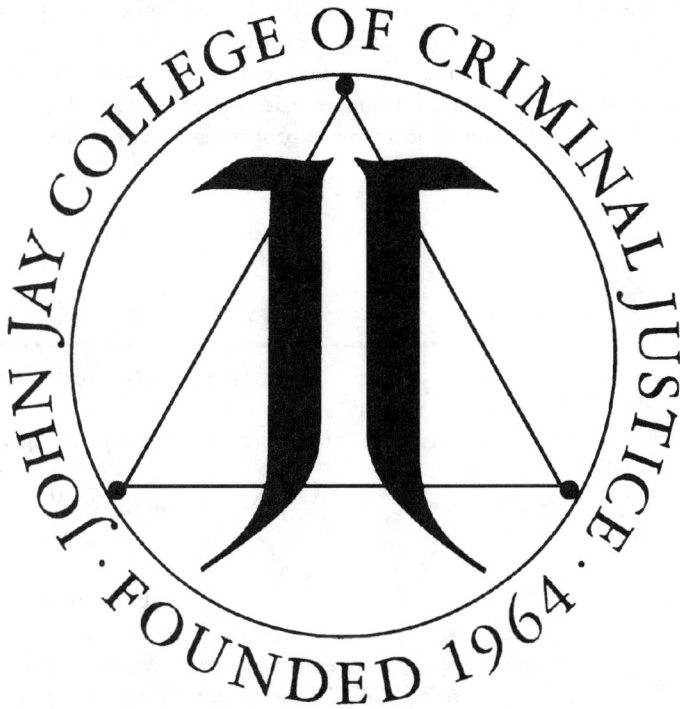

John Jay College of Criminal Justice
The City University of New York
Alumni Directory
2000

H A R R I S

The difference is service

© Bernard C. Harris Publishing Company, Inc., 2000
3 Barker Avenue
White Plains, New York 10601
(All rights reserved)

AGJH-W90-8R-15.1VA

*Inquiries may be directed to our Customer Service Department at
(800) 877-6554 or e-mail: inquiry@bcharrispub.com*

Table of Contents

John Jay College of Criminal Justice Alumni Association
899 Tenth Avenue, Suite 532T, New York, New York 10019
Telephone: (212) 237-8547 * Fax (212) 237-8546
Email: jjalumni@jjay.cuny.edu

Attorney General Janet Reno visits John Jay College, Feb. 10th, 2000

John Jay College of Criminal Justice

John Jay College and City University Officers

About John Jay College of Criminal Justice

Founded in 1964, John Jay College of Criminal Justice of The City University of New York is a liberal arts college which emphasizes as its special mission criminal justice, fire science, and other public service related fields. As such, the College is the only one of its kind in the nation.

The College serves as a major center for research in criminal justice, law enforcement, forensic sciences, and as a major training facility for local, state, federal, and international law enforcement agencies, and private security personnel. Its ethnically and culturally diverse student population, in excess of 11,000, includes 25 percent who are members of the uniformed criminal justice and fire service agencies. The majority of the students are civilian pre-professionals who plan careers in public service or already are employed in public service.

The professors and senior staff at John Jay represent a unique assemblage of talented and experienced professionals who are at the very top of their fields. The Lloyd George Sealy Library is the leading criminal justice research library in the United States.

The College hosts major conferences attracting national and world leaders to discuss crime, drug abuse, and violence and to develop meaningful solutions to these problems. With a renewed national focus on crime and violence, John Jay College is committed to play a major role in determining how these challenges are met as we approach the twenty-first century.

John Jay College in the New Millennium

INTERNATIONAL PERSPECTIVES ON CRIME, JUSTICE AND PUBLIC ORDER

Bologna, Italy, June 5-9, 2000

John Jay College will sponsor its Fifth Biennial Conference on Crime, Justice and Public Order in Bologna, Italy, June 5-9, 2000. The conference will provide practitioners and academicians with a forum to explore criminal justice issues with distinguished experts in their fields. Participants will have the opportunity to discuss current issues and trends, share research ideas and methods, and identify and develop collaborative anti-crime and public safety strategies.

Sponsors joining the College are the University of Bologna, Europe's oldest university, founded in 1088; The Interior Ministry of Italy, Department of Public Security; The Federal Bureau of Investigation; and The Johns Hopkins University, SAIS, Bologna Center.

International Conference Series

History

In 1922, John Jay College of Criminal Justice held the first in a series of conferences to advance the understanding of the global nature of crime and to encourage greater international cooperation. The conference has become one of the largest assemblies of criminal justice practitioners and academicians of its kind with more than 1,400 experts from 39 countries attending the four previous conferences. Many prominent officials, including policymakers, governors, mayors, ambassadors, business executives, and commissioners have participated in past conferences.

HUMAN DIGNITY AND THE POLICE

John Jay has taught this unique course throughout Latin America and the Caribbean and to more than twenty police forces in Eastern Europe and the former Soviet Union. The course was developed by the College under the auspices of the U.S. Justice Department's International Criminal Investigative Training Assistance Program.

International Conference Series

Sponsored by
John Jay College of
Criminal Justice

1992 *St. Petersburg, Russia.* Co-sponsored with the City of St. Petersburg, Russia

1994 *New York City, USA.* Co-sponsored with the New York City Office of the Special Narcotics Prosecutor and the New York Field Division of the U.S. Drug Enforcement Administration

1996 *Dublin, Ireland.* Co-sponsored with the Garda Síochána and the Irish Ministry of Justice

1998 *Budapest, Hungary.* Co-sponsored with the FBI and the Hungarian National Police

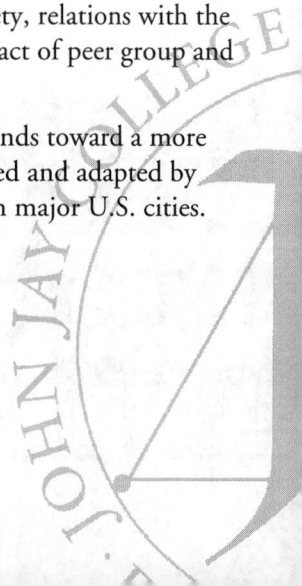

The goal of the course is to imbue police practice with a heightened understanding of human dignity as an innate quality possessed by all human beings. Using interactive exercises and innovative teaching techniques, the curriculum stresses the importance of the mutually dependent role of police in society, relations with the public, moral and ethical dilemmas in policing, and the impact of peer group and organizational influences on decision making.

Human Dignity and the Police is consistent with current trends toward a more humanistic and service-oriented model and is being developed and adapted by police in the New York City and other police departments in major U.S. cities.

PUBLICATIONS

Several important publications of the College serve to educate, inform and stimulate intellectual thought and reflection. *Law Enforcement News*, a bi-monthly newspaper, covers innovations and problems in the field, provoking thought among professionals. It disseminates critical and complex information, providing a national link between police agencies and the academic and research communities. Its readers are found in all fifty states and thirteen foreign countries. *Criminal Justice Ethics*, a scholarly journal for academics and professionals, focuses attention on ethical issues that arise in the criminal justice system. *John Jay's Finest* is an annual anthology of outstanding student writing from all disciplines.

DISTANCE LEARNING

Distance education is the process in which teaching and learning take place when instructor and student are separated by physical distance. This distance is bridged through technology, such as live, interactive video and the World Wide Web, often in concert with face-to-face communication. Presently, John Jay College is offering two types of distance learning courses. One type, called "synchronous," is taught through live, interactive video. Students enrolled in synchronous courses must meet at regularly scheduled times. Distance education is also delivered through the World Wide Web (WWW). Though Web-based courses are generally asynchronous, professors often require the students to meet "online" in a chat room for discussion at a regularly scheduled time.

A Message from the President of John Jay College

Dear John Jay College Graduate:

More and More, I am greeted by an alumnus who says with a warm smile, "I am so proud to be a John Jay College graduate."

You have good reasons to be proud. I, and the entire John Jay community, are very proud of what you have accomplished, and what you will continue to achieve in the coming years. As the 2000 Alumni Directory illustrates, there is a growing number of distinguished graduates who are leaders in law enforcement, government and private industry.

As John Jay closes in on four full decades of service, recognition of the College as a leader in criminal justice education continues to grow. Since the last edition of the directory, John Jay's Master of Public Administration Program specialization in Criminal Justice Policy earned a #1 ranking from *U.S. News & World Report*; the College hosted a major address by United States Attorney General Janet Reno about prison reform; the FBI joined John Jay as co-sponsor of an international conference on crime in Bologna; Italy; and faculty member Mike Wallace won a Pulitzer Prize in history.

There is an air of excitement on Tenth Avenue these days. The expansion of our campus is beginning. Student enrollment of undergraduates and master's candidates surpasses 10,000 each year. The number of full-time faculty is at an all time high. In an effort to meet new challenges in corporate security, John Jay is establishing a Center for Business Security and Integrity.

You are a valued part of our past and an important part of our future. Please play a role in the continued development and improvement of our unique institution. Become more involved in the activities of our Alumni Association. You will retain links to your classmates, network with other John Jay graduates and share in the pride of our College.

Sincerely,

Gerald W. Lynch
President

The John Jay College Alumni Association

The John Jay College Alumni Association provides a vital link of communication for all graduates of the College. Through its publication, *John Jay Informer*, special events, and programs, the Association keeps alumni informed and involved in the services and activities of the College.

Alumni Association members receive valuable benefits and services that assist graduates on a personal and professional level. These include: a free breakfast seminar series covering important topics such as Exploring the Internet and Personal Financial Planning; special lectures on critical criminal justice and public policy issues; and receptions featuring leading area criminal justice officials where graduates can network with colleagues.

Association members are eligible for discounts on auto and home and rental insurance through Liberty Mutual, off-Broadway shows, and college publications, like *Law Enforcement News*. In addition, the Alumni Office has a microcomputer lab where members have unlimited access to the Internet and the latest computer software. Members are also offered special career assistance and counseling services including workshops on resume writing and job interviewing. Membership dues and contributions fund merit-based scholarships, books for the Lloyd George Sealy Library, tutoring labs and other special student and program needs.

For additional information about the Alumni Association, contact the Office of Alumni Affairs, 899 Tenth Avenue, Room 532T, New York, New York 10019 (212) 237-8547.

Message from the President of the Alumni Association

Dear John Jay College Alumni:

It is with great pride that I invite you to look through the 2000 edition of our Alumni Association Directory. This is the most complete listing of John Jay College graduates every published and represents over 30 years of alumni accomplishments.

The directory serves as a great tool to re-connect with old friends and classmates, network with alumni from similar professional backgrounds and keep abreast of new developments within the John Jay College community. I am convinced you will be impressed with the College today and with its plans for an even better future.

The Alumni Association develops, coordinates, and promotes programs to attract the support and participation of our alumni. We welcome your suggestions for improvement, and look forward to serving you.

Remember, if we are to grow and improve with time, we need your participation.

Sincerely,

George C. Abraham
President, C1 '75

The Alumni Association
Executive Board

Brian Gimlett
1st Vice President
C1 '75

Jane Perlov
2nd Vice President
C1 '92

Richard Gallo
3rd Vice President
C1 '79, '82, '85

John McCabe
Treasurer
C1 '73, '79

Robert Donato
Secretary
C1 '90, '95

Guide to the Directory

DIRECTORY INFORMATION

The biographical information contained in this directory was compiled in the following manner:

a) John Jay College provided the publisher with the most recent information contained in its files at the time the project commenced;

b) Publisher attempted to update the address and telephone number information through third party research vendors with which it had executed confidentiality agreements; and

c) Publisher made every reasonable attempt to verify the biographical information via direct contact with each individual via mail and/or telephone. During telephone contact, updates given by immediate family members may have been applied as well.

If attempts to verify the information directly with individuals were unsuccessful, the information originally provided by John Jay College was utilized, with any address or telephone number updates obtained through research applied. We apologize in advance for any errors and omissions and we urge you to send corrected information regarding your listing to:

John Jay College
Office of Alumni Affairs
899 Tenth Avenue, Room 532T
New York, NY 10019
(212) 237-8547

BIOGRAPHICAL SECTION

This section lists each alumnus/a alphabetically with the following information, when available:

- class years and degrees from John Jay College
- degrees and names of other institutions attended
- title
- employer name, address, and telephone number
- residence address and telephone number
- spouse's name (in italics)
- children's names

The word "e-mail" appears at the end of the listing for each alumnus/a listed in the E-Mail Address Section.

Alumni with name changes are cross-referenced by their student names.

CLASS YEAR SECTION

This section lists alumni under the class years for their first degree programs attended at John Jay College. Following each name is a geographical cross-reference (as listed in the Geographical Section) which is either the standard U.S. postal abbreviation or country name for alumni with international addresses.

Alumni with name changes are listed by their student names. A single asterisk identifies alumni with unknown addresses; a double asterisk identifies alumni who are deceased.

GEOGRAPHICAL SECTION

This section lists alumni under their residence addresses in the following order: State, U.S. Military, U.S. Possessions and Territories, and Outside U.S.A. Following each name are class year and career networking code (in italics).

CAREER NETWORKING SECTION

This section lists alumni under their careers. Careers appear in alphabetical order.

E-MAIL ADDRESS SECTION

This section lists alumni alphabetically with class years and e-mail addresses.

CAREER NETWORKING CODES

Refer to the following career networking codes (and their translations) used in the Geographical Section:

AA	Aviation/Aerospace	JO	Journalism
AC	Accounting	JU	Judiciary
AD	Advertising	LD	Landscaping
AF	Arts—Fine	LS	Library Science
AG	Agriculture/Ranching	LW	Law/Legal Services
AM	Administrative/Clerical/Secretarial	MD	Media
AP	Arts—Performing/Creative	ME	Medical/Health Services (Other than
AR	Art		Dentistry, Nursing, Physician, Pharmacology)
AU	Architecture/Urban Planning	MF	Manufacturing
AV	Animal Science/Veterinary Medicine	MG	Management
BE	Business—Entrepreneur/Owner	MI	Military
BI	Brokerage/Securities/Investments	MK	Marketing
BK	Banking	MT	Mathematics/Statistics
CC	Construction/Contracting	MY	Ministry
CH	Childcare	NT	Nutrition
CN	Consulting	NU	Nursing
CO	Counseling	PA	Pharmacology
CP	Computer/High Technology	PB	Public Relations
CT	Communications	PH	Physician
DE	Dentistry	PJ	Publishing
EA	Education—Administration	PL	Public Service (Firefighter,
EM	Entertainment		Police, Sanitation, etc.)
EN	Engineering	PM	Pharmacy
ER	Energy Resources (Oil, Gas, etc.)	PN	Personnel/Human Resources
ES	Education—Student Affairs	PS	Personal Services
ET	Education—Teaching	RD	Research/Development
EV	Environmental Science	RE	Real Estate
FB	Fashion/Beauty	RL	Recreation/Leisure Services
FN	Funeral Services	SA	Sales
FR	Fund-raising	SN	Science
FS	Foreign Services	SO	Social Science
FV	Financial Services	SP	Sports
GD	Graphic Design	ST	Student
GE	Government—Elected	SW	Social Work
GN	Government—Non-Elected	TC	Trade/Craft
HM	Homemaking	TR	Transportation
HT	Hotel/Restaurant/Catering	TV	Travel Industry
ID	Interior Decorating/Design	UL	Utilities
IM	Import/Export	VL	Volunteerism
IN	Insurance	WR	Writing

BIOGRAPHICAL SECTION
Alphabetical Listings
Alumni of
JOHN JAY COLLEGE OF CRIMINAL JUSTICE
THE CITY UNIVERSITY OF NEW YORK

A

AARON, Grantley W.; '80 BS; 3806 Cranberry Ln., Shrub Oak, NY 10588, 914 528-0455.

ABAMWA, Osaka M.; '95 BS; Assoc. Fruad Investigator; ORI-EVR, 1716 Southern Blvd., Bronx, NY 10460, 718 617-8917; r. 274 E 175th St. Apt. 1f, Bronx, NY 10457, 718 716-1110; *Ufuoma C.;* Ese M., Kevwe M.

ABARCA, Celia J.; '78 BS; Med. Accounts Mgr.; Hosp. for Special Surgery; r. 518 E 39th St., Paterson, NJ 07504, 973 684-7835; Lindsay. e-mail

ABBATEPAOLO, Lisa M.; '92 AS; 21 Bennett Ave. Apt. 22, New York, NY 10033.

ABBOTT, Fern A.; '85 AS; 54 Boerum St. Apt. 4b, Brooklyn, NY 11206, 718 858-1072.

ABBOTT, Milton N.; '80 BS; 8604 Avenue B, Brooklyn, NY 11236, 718 858-1072.

ABDALLAH, Adib; '85 BA; 1432 White Plains, Bronx, NY 10462.

ABDELHADY, Zamyra; '92 BS; MSW Yeshiva Univ.; Private Practice; 416 E 73rd 3e, New York, NY 10021, 212 535-1073; r. 416 E. 73rd. ST., #3-E, New York, NY 10021, 212 794-2966.

ABDOOL, Rick E.; '96 AS; BS; Linx Admin./Security; Davis Polk & Wardwell, 450 Lexington Ave., New York, NY 10017, 212 450-5891; r. 4711 6th Ave., Brooklyn, NY 11220, 718 633-9263; Rishad, Ravi. e-mail

ABDUL, Christine A.; '95 BS; 1418 Garden Wood Dr., Atlanta, GA 30349, 770 414-9878.

ABDUL-KAREEM, Sanah '85 (See Cisse, Sanah).

ABDULLAH, Ms. Doris T.; '80 BA; Cash Mgr.; Pechiney World Trade USA, 475 Steamboat Rd., Greenwich, CT 06830, 203 625-9029; r. Brooklyn, NY 11220; Paul. e-mail

ABDUL-MUNTAQIM, Sayeed; '83 BS; 2260 Nameoken Ave., Far Rockaway, NY 11691, 800 950-3169.

ABDURAKHMANOV, Igor F.; '99 BA; 61-55 98th St. #14H, Rego Park, NY 11374, 718 592-3057.

ABDUR-RASHID, Sabura; '93 BA; POB 866, Bronx, NY 10453, 718 731-8494.

ABIMBOLA, Ayetigbo C.; '88 BS; 9407 King's Hwy. #2H, Brooklyn, NY 11212.

ABOLADE, Wasiu A.; '78 MA; 735 New Jersey Ave., Brooklyn, NY 11207.

ABOUSAMRA, Paul N.; '97 BS; 1107 Neill Ave., Bronx, NY 10461.

ABRAHAM, George C.; '75 BS; AS; G.C. Abraham & Assocs., 524 Willoughby Ave., Brooklyn, NY 11206, 718 388-2744; r. same; *Yasmina;* Adrienne, Geoffrey. e-mail

ABRAHAM, Harlan B.; '96 BS; 20 Clarence Pl., Staten Island, NY 10306, 718 979-1452; *Rosalie.* e-mail

ABRAHAM, Robert; '76 BS; 48 Grayson St., Staten Island, NY 10306, 718 351-7816.

ABRAMCHIK, Trudy; '82 MA; 8873 Bay 16th St., Brooklyn, NY 11214, 718 788-5146.

ABRAMOWITZ, Michael; '87 BS; 860 E Broadway Apt. 6x, Long Beach, NY 11561, 516 431-8523.

ABRAMS, Deon S.; '94 BS; Detective; NYPD Patrol Brooklyn South, Brooklyn, NY 11201; r. 534 Thatford Ave., Brooklyn, NY 11212, 718 485-1499.

ABRAMS, Fay A.; '80 BS; 697 Evergreen Ave., Brooklyn, NY 11207, 718 452-4895.

ABRAMS, Jonathan A.; '93 BS; Police Ofcr.; Suffolk Cnty. Police Dept., 30 Yaphank Ave., Yaphank, NY 11980, 631 854-6000.

ABRAMS, Robert; '85 BS; Retired Police Ofcr.; NYC Housing Authority; r. 115114 229th St., Jamaica, NY 11411, 718 978-6590; *Thelma;* Robbin, Ronard (dec).

ABRAMSON, Neal G.; '78 MA; MA City Clg. of NY, BA Lehman Clg.; Customer Svc. Rep./Tchr.; JC Penney Direct Mktg. Co., 2700 W Plano Pkwy., Plano, TX 75075; r. 1000 W Spring Valley Rd #229, Richardson, TX 75080, 972 231-3732.

ABRAMSON, Rebecca D.; '75 MA; MSW Rutgers Univ., PD Fordham Univ.; Dir. Counseling Early Intervention; Help for Families Child Elder Advocacy, Diagnostics & Sch. Findings, 312 E 84th St., New York, NY 10028, 212 288-1337; r. 312 E. 84th St., New York, NY 10028, 212 288-1337.

ABREU, Arnold; '80 BS; 2208 Newbold, Bronx, NY 10462, 718 931-0814.

ABREU, Maria A.; '93 BA; 1795 Riverside Dr., Apt. 3D, New York, NY 10034, 212 769-2015.

ABREU, Maria T.; '89 BA; 35 Hawthorne Ave., Apt. 8, Yonkers, NY 10701, 914 337-6430.

ABREU-LOTZ, Yosmari M.; '84 BA; 52 Clark St. # 5r, Brooklyn, NY 11201, 718 384-1403.

ABRUZZI, Raymond J.; '81 MA; Asst. Chief Retired; NYPD; r. 5450 66 St. Apt#2, Maspeth, NY 11378; *Deborah;* Kenneth, Karen, Raymond, Stephen. e-mail

ACEVEDO, Carmelo; '88 BS; 313 59th St., Brooklyn, NY 11220, 718 787-0126.

ACEVEDO, Cruz; '75 BA; PSC 303 Box 29t, APO, AP 96204.

ACEVEDO, Edward T.; '94 AS; Ret. Police Ofcr.,Ct. Security Ofcr; NYS, US Marshal Svc., Orlando, FL 32801, 407 426-8002.

ACEVEDO, CW4 Efrain; '76 BS; AAS Bronx Comm Clg.; Police Det. Ret/Military Intel.; NYPD; r. 382 Grandview Blvd., Yonkers, NY 10710, 914 961-9330; *Sharon;* Erick, Dayne, Daniel, Anthony. e-mail

ACEVEDO, Javier J.; '87 BS; 666 Water St. Apt. 4a, New York, NY 10002.

ACEVEDO, Louis; '81 BA; 1133 Julia St., Teaneck, NJ 07666, 201 837-8241.

ACEVEDO, Luz A.; '77 BS; 75 Wilson St. Apt. 12c, Brooklyn, NY 11211, 718 384-4573.

ACEVEDO, Marcos A.; '86 AS, '94 BS; 7 Fairfax Ct., Palm Coast, FL 32164, 904 447-0890.

ACEVEDO, Maxima K.; '99 BS; 507 Concord Ave. 1st Fl., Bronx, NY 10455, 718 585-2874.

ACEVEDO, Nancy; '89 BS; 291 King Hwy. #, Brooklyn, NY 11231, 718 787-0126.

ACEVEDO, Ramon; '80 BS; 320 51st St., Brooklyn, NY 11220, 718 449-0480.

ACEVEDO, Rene; '90 BS; 10817 48th Ave., Flushing, NY 11368, 718 777-9335.

ACEVEDO, Socrates; '93 BS; 1165 Gerard Ave. Apt. 51a, Bronx, NY 10452, 718 549-2008.

ACHA, Beraldine L.; '79 MA; 10 Waterside Plz., New York, NY 10010.

ACHINI, Antonio; '98 BS; Paralegal; r. 346 E 205th St. #5c, Bronx, NY 10467, 718 405-9635.

ACHON, Alexa M.; '99 BA; 34-90 Ft. Independence St., Bronx, NY 10463. e-mail

ACKERSON, Kimberley, PhD; (Kimberley Svec); '88 MA; BA Lawrence Univ., PHD Univ. of Alabama; Clinical/ Forensic Psychologist; r. 1027 23rd St. S, Birmingham, AL 35205, 205 324-8499; *Joseph;* Dylan, Abigail.

ACOSTA, Danae; '97 BA; 1330 Vreeland Ave., Bronx, NY 10461, 718 563-8832.

ACOSTA, Galo F.; '78 MS, '85; 7155 Calabria Ct. Apt. E, San Diego, CA 92122, 858 550-0887.

ACOSTA, Gasmary; '98 BA; Caseworker; St. Vincent's Svcs., 205 Montague St., 66 Boerum Pl., Brooklyn, NY 11201, 718 522-3700; r. 821 E. 173rd St. Apt. 2G, Bronx, NY 10460, 718 617-2571; Vanessa, Amanda, Damaris. e-mail

ACOSTA, Gloria W.; '98 MA; 100 W. 92nd St. #14C, New York, NY 10025, 212 496-5625.

ACOSTA, Indrani; '97 BS; 124 Freeman St., Brooklyn, NY 11222.

ACOSTA, Luis; '77 BA; Housing & Community Devel.; Div. of Housing & Community Revenue, 212 480-7154; r. 8702 Springfield Blvd., Jamaica, NY 11427, 718 468-7010. e-mail

ACOSTA, Michelle; '99; 33-10 Crescent St., Long Island City, NY 11106.

ACOSTA, Pilar M.; '99 BA; AS NYC Tech. Clg.; Court Liaison; Superior Ct. of Elizabeth, 1 Elizabethtown Plz., Elizabeth, NJ 07202, 908 659-3697; r. 151 Gable Cir., Lakehurst, NJ 08733, 732 408-1342.

ACOSTA, Willie R.; '75 BA; 209-11 Bardwell Ave., Queens Vlg., NY 11429, 718 416-4324.

ACOSTA-HANCOCK, Dora; '85 BS; 2110 Hermany Ave., Bronx, NY 10473.

ACTIE, Winnifred; '78 BA; 593 Marcy Ave., Brooklyn, NY 11206, 718 384-4373.

ACUNA, George A.; '95 BS; 14235 84th Dr. Apt. 2c, Jamaica, NY 11435.

ADADE, Dr. Aaron Y.; '79 BS; PHD; VP; Selicity's Inc., 6210 Chillum NW, Washington, DC 20011, 202 829-2462; r. 2921 Cheverly Oak Ct., Hyattsville, MD 20785, 301 772-4078; Nick, Timothy.

ADAMES, Flavio L.; '97; 37-26 90th St., Jackson Hts., NY 11372, 718 651-5804.

ADAMIAK, Alan B.; '83 MA; BA The Kings Clg.; Financial Planner; CJM Plng., 223 Wanaque Ave., Pompton Lakes, NJ 07442, 973 831-8020; r. 23 Potter Rd., Clifton, NJ 07013, 973 779-4793. e-mail

ADAMS, Bernard S.; '92 BS; 221 Montana Ave., Bay Shore, NY 11706, 631 968-4921.

ADAMS, C. J.; '81 BA; 15934 W. Riverside Dr., New York, NY 10032, 315 896-2780.

ADAMS, Charice Y.; '95 BS; 5401 Macalpine Cir., Apt. 1025, Glen Allen, VA 23059, 804 744-4825.

ADAMS, Charles J.; '67 BS; 10411 204th St., Jamaica, NY 11412, 718 776-1902.

ADAMS, Christopher; '96 BA; JD Hofstra Law Sch.; Student; Hofstra Law Sch.; r. 2598 36th St., Apt. 6B, Astoria, NY 11103, 718 545-9281; *Pamela Harris;* William Idrissi.

ADAMS, Dennis A.; '78 BA; 201 Crown St., Brooklyn, NY 11225, 718 493-1405.

ADAMS, De'Ron W.; '99 BS; Fraud Investigator; HRA/ORI/EVR, 260 W. 11th Ave., New York, NY 10003, 212 630-9731; r. 117 W 144 St. 5B, New York, NY 10030, 212 694-7231. e-mail

ADAMS, Elke; '90 BA; 212 Throop Ave. # 11, Brooklyn, NY 11206, 718 498-4795.

ADAMS, Eric L.; '98 BA; 425 Prospect Pl. 1k, Brooklyn, NY 11238, 718 622-7904.

ADAMS, Errol A.; '97 BA; MBA-JD Candidate/Touro Law Ctr.; Stockbrocker, T.D. Waterhouse Gr, 1 Chase Plz., New York, NY 10005; r. POB 1535, New York, NY 10276. e-mail

ADAMS, Farrell M.; '83 BA; Senior Special Agent; Dept. of Justice, INS, 425 I St. NW, Washington, DC 20536, 202 305-0613; r. Falls Church, VA 22044.

ADAMS, Gina M.; '97 BS; 42 Hurtin St., Port Jefferson Sta., NY 11776.

ADAMS, James A.; '90 BA; 171 E 89th St. #14E, New York, NY 10128, 315 896-2780.

ADAMS, Julia V.; '93 BA, '96 MA; Therapist; Devereux, Orlando, FL 32802; r. 503 Boxelder Ave., Altamonte Spgs., FL 32714, 407 682-4261. e-mail

ADAMS, Martha M.; '85 AS, '88 BS; Postal Police Ofcr.; US Postal Inspection Svc., POB 2762, New York, NY 10116, 212 330-3900; r. 435 Central Park W Apt. 5n, New York, NY 10025, 212 678-5894; Tara, Rondell.

ADAMS, Partick H.; '78 BS; 2672 Lexington Ave., E. Meadow, NY 11554, 516 221-0352.

ADAMS, Rafael D.; '82 BS; AAS Farmingdale State Univ.; Funeral Dir.; Adams Mortuary Svcs., 150 Nassau Rd., Roosevelt, NY 11575, 516 378-9183; r. 11530 166th St., Jamaica, NY 11434, 718 658-0981.

ADAMS, Robert W.; '69 AS, '71 BS; Private Practice; r. 185 Prossic Park SW, Brooklyn, NY 11218, 718 435-0827.

ADAMS, Sabrina T.; '85 BA; 10411 204th St. # 17n, Jamaica, NY 11412, 718 776-1902.

ADAMSON, Evette C.; '95 BS; 11634 141st St., Jamaica, NY 11436, 718 723-0250.

ADANSKI, Lisa M. '95 (See Romano, Mrs. Lisa M.).

ADDELSTON, Adam D.; '97 MA; 66 W. 94th St., New York, NY 10025, 212 222-1006.

ADDISON, Jeanette D.; '79 BS; 19413 112th Rd, Jamaica, NY 11412, 718 740-5656.

ADDO-LOBO, Kate; '87 MA; 3 Meadow Ct., Farmingdale, NY 11735.

ADEBIYI, Christina; '91 BS; 233 W 111th St. Apt. 3b, New York, NY 10026, 212 865-2044.

ADEGBAMIGBE, Adedeji; '95 BS; PC LAN Technician; Forest Labs, 909 Third Ave., New York, NY 10022, 212 224-6789; r. 1122 E 82nd St., Brooklyn, NY 11236, 718 968-8935. e-mail

ADELEYE, Helen; '97 BS; Eligibility Spec.; Human Resources Admin., 180 Water St., New York, NY 10038, 212 620-9491; r. 571 E 170th St. #6E, Bronx, NY 10456, 718 542-2209; *Olukayode Adeyemi;* Christopher A., Christina A.

ADELSON, Arthur; '75 BS CJ; Ret. Business Owner; Portasoft of Bergen Cnty., Hillsdale, NY 12529; r. 2960 Lake Osborne Dr., Lake Worth, FL 33461, 561 582-8276; *Carol.*

ADEMAJ, Vera; '99 BS; 2314 Fish Ave., Bronx, NY 10469, 718 519-9660. e-mail

ADENIRAN, Adeyinka; '90 BS; 2950 W 35th St. Apt. 413, Brooklyn, NY 11224, 718 522-5041.

ADESANYA, Oluwatoyin; '91 MPA; 2950 Richmond Ter., Staten Island, NY 10303.

ADESINA, Mufutau A.; '91 AS, '92 BS; 213 Lexington Ave., Brooklyn, NY 11216, 718 452-5973.

ADINOLFI, Thomas R.; '80 BS; 638 88th St., Brooklyn, NY 11228, 718 643-1659.

ADJAERO, Alphonsus A.; '95 BS; Investigator/Owner; Securities Professionals, Inc., OC Computers, 493 Nostrand Ave., Brooklyn, NY 11216, 718 789-0200; r. POB 472843, Brooklyn, NY 11247, 718 493-4188; *Ogechi;* Lotanna, Ugonna. e-mail

ADKINS, Lewis W.; '87 BS; 1457 Parkgate Ave., Akron, OH 44313, 330 865-5523.

ADLER, Harvey L.; '79 MA; BS SUNY New Paltz; USINS Border Coord.; Border Coordination Initiative (BCI), 1300 Pennsylvania Ave., Washington, DC 20229, 202 927-5387; r. 6633 Thurlton Dr., Alexandria, VA 22315, 703 922-0753. e-mail

ADLER, Morton N.; '85 BS; MA SUNY-New Paltz; Criminal Justice Tchr.; Newburgh Free Acad., 201 Fullerton Ave., Newburgh, NY 12550, 914 563-7484; r. 12 Duelk Ave., Monroe, NY 10950, 914 783-4415; *Sandra.* e-mail

ADLER, Scott J.; '95 BS; Police Ofcr. Sgt; Bronx Robbery Squad, 718 794-2186; r. 15 Kimberly Dr., Campbell Hall, NY 10916, 914 496-3609; *Andrea;* Zachary, Dylan.

ADOLFSSON, Boyd; '76; Retired, Lt. Police Ofcr.; NYC Police Dept.; r. Yonkers, NY 10705; *Lynn;* Boyd II, Dawn.

ADOLPHE, Marsiste; '94 BS; 645 E 26th St. Apt. 2k, Brooklyn, NY 11210, 718 692-1688.

ADORNO, Milinda; '97 BS; 210-21 94th Rd, Queens Vlg., NY 11428.

ADUM-BAWDAH, Hana, PhD; '78 MA; PHD CUNY; Traditional Ruler; 45 Martense St., Brooklyn, NY 11226; r. same, 718 282-6380.

AFANADOR, Deborah '91 (See Schaefer, Deborah).

AGATSTEIN, Phyllys; '88 MA; 16 W 16th St. Apt. 14hn, New York, NY 10011, 212 255-0862.

AGHO, Jeromia; '96 BA; 40-14 Vernon Blvd., Long Island City, NY 11101.

AGIRI, Iyabo; '92 BA; 257 Congressional Ln., Rockville, MD 20852, 301 881-6786.

AGLIETTI, C.; '93 BS; 76 Seneca Ave., Yonkers, NY 10710, 914 337-5288.

AGOSTO, Barbara; '93; 3019 Riverside Dr., Coral Springs, FL 33065.

AGRAPIDES, Peter; '83 BS; 7423 Ridge Blvd., Brooklyn, NY 11209, 718 833-2243.

AGRON, Mikhail M.; '98 BA; 2120 E. 14th St. 2/Fl., Brooklyn, NY 11229, 718 336-9576.

AGRUSTI, Craig D.; '95 BA; 6 E Cove Ln., Morristown, NJ 07960, 973 539-2033.

AGUERO, Maggie; '80 MA; 146 Drew Dr., Langhorne, PA 19053, 215 752-9176.

AGUGLIARO, John P.; '86 BS; 699 Laconia Ave., Staten Island, NY 10306, 718 317-5644.

AGUIAR, Yvette; '86 BS, '93 MPA; 3611 Henry Hudson Pkwyw Bsmtlc, Bronx, NY 10463, 718 884-4010.

AGUILAR, Joanne C.; '97 BS; 326 Covert St., Brooklyn, NY 11237, 718 449-3562.

AGUILERA, Emily; '91 BS; 18-16 Astoria Park, Astoria, NY 11102, 718 545-1174.

AHEL, Sabine; '93 BS; Paralegal; r. 2265 24th St., Long Island City, NY 11105, 718 721-0988.

AHERN, Dennis J.; '78 MPA; 38 Wellesley Ln., Hicksville, NY 11801.

AHERN, Kevin; '86 BA; 152 Meagher Ave., Bronx, NY 10465, 718 828-6319.

AHERN, Liam G.; '79 BS; 119 Knollwood Dr., Carle Place, NY 11514, 516 931-7090.

AHLERS, Kenneth W.; '76 BS; 150 West Dr., Massapequa, NY 11758.

AHMAD, Shiraz; '95 BA; 3095 32nd St. Apt. 2, Long Island City, NY 11102, 718 545-5838.

AHMED, Abdul M.; '89 MA; PHD Houghton Univ., MA Punjab Univ.; Retired Principal; r. 350 E. 19th St., Brooklyn, NY 11226, 718 287-1731; *Shameem;* Siara, Amjad.

AHRENS, Bree C.; '98 MA; 3435 NE 26th Ave., Portland, OR 97212, 503 694-5730.

AHYOUNG, Gary C.; '99 BS; Crisis Paraprofn.; Bd. of Educ. Dist. 11, Bronx, NY 10451; r. 3216 Bronx Blvd., Bronx, NY 10467, 718 653-3708. e-mail

AIELLO, Frank P.; '75 BS; 619 President St., Brooklyn, NY 11215, 718 836-8186.

AIELLO, Michael; '86 BS; 113 Morse Ave., Bloomfield, NJ 07003.

AIKEN, Avril A.; '87 BS, '89 MPA; 3967 Sedgwick Ave., Bronx, NY 10463, 718 601-6796.

AIKEN, Daniel; '82 BA; 3525 101st St., Flushing, NY 11368, 718 528-3862.

AIKEN, Iris A.; '91 BS; AS NYC Community Clg.; Ret; r. 3230 Magnolia Woods Pl., Quinton, VA 23141, 804 932-8950. e-mail

AIKEN, Norman F.; '90 BS; 517 E 13th St. Apt. 2c, New York, NY 10009, 212 777-8196.

AIMONE, Paul J.; '83 MA; Investigator; State Public Defender's Ofc., 25 Washington St., Morristown, NJ 07960; r. 2 Marberne Ter., Livingston, NJ 07039; *Judy;* David. e-mail

AIOSA, Claire J.; '80 MA; 248 Hollywood Ave., Flushing, NY 11363, 718 225-6745.

AITKEN, Alexandra S.; '99 MPA; BS Spring Hill Clg.; Claims Coord.; AJC Intl., 5188 Roswell Rd, Atlanta, GA 30342, 404 252-6750; r. 3993 Everett Ct., Duluth, GA 30097, 770 441-2034. e-mail

AITKEN, John J.; '81 BS; 45 NE 25th St., # A, Ft. Lauderdale, FL 33305.

AIVAZIS, Elias K.; '79 BS, '81 MA; Asst. Special Agt. in Charge; United States Secret Svc., Vp Protective Div, Old Executive Ofc. Bldg. Rm 295, Washington, DC 20502, 202 757-4800; r. 9805 Wintercress Ct., Vienna, VA 22182, 703 757-7316; *Mary Monticelli Aivazis.* e-mail

AJAH, Efut; '88 BS; POB 2080, Jacksonville, FL 32231.

AJUNWA, Ifeyinwa P.; '99 BA; Annuity Spec.; M&M Benefit Bd., 475 Riverside Dr., New York, NY 10115; r. 912 E. 220 St., Bronx, NY 10469, 718 798-4533. e-mail

AKALONU, Rosalyn B.; '80 MA, '80 BA; JD Howard Univ. Law Sch.; Atty.; Roslyn B Akalonu Atty-at-Law, 169 S Main St., #340, New City, NY 10956, 914 639-6627; r. POB 784, New City, NY 10956.

AKAPOLAWAL, Wasiu A.; '93 BS; POB 453, Bronx, NY 10473.

AKERELE, Gabriel A.; '92 MPA; BSC Rutgers Univ., RN SUNY Brooklyn; RN; Manhattan Psychiatric Ctr., 600 E. 125th, New York, NY 10035, 212 369-0500; r. POB 6157, Bronx, NY 10451, 718 329-3074; *Esther;* Christiana, Felicia, Michael. e-mail

AKERMAN, John M.; '85 BA; AA NYC Technical Clg.; Battalion Chief; NYC Fire Dept., 123 Pendleton Pl., Staten Island, NY 10301, 718 442-8723; r. same, 718 720-4797; *Suzanne;* Matthew, Andrew.

AKGUN-AUERBACH, Ms. Alice, (Alice Auerbach); '92 BS, '98 MA; AA Suffolk Cnty. Comm Clg.; Child Protective Spec.; Admin. for Children's Svcs., 90-25 161st St., Jamaica, NY 11433, 718 262-1652; r. 19 Endicott Dr., Huntington, NY 11743, 631 549-4897; *Jeffrey Auerbach.* e-mail

AKHTAB, Nazlah; '97 BS; 42 E 26th St., Brooklyn, NY 11226.

AKINS, Rachquel; '98 BA; Residential Mgr.; Anderson Sch., 875 Rte. 9, Staatsburg, NY 12580, 914 889-4034; r. 34 #2 Cedar Ln., New Windsor, NY 12553, 914 565-4070.

AKINSIKU, Frederick; '85 BS; 2 Sterling Ct., Edison, NJ 08817, 732 393-1219.

AKRIVOS, Jimmy; '95 AS; 27-09 Cres. Str, Astoria, NY 11102.

AKSELROD, Steve; '95 BS; 1833 E 16th St., Brooklyn, NY 11229.

ALAIMO, Frank A.; '77 BS; 13 E 7th St., Brooklyn, NY 11218, 718 645-0649.

ALAIMO, William N.; '80 BS; 42 Reeve Pl., Brooklyn, NY 11218, 718 645-0649.

ALAJI, Omar U.; '95 BA; POB 71622, Oakland, CA 94612, 316 262-5163.

ALAM, Ilia A.; '97 MA; 52-40 39th Dr. #4B, Woodside, NY 11377, 718 426-2035.

ALAMO, Ildefonso L.; '81 BA; 2574 Green Hills Way, Vista, CA 92084, 760 945-7442.

ALANIS, Kevin; '92 AS; 4319 39th Pl. Apt. 14, Long Island City, NY 11104.

ALAVA, Eddie J.; '98 BS; 172 E. 4 St. 7h, New York, NY 10009, 212 777-5785.

ALAVA, Tricia; '93 BA; 103 Smith St. #8, Brooklyn, NY 11201, 718 348-0447.

ALBA-GIL, Flordaliza A. '93 (See Rodriguez, Ms. Fiordaliza A.).

ALBAN, Donna A.; '95 BS; Correction Ofcr.; NYC Dept. of Corrections, New York, NY 10013, 212 225-1340; r. 35-15 102 St., Apt. 9, Corona, NY 11368, 718 446-1593.

ALBANESE, James J.; '92 BS; 5 Vivienne Ct., Valley Cottage, NY 10989.

ALBANESE, Philip P.; '76 MA; 722 Drumgoole Rd W, Staten Island, NY 10312.

ALBANO, Daniel J.; '76 BS; 92-09 241 St., Bellerose, NY 11426, 718 539-1351.

ALBARRAN, Migdalia; '97 BS; 60-57 71st Ave., Ridgewood, NY 11385.

ALBERT, Philip J.; '80 BS; 241 S.12th St., Lindenhurst, NY 11757, 631 226-8720.

ALBERT, Tracy K.; '99 BA PSYC; PhD Cand.; r. Brooklyn, NY 11224.

ALBERTI, Leonardo L.; '91 BA; 8932 196th St., Hollis, NY 11423.

ALBERTUS, Alfred J.; '72 AS, '74 BS; 30 Malvern Ln., Stony Brook, NY 11790.

ALBORNOZ, Anneris T.; '98 BA; 1042 45 St. 3g, Brooklyn, NY 11219, 718 436-4730.

ALBRIGHT, Eugene T.; '73 AA, '75 BA, '80 MPA; Retired Detective Lt.; New York Police Dept.; r. 100-7 Elgar Pl. #7E, Bronx, NY 10475, 718 671-5404. e-mail

ALBUJA, Hugo D.; '98 BS; Paralegal; NYC Law Dept., 100 Church St. 3rd Fl., New York, NY 10007, 212 442-2700; r. 11 Kiely Pl. #2, Brooklyn, NY 11208, 718 277-6052.

ALBURY, Nicholas A.; '76 BS; 880 Thieriot Ave., Bronx, NY 10473.

ALCANTARA, Mrs. Olga, (Olga Collado); '90 BS, '98 MPA, '98 MPA; Human Resources Admin.; Rsch. Fndn., 30 W. Broadway, New York, NY 10007, 212 417-8638; r. 84-31 Van Wyck Expy., Jamaica, NY 11435, 718 523-0125; *Richard E.;* Alyssa I. e-mail

ALCEE, Natalie (Giggles) S.; '97 BS; Legal Secy.; Camhy Karlinsky & Stein LLP, 1740 Broadway 16th Fl., New York, NY 10019, 212 977-6600; r. 362 Palisade Ave., Cliffside Park, NJ 07010, 201 943-4984; Kiara. e-mail

ALCOBA, Marcello; '96 BS; 6507 Ravens Crest Dr., Plainsboro, NJ 08536.

ALDOY, Anna M.; '98 MA; BA Monmouth Univ.; Mental Health Clinician; St. Barnabas Correctional Health Svcs., 19-19 Hazen St., E. Elmhurst, NY 11370, 718 546-7653; r. 317 Bellanca Rd., Brick, NJ 08723, 732 477-6077. e-mail

ALDRICH, Alicia; '91 BA; Clinical Couns.; Med. Univ. of South Carolina; r. 2494 Etiwan Ave. #H10, Charleston, SC 29414, 843 556-4193; Chase. e-mail

ALDRICH, Darcy M.; '93 MA; POB 9235, Scottsdale, AZ 85252.

ALDUENDE, Ivonne; '99 MPA; BS FL State Univ.; Staff Analyst/Press Liaison; NYC Dept. of Transportation, 40 Worth St. Rm. 1010, New York, NY 10013, 212 442-7035; r. 2979 Marion Ave. Apt. 2E, Bronx, NY 10458, 718 365-9850; Alyssa. e-mail

ALEJANDRO, Byanca; '92 BA; 2853 Dewey Ave. Ph, Bronx, NY 10465, 718 733-4805.

ALEJANDRO, Gina M.; '98 BA; Auto Ins. Underwriter; GEICO, 750 Woodbury Rd., Woodbury, NY 11797; r. 141 Ohio St., Lindenhurst, NY 11757, 516 496-5498.

ALEMAN, Jose L.; '94 BS; 1670 Bell Blvd., Apt. 703, Bayside, NY 11360.

ALEMAN, Kleber E.; '88 BS; 3564 89th St. Apt. 5g, Flushing, NY 11372, 718 423-2048.

ALEMAN, Tania E.; '95 BS; 4855 46th St. Apt. 5c, Flushing, NY 11377, 718 423-2048.

ALEO, Vito V.; '95 BA; 6913 62nd Dr., Flushing, NY 11379.

ALERS, Benjamin; '72 BA; 94 Huntington Rd, Garden City, NY 11530, 516 747-4148.

ALERTE, Gary C.; '89; Dist. Ofcr.; Immigration & Naturalization Svcs.; r. 13261 SW 99th St., Miami, FL 33186, 305 383-7845.

ALERTE, Richard C.; '97 BS, '98 BS; 919 Saint Johns Pl. #4l, Brooklyn, NY 11216, 718 636-1852.

ALEXANDER, Algernon; '93 BA; MA Valparaiso Univ.; Law; r. 907 E 58th St., Brooklyn, NY 11234, 718 444-4855; Dominus.

ALEXANDER, Alison J.; '99 BA; Administrative Asst. to Admin.; NY Cnty. Dist. Atty. Ofc., 1 Hogan, New York, NY 10013, 212 335-9675; r. 24 Warfield St., Brooklyn, NY 11221, 718 942-0069; LaQuin.

ALEXANDER, Beverly J.; '89 BA; Retired 1st Grade Detective; NYC Police Dept.; r. 4 Fordham Hill Oval Apt. 11f, Apt. 11F, Bronx, NY 10468, 718 365-0174.

ALEXANDER, Cheryl P.; '94 BS PA; CUNY; Singer/Actress/Dancer; r. 529 W 42nd St. Apt. 7B, New York, NY 10036, 212 947-0892.

ALEXANDER, Christoph; '97 BS, '98 BS; 258 W. 15th St., New York, NY 10011, 212 675-0531.

ALEXANDER, Daniel J.; '96 BS; 330 Lenox Rd # 3, Brooklyn, NY 11226, 718 469-6956.

ALEXANDER, Dawn L.; '90 BA; 832 Midwood St., Brooklyn, NY 11203, 718 469-6956.

ALEXANDER, Delvia M.; '97 BS; 30 E.Clarke Pl., Bronx, NY 10452, 718 324-2062.

ALEXANDER, Lavern K.; '92 BA; PARLEGAL LIU; Paralegal Dist. Atty's Ofc.; Brooklyn D.A. Ofc., 350 Jay St., Brooklyn, NY 11201, 718 250-3500; r. 5322 Tilden Ave., Brooklyn, NY 11203, 718 257-4409; Natasha. e-mail

ALEXANDER, Lorna V.; '86 BS; 120-25K Alcott Pl., Bronx, NY 10475, 718 654-8287.

ALEXANDER, Neva H.; '97 BS; 242 E. 25th St., Brooklyn, NY 11226, 718 277-3393.

ALEXANDER, Samuel; '79 BS; 200 Highland Blvd. Apt. 4e, Brooklyn, NY 11207, 718 604-1031.

ALEXANDER, Saundra; '83 BS; 129 W 147 St., New York, NY 10039, 315 896-2185.

ALEXANDER, Tricia; '97 BA; 405 Westminster Rd, Brooklyn, NY 11218, 718 403-9897.

ALEXANDER, Tyrone; '96 BS; 107-04 Inwood St., Jamaica, NY 11435, 718 712-1441.

ALEXANDER, Walter; '80 BS; 59 Hartman Hill Rd, Huntington, NY 11743.

ALEXANDRE, Carl; '81 BA; 10033 196th St., Jamaica, NY 11423, 718 217-5419.

ALEXANDRE, Jean W.; '97 BS; CLT; r. 11245 Seaview Ave., Apt. 3c, Brooklyn, NY 11239, 718 642-2678. e-mail

ALEXANDRE, Jphilippe; '95 BA; 1420 Bronx River A, Apt. 6k, Bronx, NY 10472, 718 328-5184.

ALEXANDRE, Nadhege M.; '96 MA; 621 S Spring St., Apt. 607, Los Angeles, CA 90014, 714 523-3066.

ALEXANDRE, Natacha; '96 BS; 12034 230th St., Jamaica, NY 11411.

ALEXIS, Monica; '94 BA; 1424 Walton Ave. # 5, Bronx, NY 10452, 718 538-5331.

ALEYNE, Aida M.; '93 BS; 2106 Bedford Ave., Brooklyn, NY 11226.

ALFRED, Rosa A.; '86 BS; MSW Fordham Univ.; Family Therapist; Steinway Family & Children Svc., 41-34 27th St., Long Island City, NY 11101, 718 389-5100; r. 8710 Avenue M, Brooklyn, NY 11236, 718 531-7435; Rickey, Racquel.

ALGARIN, Dwayne D.; '90 MPA; 24d Water Wheel Dr., Montgomery, NY 12549.

ALI, Allison; '98 BA; Columbia Univ.; Student; Columbia Univ., 203 Lewisohn Hall, MS-4114 2970 Broadway, New York, NY 10027, 212 854-2820; r. 94-42 117th St., Richmond Hill, NY 11419, 718 849-7653.

ALI, Mrs. Aneerah R., (Aneerah Riaz); '93 BA; JD Thomas M. Cooley Law Sch.; 6529 Stonebrook Ln., Flushing, MI 48433, 810 230-3333; Dr. Nasir; Bilal. e-mail

ALI, Anisa S.; '99 BA; Payroll Admin.; Instinet; r. 109-14 Ascan Ave. #2E, Forest Hills, NY 11375, 718 263-2506.

ALI, Fyza D.; '95 BS; 222 E 8th St. Apt. 7g, Brooklyn, NY 11218, 718 768-0206.

ALI, Na'imah A.; '79 BS; 10981 200th St., Jamaica, NY 11412, 718 366-5969.

ALI, Shakawat; '95 BA; MPA NYU; Computer Spec.; NYC Controller Ofc., New York, NY 10038, 212 788-5523; r. 1496 Saint Lawrence Ave., Bronx, NY 10460. e-mail

ALIBRANDE, Donald; '76 BS; 12-03 30th Rd., Long Island City, NY 11102, 718 626-0994.

ALICEA, Elliott J.; '95 AS; 365 Wilson Ave. Apt. 3t, Brooklyn, NY 11221, 718 235-5488.

ALICEA, Sigret; '96 BA; 8060 SW 152nd Ave., Apt. 513, Miami, FL 33193, 305 248-2287.

ALIHA, Kourosh M.; '98 MPA; 255 Fieldston Ter., #6j, Riverdale, NY 10471.

ALIYEV, Radmila; '96 BA; 1414 E 12th St., Apt. 6C, Brooklyn, NY 11230.

ALLAMBY, Kevin; '95 BS; 273 E 95th St. Apt. 2f, Brooklyn, NY 11212.

ALLAN, Colin P.; '80 BS; 3595 Santa Fe Trlr. Ave. 150, Long Beach, CA 90810, 562 493-6519.

ALLARD, William J.; 8727 80th St., Jamaica, NY 11421.

ALLBRIGHT, Nicole; '95 BS; Investigator; r. 1300 Gates Ave., Brooklyn, NY 11221, 718 574-0179.

ALLEN, Allen B.; '75 MA; 40 W 135th St. Apt. 8p, New York, NY 10037, 315 724-6250.

ALLEN, Alton D.; '76 BS; Retired NY Housing Police Dept.; r. 343 Kassik Cir., Orlando, FL 32824, 407 812-9777. e-mail

ALLEN, Beryl R.; '71 AS, '73 BA, '75 MA; Exec. Dir.; Harlem Interagency Council for The Aging, Inc., 50 W 139th St., New York, NY 10037, 212 234-1060.

ALLEN, Brenda R.; '81 BA; 31 Leonard St. Apt. 8s, Brooklyn, NY 11206, 718 241-8782.

ALLEN, Carl; '76 BA; Correction Ofcr.; NYS Dept. of Correctional Svcs.; r. POB 190489, S. Richmond Hill, NY 11419, 718 441-1917; Jameelah.

ALLEN, Christine V.; '76 BA; 325 E 106th St. Apt. 14c, New York, NY 10029, 315 724-1874.

ALLEN, Jacinta; '95 BA; 14 Hunt Walk # F, Bergenfield, NJ 07621, 201 244-0015.

ALLEN, James T.; '76 BS; 1881 Park Ave., New York, NY 10035.

ALLEN, Jerome; '93 MA; 568 Halsey St., Brooklyn, NY 11233, 718 443-9112.

ALLEN, John J.; '80 BA; 8123 14th Ave., Brooklyn, NY 11228, 718 645-0864.

ALLEN, Joseph A.; '96 BS, '99 MA; Release-Own Recognizance Interview; NYC Criminal Justice Agcy., 52 Duane St., New York, NY 10007, 718 330-1521; r. 707 Myrtle Ave., # 2F, Brooklyn, NY 11205, 718 246-7190; Dahlia. e-mail

ALLEN, Kelly J.; '98 BS; 15603 107th Ave., Jamaica, NY 11433, 718 322-2595.

ALLEN, Matthew C.; '86 BS; 323 Hearthstone Mews, Alexandria, VA 22314, 703 548-8571.

ALLEN, Neil G.; '94 BA; 3210 Fish Ave., Bronx, NY 10469, 718 515-9804.

ALLEN, Pauline L.; '79 BS; 281 Wyona St., Brooklyn, NY 11207, 718 748-0603.

ALLEN, Richard E.; '75 MA; BA Adelphi Univ., AS SUNY-Farmingdale; Suffolk County Police, Yaphank Ave., Yaphank, NY 11980; r. 6000 Indian Neck Ln., Peconic, NY 11958, 631 734-5914; Diane; Marianne, Richard.

ALLEN, Theresa L.; '77 BS; 130 Vanderbilt Ave., Brooklyn, NY 11205, 718 783-3764.

ALLEN, Tonya; '92 BS; 1725 Dorchester Rd, Apt. 2A, Brooklyn, NY 11226, 718 241-8782.

ALLEN, Wayne A.; '92 BA, 2000 MPA; BBA Baruch Clg., MPA; NYC Corrections Capt.; Brooklyn Detention Complex, Brooklyn, NY 11210, 718 797-8252; r. 1014 Lenox Rd, Brooklyn, NY 11212, 718 345-1894. e-mail

ALLERT, Theresa; '97 BA; AS New York Technical Clg.; Library Assoc.; Brooklyn Public Library, 2636 E 14th St., Brooklyn, NY 11235, 718 368-1815; r. 709 E.82nd St., Brooklyn, NY 11236.

ALLESSANDRO, James; '76 BA; 409 Doane Ave., Staten Island, NY 10308.

ALLETTE-DAVIS, Wendy; '97 BA; 109-41 174th St., St. Albans, NY 11433.

ALLEVA, Michael; '95 BS; 2344 E 7th St., Brooklyn, NY 11223, 718 375-5481.

ALLEVA, Nicholas; '88 BA; 8856 Aubrey Ave., Flushing, NY 11385.

ALLEYNE, Pauline A.; '93 BA; 1407 Sterling Pl., Brooklyn, NY 11213, 718 773-7922.

ALLEYNE, Peter; '90 BA; 1601 E 98th St., Brooklyn, NY 11236, 718 282-0407.

ALLMAN, Crystal C.; '90 BS; 2329 Mott Ave. # 1fl, Far Rockaway, NY 11691.

ALMA, Gilbert J.; '91 BA; 335 Wadsworth Ave., New York, NY 10040.

ALMEDINA, Joseph A.; '76 BA; 3239 Barker Ave., Bronx, NY 10467, 718 653-1578.

ALMEIDA, Esther M.; '94 BS; Gen. Mgr.; Apparel Contract Assoc., 2 Exec Dr. Ste. 521, Ft. Lee, NJ 07024, 201 302-9820; r. 724 Prospect Ave., Bronx, NY 10455, 718 585-7167. e-mail

ALMODOVAR, Lourdes; '97 BS; 82 Rutgers Slip #22G, New York, NY 10002, 212 732-3731.

ALMODOVAR, Melisa '96 (See Ocampo, Mrs. Melisa).

ALMODOVAR, Michele Y.; '95 BS, '95 CERT; Correction Ofcr.; NYC; r. 9725 64th Ave., Apt. D17, Flushing, NY 11374; *Daniel;* Danielle.

ALMODOVAR, Steven A.; '84 BS; 4234 Cardinal Blvd., Daytona Bch., FL 32127.

ALMONOR, Merault K.; '97 BA; REAL EST; Police Ofcr.; New York, NY 10030; r. 626 Riverside Dr., New York, NY 10031.

ALMONTE, Alex; '97 BA; 55 Delancey St., New York, NY 10002.

ALMONTE, Andy; '96 BA; 2115 Ryer Ave., Bronx, NY 10457, 718 893-2746.

ALMONTE, Ernesto R.; '98 BA; 59-41 58ave., Maspeth, NY 11378, 718 651-0491.

ALMONTE, Ervin J.; '97 BS; Probation Police Ofcr.; NYC Police Dept., Police Academy, New York, NY 10038; r. 97-13 75th St., Ozone Park, NY 11416, 718 827-8239.

ALMONTE, Luis A.; '96 BA; 55 Delancey St., New York, NY 10002.

ALOI, Carole A.; '80 MA; 527 81st St., Brooklyn, NY 11209, 718 998-9836.

ALOIA, Augustine C.; '90 MPA; Sgt.; NYPD; r. 1 Police Plz., New York, NY 10038, 212 533-1368.

ALOIA, Veanna M.; '99 BA; 12 Meadow Point Dr., Brick, NJ 08723.

ALOISIO, Sal; '80 BS; 40 Daley Pl. Apt. 111, Lynbrook, NY 11563, 516 887-1779.

ALONGI, Michael R.; '95 BS; 445 Union St., Brooklyn, NY 11231.

ALONSO, Michael; '72 MA; 2 Hallmark Dr., New City, NY 10956, 914 638-3728.

ALONZO, Barber; '84 BS; 71 W 112th St., New York, NY 10026.

ALPA, Yalcin; '95 BS; 829 E 10th St. Apt. 4h, Brooklyn, NY 11230, 718 851-3270.

ALPHONSO, Errol A.; '93 BA; 3805 Avenue I, Brooklyn, NY 11210, 718 282-8992.

AL-QADIRI, Talla; '93 BS; 1023 47th Rd # 2nd, Long Island City, NY 11101.

ALSTON, Barbara A.; '78 BA; 95 Old Broadway, New York, NY 10027, 212 368-5467.

ALSTON, Harry T.; '82 MA; Ret Police Ofcr./Couns.; The Jewish Bd.; r. 332 E 16th St., Brooklyn, NY 11226, 718 941-0329; *Paula;* Kimberlee, Trumane.

ALSTON, Samuel; '82 BS; Pres./Owner & Ins. Agt.; Amir Intl. Protective Svcs. Inc., 33 S. Broadway, Yonkers, NY 10701, 914 375-2906; r. 34 W. 184th St., Bronx, NY 10468, 718 733-0328; *Jean;* Malik, Akean, Kenneth, Lateefah, Zakiyyah.

ALSTON, Yvonne; '91 MA; 689 Decatur St., Brooklyn, NY 11233, 718 443-9120.

ALSWANG, Scott B.; '80 MA; BS William Paterson Clg.; Special Agt.; US Secret Svc., 7 Work Trade Ctr. 9th Fl., New York, NY 10048, 212 637-4553; r. 19 Marlin Dr., Whippany, NJ 07981, 973 503-1775; *Kay Barsdell-Alswang.* e-mail

ALTES, Alexandria '95 (See Shaw, Mrs. Alexandria).

ALTMAN, Sedric D.; '93 BS; 11426 133rd St., Jamaica, NY 11420, 718 267-1625.

ALVARADO, Darlene; '93 BA; 1727 Clinton Pl., Teaneck, NJ 07666, 201 837-7319.

ALVARADO, Gloria M.; '91 BS; 1810 Bruckner Blvd., Bronx, NY 10473, 718 378-1610.

ALVARADO, Ivonne C.; '98 BS; Confidential Investigator; NYC Dept. of Investigation, 250 Broadway Ave., New York, NY 10007, 212 306-8465; r. 80-73 Cypress Ave., Glendale, NY 11385, 718 418-8682.

ALVAREZ, Ana A.; '88 BS; 24816 88th Dr., Jamaica, NY 11426, 718 429-9585.

ALVAREZ, Betsaira; '93 BS; 1539 Hone Ave. # P, Bronx, NY 10461, 718 828-7953.

ALVAREZ, Cathy; '89 BS; 4500 Broadway #3l, New York, NY 10040.

ALVAREZ, Elvin; '84 BA; AA Manhattan Comm. Clg.; Admin. Coord.; Columbia Univ.; r. 55 La Salle St., New York, NY 10027, 212 305 6368. c mail

ALVAREZ, Jeannette M.; '96 MA; 146 Sylvan Ave., Leonia, NJ 07605.

ALVAREZ, Judith A.; '85 BS; 16 Raymond Ave., Farmingville, NY 11738, 631 732-3212.

ALVAREZ, Lucrecia; '91 BA; 34-20 24th St., Long Island City, NY 11106.

ALVAREZ, Margarita; '78 BA; 3595 Burlingame Rd, Cazenovia, NY 13035.

ALVAREZ, Michelle L.; '98 BA; Administration; HRA; r. 126-05 25th Ave., College Pt., NY 11356, 718 460-3877. e-mail

ALVAREZ, Ray; '96 BA; Claims Rep.; Social Security Admin., 7000 SW 62 Ave., Ste. 600, Miami, FL 33143, 305 662-1352; r. 9000 SW 122 Pl., Apt. 301, Miami, FL 33186, 305 274-4124; *Erica.* e-mail

ALVAREZ, Richard; '98 BS; Police Ofcr.; New York Police Dept., 2021 Ryer Ave., Bronx, NY 10453, 718 220-5211; r. 659 W 162nd St., Apt. 31, New York, NY 10032, 212 781-5845; *Jacqueline;* Paola.

ALVAREZ, Ronald J.; '94 BA; Police Lt.; New York Police Dept., 1 Police Plz., New York, NY 10038, 212 374-5323; r. 415 W. Broadway, Port Jefferson, NY 11777, 631 331-3123.

ALVEAR, Mrs. Bonnie S.; '88 BA; Regional Dir. for CBI; Dept. of Juvenile Justice, 365 Broadway, New York, NY 10013; r. 8905 3rd Ave. # 2fl, Brooklyn, NY 11209, 718 238-1951; *Douglas;* Bonnie, Joseph.

ALVERIO, Daisy M.; '81 BA; JD Drake Law Sch.; Admin. Law Judge; 917 318-8688; r. 1515 Overing St., Bronx, NY 10461, 917 318-8688. e-mail

ALVIA, Susana; '97 BA; POB 2080, New York, NY 10008.

ALWILL, Gale A.; '92 BA; 156 Hudson Ave., Red Bank, NJ 07701, 732 450-1430.

ALZANDANI, Mansoor; '95 BS; 62 Richmond Ter., Staten Island, NY 10301.

ALZATE, Jorge E.; '98 BS; 89-20 55th Ave. #3j, Elmhurst, NY 11373.

AMADI, Ogechi A.; '98 MPA; 141 30 77th Rd. #2c, Kew Gardens, NY 11367, 718 217-6022.

AMADOR, Bernard; '99 BA; BA Purchase Clg.; Student; Sage Grad. Sch.; r. 520 E 156 St. 6S, Bronx, NY 10455, 718 292-2882. e-mail

AMADOR, Doris; '81 BS; 835 Quincy Ave., Bronx, NY 10465.

AMADU, Onoriode P.; '91 MA; 271 E 164th St., Bronx, NY 10456.

AMANDOLA, Joseph J.; '79 BS; 37-18 27 St., Long Island City, NY 11101.

AMANN, Gloria D.; '87 MPA; MLS Queens Clg., BA CUNY; Sch. Librarian; CISAD2, 1700 Macombs Rd, Bronx, NY 10453, 718 583-7007; r. 195 Bennett Ave., New York, NY 10040; *Helmut.*

AMANNA, Francine M.; '97 BS; 67-15 73rd Pl., Middle Vlg., NY 11379.

AMARAL, Patrick N.; '98 BS; 45b Fox Hill Dr., Dover, NJ 07801, 973 631-4229.

AMARO, Ed; '96 BS; Meeting Planner; KPMG LLP; r. 326 Webster Ave., Englewood, NJ 07631, 201 541-9540.

AMARO, Margarita; '95 BA; Couns.; Victim Svcs., 215 E. 161st St., Bronx, NY 10451, 718 588-0038; r. 345 W 50th St. 10-Z, New York, NY 10019, 212 582-5820.

AMARO, Marta; '91 BA; Deputy City Sheriff; Sheriff's Ofc., 550 W. 59th Stree, New York, NY 10017, 212 379-0509; r. 1475 Longfellow Ave., Bronx, NY 10460, 718 842-3761.

AMARUTSANON, Kittisak; '93 MPA; FBI National Academy, Quantico, VA 22135.

AMATO, Edward J.; '76 BS; Pres.; Amato Investigative Svc. Inc., POB 482, Tuckahoe, NY 10707, 914 793-7528; r. 359 Westchester Ave., Tuckahoe, NY 10707, 914 793-4903; *Mary;* Kristen. e-mail

AMATO, Peter J.; '95; 35065th St., Brooklyn, NY 11220, 718 375-4377.

AMATO, Ronald J.; '81 BS; Ofc. Mgmt.; 212 366-7098; r. 2050 21st Dr., Brooklyn, NY 11214, 718 265-0125.

AMATO, Rosemarie A.; '79 BA; 14737 Union Tpk. # 134, Flushing, NY 11367, 718 297-2430.

AMATORE, Alfred; '92 BS; 8803 20th Ave., Brooklyn, NY 11214.

AMAY, Jasmin E.; '99 BS; 70 Maujer St., Brooklyn, NY 11206, 718 232-0556.

AMAYA, Allan F.; '88 BS; Official Court Interpreter; Kings Cnty. Family Ct., 286 Adams St., Brooklyn, NY 11201, 718 643-7680; r. 101-54 108th St., S. Richmond Hill, NY 11419, 718 845-5001. e-mail

AMBERT, Ms. Arlene; '85 MA; BA PSYCH Long Island Univ., JD Brooklyn Law Sch.; Atty.; Arlene Ambert Atty-at-Law, 505 59th St., Brooklyn, NY 11220; r. 1741 Gerritsen Ave., Brooklyn, NY 11229.

AMBRIS, Ayanna E.; '99 BA; Police Ofcr.; CUNY; r. 1098 Barbey St., Brooklyn, NY 11207, 718 649-6062; Ashantii.

AMBRIS, Marcia C.; '95 BS; Frud Investigator; HRAEVR, 30 Main St., Brooklyn, NY 11201; r. 5301 Synder Ave. Apt. H4, Brooklyn, NY 11203, 718 485-0586; Jonathan.

AMBROISE, Sabine T.; '97 BA; 158-25 78th Ave., Flushing, NY 11366, 718 932-3839.

AMBROSE, Wilma I.; '96 BA; 214 E 35th St., Brooklyn, NY 11203, 718 599-1403.

AMBROSIO, Ralph V.; '80 MA; 585 Manor Ln., Pelham, NY 10803, 914 738-4990.

AMBROSIO-DEY, Maria; '88 BA; 8441 85th Rd, Woodhaven, NY 11421.

AMEDEE, J.; '93 BS; 2475-15 Southern B, Bronx, NY 10458, 718 367-0636.

AMELIO, Anthony; '85 BS; Lt.; NYPD, Bronx, NY 10461; Phyllis; Anthony Jr, Christopher.

AMENGUAL, Margie; '83 BS; MS Yeshiva Univ.; Social Worker; Bd. of Educ., PS 165, Y34 W 109thst, New York, NY 10025, 212 678-2964; r. 224 Livingston St., Clifton, NJ 07013, 917 414-6260; Jeff; Tracey. e-mail

AMERENO, Bernice O.; '76 BA; 13827 227th St., Jamaica, NY 11413.

AMORESE, Sam A.; '78 BS; JD Fordham Law; Asst. Commissioner; NYC Dept. of Investigation, 80 Maiden Ln. 17th Fl., New York, NY 10038, 212 825-2801; r. 264-45 73rd Ave., Floral Park, NY 11004.

AMORUSO, William M.; '92 BS, '99; 31 Tallman St., Staten Island, NY 10312, 718 356-6351.

AMOUR, Johnson N.; '97 BA; 1093 E. 52nd St., Brooklyn, NY 11234.

AMPIE, Omar A.; '99 MA; 3801 S. Ocean Dr., #16p, Hollywood, FL 33019, 954 455-2169. e-mail

AMPLO, Anthony J.; '78 BS; 7714 87th St., Flushing, NY 11385, 718 441-3096.

AMPLO, Anthony S.; '90 BS; 84 Jonathan Dr., Mahopac, NY 10541, 914 628-6246.

AMUNDSEN, James E.; '99 BS; 647 Yetman Ave., Staten Island, NY 10307, 718 356-6342.

ANAIPAKOS, George P.; '82 BS; 1276 Bayview Cir., Weston, FL 33326.

ANAND, Srikala; '86 MA; 172 Luz Church R., Mylapore Madras, India, 4992582.

ANASTAS, Anthony; '96 BS; Financial Advisor; Morgan Stanley Dean Witter, 885 Third Ave., New York, NY 10022, 212 705-4532; r. 108-56 50 Ave., Corona, NY 11368, 718 592-4469.

ANASTASOPOULOS, Mrs. Cara E., (Cara E. O'looney); '92 BA; AA Nassau Community Clg.; Phoenix House-Mother & Child Div., 164 W. 74th St., New York, NY 10023; r. 5 N. Hill Dr., E. Northport, NY 11731.

ANATSUI, Edwige M.; '99 BA; Probationary Police Ofcr.; NYPD, One Police Plz. Ny Ny 10038, 235 E. 20th St., Cooper, NY 10003, 212 374-7918; r. 98-30 57th Ave. (#16G), Corona, NY 11368, 718 592-0734; Benjamin; Victoria. e-mail

ANCRUM, Alberta; '89 BA; 765 E. 163 St., Bronx, NY 10456.

ANDALUZ-SCHER, Maria; '87 BS; 1106 Mace Ave., Bronx, NY 10469, 718 881-9154.

ANDERLE, Joseph W.; '89 BS; 6056 60th Dr., Flushing, NY 11378, 718 381-6598.

ANDERS, Scott; '94 BA; Police Ofcr.; NYPD, Bronx, NY 10469; r. 2449 Throop Ave., Bronx, NY 10469.

ANDERSON, Andre '96 (See Maximum, Andre A.).

ANDERSON, Bonita M.; '96 BA; Analyst; Ofc. of Mgmt. & Budget, 75 Park Pl., New York, NY 10007, 212 788-6159; r. 3250 Broadway #13B, New York, NY 10027; Keith (Dec), Teria, Stacey, Brandesha. e-mail

ANDERSON, Ms. Carmen N.; '99 BA; Legal Hiring Assoc.; Manhattan Dist. Atty.; r. 679 Hendrix St. #2R, Brooklyn, NY 11207, 718 498-4625.

ANDERSON, Charles P.; '75 BS; Ret. Deputy Chief; NY Fire Dept.; r. 579 SW Saint Kitts Cove, #225, Port St. Lucie, FL 34986, 561 336-2670; Nancy, Charles II. e-mail

ANDERSON, Christeen; '97 BS; 4243 147th St. Apt. 3d, Flushing, NY 11355, 718 445-5887.

ANDERSON, Erik J.; '92 BA; 9216 3rd Ave. Apt. 2, Brooklyn, NY 11209, 718 622-3402.

ANDERSON, Esther G.; '85 BA; 57-15 Shore Front, Arverne, NY 11692, 718 318-2239.

ANDERSON, Eunice T., (Eunice Coleman); '82 BA; AA NYC Comm. Clg.; Social Worker; Lincoln Hall, 220 E. 23rd St., Rm. 401, New York, NY 10010, 212 696-1910; r. 12421 Flatland Ave., Brooklyn, NY 11208, 718 927-2086.

ANDERSON, Greta; '76; 11206 176th St., Jamaica, NY 11433, 718 786-5923.

ANDERSON, Harold T.; '78 BS; 22815 145th Ave., Jamaica, NY 11413, 718 978-1413.

ANDERSON, Henry; '84 BS; Asst. Duty Mgr.; Kennedy Airport, Bldg. 14, JFK, Jamaica, NY 11430, 718 244-4104; r. 3721 Marcy St., Mohegan Lake, NY 10547, 914 526-8161; Audrey V.; Amanda M., Blaire V.

ANDERSON, Jacqueline V.; '99 BA; 221 Linden Blvd., #E1, Brooklyn, NY 11226, 718 693-5488.

ANDERSON, Kevin G.; '94 MPA; BS PA State Univ.; Procurement Analyst; NYC Dept. of Health, 125 Worth St., Rm. 203 Box 74, New York, NY 10013, 212 788-4370; r. 120-19 Asch Loop #19D, Bronx, NY 10475, 718 671-8772; Stephanie. e-mail

ANDERSON, Krik C.; '96 BA; P.O.Box 160, Miller Place, NY 11764.

ANDERSON, Linda M.; '79 BA; 7925 Calamus Ave., Flushing, NY 11373, 718 446-2175.

ANDERSON, Dr. Lola H., (Lola H. Langley); '78 BS; MSW Fordham Univ., PHD Walden Univ.; Prof.; Audrey Cohen Clg., 75 Varick St., New York, NY 10039, 212 343-1234; r. 101-125 W. 147th St., #21C, New York, NY 10039, 212 234-3897; `Simon Langley-Anderson; James, Kevin, Karen, Carol, Koren, Selma, Pierre, Gary, Nicole, Kyle. e-mail

ANDERSON, Luke E.; '95 AS; 114 Garland Ct., Brooklyn, NY 11229, 718 385-8048.

ANDERSON, Margaret R.; '82 BS; 545 E. 14 St., New York, NY 10009, 212 674-5866.

ANDERSON, Martha C.; '91 BS; 6296 Taliaferro Way # Pvth, Alexandria, VA 22315, 703 799-0187.

ANDERSON, Dr. Melody M.; '75 BAH; DSW Yeshiva Univ., MS Columbia Univ.; Adjunct Prof.; Yeshiva Univ., 435 E 79th St., Ste. 1c, New York, NY 10021, 212 570-4877; r. 216 E 47th St. 4A, New York, NY 10017. e-mail

ANDERSON, Otis C.; '78 MA; 105-11 171 Pl., Jamaica, NY 11433, 718 446-2175.

ANDERSON, Paul M.; '76 BA; 13746 225th St., Jamaica, NY 11413, 718 446-2175.

ANDERSON, Robert J.; '84 MA; BS Mercy Clg., MS Long Island Univ.; Cnslt.; Robert J Anderson Municipal Cnsltg., 27 Lupus Ln., Sewell, NJ 08080, 856 218-7493; r. same. e-mail

ANDERSON, Rufus S.; State Employees Credit Union, Lansing, MI 48933, 517 351-1252.

ANDERSON, Timothy T.; '93 BA, '95 MPA; 40 E. Birch St., Mt. Vernon, NY 10552, 914 699-0842.

ANDERSON, Vanita M.; '95 BS; 730 Gates Ave. Apt. 2a, Brooklyn, NY 11221, 718 232-7679.

ANDIARENA, Wilfredo; '93 BS; 609 W 188th St. Lot I, New York, NY 10040.

ANDINO, Alcides; '97 BA; 1964 1st Ave. #3, New York, NY 10029, 212 369-8290.

ANDINO, Anita M.; '96 BA; 6425 60th Ave., Maspeth, NY 11378.

ANDINO, Eddie; '92 BS; 17 N Rockland Ave., Congers, NY 10920.

ANDO, Scott M.; '88 MPA; 1141 Rue Chinon, Mandeville, LA 70471.

ANDRADE, Karol J.; '97 BS; 25-15 18th St., Astoria, NY 11102, 718 274-7130.

ANDRADES, John, Jr.; '78 BA; Coord. of Trng. & Devel.; Retired NYC Transit Authority, 370 Jay st. Brooklyn NY, Brooklyn, NY 11212; r. 401 First Ave., Apt. 21 A, New York, NY 10010, 212 686-3996; Colleen P.; Ana, Antonia. e-mail

ANDRESS, La'donna V.; '96 MA; POB 15038, Houston, TX 77220.

ANDREW, Gregory; '96 BA; 1155 E 52nd St., Brooklyn, NY 11234, 718 493-7085.

ANDREWS, Benjamin (Ben); '90 BS; PARA Long Island Univ.; Ret Sgt;Personal Financial Analyst; Primerica Financial Services, 135 Raritan Center Pkwy, Edison, NJ 08837, 732 225-4334; r. 893 E 94th St., Brooklyn, NY 11236, 718 319-3199. e-mail

ANDREWS, Joy A.; '89 BS; 388 Quincy St., Brooklyn, NY 11216, 718 398-4587.

ANDREWS, Peter; '76 BA, AS; Retired-Sergeant; NYC Police Dept.; r. 330 W 28th St., Apt. 18J, New York, NY 10001, 212 924-9136; Michael, Katherine, Sophia, Eleni. e-mail

ANDRICOSKY, John J.; '76 BS; AS Manhattan Comm Clg., MPS CW Post Clg.; Pres.; Andricosky & Fedele, Inc., 261-02 Union Tpk., Floral Park, NY 11004, 718 347-9631; r. 147-01 16th Rd., Whitestone, NY 11357, 718 746-9447. e-mail

ANDRINI, Deanna; '96 BA; 1321 Clinton Ave., Bronx, NY 10456, 718 328-3016.

ANDROS, Frances S.; '77 BA; 277 Deems Ave., Staten Island, NY 10314.

ANDRUSZKEWICZ, Phillip M.; '80 BA; 4 Maple Ln., New Hyde Park, NY 11040.

ANDUJAR, Diana; '93 BA; 240 Madison St. Apt. 6h, New York, NY 10002, 212 732-6002.

ANDUJAR, Michael; '75 BA; 443 W. 25th St., New York, NY 10001.

ANDUZE, Kenneth R.; '89 MPA; POB 100577, Brooklyn, NY 11210.

ANDUZE, Lisa M.; '90 BA; POB 880031, Boca Raton, FL 33488.

ANELLO, Cathy; 4310 Gunther Ave., Bronx, NY 10466.

ANES, Edwin; '96 BS; Police Ofcr.; OCCB, Narcodics Division, 2768 Frederick Douglas Blvd., New York, NY 10039, 212 694-8167; r. 472 Smith St., Apt. 2R, Brooklyn, NY 11231, 718 246-1749. e-mail

ANFITEATRO, Andrea; '91 MA; 120 Watch Hill Rd, Cortlandt Manor, NY 10567, 914 528-2664.

ANGELAKIS, Kaliope; '86 BA; POB 307, E. Marion, NY 11939.

ANGELETTI, Debra; '93 MA; Trial Cnslt.; 1158 26th St., Ste. 303, Santa Monica, CA 90403, 310 449-0159; r. 1158 26th St., # 303, Santa Monica, CA 90403, 310 456-3990.

ANGELUCCI, Joann; '98 BA; 2419 Throop Ave. #1Fl, Bronx, NY 10469, 718 359-3263.

ANGERMAIER, Heather A.; '98 MA; 84 Sylvan Dr., Wading River, NY 11792, 631 929-6622.

ANGILLETTA, Joseph A.; '86 MA; 1322 Bay Ridge Ave., Brooklyn, NY 11219, 718 259-4941.

ANGLEY, Richard J.; '76 BS; 4-900 Kuhio Hwy., Kapaa, HI 96746.

ANGLIN, Brian; '86 MPA; 300 Ocean Ave. N, Apt. 2A, Long Branch, NJ 07740.

ANIELLO, Nicholas A.; '87 BS; 97-34 82nd St., Ozone Park, NY 11416.

ANISOWICZ, George; '71 BA; 1650 Melrose Dr. SW, Atlanta, GA 30310.

ANN, Ryan L. '77 (See Kessinger, Ann L.).

ANNAMUNTHODO, John C.; '97; AA Borough Manhattan Comm., BBA Borough Clg.; Adjunct Instr.; Borough Manhattan Community; r. 1405 St. Johns Pl., Apt. 1b, Brooklyn, NY 11213, 718 735-8588.

ANNARUMMA, Thomas P.; '80 BA; 7261 Shore Rd Apt. 5t, Brooklyn, NY 11209, 718 372-8187.

ANNETTS, Paul D.; '93 BS; AS Dutchess Community Clg., Marist Clg.; Correctional Facility Spec. I; NYS Commission of Correction, 4 Tower Pl., Albany, NY 12203, 518 485-9965; r. POB 1305, Hopewell Jct., NY 12533; *Maria Menconeri-Annetts*.

ANNINA, Ralph; '80 MPA; CAS NYU, CLSS NYS & Wisconsin; Technology Cnslt.; r. 11011 N Kensington Dr., # 83W, Mequon, WI 53097, 262 238-8722. e-mail

ANNINOS, John W.; BA; 17 Silver Birch Ln., Pearl River, NY 10965, 914 623-1912.

ANNIS, Christopher; '92 AS; 111 Rockne St., Staten Island, NY 10314.

ANNITTO, Paul E.; '91 BS; 8239 247th St., Jamaica, NY 11426, 718 347-8843.

ANNUCCI, Anthony J.; '76 MA; 7310 10 Ave., Brooklyn, NY 11228.

ANOBILE, John J.; '80 BS; 2709 Ave. W, Brooklyn, NY 11229, 718 891-5352.

ANSALDI, Angela '78 (See Cahill, Angela M.).

ANSCHICK, Robert H.; '74 BS, '78 MPA; CMP Columbia-Police Mgt Inst.; Inspector; NYC Police Dept., 1 Police Plz., New York, NY 10038, 212 741-8475; r. Pearl River, NY 10965.

ANSHANSLIN, James B.; '80 BA; 4925 E Calle De Las Estrellas, Cave Creek, AZ 85331.

ANTAB, Vaughn; '73 BS; 1602 10th Ave., Brooklyn, NY 11215.

ANTHOINE, Robert; '85 MA; 1065 Lexington Ave., New York, NY 10021, 212 737-9859.

ANTHONY, Ceredo F.; '94 BS; 140 Donizetti Pl. Apt. 3d, Bronx, NY 10475, 718 220-4548.

ANTHONY, Chailendra; '97 BS; 590 Clinton St., Apt. 2B, Brooklyn, NY 11231, 718 222-3371.

ANTHONY, Mark W.; '97 BS; Syst. Admin.; PAIS-OCLC, 521 W. 43 St., New York, NY 10036; r. 114-32 201st St., St. Albans, NY 11412.

ANTHONY, Tyrone; '79 BA, '84 MA; 1725 President St., Brooklyn, NY 11213, 718 756-0161.

ANTHONY, Wade D.; '93 BA; 4 Sunny Ridge Rd, Spring Vly., NY 10977, 914 362-4346.

ANTOINE, Jennifer; 186 Prospect Pl. #3G, Brooklyn, NY 11238, 718 857-0423.

ANTOINE, McFredy; '89 BA; MSED Long Island Univ.; Owner; A&M Enterprises, (Tax Svcs. & Employement Agcy.); r. 100 Lefferts Ave., Brooklyn, NY 11225, 718 826-6352.

ANTOINE, Phyllis A.; '78 BS; 538a Willoughby Ave., Brooklyn, NY 11206, 718 693-1000.

ANTOINE, Wayne A.; '79 BS, '94 MA; 150 Crown St. #F18, Brooklyn, NY 11225, 718 953-9373.

ANTOMEZ, SGT Herbert; '78 BS; MPA CW Post Univ.; Police Ofcr.; NYPD; r. 664 E 59th St., Brooklyn, NY 11234, 718 209-1866; Rickelle.

ANTON, Robert W.; '90 BA; 164 Bowers St., Jersey City, NJ 07307.

ANTONELLI, Ralph; '89 BS; 1094 Wantagh Ave., Wantagh, NY 11793, 516 221-7998.

ANTONICELLO, Giacomo; '86 BS; 276 Harrison St., Nutley, NJ 07110.

ANTONIN, Jo-Ann; '99 BA; NYS Motor Vehicle Investigator; NYS Dept. of Motor Vehicles, 30-56 Whitestone Expy., Rm. 200, College Pt., NY 11354, 718 539-8670; r. 87-04 215th Pl., Queens Vlg., NY 11427, 718 479-0680. e-mail

ANTONIOU, Antonios; '99 MA; 31-60 35 St., Astoria, NY 11106, 718 545-6556.

ANTONUCCI, Robert J.; '99 MPA; 12 Cres., Selden, NY 11784, 631 736-0725.

ANTROBUS, Jennifer B.; '79 BS; 280 Prospect Park W # 38, Brooklyn, NY 11215.

ANYANSI, James O.; '90 BA, '92 MA; 3423 Wickham Ave., # 3, Bronx, NY 10469, 718 881-7556.

ANZIANI, Victor; '76 BS; Customer Svc. Rep.; Pitney Bowes, 500 Bi-County Blvd., Farmingdale, NY 11735; r. 63 Pickwick Dr. N, Hicksville, NY 11801, 516 935-0743.

APOLINARIO, Marcia; '95 BA; 37 Prospect St., Bloomfield, NJ 07003.

APONTE, Ana; '90 BS; Probation Ofcr.; NYC Dept. of Probation, 718 657-5671; r. 88-37 80th St., Woodhaven, NY 11421, 718 296-1406; Jaclyn, Erin, Kellina, Joana, Reina. e-mail

APONTE, Bianca M.; '95 BS; 19 Hillis St., Staten Island, NY 10312, 718 984-0720.

APONTE, Cesar; '77 BS, '81 MA; Sr. In Law Enforcement; NY Dist. Attys. Ofc., 1 Hogan Pl. Rm. 1508, New York, NY 10013, 212 335-9576; r. 620 Baychester Ave. #10g, Bronx, NY 10475.

APONTE, Gina; '89 BS; 12 York Ave., Bethpage, NY 11714, 516 791-2807.

APONTE, Lydia; '98 BS; 1306 Fteley Ave., Bronx, NY 10472, 718 364-1231.

APONTE, Marlene; '96 BS; 3038 70th St., Flushing, NY 11370, 718 760-3693.

APONTE, Myriam; '79 BS; Cnslt.; r. 425 Dorsett #1, S. Burlington, VT 05403, 802 864-9719. e-mail

APONTE, Negron R.; '96 AS; C/510 Blogue Om-1, Carolina, PR 00982.

APONTE, Victor M.; '76 BA; Drug Enforcement Administrator (DEA), 700 Army-Navy Dr., Arlington, VA 22202; r. Via Valdisole, #15, Roma 00135, Italy, 7039129176; *Carmen L.;* Tracey Ann, Victoria Ruth, Ceclia Manuela. e-mail

APPADOO, Ruth S.; '94 BS; 6420C 192nd St. Apt. 3A, Fresh Meadows, NY 11365.

APPEL, Kenneth P.; '84 MA, '84 BS; Dir. of Operations; Professional Security Bur., 535 Broadhollow Rd., Ste. W-6, Melville, NY 11747, 631 454-1111; r. 2239 Troy Ave. Apt. 6J, Brooklyn, NY 11234, 718 258-5404; Emily. e-mail

APPEL, Michael A.; '80 BS, '92 MA; Loss Prevention Supv.; The Home Depot, 600 Hempstead Tpk., Elmont, NY 11003, 516 488-8500; r. 417 Parkside Ct., Copiague, NY 11726, 631 226-4568; Sue Ann; Ryan, Lindsay. e-mail

APPELBAUM, Jed; '76 BSPSCJ; Asst. Commissioner; NYC Taxi Limousine Commission, 24-55 B.Q.E. W., Woodside Facility, Woodside, NY 11377, 718 267-4598; r. POB 345, Brooklyn, NY 11236; Arlene; Jenna.

APPELT, Peter J.; '78 BS; 31 Hark Ln., Westbury, NY 11590.

APPLEWHITE, Elsie; '84 MPA; Systs. Analyst; Coney Island Hosp., 2601 Ocean Pkwy., Brooklyn, NY 11235, 718 616-5332; r. 2301 Kings Hwy., Brooklyn, NY 11229, 718 377-3551; Erain.

APTACKER, Steven I.; '87 BS; Sergeant; New York Police Dept., 49th Precinct, Bronx, NY 10461, 718 918-2000; r. 245 Verrazano Ave., Copiague, NY 11726, 631 842-1562; Naomi; Ashley. e-mail

AQUINO, Donald D.; '73 BS; 1672 W 2nd St., Brooklyn, NY 11223, 718 833-0159.

ARAMINO, Sandra L.; '83 BS; 521 Ridge Rd., Lyndhurst, NJ 07071.

ARANEO, Suzanne; '83 BS; 64 Parson Rd, # 1, Clifton, NJ 07012, 973 471-1151.

ARAUJO, Jose M.; '97 BS; 31-34 51 St. #2, Woodside, NY 11377, 718 937-6696.

ARCE, Daisy '96 (See Fortis, Daisy).

ARCE, Jose M.; '89 BS; 251 Pacific St. Apt. 15, Brooklyn, NY 11201, 718 858-7420.

ARCE, Michael H.; '78 BS; Natl. Park Ranger; Herbert Hoover Natl. Park; r. Box 1, Lake Powell, UT 84533, 435 692-1119; Mardi.

ARCE, Michele; '97 BA, '99 MA; AA BMCC; Dir.; The Ctr. for Children & Family, 718 898-2230; r. 1070 Hicksville Rd., Seaford, NY 11783, 516 795-6443. e-mail

ARCE, Nancy; '90 BA; 426 Rodney St., Brooklyn, NY 11211, 718 492-7603.

ARCE, Nelson; '95 BS; 3250 48th St. Apt. 1l, Long Island City, NY 11103, 718 932-8523.

ARCHAMBEAU, Lincoln; '97 BA; 3605 Pauling Ave., Bronx, NY 10469.

ARCHER, Mable L.; '87 BS; 139-26 86Th., Jamaica, NY 11435, 718 956-3670.

ARCHER-JOEFIELD, Shellyann M.; '92 BA, '96 MA; 1482 St. Johns Pl., 2-H, Brooklyn, NY 11213.

ARCHIBALD, Emanuel; '82 BA; 1 Roanoke Dr., Monroe, NY 10950.

ARCHIE, Michelle J.; '93 BA; 61 Glen St., Brooklyn, NY 11208, 718 574-9354.

ARCURI, Gary; '92 BA; Investigator; r. 41 Galveston Loop., Apt. 1, Staten Island, NY 10314, 718 494-2572.

ARECIUS, Claudine; '96 BS; 5216 Beverly Rd., Brooklyn, NY 11203, 718 495-4656.

ARELLANO, Arthur Wellesley; BS; Slortar, 917 915-0154. e-mail

ARELLANO, Jose; '95 BA; JD Univ. of Akron; Law Clerk; Smith & Rossi, Akron, OH 44306; r. 626 Wythe Pl. Apt. 6j, Brooklyn, NY 11211, 718 388-8475. e-mail

ARESTIE, Martin J.; '76 BS; 11100 Braesridge Dr. Apt. 1835, Houston, TX 77071.

AREVALO, Yesenia M.; '95 BA, '95 CERT; AFDC Caseworker; Texas Dept. of Human Svcs., 1501 New York Ave., Arlington, TX 76010; r. 5315 Pocassett Dr., Arlington, TX 76018, 817 417-4722. e-mail

ARGALUZA, Roberto; '95 BA; 227 Naples Ter., Bronx, NY 10463, 718 601-5742.

ARGENT, Holly B.; '75 BA; 142 Hillcrest Rd, Mt. Vernon, NY 10552.

ARGENTI, Karen M.; '78 MPA; BA Lehman Clg.; Environ. Cnslt.; r. 3330 Giles Pl., Bronx, NY 10463, 718 543-1812; Dennis Nagle. e-mail

ARGENTINE, Michele; '89 BA; 7615 35th Ave. Apt. 3h, Flushing, NY 11372.

ARGIENTO, Ralph; '76 BA; 32 Colby Dr., Kings Park, NY 11754, 631 979-8293.

ARIAS, David S.; '99 BA; 1420 Amsterdam Ave #13H, New York, NY 10027, 212 694-0621.

ARIAS, Flora; '85 MPA; 512 White Plains Rd, Bronx, NY 10473, 718 884-9546.

ARIAS, Milagros A.; '95 BA; 9 Sherman Ave. Apt. 1k, New York, NY 10040.

ARIAS-KLEIN, Marta '77 (See Klein, Marta A.).

ARIDAS, Mrs. Nanette, (Nanette Vega); '97 BA; 45-56 42 St., apt. 4C, Sunnyside, NY 11104; Donald. e-mail

ARISTY, Tommy G.; '96 BS; Criminal Investigator; US Dept of Justice, New York, NY 10001; r. 90 Park Ter. E. Apt#4c, New York, NY 10034. e-mail

ARLAIN, Nena D.; '97 BS; Courier; Fed. Express, Maspeth, NY 11378; r. 225-03 Murdock Ave., Queens Vlg., NY 11429, 718 468-2552; Michael, Ebony. e-mail

ARLEN, Jennifer; '99 MA; BA SUNY Albany; Deputy Dir. of Admissions; Inst. for Community Living, Inc., 40 Rector St., 8th Fl., New York, NY 10006, 212 385-3030; r. 264 Whitman Dr., Brooklyn, NY 11234, 718 531-6492. e-mail

ARMANI, Chris G.; '98 BA; AS Kingsborough Community Cl; Police Ofcr.; Police Cnty.; r. 1935 59 St., Brooklyn, NY 11204, 718 234-6424. e-mail

ARMAO, Robert; 239 E. 17 St., New York, NY 10003.

ARMAS, Margie; '94 BS; MA Fordham Univ.; Retired Detective; NYPD, New York, NY 10038; r. 120-17 Einstein Loop #17F, Bronx, NY 10475, 718 320-2103; Annette, David. e-mail

ARMATTI, Linda '80 (See Armatti-Epstein, Linda T.).

ARMATTI-EPSTEIN, Linda T., (Linda Armatti); '80 BS; JD Southwestern Univ.; Lawyer; Jacoby & Meyers, 175 Pinelawn, Melville, NY 11747; r. 32 Slayton Ave., Staten Island, NY 10314, 718 494-9135; Jeffrey Epstein; Debra, Amanda. e-mail

ARMENIA, Rita; '99 BA; Asst. to Dean Grad. Studies; John Jay Clg., 899 10th Ave., New York, NY 10019, 212 237-8423; r. Elmont, NY 11003.

ARMESTO, Catherine P.; '99 BA; Ofc. Operation; First Choice Real Estate, 186 St., Fresh Meadows, NY 11365, 718 886-2816; r. 75 58 198 St. 1, Flushing, NY 11366, 718 776-2176. e-mail

ARMET, Thomas F.; '79 BS; 2 Academy St., Cambridge, NY 12816, 518 677-2444.

ARMIENTO, Michael J.; '71 BS, '78 MPA; Retired; r. 225 Forest Ave., New Rochelle, NY 10804, 914 636-0742.

ARMORER, Sharifa J.; '93 BA; MSW Hunter Clg.; Social Worker; The Children's Village, Dobbs Ferry, NY 10522; r. 4067 Barnes Ave., Bronx, NY 10466, 718 547-4924.

ARMSTEAD, David; '95 BA; 201Ravine Ave. 6G, Yonkers, NY 10701.

ARMSTEAD, Kemba A.; '96 AS; 1172 Anderson Ave., Bronx, NY 10452, 718 402-9682.

ARMSTRONG, Lenore; '93 BS; 30 Richman Plz., Bronx, NY 10453, 718 515-8825.

ARMSTRONG-BARROWS, Valerie F.; '89 MPA; 1046 E. 212 St., Bronx, NY 10469, 718 231-1345.

ARNEJA, Mindy C.; '86 BA; 10512 63rd Rd, Flushing, NY 11375, 718 997-1297.

ARNEMAN, Barbara A.; '82 BA; 8116 267th St., Glen Oaks, NY 11004, 718 347-4346.

ARNIOTES, LT James V.; '97 BS, '98 BS; Lt.; NYC Police Dept., 1 Police Plz., New York, NY 10038, 718 935-9240; r. 5104 Oceanview Ave., Brooklyn, NY 11224, 718 372-3290. e-mail

ARNOLD, Henry C.; '80 MA, BA, AS; Univ. of Louisville; Lt. Detective Cdr Ret; Monroe Cnty. So, Key West, FL 33040; r. 238 W Seaview Cir., Marathon, FL 33050, 305 743-0457; Ellie; Eric, Craig, Heab, Kirk, Kim, Alex, Allison, Lyle.

ARNOLD, Richard; '96 BS; Firefighter; Village of Garden City, 347 Stewart Ave., Garden City, NY 11530, 516 746-1301; r. 3697 Somerset Dr., Seaford, NY 11783, 516 221-2504; Eva Marie; Christopher. e-mail

ARNOLD, Sharol A.; '92 BA; 300 E 138th St., Apt. 2B, Bronx, NY 10454, 718 829-4883.

AROCHO, Belinda A.; '82 BS; POB 95, Bronx, NY 10472, 718 881-9762.

AROCHO, Sonia A.; '97 BA; 1536 38th St., Brooklyn, NY 11218.

ARONS-SCHULTZE, Janet A.; '78 BS; Voc. Rehab Couns.; Rehab. West of CA, Escondido, CA 92025; r. 12397 Avenida Consentido, San Diego, CA 92128, 858 673-9599; Robert; Daniel, Stephen, Laura. e-mail

ARRIETA, Frank J.; '82 BA; JD New York Law Sch.; Managing Atty.; Fitzgerald Fitzgerald, 538 Riverdale Ave., Yonkers, NY 10705, 914 378-1010; r. 3558 Cooper St., Mohegan Lake, NY 10547, 914 551-2253; Carrie Lyn; Rachel, Emily.

ARRIETA, Marcela R.; '82 BS; 8271 160th St., Jamaica, NY 11432.

ARRINGTON, Oscar P.; '85 AS, '91 MA; 780 Concourse Village, Bronx, NY 10451, 718 881-6723.

ARRINGTON, Otis W.; '78 BA; 1132 E. 229th St., Bronx, NY 10466, 718 881-6723.

ARROYO, Anthony; '95 BA; 726 Elton Ave., Bronx, NY 10455, 718 543-1767.

ARROYO, Catherine; '96 BA; 359 Manhattan Ave., Brooklyn, NY 11211, 718 383-0584.

ARROYO, David; '89 BS; 426 E. 149 St. #4W, Bronx, NY 10455, 718 402-5809.

ARROYO, Henry; '90 BA; Administrative Assoc.; Law Department Corporation Counsel, 198 E. 161st St., Bronx, NY 10451, 718 590-6215; r. POB 85, Park Chester Sta., Bronx, NY 10462, 718 792-1287.

ARROYO, Jennifer R., (Jennifer J. Reid); '94 MA; BA City Clg. of NY; Systs. Admin.; Wachtell Lipton Rosen & Katz, 51 W 52nd St., New York, NY 10019, 212 403-1548; r. 483 Empire Blvd., Brooklyn, NY 11225, 718 756-2463; *Miguel*. e-mail

ARROYO, Jose A.; '95 AS; 1855 Schieffelin A, Bronx, NY 10466, 718 543-1767.

ARROYO, Kelly; '99 BA; 408 Beverly Rd Bsmt, Brooklyn, NY 11218, 718 633-8679.

ARROYO, Miriam E.; '81 BA; 120 W 97 St., New York, NY 10025, 212 966-9618.

ARSENAKOS, Stella, JD; '80 BA; JD Bridgeport Law Sch.; Atty.; Stella Arsenakos Atty-at-Law, 26 Court St. Ste. 606, Brooklyn, NY 11242, 718 643-1699; r. Brooklyn, NY 11209.

ARTEAGA, Ms. Luz A.; '97 BA; BA; Social Worker; New York Foundling Hosp., 11-43 47th Ave., Long Island City, NY 11101, 718 784-4422; r. 23-33 91st St., E. Elmhurst, NY 11369, 718 899-4423. e-mail

ARTES, Joseph; 102 E. 32 St., Brooklyn, NY 11226.

ARTESANI, Joanne A.; '79 BS; 3223 83 St., Flushing, NY 11370.

ARTHUR, Easlyn C.; '80 BS; 379 E 48 St., Brooklyn, NY 11203, 718 629-2315.

ARTHUR, Jude; '98 BS; SAPIS; Bd. of Educ, 110 Livingston St., Brooklyn, NY 11201, 718 657-7690; r. 116-21 169th St., Jamaica, NY 11434, 718 276-5979; Juliana.

ARTHUR, Kent; '92 BS; 980 Ocean Ave., Brooklyn, NY 11226, 718 462-4374.

ARTHUR, Mario; '81 BA; POB 1386, Sterling, VA 20167, 703 312-0522.

ARTHUR, Terri E.; '84 MA; 6 Sarrington Ct., Stafford, VA 22554.

ARUZ, Steve A.; '95 BA; 20-54 Crescent St., Long Island City, NY 11105.

ARZBERGER, Robert M.; '75 BS; 9 Harness Ln., Levittown, NY 11756, 516 796-6772; *Margaret*; Melissa, Jeffrey, Bryan.

ARZOLA, Elizabeth; '89 MA; 74 Deerfield St., Bergenfield, NJ 07621.

ARZUAGA, Juan J.; '92 BS, '99 MPA; 46 Devon Rd., Hempstead, NY 11550, 718 654-1461.

ASAD, Abdalla M.; '95 BS; 191 32nd St. # 1, Brooklyn, NY 11232.

ASAD, Jamal M.; '89 BS; 391 Prospect Ave., Brooklyn, NY 11215, 718 965-4988.

ASAMOAH, Benoni A.; '80 MA; 61 Seneca Rd, New Haven, CT 06515, 203 387-9667.

ASANTE, Tyberius D.; '96 BA; 37-36 Tenth Ave., New York, NY 10034.

ASBERY, Joseph; '93 BS; 932 E 226th St., Bronx, NY 10466, 718 547-9026.

ASENCIO, Stacy; '97 BA; 50 Herbert St., Brooklyn, NY 11222.

ASH, Sylvia G., Esq.; '76 BA; BA SUNY at Stony Brook, JD Howard Univ.; Sr. Atty.; DC37 Immigration Prog., 125 Barclay St., Ste. 667, New York, NY 10007, 212 341-4702; r. 568 Westminster Rd, Brooklyn, NY 11230, 718 693-7560. e-mail

ASHER, Jean M.; '96 MA; 730 60 St., Brooklyn, NY 11220, 718 492-2740.

ASHLEY, Jo-an G.; '84 BS; 3739 100th St., Flushing, NY 11368, 718 217-8469.

ASHLEY, Teresa L.; '97 BA; Programming Svcs. Coord.; Advent Software, New York, NY 10001; r. 255 E 18th St., Apt. 5D, Brooklyn, NY 11226, 718 941-7262. e-mail

ASHOORY, Bracha; '85 MA; 94-31 60 St. #3H, Rego Park, NY 11373.

ASHTON, Cornelius M.; '86 BA; 422 Halsey St., Brooklyn, NY 11233, 718 345-2173.

ASHWOOD, Carlos A.; '78 BA; 14432 184th St., Jamaica, NY 11413, 718 527-7835.

ASKIN, John P.; '72 AS, '75 BA; Inspector; Police Dept. City of NY, 960 Carrol St., Brooklyn, NY 11225; r. 356 Beach Rd, Staten Island, NY 10312, 718 356-4758.

ASKINS, Jisselle F.; '99 BA; 83-37 St. James Ave. #1Lb, Elmhurst, NY 11373, 718 476-8712.

ASSANTE, Philip J.; '73 BS; 2123 S Joyce St., Arlington, VA 22202, 703 683-5619.

ASSAYAG, Lyate A.; '99 BS; 1656 E 4th, Brooklyn, NY 11236, 718 645-4801.

ASSENHEIMER, Carl F.; '73 BA; 163 Grove St., Lodi, NJ 07644.

ASSIFF, Laurie A.; '97 BA; 1146 77 St., Brooklyn, NY 11228.

ASTOR, Kevin R.; '81 BS; 107 Stokesay Ct., Cary, NC 27513; *Susan;* Lindsay, Amanda.

ASTRIZKY, Beatrice N.; '80 BS; 430 Shore Rd., Long Beach, NY 11561.

ATKINSON, Donald; '75 MA; EDD Temple Univ.; Theology Student; Wesley Theological Seminary; r. 23 Baroness Ct., Owings Mills, MD 21117, 410 902-8255; *Rosemary*. e-mail

ATLAS, Gary; '75 BA; 26 Brighton 10 Ct., Brooklyn, NY 11235, 718 965-2488.

ATLAS, Thomas A.; '75 MA; 65-94 162 St., Flushing, NY 11365, 718 969-2008.

ATRISTAIN, Luis; '99 BS; 82-35 134th St. #3G, Briarwood, NY 11435, 718 261-0311.

ATTRIDGE, Walter J.; '99 BS; 119 06 28 Ave., Flushing, NY 11354.

AUDIFFRED, Jesus; '93 BS; Security Supv.; Barney NY, Lyndhurst, NJ 07071; r. 414 11th St. # 1, Union City, NJ 07087, 201 864-8155.

AUDINOT, Leila B.; '79 BA; POB 385, Rifton, NY 12471, 914 658-9644.

AUERBACH, Alan R.; '87 BS; 18 Birch Ln., Plainview, NY 11803.

AUERBACH, Alice '92 (See Akgun-Auerbach, Ms. Alice).

AUGELLO, Angelo J.; '76; 1853 76th St., Brooklyn, NY 11214, 718 331-5294.

AUGUSTE-SMITH, Portia; '99 BS; 1142 E. 58th St., 2nd Fl., Brooklyn, NY 11234, 718 222-1587.

AUGUSTIN, Kisha V.; '99 BA; 2603 Avenue D, Brooklyn, NY 11226, 718 856-6165. e-mail

AUGUSTIN, Nancy; '96 BS; 8 Gladys Ln., Freeport, NY 11520, 516 536-8524.

AUGUSTINE, Clyde L.; '80 BS, '83 MA; Sr. Detective Investigator; Ofc. of The Dist. Atty.-Kings Cnty., Renaissance Plz., 350 J St., Brooklyn, NY 11201, 718 250-3872; r. 894 E 39th St., Brooklyn, NY 11210, 718 421-0156. e-mail

AUGUSTINE, Sharmain; '96 BS; 99-20 32nd Ave., E. Elmhurst, NY 11369, 718 894-5160.

AUGUSTUS, Antoinette J. '97 (See Augustus Miller, Mrs. Antoinette J.).

AUGUSTUS, Sondra R.; '75 AA; BA Pace Univ.; Dir.; Campbell Soup Co., Campbell Pl., Camden, NJ 08103, 856 342-6358; r. 1000 Randolph Dr., Yardley, PA 19067, 215 321-8932.

AUGUSTUS MILLER, Mrs. Antoinette J., (Antoinette J. Augustus); '97 BA; BA; Police Ofcr.; 718 972-3312; r. Brooklyn, NY 11207. e-mail

AUGUSTYNOWICZ, Richard; '77 AS; Retired Police Ofcr.; r. 457 Ocean Ave., West Haven, CT 06516, 203 931-7071; *Millie*. e-mail

AULBACH, Philip E.; '71 AS, '72 BA; 11 Yale St., Port Jefferson Sta., NY 11776, 631 331-8646.

AULETA, Kent R.; '75 BA; 23 Windham Ln., Ronkonkoma, NY 11779.

AULETTA, Richard N.; '77 AS; Pres.; Summit Security Svcs. Inc., 45-34 Court Sq., Long Island City, NY 11101, 718 452-0200; r. 54 Riviera Dr. S, Massapequa, NY 11758, 516 799-5482.

AULI, Karoll; '99 BA; Child Welfare Spec.; Admin. for Children's Svcs., 55 6th Ave., New York, NY 10013, 212 941-6444; r. 360 Morris Ave., #4A, Bronx, NY 10451, 718 665-3627. e-mail

AULT, Colette E.; '99 BA; Employee Benefit Coord.; City of NY Parks & Rec., 16 W. 61st St., New York, NY 10023; r. 120-13 197 St. Bsmt, St. Albans, NY 11412, 718 949-9761.

AUSTIN, Barbara J.; '79 BS; MSED Hunter Clg.; Admissions Couns.; Hunter Clg., 695 Park Ave., New York, NY 10021, 212 772-4045; r. 18019 Linden Blvd. Ste. 2, Jamaica, NY 11434, 718 949-6201.

AUSTIN, Evelyn G.; '78 BA; 205 E 112th St. Apt. 7c, New York, NY 10029, 315 724-1603.

AUSTIN, Karen F.; '76 BA; 377 Hawthorne St., Brooklyn, NY 11225, 718 921-0024.

AUSTIN, Reginald A.; '75 BS; Retired; r. 13319 160th St., Jamaica, NY 11434, 718 527-3983; *Anez;* Reginald, Kenneth W., Kyle Janet (d).

AUSTRIA, Crisanta H.; '85 MPA; 189-03 90th Ave., Hollis, NY 11423, 718 468-1348.

AUSTRIE, Gilda; '96 BA; Law Student; Thomas M. Cooley Law Sch., Sch. Address:, 323 N. Walnut St. #605, Lansing, MI 48933; r. Permanant Address:, 3314 109th St., Corona, NY 11368. e-mail

AUTERA, Marysusan D.; '93 BA; Retired Detective; NYPD; r. 5128 30th Ave. # 4b, Woodside, NY 11377. e-mail

AVALLONE, Carolann; '89 BA; 42 Barbara St., Staten Island, NY 10306.

AVDOULOS, Robert L.; '99 BA; 66 E. 5th St., Deer Park, NY 11729, 631 586-4419.

AVELLA, Tracey E.; '95 MA; 17 Schoolhouse Rd, East Islip, NY 11730.

AVERSA, Eileen T. '98 (See Lafemina, Ms. Eileen T.).

AVERY, Earl; '80 MPA; Ins. Broker; Cambria Heights Ins. Brokerage, Inc., 114-31 226th St., Cambria Hts., NY 11411, 718 276-4534; r. 11431 226th St., Cambria Hts., NY 11411, 718 276-4534; Annie B.; Valerie C., Theresa L. e-mail

AVILA, Douglas E.; '89 BS; 1211 30th Dr. Apt. 1l, Long Island City, NY 11102, 718 846-0161.

AVILA, Gil; '93 BA; 1218 Leland Ave. Ph, Bronx, NY 10472, 718 681-8750.

AVILA, Patricio; '95 BS; 11-15 New Montrose, Brooklyn, NY 11211, 718 964-0862.

AVILES, LT Edwin R.; '92 BA, '92 MPA; CERT. Cornell Univ., FBI Academy; Commanding Ofcr.; NYC Police 25th Precinct, Detective Squad, 120 E 119th St., New York, NY 10035, 212 860-7223; r. 129 Zoe St., Staten Island, NY 10305, 718 979-3997; Pilar; Mark Edward, Jason Stewart, Denise Pilar, Natalie Jean.

AVILES, Lisa; '96 BA; 290 Suydam St., Brooklyn, NY 11237.

AVILES, Norma; '92 BS; 10 Manhattan Ave., New York, NY 10025, 212 928-0912.

AVILES, Victor; '84 BA; MS Long Island Univ., AS Westchester Community Clg; Police Ofcr.; Metropolitan Transportation Authority, 345 Madison Ave., New York, NY 10017, 212 340-2723; r. POB 1527, Ossining, NY 10562.

AVILES, Victor R.; '92 BS; 788 Columbus Ave., New York, NY 10025, 212 666-1646.

AVINGER, Denise; '95 BS; 22 Patchen Ave. #5 BSMT, Brooklyn, NY 11221, 718 443-6563.

AVRAMIDIS, Georgios; '84 BS; 26-04 Ditmars Blvd., Astoria, NY 11105, 718 278-2992.

AWEEKY, Peter A.; '84 BS; Sr. Vice President Treas.; Landsbank Hessen Turingen, 420 5th Ave., New York, NY 10018, 212 703-2500; r. 4 Knox Pl., Staten Island, NY 10314. e-mail

AYALA, Carmelo; '81 BA; 106 W Eckerson Rd, Spring Vly., NY 10977, 914 425-7986.

AYALA, Francisco, Jr.; '78 BS; Chief of Security/Exec. Dir. HNLEF; Discovery Trading Corp., HNLEF/Hispanic Natl. Law Enf. Foun., 660 Madison Ave., New York, NY 10021; r. POB 30905, New York, NY 10011, 917 802-7005; Dorothy; Frank III, Andino, Orlando, Antonio. e-mail

AYALA, Irma I.; '99 BA; 119 E. 102 St., New York, NY 10029, 212 996-1371.

AYALA, Manuel D.; '92 BA; 3456 73rd St. Apt. D10, Flushing, NY 11372, 718 426-2045.

AYALA, Maria; '89 BS; 8201 Britton Ave. Apt. 5N, Flushing, NY 11373, 718 446-4869.

AYALA, Mona C.; '98 BS; Fraud Investigator; Bur. of Fraud Investigations, 250 Church St., 3rd Fl., New York, NY 10013, 212 274-5387; r. 75 W. End Ave. Apt. C1OL, New York, NY 10023; Richard.

AYALA, Robert; '87 BA; 2319 Wallace Ave., Bronx, NY 10467, 718 329-2015.

AYALA-DEVITO, Linda; '89 BS; 10520 66th Rd, Apt. 3D, Forest Hills, NY 11375.

AYARI, Abderrahman B.; '75 BA; 286 Cortelyou Ave., Staten Island, NY 10312.

AYARI, Dalinda C.; '95 BA; 642 Washington St., Apt. 1B, New York, NY 10014.

AYERS, Charles E.; '79 BA; Supv. of Mail; Morgan Gen. Mail Facility, New York, NY 10001; r. 42 Matthews Ave., W. Babylon, NY 11704, 631 491-0822.

AYERS, Manford G.; '87 AS; 83 Woodland Ave., Morristown, NJ 07960, 973 744-1234.

AYERS, Rashida; '95 BA; 1596 Unionport Rd, Apt. 3H, Bronx, NY 10462, 718 828-1880.

AYLWARD, John; '95 BA; 13 Irma Ave., Port Washington, NY 11050, 516 944-7652.

AYRES, Richard; '85 MPA; BS Dickinson Clg./Iona Clg., JD Washington Clg. of Law; Trainer/Cnslt.; Ctr. for Labor Mgmt. Study, 1 Matoca Ct., Fredericksburg, VA 22401, 540 373-9670; r. same, 540 371-3179; Marilyn. e-mail

AYROVAINEN, Thomas; '83 AS, '85 BS; 556 N Greene Ave., Lindenhurst, NY 11757, 631 888-8734.

AZEGLIO, Anna M.; '92 BS; 50-07 5th St., Long Island City, NY 11101, 718 937-0847.

AZIZ, Amina; '95 AS, '97 BA; 650 Malcolm X Blvd. Apt. 4d, New York, NY 10037, 212 281-7263.

AZURDIA, Gilda L.; '97 BA; 87-37 110 St., Richmond Hill, NY 11418.

AZURDIA, Raul J.; '97 BA; 87-37 110 St., Richmond Hill, NY 11418.

AZZARO, Diana; '96 BA; 257-30 147th Rd., Rosedale, NY 11422.

AZZOLINI, John; '90 BA; 2112 24th Ave. # 1, Astoria, NY 11102.

B

BABAKITIS, Paul G.; '83 BS; Sgt./ NYPD; NYC Police Dept., 1 Police Plz., New York, NY 10038, 212 237-4530; r. 58 Hazelwood Dr., Jericho, NY 11753; Debbie; Michael, Zoie. e-mail

BABALOLA, Sikiru; '94 BSCJ, 2000 MSCJ; Pres./Prog. Alliance/Redir./Nigeria; Mgr. Clinical Proj. Facility-Homelss, Unifacity Treatment Ctr., 1020 Grande Concouse, Bronx, NY 10451, 718 401-2850; r. 672 Ocean Ave. #8A, Brooklyn, NY 11226, 718 856-6607; Kemi.

BABB, Harry N.; '69 BS; 491 18th St., W. Babylon, NY 11704.

BABB, Jackie R.; '99 BS; Business Analyst; American Express, 7 World Trade Ctr., New York, NY 10048, 212 306-9166; r. 1116 E. 48th St., Brooklyn, NY 11234, 718 252-1730.

BABB, Randolph; '77 BS; 245 Clifton Pl., Brooklyn, NY 11216, 718 783-1135.

BABBINI, Patricia A.; '83 BA; Senior Parole Ofcr.; Div. of Parole, 66 Hamilton St., Paterson, NJ 07505, 973 977-4256; r. 816 Prospect Ave., Ridgefield, NJ 07657, 201 945-9372; Donald Ritchie.

BABISCKO, Stephen G.; '77 BS; Ret. Asst. Secure; Pompano Race Track; r. 110 NW 53rd Ct., Pompano Bch., FL 33064, 954 421-0534; Arlene; Kevin. e-mail

BABNIK, Andrew; '77 AS; 2 Uppland Dr., Putnam Vly., NY 10579, 914 528-8192.

BABSKI, Tatjana A.; '96 BS; 86-07 86th Ave., Woodhaven, NY 11421.

BACCHI, Diana E.; '96 BA; 54 Shepherd Ave., Brooklyn, NY 11208.

BACCHUS, Garvin W.; '80 BS; 1083 E. 43rd St., Brooklyn, NY 11210, 718 338-1197.

BACCHUS, Kimberly C. '98 (See Bacchus-Larode, Mrs. Kimberly C.).

BACCHUS, Roseema S.; '93 BS; JD Touro Law Sch.; Legal Publishing; HW Wilson; r. 246 E Chester St., Long Beach, NY 11561, 516 431-4421.

BACCHUS-LARODE, Mrs. Kimberly C., (Kimberly C. Bacchus); '98 BA; Liability Adjuster; State Farm Mutual Ins. Co., 75 20 Astoria Blvd., E. Elmhurst, NY 11370, 718 803-4300; r. 159 E. 37th St., Brooklyn, NY 11203, 718 953-5305; Keith Larode; Kurston.

BACH, Robert R.; '76 BS; 54-62 63 Pl., Maspeth, NY 11378, 718 641-9120.

BACH, Roger J.; '96 MPA; BA St. Leo; Supervisory Special Agt.; DEA, 175 Pine Lawn Rd. Ste. 205, Melville, NY 11747, 631 420-4530.

BACHMANN, Peter J.; '80 BA; 3068 Harding Ave., Bronx, NY 10465, 718 792-2795.

BACHORIK, Edward S.; '73 AS, '74 BS; 1475 Theriot Ave., Bronx, NY 10460, 718 828-0236.

BACKOF, Richard W.; '76 BS; 5 Cascade St., Staten Island, NY 10306.

BACON, Cynthia; '89 BS; POB 162391, Atlanta, GA 30321, 770 978-8992.

BACOVIC, Hasan; '97 BS; 2222 E.18 St., Brooklyn, NY 11229.

BADAGLIACCA, Michael; '97 BA; 7820 14th Ave., Brooklyn, NY 11228.

BADALAMENTI, Frank; '96 BS; 7149 70th St., Ridgewood, NY 11385, 718 497-9545.

BADAMO, Robert T.; '77 BS; Police Ofcr.; New York City, 101st Precinct, 1612 Mott Ave., Far Rockaway, NY 11691; r. 11 E. 6th Rd., Broad Channel, NY 11693; Donna; Jennifer, James.

BADDOO, Juliana '88 (See Baddoo-Asare, Juliana).

BADDOO-ASARE, Juliana, (Juliana Baddoo); '88 BA; Ofc. Mgr.; Springfield Med. Ofc., 1 Cross Island Plz., Ste. 201, Rosedale, NY 11422, 718 712-1080; r. 253-36 149th Rd, Jamaica, NY 11422, 718 723-5691; Dr. Emmanuel Asare; Letitia, Christina.

BADILLO, Anderson; '92 BS; AS Bronx Com. Clg.; Retired-Police Ofcr.; NYC Transit; r. Medford, NY 11763.

BADILLO, Cristina; '99 BS; Admin. Coord.; Fed. Ex, 300 Massbest, Brooklyn, NY 11211, 718 782-4848; r. POB 320039, Brooklyn, NY 11232, 718 499-2401.

BADILLO, Elizabeth; '97; 69 Sky Meadow Pl., Elmsford, NY 10523.

BAEK, Hyon K.; '97 BS; 140-19 33rd Ave., Flushing, NY 11354, 718 392-0632.

BAEZ, Benjamin; '84 BS; 455 E 137th St. Apt. 2b, Bronx, NY 10454, 718 589-8868.

BAEZ, Eileen; '95 BS; 186 Claremont Ave., New York, NY 10027.

BAEZ, Henry; '76 BA; 99 Albion Pl., Staten Island, NY 10302, 718 698-3124.

BAEZ, Mayra M.; '96 BS; 1414 Walton Ave., Bronx, NY 10452, 718 299-8689.

BAEZ, Ricardo; '98 BS; 1173 Old Post Rd, S. Salem, NY 10590, 914 576-9182.

BAEZ, Tina M.; '95 BS; Fraud Investigator; Ofc. of Revenue & Investigation, 250 Church St., New York, NY 10013, 212 274-4874; r. 718 969-4732; Carlos.

BAEZ, Yvonne K.; '96 BS; UPR/PEP; NYC Parks & Recreation, 1234 5th Ave., New York, NY 10029, 212 437-1350; r. 111 Linwood St., Brooklyn, NY 11208, 718 277-6593.

BAEZ-FELIX, Eileen; '94 BS; 115 Alderwood Dr., Kissimmee, FL 34743.

BAGI, Gabor R.; '97 BS; 63 Saint Andrew Pl, Yonkers, NY 10705.

BAGLEY, Reginald N.; '76 BS; 3 Autumn Ln., Amityville, NY 11701.

BAHAN, Mildred; '92 BA; Social Worker; r. 6811 Owls Head Ct., Brooklyn, NY 11220, 718 745-1456; Christine.

BAHNA, Alfred M.; '88 BS; Hallmark Retailer; C.V.'s Hallmark, 236 Prospect Park W., Brooklyn, NY 11215, 718 499-6670; r. 640 Vanderbilt St., Brooklyn, NY 11218, 718 633-2231; Kerry; Matthew. e-mail

BAICHOO, Linda T.; '99 BA; 107-67 117th St., S. Richmond Hill, NY 11419, 718 843-0339.

BAIDY, Quillar; '97 BS; 590 E 3rd St., Mt. Vernon, NY 10553.

BAIERLEIN, Elizabeth; '93 BA; 1902 Everett St., Valley Stream, NY 11580, 516 679-5172.

BAILEY, Alban O.; '77 BS; 122 Ramsell St., San Francisco, CA 94132, 415 668-1187.

BAILEY, Alex T.; '94 MPA; Capt.; NYC Dept. of Corrections, 60 Hudson St., New York, NY 10013, 212 266-1000; r. POB 296, Blooming Grove, NY 10914, 914 496-6335.

BAILEY, Anthony M.; '97 BS; 382 E.51 St., Brooklyn, NY 11203, 718 258-3327.

BAILEY, April; '85 BA; 8730 204th St., Apt. B63, Hollis, NY 11423, 718 525-2495.

BAILEY, Belinda A.; '79 BS; 140 Alcott Pl. # 23, Bronx, NY 10475, 718 379-2811.

BAILEY, Betzaida; '97 BS; 245 Wortman Ave., Brooklyn, NY 11207, 718 649-0272.

BAILEY, Christine; '89 BA; 672 E 232nd St., Bronx, NY 10466, 718 538-3346.

BAILEY, Edmarine A.; '97 BA; 2076 Dean St., Brooklyn, NY 11233, 718 602-2632.

BAILEY, Kimesha; '97 BA; 42-66 Phlox Pl., Flushing, NY 11355, 718 525-2495.

BAILEY, Lisa; '87 BS; 15312 120th Ave., Jamaica, NY 11434, 718 776-4577.

BAILEY, Nigel R.; '95 BS; 333 E. 150 Stree, Bronx, NY 10451, 718 292-2815.

BAILEY, Patricia A.; '81 BS; 606 N Van Buren St., Wilmington, DE 19805, 302 369-6440.

BAILEY, Stephen H.; '76 BS; PARALGL Adelphi Univ., MPA; Inspector/Inspections Postal Police; Treasury Dept. US Customs/ US Postal Svc, JFK Airport, Jamaica, NY 11430, 718 553-7372; r. 112 Spray St., Massapequa, NY 11758, 516 797-1750; Sharon; Jason, Sherita, Stephani, Christel. e-mail

BAILEY, Steven D.; '97 BS; State Corrections Ofcr.; r. 330 Cypress Dr., Colonia, NJ 07067, 732 381-7252.

BAILEY, Sweden M.; '97 BS, '98 BS; 19222 Williamson Ave., Springfield Gardens, NY 11413, 718 525-2495.

BAILEY, William S.; '82 BS; Security Mgr.; Victoria Secret Catalog, 1114 Ave. of The Americas, 25th Fl., New York, NY 10036; r. 699 Seaman Ave., Baldwin, NY 11510, 516 378-0851. e-mail

BAIRD, Ernest; '75 BS; 720 Lenox Ave., New York, NY 10039, 315 839-5866.

BAIRD, Omadeli S.; '95 BS; 11030 197th St., Jamaica, NY 11412, 718 479-6542.

BAIRD, Scott; '97 BA; 240 E.35th St. #8, New York, NY 10016, 212 889-3308.

BAIRD-ALLEYNE, Arlene; '91 BA; 1055 Lincoln Pl., Brooklyn, NY 11213, 718 467-4192.

BAISDEN, Ms. Jilyon; '99 BS; Info. Syst. Security Analyst; TD Waterhouse Investor Svcs., 95 Christopher Columbus Dr., Jersey City, NJ 07302, 201 369-8358; r. 95 Eastern Pkwy. 2B, Brooklyn, NY 11238, 718 398-7307; Rainier Jeffrey, Akeem. e-mail

BAKER, April M.; 466 S Columbus Ave., Mt. Vernon, NY 10553, 716 834-1099.

BAKER, Candiace V.; '91 BS; 13343 157th St., Jamaica, NY 11434, 718 529-3809.

BAKER, Harold C.; '73 BS; MA NYU; Safety Engr. Ret; Lucent Technologies; r. 71 Tall Timber Rd, Middletown, NJ 07748, 732 671-5467; Vivian M. e-mail

BAKER, James; '85 MA; BS USMA, JD Univ. of Oregon Law; Asst Dist. Counsel; USA Engr. Dist. Walla Walla, 201 N 3rd Ave., Walla Walla, WA 99362, 509 527-7717; r. 1746 Hillbrooke Dr., Walla Walla, WA 99362, 509 522-3344.

BAKER, Janice L.; '95 BS; MLS Queens Clg.; Information Specialist; Clifford Chance Rogers & Wells LLP, 200 Park Ave., New York, NY 10166; r. 25340 147th Rd., Jamaica, NY 11422, 718 527-7600. e-mail

BAKER, Jimmie R.; '77 BS; MPA NYU; Probation Ofcr.; Floyd Cnty. Probation Ofc., 400 Broad St., Rome, GA 30161, 706 295-6323; r. 314 Viewmont Dr., Tunnel Hill, GA 30755, 706 673-9893; Deanna; Michael, Ashlee Partlow. e-mail

BAKER, Michele C.; '87 BS; 738 Park Ave., Uniondale, NY 11553, 516 569-4347.

BAKER, Noel M.; '97 BS; 297 Grafton St., Brooklyn, NY 11212, 718 338-6707.

BAKER, Robert D.; '97 BS; JD Fordham Univ.; Ofcr.; New York Police Dept., Precinct 102, Richmond Hill, NY 11418, 718 805-3200; r. 175-45 88th Ave., Jamaica, NY 11432; Simone. e-mail

BAKER, Teresa; '86 BA; 2425 Lorillard Pl., Bronx, NY 10458, 718 792-5396.

BALA, James W.; '76 BS; BS; Sr. Deputy Sheriff; NYC Sheriff; r. 159 North Rd., Topsfield, ME 04490. e-mail

BALANGON, Janelle P.; '99 BS; 67-123 Burns St., Forest Hills, NY 11375, 718 520-4544.

BALASH, Andre; 3325 92nd St. Apt. 4h, Flushing, NY 11372.

BALCOM, MAJ Jerome (Jerry) K.; '73 BS CJ; MPS C.W. Post-LI Univ., CERT. Inst. for Ct. Mgmt.; Cmd. Ofcr-Supreme & Cnty. Courts; 9th Judicial Dist., State of NY, White Plains, NY 10602, 914 285-3864; r. 61 Mayfair Rd., Poughquag, NY 12570; Laura; Bernadette, Judith. e-mail

BALCOM, Mrs. Laura, (Laura Moeser); '73 BA, '87 MA; Crisis Couns.; r. 61 Mayfair Rd., Poughquag, NY 12570, 914 724-4050; Jerome K.; Bernadette, Judith. e-mail

BALCOMBE, Marcelle; '93 BS; 1023 E 80th St., Brooklyn, NY 11236.

BALDUCCI, Frank; '94 BS; Police Ofcr./Instr.; NYC Police Dept., 1 Police Plz., 235 E. 20 St., New York, NY 10003; r. 2260 37th St., Long Island City, NY 11105, 718 726-7036.

BALDWIN, Robert M.; '76 BA; MBA Pace Univ.; Corporate Security Dir.; Movado Grp. Inc., 125 Chubb Ave., Lyndhurst, NJ 07071, 201 460-3860; r. 4642 189th St., Flushing, NY 11358. e-mail

BALECHA, Joanne; 340 W. 55th St., New York, NY 10019, 212 262-1320.

BALFOUR, Joshua H.; '92 BS; Security Mgmt.; Pinkerton, Hicksville, NY 11802; r. 10736 139th St., Jamaica, NY 11435, 718 657-6958.

11

BALGOBIN, Hemant K.; '99 BS; Records Clerk; Simpson Thacher & Bartlett, 425 Lexington Ave., New York, NY 10017, 212 455-2000; r. 87-61 109 St., Richmond Hill, NY 11418, 718 849-2780.

BALGOBIN, Ms. Julianna; '98 BA; AA Manhattan Community Clg.; Tchr.-1st Grade & Grad. Student; City of NY Public Schs., 5010 Sixth Ave., Brooklyn, NY 11220.

BALIKO, Jaclyn M.; '97 BA; 72 Columbia Ave., Jersey City, NJ 07307.

BALL, Raymond H.; '90 BA; Rsch. Cnslt.; r. 230 W. 129th St. #8B, New York, NY 10027, 212 663-8439.

BALL, Robert; '82 BS; Retired Paralegal; r. 230 W 129th St. Apt. 8b, New York, NY 10027, 212 663-8439; *Sadie*. e-mail

BALLANTINE, Jean M.; '82 BA; 4415 Montecello Ave., Bronx, NY 10466.

BALLARD, Celeste I.; '96 BS; 1600 Metropolitan Ave. Apt. 1h, Bronx, NY 10462, 718 681-4985.

BALLARD, Michael A.; '79 BS; 967 E 225th St., Bronx, NY 10466, 718 681-4985.

BALLERO, Hilda E.; '77 BS; 8714 97th Ave., Jamaica, NY 11416.

BALLIRAJ, Ramjit; '79 BS; 563 41st St., Brooklyn, NY 11232.

BALOGUN, Raheem; '85 BS; 116a Macon St., Brooklyn, NY 11216.

BALSAMO, Patricia; '93 BS; 441 Beach 130th St., Rockaway Park, NY 11694, 718 848-7620.

BALUNAS, William E.; '89 BS; 1349 F St., Elmont, NY 11003.

BAMRICK, Kenneth G.; '69 BS; MBA St. Johns Univ.; Ret.; r. 2079 Palo Alto Ave., The Villages, FL 32159, 352 259-0997; *Ann*. e-mail

BANACH, Paul F.; '86 BS; 30 Vincent Dr., Burlington Twp., NJ 08016.

BANATTE, Carline; '94 BS; 444 Bergen St., Brooklyn, NY 11217, 718 399-6171.

BAND, Nora H.; '77 MA; 1610 E 94th St., Brooklyn, NY 11236, 718 338-8528.

BANDIK, Mark G.; '82 BS; Unit 3900, APO, AA 34032.

BANEY, James M.; '75 BS; 145 Henrietta Ave., Oceanside, NY 11572, 516 678-4852.

BANIEVICZ, Alexander; '96 BA; Supports Spec.; FBI, 26 Federal Plz., New York, NY 10278, 212 384-4338; r. 3155 Rochambeau Ave. 2D, Bronx, NY 10467; *Heade*.

BANK, Maurice H.; '76 BS; State Tax Agt. Compliance; NYS Dept. of Taxation & Finance, 55 Hanson Pl., Brooklyn, NY 11217; r. 3000 Ocean Pkwy. Apt. 23v, Brooklyn, NY 11235, 718 372-3785. e-mail

BANKO, Ellen '84 (See Banko -Ross, Dr. Ellen).

BANKO -ROSS, Dr. Ellen, (Ellen Banko); '84 MA; PSYD; Psychotherapist; 305 Metcalf Plz., Auburn, NY 13021, 315 255-2448; r. Canoga Rd., Auburn, NY 13021.

BANKOVIC, Milan; '94 BS, '96 MA; CERT. Natl Foreign Svc Trg Inst; Asst. Regional Security Ofcr.; US Dept. of State-Diplomatic Security, US Embassy Kiev Ukraine, Washington, DC 20521; r. 430 E. 6th St., Apt. 3B, New York, NY 10009, 212 677-8766. e-mail

BANKS, Celia B.; '81 BA; 190 Cozine Ave., Brooklyn, NY 11207, 718 927-4867.

BANKS, Cynthia '81 (See Sow, Ms. Cynthia B.).

BANKS, Deborah M.; '96 BA; 122-02 Irwin Pl., St. Albans, NY 11412, 718 335-4252.

BANKS, Demorris J.; '79 BS; 1109 Sussex Rd, Teaneck, NJ 07666, 201 587-0805.

BANKS, Hermon J.; '76 BA, '79 MPA; CERT. FBI Acad.; Security Dir., Former Sec. Dir.; Mt. Sinai Med. Ctr./World Trade Ctr., One Gustave L. Levy Pl., New York, NY 10029, 212 241-5661; r. 2 Fordham Hill Oval Apt. 6D, Bronx, NY 10468, 718 733-6089; *Katie (dec)*; Sadiqa, La Sawn, Keri Taylor. e-mail

BANKS, Latisha V. '99 (See Banks-Catoe, Latisha V.).

BANKS, Linda; '91 MPA; 315 W 232nd St. Apt. 4a, Bronx, NY 10463, 718 583-2779.

BANKS, Sadiqa; '99 BA; Special Asst. to Dir.; 212 572-3335; r. 10 Benchley Pl., Bronx, NY 10475, 718 320-3236.

BANKS, Shaundra L.; '82 BS; 405 Grand Ave., Brooklyn, NY 11238, 718 348-4999.

BANKS-CATOE, Latisha V., (Latisha V. Banks); '99 BA; Principal Community Liaison Worker; NYC Dept. for The Aging, 2 Lafayette St., 16th Fl., New York, NY 10007, 212 442-3069; r. 286 W. 147th St., #2B, New York, NY 10039, 212 283-1842; *Derrick Catoe*; Katiera. e-mail

BANNON, John W.; '73 BS; 6623 E Noel Pl., Inverness, FL 34452.

BAPTISTE, Camille A.; '98 BS; Telecommunication; Motorola, Atlanta, GA 30342; r. 5864 Fornof Rd, Columbus, GA 31909, 706 569-0876; *Karim Lowers*. e-mail

BAPTISTE, Wilfred E.; '83 MA; BS Morgan State Univ.; Agt.; Dept. of Justice, 26 Federal Plz., New York, NY 10278, 212 384-3275; r. POB #1956, New York, NY 10013, 212 384-3275. e-mail

BARAJAS, Robert J.; '81 MA; BS St. Johns Univ.; Security Cnslt.; Palladium Security Svcs., POB 296, Colonia, NJ 07067, 732 283-3031; r. 971 Green St., Iselin, NJ 08830, 732 283-4572; *Nancy*. e-mail

BARAKET, Tamara M.; '97 BS; Law Student; Quinnipiac; r. 13235 82nd St., Ozone Park, NY 11417, 718 835-5024. e-mail

BARANELLO, James P.; '86 BS; 103 Landau Ave., Floral Park, NY 11001, 516 328-1974.

BARATTA, Anthony; '80 BS; 2150 Bay Ridge Ave., Brooklyn, NY 11204, 718 232-1784.

BARATTINI, Peter F.; '78 MA; 15 Devonshire Dr., White Plains, NY 10605.

BARBA, Maria E.; '75 BS; 3202 Sweetmeadow Ct., Oakton, VA 22124, 703 273-7889.

BARBATO, Michael; '93 AS; Retired Firefighter; NYC; r. 6224 65th St., Flushing, NY 11379, 718 497-7420. e-mail

BARBATO, Ralph A.; '84 BA; 152 Thompson St., New York, NY 10012.

BARBER, Glenn M.; '78 BS; 1927 Orchard Dr., Daleville, VA 24083, 540 992-4270.

BARBERA, Joseph; '92 BS; 38 Morris Ave. W, Malverne, NY 11565, 516 887-9570.

BARBETTA, Mary T.; '95 BS; 5814 186th St., Fresh Meadows, NY 11365, 718 357-1754.

BARBIERI, Ellen B.; '75 MPA; BSN Hunter Clg.; Retired-Community Health Nurse Coor; Veterans Admin.; r. 1116 Akron St., San Diego, CA 92106, 619 226-0803; *Salvatore*. e-mail

BARBIERI, William T.; '95 AS; 30 Greencroft Ave., Staten Island, NY 10308.

BARBOSA, Jose A.; '99 BS; 71 W 107 St. 4C, New York, NY 10025.

BARBOUR, Ms. Susan M.; '85 BS; JD Brooklyn Law Sch.; Asst Atty. Gen.; NYS Dept. of Law, 120 Broadway, New York, NY 10271, 212 416-8623; r. 230 Park Pl. Apt. 2N, Brooklyn, NY 11238, 718 385-9208.

BARCLAY, Keith G.; '80 MA; 54 Ivy Hill Rd, Red Bank, NJ 07701, 732 219-9571.

BARDALES, Michael G.; '96 BS; Assoc. Fraud Investigator; NYC Human Res. Admin., 180 Water St., New York, NY 10038, 718 237-1170; r. 7142 150th St., Flushing, NY 11367, 718 575-3034; *Alma*.

BARFIELD, Miriam; '82 AS; 161 S. Elliott, Brooklyn, NY 11217, 718 443-3076.

BARFIELD, Shawn; '97 BA; 695 E.163rd St., Bronx, NY 10456, 718 842-5409.

BARGEBUHR, Nancy E.; '79 BA; MDA, MSW Fordham; Psychotherapist/ Geriatric CSW; r. 410 E 65th St., New York, NY 10021; *Terri Krsulich*. e-mail

BARGELINI, Gionata M.; '95 BS; 121 Inwood Ave., Pt. Lookout, NY 11569, 516 897-3142.

BARGELLINI, Gionata; 121 Inwood Ave., Pt. Lookout, NY 11569, 516 897-3142.

BARIBAULT, Richard; '72 BS; 1113 South Dr., Baldwin, NY 11510, 516 223-0518.

BARICELLI, Patrick C.; '92 BS; Law Enforcer; r. 17 Allegheny Dr. W., Farmingville, NY 11738, 631 698-4970.

BARKER, Cathy-anne O.; '95 BS; 1222 Saint Johns Pl. Apt. 3a, Brooklyn, NY 11213, 718 773-7059.

BARKLEY, Darlene; '89 BS; 104 Pearsall Dr., Mt. Vernon, NY 10552, 914 668-3119.

BARLOW, Christopher; '97 BA; 3820 Waldo Ave., Bronx, NY 10463, 718 549-5047.

BARLOWE, Brian K.; '87 AS; 26-26 96st St., Flushing, NY 11369.

BARMINKO, Svetlana; '98 BA; 310 102nd St. #8M, New York, NY 10029.

BARMORE, Ellen J.; '82 BS; 1350 5th Avre., New York, NY 10026, 212 722-7820.

BARNA, John A.; '75 BS; 19 Hester Pl., Garnerville, NY 10923, 914 947-1293.

BARNES, Bray; '80 MA, '80 BA; 1924 Kenilworth Ct., Toms River, NJ 08753, 732 255-0276.

BARNES, Charles E.; '80 BS; 192 Sands St. #1G, Brooklyn, NY 11201, 718 331-3557.

BARNES, Enobia E.; '80 BA; 332 E 4 St. #55, New York, NY 10009, 315 841-8085.

BARNES, Shurrel Y.; '96 BS; AA SUNY-Farmingdale; Computer Tech.; r. 1289 Brooklyn Ave., Brooklyn, NY 11203.

BARNES, Wallace; '89 BS; 18 Landscape Ave., Apt. 3, Yonkers, NY 10705, 914 375-3852.

BARNETT, Denise E.; '90 BS; JD William Mitchell Clg. Law; Atty.; Pinkston & Pinkston, PA, POB 4608, Jacksonville, FL 32202, 904 354-3147; r. 4436 Woodmere St., Jacksonville, FL 32210, 904 998-0942; *M. Everett George Esq.* e-mail

BARNETT, Robert; '95 BA; 43 Bronx River Rd, Apt. 5N, Yonkers, NY 10704, 914 969-2660.

BARNETT, Rodney A.; '93 BS; 620 Malcolm X Blvd. Apt. 9d, New York, NY 10037, 212 283-0286.

BAROMETRE, Reginald; '96 BA; Caseworker; HR Human Resources Admin., 132 W. 125th St., New York, NY 10027, 212 666-4754; r. 1704 Troy Ave., Brooklyn, NY 11234, 718 677-1053.

BARQUIN, Armando X.; '92 BS; State Trooper; NYS Police, Troop K Sp Somers, Rt100, Somers, NY 10589, 914 277-3651; r. POB 246, Mahopac, NY 10541, 914 628-6517; *Joan;* Christina, Armando Jr. e-mail

BARR, Charles S., CPP, CFE; '75 BA; Assoc. Dir.; UBS Warburg, 299 Park Ave., New York, NY 10171; r. 3840 Morton Ln., Seaford, NY 11783, 516 826-4175. e-mail

BARR, Keith; '97 BA, '98 BA; 364 Beach 56th #2C, Far Rockaway, NY 11692, 718 631-9596.

BARR, Leroy; '71 BS; 19b Defoe Pl., Bronx, NY 10475, 718 991-7745.

BARREIRO, Ramon G.; '97 BS, '98 BS; 712 Fox St. #2E, Bronx, NY 10455, 718 542-4164.

BARRETO, Amelia R.; '90 BA; AT&T Wireless, Orlando, FL; r. 5578 Red Bone Ln., Orlando, FL 32810, 407 291-3135. e-mail

BARRETO, Samuel; '92 BA; MA, JD St. Johns Univ.; Supv.; NYC Transit Co., New York, NY 10001; r. 7349 198th St., Fresh Meadows, NY 11366. e-mail

BARRETT, Calvin A.; '77 BS; 599 E 7th St. Apt. 1n, Brooklyn, NY 11218, 718 284-3553.

BARRETT, Daniel J.; '81 MA; 40 Brendan Ave., Massapequa Park, NY 11762, 516 785-3248.

BARRETT, Doreen A.; '83 BS; 160 E 37th St., Brooklyn, NY 11203, 718 629-4274.

BARRETT, John J.; '74 BA; 81 Pilgrim Ave., Yonkers, NY 10710.

BARRETT, Katherine E.; '82 BA; 4161 Baychester Ave., Bronx, NY 10466, 718 325-7427.

BARRETT, Kevin; '91 MA; Assoc. Prof.; Palomar Clg., 140 W Mission Rd, San Marcos, CA 92069, 760 744-1150; r. 2476 Country View Gln, Escondido, CA 92026, 760 436-0806; *Janine.*

BARRETT, Kevin J.; '80 MA; Police Ofcr.; Inglewood New Jersey Police, Englewood, NJ 07631; r. 52 Edwin St., Ridgefield Park, NJ 07660, 201 641-6230.

BARRETT, Thyrone V.; '80 AS, '81 BS; 1320 Amsterdam Ave., New York, NY 10027, 315 839-5469.

BARREYRE, Raymond; '76 BA; Captain Retired; NYC Police Dept.; r. 159 Cherry St., Floral Park, NY 11001, 516 437-9234; *Marie;* Raymond J., Stephen. e-mail

BARRIERE, Wilfred M.; '91 AS; 4367 170th St., Flushing, NY 11358, 718 746-4519.

BARRINGTON, Nichelle; '94 BA; 431 Eldert Ln. # 2, Brooklyn, NY 11208, 718 703-1439.

BARRIOS, Leonthe; '92 AS, '93 BS; 226 E 203rd St. Apt. 7d, Bronx, NY 10458, 718 364-5194.

BARRIOS, Luz; '98 BA; 149-05 79th Ave.#736, Flushing, NY 11367, 718 366-5950.

BARRITEAU, Gemma M.; '86 BA; 45 Overlook Ter., New York, NY 10033.

BARRITEAU, Marsha A.; '92 BS; 1551 Eastern Pkwy., Brooklyn, NY 11233.

BARROIS, Sebastien E.; '96 BS; 35-55 80 St. #4, Jackson Hts., NY 11372.

BARROS, Anna M.; '78 BS; 2453 Kingfisher Ln., Clearwater, FL 33762, 727 725-8892.

BARROW, Audra J.; '92 BS; JD NY Law Sch.; Private Practice; 291 Macon St., Ste. 1, Brooklyn, NY 11216, 718 452-4323; r. Brooklyn, NY 11216; *Daniel Hall.*

BARROW, Mary '96 (See Barrow-Baez, Mary).

BARROW-BAEZ, Mary, (Mary Barrow); '96 BA; Community Svc. Assoc.; NYC Housing Auth., 250 Broadway, New York, NY 10007, 212 285-0037; r. 10 Catherine Slip, 7H, New York, NY 10038, 212 285-0037; *Henry Baez;* Delfina Lugo. e-mail

BARROWS, Aileen A.; '93 BA; 912 E 214th St. # 3, Bronx, NY 10469, 718 519-1721.

BARRY, Billjeanna A.; '95 BS; 1432 144th Pl., Whitestone, NY 11357, 718 474-1957.

BARRY, Charles P.; '77 BS; 15165 26th Ave., Flushing, NY 11354, 718 821-3545.

BARRY, Edward P.; '80 BS; 3 Belle Terre Dr., Manalapan, NJ 07726, 732 308-0906.

BARRY, Elaine, (Elaine Cantaves); '82 MA; Legal Secy.; Richards & O'Neil, LLP, 885 Third Ave., New York, NY 10022, 212 207-1242; r. 83-80 118th St. #6T, Kew Gardens, NY 11415, 718 441-6897. e-mail

BARRY, Gail L.; '84 BS; 780 W. Concourse Vlg., Bronx, NY 10451, 718 991-8334.

BARRY, James P.; '92 BS, '99 MS; Deputy Warden; NYC Corrections Dept.; r. Staten Island, NY 10312.

BARRY, John J.; '66 BA; 73 Pleasantville Rd, Pleasantville, NY 10570, 914 962-3972.

BARRY, Karl S.; '81 BA; 5 Columbia Ave., Jersey City, NJ 07307, 201 656-7093.

BARRY, Kevin B.; '75 BS; Detective 1st; NYPD Bomb Squad, 233 W. 10th St., New York, NY 10014, 212 741-4835; r. 186 Pennsylvania ave., Freeport, NY 11520, 516 378-0012. e-mail

BARRY, Patrick T.; '78 BS; FBI Natl. Acad.; Owner & CEO; Alliance Investigative Grp. Ltd., 69 Brookside Ave., Ste. 223, Chester, NY 10918, 914 469-6403; r. 4 Trotting Dr., Chester, NY 10918, 914 469-2468; *Maureen;* Dawn, Kevin, Dennis, Erika. e-mail

BARRY, Rupert J.; '78 MA; 385 Argyle Rd, Brooklyn, NY 11218, 718 856-6164.

BARTELS, Ms. Elizabeth C.; '98 MA; BA Barnard Clg.; PhD Student; John Jay Clg. of Criminal Justice, 899 Tenth Ave., New York, NY 10019; r. 45 Farley Rd., Short Hills, NJ 07078, 973 379-5933. e-mail

BARTH, Christine; '85 MA; 130 W. 28 St., New York, NY 10001, 315 841-8135.

BARTIROMO, Michael; '89 BS; 48 Bedell Ave., Staten Island, NY 10307.

BARTKOVICH, Michelle; 145 Union Hill Rd., Manalapan, NJ 07726, 732 446-4174.

BARTLETT, Glen E.; '82 BA; 157 W 21st St., Huntington Sta., NY 11746, 516 783-1959.

BARTLETT, Ms. Judith R.; '95 BS; Correction Capt.; NYC Dept. of Corrections, 1606 Hazen St., E. Elmhurst, NY 11370, 718 546-4191; r. 147-20 258th St., Rosedale, NY 11422, 718 341-9282.

BARTLETT, Thomas W.; '76 MA; BA Rutgers Univ., MBA Rider Univ.; Regional Supv.; Intensive Supervision Prog., Administrative Ofc. of The Cts., Trenton, NJ 08650, 732 286-6447; r. 17 Cardiff Ln., Hamilton Sq., NJ 08690, 609 890-9001; *Cynthia;* Devon, Thomas, Morgan.

BARTLETT-JOSIE, Mrs. Christine; '90 BS; Vice Consul; Consulate Gen. St. Lucia, 800 Second Ave., 9th Fl., New York, NY 10017, 212 697-9360; r. One University Pl., New Haven, CT 06511, 203 498-2525; *Lancelot;* Imani, Najah, Magarvey. e-mail

BARTLEY, Laverne D.; '97 BA; 215 Trantor Pl.#2, Staten Island, NY 10302, 718 981-0451.

BARTOLONE, Maria; '83 BS; 6108 23rd Ave. Apt. 1r, Brooklyn, NY 11204, 718 946-8557.

BARTOLOTTA, John; '92 BS; 2534 Cruger Ave., Bronx, NY 10467, 718 931-7784.

BARTON, Claudia J.; '99 BS; 182-25 Waxford Trrc/605, Jamaica Estates, NY 11432, 718 571-7100.

BARTON, Jeffrey A.; '89 BS; 3561 Casa Real Way, Las Vegas, NV 89147, 702 456-8069.

BARTON, Kenneth L.; '84 BA; 18211 145th Ave., Jamaica, NY 11413, 718 740-6062.

BARTON, Lisa M.; '90 BS; 182-11 145th, Springfield Gardens, NY 11413, 718 527-1769.

BARTON, Shari L.; '93 MA; POB 52032, Shreveport, LA 71135, 318 797-6076.

BARTON, Wade J.; '80 BS; 438 99th St., Brooklyn, NY 11209, 718 388-0901.

BARTOSZEK, Peter C.; '72 BS; CERT. FBI Natl. Acad.; Security Supv.; NY Botanical Garden, 200 St. & Southern Blve, Bronx, NY 10458, 718 817-8664; r. 43 Linden Ave., Pelham, NY 10803. e-mail

BARUCH, Marcia L., (Marcia Nelson); '80 MA; PHD Hofstra Univ., BA Brooklyn Clg.; Chief Psychology; Ft. Dix Fed. Correctional Institution, 856 723-1100; r. 28 Chippenham Dr., Voorhees, NJ 08043, 856 784-1849; *Dr. Edward;* Mollie, Hannah. e-mail

BASCIANO, Patricia R., (Patricia R. Karalis); '80 BS; Substitute Elem. Tchr.; PS 226; r. 39 Hemlock Ct., Staten Island, NY 10309, 718 317-0453; *Anthony;* Mallory, Alexander, Dawn. e-mail

BASHIR, Benjamin M.; '75 BA; 3320 Kingsland Ave., Bronx, NY 10469, 718 882-5256.

BASIL, John; '95 BS; 141 Mulberry St., Apt. C1, New York, NY 10013.

BASLER, Craig C.; '99 BS; 65 37 172 St., Fresh Meadows, NY 11365, 718 359-2787.

BASS, Jeffrey I.; '96 BA, '98 MA; Doctoral Student; CA Sch. of Professional Psychology, San Diego, CA 92138; r. 6070 Rancho Mission Rd Apt. 441, San Diego, CA 92108, 619 282-0962. e-mail

BASS, Mildred C.; '99 MA; AA Westchester Community Clg; 13 Oakwood Dr., Peekskill, NY 10566, 914 788-8624; *Christopher McCaskill Sr.;* Christopher.

BASSETT, Gregg R.; 109-52 172nd St., Jamaica, NY 11433.

BASSETT, Patricia A.; '84 BS; 4272 Carpenter Ave., Bronx, NY 10466.

BASSINGER, Deborah N.; '84 MPA; 6903 Linbrook Blvd., Columbus, OH 43235.

BAST, Molly A.; '97 MA; 416 E. 237th St., Bronx, NY 10470, 718 325-6295.

BASTIDAS, Patricia E.; '99 BA; 31 33 90 St. D6, E. Elmhurst, NY 11369.

BATANUS, John; '95 BS; Police Ofcr.; r. 34 Lillie Ln., Staten Island, NY 10314.

BATISTA, Carmelo; '80 BA; 1337 Commonwealth Ave., Bronx, NY 10472.

BATISTA, Julio; '86 BA; 530 W. 153 St., New York, NY 10031.

BATISTA, Manuel L.; '89 BS; 81 Jersey St. Apt. 7c, Staten Island, NY 10301.

BATISTA, Maria; '97 BA; 1949 Mcgraw Ave. 4, Bronx, NY 10462, 718 561-0410.

BATISTA, Nelsa; '95 BS, '97 BA; 105 Audubon Ave. # 3, New York, NY 10032.

BATISTA, Ruth; '80 BS; 1485 Park Ave. #4C, New York, NY 10029, 212 427-9253.

BATISTA, Shenoeck; '98 BA; Aide; City Hall; r. 1337 Herschell St. #1, Bronx, NY 10461, 718 409-1060.

BATNICK, Christie J.; '83 BS; 9921 63rd Ave., Flushing, NY 11374.

BATT, Jerome P.; '75 MPA; 162 79th St., Brooklyn, NY 11209, 718 836-4236.

BATTAGLIA, Donna '81 (See Varga, Donna M.).

BATTAGLIA, Eugene F.; '78 BA; 3128 Gershwin Ln., Silver Spring, MD 20904, 301 890-9476.

BATTAGLIA, William; '99 BA; 1372 Belmont Ave., N. Haledon, NJ 07508, 973 427-8028.

BATTEL, Patrick J.; '71, '73 BA; 77 Jefferson St., Franklin Sq., NY 11010, 516 437-9083.

BATTISTA, Michael N.; '97 BA, '98 BA; 7 Caroline Ct., N. Babylon, NY 11703, 631 667-6063.

BATTISTE, Denise; '84 BA; Owner; DB Financial Svc, 314 2nd St., Liverpool, NY 13088, 315 410-0467; r. 8418 Theodolite Dr. Apt. 715, Baldwinsville, NY 13027, 315 622-4059.

BATTLE, Lisa M.; '93 BS; Secy.; Dependable Glass, 305 3rd Ave., Brooklyn, NY 11215, 718 797-1717; r. 57 Herkimer St., Apt. 205, Brooklyn, NY 11216, 718 857-2145.

BATTLE, Tamika S.; '99 BS; Paralegal; Macalino, Pruz & Assocs, 232 Madison Ave., New York, NY 10016, 212 755-7777; r. 84-50 169th St. #101, Jamaica, NY 11432, 718 297-1517.

BAUER, George M.; '99 BA; AS; Police Ofcr.; New York Police Dept., 481 Morris Park Ave., Transit Dept., Bronx, NY 10460, 718 430-0608; r. 164 Phyllis Ct., Yorktown Hts., NY 10598, 718 430-0608; *Eileen Mahoney;* Ryan, Brianna. e-mail

BAUER, Michael; '80 BS; 650 Fox Mountain Rd, Livingston Manor, NY 12758, 914 292-1394.

BAUER, Richard B.; '81 BS; 110 Forresta Dr., Butler, PA 16002, 724 586-6351.

BAUER, Richard C.; '76 AS; 110 Forresta Dr., Butler, PA 16002, 724 586-6351.

BAUMANN, Daniel; '97 BA; Police Ofcr.; NYC Police Dept., 1 Police Plz., New York, NY 10038; r. 60 Poplar Ave., Bronx, NY 10465, 718 828-4438.

BAUMANN, Ms. Deborah C.; '84 MA; Exec. Admin.; Oltarsh Oltarsh PC, 26 Broadway 24th Fl., New York, NY 10004, 212 747-1410; r. POB 116, Florida, NY 10921, 914 651-7801. e-mail

BAUMANN, Kevin P.; '76 MA; 9 Garden City Ave., Pt. Lookout, NY 11569, 516 889-2857.

BAUMERT, Robert (Boomer) J.; '66 BS, '75 MA; Deputy Chief-Org Cr Ctrl; NYC Police Dept., 1 Police Plz., Organized Crime Control Bureau-1310, New York, NY 10038, 212 374-6741; r. 3820 Avenue P, Brooklyn, NY 11234; *Sheila;* Marie, Robert Jr, Christine, Jacqueline, James.

BAUMGART, Edward W.; '80 BS; 23 Quarry Ter., W. Orange, NJ 07052.

BAUSO, Louis J.; '81 BS; Police Ofcr.; New York Police Dept., Queens, NY 11412.

BAUZA, Luis N.; '93 BS; 55 Winthrop Dr., Cortlandt Manor, NY 10567.

BAVARO, Nicholas; '91 AS; 261-85 Langston Ave., Glen Oaks, NY 11004, 718 767-4911.

BAVOLAR, SGT Keith A.; '98 BS; Sergeant; NYPD Narcotics Borough Queens, 80-45 Winchester Blvd. Bld#70-L, Queens Vlg., NY 11427, 718 736-8972; *Amy;* Gary, Claire. e-mail

BAWER, Patricia; '96 BS; 132-45 Maple Ave., Flushing, NY 11355.

BAX, Wayne F.; '92 BA; Deputy Inspector; NYC Police Dept., 1 Police Plz., New York, NY 10038; r. 45 Continental Dr., W. Nyack, NY 10994, 914 353-3533; *Marianne;* Christopher, Danielle.

BAXTER, George T.; '79 MA; 46 Sutton Dr., Ho-Ho-Kus, NJ 07423.

BAXTER, Gregory; '97 BS; 365 Ford St. #4, Bronx, NY 10457.

BAXTER, Katherine; '78 MA; 1818 Newkirk Ave. #6S, Brooklyn, NY 11226, 718 399-6677.

BAYARD, Marie-denise; '76 MA; 66 Wisconsin Ave., Bay Shore, NY 11706, 631 273-4375.

BAYLEY, George A.; '77 BS; 22223 143rd Ave., Jamaica, NY 11413, 718 297-9227.

BAYLISS, Bridget G.; '98 MA; 43-10 Kissena Blvd., Flushing, NY 11355, 631 399-2070.

BAYLOR, Charlene; '89 BS; 1455 Geneva Loop Apt. 5f, Brooklyn, NY 11239.

BAYNE, Melvin; '92 BS; Investigator; NYS Atty General's Ofc., 212 416-6176; r. 1534 E 48th St., Brooklyn, NY 11234, 718 258-5988.

BAYUELO, Claudia S.; '91 BA; MPA Baruch Clg.; Exec. Dir.; NYS Assembly of Task Force of New Amer, 718 931-2620; r. 17-14 147th St., Whitestone, NY 11357, 718 747-1547; Angela.

BAZAZIAN, Dennis G.; '77 BA; 7 Flora Ct., Stony Point, NY 10980.

BAZILE, Steven G.; '99 BS; 255 E. 18th St. #6G, Brooklyn, NY 11226, 718 287-5694.

BEACCO, Joseph M.; '88 BS; 4822 190th St., Flushing, NY 11365, 718 357-8150.

BEAL, Susan; '95 BS; JD CUNY-Law; Criminal Atty.; r. New York, NY 10009. e-mail

BEAMAN, Paige A.; '96 BS; 10825 173rd St., Jamaica, NY 11433.

BEAMON, Tanya J.; '90 BS; 333 Jefferson Ave., Brooklyn, NY 11216.

BEARD, Darryl; '92 BS; 84 Elderberry Ln., Willingboro, NJ 08046.

BEARY, Richard A.; '99 BS; Paralegal; Pfizer Pharmaceuticals, 150 E. 42Nd. St., New York, NY 10017; r. 9416 209th St., Queens Vlg., NY 11428, 718 468-9171. e-mail

BEATO, Marino; '93 BS; 3 W Farms Pl. # 21, Bronx, NY 10460, 212 865-1578.

BEATO, Rafael A.; '99 BA; Fraud Investigator; Human Resources Admin, 330 Jay St., 4th Fl., Brooklyn, NY 11201, 718 237-8471; r. 5115 92nd St. Apt. 3, Elmhurst, NY 11373, 718 699-7877.

BEATTIE, Henry J.; '99 BA; EOC Security Trng., 39 Onderdonk Rd, Warwick, NY 10990, 914 987-4400; r. 39 Onderdonk.Rd., Warwick, NY 10990, 914 986-0450; *Kathleen;* Richard, Tim, Tom, Steve, Bill. e-mail

BEATTY, Cephus J.; '85 BS; 4022 Ely Ave., Bronx, NY 10466, 718 829-6992.

BEATTY, Gerard V.; '72 BA; MA SUNY-Albany; Prof.; Hartnell Clg.; r. Carmel Vly., CA 93924; *Terri;* Joseph, Gerard, Donna, Bonnie, Laura. e-mail

BEATTY, John P.; '98 BA; 8816 91st Ave., Woodhaven, NY 11421, 718 849-3197.

BEATTY, Pamela Y.; '94 BA; 1552 Brooklyn Ave., Brooklyn, NY 11210, 718 434-7254.

BEAUCHAINE, David J.; '75 AS; POB 606, Booneville, AR 72927.

BEAUVAIS, Reginald; '90 BS; 1103 Carroll St., Brooklyn, NY 11225, 718 756-2184.

BEAUZILE, Tamara M.; '92 BA; 11416 126th St., Jamaica, NY 11420.

BEBERAGGI, Ralph; '78 BA; 567 Ft. Wasington Ave. 1G, New York, NY 10033.

BECCHINA, Victoria A.; '97 BA; 128 Raintree Ln., Mahwah, NJ 07430.

BECKER, Cynthia; '77 MA; 500 Westend Ave., New York, NY 10024, 212 873-1437.

BECKER, John J.; '77 AS; 490 Amherst Ave., Staten Island, NY 10306.

BECKER, Lester; '72 BS; 12 Irving Ct., Hicksville, NY 11801, 516 932-4514.

BECKER, Robert L.; '72 BS; Retired NYPD; r. 230 E 88th St. Apt. 7g, New York, NY 10128, 212 741-6603.

BECKER, Mrs. Susan, (Susan Butkiewicz); '88 BS; BA Queens Clg.; Audit Ofcr./CPA; Chase Manhattan Bank, 300 Jericho Quad, Jericho, NY 11753, 516 828-4359; *Al;* Robert.

BECKETT, Michael L.; '79 BA; 12020 201st Pl., Jamaica, NY 11412, 718 740-6083.

BECKFORD, Maxine A.; '97 BS; Child Protective Spec.; Admin. for Children's Svcs., 150 William St., New York, NY 10038, 212 676-6585; r. 51 Henry St., Valley Stream, NY 11580, 516 285-2612. e-mail

BECKLES, Arlene D.; '87 BS; Detective; NYPD; r. 311 E 92nd St., Brooklyn, NY 11212, 718 345-7192. e-mail

BEDROSSIAN, Anne-Marie M.; '97 BS; MS Univ. of IL at Chicago; Forensic Scientist; I.S.P. Div. of Forensic Svcs., 1941 W. Roosevelt Rd., Chicago, IL 60608, 312 433-8000; r. 1624 Louise, Laval, QC, Canada H7S 1E4. e-mail

BEECHER, Evelyn; '94 BS; 13411 232nd St., Springfield Gardens, NY 11413.

BEEKMAN, Mary E.; '78 MA; 8236 248th St., Jamaica, NY 11426, 718 831-9733.

BEEKRAM, Anita L.; '97 BA; 225 E 6th St., Apt. 2C, New York, NY 10003.

BEEN, Monette L.; '89 BA; 177 Halsey St. # Pvt, Brooklyn, NY 11216.

BEERS, Albert S.; '89 MS; AS Atlantic Community Clg., BS Thomas A Edison; Fire Marshal; Crest Haven Complex, Dn 306, Cape May Court House, NJ 08210, 609 465-2570; r. 7205 Pacific Ave., Wilowood Crest, Wildwood, NJ 08260, 609 522-1495. e-mail

BEERS, Lisa M.; '94 BS; 1327 Creek St., Webster, NY 14580.

BEHAN, Cornelius (Neil) J.; '68 BS; EXEC RES Johns Hopkins Univ.; Cnsltg.; Cornelius J. Behan Assocs., Inc., 8 Midcrest Ct., Towson, MD 21286, 410 321-1641; r. same; *Patricia.* e-mail

BEHLIN, Charlotte E.; '89 BS; 420 Kingsborough 4th, Brooklyn, NY 11233, 718 326-4333.

BEICHNER, Karen R.; '95 MA; 108 Chaucer Pl., Cherry Hill, NJ 08003.

BEIRNE, Margaret; '76 MA; 3834 Bailey Ave., Bronx, NY 10463.

BEJA, Zachary; '79 MA; Ret.; NYC Police Dept.; r. 70 Ketcham Rd, Hicksville, NY 11801, 516 433-5102.

BEJGROWICZ, Lisa M. '96 (See Cook, Mrs. Lisa M.).

BELASCO, Mrs. Barbara A., (Barbara A. Serviss); '85 BA; Tchr.; Oceanside Public Sch. Dist., Supervisor of CARES, Oceanside, NY 11572; r. 14 Oakview Ave., Oceanside, NY 11572, 516 764-7928; *Michael;* Tiana, Matthew, Sean, Sabrina. e-mail

BELCHER, Penney L.; '99 MA; POB 648, Binghamton, NY 13905, 212 613-6335.

BELDO, Gina; '94 BA; Leg. Asst.; NYS Assembly, 2294 Nostrand Ave., Brooklyn, NY 11210; r. 2940 W 33rd St. Apt. 2e, Brooklyn, NY 11224, 718 714-1925; Saba, Asaba. e-mail

BELEN, Irene M.; '97 BA; 205 W 88th St., New York, NY 10024.

BELENKY, Dmitry; '94 BA, '96 MA; Child Welfare Spec./Psychotherapist; NYC A.C.S./Private Practice, New York, NY 10038, 212 676-6632; r. 3554 12th Ave., Brooklyn, NY 11218, 718 972-6219. e-mail

BELFI, Brian J.; '97 MA; 6340 Lake June Rd, Hialeah, FL 33014, 305 512-0052.

BELFIORE, Thomas E.; '79 BS, '97 MA; 10 Birch Dr., Brewster, NY 10509.

BELFON, Joyce P.; '78 BA; 4415 Bruner Ave., Bronx, NY 10466, 718 324-7690.

BELFORD, Curtis S.; '99 AS, 2000 BS; Police Ofcr.; Republic of Trinidad & Tobago, E P #58 E Basanta Trace,, St. Johns Rd, St. Augustine, Trinidad and Tobago, 8686459967; r. 373 E 29 St., Brooklyn, NY 11226, 718 462-3306.

BELFORD, Mary J.; '87 BA; 664 Ashford St., Brooklyn, NY 11207.

BELGRAVE, Carl C.; '83 BA, '85 MA; Atty.; Law Ofc. of Carl C Belgrave, 60 Park Pl. Ste. 202, Newark, NJ 07102, 973 824-5900; r. 35 Burnett Ter., W. Orange, NJ 07052, 973 736-1356. e-mail

BELGRAVE, Jessica A.; '96 BS; 846 E 51st St., Brooklyn, NY 11203, 718 462-2578.

BELGRAVE, Reginald; '74 BS; Retired; r. 11635 226th St., Jamaica, NY 11411, 718 276-5773.

BELIN, Thelma; '86 BS; Ofc. Mgr.; NYC Church of Christ, 360 W. 31st St., New York, NY 10001, 212 736-2413; r. 840 E 232nd St. # 1, Bronx, NY 10466, 718 994-2598.

BELL, Anna K.; '97 BA; 22 Minkel Rd, Ossining, NY 10562, 914 762-1075.

BELL, Christopher; '92 BS; 212 828-1058; r. 1410 Park Ave., New York, NY 10029, 212 828-1312.

BELL, James K.; '97 BA, '98 BA; 110-11 179 St., Jamaica, NY 11433, 718 658-1493.

BELL, Rolando J.; 13058 226th St., Jamaica, NY 11413, 718 276-6705.

BELL, Tasmiya J.; '93 BS; 445 W. 240th St., Bronx, NY 10463, 718 884-8432.

BELLAFLORES, Jamari; '95 BS; 120 Erskine Pl. # 5, Bronx, NY 10475.

BELLAMY, Beverly J.; '80 BS; 2009 Turnbull Ave., Bronx, NY 10473, 718 654-4040.

BELLAMY, Charlie M.; '78 BA; MA Columbia Univ.; New York State Parole Ofcr.; NYS Div. of Parole, 314 W. 40th St., New York, NY 10018, 212 239-6198; r. 22220 145th Rd, Springfield Gardens, NY 11413, 718 949-1542.

BELLAMY, Doris J.; '76 MA; 12 Hansbury Ave., Newark, NJ 07112, 973 926-9774.

BELLAMY, Myra D.; '85 BA; 1000 Grand Concourse, Bronx, NY 10451, 718 681-4251.

BELLE, Franklin D.; '89 AS; 94 Cone Ave., Central Islip, NY 11722.

BELLEJAMBE, Melanie; '80 BS; 140 Dekruif Pl., Bronx, NY 10475.

BELLO, Joseph J.; '89 BA, '93 MPA; 3414 Fillmore Ave., Brooklyn, NY 11234, 718 376-5909.

BELLO, Muhammad A.; '82 BA; MA City Clg. NY, DIPLOMAT Universite De Paris; Supv. Social Work; NYC Admin. for Children Svcs., Linden Blvd., Brooklyn, NY 11208, 718 348-8055; r. 150 Crown St. Apt. B22, Brooklyn, NY 11225, 718 735-9310.

BELLO, Valerie; '99 BS; Rsch. Analyst; Russell Reynolds Assocs., 212 351-2057; r. 2023 Colonial Ave., Apt. 6-D, Bronx, NY 10461, 718 597-7056; Ashely. e-mail

BELLUARDO, Joseph B.; '79 BA; 5852 197th St., Flushing, NY 11365, 718 428-4033.

BELOTTE, Myriam; '96 BA; MS Hofstra, NYIT; Tchr.; Roosevelt JH, Roosevelt, NY 11575; r. 29 Frederick Ave., Elmont, NY 11003, 516 488-2377.

BELTON, Deborah E.; '08 BS; 432 Country Club Ln., Pomona, NY 10970, 914 354-6103.

BELTRE, Gustavo A.; '95 BA; 289 Convent Ave. Apt. 4, New York, NY 10031, 212 234-6772.

BELTREZ, Manuel; '91 BS; 239 Elizabeth St., New York, NY 10012, 212 334-3014.

BELVISO, Lawrence M.; '81 BS; Police Ofcr.; Henrico Cnty. Div. of Police, POB 27032, Richmond, VA 23273, 804 501-5896; r. 1206 Amesbury Ln., Richmond, VA 23227, 804 264-3764; *Sherrie;* Vincent, Victoria. e-mail

BENAIM, Charlie; '97 BA; New York Police Dept., New York, NY 10038; r. 210 W. 101 St., New York, NY 10025; *Rachel;* Ayalon, Adiva, Aitan, Ariel. e-mail

BENASUTTI, Kathleen; '97 BS; 82 Potomac Ln., Sayville, NY 11782.

BENCOSME, Odette M.; '98 BA; 35-42 100 St. 2nd Fl., Flushing, NY 11368, 718 898-9332.

BENDER, John R.; '77 BS; Corporate Dir. of Security; Triarc Companies, Inc., 280 Park Ave.-24West, New York, NY 10017, 212 451-3161; r. 12 Glazer Ln., Levittown, NY 11756. e-mail

BENDETSON, Robert; '79 BS; Special Agt.; FBI, 26 Federal Plz., New York, NY 10278, 212 384-1000.

BENEBY-PLAZA, Cathy; '84 BA; 16633 89th Ave. Apt. 2g, Jamaica, NY 11432, 718 296-2347.

BENEDETTO, Anthony S.; '75 BA; 1150 40th St., Brooklyn, NY 11218, 718 436-5960.

BENEDETTO, George; '89 BS; 74 Independence Ave., Freeport, NY 11520.

BENEDETTO, Michael; '93 BS; 4216 203rd St., Flushing, NY 11361, 718 634-1951.

BENEDICT, Clare T.; '77 BS; 299 Saint Marks Pl. # 5d, Staten Island, NY 10301.

BENEDISUK, Mary R.; '76 BA, '82 MA; MSW New York Univ.; Assoc. Staff Analyst; NYPD Grants Devel. Unit, 1 Police Plz., New York, NY 10038, 212 374-6501; r. 273 Saint Marks Pl. Apt. 5d, Staten Island, NY 10301, 718 981-3770.

BENEJAN, Robert; '97 AS; POB 486, Bronx, NY 10468, 718 584-4231.

BENERI, Fred P.; '78 BS; Lt.-New York State Court Ofcr.; Queens Cnty. Family Ct., 89-14 Parsons Blvd., Jamaica, NY 11432, 718 520-3960; r. 242-32B Oak Park Dr., Douglaston, NY 11362.

BENES, Kenneth J.; '76 BS; 84 Park Ave., Port Washington, NY 11050, 516 944-5737.

BENEVENTO, Peter R.; 185 Hart Blvd., Staten Island, NY 10301, 718 981-5145.

BENFANTI, Louis A.; '93 MPA; POB 64, Ossining, NY 10562, 858 581-0451.

BENFATTI, Kristeine; '90 BA; MSED Brooklyn Clg.; Guid. Couns.; The Wakefield, Bronx, NY 10470, 718 324-1278; r. 1819 Matthews Ave., Bronx, NY 10462. e-mail

BENINTENDO, John; '98 BS; 61-76 79th St., Flushing, NY 11379, 718 330-5931.

BENITEZ, Gustavo; '92 BS; Probation Ofcr.; NYC Dept. of Probation, 198 E. 161st, Bronx, NY 10451, 718 537-5378; r. 1210 Croes Ave., Bronx, NY 10472, 718 542-2836.

BENITEZ, John J.; '95 MA; 171 E 77th St. Apt. 2b, New York, NY 10021, 212 628-4909.

BENITEZ-RIVERA, Mild; '97 BA; Paralegal; Bronx Dist. Atty's. Ofc., 215 E 161st, Bronx, NY 10453, 718 590-2000; r. 2812 Heath Ave., Bronx, NY 10463, 718 239-0557.

BENJAMIN, Candace E.; '93 MA; 172-34 133 Ave., Jamaica, NY 11434, 718 723-1102.

BENJAMIN, Carole R. '86 (See Samples, Mrs. Carole R.).

BENJAMIN, Edward; '75 BA; 698 Rivertree Dr., Oceanside, CA 92054, 858 756-6600.

BENJAMIN, Gilda E.; '94 BS; 1323 Croes Ave., Bronx, NY 10472, 718 671-3967.

BENJAMIN, Helman O.; '96 BS; Principal Investigator; NYS Inspector Gen. Ofc., New York, NY 10001; r. 200 W 111th St., Apt. 4B, New York, NY 10026, 212 865-4443; *Hilliary*. e-mail

BENJAMIN, Lesley V.; '91 BS; 575 Hancock St. Apt. 5c, Brooklyn, NY 11233, 718 241-9346.

BENJAMIN, Paul; '99; 132-25 Maple Avenue L-2, Flushing, NY 11355, 718 217-4283.

BENJAMIN, Yvonne E.; '94 BA; NY Police Ofcr.; NY City Med. Div. Psych Univ., 5917 Junction Blvd., Rego Park, NY 11368; r. 1282 Brooklyn Ave., Brooklyn, NY 11203, 718 462-0397; *Shari*. e-mail

BENNETT, Curtis L.; '91 BS; POB 938, Bronx, NY 10453, 718 828-6969.

BENNETT, Keren M.; '94 BA; 2800 University Ave., Bronx, NY 10468, 718 828-6969.

BENNETT, Ms. Kerry-Ann; '99 BA; Mental Health Worker; Long Island Jewish Hosp. Hillside Div., 75-59 263rd St., Glen Oaks, NY 11004, 718 470-8540; r. 113-15 Colfax St., Queens Vlg., NY 11429, 718 464-6994. e-mail

BENNETT, Margaret G.; '78 MA; 19045 112th Ave., Jamaica, NY 11412, 718 465-1776.

BENNETT, Margaret M.; '79 BA; 11846 221st St., Jamaica, NY 11411, 718 657-6955.

BENNETT, Sylvia L.; '79 BS; Detective; NYC Police Dept., 1 Police Plz. Rm 1402, New York, NY 10038, 212 374-5424; r. 333 Lafayette Ave., Brooklyn, NY 11238, 718 789-8138; Jared Barchus. e-mail

BENNETT, Winsome Y.; '98 BS; 860 E 221 St. 2f, Bronx, NY 10467, 718 828-6969.

BENNETTI, Joseph J.; '90 MS; Firefighter; City of NY; r. 70 Lake Shore Dr., Pleasantville, NY 10570, 914 741-0666.

BENSON, Irving; '69 AS, '70 BS; Retired; r. 10752A Ladypalm Ln., Boca Raton, FL 33498, 561 883-0216; *Mae*; Eugene, Jerome, Jeffrey.

BENSON, Michael J.; '77 BA; 50 Pkwy. Cir., Scarsdale, NY 10583, 914 533-3065.

BENSON, Rodney B.; '76 BA, '79 MPA; Personnel Admin.; NYC Dept. of Corrections, 2 Washington St., 10th Fl., New York, NY 10004, 212 487-6673; r. 13870 Elder Ave. Apt. 4-W, Flushing, NY 11355, 718 961-0878.

BENT, Pamela A.; '97 BA; Legal Secy.; Akin Gump, New York, NY 10022; r. 160 Ocean Pkwy., Brooklyn, NY 11218, 718 853-2132.

BENTHAM, Colin H.; '83 BA; 11615 169th St., Jamaica, NY 11434, 718 949-7834.

BENTLEY, Cheryl A.; '96 BA; 1708 62nd St., Brooklyn, NY 11204, 718 596-0180.

BENTLEY, Mala D. '78 (See Walker, Mala D.).

BENTON, Delores; '85 BA; 13719 171st St., Jamaica, NY 11434, 718 454-0821.

BENTON, F. W.; '73; 149 Beach Ave., Larchmont, NY 10538, 914 834-2893.

BENTON, Stephanie G.; '83 BA; 1430 Amsterdam Ave., New York, NY 10027, 212 862-7393.

BENZAN, Lourdes M.; '82 BA; 487 Pennsylvania A, Brooklyn, NY 11207.

BERDAN, Warren C.; '75 BS; 47-08 31 Ave. #1A, Astoria, NY 11103, 718 727-1507.

BERGER, Richard; '92 BS; Parcel Post Carrier; USPO, Cppf@morgan.gmf, 341 9th Ave., New York, NY 10199, 212 330-2330; r. 273 Saint Marks Pl., Apt. 5 C, Staten Island, NY 10301, 718 727-1507; *Roberta*.

BERGERON, John D.; '72 BS; Cnslt./ Educator; r. 26 Maritime Dr., Wareham, MA 02571, 508 291-3453; *Catherine*. e-mail

BERGERSEN, John R.; '76 BS, AS; Dir.-Security; Natl. Broadcasting Co., 30 Rockafeller Plz., New York, NY 10112, 212 664-6179; r. 43 Ribbon Ln., Wantagh, NY 11793, 516 731-2843; *Carol*; John Kevin, Barbara Curry, Carolyn Michele, Keith, Troy, Christopher.

BERGNER, Kevin; '88 MPA; 58 Chowning Dr., Hampton, VA 23664, 757 851-4215.

BERISHA, Xhavid; '84 BS; 2455 Cruger Ave'B, Bronx, NY 10462, 718 653-0269.

BERITAN, Jorge L.; '95 AS; 176 Union St. Apt. 1l, Brooklyn, NY 11231, 718 855-0994.

BERKE, Marshall L.; '95 BS; Payroll Supv.; CCFA, 386 Park Ave. S. 17th Fl., New York, NY 10016, 212 685-3440; r. 8911 Avenue M 2nd Fl., Brooklyn, NY 11236, 718 251-4765. e-mail

BERKLEY, Denise; '89 BA; 112 E. 98th St., New York, NY 10029, 212 289-6877.

BERKLEY, Desiree M.; '95 BA; 2173 Davidson Ave., Bronx, NY 10453, 718 293-1947.

BERKOWITZ, Charles R.; '98 MA; 16 E Maple Rd, Greenlawn, NY 11740.

BERKOWITZ, Gwynne '91 (See Wicks, Gwynne).

BERMAN, Merrily A.; '80 BS; 10614 Otis Ave., Flushing, NY 11368, 718 352-0976.

BERMAN, Stacey; '83 MPA; 2220 Burnett St., Apt. 4H, Brooklyn, NY 11229, 718 677-7940.

BERMANN, Julia; '87 MA; 351 Griggs Ave., Teaneck, NJ 07666, 201 836-3049.

BERMUDEZ, Carlos R.; '94 BS, '99; Police Lt.; City of NY Police Dept., 9th Precinct, 321 E. 5th St., New York, NY 10009, 212 477-7804; r. 109 Rockland Ln., Spring Vly., NY 10977, 914 356-3547; *Yvette Larracuente-Bermudez*; Samantha, Isabella. e-mail

BERMUDEZ, Iris E.; '86 BA; 119 S 8th St. # 3, Brooklyn, NY 11211, 718 802-9416.

BERMUDEZ, Leyla V.; '95 BS; 2415 93rd St. # P, Flushing, NY 11369, 718 740-7610.

BERMUDEZ, Michael; '79 BA; Auditor; NYC Human Resources Admin., 180 Water St., New York, NY 10030, 212 331-5903; r. 122-01 Linden Blvd., S. Ozone Park, NY 11420, 718 738-3158.

BERMUDEZ, Rosa A.; '92 BS; 527 Graham Ave., Brooklyn, NY 11222, 718 782-8967.

BERMUDEZ, Yvette; '88 BA; 45 Fleet Walk Apt. 2d, Brooklyn, NY 11201.

BERNARD, Brenda '85 (See Richardson, Brenda).

BERNARD, Derwin M.; '96 BA; 5201 Clarendon Rd., Brooklyn, NY 11203, 718 919-0190.

BERNARD, Diane M.; '87 BA; 116-02 228th St., Jamaica, NY 11411, 718 276-2134.

BERNARD, Joseph; '93 AS, 2000 BS; Security Ofc.; MetLife; r. 319 Avenue C Apt. 1a, New York, NY 10009, 212 614-0799; *Yanique.* e-mail

BERNARD, Ronald P.; '78 BS; 213 Stanford Dr., Wallingford, PA 19086, 610 872-7034.

BERNARDEZ, Mirtha C.; '92 BS; 1695 Hoe Ave. Apt. 5c, Bronx, NY 10460.

BERNSTEIN, Faye K.; '94 MA, '94 BA; Psychologist; ReEntry House, 5812 Lyndale Ave. S, Minneapolis, MN 55419, 612 869-2411; r. 3346 Blaisdell Ave. S, Minneapolis, MN 55408, 612 824-5119. e-mail

BERNSTEIN, Ms. Leslie; '83 BS; Trng. Spec.; 7-Eleven, 5640-70 Sunrise Hwy., Sayville, NY 11782; r. 3 Pontiac Rd, Selden, NY 11784, 631 698-5140; Eva.

BERNSTEIN, Richard W.; '76 BS; 89 Whispering Hills, Chester, NY 10918.

BERNSTEIN, Stuart L.; '83 BS; 2045 Rockaway Pkwy., Brooklyn, NY 11236, 718 373-6990.

BERRIDGE, Heather; '95 BS; 10220 185th St. # 1, Jamaica, NY 11423.

BERRIOS, Aaron; '98 BA; 2078 2nd Ave. Apt. 1E, New York, NY 10029.

BERRIOS, Carmen M.; '83 BS; Sr. Counselor; Juvenile Hall, 375 Woodside Ave., San Francisco, CA 94127, 415 753-7500; r. 25 Corwin St. Apt. 5, San Francisco, CA 94114, 415 821-5719.

BERRIOS, Frank J.; '93 BA; 907 Quincy Ave., Bronx, NY 10465, 718 931-4782.

BERRIOS, Johnny; '98 BS; Police Ofcr.; NYC Police Dept., 1 Police Plz., New York, NY 10038, 212 374-2801; r. 357 W 55th St. #1-m, New York, NY 10019, 212 459-2901.

BERRIOS, Laura M.; '83 BA, '93 BA; 830 Revere Ave., Bronx, NY 10465, 718 220-1266.

BERRIOS, Lynelle; '96 BA; 1820 Harrison Ave., Bronx, NY 10453, 718 220-1266.

BERRIOS, Rafael; '95 BS; 1256 Union Ave., Newburgh, NY 12550, 914 566-3173.

BERROA, Ms. Janice, RN; '91 BA; MBA Dowling Clg., BSN Clg. of New Rochelle; Direct Patient Care Mgr.; Dept. of Health-Tuberculosis Prog., 34-33 Junction Blvd., 225 Broadway, Jackson Hts., NY 11372, 718 803-6406; r. 611 W 204th St. # 619, New York, NY 10034, 212 304-1977. e-mail

BERROUET, Gerard E.; '97 BS; 309 E. 18th St., Brooklyn, NY 11226.

BERRY, Joseph S.; '84 BS; 78-06 46th Ave. #2H, Elmhurst, NY 11373, 716 665-2652.

BERRY, BG Robert W., USA(Ret.); '81 MA; BA Washington State Univ., JD Harvard Law Sch.; Lawyer; Messner & Reeves, 600 17th St., #2800 S, Denver, CO 80202, 303 605-1577; r. Lakewood, CO 80227. e-mail

BERRY, Siobhan L.; '99 BA; Community Asst./Paralegal; The Bronx Dist. Attorney's Ofc., 198 161st, Appeals Bur, Bronx, NY 10451, 718 590-2123; r. 591 1st Ave., New York, NY 10016, 212 779-8941.

BERRY, Stephen D.; '86 MA; RR2 Box 2198, Saylorsburg, PA 18353, 610 515-0555.

BERRYMAN, John H.; '62 MPA; POB 205, Southold, NY 11971, 631 765-5472.

BERT, Gerard; '96 MA; 22 Cheryl Rd, Massapequa, NY 11758, 516 938-8431.

BERT, Richard A.; '95 BA; MAED Bank Street Clg. of Educ.; Retired Detective; NYS Police Dept.; r. Grondzeiler # 68, Pc 1035 An, Amsterdam, Netherlands. e-mail

BERTHLEY, Maria D.; '95 BS; 10120 111th St., Jamaica, NY 11419.

BERTOLINI, Vinicio; '81 BS; RR 3 Box 69, Walton, NY 13856, 607 865-4211.

BERUBE, Michael; '96 BA; US Immigration Officer; US Immigration, Buffalo District-New York, Buffalo, NY 14201; r. 550 Webb Dr. #1803, Mississauga, ON, Canada L5B 3Y4.

BESS, Tara S.; '95 MA; 2467 State Rte. 10 Apt. 7-1a, Morris Plains, NJ 07950.

BEST, Aromah; '97 BS, '98 BS; Corrections Ofcr.; NYC Dept. of Corrections; r. 41-10 12th St. 1b, Long Island City, NY 11101, 718 784-1879; *Phillip Shands.*

BEST, George M.; '75 MA; Asst. Dean of Students; John Jay Clg., 445 W. 59th St., New York, NY 10019, 212 237-8115; r. 626 Linden Blvd., Brooklyn, NY 11203, 718 856-5424.

BEST, Jennifer A.; '94 BA; 6821 6th Ave. # 4, Brooklyn, NY 11220, 718 748-5094.

BEST, Racine A.; '96 BS; Customer Svc.; Bell Atlantic, 395 Flatbush Ave. Ext., Brooklyn, NY 11201, 718 890-1219; r. 266 Rochester Ave., Brooklyn, NY 11213, 718 467-4760.

BEST, Sandra; '97 BA; 55-30 98th Pl. 2, Rego Park, NY 11368, 718 658-1757.

BEST, William S.; '89 BAS; 5808 Farragut Rd, Brooklyn, NY 11234, 718 467-2837.

BESTHOFF, Eric A.; '90 BS; 1 Birchwood Ct. Apt. 3d, Mineola, NY 11501.

BETANCES, Neftali, Jr.; '96 BA; Police Ofcr.; City of NY, New York, NY 10001; r. 221 W. 233rd St. Apt. #5l, Bronx, NY 10463, 718 432-9316; *Alba Rodriguez.* e-mail

BETANCOURT, Brian; '96 BA; 6 Second St., Nesconset, NY 11767, 631 471-5121.

BETHEL, Cassandra V.; '83 MPA; 1234 Halsey St., Brooklyn, NY 11207, 718 453-5043.

BETSO, Philip R.; '79 BS; 2 Grace Ct., Brooklyn, NY 11201, 718 643-9484.

BETTMAN, Michael; '86 MA; 15 Colborne St., Kingston, ON, Canada K7K 1C5, 613 549-8042.

BETTS, Mary-ann C.; '96 BA; 180 Senator, Brooklyn, NY 11220, 718 429-2953.

BETTS, Steven D.; '95 BS; 981 Hayes St., Baldwin, NY 11510.

BETTY, Melvin L.; '76 BA; 22015 139th Ave., Jamaica, NY 11413.

BETZ, William; '85 BA; 16339 25th Dr., Flushing, NY 11358.

BEVERIDGE, Alvin J.; '78 MA; Mgmt. Analyst; NJ Ofc. of Atty. Gen., 25 Market St., Trenton, NJ 08625, 609 984-4934; r. 78 Winding Way, Trenton, NJ 08620, 609 984-4934; *Linda;* David, Karen.

BEVINETTO, Santo; '97 BS; 67-41 Central Ave., Glendale, NY 11385.

BEY, Robert F.; '97 BS; Financial Advisor; Prudential Securities, 118-35 Queens Blvd., Forest Hills, NY 11375, 718 268-3600; r. 114 Elm St., Woodmere, NY 11598.

BEYER, Howard L.; '79 MPA; 498 2nd St., Trenton, NJ 08611, 609 882-6201.

BHAN, Alvin J.; '97 BA; 93-34 214 St., Queens Vlg., NY 11428.

BHOJWANI, Manny; '93 BS; 9430 58th Ave. Apt. 6e, Flushing, NY 11373, 718 592-0884.

BHOLA, Ms. Patti-lou S.; '96 MA; BS Mercy Clg.; Sr. Domestic Violence Counsel; Northern Westchester Shelter, Inc., Box 203, Pleasantville, NY 10570, 914 747-0828.

BIADA, Charles; '96 BS; Operation Dir.; Natl. Acad. of Design, New York, NY 10128; r. 359 Stanley Ave., Staten Island, NY 10301, 718 720-5094.

BIANCHI, Joseph A.; '75 MPA; BBA Iona Clg.; Retired; r. 1695 Bard Ln., E. Meadow, NY 11554, 516 794-0246; *Eileen.*

BIANCO, Aniello R.; '76 BA; Retired Det. Sergeant; NYC Police Dept.; r. 1937 Jackson Ave., W. Islip, NY 11795, 631 587-6455.

BIANCO, Anthony V.; '96 BA; 3625 E Ray Rd, Apt. 1022, Phoenix, AZ 85044, 602 233-0430.

BIANCULLI, Frank C.; '76 BS; 6908 Alderton St., Flushing, NY 11374, 718 497-7593.

BIBERAJ, Hasan; '76 BA; 234 W 56th St. Fl. 3rd, New York, NY 10019.

BIDO, Antonia F.; '97 BA; AS Macalester; 911 Dispatcher; NYC; r. 1141 FDR Dr., Apt. 6E, New York, NY 10009, 212 533-0761; Candace.

BIEGEL, Stephen W.; '97 BS; 159 Madison Ave., New York, NY 10016.

BIELING, Christopher; '78 BS; 3604 Byron Dr., Finksburg, MD 21048.

BIELSKI, Chester W.; '74 BS; Hc 88 Box 655, Pocono Lake, PA 18347, 570 646-0943.

BIENIEWICZ, Linda M.; '93 BA, '95 MA; 618 Vincent Ave., Bronx, NY 10465, 718 823-0310.

BIESTY, William F.; '76 BS; Retired Battalion Chief; NYC Fire Dept.; r. 20449 8th Ave., Far Rockaway, NY 11697, 718 945-4750.

BIFULCO, Anthony P.; '90 BS; 125-04 115th Ave., S. Ozone Park, NY 11420, 718 843-5924.

BIFULCO, Frank J.; '84 BS; 125-04 115 Ave., S. Ozone Park, NY 11420, 718 843-5929.

BIGGERS, Crystal L. '86 (See Screen, Crystal L.).

BIGGINS, Patrick N.; '77 MA; 1 Birch Rd, Sloatsburg, NY 10974.

BILA, Anthony; '91 BS; MA St. John's Univ.; Claims Spec.; NYC Law Dept., 100 Churc St., New York, NY 10007, 212 788-1698; r. 9120 Gold Rd., Jamaica, NY 11417, 718 845-5703.

BILELLO, Anthony; '79 BS; POB 2018, Sedona, AZ 86339.

BILITY, Mohammed S.; '99 BS; Tchr./ Soccer Coach; MS 53; r. 490-A Lexington Ave. Basement, Brooklyn, NY 11221, 718 443-0381; *Felicity;* Amadee.

BILLER, CDR Ronald D.; '97 BA; Fire Ofcr.; NYC, New York, NY 10001; r. 207 Yetman Ave., Staten Island, NY 10307, 718 984-6475.

BILLIE-COSBY, Bridget; '86 BS; 42-31 Elberton St., Elmhurst, NY 11373, 718 565-8313.

BILLIK, Philip A.; '92 MA; 3 Rockridge Dr., Thiells, NY 10984.

BILLINGS, Robert P.; '76 MA; 134 Nugent St., New Hyde Park, NY 11040.

BILLINGS, Saiheme; '93 AS; 2253 3rd Ave. Apt. 2203, New York, NY 10035.

BILLITTERI, Christina; '88 BA; 1519 Wood Violet Dr., Orlando, FL 32824.

BILLS, Sylvester; '80 MPA; 4005 College Pt. Blvd. Apt. 10b, Flushing, NY 11354, 718 461-1764.

BILLUPS, Leeanna; '84 BS; 2130 1st Ave. # 2, New York, NY 10029, 212 289-7096.

BILLY, Joseph; '82 BA; 518 Hemlock St., Rahway, NJ 07065.

BILOUS, Stephen R.; '81 BA; 506 Victor St., Scotch Plains, NJ 07076, 908 889-6860.

BINCAROWSKY, George; '58 MPA; Prof. Emeritus/Lt. NYPD Ret; Rutgers Univ.; r. 20711 43rd Ave., Bayside, NY 11361; *Mary;* Barbara, Jeanne, Maryellen, George (dec).

BINES, Joseph G.; '76 BA; 17761 Ursina Rd, Jamaica, NY 11434, 718 276-2333.

BINFORD, Nina '91 (See Wilson, Nina M.).

BIOT, Deborah M.; '96 BS; 112 Rudder Dr., Holtsville, NY 11742, 631 472-1013.

BIRBIGLIA, Joseph M.; '75 BS; Tax Examiner; Internal Revenue; r. 234 Oceanside St., Islip Terrace, NY 11752, 631 277-3338; *Marion.*

BIRCH, Judith E.; '77 BA; 779 Concourse Village13A, Bronx, NY 10451, 718 538-4120.

BIRD, Edwin T.; '93 MPA; 60 Sycamore Ave., Floral Park, NY 11001.

BIRNBAUM, Lewis R.; '90 BA; Landscaping; Peartree Landscaping, C W Briggs Rd., Croton-on-Hudson, NY 10520; r. C.W. Briggs Rd, Croton-on-Hudson, NY 10520, 914 271-3010.

BIRNER, Jolene N.; '98 BA; 11 Centre St., Lynbrook, NY 11563, 516 593-0945.

BISCUTI, Anthony J.; '93 AS; '97 BS; 13 Belt St., Bellmore, NY 11710.

BISHOP, Barbara A.; '90 BA; 160 Lamport Blvd., Staten Island, NY 10305, 718 720-8063.

BISHOP, John H.; '82 BS; Corrections Ofcr.; NYS Dept. of Corrections-Sing Sing, 354 Hunter St., Ossining, NY 10562; r. same.

BISHOP, Robert J.; '92 AS, '93 BS; 80 Seaman Ave. Apt. 5f, New York, NY 10034, 315 853-2637.

BISHOP, William B.; '86 BS; 3204 Park Ave., Apt. 2G, Bronx, NY 10451, 718 681-3039.

BISHUN, Peter R.; '81 BS; 6 Ocean Ave., E. Rockaway, NY 11518, 516 593-9516.

BISWANGER, Terri P.; '99 BS; 331 W 57th St. # 299, New York, NY 10019, 212 582-1055.

BITKOWER, Amy J.; '93 MA; 36 Taylor Rd, Valhalla, NY 10595, 914 592-4015.

BITNER, Iwona E.; '96; 6901 E Lake Mead Blvd., Apt. 2020, Las Vegas, NV 89156.

BITSIMIS, Jeffrey; '80 BS; Pres.; Software Reproduction Technologies Inc., 11 E 26th St., 7th Fl., New York, NY 10010, 212 447-4475; r. 23 Beach Plum Dr., Centerport, NY 11721, 631 912-9581; *Theresa.* e-mail

BITTAR, Dennis; '93 BS; 425 Prospect Ave., Brooklyn, NY 11215, 718 832-6225.

BITTAR, Robert N.; '87 BS; 1617 E 33rd St., Brooklyn, NY 11234, 718 382-8797.

BITTLES, Richard J.; '83 BA; Retired Ofcr.; NYC Fire Dept.; r. 2 Paula Ct., Cornwall on Hudson, NY 12520, 914 534-2234; Richard, James.

BITTMANN, Brenda L.; '97 BA; 1 Kimberly Ln., Pomona, NY 10970.

BLACHMAN, Eric J.; '97 BSCJ; Special Agt.; US Dept. of Justice, 77 N. Boundary Rd., Jamaica, NY 11430, 718 553-7520.

BLACK, Anne; '79 BS; 716 Tysens Ln., Staten Island, NY 10306, 718 984-4927.

BLACK, David W.; '99 BS; 180 Kirshon Ave., Staten Island, NY 10314, 718 984-4927.

BLACK, Sally E.; '90 BS; Police Ofcr.; Town of Newburgh Police Dept., 300 Gardnertown Rd, Newburgh, NY 12550, 914 564-1100; r. 479 Ridge Rd, Campbell Hall, NY 10916, 914 496-1813.

BLACK, Samuel (Sam); '98 MA; BA PSYCH Castleton State Clg.; Account Exec.; Street Fusion, 100 Spear St., San Francisco, CA 94104, 415 343-3140; r. 3233 Scott St., Apt. 9, San Francisco, CA 94123, 415 614-0545. e-mail

BLACK, Sylvia C.; '94 BA; AA Kingsborough Clg.; Fraud Investigator; r. 390 Gates Ave. #7X, Brooklyn, NY 11216, 718 399-6704; Gerald.

BLACKMAN, Colin J.; '96 BA; 253-33 147th Dr., Rosedale, NY 11422, 516 546-4650.

BLACKMAN, David B.; '90 BS; AAS St. Francis Clg., JD CUNY Sch. of Law; 14643 183rd St., Springfield Gardens, NY 11413, 718 723-1408; *Leila.*

BLACKMAN, Michael J.; '80 BS; Sergeant; PG Cnty. Dept. of Corrections, 13400 Dille Dr., Upper Marlboro, MD 20772, 301 952-7030; r. 3506 Strawberry Ct., Clinton, MD 20735, 301 930-3168; Michael.

BLACKMAN, Michelle; '95 BA; 398 Grand Ave. P.h., Brooklyn, NY 11238.

BLACKMAN, Salena M.; '92 MA; 35 Elderwood Ln., Melville, NY 11747, 631 421-0329.

BLACKMAN, Te'shanee M.; '98 BA; 1000 Freeman St., #6h, Bronx, NY 10459, 718 328-1489.

BLACKSBURG, Michael; '96 BA; 29 Howard Ave., Tappan, NY 10983.

BLACKSHEAR, Cornelius; '71 BS; 17120 Mayfield Rd, Jamaica, NY 11432.

BLACKSHEAR, Norman; '96 BA; 1310 Nostrand Ave., Brooklyn, NY 11226.

BLACKWELL, Darius S.; '93 BS; 666 St. Nicholas Ave., New York, NY 10030, 212 926-5351.

BLACKWELL, Dru Janin; '97 BS; 18535 Hilburn Ave., St. Albans, NY 11412, 718 528-8653.

BLACKWOOD, Nicola G.; '97 BS; 146-26 226th St., Springfield Gardens, NY 11413, 516 333-6063.

BLACKWOOD-AHMED, Melrose; '98 BA; 589 E 94 St., Brooklyn, NY 11236, 718 677-3021.

BLAHA, Jana L.; '97 BS; Systs. Admin.; Human Res. Mgmt., 100 Park Ave. Ste. 1110, New York, NY 10017, 212 843-0400; r. 902 Mcdonald Ave., Brooklyn, NY 11218, 718 853-9059; *Scott.* e-mail

BLAHA, Richard; '95 BS; 19 Overlook Dr., Washingtonville, NY 10992, 914 361-5253.

BLAICH, Charles R.; '98 MS; BS St. Johns Univ.; Deputy Chief-Fire Dept.; Fire Dept. City of NY; r. 122 Mada Ave., Staten Island, NY 10310, 718 981-8631; *Mary;* Andrew, Daniel. e-mail

BLAIKIE, Melanie A.; '99 MA; 2 Tyburn Ln., S. Setauket, NY 11720, 631 698-2814.

BLAIR, Bernardo R.; '80 BS; 131-43 135th, S. Ozone Park, NY 11420, 718 529-7358.

BLAIR, Dwight A.; '78 BA; 773 Concourse Village, Bronx, NY 10451, 718 320-4820.

BLAKE, Christopher; 730 Spur Dr. N., Bay Shore, NY 11706, 631 968-1393.

BLAKE, Ernestine; '97 BS; Licensed Sales Cnslt.; Century 21, 1353 Castle Ave., Bronx, NY 10462, 800 322-3716; r. 820 Colgate Ave., Apt. 17E, Bronx, NY 10473.

BLAKE, Dr. Henry E. E.; '67 BS; MA Baylor Univ., MPA Nova Southwestern FL; Chairperson Criminal Justice; Central Texas Clg.-Retired, Killeen, TX 76541; r. 905 Verna Lee Blvd., Harker Hts., TX 76548, 254 698-2135; *Pearl A.*

BLAKE, Micheryl R.; '85 BS; 577 Madison St. Apt. 2, Brooklyn, NY 11221, 718 452-8404.

BLAKE, Richard A.; '93 AS; Police Ofcr.; Ocoee Police Dept., 175 N. Bluford Ave., Ocoee, FL 34761, 407 656-1313; r. POB 271, Ocoee, FL 34761. e-mail

BLAKE, Ms. Vera A.; '92 MA; Housing Asst.; NYC Housing Authority, 90 Church St. 9th Fl., New York, NY 10007, 212 306-8170; r. 5526 Jodie Ct., Brooklyn, NY 11203, 718 451-0923.

BLAKELEY, Dawn; '98 BA; Ins. Broker; Acadia Risk Mgmt., 1 Rockefeller Ctr., Rm #1502, New York, NY 10020, 212 698-8574; r. 350 Merrick Rd, Apt. 1-T, Rockville Centre, NY 11572, 516 536-1098. e-mail

BLANCO, Fior D.; '96 BA; 65 W 96th St. # 12, New York, NY 10025.

BLANK, Dorothea; '82 MA; 283 Bay 17th St. Apt. 1c, Brooklyn, NY 11214, 718 398-4732.

BLANKS, Juanita D.; '81 BS; 169-15 89 Ave. #2B, Jamaica, NY 11432, 718 712-9899.

BLASSINGAME, Paul; '93 BA; Computer Analyst; Human Resources Admin., 109 E 16 St., New York, NY 10003, 212 896-5661; r. POB 6651 Yorkville Sta., New York, NY 10128; *Lindy*.

BLASZCYK, Theodore W.; '81 MA; BA LIU-C.W. Post, JD Touro Law Sch.; Atty.; Gilbert & Blaszcyk, 440 Waverly Ave., Patchogue, NY 11772, 631 447-6500; r. 6 Saddlebrook, Manorville, NY 11949, 631 878-7309; *Debra; Laura, William, Lindsay, Lillian, Liza*.

BLATT, Barry A.; '84 MPA; 477 Fdr Dr., Apt. 106, New York, NY 10002, 212 473-2712.

BLEEKER, Stanley W.; '78 MA; 2405 E 63rd St., Brooklyn, NY 11234.

BLEIBERG, Bruce A.; '80 BS; 68 Chapin Ave., Merrick, NY 11566, 516 223-7044.

BLEIBERG, Michael S.; '76 BS; 2018 Avenue X #2R, Brooklyn, NY 11235, 718 783-5944.

BLIACH, Tinamarie, (Tinamarie Ventrice); '84 BS; Customs (Semi-Ret)/Preschool Tchr.; Excel Learning Ctr.; r. 4523 Anglers Crossing, Palm Harbor, FL 34685.

BLIGE, Slater S.; '74 BA; Retired Correctional Couns.; Correctional Svcs.; r. 1871 Belfast Keller Rd., Richmond Hill, GA 31324, 912 727-3896; Slater S. III, Shelby, Lora A.

BLISS, Donald; '96 BA; 14 Corn Hill Rd, Shelton, CT 06484, 203 929-1402; *Christine;* Jonathan. e-mail

BLISS, Stuart; '85 BA; 141-15 28 Ave., Flushing, NY 11354, 718 786-1692.

BLOCK, James B.; '91 BA; 132 East Dr., Massapequa, NY 11758, 718 343-5841.

BLOIS, James H.; '79 BS; 86 Simonson Ave., Staten Island, NY 10303.

BLOMQUIST, Bryan D.; '95 MA; BS NY Inst. of Technology; Police Lt.; Lynbrook Police Dept., 1 Columbus Dr., Lynbrook, NY 11563, 516 599-3300; r. 33 Harding Ave., Lynbrook, NY 11563; *Diane;* Tara, Corinne, Brett.

BLOOM, Jason S.; '96 MA; BA Univ. of TX Austin; Rsch. Assoc.; Courtroom Sciences Inc., 4950 N O'connor Rd., Irving, TX 75062, 972 717-1773; r. 5424 Tanbark Rd., Dallas, TX 75229, 214 871-9646. e-mail

BLOOM, Michael H.; '96 BA MPA; Ofc. Admin.; United States Military Acad., Staff Judge Advocates Ofc., West Pt., West Point, NY 10996, 914 938-4541; r. 109 Bennett Rd., Newburgh, NY 12550, 914 562-0912. e-mail

BLOTNER, Roberta; 10 East End Ave. Apt. 5C, New York, NY 10021.

BLOUNT, Danny H.; '81 AS; BA Univ. of Pennsylvania, BA Edison State Clg.; US Postal Svc.; 308 Market St., Philadelphia, PA 19106, 215 875-8888; r. 1668 N Wilton St., Philadelphia, PA 19131; *Priscilla;* Tyisc, Maurice.

BLOUNT, Ms. Heather; '98 BS; Coord. of Special Events; United Fedn. of Tchrs., 260 Park Ave. S, New York, NY 10010, 212 388-9623; r. 574 Greene Ave. #2B, Brooklyn, NY 11216, 718 857-2732. e-mail

BLUE, Sheila E.; '97 BA; 604 St.nicholas Ave., New York, NY 10030.

BLUEFORD, Helen J.; '83 BS; 24012 128th Ave., Jamaica, NY 11422.

BLUETHGEN, Jane M.; '94 BS; 18 Loret Ln., E. Northport, NY 11731.

BLUGH, Eneida A.; '91 MPA; 73 E 42nd St., Brooklyn, NY 11203.

BLUGH, Michael; '93 BS; 388 Quincy St., Brooklyn, NY 11216.

BLUM, Dominic K.; '96 BA; Court Ofcr.; Manhattan Family Courts, 60 Lafayette St., New York, NY 10013, 212 374-8711; r. 936 52nd St., Brooklyn, NY 11219, 718 437-9768; *Mary Gotsotouli;* Katerina, Gabriella.

BLUME, Rene M.; '98 BA; 149 Union St. #4, Brooklyn, NY 11231, 718 625-4216.

BLUMENSTEIN, R.; '97 BS; 269 Prescott Ave., Staten Island, NY 10306.

BLUMENTHAL, George; '69 MPA; 17891 N 99th Dr., Sun City, AZ 85373, 623 974-1231.

BLUMLEIN, Michael; '85 BA; 78-08 95 Ave., Jamaica, NY 11416.

BLUMSTEIN, Evan P.; '98 BA; 157 Mackenzie St., Brooklyn, NY 11235, 718 615-0685.

BLUSZCZ, Frank J.; '79 BS; 4 Darien Ct. Apt. 2a, Pomona, NY 10970.

BOAKYE-YIADOM, Kwame; '87 BA, '89 MPA; Sr. Public Health Advisor; Dept. of Health-NY, 917 769-0808; r. 40 Lincoln Rd Apt. 3h, Brooklyn, NY 11225, 718 282-4735; *Mary;* Osdert Owusu, Jennifer.

BOATENG, Akua A.; '96 BA; 227 Haven Ave. #, New York, NY 10033.

BOATRIGHT, Gina E.; '83 BA; 305 Livonia Ave., Brooklyn, NY 11212.

BOBB, Gavin E.; '98 BA; 1268 Findlay Ave., Bronx, NY 10456, 718 992-1021.

BOBB, Hamilton E.; '82 MA; 1323 Ginger Cir., Weston, FL 33326, 954 385-6957.

BOBB, Ms. Irma Diane, Esq.; '94 BS; Atty.; r. 135 Morris St. #F2R, Jersey City, NJ 07302. e-mail

BOBECZKO, Aleksandra; '96; 88-46 53rd Ave., Elmhurst, NY 11373.

BOCHETTE, Louis R.; '73 BS, '75 MPA; Staff Dir.-Retired/Cnslt.; NY Assembly Corrections Committee; r. 655 E. 14 St., New York, NY 10009, 212 533-8961; *Jeannie.*

BOCIAN, Stephen J.; '77 BS; 33 Merrywood Ln., Short Hills, NJ 07078, 973 912-9823.

BODDEN, Cheryl L.; '97 BA; Public Health Epidemiologist; NYC Dept. of Health, 2 Lafayette St., New York, NY 10019; r. POB 936, New York, NY 10156.

BODDEN, Juana; '94 BA; 601 E 149th St. # 6, Bronx, NY 10455, 718 991-1628.

BODKIN, John E.; '75 BS; 219 Chase Ave., Yonkers, NY 10703, 914 965-7949.

BOETTCHER, Donna M.; '98 MPA; 7 Brookview Rd., Whitehouse Sta., NJ 08889, 908 534-5972.

BOGDANOWICZ, Kathleen; '81 BS; 101 Wyona Ave., Staten Island, NY 10314.

BOGGIANO, Daniel; '94 BS, '99 MS; Policeman; NYC Police Dept., P S A #3, Brooklyn, NY 11206, 718 386-4101; r. 48-38 38th St., Long Island City, NY 11101, 718 786-4718; *Becky*. e-mail

BOGGIO, Linda M.; '82 BA; JD New York Law Sch.; Court Atty.; State of NY, Family Ct., 283 Adams St., 6th Fl., Brooklyn, NY 11201, 718 643-6277; r. 238 W. 106 St., New York, NY 10025, 212 865-3943. e-mail

BOGGIO, Marco A.; '95 BS; 666 West End Ave., New York, NY 10025.

BOGOVIC, Anthony P.; '79 BS; Systs. Analyst; PaineWebber, 51 W 52nd St., 21st Fl., New York, NY 10019, 212 882-5022; r. 31-40 35 St., Astoria, NY 11106, 718 278-4652. e-mail

BOHACK, Susan; '91 MA; 59-19 69th Pl., Maspeth, NY 11378.

BOHIGIAN, Valerie; '91 MA; PHD CUNY; Investigative Reporter-Writer; Valerie Bohigian, 225 Hunter Ave., Sleepy Hollow, NY 10591, 914 631-8866; r. same, 914 631-1547; *Dr. Haig;* Kara, Melanie Winn. e-mail

BOHRER, Philip; '80 MA; 53 Forest Green, Staten Island, NY 10312.

BOHRINGER, Ernest W.; '99 BS; Police Ofcr.; NYC Police Dept., 1 Police Plz., New York, NY 10038; r. 113 Pilgrim Pl., Valley Stream, NY 11580, 516 872-8030. e-mail

BOISROND, Marie-Fran; '92 BA; 509 W. 142nd St., New York, NY 10027.

BOISSEAU, Dominique; '97 BS; 39-43 50th Ave. 1, Sunnyside, NY 11104.

BOLDEN, Denise; '87 BA; 2328 W 8th St., Brooklyn, NY 11223, 718 498-1416.

BOLDIN, Teresa S.; '93 BS; 238 MacDonough PH, Brooklyn, NY 11233, 718 443-9382.

BOLE, Nicholas; '76 BA; 105 Vincent Ave., Staten Island, NY 10306, 718 727-7508.

BOLEN, Thomas J.; '85 BA; 3236 201st St., Flushing, NY 11361.

BOLGER, Barbara; '91 AS; 334 W 47 St. #3, New York, NY 10036, 212 333-7780.

BOLGER, John P.; '81 BS; 808 Barbara Blvd., Franklin Sq., NY 11010, 516 489-1883.

BOLGER, William J.; '91 AS; 440 W. 238th St., Apt. Ground S., Riverdale, NY 10463.

BOLIVAR, Matilde; '90 BA; Computer Programmer; John Jay Clg. of Criminal Justice, 555 W. 57th St., Rm. 609 BMW Bldg., New York, NY 10019, 212 237-8203; r. 8 Lomala Rd., Hopewell Jct., NY 12533, 914 897-5675. e-mail

BOLLANDER, Richard C.; 11540 Chmy Rock Rd #209, Houston, TX 77035.

BOLLING, Charise M. '83 (See Bolling Sharpe, Mrs. Charise M.).

BOLLING SHARPE, Mrs. Charise M., (Charise M. Bolling); '83 AS; BS St. Johns Univ.; Paralegal; Salomon Smith Barney, 388 Greenwich St., New York, NY 10013, 212 816-7225; r. 113-32 209th St., Queens Vlg., NY 11429, 718 465-2596; *Justin Sharpe.* e-mail

BOLOGNA, Anthony (Tony) V.; '92 BS; GRAD FBI Natl. Acad.; Capt.; NYC Police Dept., Manhattan S. Task Force, New York, NY 10036, 212 760-8344; r. Staten Island, NY 10314. e-mail

BOLOGNA, Joe; '85 BA; 2 David Rd, Plainview, NY 11803, 516 433-6456.

BOLSTAD, Robert; '97 BA; 15 Battery Ave., Brooklyn, NY 11228, 718 491-0063.

BOLT, Ronald G.; '82 BS; 1995 Sedgwick Ave. Apt. 1g, Bronx, NY 10453, 718 299-0599.

BOLTON, Cheryl C.; '97 BS; 89-42 201st St., Hollis, NY 11423.

BOLTON, Garfield L.; '93 BS; Parole Ofcr.; NYS Div. of Parole, 314 W. 40th St., New York, NY 10018, 212 239-6337; r. 107-12 Farragut Rd, Brooklyn, NY 11236, 718 600-0477.

BOLTON, Judy L.; '78 BA; 116-06 202 St., Jamaica, NY 11412, 718 276-4069.

BOLZ, Francis A., Jr.; '68 BS; Cnslt. Lecturer; Bolz Assocs. Inc., POB 2678, Huntington Sta., NY 11746, 631 462-9706; r. 9 Candlewood Path, Dix Hills, NY 11746, 631 462-9706; *Ruth.* e-mail

BON, Johnny; '77 BA; 25 Roma Ave., Staten Island, NY 10306, 718 351-7464.

BONA, Alan J.; '83 MPA; 305 Raff Ave., Carle Place, NY 11514, 516 742-1123.

BONACCHI, Eugene; '76 BS; 271 Tanglewood Dr., Staten Island, NY 10308.

BONACORSA, Michael F.; '91 BA; 55 Anchor Ave., Oceanside, NY 11572, 516 331-5121.

BONACUM, William T.; '75 MPA; 64 Griffing Ave., Amityville, NY 11701.

BONANEY, Polanges R.; '97 BA; Health Advisor; Dept. of Health Brooklyn, NY; r. 732 E. 48th St., Brooklyn, NY 11203, 718 629-2609; Gerta, Dimitry, Elida Dorismond. e-mail

BONANNO, Douglas A.; '82 BS; 161-06 Jewel Ave., Flushing, NY 11365, 718 515-4736.

BONANNO, Patsy; '91 BS; 9 Barnum Ct., Brewster, NY 10509, 914 965-9297.

BONANO, Aracelis; '96 BA; 111 Marble Hill, Bronx, NY 10463, 718 563-9113.

BONANO, Gregory; '83 BA; 4861 Broadway, New York, NY 10034.

BONAPARTE, Henry; '75 BA; 319 6th Ave., Pelham, NY 10803, 914 738-0241.

BONAS BENJAMIN, Laura Z.; '98 BS; 667 E 34 St. 4p, Brooklyn, NY 11203, 718 241-9346.

BONDOR, Stephen A.; '82 BS; 165 Division Ave., Brooklyn, NY 11758.

BONDS, Charles W.; '89 BS; AS Clg. of Staten Island; Security Mgr.; Wackenhut, DC Area; r. 10219 Cove Ledge Ct., Montgomery Vlg., MD 20886, 301 963-1440; Christopher.

BONDS, Cheryl D.; '89 BS; Retired; r. 335 Lake Ave., Brooklyn, NY 11233, 718 498-4928.

BONELLI, Basil A.; '79 BS; Retired; r. 257 A Third Ave., Bay Shore, NY 11706, 631 968-2387.

BONET, Deborah H.; '92 BS; 1118 39th St. 2nd F, Brooklyn, NY 11218.

BONGIOVANNI, R.; '88 BA; 3 Woodsorrel Ln., E. Northport, NY 11731, 631 368-2069.

BONILLA, Anthony; '99 BA; 53 19 46 St., Maspeth, NY 11378, 718 706-7105.

BONILLA, Cesar A.; '94 BS; Police Ofcr.; NYC Police Dept.; r. 112-09 111th Ave., S. Ozone Park, NY 11420, 718 476-1604.

BONILLA, Jose E.; '98 BS; Case Mgr.; Voc. Couns.; Correction Corp.; r. POB 1171, New York, NY 10040, 212 923-1525. e-mail

BONILLA, Jose L.; '85 BS; 108 Avenue D Apt. 7g, New York, NY 10009.

BONILLA, Nilda; '85 BA; 1815 Grand Concourse, Bronx, NY 10453, 718 561-6386.

BONILLA, Rosa Y. '98 (See Gomez, Rosa Y.).

BONILLA, Sandra G.; '92 BS; 342 52nd St., Brooklyn, NY 11220, 718 492-5733.

BONITA, Thomas J.; '81 MPA; BS Pace Univ.; Court Admin.; US Dept. of Justice, New York, NY 10014, 212 620-6279.

BONNER, Edward J.; '74 BS; 3760 Jerusalem Ave., Seaford, NY 11783, 516 752-0060.

BOODHOO, Joanne; '97 BA; 130-22 123rd St., S. Ozone Park, NY 11420.

BOODRAM, Natalie; '87 BS; 109-49 123 St., Flushing, NY 11354.

BOOKER, Eric G.; '84 BS; 300 S Kirschling Dr., Swedesboro, NJ 08085.

BOOKER, Kwesi L.; '98 BA; Child Protective Spec.; Admin. for Children Svcs., 7 Laight St., New York, NY 10013; r. Apt. 4C, Brooklyn, NY 11234, 718 859-1920. e-mail

BOOKER, Walter L.; '79 BS; MPA CW Post/Long Island Univ.; Lt. Ret/Adjunct Prof./Asst.; Campus Dir., NYPD/Clg. of New Rochelle, Bronx, NY 10454, 718 665-1310; r. 133-01 226th St., Laurelton, NY 11413, 718 723-8854.

BOOKER, Wayne R.; '79 BS; 619 E 29th St., Brooklyn, NY 11210, 718 859-2320.

BOONCOME, Sanrit; '99 BS; 61 15 43 Ave. 5F, Woodside, NY 11377, 718 507-5702.

BOONE, Bruce A.; '94 BA; Transportation; NYC Transit Authority, 370 Jay St., New York, NY 10001, 718 243-4751; r. 319 Macdonuogh St., Brooklyn, NY 11233, 718 573-6592. e-mail

BOONE, Nikita M.; '97 BA; 116-11 131st St., Jamaica, NY 11420, 718 659-8993.

BOONE, Theresa L.; 75 Sunnyside Dr., Warwick, RI 02889, 401 739-6177.

BOONE, Vernette L.; '89 BA; 11611 131st St., Jamaica, NY 11420, 718 659-5072.

BORAKOV, Fred S.; '80 MA; POB 393, New York, NY 10008.

BORBON, Daysi A.; '98 BA; CERT. Drake Bus. Sch.; Clerk; Brooklyn Supreme Library, 360 Adams St., Brooklyn, NY 11201, 718 643-8080; r. 966 St. Nicholas Ave. #5f, New York, NY 10032, 212 234-3120; Keilah Adames, Tiffany Adames.

BORBON, Manuel J.; '97 BS; 65 Fortwashinton Ave. #34, New York, NY 10032.

BORCHERS, Henry J.; '79 MA; 9 Fairgreen Ct., Cortlandt Manor, NY 10567, 914 737-6929.

BORCHERS, James E.; '85 BS; 419 Colonial Ave., Westfield, NJ 07090, 908 232-5581.

BORDAS, David M.; '99 BA; Teacher; Sacred Heart High School, 34 Convent Ave., Yonkers, NY 10703, 914 965-3114; r. 100 Herriot St. Apt. #4L, Yonkers, NY 10701; *Aleida.* e-mail

BORDEN, Lesley '95 (See Smith, Mrs. Lesley B.).

BORDERS, Delisa Y.; '83 BA; 572 Washington Ave., Brooklyn, NY 11238.

BOREA, William P.; '97 BS; 19 Grand Ave., Ridgefield Park, NJ 07660, 201 440-0625.

BORELLI, Anthony M.; '82 BS; 141 W 2nd St., W. Islip, NY 11795, 631 587-7648.

BORESKY, George M.; '80 MA; 164 W Cedarview Ave., Staten Island, NY 10306.

BORESKY, Peter J.; '78 MA; 164 W Cedarview Ave., Staten Island, NY 10306.

BORFITZ, Irving E.; '76 BS; 8932 Vanderveer St., Queens Vlg., NY 11427.

BORGES, Cibella R.; '85 BS; 192 Orchard St. Apt. 4, New York, NY 10002.

BORGIA, Donald D.; '80 MPA; 61 13th Ave., Ronkonkoma, NY 11779.

BORGSTRAND, Margaret A.; '74 BA; Retired; r. 3516 80 St. #42, Jackson Hts., NY 11372.

BORIS, Elizabeth; '80 MA; 1019 Northfield Rd, Woodmere, NY 11598, 516 374-1849.

BORITZA, Ms. Patricia A.; '80 BS; Paralegal; Mayer Brown & Platt, 700 Louisiana St., Houston, TX 77002, 713 546-0531; r. 7751 High Village Dr., Houston, TX 77095, 281 856-2234; Danielle, Sanchez. e-mail

BORJA, Ivan; '96 BS; 511 Pennsylvania Ave., Williston Park, NY 11596.

BORKER, Vito; '97 BA; Police Detective; NYC Police Dept; r. 1213 Avenue Z #E8, Brooklyn, NY 11235, 718 332-5730. e-mail

BORMAN, Charles J.; '75 BS; 68-17 Myrtle Ave., Brooklyn, NY 11227.

BORMAN, Gary M.; '77 AS, '78 BS; Lieutenant; NYC Police Dept.; r. #2 Cottonwood Ct., Bardonia, NY 10954, 914 627-3007; *Frances;* Gail, Gary Jr, Carolann.

BORMAN, William G.; '75 MPA; 28 Larkspur Ave., Merrick, NY 11566, 516 486-0315.

BORNMANN, Ines C.; '84 BS; 417 Taurus Rd, Schenectady, NY 12304.

BORQUAYE, Marylin, (Marylin Reed); '81 BA; MS New Sch. Grad. Division; Retired Deputy Dir. of Contracts; City of NY; r. 100-31 Alcott Pl., Bronx, NY 10475, 718 671-4851; Shelly, Erik, Lisa. e-mail

BORRELLI, Kristin K.; '98 MA; 23-38 31 Street Rd. 4d, Astoria, NY 11106, 718 738-3212.

BORRERO, Hiram T.; '96 BA; 186 32nd St., Brooklyn, NY 11232, 718 832-1573.

BORRERO, Kenneth; '98 BA; Financial Systs. Coord.; St. Barnabas Hosp., 4750 3rd Ave., Bronx, NY 10457, 718 960-3879; r. 118 Palisade Ave., Cliffside Park, NJ 07010, 201 941-1252. e-mail

BORRUSO, Mariano; '75 BS; Pres.; Utility Metal Rsch., 14 Van St., Staten Island, NY 10310, 718 720-6646; r. 26 Flagship Cir., Staten Island, NY 10309, 718 984-0729; *Arleen;* Marleen, John. e-mail

BORSILLI, Mildred O.; '88 BA; 432 Elventon Ave., Staten Island, NY 10308, 718 979-9550.

BORWORNTHAMMARAT, A.; '95 MS; 147 N. 8th Aven, Mt. Vernon, NY 10550.

BORZOTTA, David R.; '93 MA; 118 Division Ave., Hasbrouck Hts., NJ 07604, 201 331-1299.

BOSCO, Michael; '92 BS; 64 Ridge Ave., Staten Island, NY 10304, 718 980-3985.

BOSCO, Vicent I.; '63 MPA; 35 Rudolph Ter., Yonkers, NY 10701.

BOSELLI, Denise M. '91 (See Goldberg, Mrs. Denise M.).

BOSHELL, Kevin M.; '95 BS; 577 Bay Ridge Pkwy., Brooklyn, NY 11209.

BOSIO, Franklin J.; '81 BS; AS CCNY; Cert. Latent Fingerprint Examiner; N.Y.P.D, Police Headquarter, New York, NY 10001; r. 48-03 195 St., Fresh Meadows, NY 11365, 718 357-6458; *Thomasina;* Franklin Jr., Maryann.

BOSKO, George M.; '81 BS; Retired; NYC Police Dept.; r. 2131 SW Mayflower Dr., Palm City, FL 34990, 561 220-3390; *Dolores.* e-mail

BOSSA, Anna L.; '89 BA; 2113 Haviland Ave., Bronx, NY 10472, 718 239-9708.

BOSSONG, Denise '85 (See Di Benedetto, Denise).

BOSTICK, Denise G.; '82 BA; 325 E. Vivian St., POB 565, Candor, NC 27229, 910 974-3553; *Booker T.*

BOSTON, Denver G.; '72 AS, '73 BS; Regional Trng. Ofcr.; US Govt, 26 Federal Plz., New York, NY 10278, 212 264-3918; r. 7 Indian Hill Rd, Rye, NY 10580, 914 921-0950. e-mail

BOSTON, Karen; '88 BA, '90 MPA; 583 Midwood St., Brooklyn, NY 11203, 718 774-0102.

BOSWELL, Joseph A.; '80 MPA; 301 Taylor St., Staten Island, NY 10310, 718 447-4252.

BOTA, Heidi; '89 BS; 2405 1st Ave. Apt. 7d, New York, NY 10035.

BOTHOS, Demetrios; '96 BS; JD Cand.; CUNY Law Sch.; r. 3440 9th St., Long Island City, NY 11106, 718 267-6430.

BOTTARINI, Carlos; '91 BS; 3614 Corporal Stone St., Flushing, NY 11361, 718 423-4954.

BOTTE, Dominick, Jr.; '80 BS; Pres.; New Yorks Finest French Cleaners, 144 Reade St., New York, NY 10013, 212 431-4010; r. 8651 16th Ave., Brooklyn, NY 11214, 718 837-7345; *Carol Ann;* Dominick III, Stephanie, Nicholas, Christopher. e-mail

BOTTINO, Roland; '92 BA; 1646 1st Ave. Apt. 18g, New York, NY 10028, 212 628-9899.

BOUDIETTE, Charles T.; '80 BS; 1837 124th St., Flushing, NY 11356, 718 461-3147.

BOUILLON, Stephen; '89 BA; 9317 197th St., Jamaica, NY 11423, 718 736-0062.

BOURDON, Ana M.; '92 BS, '97 MPA; Postal Inspector; USPO, New York, NY 10001; r. 370 Brook Ave., Bronx, NY 10454, 718 993-8313. e-mail

BOURDON, Edwin L.; '91 BS; 203 W 108th St. Apt. 1, New York, NY 10025.

BOURDON, Martha L.; '89 BA; 1922 Ditmars Blvd., Long Island City, NY 11105, 718 204-7852.

BOURQUIN, Peter E.; '77 BS; 6483 83rd Pl., Flushing, NY 11379.

BOUTE, Yvrande; '96 BS; 1694 Troy Ave., Brooklyn, NY 11234, 718 934-0197.

BOUTINEAU, Robert G.; '76 BS; 4 Rose St., # 5A1, Oceanside, NY 11572, 516 678-2437.

BOUTSIKAKIS, Margrte; '81 BA; 2142 80th St., Flushing, NY 11370, 718 726-7719.

BOUZA, Anthony V.; '68 MPA; 10 Winthrop Ln., Scarsdale, NY 10583.

BOVE, John D.; '78 BS; MS Iona Clg.; Pharmaceutical Chemist; Wyeth-Ayerst Labs., 914 732-4511; r. 31 Overlook Rd, W. Haverstraw, NY 10993, 914 786-2325. e-mail

BOVEA, Liana '89 (See Casalins, Liana C.).

BOVELL, Donna A.; '93 AS, '96 BS; Correction Ofcr.; NYC Dept. of Corrections, 275 Atlantic Ave., Brooklyn, NY 11201, 718 797-8305; r. 1059 Schenectady Ave., Brooklyn, NY 11203, 718 922-0072; *Davonni.* e-mail

BOWDEN, Bradd D.; '97 BA; 2550 Independence, Bronx, NY 10463, 718 548-2528.

BOWEN, Anthony; '96 MPA; CERT. ICTA; Dir. of Sales Northeast Reg.; DER/German Rail, 171-20 103 Rd., Jamaica, NY 11433, 718 523-7882; r. 17120 103rd Rd, Jamaica, NY 11433, 718 291-0145. e-mail

BOWEN, Fielding W.; '91 BS, '91 MPA; 104 Decatur St., Brooklyn, NY 11216, 718 493-5878.

BOWEN, Gerard; '92 BA; 340 Crown St., Brooklyn, NY 11225, 718 774-9071.

BOWENS, Hermine E.; '78 BS; 16820 Liberty Ave., Jamaica, NY 11433.

BOWENS, Renita D.; '94 BS; Social Worker; Care for The Homeless, 2727 Jerome Ave., Bronx, NY 10468; r. Bronx, NY 10463; *David Marshall.* e-mail

BOWES, Vincent; '75 BS; AS Kingsborough Community; Investigator-Corporate Security; Salomon Smith Barney, 388 Greenwich St., New York, NY 10013, 212 816-1703; r. 105 Wood St., Lynbrook, NY 11563, 516 887-4587; *Carole;* Kristen, Brian. e-mail

BOWLER, William T.; '77 BS; AAS North Country, AAS Nassau Community; Sr. Programmer Analyst; Chase Manhattan Bank, Garden City, NY 11530, 516 745-3117; r. 334 W Nicholai St., Hicksville, NY 11801, 516 935-1369; *Christine.* e-mail

BOWLES, Aries; '95 BA; 185 Wortman Ave., Brooklyn, NY 11207.

BOWLES, Leslie M.; '94 BS; 333 Lafayette Ave., Brooklyn, NY 11238, 718 302-4992.

BOWLES, Mark E.; '99 BA; 230 E. 88 St. Apt. 3B, New York, NY 10128, 212 289-3193.

BOWMAN, Debra; '84 BA; Retired Police Ofcr.; Dist. 33; r. 13856 232nd St., Springfield Gardens, NY 11413; Jamel Pinckney, Christopher Pin, Candice Pinckne. e-mail

BOWMAN, Jeffrey H.; '84 MPA; 57 Parkway Dr., Rye, NY 10580.

BOWMAN, Lawson D.; '97 BA; Data Entry; Continental Airline, JFL Bldg. #75; r. 41-40 Union St. 10R, Flushing, NY 11355, 718 526-9766. e-mail

BOWMAN, William D.; '83 MPA; 87 Susan Dr., New City, NY 10956, 914 638-0732.

BOWRY, Letitia R.; '84 BS; 773 Concourse Village, Bronx, NY 10451, 718 293-4205.

BOYCE, Audrei T.; '75 MPA; 8718 Avenue J # A1, Brooklyn, NY 11236, 718 377-1337.

BOYCE, Karentessa D.; '92 BS; 352 Chester St. # D, Brooklyn, NY 11212, 718 385-2073.

BOYCE, Robert; '98 BA; 23-08 42nd St., Astoria, NY 11105, 718 322-4264.

BOYCE, Rodney C.; '97 BS, '98 BSCRIM, '98 BS; Police Ofcr.; NYC Dept. of Corrections; r. 1199 E. 53rd St., Brooklyn, NY 11234, 718 531-6903.

BOYD, Crystal; '97 BS; Sch. Safety; r. 1234 Lincoln Pl., Brooklyn, NY 11213, 718 493-8794.

BOYD, Tracey '79 (See Boyd-vega, Tracey).

BOYD, William S.; '78 BS; 1975 54th St., Brooklyn, NY 11204, 718 377-1502.

BOYD-VEGA, Tracey, (Tracey Boyd); '79 BS; MS George Washington Clg.-DC; Asst. Chief Textile Acquisitions; Dept. of Justice, 400 First St., Washington, DC 20537, 202 305-7260; r. 5555 Neddleton Ave., Woodbridge, VA 22193, 703 730-5674.

BOYESON, Warren; '85 AS; Processor; US Postal Svc., 2001 Dixiana Rd, W. Columbia, SC 29172, 803 926-6121; r. 107 Wilton Hill Rd, Columbia, SC 29212, 803 407-1549; *Christine;* Matthew, Amanda.

BOYKIN, Thomas; '78 BA; 1021 Philadelphia Rd., Westerville, OH 43081, 614 436-6403.

BOYKO, Kevin E.; '76; 115 9th St. SE, Minot, ND 58701, 701 852-8150.

BOYLAN, Joan; '89 BS; 3987 New York Ave., Seaford, NY 11783.

BOYLAN, Kathleen; '96 BA; Homemaker; r. 5 Glenwood St., Clifton, NJ 07013; *Peter Erdman; Henry.* e-mail

BOYLAN, Lauren E.; '96 BA; Brooklyn Law Sch.; Police Ofcr.; NYPD, 1 Police Plz., New York, NY 10038, 212 374-5000; r. 143 Kirshon Ave., Staten Island, NY 10314. e-mail

BOYLAN, Michael P.; '78 BS; 485 Bard Ave., Staten Island, NY 10310, 718 720-8946.

BOYLE, Donald J.; '77 BS; 475 Greeley Ave., Staten Island, NY 10306, 718 981-8110.

BOYLE, Edward R.; '83 AS; 1302 Woodlake Dr., Denton, TX 76205.

BOYLE, James J.; '77 BS; AS NY Tech; Higher Educ. Ofcr.; John Jay Clg., 555W 57 St., New York, NY 10019, 212 237-8650; r. 523 Oxford St. W, Westbury, NY 11590, 516 997-6107; *Barbara;* James, Michael, Mary, Peter, Jean. e-mail

BOYLE, John F.; '63 MPA; Retired Det. Sgt.; New York Police Dept.; r. 11 Cougar Run, Hilton Head Island, SC 29926, 843 681-6871.

BOYLE, John J.; '71 BS; 8 Van Cott Ave., Farmingdale, NY 11735, 516 249-7385; *Margaret;* John Kevin, Anne Marie, Timothy James, Michael Neil. e-mail

BOYLE, Sheila A.; '80 BS; 2062 79th St., Brooklyn, NY 11214, 718 745-7450.

BOYLE, William M.; '84 MA; 141 Apponegansett St., New Bedford, MA 02744, 508 996-6274.

BOZZI, Elissa; '77 MA; 15145 28th Ave., Flushing, NY 11354, 718 353-6089.

BRACCINI, Stefano A.; '95 BS; 628 Annadale Rd, Staten Island, NY 10312.

BRACERO, Denise; '98 BS; Syst. Analyst; Metropolitan Hosp., 1901 First Ave., New York, NY 10029, 212 423-7532; r. 2684 Fulton St. 2nd Fl., Brooklyn, NY 11207, 718 346-5379; *Orlando;* Christian. e-mail

BRACEY, Louise A.; 176-20 Sunbury Rd., Jamaica, NY 11434.

BRACY, Marshandra D.; '99 BS; 1515 Grand Concourse, #5D, Bronx, NY 10452, 718 299-9596.

BRADLEY, Donna M.; '87 MA; BA Fordham Univ.; Asst. Admin.; Teamster Trust Fund Ofc.; r. 3505 Bruckner Blvd., Bronx, NY 10461, 718 828-0457; Kasey O'Reilly.

BRADLEY, Kevin; '95 BS; 6305 Kennedy Blvd. E # C, W. New York, NJ 07093.

BRADLEY, Richard A.; '97 BA; 3784 10th Ave., Apt. 13H, New York, NY 10034, 212 569-8421.

BRADSHAW, Robert N.; '97 BS; Technical Asst.; NASA Community Clg.; r. 2521 4th Ave., E. Meadow, NY 11554, 516 781-6152.

BRADY, Bryan; '96 AS; POB 117, Florida, NY 10921, 914 357-2097.

BRADY, COL Edward T., USA(Ret.); '77 MA; BS Univ. Nebraska, Omaha, JD CA Western Sch. Law; Atty-at-Law; Brady & Brady, 325 Green St., Fayetteville, NC 28301, 910 323-5600; r. same. e-mail

BRADY, Gerard D.; '87 BA; POB 274, Islip Terrace, NY 11752.

BRADY, James S.; '77 BS; 576 W Park Ave., Long Beach, NY 11561, 516 627-7198.

BRADY, John J.; '93 BS; HR-Background Investigator; US Dept. of Justice, 100 29th St., Ext. 5328, Brooklyn, NY 11232, 718 840-4200; r. 23 Bayview Ave., Bayport, NY 11705, 631 472-1149; *Michelle;* Shannon, Sean. e-mail

BRADY, John J.; '82 MPA; 29 Water Ln. N, Levittown, NY 11756, 516 796-1808.

BRADY, Matthew; '93 BA; 309 Cherry St., Belford, NJ 07718.

BRADY, Matthew E.; '79 BS; Mgr.; US Postal Svc., 2191 Ebenezer Rd., Rock Hill, SC 29732, 803 327-4599; r. 205 Wessex Way, Ft. Mill, SC 29708, 803 547-6038; *Joan M.;* Matthew I., Kaitlin S., Sean A.

BRADY, Michael J.; '69 BS; 24 Park Ave., Congers, NY 10920, 914 268-6450.

BRADY, Oral W.; '92 BS; 771 St. Johns Pl., Brooklyn, NY 11216, 718 241-6850.

BRADY, Richard J., Esq.; '82 BA; Police Chief; Waldwick Police Dept., 201 652-5700; r. 112 Franklin Tpk., Waldwick, NJ 07463, 201 652-6521.

BRADY, Sandra A.; '96 MA; 109 Avenue C, Haledon, NJ 07508.

BRADY, Sylvia T.; '72 BS, '72 AA, '81 MA; Ret. Asst. Deputy Warden,Unit Leadr; Dept. of Corrections, Mental Health Clinic; r. POB 958, Christiansted, VI 00821, 340 778-9745; *Michael.*

BRAFF, Jeraldine; '75 MA; 1477 Levey Rd, Pattersonville, NY 12137, 518 864-5564.

BRAFF, Neil S.; '88 BS; 2942 W 5th St. Apt. 7g, Brooklyn, NY 11224, 718 946-6438.

BRAGG, Joseph L.; '76 BA; 95 W. 95 St., New York, NY 10025, 212 866-2169.

BRAITHWAITE, Deborah; '85 BS; 30c Seafoam Ave., Winfield, NJ 07036, 908 925-4357.

BRAITHWAITE, George F.; '77 BA; 1321 St. Johns Pl., Brooklyn, NY 11213, 718 277-1439.

BRAITHWAITE, Reginald, Esq.; '75 BS, '84 MA; JD Touro Clg. Law Sch.; Atty.; Law Ofc. of Reginald L. Braithwaite, 139-18 228th St., Laurelton, NY 11413, 718 344-4718; r. 13918 228th St., Laurelton, NY 11413, 718 527-8572; *Angelica;* Reginald Jr., Antonio, Lawrence. e-mail

BRAMBLE, Anthony S.; '97 BS; Collections Rep.; Bayridge Physcial Medicine; r. 1111 Lafayette Ave., Apt. 2A, Brooklyn, NY 11221, 718 919-8059. e-mail

BRAMBLE, Elvira T.; '75 BS; 119-39 Nsvile Blvd., St. Albans, NY 11412.

BRAMBLE, Michael P.; '93 MA; BA City Clg. of New York, MA; Lt.; NYC Police Dept., Detective Boro Bronx, 450 Cross Bronx Expyway, Bronx, NY 10457, 718 299-4065; r. 223 W 139th St., New York, NY 10030, 212 307-1263.

BRAMBLE, Rachel; '93 MA; POB 2225, Crestline, CA 92325, 503 240-0141.

BRAMSON, Joy A.; '78 BS; MS Audubon Expedition Inst.; Tchr.; Bronx Zoo; r. 44 Tier St., Bronx, NY 10464, 718 885-1991.

BRANCATO, Gregory R.; '87 BS; 404 Churchill Rd, Teaneck, NJ 07666, 201 833-1731.

BRANCELLA, Silvano; '69 AS, '70 BS, '93 MA; 9808 158th Ave., Jamaica, NY 11414, 718 592-2787.

BRANCH, Joseph; '85 MPA, '86 BS; Retired Police Ofcr.; NYC Police Dept.; r. 126 Norway Ln., Lebanon, PA 17042, 717 274-6086; *Aurora;* Joshua.

BRANCH, Robert L.; '77 AS; 3043 Tiemann Ave., Bronx, NY 10469.

BRANDI, Daniel J.; '76 BS; 2563 Seminole Ave., Seaford, NY 11783.

BRANDOFINO, Elaine M.; '79 BS; JD Hofstra Law Sch.; Elaine Brandofino, Esq., 305 Braodway, New York, NY 10007, 212 267-5600; r. 185 West End Ave. 5E, New York, NY 10023.

BRANDON, John; '80 BS; 13066 228th St., Jamaica, NY 11413.

BRANDT, William J.; '68 BS; Retired NYC Police; r. POB 358, Rehoboth Bch., DE 19971, 302 226-9779; *Anissa;* Gary. e-mail

BRANGMAN, Philip H.; '77 BS; 10925 201st St., Jamaica, NY 11412.

BRANIC, Doretha; '88 BS; Social Worker; Fedn. of Puerto Rican Org of Brownsville, 454 Chester St., Brooklyn, NY 11212; r. 65 Ocean Ave. Apt. 4-C, Brooklyn, NY 11225, 718 287-2479; Evelyn T., Roosevelt Keith, Glen W., Lisa S.

BRANIGAN, Robert J.; 632 Palmer Rd. #5J, Yonkers, NY 10701, 914 337-7392.

BRANNAN, Amy A.; '97 BS, '99 BS; 859 Fairfield Ave., Westbury, NY 11590, 516 333-7305.

BRANT, Clifford E.; '78 BS; Forensic Scientist III; NYS Defense-Forensic Investigations, State Campus, Albany, NY 12201; r. 3 Francis Pl., Latham, NY 12110, 518 783-3492.

BRANT, John J.; '78 BA; 21826 104th Ave., Queens Vlg., NY 11429, 718 441-8991.

BRASERO, Rever; '84 BS; 801 Manor Rd Apt. 6d, Staten Island, NY 10314, 718 983-0734.

BRASH, Ronald A.; '97 BS; 1530 Archer Rd., Bronx, NY 10462.

BRASSINGTON, Michael; '90 BS; 4209 Quentin Rd, Brooklyn, NY 11234.

BRATCHER, Illene; '92 BS; 4-21 Astoria Blvd., Long Island City, NY 11102.

BRATHWAITE, Earl R.; '96 BS; MS City Clg.-NY; Law Instructor; NY Bd. of Educ., HS For Legal Studies, 850 Grand St., Brooklyn, NY 11211, 718 387-2879; r. 205 West End Ave., Apt. 6W, New York, NY 10023, 212 875-0505.

BRATHWAITE, Henderson O.; '98 AS; 212 Bristol St. #1, Brooklyn, NY 11212, 718 493-8688.

BRATHWAITE, LeRoy L.; '74 BA; Retired Lt.; NYC Police Dept.; r. 144-01 133rd Ave., Jamaica, NY 11436, 718 322-6314; *Harriet;* Helene. e-mail

BRATHWAITE, CAPT Rafael; '90 BA; Quality Spec.; US Postal Svc., 421 8th Ave. Rm 5030, New York, NY 10199, 212 330-3123; r. 18912 118th Ave., Jamaica, NY 11412, 718 723-5325; *Denise;* Alexander, Jessica. e-mail

BRATHWAITE, Sheron; '95 BS; 3 W. 101 St. Stre, New York, NY 10025.

BRATHWAITE, Tasha Y.; '96 BA; CERT. Police Acad.; Police Ofcr. Tracer Unit; NYC Police Dept., 72nd Precinct, Brooklyn, NY 11232, 718 965-6311; r. 3702 Avenue I, Brooklyn, NY 11210, 718 258-8654.

BRATTON, James G.; '74 BA; 13726 158th St., Jamaica, NY 11434.

BRAUN, Eileen E.; '89 BS; JD Touro Law; Administrative Law Judge; NYC Dept. of Finance, 210 Joralemon St., Brooklyn, NY 11201; r. 4 Terrace Ct., Albertson, NY 11507, 516 466-8060; *Hermann;* Catherine, Megan, Kaylie.

BRAVO, William A.; '98 AS; POB 606, Babylon, NY 11702.

BRAXTON, Aubrey S.; '91 BS; Police Ofcr.; NYPD, 1 Police Plz., New York, NY 10038, 212 239-2221; r. 219 Montauk Ave., Brooklyn, NY 11208, 631 968-8521; *Karen;* Nailah.

BRAXTON, Valerie D.; '98 MPA; 120-02 Sutphin Blvd. #104D, Jamaica, NY 11434, 718 659-0081.

BREA, John; 120 S 17th St., Philadelphia, PA 19103.

BREA, Lizette; '95 BA; 211 E. 205th St., Bronx, NY 10458.

BREAULT, Suzanne M.; '99 BA; 24 N Beverwyck Rd, Ste. B, Lake Hiawatha, NJ 07034, 973 402-7214.

BRECH, Todd R.; '96 BS; Police Ofcr.; NYPD, 1st Per., 16 Ericsson Pl., New York, NY 10003, 212 791-4062; r. 20 Rainbow Ave., Staten Island, NY 10302, 718 447-2927; *Elizabeth;* Michael, Matthew. e-mail

BREDEFELD, Nicole J.; '99 BA; 20 Maryann Rd, Oak Ridge, NJ 07438, 973 742-3363.

BREDER, Donald J.; '95 AS; 1713 E 37th St., Brooklyn, NY 11234.

BREEN, Susan L.; '90 BS; 59 Cayuga Ave., Staten Island, NY 10301, 718 981-3448.

BREN, Fern M.; '85 BS; 1740 Ocean Ave., Apt. 6B, Brooklyn, NY 11230, 718 252-9691.

BRENNAN, Daniel K.; '75 MA; 47 W 75th St. Apt. 1r, New York, NY 10023, 212 501-9513.

BRENNAN, Denise; '99 BA; 1354 Sidney Ct., Seaford, NY 11783, 516 783-8581.

BRENNAN, Eileen M.; '79 BA; 94 Iceland Dr., Huntington Sta., NY 11746, 516 783-8581.

BRENNAN, James J.; '68 BS; 13 Whippoorwill Dr., Hackettstown, NJ 07840, 973 584-0091.

BRENNAN, John J.; '78 MA; Retired Capt./Fire Security; NYC Fire Dept.; r. 765 Riverside Dr., New York, NY 10032, 212 927-3399; *Maria.*

BRENNAN, John P.; '68 MPA; 451 60 St., Brooklyn, NY 11220, 718 859-1812.

BRENNAN, Joseph R.; '83 MPA; 3072 Governors Xing, Belmar, NJ 07719, 732 280-2588.

BRENNAN, Kenneth D.; '77 BS; Tavern Owner; Deer Head Inn, 140 Western Hwy., W. Nyack, NY 10994, 914 358-9821; r. 80 Branchville Rd, Valley Cottage, NY 10989, 914 268-4157; *Delia; Lauren,* Joseph. e-mail

BRENNAN, Michael J.; '75 AS, '77 BS; VP; Staten Island Savings Bank, 15 Beach, Staten Island, NY 10304, 718 727-8863; r. 208 Mann Ave., Staten Island, NY 10314.

BRENNAN, Thomas F.; '75 BS; 1936 SE 35th St., Cape Coral, FL 33904, 631 567-8074.

BRENNAN, Thomas H.; '80 BS; 44 Charleston Ave., Staten Island, NY 10309.

BRENNEMAN, Suzanne N.; '99 MA; 2109 Broadway #7-160, New York, NY 10023, 212 595-3398.

BRENORD, Celius; '95 BS, '97 MPA; 1189 E 59th St., Brooklyn, NY 11234, 718 251-1697.

BRESLIN, Daniel E.; '77 BS; 49 Spence Ave., Holtsville, NY 11742.

BRESLIN, Ethel T.; '74 MA; 4 Seacliff Ave. Box 823, Miller Place, NY 11764.

BRESLIN, Michael; '96; 398 Oliver Pl. #, Bronx, NY 10458.

BRESLIN, Michael D.; '94 BS; 1767 E 34th St., Brooklyn, NY 11234, 718 833-0307.

BRESNAN, Eilish B.; '93 BS; Probation Ofcr.; Bergen Cnty. Juvenile Intake Unit, Bergen Cnty. Courthouse, 10 W. Main St., Rm. 142, Hackensack, NJ 07601, 201 752-4484; r. 39 7th St. # 1, Cresskill, NJ 07626, 201 568-6030. e-mail

BRETON, Lydia E.; '97 BA; 2156 Cruger Ave., Bronx, NY 10462, 718 892-5629.

BRETT, Veronica E.; '84 BS; CER; Substance Abuse Couns; Extra Care Health Svcs., 201 Hwy. 34, Matawan, NJ 07747, 732 721-0060; r. 83 Dodd St., Laurence Harbor, NJ 08879. e-mail

BRETTON, Ronald; '76 BA; 475 Atkinson Dr., Honolulu, HI 96814, 808 944-8411.

BREWER, Denize; '77 BA; 10811 175th St., Jamaica, NY 11433, 718 897-1031.

BREWER, Howard; '79 BS; 2653 30th St., Long Island City, NY 11102.

BREZNY, Charles G.; '85 AS; Chmn.; Dudley, MA 01571; r. 5 Cswy. Shore, Dudley, MA 01571, 508 943-9055; *Denise;* Brian, Donna, Denise, Dianna.

BRIANT, Anita K.; '85 BS; 131-09 134 St., S. Ozone Park, NY 11420.

BRICE, Cassandra Y. '95 (See Souvenir-brice, Mrs. Cassandra Y.).

BRICKWOOD, Dale; '95 BS; 776 Pinesbridge Rd, Ossining, NY 10562, 914 941-4954.

BRIDESON, Dawn M.; '94 BS; 78 Utter Ave., Staten Island, NY 10314.

BRIDGES, Rhonda; '92 BS; 13825 248th St., Rosedale, NY 11422.

BRIDGEWATER, Joel A.; '74 BS; 288 E Pleasant Grove Rd, Jackson, NJ 08527.

BRIEBA, Lorenzo A.; '86 BS; 4 Wilson Dr., Hampton Bays, NY 11946, 631 728-3829.

BRIEN, William E.; '95 BS; 43 Ashton Dr., Staten Island, NY 10312.

BRIENZA, Jeffrey T.; '95 BS; Police Ofcr.; NYC Police Dept., 1 Police Plz., New York, NY 10018; r. 84-06 88th St., Woodhaven, NY 11421.

BRIGANDI, Douglas; '76 MA; 50-01 217 St., Bayside, NY 11364.

BRIGGS, Errol; '95 BA; MA Brooklyn Clg.; Social Worker; Jasa; r. 471 E 45th St. Apt. A3, Brooklyn, NY 11203; *Dianne Franklin;* Karil, Kyle, Karlvin, Nicholas. e-mail

BRIGGS, Renee; '91 BS; MS Long Island Univ.; Guid. Couns.; NYC Bd. of Educ., 718 773-2894; r. 30 Bush St. Apt. 4b, Brooklyn, NY 11231, 718 858-1356.

BRIGHTON, China T.; '99 MS; 16022 Randall Ave., Fontana, CA 92335, 718 267-7260.

BRIGNONI, Amy B.; '90 BA; 2086 2nd Ave. Apt. 3e, New York, NY 10029.

BRILL, Adam H.; '88 BS; 1273 North Ave. # Ent1-1H, New Rochelle, NY 10804, 914 241-6396.

BRILL, John J.; '76; 1674 Troy Ave., Brooklyn, NY 11234, 718 615-2160.

BRINADZE, Anna; '95 BS; Legal Asst.; r. 3903 Nostrand Ave., 2N, Brooklyn, NY 11235, 718 891-1807. e-mail

BRINDISI, Frank A.; '81 BA; 155-01 Cohancy St., Howard Bch., NY 11414.

BRINKMAN, Mrs. Diane M., (Diane M. Langlan); '94 MA; Victim Advocate; Ofc. of Victim Svcs. State of CT, c/o States Attys Ofc., 235 Church St., New Haven, CT 06510, 203 789-7894; r. 229 Branford Rd #508, N. Branford, CT 06471, 203 488-9502; *Eric.* e-mail

BRINSON, Allyson C.; '83 BS; 1760 Watson Ave., Bronx, NY 10472, 718 884-6585.

BRISBANE, Joyce L.; '88 BS; 210 Clinton Ave. Apt. 10H, Brooklyn, NY 11205.

BRISCOE, Harold P.; '69 BS; 54 Boerum St., Brooklyn, NY 11206, 718 486-6759.

BRISCOE, James J.; '91 BS; Lt.; NYC Police Dept.; r. 818 Sheldon Ave., Staten Island, NY 10309, 718 967-2729; *Lisa;* Karla Rose, Tina Marie. e-mail

BRISKIE, Michael S.; '97 MA; 4600 9th Ave. #103, Brooklyn, NY 11220, 718 436-3156.

BRISSETT, Jacqueline; '93 BA; 219 E 38th St., Brooklyn, NY 11203.

BRITAN, Judith S.; '79 MA; 325 Pease Rd., E. Longmeadow, MA 01028.

BRITO, Michael J.; '95 BS; Special Agt.; DOJ/DEA, 8400 NW 53 St., Miami, FL 33166, 305 597-2031; r. 7891 W. Flagler St. #339, Miami, FL 33144, 305 590-4970. e-mail

BRITT, Deborah L.; '79 BA; Deputy Center; Dept. of Parks City of NY; r. 1411 Linden Blvd., Brooklyn, NY 11212, 718 342-3531.

BRITTON, John J.; '77 BS; Sr. Special Agt.; US Immigration, 7880 Biscayne Blvd., Miami, FL 33138, 305 654-3352; r. 5530 Castlegate Ave., Ft. Lauderdale, FL 33331, 954 434-2035; *Roxanne;* Matthew, Rebecca. e-mail

BRITTON, Lyria K.; '89 BS; 1537 Nelson Ave., Bronx, NY 10452, 718 294-9334.

BRIU, Yolanda; '97 BA; 924 E. 181st St., Bronx, NY 10460.

BROACH, Myra K.; '92 MA; BA Louisiana State Univ.; Owner; Black Cat, 31 Larson Rd., Muncy, PA 17756, 570 437-2319; r. same; Jeff.

BROADHURST, William; '75 BS; 248 Oakwood Ave., Staten Island, NY 10301.

BROCK, Beverly W.; '90 BS; AAS NYC Technical Clg.; RN; United Cerebral Palsy; r. 11111 168th St., Jamaica, NY 11433; *Ralph.*

BROCK, Mrs. Daisy H.; '99 BA; Case Mgr.; Correctional Svcs. Corp., 988 Myrtle Ave., Brooklyn, NY 11206, 718 574-4866; r. 2108 Ryer Ave. #G2, Bronx, NY 10457, 718 365-8636; *Sean;* Ashley, Sean, Justin.

BROCK, Ralph E.; '91 BS; Supervising Fire Marshal; NYC Fire Dept., Bureau of Fire Investigation, 9 Metro Tech Ctr., Brooklyn, NY 11201; r. 11111 168th St., Jamaica, NY 11433; *Beverly.*

BROCKWAY, Alvin J.; '87 BS; 58-32 84th Pl., Elmhurst, NY 11373.

BROCKWAY, Mary Z.; '84 BA, '90 MPA; Crime Prevention & Investigation Mg; Chase Manhattan Bank, 2 Chase Plz., New York, NY 10081; r. Suffern, NY 10901.

BRODACK, Jeffrey; '95 BS; 19840 32nd Ave., Apt. D5, Flushing, NY 11358, 718 445-9096.

BRODERICK, Harold T.; '85 MPA; 16 Jansen St., Staten Island, NY 10312, 718 273-2921.

BRODERICK, Stephen J.; '98 BS; 1089 Thompson Dr., Bay Shore, NY 11706, 631 666-0597.

BRODMAN, Mathew H.; '97 BA; Spec. Agt.; US Dept. of State, 26 Federal Plz., Ste. 3409, New York, NY 10278, 212 415-4479; r. Brooklyn, NY 11229. e-mail

BRODY, Stephen D.; '81 BA; 97 Greenleaf Ave., Staten Island, NY 10310.

BROGAN, Francis J.; '79 BS; 35 McGuinness Blvd., Brooklyn, NY 11222, 718 259-8884.

BROGAN, Michael P.; '80 MPA; BA, AAS Ocean Cnty. Clg.; Police Lt.; Port Authority Police Dept., New York, NY 10004, 800 367-7679; r. 4 Cambridge Ct., Manalapan, NJ 07726. e-mail

BROGAN, Robert J.; 12 Mallory Rd., Spring Vly., NY 10977.

BROGAN, Thomas M.; '85 BS; 167 Delancey Pl., Bronx, NY 10462, 718 892-9583.

BROGLI, Maria C.; '91 BS; 2643 Harding Ave., Bronx, NY 10465.

BROKER, Steven J.; '96 BA; Special Investigator; r. 2953 Lawton Ave., # 2, Bronx, NY 10465, 718 823-4796. e-mail

BROMLEY, Stephen T.; '80 MA; 2830 45th St., Long Island City, NY 11103, 718 274-2134.

BRONAUGH, Ronald A.; '99 BS; Police Ofcr.; NYPD, Task Force; r. 24 Mt. Morris Park W, Apt. 2 N, New York, NY 10027, 212 987-4987. e-mail

BRONFMAN, Judith; 125 W 76th St. Apt. 4c, New York, NY 10023, 212 580-6792.

BRONKHURST, Frank X.; '78 BS; 7 E. Oakdale St., Bay Shore, NY 11706.

BROOK, Jonathan A.; '83 MA; 5310 Wigton Dr., Houston, TX 77096, 713 726-9296.

BROOKS, Eurita '80 (See Daniels, Eurita).

BROOKS, Gloria; '87 BS; Retired NYC Correction Ofcr.; NYC; r. 92 Camille Ln., E. Patchogue, NY 11772, 631 475-6455; *Ralph Cardone;* Tameca.

BROOKS, Lorraine K.; '81 BS; 8412 35 Ave., Jackson Hts., NY 11372, 718 205-5945.

BROOKS, Ms. Marvie B.; '90 MA; BA Morris Brown, MLS Clark Atlanta Univ.; Ref. Librarian Rsch. Security Mgmt.; Lloyd Sealy Library John Jay Clg., New York, NY 10001, 212 237-8261; r. 700 Columbus Ave., New York, NY 10025, 212 666-4141. e-mail

BROOKS, Michele; '89 BS; 2820 Ocean Pkwy., Brooklyn, NY 11235, 718 574-0088.

BROOKS, Robert A.; '78 BA; 103 Point Pleasant Dr., Palm Coast, FL 32164, 904 437-1711.

BROOMFIELD, Arthur; '86 AS; 10 Wedge Pl., Palm Coast, FL 32164, 904 447-0228.

BROPHY, Edward J.; '75 BA, '79 MPA; Picture Painter/Educator; r. 43 Southward Ave., Congers, NY 10920, 914 268-7486.

BROSNAN, David J.; '85 BS; 20 Day Rd, Campbell Hall, NY 10916.

BROSNAN, Donald P.; '76 MA; 4 Beach 220th St., Far Rockaway, NY 11697, 718 318-5788.

BROSOKAS, Victor J.; '77 BS; 190 Lincoln St., Elmont, NY 11003, 516 352-0103.

BROUARD, Michelle; '96 BS; 167-25 144th Ter., Springfield Gardens, NY 11434.

BROUSSEAU, Joseph O.; '81 BS; 55 Littlefield Ave., Staten Island, NY 10312, 718 442-1162.

BROWN, Alan R.; '75 MA; POB 243, Huntington, NY 11743, 516 795-4755.

BROWN, Angela R. '89 (See Dean, Mrs. Angela R.).

BROWN, Annette M.; '81 BS; 119-05 Long St., Jamaica, NY 11434, 718 268-2691.

BROWN, Annie D.; '94 BA; 690 Gates Ave. Apt. 6d, Brooklyn, NY 11221, 718 452-4870.

BROWN, Arline D.; '82 BA; AS Bronx Community Clg.; Tchr.; NYC ISD Dist. 9, Bronx, NY 10451; r. 1000 Grand Concourse, Bronx, NY 10451, 718 538-7442; *John;* James, Ralph, Gloria, Eric.

BROWN, Arthur M.; '70 BA, '80 MA; Lecturer-Thematics Studies-Police; Sci., African Amer. Studies, John Jay Cl, of Criminal Justice, 889 10th Ave., Consulting-Police Recruitment, New York, NY 10019, 212 237-8460; r. Community Seminars-Policing, 4240-21G Hutchinson River Pkwy. E, Bronx, NY 10475, 718 671-9744; *Shirley;* James, Elizabeth, Arthur II.

BROWN, Belviana J.; '77 BA SD; Keyboard Spec.; State Atty. Gen. Ofc., New York State Dept. of Law, Justice Youth Atty.; r. 3412 113th St. Apt. 2-L, Corona, NY 11368, 718 478-3841.

BROWN, Beverley M.; '82 BS; 800 Cortelyou RD 3 d, Brooklyn, NY 11218, 718 257-2147.

BROWN, Brian K.; '89 BS; 120 Donzetti Pl., #18F, Bronx, NY 10475, 718 991-4213.

BROWN, Candra L.; '92 BS; 215 Wortman Ave. #4, Brooklyn, NY 11207, 718 218-7379.

BROWN, Carla S.; '84 BA; 11931 229th St., Cambria Hts., NY 11411, 718 712-0053.

BROWN, Carol N.; '83 BA; 738 Warwick St., Brooklyn, NY 11207, 718 649-1528.

BROWN, Cathy; '94 MS; JD Columbia Univ.; Atty.; Riker Danzig Scherer Hyland & Perritti, Llp, 1 Speedwell Ave., Morristown, NJ 07962, 973 538-0800; r. 31 Lloyd Rd, Montclair, NJ 07042, 973 655-1249. e-mail

BROWN, Charlane O.; '87 BA; 13041 226th St., Jamaica, NY 11413, 718 481-8959.

BROWN, Charles L.; '79 AS, '80 BS; 24 Covert St., Brooklyn, NY 11207, 718 218-7379.

BROWN, Charles R.; '89 BS; 1571 Vyse Ave., Apt. 3B, Bronx, NY 10460, 718 329-2222.

BROWN, Charlton A.; '96 BA; Civil Svc.; r. 278 Nichols Ave., Cypress Hls., NY 11208, 718 827-5456; Isaiah.

BROWN, Cheryl M.; '96 BA; 14967 255th St., Jamaica, NY 11422, 718 217-0535.

BROWN, Clifford E.; '90 BS; 397 E 46th St., Brooklyn, NY 11203, 718 218-7379.

BROWN, Colin R.; '95 BS; 120 Benchley Pl. Apt. 17e, Bronx, NY 10475, 718 329-2222.

BROWN, Courtney L.; '99 BA; Sales Rep.; Frontier Communications, Monroe, NY 10950, 914 783-5220; r. POB 191, Blooming Grove, NY 10914, 914 496-7104. e-mail

BROWN, Deborah L.; '95 BS; Nelson A Rockefeller Univ; Family Support Advocate; Albany Cmty. Opportunities Inc., 35 Clinton Ave., Albany, NY 12210, 518 432-3606; r. 275 Colonie St., Apt. 1D, Albany, NY 12210; *Daryl Higgins;* Rarrmel, Shannon, Lexus. e-mail

BROWN, Debra E.; '81 BS; 5085 Broadway, New York, NY 10034, 315 339-2946.

BROWN, Delroy; '89 BS; 22123 103rd Ave., Jamaica, NY 11429, 718 595-1909.

BROWN, Derrick; '96 BA; 1327 Sterling Pl., Brooklyn, NY 11213, 718 857-6015.

BROWN, Desiree; '85 BA; 119-05 Long St., Jamaica, NY 11434, 718 595-1909.

BROWN, Doslyn V.; '90 BS; Child Welfare Spec.; Admin. for Children's Svcs. NYC, 150 William St., New York, NY 10036, 212 676-9216; r. 811 Walton Ave. Apt. C20, Bronx, NY 10451, 718 993-1238.

BROWN, Elizabeth A.; '80 BS; 151 Throop St., W. Babylon, NY 11704, 631 595-2626.

BROWN, Ms. Estelle A.; '93 BS; Correction Ofcr.; NYC, 100 Centre St., New York, NY 10013, 212 374-4470; r. POB 610, Morningside, NY 10026, 212 860-2725.

BROWN, Francisco A.; '82 BS; Fire Marshal; Manhattan Cnty., 9 Metro Tech, Brooklyn, NY 11201, 212 966-4384; r. 1281 Albany Ave., Brooklyn, NY 11203, 718 629-0380; Francisco Jr, Tina Maria. e-mail

BROWN, Gene A.; '78 MPA; 2 Horatio St. Apt. 11j, New York, NY 10014, 315 336-3485.

BROWN, Herbert; '80 BS; Retired Police Ofcr.; NYC Transit Police Dept.; r. 111-11 202nd St., Hollis, NY 11412, 718 776-1109; *Jamie*; Herbert Jr, Harriet, Gregory Kinley, Waymon Kinley. e-mail

BROWN, Herbert A., Jr.; '97 BS; Detective; New York Police Dept., 718 495-5282; r. 97-28 57th Ave. Apt# 3k, Rego Park, NY 11368, 718 699-5749. e-mail

BROWN, Herman; '87 BA; 1170 E 229th St. #8, Bronx, NY 10466, 718 589-1144.

BROWN, Ian L.; '87 BA; 4005 Carpenter Ave., Bronx, NY 10466, 718 325-0271.

BROWN, Iris D.; '77 BS; 197 Kosciusko St., Brooklyn, NY 11216, 718 345-5023.

BROWN, Isaac L.; '95 BS; 903 E 106th St., Brooklyn, NY 11236, 718 345-5023.

BROWN, James D.; '83 MPA; POB 668, Beacon, NY 12508, 914 838-0464.

BROWN, James M.; '64 MPA; 9 Reid Ave., Bloomfield, NJ 07003, 973 429-9584.

BROWN, Janean A.; '95 MA; Detention Enforcement Ofcr.; US DOJ Immigration & Naturalization Svc, 201 Varick St., New York, NY 10014, 212 620-3441; r. 124 Crotona Ave., Harrison, NY 10528, 914 835-7324; Sierra. e-mail

BROWN, Janet; '96 BS; 5411 Avenue H, Brooklyn, NY 11234, 718 222-9003.

BROWN, Ms. Janet L.; '91 BS; JD Seton Hall Univ. Law Sch.; Asst. Corp. Council; NYC Law Dept., 718 658-0500; r. 210-45 119 Ave., St. Albans, NY 11412; *Thomas Chavis;* Caelah S Chavis. e-mail

BROWN, Joanna U.; '83 BS; 442 Swinton Ave., Bronx, NY 10465, 718 823-2246.

BROWN, Joseph G., Jr.; '98 MPA; BS Fordham Univ./Lincoln Cnt; Asst. Deputy Chief; Brooklyn Criminal Ct. Room 510, 120 Schermerhorn St., Chief Clerks Ofc., Brooklyn, NY 11201, 718 643-3909; r. 1945 Third Ave. #7F, New York, NY 10029; *Althesteen;* Michele, Christine.

BROWN, Joyce C.; '80 BS; Capt.; NYC Dept. of Corrections; r. 25-02 Gillmore St., E. Elmhurst, NY 11369; Kyle.

BROWN, Julia C.; '83 BA; 648 Coster St., Bronx, NY 10474, 718 239-1335.

BROWN, Juliet D.; '97 BS; 2756 Barnes Ave., Bronx, NY 10467, 718 239-1335.

BROWN, Kenya D.; '99 BA; 116-51 157 St. 4F, Jamaica, NY 11434, 718 527-5675.

BROWN, Latisha Y.; '97 BA; Child Protective Spec.; Child Protective Svcs. Agcy., Brooklyn, NY 11233, 718 953-8283; r. 519 Lexington Ave., Brooklyn, NY 11221, 718 452-1090; Annia. e-mail

BROWN, Leah D.; '99 MA; 65 Berry St., Valley Stream, NY 11580, 516 538-8317.

BROWN, Leonetta M.; '80 BA; 400 Cozine Ave., Brooklyn, NY 11207, 718 230-5817.

BROWN, Leslie C.; '78 BS; 219-46 113 Dr., Queens Vlg., NY 11429, 718 262-8548.

BROWN, Linata; '99 BA; Prog. Spec.; Madison Square Boys & Girls Club, 2315 Surf Ave., Brooklyn, NY 11224, 718 996-3170; r. 2920 W 21st St. #5M, Brooklyn, NY 11224, 718 996-6468; Cequan Wynn, Gary.

BROWN, Louis; '76 BA; POB 646, Bronx, NY 10462, 718 584-2999.

BROWN, Marcia S. '92 (See Brown-Acosta, Marcia S.).

BROWN, Marie B.; '86 BA; Socio Economic Researcher; Rsch. Triangle Inst., Chicago, IL 60615; r. 80 Ft. Washington, New York, NY 10032.

BROWN, Melvin R.; '81 BA; 4220-15 Hutch River, Bronx, NY 10475, 718 329-4700.

BROWN, Milton E.; '98 BA; 909 E. 213th St., Bronx, NY 10469, 718 329-4700.

BROWN, Moreale P.; '97 BS; Dir. of Day Care; r. 2115 Rockaway Pkwy., Brooklyn, NY 11236, 718 241-2877.

BROWN, Myrtle M.; '85 BA; 436 Eastern Pkwy., Brooklyn, NY 11225, 718 363-8328.

BROWN, Patricia R.; '79 BS; MSW Hunter Clg.; Prog. Dir.; FEGS, NYC Link Program, New York, NY 10038, 917 606-6560; r. 1505 Archer Rd, Apt. TC, Bronx, NY 10462, 718 828-7899. e-mail

BROWN, Patrick J.; '80 BA; Capt.; New York Fire Dept., 9 Metrotech Pl., Brooklyn, NY 11201, 212 570-4303; r. 319 Avenue C Apt. 11a, New York, NY 10009, 212 677-5517.

BROWN, Paul R.; '98 BA; 709 Lenox Rd., Brooklyn, NY 11203, 718 467-9102.

BROWN, Paul S.; '98 BA; 376 E. 94th St.#18B, Brooklyn, NY 11212, 718 345-7044.

BROWN, Ralph J.; '76 BS; 1950 Hutch River Pkwy., Bronx, NY 10461, 718 378-0119.

BROWN, Raymond M.; '76 BS; MSW NYU; Retired Deputy Chief-NYC Fire Dept ; Manager-Port Authority, 241 Erie St., Jersey City, NJ 07310, 201 216-2300; r. 36 W Walnut St., Long Beach, NY 11561, 516 897-6692.

BROWN, Renelle; '90 BA; 1302 Avenue K #1E, Brooklyn, NY 11230, 718 230-8045.

BROWN, Richard W.; '82 BA; 10030 Ditmars Blvd., Flushing, NY 11369, 718 291-4673.

BROWN, Robin; '88 BA; 2850 W Silverado Ranch Blvd., Apt. 101, Las Vegas, NV 89123, 702 228-5660.

BROWN, Rodney W.; '93 BA; 2907 Kingsbridge Ter., Bronx, NY 10463, 718 220-3017.

BROWN, Ronald E.; '76 BS, '81 MPA; 2389 Wexford Dr., Atlanta, GA 30349, 770 907-2065.

BROWN, Ronda R.; '98 MPA; Mgmt. Analyst; West Chester Cnty.-Supreme Ct., 111 Dr. Martin Luther King Jr. Blvd, White Plains, NY 10607, 914 285-3816; r. 945 Teller Ave. #3d, Bronx, NY 10451, 718 681-8976. e-mail

BROWN, Shanteil; '88 BA MPA; Sr. Organizational Spec.; Dept. of Housing Preservation/Devel., New York, NY 10038; r. 10 W. 135 St. Apt. 14a, New York, NY 10037, 212 368-3592; *Gary McMunn.* e-mail

BROWN, Sherise N.; '95 BS; 606 W Cornelia Ave., Apt. 473, Chicago, IL 60657, 773 755-4665.

BROWN, Stevelle M.; '93 BS; 459 Milford St., Brooklyn, NY 11208, 718 284-5673.

BROWN, Tara C.; '90 CERT, '90 BA; Teen Ministry Coord./Cnslt.; Bethal Gospel Assembly, 1832 Madison Ave., New York, NY 10035, 212 860-1516; r. 1695 Madison Ave., New York, NY 10029, 212 860-0491. e-mail

BROWN, Tara N.; '96 BS; Sr. Correctional Ofcr.; Fed. Correctional Institution, 501 Gary Hill Rd., Edgefield, SC 29824, 803 637-1500; r. 506 Carberry Ct., W. Columbia, SC 29169, 803 951-7106. e-mail

BROWN, Tarsha S.; '99 BA; 2354 Batchelder St. 5B, Brooklyn, NY 11229, 718 891-7725.

BROWN, Timothy; '98 BA; Fraud Investigator; City of NY, 330 Jay St., Brooklyn, NY 11201, 718 237-8222; r. 355 E. 49th St. #1, Brooklyn, NY 11203, 718 941-1598. e-mail

BROWN, Timothy J.; '99 BS; Police Ofcr.; NYC Police Dept., New York, NY 10038; r. 1607 E 34 St., Brooklyn, NY 11234, 718 377-1371.

BROWN, Tracy-Ann M.; '99 BA; Business Mgr.; JMH Communications, 1133 Broadway, Ste. 1123, New York, NY 10010, 212 924-2944; r. 143-25 84th Dr. #6K, Briarwood, NY 11435, 718 739-2071. e-mail

BROWN, Tyrone S.; '97 BS; 56 French Ridge, New Rochelle, NY 10801, 914 944-9035.

BROWN, Valerie A.; '95; 102-62 185th St., Hollis, NY 11423, 718 337-1970.

BROWN, Valerie L.; '77 BA; MA Miami Univ.-Ohio, JD Howard Univ.; Atty./Lobbyist; New Jersey Bar Assn., Constitution Sq., New Brunswick, NJ 08901, 732 937-7512; r. 87 York St., Lambertville, NJ 08530. e-mail

BROWN, Van; '95 BS; 370 Cochran Pl., Valley Stream, NY 11581, 516 377-1188.

BROWN, Verley; 5608 NW 19th St., Lauderhill, FL 33313, 954 733-7446.

BROWN, Wilma '82 (See Philips, Wilma).

BROWN, Yvette E.; '95 BS, '97 MA; Asst. Dir.; Church Ave Merchant Block Assoc., 1720 Church Ave., Brooklyn, NY 11226, 718 237-8130; r. 135 Clarkson Ave. Apt. A5, Brooklyn, NY 11226, 718 287-8571. e-mail

BROWN-ACOSTA, Marcia S., (Marcia S. Brown); '92 BS; CERT Adelphi Univ.; Caseworker; Admin. for Children's Svcs., Queen Family Ct., 89-14 Parsons Blvd., Jamaica, NY 11432, 718 739-6230; r. 11837 225th St., Jamaica, NY 11411, 718 978-7490; *Alex;* Allan.

BROWNBILL, Susan '86 (See Brownbill-vega, Susan).

BROWNBILL-VEGA, Susan, (Susan Brownbill); '86 BS; JD Pace Univ.; Asst Dist. Atty; Bronx Dist. Attorney Ofc., 215 E. 161 St., Bronx, NY 10451, 718 590-2000; r. 33-16 96th St., Corona, NY 11368, 718 672-2168; *Ricardo; Olivia, Stephanie.*

BROWN-CATHEY, Ms. Gertrude; '84 MPA; BS Hunter Clg; Ret. RN, Asst. Dir.; Bellevue Hosp. Pediatric Dept.; r. 35 Union Ave., E. Rutherford, NJ 07073, 201 438-8461; *Delter Cathey (dec);* William, Colleen, Eileen, Christopher.

BROWNE, Amy (Amelia); '92 BS; Investigator; US Dept. of Labor, 6 World Trade Ctr., New York, NY 10048; *Anthony M. Losito.*

BROWNE, Cleo-renee; '90 BA; 1016 Bryant Ave. # 2, Bronx, NY 10459, 718 824-7784.

BROWNE, James; '75 BS; Retired; r. 5915 47 Ave., Woodside, NY 11377, 718 457-0309.

BROWNE, Phillip A.; '99 BS; AA Kingsborough Comm. Clg.; Fraud Investigator; NYC, Dept. Revenue & Investigations, 260 11th Ave., New York, NY 10001, 212 630-9756; r. 2007 Linden Blvd., Brooklyn, NY 11207, 718 257-0163. e-mail

BROWNE, Robert J.; '71 MS; JD Fordham Univ. Sch. of Law; Atty.; Robert J Browne Esq, 301 E 66th St. Apt. 16h, New York, NY 10021, 212 734-5089; r. same, 212 861-3983; *Helen Page.*

BROWNE, Samuel A.; '82 MA; BS NYIT; Asst. Deputy Warden Ret; NYC Dept. of Corrections; r. 257 Kissel Ave., Staten Island, NY 10310, 718 273-4287.

BROWNE, Vivian C.; '81 BA; 50 W 97 St., New York, NY 10025, 315 736-3672.

BROWNING, Darlene; '92 BS; MSW Hunter Clg.; Child Protective Spec Supv; Admin. for Specialist Supervisor, 55 Sixth Ave., New York, NY 10013; r. 20 Graves St., Staten Island, NY 10314, 718 720-9009. e-mail

BROWNING, Monique '97 (See Ucelli, Monique S.).

BROWNLEE, Michelle; '86 BA; 222 E. 93 St., New York, NY 10028, 212 369-5196.

BROWNSTEIN, Brian J.; '86 BA; 9591 NW 48th Mnr, Coral Springs, FL 33076.

BROWNSTEIN, Daniel; '77 BA; 1449 Granada Pl., Far Rockaway, NY 11691, 718 337-6908.

BROWNSTEIN, Herbert; '69 BS; 6708 Stardust, N. Lauderdale, FL 33068.

BRUCCULERI, Giovanna R.; '98 BS; 22-38 Crescent St., Astoria, NY 11105, 718 728-1826.

BRUCCULERI, Maryann; '97 BA; 151-32 24th Rd, Whitestone, NY 11357, 718 352-3294.

BRUCE, Prince A.; '99 BS; Security Ofcr.; New York Presbyterian Hosp., 525 E. 68 St., New York, NY 10021, 212 746-5454; r. 1592 Jesup Ave.#2D, Bronx, NY 10452, 718 294-6176. e-mail

BRUCE, Tommy; '93 BS; Security Ofcr.; United Nations Org., AICC Bldg., POB 6016, Arusha, Tanzania, 2129632850; r. 1525 Walton Ave. Apt. 3C, Bronx, NY 10452, 718 583-3488; *Agathe;* Mawuli, Eden, Mawuena. e-mail

BRUCKENSTEIN, K.; '92 BA; 28-08 141 st. Apt. 4A, Flushing, NY 11354, 718 461-4594.

BRUCKENTHAL, Eric A.; 83 University Hgts, Stony Brook, NY 11790.

BRUDENT, Sandra; '98 BA; Dir. of Admission; One Step Data Inc., 70 W. 36th St., New York, NY 10018, 212 355-9197; r. 594 Lenox Rd, Brooklyn, NY 11203, 718 771-1866. e-mail

BRUDER, William J.; '77 BS; 39-66 64 St., Woodside, NY 11377, 718 591-0080.

BRUECHERT, Nicolle; '98 BS; 215 Brendan Ave., Massapequa Park, NY 11762, 516 798-8863.

BRUEN, Noel F.; '91 BS; 107 Wayacross Rd, Mahopac, NY 10541, 914 621-0443.

BRUMER, Steven N.; '83 MPA; BS Univ. of South Florida; Pres.; Global Wireless Data, 5380 Peachtree Ind Blvd., Ste. 247, Norcross, GA 30071, 770 447-4490; r. 1089 Croftmoore Lndg, Suwanee, GA 30024, 770 614-5680; *Jessica;* Hannah, Max. e-mail

BRUN, Gina; '88 BA; MS Adelphi Univ.; Tchr.; Health Opportunities HS, 350 Gerard Ave., Bronx, NY 10451, 718 401-1826; r. 1560 Silver St. Apt. 4E, Bronx, NY 10461, 718 823-3702.

BRUNEAU, Johanne; '91 BS; 933 E 101st St. # 2n, Brooklyn, NY 11236, 718 257-3489.

BRUNETTI, Joseph; '96 BS; 1411 E.4th St., Brooklyn, NY 11230, 718 645-4790.

BRUNING, Howard A.; '79 BS; RFD 11 Longview Rd, Carmel, NY 10512, 914 225-7914.

BRUNO, Daniel J.; '95 BS; Litigation Asst.; Fried, Frank, Harris, Shriver & Jacobson, 1 New York Plz., New York, NY 10004, 212 859-8336; r. 1073 E 43rd St., Brooklyn, NY 11210, 718 258-2653. e-mail

BRUNO, Frank W.; '82 BS, '92 MA; Lt.; NYC Police Dept., 90th Precinct, 211 Union Ave., Brooklyn, NY 11211; r. 54 Daffodil Ave., Franklin Sq., NY 11010, 516 538-5234. e-mail

BRUNO, Joan; '77 BA; 3945 Tarmigan Dr., Antelope, CA 95843.

BRUNO, Michael A.; '96 BS; 8891 20th Ave., Brooklyn, NY 11214, 718 372-3249.

BRUNO, Richard F.; '91 BS; 152 Gervil St., Staten Island, NY 10309, 718 448-1037.

BRUNSON, Jacqueline; '97 BS; 1210 Croes Ave., Bronx, NY 10472, 718 893-2843.

BRUNSON, Lakisha D.; '98 BS, '99 BS; CRC; Cablevision, 150 Crossways Park Dr., Woodbury, NY 11797, 516 803-9314; r. 117-63 126th St., S. Ozone Park, NY 11420, 718 843-4338; *William Stewart Jr;* Joseph Walker, Davon Walker, Kyla Stewart. e-mail

BRUNSON, Sharon B.; '89 BA; 580 Main St. # 4, New York, NY 10044.

BRUNTEL, Doris H.; '95 MA; MPA Syracuse Univ.; Info. Syst. Mgr.; r. 345 Eighth Ave., New York, NY 10001, 212 243-3113.

BRUSCHI, Mario J.; '76 MA; 1154 First Ave., New York, NY 10021, 212 755-2643.

BRUSCO, Lisa; '93 BA; 313 w 76th St., New York, NY 10023, 212 877-8676.

BRUZZICHESI, William; '91 BS; Firefighter; Twp. of Belleville, Belleville, NJ 07109; r. 84 Division Ave., Belleville, NJ 07109, 973 751-1671.

BRYAN, Anita; '83 BS; 11815 222nd St., Jamaica, NY 11411, 718 525-4640.

BRYAN, Annmarie L.; '83 BS; 188 E 55th St., Brooklyn, NY 11203, 718 287-0954.

BRYAN, Egan E.; '80 MA; 16127 85th Ave., Jamaica, NY 11432, 718 526-6527.

BRYAN, Stephanie A.; '98 BS; 1355 Bushwick Ave. 1, Brooklyn, NY 11207, 718 452-9430.

BRYAN-PIPER, Hannah; '92 BA; 4217 Gunther Ave., Bronx, NY 10466, 718 325-1862.

BRYANT, Brenda A.; '86 BS; 210 Cassata Dr., Copiague, NY 11726.

BRYANT, Julia; 191 St. Marks Ave., Brooklyn, NY 11238, 718 783-4912.

BRYANT, Kevin J.; '79 BS; 66 W. 89 St., New York, NY 10024, 518 377-5314.

BRYANT, Nicole; '95 MA; 696 Remsen Ave., Brooklyn, NY 11236.

BUBBICO, Francesco D.; '97 BS; 23 Oakridge Rd. W., W. Paterson, NJ 07424.

BUBNIS, Christalie J.; '98 MA; POB 102, Stockertown, PA 18083.

BUCAJ, Alfons; '93 BS; 123 4th Ave., Pelham, NY 10803, 914 761-1498.

BUCCA, Maria; '94 BS; 1341 84th St., Brooklyn, NY 11228.

BUCCI, Joseph R.; '82 BS; 2302 Glebe Ave., Bronx, NY 10462, 718 822-6846.

BUCCINO, Peter J.; '89 MA; 417 Lake Ave., Deer Park, NY 11729, 631 242-3865.

BUCHALTER, Steven; '75 BA; Investigator; State of NJ; r. 11 Wisteria Ln., Hamilton Nj, Hamilton, NJ 08690, 609 689-0526; *Ava.*

BUCKLEY, Anna M.; '85 BS; 20 Gesner St., Linden, NJ 07036.

BUCKLEY, Maurice; '80 MPA; BA Fordham Univ.; Retired; NYCPD; r. 4 Minor Ct., W. Nyack, NY 10994, 914 623-5374; *Arlene;* John, Kevin, Eileen. e-mail

BUCKNER, Martha; '95 BS; News Anchor; Bronxnet TV, 250 Bedford Park Blvd., Bronx, NY 10468, 718 960-1189; r. 211 W 53rd St. Apt. 5f, New York, NY 10019, 212 757-0799.

BUDA, Richard; '78 BA, '80 MA; Assoc. Prof.; Hofstra Univ., 134 Hofstra Univ, Hempstead, NY 11549, 516 463-5732; r. 541 E 20th St., Apt. 4 H, New York, NY 10010, 516 463-5732; *Susan.* e-mail

BUDENAS, John M.; '91 BS; Sr. Parole Ofcr.; New Jersey Juvenile Justice Commission, 9 Quaker Bridge Plz., POB 108, Trenton, NJ 08625, 609 631-4711; r. 57 Cliffside Dr., Toms River, NJ 08755, 732 341-9046; *Shannon.*

BUDRAM, Anil; '99 BA; Tchr.; NYC Bd. of Educ., 1111 Pugsley Ave., Bronx, NY 10472, 718 822-5186; r. 2002 Blackrock Ave., Bronx, NY 10472, 718 597-3799. e-mail

BUENO, Josner; '95 BA; 35-06 73rd St. #4j, Jackson Hts., NY 11372.

BUFFALOE, Kenneth S.; '86 BA; 409 Myrtle Ave., Brooklyn, NY 11205, 718 875-8113.

BUGGE, Brian K.; '78 MA; Security Cnslt.; ICFLESDI Inc., POB 150, Centereach, NY 11720, 631 467-5257; r. same. e-mail

BUGGS, Mrs. Veronica V., (Veronica V. Clark); '94 MA; Case Mgr.; Fed. Bur. of Prisons, USAR, Fairton, NJ 08320, 856 453-1177; r. 724 Mallard St., Millville, NJ 08332.

BUGROS, Michelle '95 (See Kalian, Mrs. Michelle A.).

BUHRMEISTER, Robert K.; '95 BS; 128 Lombardi Rd, Pearl River, NY 10965, 914 735-6530.

BUICA, Lucy; '97 BA; 5225 14 Ave. #C1, Brooklyn, NY 11219.

BUIE, Deborah L.; '90 BS; 455 Carlton Ave. Apt. 3F, Brooklyn, NY 11238.

BUIE, Teresa; '92 BA; 259 Halsey St., Brooklyn, NY 11216, 718 574-4820.

BUITRAGO, Michael; '96 BS; 91-55 84th St., Woodhaven, NY 11421, 718 639-3119.

BUJOLD, Daniel J.; '96 BA; 7533 217th St., Flushing, NY 11364, 718 740-2170.

BUKATMAN, Tessie; 6910 Avenue U Apt. 6k, Brooklyn, NY 11234.

BUKOWSKI, Gary; Mercyhurst Clg., 501 E. 38, Erie, PA 16501, 570 256-7775.

BUKSHA, Raymond M.; '96 BS; 2186 Grand Concour, Bronx, NY 10457.

BULL, Rhudean; '98 MPA; Human Resources Admin.; City of Stanford; r. 342 New Haven Ave., Milford, CT 06460, 203 874-2263. e-mail

BULLARO, Marc J.; '80 BS; 31-19 35 St., Astoria, NY 11106, 718 961-6537.

BULLEN, Alicia; 451 E. 43rd St., Brooklyn, NY 11203, 718 629-0806.

BULLOCK, Doris K.; '83 BS; 435 E. 105th St., New York, NY 10029.

BULLWINKEL, John A.; '99 MA; 7245 Brentford Dr., Colorado Spgs., CO 80919, 719 594-0932.

BULTER, Bernard P.; '95 BS; 16010 89th Ave. Apt. 6h, Jamaica, NY 11432.

BUNCH, Robert L.; '74 AS, '74 BS, '80 MA; Army War Clg., USAF War Clg.; 125 Prospect Ave., # 6B, Hackensack, NJ 07601, 201 342-4347.

BUNDHOO, Rakeish; '97 BA; 104-72 123rd St., Richmond Hill, NY 11419.

BUNDY, Elizabeth B.; '99 MA; BA Univ. of Wisconsin; Substance Abuse Couns.; TRI Ctr., Inc., 2488 Grand Concourse, Bronx, NY 10458, 718 584-7204; r. S54W34121 Private Sanctuary Ln., N. Prairie, WI 53153, 262 392-2582. e-mail

BUNIS, Joy; '84 BA; 35 Winding Way, Binghamton, NY 13905, 607 723-3621.

BUNKEDDEKO, Sully; '97 BS, '98 BS; 84-11 Elmhurst Ave. #4f, Elmhurst, NY 11373, 718 565-2203. e-mail

BUNTIN, Mark M.; '80 BS; AS Tunxis Community Clg.; Pres.; New England Woodworking, 912 Old Colony Rd., Meriden, CT 06451, 203 235-0085; r. 12 Leigus Rd., Wallingford, CT 06492, 203 284-0128. e-mail

BUNYAN, Michael C.; '78 MA; 85 Earley St., Bronx, NY 10464.

BUONO, Alisa; '97 BA; 96 Parma Rd., Island Park, NY 11558.

BUONO, Joseph F.; '77 BS; Fire Dept. Capt./Field Ops. Coord.; FDNY/NYC-OEM, 885 Howard Ave., Brooklyn, NY 11212, 718 965-8315; r. 2320 Stuart St., Brooklyn, NY 11229, 718 332-0385; *Barbara;* Joseph Jr., Nicholas. e-mail

BUONPANE, Angelina; '78 BA; POB 692, New York, NY 10268.

BURAKIEWICZ, Lisa M.; '97 BA; Supportive Case Magr; Puerto Rican Family Inst.; r. 1635 Mahan Ave., Bronx, NY 10461, 718 822-9197.

BURBRIDGE, Adero; '93 BA; 709 E 213th St., Bronx, NY 10467, 718 515-5892.

BURCH, Felicia; '88 BA; 62 Etna St., Brooklyn, NY 11208, 718 768-1331.

BURCH, Jennings; 200 W. 15 St. 10C, New York, NY 10011, 315 855-4332.

BURCH, Shande D.; '96 BS; 159-14 Harlem River Dr., New York, NY 10039, 315 855-4332.

BURD, Dr. Marc A.; '88 MA; PHD New Sch. Univ.; Psychologist; St. Barnabas Rikers Island, 1500 Hazen St., E. Elmhurst, NY 11370, 718 626-3414; r. 50 E. First St., New York, NY 10003, 212 254-1096. e-mail

BURDI, Michael J.; '84 BS, '88 MPA; Regional Dir.; NYS Div. of Parole, Bronx, NY 10451, 718 292-2822; r. 541 Edison Ave., Bronx, NY 10465, 718 597-3789.

BURDIEZ, Ruby M.; '96 BA; 35-22 93 St. 1s, Jackson Hts., NY 11372.

BURGE, John S.; '81 BS; 835 Penfield St., Bronx, NY 10470, 718 655-6805.

BURGER, Frederick (Fred) R.; '76 BS FIR; Retired Fireman; POB 510985, Punta Gorda, FL 33951, 941 575-6880; r. 13723 168th St., Jamaica, NY 11434, 718 341-1842. e-mail

BURGER, James; '73 BS; 15 Brainard St., Montclair, NJ 07043, 973 783-6832.

BURGER, William C.; '76 BA; 720 E 39 St., Brooklyn, NY 11203, 718 832-0012.

BURGESS, Audrey L.; '97 BS; 370 Pelton Ave., Staten Island, NY 10310.

BURGESS, SGT Irving, Jr.; '79 AS, '80 BS; Retired; r. 4551 Breakwater Blvd., Spring Hill, FL 34607, 352 597-2000.

BURGESS, Mrs. Marjorie L.; '71 AS, '72 BA; Retired Corrections Lt.; NYS Dept. of Corrections; r. 260 Prospect Ave. Apt. 151, Hackensack, NJ 07601, 201 343-3318; Terence, Michael.

BURGESS, Thomas S.; '79 MPA; BA Fayetteville State Univ., VOCREHAB Univ. of West Virginia; Tchr., B.E.D & Elem. Educ.; East Hoke Middle Sch., Raeford, NC 28376, 910 875-5048; r. 350 Ayrshire Ct., Fayetteville, NC 28311, 910 822-8015; Tamara B. Johns, Tonya.

BURGESS, Victoria; '99 MA; BA Univ. NY; Acct. Exec.; Ten Ten Wins Radio, 888 7th Ave., New York, NY 10106, 212 315-7064; r. 55 Overlook Ter. #3A, New York, NY 10033, 212 781-3066.

BURGH, Todd D.; '96 BS; AS Manhattan Community Clg.; Community Assoc./Paralegal; Bklyn Dist. Attorney's Ofc., 350 Jay St., Brooklyn, NY 11201, 718 250-3500; r. 2675 W 36th St. Apt. 12-D, Brooklyn, NY 11224, 718 390-7242; Zachary. e-mail

BURGOIS, John M.; '81 BA; Corporate Security Mgr. & Asst. VP; Salomon Smith Barney, 388 Greenwich St., New York, NY 10013, 212 816-1702; r. 65 Silver Ln., Levittown, NY 11756.

BURGOS, Angela I.; '98 BA; 1234 Pacific St., F1, Brooklyn, NY 11216, 718 348-0607.

BURGOS, Brenda; '90 BS; 2800 Lexington Rd. NE Apt. 94, Albuquerque, NM 87112, 505 292-5860.

BURKE, Derek; '92 BA; 3210 Avenue H Apt. 4c, Brooklyn, NY 11210, 718 444-4686.

BURKE, Donald H.; '87 BS; AS SUNY-Farmingdale; Supv.; USPS AMC JFK, Bldg. 250, Jamaica, NY 11430, 718 553-7286; r. 116 E Greenwich Ave., Roosevelt, NY 11575, 516 868-1026; *Roveda;* Erik, Dymonique, Anthony, Jenna.

BURKE, Francis D.; '70 BS; Retired; NYC Police Inspector; r. 3 Peter Cooper Rd Apt. 5b, New York, NY 10010, 212 677-5374; *Marian;* Christopher.

BURKE, Glenn E.; '78 BS; 7119 70th St., Flushing, NY 11385, 718 949-1092.

BURKE, James J.; '77 BS; Sgt.; NYPD, 1 police Plz., New York, NY 10038, 212 374-5000; r. 44 Northern Blvd., Staten Island, NY 10301; *Annette;* James.

BURKE, Jeremiah M.; '76 BS; 89-32 Vanderver St., Jamaica, NY 11427, 718 416-1546.

BURKE, John F.; '97 BS; 24 Graney Ct., Pearl River, NY 10965, 914 429-4620.

BURKE, Kevin E.; '99'; 280 Guy Lombardo Ave., Freeport, NY 11520, 516 868-4501.

BURKE, Michael N.; '87 BS; Valley View, Mohegan Lake, NY 10547, 914 632-0768.

BURKE, Patrick; '97 BA; P.O.Box 377 Churc, New York, NY 10008, 315 839-6298.

BURKE, Redmond P.; '81 MA; Ret. Capt.-Nypd, Prof.; Nassau Community Clg., Criminal Justice; r. 3050 Fairfield Ave., Bronx, NY 10463, 718 543-1194.

BURKE, Robert F.; '65 BBA, AAS; Asst. Chief Retired; NYC Police Dept.; r. 132 Sequams Ln. Ctr., W. Islip, NY 11795, 631 422-8155.

BURKE, Robert M.; '77 BS; 5819 80th St., Flushing, NY 11373, 718 276-3423.

BURKE, Thomas; '82 BS; 1304 Stratford St., W. Palm Bch., FL 33414, 561 968-7290.

BURKE, William J.; '74 BA; 216 Valley Rd, Valley Cottage, NY 10989, 914 268-6504.

BURKHALTER, Gerald; '77 MA; 12831 233rd St., Jamaica, NY 11422.

BURNETT, Byron K.; '71 BA; MPP Harvard Univ., JD Harvard Law Sch.; Atty.; Spooner & Burnett, 90 Broad St., 18th Fl., New York, NY 10024, 212 785-4333; r. 16 W. 83rd St., New York, NY 10024, 212 580-0062; *Margaret-Ellen Pipe;* Alison. e-mail

BURNETTE, Lebro C.; '86 BS; 509 Beach 67th St., Arverne, NY 11692, 718 474-6974.

BURNS, Christopher A.; '77 BS; 6136 78th St., Flushing, NY 11379, 718 457-2496.

BURNS, John W.; '82 BS; Atty.; Worth, Longworth Bamundo & London, 111 John St., New York, NY 10038, 212 964-8038; r. Brooklyn, NY 11215. e-mail

BURNS, Junious L.; '81 MA; 662 Grand Blvd., Deer Park, NY 11729.

BURNS, Robert T.; '82 BA; 95-19 149th Ave., Ozone Park, NY 11417, 315 826-7682.

BURNSIDE, Robert W.; '92 BA; 10 Park Ter. Ea, New York, NY 10034.

BURNS-LEMP, Patricia; '78 BA; 6015 Riverdale Ave., Bronx, NY 10471.

BURRELL, Monica; '98 BS; POB 920, Woodridge, NY 12789, 914 292-2970.

BURRELL, Tracey, PhD; '91 MA; MA CSPPLA, PHD CSPP-LA; Clinical Psychologist; 562 654-6674; r. 400 Lavender Ln., Placentia, CA 92870, 714 528-6902. e-mail

BURRELL, William D.; '76 MA; BA Susquehanna Univ.; Chief of Probation Svcs.; The Administrative Ofc. of The Courts, POB 987, Trenton, NJ 08625, 609 292-8925; r. 37 Cliveden Ct., Lawrenceville, NJ 08648.

BURROUGHS, Jamel; '99 BA; 107-11 221 St., Queens Vlg., NY 11429, 718 479-1041.

BURROUGHS, Ninette; '98 BA; 14946 Cherry Ave., Flushing, NY 11355.

BURROWS, Jonathan; '94 MA, '96 MA; MA; Marathon Substance Abuse Outpatient, Westerly, RI 02891; r. Bradford, RI 02808; *Kimberly;* Jordan. e-mail

BURROWS, Kenneth A.; '93 BS; 63-11 Queens Blvd., Woodside, NY 11377, 718 224-1801.

BURROWS, Winston A.; '80 BS; 131-08 160 St., Jamaica, NY 11434, 718 224-1801.

BURRUANO, Vivian S.; '81 BA; 12 Iris Cir., Manalapan, NJ 07726.

BURSHTEYN, Pavel; '98 BS; Driver; Joan Charles Flatbed, Inc.; r. 3856 Bronx Blvd. 9b, Bronx, NY 10467, 718 798-9243.

BURSUK, Paulette R.; '78 MA; 415 E 80th St. Apt. 2h, New York, NY 10021.

BURTON, Ines V.; '95 BA; 1615 Union St. Apt. 3e, Brooklyn, NY 11213, 718 467-4624.

BURTON, Lisa L.; '79 BA; 204-02 109th Ave., Hollis, NY 11412, 718 322-5240.

BURTON, Robert; '92 BS; 14226 Fredricksburg Dr. Apt. 205, Orlando, FL 32837, 407 384-6236.

BURWELL, Louise M.; '89 BS; MSEE City Clg.; Tchr.; Family Acad., 240 W. 113th St., New York, NY 10026, 212 678-2898; r. 350 E 124th St. Apt. 5E, New York, NY 10035, 212 289-9014.

BURWELL, Shawna M.; '91 BA; York; Tchr.; Dist. 19 IS 292, 718 498-6560; r. 117-26 239th St., Elmont, NY 11003, 516 285-0829. e-mail

BUSACCO, Angelo; '71 AS, '73 BA; 8510 Liberty Ave., N. Bergen, NJ 07047.

BUSBY, Dyedra P.; '95 BS; 409 E 56th St. # Pvt, Brooklyn, NY 11203, 718 451-3749.

BUSCAGLIA, Joann; '88 MS; 8001 12th Ave., Brooklyn, NY 11228, 718 366-3071.

BUSCEMI, Salvatore; '74 BA; 1430 31st Dr., Long Island City, NY 11106, 718 274-3206.

BUSER, Robert J., CFE; '95 BS; 718 386-4101; r. 26 Brixton Rd, Garden City, NY 11530; *Eileen.* e-mail

BUSH, Christopher P.; '95 BS; 5185 Long Dr., Bethlehem, PA 18020, 610 861-3026.

BUSH, Randall S.; '99 BA, '99 MPA; Colby Clg.; Sgt; NYPD, One Police Plz., New York, NY 10038, 212 614-6755; r. 18 Stuyvesant Oval Apt. 11-B, Apt. 11-B, New York, NY 10009, 212 533-2868.

BUSH, Robert C.; '96 BS; 13 Stone Row Ln., Oak Ridge, NJ 07438, 973 697-8575.

BUSHELON, Jennifer; '95 BS; 17 Old Rd, Kings Park, NY 11754, 631 269-3885.

BUSKA, Richard M.; '86 BS; MA NYU; Buyer; Cnty. of Union, 10 Elizabeth Twn., Elizabeth, NJ 07207, 908 527-4135; r. 518 Brooklawn Ave. #F2, Roselle, NJ 07203, 908 298-0154. e-mail

BUSTILLOS, Norma I.; '93 BS; 111 Bruce Ave. Apt. 7d, Yonkers, NY 10705.

BUTCHER, Mrs. Judith A., (Judith A. Miller); '83 MPA; BA Hunter Clg.; Dir.; NYS Div. of Human Rights, 55 W. 125th St., New York, NY 10027, 212 961-8608; r. 2037 Cicero Ave., Bronx, NY 10473.

BUTCHER, Margaret P.; '83 BA, '99 MPA; Mktg. Asst.; Jones Lang LaSalle, 40 Massachusetts Ave., Washington, DC 20002, 202 289-1908; r. 10500 Dee Ln., Clinton, MD 20735. e-mail

BUTE, Jessica A.; '91 BS; 599 E 7th St. Apt. 2u, Brooklyn, NY 11218, 718 856-7715.

BUTKIEWICZ, Susan '88 (See Becker, Mrs. Susan).

BUTLER, Harold W.; MA; 855 Baldwin Dr., Westbury, NY 11590, 516 997-9860.

BUTLER, Jason L.; '94 BA; 103 Bainbridge St., Brooklyn, NY 11233, 718 346-7192.

BUTLER, Joanne L.; '84 BS; 13 Bell St., Irvington, NJ 07111.

BUTLER, Katrina A.; '97 MA; 31 Midwood St., Brooklyn, NY 11225, 718 287-8735.

BUTLER, Raymond M.; '95 AS; BA Clg. of Staten Island; Police Ofcr.; NYCPD; r. 46 Cambridge Ave., Staten Island, NY 10314.

BUTLER, Robert E.; '88 BA, '91 MA; 20425 8th Ave., Far Rockaway, NY 11697, 718 343-2232.

BUTLER, Ruth M.; '98 BA; 134 53 219 St., Springfield Gardens, NY 11413, 718 343-2232.

BUTLER, Sandra; '92 BS; 1303 Saint Johns Pl., Apt. 4B, Brooklyn, NY 11213, 718 647-7108.

BUTLER, Tawanna C.; '98 BS; Assoc. Fraud Investigator; NYC Dept. of Homeless Svcs.; r. 1465 Fulton Ave. #3c, Bronx, NY 10456, 718 681-8939. e-mail

BUTLER, Tyrone T.; '77 BA; 425 E 35 St., Brooklyn, NY 11203, 718 265-3709.

BUTTARO, Victor A.; '97 BA; 1395 E. Second S, Brooklyn, NY 11230, 718 336-1353.

BUTTARO-SANCHEZ, Joann; '90 BA, '92 MA; 1395 E 2nd St., Brooklyn, NY 11230, 718 218-7114.

BUTTERFIELD, Anna; '86 BS; 1505 Metropolitan Ave. Apt. 3e, Bronx, NY 10462.

BUYLDING, Douglas W.; '91 AS; 17919 Selover Rd, Jamaica, NY 11434.

BYER, Charles; '92 BS; 140 Benchley Pl. # 33, Bronx, NY 10475, 718 561-3032.

BYER, Renee A.; '99 BA; Contracts; Penguin Putnen, 375 Hudson St., New York, NY 10014, 212 366-2000; r. 817 Schenck Ave. 4B, Brooklyn, NY 11207, 718 272-6366. e-mail

BYKES, Jennifer V. '96 (See Bykes-Guzman, Jennifer V.).

BYKES-GUZMAN, Jennifer V., (Jennifer V. Bykes); '96 BS; Homemaker; r. 1952 First Ave., New York, NY 10029, 212 410-0656; *Aaron;* Aaron II.

BYNDE, Darice B., (Darice B. Harris); '93 BS; Educator; Bd. of Educ.; r. 132-45 Bennett Ct., Jamaica, NY 11434, 718 276-3064; *Bertram Jr;* Aliyah, Ny.

BYNUM, Nora B.; MED Long Island Univ., BA City Clg.; Parent Advocate Liaison/Poetry; NYC/Belle, Brooklyn, NY 11216, 718 398-3499; r. 301 St. Nicholas Ave., Apt. #65, New York, NY 10027, 212 864-5195; Angela, Mayo. e-mail

BYRD, Paul H.; '73 BS; 14551 179th St., Jamaica, NY 11434.

BYRD, Shasun (Germaine); '99, '99 BA; 916 Lafayette Ave., Brooklyn, NY 11221, 718 602-4633.

BYRD, Vanessa A.; '82 BA; 1102 Jefferson Ave., Brooklyn, NY 11221, 718 573-7709.

BYRNE, Daniel C.; '91 BS; 510 E 23rd St. Apt. 6b, New York, NY 10010, 212 673-7477.

BYRNE, George; '96 BA; 33 Berkeley Sq., Suffern, NY 10901, 914 368-3439.

BYRNE, James F.; '92 BS, '98 MA, '98 MA; 933 Lester Rd., Yorktown Hts., NY 10598, 914 245-6854.

BYRNE, John T.; '76 BA; 1338 Croes Ave., Bronx, NY 10472, 718 543-0265.

BYRNE, Lawrence P.; '85 AS; BA MA Queens Clg., MS NYU; Sergeant; NYC Police Dept., 1 Police Plz., New York, NY 10038, 212 374-3888; r. 219-05 75th Ave., Bayside, NY 11364, 718 465-5338.

BYRNE, Therese M.; '84 BA; 1017 The Hideout, Lake Ariel, PA 18436.

BYRNES, James E.; '78 BS; 21-59 42 St., Astoria, NY 11105, 718 843-5988.

BYRNES, Jennifer L.; '99 MA; BA Pace Univ.; Sex Offender Therapist; Special Svcs.; r. 8408 Chelsea Cove Dr. N., Hopewell Jct., NY 12533, 914 223-7747. e-mail

BYRNES, John P.; '75 MA; 1320 Schenectady Ave., Brooklyn, NY 11203, 718 369-2770.

BYRNES, Ms. Kirsten M.; '99 MA; Clinician; Svc. Ctrs. of New Jersey, 197 Rte. 18 S. Ste. 306, E. Brunswick, NJ 08816, 732 937-6699; r. 134 Arlington Dr., Fords, NJ 08863, 732 225-0630. e-mail

BYRNES, Robert G.; '95 BS; Police Ofcr.; NYS MTA; r. 44 Highview Ter., Yonkers, NY 10705, 914 476-7158.

BYRNES, Robert M.; '76 MS, '81 MPA; Special Agt.; US Environ. Protection Agcy., 290 Broadway, New York, NY 10007, 212 637-3034; r. 44 Highview Ter., Yonkers, NY 10705, 914 476-7158.

BYRON, Brendan; 99 Kelly Rd., Carmel, NY 10512.

BZIK, Susan M.; '97 MA; 15-50 Elmary Pl., Fair Lawn, NJ 07410.

C

CABALLERO, Joyce E.; '98 BA; 67 Marcus Garvuy BLD 7C, Brooklyn, NY 11206, 718 443-9509.

CABALLERO, Nester J.; '95 BS; 112-09 95th Ave., Richmond Hill, NY 11419.

CABALLERO, Ricardo M.; '82 BS; 3715 81st St. Apt. 5g, Flushing, NY 11372.

CABAN, Deboral '98 (See Caban-Gonzalez, Deborah).

CABAN, Juan A.; '83 MPA; Ins. Investigator; Sterling Investigator Svcs., 2 Executive Dr., Somerset, NJ 08873, 732 356-3238; r. 60 Puritan Ave., Yonkers, NY 10710, 914 961-0155; *Gladys;* John, Steven, James, Edward, Richard.

CABAN, Wilfred; '95 BS; 19 Radburn Dr., Farmingville, NY 11738.

CABAN, Wilfred, Sr.; '75 BS; Asst. Dir Hosp. Policeman/Security; Kings Cnty., 451 Clarkson Ave., Brooklyn, NY 11203, 718 245-4300; r. 11634 230th St., Jamaica, NY 11411.

CABAN-GONZALEZ, Deborah, (Deboral Caban); '98 BA; Special Educ. Tchr.; PS 116, 515 Knickerbocker Ave., Brooklyn, NY 11237; r. 145 Freedom Ave3, Staten Island, NY 10314, 718 983-6487; *Robert.*

CABRAL, Aileen I.; '99 BS; Admin. Asst. Business Affairs; Affiliate Relations, USA Networks, r. Elmhurst, NY 11373. e-mail

CABRAL, Raymond; '89 AS, '93 BS; 54 S Rockland Ave., Congers, NY 10920.

CABRERA, Daniel; '87 BS, '92 MPA; POB 80, Old Bridge, NJ 08857.

CABRERA, Maritza; '93 BA; Data Transcriber; Dept. of Justice; r. 21 Kingsland Ave., Brooklyn, NY 11211.

CABRERA, Marjorie; '93 BS; 1801 University Ave., Bronx, NY 10453, 718 378-1377.

CABRERA, Milagros; '97 BA; 408 Prospect Ave., Brooklyn, NY 11215, 718 266-3832.

CABRERA, Sara; '97 BA; 34-58 74th St., Jackson Hts., NY 11372, 718 291-6585.

CABRERA, Yokasta; '95 BS; Release Own Recognizance Interview; New York Criminal Justice Agcy., 12501 Queens Blvd., Queens, NY 11412, 718 286-3146; r. 608 W 140th St. # 5, New York, NY 10031, 212 926-9153; Dariel.

CACCAVALE, Andrew C.; '90 BA; 1749 79th St. Apt. 3, Brooklyn, NY 11214, 718 232-6522.

CACCAVO, Christine; '99 MA; 5 Mary Beth DriveSuffern, Suffern, NY 10901, 914 368-4287.

CACCIATORE, Robert J.; '92 BS; MS Hunter Clg.; Capt./Lect. Urban Studies; NYC Police Dept., Hunter Clg., New York, NY 10021. e-mail

CACERES, Elisabeth; '95 BA; Sales Coord.; Peninsula New York, 700 Fifth Ave., New York, NY 10019, 212 903-3922; r. 561 W. 141 St. #58, New York, NY 10031, 212 491-1196; Sebastian. e-mail

CADDLE, Carolyn A.; '95 BA; 338 Prospect Pl. Apt. 4J, Brooklyn, NY 11238, 718 636-9513.

CADE, David W.; '78 BA; 5616 Tilden Ave., Brooklyn, NY 11203.

CADET, Bella C.; '93 BS; 24540 147th Rd, Jamaica, NY 11422, 718 846-2833.

CADET, Darley; '86 BA; 37-28 102 St., Corona, NY 11368, 718 846-2833.

CADET, Flobert; '97 AS; 799 E.40th St., Brooklyn, NY 11210, 718 469-3390.

CADET, Myrtelle; '93 BA; 10913 123rd St., Jamaica, NY 11420, 718 846-2833.

CADET, Rachelle; '99 BA; 347 E 51 St., Brooklyn, NY 11203, 718 346-0813.

CADET, Robinson; '93 BS; 674 E 52nd St., Brooklyn, NY 11203, 718 287-6855.

CADET, Yves; '83 BS; 5313 Tilden Ave., Brooklyn, NY 11203, 718 469-3390.

CADICAMO, Maria '77 (See Clifford, Maria C.).

CADOGAN, Darwin D.; '73 BA; Unit 45004 Box 210, APO, AP 96337.

CADOT, Marie M.; '91 BS; MS Hunter Clg.; Tchr./Coord Student Affairs; r. 6 Shade Tree Ln., E. Patchogue, NY 11772, 631 286-2674; *Joseph St Hilaire.* e-mail

CAESAR, Tessa V.; '95 BA; Police Ofcr.; NYC Dept.; r. 105 Winthrop St., Apt. 6F, Brooklyn, NY 11225, 718 940-0761; Briana, Brian. e-mail

CAFARELLI, Michael L.; '88 BS; 175 Glenwood Ave., Leonia, NJ 07605. e-mail

CAFFREY, James; '90 BS; 14 Smith St., E. Rockaway, NY 11518, 516 887-0146.

CAFFREY, James D.; '80 BA; 614 S. Carr St., Lakewood, CO 80226.

CAFFREY, Ronald; '85 MPA; 13 Darlene Ter., Washington Twp., NJ 07675.

CAGGIANO, Andrew C.; '96 BS; 199C N Beverwyck Rd, Apt. 3, Lake Hiawatha, NJ 07034.

CAGLIUSO, Nicholas; '95 BS; 1308 E 7th St., Brooklyn, NY 11230.

CAHILL, Angela M., (Angela Ansaldi); '78 BA; Homemaker; r. 5 Harrison St., Stony Point, NY 10980, 914 429-0641; *Patrick.*

CAHILL, Donna M.; '77 BA; 4 Col Glenn Dr., Carmel, NY 10512, 518 789-9354.

CAHILL, Patrick; '78 BA; Retired Capt.; NYPD; r. 5 Harrison St., Stony Point, NY 10980, 914 429-0641; *Angela.* e-mail

CAICEDO, Astrid; '94 AS; 31-24 85 St., Jackson Hts., NY 11370, 718 699-4514.

CAICEDO, Jose; '97 BA, '98 BA; 1710 Caton Ave. #56, Brooklyn, NY 11226, 718 284-4350.

CAIN, Thomas; 37-14 Parsons Blvd., Flushing, NY 11354, 718 341-2004.

CAIRL, Brian D.; '83 BS; Assoc. Dir.; Kroll Assocs., 900 Third Ave., New York, NY 10022, 212 835-3485; r. 5 Bettina Ct., Huntington Sta., NY 11746; *Cindy;* Brian Richard, Joseph John. e-mail

CAJIGAS, Veronica; '95 BA; 489 Hart St. # 1, Brooklyn, NY 11221.

CAJOU, Jean Claude; '96 BS; Tchr.; John Jay HS, Brooklyn, NY 11201; r. 621 Lefferts Ave., Apt. B14, Brooklyn, NY 11203, 718 467-2463. e-mail

CALABRIA, Michael; '93 BS; 15918 100th St. Apt. 2, Jamaica, NY 11414.

CALABRO, Andrew J.; '77 BS; 733 Crescent St., Brooklyn, NY 11208.

CALABRO, Dennis P.; '93 MA; BA Pace Univ.; Capt.; NYC Police Dept.; r. 190 Lindenwood Rd, Staten Island, NY 10308; *Joann;* Tara, Toniann, Dennis.

CALANDRIELLO, Maria; '96 MPA; 61 N Montague St., Valley Stream, NY 11580.

CALATHES, Dr. William; '83 MA; JD City Univ of NY Law Sch., PHD City Univ. of New York; Assoc. Prof.; New Jersey City Univ., Dept. of Criminal Justice, 2039 Kennedy Blvd., Jersey City, NJ 07305, 201 200-3492; r. 100-19H DeKruif Pl., Bronx, NY 10475; Whitney. e-mail

CALBY, Paula M.; '79 MA; PHD Fordham; Dir.; Victim Svcs., 2 Lafayette St., New York, NY 10007, 212 577-3890; r. 50 Pierpont Pl., Staten Island, NY 10314, 718 761-4189. e-mail

CALDARARO, John V.; '76 BS; 63 Tennyson St., Carteret, NJ 07008, 732 969-1417.

CALDARELLI, John L.; '76 BS; Asst. Area Dir.; Occupational Safety & Health Admin., 1400 Old Country Rd, Westbury, NY 11590, 516 334-3344; r. 290 Vernon Valley Rd, Northport, NY 11768, 631 261-3807.

CALDAROLA, Anthony E.; '80 BS; 364 7th Ave., Brooklyn, NY 11215, 718 832-5464.

CALDERON, Angel; '77 AS; 888 Flushing Ave., Brooklyn, NY 11206, 718 452-9711.

CALDERON, Jose; '87 BS; 315 E 143rd St. Apt. 6e, Bronx, NY 10451, 718 365-0550.

CALDERON, Marilyn; '97 BS; 102 Post Ave. #4, New York, NY 10034.

CALDERON, Nubia C.; '97 BS; 35-29 87th St. P, Jackson Hts., NY 11372, 718 849-6821.

CALDERON, Peter; '93 BS; Fresh Meadows, NY 11365.

CALDERONE, Vincent A.; '79 BA; 104 Alta Vista Dr., Ringwood, NJ 07456.

CALDERONE, William D.; '80 MA; 3018 Philip Ave., Bronx, NY 10465.

CALDWELL, Antilla; 65-32 Parsona Blvd. #1A, Flushing, NY 11365, 718 591-5342.

CALDWELL, Lynnette; '97 BS; Legal Asst.; Nixon Peabody; r. 45 Gardenia Dr., Maple Shade, NJ 08052.

CALHOUN, James J.; '73 BS; 420 Howe Ave., Bronx, NY 10473, 718 792-1985.

CALHOUN, Roy L.; '82 MA; 970 Wilson Blvd., Central Islip, NY 11722.

CALHOUN, William F.; '76 BS; 145 Corbin Ave., Staten Island, NY 10308, 718 948-2922.

CALI, Jack; '84 BS; 31 Horn Ln., Levittown, NY 11756, 516 759-1237.

CALI, Richard J.; '80 MA; Mortgage Processor; US Capitol; r. 1147 N Miramar, Mesa, AZ 85213, 480 830-0482; *Toni.*

CALICHIO, Frank J.; '78 BS; 1920 Henry St., N. Bellmore, NY 11710.

CALIFANO, John J.; '77 AS; BS; Proj. Mgr.; Kennedy Airport, Bldg. 14, Jamaica, NY 11430, 718 244-4227; r. 1 Terry Ln., Plainview, NY 11803.

CALIN, Ovidiu M.; '99 MS; 8-15 27th Ave. (#600), Astoria, NY 11102, 718 777-5620.

CALISE, Diane; '98 BA; Police Ofcr.; Bronx, NY 10465. e-mail

CALKIN, Ronald F.; '76 BS; 3053 Erwin Pl., Oceanside, NY 11572.

CALLAHAN, Michael P.; '75 BS, '78 MA; Retired; r. 2176 Mohansic Ave., Yorktown Hts., NY 10598.

CALLAHAN, Patricia; '93 BS; 7025 Yellowstone Blvd. # 11, Flushing, NY 11375, 718 793-6643.

CALLAHAN, Robert M.; '76 BS; Retired; NYC Police Dept.; r. 96 Burnside Ave., Staten Island, NY 10302, 718 981-7390.

CALLAHAN, William J.; '95 MA; 28 S 3rd Ave., Highland Park, NJ 08904, 732 937-5790.

CALLAN, Cesar A.; '80 BS; Young Rd., Katonah, NY 10536, 914 232-1806.

CALLAN, Kathleen A.; '93 BA; 3235 68th St., Flushing, NY 11377.

CALLANAN, Maureen F.; '78 BA; 2598 Harvey Ave., Oceanside, NY 11572.

CALLAS, George S.; '69 MPA; 632 Valley Rd, Brielle, NJ 08730.

CALLE, Ana Maria; '86 BA; Trng. Spec.; ABN AMRO North America, Uniondale, NY 11553; r. 5054 46th St., Flushing, NY 11377, 718 937-3388.

CALLE, Juan G.; '80 BS; 33-37 69 St., Woodside, NY 11377, 718 545-1343.

CALLE, Maria I.; '95 BA; 5054 46th St., Flushing, NY 11377, 718 545-1343.

CALLE, Washington R.; '78 BA; 4121 Benham St., Flushing, NY 11373, 718 457-3893.

CALLENDER, Colette D.; '92 MPA; 1164 Sherman Ave. Apt. 2, Bronx, NY 10456, 718 792-6934.

CALLENDER, Cynthia; '94 BA; Contracting Ofcr.; US Immigration & Naturalization Svc., 26 Federal Plz., Rm. 3907, New York, NY 10278; r. 3825 Kings Hwy., Brooklyn, NY 11234. e-mail

CALLISTRO, Cynthia Y.; '90 BA; Theol. Inst., Bronx, NY; Day Care Provider; Day Care Provider,Rivers Of Living Water, Christian Family Day Care Ctr., Bronx, NY 10451, 718 992-7438; r. 1353 Sheridan Ave., Apt. 3-A, Bronx, NY 10456, 718 992-7438; Asia Latimer, Nairobia, Latimer.

CALOURO, Joseph; '80 BS; 19 Furness Pl., Staten Island, NY 10314.

CALTABIANO, Lisa J.; '99 BA; Case Mgr.; AIDS Svc. Ctr. of Manhattan; r. Woodhaven, NY 11421.

CALVANESE, Jerry F.; '74 BS, '74 BA; Mort Banker; M&T, 401 Broad Hollow Rd, Melville, NY 11747, 631 501-0123; r. 37 Carrington Dr., E. Northport, NY 11731, 631 266-2468; Jerry M., Catherine.

CALVERT, John T.; 69 Maple St., Croton-on-Hudson, NY 10520.

CALVERT, Vashti N.; '98 BS; 535 Essex St., Brooklyn, NY 11208.

CALVO, Jenny M.; '89 MA; 45-01 Newtown Rd, Long Island City, NY 11103, 718 478-4597.

CALVO, Ramon; '82 BS; 16041 95th St., Jamaica, NY 11414, 718 478-4597.

CALVOSA, Ronald P.; '81 BA, '81 MA; Inspector Gen.; NYC Dept. of Investigation, 40 Worth St., Rm. 821, New York, NY 10013, 212 442-8100; r. 718 351-2150.

CALZADILLA, Esme M.; '86 BA; 333 Prairie Dune Way, Orlando, FL 32828.

CALZERANO, Joseph P.; '62 MPA; 1862 Matthews Ave., Bronx, NY 10462, 718 792-8964.

CAMA, Pasquale A.; '75 MPA; 14455 25th Dr., Flushing, NY 11354, 718 575-3211.

CAMACHO, Angel J.; '97 BS, '99; 401 E. 145 St., Bronx, NY 10454, 718 547-2678.

CAMACHO, Edgar M.; '84 AS, '99 BA; Customs Inspector; US Customs Svc.; 1210 Corbin St., Elizabeth, NJ 07201, 973 645-2236; r. 2300 Olinville Ave., Bronx, NY 10467, 718 653-2105; Miriam; Christopher, Gabriel, Corinne. e-mail

CAMACHO, Gabriel; '95 BS; Deputy Dir. of Inspection; Dept. of Transportation, Bowling Green, NY 10004; r. 125 E 101st St. Apt. 2w, New York, NY 10029, 212 410-1160. e-mail

CAMACHO, Michael; '98 BS; 2945 White Plain Rd, Bronx, NY 10467, 718 655-9186.

CAMACHO, Sarita; '83 BA; 340 Alexander Ave., Bronx, NY 10454, 718 665-0984.

CAMARDA, Susan A.; '86 BS; 1 Greystone Cir., Bronxville, NY 10708, 914 337-5268.

CAMARGO, Catherine; '96 BA; 23-39 92nd St., E. Elmhurst, NY 11369, 718 575-3211.

CAMARGO, Ruth E.; '98 BS; 11-03 Welling Ct., Long Island City, NY 11102, 718 424-6733.

CAMERON, Norman E.; '97 BA; Supv.; USPO, Church St. Sta., New York, NY 10002; r. 2822 W.36th St., Brooklyn, NY 11224, 718 946-0923; Douglas.

CAMERON, Peter F.; '76 BS; 4-31 28th St., Fair Lawn, NJ 07410.

CAMERON, Rosalind R.; '90 MPA; BS HADM St. Joseph's Clg., BSN Molloy Clg.; Supervising Public Health Nurse; Dept. of Health Bur. of Sch. Health, 120-34 Queens Blvd., Kew Gardens, NY 11415, 718 575-2390; r. 166-05 Highland Ave., Apt. 8 Y, Jamaica Estates, NY 11432, 718 523-0544; Jeffrey.

CAMILLERI, Michele; '94 BA; Financial Advisor; r. 19 Sunset Ave., Amityville, NY 11701, 631 789-5398; Charles. e-mail

CAMILLERI, Michelle; '96 BS; 60 Pleasantview Ct., Copiague, NY 11726.

CAMILO, Gilberto J.; '99 BS; Police Ofcr.; NYPD; r. 933 E. 181 St. 2Fl, Bronx, NY 10460, 718 365-5351. e-mail

CAMILO, Wilton; '96 BA; 509 W. 212 St., New York, NY 10034.

CAMINERO, Elbi M.; '99 BA; Asst. Gas Svc. Mgr.; Holiday Inn, 440 W 57th St., New York, NY 10019, 212 581-8100; r. 108-18 37th. Dr. 1st Fl., Flushing, NY 11368, 718 533-8608.

CAMINSKE, Russell L.; '84 BA; 669 N Greene Ave., Lindenhurst, NY 11757.

CAMMALLERE, Catherine; '82 BA; MSED Hunter Clg.; Sr. Disability Mgmt. Spec.; Intracorp, 800 532-2205; r. POB 459, Brooklyn, NY 11231, 718 832-6252.

CAMMALLERE, M. J.; '76 MA; 155 Huntington St., Brooklyn, NY 11231, 718 624-0425.

CAMMETT, John M., PhD; BA Wayne State Univ., PHD Columbia Univ.; Prof. Emeritus History/Provost; John Jay College of Criminal Justice; r. 905 West End Ave., New York, NY 10025, 212 316-2613; Sandi Cooper; Lisa, Anni, Melani. e-mail

CAMP, Nicole; '92 BS; 19 Leona St., Staten Island, NY 10314, 718 948-1533.

CAMPAGNOLA, Alfonso; '75 BS; Special Agt.; NYS Commission of Investigation, 59 Maiden Ln., 31st Fl., New York, NY 10038, 212 344-6660; r. 11 Cedar St., Massapequa, NY 11758, 516 798-0544; Roseann.

CAMPANILE, Anthony; '95 BA; 120 Pennsylvania Ave., Tuckahoe, NY 10707, 914 779-9452.

CAMPBELL, Annecia A.; '97 BS; Fed. Ofcr.; US Dept. of Justice, Brooklyn, NY 11201; r. 114-42 157th St., Jamaica, NY 11434. e-mail

CAMPBELL, Bradley S.; '90 BS; 190 Willoughby St., Brooklyn, NY 11201, 718 622-7099.

CAMPBELL, Carol G.; '86 BS; 494 Putnam Ave., Brooklyn, NY 11221, 718 221-9262.

CAMPBELL, Duncan; '82 MPA; 2922 Barnes Ave., Apt. 5F, Bronx, NY 10467, 718 653-8867.

CAMPBELL, Hopeton A.; '90 BA; Fordham Univ.; Adjunct Prof.-Tech. Supv.; Digital Media Lab, Fordham University; r. 1422 Harrod Ave., Bronx, NY 10472, 718 542-6256. e-mail

CAMPBELL, Isaac J.; '82 MA; 123 Plumtree Ln., Willingboro, NJ 08046, 609 871-9116.

CAMPBELL, John J.; '72 BS, '76 MPA; Retired; r. 2748 Anthony Ave., Bellmore, NY 11710, 516 785-7177.

CAMPBELL, Morven A.; '95 BA; Supv.; Dept. of Homeless Svcs., 151 E 151 St., Bronx, NY 10451, 718 402-6261; r. 4149 De Reimer Ave., Bronx, NY 10466, 718 994-7846.

CAMPBELL, Patricia A.; '95 BA; 1179 President St., Brooklyn, NY 11225, 718 493-4520; Ayanna.

CAMPBELL, Rita; '80 BA; 2 Charlton St., New York, NY 10014, 315 697-5512.

CAMPBELL, Robert; '76 BS, '86 MPA; 33 James St., Montclair, NJ 07042, 973 744-2917.

CAMPBELL, Robert; '98 BS; 146-26 222 St., Springfield Gardens, NY 11413, 718 527-9359.

CAMPBELL, Robert E.; '71 MPA; 15 Midway Pl., Staten Island, NY 10304, 718 987-5402.

CAMPBELL, Robert J.; '78 BS; 184 Pine St., Rockville Centre, NY 11570, 516 355-0383.

CAMPBELL, Sheilah N.; '85 BA; 970 Boston Rd #4-B, Bronx, NY 10456, 718 409-3727.

CAMPBELL, Steven T.; '78 MA; BA C.W. Post Clg., LIU; Pres./Owner; Corporate Security Resources, Inc., 11 Penn Plz., 5th Fl., New York, NY 10001, 212 946-4800; r. 31-519 River Ct., Jersey City, NJ 07310; *Julia*. e-mail

CAMPBELL, Tricia T.; '96 BS; 257 Clocks Blvd., Massapequa, NY 11758.

CAMPBELL, Wilfrid R.; '76 BS; 6 Chatham Rd, Commack, NY 11725.

CAMPBELL, Yolan; '94 BS; 553 E 84th St. # 1, Brooklyn, NY 11236.

CAMPER, Deborah F., Esq.; '84 BS; JD Touro Law Sch.; Dir.-Housing Dept.; City of Cambridge, Maryland, 705 Leonard Ln., Cambridge, MD 21613, 410 228-6466; r. 501 Penn St., Hurlock, MD 21643, 410 943-0250; *Stanley Lake;* Brandon, Stanley Jr., William. e-mail

CAMPION, Edmund J.; '74 BS; 9413 E Fairway Blvd., Sun Lakes, AZ 85248.

CAMPION, John D.; '74 BS; 1650 Woodstock St., Elmont, NY 11003.

CAMPISI, Charles V.; '78 MA; 7239 52nd Ave., Flushing, NY 11378, 718 204-8859.

CAMPISI, Ronald P.; '80 BS; Fraud Investigator; Dime Savings Bank, EAB Plaza, E. Twr., 11th Fl., Uniondale, NY 11553, 516 745-2057; r. 15 Denise Dr., N. Babylon, NY 11703, 541 893-0295; *Rose Marie;* Elena, Matthew.

CAMPOCCIO, Deborah A.; '97 BS; Caseworker; Oneida Cnty. Dept. of Social Svcs., 800 Park Ave., Utica, NY 13501; r. 1333 Mary St., Utica, NY 13501. e-mail

CAMPOLO, Jennifer; '96 BA; Probation Ofcr.; State of New Jersey, Somerville, NJ 08876, 908 231-7600; r. 18 Main St., Succasunna, NJ 07876, 973 252-6888.

CANACOO, Seth; '88 BA; 20-32d W Mosholu, Bronx, NY 10468, 718 220-5308.

CANADY, Donna A., (Donna A. Morris); '96 BS; Admin.; Prudential Ins., 379 Thornall St., Edison, NJ 08837; r. 6 Kettle Ct., Howell, NJ 07731, 732 730-0856; *Otis;* Paul. e-mail

CANAII, Angel B.; '75 BA; 282 Linden Blvd., Brooklyn, NY 11226.

CANAL, Eugene; '72 BS; 4 James Anx, Shoreham, NY 11786.

CANAL, Wilvina; '98 BA; AA American Acad. McAllister; Community Affair Rep.; NYPD, Brooklyn, NY 11230; r. 1745 Caton Ave. #4F, Brooklyn, NY 11226, 718 856-2866.

CANALS-ROSA, Mildred C.; '80 BS; 500 W 123rd St. Apt. 7, New York, NY 10027, 315 734-0153.

CANAVAN, Andrew J.; '80 BS; 138 Jefferson Ave., Emerson, NJ 07630.

CANAVAN, Francis P.; '78 BS; 8823 53rd Ave., Flushing, NY 11373, 718 263-8678.

CANCEL, Blanca I.; '77 BS; 845 Columbus Ave. Apt. 20a, New York, NY 10025.

CANCEL, Juan A.; '96 BS; Police Ofcr.; NYC Police Dept.; r. 2030 Seagirt Blvd., 4 F, Far Rockaway, NY 11691, 718 337-3479; *Sherena.* e-mail

CANDELARIA, Gladys; '85 BS; 9818 Flatlands Ave., Brooklyn, NY 11236.

CANDIA, Fernando A.; '89 BS; AS Bronx Comm. Clg.; Claims Investigator; Progressive Ins., 3250 Westchester Ave., Bronx, NY 10461, 718 409-7615; r. 100 Elgar Pl. Apt. 21d, Bronx, NY 10475. e-mail

CANELO, Juan; '76 BS; POB 350741, Miami, FL 33135.

CANFIELD, Dennis V., PhD; '76 MPA; BS BIOL. Lynchburg Univ., PHD Northeastern Univ.; Mgr. Toxicology & Accident Res.; Fed. Aviation Admin., 6500 S. MacArthur Blvd., Oklahoma City, OK 73125, 405 954-6252; r. 904 Richmond Rd., Edmond, OK 73034, 405 359-0533; *Liese;* Jason, Christina, Wayne, Gabriele, Heather, Noel, Tiffany. e-mail

CANGELOSI, Robert S.; '93 BS; Deputy US Marshal; US Marshals Svc., 225 Cadman Plz. E., Brooklyn, NY 11201, 718 254-6700; r. 1232 82nd St., Brooklyn, NY 11228.

CANGRO, Frank F.; '83 BS; POB 131656, Staten Island, NY 10313.

CANIZALES, Christina; '96 BS; 47-30 59th St. #5A, Woodside, NY 11377.

CANKAT, Johnny A.; '84 BA; 14480 Sanford Ave. Apt. 5b, Flushing, NY 11355.

CANNADY, Sheletha S.; '96 BA; 811 St.Ann's Ave., Bronx, NY 10456, 718 294-4177.

CANNADY, Terri; '92 BA; 1305 Amsterdam Ave., New York, NY 10027.

CANNATA, Augustine M.; '77 BS; 87 Baltimore St., Staten Island, NY 10308, 718 983-8180.

CANNELLA, Joseph D.; '76 BA; 1709 Willoughby Ave., Ridgewood, NY 11385, 718 366-7030.

CANNING, Candia C.; '99 BA; Bldg. Expeditor; Mt. Sinai Hosp.; r. 185 Malcom X Blvd., Brooklyn, NY 11221, 718 452-2883. e-mail

CANNING, Thomas P.; '80 BS; 138 N. Egermont Rd., Alford, MA 01230.

CANNIZZARO, Mariann; '98 BA; 40-36 203rd St., Flushing, NY 11361, 718 229-3818.

CANNIZZO, Enzo F.; '85 MPA; 19 Commerce St., Staten Island, NY 10314.

CANNON, Austin E.; '90 BS; Loss Prevention Spec.; Airborne Express, 165 Cantiague Rock Rd., Westbury, NY 11590, 516 942-3796; r. 2066 Jacqueline Ave., Bellmore, NY 11710, 516 826-2357; *Laurie;* Matthew. e-mail

CANNON, Edward T.; '95 BA, '95 MA; 24 Wyandanch Ave., East Islip, NY 11730.

CANNY, Joseph; '96 BA; 145 President St., Lynbrook, NY 11563.

CANO, Jeanette; '95 BS; 652 Faile St. Fl. 1st, Bronx, NY 10474, 718 220-1936.

CANTALINO, Carmine C.; '79 BS; 749 E 88th St., Brooklyn, NY 11236, 718 257-8453.

CANTALUPO, Lotteann; '96 BS; 172 E. 4th St., New York, NY 10009.

CANTAVE, Alexandra M.; '86 BA; 701 Fenimore St., Brooklyn, NY 11203, 718 774-6434.

CANTAVE, Barbara E.; '97; 66 W. Broad St., Haverstraw, NY 10927.

CANTAVES, Elaine '82 (See Barry, Elaine).

CANTO, Salvatore; '93 BS; 2234 73rd St., Flushing, NY 11370, 718 544-4663.

CANTONE, Michael D.; '89 BS; 14E Dorado Dr., Morristown, NJ 07960.

CANTY, Maria A.; '95 BS; 926 Lafayette Ave., Brooklyn, NY 11221, 718 638-7914.

CANZONERI, Leah A.; '83 BS; POB 3721, New Hyde Park, NY 11040.

CAOLA-OSKIN, Courtney B.; '95 MA; 2518 Lavin Ct., Troy, NY 12180.

CAPAOBIANCO, Sr. Carmela; '93 MA; MA HIST Fordham Univ., BAES Boston Clg.; Prison Ministry; Srs of The Good Shepherd, 39 W. 19th St., New York, NY 10011, 212 206-7070; r. 337 E. 17th St., New York, NY 10003, 212 475-4245. e-mail

CAPARCO, Randy M.; '79 BS; 208 Mooney Pond Rd., Selden, NY 11784.

CAPASSO, Geraldine C.; '79 BS; 20 Highland Blvd., Lynbrook, NY 11563, 516 538-4313.

CAPELLA, Ms. Jeanette; '76 BA; MED Fordham Univ.; Tchr. ESL; IS 93; r. 1821 Stockholm St. # 3L, Flushing, NY 11385. e-mail

CAPELLA, Peter C.; '89 BS; 439 Elderts Ln., Brooklyn, NY 11208.

CAPELLAN, Awilda J.; '98 BS; 182 N. Broadway La, Yonkers, NY 10701, 914 963-9056.

CAPELLI, Robert; '95 BA; 75 Leif Blvd., Congers, NY 10920, 914 268-4858.

CAPOBIANCO, John J.; '76 BA; 236 Naples Ter., Bronx, NY 10463.

CAPOBIANCO, Joseph J.; '97 BA, '98 BA; Acct. Exec.; Fox TV Sales, 635 Madison Ave., New York, NY 10001, 212 537-5800; r. 82 Sutton St., Brooklyn, NY 11222, 718 349-6452.

CAPON, Joseph; '90 BS; 213 Douglas Ave., W. Islip, NY 11795, 631 422-8540.

CAPONE, Peter; '92 BS; 261 Eltingville Blvd., Staten Island, NY 10312, 718 227-6730.

CAPPARELLI, Madeline C.; '95 BS, '97 MA; 6912 17th Ave., Brooklyn, NY 11204.

CAPPARELLI, Robert (Rob); '96 BA; Corporate Paralegal; Pryor Cashman Sherman & Flynn LLP, V10 Park Ave., New York, NY 10022, 212 326-0470; r. 58-26 75 St., Elmhurst, NY 11373, 718 803-9394; *Virginia.* e-mail

CAPPELLA, Albert M.; '81 BS; 36 Beacon St., Shirley, NY 11967.

CAPPELLO, Edward; '77 BS, '80 MPA; AS; Retired Deputy Chief; NYC Police Dept.; r. 1984 W. 12th St., Brooklyn, NY 11223, 718 266-7057; *Joanne;* Linda, John. e-mail

CAPPELLO, Mary G.; '79 BS; 1029 Van Nest Ave., Bronx, NY 10461, 718 829-7856.

CAPPIELLO, Dominick A.; '97 BS; SCC, AS; Police Ofcr.; NYPD, Brooklyn, NY 11201, 718 797-1270; r. Huntington, NY 11743. e-mail

CAPPIELLO, James T.; '90 BS, '92 MPA; 193 Peach Tree Pl., Freehold, NJ 07728, 732 303-8995.

CAPPONI, Louis J.; '72 BS, '75 MPA; Retired; r. 79 Manor St., Plainview, NY 11803, 516 822-3859.

CAPRIA, Britt A.; '96 BA; Homemaker; r. 25 Meridian Rd, Norwalk, CT 06853, 203 838-6060; *Tom;* Anton, Sofia. e-mail

CAPRICES, Nadalyn; '97 BS; 2700 Marion Ave., Bronx, NY 10458, 718 562-2392.

CAPUTO, James M.; '89 BA, '95 MPA; 55 Clover Ave., Floral Park, NY 11001, 516 437-5591; *Kristin;* James.

CAPUTO, John; '88 BS, '92 MPA; 994 Fenworth Blvd., Franklin Sq., NY 11010, 516 328-9428.

CAPUTO, Joseph; '85 BS; CERT. Police Acad.; Deputy Inspector Gen.; Dept. of Investigation, 180 Water St. 2nd Fl., New York, NY 10038, 212 331-3005; r. 120 Timber Ridge Dr., Staten Island, NY 10306, 718 667-8471; *Diana;* Grace, Anthony, Frank.

CAPUTO, Rosemarie; '84 BS; 3820 13th Ave., Brooklyn, NY 11218, 718 748-6523.

CARABALLO, Gesselle; '99 BS; 2559 Gr Concourse 5-B, Bronx, NY 10468, 718 733-1376.

CARACOLA, John A.; '76; 84-63 129 St., Kew Gardens, NY 11415.

CARAGIULO, Dominic; '90 BS; 210 Allison Ave., Staten Island, NY 10306, 718 979-7482.

CARATTINI, Esteban; '94 BS; 9414 125th St., Jamaica, NY 11419.

CARAVELLO, Kelly A.; '96 BS; 1407 Gravesend, Brooklyn, NY 11229.

CARBERRY, George M.; '76 AS; 2111 28th St., Long Island City, NY 11105.

CARBERRY, James E.; '97 BS; 6738 108 St. #B, Flushing, NY 11375.

CARBIN, Bernard J.; '75 BA; 549 E Penn St., Long Beach, NY 11561.

CARBONARO, Lawrence; '96 MA; 3823 Bedford Ave., Brooklyn, NY 11229, 718 375-4534.

CARBONELL, Elisa M.; '95 BS; 255 W 22nd St. Apt. 5b, New York, NY 10011.

CARBUCCIA, Julio C.; '78 BS; 108-51 39th Ave., Corona, NY 11368.

CARDET, Carolyn; '93 BS; 1243 Brooklyn Ave. Apt. 2l, Brooklyn, NY 11203.

CARDICHON, D.; '92 BS; 138-67 Brookville, Rosedale, NY 11422.

CARDILLO, Bob J.; '78 BA; Retired Police Ofcr.; NY Port Authority; r. 351 W. 51st, New York, NY 10019, 212 247-1354. e-mail

CARDILLO, Joseph L.; '74 BS; Secy. Treas.; r. 8 Davis Dr., Armonk, NY 10504, 914 273-8007; *Susan.* e-mail

CARDONA, Jimmy E.; '97 BA; Fraud Investigator; NYC; r. 34-56 73rd St. B9, Jackson Hts., NY 11372; *Lourdes Dominguez.*

CARDONA, Michael A.; '91 AS; Police Ofcr.; New York Police Dept., Bronx, NY 10463; r. 33-35 E. 208th St. #2G, Bronx, NY 10467, 718 547-9014.

CARDONE, Robert A.; '80 BS; 252 Greencroft Ave., Staten Island, NY 10308, 718 356-1749.

CARDOZA, Jamie M.; '98 MA; BA Villanova Univ.; Caseworker; St. Mary's Children & Family Svcs., 525 Convent Rd., Syosset, NY 11791, 631 243-2824; r. 25 Harvard St., Westbury, NY 11590, 516 997-5087; *Ron.*

CARDOZA, Zachary A.; '97 BA; Sr. Ins. Advisor; Direct Response Corp., 4 Gannett Dr., White Plains, NY 10604, 914 640-2199; r. 30 Ambassador Ln., Newburgh, NY 12550; *Christine L.* e-mail

CARDWELL, Linda '76 (See Williams, Ms. Linda).

CARELA, Wanda; '93 BA; 170 Nagle Ave., New York, NY 10034, 212 569-1090.

CAREY, Arlene; '96 BS; 1478 Commonwealth Ave., Bronx, NY 10460, 718 547-0215.

CAREY, Gary T.; '76 BS; Retired; r. 24668 87th Ave., Bellerose, NY 11426, 718 343-3508; *Susan;* Jason, Justin.

CAREY, James P.; '89 BA; RD 2 Box 53 Skirun, Bloomingburg, NY 12721.

CAREY, John J.; '79 BA; 265 07 83rd Ave., Floral Park, NY 11004, 516 676-9291.

CAREY, Vincent M.; '83 MPA; 5230 39th Dr. # 11, Flushing, NY 11377, 718 628-8704.

CAREY, William G.; '79 BS; 6341 55th Ave., Flushing, NY 11378, 718 899-3659.

CAREY, William J.; '80 BS; 2 Bank St., New York, NY 10014, 212 255-0253.

CARILLO, C.; '82 BA; 60 Dougherty Blvd. #406, Far Rockaway, NY 11696.

CARILLO, Joseph A.; '78 BA; 19-02 Astoria Park S, Long Island City, NY 11102.

CARLE, William R.; '83 BS; Hc 2 Box 219, Satsuma, FL 32189.

CARLEY, Joseph; '90 BS; 8 Beach 220th St., Far Rockaway, NY 11697, 718 634-6436.

CARLO, John R.; '69 AS; '70 BS; Pastor; Christian Pentecostal Church, 900-910 Richmond Rd., Staten Island, NY 10304, 718 273-5850; r. 36 Garden St., Staten Island, NY 10314, 718 494-4168; *Sandra;* Yvonne, Sharon, Lynne, John Jr. e-mail

CARLSON, Glenn A.; '99 BS; Police Sergeant/Youth Bureau Supv; Town of Mt. Pleasant PD, 1 Town Hall Plz., Valhalla, NY 10595, 914 769-1941; r. Valhalla, NY 10595, 914 769-6292. e-mail

CARLSON, Karen F.; '81 BS; 310 Windsor Pl., Brooklyn, NY 11218, 718 330-1997.

CARLSON, Mary; '92 MPA; 20 Arnhem Rd., Whitehorse, YT, Canada Y1A 3B4.

CARLSON, Richard D., Jr.; '75 BS, '82 MA; CPM Fairleigh Dickinson Univ.; Leonia Police Dept. Sergeant; Adjunct Professor-Fairleigh Dickinson, Leonia, NJ 07605, 201 944-0800; r. 111 Summit Rd, Sparta, NJ 07871, 973 726-7163; *Kathleen;* Richard D. III, Matthew G. e-mail

CARLSON, Todd S.; '92 BS; Ofcr.; Secret Svc., White House, 1600 Pennsylvania Ave. NW, Washington, DC 20500, 202 395-2020; r. 2902 Bentley Ave., Jamestown, NY 14701, 716 483-1019.

CARLTON, Erik; '97 BS; 2766 Mill Ave., Brooklyn, NY 11234, 718 919-0490.

CARLUCCI, Jean M.; '97; USA Soldier; USA, CMR 440 Box #826, APO, AE 09175, 496 151-6816; r. 17 Ruzzi St., Cranston, RI 02920. e-mail

CARMICHEL, Debora L.; '85 BS; POB 210559, Brooklyn, NY 11221.

CARMONA, Amada; '86 BA; 191 E 42 St. #5C, Brooklyn, NY 11203.

CARMONA, Marco A.; '97 AS, '98 BA; Law Enforcement; r. 47-16 49th St., Woodside, NY 11377, 718 729-0687.

CARNEY, Raymond J.; '93 AAS, '96 BA; Cab Driver; Seyle Mgmt. Corp.; r. 70 E 162nd St. Apt. 1g, Bronx, NY 10452, 718 293-0228; *Edith.*

CARNEY, William F.; '72 AS, '74 BS; 542 The Hideout, Lake Ariel, PA 18436, 570 698-9319.

CARO, Shirley; '95 BA; 189-04 64th Ave., Fresh Meadows, NY 11365, 718 458-5591.

CAROLAN, Edward; '90 AS; 123 Sweetfield Cir., Yonkers, NY 10704. e-mail

CAROLAN, John J.; '79 AS, '81 BS; Retired Detective; NYPD; r. 90 Perry Ave., Bayville, NY 11709, 516 628-8535; *Maureen;* Sean, Daniel, Christine, Kathleen, Gregory.

CAROLINA, Tanya L.; '93 BS; Brooklyn, NY 11233.

CAROLLO, Anthony M.; '83 BS; 77 Corona Ave., Staten Island, NY 10306, 718 448-6492.

CAROZZA, John P.; '91 BA; 10207 NW 7th Ct., Plantation, FL 33324, 954 452-6968.

CARPANINI, Nancy M.; '79 BS; 43-02 21 Ave., Long Island City, NY 11105.

CARPENDER, Scott; '90 BS; 1225 Midland Ave., Apt. 4M, Bronxville, NY 10708.

CARPENTER, Annissa L.; '97 BS; 914 Hickory Rd, Ocala, FL 34472.

CARPENTER, Ms. Edna E., (Edna E. Garay); '80 AS; Legal Secy.; Marvin Newberg, Esq., 33 North St., Monticello, NY 12701, 914 794-8413; r. 3216 Rte. 42, Monticello, NY 12701, 914 796-3362. e-mail

CARPENTER, Jeffrey S.; '92 BS; 437 Kirbytown Rd, Middletown, NY 10940, 914 344-3861.

CARPENTER, Taurina; '94 BS; 11625 Marsden St., Jamaica, NY 11434, 718 525-6136.

CARPINELLI, Paul; '96 BS; 1392 Madison Ave., Apt. 24, New York, NY 10029, 212 722-4590. e-mail

CARPIO, Marcus; '89 BS; 4706 Bronx Blvd., Bronx, NY 10470, 718 655-5547.

CARR, Autuam D.; '89 BA; 518 Evergreen Ave., Brooklyn, NY 11221, 718 467-9833.

CARR, Danielle M.; '82 BA, '97 MA; 3017 Eastchester Rd, Apt. 2, Bronx, NY 10469, 718 562-4445.

CARR, Dietrich M.; '95 BS; 10945 167th St., Jamaica, NY 11433, 718 526-4819.

CARR, Robert J.; '75 AS; 68 Parkway Dr. N, Blauvelt, NY 10913, 914 623-4698.

CARRADERO, Wilfredo; '88 BA; 33 Redlef Ct., E. Patchogue, NY 11772.

CARRANZA, Oscar; '96 AA, '99 BA; Correctional Ofcr.; NYS Dept. Correctional Svcs., Sing-Sing, Ossining, NY 10562; r. Nys Dept. of Correctional Services, Sing-Sing, Ossining, NY 10562. e-mail

CARRARA, Benjamin J.; '97 MA; 150 Dogwood Dr., Oakland, NJ 07436.

CARRASCO, Edward; '95 BS; 563 Soundview Ave., Bronx, NY 10473, 718 325-9337.

CARRASCO, Edward (Ed) G.; '99 MA; BA St. Francis; Law Enforcement; r. 50-57 39th Pl., Sunnyside, NY 11104, 718 392-9135. e-mail

CARRASQILLO, Myriam; '85 BA; 890 E 6th St. Apt. 4d, New York, NY 10009.

CARRENARD, Jack A.; 2522 Curtis St., Flushing, NY 11369.

CARRERA, George; '93 AS; 3962 56th St., Flushing, NY 11377, 718 651-5886.

CARRERA, Margarita; '98 BA; Ofc. Mgr.; Air Europa; r. 37-38 91St. 2nd Fl., Jackson Hts., NY 11372, 718 779-1850. e-mail

CARRERA, Miguel A.; '96 BA; 104-14 89th Ave., Richmond Hill, NY 11418.

CARRERAS, Ralph; '75 BA; 29 W Belmont St., Bay Shore, NY 11706.

CARRIGAN, Richard M.; '76 BS; 29 St. Joseph Ave., Ronkonkoma, NY 11779.

CARRILLO, Anaida W.; '98 BA; 5509 4th Ave. #114, Brooklyn, NY 11220, 718 486-8390.

CARRINGTON, Charlotte; '77 BA; 669 Franklin Ave., Brooklyn, NY 11238, 718 258-1233.

CARRINGTON, Eric; '95 BS; 515 Clinton Ave. Apt. 5, Brooklyn, NY 11238, 718 789-2229.

CARRINGTON, Frederic; '75 BS; 11134 Witthoff Ave., Queens Vlg., NY 11429, 718 776-4035.

CARRINGTON, Ron E.; '96 BA; Special Investigator; Bur of Fraud & Investigation, 250 Church St., New York, NY 10013, 718 626-4837; r. 149-46 117th St., S. Ozone Park, NY 11420, 718 848-1869.

CARRION, Ana R. '99 (See Colon, Ana R.).

CARRION, Axel; '96 BS; 85 Graham St., Jersey City, NY 07307.

CARRION, Luis A.; '93 BS, '97 MS; Probation Ofcr.; NYC Dept. of Probation, 215 E. 161st. St., Bronx, NY 10461, 718 590-3151; r. 2749 Tenbroeck Ave., Bronx, NY 10469, 718 652-2952. e-mail

CARROLL, Ellen M.; '76 BA; 37-03 69 St., Woodside, NY 11377, 718 634-2677.

CARROLL, James W.; '85 BA; 15 Abbott Rd, Somerset, NJ 08873.

CARROLL, John J.; '73 BS; 230 Koehl St., Massapequa Park, NY 11762, 516 797-8220.

CARROLL, Michael J.; '99 MA; BS Mt. St. Vincent; Adjunct Prof; St. Thomas Aquinas Collge, Sparkill, NY 10976; r. Congers, NY 10920.

CARROLL, Patrick J.; '72 BS; MA Hunter Clg.; Police Commissioner; New Rochelle Police, New Rochelle, NY 10801, 914 654-2228; r. 475 North Ave., New Rochelle, NY 10801; *Kathleen.* e-mail

CARROLL, Thomas J.; '91 BS; 800 Victory Blvd., Staten Island, NY 10301, 718 442-8399.

CARROLL, Thomas R.; '73 MPA; Owner; r. POB-363 Parkchester St., Bronx, NY 10462, 718 796-5777. e-mail

CARROLL, William J.; '86 BA; 39-50 50 St., Woodside, NY 11377, 718 565-8482.

CARR-SHEPPARD, Kim D.; '85 BA; Correction Ofcr./Investigator; NYC Dept. of Corrections; r. 24 Windsor Pkwy., Hempstead, NY 11550, 516 432-3899; *Kinsey Ryan.*

CARRUTHERS, Bevan; '84 BA; 15 Galaxy Ln., Willingboro, NJ 08046.

CARSON, Andrew F.; '76 BA; 25 Soloff Rd, Massapequa, NY 11758.

CARSON, Jonathan; '98 BA; 34-33 97th St., Corona, NY 11368, 718 651-0671.

CARTAGENA, Hector; '94 BS; 108-41 Flatlands, Brooklyn, NY 11236, 718 567-2959.

CARTER, Arnold; '91 BA; Correction Ofcr.; r. 767 Eastern Pkwy., Brooklyn, NY 11213, 718 773-4160; *Antwin, Arnold, Kelli.*

CARTER, Corynne D.; '92 BA; 289 Empire Blvd., Apt. 4L, Brooklyn, NY 11225, 718 771-4285.

CARTER, Dawn E.; '85 BA; 2725 1st St., Apt. 6G, Astoria, NY 11102, 718 471-6696.

CARTER, Debbie N.; '96 BA; 46-40 Bowne St., Flushing, NY 11355, 718 471-6696.

CARTER, James E.; '76 BS; Retired Police; NYPD; r. 258 Kennedy Ave., Hempstead, NY 11550, 516 483-9258; *Celia;* Marvell, Sheree, James E. Jr. e-mail

CARTER, Kim; '85 BS; 5706 Farragut Rd., Brooklyn, NY 11234, 718 444-8486.

CARTER, Luis A.; '79 BS; Confidential Investigator; NYS Dept. of Law, 120 Broadway, New York, NY 10270, 212 416-8790; r. 72-21 Shawnee Ave., Yonkers, NY 10710, 914 779-5120.

CARTER, Mary A.; '81 BA; Indep Assoc.; Prepaid Legal Svcs., 803 819-1161; r. 355 Murrah Rd, N. Augusta, SC 29860, 803 279-6632; *Willie M.;* Doris. e-mail

CARTER, Melvin A.; '91 AS; 3324 Avenue J, Brooklyn, NY 11210, 718 703-3127.

CARTER, Melvina M.; '93 BS; MPA Pace Univ.; Fiscal Ofcr.; City of Yonkers; r. 33 Centre St., Yonkers, NY 10701, 914 376-9721; *Carlton.*

CARTER, Michael R.; '92 BS; 72 Gilman St., Bridgeport, CT 06605, 203 576-0138.

CARTER, Owen; '76 BS; Real Estate Broker; Owen Carter Realty, Springfield Garden, Queens, NY 11412, 718 341-1100; r. 11611 157th St. Apt. 7b, Jamaica, NY 11434, 718 341-1552. e-mail

CARTER, Ronald; '97 BS; 605 Louisiana Ave., Apt. 13E, Brooklyn, NY 11239, 718 642-2797.

CARTER, Wylene Y.; '81 MA; 652 Wilderness Acres, E. Stroudsburg, PA 18301, 610 599-2605.

CARTHON, Arlene; '90 BS; ASN Bronx Community Clg.; Nurse Mgr.; Sutter Psych, 7600 Folsom Blvd., Sacramento, CA 95826, 916 386-3000; r. 2626 Coho Ct., Sacramento, CA 95826, 916 366-7779.

CARUANA, Vincent J.; '84 BS; 172 Armstrong Ave., Staten Island, NY 10308.

CARUSO, Michael L.; '94 MA; 1785 215th St. Apt. 1g, Flushing, NY 11360, 718 446-4333.

CARUSO, Rosemary; '85 BS, '91 MA; AS Nassau Comm. Clg.; Special Investigator; NYC Dept. of Investigation, 250 Broadway, 28th Fl., New York, NY 10007, 212 306-3361; r. 72-09 45th Ave., Woodside, NY 11377. e-mail

CARUTH, Godson R.; '95 BS, '98 MPA; CERT. John Donaldson Tech Inst.; Fraud Investigation; City of NY, 30 Main St., Brooklyn, NY 11205, 718 260-7115; r. 681 Ocean Ave. D7, Brooklyn, NY 11226, 718 284-7410; *Winnifred D.;* Joel, Nigel, Crystal, Reynel.

CARVAJAL, Patricia; '95 BS; Supv.; NYC Criminal Justice Agcy.; r. 6929 Little Neck Pkwy., Glen Oaks, NY 11004.

CARVAJAL, Rita M.; '86 BS; 38-02 30th St., Long Island City, NY 11101, 718 478-8831.

CARVAJAL, Tania M.; '99 BS; Purchasing Admin.; Estee Lauder, 767 5th Ave., New York, NY 10153, 212 572-4711; r. 122 E. 103rd St. #14, New York, NY 10029, 212 876-3695. e-mail

CARVAJAL, Xiomara G. '95 (See Carvajal-Nunez, Mrs. Xiomara G.).

CARVAJAL-NUNEZ, Mrs. Xiomara G., (Xiomara G. Carvajal); '95 BS; Brooklyn Clg., PPT Bd. of Educ., Brooklyn; Elem. Special Educ., Teacher; I71-I141, 181 Hayward, Brooklyn, NY 11225, 718 287-2131; r. 520 E. 21st St., Apt. L, Brooklyn, NY 11226, 718 693-6319; *Pablo R. Nunez;* Paola Xiomara, Xiomara Paola. e-mail

CASABURI, Joseph A.; '71 BS, '76 MPA; AAS NYC Comm. Clg.; Retired Chief of Dept.; NYC Fire Dept., Distinguished Alumnus Award From, John Jay Clg. of Criminal Justice; r. 39 Elm St., Sayville, NY 11782, 631 567-9188; *Sheila;* Michael, Christopher, Mark, Melissa.

CASALE, Charles; 503 Maguire Ave., Staten Island, NY 10309, 718 966-5802.

CASALE, Donald E., II; '96 BS; JD New England Sch. of Law; Atty.; r. 62 Boylston St. Apt.-517, Boston, MA 02116, 617 426-9089. e-mail

CASALETTO, Craig J.; '96 BS; 44 Ctr. Grove Rd, Apt. H43, Randolph, NJ 07869.

CASALINS, Liana C., (Liana Bovea); '89 BS; Paralegal; Amedex Ins. Co., 7001 SW 97th Ave., Miami, FL 33173, 305 275-1416; r. 8888 SW 131st Ct., Apt. 204, Miami, FL 33186, 305 385-6007. e-mail

CASANOVA, Veronica '89 (See Casanova-Scott, Mrs. Veronica).

CASANOVA-SCOTT, Mrs. Veronica, (Veronica Casanova); '89 BA; US Probation Ofcr.; US Dept. of Probation, 500 Pearl St. 7th Fl., New York, NY 10007, 212 805-5190; r. 452 E 43rd St., Brooklyn, NY 11203, 718 629-9385; *Troy Scott; Lenn, Claudette, Anastasia.* e-mail

CASARES, Alcides; '96 BS; 320 W. 56th St., New York, NY 10019, 212 489-3312.

CASARES, 1LT John W., USA; '98 BS; Infantry Platoon Leader; Ft. Hood, TX 76545, 254 287-5999; r. 5116 Daybreak Dr., Killeen, TX 76542, 254 690-4914; *Tanya; Joshua, Charlie.* e-mail

CASARINO, Carmine J.; '70 BA, '73 BS, '79 MA; Adjunct Prof.; Miami-Dade Community Clg. (MDCC), Wolfson Campus, 300 NE Second Ave. Rm 3506-29, Miami, FL 33132, 305 237-3274; r. 1631 Egret Rd, Homestead, FL 33035, 305 245-0861; *Theresa (Dec); Philip.* e-mail

CASATELLI, Joseph A.; '83 BS; 1640 Fowler Ave., Bronx, NY 10462.

CASELLA, Nancy E.; '97 MA; 69-10 Yellowstone, Forest Hills, NY 11375, 718 459-0665.

CASELLI, Lisa A.; '96 MA; 80 Crown Ave., Elmont, NY 11003.

CASERTA, Joseph M.; '77 BA; POB 2241, Montauk, NY 11954, 631 668-2179.

CASEY, Dennis R.; '76 BS; 2778 Claflin Ave., Bronx, NY 10468.

CASEY, James J.; '67 BS; Retired Capt.; r. Staten Island, NY 10312.

CASEY, Michael J.; '95 AS, '98 BS; Sgt Police; NYC, 212 690-6302; r. 33 S Washington St., Port Washington, NY 11050.

CASEY, Michael P.; '89 BS; 39-67 65 St., Woodside, NY 11377, 718 747-3586.

CASH, Charisse R.; '83 BA; 4044 Monticello Ave., Bronx, NY 10466, 718 324-8777.

CASHIN, John G.; '79 BS; 5612 Sylvan Ave., Bronx, NY 10471.

CASHIN, Margarette; '89 BS; JD Seton Hall Univ.; Atty.; Margarette Burge Cashin, 430 55th St., Brooklyn, NY 11220, 718 439-9223; r. same; *Michael.*

CASIANO, Miguel A.; '90 BA; 11148 Addison St., Spring Hill, FL 34609.

CASILLA, Jose; '97 BA; AA Hostos Community Clg.; Housing Spec.; Proj. Basement, 542 W. 153 St., New York, NY 10031, 212 491-4600; r. 657 W 161 St. Apartament 6H, New York, NY 10032, 212 781-1478; *Yosiris Polanco; Ashley, Alexander, Allison.*

CASO, Luis; '90 MA; BS; Sr. US Probation Ofcr.; US Probation Dept., 75 Clinton St. 4th Fl., Brooklyn, NY 11201, 718 254-7413.

CASOLA, Anthony; '92 BA; 14 May Ct., Rockville Centre, NY 11570.

CASPER, Rene E.; '76 MA; 89-23 212 Pl., Jamaica, NY 11427, 718 217-2673.

CASSAGNOL, Nikole; '95 BS; Accounts Receivable Mgr.; Ambient Grp. Inc., 55 W. 39th St., New York, NY 10018, 212 463-7812; r. 376 Quincy St., Brooklyn, NY 11216, 718 638-0508.

CASSANO, Dominick J.; 164-42 90 St., Howard Bch., NY 11414, 718 746-9297.

CASSANO, Salvatore J.; '76 BS; 543 Powell St., Staten Island, NY 10312, 718 966-5540.

CASSANO, Vito M.; '77 BA; 2125 59 St., Brooklyn, NY 11204.

CASSERLY, Michael; '78 BA; 311 Joan St., Ronkonkoma, NY 11779.

CASSIDY, Jared K.; '98 BA; 10 Apex La, Ridge, NY 11961, 631 744-6838.

CASSIDY, John J.; '76 BS; BSRN Hunter Clg.; Battalion Chief; NYC Fire Dept., 9 Metro Tech Ctr., Brooklyn, NY 11209; r. 44 91st St., Brooklyn, NY 11209, 718 748-7466.

CASSIDY, Joseph T.; '99 MA; BA Syracuse Univ.; Capt; NYC Police Dept., New York, NY 10012; r. Washingtonville, NY 10992.

CASSIDY, Kevin A.; '83 BS, '86 MA; Security Cnslt.; Janus Assocs., POB 754033, (Adjunct Lecturer For John J Colg.), Forest Hills, NY 11375, 718 263-2433; r. 6817 Olcott St., Flushing, NY 11375, 718 263-4354.

CASSIDY, Michael A.; '95; 458 E Harrison St., Long Beach, NY 11561, 516 608-9088.

CASSIDY, Patrick E.; '76 BA, '79 MA, AS; Retired; NYCPD; r. 9720 118th St., Jamaica, NY 11419, 718 849-4538; *Margaret (dec);* Lawrence, Michael, Kathleen, Steven.

CASSIDY, Sharon E.; '92 BA, '94 MA; 458 E Harrison St., Long Beach, NY 11561, 516 608-9088.

CASSIDY, Susan E.; '89 MA; Lt.; NYC Police Dept., 1 Police Plz., New York, NY 10038, 212 374-5420; r. 1 Buckner Ave., Hicksville, NY 11801. e-mail

CASSIDY, Thomas A.; '97 BS; 944 Old Foundry Rd, Newton, NJ 07860.

CASTAGNA, Alfred R.; '89 BA; Law Enforcement; NPDPD, 1 Police Plz., New York, NY 10038, 718 828-4282; r. 96 Ryerson Rd, Warwick, NY 10990, 914 986-5581; *Joanne;* Allison, Tracey, Melissa.

CASTAGNA, John J.; '95 BS; AS Suffolk Community Clg.; Police Ofcr.; NYS Metropolitan Transport Authority, 347 Madison Ave., New York, NY 10017, 718 558-3333; r. 24 Claire Ln., Sayville, NY 11782. e-mail

CASTANEDA, Urania; '97 BA; 132-09 Maple Ave., Flushing, NY 11355, 718 274-6760.

CASTANZA, James; '95 BA; 1646 1st Ave. Apt. 7j, New York, NY 10028, 718 204-0492.

CASTELLANI, Albertina; '98 BS; 245 E. 54th St. #6J, New York, NY 10022.

CASTELLANO, Cayetano R.; '99 MA; 1302 72nd St., N. Bergen, NJ 07047, 201 854-0322.

CASTELLANO, John; '80 BS; AAS NYC Clg.; Deputy Chief Fire Dept.; Westfield Fire Dept., 405 North Ave. W, Westfield, NJ 07090, 908 789-4138; r. 610 4th Ave., Westfield, NJ 07090, 908 518-1591; Dina, Audra, John Jr. e-mail

CASTELLAR, Kane H.; '99 BS; Human Resources Asst.; Curtis, Mallet-Prevost, Colt & Mosle LLP, 101 Park Ave., New York, NY 10178, 212 696-6000; r. 60-86 69th Ave. #1, Ridgewood, NY 11385, 718 386-4240. e-mail

CASTIGLIONE, Steven; '95 BS; AAS Corning Community Clg., AS; Chemist; Procter & Gamble Pharmaceuticals, Woods Corner Facility, Norwich, NY 13815, 607 335-2552; r. 71 Cortland St., Norwich, NY 13815, 607 336-3323; Matthew, Lexi. e-mail

CASTILLO, Alfredo; '91 BS; 236 E 112th St. Apt. 64, New York, NY 10029.

CASTILLO, Elizabeth; '93 BA; 106-07 79th St. #1, Ozone Park, NY 11417, 718 969-8078.

CASTILLO, Ernesto (Pete) A., Jr., CFE; '90 BA; MPA Marist Univ.; Investigator/Auditor; AIG, 175 Water St., 27th Fl., New York, NY 10038, 212 458-3262; Peter, Paul, Elena. e-mail

CASTILLO, Gelin M.; '97 BA; AS Kingsborough Comm. Clg.; Flight Attnd.; TWA; r. 590 W.172 St., New York, NY 10032, 212 928-2415. e-mail

CASTILLO, Karla C.; '89 BA; 420 Screvin Ave., Bronx, NY 10473, 718 863-6670.

CASTILLO, Luis R.; '79 BS; 25 Knapp Te,, Goshen, NY 10924.

CASTILLO, Maria I.; '97 BS; 35-55 73rd St. #1, Jackson Hts., NY 11372, 718 846-4920.

CASTILLO-MULLINGS, Glynnis; '95 BA; 17 Delaware St., Huntington, NY 11743, 631 351-5760.

CASTINEIRAS, Fernando; '78 BS; 222 Newman Ave., Bronx, NY 10473.

CASTRICONE, John A.; '81 BS; 1738 Billy Casper Dr., El Paso, TX 79936.

CASTRO, Aida L.; '97 BS; 1279 Noble Ave., Bronx, NY 10472, 718 515-1999.

CASTRO, Alan J.; '97 BA; 108-20 62nd Dr. #4D, Forest Hills, NY 11375, 718 352-4874.

CASTRO, Arlene; '96 BA; 23-34 96 St., E. Elmhurst, NY 11369, 718 352-4874.

CASTRO, Mrs. Ayanna T., (Ayanna T. Mobley); '95 BA; AS LaGuardia Community; Ofc. Admin.; OC Tanner, 25 W. 45th St., Ste. 500, New York, NY 10036, 212 719-1900; r. 96-08 57th Ave., Apt. 17F, Corona, NY 11368, 718 699-4162; *Mario.* e-mail

CASTRO, Cristine D.; '83 BA; 119 Yuma Ln., East Islip, NY 11730.

CASTRO, Debra; '89 BA; 51 Ross St. Apt. 3b, Brooklyn, NY 11211, 718 854-5157.

CASTRO, Deron R.; '89 BS; 305 Vanderbilt Ave., Brentwood, NY 11717.

CASTRO, Fermin; '95 BS; 503 W 111th St., New York, NY 10025, 315 822-5445.

CASTRO, Gisele; '98 BA; 1341 Taylor Ave. P.h., Bronx, NY 10472, 718 892-7217.

CASTRO, Giselle; '80 BS; 1461 E 93rd St., Brooklyn, NY 11236, 718 854-5157.

CASTRO, Jacqueline; '93 BS; 154 S. 3rd St., Brooklyn, NY 11211.

CASTRO, Maria T.; '97 BA; Sr. Mgmt. Cnslt.; New York Health & Hosp. Corps., 230 W. 41st St., New York, NY 10036, 212 730-3830; r. 225 W. 109th St., New York, NY 10025, 212 663-1711; Daniel Garcia.

CASTRO, Robert J.; '77 BS; Mgr. Fleet Svcs.; MTA Police Dept., 347 Madison Ave., New York, NY 10017; r. 50 Beekman St., Staten Island, NY 10302; *Frances; Michael, Stefanie.* e-mail

CASTRO, Sandra J. '98 (See Landivar, Mrs. Sandra J.).

CASTRO, Zinna; '99 BS; Human Resources; RR Donnelley; r. 64-34 102nd St., Rego Park, NY 11374.

CASTRO-GONZALEZ, Wilf; '78 BA; 5622 Beverly Rd, Brooklyn, NY 11203.

CATALANO, Daniel J.; '80 AS; 2521 Sedgwick Ave., Bronx, NY 10468.

CATALANO, Domenick; '81 BS; 226 Connecticut St., Staten Island, NY 10307, 718 720-8189.

CATALANO, John M.; '90 BS; 30 Jute Rd, Rocky Point, NY 11778.

CATALANO, Thomas; '73 BS; 127 Stonegate Rd, Buffalo Grove, IL 60089, 847 541-4316.

CATALFUMO, Michael; '75 BS; 2566 E 29th St. Apt. 2, Brooklyn, NY 11235.

CATANA, Alexandra D.; '98 BA; 8 W 169 St. 4e, Bronx, NY 10452, 718 829-7350.

CATANESE, Joseph J.; '95; 351 Somerset St., New Brunswick, NJ 08901, 732 247-5161.

CATANIA, Denise A.; '98 BS; Legal Asst.; Epstein, Becker & Green, 250 Park Ave., New York, NY 10177, 212 351-4500; r. 189-14 Crocheron Ave., Flushing, NY 11358, 718 358-3395; David. e-mail

CATANZARO, Joseph; '81 BS; 8888 Hamilton St., Alta Loma, CA 91701.

CATES, Bernice; '89 BS; 557 South Ave., Staten Island, NY 10303.

CATLYN, Dasha V.; '95 BA; 445 Rogers Ave. Apt. 2r, Brooklyn, NY 11225, 718 282-3914.

CATO, Kenrick F.; '87 AS; 12 Cedar St., Freeport, NY 11520, 516 379-0657.

CAULFIELD, Hugh J.; '76 MPA; 2216 146th St., Whitestone, NY 11357.

CAVAGNETTO, Lawrence; '86 MPA; Sr. US Probation Ofcr.; r. 191 Dover Pkwy., Garden City, NY 11530; *Debbie.* e-mail

CAVALIER, Dorothy P.; '91 BA; 252 W Nicholai St., Hicksville, NY 11801, 718 252-8263.

CAVALIERE, Christopher; '95 BS; Asst. Mgr. Compliance; Citigroup, 111 Wall St., New York, NY 10043, 212 820-1890; r. 2292 E 24th St., Brooklyn, NY 11229, 718 934-2993; *Tara.* e-mail

CAVANAGH, Charles W.; '75 MA; 1308 Park Ave., Mamaroneck, NY 10543, 914 698-7908.

CAVANAGH, James P.; '79 BA; Proj. Mgr.; Grumman's Syst. Support, 10 Orville Dr., Bohemia, NY 11716; r. 865 Plum Tree Rd W, Westbury, NY 11590, 516 997-4799; *Cathy;* Billy, Patrick, Jack. e-mail

CAVANAGH, Joseph G.; '77 BS; Retired Police Ofcr.; NYPD; r. 29 Deerfield Dr., New City, NY 10956, 914 634-9547.

CAVER, Cynthia L.; '99 BA; Admin. Supv.; 41st Precinct, 1035 Longwood Ave., Bronx, NY 10453, 718 542-4771; r. 2410 Barker Ave. 11G, Bronx, NY 10467, 718 542-4771. e-mail

CAVOTO, Anthony; '76 BA; POB 176b, Carmel, NY 10512.

CAVUTO, Michael T.; '78 BS; 15615 99th St., Jamaica, NY 11414.

CAWLEY, Donald F.; '71 BS; 264-12 82 Ave., Glen Oaks, NY 11004.

CAYETANO, Olga; '95 BA; 1924 Candlelight Dr., Chesapeake, VA 23325.

CAZEAU, Beatrice; '94 BS; JD New England Sch. of Law; Asst. State Atty.; State Atty's. Ofc., 175 NW 1st Ave. 2500, Miami, FL 33128, 305 360-5830; r. 17485 NW 67th Ct. 214, Brooklyn, NY 11238, 305 231-9563. e-mail

CAZZOLI, Ubaldo; '80 BA; 2416 Grand Ave., Bronx, NY 10468.

CEA, Ellen; '96 BS; 10 Hartley Ln., Basking Ridge, NJ 07920.

CEBALLOS, Amelia A.; '88 BS; 3569 Broadway Apt. 6a, New York, NY 10031.

CEBALLOS, Gloria A.; '96 BA; 600 W. 183 St., New York, NY 10033, 212 928-0265.

CEBIC, Svetlana; '92 BS; Secy./Mgmt.; r. 30-11 Parsons Blvd. #7j, Flushing, NY 11354, 718 978-2616. e-mail

CECERE, Michael A.; '83 BS; 12 Taggart Way, Saddle Brook, NJ 07663, 201 489-7011.

CEDENO, Jaime; '82 BA, '91 MA; 3604 Broadway, New York, NY 10031, 212 283-4038.

CEDENO, Mariela; '92 BA; 286 Ft. Washington, New York, NY 10032.

CEDENO, Stacey N.; '99 BA; Investigator; NYS Taxation & Finance, Tax Enforcement Division, New York, NY 10048, 212 321-4612; r. 1018 Greene Ave., Brooklyn, NY 11221, 718 455-6882.

CELEDONIO, Leonin; '92 BS; 530 W 157th St. # 6, New York, NY 10032.

CELELLA, Carolyn C.; '80 BS; 35-47 33 St., Astoria, NY 11106.

CENDAGORTA, Louis M.; '86 BS, '90 MS; 333 Pearl St., New York, NY 10038, 212 732-6532.

CENNAMO, John E.; '85 MPA; 2394 Atlantic Blvd., Wantagh, NY 11793.

CENTAMORE, Ronald J.; '81 MPA; 7641 Parkview Way, Coral Springs, FL 33065, 954 340-3543.

CENTODUCATI, Dena M. '92 (See Dahl, Dena M.).

CEPEDA, Ivan A.; '82 BA; 32-68 41 St., Long Island City, NY 11103, 718 417-1960.

CEPEDA, Luis, Jr.; '91 BS; AAS Manhattan Comm. Clg.; Police Ofcr.; Yonkers Police Dept., 3rd Precinct, 4035 Riverdale Ave., South, NY 10705, 914 377-7428; r. 420 Palisade Ave. Apt. 2H, Yonkers, NY 10703, 914 968-7229; *Nancy; Ashley, Jeffery.* e-mail

CERAMI, Victor S.; '76 MA; 122 Davison Ave., Oceanside, NY 11572.

CERASOLI, Justine M.; '92 BA; 32-09 47 St. #4, Astoria, NY 11103.

CERDA, Maria C.; '95 BA; 41 W 112th St. Apt. 2E, New York, NY 10026.

CERDA, Rafael A.; '97 BA; 207 Sunset Blvd., Bronx, NY 10473, 718 822-1652.

CEREZO, Juan E.; '96 BS; Asst. Dir. of Security; Manhattan Clg., 4513 Manhattan College Pkwy., Riverdale, NY 10471, 718 862-7240; r. 56 Park Dr. P/H, Warwick, NY 10990; *Gloria;* Juan II, Michele, Melissa. e-mail

CERON, Gladys E.; '96 BS; 400 W 43 St. #31N, New York, NY 10036.

CERRETA, Kenneth; '85 BS; Retired Asst. Chief of Operations; NYC Fire Dept.; r. 21 Hunt Pl., Bethpage, NY 11714, 516 796-9660.

CERULLO, Vincent; '72 BS; 2 Trapper Ln., S. Setauket, NY 11720.

CERVEN, James F.; '89 BS; 1267 Hobart Ave., Bronx, NY 10461, 718 824-5794.

CERVINO, Anthony R.; '79 BS; Retired Detective-Dir. of Security; ODI Inc., 44-40 11th St., Long Island City, NY 11101, 718 706-8989; r. 138 Davison Ave., Lynbrook, NY 11563.

CESARANO, Anthony; '95 BS; Sergeant; NYC Police Dept.; r. 503 1st St., E. Northport, NY 11731, 631 262-6947; *Maria.* e-mail

CESARZ, Christopher; '92 BS; 17 Lauriano Ln., New Hampton, NY 10958.

CESPEDES, Luisa Y.; '97 BA; 3440 Gates Pl., Bronx, NY 10467.

CESTARE, John; '76 BS; 423 Morris Dr., Valley Stream, NY 11580.

CETHOUTE, Guy J.; '92 BA; 72 Rugby Rd, Brooklyn, NY 11226.

CHABLA, Patricia A.; '85 BS; Deputy Agcy. Chief Contr. Ofcr.; NYC Dept. of Corrections, New York, NY 10001; r. 7636 113th St., Forest Hills, NY 11375.

CHABRAN, Jennifer; '95 BS; 3328 104th St. Ph, Flushing, NY 11368.

CHABRIER, Lydia I.; '79 BS; 3630 E Bell Dr., Davie, FL 33328.

CHACON, Karlene L.; '98 MA; 428 Midwood St., Brooklyn, NY 11225, 718 604-3611.

CHACON, Mario E.; '94 BA; 250 W 61st Dr. Apt. 4d, New York, NY 10023.

CHADWICK, Keith; '89 BS; 3324 Giles Pl., Bronx, NY 10463, 718 324-1774.

CHAFFEE, David J.; '75 MA; 920 Yucca Ct., Longmont, CO 80501, 303 651-3448.

CHAGRIN, Jay W.; '79 BA, '81 MPA; Corporate Banking; r. 150 Schenck Ave., Great Neck, NY 11021, 516 466-3140; *Robin.*

CHAHALIS, Constance; '81 BA; 35-55 Olinville Ave., Bronx, NY 10467.

CHALLITA, John-Pierre; '99 BA; AS Queensborough Community; 109 28 Park Ln. S., Richmond Hill, NY 11418, 718 805-1066. e-mail

CHALMERS, Marvin E.; 2074 Park Est. #6J, Bronx, NY 10462, 718 410-2464.

CHALMERS, Trudy O.; '87 MPA; 2695 Briggs Ave. # C, Bronx, NY 10458, 718 584-1804.

CHAMAGUA, Iris E.; '83 BA; Social Worker; Mercy Hosp., 3663 S. Miami Ave., Miami, FL 33133, 305 854-4400; r. 15853 SW 144th Ave., Miami, FL 33177, 305 378-9262.

CHAMBERS, Darrell; '92 BS; 194-08 115 Ave., St. Albans, NY 11412, 718 525-1585.

CHAMBERS, Hewitt L., Jr.; '81 BS; Gen. Expediter; US Postal Svc., W. Jersey PD & C, 54 S Jefferson Rd., Whippany, NJ 07999; r. 192 Crestview Rd., Bridgewater, NJ 08807, 908 541-0934.

CHAMBERS, Jeffrey A.; '96 BS; Corrections Ofcr.; Cnty. Dept. of Public Safety, 45 Elm Rd., Caldwell, NJ 07006, 973 226-7777; r. 144 High St., Orange, NJ 07050, 973 676-2883. e-mail

CHAMBERS, Maxine V.; '99 BA; Client Assn.; Chase Manhattan Bank, 1501 Broadway, New York, NY 10036, 212 719-2936; r. 2726 Fenton Ave., Bronx, NY 10469, 718 882-6422. e-mail

CHAMBERS, Robert; '97 BA; 201 Washington Blvd., Sea Girt, NJ 08750.

CHAMBERS, Robert F.; '89 BS; 238 E 237th St., Bronx, NY 10470.

CHAMBLE, Benjamin S.; '80 BS; 3613 Marolla Pl., Bronx, NY 10466.

CHAMETZKY, Steven A.; '91 BA; Retired Postal Svc.; r. 2461 E. 29 St., Brooklyn, NY 11235, 718 646-0857. e-mail

CHAMORRO, Sol M.; '77 BS; 80 Amsterdam Ave. Apt. 11c, New York, NY 10023.

CHAMPAGNE, Nancy F.; '80 MA; 1143 36th St., Brooklyn, NY 11218, 718 832-3887.

CHAN, Agnes; '82 BA; 122 Finley Ave., Staten Island, NY 10306, 718 227-1333.

CHAN, Danny; '92 BS; 691 FDR Dr. #12C, New York, NY 10009, 315 839-6048.

CHAN, David; '95 BS; 6413 35th Ave., Woodside, NY 11377, 718 476-0994. e-mail

CHAN, Kalung; '92 BS; 3914 Corporal Kennedy St., Bsmt, Bayside, NY 11361, 718 424-7187.

CHAN, Kathy; '97 BS; 60 Pitt St. #8C, New York, NY 10002, 212 228-0751.

CHAN, Lai F.; '94 BS; 257 Clinton St. #4, New York, NY 10002, 315 724-7881.

CHAN, Patrick; '91 BS; 62-60 108th St., Forest Hills, NY 11375, 315 724-7881.

CHAN, Steven; '93 BS; 118 Madison St. Apt. 7, New York, NY 10002, 315 724-7881.

CHAN, Suk Han H.; '99 BA; Sales; Oriental Air; r. 2624 W. 13th St., Brooklyn, NY 11223, 718 266-3766. e-mail

CHAN, Susan; '97 BS; Corp. Security; Davis Polk & Wardwell, 450 Lexington Ave., New York, NY 10017, 212 450-4500; r. 31-07 90th St., E. Elmhurst, NY 11369, 718 476-0931. e-mail

CHAN, Wai H.; '87 BS; 24 Mcguinness Blvd., Brooklyn, NY 11222, 718 853-2810.

CHAN, William; '89 BS; 31 Market St. Apt. 15, New York, NY 10002, 315 724-7881.

CHANCE-POLLARD, Sarita T.; '99 BA; 310 W. 143 St. 13A, New York, NY 10030, 212 368-3514.

CHAND, Seema; '96 BS; 142-02 Franklin Ave., Flushing, NY 11355, 718 291-0591.

CHANDLER, Jana; '86 MA; 4312 Snyder Ave., Brooklyn, NY 11203, 718 703-3905.

CHANDLER, Kinya; '95 BA; 2615 Newkirk Ave., Brooklyn, NY 11226, 718 485-1445.

CHANG, John K.; '96 BA; Police Ofcr.; MTA, 347 Madison Ave., New York, NY 10017, 212 340-2480; r. 184 Richmond St., Brooklyn, NY 11208, 718 235-6903.

CHANG, Mrs. Josephine, Esq.; '91 BS; JD Northeastern Univ.; Atty-at-Law; Fulbright & Jaworski LLP, 666 Fifth Ave., New York, NY 10103, 212 318-3147; r. 6 Esmond Ave., Melville, NY 11747, 631 424-8443; *Jo;* Delvin, Devlin. e-mail

CHANNELL, Albert M.; '83 MA; Agt.; FBI, Philadelphia, PA 19106; r. 4118 Harbour Dr., Palmyra, NJ 08065.

CHANNELL, Warren T.; '80 AS, '82 BS; Safety & Security Mgr.; Grand Cypress Resort, Orlando, FL 32836, 407 239-1981; r. 8012 Aspencrest Ct., Orlando, FL 32835, 407 294-0637.

CHANTAYAN, Angelika; '99 BA; 47 35 39 Pl., Sunnyside, NY 11104, 718 937-4949.

CHANY, Christopher P.; '77 BS, '83 MS; Forensic Scientist; Westchester Cnty. Forensic Lab, 2 Dana Rd, Valhalla, NY 10595, 914 593-5600; r. 423 Lake Shore Rd., Putnam Vly., NY 10579, 914 528-1291; *Patricia;* Christopher, Kathryn.

CHAPARRO, Hiram; '88 BA; 640 Adee Ave. #4F, Bronx, NY 10467, 718 792-9183.

CHAPMAN, Doris; '87 BA; 25 Tennis Ct. # 5, Brooklyn, NY 11226, 718 972-0348.

CHAPMAN, James L.; '90 MA; 115 Demarest Pkwy., Elmira, NY 14905.

CHAPMAN, Marilyn; '98 BA; Voc. Couns.; VIP Community Svcs., 718 731-9890; r. POB 110332, Cambria Hts., NY 11411, 718 367-5162. e-mail

CHARAN, Shamla M.; '82 BS; 186 E 164th St. Apt. 4d, Bronx, NY 10456.

CHAREST, Mark F.; '90 BS; Birch Hill Acres, Brewster, NY 10509, 914 747-6248.

CHARLA, Stephen P.; '77 MA; 974 Charrington Rd, Bloomfield, MI 48301, 248 642-7191.

CHARLES, Alice; '95 BS, '95 MA; JD Benjamin N. Cardozo; Atty.; Countrywide Ins. Co., 40 Wall St., New York, NY 10006, 212 344-8700; r. 810 Ritter Pl. Apt. 5A, Bronx, NY 10459; Camonghne, Y'ananyah. e-mail

CHARLES, Deryck; '86 BA; 474 w. 158 St., New York, NY 10032.

CHARLES, Isabelle '90 (See Charles Smiley, Isabelle).

CHARLES, Joseph; '95 BS; 1701 Albemarle Rd, Apt. B2, Brooklyn, NY 11226, 718 462-2833.

CHARLES, Marie M.; '79 BA; 438 Rockaway Pkway, Brooklyn, NY 11212, 718 774-7538.

CHARLES, Nirlaine; '96 BAPA; Case Coord.; The Assn. for Help of Retarded Children, 200 Park Ave. S., 2nd Fl., New York, NY 10003; r. Brooklyn, NY 11210.

CHARLES, Ralph M.; '99 AS; 750 Faile St. 9E, Bronx, NY 10474, 718 854-2580.

CHARLES, Ronald; '93 BA; 227-08 108th Ave., Queens Vlg., NY 11429, 718 337-5788.

CHARLES, Rose M.; '95 BA; 514 Cedar St., Uniondale, NY 11553, 516 483-7201.

CHARLES, Rulolph N.; '78 BS; Police Ofcr; PAPD; r. 1365 Saint Nicholas Ave. Apt. 21r, New York, NY 10033; *Martha.*

CHARLES, Victor; '97 BA; 1100 Grand Concourse, Bronx, NY 10456, 718 231-1186.

CHARLES SMILEY, Isabelle, (Isabelle Charles); '90 BS; New York City Regional Ofc. Mgr.; NYS Atty. Gen. Ofc.-(M.F.C.U.), 120 Broadway, New York, NY 10271; r. 120-3 Dreiser Loop, Bronx, NY 10475, 718 379-0935; *Gilbert;* Vincent, Clifton. e-mail

CHASE, Audrey; '91 MPA; 115-11 125 St., S. Ozone Park, NY 11420, 718 423-0315.

CHASE, Garel S.; '85 BS; 13714 232nd St., Jamaica, NY 11413, 718 423-0315.

CHASE, Lisa; '96 BA; 170 S Portland Ave. Apt. 14d, Brooklyn, NY 11217, 718 832-0607.

CHASON, Neil S.; '81 BS; 57 Division Ave., Massapequa, NY 11758, 516 798-5933.

CHATMAN, Mayai N. '95 (See Chatman-Whitfield, Mayai N.).

CHATMAN, Zemender; '87 BA; 10704 Courthouse Rd, Dinwiddie, VA 23841, 804 862-1146.

CHATMAN-WHITFIELD, Mayai N., (Mayai N. Chatman); '95 AS, '96 BS; Wedding Event Planner; Wedding Day Inc., 8 W. 38th St., 10 th Fl., New York, NY 10018, 212 840-2333; r. 14424 253rd St., Jamaica, NY 11422, 718 528-1262; *Omar Whitfield;* Omari. e-mail

CHATTERGOON, Suchetr C.; '97 BA; MS St. Johns Univ.; Ins. Coord.; Raytel Cardiac Svcs., 11835 Queens Blvd., Forest Hills, NY 11375, 718 520-2077; r. 94-20 210 St., Queens Vlg., NY 11428, 718 776-0259.

CHATTERJEE, Sheila; '94 MPA; 40 Morningside Ave., New York, NY 10026.

CHAU, Tony K.; '94 BA; 10 Delancey St. Apt. 2, New York, NY 10002.

CHAVEZ, Alina; '96 BS; 229 W. 97th St., New York, NY 10025, 212 678-5080.

CHAVEZ, Rocio E.; '97 BA; 333 Mcdonald Ave., Brooklyn, NY 11218.

CHAVIES, Phyllis A.; '93 AS, '96 BS; 254 Washington Ave., Amityville, NY 11701, 631 841-1996.

CHAVIS, Malcolm L.; '91 BS; 401 E 102nd St. # 10, New York, NY 10029, 212 427-4463.

CHAVIS, Rosezina; '95 AS; BA; Administrative Asst.; John Jay Clg. of Criminal Justice, 237-8169; r. 356 Rockaway Pkwy. Apt. 2, Brooklyn, NY 11212, 718 342-5974. e-mail

CHAVIS, Shawn; '95 BS; 679 Warburton Ave., Apt. 7J, Yonkers, NY 10701, 914 375-2180.

CHAZAN, Barbara A.; '84 BA; 175 W 73 St., New York, NY 10023.

CHEATHAM, Anthony; '89 BA; 8928 168th Pl., Jamaica, NY 11432, 718 820-0802.

CHEATHAM, Leroy R.; '76 BA; 1712 Ditmas Ave., Brooklyn, NY 11226, 718 941-7906.

CHECO, Christina; '95 BS; 40-66 Ithaca Stree, Elmhurst, NY 11373.

CHECO, Manuela E.; '95 BA; 618 W. 177 Stree, New York, NY 10033.

CHEEKS, Robert; '95 BA; Dir. of Promotions; Aka.com, 221 W. Seventeenth St., New York, NY 10011, 212 763-5436; r. 354 Beach 56th Str, Arverne, NY 11692, 718 868-4077. e-mail

CHEESMAN, Marguerite; '81 BS; 11445 178th St., Jamaica, NY 11434, 718 739-5265.

CHEN, Hang; '95 BS; 13402 Cherry Ave., Flushing, NY 11355, 718 423-2696.

CHEN, Jennifer W.; '99 BS; Mgr.; Hanami, 10 Engle St., Englewood, NJ 07631, 201 541-7785; r. 4202 Kissena Blvd., #5J, Flushing, NY 11355, 718 539-3103.

CHEN, Jie Chan; '97 BA; 29 E.Broadway #3A, New York, NY 10002, 212 285-1388.

CHEN, Johnny Y.; '96 BS; 229 S 7th Ave., #5B, Mt. Vernon, NY 10550, 716 668-3134. e-mail

CHEN, Jose; '85 BS; 3565 Bivona St., Bronx, NY 10475, 718 432-9644.

CHEN, Katty; '96 CERT, '96 BA; Proj. Coord.; QUNY Citizenship Proj., 101 W. 31st St., New York, NY 10001, 212 502-2904; r. 8311 34th Ave., Jackson Hts., NY 11372, 718 274-1726. e-mail

CHENG, Christoph C.; '98 BS; Police Ofcr.; NYPD, 321 E. 5th St., Precient 009, New York, NY 10009, 212 477-7811; r. 152 Conklin Ave., Brooklyn, NY 11236, 718 272-0278.

CHENG, Mei; '96 BS; Clerk; US Postal Svc.; r. 84-29 101st St., Richmond Hill, NY 11418, 718 846-2751.

CHEREGOTIS, Peter J.; '95 AS; 42 74th St. # Pvt, Brooklyn, NY 11209.

CHERENA-PACHECO, Yvonne; '78 MA; JD CUNY Law Sch. at Queens, LLM Georgetown Univ.; Assoc. Dean/Dir. of Admissions; St. Mary's Univ. Sch. of Law, One Camino Santa Maria, San Antonio, TX 78228, 210 436-3523. e-mail

CHERNICK, Steven M.; '89 BA; JD Touro Law Sch.; Public Svc./Union; r. 169 S. Main St., Pmb 351, New City, NY 10956, 914 393-8547; *Elizabeth.* e-mail

CHERNJAWSKI, Nicholas; '92 BA; 19 Roberts Dr., Putnam Vly., NY 10579.

CHERRY, Alvina T.; '98 BA; 213 Sumpter St., Brooklyn, NY 11233, 718 919-3857.

CHERRY, Jack W.; MS; 6379 Tinted Hl, Columbia, MD 21045, 410 290-8279.

CHERRY, James C.; '77 BA; 15114 33rd Ave., Flushing, NY 11354, 718 278-8633.

CHERRY, Julie; '94 BS; 445 E 120th St. # 34, New York, NY 10035.

CHERRY, Patrick J.; '77 MPA; 11 Edgewood Rd, Staten Island, NY 10308, 718 967-9738.

CHERRY, Tyrone; '89 MA; 1460 Washington Ave., Bronx, NY 10456, 718 231-8887.

CHERUBIN, Ms. Yadlynd R.; '99 BA; Child Protective Spec.; Dept. of Social Svcs., 345 Adams St., Brooklyn, NY 11201, 718 522-8150; r. 999 E 38 St., Brooklyn, NY 11210, 718 377-0583. e-mail

CHERWAK, Walter; '77 BA; 414 E 9 St., New York, NY 10009.

CHESKI, Philip M.; '93 BA; Firefighter; Clifton Fire Dept., 900 Clifton Ave., Clifton, NJ 07013, 973 470-5801; r. 60 Lee St., Elmwood Park, NJ 07407, 201 701-9496; *Robyn;* Ryan, Shannon. e-mail

CHESTER, Rochelle; '82 BS; Assoc. Dir.; NYC Dept. of Investigation, 80 Maiden Ln., New York, NY 10038, 212 825-6817; r. 160 E 3rd St., New York, NY 10009.

CHESTER, Shonette A.; '95 BA; 221 Martha Ln., Blakeslee, PA 18610, 570 992-6126.

CHETAL, Rakesh; '96 BS; 11 Plainview Rd, Bethpage, NY 11714, 516 932-5734.

CHEUNG, Zulma G.; '99 BA; 168 Deerfield Ln., Aberdeen, NJ 07747.

CHEVERE, Beverly D.; '96 BA; Child Welfare Spec.; r. 67-15 102nd St., Forest Hills, NY 11375, 718 830-9237; Christopher J., Pamela Nicole, Kecia Anne.

CHEW, Philip M.; '99 BS; Claims Investigator; State Farm Ins., Uniondale, NY 11553, 516 229-2800; r. 144-07 Laburnum Ave., Flushing, NY 11355, 718 939-3728.

CHIAPPETTA, Gennaro (Jerry); '71 BA, '81 MA; Exec. Dir., Not-for-Profit Org.; American Italian Coalition of Orgs., AMICO, 138 Bay 20th St., Brooklyn, NY 11214, 718 356-2445; r. 1743 W 3rd St., Brooklyn, NY 11223, 718 627-8363; *Alice;* Kristin.

CHIARA, Frank J.; '77 BS; 8645 251st St., Jamaica, NY 11426, 718 343-6290.

CHIARANTANO, Daniel; '87 MA, BS MPA; Detective; NYPD Joint Firearms Task Force, 1 Police Plz., New York, NY 10038, 917 506-3067; r. 1835 E 36th St., Brooklyn, NY 11234; *Mary.*

CHIARINI, George J.; '77 BA; Pres.; Chiarin Marble & Son; r. 12 Greenmoor, Irvine, CA 92604, 949 551-4612. e-mail

CHICO, Ivelisse; '95 BS; 549 51st St. Apt. 1, Brooklyn, NY 11220.

CHICOLO, Mary E.; '81 BS; 30 Thomas St., Staten Island, NY 10306, 718 979-5383.

CHICOLO, Michael; '81 BS; 14 Nassau St., Staten Island, NY 10301.

CHILDS, Harry E.; '96 BS; 130 Oswego St., Staten Island, NY 10301, 718 447-7014.

CHILDS, Iris M.; '99 BS; Police Ofcr.; NYC Police Dept.; r. 30 W. 141st St., Apt#6 L, New York, NY 10037, 212 926-1663. e-mail

CHILLE, Edward; '89 MS; 6137 Amboy Rd, Staten Island, NY 10309, 718 966-4471.

CHILLO, Generoso A.; '88 BA; 42 Bay 8th St., Brooklyn, NY 11228, 718 256-4774.

CHIMENTI, Frank J.; '75 BA; 205 Belfast Ln., Ridge, NY 11961.

CHIMENTO, William F.; '71 BS; 16059 19th Ave., Whitestone, NY 11357.

CHIMIENTI, Alexander; '76 BA; Retired Fire Dept.; r. 25956 148th Dr., Jamaica, NY 11422, 718 528-3012.

CHIN, Frank; '95 MPA, '95; 153-28 75th Ave., Flushing, NY 11367, 718 224-7607.

CHIN, George W.; '79 BS; Sr. Forensic Scientist; NJ State Police, Central Lab, 380 Scotch Rd, Ewing, NJ 08628, 609 671-0022; r. 23 Adel Ct., Lawrence, NJ 08648, 609 620-0736. e-mail

CHIN, James M.; '77 AS; 14039 34th Ave. Apt. 1p, Flushing, NY 11354, 718 461-8174.

CHIN, Rose; '76 BA; 91-12 86 St., Woodhaven, NY 11421, 718 423-4692.

CHIN, Tin Y.; '87 BS; Asst. Mgr.; Canal Gift & Varieties Inc., 261 Canal St., New York, NY 10013, 212 941-0306; r. 5654 148th St., Flushing, NY 11355, 718 461-6648; *Sharon;* Shehan.

CHIN, Victor; '99 BA; 1508 Rosedale Ave., Bronx, NY 10460, 718 829-4169.

CHINCHILLA, Maria M.; '95 BS; Apt. 60, Far Rockaway, NY 11691.

CHIRIANI, Daniel T.; '82 BS; 137 Seaview Ave., Staten Island, NY 10304, 718 351-4885.

CHISHOLM, Delores; '82 AS; Educ. Administration; r. POB 6100, Bronx, NY 10451, 718 458-8892. e-mail

CHISHOLM, Elizabeth; '76 BA; 10555 62nd Dr., Flushing, NY 11375, 718 474-4652.

CHISHOLM, Marvin A.; '79 BA; 194-05 119th Ave., St. Albans, NY 11412, 718 528-3402.

CHISOLM, Elouise J.; '77; 2632 Davidson Ave., Bronx, NY 10468, 718 584-4447.

CHISOLM, Karen A.; '88 BS; POB 817, Kingstree, SC 29556.

CHITTICK, Diane A.; '95 BS; 214 S Augusta Ave., Baltimore, MD 21229.

CHIU, Lim-chi; '97 BA, '98; Legal Asst.; r. 275 Cherry St. 6H, New York, NY 10002, 212 393-9315.

CHO, Jody; '83 BA; 375 Evergreen Blvd., Scotch Plains, NJ 07076, 908 889-4835.

CHO, Polly; '96 BA; 59-14 161st St., Fresh Meadows, NY 11365, 718 886-8227.

CHODAKIEWICZ, Thomas; '89 BA; 33 Eric Ln., Staten Island, NY 10308.

CHOE, Munyong; '96 BS; 80-06 47 Ave. #5, Elmhurst, NY 11373.

CHOMIAK, Robert H.; '78 MA; Dean of Students; Trinity Catholic HS, 926 Newfield Ave., Stamford, CT 06905, 203 322-3401; r. 115 Old Haverstraw Rd, Congers, NY 10920. e-mail

CHON, Haksoo; '96 BS; 36-15 30 Ave. 2f, Astoria, NY 11103, 718 463-1583.

CHONG, LT David E.; '80 BS; AS Queensborough CC; Lt.; NYCPD-HIDTA, 26 Federal Plz. Rm. 29-30, New York, NY 10278, 212 637-6600; r. 13 Garson Rd,, Carle Place, NY 11514.

CHONG, Gayle E.; '88 BS; 14746 230th Pl., Jamaica, NY 11413, 718 358-8198.

CHONG, Renee H.; '93 BS; Capt.; NYC of Corrections; r. 262-16 149th Rd, Rosedale, NY 11422, 718 949-5947.

CHORNEY, Tonya L.; '95 MA; MSED, PSY Pace Univ.; Student Dr. Cand. Clinical Psych.; Pace Univ., New York, NY 10038; r. 444 W 35th St. Apt. 17c, New York, NY 10001, 212 268-1997. e-mail

CHORZEWSKI, Robert; '89 AS; 622 54th St., Brooklyn, NY 11220.

CHOU, Alice M.; '93 BS; POB 3898, Flushing, NY 11386, 718 932-8137.

CHOW, Frederick R.; '85 BS; 205 Munro Blvd., Valley Stream, NY 11581, 516 428-2257.

CHOW, Julianne T.; '81 AS; 85 Columbia St., New York, NY 10002, 212 677-5726.

CHOW, Lynette S.; '95 MA; 408 W Iowa St., Urbana, IL 61801.

CHOW, Patty Y.; '92 BS; Legal Asst.; Unite-Immigration Proj., 275 Seventh Ave., New York, NY 10002; r. 76 Orchard St., New York, NY 10002.

CHOW, Richard; '93 BS; AAS Borough Manhattan CC; Security; NYC Off-Track Betting Corp., New York, NY 10036, 212 221-5200; r. 87 Columbia St. #17, New York, NY 10002, 212 777-8369.

CHOWDHURY, Tarakur R.; '99 BA; Fraud Investigator; Human Res.; r. 1925 McGraw Ave., Bronx, NY 10462, 718 518-9412. e-mail

CHOY, Yolanda; '97 BS, '99 BS; New York City Police Dept.; One Poloce Plz., New York, NY 10003, 212 334-0711; r. 83 Butler St., Brooklyn, NY 11231, 718 643-5465; *Frank Ramierez Valenrin;* Kathy, Angelica, Michelle.

CHRIST, Karen J.; '96 MA; 104 Northwood Blvd., Central Islip, NY 11722.

CHRIST, Lily E.; John Jay Clg., New York, NY 10019, 315 853-2562.

CHRISTENSEN, James; '81 BS; JD San Francisco Law Sch.; Supervisory Special Agt.; US Dept. of Justice, Immigration & Naturalization Serv., 630 Sansome St., San Francisco, CA 94111, 415 844-5281; r. 13 Narcissus Ct., Danville, CA 94506, 925 736-8589. e-mail

CHRISTENSEN, Jarl H.; '75 BS; Retired Capt.; NYC Fire Dept.; Hackettstown, NJ 07840; r. 37 Russling Rd, Hackettstown, NJ 07840, 908 852-1365.

CHRISTIAN, Crystal; '97 BS; 93 Featherbed Ln., Bronx, NY 10452.

CHRISTIAN, Elmo E.; '95 BA; CEO; Magic Christian Music, 81 Main St., Hempstead, NY 11550, 516 292-2079; r. 539 E 96 St., Brooklyn, NY 11212. e-mail

CHRISTIANO, Michael J.; '77 MA; 1627 W 13 St., Brooklyn, NY 11223.

CHRISTIANO, Steven A.; '85 BS; 288 Richard Ave., Staten Island, NY 10309.

CHRISTIANSEN, Janet E.; '78 BS; 13829 Jewel Ave. Apt. 3d, Flushing, NY 11367, 718 263-1836.

CHRISTIE, Andrew C.; '98 BS; 1187 Rogers Ave., Brooklyn, NY 11226, 718 462-1229.

CHRISTINE, Marc T.; '96 BA; Graphic Design; r. 201 St. Paul's Ave., Apt. 16A, Jersey City, NJ 07306, 201 420-8080; *Walewska;* Cameron.

CHRISTMAN, SGT Dennis L.; '73 BA; MA Long Island Univ-CW Post; Retired Sgt New York Police Dept.; r. 36 Dail St., New Hyde Park, NY 11040, 516 248-8242; *Margaret;* Michael, James, Karen, Susan, Jennifer, Cynthia.

CHRISTMAN, Thomas V.; '85 BS, '90 MS; Safety Cnslt.; CNA Ins.; r. 36 Cherry St., Floral Park, NY 11001, 516 354-1798.

CHRISTMAN, William C.; '78 BS, '85 MA; Retired; NYC HRA Fraud Investigations; r. 126 Perry Dr., Goldsboro, NC 27530, 919 734-1337. e-mail

CHRISTOPHE, Joseph; '94 BS; Detective Investigator; New York City Police Department, 1 Police Plz., New York, NY 10038, 718 482-6825; r. 585 E 81st St., Brooklyn, NY 11236, 718 444-9360; Narley.

CHRISTOPHER, Lola C.; '78 AS; 11623 Farmers Blvd., Jamaica, NY 11412, 718 458-6853.

CHUDHABUDDHI, Pichai; '85 BS; 122 Seville St., Elmont, NY 11003.

CHUGERMAN, Jacob E.; '76 BS; Retired NY State DOC; Box 4434, Boynton Bch., FL 33424, 561 439-6981; r. POB 343, Summer Address May To Oct, Hurley, NY 12443, 914 338-0330. e-mail

CHUNG, Christina J.; '94 BA; 21711 64th Ave., Flushing, NY 11364, 718 428-8815.

CHUNG, George; '76 BA; 17929 90th Ave., Jamaica, NY 11432, 718 353-3037.

CHUNG, James K.; '99 BA; Student; r. 45-55 Pike St. #13A, New York, NY 10002, 212 349-3402.

CHUNG, Jane; '93 BS; 1716 71st St., Brooklyn, NY 11204, 718 621-4291.

CHUNG, Judy Y.; '88 BA; Translator; DWM Cnsltg. Svc., 3901 Main St. #611, Flushing, NY 11354, 718 445-8851; r. 4228 Colden St., Flushing, NY 11355.

CHUNG, Michael; '95 BS; 2353 E 16th St., Brooklyn, NY 11229, 718 643-3668.

CHUNG, Thomas H.; '94 BS; Criminal Investigator; New York Cnty. Dist. Atty.'s Ofc., 1 Hogan Pl., New York, NY 10013, 212 335-9011; r. 108 Egbert Ave., Staten Island, NY 10310; *Dominique.* e-mail

CHUNG, Victor L.; '77 BS; Mgr. of Safety Analyst; Triborough Bridge & Tunnel Authority, POB 35, New York, NY 10035, 718 969-9884; r. Box 165 Peck Slip, New York, NY 10038, 718 969-7308; *Theresa.* e-mail

CHUPCAVICH, Anna J.; '98 BA; Admin. Asst.; Mt. Sinai Sch. of Medicine, 100th Madison Ave., New York, NY 10029, 212 241-6561; r. 82-46 135th St., Kew Gardens, NY 11435.

CHURCH, Robin A.; '89 BS; 13531 234th St., Jamaica, NY 11422, 718 520-6640.

CHURCH, William J.; '95 BS; 42 Wander Ln., Wantagh, NY 11793.

CHYPRE, Richard L.; '86 BS; 56 Cheever Pl., Brooklyn, NY 11231, 718 875-3098.

CHYRACK, Judy; '99 BA; 946 E. 43 St., Brooklyn, NY 11210, 718 258-7559.

CIAMPO, Michael N.; '83 BA; Firefighter; Fire Dept. City of NY, 1261 Morris Ave., Bronx, NY 10463, 718 430-0292; r. 11 Spruce Hill Ln., Goshen, NY 10924, 914 651-2186. e-mail

CIAVARELLA, Joanne; '89 BS; 20941 35th Ave., Fl. 41, Bayside, NY 11361.

CICCARELLO, Linda F.; '78 BS; 1779 West Rd. # 3, Mohegan Lake, NY 10547, 914 528-8302.

CICCHESI, Cynthia M.; '96 BA; 930 Neill Ave., Bronx, NY 10462, 718 409-3906.

CICCONE, Frank; '93 BS; 5043 42nd St., Long Island City, NY 11104.

CICCONE, Joseph F.; '76 BS; 705 Westchester Ave., Port Chester, NY 10573, 914 526-8413.

CICCOTELLI, Richard; '91 BS; 245 E. 238th St., Bronx, NY 10470.

CICERO, Alethea U.; '98 BA; Communications Asst.; Thomas Publishing; r. 644 E. 88th St., Brooklyn, NY 11236, 718 649-8273. e-mail

CICHON, Michael; '85 MA; 164 Schenck Cir., Hewlett, NY 11557.

CID, Maria; '97 MS; 47-52 44 St. #C, Woodside, NY 11377.

CIEPIERSKI, Joseph R.; '80 BS; 195 Bedell Ave., Staten Island, NY 10307, 718 984-0206.

CIHAN, Nerkiz; '93 BS; 3248 81st St., Flushing, NY 11370.

CILIONE, Jeffery; '93 BA; 229 67th St. # 1, Brooklyn, NY 11220.

CILLA, Peter A.; '77 BA; 33-27 753 St., Flushing, NY 11354.

CILLA, Veronica M.; '81 BS; 3725 Henry Hud Pkw, Bronx, NY 10463, 718 601-4722.

CIMORELLI, Gary H.; '81 MA; 22 Cedar Rd, Pompton Plains, NJ 07444.

CINI, Robert A.; '83 BA; 28-02 36th Ave., Long Island City, NY 11106, 718 565-5081.

CINNAMO, Vincent; '83 BA; 5240 69th St., Flushing, NY 11378.

CINQUEMANI, Joseph; '78 BS; 245 Betsy Ross Dr., Orangeburg, NY 10962.

CINTI, John A.; '75 BS; Pleasant Valley Dr., Brodheadsville, PA 18322.

CINTRON, Angela; '79 BS; 10118 224th St., Queens Vlg., NY 11429.

CINTRON, Anita; '97 BS; AS LaGuardia Clg.; Proj. Mgr.; Nextel Communications; r. 32-32 54th St., Woodside, NY 11377, 718 726-3477.

CINTRON, Aracelis; '95 BS; 435 E. 105th Str, New York, NY 10029.

CINTRON, David; '95 BA; 245 E 149th St., Apt. 2G, Bronx, NY 10451, 718 239-9887.

CINTRON, Dolores; '96 BA; 128 Ft. Washington Ave., New York, NY 10032.

CINTRON, Donna M.; '96 BA MA; Forensic Psychotherapist; r. 435 W. 57th St. #15N, New York, NY 10019, 212 358-5711.

CINTRON, Edwin; '98 BS; 1641 Andrews Ave. 3a, Bronx, NY 10453, 718 931-8331.

CINTRON, Yvette; '94 BS; 74 Bodine St., Staten Island, NY 10310, 718 816-0361.

CINTRON, Yvonne; '77 BA; 352 E 139th St. Apt. 2w, Bronx, NY 10454, 718 931-8331.

CIORCIARI, David J.; '80 BS; AB Queensborough Clg.; Sgt.; New York Police Dept., Special Investigation Division, New York, NY 10007, 212 374-0320; r. 5753 65th St., Maspeth, NY 11378, 718 894-3973; *Eileen B.;* Nicole M., Annamarie R.

CIPRI, Anthony J.; '95 BS; 7014 58th Rd # 1, Flushing, NY 11378, 718 347-3001.

CIPRIANO, Vincent; '99 BA MA; 274 Mott St. 2C, New York, NY 10012, 212 431-7038.

CIRILLO, Maria D.; '99 BS; 35 Gerrymander Dr., Centerport, NY 11721, 631 754-2660.

CIRINGIONE, Frank J.; '88 BS; Criminal Investigator; US Immigration, 26 Federal Plz., New York, NY 10278, 212 264-5725; r. 33 Adams Ct., Westwood, NJ 07675.

CISEK, Mary T.; '93 BA; 619 58th St., Brooklyn, NY 11220, 718 439-8270.

CISNEROS, Albert E.; '77 BS; 19 Central Dr., Mill Valley, CA 94941, 415 331-2074.

CISSE, Sanah, (Sanah Abdul-Kareem); '85 BS; MED UMASS; Asst. Resident Dir/ Conference Coord; Univ. of MA, POB 157, Amherst, MA 01004; r. 790 Concourse Village, Bronx, NY 10451, 718 538-8233; *Mahmoud;* Idris, Suhailah, Jibril, Jahan. e-mail

CITRON, Mary; '76; 40 First Ave., New York, NY 10009.

CIUZIO, Maria; '77 BA; 2081 Fatzler Rd, Melbourne, FL 32935.

CIUZIO, Richard G.; '78 BS; Ins. Agt.; Knights of Columbus, 1230 Weeping Willow Ln., Rockledge, FL 32955, 321 632-5116; r. same; *Donna Lee;* Ricky, Lacey, Billy. e-mail

CIVELLO, Joseph S.; '83 BA; 62 Delano Ct., New Hyde Park, NY 11040, 516 488-2607.

CIVITANO, Danielle L.; '95 BS; MA Lehman Clg.; Elem. Tchr.; CS150, Bronx, NY 10451; r. 628 Leland Ave., Bronx, NY 10473, 718 589-8810; Brianna, Angelique.

CLABBY, William F.; '82 BS; Fordham Univ. Sch. of SW; Police Ofcr.; Bicycle Patrol, 114 Pct., Astoria, NY 11103, 718 626-9311; r. 87-67 254th St., Bellerose, NY 11426, 718 962-7005; *Margaret;* Brendan, Bridget.

CLAHAR, Winwell; '97 BA; 1105 College Ave., Bronx, NY 10456, 718 293-3287.

CLANCY, James T.; '76 BS; 33 Carman Ave., E. Meadow, NY 11554.

CLANCY, William C.; '66 BS, '75 MA; Retired-Prof. of Crim. Justice; John Jay Clg. of Criminal Justice; r. 32 Mansfield Dr., Brick, NJ 08724, 732 458-6877.

CLAPP, Michelle D.; '95 BS, Asst. Dir. for Budget & Admin. Svc; NYU, 22 Washington Sq. N., New York, NY 10011, 212 998-4516; r. 825 Boynton Ave. # 1, Apt. 12f, Bronx, NY 10473, 718 893-6345. e-mail

CLARK, Christopher; '96 BS; 14-17 31st Rd., Astoria, NY 11106, 718 335-6310.

CLARK, Damaris X.; '86 BA; 1566 Macombs Rd, Bronx, NY 10452, 718 590-4486.

CLARK, Dennis P.; '75 BS; 111 Rosedale Rd, Colonial Hts., NY 10710, 914 693-8443.

CLARK, Georganna; '88 BA; 280 Pk Hill Ave. #24, Staten Island, NY 10304, 718 966-7547.

CLARK, Gerald C., Jr.; '85 MA; BA Edinboro Univ. of PA; Special Agt.; FBI, 200 W. 2nd St., Rm. 411, Dayton, OH 45402, 937 222-7485; r. same, 937 512-1934; *Danielle;* Michael, Jake.

CLARK, James; '78 BS; 19 Taunton St., Staten Island, NY 10306, 718 979-2428.

CLARK, Jeffrey W.; '89 BS; 1186 Debra Dr., Linden, NJ 07036, 908 925-4794.

CLARK, John B.; '77 MPA; 3800 Waldo Ave., Bronx, NY 10463, 718 548-5251.

CLARK, John L.; '77 BA; 22-04 157 St., Flushing, NY 11357, 718 528-0971.

CLARK, John W.; '78 BA; 160 Bannon Pl., Massapequa Park, NY 11762, 516 798-8532.

CLARK, Joseph F.; '75 MA; 5 Meadowbrook Ln., Cedar Grove, NJ 07009.

CLARK, Kevin M.; '80 BS; Police Ofcr.; NYC Police Dept., 1 Police Plz., 44 DCT 2E 169th st., New York, NY 10038, 718 590-5504; r. 40 W Mosholu Pkwy. S. 14A, Bronx, NY 10468, 718 295-3069. e-mail

CLARK, Kevin P.; '92 BS; 321 Union Ave. PH, Mt. Vernon, NY 10550, 716 893-6393.

CLARK, Mark; '92 AS, '95 BS; Correction Ofcr.; NYC Dept. of Corrections, Brooklyn, NY 11203; r. POB 130375, Brooklyn, NY 11213, 718 756-1154. e-mail

CLARK, Ramsey; Ramsey Clark, Atty., 36 E. 12th St., New York, NY 10003, 212 475-3232; r. 37 W 12 St., New York, NY 10011, 212 989-6613; *Georgia.*

CLARK, Rhonda C.; '80 BS; 2423 Ericsson St., Flushing, NY 11369, 718 471-4326.

CLARK, Shalima; '99 BA; 61-25 97th St. #4C, Rego Park, NY 11374, 718 760-2169.

CLARK, Veronica V. '94 (See Buggs, Mrs. Veronica V.).

CLARK, William D.; '89 BS; 29 Ira Ct., Brooklyn, NY 11229.

CLARK, William R.; '66 AAS, '69 BS, '75 MPA; Retired Police Officer; NYC; r. 53-19 80th St., Flushing, NY 11373, 718 457-1618; *Kathleen M.*

CLARKE, Al-yeru; '96 BA; 1217 E 83rd St., Brooklyn, NY 11236, 718 342-0038.

CLARKE, Barry R.; '93 BS; New York Law Sch.; Deputy Clerk of The Cnty.; NY Civil Courts, 1011 Centre St., New York, NY 10013, 212 374-8433; r. 510 E 17th St., Brooklyn, NY 11226, 718 856-2328; *Thomasena;* Ronald, Zenobya, Zachary. e-mail

CLARKE, Charmaine; '94 BA; 2110 1st Ave. Apt. 413, New York, NY 10029, 315 896-2512.

CLARKE, Cleveland; '96 BS; 14121 247th St., # 21, Rosedale, NY 11422, 516 767-0467.

CLARKE, Denise L.; '88 BA; Ofc. Administrator; Family Ct. Mental Health Svcs., Bronx, NY 10451; r. 1565 Odell St. Apt. 3e, Bronx, NY 10462, 718 863-9047.

CLARKE, James G.; '76 BS; 19 Taunton St., Staten Island, NY 10306, 718 979-2428.

CLARKE, Joan B.; '93 BS; CERT. Long Island Univ.; Paralegal; Bronx Dist. Atty's. Ofc., 215 E. 161 St., Bronx, NY 10451, 718 590-2553; r. 4256 Monticello Ave., Bronx, NY 10466.

CLARKE, John; '85 MPA; 186 Wellbrook Ave., Staten Island, NY 10314, 718 317-0976.

CLARKE, Justin H.; '95 BS; Microsoft Systs. Engr.; r. 239 E 57th St., Brooklyn, NY 11203, 718 629-6297.

CLARKE, Kathleen O.; '77 BS; 56 E 55th St., Brooklyn, NY 11203, 718 771-6111.

CLARKE, Kert L.; '97 BS; 13-34 Gipson St., Far Rockaway, NY 11691, 718 544-5488.

CLARKE, Lateacha S.; '97 BS; 3 Hurley Ct., Far Rockaway, NY 11691, 718 471-0195.

CLARKE, Laura; '99 MA; 47 Riverbend Dr., North Brunswick, NJ 08902, 732 940-9113.

CLARKE, Lois G.; '77 BA; 843 C Linwood St., Brooklyn, NY 11208, 718 421-3614.

CLARKE, Lynn A.; '80 BA; 405 Jefferson Ave., Brooklyn, NY 11221, 718 421-3614.

CLARKE, Michelle Y.; '81 MA; 475 Crown St., Brooklyn, NY 11225, 718 257-0813.

CLARKE, Ms. Nicole A.; '97 BS; AAS Westchester Comm Clg.; Child Protective Spec.; Admin. for Children's Svcs., 150 William St., New York, NY 10038, 212 676-7126; r. 139 Belknap Ave., Yonkers, NY 10710, 914 217-7632. e-mail

CLARKE, Nicole L.; '99 BA; Editor; r. 270 Parkside Ave. C1E, Brooklyn, NY 11226, 718 826-3776.

CLARKE, Nuria E.; '93 BA; Svc. Coord.; Theracare of NY, 26 Ct. Str, Ext. 223, Brooklyn, NY 11242, 718 625-4055; r. 150 Crown St., Apt. D14, Brooklyn, NY 11225, 718 778-0896; *Levy Fargharson;* Jalen. e-mail

CLARKE, Rosanna; '99 BA; Tchr.; PS 191, Brooklyn, NY 11201; r. 1655 Flatbush Ave., B1207, Brooklyn, NY 11210; *Juergen Tempel.*

CLARKE, Selwart R.; '89 BS; 519 W 150th St., New York, NY 10031, 212 694-3558.

CLARKE, Sheena D.; '81 BA; 198 2nd St., Englewood, NJ 07631.

CLARKE, Thomas J.; '76 BS; 3308 Avenue R, Brooklyn, NY 11234, 718 331-6317.

CLARKE, Thomas M.; '80 BS; 713 Hollywood Ave., Bronx, NY 10465, 718 405-0624.

CLARKE, Winston M.; '72 BA; 5480 Broadway, Bronx, NY 10463, 718 597-8387.

CLARO, Brian K.; '87 BS; 128 Champlain Ave., Staten Island, NY 10306.

CLAUDIO, Luis E.; '92 BS; 694 E 149th St. Apt. 17a, Bronx, NY 10455, 718 653-9630.

CLAUDIO, Roberto; '95 BS; 1645 Grand Concourse Apt. 3k, Bronx, NY 10452.

CLAUSE, Smyrna E.; '78 BA; 225-11 144 Ave., Rosedale, NY 11422.

CLAUSEN, Vincent J.; '74 BS; MPA Southeastern Univ., JD Reynaldo Garza SOL; Asst. Dist. Dir.; US Immigration & Naturalization Svc., 1545 Hawkins Blvd., Ste. 167, El Paso, TX 79925, 915 225-1828; r. 1921 Sun Tide Dr., El Paso, TX 79938, 915 857-2863; *Sonia.* e-mail

CLAVELL, Louis F.; '72 BS; 158-04 Cryders Ln., Beechhurst, NY 11357, 718 746-6130.

CLAY, Eugene S.; '85 BA; 247 W. 61st Dr., New York, NY 10023, 315 797-4351.

CLAY, Kareem; '99 BS; 1416 Nelson Ave. 4J, Bronx, NY 10452.

CLAYTON, James O.; '83 BS; Investigator; NYS Ins. Fraud Bur., 25 Beaver St., New York, NY 10004, 212 580-5880; r. 3843 Amundson Ave., Bronx, NY 10466, 718 994-3944. e-mail

CLEARY, Michael J.; '80 BS; 14 Hill St., Ronkonkoma, NY 11779, 631 738-7256.

CLEATON, Larry C.; '93 BS; 1940 E. Tremont, Bronx, NY 10462.

CLEMENTE, Michael A.; '89 BS; 1732 E 37th St., Brooklyn, NY 11234, 718 599-3472.

CLEMENTS, Lavonda D.; '88 BS; Sr. Court Ofcr.; Bronx Supreme Ct., 851 Grand Concourse, Bronx, NY 10451, 718 590-3704; r. 560 Lenox Ave. Apt. 1 S, New York, NY 10037, 212 926-8523; Giavonni. e-mail

CLEMENTS, Shirley; '81 BA; POB 640, Bronx, NY 10466.

CLERICO, Lucien T.; '80 MPA; BA Richmond Clg.; Deputy Chief Clerk; Surrogate Ct., 262 Old Country Rd, Mineola, NY 11501; r. 870 N Fletcher Ave., Valley Stream, NY 11580, 516 561-1690. e-mail

CLERMONT, Maxim; '92 BA; 86-04 Grand Ave. #6, Elmhurst, NY 11373.

CLEVELAND, Alfonzie; '76 BA; 645 Westchester Ave. Apt. 8c, Bronx, NY 10455.

CLIFFORD, Maria C., (Maria Cadicamo); '77 BA; MAT Rollins Clg.; Elem. Sch. Tchr.; John F. Turner Sr. Elem. Sch., 3175 Jupiter Blvd., Palm Bay, FL 32909, 321 676-5700; r. 2081 Fatzler Rd, Melbourne, FL 32935, 321 242-0733; Donald; Ricky, D.J., Danielle. e-mail

CLIFFORD, Timothy J.; '79 MPA; 196-38 Pompell Ave., Holliswood, NY 11423.

CLINE, James; '73 MS; 31 W 8th St., Bayonne, NJ 07002.

CLINTON, Brian J.; '74 BS, '77 MPA; AS New York Community Clg.; Retired Asst. Chief of Dept.; NYC Fire Dept.; r. 711 Wedelia Dr., Barefoot Bay, FL 32976, 561 664-4252.

CLINTON, Linda M.; '80 BA; 1010 Janet Dr., Lakeland, FL 33805.

CLIVE, Laurence E.; '80 BS; 19 Henry Ct., Dobbs Ferry, NY 10522, 914 693-0819.

CLOTTER, Nelly; '99 BA; 454 S. First Ave., Mt. Vernon, NY 10550, 914 668-3452; Steven Bush, J. Anthony Davi, Iman Davis.

CLOUDEN, George; '87 BS; Capt.; New York Police Dept., 1925 Bath Ave., Brooklyn, NY 11214, 718 236-2270; r. 277 Macon St., Brooklyn, NY 11216, 718 771-6247.

CLOUGH, Francis; '95 AS; 17612 134th Ave., Jamaica, NY 11434, 718 961-2195.

CLOWES, Eric J.; '98 BS; 528 Nariticong Ave., Hopatcong, NJ 07843, 973 398-4669.

CLUE, Denese A.; '95 BA; 385 Bayview Ave. # 9, Inwood, NY 11096, 516 371-1108.

CLYDE, Nicole; '98 BS; 111 52 145 St., Jamaica, NY 11435, 718 657-7029.

COAKLEY, Daniel P.; '73 BS; MS Long Island Univ.; Fraud Investigator; Apple Bank for Savings, 277 Park Ave., New York, NY 10172; r. Box 151, RFD 5, Mahopac, NY 10541, 914 628-3016.

COAKLEY, Lorianne; '95 BS; Front Line Mgr. of Finance; US Postal Svc., 909 3rd Ave., New York, NY 10022, 212 330-5597; r. 525 E 143rd St. Apt. 2a, Bronx, NY 10454, 718 292-0791; Anthony Pratt Sr; Anthony PrattJr.

COATES, John R., Jr.; '86 BS; Police Ofcr.; NYC Police Dept., 1 Police Plz., New York, NY 10038; r. 37 Capitol Dr., Washingtonville, NY 10992; Consuelo; Kevin, Kayla.

COAXUM, Stacey S.; '96 MA; 1050 E 222nd St., Bronx, NY 10469, 718 654-2520.

COAXUM, Teresa (Teri); '93 BA, '94 CERT, 2000 MPA; PARADIPL NYU, MCC Medger Evers; Community Relations Spec.; Kings Cnty. Dist. Atty's Ofc., Renaissance Plz., 350 Jay St., Brooklyn, NY 11201, 718 250-4906; r. 1188 Remsen Ave., Brooklyn, NY 11236, 718 342-9432; Jarranda, Carle'. e-mail

COBB, Mrs. Mamie O.; '95 BS; AA Hostos Community Clg.; Child Protective Spec.; Admin. for Children Svcs., 150 William St., 192 E. 151st St., Bronx, NY 10451, 718 579-9290; r. 335 E 166th St. Apt. 1e, Bronx, NY 10456, 718 992-7496; Natasha McCants.

COBB, Michael A.; '89 BA; 836 Tilden St., #4A, Bronx, NY 10467, 315 866-3224.

COBIA, Reuben T.; '95 BS; 507 E 5th St. Apt. 8, New York, NY 10009.

COCCHI, John A.; '95 AS; 328 9th St., W. Babylon, NY 11704.

COCKBURN, George A.; '72 BS; MA SUNY-Albany; Dir. of Public & Alumni Affairs; John Jay Clg. of Criminal Justice, 899 10th Ave., New York, NY 10019, 212 237-8427; r. 34 Ledgewood Commons, Millwood, NY 10546, 914 923-0402; Andrea, Kristyn, Erik. e-mail

COCOROS, Denise; '93 MA; 2127 35th St., Long Island City, NY 11105.

COCOZZA, Joseph T.; '98 AS; 1123 Calhoun Ave., Bronx, NY 10465.

CODISPOTI, Michael; '81 BS; Owner; Soar Video, 5 Tudor City Pl., Apt. B20, New York, NY 10017, 212 983-2983; r. same. e-mail

CODLING, Omar; '95 BS; 5202 Tilden Ave., Brooklyn, NY 11203, 718 346-3891.

CODRINGTON, Paula A.; '94 BS; Legal Secy.; Fidelity Natl. Title Ins. Co. of NY, 2 Park Ave., New York, NY 10016, 212 481-5858; r. 1275 E. 82nd St., Brooklyn, NY 11236, 718 241-1260; Treston. e-mail

CODRINGTON, Randolph; '87 BA; 2400-13 Hunter Ave. #13D, Bronx, NY 10475, 718 671-1760.

CODY, Gayle L.; '82 BS; 179-29 Zoller Rd., Jamaica, NY 11434, 718 461-5482.

CODY, Thomas E.; '90 BS; 36 Evans St., Staten Island, NY 10314, 718 351-8592.

COELLO, Marjorie I.; '99 BA; Student; r. 26-23 91st St., E. Elmhurst, NY 11369, 718 478-3386. e-mail

COFER, Sherlene L.; '79 BS; 789 E 211 St., Bronx, NY 10467.

COFFEY, Thomas K.; '89 BS; Lt. Police Ofcr.; NYC Police, New York, NY 10001, 718 963-5307; r. 13212 114th St., Jamaica, NY 11420, 718 835-3624.

COFFRAN, William J.; '95 BS; 41 Broadway, Ronkonkoma, NY 11779.

COGHLAN, Grace; '96 BS; 3911 62nd St. Apt. 4, Flushing, NY 11377.

COHANE, Miriam B.; '79 BS; 16 Marine Ave., Lindenhurst, NY 11757.

COHEN, Amy B.; '80 BS; 711 E 79th St., Brooklyn, NY 11236, 718 332-5013.

COHEN, Bonny A.; '78 BA; 31 Orleans Grn, Coram, NY 11727, 631 331-8276. e-mail

COHEN, David J.; '98 MA; BA Yeshiva Univ.; Investigator; USDOLOSHA, 201 Varick St. Rm. 670, New York, NY 10014, 917 953-6587; r. 260 Riverside Dr., Apt#9c, New York, NY 10025, 212 932-1471. e-mail

COHEN, David L.; '84 BS; Regional Investigator; UNUM Provident Corp., 522 US Hwy. 9 N., Box 316, Manalapan, NJ 07726, 732 972-5281; r. Marlboro, NJ 07746. e-mail

COHEN, Donna M.; '79 BA; 2140 Seward Ave., Bronx, NY 10473, 718 548-1031.

COHEN, Faith M.; '90 BA, '90 MA; Parole Ofcr./Mental Hlth Spec.; 77 PCT/ Rikers Island; r. 2165 Brigham St., Brooklyn, NY 11229, 718 474-1296.

COHEN, Fern; '80 MA; 154 Edgegrove Ave., Staten Island, NY 10312, 718 605-4220.

COHEN, Jacqueline; '97 BS; 1768 E 5th St., Brooklyn, NY 11223, 718 232-0113.

COHEN, Jeffrey L.; '74, '74 MA; BA Hunter Clg.; Court Clerk Spec.; Supreme Ct. Queens Cnty., NY, 88-11 Sutphin Blvd., Jamaica, NY 11435, 718 520-3100; r. 760 Elvira Ave., Far Rockaway, NY 11691, 718 471-2803.

COHEN, Karen; '95 BS; 1475 Townsend Ave., Bronx, NY 10452.

COHEN, Michael J.; '76 MA; 18 Everett Rd, Carmel, NY 10512.

COHEN, Rachel L.; '94 MA; Writer-Fiction; r. 26 North St., Great Barrington, MA 01230; Chris McDermott.

COHEN, Richard A.; '93 BS; 16140 90th St., Jamaica, NY 11414, 718 591-2690.

COHEN, Ronald; '79 BS; 17815 Northhagen Dr., Houston, TX 77084, 281 856-7480.

COHEN, Samuel; '75 MPA; BS NYU; Social Worker; Veteran's Admin., FDR Veteran's Hospital, Ext. 2742, Montrose, NY 10548, 914 737-4400; r. 202 Barrister Ct., Wyckoff, NJ 07481, 201 848-6828.

COHEN, Seymour J.; '77 BA; 149-19 82nd St., Howard Bch., NY 11414, 718 454-5667.

COHEN, Steven A.; '95 BA; 2070 Seward Ave. Apt. 7l, Bronx, NY 10473.

COHEN, Steven M.; '80 BS; 4 Brighton 10 Path, Brooklyn, NY 11235, 718 336-9760.

COHN, Jennifer I.; '99 MA; BS Univ. of Wisconsin; Forensic Social Work; The Legal Aid Society, 49 Thomas St., New York, NY 10013, 212 298-5045; r. 325 E. 48th St. #4D, New York, NY 10017, 212 755-2843. e-mail

COIRO, Robert M.; '83 BA; Capt.; NYC Police Dept., 1 Police Plz., New York, NY 10038; r. 12 Stonewall Ct., Warwick, NY 10990; Lili-Elyn; Mark. e-mail

COKER, Renee R.; '98 MPA; Probation Ofcr.; NYC Dept. of Probation; r. 1595 Unionport Rd. Apt.1e, Bronx, NY 10462, 718 409-1310. e-mail

COLASUONNO, Dominick; '89 BS; 1151 E. 10 St., Brooklyn, NY 11230, 718 258-3969.

COLASURDO, James F.; '96 MA; BA JOUR George Washington Univ., Ferkauf Grad. Sch Yeshiva; Student PsyD; r. 127 W 79th St. 6a, New York, NY 10024, 212 580-0892; Diane; Vito. e-mail

COLAVITA, Maria A.; '79 BA; 2 Laverne Ct., Wharton, NJ 07885.

COLCLOUGH, Andre W.; '98 BA; Police Ofcr.; NYC; r. 84 Evans Ave., Freeport, NY 11520, 516 223-5848. e-mail

COLE, Donald M.; '87 BA; 3739 Barnes Ave., Bronx, NY 10467, 718 601-2351.

COLE, Karen E.; '80 MPA; Secy.; r. 615 Western Ave., Albany, NY 12203, 518 438-4877.

COLE, Leslie, CPP; '81 MA; Security Cnslt.; Leslie Cole Assoc. Inc., 2204 Morris Ave. Ste. 301, Union, NJ 07083, 908 687-6376; r. 92 Crestview Ave., Vauxhall, NJ 07088, 908 687-5872; Sheila; Leslie Jr, Oniki. e-mail

COLE, Margie; '97 BS; 2588 7th Ave. #5, New York, NY 10039, 315 734-0758.

COLE, Opal A.; '83 BA; 1834 Andrews Ave. S, Bronx, NY 10453, 718 583-1321.

COLEMAN, Antoinetta; '96 BA; 143-24 232nd St., Springfield Gardens, NY 11413, 516 292-1832.

COLEMAN, Candance D.; '96 BA; 2407 7th Ave. #2, New York, NY 10030, 315 831-9772.

COLEMAN, Charles E.; '80 BS; MS CUNY, JD St. Johns Univ.; Prof.; NYC Technical Clg., 300 Jay St., Brooklyn, NY 11201, 718 260-5124; r. 271 Lewis Ave., Brooklyn, NY 11221, 718 443-0733. e-mail

COLEMAN, Edmond D.; '85 BA; 1133 Ogden Ave., Bronx, NY 10452, 718 295-3189.

COLEMAN, Eunice '82 (See Anderson, Eunice T.).

COLEMAN, Frieda; Owner/Agt.; Coleman Real Estate Co., 7928 Orchid Ave., Norfolk, VA 23518.

COLEMAN, James J.; '77 BA; Retired Police Ofcr./Assoc. Securit; Goldman Sachs; r. 9601Shore Rd. #6F, Brooklyn, NY 11209, 718 745-4958.

COLEMAN, Joseph W.; '90 BS; 1524 1st Ave. Apt. 4n, New York, NY 10021, 212 879-2161.

COLEMAN, Linda C.; '91 BS; 1100 Madison Ave., New York, NY 10028, 315 831-9772.

COLEMAN, Philip W.; '82 BA; 45 Seabring St., Spring Vly., NY 10977, 914 352-8229.

COLEMAN, Shermelle; '98 BA; 413 W. 147th St., New York, NY 10031, 212 926-5974.

COLEMAN, William E.; '76 BA; 65 Union Ave., Staten Island, NY 10303, 718 442-7882.

COLEY, Anthony G.; '90 BS; 530 Taylor Ave., Bronx, NY 10473.

COLEY, Helen; '95 BA; POB 195, Brooklyn, NY 11233, 718 421-5307.

COLEY, Takiya Y.; '97 BS; 363 New York Ave., Brooklyn, NY 11213, 718 385-8036.

COLGAN, George J.; '79 BA; 6 Lathrop Ln. Apt. F, Rocky Hill, CT 06067.

COLICCI, Gerald P.; '79 BS; MBA Clg. of Ins.; Pres.; SPC Investigations, Inc., 9 Inwood St., Yonkers, NY 10704, 914 423-5676; r. same; Jean M.; Gregory. e-mail

COLITTI, Madeline; '78 BS; 84-20 55th Ave., Elmhurst, NY 11373.

COLL, Thomas F.; '77 BA; 1118 E 32 St., Brooklyn, NY 11210, 718 221-8013.

COLLADO, Ms. Giselle M.; '96 BA; Police Ofcr.; NYC Police Dept.; r. 3717 108th St., Flushing, NY 11368, 718 476-2698. e-mail

COLLADO, Olga '90 (See Alcantara, Mrs. Olga).

COLLAZO, Antonio; '91 BS; Lt.; NYC Police Dept., 917 451-8700; r. 6047 Catalpa Ave., Ridgewood, NY 11385, 718 497-5661. e-mail

COLLAZO, Desiree '93 (See Collazo-soto, Ms. Desiree).

COLLAZO, Diana; '88 BA; 453 Beach 138th St., Far Rockaway, NY 11694, 718 474-8663.

COLLAZO, Fredeswinda; '96 BS; 16 Madeline Ter., Chestnut Ridge, NY 10977, 914 359-5861.

COLLAZO, Marisol; '97 BA; 94-09 95th St., Ozone Park, NY 11416.

COLLAZO-SOTO, Ms. Desiree, (Desiree Collazo); '93 BS; MS Fairleigh Dickinson; Account Exec.; Bradford Licensing Assoc., 209 Cooper Ave., Upper Montclair, NJ 07043, 973 509-0200; r. 159 New Jersey Ave., Bergenfield, NJ 07621, 201 384-3446; Michael Soto. e-mail

COLLETTI, C.; '94 MA; 643 E. 13th St., New York, NY 10009.

COLLICA, Kimberly A.; '97 BA; Care Coord.; Women's Prison Assn., Bedford Hls., NY 10507; r. Spring Vly., NY 10977, 914 426-7406. e-mail

COLLIER, Dyral; '82 BS; 575 Macdonough St., Brooklyn, NY 11233, 718 453-1070.

COLLIGAN, Mary E.; '75 BS; 1576 W 4th St., Brooklyn, NY 11204, 718 259-0379.

COLLINS, Barbara W.; '96 MS; BS SUNY; Production Mgr.; Millwood, NY 10546; r. Mahopac, NY 10541.

COLLINS, Bashiek M.; '96 AS; 1415 Bristow St. # 4, Bronx, NY 10459, 718 328-3478.

COLLINS, Cassandra L.; '85 BS; 150 W. 225th St., Bronx, NY 10463, 718 920-1393.

COLLINS, Clive M.; '97 BA; 1147 Anderson Ave. Apt#CC, Bronx, NY 10452, 718 920-1393.

COLLINS, Elliot; '91 BS; Communication Cnslt.; Bell Atlantic, 175 W. Main St., Freehold, NJ 07728, 908 717-1354; r. 6005 Hana Rd, Edison, NJ 08817, 732 819-7743. e-mail

COLLINS, Falisha R.; '97 BS; 75 Hill St. Apt. # 4N, Staten Island, NY 10304, 718 727-4933.

COLLINS, Gail M.; '75 BA; 2340 E 15th St., Brooklyn, NY 11229, 718 346-3197.

COLLINS, H. C.; 151-05 32 Ave., Flushing, NY 11354, 718 805-1199.

COLLINS, Jeremiah; '84 BS; POB 735, Remsenburg, NY 11960.

COLLINS, Kellis; '92 CERT, '92 BS; 329 Knickerbocker, Brooklyn, NY 11237, 718 837-6407.

COLLINS, Kevin P.; '90 BS; 8301 W Charleston Blvd. Apt. 2050, Las Vegas, NV 89117, 212 569-0827.

COLLINS, Louis H.; '99 BA; 3402 Gunther Ave., Bronx, NY 10469, 718 965-5040.

COLLINS, Michael; '90 AS, '93 MA; NYPD-Inspector; New York Police Dept., Detective Boro Manhattan, 230 E. 21 St., New York, NY 10010, 212 477-7747; r. 468 59 St., Brooklyn, NY 11220, 718 439-0917; Michael, James. e-mail

COLLINS, Michael J.; '72 BS; 26 Cambridge Ave., Garden City, NY 11530, 516 437-5649.

COLLINS, Ruby A.; '93 BA; 580 E 22nd St. Apt. 9, Brooklyn, NY 11226, 718 573-4076.

COLLINS, Stephen P.; '98 MA; BA SUNY Stony Brook; Firefighter; Scarsdale Fire Dept., 51 Tompkins Rd, Scarsdale, NY 10583, 914 722-1215; r. 62 Tunstall Rd, Scarsdale, NY 10583, 914 723-3097; Brendan.

COLLINS, Tara '96 (See Constant, Tara).

COLLINS, Timothy K.; '84 AS, '90 BS, '99 MA; 425 101st St. # A1, Brooklyn, NY 11209, 718 921-0791.

COLLORAFI, Mrs. Lyz S., (Lyz Palza); '98 BA; Victim Advocate/Couns.; El Paso Ctr. On Family Violence, 3800 N Piedras, Ste. C, El Paso, TX 79930, 915 562-0077; r. 345 Shadow Mtn Dr. Apt. 1413, El Paso, TX 79912, 915 845-7488; Michael. e-mail

COLON, Ana R., (Ana R. Carrion); '99 BS; Legal Secy.; Kleinberg, Caplan, Wolff & Cohen, 551 5th Ave., New York, NY 10176, 212 986-6000; r. 18 Crosby Ave. 2/Fl., Brooklyn, NY 11207, 718 348-6074; Edwin R.; Carlos, Raquel. e-mail

COLON, Anthony B.; '97 BS; ROR Interviewer; Criminal Justice Agcy., Bronx Criminal Courthouse, 215 E 161st St., Bronx, NY 10451; r. 2150 Ellis Ave., Bronx, NY 10462, 718 829-8386. e-mail

COLON, Bernardo; '92 BS; 472 Suydam St., Brooklyn, NY 11237, 718 891-6021.

COLON, Camille; '80 MA; 305 Riverside Dr., New York, NY 10025.

COLON, Carlos; '96 MA; 4410 Broadway Apt. 1f, New York, NY 10040, 212 569-2458.

COLON, Carlos A.; '97 BA, '98 BA; 30-57 32nd St., Astoria, NY 11102, 718 205-1138.

COLON, Carlos J.; '79 BS; 2764 Paulding Ave., Bronx, NY 10469, 718 583-9612.

COLON, Diana A.; '89 BS; Investigator; Civilian Complaint Review Bd., 40 Rector St. 2nd Fl., New York, NY 10006, 212 422-8790; r. 241 W. 62nd St. #6E, New York, NY 10023; *Victor Felton;* Michael David, Lisa Levina, Precious, Jonathan.

COLON, Elizabeth; '97 BA; 920 Vermont St., Brooklyn, NY 11207, 718 642-8304.

COLON, Gregory; '96 BA; Investigator; r. 4311 National St., Flushing, NY 11368, 718 426-7749. e-mail

COLON, Hector E.; '95 BS; LAN Admin.; Comcast, 800 Rahway Ave., Union, NJ 07083, 908 851-8330; r. 89 Troy Dr. Apt. C, Springfield, NJ 07081, 973 218-0655; *Maria;* Javier. e-mail

COLON, Helen; '91 BA; Correction Ofcr.; NYC Dept. Corrections, New York, NY 10001; r. 1 Lodge Ln., E. Setauket, NY 11733. e-mail

COLON, Jacqueline; '87 BS; 115 Schdes St., Brooklyn, NY 11206, 718 265-2554.

COLON, Jose M.; '96 BA; 33 Roman Acres Dr., Garnerville, NY 10923, 914 362-4380.

COLON, Jose M.; '97 BS; 100 Alcott Pl.#9l, Bronx, NY 10475, 718 563-4327.

COLON, Kazandra '96 (See Colon-Prezeau, Mrs. Kazandra V.).

COLON, Licelyn; '93 BS, '99 BA; Rsch. Coord.; Brooklyn Treatment Ct., 360 Adams St., Brooklyn, NY 11201, 718 643-8667; r. 4 Manhattan Ave. Apt. 4B, New York, NY 10025, 212 961-0919. e-mail

COLON, Ms. Luz; '93 BA; 3459 89th St. Apt. 1f, Flushing, NY 11372, 718 205-1138.

COLON, Mary; '83 BS; 85 Decker Ave., Staten Island, NY 10302, 718 967-5126.

COLON, Mirna E.; '95 MA; 1314 W. Farms Rd., Bronx, NY 10459, 718 292-9286.

COLON, Monica; '95 BS; Inmate Systs. Ofcr.; Fed. Bur. of Prisons, Dept. of Justice, Brooklyn, NY 11201; r. 9275 Ft. Hamilton Pkwy. #B2D, Brooklyn, NY 11209, 718 921-7064. e-mail

COLON, Monique; '92 BS; 2147 Clinton Ave. # P, Bronx, NY 10457, 718 292-9286.

COLON, Nancy; '83 BS; 28-07 Steinway St., Long Island City, NY 11103, 718 523-0456.

COLON, Nelson; '80 BA; 218 E 104th St. Apt. 4c, New York, NY 10029.

COLON, Norma I.; '77 BA; Labor Svc. Rep.; NY State Dept. of Labor, Albany, NY 12201, 917 305-4410; r. 140 Columbia St. Apt. 11 E, New York, NY 10002, 212 533-4564; *Nelson;* Amelia, Nelson, Gabriel.

COLON, Oswald; '96 BA; 365 Thatford Ave., Brooklyn, NY 11212, 718 891-6021.

COLON, Rafael E.; '98 BA; 709 Union St. 4l, Brooklyn, NY 11215, 718 638-7028.

COLON, Reinaldo; '77 BS; 7100 Kennedy Blvd. E, W. New York, NJ 07093.

COLON, Robert G.; '73 BS; AS Farmingdale; Security Mgr.; Ina Check Cashing; r. 1823 Avenue X, Brooklyn, NY 11235, 718 769-7585; Robert Jr, Christopher. e-mail

COLON, Rubina; '91 BS; MS Central MI Univ.; Jamaica, NY 11422, 800 466-6493; r. 25339 149th Dr., Jamaica, NY 11422.

COLON, Sandy T.; '97 BA; ACS Caseworker; City of NY; r. 1516 Plimpton Ave., Bronx, NY 10452, 718 731-2758.

COLON, Sophie M.; '86 BS; 611 Crotona Park N Apt. 10g, Bronx, NY 10457, 718 822-3668.

COLON, Walter; '81 BS; 20-35 Crescent St., Long Island City, NY 11105.

COLON, Wendy C.; '99 BS; Police Ofcr.; NYPD; r. 724 E. 6th St.(#2A), New York, NY 10009, 212 674-8367. e-mail

COLON, Yesenia; '95 BA; 395 Oliver Pl., Bronx, NY 10458.

COLONNELLO, Karen A.; '92 BA, '99 MA; Detective-Polygraphist; Nassau Cnty. Police Dept., 1490 Franklin Ave., Mineola, NY 11501, 516 573-7746; r. 51 Wyanet St., Selden, NY 11784, 631 732-8683. e-mail

COLON-PREZEAU, Mrs. Kazandra V., (Kazandra Colon); '96 MA; BA St. Johns Univ.; Fraud Investigator; Bur. of Fraud Investigations, 60 Hudson St., 8th Fl., New York, NY 10013, 212 274-5559; r. 196-52 67th Ave. Apt. 1, Fresh Meadows, NY 11365, 718 264-7203; *Stanley Prezeau.* e-mail

COLON-RAMOS, CAPT Miguel A.; '80 AS, '81 BS; MSA Central Michigan Univ.; NYC Dept. of Corrections, 14-14 Hazen St., E. Elmhurst, NY 11370, 516 662-6300; r. 114 Morris Ave., Malverne, NY 11565; *Palmira.*

COLUCCI, Jooann '75 (See Colucci-Turbett, Joann).

COLUCCI-TURBETT, Joann, (Jooann Colucci); '75 BA, '79 MA; Kean Clg; Fraud Investigator; Union Cnty. Bd. of Social Svc., 342 Westminster Ave., Elizabeth, NJ 07208, 908 965-2750; r. 701 Keep St., Linden, NJ 07036, 908 925-9834; William. e-mail

COLUMNA, Walter E.; '97 BS; 565 W 175th St., New York, NY 10033.

COLVILLE, Lorraine R.; 132 Thompson St. Apt. 4, New York, NY 10012, 212 260-6053.

COLVIN, Bernard W.; '94 BS; AS St. Johns Univ., AS Natl. Paralegal Inst.; Security Ofcr.; Beau Diethl & Assocs., 220 E. 42 St., 66-00 Long Island Expy., New York, NY 10017, 212 557-3334; r. 2 Jasmine Ln., Kings Park, NY 11754; *Christina;* Timothy. e-mail

COMADORE, Alberta; '80 BA; 170-12 130 Ave., Jamaica, NY 11434.

COMASTRI, Harold N.; '80 BS; Police Ofcr.-Hwy Div.; Lynbrook Police Dept., 1 Columbus Dr., Lynbrook, NY 11563, 516 599-3300; r. 5 Dean St., Lynbrook, NY 11563; *Donna;* Tara, Kaitlyn, Carissa. e-mail

COMENZO, Craig; '95 BS; 89 E 4th St., Deer Park, NY 11729.

COMMERFORD, Donald A.; '95 BS; 283 D Faller Dr., New Milford, NJ 07646, 201 265-6359.

COMMIKE, Eileen A., (Eileen Ulrich); '76 MPA; Sch. Social Worker; Ridgefield Park Bd. of Educ., Ridgefield Park, Ridgefield Park, NJ 07660; r. 51 Wilbur Rd # B, Bergenfield, NJ 07621; *Irving;* Laura, Myles.

COMNINEL, Irene D.; '99 BA; Svc. Coord.; Maranatha Human Svcs.; r. 47-20 44 St. Apt. 4, Woodside, NY 11377, 718 729-0636.

COMPERIATI, Joseph A.; '77 BS, AS; Retired; r. 60-49 59th Rd, Flushing, NY 11378; *Alice;* Joseph M., Daniel, Marianne, Michael, Alice M., Margaret, Elizabeth, Christopher.

CONBOY, Raymond C.; '92 MPA; Assoc. Staff Analyst; New York Police Dept., 1 Police Plz., New York, NY 10038, 212 374-6817; r. 1616 E 35th St., Brooklyn, NY 11234.

CONCANNON, John P.; '78 BS; 5309 Avenue O, Brooklyn, NY 11234, 718 253-7559.

CONCANNON, Joseph R.; '93 MPA; 8911 237th St., Jamaica, NY 11426, 718 347-0046.

CONCEPCION, Angel; '76 BA; Police Ofcr.; New York Police Dept.; r. 112 Hildreth Pl., Yonkers, NY 10704, 914 237-4764; *Linda;* Kaila, Brian.

CONCEPCION, Idaly; '89 BS; 2070 Grand Concourse, Bronx, NY 10457.

CONCEPCION, Dr. Lydia; '92 BS; Phys.; NY Presbyterian Hosp., 178 Ft. Washington Ave., New York, NY 10032, 917 899-4006; r. 2515 Poplar St., Bronx, NY 10461; *Jonie;* Jasmine Marines. e-mail

CONCEPCION, Magaly S.; '97 BA; Homemaker; r. 1188 Lake Victoria Dr., Apt. K, W. Palm Bch., FL 33411, 561 682-9614; Justin.

CONCEPCION, Melissa; '84 BS; 128-04 Gotham Rd, S. Ozone Park, NY 11420, 718 899-4493.

CONCHA, Hugo J.; '83 BS; 1350 NW 12th Ave., Miami, FL 33136, 305 742-7483.

CONDE, Matthew P.; '98 BS; Police Ofcr.; NYPD, 1 Police Plz., New York, NY 10038; r. 108 Rivington Ave., Staten Island, NY 10314, 718 727-3085. e-mail

CONDIOTTI, Irving; '76 BA; 1135 E. 59 St., Brooklyn, NY 11234.

CONDON, Richard J.; '78 MA; 126 8th St., Staten Island, NY 10306.

CONDON, Robert A.; '76 BS; 32 Arlene Ct., New City, NY 10956, 914 942-2134.

CONFINO, Sherry L.; '81 BS; 269 Jefferson Ave., Island Park, NY 11558, 516 466-6190.

CONFORT, Richard K.; '77 BS; 634 Vincent Ave., Bronx, NY 10465, 718 829-3137.

CONFORTI, Paul J.; '91 BS; BS; Sergeant; White Plains Police Dept., White Plains, NY 10602; r. 1231 Audra Ct., Mohegan Lake, NY 10547; *Louise Minutella;* Samantha M., Nicole M.

CONFUSIONE, Michael J.; '69 BA; 16 Van BurenStreetBx5011, Rocky Point, NY 11778.

CONIGLIO, Kenneth J.; '93 BS; 27387 Detroit Rd, Apt. J12, Westlake, OH 44145.

CONIGLIO, Mary J.; 2 Windsor Rd., Monroe, NY 10950, 914 496-2592.

CONKLIN, Jennifer M. '98 (See Conklin Tetor, Mrs. Jennifer M.).

CONKLIN TETOR, Mrs. Jennifer M., (Jennifer M. Conklin); '98 BA; AS Orange Cnty. Community; Ofc. Mgr.; Lento's Relocation, 2 Mill St., Cornwall, NY 12518, 914 534-2570; r. 7 Niles Rd, Patterson, NY 12563, 914 278-0273; *Eric Tetor*. e-mail

CONLEY, Nora; '94 BA; 25 Jackwill Rd, E. Patchogue, NY 11772.

CONLON, James T.; '77 BS, '83 MA; 10 Windmill Ln., New City, NY 10956.

CONLON, Joseph; '75 MA; 3 Washington Ave., Miller Place, NY 11764.

CONLON, Patricia A.; '92 BS; 3957 South St., Seaford, NY 11783, 516 783-7647.

CONLON, Peter J.; '72 BS; Retired Police Ofcr.; r. 2315 New Danville Pike, Conestoga, PA 17516, 717 872-0785; *Helen;* Rosemary, Peter Jr, Alice.

CONLON, Richard V.; '72 BA; Retired NYC Police Ofcr.; NYC Police Dept.; r. 24 Mellow Ln., Westbury, NY 11590, 516 338-0494.

CONNAUGHTON, Kenneth; '86 BA; 10434 88 Ave., Jamaica, NY 11418, 718 323-7657.

CONNELIE, William G.; '82 MA; POB 51, Sag Harbor, NY 11963.

CONNELLY, Karen T.; '84 MPA; BA Jersey City State Clg.; Resident Agt.-in-Charge; US Customs Svc., 6 World Trade Ctr., New York, NY 10048; r. 11 Alexandria Rd., Morristown, NJ 07960, 973 540-0639.

CONNELLY, Robert T.; '80 MPA; Retired Bronx Boroughs Mgr.; NYC Dept. of Environ. Protection; r. 225 Remington Cir., Tobyhanna, PA 18466, 570 894-3823; *Tara Donohue;* Christine. e-mail

CONNELLY, Susan; '86 BS; 8412 High Meadows, Plano, TX 75025.

CONNICK, Kathleen; '91 MA; 4 Lookout Pl., Ardsley, NY 10502, 914 693-2080.

CONNOLLY, Caitlin A.; '98 MA; 1081 North Ave., New Rochelle, NY 10804, 914 235-7880.

CONNOLLY, Charles P.; '76 MPA; 1st VP; Merrill Lynch, 222 Broadway, New York, NY 10038, 212 672-1052; r. 60 Cara Dr., Pearl River, NY 10965. e-mail

CONNOLLY, Daniel; '95 BS; 648 W Penn St., Long Beach, NY 11561, 516 432-7138.

CONNOLLY, John J.; '71 BS; 1052 Clay Ave., Pelham Manor, NY 10803, 914 738-4038.

CONNOLLY, John J.; '69 AS, '71 BS; Journalist/Writer; Hyperion Books, 2025 Broadway, New York, NY 10023, 718 720-3324; r. 26B Sylva Ln., Staten Island, NY 10305, 212 724-8778; Catherine, John IV, Susanne. e-mail

CONNOLLY, Mary F.; '97 BS; MS Fordham Univ.; Social Work for Drug Prevention; Bd. of Educ., 22 E. 28th St., New York, NY 10016, 917 256-4555; r. 1139 65th St., Brooklyn, NY 11219, 718 331-9667; Thomas, Larry, John. e-mail

CONNOLLY, Maryann; '86 BS; 87-87 98th Ave., Jamaica, NY 11421, 718 793-3934.

CONNOLLY, William J.; '72 AS, '74 BA; 35 Hunter Pl., Stony Point, NY 10980.

CONNOR, Brian W.; '99 BA; Brokerage Trainee; Salomon Smith Barney, 767 5th Ave., New York, NY 10153; r. 227 E 59 St. #5C, New York, NY 10022, 212 308-5324. e-mail

CONNOR, Charles; '92 BA; 663 Rugby Rd, Brooklyn, NY 11230, 718 756-4623.

CONNOR, Ghyslaine '97 (See McBean, Mrs. Ghyslaine).

CONNOR, Gregory L.; '77 BA; Healthcare Administration; New York, NY 10003; r. 8547 Coventry Rd., Brooklyn, NY 11236, 718 493-2779; Tyisha, Gregory Jr.

CONNOR, Mrs. Katrina A., (A.); '98 BA; Tchr.; Brooklyn Bd. of Educ., Brooklyn, NY 11233; r. 567 Schenck Ave., Brooklyn, NY 11207, 718 495-5468; Kyle.

CONNOR, Steven; '89 BA; 467 Prospect Ave., Hot Springs, AR 71901, 508 398-9847.

CONROY, Edward A.; '77 BS; Ret. Police Ofcr.; r. 1626 SW 30th St., Ft. Lauderdale, FL 33315, 954 525-6037; *Eileen;* Eileen.

CONROY, Gary P.; '76 BA; 132-16 60 Ave., Flushing, NY 11355, 718 591-1401.

CONROY, John T.; '96 BS; Sergeant; NYPD, 1 Police Plz., New York, NY 10038, 718 287-3522; r. 302 Hillside Ave., Rockaway Pt., NY 11697, 718 318-8129; *Peggy M.;* Mary. e-mail

CONROY, Sharon A.; '94 MA; 140 Main St., Keyport, NJ 07735, 732 264-7412.

CONRY, Steven; '87 AS, '92 BA, '92 MA; Warden; ARDC, 1111 Hazen St., E. Elmhurst, NY 11370, 718 546-4100; r. 14 Harding Way, Monroe, NY 10950, 914 782-2683; *Kelly;* Brian, James. e-mail

CONRY, Terry L.; '77 BA; 351 E 96th St., Brooklyn, NY 11212.

CONSTANT, Tara, (Tara Collins); '96 BS; MSED Hofstra Univ.; 2nd Grade Elem. Tchr.; Centereach, NY 11720; r. 802 Sara Cir., Port Jefferson, NY 11776, 631 474-1847; *Anthony.*

CONSTANTINO, Ralph V.; '70 BA; 60 Manor Ln., Yardley, PA 19067.

CONTE, Daniel P.; '97 BA; Corrections Ofcr.; NYC Dept. of Corrections, 11-11 Hazen St., E. Elmhurst, NY 11370; r. 85-92 98th St., Woodhaven, NY 11421. e-mail

CONTI, Jack, '78 BS, 6 Edward St., Lynbrook, NY 11563.

CONTI, Nicholas A.; '75 BS; 415 Gramatan Ave. Apt. 4a, Mt. Vernon, NY 10552, 914 699-9719.

CONTI, Richard P.; '97 MA; MA Fielding Inst.; PhD Candidate; Fielding Inst., Neuropsychology Certificate Program, Santa Barbara, CA 93102; r. POB 9, Convent Sta., NJ 07961, 973 267-5593. e-mail

CONTINO, Jeffrey J.; '82 BS; 46-14 Vernon Blvd., Long Island City, NY 11101.

CONTRERAS, Gloria; '97 BS, '98 BS; 234 7th St., Brooklyn, NY 11215, 718 349-1219.

CONTRERAS, Juan A.; '96 BA; Caseworker; NYC Human Resources Admin., 132 W 125th St., New York, NY 10027, 212 666-3085; r. 1166 Grand Concourse, Apt. G, Bronx, NY 10456, 718 992-7656; Favian N., Sasha M.

CONTRERAS, Lillian; '97 MA; 240 Wadsworth Ave., New York, NY 10033.

CONVERSANO, Victor M.; '93 MA; BS Jersey City State Clg.; Sgt; Guttenberg Police Dept., 6808 Park Ave., Guttenberg, NJ 07093, 201 868-3300; r. 374 Main St., Ridgefield Park, NJ 07660; *Peggy;* Erin Mary.

CONVERY, James H.; '76 MA; POB 64, Stanton, NJ 08885.

CONWAY, Gary F.; '92 BA, '93 CERT; MED Clg. Staten Island; Police Ofcr.; NYPD, One Plz., New York, NY 10001; r. 877 Rathbun Ave., Staten Island, NY 10309, 718 984-3684. e-mail

CONWAY, Judith A., (Judith A. Matiz); '86 BGOV, '87 MPA; Retired Sr. Cnslt.; NYC DMPMRAS, 718 748-1778; r. 7423 Ridge Blvd., Brooklyn, NY 11209; *Jeremiah A.;* Jeremiah W., Christopher J. e-mail

CONWAY, Loretta A.; Bd of Hghr Ed, 535 E 80th, New York, NY 10021.

CONWAY, Martin J.; '96 BS; Capt.; NYC Police Dept., #1 Police Plz., New York, NY 10038, 718 558-5400. e-mail

CONWAY, Maryelyn; '97 BS; 366 Forest Dr., Union, NJ 07083, 908 687-4218.

CONWAY, Michael A.; '81 BA; 35 Rosedale Ave., Millburn, NJ 07041, 973 228-5444.

CONWAY, Patricia M.; '84 MPA; 871 Olmstead Ave., Bronx, NY 10473, 718 320-0303.

COOK, Caudieu; '84 MA; 12124 Laurelton Pkwy., Jamaica, NY 11422.

COOK, Ida M.; '84 MPA; 4178 Central Sarasota Pkwy., Apt. 314, Sarasota, FL 34238, 941 383-1228.

COOK, Mrs. Leanne T., (Leanne T. Curcio); '99 BA; Children's Advocate; Women Aware Inc., POB 312, New Brunswick, NJ 08903, 732 249-4504; r. 11 Robertsville Rd, Freehold, NJ 07728, 732 431-7524; *Brian;* Abigail. e-mail

COOK, Mrs. Lisa M., (Lisa M. Bejgrowicz); '96 MA; Security Ofcr.; Fed. Express; r. 325 Redmont Rd., N. Plainfield, NJ 07063, 908 226-9501; *Michael.*

COOK, Lovely; '96 BS; 757 E 103rd St. # 4, Brooklyn, NY 11236, 718 272-7918.

COOK, Robert A.; '80 BS; 34-07 31 Ave., Long Island City, NY 11106, 718 341-3577.

COOK, Steven W.; '81 BS; 67 S Oxford St. Apt. 8, Brooklyn, NY 11217, 718 624-6524.

COOKINGHAM, Vincent P.; '81 MA; 176 N Main St., Florida, NY 10921.

COOPER, Alfonso A.; '78 BA; 2021 E 41st St. Apt. 3f, Brooklyn, NY 11234, 718 743-9319.

COOPER, Anthony; '84 BS; 2354 101st St., Flushing, NY 11369, 718 279-0086.

COOPER, Ava A.; '82 BS, '93 MPA; 68 Moffat St., Brooklyn, NY 11207, 718 743-9319.

COOPER, Charles D.; '80 BA; Retired Capt.; NYC Fire Dept.; r. 39 Scranton Ave., Staten Island, NY 10312, 718 356-1574; *Marie;* Donna, Christine, Allison, Ryan, Christopher, Amanda, Kayla.

COOPER, Christopher; '87 BA, '89 MA; Dept. of Sociology SUNY, Potsdam, NY 13676, 315 267-2565.

COOPER, Dermot A.; '95 CERT; BA PA CUNY, St. John Univ.; Records Mgr.; St. John's Univ., 8000 Utopia Pkwy., Jamaica, NY 11439, 718 990-2018; r. 110-01 159th St., #2, Jamaica, NY 11433, 718 291-0437; *Gail Puckerin-Cooper;* Dermot, Vaughn. e-mail

COOPER, Donna M.; '85 BA; 1130 E. 226 Dr., Bronx, NY 10466, 718 379-7320.

COOPER, Edwin B.; '74 BS; MPA C.W. Post LIU; Retired; r. 459 Winchester Rd, Satellite Bch., FL 32937, 321 773-4039.

COOPER, Gavin A.; '78 BS; Agt.; NISS; r. 784 Macon St., Brooklyn, NY 11233, 718 452-3428.

COOPER, Iris A.; '80 BA; 065 Saddle River R, Fair Lawn, NJ 07410.

COOPER, Janet; '94 MA; 550 Beach 135th St., Far Rockaway, NY 11694, 718 297-4029.

COOPER, Karl M.; '84 BS, '97 MA; AS CUNY-Brooklyn Clg., CERT.; Dir. of Technical Placement; Aquent, 71 W. 23rd St., New York, NY 10010, 212 228-7300; r. POB 1803, New York, NY 10274, 917 215-3926. e-mail

COOPER, Kenneth; '77 BS; 11469 E Carol Way, Scottsdale, AZ 85259.

COOPER, Neil J.; '70 BA; 17 Manvill Pl., Roslyn Hts., NY 11577, 516 484-0554.

COOPER, Peter J.; '91 BS; 4300 Martha Ave. #4D, Bronx, NY 10470, 718 379-7320.

COOPER, Tonya; '86 BS; 243 Albany Ave., Brooklyn, NY 11213, 718 771-6850.

COOPER, William C.; '92 BS; AS Bronx Community Clg.; Sergeant; Rockland Cnty. Sheriff, 55a New Hempstead Rd., New City, NY 10956, 914 638-5600; r. 119 E. Eckerson Rd., Spring Vly., NY 10977, 914 352-3670; *Paula;* Kyle, Brittney.

COPELAND, Nyree D.; '97 BS; 747 Rosedale Ave., Bronx, NY 10473, 718 547-5521.

COPPOCK, SGT Durwin L.; '99 MS; AS Essex Cnty. Clg., BS Rutgers Univ.; Administrative Sergeant; NJ State Police, 250 Minnisink Rd, Totowa, NJ 07512, 973 785-9420; r. 106 Reynolds Pl., S. Orange, NJ 07079, 973 762-8017; *Faye;* Daria, Danielle, Devon. e-mail

COPPOLO, James A.; '80 BS; 121 Lyman Ave. #2A, Staten Island, NY 10305, 718 448-4816.

CORA -LUNDQUIST, Marissa; '93 BS; Police Ofcr.; NYPD, 1 Police Plz., New York, NY 10038, 212 374-5000; r. 160 S. 3rd St., Brooklyn, NY 11211; *Jim Lundquist;* Samson. e-mail

CORBETT, Glenn P.; '82 BA; Asst. Prof.; John Jay Clg of Criminal Justice; r. 136 Bergen Ave., Waldwick, NJ 07463, 201 652-9224; *Sharon.* e-mail

CORBETT, Ms. Heather A.; '95 BA, '98 MA; Adjunct Prof.-Counseling; Queensborough Comm. Clg.; r. 111 Bayview Ave., Amityville, NY 11701, 631 598-5208.

CORBETT, Robert; '99 BS; Police Ofcr.; NYC Police Dept., 1 Police Plz., New York, NY 10038.

CORBIN, Christian H.; '77 BS; 5983 60th Pl., Flushing, NY 11378.

CORBIN, Stephen; '95 BS; Financial Analyst; Citigroup, Astoria, NY 11105, 718 319-3334; r. 1189 Dean St., Brooklyn, NY 11216, 718 778-7168. e-mail

CORCHADO, Diana A. '95 (See Melendez, Mrs. Diana A.).

CORCHADO, Maribel; '93 BA; 258 Bedford Ave., Brooklyn, NY 11211.

CORCORAN, Carol A. '75 (See Shomion, Carol A.).

CORCORAN, Frank E.; '80 BS; 72 Biltmore Blvd., Massapequa, NY 11758, 516 799-6941.

CORCORAN, James P.; '74 BS; Retired Asst. Chief, NY Fire Dept.; r. 213 E 3rd St., Brooklyn, NY 11218, 718 871-1665.

CORCORAN, Michael C.; '96 BA; Police Sgt.; Twp. of West Orange, W. Orange, NJ 07052, 973 325-4000; r. 21 Ravine Ave., Caldwell, NJ 07006. e-mail

CORCORAN, Michael T.; '73 AS, '75 BS; Retired; r. 302 Erik Dr., E. Setauket, NY 11733; Donna, Dawn, Debra, Darlene, Danielle. e-mail

CORCORAN, William C.; '79 BS; 401 W 52nd St., New York, NY 10019.

CORDERO, James A.; '90 BA; 394 Harold Ave., Staten Island, NY 10312, 718 876-2602.

CORDERO, Javier M.; 2440 Amsterdam Ave. #5F, New York, NY 10033.

CORDERO, Raul (Pappa Bear); '99 BA; CERT. NYS Bur. Mun.Police Trg; Fraud Investigator; NYC Human Resources Admin., 60 Hudson St., 8th Fl., New York, NY 10013, 212 274-5030; r. 257 Clinton St. #8K, New York, NY 10002, 212 267-6766. e-mail

CORDERO, Steven M., Esq.; '96 BS; AA St. Leo Univ., JD Fordham Univ.; Atty.; Kavanagh, Maloney & Osnato LLP, 415 Madison Ave., New York, NY 10017, 212 906-8338; r. 2352 Ellis Ave., Bronx, NY 10462, 718 597-3564. e-mail

CORDERO, Victor; '85 BA; 1055 Rosedale Ave. Apt. 4h, Bronx, NY 10472, 718 409-1813.

CORDES, Joseph; '97 BS; 76 E. 18th Rd, Broad Channel, NY 11693.

CORDON, Lee C.; '99 BA; 133-23 140th St. #3, S. Ozone Park, NY 11436, 718 465-4488.

CORDOVA, Leonor; '90 BA; Caseworker; Ofc. of Child Support, 115 Chrystie St., New York, NY 10002, 212 334-7660; r. 11806 Liberty Ave., 2nd Fl., Richmond Hill, NY 11419; Cuauhtemoc.

COREY, James A.; '81 BS; 77 Tanglewood Dr., Staten Island, NY 10308, 718 967-0654.

COREY, Jessica E., CPP; '87 BS; Sgt.; New York Police Dept., 167 E. 51st St., New York, NY 10021, 212 826-3211. e-mail

COREY, Peter; 57 Dorothy St., Port Jefferson Sta., NY 11776.

CORIANO, Milagros; '96 BA; Family Couns.; Victim Svcs., New York, NY 10001; r. 132 Grove St., 2nd Fl., Brooklyn, NY 11221, 718 452-6167. e-mail

CORIBELLO, Linda; '81 BS; 1343 E St., Elmont, NY 11003, 516 352-9027.

CORKE, Kathleen M.; '80 BS; 104-26 106 St., Ozone Park, NY 11417, 718 341-5122.

CORNEH, Varney M.; '80 AS, '81 BS, '84 CERT; House Ofcr.; Intercontinental Hotels, Inc., 111 E 48th St., New York, NY 10017, 212 906-3199; r. 11 Mckeever Pl., Apt. 13A, Brooklyn, NY 11225, 718 735-6716; *Bendu Y.;* Mohamed, Hassan, Hussein, Boima.

CORNELIUS, Eric J.; '92 BA; Child Care Admin./MSW Student; Jewish Bd. of Family Svcs./Fordham Univ., 914 773-7401; r. 228 Linda Ave., Hawthorne, NY 10532, 914 741-1127. e-mail

CORNELL, Richard R.; '91 BS; Police Ofcr.; Queens North-Auto Larceny; r. 208 Frederick Ave., Bellmore, NY 11710, 516 221-1822; *Anne;* Chris, Ryan. e-mail

CORNEY, Raymond J.; '79 BS; Investigator Asst. Treas.; The Bank of New York, 11 Broadway, Hicksville, NY 11801, 516 935-5381; r. 45 Garland Ct., Brooklyn, NY 11229.

CORNISH, Michael J.; '86 BS; 16 Lindstrom Rd, Stamford, CT 06902, 203 978-1122.

CORNWALL, Robert J.; '75 MPA; 249-04 81 Ave., Bellerose, NY 11426.

CORONA, Edwin R.; '95 BA; 132-57 Sanford Ave., Flushing, NY 11355.

CORPENING, La'tanya; '86 BS; 442 E. 96th St., Brooklyn, NY 11212, 718 622-3769.

CORPREW, Nitaka; '96 BA; 3941 Rosehill Rd, Apt. 1304, Fayetteville, NC 28311.

CORR, John F.; '71 BS; 815 Dean Ave., Bronx, NY 10465, 718 931-3047.

CORRADO, Vincent J.; '89 BS; Police Ofcr./Instr.; NYC Police Dept. Police Acad., In Service Training Unit, New York, NY 10038, 212 477-9200; r. Staten Island, NY 10304.

CORREA, Angel R.; '98 BS; Police Ofcr; NYPD; r. 2028 Matthews Ave., Bronx, NY 10462, 718 824-5941; *Regina.*

CORREA, Edward; '96 BA; Retired Asst. Deputy Warren; NYC Dept. of Corrections; r. 38 Bleeker Pl., Staten Island, NY 10314, 718 761-9697.

CORREA, Felix L.; '77 BA; Police Detective; 1 Police Plaza NYPD; r. 44 Columbine Ave., Islip, NY 11751; *Carmen;* Carolyn, Denise, Felix Jr.

CORREA, Jose M.; '93 BA; 131 Moore St. Apt. 19h, Brooklyn, NY 11206, 718 567-0465.

CORREA, Maritza '83 (See Perez, Maritza).

CORREA, Miguel A.; '79 BS; 12128 Goya Ct., El Paso, TX 79936, 915 855-3823.

CORREA, Rosa M.; '90 BA; 2383 2nd Ave. Apt. 2204, New York, NY 10035, 212 410-6834.

CORREA, Ruben; '97 BS; 114 E. 168th St., Bronx, NY 10452, 718 410-9550.

CORREA, Sonia '90 (See Correa-Gould, Mrs. Sonia).

CORREA, Tula J.; '95 BS; 240 Holland Ave., Elmont, NY 11003, 516 358-6383.

CORREA-GOULD, Mrs. Sonia, (Sonia Correa); '90 BS; 91-72 71st Rd., Forest Hills, NY 11375; *Drew Gould.*

CORREALE, Mark; '92 BA; 252 Reid Ave., Staten Island, NY 10305, 718 351-6147.

CORREDOR, Leonel F.; '91 BS; 2404 NE 9th St., Hallandale, FL 33009, 954 458-1284.

CORRICA, Jerome S.; '85 BS; 441 E 95th St., Brooklyn, NY 11212.

CORRIGAN, Michael J.; '82 BS; JD Natl. Univ.; Litigation Support/Private Inv.; Antrim Mgmt & Svc. Co., 800 471-8598; r. 124-09 15th Ave., College Pt., NY 11356. e-mail

CORRIGAN, Thomas F.; '91 BS; 10 Kennedy Dr., E. Quogue, NY 11942.

CORRY, Lorraine; '95 BS; Clerk/Military Police; USPS/USA, POB 863, New York, NY 10008; r. same, 973 621-6710; Angelina, Ketrina.

CORSENTINO, Anthony P.; '80 BS; 124-08 20 Ave., College Pt., NY 11356.

CORSERI, Alessandra; '85 BS; 643 W. 171 St., New York, NY 10032, 212 568-4745.

CORSEY, Priscilla; '77 BA, '89 MPA; 230-41 145th Ave., Rosedale, NY 11413.

CORSO, David J.; '99 BS; CEO; Morningstar Financial Svcs./Cortech, 176 Carson Ct., Somerset, NJ 08873, 877 613-9486; r. 1673 E. 16th St. Apt# 175, Brooklyn, NY 11229, 917 250-7478. e-mail

CORSON, Randi L.; '80 MA; 571 Maple Ct., Bensalem, PA 19020.

CORT, Martha R.; '92 BS; 1571 Carroll St., Brooklyn, NY 11213, 718 531-5115.

CORTELLINO, Gary J.; '78 BS; Police Ofcr. Lt.; Dekalb Cnty. Police/North Precinct, 4453 Ashford Dunwoody Rd., Atlanta, GA 30346, 404 294-2000; r. 2300 Pinehaven Ct., Grayson, GA 30017, 770 972-9994. e-mail

CORTES, Denise; '95 BA; 10 Pratt St., Mt. Vernon, NY 10550, 914 665-3221.

CORTES, Nelida; '89 BS; 417 Grand St. Apt. 1303d, New York, NY 10002, 315 797-6959.

CORTES, Nelson; '81 BS; 699 Pennsylvania Ave., Brooklyn, NY 11207, 718 942-1579.

CORTESE, Frank; '79 BS; 302 7th Ave., Brooklyn, NY 11215, 718 375-1114.

COSENTINO, Donna M.; '98 MA; Behavioral Spec.; AHRC, 2900 Verteran Memorial Hwy., Bohemia, NY 11716, 631 744-7158; r. 17 3rd St., Bellport, NY 11713, 631 286-1156. e-mail

COSENTINO, Louis A.; '80 BS; 8687 19th Ave., Brooklyn, NY 11214.

COSENZA, Bernard S.; '77 MA; 2532 E 19 St., Brooklyn, NY 11235.

COSENZA, Joseph; '80 BS; POB 652, Yonkers, NY 10710.

COSME, Maura; '97 BS; 771a St.ann's Ave., Bronx, NY 10456, 718 329-2779. e-mail

COSME-SATINA, Sandra M.; '86 BA; 1152 Ellsworth Ave., Ph, Bronx, NY 10465.

COSSU, Jennifer K.; '98 BA; Onsite Bldg. Mgr.; Glenwood Mgmt., 1340 york Ave., New York, NY 10021, 212 861-7790; r. 355 Clinton Ave. 1, Cedarhurst, NY 11516, 516 569-8629. e-mail

COSTA, Richard; '80 BS; 22 Hartford St., Staten Island, NY 10308, 718 979-6149.

COSTABILE, Michael J.; '73 BS; 2 K.G.Whritenour, Butler, NJ 07405.

COSTANTINO, Regina '85 (See Discenza, Regina).

COSTANZO, Keith J.; '98 MA; 231 N Middletown Rd, Apt. H, Pearl River, NY 10965.

COSTAS, Yvette-Marie; '80 BA; 369 8th St., Brooklyn, NY 11215.

COSTELLO, Mary C.; '92 MA; 8531 115th St., Jamaica, NY 11418, 718 805-2022.

COSTELLO, Vivian; '78 BA; 5821 Granger St., Flushing, NY 11368.

COSUMANO, Robert L.; '78 BS; 85 Oak Ave., Southampton, NY 11968, 718 424-8446.

COTE, Raymond A.; '92 MA; JD Pace Univ. Law School; Atty.; Rockland Cnty. Dist. Attys. Ofc., New City, NY 10956, 914 638-5000; r. 204 Cherry Hill Rd, Carmel, NY 10512, 914 277-7309; Ivone; Nicole, Eric. e-mail

COTHAM, Jeffrey D.; '94 MPA; BS Park Clg.; AAS El Paso Community Clg.; Projs. Mgr.; El Paso Police Dept., 911 N Raynor, El Paso, TX 79903, 915 564-7327; r. 10709 Jack Fleck Dr., El Paso, TX 79935, 915 592-1059; Yun Wol; Mary, Julie. e-mail

COTICELLI, Neal; '72 BS; 122 Boulder St., Staten Island, NY 10312, 718 966-6617.

COTTAM, Gerard J.; '75 MPA; 203 Carle Rd, Westbury, NY 11590.

COTTER, Daniel J.; '77 AS; 2018 Coleman St., Brooklyn, NY 11234.

COTTER, Joseph P.; '75 BA; Security Advisor; r. 4 Andover Rd, Yonkers, NY 10710, 914 337-7174; Diane; Joseph, William, Diane.

COTTER, Robert T.; '78 BS; Retired Ballistics Expert; NYPD; r. 46 Jones Dr., Highland Mills, NY 10930; June; Christine, Donna, Jennifer, William. e-mail

COTTER, William J.; '75 MPA; 10410 221st St., Jamaica, NY 11429.

COTTO, Jose L.; '90 BA, '92 MA, '95 MA; JD CUNY; Law Student; CUNY; r. 131 Moore St. Apt. 19a, Brooklyn, NY 11206, 718 455-0581; Estelle; Angelica, Jose Joel, Erica. e-mail

COTTO, Veronica; '99 BS; Govt. Immigration; r. POB 332, Brooklyn, NY 11237; Santiago Manon.

COTTO, Wilfredo; '81 BA; 125 W 109th St., New York, NY 10025, 315 866-8354.

COTTON, Eddie; '93 BS; MS Hunter Clg.; Sergeant; NYC Police Dept., 1 Police Plz., New York, NY 10038, 718 802-9202; r. 1065 Vermont St., Brooklyn, NY 11207, 718 927-0417; Mychele; Eddie, Julein.

COTTON, Gloria B.; '83 MA; 23120 126th Ave., Jamaica, NY 11413.

COTTY, Edward; '73 BS; MS St. Johns Univ.; Quality Assurance Dir.; Altana Inc., 60 Baylif Rd, Melville, NY 11747, 631 454-7677; r. 6 Wellington Rd, Merrick, NY 11566, 516 223-9343; Eileen; Edward J., Sean. e-mail

COUGHLIN, Richard D.; '91 Cloverdale Ave., Staten Island, NY 10308, 718 356-6592.

COULIANIDIS, Michael; BA Univ. of Kansas; Pres.; M.A. Rallis Corp., 2031 Hwy. 130, Monmouth Jct., NJ 08852, 732 940-0456; r. 13 Chadwick Rd, Englishtown, NJ 07726, 732 446-3650; Myrian; Anthony.

COURT, Eric; '90 AS; 16519 116th Ave., Jamaica, NY 11434, 718 261-7173.

COURTNEY, Diane T.; '95; 10 Park Dr., Putnam Vly., NY 10579.

COURTNEY, William D.; '80 BS; Deputy Dir. of Investigations; Control Risks Grp., Ltd., 1 Penn Plz., Ste. 1710, New York, NY 10119, 212 967-3955; r. POB 481, Manahawkin, NJ 08050. e-mail

COUSINS, Thomas D.; '80 BS; 19149 Roman Way, Gaithersburg, MD 20886, 301 948-3792.

COUTAIN, Kade; '98 BA; Law Clerk; Rosenman & Colin LLP, 575 Madison Ave., New York, NY 10022 840-8800; r. 222 Bedford Park Blvd. #2F, Bronx, NY 10458, 718 295-7585; Jamie Ariza.

COUTTS, Anne R.; '96 MA; Mgmt. Trainee; Royal E. Sunalliance; r. 421 Painted Post, Scarborough, ON, Canada M1G 2M7, 416 995-6753. e-mail

COVELESKI, Joyce E.; '89 MA; 94-10 24 Ave., E. Elmhurst, NY 11369.

COVIELLO, Ms. Karlee M.; '99 BA; Loss Prevention Detective; Bradlees Inc.; r. 63 N. Railroad Ave., Mahwah, NJ 07430, 201 529-4622. e-mail

COWAN, James T.; '78 BS; NYPD-Retired; r. 682 Highland Pl., Rockaway Pt., NY 11697, 718 945-3025; Alice. e-mail

COWICK, Gary L.; '95 BA; 21 Battery Ave., Brooklyn, NY 11228, 718 836-9847.

COX, Andrea; '85 BS; 41-01 Vernon Blvd., Long Island City, NY 11101, 718 468-1112.

COX, Ayoka; '94 BA; MS Hunter Clg.; 313 Tallwood Dr., Hartsdale, NY 10530; r. POB 48, Hartsdale, NY 10530. e-mail

COX, Daniel H.; '92 BA, PSY; Corporate Security Dir.; Prime Realty Svcs., 155 E 56th St. 4th Fl., New York, NY 10022, 212 927-0637; r. POB 150301, Kew Gardens, NY 11415. e-mail

COX, Ethel; '99 BS; 33 Loudoun St. #4F, Yonkers, NY 10705, 914 423-1341.

COX, Julie A.; '95 BA; 2950 S Cobb Dr. SE, Apt. 17-04, Smyrna, GA 30080, 770 514-1935.

COX, Patricia A.; '87 BS; 20 W. 102nd St., New York, NY 10025, 315 339-5616.

COX, Stephanie A. '78 (See Cox-Alston, Ms. Stephanie A.).

COX, Thomas P.; '81 MA; 9 Cornell Dr., Nanuet, NY 10954, 914 623-7016.

COX-ALSTON, Ms. Stephanie A., (Stephanie A. Cox); '78 BS; Communication Data Technician; MCI Worldcom, 2 Washington St., USAR/Ft. Totten, New York, NY 10004, 212 701-2353; r. 21 St. James Pl. Apt. 2B, Brooklyn, NY 11205, 718 399-2978; Elbert Alston; Kiya Huesca, Cine Alston. e-mail

COYLE, James G.; '79 BA; 15 Aldrich Rd, Kendall Park, NJ 08824.

COYNE, Edward J.; '79 BS; 10 Spector Ln., Plainview, NY 11803, 516 935-0512.

COYNE, James; '76 AS; Retired; r. 2433 Fish Ave., Bronx, NY 10469, 718 655-5562.

COYNE, Susan M.; '97 BS; 177-A First St., Yonkers, NY 10704.

COYNE, Thomas R.; '90 BS; 27 Row Pl., Staten Island, NY 10312.

COYNE, William P.; '90 AS; 231 Richard Ct., Pomona, NY 10970, 914 429-2393.

COZENS, Mark P.; '87 BS; Firefighter; City of Trenton, 244 Perry St., Trenton, NJ 08618, 609 393-6783; r. 339 Gordon Rd, Robbinsville, NJ 08691, 609 259-2625; *Nancy;* Brianna.

COZZOLINO, Caryn; '99 BA; Caterer; T&A Catering, Englewood, NJ 07631; r. 245 E 25th St. Apt. 6G, New York, NY 10010, 212 725-3249. e-mail

CRABB, Eric C.; '96 BA; 610 Milford Mount Pleasant Rd, Milford, NJ 08848.

CRADER, Clarissa T.; '96 BA; 412 Cornelia St., Brooklyn, NY 11237.

CRAIG, Jeffrey S.; '97 BS; 271 Avenue C #5B, New York, NY 10009, 212 388-0053.

CRAIG, Kenneth A.; '78 BS; 88 Kelvin Ave., Staten Island, NY 10306, 718 987-6837.

CRAIG, Sara Elizabeth; '95 MA; BS The PA State Univ.; PSSC; r. POB 1104, Lemont, PA 16851. e-mail

CRANDELL, Xavier O.; '95 BS; POB 340026, Jamaica, NY 11434.

CRANE, Ernest; '83 MA, BA; Retired; Police Dept.; r. 1202 Saint Marks Ave., Brooklyn, NY 11213, 718 773-0940; *Juanita;* Nicole, Candace, Makeda, Malcolm.

CRANFORD, Charles, Jr.; '88 AS; Security Ofcr.; Concord Nursing Home; r. 704 Howard Ave., Brooklyn, NY 11212, 718 345-8257; *Sarah;* Dianne, Elsie, Charles III, Clifton.

CRAVEN, Cheryl V.; '93 BA; 620 Malcolm X Blvd. Apt. 2r, New York, NY 10037.

CRAWBUCK, Charles R.; '78 BA; Fire Safety Dir./Current Assoc Pres; Dee-Cee Fire, 127-13 102nd Ave., Highrise Fire Safety Trainer/Inspec, Richmond Hill, NY 11419, 718 441-4896; r. 12713 102nd Ave., Richmond Hill, NY 11419, 718 441-4896; *Dolores;* Theresa, Barbara, Charles II.

CRAWFORD, Andrea (Angie) K.; '98 BS; Human Res. Asst.; Nike, 6 E. 57th St., New York, NY 10022, 212 891-6467; r. 616 Carlton Ave. 2fl, Brooklyn, NY 11238. e-mail

CRAWFORD, Arthur J.; '76 BA; 166-09 12th Rd, Beechhurst, NY 11357, 718 523-7705.

CRAWFORD, Audrey D.; '78 BS; MSW Hunter Clg.; Parole Revocation Spec.; NYS Div. of Parole, 97 Central Ave., Albany, NY 12206, 518 472-2984; r. 574 E 81st St., Brooklyn, NY 11236, 718 209-1172.

CRAWFORD, Bobby G.; '78 BS; 520 Caris Brook Ct., Atlanta, GA 30349, 404 997-1336.

CRAWFORD, Derek; '94 AS; 225 Willis Ave. #, Bronx, NY 10454, 718 901-3553.

CRAWFORD, Douglas T.; '78 AA; 271 Avenue C, New York, NY 10009, 212 673-1422.

CRAWFORD, Harold A.; 904 Inn Ct., Baldwin, NY 11510.

CRAWFORD, Mark R.; '98 BS; AS Kingsborough Clg.; Police Ofcr.; NY Police Dept., Brooklyn, NY 11201, 718 745-6679; r. 1224 79th St., Brooklyn, NY 11228, 718 745-6679; *Georgia.* e-mail

CRAWFORD, Michelle D.; '84 BS, '95 MS; Parole Ofcr.; NYC State, Bronx, NY 10451, 718 292-2127; r. 1500 Noble Ave. Apt. 3b, Bronx, NY 10460.

CRAWFORD, Ollie A.; '79 BS, MPA, AA; Retired; r. 305 Oak Lane Dr., Ocala, FL 34472.

CRAWFORD, Randy B.; '97 BS; Correctional Ofcr.; Dept. of Justice; r. 34 Phoenix Ct., Tinton Falls, NJ 07712, 732 493-0452. e-mail

CRAWFORD, Todd L.; '94 BA; JD Queens Clg.; 6 Catlin Ave., Roosevelt, NY 11575, 516 379-0740.

CRAWLEY, William J.; '81 BS; 197 Truman Ave., Yonkers, NY 10703.

CRAYTON, Wanda A.; '99 BA; AS LaGuardia Clg.; Tchr.; Bd. of Educ. Dist. 30, New York, NY 10001; r. 4004 Vernon Blvd., Apt. 2-D, Long Island City, NY 11101, 718 784-2168; Khristopher, Cameron, Isaiah. e-mail

CREAMER, Jeanet E.; '94 BS; Legal Asst.; Bronx Dist. Atty. Ofc., 215 E. 161st St., Bronx, NY 10451, 718 537-7221; r. 150 Dreiser Loop #7A, Dreiser Loop, NY 10475, 718 671-7444; *Allen Johnson;* Takeisha. e-mail

CREANEY, Anthony P.; '75 BS, '83 AS; BS CUNY; Retired Investigator; r. 3626 Irwin Ave., Bronx, NY 10463, 718 548-3452; *Elizabeth Ann;* Patrick, Kathy, Noel.

CREARY, Jemal D.; '93 BS; 182 Bennett Ave., Apt. 1G, New York, NY 10040.

CREARY, Michael C.; '89 MPA; 6925 Gouverneur Ave., Far Rockaway, NY 11692, 718 634-6575.

CREEGAN, John I.; '76 MPA; BS Dominican Clg., BA St. Francis Clg.; Retired; r. 24 Rochelle Dr., New City, NY 10956, 914 634-1728; *Maureen;* Helen, Peter, John, Maureen. e-mail

CREELMAN, Thomas C.; '76 BA, '91 MPA; MPA, MA; Sr. Special Investigator/ Adj. Prof.; NYS Atty. Generals Ofc./St. Johns Univ., 120 Broadway, Queens, NY, New York, NY 10271, 212 417-5638; r. POB 900144, Far Rockaway, NY 11690, 718 327-7372; *Rosemarie.*

CREGAN, Dennis J.; '76 MA; 21 Aymar Ave., Staten Island, NY 10301, 718 727-6250.

CREGAN, Michael; '75 BS; 21 Aymar Ave., Staten Island, NY 10301, 718 727-6250.

CREGAN, Robert J.; '76 BS; 21 Aymar Ave., Staten Island, NY 10301, 718 727-6250.

CREGIN, Matthew T.; '94 BS; 509 College Ave., Staten Island, NY 10314, 718 727-5651.

CREIGHTON, Brian K.; '99 BA; 250 James St., Franklin Sq., NY 11010, 516 354-3940.

CREIGHTON, Rober J.; '71 BS; 61 Avenue B, Kings Park, NY 11754.

CRENSHAW, Frank D.; '80 BA; Sr. Court Ofcr.; Kings Cnty. Supreme Ct., 120 Schermerhorn St., Brooklyn, NY 11201, 718 643-7061; r. 733 Chauncey St., Brooklyn, NY 11207.

CREPEAU, Louis J.; '75 AS; 803 Virginia Ave., N. Bellmore, NY 11710.

CREQUE, Romelia Y.; '82 BS; AAS LaGuardia Community Clg.; Staff Analyst; NYC-Dept. of Corrections, 2 Washington 10th Fl., New York, NY 10004, 212 487-6607; r. 4238 157th St., Flushing, NY 11355, 718 961-4126. e-mail

CRESCENTE, Pedro R.; '79 BS; POB 410584, Melbourne, FL 32941.

CRESPI, Ralph M.; '83 BA; 15 W 81st St., New York, NY 10024.

CRESPO, Evelyn; '83 BS; 10 Monroe St., New York, NY 10002, 212 587-8760.

CRESPO, Gladys L.; '93 BA; 51 Arlington Ave., Brooklyn, NY 11207, 718 456-4916.

CRESPO, Luisa E.; '91 BA; 2776 Pitkin Ave. Apt. 6, Brooklyn, NY 11208, 718 456-4916.

CRESPO, Marivet; '96 BS; 515 41st St., Brooklyn, NY 11232, 718 456-4916.

CRESPO, Porfirio; '85 BS; 46-48 Avenue B #3, New York, NY 10009.

CRESPO, Richard (Richie); '96 AS; Detective; NYPD, New York, NY 10001, 212 494-8259; r. Bronx, NY 10465.

CRESPO, Sylvia; '86 BS; 214 Stagg St., Apt. 3B, Brooklyn, NY 11206, 718 782-3436.

CRICHLOW, Alison F.; '96 BA; 10543 Flatlands 2nd St., Brooklyn, NY 11236, 718 222-4707.

CRICHLOW, Tracy; '81 BS, '85 MA; 2541 7th Ave., New York, NY 10039.

CRIMMINS, John D.; '76 BS; 1518 St. Peters Ave., Bronx, NY 10461.

CRIMMINS, Martin E.; '79 BS; Detective; NYC Police Dept., 34 1/2 E. 12 St., New York, NY 10013, 212 614-6755; r. 43 Mosely Ave., Staten Island, NY 10312, 718 967-3316; *Virginia Duffy;* Megan.

CRISCUOLO, Ann L.; '79 BA; 2243 Lafayette Ave., Bronx, NY 10473.

CRISCUOLO, Carol; '80 BA; 1313 Ellison Ave., Bronx, NY 10461.

CRISCUOLO, Louis; '78 BS; 1826 Mayflower Ave., Bronx, NY 10461.

CRISTIANI, Christine; '81 BS; 1466 Burton St., Whitestone, NY 11357, 718 767-3838.

CROCE, Bruce W.; '78 BS; 151 Weaver Rd, W. Sayville, NY 11796.

CROCIATA, Thomas A.; '82 BS; 7225 60th Ave., Flushing, NY 11378, 718 446-6926.

CROKE, Brian M.; '99 BA; 5415 Netherland Ave. K51, Bronx, NY 10471, 718 796-8637.

CROMWELL, Christine; '96 BA; AAS Nassau Community Clg.; Investigator; Grp. Health Inc., 441 9th Ave., New York, NY 10001, 212 615-0004; r. 281 Division Ave., Levittown, NY 11756.

CRONIN, Joseph M.; '98 MA; BA Ithaca Clg., PHD SUNY-Albany; PhD Cand.; r. 300 Rte. Nine, Gansevoort, NY 12831, 518 798-9777. e-mail

BIOGRAPHICAL SECTION

CULVERT

CRONIN, Kathleen V.; '69 BS, '72 MA; EDD Nova Univ.; Retired Tchr.; Rowan Univ.; r. 17465 Plz. Abierto, San Diego, CA 92128, 858 451-8821.

CRONIN, Michael; '98 MS; 47 Roberta Ave., Farmingville, NY 11738, 631 732-2603.

CRONNELLY, John J.; '80 MA; 44 Edgewood Ave., Farmingville, NY 11738, 631 698-4307.

CROOKS, Sonia E.; '85 MA; 16842 Liberty Ave., Jamaica, NY 11433.

CROOKS, Venesia '94 (See Welsh, Mrs. Venesia A.).

CROSBY, Delois; '76 BA; 164-01 Foch Bl #7K, Jamaica, NY 11434.

CROSBY, Karen P.; '81 BS; POB 6292, Yuma, AZ 85366, 520 317-0568.

CROSBY, Marion T.; '97 BS; Legal Tech.; US Dept. of Justice, 26 Federal Plz., New York, NY 10278, 212 264-5958; r. 412 Palisade Ave., Yonkers, NY 10703, 914 376-1921. e-mail

CROSBY, Trevor; '92 BA; 230 Park Pl. Apt. 6j, Brooklyn, NY 11238, 718 272-5141.

CROSBY, Walter V.; '74 BS; 253 Maple Pl., Mineola, NY 11501, 516 746-6755.

CROSBY-GREENE, Lee; '95 BS, '99 BA; Case Mgr.; Human Resources Agcy.; r. 21622 110th Ave., #2, Queens Vlg., NY 11429; *Laurenzo Greene.*

CROSE, Bambi M.; '96 BA; 86-25 Van Wyck Expy., Briarwood, NY 11435.

CROSS, Darrell; '87 BS; Court Ofcr./ Delegate; NYS, 1118 Grand Concourse, Bronx, NY 10456, 718 466-3102; r. 120 Carver Loop, Apt. 10-F, Bronx, NY 10475, 718 320-9723; *Renee.*

CROSS, Michelle I.; '91 BS; 4712 17th St. NW, Washington, DC 20011, 301 754-2059.

CROUTHAMEL, David E.; '98 BS; AS Cnty. Clg. of Morris; Police Ofcr.; NYCPD; r. 332 High Crest Dr., W. Milford, NJ 07480, 973 838-7482; Joanne, William, Brian, Lori, Matt. e-mail

CROWLEY, Colin; '84 BS; 106 Battery Ave. Apt. 203, Brooklyn, NY 11209, 718 833-1705.

CROWLEY, Denis F.; '84 BS; 106 Battery Ave. Apt. 203, Brooklyn, NY 11209, 718 833-1705.

CROWLEY, John G.; '80 BS; 285 Ridgewood Ave., Staten Island, NY 10312.

CRUDUP, Eartha L.; '81 BA; 212-19 102 Ave. #1E, Queens Vlg., NY 11429.

CRUDUP, Roslyn S.; '87 BA; Indep. Living Spec.; Brookwood Child Care, 25 Washington St., Brooklyn, NY 11201, 718 596-5555; r. 215 Hoyt St. Apt. 5E, Brooklyn, NY 11217.

CRUGNOLA, Charles K.; '91 AS, '92 BS; Police Detective; North Bergen Police Dept., 4233 Kennedy Blvd., N. Bergen, NJ 07047, 201 392-2100; r. 3-44 31st St., Fair Lawn, NJ 07410, 201 797-8666; *Arlene;* Kevin, Amanda.

CRUMMELL, Donna; '91 BA; Soc Wk/ Sub Abuse Spec.; McMahon Good Shepherd Svcs., 305 7th Ave., New York, NY 10001, 212 243-7070; r. 1152 E 225th. St., Bronx, NY 10466.

CRUMP, Michael; '96; 11834 228th St., Jamaica, NY 11411, 718 712-1586.

CRUSOE, Irvin; '93 BA; 500 Manhattan Ave. Apt. 1A, New York, NY 10027, 212 996-7462.

CRUZ, Angel; '83 BA; '85 MPA; Dir. of Security Queens CG; Queens Clg. CUNY, 65-30 Kissena Blvd., Flushing, NY 11367, 718 997-4443; r. 6 Waterside Pkwy., Staten Island, NY 10308, 718 984-7478; *Martha E.;* Eric, Dana.

CRUZ, Angel; '96 BS; 8693 Bay Pkwy. Apt. 15, Brooklyn, NY 11214, 718 237-4434.

CRUZ, Annette; '93 BS; 1475 Walton Ave., Bronx, NY 10452, 718 320-8358.

CRUZ, Carlos M.; '92 BS; 1430 Park Pl., Brooklyn, NY 11213, 718 771-4539.

CRUZ, Elbert; '86 BS; 941 March Hare Ct., Winter Spgs., FL 32708, 407 296-2598.

CRUZ, Gloria C.; '89 BS; 132-70 Sanford Ave., Flushing, NY 11355, 718 267-7021.

CRUZ, Heriberto; '80 BS; 36 Clovelly Dr., N. Valley Stream, NY 11580, 516 942-8186.

CRUZ, Jamie; '97 BA; 45 Cornwall Rd., Glen Rock, NJ 07452, 201 652-5806.

CRUZ, Jeanette; '91 BS; 638 Warren St. # 4, Brooklyn, NY 11217, 718 856-0764.

CRUZ, Judy; '92 BS; 1317 W. Farms Rd., Bronx, NY 10459, 718 365-3610.

CRUZ, Lillian; '86 BA; 2334 Creston Ave., Apt. 41, Bronx, NY 10468, 718 405-6715.

CRUZ, Louis A., Esq.; '76 BA; JD Fordham Univ. Sch. of Law; Atty.; Cruz & Cruz, 42-40 Bell Blvd. (302), Bayside, NY 11361, 718 428-1555; r. 4727 Little Neck Pkwy., Douglaston, NY 11362, 718 428-7357. e-mail

CRUZ, Margarita; '79 BS; 42-12 30th Ave., Astoria, NY 11103, 718 217-8965.

CRUZ, Monica C.; '92 BA; 400 Wyona St. Ph, Brooklyn, NY 11207, 718 348-0801.

CRUZ, Nancy; '88 BS; 340 Cherry St. Apt. 13d, New York, NY 10002.

CRUZ, Naomi; '97 AS; 139-34 253rd St., Jamaica, NY 11422, 718 381-9226.

CRUZ, Nelly; '92 BS; 26 Metropolitan Ov, Bronx, NY 10462, 718 466-9527.

CRUZ, Orlando; '79 BA; 1346 Morrison Ave., Bronx, NY 10472.

CRUZ, Raul; '74 BS; 1755 Westchester Ave., Bronx, NY 10472, 718 239-0527.

CRUZ, Richard; '96 BS; Court Advocate; Ctr. for Community Alternatives, 408 Jay St. Ste. 401, Brooklyn, NY 11201, 718 858-9658; r. 560 W. 175 St. Apt. 2B, New York, NY 10033, 917 443-0216. e-mail

CRUZ, Roberto D.; '81 BS; 380 Cozine Ave., Brooklyn, NY 11207, 718 919-3488.

CRUZ, Talia C. '99 (See Torres, Talia C.).

CRUZ, Victor A.; '99 BA; Retired Police Ofcr.; r. 2 Cypress Rd., Suffern, NY 10901, 914 357-0314; *Elicet;* Alex, Victor, Brittany, Tatiana. e-mail

CUBERO, Candido; '96 AS, '99 BS; MS; Detective; NYCPD, 2820 Synder Ave., Brooklyn, NY 11211, 718 287-3307; r. 536 57th St., Brooklyn, NY 11220, 718 567-9442.

CUCAJ, Xhevat; '95 BS; 980 57th St., Brooklyn, NY 11219.

CUCCIA, Anthony J.; '90 BS; 2060 E 73rd St., Brooklyn, NY 11234, 718 648-4841.

CUCCIA, Frances E.; '82 BA; 1559 E 95 St., Brooklyn, NY 11236, 718 648-4841.

CUCCIO, Rocco J.; '75 BA; 785 Brookridge Dr., Valley Cottage, NY 10989.

CUCCIOLI, Barbara V.; '97 BA, '99; 4016 9th Ave., Brooklyn, NY 11232.

CUCITI, Nicholas S.; '81 BS; 4421 Avenue I, Brooklyn, NY 11234.

CUDJOE, Michelle A.; '97 BA; Admin. Asst.; 1199 Natl. Benefit Fund, 330 W. 42nd, New York, NY 10036, 212 465-4502; r. 1246 E. 55th St., Brooklyn, NY 11234, 718 241-7629. e-mail

CUEBAS, Edwin; '77 BS; Postal Inspector; US Postal Inspection Svc., POB 555-6po, 421 8th Ave., New York, NY 10116, 212 330-3492; r. 595 7th Ave., Brooklyn, NY 11215, 718 499-1699. e-mail

CUEBAS, Tonia Y.; '84 BA; 80 W Yaphank Rd, Coram, NY 11727.

CUELLO, Francisca; '93 BS; 1 Bennett Ave. Apt. 44, New York, NY 10033, 212 568-0306.

CUESTA, George M.; '78 BS; 106-15 Queens Blvd., Forest Hills, NY 11375.

CUEVA, Patrica E.; '98 BA; 23-35 29th Ave. 15-4th Fl., Long Island City, NY 11102, 718 821-3243.

CUEVAS, Ms. Claris I.; '97 BA, '99 BA; Teacher; Bd. of Educ., 65 Livingston St., Brooklyn, NY 11201; r. 3013 Valentine Ave., Bronx, NY 10458, 718 364-7950. e-mail

CUEVAS, Doris M.; '89 BS; 189 Allen St. Apt. 3j, New York, NY 10002.

CUEVAS, Johnny O.; '96 BS; Police Ofcr.; r. 27-50 Johnson Ave. #7d, Riverdale, NY 10463, 718 432-2898; *Maritza.*

CUFF, Patrick K.; '78 MA; 16 Foreston Cir., Manorville, NY 11949.

CUFFARI, Josephine; '88 BA; 2835 Roberts Ave., Bronx, NY 10461, 718 931-9668.

CUGLIANDRO, Pasquale; '93 BS; Sr. Court Ofcr.; NYS Unified Ct. Syst., 100 Centre St., New York, NY 10013; r. 5126 48th St., Woodside, NY 11377, 718 392-7043.

CULELLA, Marycatherine E.; '98 BA; Correction Ofcr.; NYS Dept. of Corrections; r. 70 Beach Rd, Massapequa, NY 11758, 516 798-1967.

CULKIN, Margaret A. '82 (See Flammang, Margaret A.).

CULLEN, John J.; '74 BA; 7450 Mahaffey Dr. Apt. C, New Port Richey, FL 34653, 727 841-9266.

CULLUM, Christopher; '86 BS; 892 Karshick St., Bohemia, NY 11716.

CULPEPPER, Steven A.; '87 MA; 95 Minnehaha Blvd., Oakland, NJ 07436, 201 651-0104.

CULVER, Tanya L.; '95 BA; 2040 Bruckner Blvd., Bronx, NY 10473, 718 892-6641.

CULVERT, Romano; '76 MA; 726 Spring Valley Rd., Maywood, NJ 07607.

47

CUMBERBATCH, Simeon; '97 BS; Legal Aide; Law Ofc. of Lawrence S. Cumberbatch, 167 Madison Ave., New York, NY 10016, 212 251-0860; r. 2814 Beverley Rd, Brooklyn, NY 11226, 718 856-0349; *Lisa Prentiss;* Ayyuub Abdul, Baqi. e-mail

CUMMINGS, Ana; '96 BS; 135 W. 93rd St., New York, NY 10025, 315 339-0182.

CUMMINGS, Dalila C.; '98 BA; Fraud Investigator; Human Resources Admin., City of NY, Brooklyn, NY 11201; r. 636 Brooklyn Ave. #16b, Brooklyn, NY 11203, 718 773-2086.

CUMMINGS, Ivan; '99 BA; Secy.; NYS Div. of Parole, 314 W. 40th St., New York, NY 10018, 212 239-6491; r. 469 Tompkins Ave. #3F, Brooklyn, NY 11216, 718 398-1963.

CUMMINGS, James P.; '76 BS; 238 E. 58th St., New York, NY 10022, 315 339-0182.

CUMMINGS, Kathy C.; '96 BA; 236 Westervelt Ave., Staten Island, NY 10301, 718 556-2391.

CUMMINGS, Orlene F.; '96 BA; 436a Marion St., Brooklyn, NY 11233, 718 566-1861.

CUMMINGS, Vernessa; '84 BA; 275 Livonia Ave., Brooklyn, NY 11212, 718 495-0086.

CUMMO, Joseph A.; '97 MA; 13 Hoffman Rd., New Hyde Park, NY 11040, 516 354-5573.

CUNNEEN, Joseph F.; '95 MA; BS St. Francis; Inspector; NYPD, Detectives Brooklyn N., 179 Wilson Ave., Brooklyn, NY 11237, 718 573-5054; r. 116 Beach 221st St., Far Rockaway, NY 11697, 718 634-8513; *Alice Mc Carthy;* Joseph, Michael.

CUNNEEN, Judith A.; '83 BA; 96-08 221st St., Queens Vlg., NY 11429.

CUNNEEN, William A.; '67 BS; 448 Morris Dr., Valley Stream, NY 11580, 516 433-5914.

CUNNINGHAM, D.; '74 MA; Cenacle Retreat Ho #1400, Lantana, FL 33462, 561 547-4931.

CUNNINGHAM, Darrow; '79 BA, '96 MPA; Correctional Couns.; NYS Dept. of Corrections, Ossining, Sing Sing Correctional Facility, Ossining, NY 10562, 914 941-0108; r. 150 W. 225th St., Apt. 12f, Bronx, NY 10463, 718 562-2338. e-mail

CUNNINGHAM, Dennis J.; '76 BA, '76 MPA; VP of Security Natl. Hockey League; Natl. Hockey League, 1251 Ave. of The Americas, New York, NY 10020, 212 789-2000.

CUNNINGHAM, Edmund P.; '79 MPA; 750 W Broadway, Apt. 5M, Long Beach, NY 11561, 516 889-3291.

CUNNINGHAM, Eric D.; '95 BS; 420 E. 102nd St., New York, NY 10029.

CUNNINGHAM, Joseph J.; '65 MPA; 22 Cardinal Ln., East Islip, NY 11730.

CUNNINGHAM, Lawrence (Larry) H.; '97 BS; JD Georgetown Univ Law Ctr.; 3532 W Pl. NW, Washington, DC 20007, 202 625-1324. e-mail

CUNNINGHAM, Maureen; '95 BS; 220 W 24th St., New York, NY 10011, 212 675-4779.

CUNNINGHAM, Sheila; '93 AS; 699 10th Ave., Apt. 2Fs, New York, NY 10036.

CUNNINGHAM, Thomas F.; '83 MPA; 11 Quaker Ridge, Westtown, NY 10998.

CUNNINGHAM, Thomas P.; '82 BS; Fire Safety/Security; r. 44 Ridge St., Eastchester, NY 10709, 914 793-5832.

CUOMO, Anthony; '75 BA; 68-39 SW 20 St., W. Hollywood, FL 33023.

CUOMO, Vincent F.; '77 AS; 2521 25th Ln., W. Palm Bch., FL 33418.

CUPID, Irma; '99; 471 Park Ave., Brooklyn, NY 11205, 718 935-0161.

CURAS, Sophia '75 (See Foglia, Mrs. Sophia).

CURCIO, Leanne T. '99 (See Cook, Mrs. Leanne T.).

CURICH, Joseph; '96 BS; 97-11 106 St., Ozone Park, NY 11416.

CURLEY, John E.; '78 BA; 3212 58th St., Flushing, NY 11377.

CURRAN, Catherine C.; '95 BA; Mgr. of Mktg. & Admin/Student; Stratton Advisors Ltd./NYU, 575 Madison Ave., Ste. 1006, New York, NY 10022, 212 605-0572; r. 423 W. 45th St., 3FW, New York, NY 10036, 212 459-9525. e-mail

CURRAN, Eleanor A.; '74 BA; 530 Leonard St., Brooklyn, NY 11222, 718 383-2898; *James;* Maureen, Arlene, James.

CURRAN, James E.; '78 BA; Retired Fire Dept.; New York Fire Dept., Larchmont, NY 10538; r. 914 Harmon Dr., Larchmont, NY 10538, 914 834-7242.

CURRAN, John T.; '76 AS; 2 Revere Ct., Floral Park, NY 11001, 516 352-9300.

CURRAN, Matthew F.; '74 AS, '75 BA, '79 MPA; MSW Fordham Univ.; Social Worker; JRW Inst. of Addiction Studies, 705 Bronx River Rd., Yonkers, NY 10704, 914 776-7730; r. 4380 Vireo Ave. Apt. 6d, Bronx, NY 10470, 718 324-3188; *Rita;* Michael, Colleen. e-mail

CURRAN, Maureen; 530 Leonard St., Brooklyn, NY 11222, 718 383-2898.

CURRAO, Thomas J.; '90 BS; 82 Hall Ave. E, New City, NY 10956.

CURRO, Isabella; '84 BS, '90 MPA; 2525 Bouck Ave., Bronx, NY 10469.

CURRY, Anthony; '81 BA; 1131 Sogden Ave., Bronx, NY 10452.

CURRY, Heather M.; '95 MA; 18A Grandview Ave. W, Edison, NJ 08837.

CURRY, John A., Esq.; '91 BA; MA Univ. at Albany-SUNY, JD New York Law Sch.; Police Ofcr.; NYC Police Dept., 2 Lafayette St. 5th Fl., New York, NY 10007, 212 374-2534; r. 349 Bayside Ave., Rockaway Pt., NY 11697, 718 549-8685.

CURRY, Thomas P.; '76 MA; 4531 Buttonwood Rd, Great Neck, NY 11020.

CURRY, Warren P.; '95 BS; Capt.; NYC Police Dept., 1 Police Plz., New York, NY 10038, 212 374-6897; *Patricia;* Paul, Katherine, Lauren.

CURTI, Ms. Jennifer; '95 BS; Police Ofcr; NYC Police Dept.; r. 6 Burns St. #G17, Forest Hills, NY 11375.

CURTIS, Doniyell L.; '97 BA; 134-47 166th #13D, Jamaica, NY 11434, 718 712-5753.

CURTIS, Terri L.; '79 BS; 20-34 Seagrit Blvd., Far Rockaway, NY 11691, 718 712-5753.

CURYLO, Christopher J.; '92 BS; JD TX Wesleyan Univ.; Atty.; Christopher Curylo Atty-at-Law, 211 Myrtle Ave., Ramsey, NJ 07446, 201 934-7446; r. same; *Cheryl;* Asheton.

CURYLO, Phyllis J.; '98 MA; 54 Middle Island Rd, Mt. Sinai, NY 11766, 631 476-3635.

CUS, Stefanie M.; '95 BS; Sergeant; New York Police Dept.; r. 3190 140th St. Apt. 4L, Flushing, NY 11354, 718 762-0093.

CUSACK, Nancy M.; '83 BA; 8742 Van Wyck Expy., Jamaica, NY 11418.

CUSHER, Devin; '93 BS; 20 Cindy Ln., Wappingers Falls, NY 12590.

CUSIMANO, Stephanie A.; '99 BA; 17 Madison Ave., #76, Madison, NJ 07940.

CUSUMANO, Charles; '90 BS; 147 Carlyle Grn, Staten Island, NY 10312.

CUSUMANO, Patricia (Tricia); '92 BA; Caseworker; Sunrise Psychiatric Clinic, 1449 Straight Path, Ext. 21, Wyandanch, NY 11798, 631 253-9317; r. 51 Lake Promeneade, Lake Ronkonkoma, NY 11779, 631 272-2986. e-mail

CUTLER, Lynn; '74 BS; 1489 E 46th St., Brooklyn, NY 11234, 718 856-4997.

CUTLER, Robin A.; '82 BS; 49 Iroquois Ave., Lake Hiawatha, NJ 07034.

CUTRONE, Felix P.; '79 BA; 10864 42nd Ave., Flushing, NY 11368, 718 343-2832.

CUYLER, Julius T.; '81 MA; 201 King Ave., Trenton, NJ 08638, 609 882-9454.

CVIJIC, Zora '96 (See Miladinov, Mrs. Zora C.).

CYRAN, Paul; '89 BS; 888 Peconic St. Ph, Ronkonkoma, NY 11779.

CZAJKOWSKI, Raymond; '76 BS; MASTERS Clg. of Staten Island; Physical Therapist; Staten Island Univ. Hosp., Staten Island, NY 10312; r. 124 Woehrle Ave., Staten Island, NY 10312, 718 948-7140.

CZAJKOWSKI, Richard J.; '72 BS; 32 Mount Run, Neptune, NJ 07753, 732 918-0394.

CZARNECKA, Beata; '98 BS; 401 W. 45th St. 3c, New York, NY 10036, 212 459-9657. e-mail

CZARNECKI, Anthony; '75 MA; 5 Jo Dr., Cortlandt Manor, NY 10567.

D

DABKOWSKI, Dariusz; '96 BS; Ofc. Maint.; Ed Sayie Inc., 10 E. 39 St., New York, NY 10016, 212 683-1151; r. 6072 67th, Ridgewood, NY 11385, 718 417-4543; *Liza;* Andrew, Matthew.

DACKEN, Diane A.; '83 BS; 138 Stuyvesant Dr., Port Jefferson Sta., NY 11776.

DA CORTA, Elaine; '77 BA; 2220 73rd St., Flushing, NY 11370, 718 224-2752.

DACOSTA, Emmy H.; '99 BS; 88-35 Elmhurst Ave., Elmhurst, NY 11373, 718 429-1516; *Frank;* Elijah, Joshua. e-mail

DADACAY, Dominic M.; '98 MA; 744 9th Ave., New York, NY 10019.

DAGNELLO, Rudy J.; '74 BS; Ret. Mgr.; New York Crime Lab Postal Inspection, Postal Consumer Affairs; r. 217 N 4 St., Brooklyn, NY 11211. e-mail

D'AGOSTINO, John; '80 BS; 8433 149th Ave., Jamaica, NY 11414, 718 746-6896.

D'AGOSTINO, Michael; '71 BS; 312 Buchanan Ave., Mineola, NY 11501.

DAHL, Dena M., (Dena M. Centoducati); '92 BS; Business Owner; SERV-IT, 100 Sycamore Ave., Bridgewater, NJ 08807, 908 235-9149; r. same; *Ron Jr.* e-mail

DAIDONE, Anthony; '84 BS; 6222 Strickland Ave., Brooklyn, NY 11234, 718 763-6927.

DAISE, Cerita E.; '95 AS; 11616 198th St., Jamaica, NY 11412.

DALE, Thomas V.; '90 MA; 385 Seaford Ave., Massapequa, NY 11758.

D'ALESSANDRO, Joseph; '97 BA; 122 Bay 22nd St., Brooklyn, NY 11214, 718 232-4147.

D'ALESSANDRO, Paul V.; '83 BA; 2136 62nd St., Brooklyn, NY 11204, 718 891-2029.

D'ALESSIO, Berardino; 154 Walter Ave., Thornwood, NY 10594, 914 628-5210.

DALEY, Carlton A.; '93 BS; AS Kingsborough Community Cl; Mgr.; r. 590 E 165th St., Bronx, NY 10456, 718 861-6355; *Vanessa.*

DALEY, Robert E.; '76 MA; 222-17 93rd Ave., Queens Vlg., NY 11428, 718 849-3142.

DALEY, Thomas J.; '85 BA; Security Supv.; Merrill Lynch & Co., 225 Liberty St., New York, NY 10080, 212 449-3784; r. 91 Dewey Ave., Albertson, NY 11507, 516 248-1535; *Frances.*

DALLARA, Mark A.; '78 MA; BA Pace Univ.; Tax Agt.; NYS Tax Dept., 90 S. Ridge St., Rye Brook, NY 10573, 914 933-2337; r. 2055 27th St., Long Island City, NY 11105; *Theresa;* Alexis M., Angela M., Amanda M.

DALLATORRE, Elaine B.; '79 BA; 125 Withers St., Brooklyn, NY 11211, 718 349-8160.

DALLOO, Eric S.; '99 BS; Paralegal; Holland & Knight, 195 Broadway, New York, NY 10007. e-mail

DALTON, Alvaro A.; 157-10 Riverside Dr. W., New York, NY 10032.

DALTON, Angela C.; '97 BS; 441 Ocean Ave., Brooklyn, NY 11226, 718 284-4189.

DALTON, Christopher; '81 BS; 3012 Schley Ave., Bronx, NY 10465, 718 931-2991.

DALTON, Robert B.; '81 AS; AA Broward Community Clg.; Pres.; Wet Enterprises Inc., 1974 SW Bayshore Blvd., Port St. Lucie, FL 34984, 561 344-8004; r. 967 SE Bywood Ave., Port St. Lucie, FL 34983, 561 340-2125; *Jan;* Zack, Deanna, Franki, Danielle. e-mail

DALY, Daniel; '80 BS; MPA Pace Univ.; Capt.; Yonkers Police Dept., 104 S. Broadway, Yonkers, NY 10701, 914 377-7900; r. 43 Wilcox Ave., Yonkers, NY 10705.

DALY, Daren S.; '90 BA; 64 Delancey St., 3rd Fl., New York, NY 10002, 718 776-8990.

DALY, David; '74 BA; 150 W 95 St., New York, NY 10025, 315 768-7570.

DALY, Elizabeth V.; '98 BA; VS Probation Ofcr.; r. 215 29 48 Ave. 3e, Oakland Gardens, NY 11364, 718 229-3162. e-mail

DALY, CAPT Francis J.; '70 MPA; BBA City Clg.-Baruch, AS City Clg. Baruch; Retired-Police Capt.; Youth Div.-NYC Police Dept.; r. 976 78th St., Brooklyn, NY 11228, 718 833-4172; *Eileen;* Anne Marie, John, Catherine, Francis Jr.

DALY, Peter J.; '93 BS; 17 Old S. Highland Ave., Pearl River, NY 10965, 914 348-3432.

DALY, William; '85 MA; Clinical Admin. Mgr.; Staten Island Univ. Hosp., 375 Seguine Ave., Staten Island, NY 10309, 718 226-2260; r. 95 Pitman Ave., Fords, NJ 08863, 732 738-1413.

DALY, William J.; '76 BA; 91 Geranium Ave., Floral Park, NY 11001, 516 775-2774.

D'AMATO, George R.; '74 BS; BS, AS Rockland Cnty. Clg.; Criminal Investigator; NYS Dept. of Tax & Finance, 2 World Trade Ctr., New York, NY 10048, 212 321-4633; r. 33 Ebony Ct., Brooklyn, NY 11229, 718 769-8756; *Maria;* Michael, George, Jr. e-mail

D'AMATO, Michael; '71 BA; 2301 Boller Ave., Bronx, NY 10475, 718 671-8676.

D'AMBROFF, Randa; 19 Charlotte Pl., Plainview, NY 11803.

D'AMBROSIO, Jaime; '83 BA; 20-37 48 St., Astoria, NY 11105, 718 461-4555.

D'AMBROSIO, Louis J.; '76 BS; 10 Willa Way, Massapequa, NY 11758, 516 795-6207.

DAMES, Fatima C.; '95 BS; MA Univ. of Arizona, ABA Metro Clg.; Special Asst. for Legal Affairs; Mashantucket Pequot Tribal Nation, 2 Matts Path, Mashantucket, CT 06339, 860 396-2111; r. 43 Coachman Pike, Ledyard, CT 06339, 860 396-2111; *Gary;* Precious. e-mail

D'AMICANTONIO, Thomas; '91 BS; 16 Sandi Dr., Poughkeepsie, NY 12603.

DAMON, Latricia R.; '98 BS; Housing Asst.; NYC Housing Dept.; r. 235 Hoyt St., Brooklyn, NY 11217, 718 624-4429.

DAMON, Theadora P. '93 (See McSpirit, Ms. Theadora P.).

D'AMORE, Jessica M.; '99 MA; BA Wesleyan Univ.; Social Worker; Brooklyn Bur. of Community Svc., 100 Pennsylvania Ave., 3rd Fl., Brooklyn, NY 11207, 718 345-6300; r. 447 Chestnut St., Nutley, NJ 07110, 973 667-1841. e-mail

DANA, Robert J.; '77 BA; 2016 Brown St., Brooklyn, NY 11229, 718 627-5929.

DANAHER, James L.; '76 BS; 429 Ocean Ave., Massapequa Park, NY 11762.

DANCKWERTH, Edward T.; '75 BS; 6 Longview Rd, Livingston, NJ 07039, 973 992-2958.

DANCY, Ernest A.; '78 BS; 127 Franklin Ave., Brooklyn, NY 11205, 718 272-8525.

D'ANDREA, Leonardo; '97 BS; 85-17 60th Ave., Elmhurst, NY 11373.

D'ANDREA, Lorenzo J.; '96 BS; CERT. Fed. Law Enforcement Cntr; US Park Police Ofcr.; Park Police Station, Floyd Bennet Field, Brooklyn, NY 11234, 718 338-3988; r. 76 4th Pl., Brooklyn, NY 11231, 718 834-1450. e-mail

DANESE, Elizabeth Anne; '74 BS; Police Detective; Port Authority of New York & New Jersey; r. 58 Fairview Ave., Closter, NJ 07624.

D'ANGELO, Edward; '87 MA; 13 George St., Denville, NJ 07834.

DANGELO, Steven J.; '99 BA; 221 Floral Ave., Plainview, NY 11803, 516 938-6515.

DANGLER, Donald J.; '85 MA; POB 532, Convent Sta., NJ 07961.

DANIEL, Cemon F.; '97 BA; 1774 Edenwald Ave., Bronx, NY 10466, 718 325-4353.

DANIEL, David C.; '95 AS; 3319 112th St., Flushing, NY 11368, 718 527-1254.

DANIEL, George G.; '71 BS; 194-01 122nd Ave., Springfield Gardens, NY 11413, 718 380-8668.

DANIEL, Ralston; '80 AS; 1255 Commonwealth Ave., Bronx, NY 10472, 718 325-4353.

DANIEL, William A.; '78 BS; 1711 Essex Ave., Linden, NJ 07036.

DANIEL-BABB, Valerie; '96 MPA; Supv.; USPS, New York, NY 10199; r. 580 Empire Blvd. Apt. 1h, Brooklyn, NY 11225, 718 778-0594. e-mail

DANIEL-HURRY, Nadine N.; '95 BS; 1023 Bay 30th St., Far Rockaway, NY 11691.

DANIELS, Eurita, (Eurita Brooks); '80 BA; MS NYU; CEO; EUBRO Corp., 718 644-0583; r. 66-02 Grand Central, Forest Hills, NY 11375, 718 275-7618; Meka E. e-mail

DANIELS, Hilda B.; '84 BS; 2199 5th Ave., New York, NY 10037, 315 339-4163.

DANIELS, Joseph R.; '92 BS; 136 Saxon Woods Rd, Scarsdale, NY 10583, 914 762-1024.

DANIELS, Renee L.; '83 BA; 21321 Murdock Ave., Jamaica, NY 11429, 718 558-5345.

DANIELS, Mrs. Romina J.; '99 BA; AA Borough of Manhattan CC, BA; Mgr.; Godiva Chocolatier Inc., 560 Lexington Ave., New York, NY 10022, 212 980-9810; r. 1890 Lexington Ave. 5C, New York, NY 10035, 212 996-1413; *Alwyn;* Maxim.

DANIELS, Thomas L.; '95 BA; 1064 Carroll Pl., Apt. 3A, Bronx, NY 10456, 718 992-5069.

DANIELS, Yvonne; '86 BS; Probation Ofcr.; NYC Dept. of Probation, 12501 N Queens Blvd., Kew Gardens, NY 11415; r. 72 Cedar Rd., Westbury, NY 11590.

DANIELSON, Eskil S.; '75 MA; BA Lehigh Univ., MA Univ. of Virginia; Dir. of Emergency Mgmt.; Sussex Cnty. Div. of Em. Mgmt., 31 Rte. #206, Unit #2, Augusta, NJ 07822, 973 579-0380; r. 18 Hunters Ln., Andover, NJ 07821, 973 347-6676; *Judy;* Eskil Scott, Kevin William, EricChristopher. e-mail

DANIK, Mark D.; '76 MA; BA BS Rutgers Clg., JD ST Widener Law; Juvenile Justice Commission; NJ JJC, Lindbergh Rd, Hopewell, NJ 08525, 609 466-0740; r. RR #2-17 Lorton Rd, Old Bridge, NJ 08857, 732 251-7333; *Dorita Paniagua;* Denise. e-mail

DANJER, Marco V.; '95 BA; Order Patrol Agent.; US Order Patrol, 225 Kenney St., El Cajon, CA 92020, 619 557-5072; r. 2939 Laurel St., #102, San Diego, CA 92104, 619 283-0204. e-mail

D'ANTONIO, Steven A.; '76 BS, '78 MA; Lt.; NYPD Aviation Unit Coast Guard Hanger, Floyd Bennett Field, Brooklyn, NY 11234, 718 692-1220; r. 5918 23rd Ave., Apt. 3, Brooklyn, NY 11204, 718 621-0772. e-mail

DAOUAOU, Abdelilah; '97 BS; Electronic Banking; Bank of New York, New York, NY 10280; r. 25-12 Steinway St., Astoria, NY 11103, 718 721-7609. e-mail

DAOUPHARS, Jean Y.; '94 AS, '96; 443 W 51st St. Apt. 1r, New York, NY 10019, 212 586-6174.

D'AQUILA, Maureen; '79 BA; 137-17 95 St., Ozone Park, NY 11417.

DARBY, Anthony G.; '92 BS, '96 MA; 1542 Saint Lawrence Ave., Bronx, NY 10460, 718 863-7615.

DARBY, Mildred E.; '79 BS; 50 W. 97 St., New York, NY 10025.

DARCEY, Lawrence G.; '72 BS; RR3 Thistle Patch, Sag Harbor, NY 11963.

DARCY, Christopher F.; '83 BS; 103 Alan Dr., New City, NY 10956, 914 634-5156.

DARCY, Thomas J.; '72 BS; 25 Spruce Ave., Bethpage, NY 11714.

DARDEN, Lakisha M.; '99 MA; BA Iowa State Univ.; Field Investigator; US Investigations Svcs., Annandale, VA 22003; r. 4928 Fifth St. NW, Washington, DC 20011, 202 723-4857.

DARDZINSKI, Lisa A.; '95 MA; NU BS Clg. of Mt. St. Vincent, HNC A.H.N.C.C.; RN; Westchester Med. Ctr., Grasslands Rd, Valhalla, NY 10595, 914 493-7076; r. 4 Marina Dr., Mahopac, NY 10541.

DARGAN, Sabrina; '98 BA; AS; Secy.; NYS Parole, 340 Livingston St., Ext. #342, Brooklyn, NY 11217, 718596060; r. 2058 Union St. 2h, Brooklyn, NY 11212, 718 596-6060; Tatiana N Lane, Dontique L Lane.

DARGAN, Thomas J.; '76 BS; 750 Shore Rd, Apt. 3P, Long Beach, NY 11561, 516 897-3884.

D'ARPE, Gene; '93 BS; 252-07 63rd Ave., Little Neck, NY 11362.

D'ARRIGO, Joseph G.; '96 BS; 307 Onderdonk Ave., Ridgewood, NY 11385.

DARSILLO, Francis; '88 BA; 20 Lindron Ave., Smithtown, NY 11787.

DASCOLI, Francis; '76 BS; MPA Rutgers Univ.; Retired Lt./Supv.; NJ Police Dept./US Postal Svc.; r. 41 Sand Hill Rd, Kendall Park, NJ 08824, 732 821-5416; Sandra; Lisa, Victoria, Carla.

DASH, Anne M. '83 (See Michaels, Anne M.).

DASH, Randolph C.; '84 BS; 89-19 171st St., Jamaica, NY 11432, 718 746-0675.

DASHIELL, Karen; '96 BA; 9304 25th Ave., E. Elmhurst, NY 11369.

DASILVA, Gioia; '77 MA; 22 Behrendt Ct., Sayville, NY 11782.

DAUBMAN, Arthur G.; '75 BA; 770 Arlington Dr., Seaford, NY 11783, 516 735-2735.

DAUGHERTY, Cassandra; '91 BS; Corrections Ofcr.; r. 750 Grand Concourse Apt. 5F, Bronx, NY 10451; Samare.

DAUGHERTY, William; '96 BS; 21 Battery Ave., Brooklyn, NY 11228, 718 621-4217.

DAUGHTRY, Veda D.; '82 BA; 272 Pennsylvania A, Brooklyn, NY 11207, 718 604-9454.

DAUTAJ, Ylli; '95 AS; 90-19 88Ave. #D-32, Woodhaven, NY 11421.

DAVAN, Robert J.; '78 BS, '81 MA; Capt.; NYPD, 1 Police Plz., New York, NY 10038, 212 694-8205; r. 89 Lyncrest Ave., New City, NY 10956, 914 634-0845; Terry; Keith, Ryan, Rory. e-mail

DAVID, Denis P.; '78 BS; Police Ofcr.; MTA Police Dept., 346 Madison Ave., New York, NY 10017, 212 643-5079; r. Seven Denton Ave., E. Rockaway, NY 11518; Donna; Elizabeth.

DAVID, Fredrick D.; '89 BS; POB 105, Monticello, NY 12701, 315 839-6016.

DAVID, Harley; '78 AA, '79 BS; Retired Police Sergeant; NYCPD, Bronx, NY 10451; r. 149 Lions Gate Rd, Savannah, GA 31419, 912 920-7148; Mary; Harley D., Lisa, Cynthia T., Sophia.

DAVID, Joycelyn P.; '89 AS, '91 BA, '95 MPA; 11113 127th St., Jamaica, NY 11420, 718 894-5261.

DAVID, Lafleur; '90 BS; 533 E. 96 St., Brooklyn, NY 11212, 718 633-5599.

DAVID, McLawrence (Max) A.; 2000 BS; Residential Advisor; Proj. Return Fndn., 814 Amsterdam Ave., New York, NY 10025, 212 665-2010; r. 3401 Foster Ave.,Apt. 5E, Brooklyn, NY 11203, 718 469-9343; Grace H.; Terrence A., Warren R., Randy A., Damillie A. e-mail

DAVID, Wilfred; '86 MA; BA Johnson C Smith Univ.; Staff Writer/Adjunct Prof.; The Journal News/Marymount Clg., 1 Gannett Dr., W. Harrison, NY 10604, 914 966-4008; r. 32 Undercliff St., Yonkers, NY 10705, 914 965-1695.

DAVID, Yves A.; '77 BA; 2603 Avenue D, Brooklyn, NY 11226, 718 756-1641.

DAVIDS, Joseph Z.; '80 BS; 32 Lynn Pl., Bethpage, NY 11714, 516 536-4772.

DAVIDSON, Craig R.; '91 BS; POB 359, Montclair, NJ 07042.

DAVIDSON, Leslie-Ann; '90 BS, '95 MA; Probation Ofcr.; NYC Dept. of Probation, 115 Leonard St., New York, NY 10013; r. 223 Lenox Rd Apt. E11, Brooklyn, NY 11226, 718 469-4135; Trevor Gay.

DAVIDSON, Mark E.; '79 BA; 22740 Kobuk Ct., West Linn, OR 97068, 503 656-8000.

DAVIDSON, Paulette P.; '97 BS; 1129 Decatur St., Brooklyn, NY 11207, 718 384-2548.

DAVIDSON, Terrill L.; '99 BS; Loader/Unloader/Sorter; UPS, 643 W. 43rd St., New York, NY 10036, 212 631-6209; r. 1254 Prospect Pl., Brooklyn, NY 11213, 718 467-2776.

DAVIDZON, Alexander; '97 BA; 2819 W 12th St. 190, Brooklyn, NY 11224.

DAVIES, Charmaine A.; '81 BA; 19 Stoddard Pl., Brooklyn, NY 11225, 718 638-2190.

DAVIES, Christopher J.; '95 BS; 37 Sandford Rd., Fair Lawn, NJ 07410. e-mail

DAVILA, Alfredo; '97 BS; 204 W. 96th St., New York, NY 10025.

DAVILA, Jacinto; '87 BS; Divisional Loss Prevention Mgr.; CarMax, 225 Chastain Meadows Ct., Kennesaw, GA 30144, 770 792-4600; r. 4242 Willow Walk SW, Lilburn, GA 30047, 770 982-2710; Angela; Deanna.

DAVILA, Jose; '95 BS; 8839 Saint James Ave., Elmhurst, NY 11373.

DAVILA, Luis E.; '97 BS; 39-88 49th St., Sunnyside, NY 11104, 718 545-3779.

DAVILA, Nancy; '97 BA, '98 BA; 150-11 72nd Rd., Flushing, NY 11367, 718 723-4032.

DAVILA, Sandra M.; '89 BS; 150-11 72 Rd., Flushing, NY 11367, 718 723-4032.

DAVIS, Adrian C.; '84 BS; 2300 Fifth Ave. #4J, New York, NY 10037, 315 823-2601.

DAVIS, Andrew R.; '68 AS, '71 BS; 5 Pirates Cove Rd, Little Silver, NJ 07739.

DAVIS, Anthony W.; '80 MA; 221 E Pennywood Ave., Roosevelt, NY 11575, 516 371-0727.

DAVIS, Brian P.; '98 BA; Police Ofcr.; NYC Police Dept.; r. 1630 Pacific St. Apt. 2D, Brooklyn, NY 11213, 718 493-7536. e-mail

DAVIS, Chantel L.; '96 BA; 1297 Boynton Ave., # 2, Bronx, NY 10472, 718 991-3676.

DAVIS, Charles W.; '99 BS; Legislative Investigator; City Council, 250 Broadway, New York, NY 10007, 212 788-6882; r. 575 E 55 St., Brooklyn, NY 11203, 718 451-5223.

DAVIS, Cheryann '92 (See Luke, Mrs. Cherylann).

DAVIS, David; '83 BA; 3840 Greystone Ave., Bronx, NY 10463, 718 519-8523.

DAVIS, Diane L.; '95 BA; 12015 232nd St. Ph, Jamaica, NY 11411, 718 322-2690.

DAVIS, Dominique; '76 BA; 120 W 86th St. Apt. 8b, New York, NY 10024, 315 735-0839.

DAVIS, Eaton; '91 BS; AA LaGuardia Comm Clg.; Detective; NY City Police Dept.; r. 1024 E 227th St., Bronx, NY 10466.

DAVIS, Mrs. Eleanor, PhD; '78 MA; BS City Clg., PHD Union Grad. Inst.; Psychoanalytic Psychotherapist; The New Ctr. for Modern Parenthood, Family Counselor, New York, NY 10003, 212 982-7733; r. 3 Rutherford Pl., New York, NY 10003, 212 982-7733; Harold. e-mail

DAVIS, Felicia J.; '97 BA; 132-44 Bennett St., Jamaica, NY 11434.

DAVIS, Geneve E.; '96 BA; 732 E 231st St., Bronx, NY 10466, 718 294-5618.

DAVIS, Gideon; '73 AS; Chief of Operation; Triborough Bridge & Tunnel Authority, POB 35, Randalls Island, New York, NY 10035; r. 18 Dewhurst St., Staten Island, NY 10314, 718 273-3965; Miriam; Jason, Jessica. e-mail

DAVIS, Hildegarde B. '80 (See Jaliyl, Mrs. Laila A.).

DAVIS, James R.; '90 MA, '99 MSN; BA Temple Unv., PHD NYU; Adjunct Lecturer; St. Peter's Clg., Jersey City, NJ; r. 53 Vermilieaaue, New York, NY 10034, 212 567-9896; *Roberta.*

DAVIS, Jay E.; '70 BS; 20 Tareyton Dr., Victor, NY 14564, 315 597-2054.

DAVIS, Jeannette M.; '81 BS; 46 Everett St., Arlington, MA 02474, 781 861-0586.

DAVIS, Jerome; '83 AS, '86 BA; Deputy Warden; NYC Dept. of Corrections; r. 344 Fairlawn Ave., W. Hempstead, NY 11552, 516 481-8042.

DAVIS, Joanne; '99 BS; Secy.; Morgan Stanley Dean Witter, 1585 Broadway, 35th Fl., New York, NY 10036, 212 761-7185; r. 1760 Lexington Ave. 5D, New York, NY 10029, 212 876-0849. e-mail

DAVIS, Johnny E.; '87 BS; 40 E Sidney Ave. Apt. 3f, Mt. Vernon, NY 10550, 716 823-0382.

DAVIS, Judie; '95 BA; 784 Garden St. Ph, Bronx, NY 10451 900-0025.

DAVIS, Kelceda A.; '87 BS; 14509 223rd St., Jamaica, NY 11413, 718 525-3094.

DAVIS, Lawrence E.; '96 BA; 1643 Undercliff Ave., Bronx, NY 10453, 718 365-3380.

DAVIS, Londel; '78 BS; 20-32E Rothman Pl., Bronx, NY 10453, 718 365-3380.

DAVIS, Lynette; '88 BS; Investigator I; Human Resources Admin.; New York, NY 10038, 212 331-3281; r. 388 Richmond Ter. Apt. 8l, Staten Island, NY 10301.

DAVIS, Mandy D.; '96 BA; 2100 Tiebout Ave., Bronx, NY 10457, 718 597-0008.

DAVIS, Matthew; '94 BS; Child Protective Spec.; ACS, Brooklyn, NY 11208, 718 348-8061; r. 147-07 119th Ave., Jamaica, NY 11436, 718 322-4715; *Keeva Bragg.*

DAVIS, Nakisha; '98 BA; 345 W. 50th St. 1a, New York, NY 10019, 212 974-1405.

DAVIS, Regina A.; '97 MPA, '98 MPA; 851 Hancock St., Brooklyn, NY 11233, 718 443-3252.

DAVIS, Richard A.; '82 BS; POB 3124, Linden, NJ 07036.

DAVIS, Ronald J.; '76 MA; 360 E 72nd St., Apt. B1006, New York, NY 10021, 315 823-2601.

DAVIS, Roshawn B.; '95 BS; 707 Monroe St., Brooklyn, NY 11221, 718 649-7427.

DAVIS, Sonya '89 (See Roberts, Mrs. Sonya).

DAVIS, Stephen P.; '78 BS; 57 E. 95 St., New York, NY 10128, 315 839-7252.

DAVIS, Teresa A.; '95 MPA; BS SUNY; Dir. Transportation Svc.; Pennsylvania State Univ., Fleet Operations Bldg. Rm. 5, University Park, PA 16802, 814 863-4006; r. Hc 1 Box 19b, Moshannon, PA 16859, 814 387-4826; Connor. e-mail

DAVIS, Tonya; '96 CERT; 10846 Ditmars Blvd., Flushing, NY 11369, 718 465-0173.

DAVIS, Vameershala; '93 BS; MBA Adelphi Univ.; Account Exec.; United Parcel Svc., 104-01 Foster Ave., Brooklyn, NY 11236, 718 706-4166; r. 18613 Foch Blvd., Jamaica, NY 11412, 718 276-3007. e-mail

DAVIS, Wilbert; '97 BA; Legal Asst.; Willkie Farr & Gallagher, 787 7th Ave., New York, NY 10019, 212 728-8834; r. 1820 Brooklyn Ave., Brooklyn, NY 11210, 718 377-5318. e-mail

DAVIS, William T.; '98 BA; 4 Pine St., Port Washington, NY 11050, 516 883-8006.

DAVIS, Xiomara D.; '83 BS; 577 Jefferson St., Westbury, NY 11590, 516 371-0727.

DAVODOWICH, Erek G.; '93 BS, '95 MPA; 70 SW 91st Ave., Apt. 309, Plantation, FL 33324.

DAVY, Christopher S.; '92 BS; Computer Spec.; US Food & Drug Admin., 158-15 Liberty Ave., Jamaica, NY 11433, 718 340-7000; r. 604 Woodland Dr., S. Hempstead, NY 11550, 516 538-3141; *Paula;* Kalifa, Krista. e-mail

DAWBER, Mary I.; '78 BA; 152 Mayfair Ave., W. Hempstead, NY 11552.

DAWBER, Mary J.; '78 BA; 152 Mayfair Ave., W. Hempstead, NY 11552.

DAWKINS, Leslie V.; '92 BS; 31 Goshen St., Elmont, NY 11003, 516 872-3886.

DAWSON, Darlene D.; '78 BA; 758 Hendrix St., Brooklyn, NY 11207, 718 421-1962.

DAY, Thomas M.; '76 BS; 4227 Spring Ln., Lakeland, FL 33811, 863 815-0638.

DE, Holzer L.; '85 MA; 500 Kappock St. Apt. 3A, Bronx, NY 10463, 718 585-3387.

DE, Jesus B.; '90 BS; 3020 Yates Ave., Bronx, NY 10469, 718 293-9330.

DE, La; '96 BA; 99-01 Corona Ave., Corona, NY 11368, 718 279-9102.

DE, Nigris B.; '85 AS; 88 Renee Pl., Staten Island, NY 10314, 718 698-6159.

DE, Stefano; '95 AS; 1460 Pennsylvania, Brooklyn, NY 11239, 718 383-8865.

DE, Vertevil S.; '88 BS; 2 John St., Greenvale, NY 11548, 516 829-5227.

DEACON, Carol J.; '97 MA, '97 BS MA; 192 Spring St. Apt. 5, New York, NY 10012, 212 226-4618. e-mail

DEAN, Mrs. Angela R., (Angela R. Brown); '89 BS; State Traffic Ofcr.; California Hwy. Patrol, 444 N. Third St., Sacramento, CA 95814, 916 445-0752; r. 3460 Reyman Ln., Loomis, CA 95650; *Eric;* Cameron, Harley, Brianna. e-mail

DEAN, James C.; '95 MA; BA Fairfield Union; Police Inspector; NYC Police Dept., One Police Plz., New York, NY 10038, 212 374-5000; r. 381 Yale, Garden City, NY 11530; *Sarah;* James, Erin, Bridgett.

DEANE, Eric; '86 BS; Sgt.; NYPD, 49 Chambers St., Rm. 525, New York, NY 10013; r. 150 Dreiser Loop # 4, Bronx, NY 10475.

DE ANGELO, Ronnie J.; '79 BS; 15416 59th Ave., Flushing, NY 11355, 718 327-3151.

DEANS, Karen; '97 BA; Child Protective Spec.; Admin. for Children Svcs., 192 E 151st St., Bronx, NY 10451, 718 579-9259; r. 639 E. 169th St., Bronx, NY 10456, 718 378-0918.

DEARMAN, William; '71 BS; 254 Woodlands Ave., White Plains, NY 10607.

DE BEER, Rebecca; '98 MA; BA Lehman Clg.; 555 Kappock St., Bronx, NY 10463, 718 601-4785.

DEBELLIS, Michael A.; '91 BS, '97 MA; 3047 Harding Ave., Bronx, NY 10465.

DEBONO, Pierre C.; '98 BA; 43 Eric Ln., New Hyde Park, NY 11040, 516 354-7962.

DECAMBRE, Brenda; '95 BS; JD CUNY Law Sch.; Student; CUNY Law Sch.; r. 1132 Fox St., Bronx, NY 10459, 718 991-0926. e-mail

DE CANDIA, Domenic; '72 BS, '75 MA; Disaster Assistance Employee; Fed. Emergency Mgmt. Agcy., 26 Federal Plz. Rm. 1349, New York, NY 10028, 212 225-7213; r. 242 Buscher Ave., Valley Stream, NY 11580, 516 825-7242; *Joan;* Carmine, Christopher, Jeannine, Albert, Edward, Elena.

DECANDITIS, Neil; '86 MPA; 8159 156th Ave., Jamaica, NY 11414.

DE CANIO, Camille M.; '76 BA; 2915 214th Pl., Flushing, NY 11360, 718 847-4924.

DE CAPRIO, Angelo; '77 MPA; Retired; r. 36 Sutton Pl. S # 14b, New York, NY 10022, 212 751-5714; *Carol;* James, Arthur, Amanda, Mak, Ellen, Max, Catherine.

DECASTRO, Janet L.; '80 MA; BA Marymount Clg.; Ordinance Enforcement Ofcr.; Town of East Hampton, 300 Pantigo Pl., East Hampton, NY 11937, 631 324-3858; r. 118 Water Mill Towd Rd., Water Mill, NY 11976, 631 726-5718; *John Dupee;* Meredith.

DECASTRO, Lydia; '91 BS; 120-4 Donizetti Pl. #4B, Bronx, NY 10475, 718 671-0628.

DECEGLIE, Louis M.; '97 BS; 71 Henry Ave., Palisades Park, NJ 07650.

DECEILIO, Andrea E. '98 (See Tramuto, Mrs. Andrea E.).

DECHABERT, Ms. Christina; '97 BA; 1791 Bruckner Blvd., Bronx, NY 10472, 718 584-5085; Ashley.

DECHINEA, Aggrey D.; '96 BA; 18725 Keeseville Ave., Jamaica, NY 11412.

DECICCO, Dominick; '93 BS; 1569 W 3rd St., Brooklyn, NY 11204.

DE CICCO, Donna M.; '95 BSLS; Risk Mgmt. Analyst; PaineWebber, New York, NY 10019; r. 565 Graham Ave., Brooklyn, NY 11222.

DE CICCO, Timothy J.; '95 BA; POB 184, Franklin Sq., NY 11010, 516 248-1420.

DECKER, Michael J.; '96 BA; 2565 E. 11 St., Brooklyn, NY 11235, 718 368-0922.

DE CLUITT, Gerald C.; '76 BA; 427 E. 140 St., Bronx, NY 10454, 718 295-7460.

DECOCQ, Michael E.; '91 BS; 69 Park Ave., Webster, NY 14580, 716 265-3618.

DECONINCK, David A.; '95 BA; Police Ofcr.; NYPD, TMTF, New York, NY 10012, 212 239-2220; r. 47-55 39th Pl. Apt. 4F, Long Island City, NY 11104, 718 482-8448.

DECOTEAU, Francis A.; '97 BS; CERT. Long Island Univ.; Legal Asst.; NYC Law Dept., 100 Church St., New York, NY 10007, 212 442-7325; r. 705 Shepherd Ave., Brooklyn, NY 11208, 718 272-2790.

DECRESCE, Christopher; '96 BA; 30 River Ct., Apt. 602, Jersey City, NJ 07310.

DECUIR, Donna M.; '85 BS; 1617 Bayview Ave., Bronx, NY 10465.

DE DONA, Natalie; '93 MA; 439 Oak Neck Rd, W. Islip, NY 11795.

DEEGAN, Kevin T.; '95 BS; 310 Laurel Rd., Pearl River, NY 10965, 914 735-8090.

DEEN, Mohamed; '95 AS; 1963 Ryer Ave. # 2, Bronx, NY 10457, 718 299-4915.

DEERY, Edward; '76 BS; 19938 49th Ave., Flushing, NY 11365, 718 428-8965.

DEESE, Gregory; '97 BA; 2861 Bainbridge Ave., Bronx, NY 10458, 718 584-6453.

DEFELICE, John J.; 3057 Avenue U, Brooklyn, NY 11229.

DE FILIPPO, Michael; '80 BS; 527 E 42nd St., Brooklyn, NY 11203, 718 284-2150.

DEFINA, Bernice; '95 MA; BS Mt. St. Mary Clg.; Lt.; NYCPD, Police Plz., New York, NY 10038, 212 374-5000; r. 282 Potter Ave., Staten Island, NY 10314.

DEFINA, Joseph F.; '75 BS; 427 100th St., Brooklyn, NY 11209.

DEFINA, Louise M.; '75 BS; 427-100 St., Brooklyn, NY 11209.

DEFRANCESCO, Rosalie A.; '99 BS; Police Ofcr.; MTA Police Dept., 345 Madison Ave., New York, NY 10017, 212 878-1000; r. 48 Goodwin Ave., Staten Island, NY 10314, 718 876-6059.

DEFRANCO, Edward J.; '62 MPA; PHD NY Univ.; Proj. Dir.; GNNYC Div. of Criminal Justice Svc., 4 Tower Pl., Albany, NY 12203; r. 66 Mcguffey Ln., Delmar, NY 12054, 518 439-1378; *Angela;* Anthony, Edward, Stephen. e-mail

DEFRANCO, Elizabeth (Liz) C.; '97 BA; Writer; Hozro Cnsltg., 481 8th Ave., Ste. 1542, New York, NY 10001, 212 868-2364; r. Woodside, NY 11377; Chris Koth. e-mail

DEFREITAS, Ewald; '85 BS; 2311 Bedford Ave., Brooklyn, NY 11226, 718 941-5709.

DE GAETANO, Gina; '97 BS; 5 Oak Ave., Tuckahoe, NY 10707.

DE GARCIA, Carmen M.; '78 BS; 345 8th Ave. Apt. 2a, New York, NY 10001, 315 733-3343.

DE GEORGE, Joseph W.; '98 MS; BA Iona Clg.; Pres.; FYI Investigations; r. 33-03 255 St., Little Neck, NY 11363, 718 225-2798; *Cheryl.* e-mail

DEGERING, Steven V.; '76 BS; 45-31 171 St., Flushing, NY 11358.

DEGIL, Rana M.; '97 MA; 76-09 34th Ave., Jackson Hts., NY 11372.

DEGIOVINE, Arthur M.; '75 MA; BS St. Peters Clg.; Investigator; Charleston Public Defender, 2144 Melbourne Ave., POB 72065, Charleston, SC 29415, 843 740-5751; r. 2011 Hwy. 17 N. Apt. 1300-Q, Mt. Pleasant, SC 29466, 843 971-3049.

DEGIULIO, Joseph A.; '97 BS; 78 Midland Blvd., Ronkonkoma, NY 11779.

DEGNAN, Brian A.; '85 BS; Law Dept. Investigator; Atty. Generals Ofc., 120 Broadway, New York, NY 10271, 212 416-8505; r. 196 Russell St., Brooklyn, NY 11222, 718 383-7429.

DEGRAFFENREID, Adella; '85 BS; 277 W 127 St., New York, NY 10027.

DEGRENIER, Terrence; '97 BS; Mgr.-Info. Systs.; Bio-Rad Laboratories, 237 Putnam, Cambridge, MA 02139, 617 234-7196; r. 15 Highland St., Bradford, MA 01835; *Andrea;* Olivia, William. e-mail

DEGROOT, Daniel R.; '85 BA; Detective; Morris Cnty. Prosecutor's Ofc., Courthouse, POB 900, Morristown, NJ 07963, 973 285-6200; r. 142 S. Ter., Boonton, NJ 07005.

DE HART, Helen M. '74 (See Pattinson, Mrs. Helen M.).

DEHLINGER, Alfred; '83 BS; 431 W Shore Tr., Sparta, NJ 07871, 973 729-9895.

DE HOLCZER, Lauren J.; '80 BA, '85 MA; AAS Pace Univ.; RN-AIDS Spec./Public Health Nurse; NYC Dept. of Health, Dist. #9, Bronx, NY 10457, 718 681-7771; r. 500 Kappock St. Apt. #3A, Bronx, NY 10463, 718 884-0969; Julie Hansen. e-mail

DEITEL, Abraham; '75 BA; 457 Fdr Dr. Apt. A704, New York, NY 10002, 212 677-1261.

DEJESUS, Diana; '96 MA; 2740 Lurting Ave., Bronx, NY 10469.

DE JESUS, Evelyn A.; '95 BS; 501 Dean St. 3r, Brooklyn, NY 11217, 718 836-3769.

DEJESUS, Iris K.; '98 BA; Investigator; HRA, 212 491-1508; r. 4040 Bronx Blvd. 3a, Bronx, NY 10466, 718 231-9738. e-mail

DE JESUS, Jose R.; '83 BS; 3743 102 St. #1F, Flushing, NY 11368, 718 204-8644.

DE JESUS, Juan A.; '78 BS; 1048 Ward Ave. # 2f, Bronx, NY 10472, 718 293-9330.

DE JESUS, Lisa; '95 BS; Tax Spec; Fidelity Investments, 200 Liberty St., New York, NY 10281, 212 335-6757; r. 2253 Third Ave., Apt. 1801, New York, NY 10035, 212 860-1940. e-mail

DEJESUS, Nelly J.; '94 BS; 160 Wadsworth Ave., Apt. 509, New York, NY 10033.

DE JESUS, Nestor R.; '81 BS; 409 Hewes St., Brooklyn, NY 11211, 718 246-4464.

DE JESUS-RODRIGUEZ, Blanqui I.; '90 BS; AS Bronx Community Clg.; Sr. Court Clerk; Bronx Supreme Ct., 851 Grand Councourse, Bronx, NY 10451, 718 590-3729; r. 3020 Yates Ave., Bronx, NY 10469. e-mail

DE JOHN, Gregory G.; '76 BS; 4605 7th Ave., Brooklyn, NY 11220, 718 964-1510.

DEJOHN, Regina M.; '95 MPA; 1396 Long Pond Rd, Rochester, NY 14626, 716 225-0485.

DEL, Preore S.; '79 MA; 49 Wellesley St., Maplewood, NJ 07040.

DEL, Vecchio F.; '81 BS; 60 Pitt St. #10F, New York, NY 10002.

DELACRUZ, Claret; '99 BA; 1046 Amsterdam Ave., 9, New York, NY 10025.

DELACRUZ, Cruz; '97 BA; 722 E 218th St., Apt. 1, Bronx, NY 10467.

DELACRUZ, Ralph; '98 BS; CERT FEGS Business College; Temp Paralegal Ofc. Asst.; Gregory & Gregory; r. 1169 E. 226th Dr. #3D, Bronx, NY 10466; *Nilda;* Shawn, Kimberly, Tiffany, Ralph.

DE LA CRUZ, Ramon; '94 BA; 565 W 139th St. Apt. 64, New York, NY 10031, 315 245-2337.

DELAHANTY, Lt Neal C.; '72 BS; Ret Lt.; NYC Police Dept.; r. 348 Travis Ave., Staten Island, NY 10314, 718 983-0817; *Melanie;* Adam, Tiffany, Timothy. e-mail

DELAMER, John; 33 Seville Ln., Stony Brook, NY 11790.

DELANEY, Ann; '81 BS; 40 Miller Ave., Tarrytown, NY 10591, 914 631-4748.

DELANEY, Ernest S.; '93 BS; 2955 Frederick Douglass Blvd. #1, New York, NY 10039, 315 336-2669.

DELANEY, James T.; '93 AS, '96 BS; Lt.; NYC Police Dept., 76th Precinct, 191 Union St., Brooklyn, NY 11231, 718 834-3201; r. 317 100th St. Apt. 5k, Brooklyn, NY 11209.

DELANEY, Katharine '86 (See McLoughlin, Katharine).

DELANEY, Melvin; '85 BS; 141 Argyle Rd., Garden City, NY 11530.

DELANO, Donald F.; '76 MPA; PHD City Univ. of NY, BA Queens Clg.; Police Lt.; Port Authority of NY & NJ Police, Bldg. 10 Newark Intl Airport, Newark, NJ 07114, 973 961-6230; r. 8 Sherwood Rd, Manalapan, NJ 07726, 732 536-1546; *Kathleen;* Donald F. Jr.

DELAPAZ, Frank C.; '95 BS; 4130 46 St., Long Island City, NY 11104.

DE LA PENA, Mario; '81 BS; 1980 63rd St., Brooklyn, NY 11204, 718 284-2150.

DEL CASTILLO, Vincent; '84 MPA; PHD Fordham Univ.; Prof.; John Jay Clg.; r. 716 Glover Pl., Baldwin, NY 11510, 516 223-1596.

DELEO, Deirdre; '96 MA; Psychiatric Social Work; Visiting Nurse Svc. of New York, 41-61 Kissena Blvd., Flushing, NY 11355, 718 463-9494; r. 60 Grant Ave., Brooklyn, NY 11208, 718 348-5999. e-mail

DELEON, Anna M.; '95 BS; 4 W 103rd St. Apt. 5a, New York, NY 10025.

DE LEON, Rafael A.; '84 MPA; RR 3, Carmel, NY 10512, 518 789-6271.

DELERME, Carolyn; '99; Student; r. Bronx, NY 10462, 718 931-9730; Amanda. e-mail

DELERME, Stevenson; '95 BS; Investigator; H.R.A. Dept of Social Svcs., 718 237-8105; r. 709 E 78th St., Brooklyn, NY 11236; *Nadia.*

DELGADO, Benny; '82 BA; 130 E. 104 St. #6, New York, NY 10029.

DELGADO, Ms. Fatima A.; '95 BA; Asst. Supv.; TIAA-CREF, Republic Plz., Ste. 200, 370 Seventeenth St., Denver, CO 80290, 303 607-2230; r. 5563 S. Quatar St., Aurora, CO 80015, 303 766-9414; Doris, Marie. e-mail

DELGADO, Jose L.; '85 BA; 1314 Metcalf Ave., Bronx, NY 10472, 718 220-0662.

DELGADO, Tracy L.; '96 BA; 50 W. 97th St., New York, NY 10025, 212 222-8757.

DELGADO-RIOS, Lisa; '88 BS; 221 Ringwood Ave., Apt. A-13, Pompton Lakes, NJ 07442.

DELISSER, Christine A.; '99 BA; 22 Whitson St., Hempstead, NY 11550, 516 562-4262.

DELIU, Francisco C.; '99 BA; Law Student; Syracuse Univ. Clg. of Law, Syracuse, NY 13244; r. 80 05 78 Ave. 2, Flushing, NY 11385, 718 366-5573; *Gabriella.*

DELIZ, Tina Marie '92 (See Pagan, Tina-marie).

DELLA, Torre T.; '79 BS; 67 Stanley Ave., Nutley, NJ 07110.

DELL'AERA, Peter A.; '96 BA; AAS Farmingdale Univ.; Lt.; NYPD, 263 Tompkins Ave., Brooklyn, NY 11216, 718 636-6624; r. 53 Abbey Ln., Levittown, NY 11756.

DELLAPENNA, Alfrdd J.; 74 Walton St., Brentwood, NY 11717, 631 273-9086.

DELLAVALLE, Anthony; '96 BS; 1831 Edison Ave., Bronx, NY 10461, 718 597-7956.

DELLICARPINI, Joseph; '77 BA; 2025 43rd St., Long Island City, NY 11105.

DELLORTO, Melissa A.; '98 BA; 279 Spruce Dr., Brick, NJ 08723.

DELMA, Nadege; '91 BS; 215 N 7th Ave., Mt. Vernon, NY 10550, 914 699-7791.

DELMORE, John G.; '77 BS; 43-09 147, Flushing, NY 11355.

DELONG, Joseph; '73, '74 BS; 6 Ludlow Way, Oakdale, NY 11769.

DELORENZIS, Ellis R.; '95 BA; 3615 Greystone Ave., Bronx, NY 10463, 718 601-7869.

DELPIN, Pedro; '90 BS; 115 E 116th St. Apt. 2e, New York, NY 10029, 212 427-5999.

DEL PREORE, Salvatore; '79 MA; BA Montclair State Clg.; Retired Capt; r. 49 Wellesley St., Maplewood, NJ 07040; *Kay.*

DELPRINO, Robert; '86 MA; PHD Old Dominion Univ.; Assoc. Prof.; Buffalo State Clg. SUNY, Dept. Physchology, 1300 Elmwood Ave., Buffalo, NY 14222. e-mail

DELRUSSO, Christopher; '79 MA; 21 Josham Ln., Lake Hiawatha, NJ 07034.

DELUCA, Anthony F.; '79 BS; JD Brooklyn Law Sch.; Atty.; Longo & D'Apice Esq., 26 Court St., Brooklyn, NY 11242, 718 855-5684; r. 3589 Manhasset St., Seaford, NY 11783, 516 409-5196; *Theresa;* Bridget, Annelise. e-mail

DE LUCA, Fortunato J.; '75 MPA; 51 Soundview Ave., Oyster Bay, NY 11771, 516 354-5284.

DELUCA, Henry; '89; Asst. Prof.; Westfield State Clg., Westfield, MA 01085; r. 2807 Coventry Ln., E. Greenbush, NY 12061, 518 479-3941; *Loretta;* Jo-Ellen, Ann Marie Caso, Jodie Ferro, Adam Kulak. e-mail

DE LUCA, Lawrence J.; '80 BS; 1130 Bergen Ave., Brooklyn, NY 11234, 718 622-5972.

DELUCA, Lorayn; '94 CERT; BS MS CUNY/New Sch. Social Res., CERT. NYS; Asst. Dir.; NYC Bd. of Educ., New York, NY 10001; r. New York, NY 10001. e-mail

DELVALLE, Carlos; '89 BS; 44 Highland Pl., Brooklyn, NY 11208.

DELVALLE, Yesenia; '96 BA; 521 Fdr Dr. Apt. 7e, New York, NY 10002.

DEL VICARIO, Robert E.; '91 AS; Asst. Special Agt. Charge; US Customs Svc., 1780 Ste. D, Wherle Dr., Williamsville, NY 14221, 716 565-2039; r. 4230 Thornwood Ln., Williamsville, NY 14221; *Loreta;* Richard, Jonathan, Robert, Stephen. e-mail

DEMAGGIO, John M.; '75 BS; 11714 125th St., Jamaica, NY 11420, 718 784-8269.

DEMAGISTRIS, Scott J.; '92 BS; AS Cnty. Clg. of Morris; Police Ofcr.; Monteville Twp., 86 River Rd, Montville, NJ 07045, 973 334-2730; r. 19 Village Grn Apt. J, Budd Lake, NJ 07828; *Krina.*

DE MAIO, Anthony V.; '81 MA; 14214 Booth Memorial Ave., Flushing, NY 11355, 718 393-3731.

DE MAIO, Joseph; '77 BS; 8431 110th St., Jamaica, NY 11418, 718 204-8644.

DEMAIO, Vincent; '93 BA; 2239 21st St., Long Island City, NY 11105.

DEMARCO, Michael; 1551 W 6 St., Brooklyn, NY 11204, 718 234-5816.

DE MARINO, Vincent A.; '80 BS; 1346 Decker St., Valley Stream, NY 11580, 516 829-5227.

DE MARTINI, Joseph; '77 BA; 1958 Brown St., Brooklyn, NY 11229, 718 743-7888.

DE MATAS, Robert P.; '78 BS; 54 Dean Pl., Larchmont, NY 10538, 914 771-6499.

DEMBY, Janice; '89 CERT; 16 Pinho Ave., Carteret, NJ 07008, 732 969-0770.

DEMENT, William; '92 BA; 777 Father Capodanno Blvd., Staten Island, NY 10305.

DEMEO, Teresa A.; '84 MA; 116 Ravenhurst Ave., Staten Island, NY 10310, 718 273-0610.

DEMERS, Martha; '91 MPA; BS Incarnate Word Clg.; Prog. Mgr.; T.R.I.C.A.R.E. Southern California, Bob Wilson Dr., San Diego, CA 92134, 619 532-9697; r. 3140 Bonita Woods Dr., Bonita, CA 91902, 619 475-3659. e-mail

DEMING, Janet; 27 Carlson Ave., Kings Park, NY 11754, 631 269-7293.

DEMIRKAYA, Yalkin; '85 BS, '89 MA; 96 Flintridge Dr., Holbrook, NY 11741.

DEMPSEY, Dennis J.; '79 MA; 98 Steiner Ave., Trenton, NJ 08619.

DEMPSEY, John S.; '72 BA; Long Island Univ., MPA; Prof. of Criminal Justice; Suffolk Cnty. Community Clg., 533 College Rd., Selden, NY 11784, 631 451-4338; r. 10 Oak Ct., Selden, NY 11784, 631 666-1369. e-mail

DENARDO, Jeffrey J.; '80 BA; 2345-83 St., Brooklyn, NY 11214, 718 449-1985.

DE NARO, Robert J.; '81 BS; 1655 Hubbell St., Bronx, NY 10461, 718 584-5085.

DENESOPOLIS, John; '94 BS; 196 Keiber Ct., Staten Island, NY 10314.

DE NIET, Bonnie, (Bonnie McGarrell); '82 MA; MSW SUNY-Stony Brook; 349 Magnolia Dr., Selden, NY 11784, 631 642-1349; *John.* e-mail

DENIS, Chester J.; '98 BA; 255 Prospect PL., Brooklyn, NY 11238, 718 953-2047.

DENIS, Iznaldy; '99 BS; 166-05 89th Ave. #3G, Jamaica, NY 11432, 718 297-1404.

DENIS, Mrs. Karla J., (Karla J. Draffen); '87 BA; Purchasing Mgr.; New York Marriott Marquis, 1535 Broadway, New York, NY 10036, 212 704-8706; r. 129 W 147 St., Apt. #15C, New York, NY 10039, 212 281-5995; *Reginald;* Bryan, Denis. e-mail

DENNARD, Debra M.; '98 MA; Psychologist; PSCH, 718 460-5500; r. 115-42 226th St., Cambria Hts., NY 11411, 718 525-1801; Taylor.

DENNEDY, James F.; '96 BS; 845 56th St., # 2R, Brooklyn, NY 11220, 718 854-4943.

DENNELLY, Lawrence E.; '77 BA; 17 Crampton Ave., Great Neck, NY 11023.

DENNETT, Phyllis D.; '83 BS; Sr. Secy. to Supreme Court Justice; 718 520-3159; r. 155-24 Jewel Ave., Flushing, NY 11367. e-mail

DENNIGAN, Paul R.; '92 AS, '96 BS; Bridge & Tunnel Ofcr.; Triborough, Marine Pkwy. Bridge, Brooklyn, NY 11234, 718 692-5501; r. 2008 New York Ave., Brooklyn, NY 11210, 718 377-4691.

DENNIS, Gustina M.; '75 BA; 119-37 130 St., S. Ozone Park, NY 11420, 718 949-7114.

DENNIS, Jose J.; '78 BA; 401 B St., Ste. 1550, San Diego, CA 92101, 858 748-2880.

DENNIS, Ms. Tyler L.; '96 BA; Child Protective Svcs.; Admin. for Children Srvs, 192 E151St.St, Bronx, NY 10451, 718 579-9122; r. 1309 Fifth Ave., New York, NY 10029, 212 831-3734.

DENSLOW, Lisa D.; '97 BA; Couns.; Covenant House, 346 W 17th St., 6th Fl., New York, NY 10011, 212 727-4195; r. 5 Virginia Pl., Brooklyn, NY 11213, 718 778-7953. e-mail

DE NUNZIO, Steven M.; '77 BS; 8723 97th St., Jamaica, NY 11421, 718 323-9807.

DENZLER, Thomas A.; '92 MPA; 4 Thornwood Ct., Harriman, NY 10926.

DEOW, Nadira; '86 AS; 36-30 31st. St., Long Island City, NY 11106.

DEPALMA, Ms. Danielle A.; '96 MA; Psychiatric Screener; Care Plus NJ, Paramus, NJ 07652, 201 262-7108; r. 6 Vivian Ave., Emerson, NJ 07630, 201 599-0075.

DE PAOLO, Steven M.; '80 BS; 455 E 57 St., New York, NY 10022, 212 688-7358.

DE PAULO, Peter A.; '76 BA; 2025 E. 15 St., Brooklyn, NY 11229, 718 237-2262.

DE PHILLIPS, Alfred P.; '67 MPA; 19 Birchwood Park Dr., Syosset, NY 11791, 516 433-5038.

DEPIERRO, Joseph M.; '69 AAS, '71 BS; Inspector for Police Dept. Ret; r. 10 Wood Ave., Massapequa, NY 11758, 516 799-7265; *Marianne;* Carolyn.

DEPUY, Richard A.; '96 BS; 37 Bradley Ave., Staten Island, NY 10314.

DERAC, Yves P.; '84 BS; 1253 S Curson Ave., Los Angeles, CA 90019, 323 525-0997.

D'ERASMO, Maria L.; '89 BS; 5 Pine St., Elmont, NY 11003, 516 354-2092.

DERAVIN, MAJ Eric H., USAR(Ret.); '83 MPA; PHD LaSalle Univ.; NYC Correction/Hofstra Univ.; r. POB 133, Bronx, NY 10469, 718 681-5331.

DERENOWSKI, John C.; '67 BS, '67 AS, '75 MA; HS Tchr.; Social Studies; Lake Havasu City HS, Lake Havasu City, AZ 86406, 520 855-4011; r. 3121 Longview Dr., Lake Havasu City, AZ 86406, 520 855-8791; *Barbara*. e-mail

DERENTHAL, Frederick E.; '72 AS, '76 BS, '78 MPA; Lt.; NYPD, Patrol Borough Manhattan S., New York, NY 10001, 212 477-7436; *Vicki*.

DERFINYAK, Eugene S.; '99 BS; Student; r. POB 564585, College Pt., NY 11356.

DERIENZO, Thomas; '92 BS; Fire Safety Spec.; NYC Transit, 370 Jay St., Brooklyn, NY 11201, 718 243-3661; r. 107 Highland St., Park Ridge, NJ 07656, 201 391-9334; *Dorothy;* Thomas, Christopher. e-mail

DEROLUS, Jean P.; '97 BA; Govt.; r. 726 E. 49th St., Brooklyn, NY 11203, 718 451-4711. e-mail

DE ROSA, Vincent P.; '79 BS; Retired; r. 110 Louis St. # B, Massapequa, NY 11758, 516 694-8985.

DERR, Maria; MPA; 22 W 11th St., New York, NY 10011, 315 337-0275.

DERRING, Tremell; '90 AS; 1075 New Jersey Ave., Brooklyn, NY 11207.

DERVIN, Katharine M.; '99 BA; 17 Bar Beach Rd., Port Washington, NY 11050, 516 883-9648.

DESANTIS, Francesco; '76 MPA; MBA St. John's Univ.; CPA; Ft. Monmouth CECOM; r. 37 London St., Freehold, NJ 07728, 732 308-1885.

DE SANTIS, Nicholas; '76 MPA; BA Herbert H Lehman Clg., MBA Pace Univ.; Partner CPA; 914 421-5600; r. 75 Burda Ave., New City, NY 10956, 914 634-4556.

DE SANTO, Joseph A., PhD; '82 MA; BA St. Joseph Clg. & Sem, MS Iona Clg.; Criminal Justice Chair Retired; Iona Clg.; r. 18 Cherry Ave., Larchmont, NY 10538, 914 763-0589.

DESAUSSURE, Ms. Martha; '94 BS; AAS NYC Tech. Clg.; Admin. Secy. William C. Thompson; Hon. William C. Thompson, 45 Monroe Pl. 3rd. Fl., Brooklyn, NY 11201, 718 722-6351; r. 950 Rutland Rd Apt. 507, Brooklyn, NY 11212, 718 778-9424; Lorraine, Michele.

DESENSO, Eldon; 245 E Granada Ave., Lindenhurst, NY 11757.

DE SERIO, Joseph M.; '81 MPA; 1542 E 54th St., Brooklyn, NY 11234, 718 338-2479.

DESHAZO, Clant E.; '79 BS; 1346 Clay Ave., Bronx, NY 10456.

DESIDERIO, Richard A.; '80 MPA; 2772 Woodhull Ave., Bronx, NY 10469, 718 547-5920.

DESIMONE, Andrew; '92 MA; 296 Cass St., Dix Hills, NY 11746.

DESIMONE, Andrew J.; '93 BS; 9281 Shore Rd Apt. 523, Brooklyn, NY 11209.

DESIO, Frances M.; '89 MPA; 191 Keiber Ct., Staten Island, NY 10314.

DESIR, Nadine (Nadia) O.; '92 BA; Social Worker; Dept. of Social Svcs., Jamaica, NY 11435, 718 523-2934; r. 158-02 72nd Ave., Flushing, NY 11365, 718 380-6044.

DESIR, Wilfrid; '98 MA; 219-16 131St. Ave., Springfield Gardens, NY 11413, 718 978-5828.

DESIRE, Yves C.; '80 BS; Special Investigator; NYC Dept. of Investigation, 80 Maiden Ln., New York, NY 10038, 212 825-5900; r. 21 Amsterdam Ave. # 1, Staten Island, NY 10314, 718 982-6260.

DESMOND, Frances; '90 BA; 42-04 Ssaull St. #5D, Flushing, NY 11355, 718 899-4628.

DESNOYERS, Hans N.; '87 BA; 22 Prospect Pl., Brooklyn, NY 11217.

DESOLA, Anthony J.; 228 E. 42 St., Brooklyn, NY 11203, 718 258-3447.

DESOUSA, Neil; '89 BS; 17597 144th Dr., Jamaica, NY 11434, 718 712-4507.

DE SOUZA, Chris; '97 BS; 1312 Union St., Brooklyn, NY 11213, 718 648-9788.

DESROUILLERES, Jean; '92 BS; 1505 Ocean Ave. Apt. B11, Brooklyn, NY 11230.

DESSOURCES, Ralph; '98 BA; For. Investigator; Human Res. Admin., 906 E. 58th St., Brooklyn, NY 11234, 718 531-5292; r. same.

DESTEFANO, Michael; '79 MA; 1 Gateway Rd, Rochester, NY 14624.

DESURMEAUX, Paul E.; '77 MS; POB 17, Carver, MA 02330.

DETESKEY, Henry R.; '91 BS; 66 78th St., Brooklyn, NY 11209.

DETRES, Cynthia; '95 BA; 84 Ross St. Apt. 3a, Brooklyn, NY 11211, 718 599-0023.

DETRES, Richard M.; '75 BS; 3132 75th St., Flushing, NY 11370, 718 639-2285.

DETTMANN, Edmund P.; '81 MA; BA NY Inst. of Tech.; Owner; Guardian Investigations/EMD & Assoc., Middle Island, NY 11953, 631 345-2687; r. 3 Mauritz Blvd., Middle Island, NY 11953, 631 924-9442; *MaryAnn;* Richard, LoriAnn, Deborah, Danielle, Debbie. e-mail

DEVER, John A.; '84 BA; Retired; Morristown Fire Dept.; r. 17 Brearly Cres., Flanders, NJ 07836, 973 584-2041; Kelly Ann.

DEVIA, Lydia M.; '83 BA, '91 MPA; 410 E 136th St., Bronx, NY 10454.

DEVINE, Edward W.; '80 BS; 452 99th St., Brooklyn, NY 11209, 718 435-5078.

DEVINE, James J.; '78 BA; Retired Fire & Safety Dir.; Compas Leasing & Mgmt.; r. 4410 Cayuga Ave., Bronx, NY 10471, 718 543-1177.

DEVINE, Patrick; '96 BS; Treatment Coord.; Cap Behavior Assocs, 175 Remsen St. 5th Fl., Brooklyn, NY 11201, 718 254-9230; r. 140 Rocklyn Ave., Lynbrook, NY 11563, 516 887-9665. e-mail

DEVINE-MOLIN, Carol; '78 MAPSYCH; BA McGill Univ.-Quebec; Probation Unit Supv.; Westchester Cnty. Probation Dept., 112 E. Post Rd., 3rd FL., White Plains, NY 10601, 914 285-3553; r. 500 High Point Dr. Apt. 608, Hartsdale, NY 10530, 914 428-0595.

DEVINS, Brian M.; '95 BS; Tchr.; The Lowell Sch., 2420 Parsons Blvd., Flushing, NY 11357, 718 422-4555; r. 11 Little Neck Rd., Douglaston, NY 11363, 718 281-9774. e-mail

DE VITO, Dennis W.; '80 BS; 685 The Plain Rd, Westbury, NY 11590, 516 593-4763.

DEVITO, Diane; '86 BS; 2063 62nd St., Brooklyn, NY 11204, 718 833-0249.

DEVITO, James M.; '93 BS; 1526 E 35th St., Brooklyn, NY 11234, 718 258-2816.

DEVITO, Louis J.; '71 MA; BBA Bernard Baruch; Owner; DeVito Assoc., 3 Sheridan Sq., New York, NY 10014, 212 924-5924; r. 23 Barrow St., New York, NY 10014, 212 924-5924.

DE VITO, Michael J.; '80 BS; 2238 61st St., Brooklyn, NY 11204, 718 284-2150.

DE VIVO, Francis (Frank) W.; '80 BS; Police Ofcr.; Kearny Police Dept., 237 Laurel Ave., Kearny, NJ 07032, 201 998-1313; r. 484 De Witt Ave., Belleville, NJ 07109. e-mail

DEVLIN, John F.; '75 MA; 12 Forest Rd, Glen Rock, NJ 07452.

DEVLIN, Kevin G.; '79 BS; 733 58th St., Brooklyn, NY 11220, 718 788-4905.

DEVLIN, Maria M.; '91 BA; 736 W. 181 St., New York, NY 10033, 917 521-2370.

DEVLIN, Patrick J.; '77 MPA; 34 Studley St., Brentwood, NY 11717.

DEVONISH, Claudette; '92 BS; 84 Carroll St., Brentwood, NY 11717.

DEVONISH, Sharon; '95 BS; 18910 120th Ave., Jamaica, NY 11412, 718 276-7672.

DEVONISH, Winston R.; '98 BA; 88 69 195 Pl., Hollis, NY 11423, 718 276-7672.

DEWBERRY, Valerie M.; '89 BS; Caseworker; Admin. for Children's Svcs., New York, NY 10001; r. 274 E 175th St., Apt. 3B, Bronx, NY 10457, 718 299-5664; Ciera Holman. e-mail

DEWELL, Wayne; '86 MPA; 3555 Kings College Pl. Apt. 1a, Bronx, NY 10467, 718 515-3796.

DEY, William F.; '88 BS; 8441 85th Rd, Woodhaven, NY 11421.

DEYO, LT David; '98 MA; Lt.; New York Police Dept., 212 477-9351; r. 7392 Springfield Blvd., Flushing, NY 11364, 718 465-7873; *Darlene;* Zachary. e-mail

DEYUBERO, Candida L.; '79 BA; 67 Chestnut Ave., Staten Island, NY 10305.

DEZIL, Patrick; '96 BA; DIPLOMA NYU, JD Howard Univ.; Legal Assistant; Davis Polk & Wardwell, 450 Lexington Ave., New York, NY 10017, 212 450-6276; r. 19 President St., Hempstead, NY 11550, 516 485-5356. e-mail

D'FORA, Fred; '92 BA; POB 20683, New York, NY 10023.

D'GRACIA, Anthony J.; '99 BS; Special Investigative Claim Rep.; State Farm Ins., POB 8011, Huntington Sta., NY 11746, 631 385-6661; r. 246 Hewlett Ave., Patchogue, NY 11772, 631 447-9660; *Stephanie Napoli*.

DIACZUK, Peter J.; '78 BS; 2577 46th St., Long Island City, NY 11103.

DIAKOS, Georgia; '97 MPA; BSN Felician Clg., MS NYU; Exec. Asst.; Paterson Economic Devel. Corp.; r. 307 Reichelt Rd Apt. A, New Milford, NJ 07646, 201 599-9251. e-mail

DIAL, Savitri D.; '96 MA; 2 River Rd. Roose, New York, NY 10044.

DIAMINT, Claudlo J.; '82 BA; 3050 81st St., Flushing, NY 11370, 718 478-7785.

DIAMOND, Darlene M.; '96 MA; 207 Ashley Pl., Edwardsville, IL 62025, 618 656-6463.

DIAMOND, Theresa A.; '80 BS; 750 E 163rd St., Bronx, NY 10456, 718 601-4434.

DIANA, Charlene K.; '99 BA; 1814 69th St. #2, Brooklyn, NY 11204, 718 331-4461.

DIAZ, Andres F.; '95 BA; Fraud Investigator; Ofc. of Revenue Investigation, 60 Hudson St., New York, NY 10001, 212 630-9732; r. 145 Wadsworth Ave., New York, NY 10033, 212 781-8789. e-mail

DIAZ, Angelica; '79 BA; 675 Water St., New York, NY 10002.

DIAZ, Anthony; '96 BS; 489 Columbus Ave., New York, NY 10024, 212 595-4981.

DIAZ, LT Arthur, JD; '91 BS, '91 MA; JD St. Johns Univ Sch of Law; Sgt/Policy Analyst; NYPD, 1 Police Plz., New York, NY 10038, 212 374-6681; r. 115-05 10th Ave., College Pt., NY 11356, 718 461-3094. e-mail

DIAZ, Carmen I.; '89 BA; MA City Clg. of NY; Tchr.; PS #65, Bronx, NY 10452; r. 5 Wildwood Dr., Apt. 23-C, Wappingers Falls, NY 12590, 914 297-7190.

DIAZ, Carmen L.; '96 BA; 2133 Daly Ave. #, Bronx, NY 10460, 718 220-2918.

DIAZ, Conception M.; '89 BA; 96-15 42 Ave., Corona, NY 11368, 718 460-3302.

DIAZ, Diana; '95 BS; 75 Shaber Rd, Patchogue, NY 11772, 631 475-8376.

DIAZ, Fanny A.; '91 BS; 1 Remsen Rd 3L, Yonkers, NY 10710.

DIAZ, Fatima; '93 BA; Caseworker; Human Resources Admin. NYC, 1910 Monterey Ave., Bronx, NY 10455, 718 901-0377; r. 348 E 194th St., # 1, Bronx, NY 10458, 718 562-4767; Juan Puesan.

DIAZ, Geneva; '87 BS; 1042 45 St., Brooklyn, NY 11219, 718 336-4683.

DIAZ, Gloria; '87 BS; 370 Ft. Washington Ave., New York, NY 10033, 212 927-8991.

DIAZ, Janice; '95 MA; Dir. of Family Svcs.; Concourse House, 2751 Grand Concourse, Bronx, NY 10468, 718 584-4400; r. 2777 Reservoir Ave., Bronx, NY 10468, 718 601-6222; Kevin. e-mail

DIAZ, Jhosandys A.; '96 BS; 9913 43rd Ave. Apt. 5h, Flushing, NY 11368, 718 459-8867.

DIAZ, John M.; '95 BS; 305 Austin Ave., Old Bridge, NJ 08857, 732 393-0295.

DIAZ, Jose R.; '92 BS, '95 MA; 3334 Ft. Independence Ave., Bronx, NY 10463, 718 220-5683.

DIAZ, Juan M.; '78 BS; 11 Louisiana Ave., Brooklyn, NY 11207, 718 266-0697.

DIAZ, Maria D.; '97 BS; P.O.Box 200313, Brooklyn, NY 11220, 718 218-6440.

DIAZ, Maria I.; '96 BA, '99 MA; Social Worker; Pius XII, 188 W. 230th St., Bronx, NY 10463, 718 562-7855; r. 596 Courtlandt Ave., Bronx, NY 10451, 718 665-6617.

DIAZ, Mercedes; '79 BS; Supervisory Criminal Investigator; US Immigration & Naturalization Svcs., 2102 Teege Ave., Harlingen, TX 78550, 956 427-8542; r. POB 3075, Harlingen, TX 78551; Jorge Martinez; Katie, Eric.

DIAZ, Michelle A.; '85 BS; 49 Green Tree Ln., Staten Island, NY 10314.

DIAZ, Migdalia M.; '99 BS; 3201 Neptune Ave. (#4B), Brooklyn, NY 11224, 718 218-6440.

DIAZ, Miguel A.; '81 BS; 521 40th St., Brooklyn, NY 11232, 718 218-6440.

DIAZ, Mildred M.; '93 BA; 940 Tiffany St. Apt. 4f, Bronx, NY 10459, 718 364-4747.

DIAZ, Nestor H.; '86 BA; JD St. John's Law Sch.; Asst. DA; Kings Cnty. Dist. Attorney's Ofc., 350 Jay St., Brooklyn, NY 11201, 718 250-2883; r. 92-83 222 St., Queens Vlg., NY 11428; Iris; Bethany, Briana. e-mail

DIAZ, Nora; '96 BA; Case Mgr.; The Kintock Grp., 50 fenwick St., Newark, NJ 07114, 973 622-1400; r. 535 W. 51st St. 1c, New York, NY 10019, 212 245-5811.

DIAZ, Norian F.; '98 BS; 94-16 34 Rd., Jackson Hts., NY 11372, 718 460-3302.

DIAZ, Rahsaan E.; '97 BA; 2524 Maclay Ave., Bronx, NY 10461, 718 824-0109.

DIAZ, Raymond J.; '75 BS; 2032 Gleason Ave. # 2, Bronx, NY 10472, 718 299-4478.

DIAZ, Valdez; '95 BA; 615 W 184th St. Apt. 1d, New York, NY 10033.

DIAZ, Virgil J.; '97 BS; Security Mgr.; First Security Svcs. Corp., 200 W. 50th St., New York, NY 10019, 212 725-3330; r. 252 W. 47th St., New York, NY 10036, 212 730-7582; Nicole Vossler; Lauren, Christian. e-mail

DIAZ, William; '85 CERT; 745 E 242nd St. Apt. 2b, Bronx, NY 10470, 718 860-2108.

DIAZ, Zulma; '92 BS; CERT Certified Pre-Post Couns.; HIV Case Mgmt. Coord.; Proj. Hospitality, 150 B Richmond Ter., Ext. # 231, Staten Island, NY 10301, 718 420-1475; r. 529 56th St. Apt. 1r, Brooklyn, NY 11220, 718 439-7441; Guillermo Cruise; Thai-Lee, Joylyn, Zulenis, Denisse, Diana.

DI BENEDETTO, Denise, (Denise Bossong); '85 BS; Detective; NYC Police Dept., 1 Police Plz., New York, NY 10029, 212 722-5440; r. Yonkers, NY 10703; Elio; Rocco.

DI BLASI, Philip A.; '81 BS; 1725 Grove St., Flushing, NY 11385, 718 740-0001.

DIBRIZZI, Michael A., Esq.; '88 BS; JD Seton Hall Sch. of Law; Detective; NYC Police Acad., 235 E 20th St., New York, NY 10038, 212 477-9248; r. 710 Hyman Ave, 2 Fl., W. Islip, NY 11795, 631 422-2806; Linda J. Gormezano. e-mail

DICKERSON, Joeann M.; '76 BA; 456 Dekalb #4F, Brooklyn, NY 11205, 718 826-6431.

DICKS, Daniel M.; '93 BS; Sergeant in New York City Police; NYPD, 718 590-3830; r. 1062 E 227th St., Bronx, NY 10466, 718 515-6156; Desiree. e-mail

DICKS, Garry S.; '78 BS; MA Trinity State; Dir. of Risk Mgmt.; Crowne Plaza Rivinia, 4355 Ashford Dunwiddy Rd, Dunwoody, GA 30346, 770 395-7700; r. 3120 Montana Way, Marietta, GA 30066, 770 977-2214; Arlene; Shannon, Brandon.

DICKSON, Paul; '91 BA, '97 MPA; 26111 86th Ave., Floral Park, NY 11001, 516 561-8471.

DIDONATO, Anthony R.; '70 AS, '72 BS; Retired; r. 120 Ocean Ave., Massapequa Park, NY 11762, 516 798-6259; Clara.

DI DONATO, Steven; '81 MA; 1134 49th St., Brooklyn, NY 11219, 718 302-2242.

DIDONATO, Vincent; '79 BS; 38 White Cliff Ln., Nesconset, NY 11767.

DIECIDUE, Charles J.; '75 BS; 3339 Sabal Cove Dr., Longboat Key, FL 34228, 941 383-7422.

DIECKMANN, Martin W.; '77 BS; 60 Lorna Ln. N, Suffern, NY 10901.

DIEGNAN, John J.; '75 AS; 13030 Lefferts Blvd., Jamaica, NY 11420.

DIEHL, William T.; '86 MA; POB 746, Miller Place, NY 11764.

DIELENSNYDER, Fred J.; '78 BS; 7211 67th Pl., Flushing, NY 11385.

DIELENSNYDER, George; '75 BS; Retired; r. 223 W Nicholai St., Hicksville, NY 11801, 516 938-5999; Eleanor; Kim, Eileen, Tracy. e-mail

DIEM, Martin E.; 34 Seitz Dr., Bethpage, NY 11714.

DIER, Daniel; '93 BS; 247 E. 3rd St., Brooklyn, NY 11218.

DIETZ, John S.; '95 BS; 24 Richmond Rd, Flushing, NY 11363, 718 224-8610.

DIEZ, Angela M.; '95 BS; 4114 68th St., Apt. 1B, Woodside, NY 11377.

DIFIGLIA, Samuel J.; '89 BS; 9712 98th St., Jamaica, NY 11416, 718 845-5865.

DIFILIPPO, Christopher B.; '98 BA; 120 Narrows Rd S, Staten Island, NY 10305.

DIFUSCO, Andrew F.; '93 BS; 7 Micieli Pl., Brooklyn, NY 11218, 718 871-6886.

DI GAETANO, Alcide V.; '76 BA; 1714 Putnam Ave., Ridgewood, NY l1385, 718 651-7390.

DIGGS, Sandra; '97 BA; 2250 W. 11th St., Brooklyn, NY 11223.

DI GIACOMO, Anthony M.; '87 BS; 48 Anpell Dr., Scarsdale, NY 10583, 914 939-1677.

DIGIACOMO, Nancy F. '83 (See Filippini, Mrs. Nancy F.).

DIGIAM, Battista J.; '96 BA; 220 Central Ave., Lawrence, NY 11559.

DIGIROLOMO, Nicholas; '95 BS; 34-11 36th Ave., Astoria, NY 11106, 718 937-0744.

DIGNON, Francis T.; '76 AS; 8 Adlai Cir., Staten Island, NY 10312.

DIGNON, Frederick L.; '68 BS, '76 MPA; Retired Asst. Dean; John Jay Clg.; r. 187 Ocean Pines Ter., Jupiter, FL 33477, 561 745-3082; Janet; Frederick Jr, Jane, Neil.

DIIH, Sorle S.; '98 MPA; 54 Ada Dr., Staten Island, NY 10314, 718 370-7319.

DI IORIO, Jeannette; '95 MA; 10834 65th Rd, Flushing, NY 11375, 718 459-8867.

DILAN, Ivan; '92 BS; Capt.; NYPD; r. 8742 115th St., Jamaica, NY 11418, 718 762-5824; *Cynthia;* Ivan, Erica.

DILLARD, Gail E.; '97 BA, '98 BA; 202 24 Hollis Ave./a2, Jamaica, NY 11412, 718 721-2497.

DILLAUNT, Gordon; 2 Robinson Ln., Highland, NY 12528.

DILLION, Richard; '71 BS; 4276 Oneida Ave., Bronx, NY 10470.

DILLON, Edward J.; '74 BA; 136 77th St., Brooklyn, NY 11209, 718 434-8582.

DILLON, Frank; '89 MPA; 231 N 7th St., Newark, NJ 07107.

DILLON, Laura A.; '97 BA; 15 W. Funston Ave., Spring Vly., NY 10977, 914 578-1724.

DILLON, Michael P.; '95 BS; 172 W 32nd St., Bayonne, NJ 07002.

DILONE, Rafael; '87 BS; Detective Investigator; NYPD, 1 Police Plz., New York, NY 10038, 718 286-7378; r. 208 Centre Ave., New Rochelle, NY 10805, 914 636-4924.

DILWORTH, Donald; Police HQ Yaphank Ave., Yaphank, NY 11980.

DI MAGGIO, Barbara A., (Barbara A. Monel); '81 BS; Secy./Specialty Basket Distributor; Good Shepherd/Longaberger Cnslt., 3139 County Rd., Old Bridge, NJ 08857, 732 679-8887; r. 15 Millburn Ct., Old Bridge, NJ 08857, 732 591-0819. e-mail

DI MANGO, Domenick; '78 BA; 1838 26th Rd, Long Island City, NY 11102, 718 205-4857.

DI MARCO, Andre N.; '72 BS; 37 Meeker St., Staten Island, NY 10306, 718 727-8207.

DI MARTINO, Steven J.; '79 BS; 245-40 61 Ave., Douglaston, NY 11362, 718 322-4322.

DI MATTEO, Philip J.; '77 BS; 65 Bay 40th St., Brooklyn, NY 11214, 718 444-5241.

DI MEGLIO, Ciro P.; '80 AS; 26 Fieldway Ave., Staten Island, NY 10308, 718 979-1462.

DIMMOCK, James A.; '93 BA; MA NYY Grad. Sch. of Educ.; Case Mgr. Parole Progs.; Ed Alliance/Proj. Return Contact; r. 128 W 120th St. # 4, New York, NY 10027, 212 316-4324. e-mail

DINEEN, William F.; '94 BA; 6 Miko Rd, Edison, NJ 08817, 732 287-1067.

DINKINS, Benjamin S.; '97 BA; 254 E. 56th St., Brooklyn, NY 11203, 718 485-9252.

DINWIDDIE, Harman B.; '79 BS; 122 Palmers Hill Rd Apt. 3118, Stamford, CT 06902.

DIOMEDE, Vito S.; '85 BS; 316 Union St., Brooklyn, NY 11231, 718 935-1326.

DIOTALLEVI, Madelyn '81 (See Thompson, Madelyn).

DI PANE, Jodi E.; '98 MPA, '98 SCH; BA Clg. of New Jersey, AA Raritan Community Clg.; Administrative Cnslt.; Jodi E Di Pane Cnsltg., 150 S. 14th Ave., Manville, NJ 08835, 908 526-3456; r. same. e-mail

DI PAOLO, Alfred J.; '81 BS; 1812 Park View Ave., Bronx, NY 10461, 718 561-7344.

DIPAOLO, Paul J.; '82 AS; 1248-79 St., Brooklyn, NY 11228.

DIPASQUALE, Tommy O.; '86 BS; 1946 Radcliff Ave., Bronx, NY 10462, 718 829-3315.

DIPIERRO, Paul; '91 BS; Sr. Ct Ofcr.; Queens Superior Ct, 125-01 Queens Blvd., Kew Gardens, NY 11415; r. 20 Berkley St., Valley Stream, NY 11581, 516 791-4774.

DIPRENDA, Daniel; '83 BS; 7 Keats Pl., Greenlawn, NY 11740.

DI RAIMONDO, Carl A.; '77 BS; 115-07 Liberty Ave., Richmond Hill, NY 11419, 718 888-9984.

DIRKIN, Walter J., Esq.; '95 BS; JD Rutgers Univ.; Asst. Prosecutor; Essex Cnty. Prosecutor's Ofc., New Courts Bldg., Newark, NJ 07102, 973 621-4700; r. 808 Hudson St., Hoboken, NJ 07030. e-mail

DIROCCO, Dana L.; '83 BS; 271 Hemlock St., Brooklyn, NY 11208, 718 277-0604.

DISARNO, James J.; '97 MS; 1005 South Ave. W, Westfield, NJ 07090.

DISARNO, Michael T.; '89 BS; 121 Pearl St., New Providence, NJ 07974, 732 714-8185.

DI SCALA, Helen M.; '84 BS; 35-58 65th St., Woodside, NY 11377, 718 262-8480.

DISCENZA, Regina, (Regina Costantino); '85 BA; 233 Sunset Dr., Forked River, NJ 08731, 609 693-6454; *Frank;* Louis, Christian.

DISKEN, Timothy J.; '82 BA; 6158 Eliot Ave., Flushing, NY 11379, 718 456-1920.

DISLAKING, Antonio; '97 BA; 975 Walton Ave.#3, Bronx, NY 10452.

DISNEY, Elizabeth D., (Elizabeth K. Driscoll); '82 MA; BA Caldwell Clg. for Women; Chief Juvenile Probation Svcs.; State of NJ; r. 3606 Chadbury Rd, Mt. Laurel, NJ 08054, 856 273-9260; *Elmer.*

D'ISSELT, Lauren; '91 MA; Proj. Dir.; NYC TASC-Link, 175 Remsev St. 505, Brooklyn, NY 11201, 718 237-9404; r. Brooklyn, NY 11215, 718 965-3902.

DI STEFANO, Vincent M.; '95 BS; Fire Marshal; NYC Fire Dept., 9 Metro Tech, Brooklyn, NY 11201; r. 20 Rustic Dr., Monsey, NY 10952, 914 357-5814.

DITORO, Christopher J.; '99 BS; Police Ofcr.; NYPD, 1 Police Plz., New York, NY 10038, 212 374-5000; r. 81 Wenlock St., Staten Island, NY 10303, 718 981-6975.

DITTO, Philip J.; '99 MA; NYC Probation Ofcr.; NYC Dept. of Probation, 345 Adams St., Brooklyn, NY 11201, 718 403-4627; r. 2043 W. 10th St., Brooklyn, NY 11223, 718 449-7675.

DITTO, Robbin A.; '80 BS; 3214 42nd St., Long Island City, NY 11103.

DIVER, Hugh J.; '74 BS; Retired Sergeant; NYC Police Dept.; r. POB 436, Mastic Bch., NY 11951, 631 399-1139; *Johanna;* Veronica, Hugh F. e-mail

DIXON, Alexandreena; '84 MPA; Supt.; Taconic Correctional Facility, 250 Harris Rd., Bedford Hls., NY 10507, 914 241-3010.

DIXON, Anthony A.; '96 BS; 2545 Sedgwick Ave., Apt. 6C, Bronx, NY 10468, 718 601-8287.

DIXON, John H.; '95 MA; BS St. John Univ.; Police Ofcr.; NYC Police Dept., 917 805-6829; r. 951 70th St., Brooklyn, NY 11228, 718 921-4622.

DIXON, Nora; '95 BA; CERT.; Clerk 2; New York Ins. Dept., 25 Beaver St., New York, NY 10004, 212 480-5171; r. 45 E 91st St., Brooklyn, NY 11212.

DIXON, Paulette; '93 BS; 1786 Albany Ave., Brooklyn, NY 11210, 718 573-1701.

DIXON, Roxann T.; '92 BS; 13833 232nd St. Ph, Jamaica, NY 11413, 718 417-0137.

DIXON, Sharon H.; '88 BA; Probation Ofcr.; Dept. of Probation, Bronx, NY 10451; r. 1996 Grand Ave., Bronx, NY 10453, 718 901-3363.

DIXON, Shellese; '86 BA; Sr. Case Mgr.; Hope Inc., 172 Waverly St., Yonkers, NY 10701, 914 964-0920; r. 678 Warburton Ave. Apt. 2b, Yonkers, NY 10701, 914 965-6826; *Curtis Rawls.*

D'MEZA, Ruth; '89 BA; 526 W 112th St. # B, New York, NY 10025.

DOBAK, James; 67 Woodbine Ave., Newark, NJ 07106.

DOBAY, Dominic; Mgr.; Dynamics, Inc., 175 Dupre Ave., Norfolk, VA 23503.

DOBBINS, William J.; '83 BS; 12 Windham Ln. S, Ronkonkoma, NY 11779.

DOBRO, Stuart; '93 BS; MA Natl. Univ.; Police Ofcr.; Memphis Police Dept., 201 Poplar Ave., 2602 Mount Moriah, Memphis, TN 38115, 901 795-3131; r. 4781 Violet Ave., Memphis, TN 38122, 901 821-0061. e-mail

DOBSON, Anthony; '98 BA; 124 Dumont Ave., Brooklyn, NY 11212, 718 346-8456.

DOBSON, Dexter A.; '87 BS; 21740 100th Ave., Queens Vlg., NY 11429.

DOBZINSKI, Zev; 888 8th Ave. #8H, New York, NY 10019.

DOCEKAL, Paul G.; '82 BS; 4238 248th St., Flushing, NY 11363, 718 224-9369.

DOCKERY, Maria; '90 BS; 11554 227th St., Jamaica, NY 11411.

DODDS, Dwayne M.; '86 BS; Analyst; Dept. of Justice, 1433 West Loop South, Houston, TX 77027, 713 693-3341; r. Missouri City, TX 77459; *Michelle;* Amir, Rashad.

DODRILL, Christopher A.; '87 BS; Police Ofcr.; Town of Ramapo, Rte. 59, Suffern, NY 10901, 914 357-2400; r. 25 Tulip Tree Dr., Garnerville, NY 10923; *Eileen;* Alanna, Christopher, Nicole.

DODSON, Kenneth L.; '98 BS; AAS Borough of Manhattan CC; Retired Police Ofcr.; NYPD; r. 141 Rockland Ln., Hillcrest, NY 10977, 914 352-4117; *Nicole;* Dominique, Danielle. e-mail

DODSON, Toshia E.; '90 BS; 192 Sands St. Apt. 2b, Brooklyn, NY 11201, 718 443-2502.

DOERRBECKER, George; '78 MA; MSW Hunter Clg.; Deputy Chief; US Probation, 75 Clinton St. 4th Fl., Brooklyn, NY 11201, 718 254-7357; r. 56 Ionia Ave., Staten Island, NY 10312, 718 254-7357.

DOGAN, Walter R.; '80 MA; JD Seton Hall Univ.; Mgr.; Nutrition Mgmt. Svc. Co., Pob725, Kimberton, PA 19442, 718 589-6865; r. 88-23 162nd St. Apt. C2, Jamaica, NY 11432, 718 526-2717. e-mail

DOHERTY, James P.; '75 BS; 10 Payne Rd, Lebanon, NJ 08833.

DOHERTY, CAPT Michael J.; '76 BS; NYPD, Queens N. Task Force, 137-58 Northern Blvd., Flushing, NY 11354, 718 321-2055; r. 75-02 189th St., Fresh Meadows, Flushing, NY 11366, 718 468-1904; *Martha;* Linda R., Kathleen N.

DOLAN, Bernard A.; '77 AS; 70-69 Walnut St., Forest Hills, NY 11375, 718 932-8314.

DOLAN, Brendan M.; '82 BS; 52-07 Skillman Ave., Woodside, NY 11377, 718 932-8314.

DOLAN, Christine; '89 BA; AS Farmingdale-SUNY; Nurse/Atty.; 516 877-0016; r. 60 Flower Hill Rd., Huntington, NY 11743, 631 549-7611; *Patrick;* Michelle.

DOLAN, Daniel S.; '99 MPA; 408 W. 57th Strret, #3K, New York, NY 10019, 212 956-9565.

DOLAN, Edward G.; '75 MA; BBA St. John's Univ., CERT. Cert. Protection Profn.; Chief of Operations/NY; The Smithsonian-Institution, 1 Bowling Green-NMAI, New York, NY 10004, 212 514-3830; r. 2406 1st St., E. Meadow, NY 11554, 516 731-3185; *Mary A.;* Edward A., Mary E., Daniel P., Thomas A. e-mail

DOLAN, Maureen A.; '79 MPA; 103 Connecticut Ave., Long Beach, NY 11561, 516 792-0177.

DOLAN, Michael F.; '70 BS; 35 Virginia Dr., Elmont, NY 11003, 516 792-0177.

DOLCIMASCOLO, Jeffrey A.; '83 BS; Asst. Inspector Gen.; NYC Dept. of Investigation, 80 Maiden Ln., New York, NY 10038, 212 825-2471; r. 54 Caswell Ln., Staten Island, NY 10314; *Christine; Marisa.*

DOLDRON, Sherena '96 (See Doldron-Cancel, Sherena N.).

DOLDRON-CANCEL, Sherena N., (Sherena Doldron); '96 BA; Police Acad.; Police Ofcr.; NYC Police Dept.; r. 2030 Seagirt Blvd., #4F, Far Rockaway, NY 11691, 718 337-3479; *Juan A. Cancel.* e-mail

DOLPHY, Keri-Ann; '99 BA; Actress/Singer; Admin. of Children Services, Angel Guardian, New York, NY 10001; r. 917 773-0235. e-mail

DOMBROSKY, Mark D.; '99 MA; BS SUNY-Cortland Clg.; Therapist/Psychologist; Renaissance Healthcare, 1800 Northern Blvd., Roslyn, NY 11576, 516 625-6846; r. 1225 Arden Ave., Staten Island, NY 10312, 718 356-0911. e-mail

DOMBROWSKI, Michael; '83 BA; 6965 Caldwell Ave., Flushing, NY 11378.

DOMENECH, Edgar A.; '84 BA; 110 Cody Pl., Staten Island, NY 10312, 718 466-5145.

DOMINGO, Joel J.; '77 BS; Retired Capt. of Police Dept.; r. 1050 E 224th St., Bronx, NY 10466, 718 231-8335; *Lola;* Jacqueline. e-mail

DOMINGUEZ, Denise; '96 BA; Law Student; Rutgers Law Sch.; r. 402 Mount Prospect Ave., Apt. 14B, Newark, NJ 07104, 973 485-6545. e-mail

DOMINGUEZ, Michelle A., (Michelle A. Jones); '99 BA; Admin. Asst. Bond Dept.; Lord Abbett & Co., 90 Hudson St., Jersey City, NJ 07302, 201 395-2720; r. 1914 Palmetto St., Apt. 1L, Ridgewood, NY 11385, 718 418-7064; *Rafael;* Sydney.

DOMINGUEZ, Thomas; '95 BS; Police Ofcr.; NYPD, 1 Police Plz., New York, NY 10038; r. 26 Saint James Ct., W. Babylon, NY 11704. e-mail

DOMOND, Alix; '99 BA; Dietary Aide; Dr. Benneson Rehab. Pavilion, 39-17 Parson Blvd., Whitestone, NY 11357, 718 961-4300; r. 113-16 202nd St., St. Albans, NY 11412, 718 776-8120.

DONADIO, Francis X.; '74 BA; 699 Broadway, Staten Island, NY 10310, 718 273-1038.

DONADIO, Randall J.; '80 MPA; 1686 84 St., Brooklyn, NY 11214.

DONAHUE, Daniel J.; '78 BS; 1137 E 32nd St., Brooklyn, NY 11210, 718 802-0620.

DONAHUE, Kevin D.; '79 BS; 4539 170th St., Flushing, NY 11358, 718 359-7232.

DONAHUE, Paul G.; '99 BA; 134 Stephenson Blvd., New Rochelle, NY 10801, 914 654-1220.

DONAHUE, Steven J.; '82 AS; 9414 53rd Ave., Flushing, NY 11373, 718 849-1229.

DONALDSON, Irving F.; '86 BA; 1473 New York Ave., Brooklyn, NY 11210, 718 756-3999.

DONALDSON, Michelle; '89 BS; 114-07 Springfield, Cambria Hts., NY 11411.

DONATO, Donna A.; '81 BS; MBA Pace Univ.; Sr. Performance Cnslt.; TIAA-CREF, 730 3rd Ave., MS 485-17-21, New York, NY 10016, 212 916-4077; r. 305 E 40th St., Apt. 16G, New York, NY 10016; *Antonio.* e-mail

DONATO, Roberto; '90 BA, '95 MA; Lt.; New York Police Dept., 49-51 Chambers St., Rm 223, New York, NY 10007, 212 374 5434; r. 2040 Gerritsen Ave., Brooklyn, NY 11229. e-mail

DONELAN, Michael J.; '76 BS; 17 Chestnut Hill Rd, Chelmsford, MA 01824, 978 250-0507.

DONGO, Marsha M. '91 (See Dongo-Williams, Mrs. Marsha M.).

DONGO-WILLIAMS, Mrs. Marsha M., (Marsha M. Dongo); '91 BA; Sta. Agt.; NYC Transit Authority, 370 Jay St., Brooklyn, NY 11234, 718 243-4444; r. 97-22 57th Ave. Apt. 14B, Corona, NY 11368, 718 760-3124; *Douglas Sr Williams;* Douglas Jr, Jasmine. e-mail

DONLEAVY, William P.; '71 BS; 1255 The Hideout, Lake Ariel, PA 18436.

DONLON, John L.; '89 BS; 20425 12th Ave., Breezy Pt., NY 11697, 718 634-6465.

DONLON, Megan; '99; 252 Sunset Blvd., Sylvan Bch., NY 13157.

DONNELLAN, Roger W.; '73 BS; 187 Great Rock Dr., Wading River, NY 11792, 631 929-8823.

DONNELLY, Gerald M.; '74 BA, '77 MA; 3255 Randall Ave., Apt. 3K, Bronx, NY 10465.

DONNELLY, James E.; '90 BS; 123 Waldron Ave. #N, Staten Island, NY 10301, 718 227-5760.

DONNELLY, Matthew T.; '79 BS; 32-06 35th Ave., Long Island City, NY 11106, 718 786-2054.

DONNELLY, Stephen J.; '69 BS, '73 MS; Retired-Police Capt.; NYPD; r. 8 Wilden Ct., New Hyde Park, NY 11040, 516 437-9452. e-mail

DONNELLY, Stephen M.; '98 BS; 449 Herricks Rd., New Hyde Park, NY 11040, 516 294-1035.

DONNELLY-BRINKLEY, Virginia; '94 MPA; BS AP SUNY-Brockport; Law Student; r. 2010 Bruckner Blvd. Apt. 9k, Bronx, NY 10473, 718 792-3989. e-mail

DONNERY, Mary C.; '93 MPA; MLS SUNY Albany; Dir.; Croton Free Library; r. 6 Laurel Ln., Highland Falls, NY 10928, 914 446-5204. e-mail

DONNLEY, Eleanor T.; '74 BS; CRT ICT NY Foundling Hosp.; Real Estate Sales; O.M. Carter Realty, 122-44 Farmers Blvd., Jamaica, NY 11434, 718 341-1100; r. 120-12 DeKruif Pl. #12D, Bronx, NY 10475, 718 379-1297; Deneen, Drexel.

DONOHUE, Brian A.; '82 BS; POB 6133, Bridgeport, CT 06606, 203 459-1550.

DONOHUE, Brian E.; '95 BA; 5805 Avenue D, Brooklyn, NY 11203, 718 246-2520.

DONOHUE, Dennis W.; '98 BA; 335 E. 238 St., Bronx, NY 10470, 718 324-9340.

DONOHUE, Eileen; '94 BS; 319 Beach 98th St., 10B, Rockaway Bch., NY 11694, 718 358-0335.

DONOHUE, Luisa M.; '89 BA; 189 Audubon Ave. Apt. 4s, New York, NY 10033.

DONOHUE, Patricia M.; '78 BS; 52 Parrott Pl., Brooklyn, NY 11228, 718 246-2520.

DONOHUE, Patrick J.; '92 BS; Police Sgt; New York Police Dept., 19 Elizabeth St., New York, NY 10013, 212 334-0711; r. 89 Saint Marks Pl., Staten Island, NY 10301, 718 981-6930.

DONOHUE, Patrick T.; '75 MA; 89 Saint Marks Pl., Staten Island, NY 10301, 718 981-6930.

DONOVAN, Arundell (Tony) A.; '75 BA; MS Fordham Univ.; Security Mgr.; NYU Med. Ctr., 550 First Ave., New York, NY 10016, 212 263-5038; r. 1380 Riverside Dr., New York, NY 10033, 212 568-3147; *Joan;* Stephen.

DONOVAN, Edwin J.; '72 BS, '76 MA; Advisor for Special Projects; PA State Univ., 305 Lubert Bldg., University Park, PA 16802, 814 863-0079; r. 234 S Buckhout St., State College, PA 16801, 814 238-3614; *Delores M.;* Kathleen, Edwin Michael. e-mail

DONOVAN, Gerald J.; '72 AA, '73 BS, '75 MA; Security Cnslt.; The Protectors, 3100 Ocean Pkwy., Ste. A27, Brooklyn, NY 11235, 718 930-7250; r. same, 718 996-6407; *Nanamira;* Ariana, Noelle. e-mail

DONOVAN, John J.; '77 BS; 247 Manor Rd, Huntington, NY 11743.

DOOLAN, Shane R.; '99 BS; 352 Chester St. Apt. B, Brooklyn, NY 11212, 718 346-8509.

DOOLEY, Bradford O.; '79 MA; AA Temple Univ., BARE MAR Evangelical Bible Sem.; Student/Licensing Ornation; Evangelical Church Alliance, POB 9, Bradley, IL 60915; r. 2041 Spring Mill Rd, POB 308 Merrimack Nh 03054-0308, Conshohocken, PA 19428, 610 828-8185.

DOOLEY, Daniel; '96 BA; 64-02 80th Ave., Glendale, NY 11385, 718 463-1337.

DOOLEY, Joan T.; '89 MPA; Lt.; NYC; r. Franklin Sq., NY 11010.

DOOLITTLE, Timothy; '82 BA; 992 Stillwater Rd, Stamford, CT 06902, 203 327-7452.

DOPFEL, Robert; '96 BA; 147 Broadfield Rd, Hempstead, NY 11550, 516 489-9812.

DORANS, Edward T.; '75 AS, '77 BA; Hunter Clg., Keane Clg of NJ; Retired-Sgt.; NYPD/Bank of NY; r. 312 Van Name Ave., Staten Island, NY 10303, 718 727-0450.

DORCH, Joyce M.; '93 BS; 80 Bleecker St., Apt. 2, Brooklyn, NY 11221, 718 467-7762.

DORFF, Michael G.; 305 E 40th St. # 3-0, New York, NY 10016.

DORFMAN, Abraham; '73 BS; 419 W Beech St., Long Beach, NY 11561, 516 432-4478.

DORMENA, Marie-Suze; '99 BA; Case Mgr.; Concord Home Svcs. for The Elderly, 1958 Fulton St., Stuyvesant, NY 11233, 718 363-9833; r. 1655 Flatbush Ave., Apt. B-1007, Brooklyn, NY 11210, 718 282-2771.

DORMI, Edward J.; '93 BA; 1839 Tomlinson Ave., Bronx, NY 10461.

DOROGOFF, Paul A.; '89 MA; 1913 E 51st St., Brooklyn, NY 11234.

DORRITIE, Raymond J.; '81 BS; 270 Longstreet Ave., Bronx, NY 10465, 718 828-6732.

DORSETT, Floyd W.; '74 BA; 11812 224th St., Jamaica, NY 11411.

DORSINVILLE, Yolande; '79 BS; Retired Edu Assoc.; Bd. of Educ.; r. 4219 Forley St. Apt. 2, Flushing, NY 11373, 718 507-1162; Nancy, Ralph.

DORTA, Edward; '97 BS; 69 Montrose Ave., Brooklyn, NY 11206, 718 599-6692.

DORVAL, Marcoris; '97 BS; 1259 E 56th St., # 24, Brooklyn, NY 11234.

DORVIL, Rommelle T.; '95 BS; Police Ofcr.; 5th Precinct, 212 334-0711; r. 254 Shotwell Ave. 1st Fl., Staten Island, NY 10312, 718 227-6992. e-mail

DOSS, C. Brian; '99 MPA; BS SUNY-Brockport; Rsch. Analyst; The State Controllers Ofc., 615 532-1111; r. 1295 Countryside Rd., Nolensville, TN 37135, 315 682-4515. e-mail

DOS SANTOS, Kerry; '97 MA; 199 Second St., Newark, NJ 07107, 973 485-3391.

DOS SANTOS, Richard D.; '73 BS; 75 Royal Dr., Freeport, NY 11520, 516 239-3383.

DOTSON, Allen; '84 MA; 207 US Crthouse Foley Sq., New York, NY 10007.

DOTTERELL, Monica H.; '83 BA; 230 E 179th St. # 3, Bronx, NY 10457.

DOTZLER, Paul P.; '80 BS; 1929 Quintus Dr., Bellmore, NY 11710.

DOUGALL, Angela K.; '93 BA; 21 Ashby Ln., Newark, NJ 07103, 973 623-3295.

DOUGE, Max; '79 BS; 10 Stratford Rd, Brooklyn, NY 11218, 718 693-7407.

DOUGHERTY, Roger B.; '84 BS; Personnel Analyst; Goldman & Co., 85 Broad St., New York, NY 10004, 212 902-7193; r. 314 Lake Ave., Staten Island, NY 10303.

DOUGHERTY, Shawn M.; '94 BS; 60 Fairview St., Huntington, NY 11743.

DOUGHERTY, Vincent J.; '75 MA; 677 83rd St., Brooklyn, NY 11228, 718 284-7059.

DOUGHERTY, William; '89 BS; 53 Allen Ct., Staten Island, NY 10310.

DOUGHNEY, Joseph C.; '74 BS; 7123 4th Ave., Apt. D4, Brooklyn, NY 11209.

DOUGLAS, Cornelius J.; '92 BS; 10 Bull Run Dr., W. Nyack, NY 10994.

DOUGLAS, Darien; '97 BA; Asst. Supv.; Leake & Watts, 1967 Turnbull Ave., Bronx, NY 10473, 718 829-8174; r. 99 Metropolitan Ave., Bronx, NY 10462, 718 829-8174; Yasmin. e-mail

DOUGLAS, Gibbon E.; '89 MA; 14728 Arlington Ter., Jamaica, NY 11435, 718 523-1654.

DOUGLAS, Glenda E.; '79 BS; 237 Saint James Pl., Brooklyn, NY 11238, 718 338-6257.

DOUGLAS, John F.; '99 BA; 95-04 111th, Richmond Hill, NY 11419, 718 297-4305.

DOUGLAS, Laura V. '88 (See Douglas-Robinson, Laura V.).

DOUGLAS, Marsha D.; '98 BS; Tchr.; PF 189, Brooklyn, NY 11203; r. 444 E 46 St., Brooklyn, NY 11203, 718 462-5041. e-mail

DOUGLAS-RICHARDS, La; '96 BA; 668 Autumn Ave., Brooklyn, NY 11208, 718 467-7021.

DOUGLAS-ROBINSON, Laura V. (Laura V. Douglas); '88 BA; Police Sergeant; City of NY; r. 131 Lakeview Ave., Freeport, NY 11520, 516 623-7932; Gilbert Sr.; Gilbert III, Douglas. e-mail

DOUGLASS, Robert L.; '98 BA; 1186 Grenada Pl., Bronx, NY 10466, 718 798-7417.

DOUR, Daniel F.; '79 BS; Police Ofcr.; Glen Rock Police Dept., 1 Harding Plz., Glen Rock, NJ 07452, 201 652-3800; r. 67 Woodvale Rd., Glen Rock, NJ 07452; Ellen; Lindsey, Stephanie, Ashley. e-mail

DOURMAS, Georgia; '84 BS; 2320 29th St., Long Island City, NY 11105.

DOUSE, Patricia A.; '79 BS; 1646 Union St., Brooklyn, NY 11213, 718 771-3956.

DOUTE, Jemal L.; '98 BA; Police Ofcr.; NYC Police Dept., One Police Plz., New York, NY 10038, 212 927-3200; r. 58 Brewster Dr., Middletown, NY 10940, 914 263-9727; Debra; Nadesia, Ebonee. e-mail

DOUTHIT, Teresa M.; '88 BA; JD Univ. of Baltimore Law; Atty.; r. 5302 Eastbury Ave., Baltimore, MD 21206.

DOVE, Darlene C.; '89 BS; Secy. Acting Supreme Court Justice; Bronx Supreme Ct., 851 Grand Concourse, Bronx, NY 10451, 718 590-3985; r. 120 Einstein Loop, Apt. 18B, Bronx, NY 10475. e-mail

DOVE, Sheila T.; '97 BA, '98 BA; 21 St. James Pl. #2C, Brooklyn, NY 11205, 718 566-1292.

DOWD, Charles F.; '77 BS; Capt.; NYPD, 107th Precinct; r. 45 Bache Ave., Staten Island, NY 10306, 718 667-3087; Madeline; Katie, Robert, Garrett.

DOWD, James J.; 34 West St., W. Nyack, NY 10994, 914 358-8434.

DOWD, John E.; 47 Club La, Levittown, NY 11756, 516 873-1938.

DOWD, Lorraine E.; '89 BS; 480 St. Nicholas Ave., New York, NY 10030, 315 858-0926.

DOWD, Peter J.; '96 MA; BA Hunter Clg.; Investigator; FBI, 26 Federal Plz., New York, NY 10278, 212 384-1000; r. 62-28 84th St., Middle Vlg., NY 11379, 718 899-8414. e-mail

DOWD, Timothy M.; '78 MA; BA SOC St. John Univ.; Detective Supv. NYCPD; NYC Police Dept., #1 Police Plz., New York, NY 10038, 718 712-2865; r. 43 Virginia Dr., Manhasset, NY 11030, 516 365-8689; Janice; Timothy F., Jennifer L.

DOWE, Ferron C.; '97 BA; 4138 Paulding Ave., Bronx, NY 10466, 718 824-0814.

DOWIE, Heather M.; '95 BS; 20 Henry St. Apt. 2f, Brooklyn, NY 11201.

DOWLING, Edward J.; '71 BS; 32 Ashwood Dr., Blauvelt, NY 10913, 914 359-2170.

DOWLING, Jack F.; '77 MA; BS DePaul Univ.; Dir. of Safety & Security; Philadelphia Univ., Sch. House Ln. & Henry Ave., Philadelphia, PA 19144, 215 951-2620; r. 3950 Vaux St., Philadelphia, PA 19129, 215 849-6412. e-mail

DOWLING, Richard J.; '75 BA; Shore Ave. Forest Park, Greenwood Lake, NY 10925, 914 477-2538.

DOWNES, Thomas A.; '70 BA; 39-88 49 St., Astoria, NY 11104, 718 464-8978.

DOWNEY, John R.; '92 BS; Firefighter; NYC Fire Dept.; r. 89-21 Aubrey Ave., Flushing, NY 11385, 718 896-3571.

DOWNEY, William A.; 2000 BA; Firefighter; NYC Fire Dept.; r. 89-21 Aubrey Ave., Glendale, NY 11385, 718 896-3571. e-mail

DOWNS, Henry; '97 BS; 1594 Third Ave.2C, New York, NY 10128, 315 697-9113.

DOWNS, Maureen F.; '78 MA; POB 896, New York, NY 10156, 315 697-9113.

DOWTIN, Ronda; '94 BS; AS VA Tidewater Community, AS Farmingdale Univ.; Physical Therapy Asst.; Harborview; r. 1 Ashley Park Dr., N. Branford, CT 06471, 203 484-1496; Michael.

DOYLE, Arthur; '74 BS; Writer; r. 320 E. 25th St., New York, NY 10010, 212 686-0829; Mattie; Trecia, Christopher.

DOYLE, Catherine; '86 MA; POB 771, New Paltz, NY 12561.

DOYLE, Michael P.; '96 BA; Police Ofcr.; NYC Police Dept.; r. 217 Beach 99th St., Far Rockaway, NY 11694, 718 843-3998.

DOYLE, Thomas M.; '82 BA; 68 Kane Pl., N. Babylon, NY 11703, 631 667-8551.

DOZIER, Shaunda; '90 BA; 511 Chauncey St., Brooklyn, NY 11233.

DRAFFEN, Karla J. '87 (See Denis, Mrs. Karla J.).

DRAFFIN, Beverly H.; '78 BA; Ret. VP/Polygraphist; New York Lie Detection Labs; r. The Glenview, 5100 US Hwy. 42, Louisville, KY 40241, 718 625-3650; *Victor C. Kaufman;* Rayne, Dawne.

DRAGHI, Paul; '71 BS; Retired Intelligence Div.; NYC Police Dept.; r. 771 41 St., Brooklyn, NY 11232, 718 972-0673. e-mail

DRAKE, Jeanne M.; '96 MA; 335 Est 92nd St. #5A, New York, NY 10128, 212 996-2197.

DRAKES, Imogene; '94 MS; 1208 Pacific St., Brooklyn, NY 11216, 718 531-6934.

DRAKES, Ingrid L., (Ingrid L. Nurse); '85 BS; Police Ofcr.; 103 Precinct, 168-02 91st Ave., Jamaica, NY 11432, 718 657-8181; r. 216 Arcadia Ave., Uniondale, NY 11553. e-mail

DRAYTON, Kenneth R.; '76 BA; Dir. of Security; Fashion Inst. of Technology, 7th Ave. At 27th St., Rm. D442, New York, NY 10001, 212 217-8777; r. 2292 Walnut Ave., Ronkonkoma, NY 11779; *Eva;* Gieselle, Dawn. e-mail

DRAYTON, Sabrina R.; '92 BA; 288 W 137th St., New York, NY 10030.

DRESSLER, Marcella; '91 BA; 214 Ocean Ave., Middletown, NJ 07748.

DREW, Isola S.; '98 BA; AS BMCC; Admin. Asst.; Med. Network Svcs.; r. 3102 Newkirk Ave. 5c, Brooklyn, NY 11226, 718 469-6960.

DREWAL, Roger F.; '81 MA; 66-92 Selfridge ST., Forest Hills, NY 11375.

DRIELAK, Steven C.; '78 MA; 12 Ashford Dr., Ridge, NY 11961.

DRISCOLL, Elizabeth K. '82 (See Disney, Elizabeth D.).

DRISCOLL, John G.; '89 BS; 6010 69th Pl., Flushing, NY 11378, 718 847-4374.

DROBNY, Charlene; '84 MA; BA Roosevelt Univ.-Chicago; Researcher-Child Maltreatment; Hebrew Univ. of Jerusalem, Mount Scopus, Jerusalem, Israel; r. POB 13003, Jerusalem 91130, Israel, 7229942718; *Dr Vladimir Godin.*

DROGALIS, John J.; '73 BS; 35 Locust St., Floral Park, NY 11001.

DRONER, Gerard P.; '79 MA; 123 Wieland Ave., Staten Island, NY 10309.

DRUCKER, Eric G.; '90 MPA; BA Hamline Univ.; Special Asst. to the Dean; Human Resources, John Jay Clg., 555 W. 57th St., Rm. 612, New York, NY 10019, 212 237-8513; r. 40 Heritage Dr. Apt. F, New City, NY 10956, 914 638-3150; *Marilyn;* Jason, Adam, Daniel. e-mail

DRUCKER, Leslie; '86 BS; MSR Hunter Clg., SELC NYU; Rsch. Analyst; 160 Bleecker St. Apt. #2Bw, New York, NY 10012, 212 260-6097; r. 160 Bleecker St. Apt. 2BW, New York, NY 10012, 212 260-6097. e-mail

DRUCKER, Mitchel E.; '75 BS; 2154 Ford St., Brooklyn, NY 11229, 718 259-9212.

DRUKER, Courtenae; '90 MA; Christine Ct., Stormville, NY 12582.

DRUMMOND, Junior A.; '99 AS; Student; John Jay Clg. of Criminal Justice; r. 57 St. Pauls Pl., Brooklyn, NY 11226, 718 282-1244. e-mail

DRUSS, Philip M.; '76 MA; 28 Old Fulton St., Brooklyn, NY 11201.

DRZEWIECKI, Helena D.; '83 BA; 233 23rd St., #3R 1, Brooklyn, NY 11232.

DUANE, William D.; '75 BA; 80 Nethermont Ave., White Plains, NY 10603, 914 761-5869.

DUARTE, Anthony C.; '82 BA; 39 Creamery Dr., New Windsor, NY 12553.

DUARTE, Delilah S.; '90 MA; 498 College Rd., Farmingville, NY 11738.

DUARTE, Ms. Ruth; '97 BA; Supv.; Lincoln Hosp., 234 E. 149th St., Bronx, NY 10455, 718 579-5400; r. 827 Fox St. #2A, Bronx, NY 10459, 718 860-9205.

DUBOIS, Charmian E.; '89 BA; 945 Wheeler Ave., Bronx, NY 10473, 718 822-5517.

DUBOSE, Kenneth E.; '94 BA; 2705 Callery Ct., Chesapeake, VA 23323.

DUCHAINE, Nina S.; '77 MA; 888 7th Ave. Ste. 801, New York, NY 10106.

DUCOS, Eric; '96 BA; Customer Svc. Rep.; Bell Atlantic, 8808 164th St., Jamaica, NY 11432; r. 5155 47th St., Flushing, NY 11377, 718 392-5822.

DUCTAN, Cohetta; '98 BS; 1165 Stanley Ave. 4b, Brooklyn, NY 11208, 718 647-1094.

DUDA, Joseph (Joe) T.; '76 MA, BA; Retired Police Sgt; NYC Police Dept., 50th Precinct; r. 62 South St., Goshen, NY 10924, 914 294-9463; *Margaret, Mary;* Donna Daley, Maureen Horn, Patricia M., Therese Quinn, Ann Grossbard.

DUDA, Nicola M. '94 (See Shea, Nicola D.).

DUDASH, Stephen; '80 BA; 461 68th St., Brooklyn, NY 11220, 718 748-4542.

DUDLEY, Shawn L.; '95 BS; 10935 157th St., Jamaica, NY 11433.

DUESTERDICK, Kurt A.; '82 BA; Corporate Investigator; Roadway Express Inc., 1077 Gorge Blvd., Akron, OH 44310, 732 566-8999; r. 2 Fawn Dr., Matawan, NJ 07747, 732 566-0459. e-mail

DUFF, James P.; '75 AS, '77 BA; Retired; Security Trainer Wackenhut, 33 W Main St., Rm 303, Elmsford, NY 10523; r. 14 Park Ter., Rockland Lake, NY 10989, 914 268-7636; *Maureen;* Matthew, James.

DUFFY, Charles P.; '95 BA; Sergeant; NYC Police Dept., One Police Plz., New York, NY 10038, 212 374-2366; r. 25254 60th Ave. 2nd Fl., Little Neck, NY 11362, 718 279-4668; *Harriet;* Ilana, Cassie. e-mail

DUFFY, Craig T.; '94 MA; BA Seton Hall Univ.; Admissions Coord.; Bonnie Brae, 3415 Valley Rd. POB 825, Liberty Corner, NJ 07938, 908 647-4701; r. 105 Bermuda Dr., Neshanic Sta., NJ 08853, 908 369-9674. e-mail

DUFFY, David; '93 AS; 3104 Kingsbridge A, Bronx, NY 10463, 718 796-2546.

DUFRESNE, Raymond K.; '79 BS; MPA Baruch; US Deputy Marshal; US State Fed. Ct., Federal Ct. Bldg., Cheyenne, WY 82001; r. 10121 Branding Iron Dr., Cheyenne, WY 82009, 307 772-0528; *Roserita;* Antoinette M. e-mail

DUFRESNE, Roserita; '92 BA; Admin. Dir.; The Wyoming Trans. Museum & Learning Ctr, POB 704, Cheyenne, WY 82003, 307 637-3376; r. 10121 Branding Iron Dr., Cheyenne, WY 82009, 307 772-0528; *Raymond K.;* Antoinette M. e-mail

DUGAN, Martha; 445 W 59th St., New York, NY 10019, 315 733-8064.

DUGGAN, Frank; '76 MA; 69 Clove Rd #9C, Stamford, CT 06902, 203 461-9546.

DUHANEY, Shirene A.; '96 BS; P.O.Box 799, New York, NY 10116.

DUIGNAN, Daniel; '93 BA; 60-19 68 Rd. 33R, Ridgewood, NY 11385.

DUIGNAN, Ms. Mary T.; '67 BS; Retired Police Ofcr.; r. 4036 70th St., Woodside, NY 11377, 718 457-7041.

DUKE, Daniel L.; '79 BA; Facilities Mgr.; US Govt., General Services Admin., 290 Broadway, New York, NY 10278, 212 637-2968; r. 2790 W. 5th St., Apt. 23F, Brooklyn, NY 11224, 718 946-2967. e-mail

DUKE, Lara M.; '98 MA; 2175 North Hwy. 360, Apt. 923, Grand Prairie, TX 75050.

DULA, Eva M.; '93 BA; 150 Hawthorne St., Brooklyn, NY 11225, 718 336-3584.

D'ULISSE, Carl; '81 AS, '89 BS; Retired; NYC Empl.; r. 3427 205th St., Flushing, NY 11361, 718 423-1452.

DUMAS, Peter R.; '75 MPA; 25 Aldred Ave., Rockville Centre, NY 11570.

DUMMETT, Dexter C.; '95 BS; 11152 169th St., Jamaica, NY 11433.

DUMOIS, Jesus; '91 BA; MPA Hostos Community Clg.; Public Administration; Bellevue Hosp., 28th St. & 5th Ave., New York, NY 10009, 212 254-4933; r. 309 E 8th St. Apt. A, New York, NY 10009, 212 677-3914; *Anna;* Jesus.

DUNBAR, Arlene; '96 BA; 730 Schenectady Ave., Brooklyn, NY 11203, 718 774-8116.

DUNCAN, Abraham D.; '72 BS; 30 Lamar Pl., Yonkers, NY 10710, 914 289-0803.

DUNCAN, Bernadette '98 (See Peters, Bernadette V.).

DUNCAN, Charles A.; '91 BS; 960 Grand Concourse, Bronx, NY 10451.

DUNCAN, Clarence; '92 BA; POB 14, Bronx, NY 10464, 718 892-4151.

DUNCAN, Donald G.; '92 BS; 121-02 111 Ave., Richmond Hill, NY 11419, 718 961-4043.

DUNCAN, Garfield S.; '89 BS; 1041 Sterling Pl., Brooklyn, NY 11213, 718 826-0787.

DUNCAN, Jesse J.; '99 BS; Police Ofcr.; NYPD, 1000 Sutter Ave. 75th Precinct, New York, NY; r. Brooklyn, NY 11235. e-mail

DUNCAN, Kathy; '92 MA; 610 W. 150th St., New York, NY 10031, 315 858-2064.

DUNCAN, Mrs. Louise L.; '73 BA; Police Officer; r. 3125 Tibbett Ave. Apt. 5C, Bronx, NY 10463, 718 601-5596; *Lawrence;* Robert.

DUNCAN, LT Robert W.; '85 BS; Retired; r. 4079 Edson Ave., Bronx, NY 10466, 718 994-3268; *Juanita;* Venita, Dwayne, Justin.

DUNCAN, Shakima; '96 BA; Asst. VP; Chase Manhattan Bank, 55 Water St., New York, NY 10041, 212 252-5960; r. 390 Rugby Rd, Apt. 4G, Brooklyn, NY 11226, 718 940-4396.

DUNDON, John W.; '92 BS; 251 N Pine St., Massapequa, NY 11758, 516 798-1002.

DUNDON, Reilly J.; '89 MPA; 39 Nostrand Rd, Somerville, NJ 08876.

DUNICAN, Thomas A.; '74 AAS, '76 BA; Magistrate; North Carolina Ct. Systs., 316 Princess St., Wilmington, NC 28401, 910 256-7944; r. 1324 Williamsburg Ct., Wilmington, NC 28411, 910 350-2741. e-mail

DUNIGAN, Bryan P.; '80 BA; 80 Chelsea St., Staten Island, NY 10307, 718 984-3191.

DUNLAP, Daniel; '90 BS; CERT TCI, PI NRA; Police Admin Aide; NYCPD, New York, NY 10007; r. POB 080055, 760 Elderts Ln. #9T, Brooklyn, NY 11208, 718 827-0905.

DUNLEAVY, Sean; '92 BA; 3800 Independence Ave., Apt. 6G, Bronx, NY 10463, 718 796-1914.

DUNLOP, Winston I.; '85 MA; 1663 Thornhill Cir., Oviedo, FL 32765, 407 366-0291.

DUNLOP, Winston I.; '92 BS; 32 Mccall Pl., Newburgh, NY 12550, 914 343-5264.

DUNN, Hayley; '95 BA; Applications Spec.; New York, NY 10017; r. same.

DUNN, Michael F.; '77 MPA; POB 377, Westtown, PA 19395, 610 998-0934.

DUNN, Thomas J.; '88 BA; 18 Willo Ln., Albany, NY 12211, 518 432-0760.

DUNNE, Charles G.; '96 MA; 115 Sackville Rd., Garden City, NY 11530, 516 746-4254.

DUNNE, Jay C.; '75 AA, '76 BA, '77 MA; Retired Securities Supv.; Merrill Lynch; r. 115 Sackville Rd, Garden City, NY 11530, 516 746-4254. e-mail

DUNNE, Joseph A.; '71 MPA; 10777 W Sample Rd Apt. 219, Coral Springs, FL 33065, 954 755-1898.

DUNNE, Peter J.; 15 Hemlock Ct., Selden, NY 11784.

DUNNE, Richard A.; '72 BS; Ret.; r. 2 Woodlawn Ave. # 2, Valley Stream, NY 11581, 516 872-3354; *Antoinette;* Richard, Geri.

DUNPHY, Timothy G.; '79 BS; 1545 E 21st St., Brooklyn, NY 11210, 718 377-4650.

DUPOUX, Mrs. Marie-Maud, (Marie-Maud Thomas); '94 BA; Dressmaker; The Fashion Gallery, 404 W 56th St., Ste. 22, New York, NY 10019, 212 489-4857; r. 404 W 56th St. Apt. 22, New York, NY 10019, 212 489-4857; Ricky T. e-mail

DUPREE, Angela; '98 BA; 880 Post Rd, Scarsdale, NY 10583, 914 422-3315.

DUQUE, Ruben D.; '97 AS, '98 BA; AS, BA; Police Ofcr.; NYPD, Police Plz., New York, NY 10038, 718 574-1605; r. 330 42st, Brooklyn, NY 11232, 718 369-4821; *Rosenary.* e-mail

DURAN, Heidi L.; '97 MS; Forensic Sci.; r. 76 White Tail Ln., Wallingford, CT 06492. e-mail

DURAN, Jimmy; '98 BS; Grad. Student; Brooklyn Clg.; r. 626 40 St., Brooklyn, NY 11232, 718 854-0542. e-mail

DURAND, Maria A.; '98 BA; 507 W. 134th St., New York, NY 10031, 212 862-2676.

DURANDO, Doanld M.; '76 AS; 36-36 Crescent St., Astoria, NY 11106.

DURANDO, Donald M.; '80 BS; 59-39 157 St., Flushing, NY 11355.

DURANT, Portia R.; '79 BA; 49 Crown St. Apt. #2, Brooklyn, NY 11225, 718 693-1029.

DURANTE, Eugene G.; '95 BA, 2000 MPA; Police Ofcr.; NYPD, 718 645-4798; r. 2243 E 3rd St., Brooklyn, NY 11223, 718 645-4798. e-mail

DURE, Jacques P.; '82 BS; 11211 S Military Tr., Apt. 511, Boynton Bch., FL 33436.

DURFEE, Douglas M.; 16 Wisconsin Ave., N. Massapequa, NY 11758.

DURHAM, Bette L.; '88 BS; Child Protective Spec.; Admin. for Children Svcs., 150 William St., New York, NY 10038, 212 676-7303; r. 907 Belmont Ave., Brooklyn, NY 11208.

DURHAM, Elaine C.; '78 BA; 1824 2nd Ave., Toms River, NJ 08757, 732 244-7886.

DURISIN, George G.; '77 MA; 6 Quailhollow Dr., Mt. Holly, NJ 08060.

DURKIN, Mary A.; '89 MA; 750 Pipes Neck Rd, Greenport, NY 11944.

DURKIN, Robert T.; '99 MPA; BA SUNY-Buffalo, MS Nav. War Clg.; Maj.; USMC, 6448 Patuxent Vista Dr., Alexandria, VA 22312; r. 531A Winans, West Point, NY 10996; *Kathleen.*

DURNACK, Robert (Bob) P.; '76 BS FIR; Retired Loss Control Spec.; CIGNA Ins. Co.; r. 4 Croyden Ln., Hicksville, NY 11801.

DURNEY, William C.; '83 BA; 521 W 185th St. #3F, New York, NY 10033.

DURNIN, Thomas A.; '77 BA; 38 Lincoln Pl., Massapequa, NY 11758, 516 541-5057.

DURO, Christopher M.; '95 BS; 57 Colin St. Apt. 1, Yonkers, NY 10701.

DURR, Johershey; '76 AS; 787 E 46th St., Brooklyn, NY 11203.

DURSO, Vivian V.; '96 BS; 9281 Shore Rd #600, Brooklyn, NY 11209, 718 256-7437.

DURU, Athanasius O.; '91 AS, '92 BS; 187-35 Hillside Ave., Jamaica, NY 11432.

DURUDOGAN, Agah; '96 BS; 300 E. 57th St., New York, NY 10022.

DUSSEK, Philippe R.; '83 BS; 485 E 52nd St., Brooklyn, NY 11203.

DUTES, Ronald; '93 BS; MED Long Island Univ-Brooklyn; HS Guid. Couns; HS of Arts & Business, 105-25 Horace Harding Expy., Corona, NY 11368, 718 271-8383; r. 120 Buscher Ave., Valley Stream, NY 11580, 516 561-7925; *Christine H.;* Keisha, Ronald J., Garvey A. e-mail

DUVAL, Christopher D.; '97 BS; 106 Downes Ave., Staten Island, NY 10312, 718 317-7657.

DUVERNE, Madeleine M.; '98 BS; 150 02 88 Ave. E2, Jamaica, NY 11432, 718 523-6588.

DUVIL, Jack P.; '92 BA; 811 Cortonia Park N, Bronx, NY 10460.

DUVILLE, Richard L.; '96 BS; Database Asst.; UN, New York, NY 10001; r. 9422 210th St., Queens Vlg., NY 11428, 718 776-6611.

DWYER, Donna M.; '92 BA; 1560 Lincoln Pl., Brooklyn, NY 11233, 718 789-0784.

DWYER, Douglas R.; '88 BS; MS CW Post-Long Island Univ; Lt.; Nassau Cnty. Police Dept., 1490 Franklin Ave., Mineola, NY 11501, 516 573-7000; r. Carle Place, NY 11514.

DWYER, Karen; '95 BA; 9 Campus Pl. # Apt., Scarsdale, NY 10583, 914 637-6162.

DWYER, Lauren A.; '99 MA, '99; PSYD Hofstra Univ.; Tchr.; MS 180, Bronx, NY 10475, 718 904-5671; r. 24 Gilbert Pl., Yonkers, NY 10701, 914 968-7157.

DWYER, Lawrence T.; '79; 8935 155th Ave. Apt. 1e, Jamaica, NY 11414, 718 848-7205.

DYBSKI, Thomas; '99 BS; Fire Protection Inspector; NYC Fire Dept., 1129 E 180 St., Bronx, NY 10460, 718 430-0291; r. 40 Van Cortlandt Pk, Yonkers, NY 10701, 914 963-0243. e-mail

DYER, Mark; '93 BS; Law Student; Quinnipiac University, 275 Mt Carmel Ave., Mt. Carmel, CT 06518. e-mail

DYMINSKI, Edward A.; '99 MA; 38 Knoll Ct., Matawan, NJ 07747, 732 583-9521.

DZAIRI, Ali; '97; 8-10 27th Ave. #714, Astoria, NY 11102.

DZIEKONSKI, Barbara; '92 BA; Mortgage Svc. Rep; Masteth, 5605 69th St., Maspeth, NY 11378; r. 6821 53rd Rd, Maspeth, NY 11378, 718 779-0096. e-mail

DZIELSKI, Michael; '87 MPA; 4614 Farragut Rd, Brooklyn, NY 11203.

DZIENISZEWSKA, Ewa; '95 BS; Assoc. Programmer; Salomon Smith Barney; r. 176 Emily Ln., Staten Island, NY 10312, 718 227-3186; Kamila. e-mail

E

EAGLE, Tanya M. '95 (See Eagle-Agard, Tanya M.).

EAGLE-AGARD, Tanya M., (Tanya M. Eagle); '95 BS; Interviewer; NYC Criminal Justice Agcy., 16 Court St., Brooklyn, NY 11201, 718 330-1500; r. 1350 Bedford Ave. Apt. 5E, Brooklyn, NY 11216, 718 857-4600; *Eddie-Brian Agard.*

EANES, Ms. Barbara A.; '75 BS; MPA Baruch, MSED Hunter Clg.; Academic Advisor; Borough of Manhattan Community Clg., 199 Chambers St., New York, NY 10007, 212 346-8140; r. 101 W 87st #6C, New York, NY 10024, 212 874-8788. e-mail

EANNIELLO, Andrew; '87 BS; 49 Meadow St., Pearl River, NY 10965.

EARLE, Lynda E.; '86 BS; 8605 21st Pl., Hyattsville, MD 20783, 301 772-3012.

EARLE, Thomas; '81 BS; 1469 Teller Ave., Bronx, NY 10457, 718 994-2502.

EARLE, Winston S.; '83 BS; 1469 Teller Ave., Bronx, NY 10457, 718 994-2502.

EARLY, Kimberly M.; '85 BS; 20 Madeline Ter., Chestnut Ridge, NY 10977, 914 267-5369.

EARS, Joannee; '76 BA; 8617 103rd Ave., Jamaica, NY 11417.

EASON, Erica M.; '95 BS; Police Ofcr.; NYC Police Dept., 1 Police Plza, New York, NY 10038; r. 608 Rugby Rd, Apt. 5d, Brooklyn, NY 11230.

EASON, Marcus; '85 BA; 5814 Farragut Rd., Brooklyn, NY 11234.

EASON, Pansy; '93 BA; 5814 Farragut Rd., Brooklyn, NY 11234.

EASON, Rufus J.; '83 BA; 1206 Summerstone Ce, Austell, GA 30168, 770 969-4591.

EASTERLING, Dolores L. '95 (See Johnson, Dolores L.).

EASTMAN, Elkan H.; '95 BS; 1218 E 45th St., Brooklyn, NY 11234, 718 771-0503.

EASTMAN, Kenneth N.; '87 BA; Public Assembly Ofcr.; United Nations Sec. & Safety Svcs.; r. 1 Meadow Haven Ln., E. Northport, NY 11731, 631 499-2738. e-mail

EBANKS, Norman A.; '87 BA; 232-09 Mentone Ave., Laurelton, NY 11413, 718 337-2003.

EBERHARDT, Ruth A.; '71 BS; 8 Dover Hill Dr., Nesconset, NY 11767.

EBRAHIM, Linda; '93 MPA; 4819 43rd St. Apt. 6d, Flushing, NY 11377, 718 626-6659.

ECCLES, Kern; '96 BA; 515 W. 59th St. # 9N, New York, NY 10019, 212 765-1834.

ECHENIQUE, Patricia S.; '84 BS; 94-34 211 St., Queens Vlg., NY 11428.

ECHEVARRIA, Daliza E.; '85 BS; MSW Hunter Clg.; Exec. Dir.; Aspiring Youth Inc., 921 Hegaman Ave., Brooklyn, NY 11208, 718 647-2600; r. 8210 101st Ave., Ozone Park, NY 11416, 718 843-5457; Jasmine Munoz, Jesse, Julian Nieves. e-mail

ECHEVARRIA, Mabel; '90 BS; 1134 W. Farms Rd., Bronx, NY 10459, 718 410-2572.

ECHOLS, Phyllis A.; '83 BS; 545 W 158th St. Apt. 3, New York, NY 10032.

ECKHOFF, Karen '82 ʹ(See Eckhoff-Pieratt, Ms. Karen).

ECKHOFF-PIERATT, Ms. Karen, (Karen Eckhoff); '82 AS, '84 BS; Liquidating Aide; US Customs, World Trade Ctr., New York, NY 10048, 212 637-7688; r. 25 Jones St. Apt. 4a, New York, NY 10014; David.

ECKSTEIN, Robert; '97 BA, '98 BA; 23 Berkshire Rd, Merrick, NY 11566, 516 746-2761.

EDDINGTON, Mark; '83 BS; Sergeant; NYC Police Dept., New York, NY 10038; r. 2268 Story Ave., Bronx, NY 10473, 718 829-0265.

EDDY, Eric; '87 MPA; 135 W 106th St. # 2, New York, NY 10025, 315 363-6509.

EDELMAN, Steven P.; '95 MPA; 240 S Broadway Apt. 14b, Tarrytown, NY 10591, 914 332-0425.

EDISON, Mel; '79 MA; BA Brooklyn Clg.; Asst Loan Prog Mgr/V.A. Cert Offcr; John Jay Clg., 445 W. 59th St., Rm #3400 N, New York, NY 10019, 212 237-8156; r. 711 Montauk Ct., Brooklyn, NY 11235, 718 934-1943; Rebecca. e-mail

EDLAM, Lionel; '91 BS; 1016 E 213th St., Bronx, NY 10469.

EDMONDS, Garfield N.; '96 AS, '99 BS; 5022 Tilden Ave., Brooklyn, NY 11203, 718 922-5676.

EDOKPOLO, James O.; '93 BS, '96 MPA; Paralegal; NYC Human Resources Lig. Div., New York, NY 10013, 212 274-6781; r. 97-20 57th Ave., Corona, NY 11368; Belinda, Leonard. e-mail

EDREIRA, Anna-marie; '89 BS; Child Protective Supv.; NYC Admin. for Children's Svc., 150 William St., New York, NY 10038, 212 676-7270; r. 20 Shadow Ln., Great Neck, NY 11021, 516 466-7854.

EDWARD, Selvin F.; '81 BS; 248 Harvest Ave., Staten Island, NY 10310, 718 727-0956.

EDWARDS, Bernard E.; '74 BS; MED Fordham Univ.; Retired-1st Deputy Inspector Gen.; r. 120-11 Casals Pl., Bronx, NY 10475, 718 379-7297; Lisa, Cindei.

EDWARDS, Carla; '91 BA; 283 Barrow St. # 2, Jersey City, NJ 07302.

EDWARDS, Colleen V.; '96 BS; 1571 Sheridan Ave., Bronx, NY 10457, 718 401-4125.

EDWARDS, Evelyn M.; '87 MPA; 11448 132nd St., Jamaica, NY 11420, 718 274-6042.

EDWARDS, James W.; '74 BA; 51 Morton St., New York, NY 10014, 315 822-6043.

EDWARDS, Joseph B.; '77 MA; Assoc. Investigator; State Ins. Dept., New York, NY 10004, 212 480-5884; r. 362 Hussey Rd, Mt. Vernon, NY 10552, 914 665-1104.

EDWARDS, Joyce A.; '81 BA, '89 MPA; 254 W 139th St., New York, NY 10030, 315 822-6043.

EDWARDS, Katrina; '97; Mgr.; Natl. Assn. On Drug Abuse Problems, 35 4th Ave., Brooklyn, NY 11217, 718 623-7451; r. 8 Veteran's Way, Edgewater, NJ 07020, 201 969-1039.

EDWARDS, Latisha; '94 BA; Customer Svc.; r. 1203 Westchester Ave., Bronx, NY 10459, 718 328-1827.

EDWARDS, Martin W.; '83 MPA; 105 Patchen Ave., Brooklyn, NY 11221, 718 919-1639.

EDWARDS, Rev. Michael; '80 BA; MDIV New Brunswick Theological, MS Fordham Univ.; Asst. Principal; Bd. of Educ., New York, NY 10014, 212 337-6800; r. POB 824, New York, NY 10035, 315 822-6043; Pamela; Jamal, Tremayna, Davona.

EDWARDS, Nicole R.; '92 BS; 18728 Jordan Ave., St. Albans, NY 11412.

EDWARDS, Patrick L.; '89 BA; 789 E 40th St., Brooklyn, NY 11210, 718 443-6551.

EDWARDS, Randy M.; '89 BA; 806 Albany Ave., Brooklyn, NY 11203, 718 485-5750.

EDWARDS, Roxanne D.; '97 BA; Pace Law Sch.; Student; r. 750 Croes Ave., Bronx, NY 10473, 718 991-7202.

EDWARDS, Sam L.; '72 BS, AAS; Retired Detective Sgt/Tax Auditor; NY Police Dept./IRS; r. 312 Roquette Ave., S. Floral Park, NY 11001, 516 437-8511; Samuel Jr, Angela, Vincent, Daniel.

EDWARDS, Theresa A.; '75 MA; 1315 18th St., San Francisco, CA 94107, 415 566-2154.

EFFRECE, Frank P.; '81 BA; 544 W 163rd St. Apt. 31, New York, NY 10032.

EGAN, Abbe I.; '99 MA; Student; Villanova Sch. of Law/MCP Hahnemann Univ, Villanova, PA 19085; r. 8200 Henry Ave., Apt. A-16, Roxborough, PA 19128, 215 508-0619. e-mail

EGAN, John J.; '75 MPA; 6 Gurran Dr., Stony Point, NY 10980, 914 942-1323.

EGAN, Mary; '95 BS; 174 Chandler Ave., Staten Island, NY 10314.

EGAN, Patrick J.; '76 BA; AA, CERT. New York; Acctg. Tax Preparation/Ser; Patricks Tax & Bookkeeping Svc., 114-04 Beach Channel Dr., Rockaway Park, NY 11694, 718 945-9685; r. 244 Beach 127th St., Belle Harbor, NY 11694, 718 318-1547; Patricia A.; Michael, Kathleen, Thomas, John. e-mail

EGAN, Thomas P.; '76 BS; 15 E. 199 St., Bronx, NY 10468, 718 365-6104.

EGGER, Stephen L.; '81 BS; Computer Prog. Developer; SLE Development; r. 2345 Royce St., Brooklyn, NY 11234, 718 444-4956. e-mail

EGGLESTON, Lester R.; NYCPD Detective; NYCPD, Bronx, NY 10457, 718 299-3959; r. 22 Jerome St., Medford, MA 02155, 914 949-2198.

EGHAGHE, James O.; '81 MA; 656 Miller Ave., Brooklyn, NY 11207.

EGL, Anthony E.; '77 BA; 2663 Harding Ave., Bronx, NY 10465.

EGNER, Elizabeth; '81 BS; 293 White Rd, Mineola, NY 11501, 516 741-5273.

EHRLICH, Neil; '96 BA; 66 Bay 29th St., Brooklyn, NY 11214, 718 265-7090.

EHRLICH, Sidney; '72 BS; 455 Fdr Dr. # B, New York, NY 10002, 212 228-2737.

EICH, Thomas J.; '77 MA; 302 E 88th St. Apt. 3j, New York, NY 10128, 212 348-1349.

EICHHORN, Barbara L.; '79 BS; 222 E Curtis St., Linden, NJ 07036, 908 486-6421.

EICHNER, Andrew J.; '89 BS; 90-60 Union Tpk., Glendale, NY 11385.

EILBECK, Jean C.; '89 BS; 12 Byan St., Huntington, NY 11743.

EISENBERG, Mark C.; '75 BS CJ; Investigative Cnslt.; Kroll-Ogara-Inphoto Surveillance Inc., 342 E. Jericho Tpk. PMB #139, Mineola, NY 11501, 516 486-0651; r. 516 486-0651; Betty; Neil, Lauren. e-mail

EISENBERG, Scott; '95 MA; 5 Munson Ct., Melville, NY 11747, 516 797-1824.

EISENBERG, Shauna L.; '96 BA; 19 Beth Ln., Plainview, NY 11803, 516 931-0799.

EISENHAUER, Letty; '93 MA; 42 N. Moore St., New York, NY 10013, 212 966-0940.

EISNER, Judy; '82 MA; 55 Pierpont Pl., Staten Island, NY 10314.

EKIZIAH, Stephen K.; '95 BS; 78-09 46th Ave., Elmhurst, NY 11373.

EKSTER, Martin B.; 850 Fairway Dr., # 903Ee, Longs, SC 29568.

EKSTROM, Charles A.; '89 BS; Police Ofcr.; Ridgefield, Ridgefield, CT 06877; r. 165 Prayer Spring Rd, Stratford, CT 06614, 203 378-5653.

EL-AMIN, Ms. Zamirah K.; '96 BS; Law Clerk; Paul, Hastings, Janofsky & Walker LLP, 399 Park Ave., New York, NY 10022, 212 318-6667; r. 700 Lenox Ave. #25l, New York, NY 10039, 212 690-0214. e-mail

ELCIK, James J.; '88 BS; 5411 63rd St., Flushing, NY 11378.

ELCOCK, Erskine L.; '90 BS, '93 MPA; DIPLOMA Univ. of The West Indies; Police Sergeant/Tchr.; TNT Police Svcs., Sackville Str., Port-of-Spain, Trinidad And Tobago; r. 620 W 170th St. Apt. 3d, New York, NY 10032, 212 568-5218; *Betty;* Joel, Sherwin, Dwinnel, Erskine, Kyle, Kwesi, Keron, Shellon.

ELCOCK, Mark G.; '98 BS; Chemist; Polytex Environ. Inks. E. 140th St., Bronx, NY 10454, 718 402-2000; r. 1752 Brooklyn Ave., Brooklyn, NY 11210, 718 859-6299.

ELDER, Margaret A.; '97 BS, '98 BS; 1601 3rd Ave./25g, New York, NY 10128, 212 987-1042.

ELDER, Velma '95 (See McKain, Velma A.).

ELEFTHERIOU, Eleftherios A.; '99 BA; Full-time Student/Drug/Rehab Co; John Jay Clg. of Criminal Justice; r. 26-24 29th St. Apt. 2, Astoria, NY 11102, 718 956-3729.

ELEY, Regina E.; '85 BS; 22319 109th Ave., Queens Vlg., NY 11429.

ELFELD, Elizabeth, (Elizabeth Oettinger); '83 BS; Investigator; American Trademark Investigations Inc., POB 907, Long Beach, NY 11561, 516 897-0374; r. 23 Curley St., Long Beach, NY 11561, 516 431-9553; *Wallace;* Amy, Ryan. e-mail

ELIE, Yves; '96 BS; 5140 30th Ave. Apt. 3b, Flushing, NY 11377, 718 776-5709.

ELIO, Cynthia; 1375 Hollywood Ave. #PH, Bronx, NY 10461, 718 823-8085.

ELIO, Michael F.; '75 BS; 122 E 235th St., Bronx, NY 10470.

ELISSON, Chris; '90 BS; Lt.; NYPD; r. 7017 Ridge Crest Ter., Brooklyn, NY 11209, 718 833-4085.

ELKIN, Denise R.; '75 BS; 8870 Fntnb Bl #202, Miami, FL 33172, 305 559-2428.

ELLIOTT, Johnathan R.; '82 MA; 2459 Bedford Ave., Brooklyn, NY 11226, 718 621-1718.

ELLIOTT, Sandra E.; '81 BA; MA CA State Univ.-Hayward; Claims Supv.; Cobb Cnty. Sch. Dist., Marietta, GA 30061; r. Marietta, GA 30062, 770 509-7770.

ELLIOTT, Sean M.; '88 BS; 45 Doral Ln., Bay Shore, NY 11706.

ELLIS, Anthony; '96 BA; 5240 Broadway #7F, Bronx, NY 10463, 718 893-8480.

ELLIS, Iretha; BA; POB, New York, NY 10008, 315 736-9119.

ELLIS, Joseph S.; '99 AS; 1675 E. 21st St., Brooklyn, NY 11210, 718 768-5365.

ELLISON, Henry J.; '75 BA; 15562 116th Rd, Jamaica, NY 11434.

ELLISON, Phillip; '96 BS, '99; 30 Hunters Ln., Westbury, NY 11590, 516 333-8514.

ELLMAN, Louis M.; '82 BS; 22123 64th Ave., Flushing, NY 11364.

ELLSON, James P.; '75 BA, '91 MS; Dept. Dir.; Mayors Ofc. NYC, 7 World Trade Ctr., New York, NY 10013, 212 341-0447; r. 370 First Ave. #2D, New York, NY 10010, 212 228-7934.

ELLSWORTH, Thomas; '76 MA; BA Central Methodist Clg.; Prof.; Illinois State Univ., Normal, IL 61790, 309 438-7626; r. 210 Doud Dr., Normal, IL 61761, 309 452-2731. e-mail

ELMORE, Allan F.; '71 BA; 11805 Cleaver Dr., Mitchellville, MD 20721, 301 486-1900.

ELMORE, William (Bill) L.; '78 BS; Private Investigator; r. 871-A Underhill Ave., Bronx, NY 10473, 718 518-0150.

ELSAYED, Judith; '98 BA; Social Studies; Bd. of Educ., 718 822-5082; r. 400 Brook Ave. 7g, Bronx, NY 10454, 718 665-8460; Susan, Sandra, Miriam, Jennifer.

EMANUEL, Michael A.; '99 BS; 90 Kent Rd, Wappingers Falls, NY 12590, 914 297-0820.

EMANUEL, Michael L.; '84 MA; BA Rutgers Univ.; Forensic Toxicologist; NJ Med. Examiners Ofc., 325 Norfolk St., Newark, NJ 07103, 973 648-3915; r. 100 Cori St., Parlin, NJ 08859, 732 727-3711; *Evangeline;* Louis, Nicholas. e-mail

EMANUEL, Peter S.; '88 BS; 2823 Gunther Ave., Bronx, NY 10469, 718 320-7242.

EMBDEN, David R.; '95 MPA; 1347 Webster St. NE, Washington, DC 20017.

EMBRY, Alicia J.; '96 BS; MSW NYU; Legal Secy; Kirkland & Ellis, 153 E 53rd St., New York, NY 10022, 212 446-4872; r. 236 Greene Ave., Apt. 4D, Brooklyn, NY 11238, 718 398-7094; *Barry Walton;* Derrek Oliver. e-mail

EMERSON, James C.; '90 BS; Central Ofc. Supv.; Frontier Communications, 145 N. Main St., Monroe, NY 10950, 914 782-1032; r. 29 Jackson Ave., Middletown, NY 10940, 914 344-1354; *Laura;* Alaina, Christian. e-mail

EMIDIH, Jones F.; '99 MPA; BA Clg. of New Rochelle, MS Audrey Cohen Clg.; Prog. Dir.; Unique People Svcs., 136 W 44 St., New York, NY 10036; r. 48 St. Paul's Pl., Apt. 3A, Brooklyn, NY 11226, 718 462-6371; Rene Ovie, Jeremiah O.

EMILIAN, Ivan; '97 BA; 140 Bentley Ave., Jersey City, NJ 07304.

EMLOCK, John S.; 10932 110th St., Jamaica, NY 11420.

ENCARNACION, Felicito; '78 BS; Police Ofcr.; Port Authority Police Dept., Police Bldg. 30, Marine Terminal Rd, Flushing, NY 11371; r. POB 710054, La Guardia Sta., Flushing, NY 11371, 718 533-3947.

ENCARNACION, Gregory; '97 BS; 70 Beach Rd, Massapequa, NY 11758.

ENG, Lorna; '79 BS; 328 Bay Ridge Ave., Brooklyn, NY 11220, 718 238-9295.

ENG, Shawn; '99 BS; 1224 Tabor Ct., Brooklyn, NY 11219, 718 331-7249. e-mail

ENG, Thomas; '87 BS; 9 Allen St. Apt. 5c, New York, NY 10002, 315 797-6098.

ENGEL, Peter W.; '84 MPA; 387 8 St., Brooklyn, NY 11215, 718 768-4250.

ENGEL, William; '95 BA; 2300 Kings Hwy., Brooklyn, NY 11229.

ENGLETON, Lena D.; '84 BA; 939 Castle Hill Ave., Bronx, NY 10473.

ENGLEY, William C.; 4466 Drayton Ln., Oviedo, FL 32765.

ENGLISH, Christopher; '90 BS; 91 Athens Ave., South Amboy, NJ 08879, 732 727-5038.

ENGLISH, Claudia M.; '97 BS; 363 Forbell St., Brooklyn, NY 11208, 718 827-0918.

ENGLISH, David J.; '95 BS; Owner/Mgr.; David's Protective Svcs., Brooklyn, NY 11233, 718 443-3292; r. 239 A Sumpter St., Brooklyn, NY 11233, 718 443-3292; Dana.

ENGLISH, Eleanor A.; '84 MA; Ret Probation Ofcr.; r. 10 Stuyvesant Oval, New York, NY 10009; *Peter W.*

ENRIGHT, Mary E.; '82 MA; 254 Prospect Ave., Staten Island, NY 10301.

ENRIQUEZ, Evelyn; '86 BA; 84-25 Elmhurst Ave., Elmhurst, NY 11373.

ENRIQUEZ, Jorge; '90 BA; 204 W 109th St. Apt. 4d, New York, NY 10025.

ENRIQUEZ, Lister V.; '99; 416 Frist Pl., Uniondale, NY 11553.

EODUMEGWUHU, Khalika U.; '99 BA; Telecommunications; Millennium Broadway; r. 622 Lafayette Ave., Brooklyn, NY 11216, 718 230-3271.

EPPS, Shirley A.; '85 BS; 165 E 179th St. Apt. 5l, Bronx, NY 10453, 718 563-4914.

EPSTEIN, Bonnie; '95 BA; 2728 Kings Hwy. Apt. C1, Brooklyn, NY 11229.

EPSTEIN, Trevor J.; '70 BS; RR 2 Box 2086, Stroudsburg, PA 18360, 570 424-1291.

ERAZO, Elliot; '89 BS; 318 Sip Ave., Jersey City, NJ 07306.

ERB, Justin C.; '95 BS; 1621 Terrill Rd, Scotch Plains, NJ 07076, 908 322-6819.

ERB, Kenneth G.; '83 BA; 34 Dunn Ct., Sayville, NY 11782.

EREKUFF, Gary; 2185 Bolton St., Bronx, NY 10462, 718 792-7608.

ERGUN, Halime; '95 BS; 11 Hillside Ave., Rockville Centre, NY 11570.

ERHUNMWUNSEE, Isaac; '82 MA; MLW Fordham Univ.; Mgr.; Admin. of Children Svcs. NY, 1958 40th St., Brooklyn, NY 11233, 718 953-8455; r. 50 S.9th St. Apt. 1B, Brooklyn, NY 11211, 718 384-1036; *Boroh.*

ERICKSON, Kathleen; '92 MA; 95 76th St., Brooklyn, NY 11209, 718 339-2343.

ERICKSON, Scott W.; '98 BA; MED Wagner Clg.; Educator; Staten Island Sch. Dist. 31; r. 79 Simonson Pl., Staten Island, NY 10302, 718 981-2942. e-mail

ERICKSON, Tom E.; 157-10 Riverside Dr., New York, NY 10032.

ERICSON, Marvin F.; '69 MPA; POB 1218, Palm Coast, FL 32037.

ERNST, James C.; '98 BS; Firefighter; r. 14 Rockaway St., Holtsville, NY 11742, 631 475-2393.

ERNST, James T.; '79 BA, '86 MA; 1630 Melville St., Oakhurst, NJ 07755.

EROSA, Manuel L.; '88 BA; 9718 76 St. #1, Ozone Park, NY 11416.

ERRICO, Joseph; 16 Peachtree Ln., Levittown, NY 11756.

ERTRACHTER, Jana G.; '86 BS; 18-01 160 St., Whitestone, NY 11357, 718 846-2634.

ERVIN, Irene E. '91 (See Ervin Bullock, Irene E.).

ERVIN, Minnie G.; '79 BA; 163-19 130 Ave. #8E, Jamaica, NY 11434.

ERVIN BULLOCK, Irene E., (Irene E. Ervin); '91 BA; CSW Columbia Univ. SW; Prog. Dir.; Post Grad. Ctr. Mental Health, 344 W. 36th St., New York, NY 10018, 212 560-6729; r. 140 Casals Pl. Apt. 11 H, Bronx, NY 10475, 718 862-0170; *Mark Bullock;* Elijah, Ezekeil.

ESCALANTE, Norma E.; '98 BS; Estate Legal Spec.; Morgan Stanley Dean Witter, 5 World Trade Ctr., 5th Fl., New York, NY 10048, 212 392-9481; r. 2078 75 St. 2B, Brooklyn, NY 11204, 718 236-3176.

ESCHENBERG, Conrad J., IV; '76 BS; BS, BA Mercy Clg.; Lt. Police Officer; City of Peekskill, 2 Nelson Ave., Peekskill, NY 10566, 914 737-8000; r. 108 Hustis Rd., Cold Spring, NY 10516; *Pauline Simard;* Jacquelyn. e-mail

ESCOBAR, Louis; '75 BA; 620 E 20th St. Apt. 2e, New York, NY 10009.

ESCOBAR, Luis M.; '98 BA; 303 E. 5th St., B2, New York, NY 10003.

ESCOBAR, Marcus; '99 BA; 81 Columbia St. 11C, New York, NY 10002, 212 533-6735.

ESCOBAR, Nelson L.; '97 BA; Public Svc. Coord.; Columbia Univ., 525 N 120th St., New York, NY 10027, 212 678-3035; r. 219-01 99th Ave. 1st Fl., Queens Vlg., NY 11429, 718 736-1059. e-mail

ESCOBAR, Veronica; '98 BS; Police Ofcr.; NYC Police Dept., 1 Police Plz., New York, NY 10038, 212 292-6161; r. 90-15 138th Pl. #B18, Jamaica, NY 11435, 718 297-1225.

ESGUERRA, Andres; '99 BA; After Sch. Dir.; Hartley House, 413 W. 46th St. New York, Ny 10036, New York, NY 10036, 212 246-9885; r. 80-50 Baxter Ave. 1F, Elmhurst, NY 11373, 718 899-5878.

ESNARD, Richard; '76 BS; Mgr.; Esnacost Realty, 327 E. 65, New York, NY 10021, 212 988-0813; r. 33-52 81st St., Jackson Hts., NY 11372, 718 478-1732.

ESOFF, Donald J.; '82 BS; 2362 Webster Ave., Bronx, NY 10458, 718 584-2631.

ESPADA, Evelyn; '99 BA; 21 E. 107th St. Apt. 6H, New York, NY 10029, 212 289-6402.

ESPADA-WAITE, M.; '90 BS; 83-33 250th St., Bellerose, NY 11426, 718 776-6196.

ESPANET, Jennifer A.; '98 BS; Legal Asst./Paralegal; Broudy & Assocs., PC, 230 Park Ave., Ste. 2400, New York, NY 10169, 212 953-0910; r. 68-37 Central Ave., Glendale, NY 11385.

ESPANOL, Joseph L.; '80 BA; POB 600, Apopka, FL 32704.

ESPARZA, Christopher; '90 BS; 120 W. 105 St., New York, NY 10025.

ESPERTO, Patti-jo; '92 BS; 89 Benjamin Ave., Hicksville, NY 11801, 516 822-3654.

ESPINA, Elizabeth, Esq., (Elizabeth Silverio); '93 BA; JD Touro Law Sch.; Law Grad.; Nassau-Suffolk Law Sch., 1 Helen Keller Way, 5th Fl., Hempstead, NY 11550, 516 292-8100; r. 109 Yoakum Ave., Farmingdale, NY 11735, 631 756-0035; *John.* e-mail

ESPINAL, Elida; '93 BA; 13337 83rd St. Ph, Jamaica, NY 11417, 718 396-4051.

ESPINAL, Jacqueline; '99 MA; BA St. Johns Fisher Clg.; Cnsltg. Psychotherapist; Gabriel Feldmar, PhD; r. 210 W 251 St. Apt. 4G, Bronx, NY 10471, 718 548-1765; *Ed Perez;* Nailah Perez.

ESPINAL, Sandra M.; '99 BA; Legal Secy.; Coudert Bros., 1114 Ave. of The Americas, New York, NY 10036, 212 626-4743; r. 1492 Second Ave., New York, NY 10021, 212 535-5541. e-mail

ESPINOSA, Patricia; '82 BA; 429 E. 65 St., New York, NY 10021.

ESPINOZA, Fanny G.; '99 BS; 2471 Davidson Ave. #24, Bronx, NY 10468, 718 563-7894.

ESPINOZA, Jenny P.; '96 BS; 64 Highview Ave., Stamford, CT 06907, 203 968-9580.

ESPINOZA, Susan I.; '99 BA; 1329 St. Lawrence Ave. 2R, Bronx, NY 10472, 718 853-9230.

ESPOSITO, Angelina E.; '96 BS; AS Farmingdale State Univ.; Conductor; Long Island Railroad Syst.; r. 92 Heyward St., Brentwood, NY 11717, 631 435-3259.

ESPOSITO, Frances '74 (See Hettler, Mrs. Frances).

ESPOSITO, Gerald A.; '83 MPA; NYC District Mgr.; Community Board #1 Brooklyn, 435 Graham Ave., Brooklyn, NY 11211, 718 389-0009; r. 152 Conselyea St., Brooklyn, NY 11211, 718 748-3841.

ESPOSITO, Michael V.; '99 BS; AA Nassau Community Clg.; Police Ofcr.; NYC, New York, NY 10012; r. 84-07 60th Ave., Elmhurst, NY 11373, 718 565-2498. e-mail

ESPOSITO, Ralph A.; '85 MPA; Lt Detective Squad Comm.; NYC Police Dept., 1844 Brooklyn Ave., Brooklyn, NY 11210, 718 258-4400; r. 21 O'Gorman Ave., Staten Island, NY 10306. e-mail

ESPOSITO, Theresa M. '95 (See Zelaya, Theresa M.).

ESPOSITO, Vincent P.; '78 BA; 2148 E 34th St., Brooklyn, NY 11234, 718 491-8616.

ESSIG, Frank; '85 MPA; 88-02 139 St., Jamaica, NY 11435.

ESSILFIE, Coretta; '97 BA; Child Protective Spec.; Admin. for Children's Svcs., Bronx, NY 10451; r. 1807 Clinton Ave., Apt. 4D, Bronx, NY 10457.

ESTEBAN, Ricardo; '95 BS; 408 E 53rd St., Brooklyn, NY 11203.

ESTEVEZ, Javier G.; '96 BA; 203 30th St. #T, Brooklyn, NY 11232.

ESTEVEZ, Mildred; '98 BA; Madison St. #8a, New York, NY 10002, 212 962-0607.

ESTRADA, Jose; '83 BS; Correctional Ofcr.; NYS Dept. of Correctional Svcs.; r. 562 Van Nest Ave., Bronx, NY 10460, 718 597-8970.

ESTRADA, Mario B.; '94 BS; Investigator; Office of the Attorney General, State of New Jersey, Trenton, NJ 08625; r. 346 2nd St., Jersey City, NJ 07302, 201 216-9189.

ESTRADA, Orlando; '95 BS; 1485 Hoe Ave., Bronx, NY 10460, 718 542-0802.

ESTRELLA, Yojaida; '95 BS; 1546 Agate St., Bay Shore, NY 11706.

ESTURINE, Francella T.; '98 BA; 164-23 109 Rd, Jamaica, NY 11433, 718 657-2273.

ESTWICK, Gerald; '96 BS; 1959 Mcgraw Ave. # 4, Bronx, NY 10462, 718 892-0295.

ETNBINDER, Leonard; 7 Sanders Ct., W. Milford, NJ 07480.

EVANS, Aaron J.; '96 BA; 484 Marcy Ave. #, Brooklyn, NY 11206, 718 372-3129.

EVANS, April R., (April R. Hubbard); '79 BS; Review Spec.; NYS Commission of Correction, 4 Tower Pl., Albany, NY 12203, 518 457-9154; r. 11 St. Josephs Ter., Albany, NY 12210, 518 463-8996; Aja, Quinn. e-mail

EVANS, Cherisse T.; '95 BS; 875 Pennsylvania A, Brooklyn, NY 11207, 718 238-0029.

EVANS, Doris P.; '94 BS; 11155 131st St., Jamaica, NY 11420, 718 279-4682.

EVANS, Elsa; '87 MPA; 11165 Inwood St., Jamaica, NY 11435, 718 279-4682; *Grady;* Gregory, Rodney, Lauri.

EVANS, Gerard T. '92 (See Nkrumah, Kafahni T.).

EVANS, Jasseth M.; '93 BS; Ofcr.; Nassau Cnty. Police Dept.; r. 486 Rhodes Ln., W. Hempstead, NY 11552.

EVANS, Jonathan; '75 BA; 241 N Long Beach Ave., Freeport, NY 11520, 516 626-6712.

EVANS, Kenya L.; '97 BS; 1526 Park Pl., Brooklyn, NY 11213, 718 349-6767.

EVANS, Madeline C.; '80 BA; 48 Fleet Walk #6D, Brooklyn, NY 11201, 718 372-3129.

EVANS, Michael; '97 BS, '98 BS; CEO; Mike Daddy Unlimited Inc., 502 S 2nd Ave., Mt. Vernon, NY 10550, 212 468-8110; r. 502 S. 2nd Ave., Mt. Vernon, NY 10550, 877 344-2303; Unique, Jacen. e-mail

EVANS, Robert; '91 CERT, '91 BS; 43-22 45th St., Long Island City, NY 11104, 718 254-6778.

EVANS, Robert C.; '92 BA, CERT; Deputy US Marshal; US Marshal Svc., 225 Cadman Plz. E. Rm G80, Brooklyn, NY 11201, 718 254-6778; r. same.

EVANS, Telora; '93 BS; 159-00 Riverside Dr., New York, NY 10032, 315 732-2026.

EVELYN, Spencer E.; '95 BS; 2350 Crotona Ave. #, Bronx, NY 10458, 718 562-7289.

EVENTERIS, Steve; '96 BS; 35-18 Ditmars Blvd., Astoria, NY 11105.

EVERETT, Hilda W.; '79 BA; 6254 97th Pl. Ste. H, Flushing, NY 11374, 718 592-6442.

EWALD, William E.; '80 BA; 1863 Harmon St., Flushing, NY 11385, 718 366-1951.

EYMAN, Buster D.; '77 BA; 408 Bergen St., Brooklyn, NY 11217.

EZECHIELS, Richard E.; '97 BA; 131-40 231 St., Jamaica, NY 11413.

F

FABER, Eli; 147-03 77 Rd., Flushing, NY 11367, 718 225-3962.

FABIAN, Raymond; '95 BS; Private Investigator; Roman & Assocs., Lynbrook, NY 11563, 800 325-1630. e-mail

FABIEN, Margareth; '98 BA; 848 Knickerbocker #1, Brooklyn, NY 11207, 718 443-3356.

FABOZZI, Michael; '93 BS; 180 Hamilton Ave., Staten Island, NY 10301.

FABRIZIO, Ralph A.; '81 MS; 937 81st St., Brooklyn, NY 11228.

FACCHINI, Paschal; '96 BS; MAE Seton Hall Univ.; Security Mgr.-Ventis Pharma; SOS Security, Rte. 202-206, Bridgewater, NJ 08807; r. 26 Arie Dr., Marlboro, NJ 07746, 732 577-2806; *Antoinette;* Peter, John, Anthony. e-mail

FACCIPONTI, Ronald; '94 BS; 159 Garrison Ave., Staten Island, NY 10314.

FACEY, Julia C.; '92 BA; 3063 Edson Ave. Bsmt, Bronx, NY 10469.

FACILLA, Theresa M.; '76 BS; 5503 69th Pl., Flushing, NY 11378.

FACKNER, Robert E.; '76 BS; 178 Beach 92nd St., Far Rockaway, NY 11693.

FACONTI, Christiane; '96 BA; 6618 Ovington Ct., Brooklyn, NY 11204, 718 259-3652.

FAFOUTIS, Nicholas A.; '84 MA; NY State Correction Ofcr.; r. 62 Overlook Ct., Philmont, NY 12565, 518 672-0059.

FAGAN, Harry J.; '74 BS; 44 Howell Dr., Smithtown, NY 11787, 631 265-7605.

FAGAN, Kenneth F.; '71 BS, AS; Retired; r. 6322 SE Tory Pl., Hobe Sound, FL 33455.

FAHERTY, Donald J.; '77 BS, '79 MPA; Retired Inspector; NYC Police Dept., 1 Police Plz., New York, NY 10038; r. 5943 69th Ln., Flushing, NY 11378, 718 651-3770.

FAHEY, John W.; '78 BS; MA Fordham Univ.; Retired Capt. NYFD; r. 7 CEDAR Rd., Mastic Bch., NY 11951; *Maureen;* Mary, Noreen, Joann, Geraldine, William, Thomas, Catherine.

FAHJE, Donald; '93 BA; Retired Dist. Supt.; NY Sanitation; r. 798d Bluegrass Cir., Somers, NY 10589, 914 276-7868.

FAIR, Craig D.; '96 MA; 37 N Woodhill Ave., Binghamton, NY 13904, 607 775-3060.

FAIRCONETURE, Stace; '85 MPA; 15324 120th Ave., Jamaica, NY 11434, 718 529-0495.

FAIRLEY, Norman S.; '95 BS; 54 Benburb St., Amityville, NY 11701.

FAISON, Alma J.; '79 BA; 3511 Barnes Ave. Apt. 6h, Bronx, NY 10467, 718 320-4897.

FAISON, Sylvia; '89 BS; 801 Manor Rd Apt. 4d, Staten Island, NY 10314.

FAISON, Thomas A.; '90 MPA; 656 Marcy Ave., Staten Island, NY 10309, 718 984-4140.

FAISON, Venessa; '93 BS; 672 Ocean Ave. Apt. D7, Brooklyn, NY 11226, 718 642-7674.

FAITH, Francis L.; '80 BS; NYC Police Capt.; NYC; r. Hc 1 Box 28, Acra, NY 12405, 518 622-2206; *Helen;* John, Michael, Peter, James.

FAJARDO, Edward; '91 BS; 13-06 34th Ave. #1C, Long Island City, NY 11106.

FAJARDO, Juan Carlos; '99 BS; Law Student; City Univ. of NY Law Sch.; r. Middle Vlg., NY 11379; *Suzanna.*

FALCON, Mercedes; '95 BA; 941 Jerome Ave. # 1, Bronx, NY 10452, 718 378-5343.

FALCONE, Loretta T.; '80 BS; 598 7th Ave., Brooklyn, NY 11215, 718 499-9248.

FALKENHAINER, William; '84 BS; 423 Stobe Ave., Staten Island, NY 10306, 718 667-0321.

FALLEY, Roy B.; '79 MA; 7211 Alwell #26, Houston, TX 77081.

FALLON, Ms. Bessie A., (Bessie Knicos); '95 BA; AS LaGuardia Community Clg.; Operations Coord.; US Postal Inspection Svc., POB 555, New York, NY 10116, 212 330-2784; r. 18 Beech Dr., Stockholm, NJ 07460, 973 697-2123; *George.* e-mail

FALLON, Jeffrey C.; '99 MPA; 40 Collfield Ave., Staten Island, NY 10302, 718 442-3554.

FALLON, John G.; '76 BS; 68 Carlton Ter., Garden City, NY 11530, 516 791-8599.

FALLON, Thomas W.; '76 MA; 315 S Kensington Ave., La Grange, IL 60525, 708 482-4013.

FALVEY, Lynn R.; '75 BS; Protective Svc. Worker; Cnty. of San Diego; r. 843 Sumac Pl., Escondido, CA 92027, 760 432-9227; *Stephen;* Heather, Sean.

FALVEY, Stephen J.; '75 BS; VP; Bank of America; r. 843 Sumac Pl., Escondido, CA 92027, 760 432-9227; *Lynn;* Heather, Sean.

FANA, Fermin E.; '93 BS; 87-03 75th St. 1st, Woodhaven, NY 11421, 718 445-3918.

FANELLI, Ronald J.; '81 MA; 144-62 25th Rd., Flushing, NY 11354, 718 728-6807.

FANNON, Richard P.; '89 MPA; 443 56th St., Brooklyn, NY 11220.

FANTAUZZI, Douglas; '92 BA; 27 Fieldstone Dr. #, Hartsdale, NY 10530.

FARAGO, Stephen T.; '79 BS; RR 2 POB 144, Oneonta, NY 13820.

FARAH, Lyes; '90 AS, '92 MPA; 14739 73rd Ave. # 2, Flushing, NY 11367, 718 544-0530.

FARAONE, Ms. Teri; '95 MA; MA Columbia Tchrs. Clg.; Student & Public Relations; r. 75 W. end Ave., Apt. R9A, New York, NY 10023, 212 489-1313; *Ted.* e-mail

FARES, Ali; '94 BS; 457 86th St., Brooklyn, NY 11209.

FARIAS, Jeanine V.; '95 AS, '97 BS; 377 Ridgewood Ave., Brooklyn, NY 11208, 718 348-5996.

FARINO, Thomas; '93 BS; 1004 Church St., Bohemia, NY 11716.

FARKAS, Diana A.; '96 MA; 65 W. 90th St., New York, NY 10024, 212 787-8758.

FARKAS, Howard G.; '76 MA; AAS, BBA CCNY/Baruch Sch.; Sr. Custom Inspector/Retired NYPD; US Custom Svc., 6 World Trade Ctr., New York, NY 10048, 212 637-7637; r. 730 Ft. Washington Ave., New York, NY 10040; *Geneva Eleutice;* Jonathan Zoltan, Zachary Meyer. e-mail

FARLEY, James F.; '95 MA; 719 Manette Ln., Valley Cottage, NY 10989, 914 354-1102.

FARMER, Clezel D.; '83 MA; 20 Sherman Ave. #5B, New York, NY 10040, 315 855-4668.

FARNES, Milagros; '84 BA; 14 Kay Ct., Brooklyn, NY 11229, 718 769-2007.

FARO, James J.; '74 BS; JD St. John's Law Sch., LICENSE Series 7-Broker License; Atty./Financial Rep.; 159-18 Northern Blvd., Flushing, NY 11358, 718 460-9500; r. 31 Roger Pl., Floral Park, NY 11001, 516 328-7414; *Patricia;* James, Nicholas. e-mail

FARQUHARSON, Paul; '88 BS; 3526 Ely, Bronx, NY 10466, 718 519-0161.

FARRAR, Deborah R.; '88 MPA; 120 Co Op City Blvd. Apt. 7d, Bronx, NY 10475.

FARRELL, Clare T.; '98 MA; 8821 16th Ave., Brooklyn, NY 11214, 718 767-1479.

FARRELL, Denise M.; '97 BA, '98 MA; 1211 86th St., Brooklyn, NY 11228, 718 680-9104.

FARRELL, Edward J.; '78 MA; 5038 60th St., Flushing, NY 11377, 718 850-0108.

FARRELL, Franklin H.; '78 BA; 89 Panorama Dr., Patterson, NY 12563.

FARRELL, James M.; '76 BA; 4620 157th St., Flushing, NY 11355, 718 357-3018.

FARRELL, John; '77 BS; 177 Bedell Dr., Port Jervis, NY 12771.

FARRELL, John F.; '80 MA; 20422 8th Ave., Far Rockaway, NY 11697, 718 357-3018.

FARRELL, John J.; '78 BS; 18 Prudence Dr., Stamford, CT 06907.

FARRELL, John R.; '73 MPA; 85 Viscount Dr., Unit A64, Milford, CT 06460.

FARRELL, Kevin P.; '74 BA; 58 76th St., Brooklyn, NY 11209, 718 680-9611.

FARRELL, Marianne J.; '77 BS; Physical Educ.; Diocese of Bklny; r. 1554 E 66 St., Brooklyn, NY 11234, 718 763-3837; *John J. Jr;* Joanne.

FARRELL, Mel G.; '98 BA; Real Estate Managing Agt.; Alexander Wolf & Co. Inc., One Dupont St., Plainview, NY 11803, 516 349-0540; r. 1771 1st Ave. #2, New York, NY 10128, 315 845-8592. e-mail

FARRELL, Patrick J.; '80 BS; 8011 SE Evergreen St., Hobe Sound, FL 33455.

FARRELL, Patrick R.; '80 BA; 68 Island Pkwy., Island Park, NY 11558, 516 223-1607.

FARRELL, Thomas; '89 BS; 24 Bluebell Ln., Levittown, NY 11756.

FARRELL, Walter D.; '75 MA; Retired Fed. Agt.; US Govt.; r. 120 Cambridge Ave., Garden City, NY 11530, 516 483-9865; *Alicia.*

FARRELLY, Francis J.; '74 BA; 10 Duhaime Rd, Pearl River, NY 10965, 914 735-9121.

FARRICE, Edward P.; '89 BA; 2402 65th St., Brooklyn, NY 11204.

FARRON, Mrs. Heidi M., (Heidi Graney); '95 BS; US Customs Inspector; US Customs, JFK Airport, Jamaica, NY 11430, 718 553-1551; r. 5205 Manor Dr., Peekskill, NY 10566; *Lou;* Madison.

FARRUGIA, Matthew P.; '96 BA; AS Nassau Community Clg.; Immigration Ofcr.; Dept. of Justice INS, 711 Stewart Ave., Garden City, NY 11530, 516 228-9246; r. 244 N. Pine St., N. Massapequa, NY 11758, 516 799-3907; *Teresa.* e-mail

FARRY, Richard D.; '75 BS; 113 Dederer St., Tappan, NY 10983, 914 365-2545.

FASANO, Richard A.; '99 BS; Title Closer; r. 47 Jerome Ave., Staten Island, NY 10305, 718 981-9333; *Patricia;* Richard Jr, Lauren, Matthew, Alexis. e-mail

FASSBERG, Stuart L.; 1362 E 86 St., Brooklyn, NY 11236.

FASSNACHT, Irene E.; '76 MA; 57-50 80th St., Elmhurst, NY 11373.

FATONE, Anthony P.; '81 BA; 2382 Hughes Ave., Bronx, NY 10458, 718 364-7813.

FATSIS, Kyriakoula; '95 MA; 1644 Rte. 9w, Highland Falls, NY 10928, 718 726-8614.

FAUCI, Richard A.; '71 BS; AA CUNY; Ret Capt.; NYC Fire Dept.; r. 3 Drayton Rd, Lakehurst, NJ 08733, 732 657-5775; *Mary T.;* Richard Jr, Lori A., Lisa M. e-mail

FAULK, Alisa; '95 BS; 37 Centre St., Yonkers, NY 10701, 914 632-8013.

FAUNTLEROY, Irma C.; '98 BA; 20611 46th Rd # 2, Bayside, NY 11361, 718 298-6713.

FAUSTIN, Brigette; '83 BS; 32-12 Mott Ave., Far Rockaway, NY 11691.

FAUSTINO, Allison; '95 BA; 22735 114th Rd, Jamaica, NY 11411, 718 479-1747.

FAVARA, Anthony J.; '78 BA; 802 Harrison St., W. Hempstead, NY 11552.

FAY, Catherine; '89 BS, '93 MA; POB 805, N. Bennington, VT 05257, 802 867-5524.

FAYAD, Abdul; '99 BA; Ofc. Mgr.; Law Offices of Micahel E. Curan, 59 John St., New York, NY 10038, 212 513-1578; r. 48 56 47 St. 3F, Woodside, NY 11377, 718 937-3472. e-mail

FEALEY, Joseph C.; '76 AS; BA; Retired., Lt.; NYCPD, New York, NY; r. 3516 Waverly Ave., Seaford, NY 11783, 516 826-1457.

FEALY, Michael D.; '95 BS; Police Ofcr.; Manhattan Task Force; r. 200 Hart Blvd. Apt. 4c, Staten Island, NY 10301.

FEARON, William G.; '92 BS; State Trooper; New Jersey State Police, W. Trenton, NJ 08628, 609 882-2000; r. 87 Union St., Cedar Grove, NJ 07009, 973 857-8268. e-mail

FEATHERSTONE, Aubrey; '80 MPA; Deputy Commissioner; Administration for Children Svcs., 150 William St., New York, NY 10038, 212 341-0943; r. 17224 Henley Rd, Jamaica, NY 11432, 718 297-1678; *Hazelien;* Audriene, Alistair.

FEBLES, Aida C.; '96 BS; Clerk; US Postal Svc., Kensington Sta., Brooklyn, NY 11218, 718 531-5903; r. 1115 E. 83rd St., Brooklyn, NY 11236, 718 531-5903.

FEDERICI-LAFARGUE, Ms. Marietta; '95 BA, '98 MA; CO-Director Women's Ctr/Prof.; John Jay Clg., 445 W. 59th St., Rm #1112, New York, NY 10019, 212 854-8858; r. 484 W. 43rd St., New York, NY 10036, 212 947-7163. e-mail

FEDOR, Chester; '79 BS; 85-01 79th St., Woodhaven, NY 11421, 718 426-8755.

FEDORSCHAK, Leonard; '62 MPA; 153 Todt Hill Rd, Staten Island, NY 10314; *Audrey;* Michael, John, Paul.

FEDOTOV, Alex V.; '96 BS; 4800 14th Ave. Apt. 6h, Brooklyn, NY 11219.

FEE, Christopher J.; '95 BS; AAS Corning Community Clg.; Prepress Tech.; New Elmira APT, Horseheads, NY 14845; r. 66 John St. Apt. 2, Corning, NY 14830, 607 962-5997; *Kelly;* Alexander. e-mail

FEEHAN, Jeremiah K.; '77 MA; BA St. Marys Univ, Baltimore; Retired; r. 469 Kissel Ave., Staten Island, NY 10301, 718 273-1499; *Andrea.*

FEELEY, Warren J.; '76 BA; 113 Greaves Ave., Staten Island, NY 10308, 718 967-9348.

FEELEY, William F.; '79 MPA; Cnslt.; 207 Bertram Pl., Bethpage, NY 11714; r. same; *Juliet;* Christopher, Lisa.

FEELY, Thomas J.; '77 BS; 158-38 95 St., Howard Bch., NY 11414, 718 525-7277.

FEENEY, Kathleen; '94 BA; 201 Raymond St., Rockville Centre, NY 11570, 516 766-4095.

FEENEY, Mary D.; '76 BS; 18 Glenwood Ln., Sussex, NJ 07461, 973 875-2782.

FEFFER, Lawrence; '75 BS; Police Lt.; Nassau Cnty. Police Dept., 1490 Franklin Ave., Mineola, NY 11501, 516 573-6400; r. 2 Howland Rd, E. Rockaway, NY 11518, 516 573-6450.

FEGAN, Ewart; '86 BS; Chmn.; Alcott Capital LLC, 545 Eighth Ave., Ste. 402, New York, NY 10018, 212 613-3000. e-mail

FEGLEY, Venessa M.; '99 MA; Miami Inst. of Psychology; Psychological Spec.; FL Dept. of Corrections; Dade Correctional, Florida City, FL, 305 242-1847; r. 11698 Bayshore Dr., Crystal River, FL 34429, 352 564-9502. e-mail

FEIGENBAUM, Daniel; '92 BS; Detective; Suffolk Cnty. Police Dept., 20 Yaphank Ave., Yaphank, NY 11980, 631 852-6000; r. 45 Ruth Blvd., Commack, NY 11725. e-mail

FEIGENBAUM, Roy A.; 110 Caton Ave., Brooklyn, NY 11218, 718 338-2448.

FEILER, Christopher; '95 BS; 1195 Tusk Ln., Wantagh, NY 11793, 516 409-0815.

FEINBERG, Mark S.; '91 BA; 9918 Avenue L Ph, Brooklyn, NY 11236, 718 488-7606.

FEINHOLTZ, Leslie; '95 MA; 242 Newark Ave., Lyndhurst, NJ 07071.

FEIT, Harvey D.; '78 BS; 447 Eltingville Blvd., Staten Island, NY 10312.

FELDER, Calvin L.; '84 BS; 826 Putnam Ave., Brooklyn, NY 11221, 718 574-7383.

FELDER, Venitia; '92 MPA; BA Hunter Clg. CUNY; Social Worker; City of NY, New York, NY 10029; r. Jamaica, NY 11434.

FELDER, William J.; '98 BA; 830 Prospect Pl., Brooklyn, NY 11216, 718 735-6831.

FELDMAN, David A.; '79 BS; MS Adelphi Univ.; Special Educ Tchr.; 45th Street Mental Health Ctr., 1041 45th St., W. Palm Bch., FL 33407, 561 844-3360; r. 8672 Tourmaline Blvd., Boynton Bch., FL 33437, 561 369-4182; *Barbara;* Daniel, Laura.

FELDMAN, Felix P.; '95 BS; Litigation Paralegal; Lozner Mastropietro, 1901 Emmons Ave., Ste. 206, Brooklyn, NY 11235, 718 615-0044; r. 1515 Penn Ave., Brooklyn, NY 11239, 718 642-6607.

FELDMAN, Irene; '77 BA; 140-21 Burden Cres., Jamaica, NY 11435, 718 847-7127.

FELDMANN, Dalia; '77 MA; 62-61 Wetherole St., Rego Park, NY 11374.

FELDSTEIN, Kenneth I.; '79 BA; Dir. of Mfg.; Talbots Inc., 175 Beal St., Hingham, MA 02043, 781 741-4869; r. 209 Central St., Norwell, MA 02061, 781 659-5912. e-mail

FELDSTEIN, Robert A.; '83 BA, '86 MPA, '89 MA; 2790 Bragg St., Brooklyn, NY 11235, 718 934-1558; *Debra Rothman.*

FELICIANO, Elizabeth; '98 MS MPA; '98 BA; Mktg. Coord.; Health Mgmt. Systs., New York, NY 10016, 212 857-5628; r. 442 Degraw St., Apt 1, Brooklyn, NY 11217, 718 852-5536. e-mail

FELICIANO, Elsa M.; '97 BA; 2839 W. 33 St., Brooklyn, NY 11224.

FELICIANO, Evelyn; '87 BS; 1735 Madison Ave., New York, NY 10029, 315 339-2589.

FELICIANO, George; '87 BS; 36 Island St., Plainview, NY 11803.

FELICIANO, Gloria; '94 BS; Mental Health Couns.; Puerto Rico Family Inst., 217 Havermeyer St., 4th Fl., Brooklyn, NY 11211, 718 963-4430; r. 278 S. 2nd St., Brooklyn, NY 11211, 718 782-0615; *Toni Bernadette.* e-mail

FELIU, Maria D.; '97 BA; 1190 Shakespeare A, Bronx, NY 10452.

FELIX, Lesly; '86 BS; 1078 E 38th St., Brooklyn, NY 11210, 718 252-3432.

FELIX, Suzanne; '88 BA; 5644 Christian St., Philadelphia, PA 19143.

FELIZ, Luisa A.; '98 BA; 570 W. 204th St. #6i, New York, NY 10034, 212 567-6902.

FELL, Ronald; '97 BA; 68 Beech St., Central Islip, NY 11722.

FELTON, Crystal Y.; '86 BS; 140 Menahan St. Apt. 3b, Brooklyn, NY 11221, 718 649-1932.

FELTON, Karen G.; '84 BA; 427 W. 154 St., New York, NY 10032.

FELTON, Ronald; '78 BA; 1246 Evergreen Ave. # 1a, Bronx, NY 10472, 718 792-0999.

FEMINELLA, Ralph J.; '76 AS; Retired; r. 9132 Bassett Ln., New Port Richey, FL 34655, 727 376-1659; *Helen.*

FENEQUE, Samuel; '95 BS; 210 E 58th St., Apt. 8A, New York, NY 10022, 212 486-2852.

FENKEL, Robert I.; '82 MA; Police Capt.; New Brunswick, New Brunswick, NJ 08901, 732 745-5200; r. PO #1346 Nixon Sta., Edison, NJ 08818, 732 528-9332; *Diane; Cassie.*

FENNELL, Gerard; '75 MPA; 123 E 237 St., Bronx, NY 10470.

FENNER, Rosalynde M.; '97 MA; P.O.Box 30339, New York, NY 10011.

FENNESSY, Adriana, (Adriana Mairanda); '93 BS; Scientist; Novartis Pharmaceuticals Corp., 25 Old Mill Rd., Suffern, NY 10901, 914 368-6190; r. 105 School Rd., Monroe, NY 10950, 914 774-2759; *Ed;* Mairanda. e-mail

FENRICH, Ronald J.; '75 MPA; 61-10 67 St., Middle Vlg., NY 11379.

FENTY, Jill M.; '96 BA; Special Agt.; Fed. Aviation Admin., Laguardia Airport, POB 441, Flushing, NY 11371, 718 533-8343; r. 6 Stevens Rd., Apt. 52, Wallington, NJ 07057, 973 249-8836.

FERBER, Eric M.; '93 BS; Detective; NYPD, Precint 110, Elmhurst, NY 11373; r. 725 Miller Ave. # 130, Freeport, NY 11520, 516 867-7059. e-mail

FERDENZI, Joseph N.; '75 BA; 39-20 104 St., Corona, NY 11368.

FERDINAND, David; '90 BA; 335 E. 22nd St. #, New York, NY 10010, 212 674-0131.

FERENCE, Thomas J.; '87 MPA; POB 699, Smallwood, NY 12778.

FERGUS, Kathyann J.; '97 BS; 750 E. 52nd St., Brooklyn, NY 11203, 718 453-6193.

FERGUSON, Adriane; '92 BS; Customer Svc. Supv.; US Postal Svc., 534 W. 112th St., New York, NY 10025, 212 864-1874; r. 720 Esplanade Gardens Plz. Apt. 8a, New York, NY 10039, 212 491-8433.

FERGUSON, Andre; '98 BS; Security; Corporate Security Resources, 1110 Plz., New York, NY 10001; r. Brooklyn, NY 11203, 718 778-2757. e-mail

FERGUSON, Anselma; '92 BA; 22128 110th Ave., Queens Vlg., NY 11429, 718 712-4332.

FERGUSON, Brian; '91 BS; 23 Hall Ave. E, New City, NY 10956, 914 634-8598.

FERGUSON, Brian P.; '94 BS; POB 151, Leeds, NY 12451, 518 733-6525.

FERGUSON, Charles J.; '76 BA; 313 Riedel Ave., Staten Island, NY 10306.

FERGUSON, Craig D.; '82 BS; AAS NYC Comm. Clg.; 3029 Fairfax Ave., San Jose, CA 95148.

FERGUSON, Deborah A.; '93 BA; 1422 Avenue Y # 2nd, Brooklyn, NY 11235, 718 789-4258.

FERGUSON, James G.; '76 BA; American Embassy Manilla, APO, AP 96528.

FERGUSON, Lisa A.; '80 BA; 90 Gold St., New York, NY 10038, 315 866-1907.

FERGUSON, Madree; 3856 Bronx Blvd. #5M, Bronx, NY 10467, 718 798-6012.

FERGUSON, Terry A.; '89 BA; 955 Evergreen Ave., Bronx, NY 10473, 718 654-0640.

FERGUSON, Wanda; '84; Customer Svc.; Healthworks, 1546 Union Tpk., New Hyde Park, NY 11040; r. New Hyde Park, NY 11040.

FERMAN, Yolanda D.; '79 BA; Police Lt.; NYC Police Dept., New York, NY 10038; r. 282 Sneden Pl. W, Spring Vly., NY 10977.

FERMATURE, Thomas L.; 44 Lincoln Ave., Massapequa Park, NY 11762.

FERNADEZ, Patricia; '98 BA; 1744 E 34th St., Brooklyn, NY 11234, 718 851-6733.

FERNANDEZ, Adamilka; '98 BA; AA SUNY-Farmingdale; Fraud Investigator; Dept. of Homeless Svcs., 151 E. 151st St., Bronx, NY 10451, 718 402-6261; r. 1315 Amsterdam Ave. 19A, New York, NY 10027, 212 864-2655.

FERNANDEZ, Alexis V.; '92 BA; 5174 Pedro A Campos St., Isabela, PR 00662.

FERNANDEZ, Australia; '89 BA; 606 45th St. #24, Brooklyn, NY 11220, 718 596-2185.

FERNANDEZ, Carlos A.; '97 BS; Seton Hall Univ.; Police Ofcr.; NYPD, 212 927-0701; r. 511 W. 172 St., New York, NY 10032, 212 927-0701; *Karen Jagassar.*

FERNANDEZ, Mrs. Daysi, (Daysi Garcia); '90 BA; MA Queens Clg.; Guid. Couns.; Dist. 25, Flushing, NY 11368, 718 747-2516; r. 2933 Curtis St., Flushing, NY 11369, 718 424-3024.

FERNANDEZ, Evelyn; '93 BS; 511 W. 175 St. #1, New York, NY 10033.

FERNANDEZ, Jeffrey J.; '91 BS; 3776 62nd St. Apt. D2, Flushing, NY 11377, 718 297-6552.

FERNANDEZ, John A.; '98 MA; PhD Candidate, I/0 Psychology; CUNY; r. 998 Amsterdam Ave. #2C, New York, NY 10025, 212 662-5668. e-mail

FERNANDEZ, Luis; '97 BA; 37-22 101st St., Corona, NY 11368, 718 297-0220.

FERNANDEZ, Maria C. '99 (See Lisanti, Mrs. Maria C.).

FERNANDEZ, Mercedes; '89 BS; 22-16 26 St., Astoria, NY 11105, 718 441-2078.

FERNANDEZ, Michael; '92 BS; 74 Nassau Ave., Malverne, NY 11565, 516 674-0826.

FERNANDEZ, Odalys; '87 BA; Banking Asst.; Lehman Bros., Inc., 3 World Financial Ctr., 15th Fl., New York, NY 10285, 212 526-2744; r. 441 E. 20th St., Apt. 10G, New York, NY 10010. e-mail

FERNANDEZ, Theodore (Ted); '93 BA; MA Hunter Clg.; Adjunct Lecturer; John Jay Clg.; r. 130 E 93rd St. Apt. 2d, New York, NY 10128, 212 427-0012. e-mail

FERNANDEZ, Yvette; '99 BA; Grad. Student Forensic Psych.; John Jay Clg. of Criminal Justice; r. Clifton, NJ 07012, 973 777-5370. e-mail

FERRAIOLI, Steven J.; '87 BS; AS St. Francis Clg.; Police Ofcr.; Morris Cnty. Park Police, 300 Mendham Rd., Morristown, NJ 07960; r. 26 Buttonwood St., Jersey City, NJ 07305; *Tara Ann; Joseph.*

FERRALL, Christopher T.; '95 MA; 60 N Cottage St., Valley Stream, NY 11580.

FERRANTE, Carol A.; '75 BA; 3116 75th St., Flushing, NY 11370, 718 767-8626.

FERRANTE, Victor; '95 AS, '97 BS; Police Ofcr.; NYPD, 1 Police Plz., New York, NY 10003; r. 574 Edison Ave., Bronx, NY 10465, 718 822-5702. e-mail

FERRARA, Albert A.; '76 BA; 1824 W. 12 St., Brooklyn, NY 11223, 718 209-0442.

FERRARA, Toni A. '74 (See Medwick, Toni A.).

FERRARA, Vivian '88 (See Ferrara-Machado, Vivian M.).

FERRARA-MACHADO, Vivian M., (Vivian Ferrara); '88 BA, '94 MA; Psycho-Forensic Evaluator; Prison Health Svcs., Baylor Womens Correctional Inst., Delores Baylor Blvd., New Castle, DE 19720, 302 577-3004; r. 29 Stirrup Dr., Elkton, MD 21921, 410 398-6098. e-mail

FERREIRA, Jeannette '97 (See Rodriguez, Mrs. Jeannette).

FERRELL, Shaniqua N.; '96 BS; 201 W. 121 St., New York, NY 10027.

FERRER, Awilda; '84 BS; 321 45 St. 1 Fl., Brooklyn, NY 11220, 718 972-7442.

FERRER, Jorge M.; '94 BA; POB 28, Stony Point, NY 10980, 914 429-7470.

FERREYRA, Orlando F., Jr.; '81 BS; Retired NYPD Police Lt.; MPS Financial Svcs., 911 Police Plz., Hicksville, NY 11801, 516 932-1013; r. 1394 Apple Ln., E. Meadow, NY 11554, 516 486-8042; *Karen;* Orlando III, Cher, Christopher, Jennifer, Michael. e-mail

FERRIGNO, Mario; '86 MPA; 10 Raphael Pl., Middletown, NJ 07748, 718 624-1849.

FERRIS, Andrew P.; '94 BS; 30 Eastman St., Staten Island, NY 10312.

FERRIS, Lauraine E.; '90 BS; 1411 Kilby St., Burlington, NC 27215, 336 222-7722.

FERRSON, Norita; '93 BA; 973 Marcus Dr. Apt. 7, Newport News, VA 23602.

FETONTI, Paul J.; '76 BS; Retail Mgr.; Epstein's Dry Goods, Tuckahoe, NY 10707, 914 961-2833; r. 447 Bronxville Rd, Bronxville, NY 10708, 914 337-1632; Tess, Emma, Charlotte. e-mail

FETUS, Patrick; '93 BA; 191 E 32nd St., Brooklyn, NY 11226, 718 703-8657.

FEVELO, John F.; '76 BS; 195 Chandler Ave., Staten Island, NY 10314.

FEW, Terry R.; '87 MPA; 94-04 23rd Ave., E. Elmhurst, NY 11369.

FEX, George T.; '95 BA; 70-38 65th Pl., Glendale, NY 11385.

FEY, Alfred; '69 BS; 8336 255th St., Glen Oaks, NY 11004.

FIDANQUE, Claudia S.; '81 MA; Rte. 9, Garrison, NY 10524.

FIELD, Heather L.; '84 BS; 166 E 59th St., Brooklyn, NY 11203, 718 596-9280.

FIELDS, Bernadette (Michelle); '93 BA; Paralegal; r. 217 Eastern Pkwy., Apt. 3a, Brooklyn, NY 11238, 718 623-2560; Takyira Wash., Ron, Khalil Wash. e-mail

FIELDS, Dana; '98 BA; Tchr.; Dist. 13, Brooklyn, NY 11201; r. 188-15 Dunkirk Dr., Jamaica, NY 11412, 718 276-1308. e-mail

FIELDS, Jennifer A.; '95; 141 E 89th St., Apt. 3C, New York, NY 10128.

FIELDS, Mark A.; '98 BS; 2286 Light St., Bronx, NY 10466, 718 798-7583.

FIELDS, William F.; '96 CUBA; 29 W 69th St. Apt. 2, New York, NY 10023.

FIGUEROA, Annette M.; '83 MPA; 2778 Schley Ave. # 1, Bronx, NY 10465, 718 294-3581.

FIGUEROA, Blanche; '89 BS; 10464 115th St., Jamaica, NY 11419, 718 297-0051.

FIGUEROA, Carmelo J.; '95 BS; 561 W. 144th Stree, New York, NY 10031.

FIGUEROA, Cynthia L.; '85 BA; 170 Avenue C Apt. 21f, New York, NY 10009.

FIGUEROA, Dominga; '99 BA; 618 W. 187th St. #41, New York, NY 10033, 212 543-2908.

FIGUEROA, Genoveba N.; '98 BA; 528 Leland Ave. #1, Bronx, NY 10473, 718 589-6758.

FIGUEROA, Iris; '96 BS; 847 Forest Ave., Bronx, NY 10456, 718 294-0466.

FIGUEROA, Ivan F.; '81 BS; 244 Bond St. Apt. 4e, Brooklyn, NY 11217, 718 333-0062.

FIGUEROA, Jodie L.; '99 BA; 4717 6th Ave., Brooklyn, NY 11220, 718 331-6957.

FIGUEROA, Juana A.; '97 BS; 98 BS; 519 W.160th St. 3D, New York, NY 10032.

FIGUEROA, Lisset; '93 BS; 54 Rutgers St., Belleville, NJ 07109.

FIGUEROA, Lois M.; '96 BA; 8402 Smedley St. #2fl, Briarwood, NY 11435, 718 479-2621.

FIGUEROA, Lucinda; '87 BS; 535 E 148th St. # 2, Bronx, NY 10455, 718 993-5706.

FIGUEROA, Luis A.; '82 MA; 247 E Walnut Park, Philadelphia, PA 19120, 215 634-2845.

FIGUEROA, Luis A.; '89 BS; 285 E.138th St., Bronx, NY 10454, 718 294-0466.

FIGUEROA, Luz I.; '87 BA; 9122 91st Ave., Jamaica, NY 11421, 718 479-2621.

FIGUEROA, Maria E.; '96 BA; 197 Willow Ave., Cornwall, NY 12518, 914 566-4278.

FIGUEROA, Melissa; '95 BA; AAS Bronx Comm Clg.; Paralegal; Weitz & Luxemberg, New York, NY 10038, 718 547 8003; r. 2785 University Ave. Apt. 5a, Bronx, NY 10468, 212 795-6789.

FIGUEROA, Melissa; '97 BA; 210-40 Grand Ctr., Queens Vlg., NY 11427, 718 641-7333.

FIGUEROA, Miguel A.; '88 BS; 3019 94th St., Flushing, NY 11369, 718 641-7333.

FIGUEROA, Monica P.; '89 BS; 3060 48th St. Apt. 4e, Long Island City, NY 11103, 718 641-7333.

FIGUEROA, Paola A.; '97 BA; Fed. Law Enforcement Ofc.; r. 420 44th St. #1, Brooklyn, NY 11220, 718 438-3851. e-mail

FIGUEROA, Paul A.; '95 BS; 2790 Randall Ave. #, Bronx, NY 10465, 718 892-9913.

FIGUEROA, Saul; '83 BS; 100 W. 93rd St., New York, NY 10025.

FIGURSKI, Susan A.; '91 BS; 8624 233rd St., Queens Vlg., NY 11427.

FILINGERI, Joseph J.; 310 E. 19 St., New York, NY 10003.

FILION, Elizabeth; '99 BA; Patient Service; NY Hosp., 5121 Broadway St., New York, NY 10032, 212 932-5079; r. 150 W. 225 St. 26F, Bronx, NY 10463, 718 295-7258.

FILIPIAK, Paul J.; '83 BA; Police Ofcr; Suffolk Cnty. Police Dept., W. Babylon, NY 11704; r. Merrick, NY 11566. e-mail

FILIPOWICZ, Renata; '99 BA; Tchr.; John Welsh Jr. High; r. 73-23 72nd St., Flushing, NY 11385, 718 628-1235; *Jack; Bianka, Olivia.* e-mail

FILIPPINI, Mrs. Nancy F., (Nancy F. Digiacomo); '83 BS; Tchr.; Northport Middle Sch., Port St. Lucie, FL 34983; r. 201 SW Crescent Ave., Port St. Lucie, FL 34984, 561 879-0965. e-mail

FILIPPONI, Dominick; '77 BA; AA; Retired Detective; NYC Police Dept., 115th Squad, New York, NY 10001; r. 600 Burlwood Ter., Tarpon Spgs., FL 34689, 727 938-1381. e-mail

FILLYAW, Leonard D.; '73 BA; MED Dowling Clg.; Tchr.; Central Islip Sch. Dist., Central Islip HS, Central Islip, NY 11722, 631 348-5001; r. 203 Leaf Ave., Central Islip, NY 11722, 631 234-0872; *Willie; Sharon, Denise, Dr. Tyrone.* e-mail

FINAMORE, Daniel J.; '75 BS; POB 140078, Staten Island, NY 10314, 718 227-1152.

FINAMORE, James J.; '96 AS; Police Ofcr.; 78Th Precinct; r. Brooklyn, NY 11214. e-mail

FINAMORE, Sandro; '80 BS; 1559 65th St., Brooklyn, NY 11219, 718 837-2032.

FINDLAY-PAUL, S.; '93 BS; 501 New York Ave., Brooklyn, NY 11225, 718 469-2564.

FINE, Barbara J.; '95 BS; 75 East End Ave. Apt. 16h, New York, NY 10028.

FINE, Joselyn; '96 MA; BA Syracuse Univ., PSYD CA Sch. of Psychology; Graduate Student; California School of Psychology, 2021 California St., Apt. 103, San Francisco, CA 94109, 415 928-4978; r. 3299 Cambridge Ave., Bronx, NY 10463, 718 549-9006.

FINEGAN, Kevin J.; '99 BS; 3965 Sedgwick Ave. 2C, Bronx, NY 10463, 718 884-8911.

FINKELSTEIN, Eric L.; '87 AA, '92 BA; Sgt.; NYC Police Dept., 1 Police Plz., New York, NY 10038, 212 374-5000; r. 2322 36th St., Astoria, NY 11105, 718 278-7987.

FINLAYSON, Thomas C., Jr.; '95 MPAIG; BA Lehman Clg., AAS Univ. of MD; Sergeant; NYPD, Bronx Narcotics, 500 Abbott St., Bronx, NY 10470, 718 653-7053; r. Bronx, NY 10475. e-mail

FINN, Brian T.; '73 BS; 30-15 149th St., Flushing, NY 11354, 718 474-3355.

FINN, Sean P.; '91 BS; Sgt; New York Police Dept., Transit District 33, New York, NY 10038; r. 1759 E 31st St., Brooklyn, NY 11234, 718 998-9398.

FINNERTY, Frederick C.; '77 AS; 310 Willard Ave., Staten Island, NY 10314.

FINNERTY, Kevin; 5558 Kendrick Ln., Burke, VA 22015, 703 848-9029.

FINNERTY, Thomas W.; '75 AA, '76 BS; CEO; TW Finnerty Property Mgmt. Inc., 175 Locust Ave., POB 060618, Staten Island, NY 10306, 718 980-3657; r. 175 Locust Ave., Staten Island, NY 10306, 718 351-3074. e-mail

FINNEY, John H.; '87 MA, '93 MPA; 36 Hamilton Ave., New Rochelle, NY 10801, 914 632-9318.

FIORE, Albert J.; '95 BS; Midtown North Pct.; r. 176 Seeley St. Apt. 5C, Brooklyn, NY 11218, 718 851-0048. e-mail

FIORE, Anthony M.; '75 BS; Retired; r. 2373 Stuart St., Brooklyn, NY 11229, 718 743-3431; *Madeline.*

FIORE, Nicholas S.; '75 MA; BSED Upsala Clg., MA CJ; Retired Chief Probation Ofcr.; Superior Ct. of New Jersey, 41 Court St., Newark, NJ 07102; r. 27 Monroe St., Nutley, NJ 07110, 973 284-0313; *Nancy A.; Karin C., Nicholas R.* e-mail

FIORE, Sharon A.; '98 BS; Distribution Clerk; US Postal Svc., 2301 NE Savannah Rd, Jensen Bch., FL 34957; r. 550 SE Thanksgiving Ave., Port St. Lucie, FL 34984, 561 336-7694.

FIORILLO, Anthony R.; '77 BA; 403 Olmstead Ave., Bronx, NY 10473.

FIRST, Jeffrey D.; '90 BA; Licensed Nursing Home Admin.; Future Care Cnslts., 155 40th St., Irvington, NJ 07111, 973 371-7878; r. 52 Greenbrook Rd, Middlesex, NJ 08846, 732 356-2439.

FISCH, Daniel G.; '95 BS; 1518 Park St., Atlantic Bch., NY 11509, 516 922-2476.

FISCH, Roberta; '80 MA; BA; RN Retired; r. 50 W 97 St., New York, NY 10025, 212 866-2546; *Gene.*

FISCHER, Lauren J.; '92 BS; 67 Grove Ave., E. Hanover, NJ 07936.

FISCHER, Mrs. Margaret M., (Margaret Jeselnik); '77 BS; Sales Exec.; Platypus Inc., New York, NY 10001; r. 242 Van Duzer St., Staten Island, NY 10304; *Fred R.*

FISCHER, Maureen J.; '80 MA; MSW Yeshiva Univ., ABD NYU; Dir. of Clinical Svcs.; Housing Works Inc., 320 W. 13th St., 4thf Fl., New York, NY 10014, 212 645 8111; r. 135 Willow St. Apt. 306, Brooklyn, NY 11201, 718 625-0941; *Michael; Remy.*

FISCHER, Stephen F.; '69 BS, '79 MA; Retired Police Lt.; Westchester Police Dept.; r. 415 King St., Port Chester, NY 10573, 914 939-8793.

FISCHER, William R.; '78 BS; Retired; r. 552 10th St., Brooklyn, NY 11215, 718 768-2358.

FISCHER-LONG, J.; '89 BS; 750 E 225th St., Bronx, NY 10466, 718 548-5661.

FISCINA, Michael J.; '77 AS; 89-19 156 Ave., Howard Bch., NY 11414.

FISHER, Bobby; '90 BS; 13328 Laurelton Pkwy., Jamaica, NY 11422, 718 341-8259.

FISHER, Emily P., (Emily S. Phillips); '98 MA; Rsch. Exec.; Young & Rubicam, 285 Madison Ave., New York, NY 10017, 212 210-5281; r. 404 E. 79th St., Apt. 23C, New York, NY 10021, 212 988-1605; *Thomas.* e-mail

FISHER, Michael A.; '86 BS; 518 E. 39th St., Brooklyn, NY 11203, 718 252-6925.

FISHER, Steven A.; '88 MA; BA Queens Clg.; Probation Ofcr.; NYC Dept. of Probation, 162-24 Jamica Ave., Jamaica, NY 11432, 718 658-3540; r. 65-61 Saunders St., Apt#7L, Forest Hills, NY 11374, 718 275-0445.

FISHER, William E.; '80 BS; 9 East Ave., W. Nyack, NY 10994, 914 357-7232.

FISHMAN, Howard (Howie) L.; '78 MA; BA Brooklyn Clg.; Risk Mgr.; City of Manhattan Beach, 1400 Highland Ave., Manhattan Bch., CA 90266, 310 802-5254; r. 1133 7th Pl., Hermosa Bch., CA 90254, 310 372-6140; *Kathy Keane;* Aaron. e-mail

FISK, Karen B.; '81 AS; 1881 Harrison Ave., Bronx, NY 10453.

FITZGERALD, Daniel J.; '79 BS; Sergeant; NYCPD; r. 1836 S Railroad Ave., Staten Island, NY 10306; *Suzanne; Coleen, Jill.*

FITZGERALD, James J.; '93 BS; Special Agt.; US Dept. of Trans-Fed. Aviation Admin., Halmar Bldg. 77, John F Kenney International Airport, Jamaica, NY 11430, 718 553-1676; r. 317 E 241 St., Bronx, NY 10470, 718 994-1603. e-mail

FITZGERALD, John K.; '88 BS; 437 77th St. # 2, Brooklyn, NY 11209, 718 238-1487.

FITZGERALD, John W.; '70 BS; Retired; r. 312 Houston Ave., Mineola, NY 11501, 516 747-0493.

FITZGERALD, Kelly J.; '96 BS; 846 E 214th St., Bronx, NY 10467, 718 884-9359.

FITZGERALD, Loretta E.; '77 MA; 7866 83rd St., Flushing, NY 11385, 718 497-3771.

FITZGERALD, Patrick J.; '79 BA; 612 Pavonia Ave., Jersey City, NJ 07306, 201 795-3621.

FITZGIBBON, John; '88 BS; 3459 89th St. #2D, Jackson Hts., NY 11372, 718 932-5765.

FITZGIBBONS, Marie E.; '76 BS; 97-43 92 St., Ozone Park, NY 11416.

FITZMAURICE, M.; '92 BA; 4 Gifford Ct. #1, Maplewood, NJ 07040.

FITZPATRICK, Brian R.; '83 BS; AA Nassau Comm. Clg.; Capt.; NYC Police Dept.; r. 65 Sunset Ave., Farmingdale, NY 11735, 631 694-3539; *Ann;* Shawn, Brian Jr, Danielle.

FITZPATRICK, Oona M.; '91 BS; 174 Garth Rd Apt. Tr., Scarsdale, NY 10583, 914 712-0414.

FITZPATRICK, Paul J.; '94 BA; Parole Ofcr.; NYS Div. of Parole, 119 W 31st St., New York, NY 10001, 212 736-9768; r. 30-82 35th St., Apt. 1 A, Astoria, NY 11103, 718 777-0934.

FITZPATRICK, Thomas G.; '76 BS; AS NYC Community Clg.; Retired Fire Lt.; r. 29 Bartlett Ave., Staten Island, NY 10302, 718 984-6020; *Gladys.*

FLAHERTY, Jennifer J.; '99; 33 New Ln., Cromwell, CT 06416, 860 635-6049.

FLAHERTY, John H.; '76 BS; 613 Britton Ave., Staten Island, NY 10304, 718 720-8087.

FLAHERTY, John P.; '95 MPA; MBA Baruch Clg.; Dir. of Security & Public Safety; The Grad. Ctr., 365 5th Ave., New York, NY 10016, 212 817-7761. e-mail

FLAHERTY, Michael R.; 1062 E 2nd St., Brooklyn, NY 11230, 718 377-3257.

FLAHERTY, Richard J.; '74 BS; 960 Edgegrove Ave., Staten Island, NY 10309, 718 967-1988.

FLAMARIQUE-VELA, Susana; '99 BA; 499 Stratford Rd, Brooklyn, NY 11218, 718 252-4117.

FLAMMANG, Margaret A., (Margaret A. Culkin); '82 BS; 12908 NW 106th St., Yukon, OK 73099, 405 373-2533.

FLANAGAN, Christina; 6200 Riverdale Ave., Bronx, NY 10471, 718 548-5203.

FLANAGAN, Colleen M.; '99 BA; Legal Asst.; Davis Saperstein & Salmon, 375 Cedar Ln., Teaneck, NJ 07666, 201 907-5000; r. 144 S Prospect Ave., Bergenfield, NJ 07621, 201 384-4972. e-mail

FLANAGAN, Doreen M.; '78 BS; 6200 Riverdale Ave., Bronx, NY 10471, 718 548-5203.

FLANAGAN, Edward J.; '78 MPA; 3939 221st St., Flushing, NY 11361.

FLANAGAN, Leon E.; '81 BS; 140 Park Hill Ave., Staten Island, NY 10304.

FLANAGAN, Leonard; '72 BA; Retired Policeman; NYPD; r. 11 Stuyvesant Oval Apt. MG, New York, NY 10009, 212 673-3958.

FLANAGAN, Richard Y.; '75 MA; 2716 Eldon Ave. # D, Drexel Hill, PA 19026.

FLANIGAN, Sean R.; '92 BA; 651 Vanderbilt St., Brooklyn, NY 11218.

FLANNERY, Timothy J.; '97 MS; 13 Liberty Blvd., Phillipsburg, NJ 08865.

FLATEAU, Andrea; '85 MPA; 185 Hall St., Brooklyn, NY 11205, 718 919-0504.

FLEETWOOD, Yancy; '94 AS, '98 BA; Law Clerk; r. 2110 1st Ave. Apt. 2002, New York, NY 10029, 212 534-0688. e-mail

FLEISHER, David S.; '81 BS; 1412 Avenue U, Brooklyn, NY 11229, 718 891-7466.

FLEMING, April J., (April J. Hyman); '85 BA; Case Mgr.; Human Res. Admin., 2865 W. 8th St., Brooklyn, NY 11224, 718 265-5539; r. 2960 W. 24th St., Apt. 3-K, Brooklyn, NY 11224, 718 265-5067; *Anthony;* Asia, Anesha.

FLEMING, Arthur J.; '76 BS; 176 Seeley St. Apt. 8e, Brooklyn, NY 11218, 718 633-4140.

FLEMING, Donald L.; '78 BS; 19605C 65th Cres., Apt. 2C, Fresh Meadows, NY 11365, 718 507-9287.

FLEMING, Edward J.; '78 BS; Police Sergeant; Suffolk Cnty. Police Dept., 30 Yaphank Ave., Yaphank, NY 11980, 631 852-6000.

FLEMING, John F.; '97 BA MA; Addiction Couns.; St. Luke's Behavioral Health, Phoenix, AZ 85034, 602 251-8546; r. 18 Newport Ave., Selden, NY 11784, 631 696-1083; *Debbi;* Marisa, Mackenzie. e-mail

FLEMING, John M.; '86 BS, '96 MPA; Detective; Ofc. of Special Narcotics, 80 Centre St. Rm. 670, New York, NY 10013, 212 815-0469; r. 211 2nd Ave., Pelham, NY 10803, 212 815-0469; *Diane.*

FLEMING, Laqueth; '76 MPA; MBA CUNY, MPM; Pres.; MKI Constr. Corp., 6 Turner Dr. S., Chappaqua, NY 10514, 914 666-3617; r. 6 Turner Dr. S, Chappaqua, NY 10514, 914 666-3617; *Myrtle;* Penelope, Noelle. e-mail

FLEMING, Maureen; '81 BS; 1493 Ericson Pl., Bronx, NY 10461, 718 364-1642.

FLEMING, Michael J.; 416 Beach 134th St., Far Rockaway, NY 11694, 718 463-1849.

FLEMING, Patrice A.; '93 BS, '93 MPA; Auditor; US Dept. of Educ., 75 Park Pl., New York, NY 10007, 212 264-4022; r. 2044 Seagirt Blvd., Apt. 5G, Far Rockaway, NY 11691, 718 327-0690. e-mail

FLEMING, Roger; '66 MPA; 2400-25 Hunter Ave. #25C, Bronx, NY 10475, 718 466-2066.

FLEMING, Sibyl L.; '80 BS; 1405 Prospect Pl., Brooklyn, NY 11213, 718 774-7075.

FLEMING, William; '75 BA; Retired; r. 93 Blvd. W, Keyport, NJ 07735.

FLEMING, William J.; '90 BS; Police Ofcr.; NYC; r. 5 Underhill Ave., Hicksville, NY 11801, 516 433-4679; *Judy.*

FLEMINGS, Elmer W.; '76 BS; 17729 145th Dr., Jamaica, NY 11434.

FLEMING-WHITE, Merie; '96 BS; 23-08 Newtown Ave., Astoria, NY 11102, 718 478-8087.

FLEMMINGS, Lamont S.; '76 BS; Retired Capt.; NYC Fire Dept.; r. 6601 Hollow Oak Dr., Charlotte, NC 28227, 704 545-2584; *Denise.*

FLESKES, Jenna M.; '99 MA; BA Georgetown Univ.; Sr. Mental Health Worker; Bacs-Hedco House, 590 B St., Hayward, CA 94541, 510 247-8235; r. 272 9th Ave., Apt. B, San Francisco, CA 94118, 415 221-6308. e-mail

FLETCHER, Ali A.; '95 AS, '96 BA; 676 Saratoga Ave., Brooklyn, NY 11212, 718 693-3172.

FLETCHER, Daniel A.; '93 BS; 330 72nd St., Brooklyn, NY 11209, 718 693-3172.

FLETCHEREL, Ralph A.; '97 BA; 865 Amsterdam Ave., New York, NY 10025.

FLEURY, Andre; '92 BS; 775 St. John's Pl., Brooklyn, NY 11216, 718 493-3463.

FLEURY, Renime; '96 BA; Caseworker; Good Shepherd Svcs., 305 7th Ave., New York, NY 10001; r. 716 E. 105th St. Apt. 3D, Brooklyn, NY 11236. e-mail

FLOOD, James E.; '75 BA; 358 Park Ln., Massapequa Park, NY 11762.

FLOOD, Linda P.; '87 BA; 8 York Ave., Monticello, NY 12701.

FLOOD, William F.; '78 BS; 9 Hester Ln., Ronkonkoma, NY 11779.

FLORES, Andre; '79 BS; 250 Central Ave., Apt. D121, Lawrence, NY 11559, 516 876-0113.

FLORES, Anibal; '98 BS; ROR Interviewer; Criminal Justice Agcy., 100 Centre St., New York, NY 10013, 212 577-8777; r. 2846 W. 22nd St., Brooklyn, NY 11224, 718 265-5462. e-mail

FLORES, Arsenio; '89 BS; Pharmaceutical Spec.; AstraZeneca Pharmaceuticals; r. 33 Eleanor Pl., Staten Island, NY 10303, 718 983-5647; Brandon.

FLORES, Franklin; '99 BS; 4602-5 Ave., Brooklyn, NY 11220, 800 386-2121; r. 5607-6Ave, 5703-5 Ave., Brooklyn, NY 11220, 718 748-0795; *Violeta Olaz;* Constanza, Thalia, Adrien. e-mail

FLORES, Jason D.; '99 BS; Middletown, NY 10941.

FLORES, Jimmy; '89 BS; 2310 Beaumont Ave., Bronx, NY 10458, 718 862-2878.

FLORES, Primo; 535 E. 14th St., New York, NY 10009, 315 735-5594.

FLORES, Victor H.; '95 BS; 204 3rd Ave., E. Northport, NY 11731, 631 368-9288.

FLORES, Yvonne E.; '86 BA; Public Health Educator; NYC Dept. of Health, 485 Throop Ave., Brooklyn, NY 11221, 718 574-2454; r. 97a Visitation Pl., Brooklyn, NY 11231, 718 625-2082; Brandon Serra, Christian Serra.

FLORES, Yvonne Y.; '98 BA; 235 Scholes St. 2nd Fl., Brooklyn, NY 11206, 718 871-4455.

FLORKOWSKI, Thomas; '85 BS; 3610 Wyanet St., Seaford, NY 11783, 516 781-7298.

FLOWERS, Leon A.; '76 BA, '84 MPA; CERT. American Acad. McAllister; Retired Police Ofcr.; NYC Police Dept.; r. 405 Grand St., Brooklyn, NY 11211, 718 384-0026.

FLOYD, Joseph M.; '78 BA; 1866 Linden St., Flushing, NY 11385, 718 626-3984.

FLYAKS, Renata; '96 BS, '98 MPA, '98 MPA; BS; Computer Analyst; Impath, 521 W 57 St., New York, NY 10019, 212 314-5859; r. 2922 Nostrand Ave., Brooklyn, NY 11229, 718 677-0967. e-mail

FLYNN, Alexander A.; '85 BA; 12513 107th Ave., Jamaica, NY 11419, 718 897-8183.

FLYNN, Brian P.; '85 BS; 59 Morningside Ave., Yonkers, NY 10703.

FLYNN, Dennis J.; '77 MA; 9 Von Beaste Ln., Congers, NY 10920, 914 268-2926

FLYNN, Edward E.; 1014 Keeler Ave., Mamaroneck, NY 10543.

FLYNN, Eugene M.; BS; AS Comm Clg.; Retired Fire Chief; r. 435 Beach 137th St., Belle Harbor, NY 11694, 718 945-6968; *Johannah;* Eugene, John.

FLYNN, Eugene W.; '75 BS; Retired NYPD; r. 26 Brae Burn Ln., S. Yarmouth, MA 02664, 508 398-5495; *Mildred;* Stephen, Laura Jean, Kenneth.

FLYNN, Hugh P.; '75 MA; 1097 Rosegold St., Franklin Sq., NY 11010, 516 625-3676.

FLYNN, John; '90 BA; 28 W Gibbons St., Linden, NJ 07036.

FLYNN, John J.; '71 BS; 198 Elk Hill Rd, # 1391, Banner Elk, NC 28604, 828 963-8615.

FLYNN, Joseph E.; '78 BA; 747 10th Ave. Apt. 18K, New York, NY 10019, 315 858-1699.

FLYNN, Kevin C.; '93 BS; 51 Green St., Seneca Falls, NY 13148, 315 568-1234.

FLYNN, Michael; '94 MA; Student Clinical Psychology; Fordham Univ.; r. 560 Halstead Ave., Harrison, NY 10528, 914 835-5960.

FLYNN, Michael P.; '77 MA; 81 W. 6 St., Deer Park, NY 11729.

FLYNN, Raymond J.; '80; Deputy Chief; Las Vegas Metropolitan Police Dept., 400 E. Stewart Ave., Investigative Services Div., Las Vegas, NV 89101, 702 229-3511; r. 5801 Mendoza Ct., Las Vegas, NV 89108, 702 262-2350; *Linda;* Kimberly, Ray Jr., Kelli. e-mail

FLYNN, Thomas J.; '76 BS; 314 Buchanan Ave., Mineola, NY 11501, 516 248-9074.

FLYNN, William J.; '94 MA; Police Sergeant; New Brunswick Police Dept.; POB 909, New Brunswick, NJ 08901, 732 745-5200. e-mail

FODERA, Robert F.; '92 BS; JD Brooklyn Law Sch.; Atty.; NYC Police Dept., 2 Layfayette St., 5 Fl., New York, NY 10007, 212 374-2410; r. 936 Bay Ridge Pkwy., Brooklyn, NY 11228, 718 833-9787. e-mail

FOFANA, Unisa A.; '85 BS; 80 E 93rd St. #B613, Brooklyn, NY 11212.

FOGARTY, James P.; '68 BS, '75 MA; Retired-Inspector; NYPD; r. 36 Jackson Pl., Massapequa, NY 11758, 516 795-2925.

FOGARTY, Michael B.; '97 BS; 7 Hewlett Point Ave., E. Rockaway, NY 11518.

FOGG, Harry; '92 MPA; Personnel Mgmt. Tech.; Orange Cnty. Govt., 914 291-2707; r. 604 Cnty. Rte. 50, New Hampton, NY 10958, 914 374-3661.

FOGLIA, Mrs. Sophia, (Sophia Curas); '75 BS; Acting Exec. Dir.; Queens Symphony Orchestra, 31-00 47th Ave., Long Island City, NY 11101, 718 786-8880; r. 21346 33rd Ave., Bayside, NY 11361, 718 423-8680; *Dennis;* Katrina. e-mail

FOLAN, John B.; '93 BS; 2369 E 72nd St., Brooklyn, NY 11234.

FOLEY, Elizabeth A.; '79 BS; 125 Hempstead Gardens Dr. Apt. R2c, W. Hempstead, NY 11552, 516 223-8282.

FOLEY, Maura '82 (See Wrynn, Mrs. Maura A.).

FOLEY, Michael O., PhD; '75 MPA, '98 MPHIL; Prof. of Criminology; Western Connecticut State Univ., 181 White St., Danbury, CT 06810, 203 837-8597; r. 1 North Dr., Washingtonville, NY 10992, 914 496-6728. e-mail

FOLEY, Stephen P.; '83 BS; 140 Hunter Ave., Fanwood, NJ 07023, 908 322-4626.

FOLEY, Ms. Susan, (Susan Terranova); '83 BS; 204 Second St., Fanwood, NJ 07023, 908 889-5520; Daniel, Kathryn. e-mail

FOLEY, Thomas B., ACP; '72 AA, '74 BS; Investigator; US Govt., Washington, DC 20090; *Mary Ann.* e-mail

FOLEY, MAJ Thomas P.; '74 BS; AA BS; Operations Ofcr.; Dept. of Defense, Washington, DC 20090, 703 691-4065; r. 7 Harmon Pl., Hauppauge, NY 11788; *Mary Ann;* Thomas Brian, James Michael, John Joseph.

FOLEY, William J.; '95 BS; 1104 Hadley Hill Rd., Hadley, NY 12835, 212 580-0272.

FOLGAR, Karen J.; '98 BA; 1092 Willmohr St./2f, Brooklyn, NY 11212, 718 257-1786.

FOLLETT, Mary R.; '85 MA; 814 E 49th St., Brooklyn, NY 11203, 718 629-0673.

FOLMER, Gary M.; '78 BA; 3840 Greystone Ave., Bronx, NY 10463.

FOLSOM, Norman; '84 BS; 3913 Northumberland Dr., Louisville, KY 40245, 502 375-3517.

FONDE, LTC Philip, USA(Ret.); '72 BA; Ret. Deputy Chief; Financial Cnslt.; Axa Financial Grp., 80 Rte. 4 E, Paramus, NJ 07652, 201 712-4685; r. 7210 Cottage Ave., N. Bergen, NJ 07047, 201 868-7971; *Maria.*

FONFRIAS, Edna; '78 BA; 252 Cornelia St., Brooklyn, NY 11221.

FONG, Wayne M.; '85 BA; 422 W 57th St., New York, NY 10019.

FONSECA, Ms. Diana A.; '91 BS; Sr. Supv.; Criminal Justice Agcy., 52 Duane St., New York, NY 10007, 718 330-1500; r. 531 18th Ave., Newark, NJ 07103, 973 643-2014; StephenLawrence. e-mail

FONTANA, John P.; '81 BS; 5 Rossi Ct., Hackensack, NJ 07606.

FONTANA, Mrs. Laura M., (Laura M. Gumley); '98 BA; AS Suffolk Community Clg.; Asst. Dir. of Security; Fala Direct Mktg., 40 Daniel St., E. Farmingdale, NY 11735, 631 391-0668; r. 7 Smith Commons, Yaphank, NY 11980; *Steven.* e-mail

FONTANA, Susan; '92 BS; 79 Parkside Dr., Levittown, NY 11756, 516 867-9461.

FONTANE, Rudolph; 257 Harrison St., Leonia, NJ 07605.

FONTEBOA, Elizabeth; '97 BA; 4710 108th St., Corona, NY 11368.

FONTNEL, Monique A.; '95 BA, '98 BA; 340 Alexander Ave., Bronx, NY 10454, 718 665-5935.

FOODY, Liam J.; '80 BS; 47 Yale Ter., Blauvelt, NY 10913, 914 359-1386.

FORAN, Philip J.; '67 MPA; 3141 Lake Pine Way #B1, Tarpon Spgs., FL 34689, 727 944-2008.

FORBELL, Michael P.; '67 BS, '73 MA; Dir of Security; Valor Security Svcs. Inc., 748 S Village Cir., c/o Old Hyde Park Village, Tampa, FL 33606, 813 254-8554; r. 10000 Hwy. 98N #656, Lakeland, FL 33809, 863 858-3929; *Maureen.* e-mail

FORBES, Candace T.; '95 BS; 275 Rockaway Pkwy., Brooklyn, NY 11212, 718 498-4816.

FORBES, Carla M.; '87 BS; 1767 E 91st St., Brooklyn, NY 11236, 718 498-4816.

FORD, Brian F.; 116 Claywood Dr., Brentwood, NY 11717, 631 231-6171.

FORD, Christina E.; '73 AA, '75 BS; Detective Investigator; Queens Dist. Attorney's Ofc., Kew Gardens, NY 11415, 718 286-5893; r. 49-11 Broadway, Woodside, NY 11377.

FORD, Leticia; 117 Avenue C, Brooklyn, NY 11218, 718 574-5760.

FORD, Matthew C.; '78 MPA; 358 Calvin St., Washington Twp., NJ 07675.

FORD, Melvin; '81 BS; 2180 Strauss St., Brooklyn, NY 11212, 718 573-1292.

FORD, Olga; 44 Meadow Way, Hopewell Jct., NY 12533.

FORD, Vanessa D.; '84 BS; 8619 Ave. N, Brooklyn, NY 11236, 718 573-1292.

FORDE, Aine P.; '96 BA; 40-42 61 St. #D5, Woodside, NY 11377, 718 446-7661.

FORDE, Angela E.; '89 BS; 45 Roslyn Rd, Roslyn, NY 11576, 516 485-4203.

FORDE, Ivy D.; '80 BS; 780 Concourse Vlg W Apt. 19c, Bronx, NY 10451.

FORDE, Sharon; '97 BA; 385 E.16th Street#3, Brooklyn, NY 11226, 718 604-2687.

FOREMAN, Paulette; '99 BS; 1790 Bruckner Blvd. #8E, Bronx, NY 10473.

FORESTA, Jody A.; '79 BS; 433 Hillman Ave., Staten Island, NY 10314.

FORESTIERI, Paul J.; '88 MPA; 300 E 54 St., New York, NY 10022, 212 752-4296.

FORKER, Edward C.; '80 MPA; 6 Oriole St., Edison, NJ 08820.

FORLONG, Pedro A.; '99 BA; Child Protective Spec.; Admin. for Children Svcs., 165-15 Archer Ave., Jamaica, NY 11433, 718 481-6048; r. 42-05 Layton Street#2B, Elmhurst, NY 11373, 718 899-0666. e-mail

FORMAN, Morrey A.; '68 MPA; 190 Surrey Commons, Lynbrook, NY 11563, 516 593-3458.

FORMISANO, Daniel; 104 Highland Ave., Port Washington, NY 11050, 516 944-8033.

FORNER, Michael S.; '76 BA; Security Mgr.; Fed. Express, 5927 W Imperial Hwy., Los Angeles, CA 90045, 310 665-1064; r. New York, NY 10028.

FORNI, Mario T.; '73 BS, MAA; Tchr.; Haddon Ave Elem. Sch.; r. 5315 Calhoun Ave., Van Nuys, CA 91401, 818 907-9075; *Donna;* Elisa, Lia, Nick.

FORRESTER, Tamika '97 (See Gray, Mrs. Tamika S.).

FORRESTER, Vincent P.; '77 BA; 10 Impala Dr., Centereach, NY 11720.

FORSHAY, Karen; '95 BA; POB 55, Central Vly., NY 10917.

FORSTHOFF, SGT Roger A.; '87 BS; AA Univ. of Maine; Dir., Forensic Lab; Hudson Cnty. Prosecutor's Ofc., 555 Duncan Ave., Jersey City, NJ 07306, 201 915-1309; r. 210 Linwood Ave., Bogota, NJ 07603, 201 488-2041. e-mail

FORSYTHE, Farris B.; '79 MPA; BS Howard Univ.; Affirmative Action Ofcr.; John Jay Clg., CUNY, 445 W. 59th St., New York, NY 10019, 212 237-8122; r. 515 W. 59th St. Apt. 15N, New York, NY 10019, 212 307-1380; *Norman.* e-mail

FORTE, Jennifer M.; '91 BS; 1363 Dickens St., Far Rockaway, NY 11691, 718 471-4762.

FORTE, Leonard L.; '77 BS; Airport Police Officer; NY/NJ Port Authority Police, John F. Kennedy Intl. Airport, New York, NY 10001; r. 910 Brent Dr., Wantagh, NY 11793; *Valerie;* Thomas, Nicholas, Michael.

FORTE, Louis (Lou); '82 BS; MBA Long Island Univ.; Asst. VP; American Intl. Grp., 80 Pine St., New York, NY 10005; r. 212 Waters Edge Dr., Toms River, NJ 08753, 732 929-4314.

FORTEAU, Clement; '93 BA; 230 Forbell St., Brooklyn, NY 11208, 718 953-4552.

FORTINO, Denise M.; '94 MA; BA, MA Fordham Univ.; Therapist; Ctr. Comprehensive Health Practice, 1900 2nd Ave., New York, NY 10029, 212 360-7791; r. 675 Academy St., New York, NY 10034, 212 942-4197; *Roland Carlstedt PhD.* e-mail

FORTINO, Richard J.; '72 BS; Sr. Investigator/Retired Lt.; New York Central Ins., Pleasantville, NY 10570, 914 773-3672; r. 60 Woodland Rd, Pleasantville, NY 10570; *Alice;* Anthony.

FORTIS, Daisy, (Daisy Arce); '96 BS; SAPIS Drug Counselor; Bd. of Educ.; r. 223 Husson Ave., Bronx, NY 10473.

FORTUNAT, Daphnee; '96 BA; 10927 221st St., Queens Vlg., NY 11429, 718 465-7510.

FORTUNATO, Richard V.; '77 BS; Semi-Retired Security; NYS Correction Dept.; r. 37-25 98th St., Corona, NY 11368, 718 898-0720.

FORTUNE, Patricia; '84 BS, '87 MPA; St. John Univ.; Detective; Nassau CT Police Dept., 1490 Franklin Ave., Mineola, NY 11501, 516 573-5336; r. 11 Gates Ave. # C, Brooklyn, NY 11238, 718 398-8034. e-mail

FOSS, John R.; '79 BS; Retired NYPD/ Entrepreneur; Intercoastal Rsch. & Investigations, POB 1133, Little River, SC 29566, 843 280-4461; r. 4801 Lightkeepers Way 17b, Little River, SC 29566, 843 249-5261; *Dorothy;* Kelly, John. e-mail

FOSTER, Cherie S.; '95 BA; 1512 Townsend Ave., Bronx, NY 10452, 718 994-5267.

FOSTER, Valerie; '97 BA; 184 Macon St., Brooklyn, NY 11216, 718 774-1456.

FOTI, Anthony G.; '78 BS; 2128 60th St., Brooklyn, NY 11204, 718 854-3429.

FOTI, Frank G.; '94 BS; Det. Lt of NYPD; NYPD, New York, NY 10038; r. 22 Goodwin Ln., Coram, NY 11727, 631 331-6030.

FOUBISTER, Arlene J., (Arlene J. Reid); '75 BS; Material Coord.; Triarc Beverage, 709 Westchester Ave., W. Harrison, NY 10604, 914 245-0472; r. 58 Sheila Ct., Yorktown Hts., NY 10598, 914 245-0472; *Norman;* Stephen, Debra, Natalie.

FOUNTAIN, Belinda M.; '77 AS, '78 BS; Corrections Ofcr.; Beacon Correctional Facility, S.E.E.K. 1975-76 AWARD, Beacon, NY 12508; r. 17 Hudson View Dr., Beacon, NY 12508, 914 838-3034; Dionne, Debionne, Chad Walker.

FOUNTAIN, Roscoe E.; '78 BS; 887 Flatbush Ave., Brooklyn, NY 11226, 718 871-3512.

FOUNTOULAKIS, Georgios; '99 BS; CERT. NYC Police Acad.; Police Ofcr.; NYC Police Dept., 26th Precint, Harlem, NY 10030; r. 23-14 38th St., Astoria, NY 11105. e-mail

FOURCELL, Samantha; '99 BA; 195 Cross St., Bronx, NY 10464.

FOURNILLIER, Brian F.; '85 BA; 336 E 25th St., Brooklyn, NY 11226.

FOWLER, Kareem; '95 BS; 1545 Archer Rd., Bronx, NY 10462, 718 538-0344.

FOWLER, Stephanie; '97 BA; 76 Moffat St., Brooklyn, NY 11207, 718 399-2982.

FOX, Bonnie R.; '93 BA; Med. Collections; Salick Healthcare, Ccc Med. Practice, 160 E 32nd St.-2nd Fl., New York, NY 10016, 212 652-1995; r. 332 E. 66th St., 3D, New York, NY 10021, 212 396-0566.

FOX, Daniel J., Esq.; '83 BS; JD Seton Hall Law Sch.; Atty-at-Law; Law Ofc. Daniel J. Fox, 339 Main St. Ste. 2L, Orange, NJ 07050, 973 674-3733; r. 232 Sumner Ave., Plainfield, NJ 07062, 908 755-9217; *Donnette;* James D., Jordan D.

FOX, Edward L.; '77 MPA; 5655 Clearview Expy., Flushing, NY 11364, 718 229-8313.

FOX, Jason; '97 BS, '97 AA; Sr. Assoc. of Support Svcs.; V Formation, 170 Beaver Brook Rd, Lincoln Park, NJ 07035, 973 872-9400; r. 14 Linden Ave., Bronx, NY 10465, 718 824-0902. e-mail

FOX, Kemeel N.; '99 BS; Supv.; r. 2155 Haring St. 2 Fl., Brooklyn, NY 11229, 718 769-1217.

FOX, Kevin M.; '93 BS; 19 Quenzer St., Nesconset, NY 11767.

FOX, Kevin M.; '98 MA; 59-26 162 St., Flushing, NY 11365, 718 776-7634.

FOX, Lawrence J.; '77 BS; MED CUNY; Unit Supv.; August Aichhorn, 23 W 106th St., Cathedral, NY 10025, 212 316-9353; r. 11515 223rd St., Jamaica, NY 11411, 718 723-6583; *Sandy;* Nicole, Stephanie. e-mail

FOX, Thomas M.; '98 MA; 96 Filors Ln., Stony Point, NY 10980, 914 942-1655.

FOXX, John H.; '78 BA; 115-76 226 St., Cambria Hts., NY 11411.

FOY, Lawrence J.; '85 BS; Retired-Transit Police Ofc.; New York Transit; r. 130 Lincoln Rd, Brooklyn, NY 11225, 718 287-9398; *Jeirlynn;* Todd (dec), La-Wrence, John, Love. e-mail

FOY, Raymond G.; '90 MA; 80 Vanderwater Ave., Floral Park, NY 11001, 516 326-0752.

FOYE, Katrina '98 (See McGill, Mrs. Katrina A.).

FRABASILE, Carmelo; '84 BS; 2561 Lurting Ave., Bronx, NY 10469, 718 515-5641.

FRADELLA, Margaret; '87 BS; 18 Exeter 5 St., Old Bridge, NJ 08857.

FRAGAPANE, V.; '81 BA; 2276 78 St., Brooklyn, NY 11214.

FRAIOLI, Joyce A.; '82 BS; 137 Knollwood Ave., Mamaroneck, NY 10543, 914 698-7718.

FRANCES, Miguel A.; '95 AS, '97 BS; 9817 158th Ave., Howard Bch., NY 11414, 718 423-9267.

FRANCESCH, Fred R.; Dept. of Law Enforcement, Baton Rouge, LA 70803.

FRANCILLON, Joanne; '95 BS; Mgr. of Admin.; MTVI Grp./Sonic Net, 315 Park Ave. S, 18th Fl., New York, NY 10010, 212 284-3681; r. 236 Greene Ave., Apt. 1D, Brooklyn, NY 11238, 718 783-2521. e-mail

FRANCIS, Alvin D.; '86 BA; 26 Park Pl., Brooklyn, NY 11217, 718 857-4227.

FRANCIS, Charles J.; '95 BS; 91 Woehrle Ave., Staten Island, NY 10312, 718 317-7880.

FRANCIS, Howard C.; '98 BS; 53 Chapel Hill Dr., Brentwood, NY 11717, 631 273-4202.

FRANCIS, Joan C.; '77 BA; 668 E 225th St. # 1, Bronx, NY 10466.

FRANCIS, Joel M.; '98 BA; Sgt.; NYPD, 1 Police Plz., New York, NY 10038. e-mail

FRANCIS, John W.; '94 BS; 6559 Parsons Blvd. Apt. 1a, Flushing, NY 11365, 718 291-8725.

FRANCIS, Lois E.; '82 BS; 7 Chestnut Hill Ave., White Plains, NY 10606, 914 761-2472; *Darryl Jr, Latisha, Jourdan.*

FRANCIS, Mario J.; '93 BA; Mental Health; PSCH, 22-119th St., College Pt., NY 11356, 718 445-4700; r. 216-09 118th Ave., Cambria Hts., NY 11411, 718 527-9425; *Angelise; Marlique.*

FRANCIS, Mildred L.; '80 BA; 1-05 Astoria Blvd., Long Island City, NY 11102, 718 898-4721.

FRANCIS, Nicke R.; '96 BA; 20 St.Pauls #4, Brooklyn, NY 11226, 718 693-3357.

FRANCIS, Richard W.; '71 BS; 107 Norton Dr., E. Northport, NY 11731.

FRANCIS, Robert H.; '83 BS; POB 20103, New York, NY 10025, 315 363-0645.

FRANCIS, Rosemarie; '97 BA; 10559 132nd St., Jamaica, NY 11419, 718 322-1348.

FRANCIS, Willie W.; '94 BA; 2508 76th St., E. Elmhurst, NY 11370, 718 479-7537.

FRANCISCI, Bruno M.; '77 BS; 5172 72nd Pl., Flushing, NY 11377.

FRANCIS-LEWIS, Flona V.; '97 AS, '98 BA, '98 BS; Child Protective Spec.; Admin. for Children's Svcs., 1775 Grand Concorse, Bronx, NY 10453, 718 716-0491; r. 555 E 240th St., Bronx, NY 10470, 718 994-2708.

FRANCO, Maria; '97 BS; 2020 Grand Ave.3G, Bronx, NY 10453, 718 299-9382.

FRANCO, Robert J.; '95 BS; 11 Lake Tr. E, Wayne, NJ 07470.

FRANCOIS, Mrs. Christine, (Christine Villalobos); '92 BS; Fraud Investigator; NYC Dept. of Social Svcs., 250 Church St. 5th Fl., New York, NY 10013, 212 274-5650; r. 150-32 Jewel Ave. #62 A, Flushing, NY 11367, 718 268-5747; *Neil; Nia Barbara.* e-mail

FRANCOIS, Marc D.; '98 BS; POB 322, Sound Bch., NY 11789.

FRANCOIS, Mrs. Marie M.; '95 BS; Claims Rep.; Allstate Auto Liability DMS, 1 Expy. Plz., Roslyn Hts., NY 11577, 516 629-2305; r. 96-06 31st Ave., E. Elmhurst, NY 11369, 718 672-1535; *Jean Barreau; Kathleen, Francois.*

FRANCOIS, Marlene; '90 BS; Personal Inj, Paralegal,Collection; Roberts & Fidler PC, Garden City, NY 11530, 516 248-5432; r. 260 Brooklyn Ave., Westbury, NY 11590. e-mail

FRANGOS, Victoria H.; '79 BS; 394 Virginia Ave., Staten Island, NY 10305.

FRANK, Kathryn K.; '80 MA; Educ. Cnslt. Westchester Cnty.; Westchester Cnty. Family Ct., c/o Judge Coony, Dr. Martin Luther King Dr., White Plains, NY 10601, 914 285-3662; r. 3 Walker Ave., Rye, NY 10580, 914 835-0221.

FRANK, Laura; '86 MA; 60 Cherry St., Katonah, NY 10536, 914 232-1255.

FRANK, Rudolph A.; '82 AA, '84 BS; Supv. Customs Inspector; US Customs Svc.; r. 961 Ambassador Dr., Toms River, NJ 08753, 732 270-8062.

FRANKE, Patricia D.; '78 BS; 80-27 64 Rd, Middle Vlg., NY 11379, 718 321-1662.

FRANKEL, Robert R.; '74 BS; 10 Pheasant Dr., W. Nyack, NY 10994, 914 638-1923.

FRANKLIN, Kim '92 (See Lawson, Mrs. Kim).

FRANKLIN, Raymond J.; '99 BS; Long Island City, NY 11105.

FRANKS, Robert J.; '75 BA; 2274-85th St., Brooklyn, NY 11214.

FRANQUI, Mary A.; '87 BA; 1031 Seneca Ave., Ridgewood, NY 11385, 718 456-2128.

FRANZESE, Paul N.; '84 BS; 1767 W 9th St., Brooklyn, NY 11223, 718 623-9703.

FRANZESE, Peter J.; '92 BS; 8711 104th St., Jamaica, NY 11418, 718 343-3585.

FRANZESE, Peter P.; 97-12 130th St., Richmond Hill, NY 11419, 718 343-3585.

FRASCO, Elizabeth G.; '97 BA; 21 King St., Edison, NJ 08820.

FRASCO, Leonard W.; '79 BA; 116 8th St., Staten Island, NY 10306, 718 351-5427.

FRASER, Kenneth A.; '80 BS; 180 Giffords Ln., Staten Island, NY 10308.

FRASER, Walter W.; '75 MA; 345 W 145 St. #6B1, New York, NY 10031.

FRATER, Donroy S.; '99 MPA; BA Lehmann Clg.; Analyst; NYC; r. 3035 Ely Ave., Bronx, NY 10469, 718 671-6204; *Jane.*

FRATES, Michaelynn J.; '99 MA; BA Chadron State Clg.; 1160 Mamaroneck Ave., White Plains, NY 10605, 914 422-0233. e-mail

FRATTER, Jeffrey; '78 MA; Chief Clerk of Appeals; US Justice Dept.; r. 13904 Quietway Ct., Chantilly, VA 20151, 703 378-1762.

FRAY, Harold J.; '89 BS; 14 Somerset Dr., Washingtonville, NY 10992.

FRAZA, Louise J.; '81 MA; 236 E. 89 St., New York, NY 10028.

FRAZER, David; '87 BA; 88-27 211th St. 2Fl, Queens Vlg., NY 11427, 718 706-7061.

FRAZER, John H.; '94 BS; 2001 Arthur Ct., Mahwah, NJ 07430.

FRAZIER, Dawn M.; '97 BA; 601 Barbey St., Brooklyn, NY 11207, 718 797-0997.

FRAZIER, Gloria D.; '88 BA; 168 Willow Ave., Hempstead, NY 11550.

FRAZIER, Marguerite; '92 BS; CERT. Adelphi Univ.; Paralegal; Hammill, O'Brien, Croutier, Dempsey..., Pender,Pc, Mineola, NY 11501; r. 14554 159th St., Jamaica, NY 11434, 718 978-3084. e-mail

FRAZIER, Veronica '99 (See Haynes, Veronica (Roni) T.).

FRAZIER, William E.; '80 BS; 264 Maple St., Brooklyn, NY 11225, 718 443-8561.

FRECKLETON, Lloyd J.; '91 BS; Ret., Warden/Col./Police Ofcr.; NYC Dept. of Corrections/USA, US Central Co, MacDill AFB, Tampa, FL 33621; r. 540 Lambert Ave., Flagler Bch., FL 32136, 904 439-9661; *Deborah;* David, Sasha, Lloyd III. e-mail

FREDER, Drew F.; '92 BS; 144c Edgewater Park, Bronx, NY 10465, 718 904-8691.

FREDERICK, Darrell; '95 AS; 1530 Townsend Ave., Bronx, NY 10452, 718 904-8691.

FREDERICK, Ondie L.; '92 BS; 2829 Sedgwick Ave., Bronx, NY 10468, 718 904-8691.

FREDERICKS, Andrew A.; '95 MS; Fire Protection Cnslt.; Andrew A Fredricks & Assocs. Inc., 25 Forest Dr., Suffern, NY 10901, 914 369-6315; r. same; *Michelle;* Andrew J., Hayley M. e-mail

FREDERICKS, Jonathan E.; '99 BA MA; Sgt; NYPD; r. 1237 Crosby Ave., Bronx, NY 10461, 718 904-7387; *Melanie.*

FREDERICKS, Walter F.; '76 BS; 245 Jamaica Ave., Medford, NY 11763.

FREDERICKSEN, Robert; '70 BS; Lt. Retired; NYPD; r. 41 Ardsley St., Staten Island, NY 10306, 718 987-1512.

FREDUA-MENSAH; 1250 5th Ave. Apt. 4l, New York, NY 10029.

FREED, Lesly W.; '89 BS; 8835 23rd Ave. Apt. C5, Brooklyn, NY 11214, 718 444-5885.

FREEMAN, Aldric; '88 BA; Real Estate Corp Personal Injury; Law Firm of Aldric Freeman & Assocs, 26 Court St., Ste. 914, Brooklyn, NY 11242, 718 855-9141; r. 325 Clinton Ave., Apt. 10 C, Brooklyn, NY 11205, 718 399-9716; *Angela;* Dellian Sharp, Tuesdai A.

FREEMAN, Cynthia; '79 BS; 845 Columbus Ave., New York, NY 10025.

FREEMAN, Denise, (Denise Nelson); '76 BS; RN; r. 339 101 St., Brooklyn, NY 11209; *Thomas.*

FREEMAN, James H.; '95 BS; Police Ofcr.; NYPD; r. 644 Crescent St., Brooklyn, NY 11208, 718 647-8311; lan. e-mail

FREEMAN, Ronald A.; '91 BA; 11438 125th St., S. Ozone Park, NY 11420, 718 672-5718.

FREEMAN, Theodore R.; '74 BA; Ret; r. 45 E 135th St. Apt. 8b, New York, NY 10037, 212 926-2658.

FREEMAN, Thomas G.; '80 BS; Sr. Investigator; King's Cnty. Das Ofc., 350 Jay St., Brooklyn, NY 11201; r. 339 101st St., Brooklyn, NY 11209, 718 443-0706; *Denise.*

FREEMAN, Willie; 209 Rutland Rd., PH., Brooklyn, NY 11225.

FREILICH, Mark J.; '99 BS; Sales Exec.; Computer Assocs., Islandia, NY 11788, 800 248-9462; r. 2226 Eastchester Rd. #2F, Bronx, NY 10469, 718 652-1904; *Simona;* Mark Jr, Amanda. e-mail

FREIRE, Richard J.; '93 BS; Atty.; Hoey, King, Toker & Epstein, 55 Water St., 28th Fl., New York, NY 10041; r. 10128 99th St., Jamaica, NY 11416, 718 843-5295.

FRENCH, Rollo C.; '98 BA; 1421 Brooklyn Ave. 6c, Brooklyn, NY 11210, 718 940-4266.

FRET, Jeanette; '85 BA; 758 Kelly St., Bronx, NY 10455, 718 991-8023.

FREUND, Charles G.; '77 BS; 1467 Arden Ave., Staten Island, NY 10312.

FREUNDLICH, Jeffrey; '81 BS; 591 Bellevue Ave. N, Yonkers, NY 10703.

FRIAGLIA, Richard A.; '82 BS; Security Mgr.; Wackenhut Corp., New York Racing Div, POB 55, Ozone Park, NY 11417, 718 641-4700; r. 879 1st Ave., Franklin Sq., NY 11010.

FRIAS, Jose M.; '97 BS, '98 BS; 501 W. 169th St., New York, NY 10032, 212 927-6447.

FRIAS, Maria C.; '99 BA; Legal Secy.; Hanley & Goble LLP, 233 Broadway Rm 2701, New York, NY 10279, 212 233-3330; r. 160 W Manhattan Ave. #1C, New York, NY 10025, 212 866-8422; Taise. e-mail

FRICK, Henry F.; '98 BS; Lt.; NYC Police Dept., 1 Pl. Pl. Rm 1201, New York, NY 10038, 212 374-3870; r. POB 1062, Tannersville, NY 12485, 718 821-0174. e-mail

FRIED, Howard; '82 MA; 577 Grand St., New York, NY 10002, 212 673-6942.

FRIEDMAN, David; 1 Police Plz. RM 1014, New York, NY 10038.

FRIEDMAN, Jason A.; '96 MA; 9107 John Way, Fairfax Sta., VA 22039.

FRIEDMAN, Jenna; '95 AS, '99 BS; Police Officer; NYPD; r. 14934 Melbourne Ave., Flushing, NY 11367, 718 793-9746.

FRIERSON, Tom E.; '73 BS; 157-10 Riverside, New York, NY 10032.

FRIES, Timothy; '95 AS, '96 BS; Asst. Dir. of The HS Div; Frank & Carol Biondi Educational Ctr., At Leake & Watts, 463 Hawthrone Ave., Yonkers, NY 10705, 914 375-8946; r. POB 840 Lincolnton Sta., New York, NY 10037, 212 690-9012; *Angel McGee-Fries;* Samone, Timothy Jr. e-mail

FRISCO, Nick M.; '84 BA; 275 Rutherford Ave., Massapequa, NY 11758.

FRISIK, David J.; '82 BA; 27-08 Crescent St., Astoria, NY 11102.

FRITTITTA, Joseph G.; '98 BS; Assoc. Loss Prevention Mgr.; r. 16 Laforge Ave., Staten Island, NY 10302, 718 273-5133.

FROHBERG, John H.; '75 BS; 7 Dryden Way, Commack, NY 11725.

FROMAN, Gerald A.; '78 BS, '81 MA; Dir. Surveillance Svcs.; Data Source Intl., 200 Business Park Dr., Armonk, NY 10504, 914 273-6100; r. 193 Hickory Grove Dr. E, Larchmont, NY 10538, 914 834-4969.

FROST, David; '79 BS; Indep. Contractor; r. 3045 Ferncrest Dr., Yorktown Hts., NY 10598, 914 962-3885. e-mail

FRUMIN, Leonard C.; 15798 Loch Maree Ln. Apt. 3505, Delray Bch., FL 33446.

FRUSCELLA, Paul D.; '77 MPA; 73 Seaman Ave., New York, NY 10034.

FRY, James W.; '77 BS, '81 MPA; Dir. of Public Safety; Roosevelt Island Operations Corp., 591 Main St., New York, NY 10044, 212 832-4540; r. 195 Willoughby Ave. Apt. 513, Brooklyn, NY 11205, 718 398-1611; *Marie;* James.

FUCHS, Deborah; '81 MA; 38 Willow St., Selden, NY 11784, 631 736-0374.

FUCHSMAN, Alan; '74 BS, '78 MA; Real Estate Mgr.; Pinnacle Mgmt., 1 Penn Plz., New York, NY 10119, 212 564-2111; r. 2382 Langen Dr., Seaford, NY 11783, 516 826-4856.

FUCITO, Michael J.; '73 BS; 1721 Fillmore St., Bronx, NY 10460.

FUENTES, Christopher; '96 BS; 127 Stonehenge, Clark, NJ 07066.

FUENTES, Jacqueline A.; '99 BS; Child Protective Spec.; NYC Admin. for Children's Svcs., 350 St. Marks Pl. 5th Fl., Staten Island, NY 10301, 718 720-2736; r. 241 Hoyt St., Brooklyn, NY 11217, 718 834-8487.

FUENTES, James F.; '97 BA, '98 BA; 150-09 88th Ave., Jamaica, NY 11432, 718 397-0191.

FUENTES, Joseph; '91 MA; 33 Carlton Ter., Rutherford, NJ 07070, 201 670-6189.

FUKO, Curtis; '97 BS; 47 Emma Pl., Eatontown, NJ 07724, 732 544-1763. e-mail

FULCO, Anthony G.; '96 BS; 266 E 54th St., Elmwood Park, NJ 07407.

FULGENCIO, Nederland; '96 AS; 548 Decatur St., Brooklyn, NY 11233.

FULLAM, Robert F.; '73 BA; 62 Michael Ave., Farmingdale, NY 11735, 516 694-5539.

FULLARD, David A.; '93 MA; BA Sch. of Visual Arts; Correction Capt.; NYC Dept. of Corrections, 1 Shore Rd, Riker's Island, Little Neck, NY 11363, 718 546-1475; r. 129-133 W. 147 St. Bldg. 3, New York, NY 10039, 917 419-4193.

FULLER, Jane; '94 BA; 711 West End Ave., New York, NY 10025, 212 316-6952.

FULLER, Joan D.; '98 BA; 709 Lenox Rd., Brooklyn, NY 11203, 718 941-3162.

FULLER, William; '79 MA; 287 Fulton St., W. Babylon, NY 11704.

FULLER-BEY, Tayhlia; '95 BA; 13337 128th St., S. Ozone Park, NY 11420, 718 721-2928.

FULLERTON, Khalfani O.; '83 BS; 4014 Waterstone St., Missouri City, TX 77459, 281 499-7221.

FULTON, Audrey M. '78 (See Khashiun, Karamah M.).

FUMAI, John H.; '76 AS, '78 BA; Retired Police; r. 647 Leonard St., Brooklyn, NY 11222, 718 383-4119; *Marie;* Annmarie, Anthony. e-mail

FUMAI, Joseph F.; '76 AS; Retired Police Lt.; NY Transit Authority; r. 104 Meadowoods Dr., E. Meadow, NY 11554, 516 222-8842; *Marie;* Carlo, Nicholas, Annrose, Camille.

FUNG, Janet K.; '97 MA; BA CUNY; Sr. Youth Delv./Supv.; Good Shepherd, New York, NY 10023, 212 541-9747; r. 16015 77th Rd, Flushing, NY 11366. e-mail

FUNG, Kit T.; '92 BS; 46 Madison St. Apt. 7g, New York, NY 10038.

FUNK, James; '96 BS; 80 Alaska St., Staten Island, NY 10310, 718 442-8065.

FURELLI, Gianfranco; '95 BS; US Pretrial Svcs. Ofcr.; US Dist. Courts-Pretrial Svcs., 500 Pearl St., Rm. 550, New York, NY 10007, 212 805-4152; r. Queens, NY 11412.

FUREY, John; '86 MA; PHD Life Chiropractic Clg.; Chiropractor; Mule Road Chiropractic, 25 Mule Rd. Ste. B2, Toms River, NJ 08755, 732 341-3535; r. 633 Wyoming Dr., Toms River, NJ 08753, 732 506-0011. e-mail

FURLONG, Joseph; '97 BA; 290 W 232nd St., Apt. 15A, Bronx, NY 10463, 718 601-1259.

FURMAN, Cynthia; '95 BS; Eligibility Spec.; HRA; r. 111 Prospect St., Staten Island, NY 10304, 718 720-2198; *Kevin;* Samantha.

FURR, Angela R.; '80 BS; 1325 Pennsylvania Ave. Apt. 15g, Brooklyn, NY 11239.

FURTICK, Anna E.; '92 MA; BA Lehman Clg.; Social Work/Therapist; Lutheran Soc. Services./Young Adult Inst; r. 2929 Bainbridge Ave., Apt. 3D, Bronx, NY 10458, 718 519-6359. e-mail

FUSARO, Michael J.; '78 BA; 1529 71st St., Brooklyn, NY 11228, 718 627-4546.

FUSCO, Filomena J.; '84 BS; 605 W Salem Ave., Indianola, IA 50125, 515 961-4741.

FUSSALVA, Arleene J.; '96 BS; MSW Univ. of Pennsylvania; Bilingual Clinician; Fordham-Tremont C.M.H.C., 2021 GrandConcourse, Bronx, NY 10453, 718 960-0368; r. 2851 Sedgwick Ave., Bronx, NY 10468, 718 543-0807. e-mail

FUSTER, Adam; '93 BS; 66 W 94th St. Apt. 16a, New York, NY 10025.

FYFE, James; '71 BS; 25 Parkside Dr., Princeton, NJ 08540, 609 497-1061.

G

GAASKIN, Ms. Michelle D., (Michelle D. Gaskin); '98 BA; Child Protective Spec.; Admin. for Children's Services, 210 Joralemon St., Brooklyn, NY 11201, 718 802-2333; r. 1055 Greene Ave. #1, Brooklyn, NY 11221, 718 573-2604. e-mail

GABBIN, Catherine P.; '95 AS, '98 BS; 439 Hicks St., Brooklyn, NY 11201, 718 858-5243.

GABIN, Angeli; '99 BA; Dist. Adjudication Ofcr.; Immigration Dept., 26 Federal Plz., New York, NY 10028; r. 950 Jennings St., Apt. 20, Bronx, NY 10460, 718 617-5099; Amanda.

GABORA, Herman R.; '73 BS; MPS CW Post Clg., CPM Rutgers Univ.; Dir. of Security; Trinity Church, 74 Trinity Pl., New York, NY 10006, 212 602-0859; r. 2366 Sycamore Ave., Wantagh, NY 11793, 516 783-0096; *Carol;* Keith, Amanda. e-mail

GABOS, Mario; '66 BS, '72 MPA; 179 Amber St., Staten Island, NY 10306.

GABRIEL, Anne M.; '99 MS; 589 Ft. Hamilton Pl., River Vale, NJ 07675, 201 666-9223.

GABRIEL, Sandra M.; '99 BA; Child Protective Spec.; Admin. for Children Svcs., 165-15 Archer Ave., Jamaica, NY 11434, 718 481-5875; r. 29-04 Deerfield Rd. 2, Far Rockaway, NY 11691, 718 868-9087.

GABY, Thomas R.; '80 BA; Firefighter; NYC Engine 44, 221 E 75st, New York, NY 10021, 212 570-4244; r. 227 Alicia Dr., N. Babylon, NY 11703, 631 321-6530; *Janet;* Christopher. e-mail

GADDIST, Valerie '93 (See Gaddist-Dorsey, Valerie D.).

GADDIST-DORSEY, Valerie D., (Valerie Gaddist); '93 BA; Supv.; Bur. Fraud Investigation HRA, 3228 Northern Blvd., Long Island City, NY 11103, 718 626-6287; r. 111-04 223rd St., Queens Vlg., NY 11429, 718 657-3470; *Steven.*

GADDY, James; '91 BA; 10 Midwood St., Brooklyn, NY 11225, 718 462-6375.

GADLIN, Igor E.; '97 BS; Student; Univ. of Iowa; r. 1245 50th St. #6F, Brooklyn, NY 11219, 718 851-8027. e-mail

GADRY, Albert J.; '75 MA; 4911 Cannes Cir., Pascagoula, MS 39581.

GAETA, Dominic J.; '70 BS; 42 Powers St., Brooklyn, NY 11211, 718 387-3877.

GAETANO, Gregory; '91 MPA; 421 Little Britain Rd, New Windsor, NY 12553.

GAFFNEY, Kevin J.; '81 BS; 61 N Sound Beach A, Riverside, CT 06878.

GAFFORD, Hazel V.; '76 BA; 3121 Middletown Rd Apt. 2d, Bronx, NY 10461.

GAGATCH, Robert P.; '75 BA; 3 Tanager Rd, Brewster, NY 10509, 914 278-4412.

GAGER, Philip A.; '90 BA; 2010 Bruckner Blvd., Bronx, NY 10473.

GAGLIANO, Allene; '92 BS; Med. Student; Univ of VA Sch. of Med.; r. 1405 Cherry Ave., Charlottesville, VA 22903. e-mail

GAGLIARDI, Michael J.; '81 BS; 338 Tanglewood Dr., Staten Island, NY 10308, 718 698-6528.

GAGLIARDO, Diane M.; '84 BA; 3 Raphael Blvd., Nesconset, NY 11767, 631 366-1829.

GAIDIS, John T.; 59-47A 69 Ln., Maspeth, NY 11378.

GAILLARD, Andrea J.; '98 BA; Couns. Asst.; BMCC, 199 Chambers, New York, NY 10009, 212 346-8150; r. 41 Convent Ave. #3b, New York, NY 10027, 212 222-4385. e-mail

GAILLARD, Leroy; '83 BS; Retired Military/Transit Worker; NY Air Natl. Guard/ NYC Transit Auth.; r. 3026 Young Ave., Bronx, NY 10469, 718 798-8187; *Alma; Sharon Monque, Troy Allen, Brianna Naomi.*

GAINES, Dionne E.; '92 BA; 72 N 15th St., Wheatley Hts., NY 11798.

GAIONI, Robert J.; '76 MA; 39-20 210 St., Bayside, NY 11361.

GAIOTTI, Helaine J.; '87 AS; RR 1 Box 101, Danby, VT 05739, 802 293-6008.

GAITHER, Ernest; '99 AS; 290 Fountain ave., Brooklyn, NY 11208, 718 342-6127.

GALA, Michael F.; '94 BA, '98 MS; Lt.; NYC Fire Dept., 4210 12th Ave., Latter #148, Brooklyn, NY 11219, 718 965-8282; r. 39 Ocean Ct., Brooklyn, NY 11223, 718 336-0479; *Vita; Robert, Anthony, Bianca.* e-mail

GALAHER, Lilia; '97 BA; Housing Asst.; NY Housing Authority, 212 965-0095; r. 14-36 30th Rd, Astoria, NY 11102, 718 204-2179; *Towner;* Whitney, Heather.

GALARZA, Maria E.; '95 BS; 2301 Morris Ave. Apt. 3c, Bronx, NY 10468, 718 293-8391.

GALARZA, Michael M.; '97 BA; 74-10 35 Ave. #1, Jackson Hts., NY 11372, 718 628-1345.

GALASSO, Daniel T.; 2000 BA; Deputy US Marshal; US Marshal Svc., 50 Walnut St., Newark, NJ 07102, 973 645-2404; r. 289 Fencsak Ave., Elmwood Park, NJ 07407, 201 797-4809.

GALASSO, Rocco A.; '76 AS; 1812 Muliner Ave., Bronx, NY 10462, 718 931-9367.

GALBREATH, Lauren M.; '95 MS; POB 92, Ardsley, NY 10502.

GALCHUS, Frank M.; '74 BS; 15143 26th Ave., Flushing, NY 11354, 718 762-7190.

GALDI, Joseph M.; '83 BS; 45 Erie St. E, Blauvelt, NY 10913, 914 359-3374.

GALE, John D.; '81 BS; US Customs, Brooklyn, NY 11239, 718 553-1456; r. 100 Bethel Loop 10-C, Brooklyn, NY 11239, 718 642-4849.

GALEA, John A.; '76 AA, '77 BA; MPA Long Island Univ.-CW Post, CERT. FBI; Chief of Ethnography Section; NYS Ofc./ Alcoholism & Substance Abuse Sv, 501 7th Ave., New York, NY 10018, 212 399-8654; r. 1200 E 53rd St. Apt. 5x, Brooklyn, NY 11234, 718 763-0612; *Barbara;* Jonathan, Erica. e-mail

GALEANO, Sonia L.; '97 BA; Docket Clerk; US Dist. Ct. Eastern Dist. of NY, 225 Cadman Plz. E., Brooklyn, NY 11201, 718 260-2627; r. 565 E. 39th St. Apt. #1A, Brooklyn, NY 11203, 718 284-5006. e-mail

GALFY, James T.; '76 MPA; 15 Ardsley Ct., New Providence, NJ 07974, 609 207-1121.

GALIANO, Richard H.; '72 BA; Retired Police Ofcr.; r. 110 Ayelsford Dr., Cary, NC 27511, 919 851-5863; *Julie;* Michael. e-mail

GALICIA, Margo V.; '99 MA; Forensic Psychobiology Cnslt.; Ofc. of Chief Med. Examiner, Dept. of Forensic Biology, 520 First Ave., New York, NY 10016. e-mail

GALLAGHER, Brian; '90 BS; 542 1st Ave., Pelham, NY 10803.

GALLAGHER, Harold D.; '76, '77 BS; 12402 Sir Lancelot Dr., Glenn Dale, MD 20769, 301 681-8035.

GALLAGHER, J. P.; 834 N Newkirk St., Philadelphia, PA 19130, 215 355-1155.

GALLAGHER, Joseph E.; '91 MA, '91 BA; 17 Seaman Ave., New York, NY 10034, 212 942-7450.

GALLAGHER, Kevin R.; '78 BS; Police Ofcr.; NYPD Scuba Team, NYPD Harbor Unit Scuba Team, 40 58 St., Brooklyn, NY 11220, 718 832-2978; r. 77 S. Buckhout St., Irvington, NY 10533, 914 591-8462; *Donna;* John, Elizabeth, Mickey.

GALLAGHER, Michael G.; '75 BA; 2 Forge Gate Dr., Cold Spring, NY 10516.

GALLAGHER, Michael S.; '96 BS; 1215 W.Addison #2, Chicago, IL 60613, 773 868-4530.

GALLAGHER, Thomas; '74 BS, '76 MPA; Retired; r. 18 S Park Ave., Nanuet, NY 10954, 914 623-8153; *Anne Marie;* Cathy Ann, Thomas, Daniel.

GALLAGHER, Thomas E.; '72 BS; 69 Meadow St., Pearl River, NY 10965, 914 735-3789.

GALLAGHER, Walter; '66 BS; 935 Harrison Dr., Centerport, NY 11721.

GALLARDO, Diana; '98 BA; Legal Secy. Real Estate Law; Fischbein Badillo Wagner Harding, 909 Third Ave., 17th Fl., New York, NY 10022, 212 453-3802; r. POB 625, Oyster Bay, NY 11771, 516 922-7258. e-mail

GALLETTA, Cyrus B.; '76 BA; 245 88 St., Brooklyn, NY 11209, 718 232-9619.

GALLMAN, Kimberly L.; '96 BS; 1126 E. 52nd St., Brooklyn, NY 11234.

GALLO, Alfred V.; 14 Prospect Ave., Montvale, NJ 07645.

GALLO, Henry A.; 335 Linden Blvd., Brooklyn, NY 11226, 718 827-0888.

GALLO, James E.; '77 BS; 6343 60th Pl., Ridgewood, NY 11385, 718 849-8721.

GALLO, Joan '75 (See Gallo-silver, Joan M.).

GALLO, Richard; '85 MA; MPA, BS; Special Agt.; President Fleoa, 2G Federal Plz., New York, NY 10278, 212 264-8400; r. POB 140115, Staten Island, NY 10314, 718 979-6240.

GALLO-SILVER, Joan M., (Joan Gallo); '75 BA; Billing Mgr.; Cadwalader Wickersham & Taft, 100 Maden Ln., New York, NY 10038, 212 504-6687; r. 88 Bleecker St. Apt. Lb, New York, NY 10012, 212 529-9684; *Les.* e-mail

GALLO-SILVER, Les I., (Les I. Sivler); '75 BA; MSW NYU; Program Coord.; NYU Med. Ctr., 400 East 34th St., Ste. R229, New York, NY 10016, 212 263-5018; r. 88 Bleecker St., New York, NY 10012, 212 529-9684. e-mail

GALLOWAY, Robin L.; '91 BA; POB 658, New York, NY 10039.

GALLOWAY, Rulisa; '97 BA; Financial Asst. Check Liaison; John Jay Clg., 899 10th Ave., New York, NY 10019, 212 237-8555; r. 17-21 W. 118th St., Apt. 1G, New York, NY 10026, 917 863-9523. e-mail

GALLOZA, Gilbert; '98 BS; 639 Beach Ave., Bronx, NY 10473, 718 893-8358.

GALLUP, Tamara; '95 BA; 205 Rutland Rd, Brooklyn, NY 11225, 718 856-0447.

GALVEZ, Alexander J.; '94 BS; 6 Cnty. Line Rd, Farmingdale, NY 11735.

GALVIN, Christopher J.; '99 BA; 29 5th Ave. S., Huntington Sta., NY 11746.

GAMBARDELLA, Vincent; '78 BA; 9 Bevy Ct., Brooklyn, NY 11229, 718 648-8078.

GAMBER, Mark E.; '76 BA; 655 Joy Blvd., N. Baldwin, NY 11510.

GAMBICHLER, Edward F.; '95 BA; Field Tech; Bell Atlantic; r. 116 Notus Ave., Staten Island, NY 10312, 718 948-4737. e-mail

GAMBINO, Thomas; '96; 19 Canfield Ln., Matawan, NJ 07747, 732 765-0333.

GAMBLE, Derick; '92 BS; Tchr.; Dist. 5; r. 1066 Putnam Ave., # 3l, Brooklyn, NY 11221, 718 573-3507.

GAMBRELL, Vivian R.; '85 BA; 2665 Grand Concour, Bronx, NY 10468.

GANCITANO, Victor R.; '98 BS; Law Enforcement Ofcr.; r. 2922 Ave. N, Brooklyn, NY 11210, 718 252-4521.

GANDER, Edward F.; '82 BA; Battalion Chief NYC Fire Dept; ARNYC Fire Dept., New York, NY 10001; r. HC 1 Box 75a, Swiftwater, PA 18370, 570 839-1907; *Marion;* Catherine, Karen, Thomas, Susan.

GANGOO, Andrea R.; '99 BA; Tchr. 1st Grade; Highland Elem., 193-10 Peck Ave., Queens, NY 11412, 718 357-4747; r. 90-19 88 Ave. B46, Woodhaven, NY 11421, 718 850-1778.

GANNON, James F.; '73 BA; 69-02 69 St., Glendale, NY 11385, 718 726-2848.

GANNON, John F.; '60 MPA; 4 W End Dr., Bradford, PA 16701, 814 368-6488.

GANNON, John J.; '80 BS; Maj.; USA; r. 38 Reeve Pl., Brooklyn, NY 11218, 718 871-8762.

GANNON, Thomas H.; '74 MS; Retired; r. 733 Oak Ave., River Edge, NJ 07661, 201 265-4228; *Mary Rita;* Tom, Brian, John, Mike.

GANNON, Walter E.; '76 BS; 147 Lyndale Ave., Staten Island, NY 10312.

GANPAT, Mrs. Drupatie R., (Drupatie R. Toolsee); '98 BS; Homemaker; r. 1263 Boynton Ave., Bronx, NY 10472, 718 893-8472; *Sunil;* Sanjay.

GANSROW, Ruth; '87 BS; Retired Parole Ofcr.; TX Dept. Criminal Justice, 5233 I H 37, Corpus Christi, TX 78408; r. 709 Ashland Dr., Corpus Christi, TX 78412, 361 991-7135; *Abraham (Dec.);* Julie, Kenneth, Rachel.

GANTT, Jeffrey; '94 BS; 17034 130th Ave. # 50, Jamaica, NY 11434, 718 658-2449.

GANTT, Larry; '78 BS; 2410 Frederick Douglass Blvd. Apt 1c, New York, NY 10027.

GANU, Komla S.; '89 MA; 1419 NY Ave. #5D, Brooklyn, NY 11210.

GARAVITO, George E.; '79 BS; 107-15 129th St., Richmond Hill, NY 11419.

GARAY, Edna E. '80 (See Carpenter, Ms. Edna E.).

GARAY, Tracy L.; '96 BA; MSW NYU; Full-time Student/Social Worker; NYU; r. Bronx, NY 10462, 718 829-8739. e-mail

GARBARINO, Robert L.; 165 Park Row, New York, NY 10038, 646 227-9649.

GARBER, Joseph G.; '70 BS; MPA Long Island Univ.; Assoc. Staff Analyst; Police Dept City Of New York, 1 Police Plz., New York, NY 10038, 718 625-0918; r. 121 Wilson St. Apt. 4e, Brooklyn, NY 11211, 718 782-6799.

GARBOW, Bruce; '79 BS; 1287 E 52nd St., Brooklyn, NY 11234.

GARCES, Felipe A.; '98 BA; 121 Seaman Ave. 3a, New York, NY 10034, 212 569-0251.

GARCIA, Adriana; BA; 42-25 Hampton St. 604, Elmhurst, NY 11373, 718 779-5141.

GARCIA, Aixa J.; '89 BS; Probation Ofcr.; NYC Dept. of Probation, 345 Adams St., Brooklyn, NY 11201, 718 403-4677; r. 70-11 66th Pl., Apt. 2, Flushing, NY 11385, 718 386-2396; *David Rodriguez;* David Rodriguez.

GARCIA, Alan F.; '82 MA; 1955 Benedict Ave., Bronx, NY 10462, 718 364-3532.

GARCIA, Aldo J.; '98 BA; Child Protective Spec.; ACS, 90-25 161st St., Jamaica, NY 11432, 718 262-1684; r. 102-37 44 Ave., Corona, NY 11368, 718 639-2907.

GARCIA, Anaire R.; '84 BS; 31 W Mosholu Pkwy. N Apt. 2c, Bronx, NY 10467, 718 364-3532.

GARCIA, Claire M.; '89 BS; 156 E 74th St., New York, NY 10021.

GARCIA, Daniel; '92 BA; 1745 63rd St., Brooklyn, NY 11204, 718 259-6398.

GARCIA, Daysi '90 (See Fernandez, Mrs. Daysi).

GARCIA, Deborah S.; '95 BS; 317 President St., Brooklyn, NY 11231, 718 522-2488.

GARCIA, Evelyn M.; '87 BA, '95 MPA; 102-26 86th Ave., Richmond Hill, NY 11418, 718 263-4914.

GARCIA, Fausto, Jr.; '99 BA; Police Ofcr.; NYC Police Dept. 46th Precinct, 180 & Riot, New York, NY 10004; r. New York, NY 10032, 212 795-4193.

GARCIA, Isabel M.; '76 BS; 346 Brinsmade Ave., Bronx, NY 10465, 718 378-7629.

GARCIA, Jason K.; '95 BS; Police Ofcr.; NYC Police Dept., 1 Police Plz., New York, NY 10038; r. Flushing, NY 11355, 718 358-2426.

GARCIA, Jo-Alejandra; '96 BS; Asst. Pell/Perkins Coord.; John Jay Clg., 445 W 59th St., New York, NY 10019, 212 237-8161; r. 9302 101st Ave., Ozone Park, NY 11416, 718 323-6663; *Norberto Maldonado;* Justin Blaze. e-mail

GARCIA, Julio G.; '72 MPA; 8333 Austin St. Apt. 3g, Kew Gardens, NY 11415, 718 357-0417.

GARCIA, Louis J.; '96 BA; Social Work; Highbridge Advisory Council, 880 River Ave. Box NY 10452, Bronx, NY 10452, 718 992-1321; r. 320 Brinsmade Ave., Bronx, NY 10465, 718 239-0827; *Ellen;* Ariana.

GARCIA, Luis J.; '78 BS; 195 Hart Blvd., Staten Island, NY 10301, 718 477-6920.

GARCIA, Marilyn; '99 BA; 32-71 42 St. 3A, Astoria, NY 11103, 718 478-4175.

GARCIA, Martha M.; '96 MA; Cnslt.; r. 9 Van Dyke St., Wallington, NJ 07057, 201 896-1078. e-mail

GARCIA, Michelle C., (Michelle C. Soto); '98 BA; Client Relations; Bowne of Ft. Lauderdale, 350 E. Las Olas Blvd., Ft. Lauderdale, FL 33301, 954 331-3300; r. 7370 Stirling Rd, Hollywood, FL 33024, 954 437-6696. e-mail

GARCIA, Nonato; '79 BA; POB 471, Nanuet, NY 10954.

GARCIA, Pedro C.; '87 BS; 1055 Grand Concourse, Apt. 45N, Bronx, NY 10452.

GARCIA, Publio A.; '84 AS, '85 BA; 10412 49th Ave., Flushing, NY 11368.

GARCIA, Raymond; '91 BS; 1687 Vyse Ave., Bronx, NY 10460, 718 991-7275.

GARCIA, Rosa M.; '99 BS; Probationary Police Ofcr.; NYPD; r. 115-17 Linden Blvd., S. Ozone Park, NY 11420, 718 835-4993.

GARCIA, Yesenia; '96 BA; 1510 Boston Rd., Bronx, NY 10460, 718 328-4763.

GARCIA-GUZMAN, Mrs. Elizabeth; '92 BA; Hosp. Care Investigator; Health Hosp. Corp., 545 E 142 St., Bronx, NY 10454, 718 547-4005; r. 1216 Burke Ave. #2C, Bronx, NY 10469, 718 519-6315; *George.*

GARDELLA, Mark D.; '92 BA, '92 MA; 239 147th Pl., Whitestone, NY 11357.

GARDELLA, Ronald G.; '80 BS; 133 Mason St., Staten Island, NY 10304.

GARDNER, Llewelyn; '96 MA; 1090 Lincoln Pl., Brooklyn, NY 11213, 718 363-1044.

GARDNER, Marva; '86 BS; 307 E 48th St., Brooklyn, NY 11203.

GARDNER, Michael L.; '90 BS; 24 Surrey Rd, Chester, NY 10918, 914 469-2735.

GARDNER, Virginia C.; '81 MA; 3840 Greystone Ave., Bronx, NY 10463.

GARGANO, Mark D.; '82 BS; 87-44 125 St., Richmond Hill, NY 11418, 718 894-2762.

GARGIN, John J.; '78 BA; 665 45th St., Brooklyn, NY 11220.

GARGIULO, John A.; '77 BS; 15236 13th Ave., Whitestone, NY 11357, 718 441-4787.

GARLAND, Daniella; '88 BA; Probation Ofcr.; NYC Dept. of Probation, 345 Adams St., Brooklyn, NY 11201, 718 403-4664; r. Brooklyn, NY 11233, 718 443-6215.

GARNELL, David R.; 149-46 256th St., Jamaica, NY 11422.

GARNETT, Joan M.; '98 BA; Legal Div. Mgr.; Supportkids.com, POB 49459, Austin, TX 78765; r. 6800 Mcneil Dr., Apt. 1136, Austin, TX 78729. e-mail

GARNIER, Joubert; '90 BS; Probation Ofcr.; NYC Dept. of Probation, 115 Leonard St., New York, NY 10013, 212 442-2963; r. 343 Classon Ave. #5, Brooklyn, NY 11205.

GAROFALO, Michael R.; '98 BS; 48 Windle Park F3, Tarrytown, NY 10591.

GAROFANO, Graziella D.; '99 BA; 1619 70th St., Brooklyn, NY 11204, 718 234-9339.

GARRICK, Paula A.; '84 BA; 3656 Harper Ave., Bronx, NY 10466.

GARRIDO, Francisco; '96 BA; Police Officer; r. Yonkers, NY 10704, 212 694-3010; *Liana.*

GARRIDO, Richard R.; '98 BS; Security Loss Prevention Mgr.; Sports Authority, 636 Ave. of The Americas, New York, NY 10011, 212 929-8971; r. 427 Ft. Washington, Apt. 3 A, New York, NY 10033, 212 543-9098; *Janis;* Paul. e-mail

GARRIS, Tanya J.; '89 AS; Child Care Provider; Children's Castle, 12842 Sage Ter., Germantown, MD 20874, 301 428-0906; r. same; Tiffany White.

GARRISON, Wayne W.; '84 BS; Closter Rd., Palisades, NY 10964.

GARRITY, Thomas J.; '78 BS; 53 India St., Brooklyn, NY 11222, 718 833-0681.

GARRY, Thomas N.; '95 BS; Lt.; NYPD, 1 Police Plz., New York, NY 10007; r. 22 Blossom Heath Ave., Lynbrook, NY 11563; *Elizabeth;* Kaitlyn, Thomas. e-mail

GARSIDE, James H.; '77; Retired Police; r. 8549 256th St., Floral Park, NY 11001, 718 343-7750.

GARTNER, William C.; 1035 E 32nd St., Brooklyn, NY 11210, 718 253-5747.

GARVEY, Eileen P.; '88 MA; 624 W 207 St., New York, NY 10034, 212 569-2497.

GARVEY, James T., Jr.; '74 BA HIST, '91 MPA; AS ACCTG NYC Community Clg.; Correctional Operations Consultant; r. 162-01 Powells Cove Blvd. #2D, Beechhurst, NY 11357, 718 747-0990; *Sheila.* e-mail

GARVEY, Martin V.; '91 BS; 377 Andrews Rd, E. Williston, NY 11596, 516 223-3797.

GARVEY, Michael J., Sr.; '95 BS; MS LAU; Correction Capt.; NYC Dept. of Corrections, 1111 Hazen St., E. Elmhurst, NY 11370, 718 546-4681; r. 319 Barleau St., Brentwood, NY 11717, 631 231-1209; *Yvette;* Marcus J., Denise, Michael Jr. e-mail

GARVEY, Thomas D.; '76 BS; 782 Pelham Pkwy. S # S., Bronx, NY 10462, 718 828-4673.

GARVEY, Wendy '98 (See Garvey Williams, Wendy).

GARVEY WILLIAMS, Wendy, (Wendy Garvey); '98 BA; Supv.; NYC Criminal Justice Agcy., 52 Duane St., Bronx, NY 10451, 718 681-3607; r. 39 Davenport Ave. #2B, New Rochelle, NY 10805, 914 636-1924; *Horace;* Stefanie. e-mail

GARVIN, Deborah A.; '83 AS; 135-54 234th St., Laurelton, NY 11422, 718 526-1851.

GARVIN HUNTLEY, Lynn M., PhD; '86 MA; PHD MS Syracuse Univ., BA Buffalo State Clg.; South Park Psychology; 2100 52nd Avuene, Moline, IL 61265, 309 797-2900; r. 2348 25th St., Rock Island, IL 61201, 309 786-7879.

GARY, Ms. Blanca I., (Blanca Vazquez); '84 BS; Ofc. Mgr.; Kings Cnty. Dist. Atty.; 350 J St., Brooklyn, NY 11201, 718 250-2423; r. 7 Arbor Dr., New Rochelle, NY 10804, 914 576-7193; *Ernest;* Nicholas, Nija, Nailah. e-mail

GASKIN, Bill R.; '76 BA; 1115 Thieriot Ave., Bronx, NY 10472.

GASKIN, Melissa E.; '98 BS; 877 Macy Pl. #2, Bronx, NY 10455, 718 991-4357.

GASKIN, Michelle D. '98 (See Gaaskin, Ms. Michelle D.).

GASPARINO, John J.; '89 BS; 15521 86th St., Jamaica, NY 11414, 718 848-1698.

GASSER, Rosemary; '76 BS; 1410 Wood Rd., Bronx, NY 10462.

GASTON, Arnett W.; '71 BA; MA MPH, PHD City Univ. of New York; Dept. of Criminology/Psychology; Univ of MD, Ste. 2220, Le Frak Hall, College Park, MD 20742, 301 405-4641; r. 6717 Robinia Rd, Temple Hills, MD 20748, 301 449-8286; *Sandra;* Robyn, Brett. e-mail

GASTON, Kanal V.; '98 BS; Crime Spec.; r. 74-31 85th Rd, Woodhaven, NY 11421, 718 296-2209. e-mail

GATON, Errol C.; '76; 11573 Springfield Blvd., Jamaica, NY 11411.

GAUD, Juan R.; '84 AS; 200 W 9 St., Brooklyn, NY 11231.

GAUDET, Eugene C.; '95 BS; 563 E 82nd St. # Pv, Brooklyn, NY 11236.

GAUDIOSI, Nicholas C.; '98 MS; BS Fordham Univ.; Capt.; NYC Fire Dept., 234 E 29 St., New York, NY 10016, 212 570-4216; r. 1 Maria Ln., Garden City, NY 11530, 516 877-7724. e-mail

GAUGHAN, Edward T.; '78 MPA; 23 Petry Dr., E. Hanover, NJ 07936, 973 884-4282.

GAUGHAN, John M.; '94 BS; 249 Lafayette Rd, W. Babylon, NY 11704, 631 422-1202.

GAVIRIA, Janeth M.; '95 BA; 71-11 Austin St., Forest Hills, NY 11375.

GAY, Joseph B., Jr.; '95 BS; 1541 New York Ave., Brooklyn, NY 11210, 718 421-7083.

GAYLE, Armena D.; '88 BA; POB 130173, Brooklyn, NY 11213, 718 345-4118.

GAYLE, Cathy A.; '98 BA; Home Day Care; r. 7905 Kreege Dr. Apt. #106, Adelphi, MD 20783, 301 445-1440; Latoya.

GAYLE, Janet E.; '95 BS; 1927 Loring Pl. S, Bronx, NY 10453, 718 299-7253.

GAYNOR, Rabiah M.; '93 BS; MS Long Island Univ.; Probation Ofcr.; NYC Dept. of Probation, 115 Leonard St., New York, NY 10013, 212 442-9656; r. 17012 130th Ave., Apt. 1H, Jamaica, NY 11434, 718 276-0470. e-mail

GAZZOLA, Anthony J.; '74 BS; 16 Lacy Ct., Blue Point, NY 11715, 631 363-8324.

GE, Sylvester Y.; '99 BS; Police Ofcr.; NYPD, 4 Auburn Pl., Brooklyn, NY 11205, 718 222-2903; r. 95-12 89th St., Ozone Park, NY 11417, 718 476-3372; *Lan Chem;* Alexandra. e-mail

GEAGAN, Patrick C.; '97 BS; 183 W. 238th St., Bronx, NY 10463, 718 549-8346.

GEARY, Howard C.; '76 BA; 47-30 59th St., Woodside, NY 11377, 718 465-6821.

GEARY, John; 14 Hy Pl., Lake Grove, NY 11755.

GECEWICZ, Edward T.; '78 BS; 3 Sheila Dr., Syosset, NY 11791.

GEDDES, Melanie D.; '97 BA; 106-22 98th St., Ozone Park, NY 11417, 718 445-5575.

GEDEON, Elda; '96 BS; 700 Ocean Ave., Brooklyn, NY 11226, 718 638-1767.

GEE, Anthony D.; '99 BA; 20 Swisstone St., Medford, NY 11763, 631 447-2368.

GEE, Leslie; '82 BS; Special Agt.; Bur. of Alcohol Tobacco Firearms, 6 World Trade Ctr., New York, NY 10048, 212 264-1057; r. 1731 Belmont Ave., New Hyde Park, NY 11040, 516 775-6559; *Sham;* Leslie Jr.

GEE, Peter; '89 BS; Immigration Svcs.; Dept. of Justice; r. 4124 Elbertson St., Flushing, NY 11373, 718 779-5950.

GEIL, Terrence G.; '74 MA; 56 Vernon Pl., Mt. Vernon, NY 10552.

GEIST, Mitchell; '91 BS; Police Ofcr.; NYC Police Dept., 1 Police Plz., New York, NY 10038, 718 653-7149; r. 15 Mckinley St., Massapequa Park, NY 11762, 516 541-0283.

GELAJ, Maria; '77 BS; 38 E 208 St., Bronx, NY 10467, 718 547-9385.

GELB, Nelya; '99 BS; 3901 Nostrand Ave. 5p, Brooklyn, NY 11235, 718 384-6227.

GELFAND, Jeremy; '91 BS; 220 Mcnair Rd, # 803, Ft. Myer, VA 22211.

GELFMAN, George; '75 MA; 409 Leverett Ave., Staten Island, NY 10308.

GELINA, Jeffery A.; '92 BS; 5992 E Townline Rd, Williamson, NY 14589, 315 589-9017.

GELLARD, Douglas; '95 BA; 35-05 87th St., Jackson Hts., NY 11372.

GELLER, Patricia A., EdD; '80 MA; BA Bowdoin Clg., EDD Harvard Univ.; Psychologist; 76 Bedford St. #25, Lexington, MA 02420, 781 863-2434; r. 19 Irving Park, Watertown, MA 02472, 617 926-0607; *Geoffrey Packard.* e-mail

GELLMAN, Harold; '74 MPA; 1370 E 103rd St., Brooklyn, NY 11236.

GELMAN, Jennifer M.; '99 MA; 2050 E. 73rd St., Brooklyn, NY 11234, 718 763-4131.

GELY, Timothy N.; '99; 2140 Cruger Ave., Bronx, NY 10462, 718 863-5057.

GENDELL, Alexis L.; '97 MA; BA Lehigh Univ., Univ. of Hartford; Doctoral Candidate-Clinical Psych; Univ. of Hartford; r. 79-25 150th St., Flushing, NY 11367, 718 969-7629. e-mail

GENIA, James H.; '96 BS; 5239 79th St., Flushing, NY 11373, 718 335-1533.

GENOVA, Alfred F.; '80 BS; 6324 77th Pl., Flushing, NY 11379, 718 268-6279.

GENOVA, Chris A.; '97 BS; 351 W. 42nd St., New York, NY 10036.

GENOVESE, Alexander V.; '95 BA; Police Ofcr.; US Mint Police, Washington, DC 20220, 202 354-7332; r. 4017 Night Heron Ct. Apt. G, Waldorf, MD 20603, 301 932-7391.

GENOVESE, Dominic A.; '88 BA; MS Central Michigan Univ.; Lt.; FDNY, 9 Metrotech Ctr., Brooklyn, NY 11201, 718 965-8330; r. 18 Richmond Ct., Staten Island, NY 10303, 917 629-2194.

GENTIL, Mark; '87 BS; 144 Saville Rd, Mineola, NY 11501, 516 746-2708.

GENTILE, Anthony L.; '78 BS; 1820 79 St., Brooklyn, NY 11214, 718 763-4580.

GENTILE, Dominic A.; '99 BA; Capt.; NYC Police Dept.; *April;* Ashley, Ki. e-mail

GENTILE, Janene M.; '93 BA, '96 MA; 101 Pacific St., Franklin Sq., NY 11010.

GENTILE, John R.; '80 BS; POB 140459, Staten Island, NY 10314, 718 979-5115.

GENTLES, Andrea V.; '94 BS; 11242 207th St., Queens Vlg., NY 11429, 718 776-2704.

GEOGHAN, Dennis P.; '77 BS; 43-12 161 St., Flushing, NY 11358.

GEORGE, Ms. Camille A.; '99 BA; Case Aide; Bronx Dist. Atty's. Ofc., 198 E. 161st St., Bronx, NY 10451, 718 590-2718; r. 32-54 48th St. #2L, Astoria, NY 11103, 718 726-0797. e-mail

GEORGE, Deborah '83 (See West, Deborah).

GEORGE, Dick; '92 BS; 290 Putnam Ave. # 2, Brooklyn, NY 11216, 718 421-7095.

GEORGE, Farid H.; '86 BA; 50 Monument Walk, Brooklyn, NY 11205, 718 339-1480.

GEORGE, Hector A.; '86 BA; MS City Clg; 5th Grade Tchr.; r. 2224 Amsterdam Ave., New York, NY 10032, 212 781-0682.

GEORGE, Lennox; '96 BS; 928 E 58th St., Brooklyn, NY 11234, 718 339-1480.

GEORGE, Loise L., (Loise L. Williams); '75 BS; MPS NY Theological Sem., MDIV Drew Univ.; Retired, Clergy; r. Brooks-Howell Home, Asheville, NC 28801, 828 252-7644; *James, Gregory.* e-mail

GEORGE, Patrick F.; '85 BS; 56 W 119th St. # 60, New York, NY 10026, 212 348-4465.

GEORGE, Sharon J.; '99 BS; Acctg. Rep.; Lincoln Hosp., 149th & Morris, Bronx, NY 10469, 718 579-5949; r. 939 E. 219th, Bronx, NY 10469, 718 405-1241. e-mail

GEORGE, Steven N.; '81 BA; 197 Carlton Ave., Brooklyn, NY 11205.

GEORGES, Marcelle M.; '92 BA; 401 E 26th St., Brooklyn, NY 11226.

GEORGOPOULOS, Antoni; '97 BA; 31 Highland Ct., Huntington, NY 11743, 631 271-7791.

GERA, Mary E.; '86 BA; 436 E 66th St. Apt. 3w, New York, NY 10021.

GERACI, Anthony W.; '99 BS; Police Ofcr.; NYC Police Dept., Mid-Town N. Precinct; r. 95 Sherman Ave., Staten Island, NY 10301, 718 727-0752. e-mail

GERAGHTY, Christopher; '83 BS; 85-03 60th Rd., Elmhurst, NY 11373.

GERAGHTY, John F.; 3160 Kennedy Blvd., Jersey City, NJ 07306.

GERALD, Ira; '95 BA, '96 MPA; MSED C.W. Post; 6th Grade Tchr.; Graham Elem., Mt. Vernon, NY 10551, 914 665-5080; r. 209 Beechwood Ave., Roosevelt, NY 11575, 516 867-5116.

GERBUSH, Monty H.; 1 Canterbury Rd, Glen Head, NY 11545.

GERCHAK, Ralph E.; '81 MPA; 92-64 216th St., Queens Vlg., NY 11428.

GERDES, Jeffrey J.; '99 BA; 388 Guyon Ave., Staten Island, NY 10306, 718 980-3008.

GERHOLD, Lawrence R.; '75 MA; 185 Austin Ave., Tappan, NY 10983.

GERITANO, Lenore; '94 BA, '96 MA; 166 Getz Ave., Staten Island, NY 10312, 718 356-4981.

GERMANO, Erasmo A.; '72 BS; POB 413, East Hampton, NY 11937.

GERMOSEN, Otto; '95 BA; 332 127th St., College Pt., NY 11356.

GEROVICH, Yevgeny; '99 BA; 1811 Burnett St., Brooklyn, NY 11229, 718 336-6346.

GERRICK, Theckla R.; '99 BA; 933 Winthrop St., Brooklyn, NY 11203, 718 735-5159.

GERRISH, John P.; '77 BS; 1627 Yates Ave., Bronx, NY 10461, 718 892-2621.

GERSBECK, Joseph T.; '76 BS; 1521 E 34 St., Brooklyn, NY 11234.

GERSTHEIMER, Pamela; '95, '95 MPA; BE Albany State Univ.; 26 Milval Ln., Highland Mills, NY 10930. e-mail

GERVASIO, Louis A.; '76 AS; DIPLOMA NYS Police Sch.; Semi-Retired-Security Cnslt.; Effective Security; r. 12 Chanticleer Ct., Huntington, NY 11743, 631 692-5833. e-mail

GESCHWINDER, Janine, (Janine Vendetto); '94 BA; MS Adelphi Univ.; Personal Trainer; Sportset, 40 Maple Ave., Rockville Centre, NY 11570, 516 536-8700; r. 1598 Westervelt Ave., N. Baldwin, NY 11510, 516 379-2539; *Scott.* e-mail

GESTRING, Brian J.; '94 MS; 27 Hoffman St., Maplewood, NJ 07040.

GESTRING, Craig R.; '96; 27 Hoffman St., Maplewood, NJ 07040, 973 763-0073.

GESUALDI, Frank J.; '95 BS; Police Ofcr.; NYPD, 1 Police Plz., New York, NY 10038, 212 374-5000; r. 230 Frost St. #2f, Brooklyn, NY 11211, 718 389-8875.

GETTIS, Deanne R.; '97 MA; Family Therapist; Ocean Mental Health Svcs. Inc.; 122 Lien St., Toms River, NJ 08753, 732 349-3535; r. 532 San Juan, Toms River, NJ 08753, 732 831-1506.

GHALY, Ayman N.; '93 AS, '94 BS; Investigator; US Dept. of Agriculture; r. 156-15 86th St., Howard Bch., NY 11414, 718 738-1297. e-mail

GHERMEZIAN, Lily; '84 BA; 19 Cedar Ridge Ln., Dix Hills, NY 11746, 631 493-0384.

GHETA, Barbara A.; '91 BA, '93 MA; 4016 S Berkeley Lake Rd NW, Duluth, GA 30096.

GHOLSON, Leigh L.; '92 BS; Security Ofcr.; NYS Mental Health; r. 420 E 111 St., New York, NY 10029, 212 860-3277; *Shelia; Avan.* e-mail

GH'RAEL, Kelly M.; '97 BS; Real Estate Paralegal; Commonwealth Land Title Ins. Co., 212 949-0100; r. 520 E. 20th St., New York, NY 10009, 212 254-9629; *Ahmad; Ahmad Jr, Nahl.* e-mail

GIACCIO, William G.; '87 BS; 13-04 Malba Dr., Whitestone, NY 11357.

GIACOBBE, Joseph A.; '78 MPA; 142-13 37th Ave. #1, Flushing, NY 11354.

GIACOBBE, Nicholas; '86 BS; 144 Trenchard St., Yonkers, NY 10704.

GIACONELLI, Louis C.; '97 BA; 420 E. 85 St., New York, NY 10028, 212 988-6719.

GIAIMO, David J.; 5836 Golden Egale Cir., Palm Bch. Gardens, FL 33418.

GIALOBELLO, Michael; '96 BS; 23 Hewitt Ave., Hicksville, NY 11801, 516 932-9480.

GIAMBALVO, Deborah; '92 BS; 8343 255th St. # P, Glen Oaks, NY 11004, 718 426-4253.

GIAMBRONE, Alphonse; '90 BS; 1094 Rensselaer Ave., Staten Island, NY 10309.

GIAMBRONE, John J.; '81 BS; 4 Sprague St., N. Baldwin, NY 11510, 516 546-6692.

GIAMMALVO, Gregory V.; 416 Dover Rd, Wilmington, NC 28409, 910 792-1318.

GIAMMARINARO, Andrea; '83 MA; 135-34 82 Ave., Kew Gardens, NY 11435.

GIAMMARINO, Michael; '68 BS; 699 Fingerboard Rd, Staten Island, NY 10305, 718 448-7484.

GIANFRANCESCO, Paul; '89 BS; JD Dist. of Columbia Law Sch; Asst. City Solicitor; Law Dept. City of Philadelphia, 1515 Arch St. 16th Fl., One Pkwy., Philadelphia, PA 19102, 215 683-5144; r. 6440 Guyer Ave., Philadelphia, PA 19142, 215 724-0850. e-mail

GIANGERUSO, Carmine, CFPS; '97 BA; AS Brookdale Comm Clg.; Inspector,Fire Safety; NJ Dept. of Community Affairs, Division of Fire Safety, 101 S Broad St., Cn 809, Trenton, NJ 08625, 609 633-6132; r. 441 Riverside Ave., Lyndhurst, NJ 07071, 201 531-5929. e-mail

GIANGRASSO, F.; '91 BS; 113 Elmcrest Dr., Fishkill, NY 12524, 914 896-0823.

GIANNOUTSOS, K.; '93 BA; 36-07 20th Rd., Long Island City, NY 11105.

GIANNUZZI, Thomas A.; '78 BS; 1645 70th St., Brooklyn, NY 11204, 718 259-8368.

GIANTELLI, Patricia; '94 BS; 125 Chester St., Mt. Vernon, NY 10552, 914 667-4124.

GIANUSSO, BethanyAnne, (BethanyAnne Wilber); '99 BA; Rape Crisis Caseworker; Bellevue Hosp. Ctr., 462 1st Ave., Rm. 408 C&D Bldg., New York, NY 10016, 212 562-8280; r. 69-11 Yellowstone Blvd., Apt. A4, Forest Hills, NY 11375, 718 520-9900; *Peter.* e-mail

GIARDINA, Philip; PL; NYCPD, 1 Police Plz., New York, NY 10038; r. 241 E Euclid St., Valley Stream, NY 11580, 516 825-5620; *Kathleen.*

GIBBONS, Adam C.; '98 MA; BA Marist Clg.; Fraud Mgr.; Nextlink Communications, 45 Eisenhower Dr., Paramus, NJ 07652, 201 226-4773; r. 170 Myrtle Ave., Apt. A1, Ft. Lee, NJ 07024; *Kristen.* e-mail

GIBBONS, John M.; '74 BA; Retired; r. 20 Prices Ln., Staten Island, NY 10314, 718 761-1629. e-mail

GIBBONS, John W.; '76 BS; 618 Rapid Falls Dr., Brandon, FL 33511, 813 654-8137.

GIBBONS, Nicole S.; '96 BA; 190 York St. #5, Brooklyn, NY 11201, 718 622-7170.

GIBBONS, Oswald; 1010 Cottage Oak L, Houston, TX 77091, 281 265-1495.

GIBBONS, Thomas E.; '96 BA; New Tork State Trooper; NYS Police, 1014 Bruenig Rd, New Windsor, NY 12553, 914 567-1033; r. 45 Scott Dr., Wappingers Falls, NY 12590, 914 297-0309. e-mail

GIBBS, Eugene; '95 AS; Pres.; Eagle Protective & Investig Svcs. Inc., 749 St. Nicholas Ave., New York, NY 10031, 212 491-3900; r. POB 108, Bronx, NY 10453, 212 491-3900; *Latoya, Eugene Jr, Daniel.* e-mail

GIBBS, Faye V.; '82 BS; 582 E 51st St., Brooklyn, NY 11203, 718 443-6086.

GIBBS, Gail M.; '85 BA; Sr. Court Clerk; NYS Family Court, 283 Adams St., Brooklyn, NY 11201, 718 643-5291; r. 1305 Delmar Loop, Brooklyn, NY 11239, 718 272-6470; *Ronald Jones;* Tiffany Jones, Nya D. Jones.

GIBBS, James H.; '77 BS; RR 1 Box 1034, Dingmans Ferry, PA 18328.

GIBBS, Michael J.; '97 BA; 66-22 53rd Ave., Maspeth, NY 11378, 718 217-4584.

GIBBS, Nyhisha T., (Nyhisha T. Meaders); '95 MPA; Homemaker; r. 3 Mews Alley, Poughkeepsie, NY 12603, 914 452-3324; *Robert; Devin.*

GIBBS, Satisha E.; '99 BA; Case Mgr.; Special Narcotics; Dist. Attorney's Ofc., 80 Center St., New York, NY 10013, 212 815-0494; r. 1185 Carroll St. #5L, Brooklyn, NY 11225, 718 773-4914. e-mail

GIBLIN, John F.; '85 MPA, '85 BA; JD Brooklyn Law Sch.; Atty. Gen. Practice Law; John F. Giblin, Atty-at-Law, 11 Waldron Dr., Stony Point, NY 10980, 914 942-0771; r. same; *Marie;* Carmel, Caroline RN, Dierdre, Tara. e-mail

GIBSON, Sherry A.; '92 MPA; BA Hunter Clg.; CUNY Administrative Asst.; John Jay Clg. of Criminal Justice, 445 W. 59 St., New York, NY 10019, 212 237-8435. e-mail

GIDDINGS, Curtis G., Jr.; '96 BS; Corrections Ofcr.; Westchester Cnty., POB 389, Valhalla, NY 10595, 914 347-6026; r. 5 Franklin Ave., White Plains, NY 10601. e-mail

GIDDINGS, Robert J.; '73 BS; Retired Fireman; r. 70 Mud Pond Rd., Highland Lake, NY 12743, 914 557-3346; *Anita;* Robert, Andrew, Lisa.

GIDLOW, Brooke E.; '96 MA; 4733 S Elizabeth Ct., Englewood, CO 80110.

GIERER, George W.; 266 E. 236th St., Bronx, NY 10470, 718 994-8312.

GIESINGER, Marie A.; '86 BS; MS Long Island Univ.; Operations Sergeant; USA, 452Nd Cbt Spt Hosp., 4828 W. Silver Spring Dr., Milwaukee, WI 53218, 414 438-6200; r. 1721 Ryan Dr., Bismarck, ND 58501, 701 223-6931. e-mail

GIFFORD, Kompel; '98 BS; Customs Inspector; JFK Airport, Jamaica, NY 11430, 718 553-1648; r. 35 Clinton Pl., Apt. 5 H, New Rochelle, NY 10801, 914 633-0044; *Michael.*

GIGLIO, Charles J.; '78 BS; 145-36 232 St., Springfield Gardens, NY 11413, 516 488-6948.

GILBERT, Kenroy B.; '95 BS; 68 Granite St., Brooklyn, NY 11207, 718 455-6072.

GILBERT, Miguelina; '95 MA; 13729 68th Dr., Flushing, NY 11367, 718 323-9583.

GILCHRIST, Beverly R.; '98 MA; 570 Isham St. 1b, New York, NY 10034, 212 942-4097.

GILCHRIST, J.; '93 BA; 107-129 E. 126th, New York, NY 10035.

GILCHRIST, John T.; '80 BA; 2331 Cambridge St., E. Meadow, NY 11554, 516 794-5319.

GILDEA, Edward J.; '76 BS; 3149 Perry Ave., Bronx, NY 10467, 718 798-5634.

GILDEA, Michael O.; '75 BS; 431 E 5th St., Brooklyn, NY 11218, 718 389-5306.

GILER, Lorena K.; '97 BA MA; Mgr.; Bell Atlantic, Jamaica, NY 11432, 718 890-0775; r. 76-26 113th St., Apt. 6A, Forest Hills, NY 11375, 718 261-8820. e-mail

GILFORD, Valerie J.; '86 BA; 1470 Parkchester Rd., Bronx, NY 10462.

GILL, Adonica S.; '89 MPA; 600 Baychester Ave. Apt. 19a, Bronx, NY 10475.

GILL, Alyson J.; '86 BA; 230 Atlantic Ave. Apt. C2, Lynbrook, NY 11563, 516 599-3305.

GILL, Arleen A.; '90 BS; 600 E 18th St., Apt. 3C, Brooklyn, NY 11226, 718 604-4772.

GILL, Brian P.; '97 BA; 78-35 67th Dr., Middle Vlg., NY 11379, 718 726-8316.

GILL, Cody; '96 BS; 6495 Broadway, Apt. 6M, Bronx, NY 10471, 718 653-1370.

GILL, LeRoi L.; '81 BS; JD Rutgers Sch. of Law; Atty.; Central Brooklyn Churches, 140 Devoe St., Brooklyn, NY 11211, 718 302-9840; r. 280 Lefferts Ave., Brooklyn, NY 11225, 718 462-0427; *Robin;* Brooke, Ayanna, Brittany. e-mail

GILL, Michelle R.; '95 BS; 1304 New York Ave., Brooklyn, NY 11203, 718 953-6382.

GILL, William B.; '80 BA; 185 Barclay Ave., Staten Island, NY 10312.

GILLEN, Brian J.; '76 BA; 24 Crystal Farm Rd., Warwick, NY 10990, 914 986-7218; *Mary Pat;* Brian, Sean, Shannon, Brendan, Timothy.

GILLEN, Michael J.; '81 BS; 182 Beach 118th St., Far Rockaway, NY 11694, 718 846-7264.

GILLER, Randi L.; '98 MA; BA Binghamton Univ.; Homemaker; r. 212-66 16th Ave., Bayside, NY 11360, 718 279-2919; *Lee;* Jacob. e-mail

GILLESPIE, Bernard M.; '70 BS; Capt. of Police; NYCPD, Detective Borough Queens, 68-40 Austin St., Forest Hills, NY 11375, 718 520-9200; r. 166 Ann St. Apt. F, Valley Stream, NY 11580, 516 932-9455; *Margaret.*

GILLIANS, Detra S.; '98 BS; 1081 Sheridan Ave., Bronx, NY 10456, 718 538-6448.

GILLIGAN, Joseph P.; '97 BA; 2024 126th St., Flushing, NY 11356, 718 463-3422.

GILLIS, James R.; '81 AS; 3 Aster Ln., Levittown, NY 11756, 516 731-1489.

GILLIS, Michael H.; '96 CERT, '96 AS; 202 York St. # 2, Brooklyn, NY 11201, 718 858-1038.

GILLOOLY, Margaret; '79 MPA; 21540 47th Ave., Flushing, NY 11361.

GILMARTIN, James J.; '77 MPA; 169 S Montclair Ave., Glen Ellyn, IL 60137.

GILMARTIN, John F.; '76 BA; 66 Sylvia Dr., W. Islip, NY 11795.

GILMARTIN, Kerri A.; '81 BS; 36 Aberdeen Rd, Smithtown, NY 11787.

GILMARTIN, Peter J.; 113 Howton Ave., Staten Island, NY 10308, 718 356-1377.

GILMORE, Robert; '95 BS; JD Touro Law Ctr.; 137 Meagher Ave. Private House, Bronx, NY 10465, 718 597-0621. e-mail

GILMORE, Robert W.; '77 BS; 131-35 228 St., Laurelton, NY 11413.

GILROY, Terence J.; '78 MPA; 2 Maiden Ln., New City, NY 10956, 914 634-6281.

GIMLETT, Brian F.; '75 BS; 124 Wynleigh Dr. E, Greenville, DE 19807.

GIMLETT, Kevin L.; '77 MA; 2035 W. 4th St., Brooklyn, NY 11223.

GIMLETT, Linda; '77 MA; 124 Wynleigh Dr. E, Greenville, DE 19807.

GINEL, Julio A.; '97 BA; Substance Abuse Couns; NARCO Freedom Inc, 250 Grand Concourse, Bronx, NY 10451, 718 292-4455; r. 178-10 Wexford Tce, Jamaica, NY 11432, 718 658-6880. e-mail

GIONE, Gary J.; '79 BS; Lt NYPD; NYPD; r. 3524 Frost Rd, Shrub Oak, NY 10588.

GIORDANI, Anthony G.; '85 BS; 8214 60th Rd, Flushing, NY 11373, 718 528-8455.

GIORDANO, Bryan P.; '98 BA; Police Ofcr.; NYC Police Dept., New York, NY 10017, 212 826-3211; r. 103 Woodlawn Ave., Deer Park, NY 11729, 631 586-0599.

GIORDANO, Jack J.; '79 BS; 643 Edgegrove Ave., Staten Island, NY 10312, 718 351-3310.

GIORDANO, Melissa A. '98 (See Giordano-Valentin, Melissa A.).

GIORDANO, Susan E.; '80 BA; 162-03 91 St., Howard Bch., NY 11414, 718 848-5564.

GIORDANO-VALENTIN, Melissa A., (Melissa A. Giordano); '98 BS; Confidential Investigator; Dept. of Investigations, New York, NY 10007; r. 53 Crane Rd, Middletown, NY 10941; *Conrad Valentin.*

GIOVINAZZO, Alise; '93 BS; 223 Hawthorne Ave., Staten Island, NY 10314.

GIRACE, Paul A.; 548 Drew St., Brooklyn, NY 11208.

GIRARDI, James J.; '81 BS; Restaurant Mgr.; Marisa Restaurant, Port Chester, NY 10573, 914 937-6665; r. 17 Weber Dr., Port Chester, NY 10573, 914 939-7061.

GIRAULT, Marie; '89 BS; 55 Tiemann Pl., New York, NY 10027, 212 663-5104.

GIRFIN, Scott; 12614 Beach Ave., Beach Haven, NJ 08008.

GIRIMONTE, Albert (Al) W.; '81 BS; CERT. Columbia Univ Police Inst; Deputy Inspector; NYPD, 1 Police Plz., New York, NY 10038, 718 520-9200; r. 1647 Putney Rd, Valley Stream, NY 11580, 516 872-4041; *Barbara;* Joseph, Albert, Mary. e-mail

GIROLAMO, Anthony; '75 MA; 30 Walker St., Otisville, NY 10963.

GIRON, Juan C.; '95 BS; 3335 76th St., Jackson Hts., NY 11372, 718 478-9033.

GIRSHICK, Jenny Y.; '97 BS; 2074 E.22 St., Brooklyn, NY 11229, 718 375-6466.

GISCOME, Mario; '89 BS; 139-20 225 St., Laurelton, NY 11413.

GISORS, Roselyne; '87 MA; 55 63rd St., # 57, W. New York, NJ 07093.

GISSES, Jennie S.; '47 Plaza St. W, Brooklyn, NY 11217, 718 857-1646.

GITTENS, Constantino; '91 BS, '97 MPA; 1405 E. 55th St., Brooklyn, NY 11234.

GITTER, Elisabeth; 90 Riverside Dr. Apt. 14b, New York, NY 10024.

GIULIANO, Diane L. '99 (See Matuszak, Diane L.).

GIUSTRA, Robert; '86 BA; MSW NYU; Child Welfare Spec. Supv.; Admin. for Children's Svcs., 150 William St., 15th Fl., New York, NY 10038, 212 341-2800; r. 1705 60th St., Brooklyn, NY 11204, 718 238-4208.

GIUSTRA, Salvator; '84 BA; 1705 60th St., Brooklyn, NY 11204, 718 256-3438.

GIVENS, Tameika; '98 BA; 350 Est 143rd St. #13A, Bronx, NY 10454, 718 665-8808. e-mail

GIVES, Tillman W.; '78 MPA; 19 W. 127th St., New York, NY 10027, 212 860-4536.

GJELAJ, Mark; '99 MA; 824 Waring Ave., Bronx, NY 10467, 718 231-2786.

GLADSTON, Lewis F.; '83 BS; 41-21 39th Pl., Long Island City, NY 11104, 718 631-0741.

GLANSTEIN, Janelle M.; '98 BS; AA SCCC; Police Ofcr.; PSA 4 Manhattan; r. 1432 E. 10th St., Brooklyn, NY 11230, 718 375-1787. e-mail

GLASSER, Michael A.; '78 BS; 5316 214th St., Flushing, NY 11364.

GLAVEY, Edward; '91 BA; 65 Jefferson Pl., Massapequa, NY 11758.

GLAWSON, Lillian F.; '98 BA; 1260 Webster Ave. 14f, Bronx, NY 10456, 718 293-1598.

GLAZER, Sheindel; '95 AS; 2762 Barnes Ave., Bronx, NY 10467, 718 654-7078.

GLAZER, Stanley L.; 70-25 Yellowstone, Forest Hills, NY 11375.

GLEASON, Richard J.; '79 MPA; Rd#1, 28 Farview R, Carmel, NY 10512.

GLEBERMAN, Fredric P.; '78 BA; 147-49 72 Ave., Flushing, NY 11367.

GLEMAUD, Stanley; '98 BA; MPA; Admissions Couns.; F.E.G.S., 199 J St., Brooklyn, NY 11201, 718 488-0100; r. 428 Midwood St., Brooklyn, NY 11225, 718 953-1576; *Karlene;* Kayla. e-mail

GLENN, Dwight; '86 BS; 146-46 221 St., Jamaica, NY 11413, 718 341-0759.

GLENN, Gary F.; '76 BA; 144-41 25th Rd., Flushing, NY 11354, 718 341-0759.

GLENN, Tyra T.; '99; 75 Pilling St., Brooklyn, NY 11207.

GLENN, William; '97 BS; 172-10 133rd Ave., Jamaica, NY 11434, 718 341-0759.

GLIDDEN, Ariana M.; '93 BS; 228 Merrymount St., Staten Island, NY 10314, 718 698-0290.

GLOSSON, Muriel C.; '78 MA; 100 Erskine Pl. # 9, Bronx, NY 10475.

GLOVER, Alicia F.; '92 BA; 20-35M W Mosholu P, Bronx, NY 10468, 718 364-6059.

GLOVER, Elliott P.; '81 AS; 9308 Steve St., Manassas, VA 20111, 703 361-5835. e-mail

GLOVER, Trevor R.; '94 BS; 634 Hegeman Ave., Brooklyn, NY 11207, 718 272-9858.

GLUCK, Geri H.; '93 BS; 1063 Cedarhurst St., Valley Stream, NY 11581, 516 791-3890.

GLYNN, James J.; '68 BS; 447 M.I. Yaphank Rd, Yaphank, NY 11980.

GLYNN, James M.; '86 BA; JD Pace Univ. Sch. of Law; Atty.; James M. Glynn Esq.; r. 1845 Hunt Ave. Apt. 2, Bronx, NY 10462, 718 792-6773.

GLYNN, Keith A.; '93 BS; 25 Vogel Loop, Staten Island, NY 10314.

GLYNN, Martin P.; '77 BS; 55 Walter Dr., Stony Point, NY 10980, 914 429-5652.

GLYNN, Michael P.; '77 MA; 81 W. 6 St., Deer Park, NY 11729.

GLYNN, Thomas J.; BA; 7321 Little Neck Pkwy., Glen Oaks, NY 11004, 718 347-5727.

GNITECKI, Marcin; '99 BA; 80-08 Austin St. #3C, Kew Gardens, NY 11415, 718 275-4730.

GO, Jamelyn; '96 BA; Admin.; Pantina Cosmetics Inc., 30 Henry St., Teterboro, NJ 07608; r. 230 Columbus Ave., Palisades Park, NJ 07650, 201 592-0156; *Michael Wang.* e-mail

GODBY, Natasha L.; '97 BS; 223 Lenox Ave. #E, Brooklyn, NY 11226.

GODDARD, Alson D.; '95 BS; Supervising Investigator; NYC HRA Ofc. of Revenue & Investigations, 1951 Park Ave. 3rd Fl., New York, NY 10037, 212 690-9804; *Sonia;* Alison. e-mail

GODDARD, Mayfield '92 (See Goddard-Adetimirin, Mayfield).

GODDARD-ADETIMIRIN, Mayfield, (Mayfield Goddard); '92 BS; Assoc. Fraud Investigator; H.R.A., 30 Main St., Brooklyn, NY 11201; r. 100 Wyona St., Brooklyn, NY 11207, 718 235-2735; *Michael;* Michael Jr, Justin, Matthew. e-mail

GODFREY, David L.; '99 BS; 232 W 139th St., New York, NY 10030.

GODI, Mihai; '95 BS; 61-09 Gates Ave. 2nd. Fl., Ridgewood, NY 11385, 718 441-8052.

GODINO, Joseph; '79 BS; AS FBI; NYPD; r. 99-04 157 Ave., Howard Bch., NY 11414.

GOETZ, John F.; '75 MA, '95 MS; POB 286, Morrisville, PA 19067.

GOFF, Richard; '74 BS; 3875 Telegraph Rd # 335, Ventura, CA 93003, 805 497-4248.

GOICO, Noemi; '92 BS, '97 MPA; 568 W 192nd St. # 4, New York, NY 10040.

GOICOCHEA-BONILLA, S.; '88 BS; 434 E. 105 St., New York, NY 10029.

GOINGS, Alvin; '79 BA; Goings Cnsltg.; r. 970 Tinton Ave., Bronx, NY 10456.

GOLASZEWSKI, Henry; '90 BS; 16 Elm St., Lynbrook, NY 11563, 516 593-6569.

GOLD, Stanley A.; '96 MPA; BS USCG Acad.; Intelligence Analyst; USCG Atlantic Area-Govt., 431 Crawford St., Portsmouth, VA 23704, 757 398-6408; r. 3412 Coleshill Ln., Chesapeake, VA 23321, 757 686-2443; *Julia Halpern-Gold;* Chelsea. e-mail

GOLDBACH, George A.; '78 BS; 26923 Mesa Dr., Evergreen, CO 80439, 303 674-2875.

GOLDBERG, Abigail S.; '93 MA; 215 E 68th St. Apt. 29i, New York, NY 10021.

GOLDBERG, Daniel J.; '97 BA; Investigation Analyst; New York Stock Exch., New York, NY 10048, 212 656-2697; r. 1822 80th St., # 2, Brooklyn, NY 11214, 718 621-9447.

GOLDBERG, Delia W.; '99 BA MA; AS West Chester Busines Inst; Homemaker; r. 1388 E. 14th St., Brooklyn, NY 11230, 718 336-8690; *Mark;* Michal. e-mail

GOLDBERG, Mrs. Denise M., (Denise M. Boselli); '91 BA; MSW Adelphi Univ.; Social Worker; 155-55 Crossbay Blvd., Howard Bch., NY 11414, 718 641-8882; r. 10-34 166th St., Apt. 7A, Whitestone, NY 11357; *Michael;* Amanda.

GOLDBERG, Laurence S.; 13033 130th St., Jamaica, NY 11420, 718 478-7504.

GOLDBERG, Sheri; '99 MA; 2731 Ocean Club Blvd., Apt. 202, Hollywood, FL 33019, 954 924-4569.

GOLDEN, John P.; '99 BS; Detective, Master Cand. Protect Mgm; NYPD, One Police Plz., New York, NY 10038; r. 625 E. 14th St. #4C, New York, NY 10009, 212 979-2392; *Vivian Mateo.*

GOLDFARB, Matthew S.; '98 BA; Police Ofcr.; NYC Police Dept.; r. 157 Leber Rd, Blauvelt, NY 10913, 914 359-5088. e-mail

GOLDFINGER, Mary Ann; '80 BS; Customer Svc. Supv./Retired Mgr.; US Postal Svc., Bell Atlantic; r. 1235 Russell St., Elmont, NY 11003, 516 354-0153.

GOLDING, William D.; '78 BA; 65-19-166 St., Flushing, NY 11365, 718 527-2558.

GOLDMAN, Howard F.; '95 BS; Commack, NY 11725.

GOLDMAN, Robert M.; '95 MA; Probation Ofcr.; NYC Dept. of Probation, 162-24 Jamaica Ave., Jamaica, NY 11432, 718 657-6832; r. 8675 Midland Pkwy. #6P, Jamaica, NY 11432, 718 206-9106.

GOLDMAN, Stanley; '82 BS; 801 Mervin Ct., Baldwin, NY 11510, 516 627-8584.

GOLDRICK, Thomas J.; '78 MA; 41 Moehring Dr., Blauvelt, NY 10913, 914 359-0996.

GOLDSMITH, Andrea M.; '93 MPA; 21 Guymard Tpk., Middletown, NY 10940, 914 386-2579.

GOLDSMITH, Michelle; '95 MA; 4075 Monticello Ave., Bronx, NY 10466, 718 324-4341.

GOLDSON, Kenneth A.; '87 BA; 7337 Little Neck Pkwy., Glen Oaks, NY 11004.

GOLDSTEIN, Alan M., PhD; PHD Fordham Univ.; Prof. Emeritus, Adjunct Prof. Psych; John Jay Clg of Criminal Justice, 13 Arden Dr., Hartsdale, NY 10530, 914 693-7760; r. same.

GOLDSTEIN, Arthur; '74 BA; 355 S End Ave. Apt. 8j, New York, NY 10280.

GOLDSTEIN, Bruce; '78 BS; 2115 Westminster B, Parlin, NJ 08859.

GOLDSTEIN, Burton S.; '75 MA; 3398 Bedford Ave., Brooklyn, NY 11210, 718 951-6847.

GOLDSTEIN, Howard; '97 BS; 212 E.Broadway #6, New York, NY 10002, 212 777-2081.

GOLDSTEIN, Patricia; '73 BA; 355 S End Ave. Apt. 8j, New York, NY 10280.

GOLFINOPOULOS, Kostas; '83 BS; JD Cardozo Law Sch.; Private Practice; r. POB 3075, Long Island City, NY 11103. e-mail

GOLINO, Michael J.; '95 BS; 53-20 65th Pl., Maspeth, NY 11378, 718 779-6046.

GOLOMBEK, Leonard; '87 BA; 56 Briarwood Ln., Plainview, NY 11803, 516 938-3341.

GOMES, Felicia C.; '98 BS; 787 E.46th St. #4e, Brooklyn, NY 11203, 718 836-8015.

GOMEZ, Angelina; '79 BS; 23-26 92nd St., E. Elmhurst, NY 11369, 718 760-1905.

GOMEZ, Angelita; '83 AS; CERT. Baruch; VP/Paralegal; The Related Co., 625 Madison Ave., New York, NY 10022, 212 421-5333; r. 2038 E. 35th St., Brooklyn, NY 11234, 718 376-5591; *Antonio Cajigas;* Nathaniel, Stephanie. e-mail

GOMEZ, Anibal; '95 AS; 545 W 156th St. Apt. 4b, New York, NY 10032.

GOMEZ, Carmen M.; '95 BA; MSW Yeshiva Univ.; Rehab. Spec.; r. 401 Smith St., Brooklyn, NY 11231, 718 639-4423.

GOMEZ, Cecilio; '83 BS; 2202 Ralph Ave., Brooklyn, NY 11234, 718 230-4155.

GOMEZ, Elizabeth; '83 BS; 605 W. 170 St. #2F, New York, NY 10032, 212 795-7836; Elysse Camacho, Marcu Camacho, Chelsye Camacho.

GOMEZ, Freddy A.; '92 BS; 1260 Jefferson Ave., Brooklyn, NY 11221, 718 638-3433.

GOMEZ, George; '89 BA; Prog. Coord.; Dept. of Homeless Svcs., The Barbara Kleiman Residence, 300 Skillman Ave., Brooklyn, NY 11211, 718 963-9836; r. 29 Saint Nicholas Ave., Brooklyn, NY 11237, 718 497-3070.

GOMEZ, Henry J.; '91 BS; 1904 Voshage St., Baldwin, NY 11510, 516 538-5857.

GOMEZ, Marina A.; '81 BS; 246 Mott St. Apt. 10, New York, NY 10012, 212 965-9473.

GOMEZ, Orlando N.; '95 BA; Fraud Investigator; City of NY; r. 736 W. 181st Str, New York, NY 10033; *Flor;* Ana, Floritza.

GOMEZ, Paula A.; '97 BS; 401 Elkwood Ave., New Providence, NJ 07974, 908 464-7525.

GOMEZ, Rosa Y., (Rosa Y. Bonilla); '98 BA; High Sch. Educator; Vanguard HS, 317 E 68th St., New York, NY 10002, 212 517-5175; r. 239 E 110th St. # 1, New York, NY 10029, 212 831-1426; *Alexandro.* e-mail

GOMEZ, Tracie; '99 BA; Fraud Investigator; Human Resources Admin., New York, NY 10001; r. 92 Centre Mall (#1E), Brooklyn, NY 11231, 718 330-1986. e-mail

GOMEZ, Victor R.; '93 DA; Couns.; Evergreen Alcohol & Drug Treatment Pro, 230 E. Ridgewood Ave., Paramus, NJ 07652; r. 11 Terhune Ave. #6, Lodi, NJ 07644; Christopher M.

GONCALVES, Alvaro; '90 BS; 312 Teaberry Ct., Toms River, NJ 08753, 732 288-1844.

GONCALVES, Paula; '92 BS; 5620 Marathon Pkwy., Apt. 3C, Little Neck, NY 11362, 516 775-2553.

GONDRY, Nicole; '95 BS; 881 E 7th St., Brooklyn, NY 11230, 718 859-0012. e-mail

GONIN, Daniel O.; '93 BS; 1720 Maxwell Dr., Yorktown Hts., NY 10598.

GONSALVES, B.; '93 BS; 135 Stanton Blvd., Uniondale, NY 11553, 516 485-3082.

GONZALES, Burt R.; '95 BS; Deputy Sheriff; The Miami Dade Police Dept., 15665 Biscayne Blvd., N. Miami Bch., FL 33160, 305 787-1630; r. 2301 Collins Ave., Miami Bch., FL 33139. e-mail

GONZALES, Helen K.; '99 BA; AA Borough of Manhattan Comm; Administrative Asst.; Chase, 270 Park Ave., New York, NY 10017, 212 270-3119; r. 653 Park Pl. 2Fl., Brooklyn, NY 11216, 718 782-3632.

GONZALEZ, Adonis; '98 BS; 1341 Jefferson Ave., Brooklyn, NY 11221, 718 455-6827.

GONZALEZ, Alicia; '99 AS; 41 Nostrand Avenue#3C, Brooklyn, NY 11206, 718 417-3158.

GONZALEZ, Allan W.; '99 BS; 5644 Netherland Ave. Apt. 3D, Bronx, NY 10471.

GONZALEZ, Angel L.; '88; 2060 Anthony Ave., Bronx, NY 10457, 718 328-2688.

GONZALEZ, Anilexa J.; '97 BA; Timekeeper; Brown Bourgh Presidents Ofc., 718 590-3533; r. 1411 Townsend Ave., Bronx, NY 10452, 718 537-3476.

GONZALEZ, Anthony; '89 BA; Detective; NYPD, 1 Police Plz., New York, NY 10001, 212 374-5000; r. 2315 Story Ave., Bronx, NY 10473. e-mail

GONZALEZ, Antonio; '91 BA, '95 MS; NYC Firefighter; NYC Fire Dept., 74 Middugh St., Brooklyn, NY 11201; r. 12 Eleanor Pl., Staten Island, NY 10303, 718 698-4532. e-mail

GONZALEZ, Carmen L.; '99; 84-34 Fleet Ct. #7A, Middle Vlg., NY 11379, 718 932-2455.

GONZALEZ, Elizabeth; '97 BS; 94-06 34th Rd. #F, Jackson Hts., NY 11372, 718 441-6595.

GONZALEZ, Emilio; '89 BS; 315 Logan St., Brooklyn, NY 11208, 718 621-2187.

GONZALEZ, Enrique; '91 BA; Customer Svc.; Sensormatic, 6600 Congress Ave., Boca Raton, FL 33433, 561 912-6946; r. 22028 Palms Way Apt. 205, Boca Raton, FL 33433, 561 447-7938; *Ada;* Christine, Lauren.

GONZALEZ, Francisco; '77 BA; MS Long Island Univ.; Private Investigator; Strategic Solutions Grp., Inc., 475 Park Ave. S., New York, NY 10016, 212 686-0557; r. 6 Phillips Dr., Stony Point, NY 10980; *Sylvia;* Alox, Marcos, Maria, Frank. e-mail

GONZALEZ, Georgina; '90 BS; 121 Warwick St., Brooklyn, NY 11207.

GONZALEZ, Grisselle; '85 BS; 21 Norfeld Blvd., Elmont, NY 11003, 516 437-7255.

GONZALEZ, Hector; '95 MA; 325 E 79th St. Apt. 12e, New York, NY 10021, 315 337-1752.

GONZALEZ, Hector L.; '99 BS; Detective; NYC Police Dept., 42 Precinct-Detective Squad, 830 Washington Ave., Bronx, NY 10451, 718 402-5393; r. 2767 Briggs Ave., Bronx, NY 10458, 718 561-8101.

GONZALEZ, Janet; '80 BS; AA Hunter Clg.; Detective; NYC Police Dept., 1 Police Plz., New York, NY 10013, 212 694-3059; r. 1405 Park Ave., Apt. 3F, New York, NY 10029, 212 369-3375.

GONZALEZ, Jeffrey; '99 BS; 64-27 Palmetto St. Bsmt, Ridgewood, NY 11385, 718 366-1663.

GONZALEZ, Jimmy A.; '90 BS; 2775 E 12th St. Apt. 126, Brooklyn, NY 11235.

GONZALEZ, Jo A.; '84 BS; 2369 1st Ave. Apt. 9e, New York, NY 10035, 315 337-1752.

GONZALEZ, Jose A.; '94 BA; 250 W 63rd St., Apt. 2C, New York, NY 10023, 315 337-1752.

GONZALEZ, Kenneth A.; '95 MPA; BA Lehmann Clg.; Business Mgr.; Health USA, White Plains, NY 10603; r. 633 Revere Ave., Bronx, NY 10465, 718 792-1205. e-mail

GONZALEZ, Lourdes; '90 BS; 50 E. 102nd St., New York, NY 10029, 315 337-1752.

GONZALEZ, Luis M.; '79 BS; 605 E 14th St., Apt. 4C, New York, NY 10009, 315 337-1752.

GONZALEZ, Madeline; '92 BA; 135 Elmira Loop Apt. 2h, Brooklyn, NY 11239, 718 348-4541.

GONZALEZ, Manuel; '95 BS; Police Ofcr.; NYC Police Dept., New York, NY 10026, 212 678-1311; r. 345 Melrose St., Brooklyn, NY 11237, 718 628-1902.

GONZALEZ, Maria; '98 BA; 1314 Riverside Dr. #4B, New York, NY 10033, 315 337-1752.

GONZALEZ, Michelle; '97 BS, '98 BS; 1296 Putnam Ave.3, Brooklyn, NY 11221, 718 452-1314.

GONZALEZ, Monica L.; '98 BA; 370 Bushwick Ave., 8e, Brooklyn, NY 11206, 718 348-4541.

GONZALEZ, Nancy; '83 BS, '88 MPA; 655 47th St., Brooklyn, NY 11220.

GONZALEZ, Nancy L.; '86 BA; 180 W. 81 St., New York, NY 10024, 315 337-1752.

GONZALEZ, Reinaldo; '75 BA; 178 Avenue D Apt. 11f, New York, NY 10009, 315 822-6052.

GONZALEZ, Robert A.; '93 MA; 2800 Heath Ave., Bronx, NY 10463, 718 562-2452.

GONZALEZ, Rodney; '93 BS; 490 E 184th St. # 16, Bronx, NY 10458, 718 562-2452.

GONZALEZ, Sandy J.; '99 BA; Limousine Driver; Towncar, W. 19th St., New York, NY 10011, 212 727-3800; r. 1969 Amsterdam Ave. #26, New York, NY 10032, 212 281-6947; Christian.

GONZALEZ, Sylvia '84 (See Lugo, Mrs. Sylvia).

GONZALEZ, Tanya N.; '99 BA; 153 Manhattan Ave., New York, NY 10025, 315 337-1752.

GONZALEZ, Ms. Yadhira; '99 BS MA; JD New York Law Sch.; Law Student; r. 1878 Harrison Ave. Apt. 2C, Bronx, NY 10453, 718 466-0547; *Kingsley Taylor;* Tanairi, Aaliyah. e-mail

GONZALEZ JIMENEZ, Ramona G.; '79 BS; Retired; Social Svc.; r. 175 W 87th St. #4f, New York, NY 10024, 212 496-1215; Yvette, Dolores, Carlos.

GONZALEZ-USERA, Jessica '97 (See Usera, Jessica).

GOOD, Carlton; '86 MPA; 39 Grove St., Beacon, NY 12508, 518 789-3745.

GOODE

JOHN JAY COLLEGE

GOODE, Anna R.; '92 BA; Assoc. Registrar; John Jay Clg. of Criminal Justice, 445 W. 59th St., New York, NY 10019, 212 237-8880; r. 820 Thieriot Ave., Bronx, NY 10473, 718 589-8717; *Bennie;* Laleatha, Bennie Jr., Catheryn.

GOODE, Gail M.; '77 BA; MA Cambridge Clg.; Tchr.; Dist. 19, New York, NY; r. 498 Linwood St., Brooklyn, NY 11208, 718 827-8356; Ruben.

GOODE, Laleatha '93 (See Goode-Wallace, Laleatha B.).

GOODE, Norma M.; 14615 177th St., Jamaica, NY 11434, 718 723-9077.

GOODEN, Elsa G.; '79 BA; Ret Chief Dept of Traffic; NY Dept. of Transportation, Redemption Univ; r. 1524 Givan Ave., Bronx, NY 10469, 718 654-2867; *Herman;* Barbara, Joyce, David, Kenneth. e-mail

GOODEN, Herman; '75 AS, '78 BS; Ret Police Officer & Ret US Spec.; Deputy Marshal/NYC Housing Police, Southern Dist of New York; r. 1524 Givan Ave., Bronx, NY 10469, 718 654-2867; *Elsa;* Barbara, Joyce, David, Kenneth. e-mail

GOODE-WALLACE, Laleatha B., (Laleatha Goode); '93 BA; Prog. Spec.; FBI, 935 Pennsylvania Ave., Washington, DC 20535; r. 12 Boyd Dr., Stafford, VA 22554. e-mail

GOODING, Sharon; '97 BA; MSA Audrey Cohen Clg.; Owner; Joseph Sports, 508 E 48th St. #4, Brooklyn, NY 11203, 718 342-2407; r. 508 E 84th St. #4, Brooklyn, NY 11203, 718 324-2407. e-mail

GOODMAN, Alan Z.; '76 MA; MS ISD NYIT, BA Queens College; Trng. Cnslt.; Goodman Cnsltg., 69-17 197 St., Fresh Meadows, NY 11365, 718 264-2407; r. 6917 197th St., Flushing, NY 11365, 718 454-6292. e-mail

GOODMAN, Donald, PhD; BA Yale, PHD Fordham; Prof.; John Jay Clg., 899 10th Ave., New York, NY 10019, 212 237-8461; r. 20 Seville Ln., Stony Brook, NY 11790, 631 751-2374. e-mail

GOODMAN, Mary B.; '89 MA; Retired Probation Ofcr.; r. New York, NY 10024.

GOODMAN, Milton; '91 MPA; BS New York Inst. Tech, AA Edison State Clg.; 342 W 71st St., New York, NY 10023, 212 595-0928.

GOODMAN, Sabrina B.; '98 BA; 29 Warren St. #1-j, Staten Island, NY 10304, 718 420-1476.

GOODS, Samuel E.; '76 AS, '84 BS; Collector of Sports & Antiques; r. 775 Concourse Village E., Bronx, NY 10451, 718 992-4910; *Muriel.*

GOODWIN, Bruce K.; '76 MA; 11 Avondale St., Valley Stream, NY 11581, 516 883-9285.

GOODWIN, Ella D.; '99 BA; Unit Receptionist; Roosevelt Hosp., 1000 10th Ave., New York, NY 10019; r. 664 W 161st., New York, NY 10032, 212 923-6734.

GOODWIN, Patrick J.; '78 BS; Heating Contractor; Controlled Combustion Co., Inc., 2377 Washington Ave., Bronx, NY 10458, 718 367-9800; r. 100 Chadwick Pl., Glen Rock, NJ 07452; *Joann;* Megan, Thomas. e-mail

GOON, William; '93 BS; 124 Sherman Ave. Apt. 29, New York, NY 10034, 212 942-2581.

GOPEE, Brenda G.; '98 BS; 4226 Carpenter Ave., Bronx, NY 10466, 718 994-8529.

GORAL, Helen; '80 BS; 1012 Manhattan Ave., Brooklyn, NY 11222, 718 383-3257.

GORBETT, Robert; '97 BS; 11 Stuyvesant Oval, New York, NY 10009.

GORDON, Abby R.; '91 MA; 1215 Old Cannons Ln., Louisville, KY 40207, 502 895-8770.

GORDON, Andrea D.; '97 BS; ROR Interviewer; NYC Criminal Justice Agcy., 120 Schermerhorn St., Brooklyn, NY 11201, 718 330-1520; r. 1527 President St., Brooklyn, NY 11213, 718 221-4362; Jordan Harris. e-mail

GORDON, Benjamin A.; '95 BS; 12 Alyssa Ln., Manalapan, NJ 07726.

GORDON, Blanche M.; '95 BS; 45 Watervliet Ave., Albany, NY 12206, 518 426-4896.

GORDON, Davina S.; '89 BA; 2160 Caton Ave. #3A, Brooklyn, NY 11226, 718 221-8802.

GORDON, Gail M.; '81 MA; 6861 Yellowstone Blvd. Apt. 202, Flushing, NY 11375, 718 526-9485.

GORDON, Henry; '85 BA; Realtor; r. 96-09 Alstyne Ave., Corona, NY 11368, 718 565-8107.

GORDON, Karen; '92 BS, '97 MA; 943 Magenta St., Bronx, NY 10469.

GORDON, Linda; '95 BS; 100 W. 92nd St., New York, NY 10025, 315 336-3941.

GORDON, Sharon M.; '87 BS; 405 Williams Ave., Brooklyn, NY 11207, 718 339-5429.

GORDON, Troy A.; '93 BS; 291 Bradford St., Brooklyn, NY 11207.

GORDON, Vivian A.; '85 BS; 1526 Easthampton, Wellington, FL 33414, 561 798-0283.

GORDON, Wayne; '81 BA; New York Law Sch.; Law Enforcement; r. 140 Asch Loop Apt. 8d, Bronx, NY 10475, 917 825-3540; *Anna;* Alexander, Annesha. e-mail

GORDON, Winston A.; '83 BA; 10413 Farmers Blvd., Jamaica, NY 11412, 718 479-9133.

GORE, Barbara H.; '76 MA; Retired Capt.; NYPD; r. 4837 Clearview Expy., Flushing, NY 11364, 718 631-2263.

GORE, Elissa; '86 MA; 65 Park Ter. W, New York, NY 10034, 315 732-7429.

GORE, Michelle A.; '97 BS; 2181 Wallace Ave., Apt. 1E, Bronx, NY 10462, 718 828-3485.

GORELIK, Joanna K.; '98 BA; Collector; Danka Imaging, Treena St., Ste. 200, San Diego, CA 92131, 858 877-3674; r. 4364 Bonita Rd, Pmb 334, Bonita, CA 91902, 619 476-1479; *Max.* e-mail

GORELIK, Max; '99 BS; AOS Technical Career Inst.; Agt.; US Border Patrol/INS, POB 68, Imperial Bch., CA 91933, 619 662-7057; r. 4364 Bonita Rd. PMB 334, Bonita, CA 91902, 619 476-1479; *Joanna.* e-mail

GORIS, Damaris T.; '85 BA; 460 Grand St. Apt. 3f, New York, NY 10002.

GORIS, Patricio; '98 BS; 340 Cherry St. 1a, New York, NY 10002, 212 962-5320.

GORMAN, Albert J.; '84 MA; 581 Patten ave., Long Branch, NJ 07740, 732 870-0860.

GORMAN, James P.; '76 MA; BA St. Francis Clg.; Security Mgr.; Spartan Security, 1 Park Ave., S., New York, NY 10016, 212 251-7888; r. 240 Tulip Dr., Massapequa Park, NY 11762, 516 798-2296; *Eileen;* Jane, Noreen, Margaret, Christine, Nancy.

GORMAN, John; '87 BS; JD Fordham Univ.; Chairperson; Law Dept./NYC Police Acad., 235 E. 20th St., New York, NY 10003; r. 189 Lake St., Brooklyn, NY 11223, 718 375-3730. e-mail

GORMAN, Michael J.; '79 MA; JD Fordham Law Sch.; Atty.; New York Police Dept., 1 Police Plz., Rm S158, New York, NY 10038, 212 374-4311; r. 14931 21st Ave., Whitestone, NY 11357, 718 672-2441; *Vernie;* Victor, Michelle.

GORMAN, Nina; '85 MA; 4308 Arendell Ave. #4, Philadelphia, PA 19114.

GORMAN, Timothy J.; '89 BS; 5116 7th Ave. # 3, Brooklyn, NY 11220.

GORMLEY, Ann V.; '82 MA; 52-30 39 Dr., Woodside, NY 11377.

GORMLEY, Paula E.; '89 BA; 60 Cooper St., Apt. 3K, New York, NY 10034.

GOROVOY, Oleg B.; '99 BS; Programmer/Web Developer; Forbes, 28 W 23rd, New York, NY 10010, 212 366-8828; r. 812 W 181 St. #35A, New York, NY 10033, 212 928-7758. e-mail

GORRASI, Joseph R.; '80 BA; 51 Wilson St., Massapequa Park, NY 11762, 516 798-4406.

GORSUCH, Robert P.; '71 BS; 2629 Loretta St., Yorktown Hts., NY 10598, 914 243-4910.

GORTON, Michael J.; '77 BA; 115 Revilo Ave., Shirley, NY 11967.

GOSLING, Carolin; '97 BA; 1451 Prospect Pl., Brooklyn, NY 11213.

GOSS, Agnieszka; '96 BA; 4129 41st St., Apt. 3H, Sunnyside, NY 11104, 718 529-5020.

GOSS, Ronald M.; '96 BA; 217 W.62nd St. #2, New York, NY 10023, 212 245-3126.

GOSSMAN, Craig W.; '98 BA; 9 Old Anvil Ln., Middletown, NY 10940, 914 343-8343.

GOTAY, Albert; '71 BS; 47 Fieldstone Dr., Syosset, NY 11791, 516 496-3919.

GOTSOPOULIS-BLUM, Mary; '84 MA; 936 52nd St., Brooklyn, NY 11219.

GOTTLIEB, Cara; '95 BS; 774 Franklyn Ave., Bohemia, NY 11716.

GOTTLIEB, Paul; '76 BA; AS; Retired Police Ofcr.; City of NY; r. 248 Annadale Rd, Staten Island, NY 10312, 718 356-4602.

GOUDIE, David W.; '76 BS; 650 Drumgoole Rd E, Staten Island, NY 10312.

GOULBOURNE, Marilyn R.; '80 BS; 688 Nostrand Ave., Brooklyn, NY 11216.

GOULBOURNE, Norval; '85 MPA; 98-23 H. Harding E, Flushing, NY 11368.

GOULD, Luwyana C.; 534 Linwood St., Brooklyn, NY 11208, 718 277-8741.

GOUSSE, Sonhita; '88 BS; 13531 SW 114 Pl., Miami, FL 33176.

GOVERNALE, Joseph M.; '77 BS; 1428 157th St., Whitestone, NY 11357.

80

GOWINS, Ruthlee; '93 BS; 387 Ashford St. Ph, Brooklyn, NY 11207, 718 647-7971.

GRABIN, Scott D.; '79 BS; 197 Bryant Ave., Floral Park, NY 11001.

GRACIA, Jorge J.; '81 BA; 39-50 52nd St., Woodside, NY 11377.

GRACIANO, Maria C.; '98 BA; Domestic Violence Couns.; Urban Women's Retreat, POB 804, New York, NY 10037, 212 690-6490; r. 1684 Grand Concourse #3B, Bronx, NY 10457, 718 901-2515.

GRADY, Michael F.; '96 BA; 44-06 189 St., Flushing, NY 11358, 718 275-1068.

GRAF, Margaret M.; '91 MA; BA CCNY; Homemaker, Staff Analyst; r. 32 Greenwood Rd, Yonkers, NY 10701, 914 965-8820.

GRAHAM, Ardene M.; '96 BA; 717 E. 231 St., Bronx, NY 10466, 718 543-1881.

GRAHAM, Deborah A.; '94 BA; 221 W 113th St., New York, NY 10026.

GRAHAM, Harry W.; '86 BA; 857 Penfield St., Bronx, NY 10470.

GRAHAM, Janet A.; '89 BS; Child Abuse Investigator; Admin. for Children Svcs., 150 William St., New York, NY 10038, 718 430-1735; r. 1966 Newbold Ave., Bronx, NY 10472, 718 824-9097; Ashley. e-mail

GRAHAM, Kenneth; '91 MA; Prof.; Orange Cnty. Clg., 115 South St., Middletown, Middletown, NY 10940, 914 344-2424; r. 54 Beers Dr., Middletown, NY 10940. e-mail

GRAHAM, Nichole N.; '97 BS; 19 Muriel St., Freeport, NY 11520, 516 546-5728. e-mail

GRAHAM, Nicole S.; '98 BA; Release Own Recognizance Interview; NYC Criminal Justice Agcy., 2 Lafayette St., New York, NY 10007, 212 577-8775; r. 44 W. 175 St. #5a, Bronx, NY 10453, 718 716-3047. e-mail

GRAHAM, Patricia; '90 BA; 240 W 65th St. Apt. 23g, New York, NY 10023.

GRAHAM, Wendy; '92 BS; 11112 199th St., Jamaica, NY 11412.

GRAJALES, Ananias; '94 BA; 30 Scholes St. # 6, Brooklyn, NY 11206.

GRAJALES, Ednah; '91 BS; Correction Ofcr.; NYC Dept. of Corrections, 60 Hudson St., New York, NY 10013; Keith Ashley.

GRAMLICH, Ronald W.; '73 BS; 10812 NE 2 Ct., Miami, FL 33161.

GRANATA, Bryan E.; '96 BS; Loss Prevention Mgr.; Saks Fifth Ave, 230 Walt Whitman Rd, Holliston, MA 01746, 631 530-1222; r. 14 Bellewood Ave., S. Setauket, NY 11720, 631 981-9438.

GRANATA, George M.; '95 BS; Dir. of Security; The Wiz, 2045 Lincoln Hwy., Edison, NJ 08817, 917 325-8387; r. 14 Bellwood Ave., S. Setauket, NY 11720, 631 981-9438.

GRANATA, Robert; '92 MA; 121 Thiells Rd, Stony Point, NY 10980.

GRANDSTAFF, Glenn; '84 MA; 95 Taylor St., Hillsdale, NJ 07642.

GRANELLE, Anja E.; '91 BA; 226 E 1st St., Deer Park, NY 11729.

GRANEY, Heidi '95 (See Farron, Mrs. Heidi M.).

GRANT, Alphonzo S.; '76; 1250 Ocean Ave. Apt. 3r, Brooklyn, NY 11230.

GRANT, Anne C.; '95 MA; 114 Park Pl., Brooklyn, NY 11217, 718 272-3030.

GRANT, Barbara V.; '80 BA; 40-03 10 St., Long Island City, NY 11101.

GRANT, Calvin; '81 BS, '83 MPA; Drug Rehab Supv.; Beth Israel Med. Ctr., 16th St. At 1st. Ave., New York, NY 10003; r. 45 W 139th St. Apt. 12n, New York, NY 10037, 212 234-1395; Calvin Jr., Robert, Nicole.

GRANT, Cheryl M.; '94 BS; 101 W 147th St. #125, New York, NY 10039, 315 724-1412.

GRANT, Colleen; '87 BS; 1782 New York Ave., Brooklyn, NY 11210, 718 951-0219.

GRANT, E. G.; '84 BA, '85 MPA; 846 Clarkson Ave., Brooklyn, NY 11203.

GRANT, Geroy C.; '97 BS; 36 Ft. Greene Pla, Brooklyn, NY 11217, 718 596-2892.

GRANT, Harriett D.; '99 BS; 705 E. 39 St., Brooklyn, NY 11203, 718 856-2410.

GRANT, Joan; '85 MPA; 846 Clarkson Ave., Brooklyn, NY 11203.

GRANT, John C.; '81 BS; 38 Primrose Ave., Floral Park, NY 11001, 516 358-2827.

GRANT, Jule A.; '88 BA; MS Milano Grad. Sch., AS Baruch Clg.; Employment Coord.; Rheedlen, 170 Lenox Ave., New York, NY 10026, 212 369-5912; r. 218-17 119th Ave., Cambria Hts., NY 11411, 718 712-6993; D'anthony. e-mail

GRANT, Kenneth G.; '74 BS, '77 MA; Retired Mgr.; Public Utility of New York; r. 13631 Arden Dr., Hudson, FL 34667, 727 819-1297; Mildred; Amina. e-mail

GRANT, Kevin C.; '99 BA; Grad. Student; Georgia State Univ.; r. 9720 Ave. N, Brooklyn, NY 11236, 718 444-0923. e-mail

GRANT, Lillie; '89 BS, '96 MA; MA; Paralegal; US Attys. Ofc. SDNY, St. Andrews Plz., New York, NY 10007, 212 637-1023; r. 355 Clinton Ave., Brooklyn, NY 11238, 718 789-9148.

GRANT, Michael G.; '75 MA; 188 Broadway, Massapequa Park, NY 11762.

GRANT, Michael J.; '75 MA; 200 New York Ave., New Brunswick, NJ 08901.

GRANT, Sharon D.; '76 BS; 15 Himrod St., Brooklyn, NY 11221.

GRANT, Tamika S.; '99 BA; Paraprofn.; Bd. of Educ., 171-05 137 Ave., Jamaica, NY 11434, 718 528-7070; r. 122-08 153rd St., Jamaica, NY 11434, 718 659-5489.

GRANT, Vanessa; '86 BA; 2460 Adam Clayton Powell Jr Blvd. Ap, New York, NY 10030.

GRANT, Virginia L.; '82 MPA; 4110 Bowne St. Apt. 3z, Flushing, NY 11355.

GRANT, Vivienne J.; '89 BA; 205 E. 93 St., Brooklyn, NY 11212, 718 257-4778.

GRANUM, Denise L.; '90 BS; 2459 Devoe Ter., Bronx, NY 10468.

GRANVILLE, Alfonso M.; '80 BS; 501 Hope Chapel Rd, Lakewood, NJ 08701, 732 367-9890.

GRANVILLE, Stromme J., Sr.; '86 BS; Lt.; NYC Police Dept., PBM Investigations Unit, New York, NY 10001; r. 131-20 229th St., Laurelton, NY 11413, 718 625-0301; Lucille; Ajuba, Stromme Jr., Christopher.

GRASSO, John P.; '93 MS; BE Stevens Inst. of Tech, BS Jersey City State Clg.; Firefighter; Fire Dept. City of NY, 1516 Williamsbridge Rd, Bronx, NY 10461, 718 430-0251; r. 30 Grant Dr., Monroe, NY 10950, 914 782-9014. e-mail

GRASSO, Joseph; 103 Robbings Rd, Somerville, NJ 08876.

GRATTAN, Walter W.; '76 BS; 19 Stephens Ct., Hauppauge, NY 11788.

GRAVELLI, Vincent M.; '97 BS; Detective; NYPD, New York, NY 10038; r. 1234 77 St., Brooklyn, NY 11228, 718 748-4348. e-mail

GRAVES, Christine H.; '98 BS; Systs. Engr.; Chase Manhatten Bank, 55 Water St., New York, NY 10041, 212 638-0671; r. 65 Columbia St. 8k, New York, NY 10002, 212 533-9753; Natasha, Lawanda, Robert.

GRAVES, Tywana E. '93 (See Graves-Parker, Ms. Tywana E.).

GRAVESANDY, Colin S.; '89 BS; 1591 Bruckner Blvd., Bronx, NY 10472, 718 542-1628.

GRAVES-PARKER, Ms. Tywana E., (Tywana E. Graves); '93 BA; Grade Tchr.; NYC Bd. of Educ., 1330 Bristow St., Longwood, NY 10459, 718 328-3351; r. 4210 Bronxwood Ave., Bronx, NY 10466, 718 324-5877; Frederick Parker; Tianna, Toro. e-mail

GRAVITCH, Daniel J.; '90 BS; 169 Lamped Loop, Staten Island, NY 10314.

GRAY, Albert P.; '79 BS; 2253 95th St., Flushing, NY 11369, 718 335-8349.

GRAY, Boima; '87 BS; 400 Grand Ave., Brooklyn, NY 11238, 718 953-0977.

GRAY, Donald R.; '79 BS; 255 Garrison Ave., Staten Island, NY 10314.

GRAY, Earl E.; '95 BA; 100-7 Asch Loop #7E, Bronx, NY 10475, 718 320-1675.

GRAY, Edward B.; '85 BS; 783 Lenox Rd., Brooklyn, NY 11203, 718 604-1669.

GRAY, Golda; '93 BS, 2000 MPA; Recruitment Coord.; Medgar Evers Clg., 1650 Bedford Ave., Brooklyn, NY 11225, 718 270-6028; r. 1416 Brooklyn Ave. Apt. 2c, Apt. 2c, Brooklyn, NY 11210, 718 941-2858. e-mail

GRAY, John H.; '92 BS; 130-03 Rockaway Beach, Belle Harbor, NY 11694, 718 424-8313.

GRAY, Philburn W.; '80 BA; 179 E 54th St., Brooklyn, NY 11203.

GRAY, Mrs. Tamika S., (Tamika Forrester); '97 BS; Immigration Inspector; r. 738 E. 58th St., Brooklyn, NY 11234, 718 444-7542; Karen; Deshini, Michael.

GRAY, Thomas E.; '73 AS, '76 BS; CERT. Nassau Cnty. Comm Clg.; Paralegal; r. 17 Balsam Ln., Levittown, NY 11756, 516 796-0356; Sonia; Carolyn, Cynthia, Thomas, Kenneth. e-mail

GRAYS, Marguerite; '79 BA; 13751 Southgate St., Jamaica, NY 11413.

GRAZIANI, Noel E.; '88 BA; 329 E 75th St. Apt. 3d, New York, NY 10021.

GRAZIANO, Michael A.; '76 BS; 7519 21st Ave., Flushing, NY 11370.

GRAZIANO, Paul W.; '79 BS; 835 Sinclair Ave., Staten Island, NY 10309.

GREANEY, John J.; '79 BS; 2003 Paulding Ave., Bronx, NY 10462.

GREAUX, Roslyn A.; '94 BS; 31 Washington Blvd., Mt. Vernon, NY 10550.

GREAVES, Eustace L.; '76 BA; 1299 Ocean Ave. #5G, Brooklyn, NY 11230, 718 434-4766.

GREAVES, June S.; '95 BS; 1451 E 86th St. Apt. 1, Brooklyn, NY 11236, 718 399-6412.

GRECHANIK, Carolyn A.; '79 MA; 16316 22nd Ave., Whitestone, NY 11357.

GRECO, CAPT Carl J.; '74 BS; Ret. Capt.; NYPD; r. 264 N Utica Ave., Massapequa, NY 11758, 516 694-4541; *Rita P. (dec);* Eleanor, Janet Toto.

GRECO, Joseph P.; '78 MA; 95 Litchfield Ave., Elmont, NY 11003, 516 437-3699.

GREEN, Andrew; '95 BA; MPA Baruch Clg.; Sgt; NYC Police Dept., 9201 222nd St., Queens Vlg., NY 11428, 718 776-9090; r. 15330 79th St., Jamaica, NY 11414.

GREEN, Andrew P.; '95 BS; Data Coord.; NY Presbyterian Hosp.; r. 9526 Avenue D, Brooklyn, NY 11236, 718 498-5972. e-mail

GREEN, Calbert B.; '96 BA, '99 MA; Fraud Investigator; NYC-HRA, 180 Water St., New York, NY 10038, 718 617-8852; r. 865 E. 175th St., Bronx, NY 10460, 718 589-6021. e-mail

GREEN, Carlyn D.; '93 BA; 4624 Avenue I, Brooklyn, NY 11234.

GREEN, Cynthia A.; '90 BS; 173-11 108th Ave., Jamaica, NY 11433.

GREEN, Douglas; '96 MA; 7 Woods End Rd, W. Orange, NJ 07052.

GREEN, Eliot; '86 MA; 7 Weybridge Rd, Brookline, MA 02445.

GREEN, Eunice H.; '85 BS, '95 MA; 2991 Frederick Douglass Blvd. Apt 16, New York, NY 10039, 315 797-5373.

GREEN, Herman L.; '76 BS; 1235 35th Ave. Apt. 1g, Long Island City, NY 11106.

GREEN, James; '87 MA; 302 Rockaway Pkwy. # 2f, Brooklyn, NY 11212.

GREEN, James M.; '94 MA; 209 W. 80th St., New York, NY 10024, 212 873-5615.

GREEN, Kelly A.; '98 MA; 6 Smith St., W. Hempstead, NY 11552, 516 626-7269.

GREEN, Lawrence E.; '75 BA; 98-39 65th Rd., Rego Park, NY 11374.

GREEN, Margaret A.; '93 BS; 4212 Gunther Ave., Bronx, NY 10466.

GREEN, Mark A.; '93 BS; POB 187, New York, NY 10272.

GREEN, Michelle; '93 BS; 10512 Van Wyck Expy., Jamaica, NY 11419.

GREEN, Monique; '94 BS; 400 Cozine Ave., Brooklyn, NY 11207, 718 771-4993.

GREEN, Stephanie; '95 BA, '99 MA; Investigator; D.A. Kings Cnty., Brooklyn, NY 11201; r. 572 Warren St. Apt. 5l, Brooklyn, NY 11217, 718 875-0619.

GREEN, Stephen; '97 BA; 316 Hampton Green, Staten Island, NY 10312, 718 948-1744.

GREEN, Valerie M.; '89 AS; 81 Cameron Ave., Hempstead, NY 11550.

GREEN, Vanessa M.; '86 BA; 209 Kit Cir., Moncks Corner, SC 29461, 843 761-7297.

GREEN, Vincent E.; '79 BS; MS Brooklyn Clg.; Asst. Commissioner; NYC Dept. of Investigations, 80 Maiden Ln., New York, NY 10038, 212 825-2468; r. 585 E. 16th St., Brooklyn, NY 11226, 718 693-5026. e-mail

GREENBERG, Adam N.; '99 BA; 3000-23 Stevens St., Oceanside, NY 11572, 516 678-1136.

GREENBERG, George; '75 MA; 14419 68th Dr., Flushing, NY 11367.

GREENBERG, Gwynneth; '82 BS; 632 Palmer Rd Apt. 10N, Yonkers, NY 10701, 914 961-7310.

GREENBERG, Harry; '78 BS; 821 Newburg Ave., Valley Stream, NY 11581, 516 791-8667.

GREENBERG, Jonathan F.; '89 BS; 9690 NW 59th Ct., Parkland, FL 33076.

GREENBERG, Martin A.; '70 MA; BA Queens Clg., JD New York Law Sch.; Prof.; Ulster Cnty. Community Clg., Stone Ridge, NY 12484, 262 687-5156; r. 955 Inman Rd, Niskayuna, NY 12309, 518 372-3929; *Ellen Wertlieb;* Edward.

GREENE, Cheree; '97 BA; Ofc. Coord.; East Harlem Tutorial Prog., 2050 Second Ave., New York, NY 10029, 212 831-0650; r. 133-02 109th Ave., S. Ozone Park, NY 11420, 718 659-4956; *Anthony Mason;* Lenee. e-mail

GREENE, Delicia T.; '98 BS LAW, '98 BS; MLS Pratt Inst.; Adult Librarian Trainee; NYPL Kingsbridge Regional Branch Library, 280 W 231st St., Bronx, NY 10463, 718 548-5980; r. 2176 Grand Ave. #7A, Bronx, NY 10453, 718 733-0274. e-mail

GREENE, Elizabeth P.; '93 AS; 2547 Pearsall Ave., Bronx, NY 10469, 718 325-7049.

GREENE, Jeanique; '93 BS; JD Albany Law Sch.; Legislative Dir.; NYS Senate, 518 455-2441; r. 46 Trinity Pl. Apt. 1, Albany, NY 12202, 518 432-8961. e-mail

GREENE, Jiton T.; '99 BA; AS Bronx Community Clg.; Customer Svc. Rep.; Bell Atlantic, 375 Pearl St., New York, NY 10038, 212 890-2106; r. 190 Sunset St., Dumont, NJ 07628, 201 244-1342; Daijavae.

GREENE, Joe L.; BS St. Francis Clg.; Asst. Chief Ret; NYC Housing Police Dept.; r. 139 E. 45th St., Brooklyn, NY 11203, 718 493-2255. e-mail

GREENE, Kenny B.; '98 BS; 140-5 Darrow Pl. #5G, Bronx, NY 10475, 718 515-7072.

GREENE, Marlene M., (Marlene M. Peters); '74 BA; Retired Corrections Ofcr.; Corrections Dept. NYC; r. 1359 Dexter Dr. E., Daytona Bch., FL 32119, 904 788-3143; *Matthew L.;* Matthew K.

GREENE, Matthew L.; '75 BA; Retired Correction Ofcr.; Correction Dept. NYC; r. 1359 Dexter Dr. E., Daytona Bch., FL 32119, 904 788-3143; *Marlene;* Matthew K.

GREENE, Rita D. '85 (See Jones, Mrs. Rita G.).

GREENE, Stephen; '77 BA, '77 AA; MSED Bank Street Clg. of Educ.; Retired Prof.; r. 1412 Crotona Ave., Bronx, NY 10456, 718 542-1338; Stephen, Christopher, Sean, Heather.

GREENE, Tamecca L.; '99 BA; Full-time Law Sch.; Cardozo Law Sch.; r. 2159 Beverly Rd., Brooklyn, NY 11226, 718 693-0892. e-mail

GREENE, Tryphena; '92 BS; 240 Wortman Ave., Brooklyn, NY 11207, 718 443-4641.

GREENE, Valarie L.; '97 BS; Account Clerk/Data Entry; NYS Ins. Dept.; r. 1640 Montgomery Ave., Bronx, NY 10453.

GREENIDGE, Doreen T.; '82 MPA; 9026 198th St., Hollis, NY 11423, 718 479-1278.

GREENIDGE, Reginald F.; '81 MA; 278 Macon St., Brooklyn, NY 11216.

GREENWALD, Steven; '97 BA; Fire Prevention Inspector; NY Fire Dept., 100 Duane St., New York, NY 10007, 212 570-4230; r. 626 Arden Ave., Staten Island, NY 10312, 718 948-7091.

GREENWOOD, Deidra; '88 BS; 16010 89th Ave. Apt. 8c, Jamaica, NY 11432.

GREER, Michele A.; '88 BA, '92 MPA; 78-09 77 Ave., Glendale, NY 11385, 718 279-5887.

GREER, Stephanie E.; '88 BA; 243 E. 51 St., Brooklyn, NY 11203, 718 369-6533.

GREGG, Tommy L.; '79 BS; 134 Spring St., Massapequa, NY 11758.

GREGORIC, Maximilian; '84 BS; 915 E 126th St., Draper, UT 84020.

GREGORIN, Dr. David; '82 BS; MDIV Liberty Univ., DMIN Luther Rice Seminary; Pastor; Sewickley Baptist Church, 301 Beaver St., Sewickley, PA 15143, 412 741-8900; r. 516 Grimes St., Sewickley, PA 15143, 412 741-0704; *Margaret;* David, Jennifer, Sarah. e-mail

GREGORY, Helen A.; '80 BS; 1180 Dominion Dr. E, Mobile, AL 36695, 334 653-4885.

GREGORY, Raymond W.; '79 BS; 8303 14th Ave., Brooklyn, NY 11228.

GREGORY, Rita; '96 BS; Ofc. Asst.; CUNY, 212 650-7152; r. 1569 Metropolitan, Bronx, NY 10462. e-mail

GRENNAN, Sean A., PhD; '76 BA, '80 MA; PHD City Univ. of NY; Assoc. Prof.; Criminal Justice Dept., LIU/CW Post Campus, 720 Northern Blvd., Brookville, NY 11548, 516 299-2592; r. Criminal Justice Dept., Liu/Cw Post Campus, Brookville, NY 11548, 516 299-1587; Megan, Lauren. e-mail

GRESH, Ms. Marilyn B.; '97 BS; Analytical Chemist; Inter. Vitamin Corp., Freehold, NJ 07728; r. 309 Hemlock Dr., Lanoka Harbor, NJ 08734, 609 693-2789.

GRETIH, Anthony L.; '78 BS; 1820 79th St., Brooklyn, NY 11214.

GREY, Edward I.; '78 BS; 10 Bevy Ct., Brooklyn, NY 11229, 718 257-1736.

GREY, Natasha N.; '97 BS; 10 Drisler Ave., White Plains, NY 10607, 914 592-3712.

GRGAS, Susan. M., (Susan M. Matesich); '82 BA; Homemaker; Old Westbury, NY 11568; r. 7 Sandpiper Ct., Old Westbury, NY 11568, 516 626-2488.

GRIBBEN, Richard J.; 203-16 33 Ave., Bayside, NY 11361.

GRICE, Richard G.; '76 BS; 273 34th St., Lindenhurst, NY 11757.

GRICE, Yvonne S., (Yvonne Harper); '82 BS; Curriculum Writer; City of NY; r. 2714 Frederick Douglass Blvd., New York, NY 10030, 212 234-2166.

GRIDLEY, Shannon C.; '98 MA; Exch. Student Univ. of Leiden; Holland & Law Student Univ. of FL; r. 619 Darcey Dr., Winter Park, FL 32792, 407 647-6765. e-mail

GRIER, John E.; '94 BS; Retired; r. 3170 Broadway Apt. 14A, New York, NY 10027, 212 222-7681.

GRIEVE, Daniel P.; '73 BS; Sr. Fire Safety Dir.; Cushman Wakefield, Inc., 60 Wall St., New York, NY 10260, 212 648-6155; r. 8410 105th St., Jamaica, NY 11418, 718 441-9622. e-mail

GRIFFIN, Brian A.; '96 BA; 28 Bay St., E. Atlantic Bch., NY 11561, 516 889-8076.

GRIFFIN, Cheryl E.; '95 BA; 736 E 211th St. #2, Bronx, NY 10467, 718 299-8265.

GRIFFIN, Dennis M.; '89 BS; AS COMP Clg. of Staten Island; Police Ofcr.; NYPD, 1 Police Plz., New York, NY 10010; r. 473 Sierra Vista Ln., Valley Cottage, NY 10989, 914 353-4067. e-mail

GRIFFIN, Osie L.; '87 BA; 37 Morning Grove Cv S, Cordova, TN 38018, 901 386-7585.

GRIFFIN, Richard M.; '84 BS; 20-14 74 St., Jackson Hts., NY 11370.

GRIFFIN, Robin L.; '91 MA; 30 Oak Dr., Calverton, NY 11933, 631 744-1487.

GRIFFIN, Romania A.; '95 BS, '95 CERT; Investigator; 212 690-9815; r. 159-20 Harlem River Dr. Apt. 3h, New York, NY 10039, 212 283-0059.

GRIFFIN, Scott; 2600 Revere Rd, Brigantine, NJ 08203.

GRIFFIN, Uriel; '84 MPA; 320 Clifton Pl., Brooklyn, NY 11216, 718 638-5170.

GRIFFINS, Tml A.; BS; Hotel Clerk; Marriott Intl., 1221 22nd St., Washington, DC 20037, 202 872-1500; r. 6805 W. Forest Rd, Landover, MD 20785, 718 282-2910.

GRIFFITH, Anthony; '06 DS; 1127 C Baylor Ln., Gilbert, AZ 85296.

GRIFFITH, Cheryl L.; '87 BS; 718 Carroll St., Brooklyn, NY 11215.

GRIFFITH, Dorothy R.; '82 MPA; 65 Argyle Ave., New Rochelle, NY 10804, 914 948-3436.

GRIFFITH, Liddon; '81 MPA; 65 Argyll Ave., New Rochelle, NY 10804, 914 948-3436.

GRIFFITH, Rodney F.; '91 BS; Rehab Therapist; Catholic Charities, 165-15 88th Ave., Jamaica, NY 11432, 718 291-4848; r. 10338 Springfield Blvd., Queens Vlg., NY 11429, 718 464-3795. e-mail

GRIFFITH, Samantha; '95 BA; 225 Ridgewood Ave., Brooklyn, NY 11208, 718 827-1532.

GRIFFITH, Stanford A.; '75 BA; 959 Cramer Ct., N. Baldwin, NY 11510, 516 223-5733.

GRIFFITH, Todd A.; '85 BS; POB 8631, Woodcliff Lake, NJ 07675, 201 818-7894.

GRIFFITHS, Marcia J.; '93 BA; 231 Ocean Ave. #6E, Brooklyn, NY 11225, 718 566-8145.

GRIFFITHS, Robert P.; '75 MA; 3 Wellington Ct., Ronkonkoma, NY 11779.

GRIFFITHS, William; '92 BA; 15 Norge Ave., Nanuet, NY 10954.

GRIGGS, Deidre '94 (See Stewart, Deidre N.).

GRILES, Victor A.; '81 BS; 106-13 227 St., Queens Vlg., NY 11429.

GRILLO, Richard S.; '85 BA; 11 Tonbridge Ct., Toms River, NJ 08757, 732 473-1139.

GRIMALDI, John; 279 Beachview St., Copiague, NY 11726, 516 691-0307.

GRIMES, Joann E.; '76 BA; 12 Stuyvesant Oval, New York, NY 10009, 212 228-6551.

GRIMES, John J., Esq.; '67 BS, '69 MPA; JD Harvard Sch. of Law; Attorney; Grimes & Zimet, 16 S Bedford Rd, Chappaqua, NY 10514, 914 238-1377; r. 95 Deerfield Ln. N, Pleasantville, NY 10570, 914 747-1564; *Linda;* John Jr, Derrick Phelps. e-mail

GRIMES, William P.; '82 BS; POB 1322, Big Pine Key, FL 33043, 305 872-3547.

GRIMM, Matthew B.; '95 BA; Police Ofcr.; M.T.A.P.D., 341 Madison, New York, NY 10017, 212 878-1000; r. 1404 Thompson Dr., Bay Shore, NY 11706, 631 968-0798.

GRINAGE, David F.; '90 BS; MS New York Inst. of Tech; Sergeant; New York Police Dept., 1 Police Plz., New York, NY 10038, 212 374-5300; r. 271 Van Buren St., Brooklyn, NY 11221; *Penny;* David A., Nia S. e-mail

GRIPPI, Ada; '91 MPA; BA Fordham Univ., Clg. at Lincoln Ctr.; Astoria, NY 11102, 718 278-3343.

GRISALES, Claudia; '99 BA; CUNY Ofc. Asst.; John Jay Clg., 445 W 59th St., Ext. 2883, New York, NY 10019, 212 237-8000; r. 87-10 37th Ave. #406, Jackson Hts., NY 11372, 718 426-5994.

GROBLUSKI, George F.; '79 MA; 80 Lincoln Ave., Brentwood, NY 11717.

GRODE, George F.; '73 MPA; BA Univ. of Windsor; Ins. Exec.; r. 109 Allendale Way, Camp Hill, PA 17011, 717 763-0230.

GROGAN, Dennis; '92 BS; Income Tax Preparation; Dennis Grogan, 1274 Richmond Ave., Staten Island, NY 10314, 718 983-1110; r. 810 Coolidge Ave., Woodbridge, NJ 07095, 732 634-8186; *Angela.* e-mail

GROGAN, Lorna A.; '84 BA; Civil Rights Analyst; US Dept. of HUD, Five Points Plz., 40 Marietta St. SW, Atlanta, GA 30305, 404 331-5001; r. 2240 Castle Royale Dr., Lawrenceville, GA 30043, 770 513-1176.

GROGER, Kathleen M.; '76 MA; Retired; NYPD; r. 1130 Stadium Ave., Bronx, NY 10465, 718 828-0389.

GROM, Peter J.; '78 BS; 1740 Grove St., Flushing, NY 11385, 718 386-1361.

GROOMS, Cordell; '92 BA; 195 Underhill Ave., Brooklyn, NY 11238.

GROSS, Arthur; '87 BA; MD Brown Univ.; OBGYN; r. 450 Lewis St., Ft. Lee, NJ 07024. e-mail

GROSS, Daniel; '78 BA; 1055 N New York Dr., Massapequa, NY 11758.

GROSS, Jacob A.; '96 BS; 100 S Fairview Ave., Bayport, NY 11705.

GROSS, Kenneth D.; '78 BA; 6756 Greatnews Ln., Columbia, MD 21044, 410 730-8726.

GROSS, Roger A.; '77 BS; MED Marymount Univ.; Police Inspector; US Treas./Bur.of Engrv & Printing Police, 14th & C St. SW, Washington, DC 20228, 202 874-7350; r. 9120 Silver Pointe Way, Fairfax Sta., VA 22039. e-mail

GROSS, Solomon; '74 MA; 3 Gregory Ln., Simsbury, CT 06070.

GROSSMAN, David L.; '80 BS; 445 Spruce La, E. Meadow, NY 11554, 516 681-6320.

GROSSMAN, Jack; '84 MPA; 5852 212th St., Flushing, NY 11364.

GROSSMAN, Lisa; '94 BS; 264 Lexington Aven, New York, NY 10016.

GROSSMAN, Martin; '77 BA; 10460 Queens Blvd. Apt. 3t, Flushing, NY 11375.

GROSSMAN, Steven H.; '93 BS; 484 Pompey Ave., Staten Island, NY 10312, 718 698-4045.

GROSSO, Joseph D.; '73 BS; 47 Cannon Dr., Holbrook, NY 11741, 631 589-8342.

GROSSO, Ralph; '84 MPA; 3430 Aquetong Rd, Carversville, PA 18913.

GRUENSTRASS, Steven; '91 BS; Sales Rep.; MCS Canon, New York, NY 10017; r. 63 Arthur Ct., Port Chester, NY 10573, 914 939-5035; *Jennifer.*

GRULLON, Johanny; '98 BA; Tchr.; PS 189, 2580 Amsterdam Ave., New York, NY 10004, 212 923-8300; r. 2825 Claflin Ave. #2n, Bronx, NY 10468, 718 796-7741.

GRULLON, Mario E.; '89 BA; 865 Amsterdam Ave., New York, NY 10025, 212 865-3575.

GRUNSKI, Alexander F.; '77 BS; 1800 Gough St., San Francisco, CA 94109.

GRUSPIER, Charles G.; '87 BS; 86-06 155th Ave., Howard Bch., NY 11414.

GRZANKA, Emily J.; '98 MA; BS IL State Univ., Loyola Univ., Chicago-Law; Student; Loyola Univ. Chicago Sch. of Law; r. 5852 N Kingsdale Ave., Chicago, IL 60646, 773 282-0827. e-mail

GU, Christopher K.; '96 BS; Special Agt.; US Dept. of State Bur. Diplomatic Sec., 799 Un Plza, New York, NY 10017, 212 415-4479; r. 10464 42nd Ave., Flushing, NY 11368, 718 779-3414. e-mail

GUADAGNO, Carmine; '79 BA; 7261 Shore Rd Apt. 1w, Brooklyn, NY 11209.

GUAGENTI, Alfonso P.; '85 BS; 174 New York Ave., Congers, NY 10920.

GUAJARDO, Jacqueline; '96 MA; BA, DOCTOR City Clg.; Clinical Psychologist; City Clg.; r. 152 Lincoln Pl., Brooklyn, NY 11217, 718 399-3891. e-mail

GUALBERTO, Edgar M.; '94 BS; 17 Scarlet Dr., Parlin, NJ 08859.

GUARCO, Anthony; '75 BS; Correctional Sergeant; Mid-Orange Correctional Facility, Warwick, NY 10990, 914 986-2291; r. 366 Byrne Ave., Staten Island, NY 10314, 718 761-6261.

GUARDINO, Deborah; '85 BS; 85-30 80 St., Brooklyn, NY 11209, 718 743-8065.

GUARINO, Jerry C.; '94 MA; 2511 33rd St., Long Island City, NY 11102, 718 474-7015.

GUARINO, John M.; '79 MA; POB 77, Far Rockaway, NY 11695, 718 474-7015.

GUARINO, Nicholas E.; '76 MA; 9051 55th Ave., Elmhurst, NY 11373.

GUARNA, Vanessa K.; '98 BA; 1230 Avenue X 2d, Brooklyn, NY 11235, 718 648-6893.

GUARNIERI, Rosemarie; '77 BS; 105 Broadway, W. Hempstead, NY 11552.

GUARNOTTA, Jacqueline R. '93 (See Haaland, Mrs. Jacqueline R.).

GUASTELLA, Joan; '97 BS; 16-23 W. 8th St., Brooklyn, NY 11223, 718 382-6343.

GUASTELLA, Maria; '91; 103 Stafford Ave., Staten Island, NY 10312, 718 761-9942.

GUAYAMA, Juanita R.; '93 BS; 3743 88th St. Apt. 4g, Flushing, NY 11372.

GUCLEN, Ender; '97 BA; 2755 E.26th St., Brooklyn, NY 11235.

GUDAT, John F.; '83 BA, '99 MS; Battalion Chief; NYC Fire Dept., 9 Metrotech Ctr., Brooklyn, NY 11201, 718 999-2000; r. 8 Sheafe Cir., Rock Tavern, NY 12575, 914 496-7274. e-mail

GUDINO, Sheila D.; '95 BA; 41 Southridge Dr., Glen Cove, NY 11542.

GUDOWITZ, Peter M.; '89 BA; 1490 E Mineral Pl., Littleton, CO 80122, 303 797-1883.

GUERRA, Cecilia M.; '97 BA; Cargo Security Prog. Mgr.; Fed. Aviation Admin., JFK Airport Bldg. 111 Rm. 150, Aea-705, Jamaica, NY 11430; r. 60-66 60 Rd. #2R, Maspeth, NY 11378, 718 628-6372. e-mail

GUERRA, Cynthia; '87 BS; 565 Crescent St., Brooklyn, NY 11208, 718 375-2145.

GUERRA, Timothy A.; '96 BA; 3551 Dane St., Shrub Oak, NY 10588, 914 245-7039.

GUERRERO, Daniel G.; '89 BS; 31-04 32nd St. #8, Astoria, NY 11106, 718 631-0503.

GUERRERO, June A.; '83 BA; 1130 E 99 St., Brooklyn, NY 11236.

GUERRERO, Katherine; '96 BS; 90-36 149th St., Jamaica, NY 11435, 718 631-0503.

GUERRERO, Noemi; '99 BA; Student; Brooklyn Clg.; r. 294 Osborne, Brooklyn, NY 11212, 718 498-3413. e-mail

GUERRERO, Wendy D.; BA, '99; 46 Wyckoff Ave., Apt. 1R, Brooklyn, NY 11237, 718 497-2244.

GUERRIER, Marline; '93 BS; 9728 57th Ave. # 10-0, Flushing, NY 11368, 718 426-2481.

GUERRIER, Michele P.; '86 BA; 1129 E 80th St., Brooklyn, NY 11236, 718 256-4393.

GUERRIER, Wendy '95 (See Stewart, Mrs. Wendy A.).

GUERRIERO, Douglas G.; '80 BS; 2627 12th St., Long Island City, NY 11102, 718 278-2793.

GUEST, Gerard A.; '76 MA; POB 933, Hampton Bays, NY 11946.

GUEVARA-WILLIAMS, D.; '96 BS; Flight Attnd.; American Airline; r. 132 N. 7th Ave., Mt. Vernon, NY 10550, 914 665-5480.

GUGEL, William H.; '86 BS; 25 Twin Oaks Dr., Kings Park, NY 11754.

GUGGENHEIM, Cordelia; '96 MA; BA Wesleyan Univ., Univ. of Arizona; Grad. Student; Univ. of Arizona; r. 1146 E. Drachman St., Tucson, AZ 85719, 520 884-4337. e-mail

GUGLIELMI, Anthony R.; '87 AS, '93 BS; 1546 74th St., Brooklyn, NY 11228.

GUGLIELMO, Christoph; '97 MS; 220 Oakdale, Bohemia, NY 11716.

GUIDO, John; '75 MA; 8613 105th St., Jamaica, NY 11418, 718 805-2695.

GUIDO, William J.; '76 BS; AAS NYC Comm. Clg.; Deputy Fire Chief; NYC Fire Dept., Brooklyn Navy, Bldg. 292, Brooklyn, NY 11205, 718 722-3404; r. 141 Dutchess Ave., Staten Island, NY 10304; David, Tanja, Stephen, William Jr. e-mail

GUILLAUME, Christa M.; '98 BS; 118-20 227 St., Cambria Hts., NY 11411, 718 525-6922.

GUILLEBEAUX, Kiesha; '92 BS; 26015 145th Ave., Jamaica, NY 11422.

GUILLOUETTE, Darlay; '92 BS; 4-74 48th Ave. Apt. 22-C, Long Island City, NY 11109.

GUINYARD, Freddie; '95 BS; 2620 Lakeside St. NE, Orangeburg, SC 29118.

GULINELLO, Joseph J.; '76 MPA; 1034 Kennedy Blvd., Bayonne, NJ 07002.

GULLIVER, Kimberly C.; '96 MA; 2056 Stewarts Corners Rd, Scipio Ctr., NY 13147.

GUMBS, Douglas J.; '92 BS; MS Stevens Inst. of Tech.; Systs. Engr.; Datavision-Prologix, 539 Jacksonville Rd., Warminster, PA 18974, 201 995-9665; r. 35 Nottingham Rd., Ramsey, NJ 07446, 201 327-3160. e-mail

GUMBS, Nailah; '97 BA; 88-14 211th St., Queens Vlg., NY 11427, 718 341-2444.

GUMLEY, Laura M. '98 (See Fontana, Mrs. Laura M.).

GUNDERSEN, William; '76 BS; 3401 Bruswick Rd., Greensboro, NC 27407.

GUNERARD, Gabrielle R.; '95 MA; Special Agt.; US Secret Svc., 7 World Trade Ctr. 9th Fl., New York, NY 10048, 212 637-4500; r. 160-35 26th Ave., Flushing, NY 11358, 718 747-3086.

GUNERARO, Gabrielle R.; '95 MA; 119-05 28th Ave., Flushing, NY 11354.

GUNN, Robert (Bob); '76 BS; Customer Svc. Rep.; Chase Manhattan, New York, NY 10018, 212 819-2785; r. 77 Meyer Ln., Medford, NY 11763, 631 289-6185.

GUNNING, Jeanne B.; '82 BS; 35 Manchester Rd, Eastchester, NY 10709.

GURAL, Gary P.; '78 BS; 2214 35th St., Long Island City, NY 11105, 718 296-4937.

GURIELOV, Shalva; '84 BS; Police Ofcr.; NYC Police Dept./Central Warrant & Inv, 314 W 40th St., New York, NY 10018, 212 736-2834; r. 104-40 Queens Blvd., #15H, Forest Hills, NY 11375, 718 896-8308.

GURIERREZ, Geraldine '85 (See Gutierrez, Geraldine).

GUSKI, Christopher J.; '98 BS; Civil Svc.; r. 50 E Lovell St., Mahopac, NY 10541, 914 628-9386.

GUSKIN, Barbara S.; '96 BA; 2928 W. 5th St., Brooklyn, NY 11224.

GUSTAFSON, Linda A.; '79 BS; 1545 E. 45th St., Brooklyn, NY 11234.

GUSTAVE, Grevirlene; '91 BS; 94-09 199 St., Hollis, NY 11423.

GUTHRIE, Thomas J.; '69 BS; 11 Elissa Ln., Tappan, NY 10983.

GUTIERRAZ, Raisa '84 (See Gutierrez-donnard, Raisa).

GUTIERREZ, Edith; '99 BA; 98-05 23 Ave., E. Elmhurst, NY 11369, 718 456-2114.

GUTIERREZ, Geraldine, (Geraldine Gurierrez); '85 BA; Asst. Dir.; Beth Israel Med. Ctr.; r. 2911 Barnes Ave., 14 C, Bronx, NY 10467, 718 515-2984; *Ruben Lopez;* Jade Lopez, Shane Lopez. e-mail

GUTIERREZ, Johanna; '97 BA; 2950 W 24th St. Apt. 9F, Brooklyn, NY 11224, 718 919-3747.

GUTIERREZ, Shamaine; '86 BS; 261 Hollywood Ave., Bronx, NY 10465.

GUTIERREZ-DONNARD, Raisa, (Raisa Gutierraz); '84 BS; MST Fordham Univ., MSA Rutgers Univ.; Richboro, PA 18954.

GUTKIN, Jonathan M.; '95 BS; 117 Howsington Pl., Hightstown, NJ 08520, 609 448-8192. e-mail

GUTMAN, Laura; '97 MA, '98 MA; 69-39 Yellowstone Blvd. #610, Forest Hills, NY 11375, 718 380-7794.

GUTTENPLAN, Sheldon; '87 BA; 675 Avenue Z Apt. 3B, Brooklyn, NY 11223.

GUY, Victor; '96 BS; Clerk; Centrex; r. 934 Montgomery St., Brooklyn, NY 11213, 718 467-4360. e-mail

GUY, Yvette D.; '81 BA; Mgmt. Support Spec.; Social Security Admin., 67-10 Myrtle Ave., Glendale, NY 11385, 718 417-7824; r. 497 Euclid Ave., Brooklyn, NY 11208, 718 277-6306. e-mail

GUYET, Allan R.; '74 BA, '78 MA; MPA Univ. of New Haven; Dir. of Police & Security; Vanderbilt Univ., 2800 Vanderbilt Pl., Nashville, TN 37212, 615 343-9750; r. 1017 Overhills Ct., Old Hickory, TN 37138, 615 758-4875; *Alberta.* e-mail

GUYOT, Dorothy; BA Univ. of Chicago, MA PHD Yale Univ.; Dir. of Intl. Educ.; DePauw Univ., The Intl Ctr., Greencastle, IN 46135, 765 658-4373; r. 616 Ridge Ave., Greencastle, IN 46135, 765 655-1111; *James F.;* Erik, Maria Khin, Daniel. e-mail

GUZMAN, Damary; '96 BA; Fraud Investigator; City of NY, Bronx, NY 10460, 718 617-8840; r. 1265 Walton Ave. #2CC, Bronx, NY 10452, 718 538-3438.

GUZMAN, Danny R.; '99 BA; Police Ofcr.; NYPD, 1 Police Plz., New York, NY 10032, 212 927-3200; r. 989 E. 167th St., Bronx, NY 10459, 718 861-9403; *Elizabeth.* e-mail

GUZMAN, Edward E.; '99 BA; 94-25 57 Ave., Elmhurst, NY 11373, 718 393-0666; *Nyomi Miranda.* e-mail

GUZMAN, Elizabeth K.; '98 AS; AS; Community Worker; Talbot Perkins Children Svcs., 250 E. Houston St., New York, NY 10002, 212 674-7733; r. 55 La Salle St. Apt. 20E, New York, NY 10027, 212 749-4649; Jocelyn, Jasmine. e-mail

GUZMAN, Jose A.; '95 BS; 1349 Stratford Ave. Apt. 5h, Bronx, NY 10472, 718 299-8210.

GUZMAN, Neida V.; '89 BS; 2000 Daly Ave. # E, Bronx, NY 10460, 718 515-3116.

GUZMAN, Nelson; '99 BS; Employee Discipline/Investigator; NYC-Dept. of Buildings, Investigations,Audits,& Discipline, 11 Park Pl., 2nd Fl., New York, NY 10007, 212 442-2000; r. 220 E. 102nd St., #7G, New York, NY 10029, 212 996-6710. e-mail

GUZMAN, Paul N.; '79 BS; 227-05 88th Ave., Queens Vlg., NY 11427, 718 847-0344.

GUZMAN, Rosa; '97 BA; 724 Gerard Ave.F1, Bronx, NY 10451, 718 220-6096.

GUZMAN, Rosa E.; '95 BA; CERT. EOC Bronx Community; Med. Asst.; Our Lady of Mercy Med. Ctr., 600 E 233rd St., Bronx, NY 10466, 718 920-9821; r. 1309 Washington Ave. Apt. 9d, Bronx, NY 10456, 718 681-1378; Victor, Carlos.

GUZMAN, Saul; '99 BA; Political Sci. Student; Brooklyn Clg.; r. 2068 E. 18th St., #1, Brooklyn, NY 11229, 718 998-0491.

GUZZARDI, Joseph; '97 MA; 40-18 Francis, Bayside, NY 11361.

GUZZO, Louis G.; '97 BS; 154 Morris Pkwy., Valley Stream, NY 11580.

GUZZO, Scott R.; '98 BS; Svc. Sales Rep.; Siemens Bldg. Tech, POB 2034, Pine Brook, NJ 07058, 973 276-3564; r. POB 172, Greendell, NJ 07839.

GWYN, Christine, (Gwyn Johnson); '95 BS; Job Developer; Job Path,Inc., 22-24 W. 38th St., New York, NY 10018, 212 944-0564; r. 118-20 180th St., St. Albans, NY 11434, 718 525-8187; Benjamin; Darien, Britany, Daniel.

GYENES, Albert R., Jr.; '94 BS; Special Agt.; Drug Enforcement Admin., 99 Tenth Ave., New York, NY 10011; r. 47 Macarthur Ave., Hasbrouck Hts., NJ 07604.

GYSS, Henry F., '67 MPA; BS St. John's Univ.; Retired; r. 17 Beaverbrook Dr., Toms River, NJ 08757, 732 349-4678.

H

HAAG, Edward C.; '70 BA, '75 MA; JD Brooklyn Law Sch.; Gen. Practice Atty.; Edward C. Haag Atty-at-Law, 2070 Easth 65th St., Brooklyn, NY 11234, 718 763-3182; r. 2070 E 65th St., Brooklyn, NY 11234, 718 763-3182.

HAALAND, Mrs. Jacqueline R., (Jacqueline R. Guarnotta); '93 BS; NYC Police Ofcr.; NYC Police Dept., 111th Precinct, Queens, NY 11412; r. 76-01 69th Rd., Middle Vlg., NY 11379; Eric.

HAAR, Barry M.; '79 MA; JD Nova Law Sch.; Chief Investigator; NYS Dept. of Taxation & Finance, Petroleum Alcohol & Tobacco Bureau, 2 World Trade Ctr., New York, NY 10048; r. 6623 Austin St. Apt. 5f, Forest Hills, NY 11374, 718 897-4390.

HAAS, John J.; '67 MPA; 4 Pierce Dr., Commack, NY 11725, 631 499-7847.

HABASHZADA, Halai; '99; 37-07 147th St., Flushing, NY 11354.

HABER, Edward; '90 BA; c/o Celi, 15 Olive, Brooklyn, NY 11209, 718 802-1288.

HABERFELD, Maria M.; '90 MA, '92; POB 709, Closter, NJ 07624.

HABERSTOCK, John G.; '93 BA; 2170 Crescent St., Apt. 6C, Long Island City, NY 11105.

HACKENMILLER, Julie; '98 MA; BA Univ. of Northern Iowa; Mitigation Spec; Inquisitor Inc., 222 South Ave. N., Ste. 415, Nashville, TN 37201, 615 254-4181; r. 111 Old Hickory Blvd. Apt. 259, Nashville, TN 37221, 615 673-6551. e-mail

HACKETT, George A.; '76 MA, BS; AS City Univ.; Retired-Chmn.; Rockland Community Clg., Criminal Justice Dept.; r. 433 Blauvelt Rd, Blauvelt, NY 10913, 914 359-3599.

HACKETT, Joseph E.; '77 BA; 1819 Radcliff Ave., Bronx, NY 10462, 718 892-0272.

HACKETT, Michelle A.; '93 BS; Investigator/Homemaker; r. 354 Hancock St., Brooklyn, NY 11216, 718 452-7071.

HACKETT-VIERA, Tessa I., (Hackett Tessa); '79 BS; MSW Columbia Sch. of Soc Wk; Social Worker; Dist. Counsel 37, Legal Services Plan, New York, NY 10007, 212 815-1866; r. 244 Lefferts Ave., Brooklyn, NY 11225, 718 284-2866; Andre' Viera, Kevin Viera.

HACKFORD, Donald E.; '77 BS; 193 Cushing Ave., Williston Park, NY 11596, 516 873-8864.

HACKLE, Kirk D.; '89 BS; 3816 Review Pl. Apt. 2f, Bronx, NY 10463.

HADE, Patrick J.; '77 BS; Landscaper; Morgan Corp., Charlotte, NC 28204; r. 1731 Lake Lee Dr., Monroe, NC 28112, 704 292-7626; Rachel; Payton, Lois, Sydra.

HADJIDEMETRIOU, George; '93 BS; Fed. Ofcr.; Justice Dept., New York, NY 10014; r. 22-21 35 St., Astoria, NY 11105, 718 956-6581. e-mail

HADLEY, David C.; '95 BS; Caseworker; Concord Family Svcs., Clothing Designer, Brooklyn, NY 11205; r. 277 Washington Ave., Brooklyn, NY 11205, 718 622-1227.

HADLEY-BAILEY, Cynthia; '75 BA; 3 Hickory Rd, W. Orange, NJ 07052. e-mail

HADZI, Brahimovic S.; '97 BS; 25-77 38th St., Astoria, NY 11103.

HAGAN, Andrew A.; '78 BS; Firefighter; NYC Fire Dept., New York, NY 10001; r. 62 Superior Rd, Floral Park, NY 11001, 516 358-9892; Margaret; Alexander A., Thomas.

HAGAN, Thomas; '79 BS; 4171 249th St., Flushing, NY 11363.

HAGAN, William P.; '79 BS; 67 Fulton Ave., Atlantic Bch., NY 11509.

HAGERTY, Brian D.; '89 BS; 76-07 79 Pl., Glendale, NY 11385.

HAGGERTY, James J.; '80 MA; 13 Cypress St., Keyport, NJ 07735, 732 264-6029.

HAGGERTY, Michael C.; '85 BS, '90 MA; Special Agt.; Bur. Alcohol Tobacco & Firearms, 200 Chestnut St. Ste. 500, Philadelphia, PA 19106, 215 597-2167; r. Philadelphia, PA 19106; Carole; Joseph.

HAGIN, Karen M.; '77 BA; 440 Neptune Ave. #11E, Brooklyn, NY 11224, 718 375-5498.

HAGUE, George T.; '70 BS; 219 Wickley Rd, Philadelphia, PA 19154, 215 632-9076.

HAHN, Harold; '76 BS; Med. Legal Invgtr/Phys. Asst.; Chief Med. Examiner's Ofc. NYC, 616 Crawford Ave., Brooklyn, NY 11223, 212 447-2413; r. same, 718 646-7436. e-mail

HAHN, John J.; '79 MA; 181 Sprain Rd, Scarsdale, NY 10583, 914 271-0999.

HAHN, Robert; '91 BS; 100 Park Ter. W Apt. 3G, New York, NY 10034.

HAILEY, Cathy L.; '83 BA; 306 Van Buren St., Brooklyn, NY 11221, 718 443-1053.

HAINES, James V.; '77 BS, '88 BA; Retired Police Ofcr.; 20th Prec.NYCPD, New York, NY; r. 7705 30th Ave., # 1, Flushing, NY 11370, 718 397-8727; James, Scott.

HAIR, Robert A.; '71 MPA; Prof.; John Jay Clg. of Criminal Justice, 899 10th Ave., New York, NY 10019, 212 239-8380; r. 815 Park Ave., New York, NY 10021; Frances T.; Barbara, James.

HAIRE, Christine; '97 BS; Child Welfare Spec.; ACS, 150 Williams St., New York, NY 10038; r. 456 Schenectady Ave., Apt. 1R, Brooklyn, NY 11203, 718 778-8063; Iyana.

HAIRSTON, Debra R.; '84 MPA; 200 Cozine Ave., Brooklyn, NY 11207, 718 493-9370.

HAIRSTON, Lucinia; '91 BS; 194-29 111th Rd., St. Albans, NY 11412, 718 592-0820.

HAJAREE, Sabita '95 (See Hajaree-Ramsaran, Mrs. Sabita).

HAJAREE-RAMSARAN, Mrs. Sabita, (Sabita Hajaree); '95 BA MA; JD Touro Clg., Law Center; J.D. Candidate; Touro Clg.,Jacob D.Fuchsberg, Law Ctr., 300 Nassau Rd., Huntington, NY 11743; r. 1377 Brooklyn Blvd., Bay Shore, NY 11706, 631 968-8177; Anand Ramsaran; Aryanna S. e-mail

HAJISAVA, John; '83 BS; Regional Dir. of Sales NE; Prism Communication Svcs., 770 Broadway, New York, NY 10003.

HAKIM, Laurie J.; '96 BA; 3291 First St., Oceanside, NY 11572, 516 365-5750.

HALBOHN, Donald F.; '80 BS; 159-11 101 St., Howard Bch., NY 11414.

HALE, Altina M.; '91 BA; 1054 E 219th St., Bronx, NY 10469, 718 881-2649.

HALE, Thomas M.; '92 BS; 2065 59th St., Brooklyn, NY 11204, 718 857-1576.

HALECKI, Krzysztof; '89 BS; 6210 99th St. Apt. 2a, Flushing, NY 11374.

HALFPENNY, Peter; '77 BS; 94-29 109 Ave., Ozone Park, NY 11417.

HALKA, Jill A.; '94 MA; 111 College Rd., Apt. 3K, Selden, NY 11784.

HALKIAS, John E.; '95 BS; 2120 62nd St., Brooklyn, NY 11204, 718 234-2938.

HALL, Cheryl A.; '81 BS; 2726 Hone Ave., Bronx, NY 10469, 718 295-7129.

HALL, David E.; '72 BA; 11 Hilltop Tr., Andover, NJ 07821, 973 347-7786.

HALL, Debra E.; '98 BA; 654 Macon St., Brooklyn, NY 11233, 718 455-5749.

HALL, Debra L. '95 (See Hall-Martin, Mrs. Debra L.).

HALL, MSgt Everett M., USAFR; '93 BS; AA Comm.Clg of The Air Force, Aircruz Operations; Fed. Investigator; New York, NY 10001; r. 10-20K Richman Plz., Bronx, NY 10453, 718 294-8922; *Sandra;* Yvette.

HALL, James; '96 BS; CCDC, CPC Baltimore MD; Certified Chemical Dep Couns.; Baltimore Health Dept. Rehab Center, 9100 Franklin Square Dr., Baltimore, MD 21237, 410 887-6465; r. 8429 Old Harford, Apt. F, Baltimore, MD 21234, 410 882-8371; *Carole;* Marcia, Leslie, Dale, Ernie.

HALL, James R.; '76 AS, '78 BA, '82 MPA; Dir. of Public Safety; NYC Technical Clg., 300 Jay St., Brooklyn, NY 11201, 718 260-5550; r. 120-14 Elgar Pl. #14H, Bronx, NY 10475, 718 320-1152; *Olive;* Kim, Robin, Aisha. e-mail

HALL, John J.; '99 BS; Lt.; NYCPD, 1 Police Plz., New York, NY 10038; r. 38 Elliott St., Islip, NY 11751, 631 277-0262; *Kathleen;* Elizabeth, Sean.

HALL, Lesley A.; '93 BS; 1808 E 53rd St., # 2, Brooklyn, NY 11234, 718 363-2447.

HALL, Minnie M., (Minnie Majette); '82 BS; Real Estate; r. 2141 Partridge Pl., Suffolk, VA 23433; *Wilbert.*

HALL, Ruben T.; '98 BA; Police Ofcr.; NYCPD, New York, NY 10001; r. 932 E. 99th St., Brooklyn, NY 11236, 718 498-2927. e-mail

HALL, Tyson W.; '93 AA; Performer; Tyson Hall; r. 560 Main St. Apt. 705, New York, NY 10044, 800 393-0249. e-mail

HALLAHAN, Thomas R.; '80 MA; 1502 St. Lawrence A, Bronx, NY 10460.

HALLEN, Joseph T.; '79 BS; 5718 254th St., Flushing, NY 11362.

HALLETT, Sarah J.; '91 MA; 6336 N Oracle Rd, Tucson, AZ 85704, 520 408-2793.

HALLEY, Ms. Stacey A.; '93 BA, '97 MPA; Investigator; Smyrna, GA 30080, 678 309-0777; r. 2195 Q Lake Park Dr., Smyrna, GA 30080, 678 309-0777. e-mail

HALL-MARTIN, Mrs. Debra L., (Debra L. Hall); '95 BA; Res. Coord.; Ofc. of Ct. Admin., Manhatten Treatment Ct., 100 Centre St., New York, NY 10013, 212 374-7880; r. 950 Underhill Ave. Apt. 18h, Bronx, NY 10473, 718 861-0032; *David.*

HALLORAN, Frank H.; '80 MPA; 45 Lexington Blvd., Clark, NJ 07066, 732 381-1768.

HALPERN, Mitchell; '92 BS; 102-17 97 Ave., Ozone Park, NY 11416, 718 847-1777.

HALPERN, Samuel B.; '89 MA; 70 Southard Ln., Babylon, NY 11702.

HALTON, Darreiel A.; '95 BS; LAW Brooklyn Law Sch.; On Campus Coord.; Skadden Arps Slate Meagher & Flom, 4 Times Sq., New York, NY 10036; r. 2300 Sedgwick Ave. Apt. 6d, Bronx, NY 10468, 718 364-5258; Larelle. e-mail

HAM, Gustavo; '94 BS; Police Ofcr.; NYC Police Dept.; r. 332 Frederick Ave., Bellmore, NY 11710, 516 804-0012.

HAM, Sung; '97 BS; PARALEG. Long Island Univ.; Paralegal; r. 471 5th Ave.2A, Brooklyn, NY 11215, 718 768-2949. e-mail

HAMBLIN, Desmond M.; '75 BS; 317 Comstock Ave., San Marcos, CA 92069, 760 471-6984.

HAMEL, William; '91 MA; 540 Bergen St., Brooklyn, NY 11217.

HAMIDEH, Hamza; '99 BA; 94 Saint Andrews Pl., Yonkers, NY 10705, 914 966-0638.

HAMILTON, Carl; '73 AS, '84 BS; Pres.; Hamilton's Properties, POB 521, Newburgh, NY 12550, 914 883-7059; r. 284 Hull Ave., Clintondale, NY 12515, 914 883-7059; Eric, Melanie.

HAMILTON, H. S.; '90 AS; Police Ofcr.; r. 13730 68th Dr., Flushing, NY 11367, 718 793-1660.

HAMILTON, Jennifer M.; '99 BA; 50 28 193 St., Fresh Meadows, NY 11365, 718 746-0055.

HAMILTON, Kevin P.; '99 BA; Paralegal; Menicor Herrmann, 10 E 40th St., New York, NY 10021, 212 545-1900; r. 2067 Edenwald Ave., Bronx, NY 10466, 718 655-4572.

HAMILTON, Rudolph H.; '97 AS; 172-70 Highland Ave., Jamaica, NY 11432, 718 318-1769.

HAMILTON, Smallwood; '90 BA; 10934 203rd St., Jamaica, NY 11412, 718 526-4172.

HAMM, Tushan S.; '98 BA; 200 W 118th St. #2D, New York, NY 10026, 315 858-1492.

HAMMEL, Manuela M.; '80 BS; 504 Lincoln Blvd. #2, Long Beach, NY 11561, 516 897-7931.

HAMMER, Charles M.; '98 BS; Police Ofcr.; NYPD, 43rd Precient, Bronx, NY 10465; r. 101 B Edgewater Park, Bronx, NY 10465, 718 824-3840.

HAMMER, David S.; '83 MA; BA City Clg. of New York; Parole Ofcr.; NYS Div. of Parole, 260 E. 161 St., Bronx, NY 10451, 718 292-6538; r. 100 Donizetti Pl., # 10-G, Bronx, NY 10475, 718 379-0059; *Norca;* Ramsey, Melissa, Jennifer.

HAMMIE, Keith D.; '87 BS; 865 Columbus Ave. Apt. 20e, New York, NY 10025, 212 666-9487.

HAMMOND, Avis; '78 BA; 184 Washington Pk, Brooklyn, NY 11205, 718 692-2560.

HAMMOND, Gregory C.; '84 BS; 32 Grove Pl., Whippany, NJ 07981.

HANCE, Ms. Rachel; '92 BA; Police Ofcr.; NYC Police Dept., 1 Police Plz., New York, NY 10009, 212 477-9200; r. 419 E. 93rd St., New York, NY 10128; David, Devin.

HANCOCK, Stephen C.; '87 BS; 2110 Hermany Ave., Bronx, NY 10473.

HANDMAN, Stuart W.; '79 BS; AS; Bus Operator/TWU Representative; NYCTA, 2449 Harway Ave., Ulmer Park Garage, Brooklyn, NY 11214, 917 388-6260; r. 1511 Brightwater Ave., Brooklyn, NY 11235, 718 332-7899; *Carmela;* Elizabeth, Jacqueline, Stephanie, Peter.

HANDY, Mitzu E.; '95 BA; 455 Schenectady Ave. #1H, Brooklyn, NY 11203, 718 680-5337.

HANEY, Stephen M.; '90 BS; 1829 59th St., Brooklyn, NY 11204.

HANIFF, Zahirudeen; '97 BA; 1421 Fteley Ave., Bronx, NY 10472.

HANKINS, Michael; '91 BA; 665 New York Ave., Brooklyn, NY 11203, 718 771-6452.

HANLEY, Gary T.; '83 BS; 3 Derby Dr., Peekskill, NY 10566, 914 736-7760.

HANLEY, John J.; '96 BA; 64 Margaret St., Staten Island, NY 10308, 718 966-8646.

HANLEY, Samuel; '76 BS; 121 E 45th St., Brooklyn, NY 11203, 718 336-5886.

HANLON, James O.; '84 BS; 62 Chatterton Pkwy., White Plains, NY 10606.

HANNA, George J.; '76 BS; 84 E 2nd St., Brooklyn, NY 11218.

HANNA, Patrick J.; '76 BA; 17841 146th Ter., Jamaica, NY 11434, 718 978-9542.

HANNA, Richard; '96 AS; Correctional Ofcr.; Essex Cnty. Correctional Ctr., 45 Elm Rd, Caldwell, NJ 07006, 973 364-5329; r. 476 Joralemon St., E1, Belleville, NJ 07109, 973 759-9091; *Suzanne.* e-mail

HANNEY, Thomas V.; '89 BS; 22 Edsall Ave., Nanuet, NY 10954, 914 624-1524.

HANNIBAL, Louise; '80 BS, '93 MPA; Sr. Court Ofcr.; NYS Courts, 718 520-3716; r. 21134 45th Dr., Flushing, NY 11361, 718 631-3513; *James;* Maya. e-mail

HANNIGAN, James R.; '75 BS; 148 Woodland Ave., Yonkers, NY 10703, 914 965-9913.

HANOLD, George M.; '75 BA; Box 307 Scarborogh, Scarborough, NY 10510.

HANOVER, Scott W.; '95 BS; Capt.; NYPD; r. 6471 84th St. Ph, Flushing, NY 11379; *Margaret;* Jeffrey, Allison, Elizabeth.

HANRAHAN, Claire T.; '94 BS; 3982 44th St. # P, Long Island City, NY 11104, 718 428-8174.

HANRAHAN, Joseph J.; '72 BA, '75 MA; POB 2044, Westfield, MA 01086.

HANSBERRY, Wellingto; '96 BA; 9930 193rd St., Jamaica, NY 11423.

HANSEN, Brett P.; '99 BS; EMS Mgmt. Student; MCP Hahnemann Univ; r. 12 Toad Pasture Rd, Westtown, NY 10998, 914 858-4156.

HANSEN, Glenn J.; '80 BS; Pres. & CEO; BPA Intl., 270 Madison Ave., New York, NY 10016, 212 779-3200; r. 94 Rowland Rd, Fairfield, CT 06430, 203 255-7458; *Pat;* John Peter, Meredith, James. e-mail

HANSEN, Robert C.; '82 BS; 210 93rd St., Brooklyn, NY 11209, 718 383-3733.

HANSEN, Ronald; '97 BA; 81 Monitor St., Brooklyn, NY 11222, 718 383-3733.

HANSON, Charles J.; '75 BS; Retired Police Ofcr.; r. 195 Stony Bar Rd, Slate Hill, NY 10973, 914 355-3101; *Patricia;* Matthew, Patricia, Jennifer, Eric.

HANSON, Diane R.; '81 BS; 101-21 97th St., Ozone Park, NY 11416.

HAQUE, Ferdous; '98 BA; Admnistrator (CUNY-Cap); Early Childhood Ctr., Borough of Manhattan Community Clg., New York, NY 10007, 212 346-8260; r. 51-09 92nd St., 3rd Fl., Elmhurst, NY 11373, 718 393-0092; *Shahnur;* Ridwan Ferdous. e-mail

HARALAMBOUS, Lambros; '97 BA; 20-31 18 St. #2, Astoria, NY 11105.

HARAN, Patricia; '82 BS; 9138 222nd St., Queens Vlg., NY 11428, 718 465-3217.

HARAN, Stephen J.; '99 MA; 217 Noel St., Staten Island, NY 10312, 718 967-1986.

HARAN, Thomas J.; 1654 W 2nd St., Brooklyn, NY 11223.

HARB, Rifat A.; '91 BS; 2519 14th Pl. # 3, Long Island City, NY 11102, 718 932-0178.

HARCOURT, Kimberly; '95 BS; Asst. Treas.; Chase Manhattan Bank, 270 Park Ave., New York, NY 10017; r. POB 3345, New York, NY 10163.

HARDEN, Sheryl D.; '84 BS; 13312 135th Ave., Jamaica, NY 11420.

HARDING, Clive D.; '93 BA; 435 Linden Blvd. PH, Brooklyn, NY 11203, 718 277-7014.

HARDING, Rev. Curtis T., Jr.; '76 BA; MDIV NY Theological Seminary; Pastor/CEO; St. Albans Baptist Church, 196-02 119th Ave., St. Albans, NY 11412, 718 723-8005; r. 660 Ivy Pl., Uniondale, NY 11553, 516 485-6292; *Inez L.* e-mail

HARDING, Jacinth A.; '99 BS; 2911 Tenbroeck Ave. 1, Bronx, NY 10469, 718 861-5964.

HARDING, Michael L.; '87 BA; 5 Black Oak Ln., Old Bridge, NJ 08857, 732 360-0058.

HARDY, Ernest T.; '76 BS; 33-36 101 St., Corona, NY 11368, 718 659-6454.

HARDY, Kevin A.; '85 BA; 110 Pearsall Dr. Apt. 1a, Mt. Vernon, NY 10552, 914 665-9328.

HARDY, Kimberly '99 (See Regester, Mrs. Kimberly).

HARDY-MAJOR, Gloria; '83 BA; 112 Odell Clark Pl. Apt. 4A, New York, NY 10030, 315 735-8840.

HARE, Ruby E.; '83 MA; DMIN Drew Univ., MDIV Union Theological Sem.; Retired Reverend; United Methodist Church; r. 93 E. Summit St., Lakewood, NY 14750, 716 763-7336. e-mail

HARFMANN, Lawrence; '89 BA; 74-48 64 Pl., Glendale, NY 11385.

HARGRAVE, Abdula R.; '95 BS; 32 Winthrop St. Apt. 1b, Brooklyn, NY 11225.

HARGRAVE, Rhonda T.; '80 BS; 16822 119th Ave., Jamaica, NY 11434.

HARGROVE, James; '77 BS; MPA LIU, JD Queens Clg.; Retired Asst. Police Commiss; NYPD; r. 601 Hawaiian Way, Kissimmee, FL 34758; *Ruth;* Michele, Jason, Tia.

HARINSKI, James; '91 BS; JD Hofstra Univ.; Atty.; Rivkin Radler & Kremer, Eab Plz., Uniondale, NY 11556, 516 357-3000; r. 68 Maple St., Massapequa, NY 11758, 516 541-8184; *Kathleen;* Patrick James. e-mail

HARKINS, Michella R.; '98 BA; 1764 Auburn Rd, Wantagh, NY 11793, 516 221-9167.

HARLEY, Beverly D.; '90 BS; 2040 Bruckner Blvd., Bronx, NY 10473.

HARMON, Ms. Amy; '99 MA; BA Boston Clg.; Investigator; NY Dept. of Investigation, 80 Maiden Ln., New York, NY 10038, 212 825-2449; r. 32 W. 76th St. #BR., New York, NY 10023, 212 496-2808.

HARMON, Michael P.; '81 BS; Police Ofcr. MTA; NYC; r. 99 Danzig Pl., Valley Stream, NY 11580, 516 285-9328.

HARMON, Teon; '93 BS; New York City Sheriff; NYC Sheriff's Dept., New York, NY 10001; r. 9314 Avenue B # 1, Brooklyn, NY 11236, 718 922-5805.

HARMON, Timothy J.; '96 BS; 11 Squirrel Dr. E., E. Rockaway, NY 11518.

HARNETT, Michael; '95 BS; 21 Worth Rd, Neptune, NJ 07753.

HARO, David I.; '97 BA; Mitigation Spec.; Defense Advocacy Svcs., Brooklyn, NY 11201, 718 388-8887; r. 11211, Jackson Hts., NY 11372.

HARP, Jeffrey D.; '91 BA; Air Duct Tech.; Air Duct Cleaning; r. 89-22 208th St., Queens Vlg., NY 11427, 718 776-6022.

HARPER, Bennie; '81 AS; Owner; r. 52 Rhodes Ave., Hempstead, NY 11550.

HARPER, Christa J.; '95 BA; 230 Lafayette Pl. Apt. 4d, Englewood, NJ 07631, 201 569-5765.

HARPER, Deborah A.; '84 BS; 11515 141st St., Jamaica, NY 11436, 718 776-9374.

HARPER, Fabian F.; '97 BA; 546 Midwood St., Brooklyn, NY 11203, 718 221-9830.

HARPER, Lawrence; '97 BA; Police Ofcr.; NYPD, 1 Police Plz., New York, NY 10038; r. Queens, NY 11412; *Diane Walker.* e-mail

HARPER, Leonard; '78 BA; Retired-Police Ofcr; Postal Svc.; NYC Police Dept.; r. 10004 Wyngate Ridge Dr., Raleigh, NC 27613, 919 786-1195.

HARPER, Lisa S.; '83 BA; 134-17 166 Pl., Jamaica, NY 11434, 718 529-7349.

HARPER, Renee Y.; '86 BA; MA POLSC Brooklyn Clg., MED Long Island Univ.; Special Asst.; NYC Bd. of Educ., 65 Court St., Brooklyn, NY 11201, 718 935-3678; r. Laurelton, NY 11413. e-mail

HARPER, Yaphet; '97 BS; 749 Pines St., Brooklyn, NY 11208, 718 951-0106.

HARPER, Yvonne '82 (See Grice, Yvonne S.).

HARRELL, Dorothea M.; '96 BS, '99 MA; Investigator; US Dept. of Labor, 6 World Trade Ctr., New York, NY 10048, 212 637-0620; r. 1360 Ocean Ave., Brooklyn, NY 11230, 718 252-4177.

HARRIGAN, Eric J.; '99 BA; Mgr. Trainee; Enterprise Rent A Car, 759 Hylan Dr., Staten Island, NY 10304, 718 351-7662; r. 71 Cromwell, Staten Island, NY 10304, 718 980-6524.

HARRIGAN, John J.; '77 BS; 344 Blacksmith Rd, Levittown, NY 11756, 516 579-9585.

HARRIGAN, Justin; '85 BS; Annas Fancy #123, St. Thomas, VI 00802.

HARRIGAN, Thomas M.; '82 BS; 1310 E 91st St., Brooklyn, NY 11236.

HARRINGTON, Dennis; '91 BS; 419 Myrtle Ave., W. Islip, NY 11795.

HARRINGTON, Irwin C.; '96 BA, '99 MS, MPA; Cert. Fire Protection Spec.; Natl. Fire Protection Assn., 400A Ft. Totten, Bayside, NY 11360, 718 352-8092; r. 100-07 222nd St., Queens Vlg., NY 11429, 718 468-6360; *Shaquanna.*

HARRINGTON, James J.; '86 MS; 719 7th Ave., River Edge, NJ 07661, 201 261-4596.

HARRINGTON, Kevin M.; '76'; 52 Nantucket Dr., Fishkill, NY 12524.

HARRIOTT, Kerry-Ann E.; '99 BS; 88-07 208 St., Queens Vlg., NY 11427, 718 341-9941.

HARRIS, Adrienne L.; '85 BS; 223 Lenox Rd Apt. B11, Brooklyn, NY 11226, 718 462-5094.

HARRIS, Adrienne R.; '83 BA; 1372 Washington Ave., Bronx, NY 10456, 718 588-1371.

HARRIS, Arthur J.; '76 BA; MSW Howard Univ.; Dir.; NYC Dept. of Corrections, 60 Hudson St., New York, NY 10013, 212 266-1066; r. 4017 Bell Ave., Bronx, NY 10466, 718 994-6769; *Jonathan.*

HARRIS, Clotilde M.; '94 MPA; 22 Weirfield St., Brooklyn, NY 11221, 718 230-5364.

HARRIS, Crystal; '97 BS; 196 Throop Ave.#5, Brooklyn, NY 11206, 718 230-5364.

HARRIS, Cynthia R.; '83 BS; 1460 Washington Ave., Bronx, NY 10456, 718 671-0330.

HARRIS, Darice B. '93 (See Bynde, Darice B.).

HARRIS, Gabriella; '94 BS; Purchasing Agt.; NYU Dept. of Parks & Recreation; r. 611 W. 148th St., Apt. #1, New York, NY 10031, 212 690-1213.

HARRIS, Gene R.; '75 BS; Retired; r. 1166 Burke Ave., Bronx, NY 10469, 718 519-7322.

HARRIS, Hugh A.; '89 BS; 3530 Henry Hudson Pkwye Apt. 2H, Bronx, NY 10463, 718 325-0591.

HARRIS, Marilyn J.; '76 BA; 111-40 209th St., Queens Vlg., NY 11429, 718 529-5122.

HARRIS, Onya T.; '99 BA; AS Essex Cnty. Comm Clg.; Probation Ofcr.; r. 28 Wheeler St., Montclair, NJ 07042, 973 783-4040.

HARRIS, Rhonda L.; 522 Westgate Dr., Edison, NJ 08820, 732 545-9614.

HARRIS, Bishop Robert W.; '74 BS; Chaplain; Nassau Cnty. Police Dept., 1490 N. Franklin Ave., Mineola, NY 11501, 516 481-6929; r. 868 Spring Ave., Uniondale, NY 11553, 516 483-8111.

HARRIS, Rodney C.; '80 BS; 3414 Kingsland Ave., Bronx, NY 10469, 718 588-1906.

HARRIS, Sheila A.; '93 BS; 1230 Pennsylvania, Brooklyn, NY 11239, 718 385-8821.

HARRIS, Terrence H.; '91 AS, '92 BA, '95 MA; 523 W 157th St. Apt. 5d, New York, NY 10032, 212 928-1583.

HARRIS, Will C., III; '89 BA; Administrative Caseworker; Admin. for Children's Svcs., Dept. of Applications, 192 E 151st St., Bronx, NY 10451, 718 579-9500; r. 10 Richman Plz., Apt. 21-C, Bronx, NY 10453, 718 579-8869.

HARRISON, Alicia M.; '80 BA; 3505 Foster Ave., Brooklyn, NY 11203, 718 421-7516.

HARRISON, Emile R.; '87 BA; 675 E 140th St. Apt. 5cc, Bronx, NY 10454.

HARRISON, Henry A.; '71 BS; JD St. John's Univ.; Retired Atty.; r. 9 Saturn Blvd., Hauppauge, NY 11788, 631 360-0015; *Arleen;* Scott, Paul, Thomas. e-mail

HARRISON, Karen M.; '98 MBA; '98 MPA; BA Marymount Clg.; Res. Mgr.; Indep. Living Assoc., 110 York St., Brooklyn, NY 11201, 718 852-2000; r. 1587 E. 49th St., Brooklyn, NY 11234, 718 444-1972; Kasey Bloomfiel.

HARRISON, Olivia E.; '80 BS; 225 E 149th St. Apt. 9g, Bronx, NY 10451.

HARRISON, Patricia M.; '85 BA; 716 Lenox Rd, Brooklyn, NY 11203, 718 857-4988.

HARRISON, Sharlene '94 (See Harrison-Carera, Sharlene).

HARRISON, Tonya; '90 BS; 352 Butler St., Brooklyn, NY 11217, 718 783-3779.

HARRISON, Willie; '80 MA; BA Fordham Univ.; Deputy Supt. of Security; NYS Corrections; r. 262 43rd St., Copiague, NY 11726.

HARRISON-CARERA, Sharlene, (Sharlene Harrison); '94 BS; Legal Secy.; Kaye Scholer, 425 Park Ave., New York, NY 10017; r. 650 Warburton Ave. Apt. 4l, Yonkers, NY 10701, 914 375-0949; *Howard Carera;* Taelor. e-mail

HARROW, Tracy A.; '97 BA; 66 Country Club, Bellport, NY 11713.

HARRY, Lavern E.; '96 BA; 225 E 179th St., Bronx, NY 10457, 718 322-8341.

HART, Barry E.; 811 Marilyn Ln., Baldwin, NY 11510, 516 239-1573.

HART, Carrie A.; '97 BS, '98 BS; 100 Dekruif Pl. #13C, Bronx, NY 10475.

HART, Davis B.; '82 MA; POB 735, APO, AP 98733.

HART, Harvin; '99 BA; Police Ofcr.; NYPD, 1 Police Plz., New York, NY 10038, 212 927-1127; r. 421 W 57th St. 6A, New York, NY 10019, 212 245-1267. e-mail

HART, James R.; '80 MA; 537 18th St., Brooklyn, NY 11215, 718 346-4601.

HART, Joanne; 899 10th Ave. Rm 625, New York, NY 10019, 315 866-0157.

HART, Keith; '96 BS; 2 Red Hearth Ct., Baltimore, MD 21227, 410 536-1872.

HART, Keith R.; '80 BS; 4687 Hanford St., Flushing, NY 11362, 718 206-2630.

HART, Robert; '95 BA; 373 Euston Rd S, Garden City, NY 11530, 516 935-2912.

HART, Susin B.; '89 BS; 212 Prospect Ave., N. Arlington, NJ 07031.

HART, Todd J.; '95 BS; 67 Berby Pl., Smithtown, NY 11787.

HARTIGAN, George T.; '77 BA; 21 Keating St., Staten Island, NY 10309.

HARTLEY, Wayne; '94 BS; Correctional Ofcr.; NYC Dept. of Corrections; r. Brooklyn, NY 11216. e-mail

HARTMAN, Bryant; Editor; Tidewater Times, 1811 Hampton Blvd. #2A, Norfolk, VA 23517.

HARTMAN, Donna M.; '79 BS; 106-67 95th St., Ozone Park, NY 11417, 718 997-6360.

HARTNETT, Michael J.; '77 BS; 340 Lovell St., Mahopac, NY 10541, 914 628-8249.

HARTNETT, Sharon M.; '82 MA; Tchr.; LD Brandeis HS, 145 W 84 St., New York, NY 10024, 917 441-5600; r. 230 W 105th St. Apt. 2e, New York, NY 10025, 212 749-8731; *Robert Majcher;* Megan, Maeve. e-mail

HARTT, Kevin J.; '78 BS; 150 Hunter Ave., Miller Place, NY 11764.

HARTZOG, Adam C.; '99 BA; AS Manchester Community Tech; Mental Health Assoc.; Connecticut Valley Hosp., Middletown, CT 06457; r. 102 Wetherell St., Unit 30, Manchester, CT 06040, 860 646-9791. e-mail

HARVEY, Beverly; '93 BA; Correction Ofcr.; NYC Dept. of Corrections, Criminal Court Bldg., 215 E. 161st St., Bronx, NY 10451, 718 590-2981; r. 315 E. 143rd St. Apt. 7b, Bronx, NY 10451, 718 585-3709. e-mail

HARVEY, Brian F.; '77 BS; 6046 Tyndall Ave., Bronx, NY 10471, 718 681-7872.

HARVEY, Charmaine P.; '95 BS; Investigator; Human Resources Admin. City of NY, New York, NY 10001; r. 10745 166th St., Jamaica, NY 11433, 718 657-3217. e-mail

HARVEY, Edmund P.; '76 BS; 6046 Tyndall Ave., Bronx, NY 10471.

HARVEY, Ms. Wendy B.; '98 BS; Mutual Funds Rep.; Herzog Heine Geduld Inc., 525 Washington Buld., New Port Twr., Jersey City, NJ 07310, 201 418-4548; r. 740 Williams Ave., Brooklyn, NY 11207, 718 927-0437; Dane.

HARVILLA, Joseph; '91 BS; 573 E Maine Rd, Johnson City, NY 13790, 607 729-1928.

HASAN, Samiuddin; '95 BS; POB 518, Brooklyn, NY 11235.

HASAN, Zaheeruddin S.; '97 BS; 41 Brighton 10th, Brooklyn, NY 11235.

HASELL, Henry V.; 172-14 133 Ave. #13D, Jamaica, NY 11434.

HASHIMI, Muhammad; '85 MA; 274 Keller Ave., Elmont, NY 11003.

HASKETT, Kathy; Admin.; Little Creek Convalescent Ctr., 816 Cres. Trace, Chesapeake, VA 23320.

HASKINS, Kimberley A.; '89 BS; Retired Law Enforcement; r. 779 Turkey Hill Rd., Milan, NY 12571, 914 758-0121; *Stephen.* e-mail

HASKINS, Roberta H.; '80 BA; 3212 Decatur Ave. Apt. 2c, Bronx, NY 10467, 718 881-9863.

HASSA, Vincent J.; '75 MA; 1 Spinnaker Way, Lake Hopatcong, NJ 07849.

HASSETT, Ann; '96 BS; 81 Heston Rd # A, Shirley, NY 11967, 631 281-2062.

HASSETT, George C.; 1229 E 59th St., Brooklyn, NY 11234, 718 238-6316.

HASSETT, Jean M.; '72 BA; MSW Fordham Univ.; Victim Assistant; 850 Bryant St., Rm. 320, San Francisco, CA 94103, 415 558-2408; r. 1 Baker St., 3A, San Francisco, CA 94117, 415 552-7165.

HASSO, Lisa S.; '95 BA; 31 Cedar Pl., Yonkers, NY 10705, 914 963-4229.

HASTINGS, Kevin M.; '83 BS; 232 Elm St., South Amboy, NJ 08879.

HASTINGS, Mark E.; '95 MA; BS Univ. of WI, MA George Mason Univ.; Sr. Forensic Clinician; Loudoun Mental Health Ctr., Leesburg, VA 20175, 703 771-5100; r. 4949 N 64th St., Milwaukee, WI 53218, 414 464-3319; *Kathy.*

HATEM, Roy A.; POB 440021, Miami, FL 33144.

HATFIELD, Steven J.; '96 AS; Public Relations Rep.; Custom Book Bindery, Inc., 9 Sherdian Ave., Clifton, NJ 07011, 973 815-1400; r. 514 Kingsland Ave., # 2, Lyndhurst, NJ 07071, 201 935-9045; *Jeanne.* e-mail

HATGOOD, Alia A.; BS; 27 W 118st #1D, New York, NY 10026, 212 722-9391.

HATTON, Kenneth R.; '75 BS; 142 W 31st St., New York, NY 10001.

HATTON, Laurence F.; '75 BS; Battalion Chief Retired; NYC Fire Dept.; r. 8 Evelyn Rd, Port Washington, NY 11050, 516 883-0380; *Mary;* Margaret, Kathleen, Elizabeth.

HATZAKOS, Peter; '99 BA; 262 95 St., Brooklyn, NY 11209, 718 921-1608.

HATZIS, Alexander C.; '84 BS; 803 Thrasher Dr., San Antonio, TX 78245, 210 674-2376.

HATZIS, Gregory S.; '92 BS; 13 Cherrycourt, Highland Mills, NY 10930, 914 928-9375; *Pamela.*

HAUGHWOUT, Hugh O.; 100 Riverside Dr., # A-305, Cocoa, FL 32922.

HAUGK, Charles J.; '95 BS; 881 7th Ave. #1209, New York, NY 10019.

HAUPTMAN, Eric J.; '95 MA; 1 Davids Ln., Ossining, NY 10562, 914 472-8666.

HAUSSERMANN, Angela; '95 BS; 6232 60th Rd, Flushing, NY 11378.

HAVIKEN, John J.; '77 BS; 1457 Forest Lake Blvd., Wantagh, NY 11793.

HAWKINS, Carol L.; '82 BS; 1094 Bushwick Ave., Brooklyn, NY 11221, 718 345-6608.

HAWKINS, Crystal; '92 BS; 12132 192nd St., Jamaica, NY 11413, 718 481-9866.

HAWKINS, Michael L.; '89 AS; 264 Brookside Ave., Roosevelt, NY 11575, 516 223-6668.

HAWKINS, Shelly-ann L.; '95 BS, '97 MPA; 17832 145th Ave. # Pvt, Jamaica, NY 11434, 718 481-9866.

HAWKINS, Wallie E.; '76 AS; Retired Capt.; NYC Dept. of Corrections; r. 194-14-100th Ave., Hollis, NY 11423. e-mail

HAWKINS, William F.; 40 W. 135 St., New York, NY 10037, 315 495-6555.

HAWLEY, Pamela A. '94 (See Rampolla, Mrs. Pamela A.).

HAWTHORNE, Latonya '90 (See Hawthorne-Archer, Latonya).

HAWTHORNE-ARCHER, Latonya, (Latonya Hawthorne); '90 BA; Deputy Sheriff; NYC Sheriff's Dept., 210 Joralemon St., Brooklyn, NY 11201, 718 802-3539; r. 5909 Glenwood Rd Apt. 3a, Brooklyn, NY 11234, 718 495-5782; *Lonzo Archer;* Tyla. e-mail

HAWXHURST, Patricia; '85 BA; 25 Rave St., Hicksville, NY 11801, 516 433-5626.

HAY, Douglas J.; '82 BS; 131 E 2nd St., Brooklyn, NY 11218, 718 680-4786.

HAYASHI, Magen K.; '99, '99 MA; 2029 Norway Rd., Ann Arbor, MI 48104, 734 665-1853.

HAYDE, William P.; '79 BS; 182a E Shore Dr., Massapequa, NY 11758, 516 798-5246.

HAYDEN, Patricia M.; '78 BA; 29 Adelphi Ave., Harrison, NY 10528.

HAYES, Clarence E.; '88 BA; 155 Baldwin Ave., Jersey City, NJ 07306, 201 536-8079.

HAYES, Donald; '97 BA; 1287 Waterview Dr., Rockville Centre, NY 11570, 516 354-0919.

HAYES, Dorsey L.; '79 MA; 281 3rd St., Hackensack, NJ 07601, 201 489-8057.

HAYES, Emogene S.; '90 BA; CERT New York Univ.; Researcher; Dept. of Finance, 25 Elm St., Brooklyn, NY 11201, 718 935-6545; r. 4308 Richardson Ave., Bronx, NY 10466; Naim I.

HAYES, James J.; '79 BA; 1329 Smith Ave., Bellmore, NY 11710, 516 221-3612.

HAYES, John R.; '96 BS; Owner/Police Ofcr.; American Risk Analyst & Mgmt Corp., Sic, Mohegan Lake, NY 10547; r. 3736 Foothill St., Mohegan Lake, NY 10547. e-mail

HAYES, Michael; '97 BS; 735 Scranton Ave., E. Rockaway, NY 11518, 516 546-4603.

HAYES, Miranda R.; '99 BS; 30 Avenue V 5B, Brooklyn, NY 11223, 718 946-4133.

HAYES, Mrs. Pammi M., (Pammi Walker); AS Empire State; NYCPD Detective; Police Dept. City of NY, 1 Police Plz., New York, NY 10007, 212 374-5000; r. 873 Woodfield Dr., W. Hempstead, NY 11552, 516 354-0919; *McClinton; Desmond, Christopher.* e-mail

HAYES, Philip L.; '95 BS; 638 E 94th St., Brooklyn, NY 11236, 718 743-1843.

HAYES, Stephanie D.; '87 BA; 30 Avenue V Apt. 13h, Brooklyn, NY 11223, 718 941-7274.

HAYES, Tevonda; '97 BA; 50 Monument Walk 4, Brooklyn, NY 11205, 718 602-5621.

HAYES, Tracy L.; '90 BA; POB 457, Bronx, NY 10473, 718 654-1983.

HAYGOOD, Alia A.; '99 BS; Mgr.; Financial Fed., 733 3rd Ave., New York, NY 10017, 212 599-8000; r. 27 W. 118th St., New York, NY 10026, 212 289-9796. e-mail

HAYNES, Kenneth; '83 BA; 14 Morgan Dr., Clayton, NJ 08312.

HAYNES, Lisa D.; '99 BS; 117-40 231st St., Cambria Hts., NY 11411, 718 527-3117.

HAYNES, Marjorie P.; '77 BA; 32-40 91 St. #607, Jackson Hts., NY 11369, 718 528-1296.

HAYNES, Robert M.; '94 BS; 14 Magnolia St., Centereach, NY 11720.

HAYNES, Veronica (Roni) T., (Veronica Frazier); '99 BA; AAS NYC Technical Clg.; Correction Ofcr.; NYC Dept. of Corrections, 16-06 Hazen St., E. Elmhurst, NY 11370, 718 542-4120; r. 20415 Foothill Ave., Apt. A26, Hollis, NY 11423, 718 776-5551; Sean, Claude. e-mail

HAYNES, Vincent; '85 MA; 682 E 49th St., Brooklyn, NY 11203.

HAYOWYK, John A.; '98 BA; 112 Righter Rd, Succasunna, NJ 07876, 973 584-3264.

HAYWOOD, Kimberly L.; '99 BA; Child Protective Spec.; Admin for Children Services, 1775 Grand Concourse, Bronx, NY 10453, 718 716-0442; r. 635 Morris Ave. #547, Bronx, NY 10451, 718 292-5873; Andre, Nikiya. e-mail

HAZARIAN, David J.; '96 BA; 2121 Paulding Ave., Apt. 2F, Bronx, NY 10462.

HAZEL, Amelia E.; '81 BS; Paramedic; Staten Island Univ. Hosp.; r. 105 Pierpont Pl., Staten Island, NY 10314, 718 698-9533. e-mail

HAZEL, Ms. Kim R.; '91 BS; Detention Deputy; Hillsborough Cnty. Sheriffs Ofc., 1201 Orient Rd., Tampa, FL 33619, 813 247-8930; r. 4204 Grainary Ave., Tampa, FL 33624, 813 963-0689; Bryan, Kymberly.

HAZEL, William B., III; '95 MA; BS Touro Clg.; Mental Health Therapist; Child Guidance of Greater Bridgeport, Bridgeport, CT 06604, 203 394-6529; r. 1961 Broadbridge Ave., Stratford, CT 06614, 203 377-1562; *Tracey.* e-mail

HAZELHURST, Bernice; '76 BA, '83 MPA; AS NYC Technical Clg.; Ret. Asst. Dir. of Alumni Assn.; John Jay Clg.-Alumni Assn.; r. 157-10 Riverside Dr., #1R, New York, NY 10032; *Burton J.; Dawn.*

HAZIM, Gladys M.; '92 BS; 2720 Decatur Ave. #, Bronx, NY 10458.

HAZLEWOOD, Gloria; '92 BS; 184-09 Henderson Ave., Hollis, NY 11423.

HAZZARD, Rev. Carrie L.; '83 BA; Retired Minister; r. 71 Kings Ferry Way, St. Augustine, FL 32084; *Wesley (Dec).*

HEAD, Sidney W., Sr.; '89 BA, '93 MA; Retired Bureau Chief; NYC Dept. of Corrections; r. 11469 226th St., Cambria Hts., NY 11411, 718 527-4604; *Eunice; Dawan, Sidney II.* e-mail

HEADLEY, Paul A.; '97 BS, '98 BA, '98 BA; 791 Hicks St., #6e, Brooklyn, NY 11231, 718 951-8102.

HEALY, Craig C.; '90 BS; 675 Fisher Ave., Uniondale, NY 11553, 516 735-3134.

HEALY, Dorothy; 122 Sand Shore Rd, Budd Lake, NJ 07828.

HEALY, James; '85 BS; Retired Chief of NY Fire Dept.; r. 1548 Westervelt Ave., Baldwin, NY 11510, 516 379-3218; *Catherine;* Kathryn Anne, Brian James, Andrew Michael.

HEALY, John E.; '80 BA; MA SUNY at Albany; Deputy Inspector; NYC Police Dept, New York, NY 10038; r. 14 Claurome Pl., Freeport, NY 11520, 516 867-3088; *Pixie-Ann;* Karen, Chris, Eric, John.

HEALY, Michael F.; '88 BA; 103 Minna St., Brooklyn, NY 11218, 718 797-4953.

HEALY, Patrick J.; '74 MPA; BA Fordham Univ.; Ret; r. 166 W Prospect St., Nanuet, NY 10954, 914 623-8742.

HEALY, Regina A.; '90 MS; 99 Winding Rd, Massapequa, NY 11758, 516 785-4609.

HEANEY, Patrick; '98 BA; Valley Stream, NY 11580, 516 568-2006.

HEAVEY, Michael F.; '76 BS; 1399 Sweetman Ave., Elmont, NY 11003.

HECKER, Peggyanne M.; '81 BS; 231 Violet Ave., Floral Park, NY 11001.

HECKER, William A.; '81 BS; Asst. Warden; NYC Dept. of Corrections; r. 231 Violet Ave., Floral Park, NY 11001.

HECTOR, David A.; '81 MPA; Lt. CDS Retired; NYC Police Dept.; r. 120-32 224th St., Jamaica, NY 11411, 718 426-7528; *Phyllis.*

HEDDERICH, Robert F.; '78 BA; 86 86th St., Brooklyn, NY 11209.

HEE, Jackson; '85 MPA; 14221 58th Rd, 2727 Corte Ponderosa, Pleasanton, CA 94566, 925 455-1958; *Patti.*

HEER, Edward; 25 Van Reipin Ave., Jersey City, NJ 07306.

HEGARTY, James; '84 BS; Inspector; NYPD Traffic Control Div., 138 W. 30th St., New York, NY 10001, 212 239-2520; r. POB 630191, Little Neck, NY 11363; *Julie.*

HEGEMAN, Elizabeth; 100 Riverside Dr., New York, NY 10024, 315 896-2531.

HEHIR, Joseph J.; '78 MPA; 245 E 207th St. Apt. A6, Bronx, NY 10467.

HEIMINK, Thomas H.; '99 BS; 112 Aspen Rd, Kings Park, NY 11754, 631 361-7166.

HEIN, Jennifer; '96 BA; 31 Ontario Ave., Medford, NY 11763, 631 289-6384.

HEINE, Susan K.; '90 BA; 97-04 103 Ave. #1, Ozone Park, NY 11417.

HEINEMAN, Frederick K.; '75 MA; BBA St. Francis Clg.; Retired-Congressman/Chief of Police; House of Representatives; r. 8412 Yucca Tr., Raleigh, NC 27615, 919 847-7550; *Linda.* e-mail

HELD, Kenneth L.; '94 BS; Police Ofcr.; City of Yonkers, 104 S. Broadway, Yonkers, NY 10701, 914 377-7900; r. 470 Tuckahoe Rd, Apt. 5B, Yonkers, NY 10710, 914 771-5531.

HELD, Sharon Z.; '85 MPA; 2619 Bayview Ave., Wantagh, NY 11793.

HELFMAN, Michelle; '80 MA; 78-10 34th Ave., Jackson Hts., NY 11372.

HELLER, Kenneth C.; '79 BS; 931 E. 78th St., Brooklyn, NY 11236, 718 855-1470.

HELLMAN, Karen A.; '96 MA; Coun. III; Maricopa Cnty. Sheriff Ofc., Durango Jail, Phoenix, AZ 85009, 602 256-1929; r. 8810 W Grovers Ave., Peoria, AZ 85382.

HELLNER, Brian; '97 BS; Owner; Video Enterprise, 680 Vdeo Corp., Bronx, NY 10462, 718 904-9343; r. 2440 Olinville Ave., Bronx, NY 10467, 718 652-1754.

HELLTHALER, F. W.; '82 AS; 2C Overlook Commons, Yorktown Hts., NY 10598.

HELMUS, Harry H.; '75 MA; 77 Walnut Ave., Rockville Centre, NY 11570.

HEMINGWAY, Richard C.; '89 MA; 5140 30th Ave., Woodside, NY 11377, 718 278-2201.

HEMMINGS, Frank E.; '80 BA; 181 Clarkson Ave., Brooklyn, NY 11226, 718 469-7415.

HEMPFIELD, Linda D.; '80 BS; 120 Pelham Rd, Apt. 6K, New Rochelle, NY 10805.

HEMPHILL, Stephanie; '83 BA; 201 Eastern Pkwy. Apt. 1k, Brooklyn, NY 11238.

HEMRICK, Henry J.; '79 MPA; 618 N Hambletonian Dr., Inverness, FL 34453.

HEMRICK, James F.; '77 BS; 451 73rd St., Brooklyn, NY 11209.

HENAO, Rosa E.; '77; 3032 32nd St. Apt. 4f, Long Island City, NY 11102.

HENDERSON, Audrey; '83 BS; 39 Dewey St., Bloomfield, NJ 07003, 973 338-6789.

HENDERSON, David R.; '78 BS; 301 Meadowbrook Heights Dr., New Windsor, NY 12553, 914 565-6156.

HENDERSON, Joseph M.; '73 BS; 1423 Golfside Dr., Winter Park, FL 32792.

HENDERSON, Richard T.; '84 BA; Asst. Claims Mgr.; Transatlantic Reinsurance Co., 80 Pine St., New York, NY 10005, 212 770-2598; r. 6 Branford Dr., Robbinsville, NJ 08691, 914 342-1365; *Charlene.* e-mail

HENDERSON, Robert A.; '78 MS; 5 Saddle Horn Dr., Upper Saddle River, NJ 07458, 201 825-2471.

HENDERSON, Vane B.; '96 BA; 839 E 227 St., Bronx, NY 10466.

HENDRICK, Carl; '88 MPA; 8 Willard St., Port Jervis, NY 12771, 914 858-8376.

HENDRICK, John S.; '81 BS; Criminal Justice Instr.; Lampasas HS, 902 S Broad, Lampasas, TX 76550, 512 556-3617; r. RR2 Box 115, Kempner, TX 76539, 512 556-6079; *Pat.* e-mail

HENDRICKS, Andre; '96 BS; 1605 Caffrey Ave., Far Rockaway, NY 11691, 718 523-0411.

HENDRICKS, Garfield; '85 BS; 1507 Metropolitan, Bronx, NY 10462.

HENDRICKS, Jennifer; '96 BS; 4167 Monticello Ave., Bronx, NY 10466, 718 665-7636.

HENDRICKSON, Avis; '74 BA; 7 Fordham Hill Oval #, Bronx, NY 10468, 718 432-0848.

HENNEN, Christopher G.; '79 BS; MS Harvard Univ.; Asst. Headmaster; New York Military Acad., Cornwall on Hudson, NY 12520; r. 20 Faculty Rd., Cornwall on Hudson, NY 12520; *Sue-Simone;* Chris, Jr., Bethany, Caitlin.

HENNESSEY, Richard E.; '78 BA; Police Ofcr. Retired; NYCPD, 1 Police Plz., New York, NY 10038; r. 301 Willowood Dr., Wantagh, NY 11793; *Maureen;* Edward, Karen, Shelia, Patricia. e-mail

HENNIG, George D.; '76 BS; Pres. Men's Fashions; Male Attitude Inc., 2084 86th St., Brooklyn, NY 11214, 718 449-7518; r. same; *Debra;* George III, Deanna Nicole.

HENRI, Claudine L.; '92 BA; 1385 3rd Ave. Apt. 2a, New York, NY 10021.

HENRIQUES, Luciann; '98 BA; 4 South Ct., Nesconset, NY 11767, 631 724-4518.

HENRIQUES, Marie; '77 BA; 4875 Mowry Ave. #132, Fremont, CA 94538.

HENRIQUES, Zelma W.; PHD Columbia Univ.; Prof.-Dept. of Law & Police Sci.; John Jay Clg., 899 10th Ave., New York, NY 10019, 212 237-8378. e-mail

HENRIQUEZ, Deborah C.; '97 BS; JD NY Law Sch.; Atty.; r. P.O.Box 91, Godeffroy, NY 12739, 914 978-5088; Yusef.

HENRIQUEZ, Marlene; '97 BS; Legal Asst.; Segal & Meltzer, 16 Madison Ave., Ste. 914, New York, NY 10010; r. 104-35 107th St., Ozone Park, NY 11417, 718 641-1993. e-mail

HENRY, Andre B.; '81 BS; 494 Hendrix St., Brooklyn, NY 11207, 718 209-1477.

HENRY, Conrad V.; '75 BS; MS Fordham Univ; Retired Detective; NYCPD; r. 310 Convent Ave., 84 Everett Rd Demerest N.J 07627, New York, NY 10031, 212 234-1524; Conrad H. Jr. e-mail

HENRY, Florence D.; '80 BS; 140-33 Casals Pl. #33K, Bronx, NY 10475, 718 652-1070.

HENRY, Hopeton H.; '93 BS; 196 Rockaway Pkwy, Brooklyn, NY 11212, 718 234-0202.

HENRY, James W.; '78 MPA; 92 Stratford Dr., Freehold, NJ 07728, 732 577-0076.

HENRY, Josseth A.; '99 BS; Home Health Aide; Patient Care, Inc., 575 Eighth Ave., New York, NY 10018, 212 564-1944; r. 249 E. 37th St. #61, Brooklyn, NY 11203, 718 284-4226; Canika. e-mail

HENRY, Kenneth D.; '76; 100-24 Alcott Pl. #24C, Bronx, NY 10475, 718 652-1070.

HENRY, Lowana M.; '99 BA; AA New York Technical Clg.; Child Welfare Spec.; Admin. for Children Svcs., 150 William St., New York, NY 10038, 718 237-7069; r. Brooklyn, NY 11233.

HENRY, Mrs. Marie R.; '99 MA; BA Univ. of Maryland, JD George Washington Univ.; Coord. of Criminal Justice Progam; Sullivan Cnty Community Clg., 1000 Leroy Rd, Loch Sheldrake, NY 12759, 914 434-5750; r. 121 Bonnell Rd., Grahamsville, NY 12740, 914 985-7777; *Martin Lester;* Whitney, Martin, Jackson. e-mail

HENRY, Mark A.; '78 MA; 133 E 15 St. #2B, New York, NY 10003, 315 338-5872.

HENRY, Newton D.; '75 BA; 791 Maple St., Brooklyn, NY 11203, 718 377-3793.

HENRY, Shirley M.; '79 BS, '81 MA, '83 MA; Health Field; r. 5900 Arlington Ave., 18 G, Bronx, NY 10471.

HENRY, Sonya M.; '93 BA; POB 11161, Hauppauge, NY 11788.

HENRY, Valerie E.; '97 BS; 94-37 121st St., S. Richmond Hill, NY 11419, 718 736-0314.

HENSHAW, George V.; '83 MA; 462 Liberty St., Little Ferry, NJ 07643.

HENTZE, Jeanette M., (Jeanette Zupka); '84 AS; Master Firefighter; City of Portsmouth, 361 Effingham St., Portsmouth, VA 23704, 757 393-8628; r. 1921 Southaven Dr., Virginia Bch., VA 23464, 757 495-9608; *Peter;* Peter Jr., James.

HERBERT, John D.; '83 BS; Retired Police Capt.; Port Authority; r. 85 Clarke Ave., Staten Island, NY 10306, 718 667-0817.

HERBERT, Tara V.; '99 BA; 300 E 158th #10F, Bronx, NY 10451, 718 665-6484.

HERBOSCH, Alessandra D.; '98 MA; Child & Family Advocate; Brooklyn Child Advocacy Ctr., 30 Main St., Brooklyn, NY 11201, 718 260-6080; r. 1035 Park Ave. #4b, New York, NY 10028, 212 722-7932.

HERBST, Andrew J.; '99 MA; BA Ithaca Clg.; Clinical Coord.; Applied Behavioral Specialist, UCP-Intern Member, American Polygraph Assoc., Hauppauge, NY 11788, 631 232-0011; r. 47 Highview Ln., Ridge, NY 11961, 631 821-1994. e-mail

HERCULES, Keith F.; '79 BS; AS Hudson Valley Clg., MS LIU; Assoc. Dir. for Physical Plant; SUNY Health Science Ctr. at Brooklyn, 450 Clarkson, Brooklyn, NY 11203, 718 270-4446; r. 66 Buckingham Dr., Jackson, NJ 08527; Keisha, Tiffany.

HERCULES, Martineau; '84 BS; 148-28 88th Ave. #2L, Jamaica, NY 11435, 718 529-3264.

HEREDIA, Rafael J.; '97 BS, '98 BS; 716 E. 181st St., Bronx, NY 10457, 718 733-9811.

HERENCIA, Craig; '89 BS; 5454 Sylvan Ave. Ph, Bronx, NY 10471.

HERES, Ana M.; '90 BS; 523 Lexington Ave., Brooklyn, NY 11221.

HERING, Robert K.; '76 MPA; 89 Skelly Pl., Mineola, NY 11501.

HERLIHY, Patrick F.; '77 BS; 326 Noxon Rd, Poughkeepsie, NY 12603, 914 454-5446.

HERMAN, Albin A.; '65 MPA; 82 Bentley Ave., Old Bridge, NJ 08857.

HERMAN, John; 23 Euston Rd, W. Hempstead, NY 11552, 516 485-6629.

HERMAN, Michele A.; '85 BS; 3487 Mickle Ave., Bronx, NY 10469.

HERMAN, Tracy A.; '97 BA; Ins.; r. 4307 Reflections Blvd., Apt. 204, Sunrise, FL 33351, 954 578-8235. e-mail

HERMANS, Peter L.; '98 BS; Police Dispatcher; Hanover Twp., Whippany, NJ 07981, 973 428-3512; r. 23 Valley Forge Dr., Whippany, NJ 07981, 973 887-2376.

HERMIDA, Mercedes; '93 BA; 510 W. 188 St., New York, NY 10040, 212 923-0545.

HERNANDEZ, Amarilyz; '95 BA; 3408 Deerhaunt St., Yorktown Hts., NY 10598.

HERNANDEZ, Ana C. '75 (See Nourakis, Ana C.).

HERNANDEZ, Ana E.; '83 MPA; 959 43rd St., Brooklyn, NY 11219, 718 235-1729.

HERNANDEZ, Anthony P.; '86 BS; 965 Ashford St., Brooklyn, NY 11207, 718 235-1729.

HERNANDEZ, Daisy; '97 BA; 2847 Webb Ave.2D, Bronx, NY 10468, 718 561-8023.

HERNANDEZ, Elizabeth; '98 BA; 9013 91st Ave., # 2, Woodhaven, NY 11421, 718 205-4709.

HERNANDEZ, Elsa; '90 BA; 255 Havemeyer St., Brooklyn, NY 11211, 718 235-3770.

HERNANDEZ, Gertrudis; '99 BA; Tchr. 6th Grade; PS 161, 100 33rd St., New York, NY 10027, 212 690-5945; r. 87-53 94th St., Woodhaven, NY 11421, 718 458-2897; *Louis Duran;* Jeff Duran. e-mail

HERNANDEZ, Hugo F.; '82 BA; 144 Jefferson St., Brooklyn, NY 11206, 718 235-1729.

HERNANDEZ, Hyda D.; '87 BS; 672 Jamaica Ave. # 2, Brooklyn, NY 11208, 718 235-1729.

HERNANDEZ, Iris; '94 BA, '95 CERT; 130 Moore St. Apt. 4h, Brooklyn, NY 11206, 718 235-1729.

HERNANDEZ, Jeanette; BA; 1659 Cornelia St#2R, Flushing, NY 11385, 718 497-5809.

HERNANDEZ, Jenny; '92; 178 Avenue D #9C, New York, NY 10009, 315 853-6770.

HERNANDEZ, Jesus J.; '87 BA; 1127 Noble Ave. # 2r, Bronx, NY 10472, 718 231-5420.

HERNANDEZ, Jose A.; '82 BS; 100 Avenue C, New York, NY 10009, 315 853-6770.

HERNANDEZ, Jose A.; '97 BA; ME; Software Configuration Mgr.; Merant, 2908 Key West Ave., Rockville, MD 20850, 888 869-0738; r. 60-17 Cooper Ave., Glendale, NY 11385, 718 456-4159; *Jennifer;* Jahred, Diego. e-mail

HERNANDEZ, Josefina; '91 BA; 188 Noll St. #3R, Brooklyn, NY 11237, 718 456-3075.

HERNANDEZ, Luisa; '90 BS; 10237 46th Ave. # 2fl, Flushing, NY 11368, 718 848-6819.

HERNANDEZ, Michael; '98 BS; Detective; NYC Police Dept., One Police Plz., NY NY, New York, NY 10278, 212 384-3889; *Marilyn;* Michael, Jasmine, Kristina. e-mail

HERNANDEZ, Michael A.; '81 BS; 2227 Chatterton Ave., Bronx, NY 10472, 718 299-4149.

HERNANDEZ, Michael E.; '97 BS; 1130 Evergreen Ave., Bronx, NY 10472, 718 542-9861.

HERNANDEZ, Michelle; '97 BA; Receptionist; Stroock & Stroock & Lavan LLP, 180 Maiden Ln., New York, NY 10038, 212 806-5401; r. 2931 8th Aveeare Ave., Apt. 14 H, New York, NY 10039, 212 283-9381. e-mail

HERNANDEZ, Nancy M.; '80 BA; 2903 Old Yorktown Rd, Yorktown Hts., NY 10598, 914 962-8526.

HERNANDEZ, Petronio; '94 BA; 778 Driggs Ave. #1E, Brooklyn, NY 11211.

HERNANDEZ, Robert; '93 BS; 2510 Olinville Ave., Bronx, NY 10467, 718 519-8415.

HERNANDEZ, Ronald; '99 BS; 656 W 171 St. 2A, New York, NY 10032, 212 740-1310.

HERNANDEZ, Rosalia; '86 BS; MS Brooklyn Clg.; Caseworker; Greenwood Job Ctr. #85, 275 Bergen St., Brooklyn, NY 11217, 718 694-8604; r. 336-48 St., Brooklyn, NY 11220, 718 492-0113.

HERNANDEZ, Victor; '92 BA; 348 Manhattan Ave., Babylon, NY 11704.

HERNANDEZ, Virginia; '89 BA; 4108 5th Ave., Brooklyn, NY 11232.

HERNANDEZ, Yvette; '92 BS; 3042 Milburn Ave., Baldwin, NY 11510, 516 378-5832.

HERRELL, Todd M.; '99; 1035 Rte. 311, Patterson, NY 12563.

HERRERA, Carlos R.; '98 BA; 170 Dreiser Loop, Apt. 6E, Bronx, NY 10475, 718 716-7896.

HERRERA, Eduardo J.; '99 BS; 8909 37th Ave., Jackson Hts., NY 11372, 718 779-1337.

HERRERA, Edwin; '83 BS; 761 44th St., Brooklyn, NY 11220, 718 633-1860.

HERRERA, George P.; '92 BS; 640 W 170th St. # 1, New York, NY 10032.

HERRERA, Jose; '93 BS; 20-54 Crescent St., Astoria, NY 11105, 718 205-1940.

HERRERA, Juan; '95 BS; 516 E 83rd St. Apt. 2w, New York, NY 10028.

HERRERA, Julian; '84 BS; Supv.; NYC Dept. Consumer Affairs, 42 Broadway, New York, NY 10004, 212 487-4325; r. 307 Degraw St., Brooklyn, NY 11231, 718 625-4756; *Lois Tendler;* Jessica.

HERRERA, Leslie S.; '99 BS; 615 E. 3rd St., 2nd Fl., Brooklyn, NY 11218, 718 602-3881.

HERRERA, Linda; '87 BS; 880 Colgate Ave., Bronx, NY 10473, 718 861-3160.

HERRERA, Luis; '96 BS; 48 Maple Dr., Stony Point, NY 10980.

HERRERA, Robert; 2249 E. 71th St., Brooklyn, NY 11234, 718 602-3881.

HERRERA, Sergio R.; '99 BA; 402 Beach 9th St., Far Rockaway, NY 11691, 718 471-6475.

HERRING, John; '85 MPA; 10 Hamilton Rd, Wappingers Falls, NY 12590, 518 789-0130.

HERRMANN, Christophe; 2000 BS MA; 870 Edward St., Baldwin, NY 11510. e-mail

HERRON, Francis R.; '72 BA, '75 MA; Retired NYPD Police Inspector; r. 464 Herricks Rd, Mineola, NY 11501, 516 741-9607; *Rosemary;* Francis R., Michael D. e-mail

HERSHMAN, Michael; '72 BS; Chmn.; DSFX Intl., 3141 Fairview Park Dr., Ste. 850, Falls Church, VA 22042, 703 207-0600; r. 600 Deerfield Pond Ct., Great Falls, VA 22066, 703 757-1919. e-mail

HERSKOVITZ, Marian; '81 BS; 2260 Benson Ave., Brooklyn, NY 11214, 718 266-3514.

HERTING, Edward C.; '76 BS; Retired; r. 7 Stephen Ct., Bayport, NY 11705, 631 472-0951.

HERVE, Francois; '98 BS; 149-55 259th St., Rosedale, NY 11422. e-mail

HERZBERG, Edward M.; '82 BS; Social Svc. Worker; The Salvation Army, 221 E. 52 St., New York, NY 10022, 212 758-0763; r. 221 E. 52street, Apt. 2B, New York, NY 10022.

HESKIN, Kathryn F.; '87 BS; 83-26 Lefferts Blvd., Kew Gardens, NY 11415.

HESS, Brian; '97 BS; 130 Sarles Ln., Pleasantville, NY 10570, 914 747-2680.

HESS, Donna A.; '89 BS; 72 Bedford St. #5A, New York, NY 10014.

HESS, Harold J.; '75 MA; Retired Asst. Chief; NYC Police Dept.; r. 6490 Mayhill Ct., Spring Hill, FL 34606, 352 688-6362.

HETRICK, John G.; '78 BS; 139-09 84 Dr., Briarwood, NY 11435.

HETTLER, Mrs. Frances, (Frances Esposito); '74 BA; Elem. Tchr.; r. 23 Rhame Ave., E. Rockaway, NY 11518; *Kenneth Richard.*

HETTLER, Kenneth R.; '74 BS; JD St. John's Univ.; Atty./Police Supv; Kenneth Hettler LLC, 23 Rhame Ave., E. Rockaway, NY 11518; r. same, 516 593-3894; *Frances.*

HETZEL, Maureen A.; '87 BA; 633 S 13th St., New Hyde Park, NY 11040, 516 355-0705.

HEWITT, Althea E.; '92 BS; Legal Asst.; Carter Ledyard & Milburn; r. 423 Snediker Ave., Brooklyn, NY 11207. e-mail

HEWITT, Darryl F.; '90 BS; 555 E 80th St., Brooklyn, NY 11236, 718 771-2566.

HEWITT, Russell; '85 MA; 1344 Metcalf Ave., Bronx, NY 10472, 718 328-3463.

HEYM, Eugene; '79 BA; Firefighter; NY Fire Dept., 257 Bill St., Rockaway Park, NY 11694; r. 103-00 Shore Front Pkwy., Rockaway Park, NY 11694; *Mary Lou;* Eugene, Charles, Eric.

HEYWARD, Richard; '78 BS, '86 MPA; 10 Corinthian Rd, New City, NY 10956, 914 352-3780.

HEYWARD, Tina M.; '88 BS; 536 Broadway, Staten Island, NY 10310, 718 815-0640.

HEYWOOD, Angela B.; '85 BA; Assoc. Fraud Investigator; Human Resources Admin., 1716 Southern Blvd., Bronx, NY 10460, 718 617-8916; r. 1560 Metropolitan Ave., Bronx, NY 10462, 718 409-2603; Nicole.

HIBBERT, Jacqueline M.; '98 BS; 97-11 123rd, Richmond Hill, NY 11419, 718 464-1829.

HIBBERT, Marcia A.; '93 BS; 172-17 115th Ave., St. Albans, NY 11434, 718 464-1829.

HIBBERT, Melonie J.; '97 BA; 97-11 123rd St., S. Richmond Hill, NY 11419.

HIBBLER, Louise; '77 BA; 4212 Labyrinth, Baltimore, MD 21215.

HICKEY, Keri; '99 BA; 140 Regis Dr., Staten Island, NY 10314, 718 983-7007.

HICKEY, L. F.; '83 MA, '83 BA; Police Ofcr.; Los Angeles Police Dept., 150 N Los Angeles St., Los Angeles, CA 90012, 213 485-3726.

HICKEY, Stephanie M.; '99 BA; Special Educ. Tchr.; r. 64-36C 186 Ln. #2A, Fresh Meadows, NY 11365, 718 454-5779.

HICKEY, Thomas F.; '99 MPA; BA, JD NYU; Asst. Atty. Gen.; NYC; r. 524 E 20th St. Apt. 12C, New York, NY 10009. e-mail

HICKMAN, John J.; '78 BA, '95; 33 Rugby Ave., Staten Island, NY 10301.

HICKMAN, Lynn B.; '93 BS; Supv. HRA; Medicade, 88 3rd Ave., Brooklyn, NY 11217; r. 262 Quincy St., Brooklyn, NY 11216, 718 398-2765; Tiffany.

HICKS, Bruce; '85 BS; 913 E 211th St., Bronx, NY 10469, 718 584-6079.

HICKS, Frances E.; '95 BA; 9825 Horace Harding Expy. Apt. 17g, Flushing, NY 11368, 718 523-1096.

HICKS, Keith E.; '92 BA; Dir.; r. 111-44 131st St., Jamaica, NY 11420, 718 529-0817; Tyler. e-mail

HICKS, Netoya S.; '95 BA, '99 MPA; POB 555, Riverdale, NY 10463, 718 562-0434.

HICKS, Theresa; '82 BA; 440 St. Johns, Brooklyn, NY 11238, 718 774-0784.

HICKSON, Wilibelle; '80 BA, '84 MPA; 157-10 Riversde Dr., New York, NY 10032.

HIDALGO, Frank; '97 BA; 3314 Colden Ave., Bronx, NY 10469, 718 993-1645.

HIDALGO, Joanne E.; '92 BS; 10055 Winding Lake Rd, # 9-103, Sunrise, FL 33351, 954 572-6814.

HIGGINS, Adrienne C.; '98 BA MA; Prog. Therapist/HBIC; Northside Ctr. for Child Devel., 1301 Fifth Ave., New York, NY 10029, 212 426-3488; r. 6684 Fresh Pond Rd., Ridgewood, NY 11385, 718 821-0032. e-mail

HIGGINS, Albert T.; '70 BS; MPA Long Island Univ.; Ret. Lt. NYPD/Ret. Admin./ Cnslt.; AT Higgins & Assocs., 200 E. 89th St. Ste. 43A, New York, NY 10128, 212 410-4641; *Carolyn.*

HIGGINS, Daniel P.; '76 MA; Ret.; r. 10 Radcliff Dr., Great Neck, NY 11024, 516 482-3889; *Sandra;* Matthew, Mark, Kurt, Leah.

HIGGINS, Dorothy '79 (See Schuhmann, Mrs. Dorothy T.).

HIGGINS, Harry F.; '76 BS; 311 E 80 St. #15, New York, NY 10021, 315 337-3738.

HIGGINS, Kathryn; '75, '92 MA; 515 E 85th St. Apt. 5c, New York, NY 10028, 315 337-3738.

HIGGINS, Malachy T.; '70 BA, '70 BS, '75 MA; Dir.; Municipal Credit Union, Courtland St., New York, NY 10038; r. 334 Calhoun Ave., Bronx, NY 10465, 718 792-9651; *Maryanne;* Suzzane, Maureen, Ellen, Mallachy, Lorraine, Nancy, Mark (dec). e-mail

HIGGINS, Michael J.; '77 MA; 361 N Flint Ct., Yardley, PA 19067, 215 321-3591.

HIGGINS, Michael S.; '98 BA; Law Student; Brooklyn Law Sch.; r. 112 E 97 St., 2r, New York, NY 10029, 212 831-2425. e-mail

HIGGINS, Patrick (Pat) J.; '92 BS; 531 Hopper Ave., Wyckoff, NJ 07481, 201 447-2350.

HIGGINS, Mrs. Sandra E., (Sandra E. Wallace); '82 BS, '85 MPA; Asst. Dir. of Student Financial Aid; New York Technical Clg., 300 Jay St., Brooklyn, NY 11201, 718 260-5704. e-mail

HIGGINS, William J.; '80 BS; 20407 Marshall Ave., Breezy Pt., NY 11697, 718 327-8436.

HIGGS, Ruth; '77 BA; 684 E 226th St., Bronx, NY 10466.

HIGGS, William T.; 11031 173rd St., Jamaica, NY 11433, 718 977-9268.

HIGHTOWER, Sadiquah; '96 BS; Crime Victims Spec.; NYS Crime Victums Bd., 55 Hanson Pl., Brooklyn, NY 11217, 718 923-4359; r. 2730 Frederick Douglas Blvd., Apt. 5C, New York, NY 10039, 212 690-0699. e-mail

HILAIRE, Livingstone; '91 MPA; 607 Linden Blvd., Brooklyn, NY 11203, 718 363-8622.

HILAIRE, Reginald; '97 BS; 209-78 Whitehall T, Queens Vlg., NY 11427.

HILAIRE-FISHER, Marie C.; '96 MA; BA SUNY; Dir. of Youth Diagnostic Facility; Good Shepherd Svcs. Social Services, 337 E. 17th St., New York, NY 10020, 212 475-4245; r. 1412 Monroe Ave., Neptune, NJ 07753, 732 988-3207; *Joseph Fisher.* e-mail

HILARIO, Dilcia Y.; '95 BA; 11217 75th Ave., # 3, Forest Hills, NY 11375.

HILER, Edmund G.; '90 BA; 451 81st St., Brooklyn, NY 11209.

HILL, Aiyeesha L.; '97 BS; 67-15 Parsons Blvd., Flushing, NY 11365, 718 525-0756.

HILL, Arthur B.; '66 BS, '73 MPA; MA THESI; Ret. VP Public Affairs; UPS; r. 18710 Ilion Ave., Jamaica, NY 11412, 718 454-8950; *Patricia;* Arthur Jr., Ernest, Victoria, Joanne, Drew Timberlake.

HILL, Barbara G.; '83 BA; MSW Hunter Clg.; Supv II; Admin. for Children Svcs.; r. Jamaica, NY 11434, 718 528-1612.

HILL, Calvin B.; '92 BS; AA NYC Technical Clg.; Correction Ofcr.; NYC Dept. of Corrections, Rikers Island, New York, NY 10001; r. 11001 177th St., Jamaica, NY 11433, 718 658-9685; *Josie Braam;* Tracy, Helena, Calvin Jr.

HILL, Craig R.; '99 BA; 952 Ashford St., Brooklyn, NY 11207, 718 257-2664.

HILL, Damon A., (A.); '98 BS; Claims Spec.; Liberty Mutual, 50 Charles Liindbergh Blvd., Uniondale, NY 11553, 516 222-6060; r. 89 Herzl St., Brooklyn, NY 11212, 718 346-2355.

HILL, Donna; '95 BS; Claims Examiner; Nationwide Ins., 170 Froehlich Farm Blvd., Woodbury, NY 11797, 516 682-1385; r. 69 W Clinton Ave., Roosevelt, NY 11575, 516 223-4617; *Luther Jr;* Da'von, Luther, Lance. e-mail

HILL, Madlyn S.; '81 BS; 12 W 123rd St., New York, NY 10027, 315 733-4657.

HILL, Marilyn E.; '80 BS; 22411 92nd Ave., Queens Vlg., NY 11428, 718 525-0756.

HILL, Meloney E.; '98 BA; 638 Hopkinson Ave., Brooklyn, NY 11212, 718 522-5129.

HILL, Mercedes S.; '85 MA; BA City Univ.-Uptown; Ret. Probation Ofcr.; NYC Dept. of Probation, Bronx, NY 10451; r. 128 Bushey Ave., Yonkers, NY 10710, 914 969-3351.

HILL, Michael A.; '97 BS, '98 BS; 489 Ray St., Freeport, NY 11520, 516 378-7394.

HILL, Nadine A.; '97 BA; 630 Ocean Ave., Apt. 6F, Brooklyn, NY 11226, 718 282-3701.

HILL, Renee C.; '89 BS; 1626 Sedgwick Ave., Bronx, NY 10453, 718 543-0405.

HILL, Rochelle M. '77 (See Murphy, Mrs. Rochelle M.).

HILL, Shirley R.; '83 BA; 293 E. 35th St., Brooklyn, NY 11203, 718 246-4980.

HILL, Siobhan; '93 MA; 600 W 239th St., Bronx, NY 10463, 718 548-8832.

HILL, Suzanne A.; '92 MPA, '95 MPA; 1383 Park Pl., Brooklyn, NY 11213, 718 522-6879.

HILL, Veronica S.; '93 BS; 535 Williams Ave., Brooklyn, NY 11207, 718 385-5110.

HILL, Willie G.; '79 MA; 112-02 Colfax St., Queens Vlg., NY 11429, 718 525-0756.

HILLERY, Joseph F.; '77 BA; 77 Primrose Ave., Floral Park, NY 11001.

HILLIMAN, Charlyn A.; '94 BS, '96 MPA; 901-A E. 106th St., Brooklyn, NY 11236.

HILLOWE-DONAHUE, C.; '86 BA; 553 Old Bridge Rd, Northport, NY 11768, 631 757-6781.

HILLS, Tonya S.; '93 BS; 22 Lewis Ave. Apt. 3d, Brooklyn, NY 11206, 718 768-5940.

HILLSMAN, Yequarah; '96 BA; Practice Admin.; Physicians Medcenter, 137-10 Northern Blvd., Flushing, NY 11354, 718 762-6640; r. 62 Brooks Ave., Roosevelt, NY 11575, 516 868-4986; Timothy. e-mail

HILSMAN, Carla D.; '97 BS; 30 W. 63rd St., New York, NY 10023.

HILTON, Allison; '97 BA, '98 BA; 1132 E. 108th St., Brooklyn, NY 11236, 718 531-0167.

HILTON, Quiana L.; '98 BA; 1245 Ocean Ave. #2E, Brooklyn, NY 11230, 718 573-8482.

HINCHEY, Arthur F.; '76 AS; BS Downstate Med. Ctr. SUNY; Retired Fireman; NYC Fire Dept.; r. 10 Debra Dr., Nesconset, NY 11767, 631 979-1675.

HIND, David V.; '95 BA; 22667 Union Tpk., Flushing, NY 11364.

HINDS, Barry M.; '89 BS; 581 Midwood St., Brooklyn, NY 11203, 718 346-0912.

HINDS, Elizabeth C.; '95 BA; 180 E. 52 St., Brooklyn, NY 11203, 718 221-1402.

HINDS, Kelvin C.; '98 BA; AAS NYC Techncial Clg.; Safety Ofcr.; Kirby Forensic Psychiatric Ctr., Wards Island Ny, Ext3519, New York, NY 10035, 212 427-9003; r. 118 Linden St., Brooklyn, NY 11221, 718 573-3256; *Dorothy;* Sophia, Kelvin.

HINDS, Leslie M.; 3544 Holland Ave., Bronx, NY 10467, 718 324-1879.

HINDS, Marcia R.; '84 BS; 11919 221st St., Jamaica, NY 11411.

HINDS, Randolph A.; '85 BS; 983 Clinton Pl., Baldwin, NY 11510, 516 623-7073.

HINES, James R.; '78 BA; Retired; Housing Authority Police Sgt.; r. 190 E 35th St., Brooklyn, NY 11203, 718 693-4044; *Ella;* Stacey, David, Bathsheba.

HINES, Sharon; '96 BS, '99 MPA; 470 Lenox Ave. # 15, New York, NY 10037.

HINES, Sharon; '96 CERT; 470 Malcolm X Blvd. Apt. 15k, New York, NY 10037, 315 339-9872.

HINES, Vera D.; '81 BS; 10034 198th St., Jamaica, NY 11423.

HINESTROZA, Xiomara; '99 BS; Court Ofcr.; Red Hook Community Justice Ctr., 88 Visitation Pl., Brooklyn, NY 11231, 718 923-8207; r. 1580 E. 53rd St., Brooklyn, NY 11234, 718 377-8779; *Alonzo;* Jamel, Nigel.

HINKSON, Kenmore I.; '76 BA; 959 Ashford St., Brooklyn, NY 11207, 718 345-7650.

HINNRICHS, Jeffery K.; '75 MPA, '90 MS; BS Univ. of WI; Retired Fire Capt.; NYC Fire Dept.; r. 1108 Winter Haven Way, Lexington, KY 40509, 859 263-4053.

HIRBOUR, Cynthia A.; '99 BA; Grad. Student; California Sch. of Profn Psych.; r. 163 Clough Rd., Waterbury, CT 06708, 203 574-7972; *Randall Krizan.*

HIRSCH, Karl W.; '80 AS; Detective Sgt; City of Ft. Lauderdale Police Dept.; r. 2618 NE 17st, Ft. Lauderdale, FL 33305, 954 566-5436; *Jill;* Karl William. e-mail

HIRSCHBERG, Jeanette '85 (See Vinton, Jeanette).

HLAVATY, John; '96 MA; 270 Riverside Dr., New York, NY 10025.

HO, Jei-fu; '88 MPA; 4140 Union St. Apt. 4c, Flushing, NY 11355, 718 335-5976.

HO, Jon; '85 MPA; 220 W. 79 St., New York, NY 10024, 315 338-0891.

HOBSON, Anthony E.; '98 MPA; Human Resources; CBS TV, 51 W 52nd St., New York, NY 10019, 212 975-4676; r. 99-41 64th Ave. #G2, Rego Park, NY 11374, 718 830-3814. e-mail

HOBSON, Kendall G.; '88 BS; MPA; Special Agt.; FBI, 26 Federal Plz., New York, NY 10278, 212 384-3420.

HOBSON, Richard; '89 BA; 57 W 106th St. Apt. 4b, New York, NY 10025, 315 735-6007.

HOCH, Joseph B.; '95 BA; Captain; NYPD, 1 Police Plz., New York, NY 10038, 212 374-5000; r. 4 Flamingo Ln., Spring Vly., NY 10977, 914 354-2242; *Robin;* Jared, Talia. e-mail

HOCHBERG, Ian P.; '79 BS; 336 Central Park W, New York, NY 10025.

HOCHFELD, Richard P.; '79 BS; 3015 154th St., Flushing, NY 11354.

HOCHSTADT, Marc M.; '80 BS; Police Ofcr DWI/DRE; Miami Bch, FL, 1100 Washington Ave., Miami Bch., FL 33139; r. 1736 Biarritz Dr., Miami Bch., FL 33141.

HOCHSTADT, Yolanda P.; '80 BA; 1736 Biarritz Dr., Miami Bch., FL 33141.

HOCKLER, Terry M.; '93 BS; 100 Union St., Beacon, NY 12508.

HODGE, Ivy S.; '99 BA; 39 W 96 St. 3G, New York, NY 10025, 212 662-3930.

HODGE, Laverna T.; '75 BA; 467 Rockaway Pkwy., Brooklyn, NY 11212, 718 940-0525.

HODGE, Loretta E.; '90 BA; 239 W 63rd St. # 1, New York, NY 10023, 315 899-3297.

HODGE, Patricia I.; '79 BS; 661 Lefferts Ave., Brooklyn, NY 11203, 718 253-1237.

HODGES, Billieannett; '93 BA; 426 Columbia St. #3, Brooklyn, NY 11231, 718 625-1160.

HODGES, Judith L.; '87 BS; 138 Branton St., Brooklyn, NY 11236, 718 629-6546.

HODGES, Phyllis; '88 BS; 16335 130th Ave., # 3A-12C, Jamaica, NY 11434, 718 978-7951.

HODGES, Rodney R.; '90 BS; MS Long Island; Police Ofcr.; NYPD; r. 37 E 56th St., Brooklyn, NY 11203.

HODGES, Warren A.; '79 BS; 509 Beverly Rd, Teaneck, NJ 07666, 201 251-1268.

HODGINS, Joseph A.; '83 BA; POB 116, Yonkers, NY 10704, 914 237-6521.

HODGSON, Tania; '96 BS; MS Hunter Clg.; Staff Analyst; NYC Transit, 370 Jay St., Brooklyn, NY 11201, 718 243-3503; r. 50 Amsterdam Ave., New York, NY 10023, 212 757-3513; Shana, Erica. e-mail

HOEHL, Allan H.; '76 BS; 5 Country Club Ct., Mt. Sinai, NY 11766.

HOENEVELD, Robert J.; '79 BS; 3 Adele Rd, W. Nyack, NY 10994.

HOENS, Eric P.; '96 AS; 15 William St., Goshen, NY 10924.

HOFACKER, Patricia; '96 BS; 59-16 Woodside Ave., Woodside, NY 11377.

HOFFMAN, Charles; '77 MA; 2454 Sunflower Ter., Vista, CA 92083, 760 727-6946.

HOFFMAN, Howard A.; '76 BS; 122 Vista Ave., Staten Island, NY 10304.

HOFFMAN, Joseph C.; '76 MPA; Adjunct Prof.; Adelphi Univ.; r. 5 Shadow Ln., E. Williston, NY 11596, 516 747-2619; *Catherine;* Joseph, Robert. e-mail

HOFFMAN, Neil; '79 MA; BA Brooklyn Clg., BS Rutgers Univ.; VP; The Bank of NY, One Wall St., New York, NY 10286, 212 635-1491; r. 23 Bunker Hill Dr., Manalapan, NJ 07726, 732 446-3634; *Ellen C.;* Glen, Julie.

HOFFMAN, Robert J.; '82 MPA; 169 Hoover Pl., Centerport, NY 11721, 631 385-8853.

HOFFMANN, James A.; '84 AS; 5613 28th Ave., Flushing, NY 11377, 718 726-3069.

HOFFMANN, LT Russlan D.; '91 BA, '95 MPA; Dir. of Public Safety Ofc. of Chief; Ramapo Clg. of New Jersey, 505 Ramapo Valley Rd, Mahwah, NJ 07430, 201 684-7432; r. 177 E. 93rd St. Apt. 1D, POB 4226, Port Jervis, NY 12771, 212 423-0313. e-mail

HOFMEISTER, Brian; '86 MPA; 35 Hutchinson Dr., Port Monmouth, NJ 07758.

HOGAN, Brian F.; '75 BA; 2 Adam Ct., Sloatsburg, NY 10974, 914 753-2631.

HOGAN, Paul T.; '98 BS; NYPD Operations; 1 Police Plaza, New York, NY 10038; r. 1606 Madison St., Elmont, NY 11003, 516 354-4256. e-mail

HOGAN, Robert A.; '71 BA; Retired-Security Cnslt.; Bankers Trust, 732 758-0537; r. 19 Southvale Ave., Little Silver, NJ 07739, 732 758-0537; *Joan;* Christine, Barbara. e-mail

HOGAN, Steven M.; '96 BS; NYPD Sgt.; r. 4101 Victoria Dr., Mt. Kisco, NY 10549, 914 242-2027; *Patti.*

HOGAN, Tamika C.; '97 BS; 1310 Union St., Brooklyn, NY 11213, 718 643-0111.

HOGAN, Virginia M.; '75; 3224 Murray Ln., Flushing, NY 11354.

HOGANS, Mrs. Robin K.; '91 BS; MS ED Mercy Clg.; Tchr.; NYC Bd. of Educ., 213-10 92nd Ave., Queens Vlg., NY 11428; r. 113-43 194 St., St. Albans, NY 11412; *Kenneth;* Maurice, Kendra.

HOGARTH, Emmanuel J.; '85 BA; 1221 S Shasta St., W. Covina, CA 91791, 310 444-3170.

HOHL, Christine; '96 BA; 7136 66th Pl., Flushing, NY 11385, 718 386-2953.

HOLDEN, McThaddeus; '76 BA; Dir. Public Safety; Bronx Community Clg. CUNY, University Ave. & W. 181 St., Bronx, NY 10453, 718 289-5923; r. 135-04 Hook Creek Blvd., Jamaica, NY 11422. e-mail

HOLDEN, Terence; '99 BA FSA; Firefighter; City of NY; r. 14 Ann Pl., Sloatsburg, NY 10974, 914 753-2545; *Christine.*

HOLDER, Desiree A.; '84 BA; 1014 E New York Ave., Brooklyn, NY 11212, 718 493-6763.

HOLDER, Giovanna; '95 BS; 526 E 78th St., Brooklyn, NY 11236, 718 498-2106.

HOLDER, Gloria I.; '74 BS; Business Owner; Access Health, 4036-A Plank Rd., Fredericksburg, VA 22407, 540 786-0575; r. 9603 Conaty Cir., Spotsylvania, VA 22553, 540 582-7974; Jamie, Jay Jay. e-mail

HOLDER, Laura M.; '82 BS, '97 MPA; 21411 112th Rd, Queens Vlg., NY 11429, 718 468-7168.

HOLDER, Lorna I.; '89 BA; 70 Lenox Rd Apt. 2c, Brooklyn, NY 11226, 718 498-6643.

HOLDER, Lynnette N.; '77 BS; 666 Prospect Pl., Brooklyn, NY 11216.

HOLDER, Tonya; '93 BA, '96 MPA; 11024 157th St., Jamaica, NY 11433, 718 298-6449.

HOLDER, Wayne A.; '81 BA; 601 W 164th St. Apt. 27, New York, NY 10032.

HOLDER, Winthrop A.; '74 BS; 115-75 226 St., Cambria Hts., NY 11411, 718 760-5336.

HOLIAN, Kevin M.; '80 BS, '82 MPA; Security Evaluation & Oversite; IRS, 110 W 44th St., New York, NY 10036, 212 719-8500; r. 5 Dorcas Ave., Syosset, NY 11791, 516 496-4683; *Debra.* e-mail

HOLIHAN, John W.; '78 BS; Retired Sgt.; NYPD; r. 19 W. Beverly pkwy., Valley Stream, NY 11580, 516 872-0865; *Noreen;* Kerry, Nancy, Patricia.

HOLLADAY, Dorothy E.; '82 BS; 30 Norton St., Inwood, NY 11096.

HOLLAND, Daniel J.; '77 BS; 163 Carrier St., Liberty, NY 12754, 315 858-0111.

HOLLAND, Jan; '97 BA; 332 Bleecker St., New York, NY 10014, 315 732-6384.

HOLLAND, Linda J.; '88 MA; 225 Elmwood Ave., Maplewood, NJ 07040.

HOLLAND, Michael; '76 BS; 531 Silent Siesta Dr., Henderson, NV 89015, 702 565-0387.

HOLLAND, Nelson K.; '85 BS; 530 Grassmere Ter., Far Rockaway, NY 11691.

HOLLAND, Ronald P.; '76 BS; 436 Brookside Ave., Roosevelt, NY 11575.

HOLLEY, James D.; '95 BS; 432 W. 49th St., New York, NY 10019.

HOLLIMAN, Jeffrey; '88 BA; 135 Elmira Loop # 4, Brooklyn, NY 11239, 718 642-3748.

HOLLINGSWORTH, Jerald; '84 BS; Enforcement Ofcr.; Cases, 346 Broadway, New York, NY 10013, 718 643-2722; r. 709 Olmstead Ave., Bronx, NY 10473.

HOLLOMAN, G. B.; '88 BS; 26 Madison St., New York, NY 10038.

HOLLOWAY, Anthony; '94 BA; 35 Norwood Ave. Apt. 1, Staten Island, NY 10304.

HOLLOWAY, Cecelia T.; '85 BS; 375 Van Siclen Ave., Brooklyn, NY 11207, 718 257-4835.

HOLLOWAY, Harold T.; '76 MPA; 1476-3 Parkside Ct., Trenton, NJ 08638.

HOLLY, Erin K.; '99, MA; 151 E. 36th St., New York, NY 10016, 212 213-5618.

HOLLY, Jacqueline R.; '83 BA; 150 Crown St. Apt. D3, Brooklyn, NY 11225, 718 241-7545.

HOLMAN, Gregory R.; '91 BS; 66 W 109 St. #24, New York, NY 10025.

HOLMAN, Jeffrey M.; '80 BS; 392 Kosciusko St., Brooklyn, NY 11221, 718 452-3765.

HOLMES, Ms. Angela A.; '91 BS; Letter Carrier; Lenoy Hill Postal Ofc., 909 3rd Ave. 4th Fl., New York, NY 10021, 212 330-5686; r. 5702 Farragut Rd. Apt. 1D, Brooklyn, NY 11234, 718 241-6486; *Latisha.*

HOLMES, Anthony; '81 BS; 20 Moneta Ct., Mt. Laurel, NJ 08054, 856 273-8254.

HOLMES, George R.; '80 BA; Ret. Sergeant; NYS Supreme Ct.; r. 283 Kennedy Ave., Hempstead, NY 11550; *Joan;* Lori Warlock.

HOLMES, Ms. Gloria; '90 BA; AAS NYC Tech, BA; Case Mgmt.; r. 1470 St. Johns Pl., Brooklyn, NY 11213, 718 493-4018; *Sabrina.*

HOLMES, Reginald; '92 BS; 22727 Murdock Ave., Queens Vlg., NY 11429, 718 358-6855.

HOLMES, Sabrina; '81 BA; JD Seton Hall Law; Atty.; r. 134 Baltic St., Apt. 1A, Brooklyn, NY 11201, 718 237-9136. e-mail

HOLMES, Sharon R.; '98 BS; Child Protector Spec.; Admin. for Children Svcs.; r. 176 14 St. Topfl, Brooklyn, NY 11215, 718 788-8515.

HOLSEY, Sabine N.; '99 MA; 172-20 133rd Ave. #12G, Jamaica, NY 11434, 718 528-2031.

HOLST, Irma R.; '78 BS; Volunteer; r. 1843 Schieffelin Ave., Bronx, NY 10466, 718 653-0754; *Bruno.* e-mail

HOLSTEN, Gary W., Jr.; '99 BA; Patrolman; South Brunswick Police, 1 Police Plz., Monmouth Jct., NJ 08852, 732 329-4646; r. 13 Debonis Dr., Milltown, NJ 08850, 732 246-4321. e-mail

HOLT, Kevin T.; '85 BS; 264-21 Langston Ave., Floral Park, NY 11004, 516 561-9055.

HOLTZMAN, Cynthia R. '93 (See Holtzman-Waranis, Cynthia R.).

HOLTZMAN-WARANIS, Cynthia R., (Cynthia R. Holtzman); '93 MA; BA PSCYH Monmouth Univ.; Mental Health Therapist; Carrier Clinic, Rte. 601, Belle Mead, NJ 08502, 908 281-1000; r. 1810 Oak Rd, Skillman, NJ 08558, 609 466-8050; *Michael.*

HOLUB, Peter W.; '78 BA; Retired-Lt.; NYPD; r. 3011 Newport Ave., Medford, NY 11763, 631 475-3130; *Patricia.* e-mail

HOLVIK, Thor; '75 MPA; 14 Lake Rd, Huntington Sta., NY 11746, 631 271-3162.

HOM, Diane; '78 BS; 1716 64th St., Brooklyn, NY 11204.

HOM, Tak J.; '83 BS; 77 Mulberry St., New York, NY 10013, 315 866-2261.

HONE, Jacqueline; '96 BA; 418 Main St., Apt. B1, Ft. Lee, NJ 07024.

HONORE, Michelle M.; '80 BS; 386 Preston Ave., Staten Island, NY 10312.

HOOD, Melody E.; '86 MA; 523 E 12th Ave., Apt. 10, Denver, CO 80203, 303 894-8648.

HOOPER, Julian C.; '82 MA; 16 Caroline St., Staten Island, NY 10310.

HOOVER, Herbert B.; '69 MPA; AA Sacramento Jr. Clg., BS Long Beach State Clg.; Retired Bureau Chief; CA Dept. of Justice, Sacramento, CA 95814; r. 1233 Monte Vistaway, Sacramento, CA 95831, 916 424-5163. e-mail

HOPE, Jennifer; '92 MA; 102 W 75th St., New York, NY 10023, 212 874-1710.

HOPE, Quinzelle; '90 BS; 116-40 Inwood St., S. Ozone Park, NY 11436.

HOPKINS, Adria D.; '99 BA; Paralegal; Bronx Dist. Atty's Ofc.; r. 4 W 108 St. Apt. 5, New York, NY 10025, 212 222-6882; Harold Crew Jr. e-mail

HOPKINS, Farrell J.; '95 BS; 8 Bayview Dr., Stony Point, NY 10980, 315 646-2241.

HOPKINS, John K.; '79 MA; 14 Winchester Dr., Monroe, NY 10950.

HOPKINS, Kevin M.; '87 BS; 177 W 3rd St., Bayonne, NJ 07002, 201 437-8634.

HOPKINS, Steven B.; '76 BA, '78 MA; 25 Harmony St., Piscataway, NJ 08854, 732 752-9162.

HOPKINS, Warner V.; '72 BS; MA Long Island Univ.; Assoc. Court Clerk; NYS Supreme Ct.; r. 341 Beach 148th St., Neponsit, NY 11694, 718 643-2302; *Patricia;* Matthew, Maggie.

HOPP, Philip M.; '74 BS; 6308 76th St., Flushing, NY 11379.

HORACE, Sara J.; '89 MPA; 2100 Lyons Ave., Lansing, MI 48910.

HORAN, Denise A.; '98 AS; 1505 Cross Bay Blvd., Rockaway Bch., NY 11693, 718 634-3249.

HORAN, Francis J.; '70 BS; 7 Deforest Ct., W. Nyack, NY 10994, 914 348-1708.

HORAN, James J.; '75 MS; BS St. Peters, MPA City Clg.; Forensic Sci. Faculty; John Jay Clg., 445 W 59th St., New York, NY 10019, 212 237-8887; r. 219 Amber St., Staten Island, NY 10306, 718 987-0737; *Marilyn.*

HORAN, Michael; '90 MPA; 70 Bayberry Rd, Schenectady, NY 12306, 518 355-5674.

HORN, Helen L.; '96 BA; 14049 Latham Ln., Jamaica, NY 11434, 718 591-3630.

HORN, Lukas; '90 MA; 145 E 92nd St., New York, NY 10128.

HORNE, Marion R.; '83 BS; 655 Bradford St., Brooklyn, NY 11207.

HORNE, Peter; '87 PHD; Prof. & Coord.; Criminal Justice Prog.; r. 837 Jamestown Rd, E. Windsor, NJ 08520, 609 443-8696. e-mail

HOROWITZ, Lawrence J.; '75 BA; 14846 58th Ave., Flushing, NY 11355, 718 464-9474.

HOROWITZ, Robert B.; '78 BA; 525 Bronxville Rd Apt. 5b, Bronxville, NY 10708, 914 962-2383.

HORTON, Edward; '95 BS; 844 Orbit Ln., Uniondale, NY 11553, 516 292-9429.

HORVATH, Robert J.; '70 BS; Regional Claim Mgr.; Med. Liability Mutual Ins. Co., 90 Merrick Ave., E. Meadow, NY 11554, 516 794-7200; r. 12 Herman Ave., Hicksville, NY 11801, 516 681-6158; *Janice;* Christopher, Tricia, Brian.

HOSEIN, Richard A.; '93 BS; 9413 85th Rd, Jamaica, NY 11421, 718 323-7856.

HOT, Zajo E.; '97 BS; Police Ofcr.; NYC Police Dept., Bronx, NY 10451; r. 657 Edison Ave., Bronx, NY 10465, 718 319-8324; *Sauda;* Allen.

HOU, Julie; '96 BA; Special Svcs.; Cravath Swaine & Moore, 825 8th Ave., Worldwide Plz., New York, NY 10019, 212 474-3308; r. 67-100 Austin St., Forest Hills, NY 11375. e-mail

HOUDEK, Caroline M.; '99 BA; AS Nassau Comm. Clg.; Owner; DJ Houdek's Restaurant, 845 Merrick Rd, Baldwin, NY 11510, 516 223-3344; r. 922 Pacific St., Baldwin, NY 11510, 516 223-9166; *Derek.*

HOUGHTON, Richard M.; '84 BS; 45 Middlesex Ave. Apt. D, Metuchen, NJ 08840.

HOULE, Ms. Genevieve L.; '99 BS; Paralegal; Green & Cohen P.C., 319 E 91st St., New York, NY 10128, 212 983-2770; r. 4542 Oxford Ave., Montreal, QC, Canada H4A 2Y8, 514 485-7316. e-mail

HOULIHAN, Maureen A.; '83 MA; 26353 74th Ave., Glen Oaks, NY 11004.

HOUSEN, Faith D.; '94 MA; 547 Union Ave., Westbury, NY 11590.

HOUSTON, Bernard P.; '78 MPA; 104-59 Roosevelt A, Corona, NY 11368.

HOUSTON, Leonard W., PhD; '82 BS; PHD ED, JD LaSalle Univ.; Pres. CEO; American Health Inst. Corp., 67 Wall St. Ste. 2411, New York, NY 10005, 212 323-8058; r. 148 Deer Court Dr., Middletown, NY 10940, 914 343-8923; *Lucille.*

HOWARD, Bernard E.; '96 BA; Safety Engr.; New York Presbyterian Hosp., 525 E. 70 St., New York, NY 10021, 212 746-1926; r. Jamaica, NY 11412; B. Esq. e-mail

HOWARD, Bradley D.; '87 BA; 231 W. 116 St., New York, NY 10026.

HOWARD, Catherine '75 (See Kolpak, Mrs. Catherine R.).

HOWARD, Frances L. '42 (See Hudson, Frances L.).

HOWARD, George E.; '77 MA; 190 W. 152nd St., New York, NY 10039, 315 896-2760.

HOWARD, Gerard A.; '77 BS, '80 MA; 46 Ormond St., Rockville Centre, NY 11570, 516 764-3087.

HOWARD, Keith S.; '89 BS, '95 MPA; Asst. Commissioner; NYC Dept. of Transportation, New York, NY 10007, 212 676-0134; r. Bronx, NY 10451. e-mail

HOWARD, Linder J.; '83 MPA; MA City Clg.; Educ.-4th Grade; PS 30; r. 651 W 188th St., Apt. 5f, New York, NY 10040, 212 923-4428.

HOWARD, Theodora E.; '85 BS; Police Ofcr.; NYC Police Dept., Brooklyn, NY 11213; r. 496 Bradford St., Brooklyn, NY 11207, 718 495-2594. e-mail

HOWARD, Timothy; '89 BS; Police Ofcr.; Stamford, CT 06901, 203 977-4921; r. 28 Mayflower Ave., Stamford, CT 06906, 203 323-6292.

HOWE, Jason B.; '99 BS; 536 Central Ave. Apt. B, Brooklyn, NY 11221, 718 602-3011.

HOWE, Lawrence; '95 BS; 97-77 Corona Ave. (BSMT), Corona, NY 11368, 718 276-7654.

HOWELL, George A.; '76 BS; 63 Lefferts Ave., Brooklyn, NY 11225, 718 693-9392.

HOWELL, Paula M.; '98 BA; Law Student; Harvard Law Sch., 8201 HLS holmes mail center, Cambridge, MA 02138, 617 493-9047; r. 1288 E 53 St., Brooklyn, NY 11234, 718 968-0240. e-mail

HOWKINS, James O.; '80 MPA; 68 Sylvan Pl., Valley Stream, NY 11581.

HOWLEY, Mary E.; '77 BS; 122-14 Newport Ave., Rockaway Park, NY 11694.

HOWLEY, Maureen A.; '78 BA; 11713 Newport Ave., Far Rockaway, NY 11694.

HOWZE, Rosa M.; '99 BA; 1165 E. 229th, Bronx, NY 10466, 718 547-5872.

HOY, Patrick J.; '75 MA; 23 Locust Ave., Bayville, NY 11709.

HOYT, Robert M.; '81 BS; 51-12 92nd St., Elmhurst, NY 11373.

HOYT, Ms. Yvette C.; '93 BA, '95 MPA; BAMPA; Fed. Investigator; US Dept. of Labor, 201 Valick St., New York, NY 10014, 212 337-2580; r. 2090 Madison Ave., New York, NY 10037; Annikqua.

HREBENKO, Aneta; '97 BS; Workforce Devel. Spec.; US Dept. of Labor, New York, NY 10014, 212 337-1088; r. 223 Madison Ave., Cresskill, NJ 07626, 201 541-9115; Jerzy; Nina. e-mail

HSU, Peter B.; '99 BA; 2463 Ridgeway Rd, San Marino, CA 91108, 626 291-2630.

HSUEH, John K.; '87 BS; 3243 88th St. Apt. 206, Flushing, NY 11369.

HUACUZ, Rogers; '96 BS; NYC Police Ofcr.; NYPD, 1 Police Plz., #41 Precinct, New York, NY 10038; r. 80 Van Cortland Park S., Apt. #G62, Bronx, NY 10463, 718 549-7040; Narda.

HUANG, Chen Tao; '97 MPA; Mail Carrier; US Postal Svc., New York, NY 10020; r. 521 66th St., Brooklyn, NY 11220. e-mail

HUANG, Melody C.; '95 BA, '95 CERT; JD St. John's Univ.; 4126 Case St., Flushing, NY 11373, 718 458-7238.

HUANG, Yi; '89 MPA; 94-08 42 Ave. 3rd Fl., Elmhurst, NY 11373.

HUBBARD, April R. '79 (See Evans, April R.).

HUBER, Paul; '88 MA; MSW Fordham Univ.; Spec. Agt.; WV DEA, Pobox 591, Wheeling, WV 26003, 304 234-7773; Julia; Zachary, Briana, Jessica.

HUBERT, Frank J.; '77 BS; 22028 93rd Ave., Queens Vlg., NY 11428, 718 465-8294.

HUBERT, Richard B.; '79 BS; 7947 68th Rd, Flushing, NY 11379, 718 894-3467.

HUDSON, Charles T.; '76 BA; 425 Central Park W, New York, NY 10025.

HUDSON, Frances L., (Frances L. Howard); '42 BA; Homemaker; r. 12014 178th Pl., Jamaica, NY 11434, 718 528-2209.

HUDSON, John J.; '75 MPA; 203 Park Blvd., Massapequa Park, NY 11762, 516 541-7978.

HUDSON, Richard; '92 BS; 9315 123rd St. # Bs, Jamaica, NY 11419, 718 520-7575.

HUDSON, Sharen D.; '84 BA; 74 Herzl St., Brooklyn, NY 11212.

HUDYMA, Amie; '85 BA; 152 E Clinton Ave., Bergenfield, NJ 07621.

HUERTA, Maricela; '96 BA; 23592 Windsong Apt. 45F, Aliso Viejo, CA 92656, 949 363-0556.

HUEY, Ivy S.; '99 BA; Court Liaison; Children's Village, Echo Hill, Dobbs Ferry, NY 10522, 914 693-0600; r. 9 Johnson Ct., # F, Dobbs Ferry, NY 10522, 914 479-0547. e-mail

HUGEE, Angela L.; '89 BA; MSW Yeshiva Univ.; Social Work; HRA Ofc. of Employment Svcs., 109 E 16th St., New York, NY 10003, 212 835-8061; r. 984 Bedford Ave., Brooklyn, NY 11205, 718 855-0125; Johnnie; Candace, Jasmine, Jonathan. e-mail

HUGGINS, Eddie C.; '76 BS; 1636 3rd Ave., # 265, New York, NY 10128.

HUGGINS, Ms. Jocelyn; '76 BA; Correction Ofcr.; Taconic Correctional Facility, 250 Harris Rd., Bedford Hls., NY 10507, 914 241-3010; r. 11A Arlington Pl., Brooklyn, NY 11216, 718 399-3719.

HUGGINS, Laurel; '94 CERT; 930 Sheridan Ave., Bronx, NY 10451, 718 538-9059.

HUGHES, Brian J.; '79 BS; JD St. Johns Sch. of Law; Atty.; Law Ofc. of Brian J. Hughes, 631 765-6911; r. 210 Brook Ln., Southold, NY 11971. e-mail

HUGHES, Mrs. Camille R., (Camille F. Petrinc); '96 BS; GN; r. 17 Parker Dr. E., Mahopac, NY 10541; Derrick; Pamela.

HUGHES, Christina E.; '97 BA; Prog. Dir.; Community Assocs. Devel. Corp., 247 Herkimer St., Brooklyn, NY 11216, 718 857 5418; r. 441 Monroe St., Brooklyn, NY 11221, 718 452-3950; Oscar; Oscar Jr, Steven, Shaqwan, Jahmel, Selassie. e-mail

HUGHES, Denita R.; '94 AS, '96 BS; 3131 Grand Concourse, Bronx, NY 10468.

HUGHES, Ellsworth K.; '76 BS; 2 Ash Pl., New Hyde Park, NY 11040, 516 488-5459.

HUGHES, Francis J.; '69 BA, '79 MPA; 70 2nd St., Pelham, NY 10803, 914 738-0617.

HUGHES, Isabel; '92 BA; Retired Sgt.; NYPD; r. 2805 Bedford Ave., Brooklyn, NY 11210, 718 253-3055; Cliffton; Andre, Cliffton Jr, Lorraine, Denta.

HUGHES, James D.; '89 BA; 111 Haverford Rd, Hicksville, NY 11801, 516 488-5459.

HUGHES, James R.; '99 MA; Ofcr./Sergeant; Mendham Twp. Police Dept., 3 Cherry Ln. Brookside, Brookside, NJ 07926, 973 543-2581; r. 200 Western Ave., Morristown, NJ 07960, 973 540-0791.

HUGHES, Joanne P.; '82 BS; 5550 Netherland Ave., Bronx, NY 10471, 718 601-7876.

HUGHES, John E.; '98 MS; BBA Pace Univ.; Deputy Dir.; Mayors Ofc. of Emergency Mgmt, 212 442-2044; r. 206 Ridge Rd., Goshen, NY 10924, 914 294-1476.

HUGHES, Karen; '87 BS; 1811 E. 15 St., Brooklyn, NY 11229.

HUGHES, Leola M.; '93 BA; 2320 Governors Rd, Windsor, NC 27983.

HUGHES, Maria, (Maria V. Konczynin); '79 BS; 11 Nixon St., Farmingville, NY 11738, 631 698-7439. e-mail

HUGHES, Martin J.; '75 BS; 3141 Decatur Ave., Bronx, NY 10467, 718 292-0728.

HUGHES, Timothy P.; '76 BA; 25861 Tipperary Ln., Lake Forest, CA 92630, 949 498-8495.

HUIE, Brenda; '97 BS; 363 Grand Ave.6D, Brooklyn, NY 11238.

HUIETT, Ghaironesa; '97 BA; POB 20621, New York, NY 10023.

HULL, Melanie S.; '98 BA; 16625 89th Ave., Jamaica, NY 11432, 718 224-4895.

HULLER, Thomas P.; '77 MPA; AS, BA; Retired Lt NYPD; r. 69-24 Eliot Ave., Middle Vlg., NY 11379, 718 326-0764.

HULSMANN, Robert N.; '73 BA; Retired Capt.; NYC Police Dept.; r. 64 Willow St., Floral Park, NY 11001, 516 437-5386; Ann; Mark, James.

HULTS, Carol D.; '95 MA; BA Queens Clg.; Prog. Dir.; Transitional Svcs. New York Inc., 80-45 Winchester Blvd., Queens Vlg., NY 11427, 718 464-3772; r. 5526 84th St., Elmhurst, NY 11373, 718 429-5464.

HULTS, Charles E.; AS BS; MA Empire State Clg.; Pres./Prof.-SUNY; MCH Cnslts.; r. Bronx, NY 10461.

HUM, Julia S.; '93 BS; 2368 W 12th St., Brooklyn, NY 11223.

HUMBER, Charles M.; '75 BA; POB 2624, New York, NY 10027.

HUMES, Gilbert C.; '95 BA; 127 Halsey St., Brooklyn, NY 11216, 718 636-8702.

HUMPHREYS, Beverly; '93 BS; 450 W 147th St., Apt. 43, New York, NY 10031.

HUNCE, Joseph D.; '81 BS; Police Lt; Mt. Vernon, NY 10551; r. 1376 Midland Ave. Apt. 709, Bronxville, NY 10708.

HUNG, Fu-chin; '84 MA; LLM Natl. Central Police Univ; Pres.; Taiwan Ag & Industrial Devel. Corp., 6F #10 Chung-King South Rd. Sec., Taipei, Taiwan, 0223617571; r. 5F #49 Ln. 190 Sec. 1 Tun-Hua S Rd, Taipei, Taiwan, 0227810646; Yueh-Kuei Hung Lin; Shuo-Heng, Shuo-Pin. e-mail

HUNGREDER, Scott G.; '97 BS; 712 E. Gun Hill, Bronx, NY 10467.

HUNT, Curtis J.; '99 BS; Loss Prevention Assoc.; Bloomingdales, 1000 3rd Ave., New York, NY 10022, 212 705-3025; r. 1695 Watson Ave., Bronx, NY 10472, 718 617-0465.

HUNT, Kathleen T.; '77 BA; 40 Winant St., Staten Island, NY 10303.

HUNT, Marvin S.; '75 AS, '79 BS; Prof.; South Florida Community Clg., 600 W College Dr., Avon Park, FL 33826, 863 453-6661; r. POB 37, Avon Park, FL 33826, 863 452-1622; *Madeline*. e-mail

HUNT, Nicole D.; '91 BA; 1630 Forest Lakes Cir. Apt. C, W. Palm Bch., FL 33406, 561 586-8985.

HUNT, Obie; '92 BS; AAS Bronx Community Clg.; Mental Hygiene Therapy Aide; Manhattan Psychiatric Ctr., Wards Island, New York, NY 10035, 212 369-0500; r. 1150 Grand Concourse, Bronx, NY 10456, 718 992-3487.

HUNTE, Ruthven G.; '86 BS; 231-11 128 Rd Dr., Laurelton, NY 11413.

HUNTER, George A.; '92 BA; 1314 Coalter Steet, Richmond, VA 23223, 804 788-4136.

HUNTER, Gloria E.; '92 AS, '94 BS; Retired; r. 315 Beach 20th St., Far Rockaway, NY 11691, 718 868-2782. e-mail

HUNTER, Philip; '96 BA; POB 39, Malverne, NY 11565, 516 561-0395.

HUNTER, William; 25 Ash Rd, Nanuet, NY 10954, 914 627-9163.

HUNTER, Yovonda (Yoyo) B.; '99 BS; Line Cook/Student; Long Island Outback Steakhouse; r. 168-40 127th Ave., Jamaica, NY 11434, 718 525-5787.

HURLEY, Jennifer D.; '87 BS; 585 Crescent St., Brooklyn, NY 11208, 718 935-1192.

HURLEY, Michael J.; '93 MPA; BA Fordham Univ., JD St. Johns Univ. Sch. Law; Lt.; NYPD, 1 Police Plz., New York, NY 10038; r. 230 Garth Rd Apt. 1b1, Scarsdale, NY 10583, 914 472-4313. e-mail

HURLEY, William T.; '86 BA; 154 W 131st St. Apt. 5, New York, NY 10027, 212 926-4005.

HURREY, Ayanna I.; '94 BA; Student; Criminal Justice Major Sch.; r. Woodside, NY 11377.

HURST, Veta P.; '91 BS, '94 MA; 2142 Holly way, Lansing, MI 48910, 517 837-2529.

HURWITZ, Brian M.; '99 MA; 812 Grand Blvd., Westbury, NY 11590.

HUSSEY, Brian P.; '84 BS; Retired 1st Grade Detective; r. 116 Pine St., Massapequa Park, NY 11762, 516 799-1357.

HUSSEY, Robert; '76 MA; 85 5th Ave., Kings Park, NY 11754, 631 269-6214.

HUSSEY, Robert F.; '68 BA; MA Adelphi, EDD Hofstra; Ret Asst Principal; r. 89 Magnolia Ave., Garden City, NY 11530, 516 742-2756.

HUSSEY, Robert J.; '76 MA; 71 Roosevelt Dr., W. Haverstraw, NY 10993, 914 947-2183.

HUTCHINSON, Dionne; '97 BA; 1261 Merriam Ave., Bronx, NY 10452, 718 590-1709.

HUTCHINSON, J.; '89 BS; 2135 Marktrail Rd, Decatur, GA 30032, 770 987-7859.

HUTCHINSON, Marla; '93 BS; 2721 Rio Grande Tr., Kissimmee, FL 34741.

HUTCHINSON, Minerva; '91 BA; POB 6928, New York, NY 10150.

HUTCHINSON, Nadia; '97 BS; 8714 Farragut Rd, Brooklyn, NY 11236, 718 771-0922.

HUTCHINSON, Thomas; '91 BS; 2913 Pheasant Dr., Decatur, GA 30034.

HWEE, Edmund; '98 BS; 51 13 94 St., Elmhurst, NY 11373.

HYACINTH, Mario K.; '98 MA; BA Fordham Univ.; Paralegal; Simpson, Thacher & Bartlett, 425 Lexington Ave., New York, NY 10017, 212 455-3664; r. 531 A Washington Ave., Brooklyn, NY 11238, 718 622-3171. e-mail

HYAMS, Laurie; '79 MA; 8031 269th St., New Hyde Park, NY 11040.

HYDE, Dorrel A.; '87 BA, '98 MS; 2115 Washington Ave., Bronx, NY 10457, 718 220-3111.

HYDE, Phillip E.; '76 BA; Partner; Hyde-Madigan Organizational Devel., 278 Greenview Rd., Yardley, PA 19067, 215 493-0592; r. 278 Greenview Rd, Yardley, PA 19067, 215 493-2421; *Karen*; Lauren, Leah, Gregory. e-mail

HYDE, Tucker; '93 BA; 219-02 94th Ave., Queens Vlg., NY 11428.

HYLAND, Velvet A. '97 (See Hyland Reda, Mrs. Velvet A.).

HYLAND REDA, Mrs. Velvet A., (Velvet A. Hyland); '97 MA; BA Hofstra Univ.; Branch Mgr.; First Franklin Financial Corp., Tarrytown, NY 10591, 914 467-5232; r. 154 Martling Apt. S-2, Tarrytown, NY 10591, 914 524-9550; *Robert Reda*. e-mail

HYMAN, April J. '85 (See Fleming, April J.).

HYMOWITZ, Alan J.; '84 MA; 10 Carter Rd., W. Orange, NJ 07052.

HYNES, Stephen D.; '88 BS; 258 Amos Ave., Oceanside, NY 11572.

HYNES, Walter G.; '83 BA; 134 Beach 93rd St., Far Rockaway, NY 11693, 718 634-3079.

HYPPOLITE, Ms. Anne W.; '98 BS; PC/LAN Tech.; NY Public Library, 188 Madison Ave., New York, NY 10016, 212 592-7269; r. 901 Washington Ave. #40, Brooklyn, NY 11225, 718 622-3813. e-mail

I

IACONO, Richard M.; '86 BA; 6327 83rd St., Flushing, NY 11379, 718 726-9515.

IACOPELLI, Lisa; '81 BS; 373 Magnolia Dr., Selden, NY 11784.

IACOPELLI, Thomas A.; '81 BS; 84-33 60th Dr., Elmhurst, NY 11373.

IACOVOU, Jack; '87 BS; 2816 Astoria Blvd., Long Island City, NY 11102.

IADANZA, Charles; '70 BS; 9145 71st Rd, Forest Hills, NY 11375.

IANNACE, Arthur B.; '78 BS; 183 Lamoka Ave., Staten Island, NY 10308.

IANNACO, Vincent T.; '75 BS; 161-28 95th St., Howard Bch., NY 11414, 718 848-0594.

IANNONE, Barbara A.; '94 MA; 225 Connetquot Ave., East Islip, NY 11730.

IANNOTTA, Richard A.; '75 BS; Investigator; NYC Law Dept., 100 Church St., New York, NY 10007, 212 788-1696; r. Flushing, NY 11365. e-mail

IBEZIM, David; '82 BS; 600 W 113th St. # 6a3, New York, NY 10025.

IBRAHIM, Husaini; '86 BA; 8819 215th Pl., Queens Vlg., NY 11427.

IBRAHIM, Shorab; '99 BS; Law Student; Hofstra Law Sch.; r. 516 Woodbind St., Uniondale, NY 11553, 516 538-8849. e-mail

IDIART, George J.; '85 BA; Capt.; NYC Fire Dept., Engine 44, New York, NY 10021, 212 570-4244; r. 17 Montgomery Rd, Pearl River, NY 10965, 914 735-7479; *Marion*; George, Michelle. e-mail

IDLETT, Paul J.; '96 BS; 66 Bulwer Pl., Brooklyn, NY 11207.

IDOWU, Frances A.; '89 BA; 425 E 96 St. #3H, Brooklyn, NY 11212.

IERARDI, Andrew J.; '83 AA, '84 BA; Retired Police Ofcr.; r. 66 Cedar Point Dr., W. Islip, NY 11795, 631 669-7971; *Rosanne*; Michael, Richard, Andrea.

IERARDI, Peter A.; '91 BA; 9512 4th Ave., Brooklyn, NY 11209, 718 677-0837.

IFEBI, Emeka C.; '99 MPA; 470 51st St., Flr.2, Brooklyn, NY 11220, 718 439-8827.

IFIDON, Lawrence L.; '96 BA; 3530 Decatur Ave., Bronx, NY 10467.

IGIEBOR, Justice O.; '98 MA; 14404 91st Ave., Jamaica, NY 11435.

IGLESIAS, Nora M.; '97 BA; MSW Adelphi Univ.; Certified Social Worker; Long Island Jewish Hosp., Jericho Tpk., Mineola, NY 11501, 516 742-4015; r. 1549 Adams St., Elmont, NY 11003, 516 564-1340.

IGLESIAS, Rosa E.; '83 MPA; 2111 62nd St. N, Apt. 814, Clearwater, FL 33760.

IGNACIUK, Stanley; '77 BS; 5 Birch Ln., Valley Stream, NY 11581, 516 791-3397.

IGNERI, Patrick N.; '78 BS; 97-19 135 Dr., Ozone Park, NY 11417.

IHNE, Christine M.; '98 BS; Investigator; US Investigator, 291 Broadway, Ste. 1204, New York, NY 10007, 212 577-5050; r. Montgomery, NY 12549. e-mail

ILARDI, Arthur; '75 BS; 557 Pauley Dr., W. Hempstead, NY 11552.

ILLAS, David; '87 BS; 512 Grant Ave., Brooklyn, NY 11208.

ILOKA, Samuel C.; '89 BA; 220 Woodlawn Ave., Trenton, NJ 08609, 609 584-8566.

IMPARATO, Michael G.; '75 BS; 1107 E 2nd St., Brooklyn, NY 11230, 718 234-5175.

IMPAVIDO, Catherine L.; '99 BA; Grad. Student; NY Law Sch.; r. 1821 E. 32nd St., Brooklyn, NY 11234, 718 376-8596. e-mail

INDAR, Dennis K.; '90 BS; 403 Etna St., Brooklyn, NY 11208.

INDELICATO, James; '88 MA; 348 Clarendon St., Secaucus, NJ 07094, 201 319-9495.

INDIMINE, Lawrence F.; '78 BA; 11 Cortland Ct., Huntington Sta., NY 11746.

INDRATHAHER, Wahyudi; '93 BA; 182 Nelson St. # 3, Brooklyn, NY 11231.

INDUCCI, Craig G.; '80 BA; US Probation Ofcr.; US Dist. Ct. Dist. of NJ, 402 E. State St., Trenton, NJ 08608, 609 989-0433; r. 930 Putnam Dr., Yardley, PA 19067, 215 369-0855.

INGELLIS, Daniel A.; '80 BS; Detective; NYC Police Dept., 1 Police Plz., New York, NY 10038; r. 128 Rockville Ave., Staten Island, NY 10314; *Marie; Michelle, Erica.*

INGMAN, Matthew A.; '95 MPA; BMED Univ. of North Texas; Free-lance Musician; r. 317 S Broadway, Nyack, NY 10960, 914 348-0930; *Marnie.* e-mail

INGOGLIA, John V.; '94 BS; 38 Burbank Ave., Staten Island, NY 10306.

INGRAM, Carlean N.; '94 BA, '99 MPA; MJA; Social Studies Tchr.; Urban Peace Acad., 2351 1st Ave., New York, NY 10035, 212 987-1906; r. 706 Remsen Ave., Brooklyn, NY 11236, 718 485-3053; Latasha. e-mail

INGRAM, Garrett; '88 BA, '98 MA; Child Protective Spec. Supv. II; The Admin. for Children Svcs., 90-25 161st St., Clinician, Behav Mgmt Svc-Dysf Fam, Jamaica, NY 11434, 718 262-1423; r. 25534 147th Dr., # 2, Rosedale, NY 11422.

INGRAM, Margaret; '92 BA; Staff Analyst Researcher; NYC Police Dept., 1 Police Plz. Rm 1014, New York, NY 10038; r. 555 Bronx River Rd, Yonkers, NY 10704, 914 776-6939; Leah, Tracy.

INNACE, Thomas E.; '78 BS; 2096 Canarsie Rd, Brooklyn, NY 11236.

INTERLANDI, Giuseppe S.; '98 BS; 1853 W. 11th St., Brooklyn, NY 11223, 718 266-0365.

INTRIERI, Dominick D.; '87 BA; 768 Kimball Ave., Yonkers, NY 10704.

IOCCO, Luigi G.; '90 BA; 28 Elissa Ln., Yonkers, NY 10710, 914 961-9487.

IONESCU-BINDER, Beatrice; '97 BA, '98 BA; 40-51 Denman ST. #283, Elmhurst, NY 11373.

IOVINO, James; '85 BS; US Govt.; r. 11547 115th St., Jamaica, NY 11420, 718 835-1949; *Lorraine.*

IPPOLITO, Michael J.; '77 BS, '87 MA; 2161 West St., Brooklyn, NY 11223, 718 369-1751.

IPPOLITO, Steve; '79 BA, '86 MA; 26 Seminara Cir., Garnerville, NY 10923.

IQBAL, Nelly R.; '84 MPA; 114-20 120th St., S. Ozone Park, NY 11420, 718 461-4620.

IRISH, Carlcton P.; '68 BS; Rctircd Acct. of Mayor John Linsey; NYC Police Dept; r. 169 Forest Green, Staten Island, NY 10312, 718 984-5227.

IRIZARRY, Christopher F.; '98 MPA; BA Rutgers Univ.; Probation Ofcr./Prof.; Sex Offenders Unit, State of Nj Judiary, 595 Newark Ave. Rom G7, Jersey City, NJ 07306, 201 795-6823; r. 4501 Palisade Ave. #5D, Union City, NJ 07087, 201 617-0612. e-mail

IRIZARRY, Gisela; '97 BA; Dir. of Business Devel.; S.W. Childs Mgmt., 667 Madison Ave., 19th Fl., New York, NY 10021, 212 759-5588; r. 640 Blvd. E. #2, Weehawken, NJ 07087, 201 617-9534. e-mail

IRIZARRY, Sylvia E.; '82 BA; 15 Riverside Dr., Suffern, NY 10901.

IRIZARRY, Yolanda; '95 BS; 1320 Odell St. Apt. B55, Bronx, NY 10462.

IROBUNDA, Claralee; '85 MA; 1503 Metropolitan, Bronx, NY 10462, 718 931-5421.

ISAAC, Dana R.; '99 BS; Administrative Asst.; Food Network, 1180 Ave. of The Americas, 11th Fl., New York, NY 10036, 212 401-5323; r. 45 W. 139th St. Apt. 5S, New York, NY 10037, 212 368-6630. e-mail

ISAACS, Paul K.; '90 BS; Pres.; Micro Applied Systs., 455 W. 34th St., New York, NY 10001, 212 564-6683; r. 455 W 34th St. # 16, New York, NY 10001, 212 279-0597. e-mail

ISAACS, Waymond Q.; '89 BA; 779 Concourse Village, Bronx, NY 10451.

ISAACSON, Eric M.; '98 BA; AAS Kingsborough Community; Field Tech.; Bell Atlantic; r. 1836 E. 18th St. #5B, Brooklyn, NY 11229, 718 382-4692. e-mail

ISLES, Samantha; '95 BS; 1045 Montgomery St., Brooklyn, NY 11213, 718 953-9672.

ISOM, Michael; '96 BA, '99 BA; 853 Walton Ave. #2D, Bronx, NY 10451, 718 538-4251. e-mail

ISRAEL, Gary G.; '76 MPA; 44 Old Middletown Rd, New City, NY 10956, 914 638-3409.

ISRAEL, Ruth L.; '95 BS; 423 Blake Ave. Apt. 1e, Brooklyn, NY 11212.

ISRAELOV, Michelle; '98 BS; 1550 Unionport Rd 2f, Bronx, NY 10462, 718 892-1278.

ISROE, Karyn E.; '95 MA; BA Pace Univ., AA Westchester Community; Forensic Clinician; Kings Cnty. Dist. Attorney's Ofc., Renaissance Plz., 350 Jay St. 10Fl, Bbonseling Services Unit 10th Fl., Brooklyn, NY 11201, 718 250-4876; r. 42 Putnam Ave., Yonkers, NY 10705. e-mail

ITHIER, Carmen; '91 BA; Case Planner; Harlem Dowling West Side/Fam. & Children, 800 A Riverside Dr., New York, NY 10032, 212 927-9200; r. 175 W. 90 St. #2H, New York, NY 10024, 212 724-8709; *Ramon;* Erica, Jennifer.

IULIANO, Stefano; '75 BA; 28 Terrace Ave., Staten Island, NY 10309.

IVANOVA, Nathalia L.; '97 BA; 482 E. 74th St., New York, NY 10021.

IVES, Nicole J.; '98 BA; 1 Corncrib Ct., Sicklerville, NJ 08081.

IVORY, Marcheta R.; '96 BA; 5019 Beverly Rd., Brooklyn, NY 11203.

IVORY, Patrick V.; '78 BS; 46 Harvard St., Garden City, NY 11530.

IYALLA, T.; '92 BA; Dir.; Miebi, Inc., 524 W 122nd St. #3A, New York, NY 10027, 212 222-6636; r. same; *Kathleen;* Ibifaka, Iboroma, T. Jr., Tambi, Atelisik.

IYALLA, Tina A.; '89 BS, '91 MA; 273 W. 131 St., New York, NY 10027.

IYESI, Okpa; '99; 3 Haven Pl. 14F, New York, NY 10009, 212 253-2375.

IYOHA, Friday E.; '80 MPA; 158 Jacques St., Elizabeth, NJ 07201.

IZZO, Angelo; '85 BA; 2324 Morgan Ave., Bronx, NY 10469.

IZZO, Anthony J.; '78 BS; 88-30 181 St., Jamaica, NY 11423.

J

JABLONS, David N.; '90 BA; MSW Hunter Clg. Sch. of SW, AS CRJUS Nassau Community Clg.; Social Worker; r. 632 E Olive St., Long Beach, NY 11561, 516 432-9483.

JABLONSKA, Beata; '95 BA, '97 MA; Legal Asst.; Fragoman, Del Rey, Bernsen & Loewy, PC, 515 Madison Ave., New York, NY 10022, 212 688-8555; r. 217 Centre Ave., Lindenhurst, NY 11757, 631 884-1036. e-mail

JABLONSKY, William; '92 BS; POB 8, Manorville, NY 11949.

JABOUIN, Alain S.; '95 BS; Fraud Investigator; River, 330 J St., Brooklyn, NY 11201, 718 237-4179; r. POB 190501, S. Richmond Hill, NY 11419. e-mail

JABOUIN, Melone H.; '98 BS; 138-23 250th St., Rosedale, NY 11422.

JACK, Bryan A.; '95 AS, 2000 BA; Campus Peace Ofc.; Brooklyn Clg., 2900 Bedford Ave., Brooklyn, NY 11210, 718 951-5511; r. 1320 E 54th St., # 1, Brooklyn, NY 11234, 718 968-3099. e-mail

JACKMAN, Harold L.; 20 Metropolitan Oval, Bronx, NY 10462.

JACKNOW, Jayson K.; '92 BS; 2652 Cropsey Ave., Brooklyn, NY 11214, 718 372-8915.

JACKSON, Adriane R.; '98 BS; AS NYC Technical Clg.; Paralegal Aide; The NYC Law Dept., Div. of Tax & Condemation Dept., 100 Church St., New York, NY 10038, 212 788-0803; r. 65-24 162nd St. #3D, Fresh Meadows, NY 11365, 718 380-2401. e-mail

JACKSON, Albert A.; '92 BS; 140 De Kruif Pl. # 31, Bronx, NY 10475.

JACKSON, Alena R.; '80 BA; Employment Spec.; NetworkPlus Employment Svcs., 25 Flatbush Ave., Brooklyn, NY 11201, 718 797-2509; r. 21 St. James Pl., Apt. 1H, Brooklyn, NY 11205, 718 622-4366.

JACKSON, Alicia J.; '99 AS; 219 02-143 Rd, Springfield Gardens, NY 11413, 718 322-2643.

JACKSON, Archie V.; '81 AS; 15323 118th Ave., Jamaica, NY 11434, 718 322-2643.

JACKSON, Barrett; '75 BS; 14220 Laburnum Ave., Flushing, NY 11355, 718 322-2643.

JACKSON, Carol J.; '96 BA; 615 Prospect Pl., Brooklyn, NY 11216, 718 348-9833.

JACKSON, Cecile; '83 BS; 2780 86 St. #7D, Brooklyn, NY 11223.

JACKSON, Christina; '97 BS; Car Cleaner; NYC Transit Authority, 370 Jays St., Brooklyn, NY 11201, 718 330-1234; r. 1618 Benson St. Apt. #3B, Bronx, NY 10461, 718 828-8041; *Lawrence;* Ginger. e-mail

JACKSON, Collette A.; '91 BA; 17 Ave. W Apt. 3f, Brooklyn, NY 11223, 718 348-9833.

JACKSON, Derek A.; '81 AS, '82 BA; MA Columbia Univ.; Police Ofcr.; Intelligence Div., 26 Fed. Park, New York, NY 10007, 212 637-3274; r. 1170 Ferndale Blvd., Central Islip, NY 11722, 631 582-6131. e-mail

JACKSON, Dunstan O.; 2000 MPA; BA Wesleyan Univ.; Deputy Dir. of Finance; NYC Dept. of Consumer Affairs, 42 Broadway, New York, NY 10004, 212 487-4243; r. 1447 Carroll St., Brooklyn, NY 11213, 718 756-3048. e-mail

JACKSON, Edward; '85 BS; Sr. Parole Ofcr.; NJ Div. Parole, 518 Market St., Camden, NJ 08102, 856 614-3726; r. 17 Tipton Ln., Willingboro, NJ 08046, 609 835-1274.

JACKSON, Falinyi D.; '84 BS; 14551 107th Ave., Jamaica, NY 11435.

JACKSON, Hardy; '85 BA; 167 Bush St., Brooklyn, NY 11231.

JACKSON, Harvey; '70 BS; 191-15 116 Ave., St. Albans, NY 11412, 718 468-8224.

JACKSON, Hazel L.; '86 BS, '89 MA; Asst. Chief Probation Ofcr.; Monmouth Probation Dept.; Superior Ct. of Monmouth Cnty., Freehold, NJ 07728, 732 409-4806.

JACKSON, Ivory L. '86 (See Scott, Ivory L.).

JACKSON, Judy; '98 BA MA; Psychologist/Forensic Advocate/Coun; Fresh Start Prog. Inc., 681 Clarkson Ave., Brooklyn, NY 11203, 718 221-7740; r. 277 Eastern Pkwy. Apt. #5l, Brooklyn, NY 11238, 212 696-8663. e-mail

JACKSON, Karen M.; '92 BS; 117-17 220 St., Cambria Hts., NY 11411.

JACKSON, Katherine L.; '87 BA; Detective; NYPD Technical Assistance Response Unit, One Police Plz. Rm 1200P, New York, NY 10038, 212 267-3317; r. 366 Douglass St., Brooklyn, NY 11217. e-mail

JACKSON, Kim A.; '90 BS; 99-03 209th St., Queens Vlg., NY 11429, 718 322-2643.

JACKSON, La-toya; '95 BS; Sr. Claims Rep.; Grp. Health Inc., 441 9th Ave., New York, NY 10007, 212 615-0412; r. 3045 Ave. W, Brooklyn, NY 11229, 718 934-1088; Justin. e-mail

JACKSON, Latoya M.; '98 BA; 440 B 58 St. 8b, Far Rockaway, NY 11692, 718 318-1503.

JACKSON, Mertol; '83 MPA; 10635 Remington St., Jamaica, NY 11435, 718 723-9035.

JACKSON, Patrice M.; '93 BS; 126 E. 53 St., Brooklyn, NY 11203.

JACKSON, Raymond; '87 AS; 4-24 Astoria Blvd./, Long Island City, NY 11102, 718 468-9891.

JACKSON, Renee M.; '82 BS, '88 MA; 115 E. 35th St., Brooklyn, NY 11203.

JACKSON, Robert A.; '83 MA; 10100 Hobbyhill Rd, Richmond, VA 23235, 804 744-9543.

JACKSON, Shawneequa; '96 BS; 203 Scholes St., Brooklyn, NY 11206, 718 230-9472.

JACKSON, Stephen C.; '81 BA; 111-09 203 St., Hollis, NY 11412.

JACKSON, Vicki D.; '79 BA; 48 Irvington Rd, Teaneck, NJ 07666.

JACKSON, William P.; '86 AS, '90 BS; 43-35 Union St., Flushing, NY 11355.

JACKSON, Yvonne C.; '85 BA; 50 Lefferts Ave., Brooklyn, NY 11225, 718 222-8612.

JACOB, George N.; '80 BS; 141 Huddy Dr., Toms River, NJ 08755, 732 349-6251.

JACOB, Lisa G.; '92 BA; 472 Hendrix St., Brooklyn, NY 11207.

JACOB, Thomas P.; '81 BS; Capt.; NYC Police Dept., 212 666-3247; r. 789 West End Ave. Apt. 8D, New York, NY 10025, 212 666-3247; Tiffany.

JACOBELLIS, Nicholas; Staten Island, NY 10308, 718 227-6253.

JACOBS, Arthur W.; '79 MPA; 8021 269th St., New Hyde Park, NY 11040.

JACOBS, Cynthia D.; '81 BS; 11233 180th St., Jamaica, NY 11433, 718 481-6918.

JACOBS, Cyril C.; '98 BA; 1807 Clinton Ave., #4d, Bronx, NY 10457, 718 731-6764.

JACOBS, Harold; '76 BA; 69 Hastings Dr., Stony Brook, NY 11790.

JACOBS, Jerry L.; '91 BS; MS CW Post Long Island Univ; Lt.; NYC Police Dept., 1 Police Plz., New York, NY 10038, 718 287-3242; r. 217 Elm Dr., Bay Shore, NY 11706, 631 231-0065; Ronda. e-mail

JACOBS, Lawrence W.; '72 BA; Retired; NYPD; r. 16330 E Powderhorn Dr., Fountain Hls., AZ 85268, 480 837-0638; Judy; Barry, Randi.

JACOBS, Nancy; 23 W 73rd St. # 1407, New York, NY 10023, 212 769-9903.

JACOBSON, Benjamin; '76 BA; 7 Pinewood Dr., Englishtown, NJ 07726.

JACOBS-OSBORNE, Guliana D.; '95 BA, '95 MA; 128-04 107th Ave., Richmond Hill, NY 11419.

JACOUTOT, Alfred; '78 BS; 1646 First Ave., New York, NY 10028.

JACUBOVICS, Robert S.; '75 MA; 2442 Buck St., Bronx, NY 10461, 718 828-9794.

JAEN, Dimas A.; '99 BA; Child Protective Spec.; r. 175 W.87th St. Apt. 3P, New York, NY 10024, 212 496-6182. e-mail

JAFFE, Joanne; '79 BS, '84 MA; Asst. Chief; NYCPD, 450 Cross Bronx Expy., Bronx, NY 10457, 718 299-4189; Douglas Lennihan.

JAFFE, Lawrence B.; '84 BS; 2926 Bayswater Ave., Far Rockaway, NY 11691.

JAGDHARRY, Mayleen G.; '99 BA; Machine Operator; Pfizer Inc., 630 Flushing Ave., Brooklyn, NY 11206; r. 292 Maple St., Apt. C1, Brooklyn, NY 11225, 718 604-2803. e-mail

JAGHROO, Hilary; '91 BS; 1063 Morris Ave., Bronx, NY 10456.

JAIGOBIND, Carl; '98 BS; Customs Inspector; US Customs, JFK International Airport, Bldg. 77, Jamaica, NY 11430; r. 32 Highland Ave., W. Nyack, NY 10994, 914 353-2586.

JAIN, Rajiv; '96 MS; 209-40 27th Ave., Bayside, NY 11360, 718 454-2954.

JAKUBOWSKI, Steven; '81 BS; 44 Cambridge, Oxford, NJ 07863.

JAKUBOWSKI, Thomas R.; '77 BS; BATF Contact Instr.; 56 Perry Ave., Staten Island, NY 10314, 718 761-2706; r. same; Maria Aprile CPA CFE.

JALAF, Gabi G.; '88 BS; 31-06 42 St. #22, Long Island City, NY 11103.

JALIYL, Mrs. Laila A.; (Hildegarde B. Davis); '80 BA; MSN NYU; Supv./Fair Hearing Rep.; Human Res. Admin., New York City, New York, NY 10128, 212 360-5039; r. 560 Main St. # 7, New York, NY 10044, 212 588-0041; Sa-Di. e-mail

JAMADAR, Bettyann; '96 BS; 345 W 50th St. Apt. 6a, New York, NY 10019.

JAMES, Ainsworth; '90 AS; BA, MPA; Fire Safety Dir.; John Jay Clg. of Criminal Justice, 899 Tenth Ave., New York, NY 10019, 212 237-8524; r. 448 E. 45th St., Brooklyn, NY 11203, 718 941-2340. e-mail

JAMES, Arthur; '80 BS; 71 Columbia St. Apt. 19h, New York, NY 10002, 212 358-9508.

JAMES, Carol A.; '86 BA; 962 Schenectady Ave., Brooklyn, NY 11203, 718 856-3120.

JAMES, Claudia L.; '88 BA; 455 Beach 69th St., Far Rockaway, NY 11692, 718 224-1270.

JAMES, Dina M.; '94 BS; Exec. Secy. Flavor & Fragrances; J. Manheimer Inc., 47-22 Pearson Pl., Long Island City, NY 11101, 718 392-7800; r. 599 Georgia Ave., Brooklyn, NY 11207, 718 386-3383. e-mail

JAMES, Fallarasha K.; '98 BS; 300 Manhattan Ave., # 5D, New York, NY 10026, 315 363-6637.

JAMES, Israel; '99 BA; CERT. Police Acad.; Police Ofcr.; NYC Police Dept., 33rd Precinct, New York, NY 10003; r. 1375 Grand Concourse Apt. 8A, Bronx, NY 10452, 718 293-7196; Marlene Castro.

JAMES, Jemal; '96 BS; 150 Schaffer St., Brooklyn, NY 11207.

JAMES, Lisa; '96 BS; 220 S. Lendla Rd.#A-108, Maple Shade, NJ 08052.

JAMES, Marcia L.; '90 BS; 3246 Colden Ave., Bronx, NY 10469, 718 324-2384.

JAMES, Melissa A.; '89 BS; 1121 Saint Lawrence Ave., Bronx, NY 10472.

JAMES, Michael G.; '88 BA; 649 E 23rd St., Brooklyn, NY 11210.

JAMES, Michelle B.; '95 BS; MCJ Iona Clg.; Legal Admin. Asst.; Brotmann & Freedman; r. POB 816, Yonkers, NY 10702.

JAMES, Michelle R.; '91 BA, '94 MA; 10427 Lefferts Blvd., Jamaica, NY 11419, 718 746-3679.

JAMES, Peter G.; '81 BA; 752 Ninth Ave. #2FS, New York, NY 10019.

JAMES, Richard L.; '92 BS; 790 Southern Pkwy., Uniondale, NY 11553, 516 333-3542.

JAMES, Sharon; '92 MPA; BA PA State Univ.; Staff Analyst; Human Resources Admin., Family Independent Admin., 111 8th Ave., New York, NY 10014, 212 849-3881; r. 27 Lamont Ct., Brooklyn, NY 11225, 718 953-6971.

JAMES, Spencer L.; '81 BS; Tech. Support Mgr.; Bank of New York, 101 Barcley St., New York, NY 10286, 212 815-4685; r. 53 Silber Ave., Bethpage, NY 11714, 516 931-8202. e-mail

JAMES, Tyrone L.; '79 BS; 241 W 131st St. # 4, New York, NY 10027.

JAMES, Walter A.; '89 BA; 1573 August Rd, N. Babylon, NY 11703, 631 884-9743.

JAMES, Wanda A., (Wanda A. Tinsley); '91 BA; Res. Devel. Coord.; New York Law Sch., New York, NY 10001, 212 431-2192; r. 379 Washington Ave., Brooklyn, NY 11238, 718 636-7643; Matthew; Matthew Jr. e-mail

JAMIESON, Peta-gaye; '87 BS; 558 E. 31 St., Brooklyn, NY 11210.

JAMINDAR, Swati P.; '90 BS; 59 Westend Ave., Valley Stream, NY 11580.

JAMISON, Annette; '98 BS; 685 E. 225th St. #B, Bronx, NY 10466, 718 432-5945.

JAMYANG, Dekyi T.; '99 BA; 426 70 St., W. New York, NJ 07093, 201 869-7507.

JANNECK, Walter F.; '89 MA; 143 Holland Ave., New Milford, NJ 07646.

JANOUSEK, Stanislav; '76 BS, '78 MA; Parole Ofcr.; NYS, 92-36 Merrick Blvd., Jamaica, NY 11433, 718 558-5150; r. Port Washington, NY 11050.

JANSSEN, Ronald P.; '76 BA; 5284 79th St., Flushing, NY 11373.

JANVIER, Alexandra; '97 BS; 573 E. 37th St., Brooklyn, NY 11203, 718 462-1218.

JANZEKOVICH, Robert; '88 BA; 54 Renee Ct., Jackson, NJ 08527.

JARECKI, Jane M.; '93 AS; 66 Bartow St., Staten Island, NY 10308.

JARJOKIAN, Kegham A.; '99 BS; 1544 Kennelworth P, Bronx, NY 10465. e-mail

JAROSCH, Richard A.; '87 BA; 41-16 49 St., Sunnyside, NY 11104, 718 229-2010.

JARRATT, Kent D.; '85 CERT; POB 876, New York, NY 10002.

JARRETT, E. C.; '94 BA; 3335 Indian Queen Ln. #2, Philadelphia, PA 19129, 212 281-4695.

JARVIS, Venetta E.; '82 BA; 2636 95th St., Flushing, NY 11369, 718 429-0698.

JASCEWSKY, George E.; '77 MA; Fingerprint Spec.; DEA; r. 53 Bartlett Ave., Staten Island, NY 10312; *Marie; Christine, Lori, Marie.*

JASMIN, Lude; '91 BS; 5301 Snyder Ave. #B, Brooklyn, NY 11203.

JASON, Tracey; '98 BA; Fraud Investigator; City of NY, Human Resources Admin./Bureau Fraud, 33-28 Northern Blvd., Queens, NY 11412, 718 626-6299; r. 269 Reynolds Ter., Unit 9, Orange, NJ 07050, 973 677-9117. e-mail

JAUDON, David; '89 BA; POB 30498, Jamaica, NY 11430.

JAUNDOO, Madeleine; '90 BS; 405 E Regent St. Apt. 4, Inglewood, CA 90301.

JAVIER, Jonathan; '96 BS; GRAD Police Acad.; Detective; NYC Police Dept.; r. 2205 2nd Ave. # 2, New York, NY 10029.

JAVIER, Sharon; '98 BS; 23-15 Steinway St. 2f, Astoria, NY 11105, 718 545-0528.

JAVORSKY, Stephen M.; '78 AS; 1328 E 84 St., Brooklyn, NY 11236.

JAWAD, Naeil; '93 BS; 5515 7th Ave. Apt. 1r, Brooklyn, NY 11220.

JAWAD, Naim; '85 BS; 910 57th St., Brooklyn, NY 11219, 718 437-1501.

JAWORSKY, Alice, (Alice Slezak); '95 BS; AAS LaGuardia Community Clg.; Legal Secy.; Philip J Kassel Esq, 60 E 42nd St., New York, NY 10165, 212 986-0656; r. 30-06 29 St. #6G, Long Island City, NY 11102, 718 721-1355; *Walter, Christine.* e-mail

JAY, Catherine; '83 BS; 134 15th St., Brooklyn, NY 11215.

JAY, Henry, Jr.; '93 AS, '94 BS; Detective Investigator; NYC Police Dept., 1 Police Plz., New York, NY 10038, 212 374-5000; r. 920 Baychester Ave., Bronx, NY 10475, 718 320-9488; *Judith; Reginald.*

JEAN, Carlo; '85 BS, '97 MPA; 469 E 38th St. # 2, Brooklyn, NY 11203, 718 421-5742.

JEAN, Pierre Y.; '90 BS; 5314 Avenue D, Brooklyn, NY 11203.

JEAN, Roberson D.; '96 BA; 956 E 89th St. Apt. 1, Brooklyn, NY 11236, 718 259-6078.

JEAN-BAPTISTE, C.; '89 BS; 711 Amsterdam Ave., New York, NY 10025.

JEAN-FELIX, Stanley; '95 BA; Sr. Investigator Spec.; Bur. of Fraud Investigation, New York, NY 10013; r. 79-27 Calamus Ave., Apt. 2, Elmhurst, NY 11373, 718 205-0140.

JEAN-GILLES, Myriam; '98 BA; 759 E. 102nd St., Brooklyn, NY 11236, 718 272-1933.

JEAN-LOUIS, Hildere; '98 BS; 674 E 45 St., Brooklyn, NY 11203, 718 941-2272.

JEAN-LOUIS, Valerie; '96 BA; 5123 Avenue J, Brooklyn, NY 11234.

JEAN-LOUIS, Wigeby; '95 BA; 925 E 100th St., Brooklyn, NY 11236, 718 345-8498.

JEAN-PHILIPPE, Herro; '90 BA; 145-20 Ferndale Ave., Jamaica, NY 11435.

JEAN-PHILIPPE, Paulena; '96 BA, '99 MPA; Mgmt. Auditor; NYC Dept. of Corrections, 7 Mandinici Rd., E. Elmhurst, NY 11370, 718 546-8213; r. 5001 Kent Ave. #, Apt. # 4f, Brooklyn, NY 11219, 718 435-3303; *Serge.*

JEBAVY, Judith A.; '97 MA; BA Austin Clg.; Border Control Agt.; US Border Patrol, 1500 W. La Quinta, Nogales, AZ 85621, 520 377-6000; r. 1 Rodeo Ct., Nogales, AZ 85621, 520 331-8071.

JEFFERSON, Alicia; '85 BS; 95-08 Liverpool St., Jamaica, NY 11435, 718 712-2519.

JEFFERSON, Clarett; '79 BA; 12827 234th St., Jamaica, NY 11422.

JEFFERSON, Gregory; '92 BS; 21933 Murdock Ave., Queens Vlg., NY 11429, 718 465-3218.

JEFFERSON, John A.; '94 BA; 247 Sterling St., Brooklyn, NY 11225, 718 789-8517.

JEFFERSON, Kayra R.; '99 BA; Grad. Student; John Jay Clg. of Criminal Justice; r. 145-36 116th Ave., Jamaica, NY 11436, 718 659-0005.

JEFFERSON, Marsha E.; '97 BA; Administrative Asst.; Brooklyn Bur. of Community Svc., 116 Williams Ave., Brooklyn, NY 11207, 718 485-9350; r. 29 Moore St., Apt. 17S, Brooklyn, NY 11206, 718 387-8604.

JEFFERSON, Marvella; '85 BS; Seizure & Forfeiture Spec.; US Marshals Svc. EDNY, 789 St. Marks Ave., Brooklyn, NY 11213, 718 254-6808; r. 789 Saint Marks Ave. Apt. 14b, Brooklyn, NY 11213, 718 735-7389.

JEFFERSON, Oubey L.; '77 BS; 4 Conning Ave., Middletown, NY 10941.

JEFFERSON, Stephen M.; '83 BA; Private Investigator; Coastline Investigative Svcs., POB 721133, Orlando, FL 32872, 407 382-6420; r. 171 Prairie Dune Way, Orlando, FL 32828, 407 823-9998; *Paula; Stephanie, Stephen Jr, Michael, Martin, Richard, Sherri, Michelle, Jamal, Kiani, Tamara.* e-mail

JEGEDE, Babatunde S.; '98 BS; 196 Rockaway Pkwy., Brooklyn, NY 11212, 718 922-2734.

JELCIC, Thomas A.; '87 BS; 95-19 41 Ave., Elmhurst, NY 11373.

JEMMOTT, Norman A.; '93 BA; Case Mgr./Social Worker; Community Counseling & Mediation, 115 W. 31st St. 5th Fl., New York, NY 10001, 212 564-6006; r. 480 Gates Ave. Apt. 4B, Brooklyn, NY 11216, 718 638-6766. e-mail

JENIK, Alice J.; '80 MPA; 601 E 20th St. Apt. 1f, New York, NY 10010.

JENIK, Peter K.; '87 MPA; 601 E. 20th St., New York, NY 10010, 212 673-2714.

JENKINS, Alexander D.; '77 MPA; 12627 Inwood St., Jamaica, NY 11436.

JENKINS, Alice M.; '96 AS, '97 BA; 13429 154th St., Jamaica, NY 11434, 718 712-2787.

JENKINS, Andre H.; '86 BS; Supervising Investigator; Special Commissioner of Investigations, 25 Broadway, New York, NY 10004, 212 510-1400; r. 882 Kings Pkwy., N. Baldwin, NY 11510, 516 868-2209; *Patricia; Darius, Julian.*

JENKINS, Charisse N.; '95 BS; Paralegal & Writer; Sullivan & Cromwell, 125 Broad St., New York, NY 10004, 212 558-3393; r. 11739 192nd St., Jamaica, NY 11412, 718 723-6030; *Anthony; Justin, England, Dante.*

JENKINS, Douglas A.; '97 AS, '99 BS; Sub Tchr.; Holy Rosary Roman Catholic Sch., 180 Bainbridge St., Brooklyn, NY 11233, 718 493-8471; r. 8940 184th St., Hollis, NY 11423, 718 264-0431; *Lauren; Douglas Jr., Mark Anthony, Trecia Ann, Kristina, Erica, Errin.* e-mail

JENKINS, Elaine; 120-06 142 Pl., Jamaica, NY 11436.

JENKINS, Ernestine; '93 BS; 22 Herkimer St. Apt. 2, Brooklyn, NY 11216, 718 257-6658.

JENKINS, Frederick V.; '82 BS; 2394 7 Ave. #68, New York, NY 10030.

JENKINS, Gary; '91 BS; 12 Cambridge Avenue P, Bay Shore, NY 11706.

JENKINS, Gary P.; '99 BS; Principal Admin. Assoc.; City of NY, 212 630-1743; r. 32 Hawthrone St., Brooklyn, NY 11225, 718 284-3253; *Randa;* Lauren, Morgan. e-mail

JENKINS, Ida F.; '77 MPA; 98-23 Horace H Expy., Rego Park, NY 11368, 718 712-2787.

JENKINS, Michael A.; '83 MPA; 22819 139th Ave., Jamaica, NY 11413.

JENKINS, Michele; '76 BS; 675 Lincoln Ave. #12A, Brooklyn, NY 11208, 718 235-3987.

JENKINS, Nicole; '93 BA; 11720 142nd Pl., Jamaica, NY 11436, 718 712-2787.

JENKINS, Pamela S.; '96 BS; 2846 Wickham Ave., Bronx, NY 10469.

JENKINS, Patricia; '89 BS; 1361 Webster Ave. Apt. 5, Bronx, NY 10456.

JENKINS, Rshaun K.; '95 BS; Parole Ofcr; NYS, Brooklyn, NY 11201.

JENKINS, Ms. Sabrina M.; '97 BA; AOS; Personal Financial Analyst; Primerica, 44 Court St. Ste. 305, Brooklyn, NY 11201, 718 243-0855; r. 1141 E. 42nd St., Brooklyn, NY 11210, 718 474-1268. e-mail

JENKINS, Samuel N.; '75 MPA; BS CUNY Clg. of New York; Retired Admin. Probation Ofcr.; NYC Dept. of Probation; r. 172-01 143rd Rd, Jamaica, NY 11434; Jane; Linda.

JENKINS, Shirley L.; '98 BS; Personnel Asst.; US Bankruptcy Ct., Brooklyn, NY 11201; r. 135-15 83 Ave., Briarwood, NY 11435, 718 849-6261; Brandyce.

JENNINGS, Hon. Allan W., Jr.; '90 BA; Assembly Dist. Leader; 31st Assembly Dist.-Queens, 135-01 Rockway Blvd., S. Ozone Park, NY 11420, 718 359-9152; r. 12803 Sutter Ave., # 2, Jamaica, NY 11420, 718 529-5339.

JENNINGS, Charles R.; '89 MS; BS Univ. of Maryland, PHD Cornell Univ.; Prof.; John Jay Clg. of Criminal Justice, Public Management, 445 W 59 St., New York, NY 10019, 212 237-8834; r. 225 Nelson Ave., Peekskill, NY 10566; Tristi Nichols. e-mail

JENNINGS, Rubin L.; '90 BS; 220 Fairview Blvd., Hempstead, NY 11550.

JENNINGS, Sean J.; '99 MA; 18 Church St., Stockbridge, MA 01262, 413 499-7293.

JENNY, Hernandez; 178 Avenue D, New York, NY 10009.

JENSEN, Glenn A.; '77 BS; 10 Schaffner Ln., Dover, MA 02030.

JENSEN, Paul V.; '72 BA; 22 Florence Dr., Syosset, NY 11791.

JEREMIE, Yves A.; '92 BA; 13125 Mathewson Ct., Jamaica, NY 11434.

JEREZ, Mercedes C.; '86 BA; 11559 118th St., Jamaica, NY 11420.

JEREZ, Victor; '97 BA; Fraud Investigator; Human Resources Admin. of The CNY, 180 Water St., 260 11th Ave. NYC, New York, NY 10038, 212 630-9758; r. 445 W. 37th St. Apt. 2 FW, New York, NY 10018, 212 564-3007; Josette; Jovic.

JERMIN, Cyril E.; '80 BS; 803 Lincoln Pl., Brooklyn, NY 11216.

JERNIGAN, Maranda D.; '96 BA; 8241 135th St. Apt. 3b, Jamaica, NY 11435, 718 481-6439.

JEROME, Lourdes M.; '97 BS, '99; 181-12 145th Ave., Springfield Gardens, NY 11413, 718 479-5183.

JESELNIK, Joseph J.; '75 BS; Retired Div. Mgr. in Marketing; r. 61 White Birch Rd, Pound Ridge, NY 10576. e-mail

JESELNIK, Margaret '77 (See Fischer, Mrs. Margaret M.).

JESELSON, Paul J.; '97 BA; 72 Seaman Ave., New York, NY 10034.

JESIA, Bryan N.; '96 BS; 9419 52nd Ave., Flushing, NY 11373, 718 271-6217.

JETTER, David A.; '77 BS; 8275 88th Pl., Flushing, NY 11385.

JEUNE, Sergo; '96 BS; Fraud Investigator; r. 940 Grand Concours, Bronx, NY 10451, 718 590-1517.

JIGGETTS, Raymond R.; '91 BS; 1522 Bryant Ave. # 1, Bronx, NY 10460, 718 378-4507.

JIMENEZ, Agueda M.; '98 BA; Police Ofcr.; NYPD, New York, NY 10002; r. New York, NY 10029. e-mail

JIMENEZ, Cristobal F.; '95 BS; 266 Ridgewood Ave., Brooklyn, NY 11208.

JIMENEZ, Daniel; '99 BS; AA Hostos Comm. Clg.; Tchr.; CIS 339, 1660 Webster Ave., Bronx, NY 10452, 718 583-5262; r. 760 Brady Ave. Apt. 616, Bronx, NY 10462, 718 823-8435; Amanda; Danielle, Gabrielle. e-mail

JIMENEZ, Ms. Julie A.; '99 MA; BA Curry Clg.; Youth Svcs. Couns.; Div. of Family Guidance Crisis Unit, 21 Main Street Ct. Plz. S., Hackensack, NJ 07601, 201 646-2233; r. 308 Vista View Dr., Mahwah, NJ 07430, 201 825-4774.

JIMENEZ, Leyla X.; '99 BA; 595 Autumn Ave. 3F, Brooklyn, NY 11208, 718 235-7617.

JIMENEZ, Linda J.; '87 BS; 545 E 144th St. # 13, Bronx, NY 10454, 718 292-2985.

JIMENEZ, Pedro A.; '95 BS; 449 Greengrove Ave., # 1, Uniondale, NY 11553, 516 796-9633.

JIMENEZ, Ramona J.; '98 BS; 1st & 2nd Grade Tchr.; P.S. 5, Port Morris Elementary Sch., Bronx, NY 10455; r. 667 W. 161 St. #2 D, New York, NY 10032.

JIMENEZ, Robert; '99 BA; Supv.; Merck, 399 Jefferson Rd, Parsippany, NJ 07054, 973 560-6127; r. 29-14 Ave., Elmwood Park, NJ 07407, 201 796-1066.

JIMINEZ, Karen; '97 BA; 28 Molle St. W, Babylon, NY 11704, 631 587-2636.

JIMPERSON, Mary; '94 MPA; BA Paine Clg.; Rsch./Lab Asst.; Intl. Flavors & Fragrances, Inc., 521 W. 57th St., Eighth Fl., New York, NY 10019, 212 765-5500; r. 2110 First Ave., Apt. 1410, New York, NY 10029, 212 860-1971; Antonio.

JINENEZ-FRANCIS, Els; '93 BA; 24570 Stewart St., Loma Linda, CA 92354, 909 653-1608.

JINKS, Veronica; '86 BA; 402 E 35th St., Brooklyn, NY 11203.

JIRAK, Donald J.; '93 BA; 105 W 13th St. Apt. 16f, New York, NY 10011.

JIRAK, Milton; '72 MA; Ret Tchr.; r. 108 Hartford Ave., Staten Island, NY 10310, 718 448-3236; Mary (dec); Paula, Roy, Meysa.

JOCHIM, Myron W.; '88 MA; POB 133, Guilford, NY 13780.

JOE, Lloyd D.; '95 BS, '98 MA, '98 MA; Investigator; NYS, 718 722-2276; r. 673 Sterling Pl. #3r, Brooklyn, NY 11216, 718 857-6238; Celia; Allana.

JOEL, Kenneth W.; '83 BS; 15964 Stonebriar Dr., Parker, CO 80134.

JOHANNESEN, Richard; '85 BS; 1848 Peck Ave., Bay Shore, NY 11706.

JOHN, Brentnol; '97 BA; Maintainer; NYC Transit Authority, 130 Livingston St., Brooklyn, NY 11201; r. 1075 E 31st St., Brooklyn, NY 11210, 718 252-8025.

JOHN, Ceres; '97 BS; Dialysis Tech.; NY Hosp., 718 961-0400; r. 253-26 148th Dr., Rosedale, NY 11422.

JOHN, Clayton P.; '92 BS; 1575 Brooklyn Ave., Brooklyn, NY 11210.

JOHN, Jacqueline D.; '89 BS; 130 E 51st St., Brooklyn, NY 11203, 718 574-0507.

JOHN, Lisa N.; '95 BS; 14828 88th Ave. Apt. 7f, Jamaica, NY 11435, 718 264-8462.

JOHNS, Lashana M.; '99 BA; 1523 Taylor #12, Bronx, NY 10460, 718 828-5848.

JOHNSEN, David P.; '75 BS; 11638 Woollcott St., San Antonio, TX 78251.

JOHNSON, Alfred K.; '85 BS; 240 Covert St., Brooklyn, NY 11207, 718 330-9215.

JOHNSON, Anne T.; '92 BA; AA Malcolm X King Clg.; Dept. of Social Work; 280 Broadway, New York, NY 10007, 212 442-3158; r. 890 Trinity Ave. # 3J, Bronx, NY 10456, 718 585-7606; Darryl.

JOHNSON, Anthony L.; '81 BS; 17530 Mayfield Rd, Jamaica, NY 11432, 718 337-0253.

JOHNSON, Ava Y.; '93 BS; MPA New York Univ.; Mktg. Mgr.; Chase Manhattan Bank, New York, NY 10001; r. 5900 Arlington Ave. Apt. 19K, Bronx, NY 10471. e-mail

JOHNSON, Bernard; '71 BS; 220-02 135 Ave., Laurelton, NY 11413.

JOHNSON, Bernard A.; '71 BS; Supervisory Special Agt.; US Dept. of State, 26 Federal Plz., Ste. 3409, New York, NY 10278, 212 264-3577; r. 900 N. Williams St., Baldwin, NY 11510, 516 378-1508.

JOHNSON, Bruce; '92 BS; POB 649, Bronx, NY 10472.

JOHNSON, Charlene A.; '99 BA; AS Borough Manhattan CC; Part-time Data Entry Clerk; Colson Svcs. Corp., 120 Broadway, New York, NY 10021, 212 266-0610; r. POB 912, Bronx, NY 10467, 718 562-9377. e-mail

JOHNSON, Charles A.; '98 BA; 340 Dumont Ave., Apt. 4D, Brooklyn, NY 11212, 718 284-1473.

JOHNSON, Charlie L.; '76 BA; 1206 Stanley Ave., Brooklyn, NY 11208, 718 284-1473.

JOHNSON, Clinton; '87 BS; 79 Cortlandt Ave., New Rochelle, NY 10801, 914 289-0087.

JOHNSON, Crystal M.; '94 BA; 1819 Nereid Ave. # 1, Bronx, NY 10466, 718 299-3063.

JOHNSON, Danielle C.; '95 BA; Correction Ofcr.; NYC Dept. of Corrections, 60 Hudson St., New York, NY 10013, 212 266-1064; r. 722 E 168th St., Bronx, NY 10456, 718 617-3127. e-mail

JOHNSON, Darryl A.; '92 BS; 2521 Sandy Ln., Easton, PA 18045.

JOHNSON, Dean L.; '80 AS; 10 Virginia Pl., Brooklyn, NY 11213, 718 209-0326.

JOHNSON, Delores; BS; 3410 Deremier Ave#14L, Bronx, NY 10475, 718 367-5568.

JOHNSON, Dolores L., (Dolores L. Easterling); '95 BS; Paralegal; Pierpont Grp., 461 5th Ave., New York, NY 10017, 212 685-2487; r. 936 Stelle Ave., Plainfield, NJ 07063, 908 755-4670; Christopher; Miles. e-mail

JOHNSON, Donald F.; '75 AS; Retired Police; NYC; r. 126 Atlantic Ave., Massapequa Park, NY 11762, 516 799-0391.

JOHNSON, Doris W.; '78 BA; 10037 196th St., Hollis, NY 11423.

JOHNSON, Edna S.; '99 BA; 2701 Valentine Ave#206, Bronx, NY 10458, 718 993-3559.

JOHNSON, Edward J.; '85 BA; Public Safety Ofcr.; Hofstra Univ., Dept. of Public Saftey, 1000 Fulton Ave., Hempstead, NY 11550; r. 170 Grand Central Ave., Amityville, NY 11701.

JOHNSON, Erious; '91 BA; 22146 Murdock Ave., Queens Vlg., NY 11429.

JOHNSON, Evelyn; '88 BS; 300 Bushwick Ave., Brooklyn, NY 11206, 718 302-0198.

JOHNSON, Everard K.; '95 BS; 151 W 123rd St. # 153, New York, NY 10027, 315 853-2589.

JOHNSON, Franceska; '94 BS; Field Operations Spec.; Dept. of Motor Vehicles, 19 Rector St., New York NY, New York, NY 10006, 212 316-2454; r. 1020 Grand Concourse, Bronx, NY 10451, 718 992-1336.

JOHNSON, Francis R.; '76 BA; 176 Governor Ave., N. Babylon, NY 11703.

JOHNSON, Frank J.; '77 BS; Detective 1st Grade; NYC Dept.; r. 122 Chestnut St., Garden City, NY 11530, 212 815-0575; *Marilyn;* Michael, Christina.

JOHNSON, Geronia G.; '81 BA; 256 Gates Ave., Brooklyn, NY 11238.

JOHNSON, Gloria; '80 BA; 700 Morris Ave. # 14, Bronx, NY 10451.

JOHNSON, Gloria; '98 BA; Case Mgr.; Little Flowers Children's Svcs., 186 Remsen St., Brooklyn, NY 11201, 718 260-8840; r. 1295 5th Ave. #17B, New York, NY 10029, 212 427-1671.

JOHNSON, Granville; '85 MPA; AAS Hutchinson Comm Jr. Clg., BA Howard Univ.; Special Agt.; Dept. of Justice DEA, 99 10th Ave., New York, NY 10011, 340 692-9500; r. 74 Central Ave., Englewood, NJ 07631, 201 871-9293; *Shandel; Kaprea, Aamir, Tarif, Tahirah.* e-mail

JOHNSON, Gwyn '95 (Scc Gwyn, Christine).

JOHNSON, Halsey J.; '93 BA; 11435 170th St., Jamaica, NY 11434.

JOHNSON, Herbert R.; '76 BA; 566 Decatur St., Brooklyn, NY 11233.

JOHNSON, Isaiah; '97 MS; 3A Dreyer Ave., Staten Island, NY 10314, 718 948-6055.

JOHNSON, James, Jr.; '80 BS; Retired Police Lt.; r. Apt. # 3L, New York, NY 10025, 315 855-7525; Tonisha.

JOHNSON, Jeanne; '79 BS; 88 Bryson Ave., Staten Island, NY 10302, 718 720-8537.

JOHNSON, John B.; '96 BA; Retired Police Officer; r. 280 Ninth Ave. Apt. 18D, New York, NY 10001, 212 243-3108; Matthew. e-mail

JOHNSON, Joni T.; '79 MA; BS Buffalo State Clg., AAS Erie Community Clg.; Payroll Ofc.; NYS Div. of Parole, 2 Church St., Ossining, NY 10562, 914 941-1028.

JOHNSON, Joseph; '75 BA; 245 Wortman Ave., Brooklyn, NY 11207, 718 649-3472.

JOHNSON, Keith M.; '81 BA; 2569 Adam Clayton Powell Jr Blvd., New York, NY 10039, 212 234-6066.

JOHNSON, Kesha Y.; '93 BS; 8691 208th St., Apt. 2D, Queens Vlg., NY 11427, 718 529-1648.

JOHNSON, Kimberly A.; '98 BS; 2050 Seward Ave. 11J, Bronx, NY 10473, 718 822-7588. e-mail

JOHNSON, Kristel A.; '92 BS; 700 E 156th St. Apt. 9c, Bronx, NY 10455, 718 293-6792. e-mail

JOHNSON, Larry; '90 BS; 66 Hancock St., Brooklyn, NY 11216.

JOHNSON, Larry; '95 BS; 295 W 150th St. Apt. 31, New York, NY 10039, 315 495-2050.

JOHNSON, Laurie J.; '91 BS; 14 High St., Sayville, NY 11782, 631 563-9224.

JOHNSON, Lucinda; '78 BS; 359 Sumpter St., Brooklyn, NY 11233, 718 439-5689.

JOHNSON, Marcia D.; '95 BA; 8317 Glenwood Rd, Brooklyn, NY 11236, 718 209-6640.

JOHNSON, Marion; '83 BS; 40-28G W. Mosholu, Bronx, NY 10468, 718 292-5348.

JOHNSON, Martin C.; '77 BA, '91 MA; 98-07 160 Ave., Howard Bch., NY 11414.

JOHNSON, Martin G.; '95 BA; Bus Operator; NYC Transit, 130 Livingston St., Brooklyn, NY 11201; r. POB 22, Bronx, NY 10473, 718 824-8466; *Oslyn;* Lorraine, Leslyn, Martin.

JOHNSON, Michael K.; '87 BS; 2693 W 37th St., Brooklyn, NY 11224, 718 373-6226.

JOHNSON, Ms. Monique F.; '98 BA GOVT, '98 BA LAW; Tchr. Social Studies; Port St. Lucie Sch. Dist., Ft. Pierce, FL 34952; r. 2643 SE Ruffin Ter., Port St. Lucie, FL 34952, 561 337-9262. e-mail

JOHNSON, Niesha P.; '98 BS; CERT. NYU; Paralegal/6th Grade Tchr.; Bd. of Educ. of New York-MS 12, 430 Howard Ave., Brooklyn, NY 11213, 718 953-4657; r. POB 330745, Brooklyn, NY 11233, 718 953-3275, Kenyatta H.

JOHNSON, Ms. Nykelle S.; '94 AAS, '95 CERT, '96 BS; BS, CERT. Bergen Community Clg.; Business Owner; Nykai's Beauty Supplies, 2732 Eight Ave., New York, NY 10039, 212 491-4590; r. 2443 3rd St. #6, Ft. Lee, NJ 07024, 201 944-8661; Nykai. e-mail

JOHNSON, Ophelia T.; '88 BS; 4451 Richardson Ave. Pen,, Bronx, NY 10470, 718 992-0526.

JOHNSON, Pamela A.; '81 BA; 64-85 Saunders St., Rego Park, NY 11374.

JOHNSON, Mrs. Patricia A.; '99 BA; AAS Westchester Community Clg; CNA; Wartburg Home, Wartburg Pl., Mt. Vernon, NY 10552, 914 699-0800; r. 30 Ehrbar Ave. #611, Mt. Vernon, NY 10552, 914 665-7031; *Ferdinald Clarke;* Ian, Nathalia, Cardinal Jr, Michael.

JOHNSON, Patricia R.; '87 BA; 850 Herkimer St., Brooklyn, NY 11233, 718 469-3270.

JOHNSON, Phyllis R.; '84 BS; 35 E. 94th St., Brooklyn, NY 11212, 718 774-7923.

JOHNSON, Ramona C.; '89 BA; 10747 159th St. Apt. 2a, Jamaica, NY 11433, 718 658-9710.

JOHNSON, Robert; '82 AS, '85 BS; 654 44th St., Brooklyn, NY 11220, 718 257-5075.

JOHNSON, Robert C.; '77 AS, '78 BS; Sr. Security Ofcr.; United Nation Headquarters New York, New York, NY 10017; r. 16840 127th Ave., Apt. 12A, Jamaica, NY 11434, 718 712-0525; *Shelia;* Lovell, Redeena, Robert Jr.

JOHNSON, Robert J.; '98 BS; Sr. Security Mgr.; FedEx, Parsippany, NJ 07054. e-mail

JOHNSON, Roger J.; '76 BA; 15 Malibu Hl, Rensselaer, NY 12144, 518 434-1996.

JOHNSON, Samuel M.; '79 MA; Retired Deputy-Warden/HS Tchr.; r. Bronx, NY 10467, 504 781-5017; *Barbara;* Cheryl, Stacie, Samuel.

JOHNSON, Shandel; '94 BA; 867 Jefferson Ave., Brooklyn, NY 11221.

JOHNSON, Sharon A.; '97; 231 Park Pl. #15, Brooklyn, NY 11238, 718 258-0079.

JOHNSON, Stepahnie; '79 MA; 646 Rutland Rd #3E, Brooklyn, NY 11203, 718 258-0079.

JOHNSON, Stephanie; '95 BA; 1755 Edenwald Ave., Bronx, NY 10466, 718 231-8716.

JOHNSON, Theresa A.; '97 BA; 749 Fdr Dr. #3A, New York, NY 10009, 315 853-2589.

JOHNSON, Tiffany R.; '99 BS; 27 W. 118th St. #1D, New York, NY 10026, 315 853-2589.

JOHNSON, Walter E.; '79 MA; 444 E 87th St., New York, NY 10028.

JOHNSON, Wendy N.; '98 MPA; BS ACCT Lehman Clg.; Analyst; MTA Bridges & Tunnels, 2 Broadway, New York, NY 10004, 646 252-7854; r. 338 Warburton Ave., Yonkers, NY 10701, 914 376-7180. e-mail

JOHNSON, Willie B.; '85 BA; MA NY Tech; Clinical Couns.; r. 75-34 164th St., Flushing, NY 11366.

JOHNSON, Zanetta C.; '97 BA; Admin. Asst.; MTA Metro North Railroad, 347 Madison Ave., New York, NY 10017; r. 1590 Madison Ave., New York, NY 10029, 212 427-4218. e-mail

JOHNSTON, David C.; '81 BS; 55 Overlook Ter., New York, NY 10033.

JOHNSTON, Deanna M.; '89 BA; Supv.; Admin. for Children Svcs., 165-15 Archer Ave., Jamaica, NY 11433; r. 29 Sherman Rd, Farmingdale, NY 11735, 631 249-8244.

JOHNSTON, Gordom M.; '81 BS; 56 Quinn St., Staten Island, NY 10304.

JOINER, Joyce R.; '79 BS; 309 Lafayette Ave. Apt. 22n, Brooklyn, NY 11238.

JOLLY, Andrea P.; '88 BS; 11949 229th St., Jamaica, NY 11411, 718 528-6415.

JOLLY, Terry E.; '81 BS; 251 Grafton St., Brooklyn, NY 11212.

JONAS, Heather E.; '99 MA; PHD Hofstra; Grad. Student; Hofstra, Hempstead, NY 11549; r. 7 Elba Pl., E. Northport, NY 11731, 631 462-1089.

JONES, Beverly V.; '92 AS, '95 BS; 2146 Charing Cross, Brunswick, GA 31525, 912 261-0122; *Seymour.*

JONES, Bobby R.; '89 BS; 13 Silverpine Dr., Amityville, NY 11701.

JONES, Brenda L.; '98 MPA; BA Hunter Clg.; Associate/Law Student; Bell Atlantic/ New York Law School; r. 270 Convent Ave. Apt. #6D, New York, NY 10031, 212 368-6733; Ashley. e-mail

JONES, Brian T.; '90 BS; 40 E Birch St. #4B, Mt. Vernon, NY 10552, 716 849-0901.

JONES, Carolyn M.; '88 BA; 467 W. 159th St., New York, NY 10032.

JONES, Cassandra D.; '89 BA; JD Western State Clg.; Atty.; Law Ofc. of Cassandra Jones, 1202 N. Broadway, Santa Ana, CA 92701, 714 972-3141.

JONES, Cheryl M.; '93 MA; 2600 Kennedy Blvd. Apt. 3G, Jersey City, NJ 07306.

JONES, Clarissa A.; '80 BS; 11128 139th St., Jamaica, NY 11435, 718 276-1095.

JONES, Corey A.; '95 BA; 439 8th St. # Ground, Brooklyn, NY 11215, 718 235-7574.

JONES, Darrell R.; '85 BA; 6 Meadowmere Ave., Mastic, NY 11950.

JONES, David A.; '92 BA; MSW Hunter Clg.; Prog. Dir.; Visiting Nurse Svc., 86-09 Rockaway Beach Blvd., Rockaway Bch., NY 11693, 718 318-3800; r. 122 Crest Ave., Elmont, NY 11003; *Karen;* Emory, David Jr., Corey Alvin, Bryce Gregory. e-mail

JONES, Debra D.; '98 BA; Student; Pace Univ. Sch. of Law; r. 130-37 235th ST., Rosedale, NY 11422, 718 528-6723. e-mail

JONES, Derrick A.; '96 BS; 2615 Newkirk Ave., Brooklyn, NY 11226, 718 282-1089.

JONES, Eneka U.; '99 BA; Student; Dept. of Computer Programming; r. 107 66 Merrick Blvd., Jamaica, NY 11433, 718 262-9583. e-mail

JONES, Ernest K.; '64 MPA; 74 Ridgeview Ave., Yonkers, NY 10710.

JONES, Frances M.; '86 BS; 206 W 123rd St., New York, NY 10027, 315 732-0269.

JONES, George E.; '73 MA; 11118 Mayville St. # Po287, Jamaica, NY 11412.

JONES, Gertrude E.; '87 BA; 13705 Modrad Way Apt. 32, Silver Spring, MD 20904, 301 516-7958.

JONES, Gregory; '81 BS; CERT. State of CA; Police Lt.; LAPD, Parker Ctr., 150 Los Angeles St., Los Angeles, CA 90012; r. POB 982, Moreno Vly., CA 92556, 909 924-5223; *Jennifer.* e-mail

JONES, Heather D.; '93 BS; 10 Cullen Ln., Middle Island, NY 11953, 631 205-1442.

JONES, Joseph L.; '73 BS; 50 Berkeley Pl., Massapequa, NY 11758.

JONES, Kevin; '93 BS; 311 Bedell St., Freeport, NY 11520, 516 520-5888.

JONES, Kevin; '95 BA; 118-01 196 St., St. Albans, NY 11412, 718 527-4404.

JONES, Kevin D.; '98 BS; 34-20 137th St. #3B, Flushing, NY 11354, 718 358-9260.

JONES, Kimberly A.; '92 MA; 17 Roger Ave., Middletown, NY 10940.

JONES, Lamont J.; '83 BS; 13436 157th St., Jamaica, NY 11434.

JONES, Lasalle; '91 BS; 705 E 179th St. Apt. 56, Bronx, NY 10457, 718 295-2797.

JONES, Lateshia P.; '95 BS; 259 Brooklyn Avenu, Brooklyn, NY 11213, 718 282-8541.

JONES, Lois M.; '81 BS; 609 W 151 St., New York, NY 10031.

JONES, Margaret D.; '97 MA, '98 BS; Community Relations Spec.; Charter Behavioral Health Systs., 19 Prospect St., Summit, NJ 07902, 908 277-9129; r. 509 1st St., Dunellen, NJ 08812, 732 926-0004.

JONES, Marla V.; '97 BS, '98 BS, '98 BS; 300 Fisher Ave., White Plains, NY 10606, 914 476-4983.

JONES, Melissa R.; '93 BS; 773 Manor Rd #4B, Staten Island, NY 10314, 718 984-1009.

JONES, Melissa S.; '90 AS, '92 BA; Police Ofcr.; NYC Police Dept.; r. 11578 223rd St., Jamaica, NY 11411.

JONES, Michelle A. '99 (See Dominguez, Michelle A.).

JONES, Otis M.; '76 BA; 11429 198th St., Jamaica, NY 11412.

JONES, Paula; '96 MPA; Deputy Dir of Equal Opportunity Pro; Univ. of VA, Hospital W., Charlottesville, VA 22908, 804 243-6439; r. 14001 Rockbasket Turn, Chester, VA 23836, 804 530-0088. e-mail

JONES, Rehenia; '98 BA; 552 W. 141st St. Apt. 1A, New York, NY 10031, 315 841-8270.

JONES, Richard; '77 BS; 875 Boynton Ave. Apt. 4l, Bronx, NY 10473.

JONES, Mrs. Rita G., (Rita D. Greene); '85 BA; Family Children Spec.; NYS Ofc. of Children & Family Svcs., 80 Madden Ln., New York, NY 10022, 212 383-4713; r. 519 Lincoln Pl. Apt. 4F, Brooklyn, NY 11238, 718 636-4763. e-mail

JONES, Robert H., Sr.; '78 BA; MS NY Inst. of Technology; Retired; Dept. of Corrections; r. 784 Clocks Blvd., Massapequa, NY 11758, 516 799-3822; *Vivian;* Robert Jr. e-mail

JONES, Robert L.; '86 BS; 5307 Clearview Expy., Oakland Gardens, NY 11364, 718 426-4706.

JONES, Robin M.; '92 BS; 1700 Bedford Ave., Brooklyn, NY 11225. e-mail

JONES, Rodney S., Sr.; '82 BA; Private Investigator; Investigation & Security Unlimited, POB 120425, St. Albans, NY 11412, 718 978-5109; r. 19421 116th Rd, Jamaica, NY 11412, 718 978-5109; Rodney Jr., Clifford.

JONES, Roger; '77 BA; 1983 Ferry Dr., Marietta, GA 30066, 770 590-9562.

JONES, Ronnie A.; '91 BS; 518 Evergreen Ave., Brooklyn, NY 11221, 718 422-1005.

JONES, Seymour A.; '76 AS, '78 BS; MA CW Post Long Island Univ., MA SUNY-Albany; Chief, Intl. Programs; Fed. Law Enforcement Trng. Ctr., Ofc. of Training, T-726, Glynco, GA 31524, 912 261-3653; r. 2146 Charing Cross, Brunswick, GA 31525, 912 261-0122; *Beverly;* Lee, Shaniqua. e-mail

JONES, Shaamgod; '97 BS; 947 Crescent St., Brooklyn, NY 11208, 718 230-1613.

JONES, Shelanda R.; '90 BA; 4417 42nd St. N, Birmingham, AL 35217.

JONES, Shirley D.; '84 BA, '84 MPA; Dir. of Payroll & Timekeeping; NYC Dept. of Transportation, 40 Worth St., Rm 1107, New York, NY 10013, 212 442-7362; r. 45 Saint Felix St., Brooklyn, NY 11217, 718 858-8313. e-mail

JONES, Solomon; '80 BS, '83 MA, AS; Investigator; NYS Fraud Bur., 25 Beaver St. ., Bowling Green, NY 10004, 516 248-5651; r. 11 Grace Ln., Coram, NY 11727, 631 474-2798; *Virgelene.*

JONES, Stephanie E.; '97 BA; 993 Erie Rd., W. Hempstead, NY 11552, 516 520-5888.

JONES, Tracey L.; '91 AS, '92 BA; Police Ofcr.; New York Police Dept., New York, NY 10001, 212 477-7314; r. 33-34 99 Th St., Corona, NY 11368, 718 803-0561. e-mail

JONES, Ursilla E.; '76 BA; 21521 Murdock Ave., Queens Vlg., NY 11429.

JONES, Venessia S.; '98 BA; Social Worker; New York Foundling Co., 590 Ave. of Americas, New York, NY 10011, 718 993-7600; r. 60 Amsterdam Ave. #12-G, New York, NY 10023, 212 399-0579.

JONES, Vernesa '87 (See Jones-Allen, Mrs. Vernesa D.).

JONES, William; '80 BS; 17339 104th Ave., Jamaica, NY 11433, 718 658-3673.

JONES, Yvonne; '95 BA; BA, MS ED Lehman Clg.; Couns.; NYC Dept. of Probation, 115 Leonard St., New York, NY 10013; r. 1199 Madison Ave. #214, New York, NY 10035, 212 360-7201; *Stanley C.;* Chione A.

JONES-ALLEN, Mrs. Vernesa D., (Vernesa Jones); '87 BS; Special Agt.; US EPA Criminal Investigation Div., 290 Broadway, Ste. 1551, New York, NY 10007, 212 637-3610; r. New York, NY 10033.

JONES-KNIGHT, Helen; '94 BS; 13 Cognac Dr., Newark, DE 19702.

JONES-SCOTT, Vena; '92 BS; 138 Lincoln Ave., Brooklyn, NY 11208.

JONES-THORPE, Jennifer J., (Jennifer J. Thorpe); '95 BS; AS NYC Technical Clg.; Release-Own Recognizance Interview; NYC Criminal Justice Agcy., 52 Duane St., New York, NY 10007, 212 330-1519; r. 75 Martense St. # 5d, Brooklyn, NY 11226, 718 207-4375; *John Patrick Thorpe;* Jenica J. Henry, Kimraun Thorpe, John P ThorpeJr. e-mail

JORDAN, Carol A.; '79 BA; 2040 Bruckner Blvd., Bronx, NY 10473.

JORDAN, Gwendolyn; '91 AS; 530 Georgia Ave. # 1s, Brooklyn, NY 11207, 718 647-7987.

JORDAN, Ms. Janet E., (Janet E. White); '74 BS, AS; Sgt.; Camden Cnty. Prosecutor, 25 N. Fifth St., Camden, NJ 08102, 856 225-8400; r. 4 Sutley Dr., Voorhees, NJ 08043, 856 767-2455.

JORDAN, Kathleen C.; '86 MA; 32-25 60th St., Woodside, NY 11377, 718 471-0913.

JORDAN, Nazly; '98 BA; MSW NYU; Rehab. Couns.; Goodwill Industries, 4-21 27th Ave., Astoria, NY 11102, 718 777-6436; r. 3520 35th St. #33B, Long Island City, NY 11106, 718 482-0983. e-mail

JORDAN, Percival J.; '85 BA; 12205 Flatlands Ave., Brooklyn, NY 11207, 718 284-6840.

JORDAN, Robbin M.; '91 BA; Human Resources Mgr.; Newman Fitch Altheim Myers, 14 Wall St., New York, NY 10005, 212 619-4350; r. 971 Jerome St., Apt. 3C, Brooklyn, NY 11207, 718 649-4732; Deianni. e-mail

JORDAN, Robert R.; '73 BS, '77 MA; Apartment Mgr.; A.H.R.C, 189 Wheatley Rd, Brookville, NY 11545, 516 626-1000; r. 60 Madison Pl., Roslyn Hts., NY 11577, 516 621-6215; *JoAnn;* Pamela Ann, Robin Jill.

JORDAN, Shamieka S.; '99 BA; Sales Asst.; Turner Broadcasting, 420 Fifth Ave., New York, NY 10018, 212 863-3659; r. 986 Adee Ave., Bronx, NY 10469, 718 652-1152. e-mail

JORDAN, Sherryl D.; '83 BS; 288A Stuyvesant Ave., Brooklyn, NY 11221, 718 259-3738.

JORDAN, Stephen; '97 BS; 5 Hattie Jones Cou, Brooklyn, NY 11213, 718 493-4965.

JORDAN, Thomas J.; '85 BA; 222 61st St., Brooklyn, NY 11220.

JORGE, Marcelo; '82 MPA; 108-32 45th Ave., Corona, NY 11368, 718 805-8878.

JORIS, Compton; '98 BS; Fraud Investigator; NYC Dept. of Homeless Svcs., New York, NY 10038, 718 402-6261; r. 185 Erasmus St., Apt. E7, Brooklyn, NY 11226, 718 826-9421.

JOSE, Gail A.; '86 BA; 7443 Aloe Dr., Spring Hill, FL 34607, 352 597-3313.

JOSEPH, Andrea M.; '92 BA, '97 MPA, '99; 820 Prospect Pl., Brooklyn, NY 11216.

JOSEPH, Carlas; '93 MA; 16 Raleigh Pl., Brooklyn, NY 11226, 718 376-3897.

JOSEPH, Clayton; '94 BA; 601 W 151st St. Apt. 56, New York, NY 10031, 212 281-8978.

JOSEPH, Crystal; '98 BA; 501 Willoughby Ave. #1Fl, Brooklyn, NY 11206, 718 376-3897.

JOSEPH, Eddison M.; '99 AS, 2000 BA; Investigations; r. 255 Lexington, Brooklyn, NY 11216, 718 638-2212. e-mail

JOSEPH, Essy A.; '80 BA; Budget Mgmt. Spec.; Broward Sheriff's Ofc., 2601 W. Broward Blvd., Ft. Lauderdale, FL 33312, 954 321-4492; r. 2261 S Sherman Cir., # A209, Miramar, FL 33025, 954 443-2444.

JOSEPH, Eugenie; '95 BS; 25962 148th Ave., Rosedale, NY 11422, 516 358-1582.

JOSEPH, George J.; '95 BA; 11474 224th St., Jamaica, NY 11411, 718 843-9717.

JOSEPH, Ingrid; '78 BA; JD New York Law Sch.; Atty.; NYS Supreme Ct., 360 Adams St., Brooklyn, NY 11201, 718 643-3188; r. 557 Chauncey St., Brooklyn, NY 11233, 718 376-2845; *Lambert Noble.* e-mail

JOSEPH, Jean; '97 BS, '98 BS; 351 Winthrop St., Brooklyn, NY 11225, 718 953-9150.

JOSEPH, Jennifer M.; '82 BS; 9101 Schenck St., Brooklyn, NY 11236, 718 462-8222.

JOSEPH, Kirt A.; '96 BS; Product Spec./Video Conferencing; Sony Electronics, 1 Sony Dr., Park Ridge, NJ 07656, 201 358-4076; r. 511 Herkimer St., Brooklyn, NY 11213, 718 721-7601.

JOSEPH, Kisha C.; '93 BS; 161 Utica Ave. Apt. 4u, Brooklyn, NY 11213.

JOSEPH, Michael R.; '91 BS, '99; 129-37 Brookville Bldv., Rosedale, NY 11422, 516 565-4160.

JOSEPH, Patrick F.; '99 MS; BS Hofstra Univ.; Security Spec.; Tyco Intl., Long Island City, NY 11101, 516 850-6577; r. 11 W. Woodbine Dr., Freeport, NY 11520, 516 223-5396; *Ingrid.* e-mail

JOSEPH, Philip; '97 BA; 1009 E.54th St., Brooklyn, NY 11234, 718 763-7137.

JOSEPH, Ms. Rhonda F.; '95 BS; 910 Lenox Rd, Brooklyn, NY 11203, 718 573-7665. e-mail

JOSEPH, Richard T.; '79 BS; 34 Pondview Dr., Congers, NY 10920, 914 354-8990.

JOSEPH, Sheila; '93 BA; 1099 E 55th St., Brooklyn, NY 11234, 718 252-1889.

JOSEPH, Ms. Tania R.; '96 BA; Community Advisor; Manhattan Dist. Atty's Ofc.; r. 13047 223rd St., Jamaica, NY 11413, 718 978-8682.

JOSEPH, Wilfredo; '96 BA; 15 Woodruff Ave., Brooklyn, NY 11226, 718 284-4531.

JOSEPH, William; '82 MPA; 2712 Mcintosh St., E. Elmhurst, NY 11369, 718 429-3065.

JOSEPHS, Sandy L.; '77 BS; 150-26 77 Ave., Flushing, NY 11367, 718 261-4487.

JOURDAN, Marine; '97 BS; Owner; The Peoples Paralegal, POB 1063, Ft. Lee, NJ 07024; r. same. e-mail

JOURDAN, Paul J.; '97 BA; 107 Kenilworth Pl., Brooklyn, NY 11210, 718 421-6881.

JOYCE, Jennifer; '96 BA; Police Ofcr.; NYC Police Dept.; r. 2898 Terrell Ave., Oceanside, NY 11572. e-mail

JOYCE, Kevin P.; '82 BA; 1616 Parkview Ave., Bronx, NY 10461, 718 295-5770.

JOYCE, William D.; '71 BS; MA Montclair State Univ.; Police Lt.; Paramus Police Force, Paramus, NJ 07652, 201 262-3400; r. 606 Victoria Ter., Paramus, NJ 07652, 201 652-7483.

JOYE, Natarsia L.; '95 BS, 2000 MPA; Investigator; r. 100 Donizetti Pl., Apt. 6A, Bronx, NY 10475. e-mail

JOYNER, Harry; '81 MPA; 1148 Alicia Ave., Teaneck, NJ 07666, 201 837-7487.

JOYNER, Joann; '83 BS; 283 Decatur St., Brooklyn, NY 11233, 718 919-6789.

JOYNER, Tisa S.; '95 BA; Student; John Jay Clg.; r. 445 New Lots Ave., Brooklyn, NY 11207, 718 257-2886.

JOYNER, Valerie K.; '84 BS; 325 E 23rd St., Brooklyn, NY 11226, 718 735-9708.

JOYNER, William L.; '79 BS; 21659 Sawyer Ave., Queens Vlg., NY 11427, 718 528-4824.

JUBAK, Ms. Jennifer L.; '98 BA; Registered Sales Asst; Morgan Stanley, New York, NY 10017; r. 121 19 8th Ave., College Pt., NY 11356. e-mail

JUERS, Cathy A. '92 (See Vinci, Mrs. Catherine A.).

JUGMOHAN, Gopie; '96 BA; 1265 Gerard Ave. # 6, Bronx, NY 10452.

JULES, Wisner; '92 BA, '97 MS; Tchr.; NYC Sch. of Educ.; r. 131 Ward Pl., S. Orange, NJ 07079, 973 275-9150. e-mail

JULES-LOUIS, C.; '90 BA; 2-04 Astoria Blvd., Long Island City, NY 11102, 718 641-4005.

JULIA, Veronica A.; '84 BS; 568 Grand St. Apt. 1301, New York, NY 10002, 315 733-6284.

JULIAN, Michael A.; '75 BS; 8 Peter Cooper Rd, New York, NY 10010, 212 228-2228.

JULIANO, Albert T.; '93 BS; 1 Landmark Sq., Port Chester, NY 10573, 914 937-7143.

JULIANO, Maria A.; '85 BS; 407 Murray St., Avenel, NJ 07001.

JULIANO, Richard P.; '84 BS; Dir. of Operations; Lincoln Square Business Improvement Dist, New York, NY 10001, 212 581-3774; r. 3746 Foothill St., Mohegan Lake, NY 10547, 914 528-1439; *Helen.*

JULIEN, Carole A.; 501 W 113th St., #2b, New York, NY 10025.

JULIEN, Heather J.; '91 BS; 3940 De Reimer Ave., Bronx, NY 10466.

JULIEN, Simon; '95 BA; 3353 Seymour Ave., Bronx, NY 10469.

JUMAN, Tarek; '97 BS; 103-20 109th St., S. Richmond Hill, NY 11419, 718 738-2043.

JUN, Mary; '97 BA; 17 Birch Hill Rd, Locust Vly., NY 11560, 516 942-5497.

JUNCO, Jorge N.; '79 BS; 1406 Jonquil St. NW, Washington, DC 20012.

JUNG, Eleanor J.; '78; 598 E 16 St. #2, Brooklyn, NY 11226, 718 645-0927.

JUNKO, Lisa M.; '95 BA; 2571 35th St. Apt. 2f, Long Island City, NY 11103, 718 726-5331.

JURAIN, Ronald S.; '81 MA; Woodcock Mt Dr., Washingtonville, NY 10992, 914 496-3375.

JUREK, Theodore J.; 958E 99St, Brooklyn, NY 11236.

JURIS, David; '86 MA; 16 Ocean Pkwy. Apt. D19, Brooklyn, NY 11218.

JURIS, John R.; '73 BS, '78 MA; AA Queens Clg., EDUC CRT Manhattan Clg.; Supv. of Security; Cantor-Fitzgerald, One World Trade Ctr., Ste. 104, New York, NY 10048, 212 938-8924; r. 201 Davenport Ave., Davenport Neck, New Rochelle, NY 10805, 914 633-9885; *Maria T.;* Michael Anthony. e-mail

JURITSCH, Martin J.; '95 BS; 1300 Ellison Ave. # P, Bronx, NY 10461, 718 828-0530.

JUSINO, Ismael; '85 BS; 298 Stanhope St. #1L, Brooklyn, NY 11237.

JUSTICE, Jeffrey; 128-11 116th Ave., S. Ozone Park, NY 11420.

JUZEFYK, Susan M.; '83 BA; 1363 Stanley Ter., Elizabeth, NJ 07208, 908 355-2007.

K

KABAKOFF, Robert I.; '99 BS; Actor-Media & Private Investigator; New York, NY 10001; r. 5 W. 63rd St. Apt. 1160, New York, NY 10023, 212 787-4716. e-mail

KADIR, Maqsood U., PhD; '88 BS; MSC Indiana State Univ., PHD Univ. of Tennessee; Prof.; John Jay Clg. of Criminal Justice, 445 W. 59th. St.,, New York, NY 10019, 212 237-8752; r. 2612 North Ave., F 9, Bridgeport, CT 06604, 203 334-6791; *Susan.* e-mail

KAECKER, Richard J.; '73 MA; 1313 42nd St. Apt. 1, Brooklyn, NY 11219.

KAESTLE, Kathryn; '92 MA; 468 W 58th St. Apt. 2b, New York, NY 10019.

KAFFASHAN, Nazanin; '99 MA; 2420 Seladd Ave., Portland, OR 97214, 914 937-5746.

KAGAN, Donald R.; '98 MS; 472 Lake St., Brooklyn, NY 11223, 718 769-4538.

KAHLON, Tejindar S.; '76 MA; BA ARTS Dyal Singh Clg.-India, LLB Punjab Univ. Law Clg.; Hearing Examiner; Nassau Cnty. Family Ct., 1200 Old Country Rd., Westbury, NY 11590, 516 571-9284; r. 1295 Jerusalem Ave., N. Merrick, NY 11566, 516 489-0837; *Sushila;* Jyoti.

KAHN, Arlene; 39 W. 69th Ave., New York, NY 10023, 315 735-7053.

KAHN-VITERI, Michael A.; '97 BS, '98 BS.

KAJ, Karen T., (Karen T. Walfish); '93 BS; Consumer Banker; H.S.B.C., 2145 Ralph Ave., Brooklyn, NY 11234, 718 531-4500; r. 60 Lewiston St., Staten Island, NY 10314; *Steven;* Sarah. e-mail

KAKAR, Humyra; '98 BA; 595 Columbus Ave. #3A, New York, NY 10024, 212 787-9048.

KALIAN, Mrs. Michelle A., (Michelle Bugros); '95 BS; Spec. Agt.; United States Dept. of Transportation, Ofc. of Inspector General, 26 Federal Plz., New York, NY 10278, 212 264-8700; r. 8 Ridge Rd., Hartsdale, NY 10530, 914 421-9222; *Chris.*

KALISKY, Alan M.; '89 BA; 1071 Lorimer St., Brooklyn, NY 11222.

KALLAS, Leo; '74 AS, '76 BS; Retired Detective; NYC Police Dept., Intelligence Div.; r. POB 46, Shohola, PA 18458, 570 559-7483; *Kaida.*

KALLASH, Anas M.; '87 BS; 164 N 9th St., Lindenhurst, NY 11757, 631 957-6348.

KALLETTA, Edward D., Jr.; '98 MS; BS Brooklyn Clg.; Deputy Chief; NYC Fire Dept.; r. 219 Beach 131st St., Belle Harbor, NY 11694, 718 634-3036. e-mail

KALLIMANIS, George; '85 BS; 20313 34th Ave., Flushing, NY 11361, 718 352-8066.

KALMAR, Roberta; '76 MPA; 571 8th St., Brooklyn, NY 11215, 718 499-8993.

KALOGERAS, Eleni; '82 BA; 24-54 38th St., Astoria, NY 11103.

KALTENMEIER, John W.; '78 BS; Firefighter; NYC Fire Dept., Brooklyn, NY 11201; r. 222 Utter Ave., Staten Island, NY 10314, 718 727-6962.

KAMARA, Alex T.; '93 BS; 210 Clinton Ave. # 3, Brooklyn, NY 11205.

KAMARA, Samuel M.; '91 BS; JD NY Law Sch.; Atty.; 2131 2nd Ave., New York, NY 10029, 917 593-3899; r. 659 Ridgedale Ave., Woodbridge, NJ 07095, 732 750-5056; *Esther A.;* Aristotle, Bryant. e-mail

KAMINSKI, Dennis J.; '80 BS; 57 Demille Ave., Elmont, NY 11003, 718 464-2599.

KAMISAR, Yale; 333 Hutchins Hall, Ann Arbor, MI 48109.

KAMMERER, Harold W.; 37-60 63 St., Woodside, NY 11377.

KAMONA, Ruth N.; '97 BA, '99 MPA; Asst. Dir.; CUNY, Ofc. of Student Services, 101 W. 81st, New York, NY 10001, 212 502-2908; r. 212 W. 91st St. #1016, New York, NY 10024, 212 873-8591. e-mail

KANACKI, Gaye D.; '79 BS; 3030 Brighton 12 S, Brooklyn, NY 11235, 718 934-9515.

KANANOWICZ, Eugene G.; '80 BS; 15759 24th Rd, Whitestone, NY 11357, 718 746-3820.

KANE, James A.; '77 BS; 200 Corbin Pl., Brooklyn, NY 11235, 718 745-4557.

KANE, James C.; '98 MS; 8 S. 18th St., New Hyde Park, NY 11040, 718 945-1656.

KANE, John; 37-14 Parsons S4C, Flushing, NY 11354, 718 945-1656.

KANE, Peter J.; '77 BS; 140a Van Cortlandt Park S, Bronx, NY 10463, 718 931-7802.

KANE, Timothy; '90 BA; 13916 28th Rd, Apt. 2E, Flushing, NY 11354, 718 474-7051.

KANE, Veronica A.; '90 BS; 8 Montclair Ave., Monsey, NY 10952, 914 357-0158.

KANNE, Emmanuel; '95 AS, '97 BA; 1481 Dean St. Apt. 2l, Brooklyn, NY 11213, 718 638-6733.

KANNE, James A.; '93 BA, '97 MPA; 1481 Dean St. Apt. 2l, Brooklyn, NY 11213.

KANOKOGI, Jean S.; '97 BA; 9728 3rd Ave. #3, Brooklyn, NY 11209.

KANOWSKY, Tina M.; '95 MA; 50 N Evergreen Rd, Apt. 20B, Edison, NJ 08837.

KANRICH, Susan; '88 CERT; 644 Sagamore Ave., Teaneck, NJ 07666.

KANTERMAN, Ronald E.; '80 BA, '88 MS; MS ENVSC NJIT; Chief of Emergency Svcs.; Merck & Co., Inc., 126 E. Lincoln Ave., Rahway, NJ 07065, 732 594-4700; r. 474 Richard Way, N. Plainfield, NJ 07062, 908 753-9709. e-mail

KANTROWITZ, Steven H.; '80 BA; 78A Chatham Dr., Cranbury, NJ 08512, 718 332-5842.

KAO, Pu-Mao F.; '99; 140-24 Beech Ave. 3rd Fl., Flushing, NY 11355, 718 271-2114.

KAPEL, Mark; '96 BS; 140 Glenn Rd, Staten Island, NY 10314, 718 698-8262.

KAPINOS, Thomas S.; '71 BA, '85 MA; Publisher; Criminal Justice Media Inc., 516 579-5063; r. 19 Hanover Pl., #221, Hicksville, NY 11801, 516 579-5063. e-mail

KAPITAN, Gary A.; '84 BS; 166 Echo Ave., Edison, NJ 08837.

KAPLAN, Holly S.; '95 MA; 216 Springmeadow Dr., Unit L, Holbrook, NY 11741.

KAPLAN, Dr. Lawrence J.; PHD MA Columbia Univ., BA Brooklyn Clg.; Economics Prof.; John Jay Clg. of Criminal Justice, 445 W 59th St., New York, NY 10019, 212 237-8097; r. 146 Bay Driveway, Manhasset, NY 11030, 516 627-9335; *Jeanne;* Harriet, Sanford, Marcia.

KAPLAN, Leonard A.; '71 MPA; Retired Police; NYPD; r. 545 Neptune Ave., Brooklyn, NY 11224, 718 996-4787.

KAPLAN, Mark; '96 BS; 640 Pelham Rd. #6E, New Rochelle, NY 10805.

KAPLAN, Mercedes M.; '81 BS; POB 918, Greenwood Lake, NY 10925, 914 496-6631.

KAPLAN, Neil J.; '79 BS; 8914 Avenue J, # 1, Brooklyn, NY 11236, 718 648-3887.

KAPLAN, Renee E.; '87 BS; 3 E. 101 St. #2D, New York, NY 10029, 212 534-4497.

KAPLAN, Robert; '80 MA; BA Harvard Univ., MIA Columbia Univ.; VP & Rsch. Dir.; Federated Dept. Stores, Lazarus, Cincinnati, OH 45202, 212 685-9844; r. 200 E. 36th St., New York, NY 10016, 212 532-5981; *Teresa Lewin;* Magge, Jennifer, Susan. e-mail

KAPLOWITZ, Karen; 444 E. 86th St., New York, NY 10028, 212 472-8506.

KARAGEORGE, Basil A.; '85 AS; 2067 35th St., Long Island City, NY 11105.

KARALIS, Patricia R. '80 (See Basciano, Patricia R.).

KARAM, Anthony A.; '86 BS; Tchr.; Allentown Sch. Dist., 31 S Penn St., Allentown, PA 18105, 610 821-2659; r. 1943 Pierce Dr., Whitehall, PA 18052; Marc. e-mail

KARAYIANNES, John G.; '82 MA; 17 Springwood Dr., Trumbull, CT 06611, 203 452-1085.

KARCZMER, Aaron S.; '94 BA; JD Stanford Univ.; Asst. Dist. Atty.; City of Manhattan Dist. Ct., New York, NY 10003; r. 182-25 Tudor Rd, Jamaica Estates, NY 11432, 718 380-1076.

KARIRA, Raj J.; '93 BS; 8826 Alliston Hollow Way, Gaithersburg, MD 20879.

KARLOSZCZUK, Monique; '86 MA; 34-35 76 St., Jackson Hts., NY 11372.

KARLOVITCH, Jay; '89 BS; US Marshal; 300 S 6th St., Ft. Pierce, FL 34950, 561 467-1723.

KARMAZIN, Nancy; '85 MA; 88-08 32nd Ave., E. Elmhurst, NY 11369.

KARPUSIEWICZ, S.; '75 BS; 3901 NE 5th Ave., Pompano Bch., FL 33064.

KARRAS, Andrea I.; '94 BA; 3608 Park Ave., Edison, NJ 08820, 732 549-0621.

KASHIMER, Irene; '81 MA; Ofc. Mgr.; Proj. Solvers, 30 W 22nd St., New York, NY 10010, 212 226-2432; r. 171-44 Bagley Ave., Flushing, NY 11358, 718 886-0370. e-mail

KASHINSKY, Alan J.; '85 BS; 67-05 Kissena Blvd., Flushing, NY 11367.

KASLOFSKY, Thor; '97 BA; Deputy Dir.; Dept. of Homeless Svcs., 33 Beaver St., 13th Fl., New York, NY 10004, 212 361-8394; r. 163 Eastern Pkwy., Brooklyn, NY 11238, 718 399-1016. e-mail

KASPER, Daniel T.; '98 CUBA; 501 Westbrook, Ridgewood, NJ 07450.

KASSAI, Michael D.; '93 BS; Police Ofcr.; Elmwood Park Police Dept., 182 Market St., Elmwood Park, NJ 07407, 201 796-0700; r. 429 Hartley Pl., Fair Lawn, NJ 07410, 201 398-0186; *Lynn;* Ashley.

KATERIDGE, Janine M.; '95 BA; Mental Health/Prog. Supv.; Transitional Svcs.; r. 298 Boundary Ave., Massapequa, NY 11758, 516 249-0151. e-mail

KATZ, Lawrence; '80 MPA; BA Brooklyn Clg., CUNY, JD Brooklyn Law Sch.; Deputy Counsel-Asst. Insp in Charge; US Postal Inspection Svc., Ofc. of Counsel, 475 L'Enfant Plz. W., SW Rm 3411, Washington, DC 20260, 202 268-7732; r. 2418 Saint George Way, Brookeville, MD 20833. e-mail

KATZ, Marvin A.; '74 AA, '76 BS; MS CW Post LIU; Owner Pres.; Business Integrity Intl., 885 Third Ave., Ste. 2900, New York, NY 10022, 212 829-5750; r. 106 Antonia Ct., Lincroft, NJ 07738; *Susan.* e-mail

KATZ, Michael R.; '79 MPA; 25 Parkview Ct., White Plains, NY 10603, 914 375-2662.

KATZ, Richard; '88 BS; 12154 Cordia Dr., Boynton Bch., FL 33437, 561 733-4351.

KATZ, Robert G.; '76 BS; 87 Aster St., Massapequa Park, NY 11762, 516 795-2485.

KATZEFF, Martha; '98 MPA; BFA Phila. Clg. of Art; Legal Secy; Winston & Strawn, 200 Park Ave., New York, NY 10166, 212 294-4627; r. 3135 Johnson Ave. #7H, Bronx, NY 10463, 718 884-4181; *Ken;* Jeremy, Samantha. e-mail

KAUFMAN, Benjamin; '88 BS; 8481 Austin St., Kew Gardens, NY 11415, 718 263-0892.

KAUFMAN, Brian R.; '99 BA; Paralegal; Edward H Wolf Esq, 910 Grand Concourse, Bronx, NY 10451, 718 410-0653; r. 2102 Holland Ave., Apt. 5G, Bronx, NY 10462; Brianna. e-mail

KAUFMAN, Mitchell J.; '75 AS, '76 BS; Police Ofcr. Retired; Port Authority of NY NJ Police Dept.; r. 54 Summit Pl., Pleasantville, NY 10570, 914 747-1780. e-mail

KAUFMAN, Steven; '85 MA; 122 Hart Blvd. Apt. 2, Staten Island, NY 10301, 718 987-1588.

KAUFMANN, Kevin J.; '85 BS; Asst. Security Ofcr.; CFS Bank, 615 Merrick Ave., Westbury, NY 11590, 516 683-4047; r. 2415 Natta Blvd., Bellmore, NY 11710, 516 221-8755.

KAVANAGH, John P.; '76 BS; Retired Command Chief; New York Transit Police; r. 88 Glendale Ave., Staten Island, NY 10304, 718 981-1862; *Eileen;* Sean, Brian, Kevin, Eileen, Timothy, Michael.

KAVANAGH, Michael J.; '98 BS; 94-03 82nd Pl., Ozone Park, NY 11416, 718 380-7886.

KAVANAUGH, Shannon B.; '99; 221 Clinton St. #4S, Hoboken, NJ 07030, 201 222-1204.

KAY, Paul; '94 BS; Madison, NJ 07940, 973 377-0166.

KAYE, Allan H.; '76 BA; 2376 E 72 St., Brooklyn, NY 11234, 718 375-5498.

KAYE, Mrs. Marion; '76 MA; Ret. Sr. Probation Ofcr.; Nassau Cnty. Probation Dept.; r. 15 Belmont Cir., Syosset, NY 11791, 516 364-3090; *Murray;* Robert, Judith.

KAYSER, Steven B.; '98 BS; Police Ofcr.; NYPD; r. 545 Neptune Ave. #12d, Brooklyn, NY 11224, 718 946-1010; *Michele.* e-mail

KAYTON, John J.; '75 BS; 647 54th St., Brooklyn, NY 11220.

KAZYMIRCZUK, Tina G.; '99 BA; Paralegal; Willkie Farr & Gallagher, 787 7th Ave., New York, NY 10019, 212 728-8409; r. 51 Lions Ct., Freehold, NJ 07728; *Nicholas.* e-mail

KEALY, Thomas J.; '76 BA; Retired Firefighter, NYC; r. 81 Cimmaron Dr., Palm Coast, FL 32137, 904 446-4278; *Patricia.*

KEANE, Joseph P.; '99 BA; 886 White Horse Hmiltsq, Trenton, NJ 08610, 609 443-8096.

KEANE, Patrick J.; '95 BS; N.Y.C. Police Capt.; NYC Police Dept., 2820 Snyder Ave., Brooklyn, NY 11226, 718 287-3259. e-mail

KEANE, Timothy J.; '67 BS; 82-03 62 Ave., Middle Vlg., NY 11379, 718 465-2331.

KEARNEY, Kevin; '86 BA; 53 Waterman Ave., Rumson, NJ 07760, 732 747-2599; *Christine;* Katelyn, Ryan.

KEARNS, Kelly E.; '97 BS; 601 W.110 St., New York, NY 10025, 212 222-2817.

KEARNS, Margherita; '90 BA; 61 Washington Pl., Totowa, NJ 07512, 973 942-6215.

KEARSE, Russell L.; '92 BS; 251 Seaman Ave. Apt. 1a, New York, NY 10034.

KEATING, Rian T.; '94 BA; 640 10th Ave. Apt. 4n, New York, NY 10036, 212 246-2057.

KEATING, Robert P.; '93 BS; Firefighter; Ladder 21, 430 W 38th St., New York, NY 10018, 212 570-4234; r. 42 Winchester Ave., Apt. 2-B, Yonkers, NY 10710, 914 375-3076. e-mail

KEEFE, Dennis C.; '77 BA; 90 S. Riverview, Bradford, MA 01835, 978 374-6723.

KEEGAN, Scott J.; '90 BA, '90 MA; Capt. Commanding Ofcr.; NYC Police Dept. Firearms Tactics Unit; r. 2812 Beatrice Ln., N. Bellmore, NY 11710, 516 783-1116.

KEEGAN, Timothy F.; '74 MA; 1674 E 54th St., Brooklyn, NY 11234, 718 492-8634.

KEEHLISEN, Lynda M.; '99 BA; Asst. Applied Behavior Spec.; Fam. Residences & Essential Enterprises, 120 Plant Ave. Ste. 1, Hauppauge, NY 11788; r. 423 18th St., W. Babylon, NY 11704, 631 957-9164. e-mail

KEELAN, James G.; '73 BS; 108 Newbury Rd, Howell, NJ 07731.

KEELER, Garrett L.; '99 BA; 3 Moonlight Ter., Milton, NJ 07438, 973 697-2387.

KEENAN, Jane; '72 BA; 2121 New York Ave., Brooklyn, NY 11210, 718 258-4273.

KEENAN, Joseph P.; '71 BS; 2121 New York Ave., Brooklyn, NY 11210, 718 258-4273.

KEENEY, Brendan W.; '85 BS; Capt.; NYPD/Transit Bur., 370 J. St., Brooklyn, NY 11201, 718 243-3441; r. 64-24 83rd Pl., Middle Vlg., NY 11379; *Anne;* Bridget, Kevin.

KEESHAN, Edward J.; '75 MA; BA Fordham Univ.; Dep Chief Investigator; NY CQ DA's Ofc., 1 Hogan Pl. NYC NY, New York, NY 10013, 212 335-8973; r. 3413 80th St. Apt. 1, Flushing, NY 11372.

KEHOE, William J.; '76 BS; Detective; Port Authority Police NY/NJ, Bldg. 269 JFK Airport, Jamaica, NY 11430, 718 244-4370; r. 1454 Sidney Ct., Seaford, NY 11783, 917 424-5612.

KEITH, Ms. Stacy A.; '98 BS; BS; Procurement Assoc.; Maryland Port Admin., 2310 Broening Hwy. Ste. 260, Baltimore, MD 21224, 410 631-1017; r. 5632 Woodmont Ave. Apt. B, Baltimore, MD 21239, 410 323-3465. e-mail

KEITT, Veronica; '93 BA, '97 MPA; 1428 5th Ave. Apt. 212, New York, NY 10035.

KELAHER, Peter E.; '76 BS; 34 Walnut St., Floral Park, NY 11001.

KELEMAN, Robert; '88 BS; 215 Ridge Ave., Valley Stream, NY 11581, 516 791-7870.

KELLAM, Fayon; 25 Nassau Rd Apt. 3, Yonkers, NY 10710.

KELLEBREW, Ida L.; '81 BS; 601 E 20th St., New York, NY 10010.

KELLEHER, William J.; '70 BS; 177 Oceanview Rd, E. Rockaway, NY 11518.

KELLER, Christopher; '97 MA; 1105 Hayes Ave., Sandusky, OH 44870, 419 625-8747.

KELLY, Angela D.; '91 BA; 707 E 58th St., Brooklyn, NY 11234, 718 398-6356.

KELLY, Austin R.; '75 MA; 303 Town Hill Rd, Nanuet, NY 10954.

KELLY, Cheryl R.; '89 BS; 1776 Bedford Ave. #, Brooklyn, NY 11225, 718 602-1487.

KELLY, David J.; '97 MS; BS Univ. of VT-Burlington; Fire Lt.; The West Hill Fire Dept.; r. 420 Grove St., Westfield, NJ 07090, 908 789-9522; *Karen;* Jonathan, Zakary, Benjamin.

KELLY, Dennis E.; '75 BS; 1130 E 29th St., Brooklyn, NY 11210, 718 566-9630.

KELLY, Edward J.; 37 Tor Rd # F, Wappingers Falls, NY 12590, 914 297-4976.

KELLY, Gerard W.; '72 AS; 17 Ridgecrest Ave., Staten Island, NY 10312, 718 948-4579.

KELLY, James F.; '76 BS; 1648 E 38th St., Brooklyn, NY 11234, 718 398-6356.

KELLY, James F.; '77 BS; 130 Beach 121st St., Rockaway Park, NY 11694, 718 318-1778.

KELLY, James F.; '99 BS; Corporate Fulfillment Admin.; Arjay Telecom, 680 12th Ave., New York, NY 10019, 212 581-4800; r. 12 Bass St., Staten Island, NY 10314, 718 761-5411. e-mail

KELLY, James P.; '79 BS; Lt.; NYC Fire Dept.; r. 131 Collins Ave., Williston Park, NY 11596, 516 742-3607.

KELLY, John E.; '74 BS, '77 MA; Security Cnslt.; Intersecs Svcs. Corp., 914 621-0045; r. 59 Cuddy Rd., Mahopac, NY 10541, 914 712-4949. e-mail

KELLY, John J.; '76 MA; 412 Beach 137th St., Belle Harbor, NY 11694, 718 318-1778.

KELLY, Joi C.; '89 BA; 1917 Andrews Ave. #3N, Bronx, NY 10453, 718 548-3222.

KELLY, Joseph A.; '72 BA, '72 MA; Retired NYC Police Ofcr.; r. 2005 Clover Ln., Champaign, IL 61821, 217 359-5345; *Alice;* Kathleen, Kevin, Laura.

KELLY, Karen M.; '81 BS; Owner; r. 425 Willowbrook Ln., Longwood, FL 32779, 407 865-6782. e-mail

KELLY, Kiely; '91 BS; 83-75 118th St., Jamaica, NY 11415, 718 318-1012.

KELLY, Leonard; '74 BA; 258 Richard Ave., Staten Island, NY 10309, 718 351-4419.

KELLY, Margo F.; '75 BA; MA ITT; Proj. Mgr.; Marchfirst, 9449 Priority Way West Dr., Indianapolis, IN 46240, 317 575-9696; r. 5381 Shorewood Dr., Indianapolis, IN 46220, 317 465-9059; *Stephen;* Peter, Stephen. e-mail

KELLY, Martin A.; '63 MPA; MA Hunter Clg., BBA Baruch Clg.; Retired New York City Police Ofcr.; r. 25 Valdale Ave., Yonkers, NY 10705, 914 476-5773.

KELLY, Patrick H.; '92 BS; 525 W. 238 St., Bronx, NY 10463, 718 543-2678.

KELLY, Paul J.; '92 BS; 7443 64th Ln., Flushing, NY 11385, 718 381-1721.

KELLY, Robert J.; '80 BA; Ret. Fireman; r. 16 Raymond Ave., Lynbrook, NY 11563, 516 593-1829; *Judith;* Margaret.

KELLY, Stephen P.; '72 BS; MS Queens Clg.; 5381 Shorewood Dr., Indianapolis, IN 46220, 317 465-9059; *Margo.* e-mail

KELLY, Thomas F.; '79 BS; Retired; r. 88-07 Aubrey Ave., Glendale, NY 11385, 718 275-8111.

KELLY, Thomas J.; '69 MPA; 2401 Clay Ct., Longwood, FL 32779, 407 862-2202.

KELLY, Timothy P.; '83 BA; 131 Purchase St. 212, Rye, NY 10580, 914 967-1430.

KELLY, William M.; '75 BS; MPA Rutgers Univ.; Mgmt. Spec.; Div. of Criminal Justice, 25 Market St., Trenton, NJ 08611, 609 984-2718; r. 1 Ashford Ct., Spring Lake, NJ 07762, 732 974-1764; *Maryann;* Michael, Marybeth. e-mail

KELLY, William P.; '68 BS; MS MSU; Retired; NYC Police Dept.; r. 16 Banks Farm Rd, Bedford, NY 10506, 914 234-0802; *Annemarie.*

KELLY, Yvonne; '99 MA; BA Hunter Clg. CUNY; Public Health Educator; Health & Hosps. Corp.-Corr. Health Svc., 125 Worth St., Rm. 930, Box 52, New York, NY 10013, 718 546-4037. e-mail

KELTY, Patrick; '97 BS; Security Supv.; Triumph Security Corp., 65 E 55 St., New York, NY 10022, 212 644-1200; r. 577 Concord Ave., Williston Park, NY 11596, 516 294-0435; *Kathy;* Claire, Andrew.

KEMEL, Ann; '97 BA; 501 B Surf Ave., Brooklyn, NY 11224.

KEMENCZY, John L.; '79 BS; 9 Burnham Dr., Pompton Plains, NJ 07444.

KEMLY, Ronald H.; '76 BA; 9828 3rd Ave., Stone Harbor, NJ 08247, 609 368-2967.

KEMP, Donita M.; '98 BA; 135 Westervelt Ave., Staten Island, NY 10301, 718 447-1688.

KEMP, Michelle B.; '97 BS; 171-27 103rd Rd, Jamaica, NY 11433, 718 843-8718.

KEMP, Naomi; '97 BS; 527 Third Ave.123, New York, NY 10016, 315 839-5683.

KEMP, Royevette; '99 BA; Couns.; Salvation; r. 204 Malta St. P, Brooklyn, NY 11207, 718 257-0155.

KENDRICK, John V.; '80 MPA; 98-1410 Akaaka St., Aiea, HI 96701.

KENIRY, Jeanne F.; '78 BA; 2024 E. 37th St., Brooklyn, NY 11234.

KENNEALLY, James J.; '66 BS; 164 E. 88 St., New York, NY 10028.

KENNEDY, Angela; '87 BS; Captain Retired; NYC Dept. of Corrections; r. 5336 SW 21st Pl., Cape Coral, FL 33914, 941 540-9759; *Yvonne Ellen.*

KENNEDY, Deniese L.; '98 MA; BA SUNY-Stony Brook, PhD CUNY; 15 Lesoir Ave., Floral Park, NY 11001, 516 326-7480; *Joseph S. Kollar.*

KENNEDY, Donald P.; '86 BS; 4325 249th St., Flushing, NY 11363, 718 740-6061.

KENNEDY, Henry W.; '89 MPA; 1148 Union St., Brooklyn, NY 11225, 718 604-2499.

KENNEDY, Karen M.; '90 BS; Univ. of Northern Florida; Yeoman/Customer Svc. Agt.; USCG/Southwest Airline; r. 3030 Oak Green Cir. #D, Ellicott City, MD 21043, 410 313-9963; *Donald;* Julian, Caleb. e-mail

KENNEDY, Katherine; '77 BA; 3351 Seymour Ave., Bronx, NY 10469, 718 652-9441.

KENNEDY, Lillian; '92 BS; Retired-Dir. of Accounts Payable; r. 12045 170th St., Jamaica, NY 11434, 718 527-3380; *Bruce.* e-mail

KENNEDY, Lori; '91 BS; 103 Sierra St., Waterbury, CT 06704, 203 757-6022.

KENNEDY, Michael J.; '97 BS; 68 Villanova Dr., Jackson, NJ 08527.

KENNEDY, Patrick C.; '76 BA; 209 W. 107 St., New York, NY 10025, 800 327-4248.

KENNEDY, Richard J.; '75 MA; 1957 Nantucket Rd, Merrick, NY 11566, 516 565-2554.

KENNEDY, Stephen R.; '81 MPA; 89 Waverly Ave., Tuckahoe, NY 10707.

KENNEDY, Tasha K.; '96 BA; 115-71 232nd St., Cambria Hts., NY 11411, 718 740-6061.

KENNEDY-GOMES, Mrs. Candice; '95 BS; Social Worker; Volunteers of America, Bronx, NY 10451; r. Brooklyn, NY 11213.

KENNELLY, Fritz S.; '97 BS; AS Manhattan Community Clg.; US Govt., New York, NY 10278; r. 43 Reading Rd, # B, Edison, NJ 08817, 732 494-3333.

KENNER, Marvin L.; '93 AS, '96 BS; 19116 119th Ave., Jamaica, NY 11412, 718 341-3989.

KENNEY, Wilson C.; '70 BS; Retired Police Sergeant; r. 59 Sailfish Dr., Brigantine, NJ 08203, 609 266-6435.

KENNON, Shawn; '99 BS; 138-11 234 St., Rosedale, NY 11422, 718 525-6577. e-mail

KENNY, John B.; '90 BA; 10 Marjorie Ln., E. Rockaway, NY 11518.

KENNY, John D.; '98 BS; AA Suffolk Community Clg.; Sales Rep.; Dura Pharmaceuticals, 7475 Lusk Blvd., San Diego, CA 92121; r. 74 Soundview Dr., Port Jefferson, NY 11777, 631 473-3853. e-mail

KENNY, Marie; '91 BS; 126 King Ave., Yonkers, NY 10704, 914 965-8153.

KENNY, Michael J.; '71 BS; 45 Sandy Point Dr., Brick, NJ 08723, 732 920-0774.

KENNY, Raymond J.; '68 BS; 10 Koch Blvd., Staten Island, NY 10312, 718 668-1459.

KENNY, Robert E., CCA; '82 BS; MS Chapman Univ.; Intelligence Analyst; Joint Interagency Task Force West, Bldg. 51, Coast Guard Island, Alameda, CA 94501, 510 535-5396; r. 110 Bayview St., San Rafael, CA 94901, 415 454-4943. e-mail

KENNY, William J.; '78 BS, '82 MA; 1975 E. 17th St., Brooklyn, NY 11229, 718 382-8417.

KEOGH, Dennis F.; '80 BS; Lt.; NY Police Dept., 230 E. 21st St., New York, NY 10010, 212 477-7407; r. 7002 Ridge Blvd., Brooklyn, NY 11209, 718 836-5865.

KERINS, Gerard J.; '75 MA; 16218 98th St., Jamaica, NY 11414, 718 845-8132.

KERN, Neil E.; '72 BS; 20414 33rd Ave., Flushing, NY 11361, 718 628-5560.

KERR, Milagro X.; '99 BA; Child Protective Spec.; Admin. for Children Svcs., 2554 Linden Blvd., Brooklyn, NY 11208, 718 348-6680; r. 422 45 St. Apt.2, Brooklyn, NY 11220, 718 871-6019.

KERSELLIUS, Gavin I.; '89 BS; 87-16 134th St., Richmond Hill, NY 11418.

KERSHAW, Eugene, Jr.; '86 BA; NYC Probation Ofcr.; NYC Dept. of Probation, 100 Centre St. 14th Fl. Rm 14-34, New York, NY 10013, 212 442-1664; r. 24-4 Asch Loop #G, Bronx, NY 10461, 718 390-7419.

KERTON, Ervin (Ernie); '73 BA; CERT. Fordham Univ.; Pol. Ofcr.,Housing Authority Ret.; Div. of NYPD, 240 Broadway, New York, NY 10007, 407 415-0294; r. 2512 Sage Dr., Kissimmee, FL 34758, 407 518-0294; *Ruby;* Ernest, Eric.

KESSINGER, Ann L., (Ryan L. Ann); '77 BS; PARALGL NY Inst. of Tech; Paralegal; William R Boccio PC, 22 Jericho Tpk. Ste. 103, Mineola, NY 11501, 516 294-5106; r. 191 Livingston Ave., Babylon, NY 11702, 631 587-8015. e-mail

KESSLER, Dennis; '70 BS, '73 MA; MSL Yale Univ. Law Sch.; Business Owner; Kessler Grp. Inc., 410 White Spruce Blvd., Rochester, NY 14623, 716 424-5277; r. 40 Hawthorne St., Rochester, NY 14610, 716 461-0041. e-mail

KESSOPA-CABRERA, Pojana; '98 BA; Intl. Relations; r. 146 17 Willets Pt Blv, Whitestone, NY 11357, 718 539-1247; *Lt Jose Antonio Cabrera.* e-mail

KETTERING, William N.; '78 MA; 2307 Tanglevale Dr., Vienna, VA 22181, 703 255-6132.

KETTRLES, Tamiko N.; '96 BS; 2953 Ave. W #3C, Brooklyn, NY 11229.

KEY, Cheryl V.; '87 BA; 4515 Snyder Ave., Brooklyn, NY 11203, 718 946-5808.

KEY, Joseph; 605 Putnam Ave., Brooklyn, NY 11221, 718 946-5808.

KEYMER, Mary M.; '93 BA; MSW Hunter Sch of Social Work; Social Worker; Dept. of Psychiatry Harlem Hosp., 135th & Lennox Ave., Harlem, NY 10030; r. 119 W 80 St., New York, NY 10024, 212 580-9491. e-mail

KHAIMOV, Igor I.; '99 BA; Grad. Student; John Jay Clg. of Criminal Justice, 899 10th Ave., New York, NY 10019; r. 117-04 Curzon Rd., 3rd Fl., Richmond Hill, NY 11418.

KHAN, Angelina; '98 BS; Case Mgr.; Kintock Grp., 50 Fenwick St., Newark, Newark, NJ 07114, 973 622-1400; r. 401 W 48 St. 2n, New York, NY 10036. e-mail

KHAN, Arlene; '98 CERT; 39 W. 69th St., New York, NY 10023, 212 482-5418.

KHAN, Bibi N.; '96 BS; 2274 Lyon Ave., Bronx, NY 10462, 718 409-2357.

KHAN, Imran E.; '88 BS; 2131 30th Ave., Long Island City, NY 11102, 718 523-0867.

KHAN, Neil M.; '97 BA, '99 MA; Full-time Student; New York Law Sch.; r. Staff House Wards Island, New York, NY 10035, 212 410-0733. e-mail

KHAN, Nezam; '85 BA; 1766 Casper Ave., E. Meadow, NY 11554.

KHAN, Rakeela B.; '99 MPA; BSW NYU; 120-15 Linden Blvd., Richmond Hill, NY 11420, 718 848-8232; *Imran;* Naveedjamal, Nadia. e-mail

KHAN, Salima J.; '89 BA; Operation Cnslt.; Axa Advisors, 1290 Ave. of The Americas, New York, NY 10104, 212 314-3014; r. 22726 113th Dr., Queens Vlg., NY 11429, 718 479-1104.

KHAN, Shazad; '98 BA; CERT.; Fraud Investigator; Dept. of Homeless Svcs., 151 E. 151st St., Bronx, NY 10451, 718 402-8983; r. 116-43 120th St., S. Ozone Park, NY 11420, 718 641-7692; Zorina.

KHASHIUN, Karamah A., (Audrey M. Fulton); '78 BA; JD New York Law Sch.; Principal Law Clerk; The Hon. Lottie E. Wilkins, 71 Thomas St., New York, NY 10013, 212 815-0883; r. 70 Park Ter. W, New York, NY 10034, 212 567-3889. e-mail

KHEMAI, Kamlapatie; '94 BA; 2938 Wallace Ave., Bronx, NY 10467.

KHILKEVICH, Denis A.; '99 BA GOV; US Pretrial Svcs. Ofcr.; US Dist. Ct.-SD/NY, 500 Pearl St., Rm. 550, New York, NY 10007, 212 805-4147; r. 1506 Dahill Rd. Apt. 1, Brooklyn, NY 11204, 718 375-3632. e-mail

KHITERER, Inna; '99 BS; Court Interpreter; Immigration Ct., 26 Federal Plz., New York, NY 10278. e-mail

KHOBOT, Aleksandr; '97 BS; 1596 E 2 St. 2n, Brooklyn, NY 11230, 718 627-4185.

KHURANA, Rajiv R.; '98 BA; Capt.; NYPD, New York, NY 10030; r. same. e-mail

KHWAJA, Tariq M.; '96 BS; MLS Pratt Inst.; Ref. Librarian; Kaye, Scholer, Fierman, Hays & Handler, 425 Park Ave., New York, NY 10022, 212 836-7413; r. 144-67 41st Ave., Flushing, NY 11355, 718 358-7917. e-mail

KIAPOKAS, Theodora; '91 BA; MSW Temple Univ.; Special Educ. Coord.; Colonial Intermediate Unit; r. 1630 N New St., Bethlehem, PA 18018, 610 865-0814. e-mail

KICKI, Michael E.; '82 MA; 1437 Ottawa Ct., Toms River, NJ 08753, 732 929-8216.

KIELY, Deirdre; '85 MPA; 451 E. 14 St., New York, NY 10009, 212 677-0338.

KIELY, Gregory; '88 BS; 5355 Henry Hudson, Bronx, NY 10471, 718 548-3055.

KIELY, Mary A.; '83 MPA; 272 First Ave., New York, NY 10009.

KIERAN, Edward; 41-87 Frame Pl., Flushing, NY 11355.

KIERNAN, Henry; '77 BS; MTA B&T Sergeant; MTA B&T, 2 Broadway, New York, NY 10004, 212 360-3000; r. 85 Holly St., Staten Island, NY 10304, 718 979-0614; *Linda;* Matthew.

KILCULLEN, Kevin J.; '79 BA; 60 W 71st St. Apt. 3a, New York, NY 10023.

KILLEEN, Michael K.; '92 BS; 233 Livingston Ave., # 2, Lyndhurst, NJ 07071, 201 438-7110.

KILLERLANE, James J.; '70 MPA; 193 Battery Ave., Brooklyn, NY 11209.

KILLIAN, Becky; '99; 281 Windsor Pl. #9, Brooklyn, NY 11218, 718 326-0627.

KILMER, Joseph F.; '80 BS; Special Agt.; DEA, 8400 NW 53 St., Miami, FL 33166, 305 590-4870; r. POB 770025, Coral Springs, FL 33077, 954 255-3847.

KIM, Sunghoon; '95 BS; 6835 150th St., Fl. 2, Flushing, NY 11367, 718 357-2985.

KIMLICKA, Daniel E.; '74 BS; Parks Commissioner; Town of Brookhaven, 1130 old town Rd., Coram, NY 11727, 631 451-6133; r. 86 Bobolink Ln., Levittown, NY 11756, 516 796-9261.

KINAHAN, Donna M.; '95 BA; 15 Townsend Ct., Franklin Park, NJ 08823.

KINAHAN, Patrick F.; '22 Schuyler Dr., Commack, NY 11725.

KINARD, Tabitha; '99 MA; 219 Pond Way, Staten Island, NY 10303, 718 982-8433.

KING, Anthony B.; '85 BS; 3709 Avenue I, Brooklyn, NY 11210, 718 209-9060.

KING, Barbara '84 (See King-Anobile, Barbara).

KING, Mrs. Crystal-Dawn; '97 BS; AAS Rockland Comm Clg., Long Island Univ.; Case Mgr.; Rockland Cnty. Dept. of Social Svcs., 10 Waldron Ave., Nyack, NY 10960, 914 358-0114; r. 7 Columbus Ave., Spring Vly., NY 10977; Christina, Jasmine, Nallah.

KING, David W.; '76 MA; Retired Police Capt.; r. 243-04 130th Rd., Rosedale, NY 11422, 718 949-1468; *Pauline;* Craig.

KING, Edison L.; '96 BA; 18019 Linden Blvd. Ste. 2, Jamaica, NY 11434, 718 267-1530.

KING, Edith I.; '83 BA; 131 Lorraine St., Brooklyn, NY 11231, 718 857-4947.

KING, Edward J.; '77 MPA; 38 Alpine Ct., Staten Island, NY 10310.

KING, Edwina J.; '92 BS; Assoc. Fraud I-Supv.; Bur. of Fraud Investigation, 250 Church St., New York, NY 10013, 212 774-4916; r. 51 Sterling St., Brooklyn, NY 11225, 718 462-0676; *Darryl;* Shemila, Latoya.

KING, Emma C.; '81 BA; 9115 Locura Pl. SW, Albuquerque, NM 87121.

KING, Eric D.; '89 BS; LA CERT NYU, WSI CERT American Red Cross; Business Analyst; AE Travel Related Svcs. Tech, 3151 W Behrend Rd., Phoenix, AZ 85027, 602 766-6175; r. 7977 W. Wacker Rd. Unit 247, Peoria, AZ 85381, 623 487-9391. e-mail

KING, Gillian L.; '92 BS; 14946 Weller Ln., Jamaica, NY 11422, 718 446-6168.

KING, Jemma F.; '93 BS; MS Long Island Univ.; Assoc.; Bell Atlantic; r. 4520 Foster Ave., Brooklyn, NY 11203, 718 693-8487. e-mail

KING, Jerome A.; '98 BA; 3802 Bel Vista Ct. #G2, Lodi, NJ 07644, 973 546-8823.

KING, Joan A.; '97 BS; 11425 158th St., Jamaica, NY 11434, 718 464-5968.

KING, John; '87 BS; 2 Colonel Robert Magaw Pl. Apt. Aa, New York, NY 10033, 315 822-5496.

KING, John J.; '79 BS; 1 Carmans Gate, Farmingdale, NY 11735.

KING, John P.; '99; 2706 Valentine Ave. A1, Bronx, NY 10458, 718 220-0182.

KING, John T.; '75 BS; 14-81 164th St., Whitestone, NY 11357.

KING, Joseph F., PhD; '75 MA; PHD CUNY; Special Agt.; US Customs Svc., Rm-508, 6-WTC, New York, NY 10048, 212 637-0938; r. 459 Rugby Rd, Brooklyn, NY 11226, 718 774-6171. e-mail

KING, Kenneth L.; '76 BS; 27 Bidwell Ave., Staten Island, NY 10314, 718 273-0642.

KING, Martin J.; '76 BA; 281 Avenue C, New York, NY 10009, 212 777-0052.

KING, Michael A.; '91 BS; 7406 17th Ave. #A9, Brooklyn, NY 11204.

KING, Michael P.; RD 5 Hickory Tr., Carmel, NY 10512.

KING, R.; '76 BA; 25 Trescott St., Dix Hills, NY 11746, 631 667-0357.

KING, Raymond F.; '79 BS; CRT FBI Natl. Academy; Chief of Criminal Invest., IAB; NYC Police Dept., One Police Plz., New York, NY 10038, 212 741-4576; r. 315 Hudson St., New York, NY 10013. e-mail

KING, Rechelle L.; '95 BA; 9720 57th Ave. Apt. 10h, Flushing, NY 11368, 718 699-7238.

KING, Stephen J., III; '79 BA, '98 MS, '98 MS; Battalion Chief; NYC Fire Dept., 9 Metrotech Centre, Brooklyn, NY 11201, 718 476-6254; r. 29 Stevenson Pl., Deer Park, NY 11729, 631 242-0621; *Joan; Christine, Stephen, Kevin, Jacqueline.* e-mail

KING, Usheevii; '98 BA; 1380 Riverside Dr. 3b, New York, NY 10033, 315 732-6609.

KING, Vera L.; '77 BS; Ret.; r. 432 NW Sherry Ln., Port St. Lucie, FL 34986, 561 878-2136. e-mail

KING-ANOBILE, Barbara, (Barbara King); '84 BS; AS CRIM Nassau Community Clg., JD CUNY Univ. at Queens Clg.; Atty.; Gordon, Siegel Law Firm, 9 Cornell Rd., Airport Park, Latham, NY 12110, 518 690-7000; r. 1044 Helen St., Rotterdam, NY 12303, 518 356-4373; *Paul Anobile.* e-mail

KINLEY, Kevin; '89 BS; 13039 223rd St., Jamaica, NY 11413.

KINNEBREW, Deborah, (Deborah Trotman); '77 BA; Dept. of Corrections, 42 Jarvis St., Cheshire, CT 06410; r. 52 Town House Rd, Hamden, CT 06514.

KINNEY, Susan; '88 MPA; 18 Marion Ave., Wappingers Falls, NY 12590.

KINSCHERF, Cindy L.; '99 BS; Forensic Chemist; Drug Enforcement, 99 10th Ave., New York, NY 10011, 212 620-6249; r. 86-35 239th St., Bellerose, NY 11426, 718 343-3467. e-mail

KINSELLA, William F.; '75 MPA; 107 Birchwood Dr., New Hyde Park, NY 11040, 516 747-0015.

KINSEY, Barbara; '88 BA; 937 E 100th St., Brooklyn, NY 11236.

KINYATTI, Mrs. Njoki W.; '77 BA, '96 MPA; MLS St. John Univ.; Asst. Prof.; York Clg., Library Dept., Jamaica, NY 11451, 718 262-2021; r. 241-04 148th Ave., Jamaica, NY 11422, 718 276-4419; *Stephen Waiguchu;* Theresa. e-mail

KIPP, Edward C.; '80 BS; 1939 Grand Concourse, Bronx, NY 10453.

KIPPINS, Susan A.; '83 BA; 615 Macon St., Brooklyn, NY 11233.

KIRBY, Thomas H.; '92 BA; 90 Amsterdam Ave., New York, NY 10023, 315 337-9187.

KIRK, Edward J.; '75 BS; 144 Cleveland Ave., Rockville Centre, NY 11570.

KIRK, John J.; '80 BA; NYC Firefighter; r. 79 89th St., Brooklyn, NY 11209, 718 680-7739.

KIRK, Michael; '76 BS; 8 George St., Tuckahoe, NY 10707.

KIRK, Thomas A.; '80 BS; 8610 109th St. Apt. E1, Jamaica, NY 11418, 718 805-2482.

KIRKBY, Stuart T.; '96 BS; 18 Salvatore Dr., West Park, NY 12493.

KIRKLEY, John; RD 3, Box 63-A, Spencer Dr., Red Hook, NY 12571.

KIRKMAN, Edward J.; '76 BA; 183 W 22nd St., Deer Park, NY 11729.

KIRKMAN, Lisa A.; '86 BA; 169 Oakdale St., Staten Island, NY 10308, 718 967-5361.

KIRKMAN, Scott J.; '92 BS; 21 Watermelon Hill Rd, Mahopac, NY 10541.

KIRKPATRICK, Michael; '82 BS; 60-17 59th Ave., Flushing, NY 11378.

KIRSCHNER, Edward; '78 BA; 399 Ocean P'kway, Brooklyn, NY 11218.

KIRSCHNER, Milton I.; '66 BS, '76 MA; AAS; Retired Police Work; r. 425 Neptune Ave., Brooklyn, NY 11224, 718 266-0637; Robert.

KIRSCHNER, Robert D.; '77 MA; 247 W 87th St. #5B, New York, NY 10024.

KIRST, Kevin; '88 BS; 214 Ivy St., Kearny, NJ 07032, 201 997-6898.

KIRTON, Donna C.; '86 BS; 341 10th St. Apt. 4e, Brooklyn, NY 11215, 718 462-1933.

KISALA, Stanley M.; '91 BS; Police Lt.; Wallington, NJ Police Dept., Wallington, NJ 07057, 973 473-1715; r. 4 Hillside Ter., Wallington, NJ 07057; *Theresa;* Timothy.

KISHLICKY, Eric K.; '83 BS; 160 5th Ave., Kings Park, NY 11754.

KISLING, Arnol F.; '78 MPA; Lakeview River, N. Salem, NY 10560.

KISSANE, Thomas P.; '75 BA; 10 Buchanan Ave., Amityville, NY 11701.

KISSEL, John S.; '94 MA; 110 Gary Pl. # 1, Staten Island, NY 10314.

KITCHENS, Leyla; '90 BS; 4615 Hill Avenue P, Bronx, NY 10466.

KITCHING, Tselanee; '99 BA; AS Sullivan Cnty. Com Clg.; Police Ofcr.; 1 Police Plz., New York, NY 10038, 212 374-5000; r. 2970 W. 27th St., Brooklyn, NY 11224, 718 265-0510; Brienna.

KITSON, Daniela S., (Daniela S. Matysiak); '79 BS; Homemaker; r. 10330 NE 151st Pl., Bothell, WA 98011; *Robert;* Lola.

KITTRELL, Frances E. '98 (See Kittrell-Coley, Frances E.).

KITTRELL, John E.; '76 BS; 111 Valentine Ln., Yonkers, NY 10705.

KITTRELL-COLEY, Frances E., (Frances E. Kittrell); '98 BS; Child Protective Spec; Admin. for Children's Svcs., 150 William St., New York, NY 10038, 212 676-8060; r. Columbus Cir. POB 20050, New York, NY 10023, 718 230-1904; *Aundre Coley;* T'Keyah. e-mail

KITZ, Alfred F.; '78 BS; 35 E Main St., Stony Point, NY 10980.

KLAMAN, Richard; '76 BS; 680 Larkfield Rd, E. Northport, NY 11731.

KLAPAKIS, Diana M.; '83 BS; 125-19 Hillside Ave., Richmond Hill, NY 11418.

KLAR, Marc E.; '75 BS; 26 Pineview Ct., Springfield, NJ 07081.

KLAS, Brian E.; '95 MA; 10 Canterbury Ct., Orchard Park, NY 14127, 716 662-2014.

KLAUS, William A.; '90 BS; 24 Gotham Ave., Brooklyn, NY 11229.

KLEIN, Fredric C.; '76 BS; Account Mgr.; Copstat Security Inc., 1860 E. Tremont Ave., Bronx, NY 10460, 212 314-2900; r. 39 Fern Ave., Staten Island, NY 10308, 718 984-2653; *Hanora;* Fredric Jr, Kevin, Timothy. e-mail

KLEIN, Gilah F.; '99 BA; 2214 E. Main St., Bridgeport, CT 06610, 203 377-6633.

KLEIN, Irving; Prof Emeritus; John Jay Clg. of Criminal Justice; r. 8261 SW 89th St., Miami, FL 33156, 305 598-4619; *Marta;* Linda, Michael.

KLEIN, Leon E.; '76 MPA; BA NYU; Pres.; Business Assistance Svc. Inc., 46-10 Queens Blvd., Sunnyside, NY 11104, 718 392-7119; r. 8155 260th St., Floral Park, NY 11004, 718 347-7444; *Dorothy;* Robert, Stephen.

KLEIN, Marta A., (Marta Arias-Klein); '77 MA; EDD Univ. of Havana-Cuba; Prof. of Criminal Justice/Editor; Law for Criminal Justice Profn., New York, NY 10001; r. 8261 SW 89th St., Miami, FL 33156, 305 598-4619; *Irving J.;* Linda B Diamond, Michael R.

KLEIN, Martha E.; '79 BS; 33 Gold St. Apt. 107, New York, NY 10038, 315 839-5205.

KLEIN, Richard J.; '89 BA; Capt.; NYC Fire Dept., 6416 80th Ave., Glendale, NY 11385, 718 497-7739; r. Flushing, NY 11385.

KLEIN, Robert E.; '89 BS; Asst. Dir. Public Safety; New Jersey City Univ., 2039 Kennedy Blvd., Jersey City, NJ 07305, 201 200-3127; r. 76 Upper High Crest Dr., W. Milford, NJ 07480, 973 838-8802; *Kimberly;* Robert Jr. e-mail

KLEIN, Thomas N.; '91 BS; 9118 104th St., Jamaica, NY 11418, 718 261-1932.

KLEINER, Richard L.; '81 MA; POB 532, Divide, CO 80814.

KLEINHEIDT, William; '77 BA; 53-33 194 St., Flushing, NY 11365.

KLEINMAN, Mandy K.; '98 MA; 68-16 Groton St., Forest Hills, NY 11375, 718 263-0687.

KLEMAN, Maryline E.; '88 MA; 300 E 56th St. Apt. 3a, New York, NY 10022.

KLEMENT, Susan M., (Susan Kozicki); '97 BS; Social Sci. Tchr.; Palm Beach Cnty. Sch., 15245 Military Tr., Jupiter, FL 33458, 561 745-7200; r. 2419-15 Treasure Isle Dr., Palm Bch. Gardens, FL 33410, 561 627-2717; James.

KLIMAS, Jeffrey W.; '79 BA; 909 N 6th St., New Hyde Park, NY 11040.

KLIMEK, Katherine A.; '82 BS; 23218 88 Ave. Grd Fl., Jamaica, NY 11427.

KLIMOSKI, Frank; '92 BS; MPA Marist Clg.; Capt.; NYC Police Dept., 5315 58th St., Woodside, NY 11377, 718 476-7510; r. 201 E 21st St. Apt. 17e, New York, NY 10010, 212 260-3127. e-mail

KLINE, Byron; '95 MA; 114 Proctor Ave., Buffalo, NY 14215, 716 892-5777.

KLINGENER, Lawrence J.; '79 BS; 26315 83rd Ave., Glen Oaks, NY 11004, 718 347-1710.

KLINK, Gunther J.; '75 BS; 225 Diane Pl., Paramus, NJ 07652.

KLINK, John H.; '79 BS; 2040 Bruckner Blvd., Bronx, NY 10473.

KLINKENBERG, William (Bill) H.; '75 MA; BA City Clg., NY; Retired Instr.; Center for Mgmt. Devel. & FAA Sch.; r. POB 350446, Palm Coast, FL 32135; *Frances.*

KLOTKO, Steven G.; '92 BS; Job Devel.; Help USA, 50 E 168th St., Bronx, NY 10452, 718 839-1196; r. 80 Van Cortlandt Park, Bronx, NY 10463, 718 543-8931; *Cheer E.;* Sapphire K. e-mail

KLUCHARITS, John C.; '97 AS; 131 Pine Dr., Emerson, NJ 07630.

KLUFT, Elizabeth R.; '91 BS; 7000 Kennedy Blvd. E Apt. 24f, W. New York, NJ 07093.

KLUG, Kenneth C.; '88 MA; 1021 80th St., Brooklyn, NY 11228.

KLYDE, Catherine H.; '93 MA; 14115 72nd Ave., Flushing, NY 11367, 718 261-8171.

KMETZ, Thomas R.; '90 BS; 91 Philadelphia Ave., Massapequa Park, NY 11762.

KNAPLUND, Virginia; '73 MA; 5 Pinecrest Rd., Scarsdale, NY 10583.

KNEZEVIC, Antoaneta '98 (See Knezevic-Xanthos, Mrs. Antoaneta).

KNEZEVIC-XANTHOS, Mrs. Antoaneta, (Antoaneta Knezevic); '98 BA; Master's Prog.; r. Long Island City, NY 11106; *Nicholas Xanthos.* e-mail

KNICOS, Bessie '95 (See Fallon, Ms. Bessie A.).

KNIGHT, Alisa G.; '96 BS; Front Desk Clerk; Marriott Hotel, Adams St., Brooklyn Hts., NY 11201, 718 246-7000; r. 149 N.Portland Ave., Brooklyn, NY 11205.

KNIGHT, Angela N.; '95 BA; 725 Riverside Dr., Apt. 11E, New York, NY 10031.

KNIGHT, Lamona O.; '95 BS; Police Ofcr.; NYPD; r. 20 Brooklyn Ave., Roosevelt, NY 11575, 516 377-1812. e-mail

KNIGHT, Petrice A.; '99 BS; Social Worker; 17 Bristol St., Brooklyn, NY 11212, 718 915-8160; r. 603 E 57 St., Brooklyn, NY 11234, 718 209-1012. e-mail

KNIGHT, Roger V.; '82 BS; Social Work Supv.; City of NY, 400 8th Ave., New York, NY 10001, 212 971-2964; r. 23 E 91st, Brooklyn, NY 11212, 718 774-1576; *Deborah.*

KNIGHT, Thaddeus A.; '85 BA; 11310 NW 23rd Ct., Coral Springs, FL 33065, 954 340-6341.

KNIGHTS, Robert A.; '89 BS; Sergeant-NYPD-Narcotics Div.; NYPD-Organized Crime Control Bur., 1086 Simpson St., Bronx, NY 10459, 917 252-9117; r. Bronx, NY 10462. e-mail

KNIPPLER, Wesley R.; 1838 Stuart St., Brooklyn, NY 11229.

KNOBLICH, James P.; '88 BS; NYC Fire Dept., Prudential Faneuli Real Estate, 1820 Commerce St., Yorktown Hts., NY 10598, 914 245-2300; r. 860 Salem Rd, Yorktown Hts., NY 10598, 914 472-8317. e-mail

KNORR, Jill L.; '98 BA, 2000 MA; AS Gloucester Cnty. Clg.; Violations Clerk; Ocean City Municipal Ct., 8211 Central Ave., Ocean City, NJ 08226; r. 13 E Jimmie Leeds Rd., Absecon, NJ 08201, 609 404-1749. e-mail

KNOTT, Clare A.; '79 AS; 330 Beach 91st St., Far Rockaway, NY 11693, 718 474-4230.

KNOX, Blanche M.; '78 BA; 128-18 Gonston Ave., Belle Harbor, NY 11694, 718 479-3923.

KNOX, Charles; '74 BA; 487 Penn Est, E. Stroudsburg, PA 18301.

KNOX, Theresa J.; '86 BA; 952 E 156th St., Bronx, NY 10455, 718 829-8013.

KNOX, Trina M.; '97 BA; 482 E. 167th St., Bronx, NY 10456.

KO, Mrs. Eliza, (Eliza Lo); '89 MPA, '89 BA; Contracting Ofcr./Branch Chief; US Dept. of Housing & Urban Devel., 26 Federal Plz., New York, NY 10278, 212 264-8000; *Ivan;* Deanna. e-mail

KO, Ivan; '86 AA, '89 BS; Det; NYC Police Dept.; r. 6005 264th St., Little Neck, NY 11362; *Eliza;* Deanna.

KO, Michelle; '96 BA; 4823 40th St., Fl. 2, Sunnyside, NY 11104, 718 423-2148.

KOBAYASHI, Beatriz; '85 BA; 8929 215th St., Queens Vlg., NY 11427, 718 204-8556.

KOBEL, Richard T.; '84 BA; 4721 213th St., Flushing, NY 11361.

KOBILINSKY, Lawrence; 504 Rebecca Ln., Oceanside, NY 11572.

KOBYRA, Raymond E.; '77 MA; 2929 SE Ocean Blvd. # 0-1, Stuart, FL 34996, 561 286-2067.

KOCH, Christopher J.; '98 BS; 211 34 34th Rd., Bayside, NY 11361, 718 224-0543.

KOCH, Robert P.; '75 BA; JD St. Johns Law Sch.; Atty. Gen. Counsel; HealthPlex, 60 Charles Lindbergh Blvd., Uniondale, NY 11553, 516 794-3000; r. 107 Webster St., Westbury, NY 11590, 516 333-6651; Bernadine, Christine, Kevin, Daniel.

KOEHLER, Karl F.; '72 BA, AA; Ret., Police Ofcr., Investigator; City of Clifton, New Jersey, New Jersey State; r. 204 Lauren Ct., New Bern, NC 28562, 252 635-2820; *Ruth;* Robert, Richard. e-mail

KOEHLER, Richard J., JD; '73 BA; MA Hunter Clg., JD Fordham Univ. Law Sch.; Atty., Koehler & Isaacs LLP; Prof., John Jay Clg., Dept. Law & Police Science, 899 Tenth Ave., New York, NY 10019, 212 237-8037; r. 1 Radford Ct., Princeton Jct., NJ 08550, 917 551-1332. e-mail

KOENIG, Patricia A., (Patricia Swayne); '74 BS; CERT. Fairleigh Dickinson; Dir. of Operations; Lincoln Controls, Inc., 172 Madison Ave., New York, NY 10016, 212 545-7705; r. 33 Madison St., Pequannock, NJ 07440; *Ralph;* Kristen.

KOESTER, Arlene L.; '98 MA; 16-05 Putnam Ave. #5c, Ridgewood, NY 11385, 718 456-9039.

KOGAN, Darina '99 (See Krutovsky, Mrs. Darina).

KOHN, Deena R.; '96 MA; 210 W. 70th St., New York, NY 10023.

KOKIS, Peter W.; '91 BA; 1921 E 17th St., Brooklyn, NY 11229, 718 645-5462.

KOKUBON, Shoko; 255 E. 10th St. Apt. 5C, New York, NY 10009.

KOKUBUN, Shoko; '99 BA, '99 MA; The Forensic Panel, 224 W. 30th St., Ste. 807, New York, NY 10001, 212 396-3246. e-mail

KOLARIK, Sean; '81 BS; 25-81 36 St., Astoria, NY 11103, 718 721-2549.

KOLARIK, Timothy D.; '79 BS, '86 MPA, '99 MS; 45-14 30th Ave., Astoria, NY 11103, 718 721-2549.

KOLBECK, David A.; '92 BS; Corporate Security Dept.; Philip Morris, 120 Park Ave., New York, NY 10017, 917 663-4080; r. 10 Columbia Pl., Brooklyn, NY 11201, 718 403-0319.

KOLEGA, Lorraine; '82 BA; 154-27 23 Ave., Whitestone, NY 11357.

KOLENOVIC, Medzit; '99 BA; Police Ofcr.; NY Police Dept., 212 253-7511; r. 110-35 72nd Rd, Forest Hills, NY 11375, 718 263-9786. e-mail

KOLLER, Joseph J.; '95 BS; 285 Concord Ave., W. Hempstead, NY 11552, 516 565-9189.

KOLMAN, David O.; '76 BS; 7 Harwich Rd., E. Rockaway, NY 11518, 516 887-9285; *Mariann;* James, Susan. e-mail

KOLODNY, Nathan; '69 BA, '75 MA; Security Mgr.; American Broadcasting Co., 125 West End Ave., New York, NY 10023, 212 456-5487; r. 325 E. 12th St., New York, NY 10003. e-mail

KOLPAK, Mrs. Catherine R., (Catherine Howard); '75 BA; Asst. to The Editor; Magnificat USA, 201 Seminary Ave., Yonkers, NY 10704, 914 377-8513; r. 4215 Throggs Neck Expy., Bronx, NY 10465; *Frank.*

KONCZYNIN, Maria V. '79 (See Hughes, Maria).

KONESKY, Karilyn; '81 MA; 1012 Manhattan Ave., Brooklyn, NY 11222.

KONG, Corwin; '95 BA, '98 MS; MS; Asst. Staff Dir.; Fed. Reserve Bank of New York, 33 Liberty St., New York, NY 10045, 212 720-5108; r. 18 Stuyvesant Oval Apt. 7D, New York, NY 10009. e-mail

KONG, Yuen F.; '95 BS; 33 70th St., Brooklyn, NY 11209, 718 765-1051.

KONIG, Eric L.; '79 BS; 24832 Deepdale Ave., Flushing, NY 11362.

KONIG, Irving; '80 MA; 24832 Deepdale Ave., Flushing, NY 11362.

KONIG, Norman; '79 BS; 1259 E 68th St., Brooklyn, NY 11234.

KONOPKA, Edward A.; '71 BS; 92-02 Woodhaven Bl, Jamaica, NY 11421.

KOONMEN, Mary B.; 24 Ackley Ave., Malverne, NY 11565, 516 887-2636.

KOONTZ, Kyristel P. '96 (See Wright, Mrs. Kyristel P.).

KOOPALETHES, Alexander J.; '95 MPA; 100 Pierson Miller Dr. Apt. D53, Pompton Lakes, NJ 07442.

KOPP, Barbara A.; 305 Ansboro Pl., Bellmore, NY 11710.

KOPSTEIN, Jay I.; '82 MA; Deputy Inspector; Police Dept., City of NY, Operations Division, 1 Police Plz., New York, NY 10038, 212 374-5501; r. 2239 Van Cortlandt Cir., Yorktown Hts., NY 10598, 914 245-0735. e-mail

KORB, Adriana; '95 BA; US Probation Ofcr.; US Probation Ofc., Eastern Dist. NY, 75 Clinton St., Brooklyn, NY 11201, 718 254-7284; r. Elmhurst, NY 11373.

KORB, Alan H.; 1658 E 56th St., Brooklyn, NY 11234.

KOREN, John; '70 BS; Fairleigh Dickinson; Retired; r. 45 Jackson St., Fair Haven, NJ 07704, 732 212-0285; *Marilyn.*

KORMAN, Arnold I., Esq.; '73 BS; JD Brooklyn Law Sch.; Ret. Detective Squad Cdr.; NYPD, Laywer; r. 6124 220th St., Flushing, NY 11364, 718 225-9102.

KORMENDI, Robert; '75 BS; 57-41 Van Horn St., Elmhurst, NY 11373.

KORNBLUM, Allan; '69 MPA; JD NYU Law Sch., PHD Princeton Univ.; Sr. Counsel for Intelligence; US Dept. of Justice, Oipr Ste. 3305, 950 Pennsylvania Ave. NW, Washington, DC 20530, 202 514-2882; r. Rm 3305 Just. Dept., Washington, DC 20530; *Helen;* Aaron, Jesse.

KORNEEV, Tanya V.; '98 BS; 94 27 St., Copiague, NY 11726.

KORNEGAY, Kenyetta A.; '99 BA; 460 W. 126 St. 1B, New York, NY 10027, 212 665-5467.

KORNFELD, Mitchell; '94 BS; 88-09 35th Ave. #3M, Jackson Hts., NY 11372, 718 396-4851.

KOROL, Natalya; '98 BS; Computer Consultant; Bond Technology, 317 Madison Ave., 4th Fl., New York, NY 10017, 212 697-4700; r. 420 Avenue F, Apt. 4E, Brooklyn, NY 11218, 718 871-6723. e-mail

KOROLYEV, Dina; '99 BA; 3045 Ocean Pkwy. 1D, Brooklyn, NY 11235.

KORTRIGHT, Augusto; '95 BA; 341 E. 146th St., Bronx, NY 10451, 718 742-9556.

KORZEKWINSKI, Jack T.; '75 BS; Retired-Patrolman; NYC Police Dept./ Housing Authority; r. 21 Pearl St., Staten Island, NY 10304, 718 981-4049; *Emily.*

KOSCINSKI, Robert; '77 BS; Sergeant; NYC Police Dept. PSA #3, 25 Central Ave., Brooklyn, NY 11226; r. 23 Middle Loop Rd, Staten Island, NY 10308.

KOSCIUSKO, Charles; '94 BS; 4587 Chippendale Dr., Naples, FL 34112.

KOSHAK, William; '83 BS; Private Security Armored Car; American Armored Car Ltd., 44 N Saw Mill River Rd, Elmsford, NY 10523, 800 831-2158; r. 59 Franklin Ave., # 1, Monroe, NY 10950, 914 735-8617; Alexa, Nicholas. e-mail

KOSINSKI, Monica D.; '97 BA; Legal Rsch. Mgr.; Courtexpress, 1538 F Honeygrove Dr., Richmond, VA 23229, 804 288-4880; r. 1538 Honey Grove Dr., Apt. F, Richmond, VA 23229, 804 673-5324. e-mail

KOSKI, Richard A.; '82 BS; 757 Marcellus Dr., Westfield, NJ 07090, 908 233-2712.

KOSMETATOS, Marina; '99 BA; Law Student; r. 84-48 159th St., Jamaica, NY 11432, 718 297-6705.

KOSOFF, Edward; '75 MA; 1438 Bay 28th St., Far Rockaway, NY 11691.

KOSOWSKI, Mrs. Frances E. (Frances E. Micucci); '80 BS; REAL EST State of NY; Real Estate Salesperson; Precious Properties, 54 Tenth St., Staten Island, NY 10306, 718 980-7222; r. 319 Rose Ave., Staten Island, NY 10306, 718 979-4685; *Michael;* Rachele, Michael. e-mail

KOSSEIM, Amin; '92 BS; 107-09 86th Ave., Richmond Hill, NY 11418.

KOST, Martin L.; '71 BS; 22 Duke Pl., Glen Cove, NY 11542.

KOSTANOSKI, John I.; '69 BS; 891 Karshick St., Bohemia, NY 11716.

KOSTEAS, Panagiotes; '98 BA; 21 60 24 St., Astoria, NY 11105, 718 728-6846.

KOSTNER-ARMATO, Michele; '92 BS; 6712 64th St., Flushing, NY 11385.

KOSTOLNI, Vincent P.; '85 BA; POB 523, Levittown, NY 11756.

KOTTERHEIDT, Walter C.; '81 BS; 357 E 201st St. Apt. 5e, Bronx, NY 10458, 718 733-8024.

KOULOMBINIS, Nicholas; '78 BA; 30-35 31 St., Astoria, NY 11102.

KOULOUMBINIS, N.; '91 MPA; 209-31 42 Ave., Bayside, NY 11361.

KOUMBA, Patricia S.; '99 BS; Student-Protection/Security/Rsch.; John Jay Clg. of Criminal Justice; r. 591 Ocean Ave. #2-H, Brooklyn, NY 11226, 718 826-3002. e-mail

KOUMIDES, Steve; '87 BS; 57-10 73rd Pl., Maspeth, NY 11378.

KOUMPOURAS, John; '95 BS; 3177 33rd St. # 4, Long Island City, NY 11106.

KOURAKOS, Joseph C.; '99 BA; Police Ofcr.; NYPD; r. 3622 Corlear Ave., Bronx, NY 10463, 718 432-6326. e-mail

KOUTOURATSAS, Nick; '96 BS; 32-38 190 St., Flushing, NY 11358.

KOUZEL, Margarita; '95 BS; MSS Natl. Univ.-CA; Criminologist; r. 1330 Eureka St., San Diego, CA 92110, 212 496-7795. e-mail

KOUZOUJIAN, Gary B.; '85 BS; MSE, PD AS Fordham Univ.; Tchr.; Christopher Columbus HS, 925 Astor Ave., Bronx, NY 10469; r. 270 Lung St. Ave., Apt. 6-J, Bronx, NY 10465, 718 863-3378. e-mail

KOVACS, John; '92 BA, '99 MA; AS LaGuardia Community Clg.; Physical Therapist; Bronx V.A. Med. Ctr., 1417 37th St., N. Bergen, NJ 07047.

KOVAL, Robert; '86 MPA; 456 Greenbelt Pkwy., Holtsville, NY 11742.

KOWALEWSKI, Steven A.; '91 BS; 1009 Ship Ave., Beachwood, NJ 08722, 732 341-5491.

KOWSKY, Claire; 157 Beach 121st St., Far Rockaway, NY 11694, 718 634-8375.

KOZAKIEWICZ, Jennifer L.; '95 BS; 26 Furman Ct., Mahwah, NJ 07430, 201 512-9125.

KOZEL, Joseph D.; '76 BS; 3235 Hicksville Rd, Bethpage, NY 11714.

KOZICKI, Susan '97 (See Klement, Susan M.).

KOZLOW, Mary; '86 BS; Confidential Investigator/Supv.; NYC Dept. of Investigation, 80 Maiden Ln., New York, NY 10038, 212 825-2424; r. 21-22 31 Ave., Long Island City, NY 11106, 718 278-0724.

KOZMA, John F.; '77 BA; 21533 40th Ave., Flushing, NY 11361.

KOZMA, Mariann E.; '77 MA; 6531 70th Ave., Flushing, NY 11385.

KRAEMER, Richard E.; '80 MA; 291 James St., Teaneck, NJ 07666, 201 836-5813.

KRAJCI, Stephen C.; '83 BS; 21 Mercury Ln., Levittown, NY 11756.

KRAMER, David A.; '81 MA; POB 367, Hillsdale, NJ 07642.

KRAMER, Kathleen M.; '81 BS; 6753 152nd St., Flushing, NY 11367, 718 471-9505.

KRAMER, Sean C.; '95 BS; 60-89 60th Rd., Maspeth, NY 11378, 718 471-9505.

KRAMER, William; '76 MA; 82 Duhaime Rd, Pearl River, NY 10965, 914 735-6157.

KRANE, Thomas W.; '79 BS; 153 Dunham St., Staten Island, NY 10309, 718 984-0255.

KRASNOV, Felix; '94 BS; 200 Rector Pl. Apt. 23k, New York, NY 10280.

KRAUS, Andrew E.; '70 BA; 226 72 St., Brooklyn, NY 11209, 718 743-0381.

KRAUS, David T.; '98 BS; PTL/Police Ofcr.; Hopatong Police Dept., 111 Rinerstyx Rd, Hopatcong, NJ 07843, 973 398-5000; r. One Keewadin Ave., Hopatcong, NJ 07843, 973 770-4026. e-mail

KRAVATH, Pauline; '75 MA; Ret. Meeting Planner; r. 6 Scott St., Dobbs Ferry, NY 10522, 914 693-3579.

KRAVCHENKO, Leonid; '98 BS; Fraud Investigator #1; HRA-Bur. of Fraud Investigations, 250 Church St., New York, NY 10013, 212 274-4908; r. 98-41 Queens Blvd., Apt. 6-G, Rego Park, NY 11374, 718 896-6352; *Calina.*

KREDATUS, Edward J.; 285 Grove St., Clifton, NJ 07013, 973 472-2109.

KRESS, Robert J.; '79 MA; 50 Goff Ave., Staten Island, NY 10309.

KRETSCHMANN, George; '70 BS; 288 Linda Ave., Hawthorne, NY 10532, 914 769-3761.

KREUSCHER, Robert L.; '96 BA; 740 Dogwood Ave., Franklin Sq., NY 11010, 516 489-5234.

KREYMER, Rita; '99 BS; 464 Neptune Ave., Apt. 7G, Brooklyn, NY 11224, 718 258-7026.

KRIEG, Barry M.; '92 BS; 145 Oakdale St., Staten Island, NY 10308, 718 984-3544.

KRIEGSMAN, Jeffrey; '79 MPA; 501 A Surf Ave., Brooklyn, NY 11224.

KRINICK, Norman; '80 BA; 249 E 7th St., New York, NY 10009.

KRISHNANAN, Annita; '95 BA; 4128 Belvedere Sq., Apt. C, Decatur, GA 30035.

KRIVITZKY, Marvin H.; '68 BS, '75 MPA; CEO/Ret. Asst. Police Chief; Northeast Vanguard Assoc. Inc., 11 Berkshire Dr., New City, NY 10956, 914 639-1790; r. same; *Susan;* Steven, Stacey, Sharon, Karen.

KRIVOSTA, George G.; 46 Van Siclen Ave., Brooklyn, NY 11207.

KROL, ILya; '97 BS, '99 BS; 701 W.189th St. 6, New York, NY 10040, 315 858-0908.

KROLL, Irwin S.; '82 BA; 12 Starks Pl., Lynbrook, NY 11563, 516 484-5094.

KROLL, Rainer D.; '98 BA; 195 Canopus Hollow Rd, Putnam Vly., NY 10579, 914 234-6073.

KRONCHER, Alex T.; '94 BS; 3505 N 12th St. Apt. A3, Grand Jct., CO 81506.

KRONENFELD, Jeffrey; '86 BS; 38-50 Northern Dr., Fair Lawn, NJ 07410.

KROUSLIS, William J.; '86 BS; 5912 Madison St., Flushing, NY 11385.

KRUEGER, Robert W.; '93 MA; BA Northeast Louisiana Univ.; Elem. Tchr.; Halsey IS 296, 125 Covert St., Brooklyn, NY 11207, 718 574-0288; r. 4 Assembly Pl., Huntington Sta., NY 11746, 631 549-6884; *Victoria J. Bell.* e-mail

KRUESI, Arthur W.; '76 BA; 409 Robinson Ave., Staten Island, NY 10312.

KRUGER, Henry J.; '83 BS; Law Enforcement; Bur. ATF; r. 7871 82nd St., Flushing, NY 11385, 718 386-5537.

KRUKIN, Ms. Avalon S.; '90 CERT; MA, BS Tchrs. Clg. Columbia; Volunteer Tutor; Dome Proj.; r. 30 W 90th St. Apt. 6b, New York, NY 10024, 212 724-2404.

KRUS, Carol A.; '81 BS; 949 Webster Ave., New Rochelle, NY 10804, 914 967-8009.

KRUTOVSKY, Mrs. Darina, (Darina Kogan); '99 BA; Claim Examiner; Household Intl.; r. 230 Brighton 2nd Ln., Brooklyn, NY 11235, 718 332-8195; *Alexander.*

KRUTYS, Edward J.; '71 BA; 65 Westgate Rd, Massapequa Park, NY 11762.

KU, Jara-na-ayut W.; '82 BS; 40-44 70th St., Woodside, NY 11377, 718 204-5301.

KUAN, Andres; '95 BA; 497 W. 182nd St., New York, NY 10033.

KUBERSKI, Richard S.; '82 BA; 45 Beekman St., Staten Island, NY 10302.

KUCELUK, Joseph R.; '78 BS; Dir. Special Investigations; NYC Transit, 25 Jamaica Ave., Rm. 10, Brooklyn, NY 11207, 718 927-7478; r. 75-25 210 St., Bayside, NY 11364, 718 468-5435; *Mona Marie.* e-mail

KUDRY, Joseph S.; '91 MPA; 2045 Williamsbridge Rd, Bronx, NY 10461.

KUEHNLE, William A.; '78 BA; 95/19 106 St., Ozone Park, NY 11416.

KUHN, Ann; '92 BS; MFA City Clg. of New York; Profn. Photographer; Professor of Photography; r. POB 20556, New York, NY 10023.

KUHN, Donald A.; '74 AS, '76 BS; MPS New York Inst. Technology; Retired Inspector; NYC Police Dept.; r. 98 Ellensue Dr., Deer Park, NY 11729, 631 586-6183; *Anne P.; Debra, Anne Marie.*

KUHNER, Vance T.; '96; 7316 220th St. #1 Fl., Oakland Gardens, NY 11364.

KUKAJ, Mustafa M.; '83 BS; 300 Ft. Washington, New York, NY 10032.

KUKURINIS, Theologia; '97 BS; 54-36 Nurge Ave., Maspeth, NY 11378.

KULAH, Kofua Z.; '95 BS; 309 Simonson Ave., Staten Island, NY 10303, 718 815-2554.

KULESA, LT Edward J.; '80 BA, '84 MPA; Lt.; NYPD, 1 Police Plz., New York, NY 10038, 212 374-6640; r. 85-09 87 St., Woodhaven, NY 11421, 718 441-6133; *Kim; Daniel, Ryan, James.* e-mail

KULYRYCH, Lubomyr P.; '89 BA; 86 Landscape Ave., Yonkers, NY 10705.

KUMAGAI, Koshin; '99 BS; BS Fukui Univ.-Japan, AS LaGuardia Community CC; Student; John Jay Clg. of Criminal Justice; r. 31-74 29th St. #5E, Long Island City, NY 11106, 718 626-6270. e-mail

KUMP, Erwin; '79 BS; 6340 77th Pl., Flushing, NY 11379.

KUNITZKY, Michael; '98 BA; Account Mgr.; Mediaplex, 177 Steuart St., Ste. 600, San Francisco, CA 94105; r. 679 2nd Ave., San Francisco, CA 94118, 415 387-7559. e-mail

KUNKIS, Robert; '77 MCJ; BA CW Post, JD Seton Hall Univ. Sch. Law; Mgmt. Analyst; NYS Ofc. of Ct. Admin., 25 Beaver St., New York, NY 10004, 212 428-2539; r. 9 Millbrook Ct., Livingston, NJ 07039, 973 992-7339; *Lois; Adam, Jennifer.*

KUPFER, James R.; '82 BS; 66 Georgia Ave., Lake Hopatcong, NJ 07849.

KUPIEC, Joseph; '72 BS; 166-09 25 Dr., Flushing, NY 11358.

KUPPER, Donald F.; '76 BS, '76 AAS; Det. SSGT; Port Authority NY NJ; r. 311 Watson Ave., Lyndhurst, NJ 07071, 201 507-0466; *Mary; Jennifer, Christopher, Kimberly.* e-mail

KURAS, Thomas J.; '78 BS; 38 Whitewood Pl., Old Bridge, NJ 08857.

KURAU, William R., Jr.; '74 BA; Antique Dealer; r. POB 457, Lampeter, PA 17537, 717 464-0731; *Teresa; William, Jonathan, David.* e-mail

KURKA, Jeffrey S.; '93 BS; 104 Monell Ave., Islip, NY 11751.

KURNATOWSKI, C.; '91 BS; 203 Norman Ave. #1, Brooklyn, NY 11222.

KURT, Cihan; '96 BA; 690 Ocean Pkwy., Brooklyn, NY 11230, 718 339-6258.

KURTEK, Richard; '95 BS, '96 BS; POB 175, Flushing, NY 11378.

KURTYKA, George F.; '90 MA; 46 Mohawk Ave., Derby, CT 06418.

KURTZ, Gary S.; '81 BS; 35-21 149 St., Flushing, NY 11354, 718 268-1425.

KURTZ, Michael J.; '76 BS; Mgr.; Fidelity Investments, 1 World Financial Ctr., New York, NY 10281, 212 335-5719; r. 20 Van Nostrand Ct., Little Neck, NY 11362, 718 224-7618. e-mail

KURTZ, Robert T.; '70 BS; Pres.; The Lunt Agcy., 138 S. 1st St., Lindenhurst, NY 11757, 631 226-3112; r. 2439 Mermaid Ave., Wantagh, NY 11793, 516 221-1021; *Jane; Robert, Suzanne.*

KURTZBERG, Jared; '93 MA; 8 Leeward Ln., Commack, NY 11725.

KURYS, Mark C.; '96 BS; 2890 Harrington Ave., Bronx, NY 10461, 718 823-8127.

KURZ, Edward A., '75 BA AA, Retired; NYPD; r. 4764 Polaris Ct., New Port Richey, FL 34652, 727 848-3175; *Josephine.*

KURZWEIL, Andrew; '99 BA; AAS Kingsborough Comm Clg.; Comptroller; Quinn & Co., 237 W. 35th St., X 233, New York, NY 10001, 212 868-1900; r. 2216 E. 22nd St., Brooklyn, NY 11229, 718 743-6274. e-mail

KUSHNER, Abraham; '73 BS, '75 MA; ASN CCNY; Retired-Lt. Police Ofcr.; r. 67-12 164th St., Flushing, NY 11365, 718 591-4417. e-mail

KUSMIERSKA, Grazyna; '98 BA; CTS; YAI, 175 Remsen St., Brooklyn Hts., NY 11201, 718 855-6240; r. 732 Lorimer St. #2R, Brooklyn, NY 11211, 718 782-9147.

KUSZEL, Philip; '89 MA; 2700 Hering Ave., Bronx, NY 10469, 718 652-0336.

KUTCHER, Raymond; '76 MA; 8 Cranbrook Dr., Centerport, NY 11721.

KUTTLER, George P.; '78 BA; Loss Prevention Mgr.; The Wiz, 915 Central Park Ave., Scarsdale, NY 10583, 914 472-8800; r. 6 Clark Rd., Goshen, NY 10924; *Pat.*

KUZYSZYN, Katrina N.; '99, MA; 324 Calloway Rd., Boone, NC 28607, 718 396-9543.

KWAKYE-BERKO, B.; '89 BS; 365 E. 184th St., Bronx, NY 10458, 718 601-1937.

KYEI, Patricia C.; '93 BA; 11 Crooke Ave. Apt. 4d, Brooklyn, NY 11226.

KYPRIOTIS, Theodosios; '95 BS, '98 MS; 3605 Kingsbridge #5b, Bronx, NY 10463, 718 884-8066.

KYRIAKIDES, Michael N.; '99 BS; 3411 29th St., Astoria, NY 11106, 718 721-1167.

L

LA, Barbera I.; '84 BS; 6543 168th St., Flushing, NY 11365, 718 217-0461.

LA, Rose M.; '87 BS; 482 E 53rd St., Brooklyn, NY 11203, 718 256-7474.

LA BARBERA, Dennis; '77 BS; 2383 Elbert Ave., N. Bellmore, NY 11710, 516 826-1047.

LABIENTO, Daniel; '95 BS; 23 Taylor Ave., Centereach, NY 11720.

LABOY, Luis; '84 BS; 55 Troutman St., Brooklyn, NY 11206, 718 381-5711.

LABOY, Michelle; '95 BS; 733 Amsterdam Ave. Apt. 10c, New York, NY 10025.

LA BOZZETTA, Victor; '81 BA; 4311 Queens Blvd., Long Island City, NY 11104, 718 846-4206.

LABRENZ, Bettyann M.; '83 BA; 166-31 9th Ave., Whitestone, NY 11357.

LABUS, Heather A.; '99 BA; 155 E. Mosholu Pkwy. N., Bronx, NY 10467, 718 515-2749. e-mail

LACASSAGNE, Monica; '89 MPA; 443 W 51st St. Apt. 1w, New York, NY 10019.

LACHANAS, Christiano; '88 MA; 350 W. 48 St., New York, NY 10036.

LACICERO, Diane R.; '98 MA; Social Worker; Easter Seals, Somerville, NJ 08876; r. 10 Hetherington Rd., Nutley, NJ 07110, 973 667-9875.

LACOBS, Scott L.; '96 BS; 2475 W. 16 St. #9, Brooklyn, NY 11214.

LACOMBE, Stanley B.; '99 BS; 785 Autumn Ave., Brooklyn, NY 11208, 718 827-5507.

LACONDRE, Earl; '81 BS; Housing Police Dept. Retired; r. 11660 232nd St., Jamaica, NY 11411, 718 723-4180; *Willy Ruth.*

LA COVARA, Margaret M.; '77 BA, '80 MA; Sr. US Probation Officer; US Dept. of Probation, Southern Dist. of Ny, US Courthouse, 500 Pearl St., New York, NY 10007, 212 805-5172; r. 2272 28th St., Long Island City, NY 11105, 718 728-4905.

LA DE, La; '95 BS; 210 Eldridge St. # 3, New York, NY 10002.

LADSON, Anthony M.; '90 BS; 2042 Strauss St., Brooklyn, NY 11212.

LAFEMINA, Ms. Eileen T., (Eileen T. Aversa); '98 BS; AS Orange Cty Community Clg.; State Trooper; NYS Police Dept., 55 Crystal Run Rd., Middletown, NY 10940, 914 344-5300; r. 175 Deer Ct., Middletown, NY 10940, 914 344-1535; *Joseph (Dec.).*

LAFERLA, Linda J.; '96 MA; 5 Wandering Way, Smithtown, NY 11787.

LAFERRERA, Anthony F.; '77 BS; 72 Nichols Ave., Brooklyn, NY 11208, 718 647-3211.

LAFFEY, Christopher; '93 BS; 179 Oaks Rd, Millington, NJ 07946, 908 647-3869.

LAFFEY, John J.; '83 BA, '95 MA; Deputy Chief; NYPD, 2768 Frederick Douglas Blvd., New York, NY 10039, 212 694-7760; r. 765 Neptune Blvd., Long Beach, NY 11561.

LAGANO, Christopher; '89 BS, '89 MA; JD Temple Univ. Sch. of Law; Atty.; Troy T Sank PC, 30 Oak St., Stamford, CT 06905, 203 357-1190; r. 41 Wildwood Dr., Greenwich, CT 06830, 203 862-9848; *Judith;* Jessica, Maxwell. e-mail

LAGODA, Anthony A.; '79 BS; 108 Degraw St., Brooklyn, NY 11231.

LAGOFF, John S.; 635 Macon St., Brooklyn, NY 11233, 718 453-5851.

LAGUERRE, John; '95 BS; 564 Kingston Ave., Brooklyn, NY 11203, 718 769-8515.

LAI, Laura; '81 BA; 67-66 Exeter St., Forest Hills, NY 11375, 718 263-0120.

LAI, Raymond; '96 BA; 68-36 Burns St., Forest Hills, NY 11375, 718 271-9153.

LAIRD, Donald (Don) A., CFE; '74 MA; BA Brooklyn Clg., CFE LIC State of Texas; Fraud Investigator; Donaldo A. Laird, CFE, Kissimmee, FL, 917 653-7258; r. 629 Midiron Dr., Poinciana, FL 34759; Shivonne. e-mail

LAJSZKY, Werner P.; '97 BA; 30-05 Broadway, Long Island City, NY 11106.

LAKE, Ms. Deborah (Debbie) R.; '91 BA, '93 MA; Food Nutrition Coord.; Police Athletic League, 34 1/2 E 12th St., New York, NY 10003, 212 477-9450; r. New York, NY 10019; *John.* e-mail

LALAK, Patsy A.; '99 BS; Benefit Analyst; Amalgamated Ins. Co., 730 Broadway, 8th Fl., New York, NY 10003, 212 539-5710; r. S. Ozone Park, NY 11420; Sabrina Caride.

LALARAM, Anjani; '99 BS; 363 Bradford St., Brooklyn, NY 11207, 718 566-1754.

LALJIE, Vishnu D.; '93 BS; 180 E 163rd St. Apt. 3k, Bronx, NY 10451.

LALL, Christopher; '96 BA; 8915 84th St., Woodhaven, NY 11421, 718 521-0508.

LALLY, Patrick; 425 W. 47th St., New York, NY 10036.

LALONDE, Marie; '84 BA; 440 Lenox Rd, Brooklyn, NY 11203.

LAM, Alan; '94 BS; 2053 Shore Pkwy., Brooklyn, NY 11214, 718 743-3727.

LAM, Alfred; '87 BS; POB 16376, San Francisco, CA 94116, 415 822-0823.

LAM, Kwai; '98 BA; Inspector; SPCA, Hong Kong, China; r. 4/F 90 Pan Hoi St., Apt. 1, Quarry Bay, China, 7182596335. e-mail

LAM, Sindi H.; '96 BS; 10847 46th Ave., Corona, NY 11368, 718 977-1390.

LA MADRID, Ms. Yvette; '97 BA; Dist. Exec.; Boy Scouts of America, 350 Fifth Ave., Empire State Bldg., New York, NY 10118, 212 651-2921; r. 55-A Brighton 10 Ct., Brooklyn, NY 11235, 718 646-6569. e-mail

LA MALFA, James J.; '77 BA; 65 Cambridge Ave., Staten Island, NY 10314, 718 698-5245.

LAMARCA, Daniel P.; '97 AS; 1821 W. 10th St., Brooklyn, NY 11223, 718 648-4194.

LAMB, James P.; '98 MA; BA SUNY at Albany; Network Compliance Mgr.; Mail.com, 11 Broadway, New York, NY 10004, 212 425-4200; r. 2983 Bayside Ct., Wantagh, NY 11793, 516 826-7273; *Roberta;* Robert. e-mail

LAMB, James S.; '77 BS; 4338 247th St., Flushing, NY 11363, 718 949-9489.

LAMB, Jerry D.; '91 BS; MS Hunter Clg., MSED Baruch Clg.; Entrepreneur; Visions of Millennia Entertainment, POB 475, Bronx, NY 10471, 212 592-9145; r. 110 Highland Ave., # 4A, Yonkers, NY 10705. e-mail

LAMB, Owen H.; '82 BS; Lawyer; Owen H Lamb; r. 353 W 57th St. # 1916, New York, NY 10019, 212 333-4444.

LAMBDIN, George C.; '76; 4510 111th St., Flushing, NY 11368.

LAMBE, Joan S.; '79 BA; 1313 126th St., College Pt., NY 11356, 718 843-3881.

LAMBERT, Edwin F.; '72 AAS, '75 BA; Polygraphist/Entrepreneur; Wall Street Investigations, 80 Wallstreet, Rm. 717, New York, NY 10005, 212 635-0900; r. 342 Edinboro Rd, Staten Island, NY 10306, 718 351-3005; *Patricia;* Edwin F. Jr., Thomas, Nancy Ozman. e-mail

LAMBERT, Joseph M.; '93 BS; 287 E 94th St. Apt. 2f, Brooklyn, NY 11212, 718 346-4811.

LAMBERT, Vanessa; '97 BS; 62 Grant St., Farmingdale, NY 11735, 631 694-3909.

LAMBERTI, Anthony J.; '78 BA; JD Brooklyn Law Sch.; Atty.; Anthony J Lamberti, 6807 11th Ave., Brooklyn, NY 11219, 718 234-3079; r. 621 76th St., Brooklyn, NY 11209, 718 238-4698; *Nancy;* Alexandra, Juliana, Anthony. e-mail

LAMBERT-MARTINEZ, Efrain; '95 BS; 597 E 139th St. Apt. 2n, Bronx, NY 10454, 718 402-6377.

LAMBIE, M'balia B.; '95 BS; 15509 SW 99th Ter., Miami, FL 33196.

LAMBKIN, John J.; '76 BA; 1824 E. 32 St., Brooklyn, NY 11234.

LAMBKIN, John M.; '95 BS; 15 Able Noble Dr., Chester, NY 10918, 914 469-1813.

LAMBRIANIDOU, Kyriaki; '99 BS; 31-64 30th St. (#42), Long Island City, NY 11106, 718 956-0398. e-mail

LAMONT, Naeemah; '92 BA; MA Hunter Clg., JD Rugters Univ. Sch. of Law; Educator; NYC Bd. of Educ, Brooklyn, NY 11203; r. 8750 204th St. Apt. A55, Hollis, NY 11423, 718 465-5671. e-mail

LA MONT, Olivia E.; '77 BA; Transportation Industry Analyst SA; US Dept. of Transportation; r. 628 Atherton Pl., Hayward, CA 94541, 510 537-4254; Brigette A., Stacy M. e-mail

LA MORTE, David; '98 MPA; Clains Examiner; Prudential, One Raritan Ctr. Pkwy., Edison, NJ 08837, 732 346-5546; r. 158 Princeton Rd, Elizabeth, NJ 07208, 908 289-9143. e-mail

LAMORTE, Lisa; '80 BA; 38 Court Dr., Huntington Sta., NY 11746, 631 427-2984.

LAMOT, Michael D.; '84 BS; 702 Woodsbrook Dr., Mahopac, NY 10541, 914 621-7135.

LAMOTHE, Michael F.; '82 BA; Sr. Prog. Analyst; IRS, Ofc. of Fedstate Relations, 1111 Constitution Ave. NW Op:Gld:Fs, Washington, DC 20224, 202 622-3346; r. 8123 Londonderry Ct., Laurel, MD 20707, 301 725-8956; *Haeng Suk;* Mickey, Christine, Thomas. e-mail

LAMOUR, Barbara M.; '97 BA; Paralegal/Mortgage Cnslt.; Manoussos Assocs., PC, Seven Twelfth St., Garden City, NY 11530, 516 741-1032; r. 25556 147th Rd, Rosedale, NY 11422, 718 723-5649; Denny. e-mail

L'AMOUR, Mousslin; '90 BS; 751 Bonnie Dr., Baldwin, NY 11510.

LAMPASSO, Albert J.; '86 MA; BA NYU; Criminal Investigator; r. 327 Central Park W, New York, NY 10025, 212 662-3412.

LAMPERT, Donna L.; '81 BS; 207 Meadowoods Dr., E. Meadow, NY 11554, 516 227-3576.

LAMPERTI, Edward P.; '92 MPA; 25 Van Reipen Ave., Apt. 306, Jersey City, NJ 07306.

LAMPF, Jesse D.; '99 MA; BA Boston Univ.; Intelligence Analyst; Justice Dept./DEA, 80 Mulberry St., Newark, NJ 07102, 973 273-5000; r. 141 Old Short Hills Rd, Apt. 118, W. Orange, NJ 07052. e-mail

LAMPINSTEI, Edward S.; '77 MA; 142 Nippon Ave., Staten Island, NY 10312.

LANCASTER, Michael O.; '95 BA; Asst. Prog. Dir.; Mental Health Assoc. of New York, 3280 Broadway, New York, NY 10027, 212 862-0205; r. 373 W 126th St. # 2 B, New York, NY 10027.

LANCE, Deborha A.; '83 BA; 12820 144th St., Jamaica, NY 11436, 718 949-1214.

LAND, Johannie; '77 BA; 696 E 52nd St., Brooklyn, NY 11203, 718 499-2631.

LANDAIS, Martine; '92 BS; 5662 Kings Hwy., Brooklyn, NY 11203.

LANDE, John; '71 BS; Financial Advisor; American Express; r. Andes Star Rte. Box 213, Delhi, NY 13753, 607 746-3636. e-mail

LANDIN, Rudolph; '93 BA; 656 Greeley Ave., Staten Island, NY 10306.

LANDIS, James L.; '75 MA; 0-40 34 St., Fair Lawn, NJ 07410.

LANDIVAR, Mrs. Sandra J., (Sandra J. Castro); '98 BA; Homemaker; r. 677 9th Ave. # 4S, New York, NY 10036, 212 977-6102; *Jose;* Joseph. e-mail

LANDSBERG, Barry; '81 MPA; 105 Sturges St., Staten Island, NY 10314, 718 834-9340.

LANE, Betty A.; '79 BS; AAS Bronx Community Clg.; Court Asst.; White Plains City Ct., 914 422-6054; r. 2045 Story Ave., Bronx, NY 10473, 718 829-9653; *Daniel (Dec); Brien, Ninette.*

LANE, Edward B.; '76 BS; 109-51 Cntrvr, Ozone Park, NY 11417, 718 229-7943.

LANE, Henry L.; '76 BA, '76 AS; Detective Retired; r. 68 Conlon Rd, Roosevelt, NY 11575, 516 868-4530. e-mail

LANE, Michael; POB 44, Putnam Vly., NY 10579.

LANE, Thomas R.; POB 218, Mastic, NY 11950.

LANG, Pamela D.; '89 BS; 175 Eastern Pkwy., Brooklyn, NY 11238, 718 922-1878.

LANG, Wayne L.; '98 MS; BS New York Tech; Chief; NYC Fire Dept.; r. 202 Wood Ave., Staten Island, NY 10307, 718 317-9213; *Renee; Michelle, Wayne J., Melissa.* e-mail

LANGAN, Mary K.; '95 BA; 778 Metropolitan Ave., Brooklyn, NY 11211.

LANGARICA, Ernesto; '98 BS; AS Suffolk Community Clg.; Intern/Mgmt. of Actress & Actors; Greson Saines Mgmt., New York Inst of Tech; r. 6 Williams Blvd., Apt. 2E, Lake Grove, NY 11755; *Noelle.* e-mail

LANGELLOTTI, Phillip; '71 BS; Sr. Clg. Lab Tech.; John Jay Clg., 15th St., New York, NY 10019; r. 89 Adelphi Ave., Harrison, NY 10528, 914 835-6519; *Patti; Michael, Elizabeth.* e-mail

LANGEVIN, Guy; '91 MA; RR 4 Box 539A Old, Biddeford, ME 04005, 207 934-4695.

LANGLAN, Diane M. '94 (See Brinkman, Mrs. Diane M.).

LANGLEY, Lola H. '78 (See Anderson, Dr. Lola H.).

LANGONE, Darin; '90 MA; 237-07 93 Rd., Bellerose, NY 11426, 516 775-1786.

LANGSTON, Sandra D.; '93 BS; MPA NYU, CERT. Cornell Univ.; Deputy Warden; NYC Correction Dept., 19-19 Hazen St., E. Elmhurst, NY 11370, 718 546-7510; r. 11612 218th St., Cambria Hts., NY 11411, 718 712-6904; *Aaron Stephens, Donald Stephens.* e-mail

LANIADO, Elliot J.; '80 BS; 2004 E 56 St., Brooklyn, NY 11234.

LANIER, Louis I.; '90 MPA; 925 Ocean Ave., Brooklyn, NY 11226.

LANIGAN, Maria; '95 BS; 31-25 49th St., Woodside, NY 11377.

LANZA, James J.; '83 BA; Firefighter; FDNY, 1836 3rd Ave., New York, NY 10029, 212 570-4253; r. 5625 28th Ave., Woodside, NY 11377, 718 726-0450.

LANZILOTTI, Carlo J.; '80 BA; 140 7th Ave., New York, NY 10011, 212 366-1816.

LAO, Jorge L.; '94 BS; 96 Sprague Ave., Middletown, NY 10940.

LA PADULA, Vincent A.; '95 MPA; JD St. Johns Univ Sch of Law; Atty.; r. 300 E 61st St. Apt. 2w, New York, NY 10021.

LAPERUTA, Domenick A.; '74 AS, '77 BS, '84 MPA; AS Westchester Community Clg; Assoc. Dir. Public Safety; Herbert H Lehman Clg. CUNY, 250 Bedford Park Blvd. W., Bronx, NY 10468, 718 960-8594; r. 1100 Midland Ave., Bronxville, NY 10708, 914 423-8255; *Magdalena;* Domenick Jr, Anthony, Daniel, Katrina. e-mail

LAPERUTA, Domenick A.; '95 MS, '99 MS; Detective; NYPD, 1 Police Plz., New York, NY 10038, 914 237-7425; r. 125 1st St., Yonkers, NY 10704; *Karin; Anita, Dominick.* e-mail

LA PIETRA, Louis C.; '91 BS; JD Brooklyn Law Sch.; NYPD Sgt/Atty./ Adjunct Prof.; Law Ofc. of Louis C. LaPietra, 77 Joyce Rd., Hartsdale, NY 10530, 914 693-6035; r. same, 914 693-7080; *Josephine; Michael, Nicole.* e-mail

LAPORTE, Angel L.; '79 BS; 444 2nd Ave., New York, NY 10010, 315 361-1267.

LARA, Antonio L.; '91 BA; 184-03 Jamaica Ave., Hollis, NY 11423, 718 721-4933.

LARA, Guisela J.; '97 BA; 39-65 52nd St., Woodside, NY 11377, 718 721-4933.

LARA, Manuel E.; '94 BA; Detective; Bronx Dist. Atty. Office, Bronx, NY 10451; r. 272 Lake Shore Dr., Brewster, NY 10509. e-mail

LA RAC, Natasha; '98 BA; 1024 E. 40th St., Brooklyn, NY 11210, 718 940-3377.

LARGO, Alfred E.; '80 MPA; 52 Hendrickson Ave., Lynbrook, NY 11563.

LARKEY, David H.; '97 BA; 26 Aubrey Rd., Montclair, NJ 07043, 973 746-6356.

LARKIN, Cheryl A. '82 (See Larkin-Bowman, Cheryl A.).

LARKIN, Susan; 435 W. 57th St., New York, NY 10019, 315 735-5922.

LARKIN-BOWMAN, Cheryl A., (Cheryl A. Larkin); '82 BA; MSW Hunter Clg.; Supr II; Admin. for Children's Svcs., Family Preservation Prgm., 1360 Fulton St., Brooklyn, NY 11216, 718 399-8224; r. 950 Rutland Rd, Brooklyn, NY 11212, 718 773-3090; *Tenae, Cherise.* e-mail

LAROC, Natasha E.; '98 BA; 1024 E 40 St., Brooklyn, NY 11210, 718 377-7027.

LAROSA, Anthony; '93 BA; 1774 E 31 St., Brooklyn, NY 11234.

LAROSA, Michael A.; '95 BS; POB 950054, Far Rockaway, NY 11695, 718 456-4084.

LA ROSA, Mickey; '80 BS; 1727 2nd Ave., New York, NY 10128, 315 337-9622.

LARROCHE, Odette Y.; '99; 615 W 183rd St. #1J, New York, NY 10033.

LARRYMORE, Cynthia; '90 BA; 12814 116th Ave., Jamaica, NY 11420.

LARSEN, Jeremy; '99 MS; BA Univ. of Albany; Assoc. Dispatcher; Metropolitan Museum of Art, 1000 5th Ave., New York, NY 10028; r. 100 Overlook Ter., Apt. 710, New York, NY 10040, 212 795-7271. e-mail

LARSON, Allan G.; '83 MPA; Lt.; NYPD; r. 186 Merrymount St., Staten Island, NY 10314, 718 761-5751.

LARTIGAUT, Sandra; '85 BS; 526 Tinton Ave., Bronx, NY 10455.

LASACK, Ian N.; '84 MPA; Pres.; Com-Tulse Inc.; r. 3253 43rd St. #2, Long Island City, NY 11103.

LA SALA, Stephen F.; '79 BS; 91-07 101 Ave., Jamaica, NY 11416, 718 359-7484.

LASALLE, Jeffrey J.; '85 BS; 105 N Linden Ave., Hatboro, PA 19040, 717 392-0516.

LASCANO, Mercy; '83 BS; 4204 50th Ave., Woodside, NY 11377, 718 463-2428.

LASCHET, Alice; '98 MPA; BA SOC. Hofstra Univ.; Police Ofcr.; Rockland Cnty. Sheriff's Dept., New City, NY 10956, 914 638-5400; r. New City, NY 10956.

LASHLEY, Michelle L.; '87 BA; BS Health Sci. Ctr.-Brooklyn; Rsch.; In Demand, New York, NY 10001; r. 1036 E 42nd St., Brooklyn, NY 11210, 718 377-9270; *Jharod.* e-mail

LASKIN, Edward S.; '83 BS; 157 Cedar Rd, E. Northport, NY 11731.

LA SPISA, Salva; '97 AS, '98 AS; 801 Peconic Ave., N. Babylon, NY 11703.

LASSEN, Christopher M.; '98 BA; 3136 Kings Hwy., Brooklyn, NY 11234, 718 692-2789.

LASSEN, Joseph; '93 BS; Police Sergeant/Law Student; NYPD, New York, NY 10003; r. 288 Swinnerton St., Staten Island, NY 10307, 718 967-7516. e-mail

LASSI, Luisa E.; '97 BA; Child Protective Spec.; NYC Admin. for Children Svcs., 150 William St., New York, NY 10038, 212 676-6430; r. 506 W. 177 St. Apt. 3E, New York, NY 10033, 212 795-6850; *Victor Capellan; Chanel Victoria.*

LASSITER, Yvonne, (Yvonne Nelson); '95 BS; Police Ofcr.; NYPD; r. 98 Half Mile Rd, Central Islip, NY 11722, 631 582-6649; *Quincy; Kelvin, Queue, Quince'.* e-mail

LASTER, Keena M.; '98 BA; VP; Starwood Corp., 36 W 44th St., Ste. 905, New York, NY 10036, 212 354-7742; r. 215 W 139th St., Apt. 5, New York, NY 10030, 212 283-2939. e-mail

LASTIQUE, Sharon D.; '98 MA; 138-45 77th Ave., Flushing, NY 11367, 718 793-7054.

LATARSKI, Sigmund J.; '71 BS; MPH C W Post; 9 Parklyn Ct., Bardonia, NY 10954.

LATAWIEC, Robert F.; '80 BA; 2268 E 18th St., Brooklyn, NY 11229.

LATHAM, John F.; '85 BA; 711 Raritan Ave., Highland Park, NJ 08904.

LATHAN, Rosemyer; '75 MPA; 775 Concourse VI E, Bronx, NY 10451.

LATIMER, George A.; '73 BA; 309 Sterling Pl., Brooklyn, NY 11238, 718 345-7766.

LATORA, Vincent; '81 BA; 484 60 St., Brooklyn, NY 11220.

LATOUR, William J.; '78 BS; 94 Gansevoort Blvd., Staten Island, NY 10314, 718 761-1962.

LATTY, Gregory C.; '84 BA; 22 Northridge Dr., Coram, NY 11727.

LAU, Ricardo C.; '92 BS; 6746 Harrow St., Flushing, NY 11375.

LAUB, George J.; '79 MPA; 22 Bolivar St., Staten Island, NY 10314, 718 351-6552.

LAUDA, Edward C.; '80 MA; BA CUNY; Sr. Investigator; Atty. Gen. Ofc., Ft. Lauderdale, FL 33310, 954 958-5457; r. 20275 Hacienda Ct., Boca Raton, FL 33498, 561 852-2190.

LAUER, Deborah A.; '82 BS; 34 Farm Ln., Levittown, NY 11756, 516 579-1621.

LAUGHLIN, Paula; '84 MS; 56 N Hamilton St., Doylestown, PA 18901.

LAURENCE, Oscar; '82 BA; 661 E 92nd St., Brooklyn, NY 11236.

LAURENDI, Domenick A.; '82 BS; 2276 E 2nd St., Brooklyn, NY 11223, 718 339-5989.

LAURENSON, Barbara J.; '96 BA; Grad. Sch. of Brooklyn; Elem. Tchr.; Dist. 22, Brooklyn, NY 11235; r. 1212 Newkirk Ave., Brooklyn, NY 11230, 718 859-8681; Dominique M., Thomas L.

LAURIA, James; '86 MPA; 1 King Rd W, Mastic Bch., NY 11951.

LAURIA, Michele A.; '85 BS; 2 Fielding Pl., Palm Coast, FL 32137, 904 446-2357.

LAUTENBERGER, R.; '93 BS; 363 52nd St., Brooklyn, NY 11220.

LAUTHER, Beverly; '83 BS, '94 MPA; 121-40 133rd St., S. Ozone Park, NY 11420.

LAVAGNA, Peter J.; '82 BS; 455 Hoboken Rd, Carlstadt, NJ 07072.

LA VAUGHN, Deanna A.; '80 BA; 521 Black River Rd, Georgetown, SC 29440.

LA VEGLIA, Anthony J.; '75 AS; MA, BA Long Island Univ.; Dir.-Asset Protection; Cablevision, 1111 Stewart Ave., Bethpage, NY 11714, 516 803-2610. e-mail

LAVEGLIA, Joseph A.; '75 MA; 79 5th Ave., Kings Park, NY 11754.

LAVELLE, Joseph T.; '91 BA; 381 Cheves Ave., Staten Island, NY 10314.

LAVERDE, Jacqueline; '93 BS; 370 Adams Ave., Staten Island, NY 10306.

LAVILLE-WILSON, Debra; '94 BS; MA Old Dominion Univ.; Business Owner; Home-Works; r. 1204 Mondrian Loop, Virginia Bch., VA 23456, 757 368-2204; Davida, Nai'Je, Maria. e-mail

LAVIN, Brian F.; 3636 Fieldstone Rd, Riverdale, NY 10463.

LAVIN, Christopher; '89 MA; BS Silve Regina Univ.; Chief of Police; Town of East Greenbush Police, 225 Columbia Tpk, Rensselaer, NY 12144, 518 479-2525. e-mail

LAVIN, John F.; '90 BA; 3047 29th St. Apt. 4, Long Island City, NY 11102, 718 229-7964.

LAVIN, Michael B.; '82 BS; 19 Linden St., Selden, NY 11784.

LAVINGTON, Chelsea R.; '99 MPA; BA Univ. of Virginia; Asst. Dir. of Admissions; CUNY-Queensborough Community Clg., 222-05 56th Ave., A210, Bayside, NY 11364, 718 631-6629; r. 130-03 229th St., Laurelton, NY 11413, 718 978-6915. e-mail

LAWLOR, Jason A.; '93 BS; POB 375, Convent Sta., NJ 07961.

LAWRENCE, Andrea L.; '91 BS; Probation Ofcr.; NYC Dept. of Probation, 283 Adams St. Rm 107, Brooklyn, NY 11201, 718 643-2356; r. 128 Hancock St., Brooklyn, NY 11216, 718 783-3169.

LAWRENCE, Barbara J.; '94 BS; 46 Madison St., New York, NY 10038, 315 245-0015.

LAWRENCE, Brent L.; '73 BS; Chief of Police; Town Fallsburg Police Dept., S. Fallsburg, NY 12779, 914 434-4422; r. POB 67, Fallsburg, NY 12733.

LAWRENCE, Carle R.; 1028 Ogden Ave., Bronx, NY 10452, 718 652-5290.

LAWRENCE, Claude; '95 BA; 346 Southside Ave., Freeport, NY 11520, 516 377-1131.

LAWRENCE, Darcel Y.; '88 BA; 114-24 155th St., Jamaica, NY 11434, 718 225-4676.

LAWRENCE, Denise A.; '83 BA; 776 Salem Rd, Uniondale, NY 11553, 516 536-0313.

LAWRENCE, Gustave J.; '83 BS; POB 6113, Bronx, NY 10451, 718 652-5290.

LAWRENCE, Janet M.; '83 BA; 102-58 Nicolls Ave., Corona, NY 11368, 718 657-1150.

LAWRENCE, Julia J.; '98 BA; 516 E 28th St., Brooklyn, NY 11210, 718 455-3466.

LAWRENCE, Michael G.; '78 BS; 151-05 20 Rd, Whitestone, NY 11357, 718 397-1229.

LAWRENCE, Robert M.; '85 MPA; 36 Willett Pl., Roosevelt, NY 11575, 516 623-5614.

LAWRENCE, Talaia; '99 AS; BA; Bank Teller; Chase Manhattan, Bronx, NY 10467; r. 711 Magenta St. 6B, Bronx, NY 10467, 718 881-1553. e-mail

LAWRENCE, Veronie; '97; 25 Beekman Ave., Mt. Vernon, NY 10553, 716 688-0948.

LAWRENCE, Yvonne J.; '85 AS, '97 MPA; 162 W. 122nd St., New York, NY 10027, 315 245-0015.

LAWSON, Blair; '95 MPA; BS Syracuse Univ.; Dir. of Client Svcs.; LIAAC Inc., 755 Park Ave., Huntington Sta., NY 11746, 631 385-2451; r. 8959 210th St., Queens Vlg., NY 11427, 718 468-6810; *Pascale; Arielle*. e-mail

LAWSON, Cecelia B.; '88 BA; 2456 Bedford Ave. 2, Brooklyn, NY 11226, 718 774-3388.

LAWSON, James; '91 BS; 1670 E 174th St., Bronx, NY 10472, 718 991-5355.

LAWSON, Mrs. Kim, (Kim Franklin); '92 BS; PARALGL Kaplan Clg.; Paralegal; Gentiva Olson, Melville, NY 11747; r. 15 Washington Ave., Amityville, NY 11701, 516 489-8154.

LAWTON, Kim R.; '87 BS; 102-27 186th St., Hollis, NY 11423.

LAYNE, Christopher; '94 BS; 11119 126th St., Jamaica, NY 11420, 718 738-5542.

LAYNE, Frederick R.; '79 AS; 118 Soundview Dr., Hampstead, NC 28443, 910 270-9164.

LAZANSKY, George; '73 BS; 450 W 27th Street Dr. Apt. 11e, New York, NY 10001.

LAZARRE, Marie; '99 BA; 1725 Dorchester Rd. #5A, Brooklyn, NY 11226, 718 282-0801.

LAZO, Herlis A.; '98 BS; Systs. Litigation Clerk; O'Sullivan Grave & Karavell, 30 Rockefeller Plz., New York, NY 10112, 212 728-5801; r. 314 72nd St., Brooklyn, NY 11209, 718 238-8932.

LAZZARO, Paul J.; '95 BS; Special Agt.; US Dept. of Defense, Airforce Ofc. of Special Inv.; r. 31 Stagg Rd, Wayne, NJ 07470, 973 305-8695.

LE, Brew V.; '84 BS; 35 Cornelia St., Brooklyn, NY 11221, 718 375-2060.

LEACH, Anthony; '97 BS, '99; 2835 Bedford Ave., Brooklyn, NY 11210.

LEACOCK, Colleen E.; '93 BS; 990 Sterling Pl., Brooklyn, NY 11213, 718 573-0139.

LEADER, David K.; '87 BS; 1861 Andrews Ave. S, Bronx, NY 10453, 718 665-5539.

LEADER, Martin L.; '77 AS; 9527 102nd St., Jamaica, NY 11416, 718 261-4274.

LEADERMAN, Ian C.; '99 MA; 150 Zeblin Rd., Atlanta, GA 30342, 404 843-9422.

LEAH, Magnuson; '93 BS; JD New York Law Sch., MA; Atty.; 9728 3rd Ave. #459, Brooklyn, NY 11209; r. 718 238-9730. e-mail

LEAHEY, John G.; '86 BS; 43-02 56 St., Woodside, NY 11377.

LEANDRY, Victor; '98 BA; Police Ofcr.; NYC Police Dept.; r. 3285 Broadway #3, New York, NY 10027, 212 694-6119.

LEARY, Jeremiah J.; '85 AS; 489 9th St., Brooklyn, NY 11215, 718 522-5732.

LEASK, William M.; '71 BS; MS NY Inst. Tech.; Free-lance; 8819 76th St., Woodhaven, NY 11421, 718 296-7030; r. 8819 76th St., Jamaica, NY 11421, 718 296-7030.

LEATHER, Joseph J.; '77 AS, '80 BS; 107 Norwood Ave., Avon By The Sea, NJ 07717, 732 775-6592.

LEAVEY, Marion A.; '82 MA; BS St. Thomas Aquinas; Probation Ofcr.; Rockland Cnty., Cnty. Ofc. Bldg., New City, NY 10956; r. 19 Cypress Ln., Orangeburg, NY 10962, 914 359-3249.

LEAVITT, Catherine B.; '96 MA; 3131 N 70th St., Scottsdale, AZ 85251.

LEBLANC, Louis M.; 21-13 22 Dr., Long Island City, NY 11105, 718 225-3374.

LEBOWITZ, Raymond; '79 BA; Retired; NYC Fire Dept.; r. 3950 Cocoplum Cir., Apt. D, Coconut Creek, FL 33063, 954 968-7426. e-mail

LEBRON, Nancy; '80 BS; 23-50 97th St., E. Elmhurst, NY 11369, 718 937-2013.

LECKEY, Sabrina M.; '99 BS; 37 New Lots Ave. #6E, Brooklyn, NY 11212, 718 495-9786.

LECKLER, Francis P.; '96 BS; Police Ofcr.; Nassau Cnty.; r. 43-17 Bowne St., Flushing, NY 11355.

LEDEE, Robert; '76 MPA; Retired; Reliable Investigations Inc., POB 340657, Rochdale Vlg., NY 11434, 718 527-2295; *Victoria*; Yvonne, Robert Jr., Reginald, Anthony.

LEDESMA, Andres; Legislative Aide; City Council NYC; r. 1404 Hancock St., Brooklyn, NY 11237. e-mail

LEDFORD, Kathleen T.; '80 BS; 31 Wren Dr., Hauppauge, NY 11788.

LEDFORD, Marsha; '95 BS; Expeditor; Dist. Atty. Ofc.; r. 13716 156th St., Jamaica, NY 11434, 718 712-9727.

LEDGISTER-DENNIS, Carla; '94 BS; 655 E 81st St., Brooklyn, NY 11236, 718 342-7054.

LEDROIT, Delphine Y.; '99 MA; 214 W 16th St. #5S, New York, NY 10011, 917 553-9479.

LEE, Amy R.; '89 BA; 11 Covington St., S. Huntington, NY 11746.

LEE, Andreas Y.; '97 BA; 142-09 Bayside Ave., Flushing, NY 11354, 718 997-6863.

LEE, Barbara S.; '99 BS; Dir.; Proedge Grp., POB 7465, Miami, FL 33152, 305 871-8090; r. 6852 SW 9th St., Pembroke Pines, FL 33023, 305 871-8090. e-mail

LEE, Brenda; '94 BA; 91 Boerum St. Apt. 3n, Brooklyn, NY 11206, 718 836-9492.

LEE, Chak Y.; '84 BS; 18 Racine Ln., Matawan, NJ 07747, 732 583-6001.

LEE, Chang-Ming; '85 MPA; 37-05 Main St. 2nd, Flushing, NY 11354, 718 204-7141.

LEE, Chon J.; '98 BA; Investigator; Dept. of Buildings, Investigation's Ofc., 11 Park Pl., New York, NY 10007, 212 442-2000; r. 36-11 23 Ave. #2F, Astoria, NY 11105, 718 728-4581. e-mail

LEE, David; '83 BA; 224 Old Bergen Rd., Jersey City, NJ 07305, 201 659-3366.

LEE, Donald F.; '98 MA; Psychologist; Manhasset Public Schs., 200 Memorial Pl., Manhasset, NY 11030; r. 270 5th St., Apt. 4l, Brooklyn, NY 11215, 718 832-0424.

LEE, Fei; '92 BS; 2843 Steinway St., Long Island City, NY 11103, 718 575-1979.

LEE, Franklin; '86 BS; Sr. Court Ofcr.; Manhattan Supreme Ct., 100 Centre St., New York, NY 10013, 212 374-4768; r. 45 Malone Ave., Belleville, NJ 07109, 973 450-8499.

LEE, Dr. Henry C.; '72 BS; MS, PHD NYU; Commissioner/Dir. of Forensic Lab; State of CT Dept. of Public Safety, 1111 Country Club Rd., Middletown, CT 06457, 860 685-8000; r. 82 Limewood Ave., Branford, CT 06405, 203 488-1475; *Margaret;* Dr Stanley, Sherry.

LEE, James C.; '77 BS; 6360 83rd St., Flushing, NY 11379, 718 205-3332.

LEE, James M.; '84 BA; 423-1 Willow Rd., Staten Island, NY 10314, 718 420-1988.

LEE, Jin; '96 BA; Sr. Dist. Exec.; Boy Scouts of America, Greater New York Council, 350 5th Ave., Empire State Bldg., New York, NY 10118, 212 651-2893; r. 660 Thwaites Pl., Bronx, NY 10467, 718 655-4939. e-mail

LEE, Judy; '99 BS; Mktg. Asst.; America Society, 1865 Broadway, New York, NY 10023, 212 408-1342; r. 31 Henry St. Apt. 7, New York, NY 10002, 212 608-1983. e-mail

LEE, Mrs. Karen B.; '90 BA, '96 MA; Psychologist ABSS MR DD; Builders for The Family & Youth Inc., 29 Catherine St., Brooklyn, NY 11211, 718 388-5900; r. 183 Beach 96th St., Rockaway Bch., NY 11693, 718 945-3448; *Robert.*

LEE, Kenneth; '96 BA; 2063 E. 17th St., Brooklyn, NY 11229, 718 336-0060.

LEE, Kin; '84 BS; Police Detective; NYPD, 1 Hogan Pl. #929, New York, NY 10013, 212 335-8968; r. 108 Herman Blvd., Franklin Sq., NY 11010, 516 739-8514. e-mail

LEE, Lisa; '90 BS; JD Benjamin Cardozo Law Sch.; Atty.; NYC Dept. of Investigation, 51 Chambers St., Ste. 1113, New York, NY 10007, 212 788-8010; r. New York, NY 10002. e-mail

LEE, M. J.; '89 BA; 103-05 91st St., Ozone Park, NY 11417, 718 297-8075.

LEE, Ms. Michele; '98 BA; GRAD NYC Police Acad; Police Officer; Housing-PSA 3, 25 Central Ave., Brooklyn, NY 11206, 718 386-4101; r. 1702 W. 6th St., Apt. 2N, Brooklyn, NY 11223, 718 627-0266.

LEE, Monique L.; '88 BA; 1466 First Ave., New York, NY 10021, 315 841-8679.

LEE, Pamela; '83 BA; 771 St. Nicholas Ave., New York, NY 10031, 212 926-5998.

LEE, Philip W.; '79 BS; 3933 Peter St., Seaford, NY 11783, 516 409-1497.

LEE, Richard; '75 MPA; 403 Clermont Ave., Brooklyn, NY 11238, 718 857-1830.

LEE, Robert; '90 BS; 3441 Corlear Ave., Bronx, NY 10463.

LEE, Ruthsana M.; '91 BS; 100 Daly Blvd. Unit, Oceanside, NY 11572, 516 536-9447.

LEE, Shashana R.; '90 BA; 11955 177th St., Jamaica, NY 11434, 718 225-6528.

LEE, Shawn A.; BA; 329 Wyona St., Brooklyn, NY 11207, 718 234-1731.

LEE, Sherman; '97 BS; 288 E. 3rd St., Brooklyn, NY 11218, 718 234-1731.

LEE, Sun; '91 BS; 91-55 86st 1Fl, Woodhaven, NY 11421, 718 225-6528.

LEE, Theresa; '79 BS; 297a Cooper St., Brooklyn, NY 11237, 718 497-8575.

LEE, Tiffany M.; '99 BA; Deputy Sheriff; r. 6905 Carnation Rd., Apt. G, Richmond, VA 23325, 804 560-3034.

LEE, Vernon; '98 BS; 55 Alexander St., Babylon, NY 11702, 631 422-3547.

LEE, Wai L.; '96 BA; 64 Rutgers St. apt#15A, New York, NY 10002, 212 233-7082.

LEE, Yoon S.; '95 BS; 315 7th Ave. Apt. 8b, New York, NY 10001, 315 338-0117.

LEE-WYSS, Mrs. Helen; '92 BS, '94 MS; Forensic Scientist; The Ofc. of Chief Med. Examiner, 520 1st Ave., New York, NY 10016, 212 447-7511; r. 303 E. 93rd St., New York, NY 10128, 212 348-7662; Teddy Wyss, Tania. e-mail

LEFKOF, Alan; '06 BA; AS Nassau Comm. Clg.; Investigator; NYC Dept. of Investigation, New York, NY 10038.

LEFKOWITZ, Abraham Z.; '75 BA; 1289 E 91st St., Brooklyn, NY 11236, 718 437-7887.

LEFTOFF, Sondra; 36 Gramercy Park, New York, NY 10003.

LEFTT, Andrew D.; '98 BA; Full-time Law Student; r. 1320 York Ave. #23l, New York, NY 10021, 212 517-9083; Samantha.

LEGER, Reguerre; '96 BA; 2509 Avenue D, Brooklyn, NY 11226.

LEGGETT, Kenyon E.; '98 BS; Police Ofcr; NYPD, 1 Police Plz., New York, NY 10003, 212 374-5000; r. New York, NY 10037. e-mail

LEGGETT, Ms. Renee; '99 BA; Child Protection; Admin. of Children's Svcs., 165-15 Archer Ave., Jamaica, NY 11433, 718 481-5887; r. 113 42 211 St., Queens Vlg., NY 11429, 718 465-6793. e-mail

LEGIEC, Mark; '97 BS; 807 Riverbend Dr., Clark, NJ 07066.

LEHMAN, Joanne; '96 BS; 311 W. 24th St., New York, NY 10011, 315 337-0398.

LEIBMAN, Faith; '85 MA; JD Widener Univ.; Adjunct Prof/Atty.-Expert Testimony; On Forensic Issues/Natl. Forensic, Villanova Univ/American Academy of, Clinical Sexology & Advanced Inst; r. POB 233, 304 Melrose Rd, Merion Sta., PA 19066, 610 664-9440.

LEIBOWITZ, Gail D.; '79 BS; 2462 E 22nd St., Brooklyn, NY 11235, 718 769-6162.

LEIBOWITZ, Harold; '76 MA; 92 Skyline Dr., Coram, NY 11727.

LEIBOWITZ, Jill D.; '96 BA; Police Ofcr.; PSA2, 560 Sutter Ave., Brooklyn, NY 11208, 718 922-8001; r. 8143 156th Ave., Howard Bch., NY 11414; *G.*

LEIBOWITZ, Morton J.; '72 BS; MA Sam Houston Univ.; Retired Jail Admin.; r. 28 Woodlawn Ter., Fredericksburg, VA 22405, 540 373-5636. e-mail

LEICHT, Paul F.; '90 BS; 8225 264th St., Glen Oaks, NY 11004.

LEIFER, George; 360 1 Ave., New York, NY 10010.

LEIKER, David C.; '75 MA; POB 1087, Sparta, NC 28675.

LEITCH, Noel E.; '93 BS; 300 Linden Blvd. Apt. 6c, Brooklyn, NY 11226, 718 623-1313.

LEITERMAN, Jason E.; '95 BS; Police Ofcr.; NYPD, 1 Police Plz., New York, NY 10038; r. 39 Wedgewood Dr., Coram, NY 11727.

LEITGEB, Edward C.; '80 BS; 227 E 22nd St., Paterson, NJ 07514.

LEJBZON, Mimi; '79 BA; 124 W 79th St., New York, NY 10024.

LEJUEZ, Kim M.; '92 BA; 1270 Gerard Ave. # 6, Bronx, NY 10452.

LEKACH, Jakub; '75 BS; MD Downstate; Phys.; 536 Edrinker St., Dunmore, PA 18512, 570 343-6444; r. 1404 Fords Pond Rd, Clarks Summit, PA 18411, 570 587-1213; *Sharyn Comeau MD;* Maximillian. e-mail

LEKOS, Ronald N.; '78 BS; 8523 106th St., Jamaica, NY 11418.

LEMA, Kathy; '99 BA; 36 Ditmars St., Brooklyn, NY 11221, 718 574-3981; *Robert Adamos;* Tylor. o-mail

LEMBERSKY, Victoria D.; '99 BA; Student; r. 2142 E. 8th St. #4, Brooklyn, NY 11223, 718 645-1923. e-mail

LEMBO, Stephen J.; '76 MA; 46 Reney St., Toms River, NJ 08753.

LEMMONDS, Michelle '89 (See Perez, Michelle).

LEMO, Edina; '99 BS; AS Kingsborough Community Cl; Asst. to Sr. Dir; Property Mgmt., Rego Park, NY 11374.

LEMONS, Henry; '78 BS; 11630 228th St., Jamaica, NY 11411.

LEMPERT, Vladimir; '98 BS; Database Admin./Operations Analyst; Doefunt-Ready, Willing, & Able, 232 E 84th St., New York, NY 10028, 212 690-6480; r. 8814 Bay Pkwy., #5j, Brooklyn, NY 11214, 718 373-4356. e-mail

LENAHAN, William R.; '78 BS; Team Photographer; New York Jets; r. 820 Clauss Ln., River Vale, NJ 07675, 201 666-6481; *Jackie;* Taylor, Riley, Michael. e-mail

115

LENARD, Jill R.; '95 MA; BA SUNY-Albany; Parole Ofcr.; NYS Div. of Parole, Green Haven C.F. -- Route 216, Ext. 1114, Stormville, NY 12582, 914 221-2711.

LENNEK, Christopher; '92 BS; MASTERS Dowling Clg.; Elem. Tchr.; r. 11 Locust Ln., Miller Place, NY 11764, 631 473-5850. e-mail

LENNON, Gerard M.; '87 BS; 5861 41st Dr., Flushing, NY 11377, 718 712-5165.

LENNON, James; '84 MA; 151 Longview Dr., Princeton, NJ 08540, 609 924-1519.

LENNON, Madeline D.; '82 BS; 4382 E. 177th St., Bronx, NY 10465, 718 796-7625.

LENTO, Anthony; 12 Ross St., Port Jefferson Sta., NY 11776.

LENTZ, Jennifer P.; '97 MA; 175 Logan Ave., Staten Island, NY 10301.

LENZ, Tracy; '89 BS; 555 Kappock St., Bronx, NY 10463, 718 796-0775.

LENZE, William R.; '99 BS; Police Ofcr.; NYPD; r. 30 Chestnut St. 1A, Brooklyn, NY 11208, 718 827-4153. e-mail

LEON, Margarita; '92 BS; 635 Arnow Ave. Apt. 5e, Bronx, NY 10467, 718 402-8895.

LEONARD, Daniel F.; 341 Violet St., Massapequa Park, NY 11762.

LEONARD, Gerald M.; '64 MPA; Retired VP & Colonel; Mutual of America; r. 277 W 261st St., Bronx, NY 10471, 718 601-6043; *Eileen;* Mary P., Jerald X., Eileen, Patrick M.

LEONARD, John J.; '93 BS; 255 W 23rd St. Apt. 2GE, New York, NY 10011, 315 733-5213.

LEONARD, Michael M.; '81 BS; Bor Mgr. for Community Svcs.; NYC Probation Dept Criminal Justice Con; r. Brooklyn, NY 11208.

LEONARD, Sean R.; '89 BS; 61 Bergen Ave., Waldwick, NJ 07463, 201 445-0667.

LEONARDI, Angela; '91 MA; 173 Bay 13th St., Brooklyn, NY 11214, 718 236-7166.

LEONE, Christopher M.; '98 BA; 29 Oakland Pl., Nanuet, NY 10954, 914 623-3165.

LEONE, Michael J.; '94 BA; AAS Kingsborough Community; Police Ofcr.; MTA Police Dept., 347 Madison Ave., New York, NY 10017, 212 878-1000; r. 1825 Madison Pl., Brooklyn, NY 11229, 718 376-1872; *Rachel;* Michael. e-mail

LEONE, Michell; '97 BA; Retail Mgr.; Pathmark, Forest Ave., Staten Island, NY 10302, 718 981-1900; r. 693 Oceanside Ave., Staten Island, NY 10305, 718 667-0735. e-mail

LEONE, Steven C.; '88 BS; 9511 Sea View Ave., Brooklyn, NY 11236, 718 802-1370.

LEONG, Lai L.; '84 BS; 745 Stafford Ave., Staten Island, NY 10309, 718 720-4532.

LEOPOLD-HOOKE, Fred L.; '90 BS, '95 MPA; 3015 Riverdale Ave. Apt. 1g, Bronx, NY 10463.

LE PAGE, Robert J.; '82 AS; 7 Pershing St., Staten Island, NY 10305, 718 981-8172.

LEPORE, Silvano; '86 BA; 11 Dixon Lake Dr., Mahopac, NY 10541.

LERNER, Larisa; '97 BA; 62-25 84th St. #C, Middle Vlg., NY 11379, 718 544-4341.

LERNER, Steven A.; '88 BS; MS NY Inst. of Technology; 717 E 26th St., Brooklyn, NY 11210, 718 434-8545.

LESSEN, Nicholas J.; '96 BA; 90-33 56th Ave., Elmhurst, NY 11373.

LESSER, Debra E.; '84 MPA; POB 241, E. Norwich, NY 11732.

LESSER, Marc H.; '98 BA; Crew Leader/Supv.; US Dept. of Commerce Bur. of Defenses, 333 Avenue X, Brooklyn, NY 11224, 718 382-3910; r. 460 Neptune Ave. 9G, Brooklyn, NY 11224, 718 449-4389. e-mail

LESSNER, Lee; '87 BA; 13 Trafalgar Ct., Nanuet, NY 10954, 914 352-5659.

LESSNER, Mrs. Mary V., (Mary V. Reill); '77 BS; AS LaGuardia Community Clg.; Veterinary Tech; Hunter Clg. Animal Facility; r. 305 Hurley Ave.-Bldg. 9E, Kingston, NY 12401, 914 339-0005; *Albert.* e-mail

LETO, Teresa A.; '79 BS, '81 MA; Detective; NYC Police Dept., 718 287-3225; r. 444 Degraw St., Brooklyn, NY 11217, 718 802-0717. e-mail

LETT, John A.; '78 BA; MPA NYU; Retired Police Lt.; NYC Police Dept.; r. POB 383, 830-B Cauldwell Ave., Bronx, NY 10456, 718 993-3033; *Lorraine;* Deborah Ann, Cynthia, Stanley.

LETT, Lorraine; '78 BS, '80 MPA; AS; Retired Administrative Asst.; JFK Airport; r. 830B Cauldwell Ave., Bronx, NY 10456, 718 993-3033.

LETTIERI, Peggy C.; '77 BA; 619 Hudson St., New York, NY 10014.

LETTIS, Paul M.; '83 MA; Court Ofcr.; NYC; r. 22 Gladiolus Ave., Floral Park, NY 11001, 516 775-0974.

LEUNG, Chiu H.; '94 BS; 2232 62nd St., Brooklyn, NY 11204, 718 935-1158.

LEUNG, Emily; '98 BA; 71-15 172 St., Fresh Meadows, NY 11365, 718 321-7529.

LEUNG, Rose; '81 BS; POB 799, New York, NY 10002.

LEVANT, Cassandra D., (Cassandra Warren-Levant); '91 BS; MS; Administrative Profn.; Dept. of Justice; r. 2530 Atlantic Ave., Brooklyn, NY 11207, 718 345-5634; Dzhantam, James, Brandon, Cordiero. e-mail

LEVENTIS, Angela B.; '95 MA; 305 Madison Ave., # 1132, New York, NY 10017.

LEVENTON, Douglas C.; '94 BS; Sec. Mgr.; The American Museum of Natural History; r. 26 Hastings St., Brooklyn, NY 11235, 718 891-5140.

LEVERS, Leona; '85 BA; 130 Martense St., Brooklyn, NY 11226, 718 826-3556.

LEVI, Barbara; '75 MA; 39-60 54 St. #6N, Woodside, NY 11377, 718 229-5345.

LEVI, Dmitry; '99 BS; 324 Van Sicken St., Brooklyn, NY 11223, 718 372-3510.

LEVIEN, Michael C.; '99 MS; 2124 Broadway, New York, NY 10023.

LEVIN, David J.; '78 BS, '80 MA; Private Investigator; David Levin PI, POB 610430, Bayside, NY 11361, 718 428-8169. e-mail

LEVIN, Michael; '94 BS; MA City Clg. of NY; Chemist; FDA, 18515 Liberty Ave., St. Albans, NY 11412; r. 7216 Bay Pkwy., Brooklyn, NY 11204, 718 256-8662.

LEVINE, Cari; '99 MA; 301 W. 53rd St., New York, NY 10019, 212 765-8436.

LEVINE, David A.; '82 BS; 18 Howell St., Pine Bush, NY 12566.

LEVINE, Fran N.; '77 BA; Mgr. of Credit & Collections; MCI Worldcom, 201 Centennial Ave., Piscataway, NJ 08854, 732 885-4595; r. 1230 Avenue Y Apt. B24, Brooklyn, NY 11235, 718 332-6699. e-mail

LEVINE, Harriett J.; '82 BS; 311 W. 82nd St., New York, NY 10024.

LEVINE, Irwin S.; 9 Mariana Dr., Hastings-on-Hudson, NY 10706.

LEVINE, Kenneth H.; '80 MPA; 3040 Ave. W, Brooklyn, NY 11229, 718 768-7173.

LEVINE, Lenore H.; '90 BA, '96 MPA, '96 CERT; CUNY, 535 E. 80th St., New York, NY 10021, 212 794-5628; r. 525 E 82 St., New York, NY 10028, 718 474-5119; *Kenneth;* Mark.

LEVINE, Morris; '80 BS; 304 Fairbanks Ave., Staten Island, NY 10306, 718 979-1914.

LEVINE, Stuart J.; '99 BA; 117-14 Union Tpk. #Fc-3, Kew Gardens, NY 11415, 718 261-9071.

LEVINE, Susan; '82 BA; 146 Evergreen St., Staten Island, NY 10308, 718 442-7508.

LEVINSON, Peter A.; '85 BS; 1720 Maham Ave., Bronx, NY 10461.

LEVITZ, Jennifer, (Jennifer Walther); '96 MA; Dir.; Council on Accreditation for Child.& Fam; r. 654 Carroll St., Brooklyn, NY 11215, 718 965-0818; *Lonny.* e-mail

LEVY, Amir; '85 BA; 695 Doblin St., Elmont, NY 11003, 516 568-0255.

LEVY, Amy B.; '95 BA; 220 E 26th St. Apt. 2n, New York, NY 10010, 315 797-6326.

LEVY, Antoinette T.; '96 BS; 3150 Broadway Apt. 4i, New York, NY 10027, 212 665-2832.

LEVY, Baron O.; '86 BA; Pres.; Baron Transportation, 13031 225th St., Jamaica, NY 11413, 718 481-6605; r. 13031 224th St., Jamaica, NY 11413, 718 481-6605; *Dawn;* Phillip. e-mail

LEVY, Erez; '96 BS; 814 Avenue V, Brooklyn, NY 11223, 718 375-3702.

LEVY, Patrick; '91 BS; 1850 Lafayette Ave., Apt. 13H, Bronx, NY 10473, 718 716-6409.

LEVY, Shari; '96 BS; 5995 Shore Pkwy., Brooklyn, NY 11236, 718 437-6394.

LEVY, William; '95 AS; 9421 199th St., Jamaica, NY 11423.

LEW, Larry; '95 BA; 2244 Haviland Ave., Bronx, NY 10462, 718 325-5425.

LEW, Lisa A.; '87 BA; 8034 246th St., Jamaica, NY 11426, 718 347-4690.

LEW, Steven; '90 BS; 1029 E 80th St., Brooklyn, NY 11236; *Michele.* e-mail

LEWANDOWSKI, S. J.; '76 BS; 69-08 66 Pl., Glendale, NY 11385, 718 386-0442.

LEWIN, Georgia M.; '95 BS; 3261 71st St., Flushing, NY 11370, 718 898-1285.

LEWIN, Ms. Ouida O.; '97 BS; MS Fordham Univ.; Tchr.; PS 340, Bronx, NY 10468, 718 220-1830; r. 3903 Duryea Ave., Bronx, NY 10466, 718 405-5689. e-mail

LEWIS, Alison; '96 BS; 113 Chester St., Brooklyn, NY 11212, 718 346-0770.

LEWIS, Ms. Annamarie; '78 BA; MA St. John's Univ.; 594 Lasher Rd, Tivoli, NY 12583, 914 756-5323. e-mail

LEWIS, Anthony; '90 BS; 3 Elizabeth St., Valley Stream, NY 11580, 516 625-7352.

LEWIS, April A.; '83 BA; 469 Lakeview Dr., Coral Springs, FL 33071, 954 757-8623.

LEWIS, Arnold C.; '83 BA; 11822 230th St., Jamaica, NY 11411, 718 268-6691.

LEWIS, Bernice; '78 BS; Retired Couns.; r. 794 E 160th St., Bronx, NY 10456, 718 328-2913; Joseph.

LEWIS, Ms. Deidre Y.; '85 BA, '93 MPA; Hearing Ofcr.; Admin. for Children's Svcs., City of New York, New York, NY 10002, 212 274-6020; r. 25736 148th Ave., Rosedale, NY 11422; Deanna. e-mail

LEWIS, Derrick L.; '92 BA; 4 Park Ln., Apt. 3H, Mt. Vernon, NY 10552.

LEWIS, Diane; '81 BS; 1201 Fountain Ct., Memphis, TN 38106, 901 948-5456.

LEWIS, Dora M.; '82 BA; Legal Asst.; NYS Ins. Dept., 25 Beaver St., New York, NY 10004, 212 480-5253; r. 1271 Ocean Ave. Apt. 3H, Brooklyn, NY 11230, 718 434-7559.

LEWIS, Ellen R.; '84 MPA; 406 Lenox Ave. #3N, New York, NY 10037, 315 337-5999.

LEWIS, Everad H.; '97 BS; 348 E. 28th St., Brooklyn, NY 11226, 718 462-3598.

LEWIS, Frederick H.; '98 BS; Lt.; NYC Police Dept., 179 Wilson Ave., Brooklyn, NY 11237, 718 573-5049; r. 65 E. 19th St., Apt. 7F, Brooklyn, NY 11226, 718 282-7359; Claudette; Layne. e-mail

LEWIS, Geoffrey B.; '96 BS; Aircraft Maint.; JFK, Twr. Air JFK Airport, Jamaica, NY 11430, 718 553-4637; r. 208 E 51st St., Brooklyn, NY 11203, 718 467-1380; Velita; Jamaal, Kimiko. e-mail

LEWIS, Georgene L.; '92 BS; Driver; UPS, One Penn Plz., New York, NY 10111, 212 967-4210; r. 30-32 St. Nicholas Pl. Apt. 1C, New York, NY 10031, 212 862-0367; Peter Martinez; Jada.

LEWIS, Holly Y.; '98 BS; 430 44th St. Apt. 1, Brooklyn, NY 11220, 718 258-6821.

LEWIS, Ingrid P.; '84 BS; 285 Montgomery St., Brooklyn, NY 11225, 718 773-0769.

LEWIS, Kevin; '80 BS; 50-41 Newtown Rd, Flushing, NY 11377, 718 739-3631.

LEWIS, Marian R.; '83 BS; 165 E 179 St., Bronx, NY 10453, 718 220-8472.

LEWIS, Mazel B.; '96; 67-07 Kissena Blvd., Flushing, NY 11367, 718 526-6508.

LEWIS, Michael; '78 BA; 1058 Ralph Ave., Brooklyn, NY 11236, 718 272-8109.

LEWIS, Michael G.; '99 BA; AA NYC Technical Clg.; Photographer; TRUS Photography, 526 E. 54th St., Brooklyn, NY 11203; r. 507 E. 51 St., Brooklyn, NY 11203, 718 485-1077. e-mail

LEWIS, Raphine J.; '99 BS; 956 E 217 St., Bronx, NY 10469, 718 294-1049.

LEWIS, Roslyn R.; '80 BS, '86 MPA; Asst. Dir.; NYC Dept. Social Svc., 60 Hudson St., New York, NY 10013, 212 274-5652; r. 487 Christopher Ave., Brooklyn, NY 11212, 718 922-4516; Britney Wilson. e-mail

LEWIS, Sandra Y.; '92 BS; 2 Stoddard Pl. 6 G, Brooklyn, NY 11225, 718 453-4459.

LEWIS, Satia M.; '79 BA, '83 MPA; 8737 123rd St., Jamaica, NY 11418, 718 341-5406.

LEWIS, Sonya A.; '97 BA, '98 BA; 4120 H.river Pkwy. E #12f, Bronx, NY 10475, 718 654-9391.

LEWIS, Steven R.; '93 BS; 190 Edith Ave., Staten Island, NY 10312, 718 966-1175.

LEWIS, Tonya '93 (See Taylor, Tonya).

LEWIS, Yolanda Y.; '89 BS; 5430 Kings Hwy., Brooklyn, NY 11203.

LEWIS SARDIA, Sardia F.; '99 AS; 8 Seymour Ln., Medford, NY 11763, 212 281-5514.

LEWIS-SHORT, Verna; '94 MPA; 175 E. 112th St., New York, NY 10029, 315 762-4641.

LEZCANO, Eduardo D.; '96 AS; 76-09 34th Ave., Jackson Hts., NY 11372.

LI, Bonnie Y.; '99 BA; 84 Madison St., New York, NY 10002, 315 797-7267.

LI, James; '96 BS; 45 Pike St. 7A, New York, NY 10002, 212 964-3371.

LI, Kathy; '97 MA; Legal Secy.; Salomon Smith Barney, 388 Grennwich St., New York, NY 10013; r. 165 Park Row, Apt. 8B, New York, NY 10038, 212 619-2172.

LIAN, Leon E.; '97 AS; 7015 19th Ave. 2, Brooklyn, NY 11204, 718 633-8223.

LIATTO, Joann; '99 BA; AS Borough Manhattan CC, BA; Fraud Investigator; City of NY Officer Revenue & Invst., 330 Jay St., Brooklyn, NY 11214, 718 254-0437; r. 1219 Wheedler Ave. #6, Bronx, NY 10472, 718 378-6137.

LIBERATORE, Benedett; '91 MPA; BS Long Island Univ., AAS Kingsborough Community; Tax Compliance Agt.; NYS Tax Dept., 55 Hanson Pl., Brooklyn, NY 11217, 718 722-4588; r. 2556 E 23rd St., Brooklyn, NY 11235, 718 648-5455.

LICHTENSTEIN, Barry J.; '75 MPA; 121 Evans St., New Hyde Park, NY 11040.

LICITRA, Joseph; '81 BA; 2122 65th St., Brooklyn, NY 11204.

LICKLIDER, Patricia; 124 W 79th St., # 12B, New York, NY 10024.

LIDDIE, Michael A.; '91 BA, '93 MPA; 23118 118th Ave., Jamaica, NY 11411, 718 527-0115.

LIEB, Kristen M.; '97 BA; 331 E. Main St., Centerport, NY 11721, 631 423-0095.

LIEBERSTEIN, Steven I.; '98 BA; Mgr. of Special Events; Israel Humanitarian Fndn., 276 Fifth Ave., New York, NY 10001, 212 683-5676; r. 82-05 134th St. #6J, Jamaica, NY 11435, 718 793-2441; Fabiola. e-mail

LIEBERT, Bennis; 5022 Ruthenia Rd, Tallahassee, FL 32310.

LIEBOWITZ, David A.; '94 BS; File Clerk; US Dist. Ct., 500 Pearl St., New York, NY 10007, 212 805-0710; r. 111-40 76th Dr., Forest Hills, NY 11375, 718 459-0940. e-mail

LIEDE, James M.; '72 BS; 428 97th St., Brooklyn, NY 11209.

LIEFF, John C.; '81 MPA; 41-12 41 St., Long Island City, NY 11104.

LIENDO, Luis E.; '82 BS, '83 MPA, '93 MS; Master's Candidate Education; Pace Univ.; r. POB 984, New York, NY 10002, 212 227-0358. e-mail

LIENHART, Richard; '96 BS; 69 Beaumont Cir., Yonkers, NY 10710, 914 337-6654.

LIESKE, Donald G.; '84 BS; 69-29 66th St., Glendale, NY 11385.

LIFFEY, Joseph A., Jr.; '98 BS; CERT. NYPD Police Acad., CERT. FLETC Fed. L/E Trng. Ctr.; Deputy US Marshal/Crim Investigator; US Marshals Svc., US Courthouse, 500 Pearl St., Ste. 400, New York, NY 10007, 212 331-7200. e-mail

LIFRIERI, Michael D.; '96 BS; 17 Lighthouse Ct., Tomkins Cove, NY 10986, 914 786-3814.

LIFSHUTZ, George; '76 BA; 1233 E. 104 St., Brooklyn, NY 11236.

LIGGIANS, Rhonda L.; '95 MPA; BA Capital Univ., MPA; Financial Mgr.; Chief Cornerstone Productions Inc., 1117 Manor Ave., Bronx, NY 10472, 718 842-4089; r. same; Tyrone; Janelle, Lamar, Ashley, Shauntel, Shawn, Shannon. e-mail

LIGHTFOOT, Jerome; '71 BS; Deputy Chief Investigator; NYS Commission of investigation, 270 Broadway, New York, NY 10007, 212 577-0719; r. 504 Ronkonkoma Ave., W. Hempstead, NY 11552, 516 766-7930. e-mail

LIGHTY, Michael; '87 BA; 13515 226th St., Jamaica, NY 11413.

LIGUORI, Michael T.; '99 BA; Law Student; Quinnipiac Clg. of Law; r. 24 Orchard Ct., Brewster, NY 10509, 914 279-1469. e-mail

LILLEY, William P.; '96 MA; 117 Walbrooke Ave., Staten Island, NY 10301.

LIM, Elizabeth O.; '99 MA; 820 Richards Cres., Brooklyn, NY 11220, 718 923-1779.

LIMITONE, Anthony V.; '79 MA; 233 Lincoln Ave., Orange, NJ 07050, 973 672-6463.

LIN, Ching-Hua; '93 MA; 332 Konan St., Taipei, Taiwan.

LIN, David; '99 BA; Clerk; Arthur Andersen, New York, NY 10001, 917 699-5438; r. 70-09 Woodside Ave. #1, Woodside, NY 11377.

LIN, Nisha; '95 BS; 1204 78th St., N. Bergen, NJ 07047.

LIN, Showsan; '96 BS; 11 Valley View Rd, Great Neck, NY 11021, 516 773-7710.

LINARES, Antonio; '80 BS; 158 Adelphi St. #1, Brooklyn, NY 11205, 718 638-2446.

LINARES, Boris; '94 BA; 86-14 Ana Pl., Jamaica, NY 11432, 718 429-6858.

LINARES, Israel; '95 BA; Police Ofcr.; NYC Police Dept., Brooklyn, NY 11201; r. 8511 Commonwealth Blvd., Bellerose, NY 11426, 718 831-6187; Damaris; Rebecca, Israel Jr.

LINARES, Virginia; '88 BS; 3138 79th St., Flushing, NY 11370, 718 639-6598.

LINDEN, Jack; '72 MA; 11 Tuten Ct., Okatie, SC 29910, 843 705-5632.

LINDEN, Scott L.; '78 MA; 69-19B 210 St., Bayside, NY 11364, 718 321-9390.

LINDENMAYER, Rose M.; '95 BA; Rsch. Assoc.; r. 228 W 63rd St., Apt. 6 E, New York, NY 10023, 212 757-9267; *Carmen, Santos.* e-mail

LINDER, Myril I.; '75 BA; 319 E 24th St., Apt. 15B, New York, NY 10010.

LINDGREN, George A.; '89 BA; 875 Blvd. E Apt. 42, Weehawken, NJ 07087.

LINDNER, LT Peter M.; '90 BS; Lt.-New York Police Dept.; 1 Police Plz., New York, NY 10038; r. 131 Evelyn Ave., Westbury, NY 11590, 516 997-6706; *Debra.* e-mail

LINDO, Chelcea O.; '80 BS; 3424 102nd St., Flushing, NY 11368, 718 527-3617.

LINDO, Renee; '99 BA; 261 W 116 St. #5A, New York, NY 10026, 212 280-4213.

LINDSAY, Clive B.; '80 BA; 115 E 52 St., Brooklyn, NY 11203.

LINDSAY, Cordelia; '92 AS, '95 BA; Sr. Faculty Practice Asst. #6; NYU Med. Ctr.; Owner, Pat's Exotic Beverage Inc; r. 3419 Barker Ave., Bronx, NY 10467, 718 655-4106; *Howard (dec);* Howard, Tricia, Shedene. e-mail

LINDSAY, Garth; '95 BS; 1330 E 99th St., Brooklyn, NY 11236, 718 467-8115.

LINDSEY, Wayne; '79 BA; 33-19 109th St., Flushing, NY 11368.

LINDWORM, Joseph I.; 86-70 Francis Lewis Blvd., Hollis, NY 11427.

LINEHAN, Edward T.; '84 BA; 146-32 Booth Mem., Flushing, NY 11355.

LINETSKAYA, Yuliya; '99 BS; 2790 W. 5th St. 19F, Brooklyn, NY 11224, 718 996-3174.

LINKLETTER, David P.; '90 BS, '92 MA; POB 563, Smithtown, NY 11787.

LINN, Edith; '82 MA; Lt.; NYPD Ct. Section, 125-01 Queens Blvd., Queens, NY 11412, 718 268-4899; r. 188 Ocean Pkwy., Brooklyn, NY 11218, 718 438-8685; *Elliot;* Hillel, Shoshana.

LINSTROM, Gregory M.; '95 AS; 32 High St., Greenwich, CT 06830, 203 531-5676.

LIOU, Choa-po; '85 MA; 41-08 76 St., Elmhurst, NY 11373.

LIPARI, Anthony J.; '79 BA; Firefighter Lt; NYC Fire Dept., 212 570-4216; r. 31 Grist Mill Dr., Kings Park, NY 11754, 631 366-4351; *Patricia;* Caroline, Jennifer, Danielle, Patrick.

LIPARI, Donna M.; '87 BA; 25 Wadsworth St., Wallington, NJ 07057.

LIPP, James O.; '99 BA; 600 N Broadway A10, Amityville, NY 11701, 631 841-1955.

LIPPER, George D.; '75 BA; 387 Plymouth St., W. Hempstead, NY 11552, 516 481-2455.

LIPPI, Ms. Francine J.; '97 BA, '99 MA; 2908 Clark Ave., Oceanside, NY 11572, 516 764-2484. e-mail

LIPSCHITZ, Stephen; '76 BS; 108 Neptune Ave., Brooklyn, NY 11235, 718 633-6335.

LIPTAK, Thomas J.; '75 BA; 1228 Eastview Ave., Wantagh, NY 11793, 516 785-0647.

LIPUMA, John P.; '83 BA; 528 Stevens Ave., Ridgewood, NJ 07450, 201 652-8035.

LIQUORI, Maureen A.; '93 MPA; 84 Charles St., New York, NY 10014, 212 989-3159.

LIRANZO, Mrs. Yahaira M., (Vapaira M. Rosa); '99 BA; Labor Svc. Rep.; Dept. of Labor, Jamaica, NY 11431; r. 1334 Hancock St., Apt. 2A, Brooklyn, NY 11237; *Kelvin;* Kelvin Jr.

LISA, Thomas M.; '95 CERT; 646 9th Ave. Apt. 4rn, New York, NY 10036, 212 265-4899.

LISANTI, Mrs. Maria C., (Maria C. Fernandez); '99 BA; AAS Hostos Comnunity Clg., BA; Public Admin.; r. 1649 Yates Ave., Bronx, NY 10461, 718 409-3239; *Ralph.*

LISCINSKY, James K.; '95 BS; 49 Cutler St., Wharton, NJ 07885.

LISCOUSKI, Robert P.; '78 BS; American Embassy, APO, AE 09794.

LISOGORSKY, Michael N.; '75 MPA; 1148 E. 108th St., Brooklyn, NY 11236.

LISSNER, Michael A.; '95 MPA; BA SUNY Plattsburgh; Probation Ofcr.; Orange Cnty. Dept. of Probation, Cnty. Government Ctr., Goshen, NY 10924, 914 291-4777; r. 21 Delaware Dr., Sparrow Bush, NY 12780.

LITCHMORE, Monique E.; '96 BS; CERT. NY Paralegal Sch., AAS Borough of Manhattan CC; Paralegal, Law Firm; r. 1029 E 104th St., Brooklyn, NY 11236.

LITTLE, Brian R.; '90 BA; 960 Grand Concourse, Apt. 5A, Bronx, NY 10451, 718 588-2880.

LITTLE, Sheremah; '97 BS; 104-43 164th St., Jamaica, NY 11433, 718 337-9244.

LITTLEBERRY, Dorothy; '90 BA; 1022 Westminster Ave., Dix Hills, NY 11746.

LITTLEJOHN, Robert F.; '73 BS; 7 Vassar Pl., Scarsdale, NY 10583, 914 722-4776.

LITTLES, Willette C.; '85 BS; 395 Ocean Ave., Brooklyn, NY 11226, 718 627-8775.

LITTLE-TORRES, Elyse; '95 BS; 811 45th St., Brooklyn, NY 11220, 718 302-2496.

LITVIN, Lawrence H.; '87 BS; 5626 Royal Lake Cir., Boynton Bch., FL 33437, 561 496-7913.

LITWACK, Tom; Prof.; John Jay College of Justice; r. 57 W. 70th St., New York, NY 10023, 212 362-8741. e-mail

LIU, George; '79 BS; 3146 48th St., Long Island City, NY 11103, 718 793-5319.

LIVINGSTON, Gregory; '85 BA; 1505 Park Ave. # 110, New York, NY 10029, 212 426-1214.

LIVINGSTONE, John E.; '97 AS; 144-10 123rd Ave., Jamaica, NY 11436.

LIVINGSTONE, Lennox; '77 BA; 452 Empire Blvd., Brooklyn, NY 11225, 718 771-3397.

LIZARDI, Joseph; '91 BS; 2029 Muliner Ave., Bronx, NY 10462.

LIZZIO, Peter J.; '81 BS, '88 MPA; 23 Colony Ln., Syosset, NY 11791.

LLANO, Robert J.; '78 BS; 2919 201st St., Flushing, NY 11360.

LLOYD, Claudette '96 (See Nelson, Claudette A.).

LLOYD, Mauline M.; '97 BS; MPA Candidate; John Jay Clg. of Criminal Justice, New York, NY 10001, 718 528-1988; r. 141-18 247th St., Rosedale, NY 11422, 718 949-9499; *Ken;* Ainsworth, Andre, Audley (Dec), Patrice. e-mail

LLOYD, Tasha N.; '98 BA; Law Student; Quinnipiac Univ.-Sch. of Law; r. 457 Yale Ave., Rockville Centre, NY 11570.

LLOYD-BEY, Ridwana; '91 BA; Fashion Acct. Mgr.; Time Out New York, 627 Broadway, New York, NY 10012, 212 539-4428; r. 312 Carlton Ave., Brooklyn, NY 11205, 718 624-5839. e-mail

LLOYD-SEALEY, Michele; '90 BS; Police Ofcr.; NYC Police Dept., One Police Plz. Rm 204, New York, NY 10038, 212 374-5305; r. 50 Kernochan Ave., Hempstead, NY 11550; *Leon Sealey.*

LLYOD, Massa N.; '99; 118-46 191st, St. Albans, NY 11412, 718 528-6530.

LO, Chun-on; '95 BS; Computer Programmer; NYC Employee Retirement Syst, 335 Adams St., Brooklyn, NY 11201, 347 643-3064; r. 21-12 123rd St. Apt. 2F, College Pt., NY 11356, 718 539-0091; *Lydia Chiu;* Amethyst. e-mail

LO, Eliza '89 (See Ko, Mrs. Eliza).

LOBL, Alin; '99 BS, 2000 MPA; Fraud Investigator; Bur. of Fraud Investigations; r. 864 Woodward Ave., Ridgewood, NY 11385, 718 456-4456. e-mail

LOBODA, Henry J.; '79 BS; MS Fairleigh Dickinson; Ret. Lt.; NJ State Police Dept.; r. Williamsburg, VA 23188. e-mail

LO BRAICO, Mrs. Dawn M., (Dawn M. Squarcino); '84 BA; Asst. Trust Ofcr.; The First Natl. Bank of Long Island, 800 Woodbury Rd., Woodbury, NY 11797, 516 364-3436; r. 573 N Broome Ave., Lindenhurst, NY 11757; *Richard;* Kristen.

LOBRUTTO, Salvatore; '98 BS; 151 36 27 Ave., Flushing, NY 11354, 718 961-1480.

LOCADIA, Janet B.; '75 BA; 244 E 58th St., Brooklyn, NY 11203.

LOCANTRO, James C.; '84 BS; 10628 79th St., Jamaica, NY 11417.

LOCASCIO, Salvatore; '81 BS; Police Lt.; Passaic Police Dept., 330 Passaic St., Passaic, NJ 07055, 973 365-3900; r. 86 Howard Ave., Passaic, NJ 07055, 973 777-4648; *May;* Salvatore Jr., Darlene, James.

LOCHNER, Colin D.; '97 MA, '98 MA; MS Fordham Univ.; Dean of Students; Berkeley Clg., 3 E. 43rd St., New York, NY 10017, 212 986-4343; r. 31 E 12th St. Apt. 4-B, New York, NY 10034, 212 529-6157; *Rubi.* e-mail

LOCK, Clifford A.; '77 AS, '78 BS; DIPLOMA Cmd. & Gen. Staff Clg.; Owner/ Police Ofcr.; Ashley Investigative Svcs.; POB 4241, Atlanta, GA 30302, 404 996-6749; r. 2035 Allen Ct., Riverdale, GA 30296, 770 996-6749; *Madie.* e-mail

LOCK, Linda C.; '76 BS; 554th MP Company, APO, AE 09131, 716 434-4378.

LOCKE, Stephen R.; 19 E Evergreen Rd, New City, NY 10956.

LOCKER, Martin; '79 MA; 8806 Tammaron Dr., Plainsboro, NJ 08536.

LOCKETT, Athina L.; '97 BS; 565 Rutland Rd., Brooklyn, NY 11203, 718 642-1495.

LOCKHART, Colleen M.; '87 BS, '97 MS; Forensic Scientist III; Yonkers Police Dept., 104s Broadway, Yonkers, NY 10701, 914 377-7757; r. 279 N. Broadway, Yonkers, NY 10701; Lauren. e-mail

LOCKWOOD, May R.; '77 BA; 110 E 29th St., Brooklyn, NY 11226, 718 469-1115.

LODVIL, Murielle; '97 BS; 1121 Rogers Ave., Brooklyn, NY 11226, 718 282-2829.

LOECHER, Daryl C.; '99 MA; 445 E. 77th St. #6B, New York, NY 10021, 212 737-0632.

LOEFFLER, Raymond W.; '76 BA; 148-08 12th Ave., Whitestone, NY 11357.

LOERBS, Heather A.; '97 BS, '98 BS; 87 68 110 St., Jamaica, NY 11418, 718 846-6816.

LOESCH, Lawrence F.; '77 BA; 16043 88th St., Jamaica, NY 11414, 718 843-1743.

LOGAN, Benjamin; '79 MA; 7800 SR Fr Py #1-0, Rockaway Bch., NY 11693, 718 297-5639.

LOGAN, John J.; 163 Hillcrest St., Staten Island, NY 10308, 718 356-0306.

LOGAN, Mark R.; '84 MPA; 612 57th Ave. E, Bradenton, FL 34203, 941 758-3306.

LOGAN, Mary A.; '81 MA; 17 Rover Ln., Hicksville, NY 11801, 516 796-8846.

LOGAN, Tracy '96 (See Logan- Watson, Mrs. Tracy R.).

LOGAN- WATSON, Mrs. Tracy R., (Tracy Logan); '96 BS; Law Sch. Student; r. 1544 Union St., Brooklyn, NY 11213, 718 493-9491. e-mail

LOGIE, Mason; '84 MPA; 786 Stafford Ave., Staten Island, NY 10309.

LOGOZZO, Allison; '92 BS; 1798 E 53rd St., Brooklyn, NY 11234, 718 745-1553.

LOGRANDE, Antonino; '90 BS, '99 MA; BS, CERT. NYU; Special Agt.; Drug Enforcement Admin., 1000 N Water St. Ste. 1010, Milwaukee, WI 53202, 414 297-3395; r. 740 W Wisconsin Ave. Apt. #422, 6736 80th St. Ny, Ny, Milwaukee, WI 53233, 414 289-8759; *Debbie;* Brittany. e-mail

LOHNES, Robert C.; '78 MA; BA; Retired Detective NYPD; r. 1522 145th Pl., Whitestone, NY 11357, 718 767-6618; *Magaly Lopez-Lohnes;* Robert, Melissa. e-mail

LOILA, Dan; '95 MA; 31 Hickory Ln., Garnerville, NY 10923.

LOMASCOLO, Frank J.; '75 BS; 755 E 216th St., Bronx, NY 10467, 718 882-2997.

LOMBARD, Alexander; '91 BS; 2171 Madison Ave., New York, NY 10037.

LOMBARD, Gary J.; '95 BS; Investigator; City of NY, 1234 Fifth Ave., New York, NY 10029, 212 360-1411; r. 1634 Brooklyn Ave., Brooklyn, NY 11210, 718 434-6518. e-mail

LOMBARDO, Blase D.; '75 BS; 2073 Kimball St., Brooklyn, NY 11234, 718 875-6369.

LOMBARDO, Frank A.; '75 BS; MS Hunter Clg.; Cnslt.; Rems Tutorial Assocs., 32 Ash St., Floral Park, NY 11001, 516 352-2059. e-mail

LOMBARDO, Joseph A.; '77 BS; 4637 Furman Ave., Bronx, NY 10470, 718 325-6955.

LOMBARDO, Michael D.; '75 BS; 793 Cleveland St., Brooklyn, NY 11208, 718 875-6369.

LOMBARDO, Richard; '85 BS; 16 Southminster Dr., W. Harrison, NY 10604, 914 476-8550.

LONG, David S.; '88 BS; JD Fordham Law Sch.; Atty.; NYC Dept. of Probation, 115 Leonard St., Rm. 4D5, New York, NY 10013, 212 442-4553; r. 30 Portnellan Ave., New Rochelle, NY 10804, 914 632-6324; *Rachel;* Matthew.

LONG, Demosthenes; '83 BS, '86 MA; 339 A Grand Ave., Brooklyn, NY 11238, 718 782-6410.

LONG, Jacqueline; '96 BA; 80 Lenox Rd Apt. 3a, Brooklyn, NY 11226, 718 941-0980.

LONG, Jeffrey E.; '99 BA; MA City Clg. of New York; Tchr.; NYC Bd. of Educ.; r. 384 Grand Concourse, Bronx, NY 10451, 718 665-2936.

LONG, William F., III; '93 MPA; BS Univ. of West FL, AA FL Jr. Clg.; CEO; Campus Auxiliary Svcs., 75 S. Manheim Blvd., New Paltz, NY 12561, 914 257-3371; r. 185 Clinton St., Montgomery, NY 12549, 914 457-3399; *Susan;* Jennifer, Billy, Zachary. e-mail

LONGARO, Brian J.; '99 BS; 2857 Royle St., Bellmore, NY 11710, 516 785-4722.

LONGO, Dolores A.; '94 BA; 15251 S 50th St., Apt. 2020, Phoenix, AZ 85044.

LONGO, Paul J.; '96 BS; Court Ofcr.; NYS Courts; r. 74 Chestnut St., Rockville Centre, NY 11570, 516 536-3534.

LONGO, Rudolph A.; '97 BA; 285 Avenue C Apt. 8B, New York, NY 10009, 315 733-1422.

LONGO, Steven; '93 BS; 195 E Shore Dr., Massapequa, NY 11758.

LONGOBARDI, Alfred C.; '77 MA; Retired; Laguardia Univ.; r. 147 Huntley Dr., Ardsley, NY 10502, 914 693-6118.

LONGOBARDI, Ms. Josephine A.; '87 BA; Court Ofcr.; Unified Ct. Syst., 100 Centre St., New York, NY 10013, 212 374-5835; r. 226 Glonmoro Rd, Chector, NY 10918, 914 469-3564. e-mail

LONGSWORTH, Patrick; '93 BS; 34 Edgecombe Ave., New York, NY 10030, 212 292-9611.

LOO, George; '95 MPA; 85 4th Ave. Apt. 6ff, New York, NY 10003, 315 733-7605.

LOOBY, Lisa; '99; Fed. Ofcr.; Fed. Bur. of Prisons, New York, NY 10007; r. 335 Beach 54th St. Apt. 6c, Far Rockaway, NY 11692, 718 318-1527. e-mail

LOOX, Michael J.; '86 BS, '88 MA; West Coast Dir. Loss Prevention; Gucci, Beverly Hls., CA 90210, 310 550-5623; r. 747 Gayley Ave. Apt. 101, Los Angeles, CA 90024, 310 550-5623. e-mail

LOPEN, Nicole; '96 MA; 4420 Broadway, New York, NY 10040.

LOPES, James; '85 MPA; 248 Demorest Ave., Staten Island, NY 10314, 718 816-7379.

LOPEZ, Albertina F.; '93 BS; 518 Balmoral Dr., New Windsor, NY 12553, 914 562-6439.

LOPEZ, Anthony; '91 MA; BA Iona Clg., JD Queens Clg.-CUNY; Staff Atty.; Prisoners Legal Svcs. of New York, 301 S. Allen St., Albany, NY 12208, 518 438-8046; r. 50 E. 104th St., New York, NY 10029, 212 289-0112; *Justine.*

LOPEZ, Antonio E.; '89 BS; 129 Wadsworth Ave., New York, NY 10033, 315 733-3058.

LOPEZ, Carmen L.; '88 BS; 8830 146th St., Jamaica, NY 11435, 718 820-0062.

LOPEZ, Charles; '90 BA; 330 E 115th St. Apt. 4b, New York, NY 10029, 212 860-2248.

LOPEZ, Cuahutemoe; '93 BS; 835 Kent Ave. # 3flr, Brooklyn, NY 11205, 718 638-3018.

LOPEZ, Daisy; '80 BS; 40-34 68th St., Woodside, NY 11377, 718 533-0148.

LOPEZ, Daisy, (Daisy Torres); '98 BA; Account Asst.; Bank Julius Baer; r. 85-17 101st St., Richmond Hill, NY 11418; *Edward.*

LOPEZ, David R.; '83 AS, '84 BS; Sr. US Probation Ofcr.; US Probation Ofc., Southern District of New York, 500 Pearl St., New York, NY 10007, 212 805-5072. e-mail

LOPEZ, Della L.; '92 BS; 425 E. 63rd St., Apt. E4D, New York, NY 10021, 212 388-7486.

LOPEZ, Diana; '95 BA; Clerk; NYPD, 230 W 20th St., New York, NY 10011, 212 741-8211; r. 170 Avenue C Apt. 13a, New York, NY 10009.

LOPEZ, Edgar; '99 BS; 40 Richman Plz. #7K, Bronx, NY 10453, 718 401-2352.

LOPEZ, Eric; '79 BS; 663 41 St., Brooklyn, NY 11232, 718 241-0746.

LOPEZ, Erik C.; '94 BA; 64-66 Essex St. #11, New York, NY 10002, 315 733-3058.

LOPEZ, Eugenia; '83 BA; 8726 143rd St. # 2, Jamaica, NY 11435, 718 275-0191.

LOPEZ, Frank; '95 BS; 7523 Weather Worn Way, Unit A, Columbia, MD 21046.

LOPEZ, Gabriel R.; '72 BS; Police Lt.; The Police Acad., 20 E 23rd. St., New York, NY 10010; r. 5 Tree Ct., E. Setauket, NY 11733, 631 751-0695; *Nicolette;* Gabrielle, Lee, Dylan.

LOPEZ, Israel; '90 BS; Field Trainer; Nielsen Media Rsch.; r. 2198 Cruger Ave. Apt. 5e, Bronx, NY 10462, 718 828-7786; Jasmine. e-mail

LOPEZ, Jackeline Y.; '95 BS; 2491 Arthur Ave., Bronx, NY 10458, 718 716-8553.

LOPEZ, Jamal D.; '96 BS; 28 Waterford Cir., Washingtonville, NY 10992, 914 856-8319.

LOPEZ, Jose I.; '76 BS; 85 W 181 St., Bronx, NY 10453, 718 716-8553.

LOPEZ, Jose L., Sr.; '82 BS; FBI Natl. Acad.; Lt. Cdr. Hartford Police Acad.; Hartford Police Dept., Hartford, CT 06120, 860 527-6300; r. 24 Cornell Dr., Enfield, CT 06082, 860 763-5100; *Rebecca;* Lalenya, Jose Jr.

LOPEZ, Judith; '94 BA; 549 51st St. Apt. 2f, Brooklyn, NY 11220, 718 342-1251.

LOPEZ, Kevin; '97 BS, '98 BS; 400 E.105th St., New York, NY 10014, 315 733-3058.

LOPEZ, Linda I.; '95 BS; 1057 Boynton Ave. 3G, Bronx, NY 10472.

LOPEZ, Lisa J.; '91 BS; Histotechnologist; St. Charles Hosp., 200 Bell Terre Rd, Port Jefferson, NY 11777, 631 476-5515; r. 3773 White Birch Ct., Wantagh, NY 11793, 516 796-2384. e-mail

LOPEZ, Lisa L.; '92 BS; 82 Sheridan Ave., Brooklyn, NY 11208, 718 921-5947.

LOPEZ, Lorraine; '81 BA; Nurse; North Central Bronx Hosp.; r. 2185 Reeds Mill Ln., Bronx, NY 10475, 718 515-0904.

LOPEZ, Lucy; '84 BA; 433 Van Duzer St., Staten Island, NY 10304, 718 317-9489.

LOPEZ, Lucy C.; '80 AS, '82 BS; 46 Madison St. #12C, New York, NY 10038, 212 962-7875.

LOPEZ, Luis A.; '79 BS; Pres.; Alante Security Grp. Inc., 10 Hyacinth Rd., Levittown, NY 11756, 516 579-9532; r. 10 Hyacinth Rd, Levittown, NY 11756, 516 579-9532. e-mail

LOPEZ, Luis M.; '91 BS; 1709 Centre St. #2, Ridgewood, NY 11385, 718 760-5720.

LOPEZ, Malgorzata K.; '97 BS; 218 E 11 St. #2, New York, NY 10003, 315 733-3058.

LOPEZ, Manuel W.; '77 BS; 714 59th St., Brooklyn, NY 11220, 718 384-1047.

LOPEZ, Marisel; '99 BA; 1001 Jerome Ave., Apt. 6L, Bronx, NY 10452, 718 538-8567.

LOPEZ, Marla; '99 BS; Asst. Dir.; Community Law Advocates, 1150 Grand Concourse, Bronx, NY 10456, 718 538-8106; r. 3075 Heath Ave. 3D, Bronx, NY 10463, 718 549-5918.

LOPEZ, Mayra; '89 BA; 1710 E. 8 St., Brooklyn, NY 11223, 718 384-1047.

LOPEZ, Melind A.; '97 BS; 1061 Myrtle Ave., Brooklyn, NY 11206, 718 384-1047.

LOPEZ, Michael A.; '98 BS; Police Officer; NYC Police Dept.; r. 1878 Harrison Ave. #4e, Bronx, NY 10453, 718 299-4166.

LOPEZ, Michelle B.; '86 BA, '95 BS; 2198 Creger Ave. 2, Bronx, NY 10462.

LOPEZ, Miguel; '91 BS; Police Ofcr.; NYCPD; r. Middletown, NY 10940. e-mail

LOPEZ, Monserrate; '97 BS; 3345 Reservoir Ova, Bronx, NY 10467, 718 519-0084.

LOPEZ, Raymond J.; '75 BA; 353 58th St. Apt. 2r, Brooklyn, NY 11220, 718 439-3156.

LOPEZ, Sabrina I.; '95 MA; Asst. Prog. Dir.; The Educational Alliance, Pride Site II, 25 Avenue D, New York, NY 10009, 212 780-5475; r. 790 Eldert Ln. # 1U, Brooklyn, NY 11208, 718 235-1319.

LOPEZ, Sandra; '96 BA; 3203 Park Ave. Apt.2A, Bronx, NY 10451, 718 653-2886.

LOPEZ, Sharon; '95 BA; 78-06 Pitkin Ave. #, Ozone Park, NY 11417, 718 478-4110.

LOPEZ, Stanley; '91 BS; 330 47th St. # 2, Brooklyn, NY 11220, 718 230-0562.

LOPEZ, Terron; '96 AS; Urb.vistas De Camu, Camuy, PR 00627.

LOPEZ, Victoria; '97 BS; 1541 Commonwealth, Bronx, NY 10460, 718 824-4610.

LOPEZ, Wanda L.; '90 BA; BSMA; Tchr.; 309-47th St., Brooklyn, NY 11220, 718 330-9270; r. 4413 7th Ave., Brooklyn, NY 11220, 718 871-0148.

LOPEZ-CORIANO, C. L.; '84 BS; 420 E 105th St. #5B, New York, NY 10029.

LOPEZ-RIVERA, Pedro; '79 BS; 110 Park Hill Ave., Yonkers, NY 10701, 914 667-0524.

LOPEZ-SIRVENT, Fernando; '81 BA; Sgt Security Svcs.; United Nations; r. 236 Kearney Ave., Bronx, NY 10465. e-mail

LORA, Krupskaia (Sky); '98 BA; Clg. Asst. Events Coord.; John Jay Clg. Alumni Affairs, 899 10th Ave. Rm. 532T, 59th St., New York, NY 10019, 212 237-8547; *Joseph Curich.* e-mail

LORANGER, Michelle; '95 MA; 937 N Erie Ave., Lindenhurst, NY 11757.

LORDE, Shannon G.; '97 BA; Caseworker; Dept. of Social Svcs., 180 Water St., New York, NY 10038; r. 740 E. 103rd St. Apt. D, Brooklyn, NY 11236, 718 257-3923.

LORE, Charles J.; '98 MA; 6615 Saunders St., Rego Park, NY 11374, 718 275-7830.

LORE, Frank A.; '96 BS; Police Ofcr.; MTA Police Dept., 345 Madison Ave., New York, NY 10017, 212 878-1000; r. 120 Arthur Ave., Thornwood, NY 10594, 914 769-3606.

LORE, Joseph M.; '77 MPA; 6435 78th St., Flushing, NY 11379, 718 461-5299.

LORENC, Iwona; '98 MA; 30-95 29th St.#5B, Astoria, NY 11102, 718 274-3661.

LORESTO, Emil J.; '89 BS; 245 Kiswick St., Staten Island, NY 10306.

LORIMER, Philip, CPM; '88 MS; BA William Paterson Univ., CPM Rutgers Grad. Sch. Public; Technical Dir.; New Jersey State Police 120, E. Rutherford, NJ 07073, 201 460-4126; r. 60 Hooyman Dr., Clifton, NJ 07013, 973 778-6383; *Ellen.*

LOS, Sandra A.; '95 MA; Psychology Assoc.; State of Ohio Dept. of Rehab. & Correcti, 2500 S. Avon-Belden Rd., Grafton, OH 44044, 440 748-1161; r. 4172 Dennis Ln., Brunswick, OH 44212. e-mail

LOSAK, Raymond J.; '79 BS; 24-09 93 St., Jackson Hts., NY 11369.

LOSCHIAUO, T.; 153 Waters Ave., Staten Island, NY 10314.

LOSI, Stephen H.; '79 BS; 16329 23rd Ave., Whitestone, NY 11357.

LOTIERZO, James D.; '81 BS; 98 Conselyea St., Brooklyn, NY 11211.

LOUALLEN, Fatima G.; '96 BA; 3211 Avenue I, Apt. 3H, Brooklyn, NY 11210.

LOUALLEN, Keith; '98 BA; Grad. Student; Hofstra Univ.; r. 158-06 76th Ave. Apt. 1C, Flushing, NY 11366, 718 591-3184. e-mail

LOUDEN, Dr. Robert J.; '77 MA; PHD CUNY Grad. Sch., BBA Baruch Clg.; Dir.; Criminal Justice Ctr., John Jay Clg., 899 Tenth Ave., Ste. 636, New York, NY 10019, 212 237-8639; r. 120 Journaug Brook Rd, Lincroft, NJ 07738, 732 747-2640; *Verna Cassetti-Louden;* Coleen M., Robert G. e-mail

LOUGHERY, Michael J.; '73 AS, '77 BS; Asst. VP; Allied Spectaguard, 9 E. 38th St., New York, NY 10016, 212 481-5777; r. 691 Bard Ave., Staten Island, NY 10310, 718 448-2819; *Mary.* e-mail

LOUGHLIN, Bernard E.; '78 BS; 120 42nd St., Lindenhurst, NY 11757, 631 226-0488.

LOUGHLIN, Michael; '72 BA; Real Estate Broker; Jack Conway Real Estate Co., 1815 Centre St., W. Roxbury, MA 02132, 617 469-9200; r. 23 Spellman Rd, Westwood, MA 02090, 781 326-1740; *Elizabeth C.;* Michael T., Mary E., Gerald P., Rita M., Robert F.

LOUGHLIN, Terence A.; '89 BS; 375 Bryn Mawr Rd, New Hyde Park, NY 11040, 516 747-7121.

LOUGHMAN, Robert P.; '72 BS, '80 MA; Tchr.; Albertus Magnus HS; r. 121 Call Hollow Rd, Pomona, NY 10970, 914 354-2473; *Ann;* Brendan, Emonn, Patricia.

LOUGHREY, Leo C.; '64 MPA; 79-08 211 St., Flushing, NY 11364.

LOUIS, Barbara; '97 BA; 253 E. 28th St., Brooklyn, NY 11226, 718 388-2816.

LOUIS, Edward; 31 Heminway Ave., New Rochelle, NY 10801, 914 632-1082.

LOUIS, Jean R.; '91 BS, '96 MPA; 958 E 104th St., Brooklyn, NY 11236, 718 469-0614.

LOUIS, Jeeny M., (Jeeny Macdalie); '98 BS; Law Enforcement; r. 218-27 104th Ave., Queens Vlg., NY 11429, 718 468-4296.

LOUISON, Kirk; '95 BA; 211 Prospect Pl., Brooklyn, NY 11238.

LOUISOR, Mike P.; '96 BA; Human Res. Rep.; Fed. Ex Ground, 55-90 47th St., Maspeth, NY 11378, 718 381-6789; r. 1171 E. 105th St., Brooklyn, NY 11236, 718 444-3710.

LOUISSAINT, Halaby; '95 AS; 4004 Avenue J Fl. 1st, Brooklyn, NY 11210, 718 693-3971.

LOUISSAINT, Harmelle M.; '98 BA; 130-27 125 St., S. Ozone Park, NY 11420.

LOUISSAINT, Medeline; '97 BA; 1048 E. 84th St., Brooklyn, NY 11236, 718 951-3369.

LOUISSAINT, Ravhelle; '95 BS; 1800 Albemarle Rd., Brooklyn, NY 11226, 718 951-3369.

LOUREIRO, John M.; '98 BS; Admin.; Iberia Restaurant, 6369 Ferry St., Newark, NJ 07105, 973 344-5611; r. 81 Congress St., Newark, NJ 07105, 973 344-0526. e-mail

LOUTTIT, Robert J.; '79 BS; JD Fordham Univ.; VP of Operations; 5th Ave Assn. Business Improvement Dist, 1230 Ave. of The Americas, Ste. C12, New York, NY 10020, 212 265-1310; r. 77 Westgate Rd., Massapequa Park, NY 11762, 516 795-3928; *Bridget M.;* Michelle D., Robert P. e-mail

LOUVADO, Ivo M.; '98 BS; Police Ofcr.; Baltimore City, 1900 Argonne Dr., Baltimore, MD 21218, 410 396-2444; r. 40 Windy Falls Way, Cockeysville, MD 21030, 410 683-4689; *Joanne.*

LOVE, Archie C.; '75 BA; 321 Detroit Ave., Staten Island, NY 10312, 718 984-3491.

LOVE, Jason C.; '93 BS; Detective Law Enforcement; Bergen Cnty. Prosecutor's Ofc., Justice Ctr., Hackensack, NJ 07601, 201 646-2300; r. 240 Prospect Ave. Apt. 487, Hackensack, NJ 07601, 201 488-9427. e-mail

LOVE, William A.; '84 BS; 2911 Laurel Ave., Baldwin, NY 11510, 516 623-6731.

LOVE-FOX, Chris; '84 BA; Regional Dir.; NYC Dept. of Juvenile Justice, 365 Broadway, New York, NY 10013, 212 925-7779; r. 964 E 58th St., Brooklyn, NY 11234, 718 209-0378; *Maurice Fox;* Latosha, Roxanne, Sharon, Tatia, Eddie.

LOVELL, Brian I.; '89 BS; 182 Stoneheights Dr., Waterford, CT 06385, 860 437-1922. e-mail

LOVELL, David E.; '95 BS, '97 MPA; Educational Prog. Asst.; NYS Educ. Dept., Madison Ave., Albany, NY 12230, 518 486-2092; r. 212 Executive Dr., Guilderland, NY 12084, 518 452-1512; *Cynthia;* Kerwin, Kerlan. e-mail

LOVELL, Frederick J.; '98 BA; Supv., Smith Barney; Student,John Jay Clg Of Criminal Justice, New York, NY 10001; r. 1680 Bedford Ave. 19 A, Brooklyn, NY 11225, 718 747-4005; *Marilyn;* Adrian, Jiselle. e-mail

LOVETT, Joseph; '77 MPA; 4329 160th St., Apt. 1, Flushing, NY 11358, 718 229-8906.

LOW, Elvis T.; '89 BA; 6520 12th Ave., Brooklyn, NY 11219, 718 629-3691.

LOW, Timothy J.; '81 BS; 312 Portsmouth Rd, Cape May, NJ 08204, 609 898-0958.

LOWE, Eulisha T.; '98 BS; Police Ofcr.; The Port Authority, 1 World Trade Ctr., New York, NY 10048; r. 97-20 57th Ave. 8 C, Flushing, NY 11368, 718 592-5821.

LOWE, Jacqueline P.; '97 BA; Case Mgr.; S.V.S The Brooklyn Clubhouse, 921 E. New York Ave., Brooklyn, NY 11203, 718 467-6876; r. 1802a Sterling Pl., Brooklyn, NY 11233, 718 855-4915. e-mail

LOWE, John P.; '76 MA; 197 Sackville Rd, Garden City, NY 11530, 516 294-9539; *Julia B.;* William J., Johh P. Jr, Thomas F., Genevieve M., Robert J., James E., Edward V.

LOWE, Rudolph E.; '77 BA; 1035 Manor Ave., Bronx, NY 10472, 718 893-4290.

LOWE, Victoria L.; '97 MA; Social Worker; Gilford Cnty. Dept. of Social Svcs., 315 W. Lyndsey, Greensboro, NC 27402, 336 412-3967; r. 6400 Old Aokk Ridge Rd Apt. H2, Greensboro, NC 27410, 336 662-8173. e-mail

LOWENSTEIN, Bruce H.; '83 MA; 2 Hoover Ln., New City, NY 10956.

LOWERY, John P.; '95 BS; 56 Brook Ave. Ph, Staten Island, NY 10306, 718 987-7225.

LOWERY, John W.; '95 BS; 86-22 Jamaica Ave., Woodhaven, NY 11421, 718 296-5313.

LOWERY, Lee R.; '85 BS; 8084 N. Davis Hwy., Pensacola, FL 32514, 850 968-3760.

LOWNEY, Michael P.; '95 MPA; 25 Knolls Cres. Apt. 7h, Bronx, NY 10463, 718 884-1660.

LOWY, Kenneth M.; '95 MS, '96 MA; Police Ofcr.; NYPD, 1 Police Plz., New York, NY 10038; r. 75 Chardonnay Dr., Coram, NY 11727, 631 696-1839; *Catherine;* Samantha. e-mail

LOZANO, Elsa M.; '98 BA; Caseworker; Westhab Inc., 156 S. First St., Mt. Vernon, NY 10550, 914 667-0638; r. 3150 Bailey Ave., Apt. 5l, Bronx, NY 10463, 718 884-5047; Matthew, Gabriel. e-mail

LUBIN, Suze; '98 BS; 421 35th St., Lindenhurst, NY 11757, 631 226-1271.

LUBIN, Theodule B.; '96 BS; MSW SUNY-Stony Brook; Psychiatric Social Worker; New York Psychiatric Inst., 1025 Riverside Dr., New York, NY 10032, 212 543-6713; r. 3 Waterford Dr., Wheatley Hts., NY 11798, 631 491-1560. e-mail

LUBOMSKI, CAPT Joseph E.; '73 BA; Commanding Ofcr., Transit Dist. 23; NYC Police Dept., 718 474-3319; r. 5319 212th St., Bayside, NY 11364, 718 428-1348. e-mail

LUCARELLI, Modestino; '76 BA; MS CUNY; Tchr.; NYC Bd. of Educ.; r. 247 Park St., Staten Island, NY 10306, 718 351-5605; *Rose;* Maria, Thomas, Lori.

LUCAS, Carl; '82 BS; JD NY Law Sch.; Counsel; Public Admin. Bronx Cnty., 718 293-7663; r. 6 Tanner Dr., Princeton, NJ 08540, 732 274-2948; *Melissa;* Corey, Imani. e-mail

LUCAS, Ms. Patricia A.; '99 BS LS; AS NYC Tech; Police Ofcr.; NYPD, One Police Plz., New York, NY 10038; r. 471 39th St., Brooklyn, NY 11232, 718 854-4840; Stephanie.

LUCES, Antoinette; '92 BA; Social Worker; Admin. for Children Svcs., 718 488-5428; r. 25 Lafayette Ave., Brooklyn, NY 11217.

LUCHER, Lasean; '93 BS; 2101 Cedar Ave., Bronx, NY 10468, 718 584-0553.

LUCIA, Kimberly A.; '97 MA; 92 Greenwich Ave. # 2, New York, NY 10011, 315 724-2061.

LUCIANO, Ana V.; '93 AS; 1841 University Ave., Bronx, NY 10453, 718 295-4428.

LUCIEN, Steeves, '99 BA; Microsoft Certified Profn.; 50 Kenilworth Pl. #3K, Brooklyn, NY 11210, 718 421-3617; r. same; *Carlien.*

LUCK, Teresa; '97 BA, '99 BA; 264 Malcolm X Blvd., Brooklyn, NY 11233, 718 387-4114.

LUCKEY, Joyce C.; '99 BS; Community Svc. Aide; Bronx Dist. Attorney's Ofc., 215 E. 161 St., Bronx, NY 10451, 718 537-7245; r. 778 Brook ave. #A, Bronx, NY 10451, 718 292-8293. e-mail

LUDWIG, William J.; '79 BS; 154-08 58th Rd, Flushing, NY 11355, 718 274-9416.

LUENGAS, Jose A.; '95 BA, '95 MPA; 1227 White Plains, Bronx, NY 10472, 718 681-2115.

LUFTMAN, Lance J.; '86 MPA; BS Univ. of Iowa; Detective; Riley Cnty. Police Dept., Manhattan, KS 66502, 785 537-2108; r. 3434 Stonehedge Dr., Manhattan, KS 66503. e-mail

LUGO, Elizabeth; '97 BS; Police Ofcr.; New York Police Dept, 2120 Amsterdam Ave., New York, NY 10033, 212 927-3200; r. 151 Nagle Ave., New York, NY 10040, 212 304-4032; Gabriel.

LUGO, Jose A.; '88 BS; 29 Moore St. Apt. 12t, Brooklyn, NY 11206, 718 246-9190.

LUGO, Nelson J.; '79 MA; 51 Hilton Ave., New Hyde Park, NY 11040.

LUGO, Olga I.; '92 BS; 21 E. 107th St. #, New York, NY 10029.

LUGO, Mrs. Sylvia, (Sylvia Gonzalez); '84 BA; Deputy Clerk; US Dist. Ct., 500 Pearl St., New York, NY 10007, 212 805-0624; r. 254 E 206 St. Apt. 2R, Bronx, NY 10467, 718 231-9502; *William;* Ernest, Michael, Erika.

LUGO, William; '90 AS; 1855 Bogart Ave. # A, Bronx, NY 10462, 718 365-0466.

LUI, Alan S.; '84 BS; Asst. Commissioner; NYC Sheriff's Ofc., 31 Chambers St., New York, NY 10007, 212 240-6702; r. Brooklyn, NY 11235.

LUI, Elena; '97 BS; 57-22 Van Doren St., Corona, NY 11368, 718 267-7144.

LUIS, Hector; '76 MPA; 9 Chiswell Dr., Melville, NY 11747.

LUIS, Marvin; '93 BS; 10527 Avenue M, Brooklyn, NY 11236, 718 256-0957.

LUKE, Mrs. Cherylann, (Cheryann Davis); '92 BA, '97 MA; Mktg., Title Closing; JC Land Abstract, 63 W. Main St., Babylon, NY 11702, 631 669-3241; r. 131 S Broadway, Lindenhurst, NY 11757, 631 226-7223; *Brian.* e-mail

LUKOWSKI, Fred J.; '94 MA; BS Trenton State Clg.; Police Lt.; NJ Inst. of Technology Police Dept., 154 Summit St., Newark, NJ 07102, 973 546-3120; r. 320 Winona Lks, E. Stroudsburg, PA 18301; *Joanie.* e-mail

LUKULA, Audrey; '91 BA, '95 MPA; 143 North St., Auburn, NY 13021.

LUM, Geraldine W.; 28 E. Walnut St., Long Beach, NY 11561, 516 248-3057.

LUMA, Yoleine; '97 BS; CERT. Long Island Univ.; Paralegal; Greater New York Ins. Co.; r. 415 Argyle Rd. 7F, Brooklyn, NY 11218, 718 287-6533; *Rony;* Nile, Neila. e-mail

LUNA, Erika; '96 BS; 264 E Broadway Apt. C1007, New York, NY 10002.

LUNA, Nallibe; '99 MA; 34-16 88th St., Jackson Hts., NY 11372, 718 699-9807.

LUNA, Sandra; '89 BS; 4015 95th St., Flushing, NY 11373, 718 565-1615.

LUNCHEON, Pedro O.; '90 BA; POB 1090, New York, NY 10035.

LUNDQUIST, James M.; '90 AS; 189 Thomas Dr., Paramus, NJ 07652.

LUNDQUIST, Tracey L.; '99 BA; Fragrance Evaluation; Intl. Aromatics, 200 Anderson Ave., Moonachie, NJ 07074, 201 964-0900; r. 3715 Liberty Ave., N. Bergen, NJ 07047, 201 863-8794. e-mail

LUNDY, Romero; '99 BS; Mgr.; NYS Unified Court Syst., 216 E 161st St., Bronx, NY 10451, 718 590-4122; r. 245 W. 109th St. Apt. 8, New York, NY 10025, 212 663-1805; Romero, Jasmine, Shaila. e-mail

LUNN, Joyanne E.; '89 BS; 647 Glafil St., Elmont, NY 11003.

LUNN, Kitty; '95 BS; Artistic Dir. & Founder; Infinity Dance Theater, 220 W 93rd St. #6C, New York, NY 10025, 212 877-3490; r. 220 W 93rd St. Apt. 6c, New York, NY 10025, 212 877-3490; *Andrew Macmillan.* e-mail

LUONGO, Gregg A.; '99 MA; 4 Kingston St., Reading, MA 01867, 781 942-7882.

LUONGO, John D.; '72 BS; 65 Roma Ave., Staten Island, NY 10306, 718 987-7005.

LUPI, Melissa A.; '99 MA; 11 Halko Dr., Cedar Knolls, NJ 07927, 973 538-4642.

LUQUIS, Annette; '91 BS; 448 47th St., Brooklyn, NY 11220, 718 492-3603.

LURRY, Mary L.; '85 BS; 12 Queens St., Egg Harbor Twp., NJ 08234.

LUSTBERG, Robert M.; '75 BA; 127-17-102nd Ave., Richmond Hill, NY 11419, 718 523-4353.

LUSTGARTEN, Adam; '87 BS; 88 Country Dr., Plainview, NY 11803, 516 433-1429.

LUSTIG, Marsha L.; '79 MA; 41 Suffolk Way, Marlboro, NJ 07746, 732 536-9683.

LUTCHMANSINGH, David A.; '99; 3025A Mickle Ave., Bronx, NY 10463.

LUTHER, John J.; '97; 260 Beauregard Pl., Apt. A, West Point, NY 10996, 914 446-1278.

LUTKENHOUSE, Nancy E.; '75 BS; 64 Bishop St., Staten Island, NY 10306, 718 727-4325.

LUTZKER, Erik L.; '95 MPA; Sr. Safety & Health Inspector; NYS Dept. of Labor, 345 Hudson St., 7th Fl., New York, NY 10014; r. 4901 Henry Hudson Pkwy. W, Bronx, NY 10471, 718 548-0151; *Clara.*

LUTZKER, Marilyn; 3977 48th St., Long Island City, NY 11104.

LUYANDO, Elizabeth; '91 BS; 854 Leland Ave. B52, Bronx, NY 10473.

LUYANDO, Luz I.; '97 BA; Patient Svcs. Supv.; North Gen. Hosp., 1879 Madison Ave., New York, NY 10035, 212 243-4660; r. 50 Park Ter. W, Apt. 1B, New York, NY 10034.

LUYANDO, Rafael A.; '95 BS; Law Enforcement; NYPD, 306 W. 54th St., New York, NY 10019, 212 767-8415; r. Pelham, NY 10803.

LUYANDO, Ray F.; '95 AS; POB 395, Bronx, NY 10465, 914 738-3060.

LYNAM, David S.; '86 BS; 105 Ontario Ave., Massapequa, NY 11758, 516 798-2070.

LYNCH, Christopher B.; '95 BS; Correction Ofcr.; NYC Dept. of Corrections, 718 546-8255; r. 271 E. 9th St. Ph, Brooklyn, NY 11218, 718 854-8009. e-mail

LYNCH, Elda M.; '88 BA; 1066 Hartman Ln., Far Rockaway, NY 11691, 718 297-1191.

LYNCH, John S.; '81 BS; 1639 Undercliff Ave., Bronx, NY 10453, 718 653-8194.

LYNCH, Richard T.; '70 BS; Retired Deputy Inspector NYCPD; r. 85-03 55th Ave., Elmhurst, NY 11373; *Julia;* Mary, Julia, Richard.

LYNCH, Rodolfo R.; '83 BA; Detective; NYC Police Dept., 1 Hogan Pl., 2123359045, New York, NY 10013; r. 19 S Portland Ave. # 3, Brooklyn, NY 11217; *Edwina;* Bayete. e-mail

LYNCH, Sean J.; '96 BS; 3270 Barkley Ave., Bronx, NY 10465, 718 931-7441.

LYNCH, Thandi N.; '99 BS; Clg. Asst.; John Jay Clg. Library; r. 125 E 93rd St. #3, Brooklyn, NY 11212, 718 735-1352. e-mail

LYNCH-IVINS, Ellen P.; '82 BA; 240 Madison St. Apt. 12d, New York, NY 10002.

LYNN, Kandia O.; '95 BA; Case Mgr.; NYC; r. Brooklyn, NY 11237.

LYNN, William J.; '80 BS; 1535 E 36th St., Brooklyn, NY 11234, 718 373-3936.

LYONS, Daphony P.; '85 BS; 102 Mastic Blvd. W # We, Shirley, NY 11967.

LYONS, Hester; '75 MA; 285 Henry St. #6, Brooklyn, NY 11201, 718 398-2038.

LYONS, Janine Q.; '95 BA; 370 E 31st St. Apt. 3b, Brooklyn, NY 11226, 718 444-9310.

LYONS, John J.; '90 BS; 1203 Rockland Ave., Staten Island, NY 10314, 718 761-5117.

LYONS, John R.; '78 BS; 57 Hillcrest St., Staten Island, NY 10308, 718 816-5908.

LYONS, Leonie A.; '95 BA; 119-01 222 St., Cambria Hts., NY 11411.

LYONS, Robert T.; '93 BA; AS Slaughter Mem.; Lt./Asst. Dir. of Public Safety; Hunter Clg. City Univ. of NY, 212 772-4521; r. 55 N. Elliot Pl., 8f, Brooklyn, NY 11205, 718 834-9778; *Annette;* Courtney.

LYONS, Ronald C.; '79 BS; 1114 New York Ave., Brooklyn, NY 11203, 718 398-2038.

LYONS, Thomas; '77 BS; Court Ofcr.; NY Criminal Ct., 100 Centre St., New York, NY 10013, 212 374-5835; r. 117-12 Ocean Promenades, Rockaway Park, NY 11694.

LYTLE, Emanuel; '80 BS; 123-25 82nd Ave. #5, Kew Gardens, NY 11415.

LYTTLE, John P.; '80 BS; MSED Hunter Clg.; Lieutenant; NYC; r. 320 Atlantic Ave. #A-16, E. Rockaway, NY 11518; *Joan.*

LYTTLE, Judith; '86 BS; 1135 Evergreen Ave., Bronx, NY 10472, 718 860-4440.

LYUDMIR, Alex; '92 BA; 458 Neptune Ave. Apt. 7d, Brooklyn, NY 11224, 718 373-8016.

M

MACALUSO, Leonard; '98 BS; Detective; NYC Police Dept.; r. 79 Sherman Ave., N. Merrick, NY 11566.

MACARI, Valerio F.; '99 MPA; 137 Villa At The Woods, Peekskill, NY 10566.

MACCARONE, Virginia; '80 MPA; 425 Willow Brook Rd., Staten Island, NY 10314.

MACCHIA, Anthony P.; '94 BA; 101 Gedney St., Nyack, NY 10960.

MACCHIAROLI, Joseph; '84 MPA; 109 Park Ave., Midland Park, NJ 07432.

MACCONE, Joseph; '77 MA; Inspector; r. 6 Crystal Ln., Westbury, NY 11590, 516 997-6285; *Mary Ann.*

MACDALIE, Jeeny '98 (See Louis, Jeeny M.).

MACDONALD, Mrs. Nirvana L., (Nirvana Marriott); '96 BS; Exec. Asst.; Bell Atlantic, 245 Park Ave. 40th Fl., New York, NY 10167, 212 557-5492; r. 6 Hudson View Dr., Beacon, NY 12508, 718 520-8698; *John.* e-mail

MACDONNELL, Mark C.; '95 AS, '99 BS; Police Ofcr.; NYPD, 1 Police Plz., New York, NY 10038, 212 374-5000; r. 5 Clubway, Eastchester, NY 10709, 914 395-1183.

MACDOUGALL, John; '76 BA; Police Capt.; City of Yonkers, Yonkers, NY 10702, 914 377-7900; r. 175 Brewster Hill Rd, Brewster, NY 10509, 914 279-6593.

MACDOUGALL, Michael; '90 BS; 43 Canton Ct., Brooklyn, NY 11229, 718 615-0441.

MACDOWELL, Kenneth M.; '84 BS; 5128 72nd St., Flushing, NY 11377, 718 446-7451.

MACDOWELL, Rick W.; '88 BS; NYPD Sergeant; 107 Precinct, 7101 Parson Blvd., Fresh Meadows, NY 11365; r. Long Island City, NY 11101; *Janet;* Danielle, Dylan.

MACFARLANE, Maria L.; '90 BS; 6000 NE 22nd Way, Apt. 3F, Ft. Lauderdale, FL 33308, 954 370-0280.

MACHIN, Annette M.; '81 BS; 12 Tulip Ave., Oakdale, NY 11769.

MACK, Alice; '79 BS; 11729 225th St., Jamaica, NY 11411, 718 949-3290.

MACK, Gerard C.; '93 BA; 8910 199th St., Jamaica, NY 11423, 718 659-1073.

MACK, John B.; '79 AS; 16b Defoe Pl., Bronx, NY 10475, 718 862-0222.

MACK, Robert J.; '77 MA; BA St. Johns Univ.; Supervisory Special Agt.; FBI, 11000 Willshire Blvd., Ste. 1700, Los Angeles, CA 90024, 310 477-6565; r. 2236 Bermuda Dunes Pl., Oxnard, CA 93030, 310 477-6565.

MACK, Ms. Stephanie M.; '95 BS; Chase Capital Partners, New York, NY 10001; r. 2541 Adam C Powell Blvd., New York, NY 10039, 212 281-2859; *Lucius Thomas;* Stephen. e-mail

MAC KAY, Donald R.; '75 BS; 2160 Larch St., Wantagh, NY 11793, 516 785-3709.

MACKESY, Richard; '84 BS; Prog. Coord; Sussex Cnty. Community Clg., College Hill Rd., Newton, NJ 07860, 973 300-2182; r. POB C, Tobyhanna, PA 18466. e-mail

MACKEY, Daniel; '85 BS; Detective; New York Police Dept., One Police Plz., New York, NY 10038, 212 374-5000; r. 140 58th St.-Ste. 6B, Brooklyn, NY 11220, 718 765-4300; *Pogmehon O'Macdea;* Eejit. e-mail

MACKEY, Elayne S.; '82 MA; 63-11 Queens Blvd., Woodside, NY 11377, 718 464-1598.

MACKIE, Dawn R.; '83 BS; 438 Bainbridge St., Brooklyn, NY 11233, 718 453-4108.

MACNAMARA, Donal E.; Distinguished Prof.; John Jay Clg. of Criminial Justice, Dept. Law & Police Science; r. 76 Four Corners Rd, Warwick, NY 10990, 914 986-0260; Dr. Brian.

MACOLINO, Eric J.; '90 BS; 5406 69th Pl., Maspeth, NY 11378.

MACON, Olivia Y.; '95 BA; Coord.; United Health; r. 1384 Lakeside Way, Apt. 206, Atlanta, GA 30319; Lawrence, Zinnae.

MACPHERSON, Ian C.; '98 MS; BA COMM Brooklyn Clg.; Protection Security; r. 279 Pleasant Ave. #5n, New York, NY 10029, 212 348-1183; *Charmaine;* Sabrina, Kamal. e-mail

MACWITHEY, Thomas J.; '95 BS; 14340 Ash Ave., Flushing, NY 11355, 718 539-5139.

MADDALENA, Leopold; '70 BS; 10 Greenway W., Sloatsburg, NY 10974.

MADDEN, Dennis J.; '77 BS; 756 Village Dr., Hauppauge, NY 11788, 631 979-2880.

MADDOX, Charles; '76 BA; 10240 62nd Ave. Apt. 3l, Flushing, NY 11375, 718 271-0813.

MADDUX, Davina P.; '94 BS; Child Protective Spec.; Admin. for Children's Svcs., 19 Grant Sq., Brooklyn, NY 11216, 718 735-0312; r. 1415 Linden Blvd., Brooklyn, NY 11212, 718 485-0176; Joshua, Dante Jackson. e-mail

MADERA, Brenda; '90 BS; POB 21522, Philadelphia, PA 19131, 215 426-2611.

MADGETT, Brian; '89 BS; 6732B E Cedar Ave., Denver, CO 80224.

MADRID, Nelson; '96 BS; 4216 82nd St., Apt. 1B, Elmhurst, NY 11373.

MADRIGAL, Elvira '96 (See Madrigal-Fernandez, Elvira).

MADRIGAL-FERNANDEZ, Elvira, (Elvira Madrigal); '96 BS; Prog. Coord.; Manhattan Dist. Attorney's Ofc., 1 Hogan Pl., New York, NY 10013, 212 335-9907; r. 117-14 Union Tpk. Apt. Da2, Kew Gardens, NY 11415, 718 268-7741; *Carlos Fernandez.*

MADSEN, Theodore S.; '76 BA; 16 Rochelle St., Staten Island, NY 10304, 718 979-3416.

MAEKAWA, Yoshimitsu; '95 BS, '99; 5 Stratford CT., Staten Island, NY 10314, 718 477-0595. e-mail

MAFFETTONE, Dennis; '92 BA, '92 MPA; Librarian; Metropolitan Transportation Authority, 347 Madison Ave., New York, NY 10017, 212 878-7192; r. 510 E. 23rd St., New York, NY 10010, 212 533-0632. e-mail

MAGADIA, Paul; '83 BS; 119-04 80th Rd., Kew Gardens, NY 11415.

MAGGIACOMO, Eddie M.; '91 BS; 330 E. 26th St., New York, NY 10010.

MAGHAN, Jess; '86 MPA; 800 S Wells St. Apt. 846, Chicago, IL 60607, 312 431-7927.

MAGID, Stephen H.; '77 BS; JD Touro Law Sch.; Court Clerk; NYS Supreme Ct.-Richmond Cnty., 355 Front St., Staten Island, NY 10304, 718 876-6411; r. 45 Seneca Loop, Staten Island, NY 10314, 718 698-4921; *Esther;* Regina.

MAGISTRO, Anthony J.; '96 BS; 22025 Chelan Loop, West Linn, OR 97068.

MAGLIACANO, Anthony; '96 BS; 2629 Juliat Pl., Union, NJ 07083.

MAGLIARO, Joseph L.; '78 MA; 9 Flintlock Dr., Barnegat, NJ 08005.

MAGLIONE, Diane C.; '80 BS; 71 7th St., Ridgefield Park, NJ 07660, 201 440-0062.

MAGNUS, Connie L.; '84 BS; Detective Sergeant; NYPD, 1 Police Plz., New York, NY 10038, 212 374-5000; r. Massapequa, NY 11758; *Maria E. Melendez.* e-mail

MAGNUSON, Ms. Leah; '92 BS; JD New York Law Sch.; Atty.; 973 481-0900; r. 9728 3rd ave. #459, Brooklyn, NY 11209. e-mail

MAGNUSSEN, Erik M.; 1824 Stuart St., Brooklyn, NY 11229.

MAGRINO, Robert; '90 AS; 1787 Washington Ave., Seaford, NY 11783, 516 221-2067.

MAGUIRE, John T.; '79 BS; 51 Mimosa Ct., Ridgefield, CT 06877, 203 431-6693.

MAHADY, Myles; '97 BA MA; Police Ofcr.; 9th Precinct, New York, NY 10009; r. 5365 65th Pl., Maspeth, NY 11378, 718 457-2452. e-mail

MAHAMAH, Chidinma, (Chidinma Onwuchekwa); '86 BS; Deputy Dir.; Ofc. of Revenue & Investigation/EVR, 260 11 Th Ave., New York, NY 10001, 212 630-9733; r. 733 Amsterdam Ave. Apt. 6e, New York, NY 10025. e-mail

MAHANY, Annemarie; '89 BS; Mental Health Couns.; Lakeside Alternatives, 434 W. Kennedy Blvd., Orlando, FL 32810, 407 875-3700; r. 8243 Golden Chickasaw Cir., Orlando, FL 32825, 407 382-6240; Christian. e-mail

MAHER, Anne M.; '95 MA; MSW NYU; Coord. of Residential Svcs; St. Mary's Hosp., Passaic, NJ 07055, 973 470-3507; r. 95 Kennedy Dr., Lodi, NJ 07644, 973 472-0631.

MAHER, Dennis; 3800 Waldo Ave., Bronx, NY 10463.

MAHER, James M.; '75 MPA; 29 Kim Ct., Tappan, NY 10983.

MAHER, John P.; '78 BS; 405 Latham Rd, Mineola, NY 11501, 516 742-4318.

MAHER, John W.; '82 BS; 2424 79th St., Flushing, NY 11370, 718 728-7265.

MAHER, Lisa-marie; '96 MA; 305 E 21st St., Apt. 29, New York, NY 10010.

MAHFOOD, Jad P.; '83 MA; 260 E 28 St., Brooklyn, NY 11226.

MAHON, Edward T.; '78 BA; 1092 Olympia Blvd., Staten Island, NY 10306, 718 351-4119.

MAHON, Jennifer; '98 BS; 515 W 110th St. 6C, New York, NY 10025, 212 721-3495.

MAHON, John F.; '76 BA; 759 51 St., Brooklyn, NY 11220, 718 921-7477.

MAHONE, Ernest; '81 BS; 16315 130th Ave. Apt. 10G, Jamaica, NY 11434.

MAHONE, Robert L.; '80 BS; 853 E 227th St., Bronx, NY 10466, 718 798-8118.

MAHONEY, Catherine V.; '99 BS; Police Ofcr.; NYPD, Bronx, NY 10451; r. 180 Briggs Ave., Yonkers, NY 10701, 914 423-6430.

MAHONEY, Daniel P.; '77 BA; 30 Gardenia Ln., Levittown, NY 11756, 516 255-0424.

MAHONEY, Dawn; '90 BS; 1338 August Rd, N. Babylon, NY 11703, 631 586-6613.

MAHONEY, Edward D.; '77 BS; 314 Nichols Ave., Brooklyn, NY 11208, 718 265-5595.

MAHONEY, Edward J.; '80 MA; 583 W 215th St. Apt. C11, New York, NY 10034.

MAHONEY, Francis J.; '79 BS; Retired; r. 9 Clark Rd, Stony Point, NY 10980, 914 429-8003.

MAHONEY, Matthew; '92 BS; 9189 Village Glen Dr. Unit249, San Diego, CA 92123, 619 284-4002.

MAHONEY, Patrick D.; '76 BS; Retired-RN; Nevada State Prison; r. 149 Lake Glen Dr., Carson City, NV 89703, 775 882-5488.

MAHONEY, Richard A.; '75 BS; 3410 56th St., Flushing, NY 11377, 718 424-4511.

MAHONEY, Robert E.; '82 MA; BS St. Johns Univ., BS NYU; Retired NY State Dept of Correction; r. 31 Moccasin Dr., Whiting, NJ 08759, 732 849-0055; *Rita;* Robert, Robyn, Karen, Sandra, Lisa, Jane, James. e-mail

MAHONEY, Sheila; '93 BS; 72 Huntsbridge Rd., Yonkers, NY 10704, 914 423-6430.

MAI, Herbert L.; '93 BA, '96 MA; 51-41 Codwise Pl., Elmhurst, NY 11373, 718 898-4903.

MAIELI, Mark S.; '81 BA; 35 Washington Ave., Miller Place, NY 11764.

MAILLARD, James H.; '75 MPA, AAS; Retired Supv Detective; DA Ofc.; r. 18837 Ilion Ave., St. Albans, NY 11412, 718 454-4078; *Elma.* e-mail

MAILLARD, Patricia L.; '88 BS; MA Queens Clg.; Principal Admin. Assoc.; NYC Bd. of Educ., 110 Livingston St. Rm 500A, Brooklyn, NY 11201, 718 935-3723; r. 376 New York Ave., Brooklyn, NY 11213, 718 774-9815; Phillip. e-mail

MAILLARD, William L.; '73 BA, '73 AA; Retired; r. 4818 Labrador Ln., Orlando, FL 32818, 407 297-1272; *Vivian;* Phillip, Donna, Katrina, Dawn. e-mail

MAINI, John; '80 BA; 169 N Cottage St., Valley Stream, NY 11580, 516 561-8964.

MAIRANDA, Adriana '93 (See Fennessy, Adriana).

MAIS, Byran R.; '94 BS; 267 E. 55th St., Brooklyn, NY 11203.

MAISANO, Michael P.; '93 BS; 2055 E 14th St., Brooklyn, NY 11229.

MAITLAND, Michelle; '95 BS; 11330 198th St., Jamaica, NY 11412, 718 978-4342.

MAJESKI, William J.; '76 BS; Private Investigator; Majeski Assocs. Inc., 301 Warburton Ave., Hawthorne, NJ 07506, 973 304-6007; r. same; *Evelyn.* e-mail

MAJESTIC, C.; '93 BS; 1126 Pelham Pkwy. S, Bronx, NY 10461.

MAJETTE, Minnie '82 (See Hall, Minnie M.).

MAJID, Syed M.; '97 MA; 206 N.Detroit Ave., Massapequa, NY 11758, 516 752-9659.

MAJOR, Curstlinia S.; '98 BA; Child Protective Spec.; Admin. for Children's Svcs., 350 St. Mark's Pl. 5th Fl., Staten Island, NY 10301, 718 720-8558; r. 75 Hill St. #2L, Staten Island, NY 10304, 718 720-6492; Kalif Mapp.

MAJOR, Gilbert H.; '95 BS; Sgt.; NYC Police Dept., 120 E 119th St., New York, NY 10015, 212 860-6551; r. 139-28 254th St., Rosedale, NY 11422; *Debbie;* Joshua.

MAJOR, Livingstone R.; '88 BA, '91 MA; Corrections Capt.; NYC Dept. of Corrections, New York, NY 10001, 718 546-6479; r. 222 Conklin Ave., Patchogue, NY 11772, 631 758-5287.

MAJOR, Sharon; '92 BS; 1931 Madison Ave., New York, NY 10035, 315 735-8840.

MAKAHON, James R.; '88 MA; POB 790178, Middle Vlg., NY 11379.

MAKANJUOLA, Rafiu T.; '96 BS; AA Kingsborough Comm. Clg.; Law Enforcement Police Ofcr.; Baltimore City Police Dept., 500 E Baltimore St., Baltimore, MD 21201, 410 396-2411; *Christiana;* Kristy, Richard, Robert.

MALAGOLI, Tara D.; '99 BA; Fordham Univ., MS; Educator; r. 80 15 41 Ave. 623, Elmhurst, NY 11373, 718 505-0818.

MALAHY, James E.; '99 BA; Client Asst.; Computer Assocs., 1 Computer Associates Plz., Islandia, NY 11749, 631 342-5361; r. 7 Williams Blvd., Apt. 2D, Lake Grove, NY 11755, 631 737-3005. e-mail

MALAPERO, Raymond; '68 BS; 1080 78th St., Brooklyn, NY 11228, 718 833-4316.

MALAXOS, Troy-Nicholas; '99 MACJ; BACOMM Loyola Clg.; Criminal Investigations; r. Great Neck, NY 11021. e-mail

MALCAN, Jay W.; '76 MA; 13107 Morning Hill Ln., Midlothian, VA 23112, 804 744-6876.

MALCOLM, Sedrick; '82 BA, '85 MPA; 529 E. 49 St., Brooklyn, NY 11203, 718 485-9698.

MALCOLM, Valerie V.; '75 BA; 46-A Pulaski St., Brooklyn, NY 11206, 718 485-9698.

MALDONADO, Annette; '93 BA; 746 Grier Ave., Elizabeth, NJ 07202.

MALDONADO, Aristides; '93 AS; 2949 Frederick Douglass Blvd. Apt 5d, New York, NY 10039.

MALDONADO, Carmelo; '99 BS; Math Tchr.; r. 270 E 162 St. #7, Bronx, NY 10451, 718 585-4711; Genesis. e-mail

MALDONADO, David; '95 BS; 65-10 108th St. Apt. 1G, Forest Hills, NY 11375, 718 459-6736.

MALDONADO, Ebelia; '87 BA; 14715 227th St., Jamaica, NY 11413, 718 418-5467.

MALDONADO, Edwin; '92 BS; Sergeant; NYPD, 1 Police Plz., New York, NY 10035, 212 374-5000; r. 323 Brinsmade Ave., Bronx, NY 10465, 718 863-1140. e-mail

MALDONADO, Evelyn J.; '99 BS; Rsch. Asst./Adjunct Prof.; John Jay Criminal Rsch. Ctr., 555 W. 5th St. Ste. 605, New York, NY 10019, 212 237-8356; r. 85-82 Eliot Ave. 1S, Rego Park, NY 11374, 718 426-1024. e-mail

MALDONADO, Ismael; '99 BS; AS St. John Univ.; Pres.; Blazing Hot Production, 117-16 Atlantic Ave. Ste. 147, Richmond Hill, NY 11419, 718 850-4674; r. 114-11 101st Ave., Richmond Hill, NY 11419, 718 441-7847; Siara Jasmine. e-mail

MALDONADO, Joseph B.; '96 BA; 80-17 88 Rd., Woodhaven, NY 11421, 718 418-5467.

MALDONADO, Mary; '96 BA; 601 Metropolitan Ave., Brooklyn, NY 11211, 718 965-1683.

MALDONADO, Patricia A.; '89 BA; 666 Belmont Ave., Brooklyn, NY 11207, 718 436-5778.

MALDONADO, Rose; '76 BA; 312 Webster Ave., Brooklyn, NY 11230, 718 342-3303.

MALDONADO, Xinmia M.; '96 BS; 60 Pitt St. #18, New York, NY 10002.

MALENKA, Elliot; '91 MA; Applied Behavior Spec.; r. 21 Rita Cres., Commack, NY 11725.

MALEY, James E., Jr.; '89 MA; BBA St. Bonaventure Univ.; Asst. Prof.; Monroe C.C., Rochester, NY 14623, 716 262-1765; r. 6 Adler Bch, Hilton, NY 14468. e-mail

MALHOTRA, Ravi; '93 MA; 104-07 Westside Ave., Corona, NY 11368.

MALLORY, Debra A. '83 (See Mallory-Canty, Debra A.).

MALLORY-CANTY, Debra A., (Debra A. Mallory); '83 BA; MSW NYU; Child Protective Supv. II; Admin. for Children Svcs., 19 Grant Sq., 3rd Fl., Brooklyn, NY 11216, 718 363-7462; r. 216 Rockaway Ave., Brooklyn, NY 11233, 718 485-0011; *Boyd Canty;* Michelle, Renee, Thomas, Jacquelyn.

MALONE, Daniel E.; '75 BS; Assoc Dir. of Telecommunication; New York Univ., 7 E 12th St., New York, NY 10003, 212 998-1230; r. 39 Bay Ridge Pkwy., Brooklyn, NY 11229, 718 238-3034. e-mail

MALONE, Patrick J.; '85 BS; 15 Washington Pl., New York, NY 10003, 315 793-0605.

MALONE, Victor E., Jr.; '86 BS; 20615 86th Rd Apt. 3h, Queens Vlg., NY 11427. e-mail

MALONEY, Bryan M.; '95 BSPA; BA Marist Clg.; Major Gifts Ofcr.; Bank Street Clg. of Educ., 610 W. 112th St., New York, NY 10025, 212 875-4500; r. 41 S Bridge St., Poughkeepsie, NY 12601. e-mail

MALONEY, Christopher; '96 BS; Security Supv.; American Express Co., 200 Vesey St., New York, NY 10285, 212 640-5126; r. 786 Highview Ave., Westbury, NY 11590; *Christine.*

MALONEY, Eileen A.; '79 BS; 10418 88th Ave., Jamaica, NY 11418, 718 847-3875.

MALONEY, John F.; '76 BS; Chief Mate; Crowley Marine Svcs., Jacksonville, FL; r. 49 Grand Pl., E. Northport, NY 11731, 631 368-8904; *Patricia;* Brian, James.

MALONEY, Steven E.; '95 BS; 583 W 215th St. Apt. B5, New York, NY 10034.

MALONEY, Vaughn; '96 BA; 1704 Amsterdam Ave., New York, NY 10031.

MALOOL, Paul G.; '93 MS; BS Mercy Clg., MTA Fairleigh Dickinson Univ.; Sr. Planner; NJ State Police, Emergency Mgmt, Helmetta, NJ 08828; r. 2040 Wood Rd, Scotch Plains, NJ 07076, 908 232-8936. e-mail

MALPICA, Betzaida; '82 BS; 44 Sunnyside Ave. #1, Brooklyn, NY 11207.

MALTBY, Paul H.; 525 S 13th St., Lindenhurst, NY 11757.

MALTESE, Hon. Joseph J.; '70 BA; MA JD NYU, New York Law Sch., MJS Natl. Judicial Clg. U. NV; Supreme Court Justice; NYS Supreme Ct., 355 Front St., Staten Island, NY 10304, 718 876-6429; *Jereen;* Jaclyn, Julie Ann.

MALTESE, Nicole M.; '95 BS; 128 95th St., Brooklyn, NY 11209, 718 238-0626.

MALTIN, Nancy I.; '95 BA; JD Brooklyn Law Sch.; Atty.; Ofc. of Corp. Counsel, City of New York Law Dept., New York, NY 10001; r. 324 W. 49th St., New York, NY 10019, 212 246-7294.

MALTZ, Barbara K.; '78 BA; MSW Univ. CV; Social Worker; St. John's Family Health Ctr., 9525 Queens Blvd., Rego Park, NY 11374, 718 286-1084; r. 220/71B 67 Ave., Bayside, NY 11364; Jeremy, Avery.

MALVASIO, Sylvia S.; '94 MA; 389 Bergen St., Brooklyn, NY 11217, 718 783-5385.

MALYSZ, Josephine; '92 BA, '97 MA; Legal Nurse Cnslt.; r. 84-37 63rd Ave., Middle Vlg., NY 11379.

MAMMANO, Richard A.; '78 BS; Retired-Police Sgt.; New York Transit Police; r. 44 St. Anthony Pl., Mahopac, NY 10541, 914 628-7255. e-mail

MAMMARELLI, Christopher J.; '95 AS, '96 BS; Steinway & Sons, 19 Ave. & 38 St., Astoria, NY 11105, 718 721-2600; r. 2036 33rd St., Long Island City, NY 11105, 718 932-6876.

MANAHAN, William F.; '89 MA; 9 Donna Ct., Staten Island, NY 10314.

MANASSE, Gigi R.; '84 BS; 33 Northfield Rd, Glen Cove, NY 11542.

MANCERA, Teresa; 8200 Copper St., Lamont, CA 93241, 661 831-6648.

MANCHAND, Nicole E.; '95 AS, '97 BS; 1500 Hone Ave., Bronx, NY 10461.

MANCO, Robert E.; '91 MPA; 15 Vanderbilt Dr., Highland Mills, NY 10930, 914 928-1865.

MANCUSO, Donna Marie B.; '98 MA; BA SUNY Albany; Natl. Recruiting Coord.; Deloitte Cnsltg., 1633 Broadway, New York, NY 10019, 212 492-3640; r. 1744 81 St., Brooklyn, NY 11214, 718 256-4650. e-mail

MANCUSO, Jo-Anne; '83 BS, '90 MA; Case Mgr.; Kings Cnty. Hosp., 718 245-2348; r. POB 230545, New York, NY 10023, 212 246-0553.

MANCUSO, John J.; '92 BS; 211 Zuber Pl., Maywood, NJ 07607.

MANCUSO, Peter J.; '76 BA, '79 MA; Partner/Owner; David M & Peter J Mancuso Inc., POB 667, New Hope, PA 18938, 215 862-5828; r. 6970 Ely Rd, New Hope, PA 18938, 215 862-2887; *Camille;* Joseph, Jill, Toni-Ann, Matthew. e-mail

MANDARINO, Michael A.; '80 BS; 47 Cres. Beach Rd, Glen Cove, NY 11542, 516 676-0119.

MANDEL, Michael J.; '94 MA; 94 Grove St., Pearl River, NY 10965, 914 735-4750.

MANDEL, Philip; '83 MA; 155 E 4th St Apt. 7J, New York, NY 10009.

MANDELBAUM, Marvin H.; '76 BS; BA, AA Fairleigh Dickinson Univ.; Owner; M.H. Claims Svc., 18000 Kittridge Ave., Reseda, CA 91335, 818 345-7862; r. 6600 Hesperia Ave., Reseda, CA 91335, 818 345-7862; *Nancy Sue;* Harold, Tiffany, Desiree. e-mail

MANDILE, Frank A.; '89 BS; 1303 Burlingham Rd, Pine Bush, NY 12566.

MANDZIK, Philip J.; '78 MPA; CERT. Columbia Univ.; Deputy Chief; NYC Police Dept., 1 Police Plz., New York, NY 10038, 718 299-4314; r. 136 Henry St., Valley Stream, NY 11580, 516 872-8723; *Joanne;* Christopher, Alison, Alexander, Emily. e-mail

MANER, Benjamin; '89 BS; 170 Old Mill Pt, Fayetteville, GA 30214.

MANETTE, Sean S.; '99 MA; BA Queens Clg.; Investigator; RMG Investigations Inc., 104 W. 27th St., New York, NY 10001, 212 989-2600; r. 72-36 112th St. #608, Forest Hills, NY 11375, 718 544-1983. e-mail

MANFREDY, Maria A.; '89 BS; 1955 Grand Concourse, Bronx, NY 10453.

MANGAL, Yovendra; '99 BA; 90-15 104th St. Bsmt, Richmond Hill, NY 11418, 718 849-8234.

MANGANO, Louis; '73 MA; JD Seton Hall Univ.; Atty-at-Law; Louis Mangano Esq, 395 River Dr., Elmwood Park, NJ 07407, 201 796-2727; r. Cooks Farm Rd., Montville, NJ 07045, 973 316-4849; *Arlene;* Kenneth, Eileen, Louis Jr, Michael.

MANGARELLA, Anthony; '99 BS; Student; Police Acad.; r. 2023 Colonial Ave., Apt. 6-D, Bronx, NY 10461, 718 597-7056; *Valerie Bello;* Ashley. e-mail

MANGER, Nichole; '99 BA; 240A Nassau Ave., Brooklyn, NY 11222, 718 361-6948.

MANGO, John F.; 91-11 97 St., Woodhaven, NY 11421, 718 474-3232.

MANGOME, Victor; '95 BS; 908 Rensselaer Ave., Staten Island, NY 10309.

MANGUAL, William P.; '80 BS; 2402 63 St. #F6, Brooklyn, NY 11204.

MANGUS, Denise; '70 BA; 136-42 Maple Ave., Flushing, NY 11355.

MANGUS, Peter J.; '76 MA; Not At This Address; r. 492 Nassau Blvd., Williston Park, NY 11596.

MANI, Riva; '97 MS; 7164 Shyamniwas, Mumbai 400026, India.

MANIBO, Joel R.; '94 BS; 98 Rutledge Ct. S, Matawan, NJ 07747.

MANIOS, Louis N.; '91 BA; MA CUNY; Head Technical Trainer; Sullivan & Cromwell, 125 Broad St., New York, NY 10004; r. 472 80th St., Brooklyn, NY 11209. e-mail

MANIR, Zabed; '99 BS; MIS Mgr.; Four Seasons Hotel, 58 E. 58th St., Phone Ext. 6300, New York, NY 10002, 212 758-5700; r. 23-90 29th St., Apt. 20, Astoria, NY 11105, 718 932-5795; *Tamia;* Omith. e-mail

MANIS, Ms. Jeanne D.; '99; BA LIU-CW Post; Agt.; Hudson Cnty. Pros. Ofc., 595 Newark Ave., Jersey City, NJ 07306, 201 795-6451; r. 199 Washington Ave., Tappan, NY 10983, 914 398-2412. e-mail

MANISCALCO, Raymond; '87 MA; 3048 Avenue R, Brooklyn, NY 11229.

MANISCALCO, Vito; '95 AS; 1938 64th St., Brooklyn, NY 11204, 718 256-0572.

MANISERO, Thomas R.; '79 BS; 302 Alverson Ave., Staten Island, NY 10309.

MANJARREZ, Jose L.; '98 BA; Detective; NYC Police Dept., New York, NY 10001; r. 41 Sutton St. Apt. 3L, Brooklyn, NY 11210, 718 349-1638.

MANN, Jeffrey H.; 2514 Avenue I, Brooklyn, NY 11210, 718 258-1543.

MANN, Kevin C.; '94 BS; NYC Deputy Sheriff; NYC Sheriff, New York, NY 10001, 212 397-0509; r. 816 Maple St., Brooklyn, NY 11203, 718 774-2358.

MANN, Krista J.; '99 BA; Social Worker; Cardinal McCloskey Svcs., 349 E 149th St., Bronx, NY 10451, 718 993-7700; r. 360 S 7 Ave., Mt. Vernon, NY 10550, 914 664-0807; Kasiem. e-mail

MANNA, Salvatore; '97 BS; 95 Ridge St., Eastchester, NY 10709.

MANNERS, Julia C. '80 (See Manners-Morales, Mrs. Julia C.).

MANNERS-MORALES, Mrs. Julia C., (Julia C. Manners); '80 BS FOR, '83 MPA; ED SPEC Nova SE Univ.; Assistant Principal; Boyd Anderson HS, 3050 NW 41st St., Lauderdale Lakes, FL 33309, 954 497-3800; r. 6400 SW 181st Ln., Ft. Lauderdale, FL 33331, 954 680-2549; *Wilfredo Morales;* Nina, Wilfredo Jr, Eileen, Cesar, Xavier. e-mail

MANNING, Carl E.; '94 BA; 165 Clinton Ave. # 5, Brooklyn, NY 11205, 718 852-9852.

MANNING, Delores H.; '84 BA; 46A Pulask St., Brooklyn, NY 11206, 718 852-9852.

MANNING, George J.; '76 MPA; Ret; r. 61-13 Bleecker St., Ridgewood, NY 11385, 212 477-5695.

MANNING, Joni R.; '84 MPA; 425a Decatur St., Brooklyn, NY 11233, 718 258-1543.

MANNING, Trevor E.; '89 BS; MPSC Brooklyn Clg.; Staff Analyst 1; City of NY Human Resources Admin., 180 Wter St., New York, NY 10038, 212 331-5816; r. 50 Paladino Ave. # 15H, New York, NY 10035, 212 369-1870; *Marie;* Trevor Jr., Travis, Trevena.

MANNINO, Eulalia; '99 BA; 60-79 54 St., Flushing, NY 11378, 718 418-2307.

MANNINO, Paul; '70 BS; 4421 NE 28th Ave., Lighthouse Pt., FL 33064, 954 781-2707.

MANNINO, Salvatore O.; '94 BS; AS Kingsborough Clg.; Dir. Info. Systs.; Welbro Bldg. Corp., 800 Trafalgar Ct., Maitland, FL 32751, 407 475-0800; r. 3226 Scenic Woods Dr., Deltona, FL 32725, 904 532-1659; *Lori;* Josephine. e-mail

MANNIX, William R.; '87 BS; 51 Florence Dr., Clark, NJ 07066.

MANNS, Olivien D.; '80 BS; 22641 129th Ave., Jamaica, NY 11413.

MANSKY, Orin; '79 MPA; 643 Maitland Ave., Teaneck, NJ 07666, 201 692-3949.

MANSON, James E.; '92 BS; 2230 Mott Ave. #, Far Rockaway, NY 11691, 718 352-6844.

MANTZARIS, Demetrios (Jimmy); '96 BA; Police Ofcr.; NYC; r. 2819 Schley Ave., Bronx, NY 10465, 718 892-3677.

MANUS, Raymond P.; '77 BS; 2761 Walker Dr., Yorktown Hts., NY 10598, 914 245-1069.

MANZELLO, Joseph; '97 BS; AS Kingsborough Community; Police Ofcr.; NYC Police Dept., 1 Police Plz., New York, NY 10038, 718 361-1031; r. 41-60 Glenwood St., Little Neck, NY 11363, 718 229-9026; *Jeanne;* Peter, Thomas. e-mail

MANZIONE, Robert E.; 110 Kensington Ave., Staten Island, NY 10305.

MANZOLILLO, Carmine; '77 AS; 9 Lehigh St., Williston Park, NY 11596, 516 741-1846.

MAPPS, Valeria D.; '96 BA; P.O.Box 297, Bronx, NY 10475.

MAR, Marie A.; '76 MA; BS PSYCH Fordham Univ., JD Univ. of Miami Sch.-Law; Atty-at-Law; Friedberg Green & Cohen, RE, Entertainment & Animal Law, 444 Maidson Ave. Ste. 805, New York, NY 10022, 212 829-9090; r. 1694 Second Ave., New York, NY 10128, 212 348-2480.

MARANO, Joseph C.; '67 BS; Retired; Fed. Protective Svcs. & NYPD; r. 24 Rolling Hills Dr., Huntington Sta., NY 11746, 631 673-4143; *Patricia;* Joseph (dec), Maryanne.

MARASCO, Michael J.; '99 MA; 303 Windward Pl., Oldsmar, FL 34677, 727 785-0561; *Jan.* e-mail

MARCANO, Maribel V.; '88 BA; 219 E. 97th St., New York, NY 10029.

MARCANTUONO, Melissa; '96 MA; 156 Chestnut St., Nutley, NJ 07110.

MARCEL, Jean; '85 BA; 132 Park Pl., Brooklyn, NY 11217, 718 377-7780.

MARCELLUS, Algeste; '98 MPA; BA Queens Clg.; Sr. Investigator; NYS Educ. Dept., 1 Park Ave., New York, NY 10016, 212 951-6473; r. St. Albans, NY 11412; *Clerveau;* Thalia. e-mail

MARCHELLO, Charles J.; '82 BS; 10531 89th St., Jamaica, NY 11417.

MARCHELLO, John A.; '93 BS; 15751 101st St., Howard Bch., NY 11414.

MARCHESANO, Neil; '81 BS; 4 Green Willows Dr., Lakewood, NJ 08701, 732 920-1092.

MARCHESE, Joseph J.; '72 BS, '72 AS; MA SUNY-Stony Brook; Prog. Devel. Spec.; NYS Div. of Parole, Albany, NY 12201, 518 473-9666; r. 6 Jessica Ct., Latham, NY 12110, 518 783-0602.

MARCHESE, Maria N.; '98 MA; Doctoral Candidate/Sch.-Child Psych; Pace Univ.; r. 2002 New York Ave., Union City, NJ 07087, 201 865-4442. e-mail

MARCHETTA, Raymond A.; '79 BS; 2674 N 1st St. #110, San Jose, CA 95134.

MARCHETTI, Rossin A.; '99; 115 Hampton Ct., Chapel Hill, NC 27514.

MARCHIA, Ms. Theresa; '80 BA, '82 MA; Police Ofcr.; NYC Police Dept., 357 W. 35 St., New York, NY 10001, 212 239-9811; r. 68-27 Olcott St., Forest Hills, NY 11375, 718 261-3017; *Tim Duckworth;* Christy, Sean. e-mail

MARCHINA, John E.; '77 BA; 8 Brookside Ave., New City, NY 10956, 914 634-4123.

MARCHISELLO, Geralyn; '77 BA; 2958 216th St., Flushing, NY 11360, 718 428-4143.

MARCIAL, Tanya; '96 CERT; 2816 Parkview Ter. #, Bronx, NY 10468.

MARCOS, Maria E.; '79 BS; 48-02 111th St., Corona, NY 11368, 718 323-4548.

MARCOTRIGIANO, James; '79 BS; POB 60488, Staten Island, NY 10306, 718 980-0019.

MARCUNE, Patrick; '79 BS; 150 Ilyssa Way, Staten Island, NY 10312.

MARCUS, Edward; '86 BA; Ret NYS Correction Ofcr.; r. 2085 Rockaway Park, Brooklyn, NY 11236, 718 241-2394.

MARCUS, James A.; '76 MA; 20 Lantern St., Huntington, NY 11743.

MARCUS, Shurnette M.; '96 BA; 104-10 217 St., Queens Vlg., NY 11429, 718 297-9552.

MARCUS, Steve A.; '90 BS; 351 Hancock St. # 4, Brooklyn, NY 11216, 718 287-4444.

MARECH, Craig A.; '99 BS; AA Middlesex Cnty.; Intelligence Research Analyst; US Customs Svc.; r. 2 Chatham Pl., Linden, NJ 07036, 908 587-1941; *Debra.*

MARENGO, Christopher, (J.); '83 MA; New York Law Sch.; Atty.; Law Offices of Christopher Marengo, 2116 Williamsbridge Rd., Bronx, NY 10461, 718 829-3207; r. 370 Washington Ave., Pleasantville, NY 10570, 914 769-9198; *Diana; Nicholas.*

MARGOLIS, Jason S.; '95 MA; 67-30H 186 Ln., Fresh Meadows, NY 11365, 718 465-2648.

MARGULIES, Randy B.; '82 BS; 801 Neill Ave. # 19, Bronx, NY 10462, 718 597-9599.

MARI, Daniel J.; '74 BA; Retired; r. 371 S. Walnut St., Lindenhurst, NY 11757, 631 232-2168; *Rachel.*

MARIA, Edward; '96 BS; 1295 Amsterdam Ave., New York, NY 10027, 315 841-4393.

MARIANO, Theresa '99 (See Mariano-Noreiga, Mrs. Theresa).

MARIANO-NOREIGA, Mrs. Theresa, (Theresa Mariano); '99 BS; Student; Fordham Univ.; r. 3190 Hull Ave. Apt. 25, Bronx, NY 10467, 718 515-0750; *Alsa Noreiga; Joshua.* e-mail

MARIETTE, Roberto; '87 BS; 9419 207th St., Queens Vlg., NY 11428, 718 740-4748.

MARIETTE, Yvonne M.; '83 BA; 9419 207th St., Queens Vlg., NY 11428, 718 740-4748.

MARIN, Vivian; '96 BS; Trng. Coord.; Young & Rubicam; r. 40 Franklin Ave., Brentwood, NY 11717, 631 273-4039. e-mail

MARINAKOS, Demos E.; '92 BS; Detective Spec. NYPD; 75th Precinct, 1000 Sutter Ave., Brooklyn, NY 11208, 718 827-3511; r. 9411 Shore Rd Apt. 5k, Brooklyn, NY 11209.

MARINARO, Michael V.; '85 BS; JD Univ. of Baltimore; Atty.; Marinaro Law Assocs., 53 N. Duke St., Lancaster, PA 17602, 717 397-7055; r. 150 Ridings Way, Lancaster, PA 17601, 631 261-7527; *Cheryl; Erica, Amanda, Michael.*

MARINE, Ricardo; '98 BS; Sales Asst.; Citibank, 111 Wall St., New York, NY 10043, 212 657-9958; r. 16 Keogh Ln., New Rochelle, NY 10805, 718 325-0375. e-mail

MARINES, Henry; '93 BS; JD SJU Law Sch.; Asst. DA; Kings Cnty. Dist. Atty., 350 Jay St., Brooklyn, NY 11201; r. 641 E 13th St. Apt. 3d, New York, NY 10009. e-mail

MARINI, Ivette '97 (See Marini de Aguilar, Mrs. Ivette).

MARINI DE AGUILAR, Mrs. Ivette, (Ivette Marini); '97 BS; AS City Techincal Clg.; 95 Willow Ave., Cornwall, NY 12518, 914 534-3457; *Roxi Aguilar;* Roxi Alexander.

MARINO, Carmine L.; '84 BA; 7251 NW 24th Ct., Margate, FL 33063.

MARINO, Vincent D.; '76 BS; 480 Burkhard Ave., Williston Park, NY 11596.

MARINOFF, Gary A.; '82 BA; Actor; r. 303 W. 66th St., New York, NY 10023, 212 873-7093.

MARIO, John R.; '79 MS; 181 Brookside Dr., Fairfield, CT 06430, 203 259-0642.

MARION, Dorothy M.; '89 BA; Tchr.; r. 1974 LaFontaine Ave., Apt. 2 A, Bronx, NY 10457, 718 299-4155; Robert Jr., Winsor.

MARION, Mary A.; '76 BA; AA; Retired; r. 14250 56th Rd, Flushing, NY 11355.

MARITA, Rose B.; '99 BA; Retail; r. 153 Vermilyea Ave. 4F, New York, NY 10034, 212 569-4504.

MARK, Harry; '98 BA; BMS; Lifespire, 87-21 121st St., Richmond Hill, NY 11418, 718 441-8200; r. 78-47 65th St., Glendale, NY 11385, 718 821-2039. e-mail

MARKERT, Anthony; '91 MA; 64 Rock Rd., Ridgefield, CT 06877.

MARKEY, John F.; '76 BS; 1753 E 36th St., Brooklyn, NY 11234.

MARKEY, Peter; '85 BS; 40 Daley Pl., Apt. 218, Lynbrook, NY 11563.

MARKIEWICZ, Tom A.; '97 BS; 60-36 Flushing Ave., Maspeth, NY 11378, 718 326-1863.

MARKMAN, Michael; '80 MA; 530 E 20th St. Apt. 9g, New York, NY 10009.

MARKOWITZ, Gerald; 160 W 97th St. Apt. 12l, New York, NY 10025.

MARKOWITZ, Mark; 88 Lincoln St., Montclair, NY 07042, 973 783-9067.

MARKOWITZ, Matthew; '95 BS; 27 Pond Hill Ave., Warwick, NY 10990, 914 986-0888.

MARKOWITZ, Paul B.; '89 BA; 2459 Bragg St. # Pri, Brooklyn, NY 11235, 718 645-7980.

MARKOWITZ, Thomas; '79 BA; 1379 E 19th St., Brooklyn, NY 11230, 718 627-6861.

MARKS, Bettina R.; '93 MA; 333 E. 23rd St., New York, NY 10010, 315 361-0113.

MARKS, Debbie A.; '84 MPA; 515 W 59 St. #21, New York, NY 10019, 315 361-0113.

MARKS, John G.; '74 BS; MPS C W Post, JD Benj Cardozo Sch. of Law; Judge; Nassau Cnty. Dist. Ct., 99 Main St., Hempstead, NY 11550, 516 572-2153; *Patricia;* Elizabeth, Jillian. e-mail

MARLIN, Susan E.; '75 BA; 900 Schenectady Ave., Brooklyn, NY 11203.

MARLOVITCH, Elaine A.; '74 BA; 562 W. 52th St., New York, NY 10019.

MARLOW, Kidada; '97 BS; AS Rockland Community Clg.; Wireless Exec. Spec.; AT&T Wireless Svcs., 15 E. Midland Ave., Paramus, NJ 07652; r. 21 Crystal St., Spring Vly., NY 10977, 914 425-6250.

MARMOL, Julie; '92 BS; 10824 37th Dr. # 1, Flushing, NY 11368, 718 639-0601.

MARMOLEJOS, Winston; '92 BA; 512 W. 135 St., New York, NY 10031.

MAROLDA, William G.; '79 MA; 1848 Tenbroeck Ave., Bronx, NY 10461.

MARONE, Anne L.; '79 MA; 115-78 224th St., Cambria Hts., NY 11411.

MARONE, Dominic J.; '90 BA; 7 Weaver St., Staten Island, NY 10312, 718 948-8145.

MAROONEY, Margaret A.; '81 BA; 225 Van Sicklen St., Brooklyn, NY 11223, 718 623-9693.

MAROTTA, James A.; '80 MPA; 8628 110th St., Jamaica, NY 11418.

MAROTTA, Michael G.; '79 BS; 120 Fairview Rd, Massapequa, NY 11758, 516 798-8510.

MAROTTA, Michelle; '95 BS; Asst.; H.P. Mavica Bail Bond Agcy., 284 Atlantic Ave., Brooklyn, NY 11201, 718 855-4994; r. 351 Dahill Rd, Brooklyn, NY 11218, 718 854-5791.

MARQUEZ, Elizabeth; '86 BA; 5015 Clarendon Rd, Brooklyn, NY 11203, 718 284-6670.

MARQUEZ, Jimmy; '95 AS; 2793 Claflin Ave. # P, Bronx, NY 10468, 718 295-9209.

MARQUEZ, Melinda E.; '99 BS; AS Suffolk Community Clg.; Rsch. Interviewer; Montefiore Med. Ctr; r. 1585 Odell St. Apt. Md, Bronx, NY 10462, 718 824-3240.

MARQUEZ, Miguel A.; '80 AS; 107 Cherrywood Dr., Gaithersburg, MD 20878.

MARQUEZ-DREW, Felix; '85 BA; 2951 Dewitt Pl. 1st Fl., Bronx, NY 10469.

MARRA, Anthony J., Esq.; '74 BS; JD CUNY Law Sch.; Deputy Chief NYCPD/Atty.; NYCPD/Michael Montesano PC, 2820 Snyder Ave., Brooklyn, NY 11226, 718 287-3266; r. 49 Livermore Ave., Staten Island, NY 10302, 718 273-9617; *Arlene;* Frank, Christine.

MARRERO, Andy; '92 BA; 886 Irvine St., Bronx, NY 10474, 718 589-3764.

MARRERO, Jose L.; '97 BS; 1737 Taylor Ave., Bronx, NY 10460, 718 655-6637.

MARRERO, Jose N.; '83 BS; Detective; NYPD, 25 Pct, 120E 119th St., New York, NY 10035, 212 860-6521; r. 36 Maple Dr., Mahopac, NY 10541; *Elsie;* Melissa.

MARRERO, Leticia L.; '83 BS; 301 Harman St. Apt. 1l, Brooklyn, NY 11237, 718 399-9449.

MARRERO, Miguel; '96 BA; 58 John St., Staten Island, NY 10302.

MARRERO, Ms. Rosa M.; '99 BS; Legal Secy.; Clifford Chance Rogers & Wells LLP, 200 Park Ave., New York, NY 10166; r. 34-06 45th St. Apt. 1E, Astoria, NY 11101, 718 848-2176.

MARRERO, William; '93 BS; AAS Kingsborough Community; Retired; NYS Correctional Officer; r. 2927 Smithfield Dr., Orlando, FL 32837; *Angela;* Andis, Andrew, Christine.

MARRIOTT, Nirvana '96 (See Macdonald, Mrs. Nirvana L.).

MARRO, Elizabeth A.; '87 BS; 216 Spring St., Staten Island, NY 10304, 718 273-9343.

MARRONE, Gerald H.; '82 BS; Sr. Parole Ofcr.; Div. of Parole, 208 Commerce Pl., Elizabeth, NJ 07201, 908 965-2973; r. 41 Payne Ave., Midland Park, NJ 07432.

MARS, Emmanuel; '92 BS; 859 E. 55th St., Brooklyn, NY 11234, 718 219-1493.

MARS, Nadeige; '94 BA; Public Health Advisor; NYC Dept. of Health, 125 Worth St., New York, NY 10013; r. 3815 Avenue I # 2, Brooklyn, NY 11210, 718 951-3939.

MARSEILLE, Bogard; '98 BA; AAS Rockland Community Clg.; 224 Kearsing Pkwy., Monsey, NY 10952, 914 352-2560. e-mail

MARSH, Judy C.; '97 BA; 359 E. 51st St., Brooklyn, NY 11203, 718 451-4614.

MARSH, Warren S.; '74 BA; 646 E 230th St., Bronx, NY 10466, 718 798-7712.

MARSHALL, Cliff; '96 BS; Sgt.; NYPD, 1 Police Plz., New York, NY 10038; r. 86-31 56th Ave., Elmhurst, NY 11373, 718 803-3959; *Irene.*

MARSHALL, David; '92 BS; JD Yeshiva; Atty.; Cybersettle.com; r. Bronx, NY 10463; *Renita Bowen.* e-mail

MARSHALL, Edward S.; '92 MA; PSYD Univ. of Denver; Psychologist; r. 1426 S Pennsylvania St., Denver, CO 80210, 303 748-7007.

MARSHALL, Glenn T.; '92 MPA; BA, AS Mercy Clg.; Police Ofcr./Town Historian; Town of New Windsor, 555 Union Ave., Fire Comm'r.-Town of New Windsor, New Windsor, NY 12553, 914 565-7000; r. 121 Cedar Ave., New Windsor, NY 12553, 914 562-5782. e-mail

MARSHALL, Mrs. Irene, (Irene Sanchez); '98 BA; Data Base Admin.; Davis Polk & Wardwell, 450 Lexington Ave., New York, NY 10017, 212 450-5309; r. 86-31 56th Ave. #3r, Elmhurst, NY 11373, 718 803-3959; *Cliff.* e-mail

MARSHALL, Joseph; '73 BS; AAPARALE Prince George Comm. Clg., PILOTCTF; Pilot-in-Command; Corporate Airline, Queens, NY 11412, 631 842-4588; r. POB 110741, Cambria Hts., NY 11411; *Christopher, Patricia, Robert.*

MARSHALL, Luis R.; '78 BS; MS Long Island Univ.; 1st Deputy Supt.; State of NY Dept. of Correctional Svcs., Coxsackie Correctional Facility, POB 200, Coxsackie, NY 12051, 518 731-2781; r. 10 Miller Rd, Poughkeepsie, NY 12603, 914 452-1665; *Carol;* Alfredo, Kisha, Tanja.

MARSHALL, Mauline A.; '88 BA; 104-36 203 St., Hollis, NY 11412, 718 868-1512.

MARSHALL, Ms. Monique R.; '96 BA; Probation Ofcr.; Dept. of Probation, 198 Linden Blvd., Brooklyn, NY 11226, 718 282-6761; r. POB 470 588, Brooklyn, NY 11247, 718 604-2282.

MARSHALL, Noel; '95 BS; 14538 123rd Ave., Jamaica, NY 11436, 718 545-9361.

MARSHALL, Paula '97 (See Marshall-Murrell, Paula).

MARSHALL, Vanessa M.; '89 BA; MASTERS Hunter Sch. Social Work; Social Worker; Children & Family Svcs. Agcy., 400 6th St. SW, Washington, DC 20024, 240 568-0898; r. 9562 Muirkirk Rd., Laurel, MD 20708, 240 568-0898.

MARSHALL, Vernon D.; '92 BA; Retired; Dept. of Corrections, City of New York; r. 746 E 93rd St., Brooklyn, NY 11236, 718 498-8989; *Marjorie;* Cheryl, Sherwyn.

MARSHALL-MURRELL, Paula, (Paula Marshall); '97 BA; MS ED Brooklyn Clg.; Guid. Couns.; PS 190 Elem. Sch., 590 Sheffield Ave., Brooklyn, NY 11207, 718 346-4328; r. 649 Empire Blvd. #64, Brooklyn, NY 11213, 718 774-2449; *Johnny Murrell;* Jennel.

MARSHALL-MYLES, Coleen; '97 BA; Legal Asst.; Kings Cnty. Dist. Atty., 350 Jay St., Brooklyn, NY 11201, 718 250-2513; r. 113-29 205 St., St. Albans, NY 11412, 718 776-3712; *Patrick Myles.* e-mail

MARSICOVETERE, Louis; '92 BS; 1722 61st St., Brooklyn, NY 11204.

MARSLOW, Margaret; '90 BS, '97 MA; 10611 31st Ave., Flushing, NY 11369.

MARTE, Carmen; '94 BA; 3528 95th St. # 3, Flushing, NY 11372, 718 478-8970.

MARTE, Elsa; '95 MA; 227 W 137th St., New York, NY 10030, 315 738-8933.

MARTE, Sandra; '94 BA; 89-07 34th Ave. #4T, Jackson Hts., NY 11372.

MARTELLA, Joseph; '77 MA; 21 Norman Rd, Montclair, NJ 07043.

MARTELLO, Michael; '96 BS; 323 147th Pl., Whitestone, NY 11357, 718 767-5238.

MARTI, John L.; '89 BS; Nassau Cnty. Police Ofcr.; 8th Precinct, Levittown, NY 11756; r. 20 Henry Ave., Selden, NY 11784.

MARTI, Lauren B.; '82 BA; 430 Fairway Rd, Linden, NJ 07036.

MARTIN, Alexandra; '97 BA, '98 BA; 2366 Fairway Rd, Huntingdon Vly., PA 19006, 215 657-3640.

MARTIN, Angela; '72 BA; 1333 Regal Heights Dr., Lithonia, GA 30058, 770 465-0772.

MARTIN, Angelique P.; '77 MA; 842 E 227th St., Bronx, NY 10466, 718 328-8749.

MARTIN, Annette M.; '88 BA; 329 E 26 St. 1st Fl., Brooklyn, NY 11226, 718 230-9025.

MARTIN, Betty J.; '78 BA; 4129 Teton St., Marrero, LA 70072, 504 368-3150.

MARTIN, Beverly S. '97 (See Martin-Baez, Beverly S.).

MARTIN, Carol A.; 243 Brownway, Benton Harbor, MI 49022, 616 925-5797.

MARTIN, Cecelia; '94 BS, '96 MPA; 560 Malcolm X Blvd. Apt. 6j, New York, NY 10037, 315 336-3156.

MARTIN, Dennis E.; '80 MA; 52 Oceanview Pl., Staten Island, NY 10308, 718 448-9562.

MARTIN, Duane; '88 BS, '92 MPA; Probation Ofcr.; NYC, 210 Joralemon St., Brooklyn, NY 11201, 718 802-3963; r. 545 Dean St., Brooklyn, NY 11217, 718 622-3433.

MARTIN, James (Jim) P.; '98 BS; Police Ofcr.; 46 Precinct; r. 109 N. Ridge St., Port Chester, NY 10573, 914 939-0307.

MARTIN, Jeanne E.; '93 BA; After Sch. Dir.; The Renaissance After Sch. at SP9, 100 W. 84th St., New York, NY 10024, 212 787-1200; r. 1225 Park Ave. # 10a, New York, NY 10128, 212 348-0815; *John Farago;* Belle, Sarah, Max.

MARTIN, Michael; '95 BA, '99 MA; 35-61 92nd St., Jackson Hts., NY 11372, 718 271-8424.

MARTIN, Michael A.; '84 BA; 2140 33rd St., Long Island City, NY 11105, 718 721-8857.

MARTIN, Patrick J.; '76 BA; 1118 Olmstead Ave., Bronx, NY 10472, 718 379-8687.

MARTIN, Richard A.; '80 BA; 97-09 160 Ave., Howard Bch., NY 11414, 718 464-0928.

MARTIN, Robert A.; '75 MPA; BA Wilkes Univ.; Private Investigator; R.A. Martin & Assocs., 8 Harriot Ave., Harrington Park, NJ 07640, 201 767-8186; r. same; *Linda;* Robert Jr., Kimberly. e-mail

MARTIN, Sherly M.; '89 BS; 108-10 86th Ave., Richmond Hill, NY 11418, 718 529-0082.

MARTIN, Teresa R.; '93 BA; 12 Birch Ct. # 12, Long Beach, NY 11561, 516 565-9248.

MARTIN, LCDR Vertel T.; '82 AS, '89 BS; MS NY Inst. of Technology; Police Lt.; New York City Police Dept., 315 Hudson St. 3rd Fl., New York, NY, 10013, 212 741-8401; r. 8118 268th St., Floral Park, NY 11004, 718 444-2049. e-mail

MARTIN-BAEZ, Beverly S., (Beverly S. Martin); '97 BS; PARA NY Univ.; Paralegal; Mendes & Mount, 750 7th Ave., New York, NY 10019, 212 261-8118; r. 5511 5th Ave., Apt. 4R, Brooklyn, NY 11220, 718 439-1693; *Thomas.*

MARTINETTI, Tatiana; '91 BS; 527 W. 47th St., New York, NY 10036.

MARTINEZ, Alfonso V.; '95 BA; 8920 55th Ave. Apt. 5l, Flushing, NY 11373, 718 426-6467.

MARTINEZ, Alma E.; '83 BS; 665 52nd St., Brooklyn, NY 11220, 718 282-0723.

MARTINEZ, Annette; '87 BS; 765 Hendrix St., Brooklyn, NY 11207, 718 282-0723.

MARTINEZ, Bryant; '93 BS; 205 E 82nd St. # 50, New York, NY 10028, 315 732-3761.

MARTINEZ, Carlos E.; '81 BS; 900 Pkwy. Pl., Peekskill, NY 10566, 914 337-3830.

MARTINEZ, Deborah; '93 BA; 2059 Homer Ave., Bronx, NY 10473, 718 430-0134.

MARTINEZ, Delfin; '91 BS; 1795 Riverside Dr. Apt. 3b, New York, NY 10034, 315 732-3761.

MARTINEZ, Desiree C.; '86 BS; Paralegal; Brooklyn Dist. Atty. Ofc.; r. 352 Eastern Pkwy., Brooklyn, NY 11225, 718 363-9601.

MARTINEZ, Duandie; '93 BA; 520 Richmond Ave., Deltona, FL 32725, 407 328-4390.

MARTINEZ, Edgar; '97 BA, '98 BA; Fraud Investigator; NYC Human Resources Admin., 320 Schermerhorn St., Brooklyn, NY 11217; r. 357-52nd St., Brooklyn, NY 11220, 718 567-0679. e-mail

MARTINEZ, Elizabeth; '98 BS; City Couns. Member Aide; NYC Counsel, City Hall, New York, NY 10007, 718 994-9951; r. 1580 Pelham Pkwy. S, Bronx, NY 10461, 718 792-4781; *Daniel;* Daniel M. Jr., Antonella M., Danielle M. e-mail

MARTINEZ, Esperanza; '78 BA; 82 Claywood Dr., Brentwood, NY 11717.

MARTINEZ, Eugene; '77 BS; 105 Leverett Ave., Staten Island, NY 10308.

MARTINEZ, Felix, Jr.; '97 BS; 128 Van Siclen Ave., Brooklyn, NY 11207.

MARTINEZ, George A.; '79 BS; 102-40 62 Ave. #4D, Forest Hills, NY 11375, 718 520-7547.

MARTINEZ, Irving; '93 BS; 522 52nd St. #3, Brooklyn, NY 11220, 718 346-8564.

MARTINEZ, Jocelyne; '95 BS; 42 Wendover Rd, Yonkers, NY 10705, 914 476-3671.

MARTINEZ, Jose B.; '80 BS; 1323 Rosedale Ave., Bronx, NY 10472, 718 329-9706.

MARTINEZ, Joselin; '99 BA; 88 26 211 St., Jamaica, NY 11427, 718 468-9481.

MARTINEZ, Joseph; '75 BA; CERT.; Sgt; NYPD, Division of Sch. Safety; r. 1311 Thieriot Ave., Bronx, NY 10472, 718 792-9688; Christopher M.

MARTINEZ, Kendall; '89 BS; 260 Audubon Ave. Frnt 2, New York, NY 10033, 315 732-3761.

MARTINEZ, Lucy; '91 BS; 9317 93rd Ave. # 2, Jamaica, NY 11421, 718 457-7579.

MARTINEZ, Margaret; '91 BA, '97 MA; Sergeant; NYPD, 1 Police Plz., New York, NY 10038, 212 374-5000; r. 1799 E 51st St., Brooklyn, NY 11234, 718 336-5172. e-mail

MARTINEZ, Margherita; '99 MA; BA St. John's Univ.; 137 Neptune Ave., N. Babylon, NY 11704, 631 587-8820.

MARTINEZ, Maria O.; '98 BA; 31-85 Cres. St. 107, Long Island City, NY 11106, 718 545-7314.

MARTINEZ, Marisol; '97 BS; Law Student; NY Law Sch.; r. 81-11 Pettit Ave., Elmhurst, NY 11373, 718 899-2767. e-mail

MARTINEZ, Marlene; '89 BS; 2131 73rd St., Flushing, NY 11370, 718 417-8861.

MARTINEZ, Miguel E.; '95 BS; 4791 Broadway #2F, New York, NY 10034, 315 732-3761.

MARTINEZ, Oscar A.; '96 BA, '98 MA; Mental Health Spec.; Riker's Island Dept. of Corrections, Saint Barnabas Hospital, ARDC; Hazen St., Queens, NY 11412, 718 546-7130; r. 4011 Kings Hwy. #4B, Brooklyn, NY 11234, 718 338-4758.

MARTINEZ, Richard; '94 BS; 1329 College Ave., Bronx, NY 10456.

MARTINEZ, Sandra; '95 AS; 1728 New Haven Ave., Far Rockaway, NY 11691, 718 868-8998.

MARTINEZ, Santiago; '93 AS; 241-07 86th Rd. P, Bellerose, NY 11426, 718 278-0483.

MARTINEZ, Theresa; '92 BA; POB 486, Bronx, NY 10468. e-mail

MARTINEZ, Victor M.; '95 BS; 1040 Gerard Ave. # 2, Bronx, NY 10452, 718 328-9460.

MARTINEZ, William; '77 BA; 1357 Washington Ave., Bronx, NY 10456, 718 792-8436.

MARTINEZ, Yesenia; '97 BS; 39-78 51st Apt.2, Woodside, NY 11377.

MARTINI, John F.; '77 BS; 9416 Pitkin Ave., Jamaica, NY 11417, 718 848-1858.

MARTINO, Angelo; '76 AS; 71 Fox Ct., Manorville, NY 11949, 631 878-5084.

MARTINO, Bruce F.; '77 BS; 2571 Woodhull Ave., Bronx, NY 10469, 718 597-4231.

MARTINO, Steven J.; '76 BS; 1271 80th St., Brooklyn, NY 11228, 718 399-1388.

MARTINO, Victor J.; '87 BA; 157 Beach 132nd St., Far Rockaway, NY 11694.

MARTINO, Vincent P.; 1 Path Plz., # 4, Jersey City, NJ 07306.

MARTIR, Kirby; '78 BS; Mgr. Forensic Sci. Lab; Yonkers Police Dept., Judge Cacace Justice Ctr., Forensic Sci. Lab - 104 S. Broadway, Yonkers, NY 10701, 914 377-7756; r. 11 Winston Ln., Garrison, NY 10524, 914 739-3699; *Mary Ellen;* Nicole. e-mail

MARTOCCI, Rocco A.; '76 MA; 41 Wellington Ct. Apt. 1i, Staten Island, NY 10314, 718 605-5529.

MARTORANO, Thomas A.; '78 MA; BA CCNY; Police Lt.; Suffolk Cnty. Police Dept., Yaphank Ave., Yaphank, NY 11980, 631 854-8382; r. Manorville, NY 11949. e-mail

MARTOS, Mrs. Elena L.; '84 BS; Ret. Court Clerk; State of NY; r. 415 E 187th St. Apt. 3 E, Bronx, NY 10458, 718 367-8409; *Mario Favier.*

MARTTERER, Amy K.; '96 MA; BA Marist Clg.; Asst. Coord./Nonsecured Detention; Berkshire Farm Ctr., 13640 Rte. 22, Canaan, NY 12029, 518 781-3785; r. 73 Wildwood Hts., W. Sand Lake, NY 12196, 518 674-2649.

MARTUCCI, June R.; '91 BS; 21 West St., Apt. 23C, New York, NY 10006, 315 735-4107.

MARTY, Maritza '97 (See Marty-Cuevas, Maritza).

MARTY-CUEVAS, Maritza, (Maritza Marty); '97 BA, CERT; Police Ofcr.; r. 2750 Johnson Ave. Apt. 7D, Riverdale, NY 10463, 718 432-2898; *Johnny Cuevas.*

MARUCCI, Barbara A.; '79 BS; 918 8th Ave., Brooklyn, NY 11215, 718 499-1416.

MARULANDA, William; '98 BA; 50-55 46th St. Bsmt., Woodside, NY 11377, 718 937-5864.

MARUS, James L.; '85 BS; 42-04 64th St., Woodside, NY 11377, 718 721-8848.

MARVELLI, Albert J.; '92 AS, '94 BS; 694 Saint Lukes Pl., N. Baldwin, NY 11510.

MARZOLI, Joseph L.; '74 BS; 1200 Beach 9 St., Far Rockaway, NY 11691.

MASCARI, John C.; '88 BS; JD Pace Univ. Sch. of Law; Atty.; Harrington, Ocko & Monk, LLP, 81 Main St., Ste. 215, White Plains, NY 10601, 914 686-4800; r. 11 Lake Marie Ln., Bedford Hls., NY 10507, 914 241-7952. e-mail

MASCIA, Joseph; '81 BS; 60-23 69 Ln., Maspeth, NY 11378, 718 777-8787.

MASCOLL, Carolyn P.; '84 BS; 442 Prospect Pl., Brooklyn, NY 11238, 718 444-3969.

MASELLA, Richard P.; '82 MA; 89 Little Silver Pkwy., Little Silver, NJ 07739.

MASELLI, John M.; '83 MA; 1980 Park Ave. #15, San Jose, CA 95126, 408 374-9245.

MASLOVA, Olga; '95 BS; 380 Avenue U, Apt. 1C, Brooklyn, NY 11223.

MASON, Marcia C.; '95 BA; Social Case Worker; West Chester Cnty., 914 665-3843; r. 41 Rochelle Pl., New Rochelle, NY 10801.

MASOTTI, Alexander; '87 BA; 2636 Ford St., Brooklyn, NY 11235, 718 891-8597.

MASSE, Jennifer; MPA; 1919 Linden Farms, Matinecock, NY 11560, 516 759-5918.

MASSEY, David; '97 BS; 1967 Cole Dr., E. Meadow, NY 11554, 516 794-0565.

MASSEY, Ritesh; '99 BA; Police Ofcr.; NYPD, Precinct #7, Bronx, NY 10456, 718 292-6161; r. 3556 Rochambeau Ave. 4K, Bronx, NY 10467, 718 231-2470. e-mail

MASTERSON, Charles; '95 BA; AS Kingsborough CC; New York, NY 10048; r. New York, NY 10036. e-mail

MASTERSON, Kevin M.; '89 BS; 35-30 206 St., Bayside, NY 11361, 718 457-6558.

MASTORIDES, George F.; '81 BS; 2343 Enright Rd, Far Rockaway, NY 11691.

MASTRONARDY, Michael; '79 MA; 1235 Coulter St., Toms River, NJ 08755, 732 341-1693.

MASUCCI, James J.; '82 BS; Lt. New York State Court Offices; NYS Ct. Offices, Targee St., Staten Island, NY 10304, 718 390-8406; r. 140 Manila Ave., Staten Island, NY 10306, 718 987-8992.

MATA, Angelina E.; '97 BS; Fraud Investigator; Human Resources Admin., 250 Church St., New York, NY 10013, 212 274-5673; r. 400 Ft. Washington Ave. 3D, New York, NY 10033, 212 568-4533. e-mail

MATALON, Victor C.; '80 MA; 190-05 Radnor Rd., Jamaica, NY 11423, 718 575-4163.

MATEO, Edelmira A.; '95 BA; 82 Wadsworth Ave. Apt. 53, New York, NY 10033.

MATEO, Gladys E.; '97 BA; Clinical Data Mgr.; Pfizer, Inc., 235 E. 42nd St., New York, NY 10017, 212 733-3344; r. 2910 Wallace Ave., Bronx, NY 10467. e-mail

MATEO, Josue; '81 BS; 130 Columbia St. # 1, New York, NY 10002, 212 674-0288.

MATEO, Richard E.; '76 BA; 249 6th Ave., Brooklyn, NY 11215.

MATEO, Yudelca A.; '95 BS; 509 W 179th St. # 1, New York, NY 10033.

MATERA, Michael A.; '73 BS; 2021 Ryder St., Brooklyn, NY 11234.

MATESICH, Susan M. '82 (See Grgas, Susan M.).

MATHAI, Satish; '95 BS; 2214 Story Ave., Bronx, NY 10473, 718 823-0714.

MATHEIS, Jean; '85 BS; 268 W 21st St., Deer Park, NY 11729.

MATHESON, Alethia A.; '93 BS; 448 E 94th St. Apt. 3d, Brooklyn, NY 11212, 718 467-8452.

MATHESON, Gerard J.; '78 BS; 4665 188th St., Flushing, NY 11358.

MATHEUS, Janice M.; '95 BS; 246 Centre Ave. Apt. 5l, New Rochelle, NY 10805, 914 235-6037.

MATHEWS, Achoy O.; '81 MA; 26 N Tyson Ave., Floral Park, NY 11001, 516 897-3900.

MATHEWS, Frank J.; '77 BS; Pres./ Qigong Tchr.; East West Qigong Way, Inc., Cranford, NJ 07016; r. 7 Pine St., Cranford, NJ 07016, 908 276-2469; *Susan.* e-mail

MATHEWS, Onica O.; '99 BA; Juvenile Correction Ofcr.; Harlem Valley Secure Ctr., Wingdale, NY 12594; r. 2340 North Ave., Apt. 1F, Bridgeport, CT 06604, 203 333-6474. e-mail

MATHIS, Caliph T.; '87 BA; 1062 Nostrand Ave., Brooklyn, NY 11225, 718 467-6509.

MATHWICH, Mary C.; '96 BA; 1229 1st Ave. Apt. 1, New York, NY 10021.

MATIAS, Awilda; '85 BS; 1448 Herkimer St., Brooklyn, NY 11233, 718 342-1174.

MATIAS, Edgar; '95 BA; 991 Myrtle Ave. Apt. 3c, Brooklyn, NY 11206, 718 633-6604.

MATIZ, Judith A. '86 (See Conway, Judith A.).

MATOS, Angel; '83 BS; 40-65 Carpenter Ave., Bronx, NY 10466, 718 365-2316.

MATOS, Edwin A.; '98 BA; CERT. Metropolitan Career Inst.; Correction Ofc.; Justice Dept. Bur. of Prisons, New York, NY 10007; r. 44-14 Newton Rd. #1L, Long Island City, NY 11103, 718 204-6976.

MATOS, Lisette; '99 MA; 2067 Seward Ave., Bronx, NY 10473, 718 823-3589.

MATOS, Nelson-Ness; '85 BS; Private Investigator; Matos Investigations, POB 6565, Astoria, NY 11106, 917 672-5606; r. POB 6565, Long Island City, NY 11106, 917 672-5606. e-mail

MATOS, Venessa M.; '99 BA; 1809 Albemarle Rd B58, Brooklyn, NY 11226, 718 287-5639.

MATOS, Willie; '94 BA; 90 Baruch Dr. # 1, New York, NY 10002.

MATRISCIANO, Joan; '91 MA; 28 Rockaway Pkwy., Valley Stream, NY 11580.

MATRONI, Mark; 25-23 E. 26, Brooklyn, NY 11235, 718 998-7486.

MATSUOKA, Andrew H.; '94 BS; 5822 41st Ave., Woodside, NY 11377.

MATTEIS, Salvatore; '75 MPA; AS Lehmann, BS; Deputy Chief Retired; NYCPD, 1 Police Plz., New York, NY 10038, 718 885-2431; r. 54 Marine St., Bronx, NY 10464; *Jean;* Wayne, Barbara, Andrew.

MATTERSON, Eric; '92 BS; Per Diem Substitute Tchr.; Bd. of Educ., 65 Court St., Brooklyn, NY 11201; r. 382 E. 32nd St. Apt. .d1, Brooklyn, NY 11226, 718 940-3529; *Shannon.*

MATTHEW, Kevin S.; '98 BS; 304 SW 85th Ter., #103, Pembroke Pines, FL 33025, 954 437-9743.

MATTHEW, Monique C.; '99 BA; 15 Gouveneur Pl. 7, Bronx, NY 10456, 718 829-5872.

MATTHEW, Raymond T.; '91 BS, '91 CERT; 16564 Nanticoke Way, 3rd Fl., Woodbridge, VA 22191, 718 296-4644.

MATTHEWS, Eljay; 720 Lenox Ave. 12L, New York, NY 10039, 315 831-4291.

MATTHEWS, Jermaine; '96 BS; 3337 Mott Ave., Far Rockaway, NY 11691, 718 392-3653.

MATTHEWS, Karen A.; '98 BA; HRIS Proj. Leader; Mt. Sinai Med. Ctr., 19 E. 98th St., New York, NY 10029, 212 241-9762; r. 931 E. 221 St., Bronx, NY 10469, 718 652-3818; *Steve Edwards.* e-mail

MATTHEWS, Kevin E.; '77 BS; 607 Belted Kingfisher Dr. N, Palm Harbor, FL 34683, 727 724-9294.

MATTHEWS, Tracy S.; '86 BS; 1537 Nelson Ave., Bronx, NY 10452, 718 583-1025.

MATTIACE, Christopher; '74 BS; 49 S Washington Ave., Hartsdale, NY 10530.

MATTIASICH, Fabio L.; '77 BS; Compliance With Food & Drug Admin.; r. 384 Arkansas Dr., Valley Stream, NY 11580.

MATTSON, Andrew; '95 BS; 9635 72nd Rd, Flushing, NY 11375.

MATURINE, Latoya D.; '98 BA; 147-18 Glassboro Ave. 1st Fl., Jamaica, NY 11435, 718 444-8121.

MATUSIAK, William; '90 BS; 3741 Cranberry Ln., Shrub Oak, NY 10588.

MATUSZAK, Diane L., (Diane L. Giuliano); '99 BA; Detective/Notary; NYPD, 1 Police Plz., Specializes In Private Security, New York, NY 10038, 212 334-0635; r. College Pt., NY 11356; *Michael,Matthew.*

MATUTE, Gaynell; '96 CERT; 11433 135th St., Jamaica, NY 11420, 718 565-6773.

MATYSIAK, Daniela S. '79 (See Kitson, Daniela S.).

MATZ, Markus A.; '96 BS; 2645 Harding Ave., Bronx, NY 10465, 718 518-1437.

MAUGHAN, William F.; '72 MPA; BBA Baruch Clg.; Retired Inspector; NYC Police Dept./USMCR; r. 1336 Casey Key Dr., Punta Gorda, FL 33950, 941 575-6920; *Mary C.;* Joan, William, Eileen, James, Nancy, Michael, Elizabeth, Jennifer, Brian.

MAULL, Patricia; 130 E. 75th St., New York, NY 10021.

MAURER, Daniel E.; '95 MA; 64-34 102 St., Rego Park, NY 11374, 718 894-6554.

MAURER, Michael J.; '76 BS; 19 Deer Meadow Dr., W. Nyack, NY 10994, 914 358-0053.

MAURER, Robert T.; '75 MA; 1216 E 35 St., Brooklyn, NY 11210, 718 266-2525.

MAURICE, Ms. Geraldine; '97 BA; Elem. Tchr.; St. Francis of Assisi Sch., 400 Lincoln Rd., Brooklyn, NY 11225, 718 778-3700; r. 9335 Vanderveer St., Queens Village, Queens Vlg., NY 11428, 718 740-5456. e-mail

MAURICE-MATTHEWS, D.; '92 BS; 116-01 218th St., Cambria Hts., NY 11411, 718 261-1955.

MAURILUS, Pierre S.; '96 BA; Housing Asst.; NYC Housing Authority, 1 Fordham Plz., Bronx, NY 10458, 718 329-7786; r. 185 Ardsley Loop #9d, Brooklyn, NY 11239, 718 642-3744. e-mail

MAURO, Mario F.; '93 BS; Retired-Police Dept.; r. 31 Avery Ct., Nesconset, NY 11767; *Mary;* Paul, Mary, Joseph.

MAURO, Patrick; '89 BS; 121 Milton St., Brooklyn, NY 11222, 718 383-7682.

MAURO, Thomas A.; '76 BA; POB 1032, Passaic, NJ 07055.

MAUTE, Lora L.; '84 BS; 84-42 129 St., Kew Gardens, NY 11415.

MAXIM, Ana; '93 BS; Computer Operator; GTE; r. 1993 Beaver Springs Ln. Apt. B, Norcross, GA 30071, 770 246-0779; *Ilie;* Estera.

MAXIM, Ilie; '93 BS; Computer Operator; Coca-Cola; r. 1993 Beaver Springs Ln. Apt. B, Norcross, GA 30071, 770 246-0779; *Ana;* Estera. e-mail

MAXIMUM, Andre A., (Andre Anderson); '96 BS; Investigator; Liberty Mutual, 2950 Expy. Dr. S., Islandia, NY 11722, 800 445-0446; r. 676 St. Nicholas Ave., New York, NY 10030. e-mail

MAXSON, Cree L.; '91 MA; 44th St. 7th Ave., Brooklyn, NY 11217.

MAXWELL, Gwendolyn; '98 BS; 773 Concourse Village Est. #8K, Bronx, NY 10456, 718 515-2566.

MAXWELL, Peadar G.; '95 BA; 4849 45th St., Flushing, NY 11377, 718 699-5733.

MAY, Paul D.; '84 BS; Police Sergeant; NYPD; r. POB 402, Bronx, NY 10462, 518 373-8915. e-mail

MAYBURY, Kevin C.; '76 BS; 50 Montell St., Staten Island, NY 10302.

MAYCOCK, Deborah D.; '95 BS; 5339 Penn Ave. S, Minneapolis, MN 55419.

MAYCOCK, Neville G.; '76 BS; 12039 224th St., Jamaica, NY 11411.

MAYER, Michael J.; '84 BS; 163 E New York Ave., Valley Stream, NY 11580, 516 487-8363.

MAYER, Robin L.; '99 MA; BA NYU; Mental Health Spec.; Manhattan Detention Ctr., 125 White St., New York, NY 10013, 212 225-1461; r. 434 E 75th St. #4A, New York, NY 10021, 212 755-2843; Anja.

MAYERS, John D., Jr.; '99 MA; Student; r. 194-31 115th Rd., St. Albans, NY 11412, 718 978-4280. e-mail

MAYNARD, Alicia J.; 225-15 Murdock Ave., Queens Vlg., NY 11429, 718 217-8723.

MAYNARD, Carol R.; '89 MPA; 108-07 37th Ave., Corona, NY 11368.

MAYNARD, Heather E.; '94 BS; AS Bronx Community Clg.; Serial Cataloging Clerk; US Ct. of Appeals Library, 2603 US Courthouse, New York, NY 10007, 212 857-8906; r. 4718 Bronx Blvd., Bronx, NY 10470, 718 325-2930.

MAYNARD, Reuben W.; '92 MPA; RR 1 Box 4030, Washburn, ME 04786, 207 455-5807.

MAYOL, Gerardo; '95 BS; 7016 60th St. # 2r, Flushing, NY 11385.

MAYOR, Lizette; '99 BA; Social Worker; r. 6056 Putnam Ave., Flushing, NY 11385, 718 497-1767.

MAYR, Louis A.; '95 BA, 2000 MA; Lt.; NYC Police Dept., New York, NY 10038; r. 6 Ceil Pl., Bethpage, NY 11714, 516 822-8912. e-mail

MAYS, Valerie N.; '99 BA; AAS New York Technical Clg.; Child Protective Spec.; Children Svcs.; r. 685 Gates Ave. 2B, Brooklyn, NY 11221, 718 574-0839.

MAYSONET, Christine L.; '99 BS; Law Student; Fordham Law Sch.; r. 2-24 Capstain Ct., College Pt., NY 11356, 718 767-4585. e-mail

MAYUSHAN, Avram M.; '92 BS; 180 Wave Rd, Manahawkin, NJ 08050, 609 698-6243.

MAZARIEGO, Andres; '97 BS, '98 BS; 248 Jefferson St., Brooklyn, NY 11237.

MAZEROLLE, Christian; '98 BS; Special Agt.; US Dept. of State, 26 Federal Plz., New York, NY 10278; r. 24 James Ct., Elmwood Park, NJ 07407, 201 797-5312.

MAZYCK, Marshall; '93 BS; 133 Harris Ave., Freeport, NY 11520.

MAZZA, Cajetan; '76 BA; Retired; r. 79 Highland Rd, Staten Island, NY 10308, 718 966-6166; *Barbara;* Anthony, Kathleen, Thomas, Michael, Barbara Ann.

MAZZA, Dolores R.; '80 BS; 590 19th St., Brooklyn, NY 11218, 718 437-4640.

MAZZA, Frank; '76 BA; POB 2458, Montauk, NY 11954.

MAZZELLA, James; '88 MA; 304 E. 151 St., Bronx, NY 10451, 718 654-5620.

MAZZELLA, Susan I.; '96 MA; 63-09 71st St., Middle Vlg., NY 11379.

MAZZONE, Gregory; '85 BS; 3 Truxton Rd, Dix Hills, NY 11746.

MC, Alister K.; '87 BS; 2166 Homecrest, Brooklyn, NY 11229, 718 495-2022.

MC, Anoff K.; '87 BS; 254 Covert St., Brooklyn, NY 11229, 718 495-2022.

MC, Cabe; '95 BS, '96 CERT; 6914 Ridge Blvd. # A, Brooklyn, NY 11209, 718 636-8576.

MC, Call T.; '90 MA; 501 E. Fordham Rd, Bronx, NY 10458, 718 994-5998.

MC, Corkle D.; '84 MA; 32 River Dr., Titusville, NJ 08560.

MC, Donald R.; '85 BS; 723 11th Ave., New York, NY 10019, 315 896-2415.

MC, Gowan W.; '93 BS; 105 Morningside Dr., Croton-on-Hudson, NY 10520.

MC, Nally L.; '87 MS; 60 School St., Northport, NY 11768.

MC, Nulty I.; '86 BS; 19 Bruce Ln., Farmingdale, NY 11735.

MC, Quade M.; '90 BS; 331 Sheafe Rd # Lot, Poughkeepsie, NY 12601, 518 789-3784.

MC, Quillan; '96 BA; POB 657, Cross River, NY 10518.

MCALEER, Gerard P.; '96 MPA; BS Salve Regina Univ.; Supv Special Agt.; US Drug Enforcement Admin., 700 Army Navy Dr., Arlington, VA 22202; r. 1211 S. Eads St. #413, Arlington, VA 22202, 703 751-2394.

MC ALEER, Joy; 69 Fifth Ave., New York, NY 10003, 315 896-2161.

MCALINEY, Kevin P.; '82 BA; 9402 216 St., Jamaica, NY 11428.

MC ALLISTER, Cathleen S.; '95 BS; 7 Carly Ct., Staten Island, NY 10309, 718 273-2991.

MC ALLISTER, Justice; '79 BA; 1122 New York Ave., Brooklyn, NY 11203, 718 940-9673.

MCALLISTER, Stephen; '94 MA; Capt.; NYPD, 1 Polics Plz., New York, NY 10038, 718 657-8186; r. 100 Walnut Ave., Floral Park, NY 11001, 516 922-6893. e-mail

MCALOON, Daniel K.; '95 BS; MA Lehman Clg.; English & Social Studies Tchr.; Middle Sch. 118, Bronx, NY 10457, 718 584-4950; r. 5600 Fieldston Rd., Bronx, NY 10471, 718 884-4987; *Francine.*

MCALPIN, William T., (Bill McAlpine); '99 MA; BS Empire State Clg.; Special Agent; US Customs, 6 World Trade Ctr., Ste. 508, New York, NY 10048, 212 637-3900; r. 146 Spencer Ave., Lynbrook, NY 11563, 516 593-8406.

MCALPINE, Bill '99 (See McAlpin, William T.).

MC ANDREW, Lois J.; '79 BS; Sgt; CUNY, New York, NY 10010; r. 655 Tysens Ln., Staten Island, NY 10306, 718 979-6254.

MC ANDREW, Paula L.; '78 BS; 210 Shields Rd, Red Hook, NY 12571, 518 789-3784.

MC ARDLE, Loretta; '94 BS; 19644 48th Ave., Flushing, NY 11365, 718 937-9555.

MC AREE, Anne M.; '76 BA; 453 E. 14th St., New York, NY 10009, 212 473-2827.

MCAULIFFE, John; '96 BS; 38 Mody Pl., Staten Island, NY 10310, 718 816-6156.

MCBAIN, Michael; '92 BS; 1115 Fdr Dr. # 12, New York, NY 10009.

MCBARNETTE, Wilfred; '83 MPA; 51 Mckenna Rd, Westbury, NY 11590.

MCBEAN, Mrs. Ghyslaine, (Ghyslaine Connor); '97 BA; Police Ofcr.; Suffolk Cnty. Police Dept., 555 Rte. 109, First Precinct, W. Babylon, NY 11704, 631 854-8100; r. 11 Wellington St., Hempstead, NY 11550; *Leslie.*

MC BRIDE, Hugh J.; '78 BS, '83 MA; 670 Rathbun Ave., Staten Island, NY 10312, 718 948-7671.

MC BRIDE, Richard H.; '78 BA; 18818 119th Rd, Jamaica, NY 11412, 718 454-4159.

MCBRIDE, Trone L.; '95 BS; 207 W 135th St. Apt. 2a, New York, NY 10030.

MCBRIDE, William A.; '97 BS; Lt./ Police Ofcr.; NYC Police Dept., 94-41 43rd Ave., Elmhurst, NY 11373, 718 476-9311; r. 100 Brooklyn Ave. Apt. 3G, Freeport, NY 11520, 516 546-7610. e-mail

MC CABE, Gregory R.; '75 BA; Owner; G.M. Coffee Co., Bushkill, PA 18324, 570 588-0455; r. 79 Wickes Rd, Bushkill, PA 18324, 570 588-0455.

MC CABE, James J.; '75 BS; Retired; r. 1 Hillside Ter., Nanuet, NY 10954, 914 623-3793; *Virginia;* Catherine, James, Patricia Ann. e-mail

MC CABE, Jenni; '96 BS; 3923 44th St., Sunnyside, NY 11104, 718 459-7649.

MCCABE, John P.; '73 BA, '79 MPA; Prof. of Criminal Justice; St. John's Univ., 8000 Utopia Pkway., Jamaica, NY 11439, 718 990-1688; r. 8831 237th St., Jamaica, NY 11426, 718 347-5152.

MC CABE, Joseph T.; '79 BS; 453 79th St., Brooklyn, NY 11209, 718 836-0928.

MCCABE, Mrs. Nunzia, (Nunzia Polidoro); '93 AS; Police Ofcr.; NYPD, Ozone Park, NY 11417; r. 150-05 Centerville, Ozone Park, NY 11417; *William;* Ryan, Nunziatina, Thomas.

MCCABE, Patrick M.; '91 BS; 4314 Oneida Ave., Bronx, NY 10470, 718 994-6806.

MC CABE, Robert K.; '78 BA; POB 217, Amawalk, NY 10501, 914 941-6385.

MC CAFFREY, Daniel X.; '78 MPA; 1717 E 29th St., Brooklyn, NY 11229, 718 253-8601.

MCCAFFREY, James P.; '84 BS; 25 Cres. Beach, Huntington, NY 11743, 516 798-2858.

MCCAFFREY, Sean P.; '94 BS; Deputy US Marshal; City of Minneapolis, 300 S 4th St., Minneapolis, MN 55415, 612 664-5923; r. 577-M Woodduck Dr., Woodbury, MN 55125, 651 702-0194. e-mail

MCCAIN, Jamaine; '94 AS; 159-10 109th Ave., Jamaica, NY 11433, 718 464-2157.

MCCAIN, Shanique S.; '98 BS; Administrative Asst.; American Express Financial Advisors, 80-02 Kew Garden Rd., Kew Gardens, NY 11415; r. 159 10 109 Ave. #1a, Jamaica, NY 11433, 718 657-4768.

MC CALLAN, Eugene F.; 8 Paul Rvere Ln., Centerport, NY 11721.

MC CALLUM, Dionn; '97 BS; 1534 E.98th St., Brooklyn, NY 11236, 718 253-8601.

MCCALLUM, Sonya L.; '93 BS; 157-03 110th Ave., Jamaica, NY 11433.

MCCANN, Michael; 61-66 67th St., Middle Vlg., NY 11379, 718 358-0061.

MC CANN, Michael D.; '76; 145-24 11 Ave., Whitestone, NY 11357, 718 835-1094.

MC CANN, Michael F.; '75 BS; JD New York Law Sch.; Dir. of Security & Safety Svc.; United Nations, New York, NY 10007, 212 963-7526; r. 6166 67th St., Middle Vlg., NY 11379; *Elizabeth;* Michael, Mary.

MCCANN, Patricia J.; '93 MA; BA Hunter Clg.; Sr. Addictions Couns.; Ctr. for Comprehensive Health Practices, 1900 Second Ave., New York, NY 10029, 212 360-7780; r. 35-20 73rd St., Jackson Hts., NY 11372, 718 631-1765; *William Kontz;* James, Donna.

MCCANN, Robert H.; '80 AS; 35-31 85 St., Jackson Hts., NY 11372, 718 631-1765.

MC CANN, Terence; '69 BA, '74 MA; 27 Oakley Pl., Great Neck, NY 11020, 516 487-9557.

MCCANTS, Stephanie N.; '98 BS; 600 Hylan Blvd., Staten Island, NY 10305.

MCCAREY, Colleen A.; '93 MA; BA Seton Hall Univ.; Fraud Systs. Admin.; AT&T Wireless, 15 E Midland Ave., Paramus, NJ 07652, 201 986-7045; r. 96 Trinity Ct., Paramus, NJ 07652, 201 294-4459.

MC CARREN, Charles J.; '78 BS; 6420 83rd Pl., Flushing, NY 11379, 718 897-6814.

MCCARTHA, Dawn E.; '99 BA; 40 W 115 St. 5C, New York, NY 10026, 212 722-6520.

MCCARTHER, Monifa; '95 MA; 375 S Reynolds St., Apt. 809, Alexandria, VA 22304.

MCCARTHY, Daniel; '90 BS; 2799 Carnation Ave., Baldwin, NY 11510, 516 932-8661.

MC CARTHY, Donald F.; '76 MA; 26170 Hickory Blvd., # 1, Bonita Spgs., FL 34134.

MCCARTHY, Donna M.; '97 BA; 1008 Russell St., Franklin Sq., NY 11010, 516 354-2890.

MC CARTHY, Eugene F.; '76 BS; 42 Steiner Dr., Mahopac, NY 10541, 914 628-1937.

MC CARTHY, Gerard F.; '78 BS; 914 Savoy Ct., Petaluma, CA 94954.

MCCARTHY, Geryl; '91 BS; 2 Nan Pl., Kings Park, NY 11754, 718 497-9302.

MCCARTHY, Jacqueline; '95 BA; MSW Hunter Clg.; Comm Ofcr. NY City Police Dept.; Counseling Svc. Unit, 189 Montague St., Brooklyn, NY 11201, 718 834-8433; r. 105-00 Shore Front Pkwy. #12P, Rockaway Park, NY 11694.

MCCARTHY, James N.; '97 BS, '98 BS; 239 Sterling Ave. # 2, Yonkers, NY 10704, 914 686-4052.

MCCARTHY, Jennifer; '96 MA; 3079 48th St., Astoria, NY 11103, 718 281-0738.

MCCARTHY, Justin M.; '92 MA; 138 Port Rd, Brick, NJ 08723, 908 781-5446.

MC CARTHY, Kevin M.; '81 MPA; 8000 Shore Front Pkwy. Apt. 4p, Far Rockaway, NY 11693, 718 318-1049.

MCCARTHY, Margaret G.; '77 BA; Special Agt.; FBI, 26 Federal Plz., New York, NY 10278, 212 384-1000; r. 2044 E 38th St., Brooklyn, NY 11234, 718 645-9786.

MC CARTHY, Robert A.; '78 MA; 1149 Howard Dr., Westbury, NY 11590, 516 997-6520.

MCCARTHY, Timothy; '93 BS; Capt. NYPD; r. 153 Sherman Ave., Merrick, NY 11566; *Mary Jane;* Meghan, Timothy Jr, Andrew, Ryan. e-mail

MC CARTHY, Timothy J.; '71 AS, '76 BS; Retired Human Svc.; Dept. of Human Svcs.; r. 280 Bath Club Blvd. N, N. Redington Bch., FL 33708, 727 391-1728; *Muriel;* Laura, Linda.

MC CARTHY, Vincent; '75 MPA; 93 Laurel Rd, New City, NY 10956, 914 353-2044.

MCCARTHY, William F.; '71 BA, '76 MA; PHD CUNY New York; Prof. of Criminal Justice & Sociolo; Corning Community Clg., Corning, NY 14830, 607 962-9465; r. 449 W Mombasha Rd, Monroe, NY 10950, 914 783-7211. e-mail

MCCARTON, James I.; '97 BA; Police Ofcr.; NYC Police Dept.; r. 11 Spruce Ln., New Hyde Park, NY 11040, 516 358-4618.

MCCARTY, Gerard; '97; 11 B Lawrence St., Nyack, NY 10960.

MCCAULEY, Chris; '93 BS; 90 Old Saugatuck Rd, Norwalk, CT 06855, 203 866-8854.

MCCAULEY, Marianne D.; MA Bank Street Clg., BA SUNY Purchase; Curator/Archivist; The Italian Amer Inst./Queens Clg., 25 W 43rd St., New York, NY 10036, 212 642-2031; r. 3 Knollwood Ave., Mt. Vernon, NY 10550, 914 667-3507; *Thomas;* Susan, Linda, Paul, Peter, Adam. e-mail

MCCAVERA, James; '95 BS; 222 E. 24 St., New York, NY 10010.

MC CLAIN, Joseph; '77 BS; 8078 88th Rd, Jamaica, NY 11421, 718 296-2411.

MCCLAIN, Shawn D.; '97 BA; S.A.P.I.S. Therapeutic/Couns.; Spark Prog./B.O.EDUC, 5800 Tilden Ave., 5800 Tildew Ave., Brooklyn, NY 11231, 718 629-4523; r. 710 Park Pl., Brooklyn, NY 11216; *Tara.* e-mail

MC CLANE, Kershaw C.; '75 AS; 527 Lakeway Dr., W. Babylon, NY 11704.

MCCLEAN, Monique D.; '88 BS; 945 Underhill Ave., Apt. 810, Bronx, NY 10473, 718 549-0853.

MCCLEAN, Sonia P.; '84 BA; 22326 112th Rd, Queens Vlg., NY 11429, 718 639-5612.

MC CLELLAN, John J.; '77 BS; 8615 Ft. Hamilton Pkway, Brooklyn, NY 11209, 718 680-7005.

MCCLELLAND, Laura D.; '86 BA; 2611 Frederick Douglass Blvd. Apt 4i, New York, NY 10030.

MC CLOUD, J. V.; 70-23 69 St., Glendale, NY 11385, 718 461-5405.

MCCLURE, Steven M.; '91 BS; 340 W 15th St., # 4, New York, NY 10011, 212 243-2021.

MCCOLE, Peter; '87 BS; Special Agt.; Bur. of Alcohol Tobacco & Firearms, 222 W. Seventh Ave. Box 39, Anchorage, AK 99513, 907 271-5701; r. POB 101394, Anchorage, AK 99510, 907 250-0080.

MCCOLLIN, Kathy-Ann E.; '98 BA; Child Protective Spec.; Admin. for Children's Svcs., Brooklyn, NY 11201; r. 735 Linclon Ave., Brooklyn, NY 11208, 718 827-2796; Qiana, Chance. e-mail

MCCOLLOUGH, Charmaine; '97 BA; AAS Touro Clg.; Police Ofcr.; New York Police Dept., 1 Police Plz., New York, NY 10018, 212 374-5000; r. 1520 Sedgwick Ave., Bronx, NY 10453, 718 901-7820.

MCCONDICHIE, Charise; '96 BA; 1738 Union St., Apt. E4, Brooklyn, NY 11213.

MC CONNEY, Christine; '75 BS; 645 E. 24th St., Brooklyn, NY 11210, 718 636-8576.

MCCORKLE, Emma; '91 BA; 168-07 Foch Blvd., Jamaica, NY 11434; *George F.;* Lisa Stevens, Tina Berden, Shannon Cornwal.

MCCORMACK, Paul G.; '97 BS; GRD FBI Natl Acad., MS NYU; Capt.; NYPD, 33rd Precinct, New York, NY 10032, 212 927-3272; r. 4266 Vireo Ave., Bronx, NY 10470, 718 994-5864. e-mail

MCCORMACK, Stephen F.; '95 BA; 402 Bay Ridge Pkwy. Apt. 39, Brooklyn, NY 11209, 718 238-9710.

MC CORMICK, Daniel; '74 BS; 133 Claremont St., Deer Park, NY 11729.

MC COVERY, Diane Y.; '75 BA; 109 Lewis Ave. Apt. 4k, Brooklyn, NY 11206, 718 452-5455.

MC COY, Carl L.; '81 MA; 246 Fenimore St., Brooklyn, NY 11225, 718 636-8576.

MC COY, Felix J.; '76 BS; 18068 Sunset Ct., Fountain Vly., CA 92708, 702 737-8617.

MC COY, Henry; '72 BS; MS Queens Clg.; Retired Police Ofcr./City Marshal; r. 18630 Dormans Rd, Jamaica, NY 11412, 718 712-1798. e-mail

MC COY, Michael G.; '76 BS; MS Brooklyn Polytech; Sr. Systs. Programmar; Health Mgmt. Systs., 401 Park Ave.south, New York, NY 10016, 212 857-5370; r. 28 Lake Celeste Dr., Garrison, NY 10524, 914 739-5508; *Sharon;* Sarah. e-mail

MC COY, Richard E.; '81 BS; 3122 103rd St., Flushing, NY 11369, 718 507-9687.

MCCOY, Robert N.; '94 CERT; Tchr.& Couns. Private; NYC Bd. of Educ., 65 Court St., Brooklyn, NY 11201, 718 471-6900; r. 1460 Beach Channel Dr., Apt. 2 D, Far Rockaway, NY 11691, 718 868-0520.

MCCRAY, Michelle E.; '85 BS; Brooklyn, NY 11206, 718 573-5891.

MCCRAY, Tara Y.; '95 BS; 381 Edgecombe Ave., New York, NY 10031, 212 234-7267.

MC CRAY, Tracey C.; '82 BA; 470 W 146 St., New York, NY 10031, 212 862-4038.

MC CREARY, Joanne L.; '77 BA, '82 MA; 88 08 241 St., Bellerose, NY 11426, 516 944-5492.

MC CRIE, Robert D.; 49 E 96th St., New York, NY 10128, 315 896-6558.

MC CRYSTAL, Harry J.; '69 BS; 3462 Ella Rd, Wantagh, NY 11793, 516 679-9745.

MCCUE, Frank T.; '91 MA; 1 Thompson Dr., Washingtonville, NY 10992, 914 496-7147.

MCCULLOUGH, Ayanna; '96 BA; 779 Concourse Village, Bronx, NY 10451.

MCCULLOUGH, Sylvia A.; '98 BS; 4541 Carpenter Ave. #2r, Bronx, NY 10470, 718 994-7752.

MC CULLOUGH, William; '67 BS; 56-38 186 St., Flushing, NY 11365, 718 428-7789.

MCCURDY, Leslie D.; '95 BS; 7120 Calamus Ave., Flushing, NY 11377.

MCCUTCHAN, Lisa K.; '95 BA; 183 Gervil St., Staten Island, NY 10309, 718 605-1412.

MCCUTCHEN, Aishah K.; '97 BA; 50 W Gun Hill Rd 5B, Bronx, NY 10467, 718 231-6679.

MC CUTCHEON, William; 100 NW 2nd Ave., Boca Raton, FL 33432.

MCDANIEL, Carol D.; '87 BS; 760 Old Kensico Rd, White Plains, NY 10603.

MC DARBY, Frank; '77 BS; 155-07 86 St., Howard Bch., NY 11414, 718 845-2162.

MC DERMOTT, John P.; '77 MA; 15 Crowell Pl., Valley Stream, NY 11580, 516 944-5492.

MCDERMOTT, John R.; '98 BS; 641 78th St., Brooklyn, NY 11209, 718 921-0277.

MC DERMOTT, Raymond T.; '82 AS; 326 Beach 90th St., Far Rockaway, NY 11693, 718 454-4159.

MC DERMOTT, Thomas; '76 BA; Detective Investigator; Suffolk Cnty. Dist. Atty., Hauppauge, NY 11787, 631 853-4150; r. 140 Glen Hollow Dr., Port Jefferson Sta., NY 11776.

MCDESMOTT, James E.; '96 BA; 77 S.Bay Dr., Massapequa, NY 11758.

MCDEVITT, James P.; '72 BA; Freelance Writer; Retired Ofcr.; NYPD; r. 2621 Surrey Ave., Modesto, CA 95355, 209 524-8268; *Mary;* James P. Jr, Margaret, Sean. e-mail

MCDONALD, Clarence (Chris); '79 BA; Pres.; Natl. Law Enforcement Sports Fedn., POB 76039, St. Petersburg, FL 33734, 727 822-7000; r. 1140 37th Ave. NE, St. Petersburg, FL 33704, 727 822-7000. e-mail

MC DONALD, Elizabeth; '81 BS; 11812 Newport Ave., Rockaway Park, NY 11694, 718 846-6650.

MCDONALD, Jeannette; '92 BS; 290 Ivy St., Kearny, NJ 07032.

MCDONALD, John; '92 MA; 12 Hastings St., Dix Hills, NY 11746.

MC DONALD, John E.; '76 BS; 12 Hastings St., Dix Hills, NY 11746.

MCDONALD, Lucille A.; '97 BS; 196 E.96st St., Brooklyn, NY 11212, 718 833-0567.

MC DONALD, Thomas T.; '79 BS; 2865 Roebling Ave., Bronx, NY 10461, 718 601-2113.

MCDONALD, Yajayra; '98 BS; 35 Grafton St. 2a, Brooklyn, NY 11212, 718 385-5596.

MC DONNELL, Kathleen; '81 BS; 19822 29th Ave., Flushing, NY 11358, 718 352-3214.

MCDONNELL, Patrick; '92 MA; POB 523, Buffalo, NY 14215, 716 823-1759.

MC DONNELL, Robert; '76 BS; 1971 Hemlock Farms, Hawley, PA 18428, 570 775-0254.

MCDOUGAL, Sonya B.; '83 BS; 963 New York Ave., Brooklyn, NY 11203, 718 221-1398.

MCDUFFIE, Robert; '84 BA; 2 Asate Ct., Brooklyn, NY 11213, 718 209-1825.

MCEACHIN, Betty J.; '84 BA; 151 E. 26 St., New York, NY 10010.

MC ELLIGOTT, Peter; '81 BA; 138-06 78 Ave., Flushing, NY 11367, 718 712-9298.

MC ELROY, Andrew C.; '75 BA; 4 Pebble Beach Dr., Purchase, NY 10577, 914 237-8146.

MC ELROY, Patrick J.; '81 BA; 113 South St., Bogota, NJ 07603, 201 968-1208.

MCENEANEY, Catherine; '85 BA; 61 Jane St. Apt.2N, New York, NY 10014.

MCENIRY, John A.; '74 AS, '76 BS; 1539 Spring St., E. Meadow, NY 11554, 516 538-3447.

MCENTIRE, Catherine Duffy; '98 BA; Lehmann Clg.; Ret-Lt. NYPD; r. Bronx, NY 10463.

MCEVOY, Barbara '77 (See Pincar, Barbara.)

MCFARLANE, Barbara; '89 BS; 3206 Mickle Ave., Bronx, NY 10469, 718 655-9731.

MCFARLANE, C.; '93 BS; MA Long Island Univ.; Grad. Student Public Admin.; r. 106A E. 29th St., Brooklyn, NY 11226, 718 287-0714. e-mail

MC FARLANE, Charlene A.; '95 BS; 52 Vermont Ave., Hempstead, NY 11550, 516 431-7126.

MCFARLANE, Elaine C.; '86 BS; 4157 Boyd Ave., Bronx, NY 10466, 718 409-0515.

MCGAHAN, George E.; '75 BS; 185 roselle st., Mineola, NY 11501, 516 747-0376.

MCGANN, Charles; 7 Henry St., Orangeburg, NY 10962, 914 365-4050.

MC GANNEY, Mary L.; '78 MA; 285 Central Park W, New York, NY 10024, 315 736-0530.

MCGARRELL, Bonnie '82 (See De Niet, Bonnie.)

MC GARRY, MAJ Frederick S., USA(Ret.); '75 MA; BA St. Francis Clg., The Citadel; Ret. Detective/Tchr. NYC Bd. of Edu; FEMA Security Div.; r. 7145 71st St., Flushing, NY 11385, 718 417-9630; Tara Ann, Stephen, Suzanne.

MC GARY, Roger A.; '76 MPA; 1311 Gresham Rd, Silver Spring, MD 20904.

MC GEADY, Robert J.; '81 BS; 2837 Collis Pl., Bronx, NY 10465, 718 731-6973.

MC GEARY, Joseph T.; '82 BS; Flight Safety Mgr.; Merrill Lynch, 225 Liberty St., New York, NY 10281, 212 236-5661; r. 146 Windsor Pkwy., Oceanside, NY 11572, 516 536-0702.

MC GEE, Kathy; '90 BS; 925 Rogers Ave., Brooklyn, NY 11226, 718 218-8708.

MCGEE, Patrick J.; '97 MA; 650 Bement Ave., Staten Island, NY 10310, 718 979-0227.

MC GEE, Peter P.; '72 BS; 89 Circle Dr., Syosset, NY 11791, 516 433-1973.

MCGEHEAN, Donna G.; '92 BS; JD WNEC Sch. of Law; Human Resources Management; r. 4455 Bitterroot Dr., Westerville, OH 43081, 614 901-0621; Sarah. e-mail

MC GEOUGH, Sherry A.; 273 Heritage Vlg # A, Southbury, CT 06488.

MC GEOWN, James R.; '77 MA; 3165 Dorset Ln., Levittown, NY 11756, 516 944-5492.

MC GHEE, Denise-Ann; '80 BS; 33-24 Parson Blvd., Flushing, NY 11354, 718 318-1077.

MCGHEE, Lisa; '98 BS, '98 MA; Paralegal; US Fed. Govt., 111 Livingston St., Brooklyn, NY 11201, 718 330-2086; r. 205 E 95 St., New York, NY 10128.

MCGHEE, Liza; '89 BS; Mgr.; E Commerce Grp. Prods. Inc., 7 Dey St., 4th Fl., New York, NY 10007, 212 791-9700; r. 968 Troy Ave., Brooklyn, NY 11203, 718 469-3866. e-mail

MC GILL, John J.; '70 BS; Retired Capt.; NYPD; r. 556 Longleaf Rd, Virginia Bch., VA 23454, 757 498-1385; *Dorothy;* Joann, John K.

MCGILL, Mrs. Katrina A., (Katrina Foye); '98 BS; Minister/Worship & Praise Dancer; United Faith Christian Ctr., 337 Crescent St., Brooklyn, NY 11207, 718 235-9540; r. 640 Bradford St. #3A, Brooklyn, NY 11207, 718 257-4879; *Min. Venis;* Daniel, Delon, Maleek, Shavaughn, Jonquil, Nia, Venis.

MCGILL, Richard K.; '83 BS; 53 Cedarview Ave., Staten Island, NY 10306, 718 816-1465.

MCGILL, Steven J.; '93 MS; 92 Sherman Pl., Jersey City, NJ 07307, 201 963-3389.

MCGINN, LT Timothy R.; '92 BS; Lt.; NYC Police Dept., One Police Plz. Rm. 1308, New York, NY 10038, 212 374-3927; r. 179 Tanglewood Dr., Staten Island, NY 10308; *Judy;* Kevin.

MC GINNIS, Robert D.; '76 MA; 81 Boonton Ave., Kinnelon, NJ 07405.

MCGINNISS, Debra A.; '85 BS; 168 Beach 125 St., Rockaway Park, NY 11694, 718 945-4341.

MC GIVNEY, John A.; '71 BS; 475 Rathbun Ave., Staten Island, NY 10312, 718 356-5365.

MCGLINCHEY, Ms. Anne T.; '92 MA; MDIV Union Theological Sem., BA Seton Hill Clg.; Dir. Domestic Violence & Mediation; Manhattan Ct. Dispute Referral Ctr., 346 Broadway, Rm. 408, New York, NY 10013, 212 374-4904; r. 9902 3rd Ave. Apt. 1H, Brooklyn, NY 11209, 718 680-4001. e-mail

MC GLINCHEY, Ms. Catherine; '71 BS; 2 Stuyvesant Oval, New York, NY 10009, 212 217-0855.

MC GLINCY, Hugh J.; '91 BA; 1131 Portland St., Pittsburgh, PA 15206, 412 462-5388.

MC GLONE, Jim; '74 BS; Sr. Administrative Ofcr.; Cablevision, 111 New South Rd., Hicksville, NY 11801, 516 390-5439; r. 102 Syosset Cir., Syosset, NY 11791; *Catherine;* James, Brian, Page, Sharon.

MC GORTY, Donald J.; '85 MA; 53 Michael Dr., Westfield, NJ 07090, 570 698-9535.

MCGOTTY, Thomas J.; '85 BS; 104 Sherman Blvd., Edison, NJ 08820.

MCGOUGH, John J.; '96 AS; 314 50th St. # E, Brooklyn, NY 11220.

MCGOURTY, Michael J.; '69 AS, '73 BS; Court Clerk; Criminal Ct., 215 E161 St., Bronx, NY 10451, 718 590-2858; r. 47 Hunt Ave., Pearl River, NY 10965, 914 735-4773; *Kathleen;* Meghan.

MC GOVERN, Kevin M.; '77 BS; 1502 E. 91st St., Brooklyn, NY 11236, 718 218-8708.

MC GOVERN, Patrick J.; '75 MA; 820 Birdie Ln., Pompano Bch., FL 33069.

MCGOVERN, Rita; '97 BS; 1640 August Rd, N. Babylon, NY 11703.

MCGOWAN, Hugh M.; '94 MA; BA Queens Clg. CUNY, MPHIL CUNY Grad. Ctr.; Police Lt.; NYPD Hostage Negotiation Team, 1 Police Plz. Rm. 1312T, New York, NY 10038, 212 374-0792; r. 5337 194th St., Flushing, NY 11365, 718 357-3861; *Marie;* Susan, Sharon, Heather, Hugh. e-mail

MC GOWAN, Kenneth T.; '78 BA; 1005 Plimsoll Pt, Lanoka Harbor, NJ 08734.

MC GOWAN, Martin J.; '75 MA; 129-17 Newport Ave., Rockaway Park, NY 11694, 718 945-6644.

MCGOWAN, Sean M.; '96 BA; Website Mgr.; Giftwrap.com, 701 Ford Rd., Rockaway, NJ 07866, 973 625-8421; r. 47 Ackerman Ave., Elmwood Park, NJ 07407, 201 797-0635. e-mail

MCGRANN, Joseph P.; '89 BS; 7 Alberta Ct., Smithtown, NY 11787.

MC GRATH, Henry J.; '79 MA; 5 Bull Calf Ln., Centerport, NY 11721, 631 788-7340.

MCGRATH, Juzann M.; '99 BA; 164-30 Hillside Ave#6F, Jamaica, NY 11432, 718 523-4740.

MC GRATH, Kevin J.; '77 BS; POB 1712, Sag Harbor, NY 11963.

MCGRATH, Michael P.; '83 BA; 10200 Shore Front Pkwy. Apt. 7o, Far Rockaway, NY 11694, 718 474-8096.

MCGRATH, Patrick M.; '98 BA; 40 Buchanan Ave., Amity Harbor, NY 11701, 631 842-8980.

MCGRAW, Deborah S., (Deborah Smith); '91 BA; 435 Reflections Cir. #23, San Ramon, CA 94583, 262 785-2603; *Anthony;* Brianna.

MCGREAL, Edward J.; '92 BS; 43 Edgewood Rd, Cortlandt Manor, NY 10567, 914 734-1366.

MC GREAL, James J.; '76 BA; 713 Union St., Brooklyn, NY 11215, 718 773-7938.

MCGREGOR, Karyn A.; '95 BA; 590 Flatbush Ave. Apt. 9b, Brooklyn, NY 11225, 718 826-6904.

MC GUADE, John; 229 W 123 St. 28PCT, New York, NY 10027, 315 826-3934.

MCGUINNESS, Charles; '91 BA; 406 Ft. Washington Ave., Hawthorne, NY 10532, 914 747-3923.

MC GUINNESS, Francis; '75 BS; Admin. of St James Parish; St. James Parish; r. 228 Violet St., Massapequa Park, NY 11762, 516 541-5990; *Teresa;* Melanie, James.

MCGUINNESS, Hugh; '89 BA; Retired; r. 211 Beechwood Shore Dr., Moyock, NC 27958, 252 232-8750; *Elaine.*

MCGUIRE, George J.; '91 BS, '95 MPA; 5 Valentine Pl., Glendale, NY 11385, 718 205-0041.

MCGUIRE, Patrick J.; '98 BS; Sergeant; NYC Police Dept., 1 Police Plz., New York, NY 10038, 718 361-1031; r. 20 Walnut Ave., Rockville Centre, NY 11570, 516 763-6750.

MC GUIRE, Peter A.; '65 MPA; BS Fordham Univ.; Retired Lt.; NYC Police; r. 8912 Shore Ct., Brooklyn, NY 11209; *Carolyn;* Peter, Lawrence, Steven.

MCGURL, Thomas M.; '98 BS; 28 Stonehenge Dr., Ocean, NJ 07712, 732 918-1461.

MC HUGH, Edward; '76 BA; JD St. John Univ.; Edward J. McHugh, PC, 420 Jericho Tpk., Jericho, NY 11753, 516 933-8015; r. 9 Magpie Ln., Levittown, NY 11756, 516 731-0744. e-mail

MC HUGH, Edward C.; '74 BS; RFD 3 Red Mills Rd, Mahopac, NY 10541.

MC HUGH, Gerard A.; '81 BS; 21 Hillside Ave., Nutley, NJ 07110.

MCHUGH, Michael J.; 711 Ilyssaway, Staten Island, NY 10312, 917 821-1468.

MC HUGH, Robert A.; '80 BS; 2323 128th St., Flushing, NY 11356.

MCINERNEY, SGT Brian G.; '93 BS; Sgt; Police Dept. City of NY, PBMS Evidence Collection Team, 357 W 35th St., New York, NY 10016, 212 239-9350; *Leslie;* William. e-mail

MCINERNEY, Joseph; '83 BS; 60-77 55th St., Maspeth, NY 11378.

MCINERNEY, Robert (Bob) X., CPP; '77 BA; Security Consultant/Investigator; Investigative Group International, Inc., 366 Madison Ave., 9th Fl., New York, NY 10017, 212 661-6100; r. 68 Radburn Rd, Glen Rock, NJ 07452, 201 670-7671. e-mail

MC INNIS, Michael R.; '95 BS; 107 Granger Rd, Wayland, NY 14572.

MC INNIS, Ronald P.; '75 BA; 17 Hedgerow Ln., Commack, NY 11725.

MC INTOSH, Cheryl E.; '79 BS; 1299 St. Marks Ave., Brooklyn, NY 11213.

MC INTYRE, John F.; '75 MA; 19 Locust Pl., Livingston, NJ 07039, 973 992-8418.

MC JUNKIN, William M.; '80 BS; Lt. NY City Fire Dept.; Fire Protection, 10 Metrotech, Brooklyn, NY 11205; r. 13823 222nd St., Jamaica, NY 11413, 718 276-2425.

MCKAIN, Velma A., (Velma Elder); '95 BA; MPH Long Island Univ.; Fraud Investigator; NYC Dept. Human Res. Admin.; r. 88 5th Ave., Apt. 2-L, Brooklyn, NY 11217, 718 399-8654.

MC KAY, John; '76 BA; 315 Wds of Aron Rd, Staten Island, NY 10312, 718 816-6156.

MC KAY, John J.; '75 BS; 120 N Vivyen St., Bergenfield, NJ 07621.

MCKAY, Roxanne M.; '95 BA; 1577 E 45th St., Brooklyn, NY 11234, 718 253-7724.

MC KEEGAN, John J.; '73 BS; 103 Weidner Ave., Oceanside, NY 11572, 516 944-5492.

MC KENIZE, Reginald; '81 AS; 12119 235th St., Jamaica, NY 11422, 718 454-4159.

MC KENNA, Daniel J.; '77 MA, '85 BS; 28 Hillside Ter., Staten Island, NY 10308, 718 667-6077.

MC KENNA, Michael; '87 AS; 9312 112th St., Jamaica, NY 11418, 718 835-1094.

MC KENNA, Peter; '77 MA; Police Ofcr.; Dept. of Treas.-US Mint, West Point, NY 10996, 914 446-3237; r. 2679 Windmill Dr., Yorktown Hts., NY 10598, 914 962-5254; *Kathleen;* Michael, Tara. e-mail

MCKENNA, Siobhan H.; '91 BS; 42 King Ave. #BSMT, Yonkers, NY 10704, 914 934-2419.

MCKENNA, Thomas; '92 BS; AA Nassau Community College; Internal Affair; NYC Parks & Rec Dept., 212 360-1411; r. 215 34 39th Ave., Bayside, NY 11361, 718 279-2396; *Christine.*

MCKENNA, Timothy P.; '96 BS; 95 Rosebud Ave., Merrick, NY 11566, 516 546-8898.

MCKENZIE, Albert W.; '97 BA; Criminologist Tchr.; Jr. High; r. 2102 Beverley Rd. #3l, Brooklyn, NY 11226, 718 282-5704; *Cara.*

MC KENZIE, Andrew O.; '81 BA; 342 Halsey St., Brooklyn, NY 11216, 718 452-3703.

MCKENZIE, Constance; '95 MA; 40 Dongan St., Staten Island, NY 10310, 718 981-1040.

MCKENZIE, Laura; '91 BS; Intelligence Rsch. Spec.; US Secret Svc.; r. 2054 Stargrass Ct., Woodbridge, VA 22192.

MCKENZIE, Malcome; '98 BA; 734 Ocean Ave. #6E, Brooklyn, NY 11226, 718 941-7622.

MCKENZIE, Maribel E.; '91 BS; 639 Hegeman Ave. #1, Brooklyn, NY 11207, 718 686-0052.

MCKENZIE, Mark A.; '97 BA; New York City Correction Ofcr.; NYC; r. 21 Paerdegat 15th, Brooklyn, NY 11236, 718 629-4052; *Gina;* Janee.

MCKENZIE, Reginald R.; '81 AS; 12119 235th St., Jamaica, NY 11422, 718 396-3904.

MCKENZIE, Roger A.; '92 BA; 14715 232nd St., Jamaica, NY 11413, 718 396-3904.

MCKENZIE, Rohan M.; '97 BA, '98 BA; 2067 Ryer Ave., Bronx, NY 10457, 718 881-1767.

MCKEON, James E.; '76 BS; US Customs Inspector; Dept. of Treas., US Customs; r. 1921 N Railroad Ave., Staten Island, NY 10306, 718 987-0568. e-mail

MC KEON, Joseph D.; '74 BS; 2976 Marion Ave., Bronx, NY 10458, 718 365-5237.

MC KEON, William; 321A Beach 101 St., Rockaway Park, NY 11694, 718 428-7789.

MCKETNEY, L.; '83 BS; 142-17 Foch Blvd., Jamaica, NY 11436.

MC KIE, Herman; '76 BA; 539 Hancock St., Brooklyn, NY 11233, 718 636-2299.

MC KINLEY, Ronald R.; '78 BS; 1903 Buffalo Blvd., Lewisville, TX 75067, 315 322-5706.

MCKINLEY, Tenee S.; '99 BA; 685 E. 140 St. 5E, Bronx, NY 10454, 718 665-9153.

MC KINNEY, Joyce F.; '77 BA; 80 Baruch Dr., New York, NY 10002, 212 982-0206.

MCKINNEY, Tracy; '94 BS; 1445 Geneva Loop, Brooklyn, NY 11239, 718 642-4411.

MC KINZIE, Linda M.; '82 BA; 340 E Mosholu Pkwy. S Apt. 1b, Bronx, NY 10458, 718 617-1135.

MC KISSIC, Aaron; '72 BS; AS; Retired Police Lt.; r. 12 Overlook Ter., Maplewood, NJ 07040, 973 762-5724; *Elizabeth;* Aronda, Phyllis.

MCKNIGHT, Margaret; '91 MPA; 4 Mine Rd, Monroe, NY 10950, 914 783-9245.

MC KNIGHT, Thomas J.; '72 BS; 1622 Parkview Ave., Bronx, NY 10461, 718 892-7931.

MC KNIGHT, Walter D.; '76 BS; 101 Fenimore St., Lynbrook, NY 11563, 516 621-2047.

MCKOY, Barbara S.; '83 BS; 120-39 172nd St., Jamaica, NY 11434, 718 776-4528.

MCKOY, Gay L.; '96 BA; 627 Van Cortlandt Park Ave., Yonkers, NY 10705.

MCKOY, Marcia; '94 BS; 375 E 31st St., # 2, Brooklyn, NY 11226, 718 638-7006.

MCLAIN, Darrell; '90 BS; 7800 Shore Front P, Rockaway Bch., NY 11693, 718 474-2640.

MCLAUGHLIN, Deborah; '92 BA; 41 Rosalind Ave., Pleasantville, NY 10570, 914 476-1146.

MCLAUGHLIN, John P.; '80 BS; Retired Police Dept. Lt.; NYPD; r. 3309 Victory Blvd., Staten Island, NY 10314, 718 698-8854; *Linda Lee;* John III, Karen, Jennifer.

MC LEAN, Carol A.; '78 BA; 222 Lenox Rd #2Y, Brooklyn, NY 11226, 718 636-8576.

MCLEES, John C.; '99; 340 Haven Ave. #2H, New York, NY 10033.

MCLEES, Mark J.; '83 BS; 4936 Glen Robin Dr., Syracuse, NY 13215, 315 492-2656.

MCLEOD, Andrea M.; '89 BS; 169-01 144th Rd., Jamaica, NY 11434, 718 977-1170.

MC LEOD, Donald K.; '69 BS, '72 MA; Retired Dir. of Security; Museum of Modern Art, New York, NY 10019; r. 13 Knox Rd, Patterson, NJ 12563, 914 279-8973; *Catherine;* Donald, Keith, Ann Marie, Roseanne, Cathy, Marybeth.

MC LEOD, James; '77; 4158 Paulding Ave., Bronx, NY 10466, 718 823-7640.

MC LEOD, Kendall; '78 BS; 1051 Ocean Ave., Brooklyn, NY 11226, 718 373-1819.

MC LEOD, Kirk; '87 BS; 275 Linden Blvd. Apt. D1, Brooklyn, NY 11226, 718 856-9675.

MC LOUGHLIN, James F.; '79 BS; 341 Preston Ave., Staten Island, NY 10312, 718 816-6156.

MCLOUGHLIN, Katharine, (Katharine Delaney); '86 MA; West Chester Chap Dir.; New York League of Conservation Voters, 76 Manaranack Ave., Ste. 5, White Plains, NY 10601, 914 949-8438; r. 180 Locust Ave., Cortlandt Manor, NY 10567, 914 736-9546. e-mail

MC LOUGHLIN, Kevin; '82 BA; 5955 47th Ave., Apt. 8D, Woodside, NY 11377, 718 205-4140.

MC LOUGHLIN, Robert; '76 BA; 176 Livingston Ave., Babylon, NY 11702.

MCLOUGHLIN, Robert G.; 176 Livingston Ave., Babylon, NY 11702.

MCLOUGHLIN, Thomas; '90 MPA; BS Iona Clg., MS Iona; Dir. of NC Operations; Civgenic, Inc., 300 S. Salisbury St., Raleigh, NC 27602, 919 856-7063; r. 8512 Seagate Dr., Raleigh, NC 27615, 919 676-0501; *Eileen;* Tom III, Timothy, Kelly Anne. e-mail

MC MAHON, Daniel F.; '76 MA; 7 Carmen Dr., Nanuet, NY 10954, 914 624-8676.

MC MAHON, John P.; '70 BS; 216 Voss Ave., Yonkers, NY 10703, 914 478-1044.

MCMAHON, Michael; '83 BS; 316 84th St., Brooklyn, NY 11209, 718 230-9238.

MCMAHON, Michael J.; '96 BA; MS St. Joseph's Univ., AAS Mercer Cnty. Clg.; Lt., Emergency Svcs.; West Windsor Twp., POB 38, W. Windsor, NJ 08550, 609 936-1419. e-mail

MCMAHON, Michael S.; '97 BS; 65-18 79 Pl. Ph, Middle Vlg., NY 11379, 718 229-1785.

MCMAHON, Patrick J.; '92 MPA; 3415 Spruce St., Mohegan Lake, NY 10547.

MCMAHON-CARROLL, Suzanne; '75 BA; 32 Prince St., New Hyde Park, NY 11040, 516 741-6963.

MCMANAMON, Michael; '81 BS; 2478 Stuart St., Brooklyn, NY 11229.

MC MANUS, Deborah A.; '81 BS; 48 Poplar Ave., Bronx, NY 10465, 718 542-0595.

MC MANUS, Elizabeth G.; '79 BA; 8824 74th Ave., Flushing, NY 11385, 718 459-4036.

MC MANUS, George M.; 9 Oldfield Dr., New City, NY 10956, 914 735-6641.

MCMANUS, John J.; '89 BS; Sgt.; NYPD; r. 14 Wells Ave., Congers, NY 10920, 914 268-2746.

MC MANUS, Pierce B.; '70 BS, '75 MA; Assoc. Mgr.-Security; Metropolitan Museum of Art In NYC, 1000 5th Ave., New York, NY 10038, 212 923-3700; r. 20 Greendale Rd, New City, NY 10956, 914 634-2741.

MCMANUS, Siobhan A.; '96 BS; 10710 Shore Front Pkwy. Apt. 6g, Far Rockaway, NY 11694, 718 347-9313.

MC MASTER, John A.; '99 BA; Branch Mgr.; Enterprise Inc., 425 E 61st St., New York, NY 10021, 212 838-2323; r. 1545 Rhinelander Ave., Bronx, NY 10461, 718 597-5284. e-mail

MC MENEMON, Thomas P.; '77 BS; 104 Armstrong Ave., Staten Island, NY 10308, 718 948-5458.

MC MILLAN, Bonnie L.; '85 BA; 217 E. 86 St. #234, New York, NY 10028, 315 853-5735.

MCMILLAN, Bridgett; '93 BS; JD SUNY-Sch. of Law; Atty.; NYC Dept. of Corrections Private Practic, New York, NY 10013, 212 266-1134; r. 442 W 164th St. Apt. 4a, New York, NY 10032. e-mail

MCMILLAN, Ralph E.; '93 BA; 217 E 86 St. #239, New York, NY 10028, 315 761-0863.

MCMILLION, Tony; '95 AS, '97 BS; 1817 Story Ave. Apt. 7b, Bronx, NY 10473.

MC MNMON, Dennis; '76 BS; 239 Pine St., Teaneck, NJ 07666.

MCMULLEN, Mark F.; '92 BS; 84 Todd Rd, Katonah, NY 10536.

MC NALLY, Patrick M.; '74 BS; 2920 166th St., Flushing, NY 11358, 718 353-9650.

MCNALLY, Terence E.; '89 BA; 60 School St., Northport, NY 11768.

MCNAMARA, Eugene; '91 AS; 14725 22nd Ave., Whitestone, NY 11357.

MCNAMARA, Joan B.; '88 MA; 119 Laurel Rd, New City, NY 10956, 914 947-2892.

MC NAMARA, Joseph D.; '68 BS; 1317 Weaver Dr., San Jose, CA 95125, 408 264-4792.

MC NAMARA, Patrick; '79 BS; 503 E 83 St., New York, NY 10028, 315 733-6944.

MCNAMARA, Thomas G.; '91 BS; 1757 E 35th St., Brooklyn, NY 11234, 718 369-3195.

MC NEAL, Harry E.; '76 AS; 11918 231st St., Jamaica, NY 11411, 718 445-1534.

MCNEELY, Karen T.; '96 BS; Child Protective Specialist; Admin. for Children's Svcs., 2554 Linden Blvd., Brooklyn, NY 11208, 718 348-6663; r. 1270 E 51st St. Apt. #4G, Brooklyn, NY 11234, 718 531-4671.

MCNEILL, Denise L.; '92 BS; 241 Dean St. # 2n, Brooklyn, NY 11217, 718 495-3317.

MCNEILL, Ms. Jasmine K.; '99 BA; Fraud Investigator; Human Resources Admin., Ofc. of Revunue & Investigation, 30 Main St., Brooklyn, NY 11201, 718 260-6738; r. 997A Lafayette Ave., Apt. 2R, Brooklyn, NY 11221, 718 452-0713.

MCNELIS, Michael J.; '96 BA; 26-16 Southard Ave., Oceanside, NY 11572.

MC NEVIN, Arthur J.; '67 BS; 158-42 86 St., Howard Bch., NY 11414, 718 631-1765.

MC NICHOLAS, Eveann V.; '70 BS; 11 Kevan Pl., Middletown, NJ 07748, 732 706-3395.

MC NICHOLAS, James F.; '76 BS; Police Lt. Retired; r. 110 Hiawatha Dr., Brightwaters, NY 11718, 631 665-0868; *Dorothy;* Daniel, James, Charles, Dorothy. e-mail

MC NICHOLL, Robert G.; 133-50 125 St., S. Ozone Park, NY 11420, 718 454-4159.

MC NICHOLS, Keith B.; '93 BS, '98 MPA, '98 MPA; 483 Park Pl., #2r, Brooklyn, NY 11238, 718 218-8708.

MC NICKLE, Litna M., (Litna Meighan); '85 AS, '87 BS; Admin.; John Jay Clg., Rikers Island, New York, NY 10001; r. 3307 91st St., Jackson Hts., NY 11372; *Nick;* Daniel, Kathryn, Rebecca.

MCNICKLE, R. G. (Nick); '96 MPA; BA, MS Lehman Clg.; Prog. Dir.; John Jay Clg., 899 10 Th Ave., New York, NY 10019, 212 237-8633; r. 33-07 91st St., Jackson Hts., NY 11372; *Litna;* Daniel, Kathryn, Rebecca. e-mail

MC NULTY, Christopher R.; '95 BS; 3152 Hull Ave. Apt. D3, Bronx, NY 10467, 718 994-5998.

MC NULTY, Daniel J.; '79 BS; 58-35 66 St., Maspeth, NY 11378, 718 318-1077.

MC NULTY, James E.; '77 BS; 2544 163rd St., Flushing, NY 11358, 718 461-5405.

MC NULTY, Kathryn B.; '81 MA; 583 W 215th St. #B9, New York, NY 10034.

MC NULTY, Thomas P.; '97 AS, '98; Security Spec.; Salomon Smith Barney, New York, NY 10001; r. 21 Jamacia Ave. Bsmt, Plainview, NY 11803, 516 933-6951.

MC PARLAND, Thomas A.; '75 MA; 228 W Hegel Ave., Edison, NJ 08820, 732 382-5469.

MC PHERSON, Debbra S.; '95 BA; 22020 146th Ave., Springfield Gardens, NY 11413, 718 318-1077.

MC PHERSON, Dianne; '79 BA; 1235 Grand Concourse, Bronx, NY 10452, 718 542-0595.

MCPHERSON, Michele M.; '95 BA; 12632 Inwood St., Jamaica, NY 11436, 718 529-1853.

MCQUEEN, David A.; '95 BS; Sergeant; New York Police Dept.; r. 2125 St.raymond Ave., Bronx, NY 10462.

MC QUEEN, Norman E., Jr.; '98 BS; Lt.; New York Bd. of Fire Underwriters, 40 Fulton St. New York Ny 10038, New York, NY 10038, 212 563-1262; r. 297 Dekalb Ave., Brooklyn, NY 11205, 718 783-6915; *Nursel Gurler;* Christina-Mari.

MCQUEENEY, Patrick; '85 BS; 3236 Kenwood St., Ferndale, MI 48220, 248 544-4849.

MC QUILLAN, Matthew A.; '77 BS; 120 W 82 St., New York, NY 10024, 315 736-0530.

MC QUILLEN, Joseph T.; '78 BA; 13 Cherry St., Flushing, NY 11363, 718 459-7649.

MCRAE, Elizabeth A.; '85 BA; 93-14 201st St., Hollis, NY 11423, 718 831-0280.

MCSHALL, Florence I.; '86 BA; 480 E. 188 St., Bronx, NY 10458, 718 933-2577.

MC SHARRY, Talbot; '82 MA; 1607 Poplar Level Rd, Louisville, KY 40217.

MC SHERRY, Martin M.; '76 BS; 2911 Harding Ave., Bronx, NY 10465, 718 863-9203.

MCSPIRIT, Ms. Theadora P., (Theadora P. Damon); '93 MA; BA Seton Hall Univ., MA; Case Supv./Report Writer; Essex Cnty. Courthouse, 50 W. Market St., Newark, NJ 07102, 973 693-5989; r. 302 Hillside Ave., Livingston, NJ 07039, 973 716-0786; *Stephen;* Stephen II.

MC SWEENEY, Dennis F.; '74 BS; 2080 3 Ave., Merrick, NY 11566, 516 997-7839.

MCTURSH, Rachel; '93 BA; 333 E 92nd St. Apt. 3b, Brooklyn, NY 11212.

MC VEETY, James A.; '72 BS, '76 MS; Supervising Investigator; New York Cnty. DA's Ofc., #1 Hogan Pl., New York, NY 10013, 212 553-3954; r. 523 E. 14th St., New York, NY 10009, 212 677-3261.

MC WILLIAMS, John J.; '75 MA; 233 Fillmore St., Massapequa Park, NY 11762, 516 795-5595.

MCWILLIAMS, Scott R.; '96 BS; Policeman; r. 259 Mineola Ave., Carle Place, NY 11514, 516 334-4985.

MEAD, Dianne J.; '89 MA; 50 N Broadway Apt. 5E, White Plains, NY 10603, 914 762-1266.

MEADE, Lyndia F.; '86 BA, '97 MPA; Clinical Dir.; Svcs. for The Underserved Persons w/AIDS, 305 7th Ave., Old Chelsea, NY 10011, 212 633-6900; r. 244 Schaefer St., Brooklyn, NY 11207, 718 573-4984; *Mario Jonas.* e-mail

MEADERS, Nyhisha T. '95 (See Gibbs, Nyhisha T.).

MEADOW, Howard S.; '76 MA; 6800 Fruit Flower Ave., Las Vegas, NV 89130, 702 616-9875.

MEADOWCROFT, James J.; '83 BS; 80 Jefferson Blvd., Staten Island, NY 10312.

MEAGHER, Brian C.; '78 BA; MSED Long Island Univ.; Sr. Investigator; Citigroup, 250 West St., New York, NY 10013, 212 723-3653; r. 26 Strathmore Dr., New City, NY 10956, 914 426-2239. e-mail

MEAGHER, Dr. Patrick B.; '87 BS; Self; r. 36 Monmouth Rd, Elizabeth, NJ 07208, 908 353-3552.

MEALIA, Robert M.; '76 MPA; MA, PHD SUNY Albany; Prof./Chair; Iona Clg. Criminal Justice Dept., 715 North Ave., New Rochelle, NY 10801, 914 637-2747; r. 20 Latourette St., Staten Island, NY 10309. e-mail

MEARA, Charles E.; '75 MA; JD New York Law Sch.; Retired; r. 3842 216th St., Flushing, NY 11361, 718 225-1129.

MECEA, Robert; '92 BS; 1267 70th St., Brooklyn, NY 11228.

MECIR, Thomas B.; '76 BS; 4370 Kissena Blvd., Apt. 21N, Flushing, NY 11355.

MEDEIROS, Michael; '76 BS; Detective; NYC Police Dept.; r. 18 Allison Ave., Staten Island, NY 10306; *Nancy;* Tiffany, Taryn.

MEDIC, Joseph; '96 BS; Law Student; Brooklyn Law Sch.; r. 30-05 42 St. #1r, Long Island City, NY 11103, 718 721-3698. e-mail

MEDINA, Bolivar; '99 BS; Police Ofcr./ Detective; NYC Police Dept.; r. Broad Channel, NY 11693, 718 634-8016. e-mail

MEDINA, Deborah; '92 BS; Police Ofcr.; r. POB 1009, Bronx, NY 10462, 718 519-9146.

MEDINA, Francisco; '95 BS; 129 Menahan St. Apt. 3l, Brooklyn, NY 11221, 718 439-5478.

MEDINA, Jaime; '93 BA; 333 Pearl St. Apt. 2l, New York, NY 10038.

MEDINA, Jose M.; '93 BA; Comp Tech.; Bell Atlantic, 1166 Ave. of The Americas, New York, NY 10036, 212 856-1365; r. 359 S. 2nd St., Brooklyn, NY 11211, 718 381-4330.

MEDINA, Luis A.; '89 BA; 165 E 179th St. Apt. 6e, Bronx, NY 10453, 718 655-5631.

MEDINA, Ms. Marianella; '91 BS; Mgr./ Gen. Medicine/Primary Care; St. Luke's Roosevelt Hosp., New York, NY 10025, 212 523-5918; r. 2184 Richmond Ter., Staten Island, NY 10302, 718 816-4527; *Wilson Rojas;* Raquel, Nicholas B. e-mail

MEDINA, Moraima; '84 BA; 2 Marble Hill Ave., Bronx, NY 10463, 718 367-6236.

MEDINTZ, Igor; '90 BS, '93 MS; 19 Stevenson St., Lynbrook, NY 11563, 516 593-8624.

MEDOWS, Deborah; '89 MPA; 51-03 Van Loon St., Elmhurst, NY 11373.

MEDWICK, Toni A., (Toni A. Ferrara); '74 BA; Homemaker; r. 72 Linden St., Carteret, NJ 07008, 732 969-3007; *Allan;* Allan, Laura.

MEEHAN, James B.; '63 MPA; 6607 Avenue T, Brooklyn, NY 11234, 718 851-4020.

MEEHAN, Stephen G.; '96 BS; 3247 Maeterlinck Ave., Toledo, OH 43614, 419 381-2732.

MEEKS, John A.; '72 BS; 33 Rosedale Ave., Madison, NJ 07940, 973 301-0878.

MEENAN, Patrick J.; '78 MA; 417 W 263rd St. # 1, Bronx, NY 10471.

MEERES, Victoria; '93 BA, '96 MPA; 70 W 93rd St. # 2, New York, NY 10025.

MEGGETT, Cynthia Y.; '82 BS; 125-06 Francis Lew, Laurelton, NY 11413.

MEHAFFEY, Paul R.; '78 MA; 1722 Kenyon Ave., S. Plainfield, NJ 07080, 908 757-9082.

MEIER, Patricia M.; '89 BA; 18920 45th Rd, Flushing, NY 11358, 718 939-7143.

MEIGHAN, Litna '85 (See Mc Nickle, Litna M.).

MEILLEUR, Leslie M.; '85 BA; 421 W. 162 St., New York, NY 10032.

MEINE, Manfred F., PhD CGFM; '80 MA; PHD Golden Gate Univ.; Regional Dir.; Troy State Univ, 81 Beal Pkwy. SE, Ft. Walton Bch., FL 32548, 850 244-7414; r. 4233 Otterlake Cv, Niceville, FL 32578, 850 897-8222; *Rita.* e-mail

MEINKEN, Todd E.; '97 MS; 36 Cedar Branch St., Middle Island, NY 11953.

MEJIA, Ravel E.; '96 BS; 187 S Ocean Ave. #2, Freeport, NY 11520, 516 539-2092.

MEJIA, Sandra M.; '98 BA; Clerk UPS-Brooklyn Key, Housing Asst-New York City, Housing Dept.; r. 565 W 171st St., Apt. 1E, New York, NY 10032, 212 927-1671; Noelia E., David A. Jr, Vladimir.

MEJIAS, Desiree; '93 BA; 510 Avenue C, Brooklyn, NY 11218, 718 284-2118.

MEJIAS, Edgar; '87 BS; Dist. Div. Mgr.; Lorillard Tobacco Co., 1017 Elmont Rd., Valley Stream, NY 11580, 516 285-1303; r. 462 Jefferson Blvd., Staten Island, NY 10312, 718 967-7785; *Frances;* Jillian, Jessica.

MELAMED, Joel S.; '86 BS; 21 Pinetree Ln., Roslyn Hts., NY 11577.

MELBOURNE, Phyllis M.; '84 MPA; BA Fordham Univ.; Retired-Administrative Asst.; John Jay Clg.; r. 4175 Hill Ave., Bronx, NY 10466, 718 325-7206.

MELCHIONA, Diane B.; '66 MPA; 679 Cornwell Ave., Malverne, NY 11565.

MELE, Elizabeth A.; '93 BS; 506 Cross Bay Blvd., Far Rockaway, NY 11693, 718 474-7426.

MELE, Mary G.; '91 BS; 506 Cross Bay Blvd., Far Rockaway, NY 11693, 718 474-7426.

MELEKWE, Augustina M.; '84 BS, '87 MA; 2440 Hunter Ave., Apt. 23A, Bronx, NY 10475.

MELENDEZ, Abel; '99 BA; Private Investigator; r. 2766 Barnes Ave., Apt. B6, Bronx, NY 10468, 718 515-4576.

MELENDEZ, Aida L.; '78 BA; 736 6th St. SW Apt. 107, Washington, DC 20024, 202 479-0682.

MELENDEZ, David; '89 BA; 1143 Fteley Ave., Bronx, NY 10472, 718 992-4141.

MELENDEZ, Mrs. Diana A., (Diana A. Corchado); '95 BS; Detective; NYC Police Dept., 1 Police Plz., New York, NY 10038, 212 741-8441; r. 52 Seaside Ln., Staten Island, NY 10305, 718 876-8551; *David.*

MELENDEZ, Eugenio; '79 BS; DIPLOMA Police Acad.; Sheriff Ofcr.; Middlesex Cnty. Sheriff Dept., 290 Georgia St., New Brunswick, NJ 08901; r. POB 186, Spotswood, NJ 08884, 732 723-1577. e-mail

MELENDEZ, Luis E.; '82 BA; 54 W 94th St. Apt. 5a, New York, NY 10025, 718 992-4141.

MELENDEZ, Michael J.; '87 BA; 7b Asch Loop, Bronx, NY 10475.

MELENDEZ, Monserrate; '98 BA; Child Protective Spec.; NYC Admin. for Children's Svcs., 192 E. 151st St., Bronx, NY 10451, 718 579-9421; r. 987 Fox St., Apt. 11, Bronx, NY 10459; *Manuel Beltran;* Heven Nicole.

MELENDEZ-JOSEY, Maritza; '99 BA; Public Assistance Spec.; Children & Families HRS, 9350 Bay Plaza Blvd., Ste. 120, Tampa, FL 33619, 813 744-6226; r. 541 Falkirk Ave., Valrico, FL 33594, 813 727-3972; *Robert.*

MELGAR, Silvia L.; '99 BA; 107-30 115th St., Jamaica, NY 11419, 718 271-3820.

MELHADO, Godfrey R.; '99 BA; 28 Beechmont Rd Bsmt, Carmel, NY 10512, 914 225-7415.

MELIAN, Octavia A.; '88 BS; 330 Haven Ave. Apt. 2n, New York, NY 10033, 212 923-2838.

MELIDOR, Avmart; '94 BS; 92-42 212 Pl., Queens Vlg., NY 11428, 718 295-4041.

MELINO, Albert J.; '98 BS; 5615 Netherland Ave., Bronx, NY 10471, 718 884-5321.

MELIS, Paul; '97 BS, '98 BS; Pres.; Corona Ready Mix Inc., 5025 97th Pl., Corona, NY 11368, 718 271-5940; r. 3627 209Street, Bayside, NY 11361, 718 428-8281; *Melissa;* Ariana, Nicholas. e-mail

MELITA, Gregory V.; '85 BS; 43 Cheever Pl., Brooklyn, NY 11231, 718 852-7693.

MELLADO, Cristina B.; '89 BS, '91 MPA; 45-03 23 St., Long Island City, NY 11101.

MELO, Yesenia E.; '98 BA; 80 Ft. Washington 6, New York, NY 10032.

MELONE, John E.; '76 AS; 414 Tarrytown Ave., Staten Island, NY 10306.

MELROSE, Valerie L.; '78 BS, '82 MPA; Assoc. Fraud Investigator; NYC Dept. of Finance, 25 Elm Pl., Brooklyn, NY 11201; r. 20 W Mosholu Pkwy. S. #31D, Bronx, NY 10468.

MELSKY, SGT Ryan E.; '99 MA; BA Jersey City State Clg., CERT. Trenton Police Acad.; Sgt./JD Candidate, Temple Univ.; Clinton Twp. Police Dept., 1370 Rte. 31 N., Annandale, NJ 08801, 908 735-7230; r. 303 Schenck Dr., Flemington, NJ 08822, 908 284-2520. e-mail

MELVIN, Octavia F.; '97 BS, '98 BS; 390 Kosciusko St., Brooklyn, NY 11221, 718 452-8818.

MENA, Bayovanex; '95 BS; Investigator; Motion Picture Assn.; r. 503 W. 111th St., New York, NY 10025. e-mail

MENA, Eda L.; '92 BA; 132 Maple Ave., Spring Vly., NY 10977.

MENARD, Earl J., Jr.; '77 MPA, '86 MPA; Acctg. Exec.; Cablevision of NYC, Bronx, NY 10473; r. 1867 Wallace Ave., Bronx, NY 10462, 718 828-7376. e-mail

MENARDY, Jasmine; '94 BS; 1632 E 93rd St., Brooklyn, NY 11236.

MENCIA, Jose L.; '96 BSCJ; Health Services; Columbia Cornell Care, 900 Third Ave., Ste. 500, New York, NY 10022, 212 588-7361; r. 555 Kappock St., Bronx, NY 10463, 718 884-9861; *Diane.* e-mail

MENDAL, Amy; '97 BS; 8 Potomac Ct., Washingtonville, NY 10992.

MENDEL, Alan; '76 MA; 16 Wanda Ave., Wayne, NJ 07470.

MENDELL, Jonathan; '94 BS; 18 Old Farm Rd, Levittown, NY 11756, 516 796-5902.

MENDELSOHN, David; '92 MA; BS CCNY; Retired Inst; r. 20 Executive Dr., Hauppauge, NY 11788, 631 265-6830.

MENDEZ, Angel; '80 BS, '99 AS; Fraud Investigator; NYC Ofc. of Revenue; r. 500 E. Houston St. #9D, New York, NY 10002, 212 260-6638. e-mail

MENDEZ, Angela; '97 BA; Proj. Mgr.; American Bldg. Maint., 70 Pine St., New York, NY 10270, 212 770-5242; r. 461 W. 44th St., Apt. G, New York, NY 10036.

MENDEZ, Arturo; '95 BS; 1692 Lexington Ave., New York, NY 10029.

MENDEZ, Dennis M.; '99 BS; Theatre Mgr.; United Artists, 321 Merrick Rd, Lynbrook, NY 11563, 516 593-1050; r. 139 Midwood St., Valley Stream, NY 11580, 516 872-0877.

MENDEZ, Felix R.; '80 BA; 856 E 156th St. Apt. 1, Bronx, NY 10455, 718 378-4923.

MENDEZ, Francis; '95 BS; 3737 88th St. Apt. E3, Flushing, NY 11372, 718 366-3082.

MENDEZ, Irma E.; '91 BS; Police Ofcr.; New York Police Dept., 1 Police Plz., New York, NY 10001, 212 374-5000; r. 59 Arnold St., Staten Island, NY 10301; *Robert Leguillou;* Martin, Diaz, Danielle L., Steven L.

MENDEZ, Jorge A.; '87 BA; MS Columbia Pacific Univ.; Psychotherapist; St. Vincent's Ctr. for Behavioral Health, 4083 Main St., Bridgeport, CT 06606, 203 365-8400; r. POB 5891, Bridgeport, CT 06610; *Olga;* Shelly, Debbie. e-mail

MENDEZ, Lisa '98 (See Nadelbach, Lisa M.).

MENDEZ, Lourdes A.; '83 BS; 1134a Greene Ave., Brooklyn, NY 11221, 718 235-4319.

MENDEZ, Lucitania B.; '94 BS; MSED Lehmann Clg.; Guid. Couns.; NYC Dept. of Education, PS 65, Mother Hale Acad., Bronx, NY 10452; r. 2038 Morris Ave., Apt. 4D, Bronx, NY 10453, 718 583-0395; *Carlos Manuel Batista.*

MENDEZ, Maria; '92 BA; 597 Knickerbocker Ave., Brooklyn, NY 11221, 718 486-0366.

MENDEZ, Marisol; '98 BS; 220 Franklin St. 4r, Brooklyn, NY 11222, 718 349-3424.

MENDEZ, Maritza; '99 BA; AS Borough Manhattan CC; Case Planner; Scan, 307 E. 116th St., New York, NY 10029, 212 534-7800; r. 23-17 32nd St. #1Floor, Astoria, NY 11105, 718 728-4973. e-mail

MENDEZ, Mrs. Milly, (Milly Torres); '96 BA; AS SUNY-Farmingdale; Social Worker; American Red Cross, 150 Amsterdam Ave., New York, NY 10023, 212 875-2295; r. 120-33D Benchley Pl., Bronx, NY 10475, 718 671-6670; *Jabiel.* e-mail

MENDEZ, Omar A.; '93 BS; 9 N Hillside Ave., Spring Vly., NY 10977.

MENDEZ, Rafael; '94 AS, '99 BS; Claims Rep.; US Social Security, New York, NY 10027; r. 2225 1st Ave. #7A, New York, NY 10029, 212 722-7401. e-mail

MENDEZ, Zenaida; '89 BA; Special Asst. to Congressman; US Household Rep, 2354 Rayburn House Ofc. Bldg., Washington, DC 20515, 212 315-2580; r. 790 11th Ave. Apt. 26a, New York, NY 10019, 212 315-2580; Dora, Clarissa, Rocio. e-mail

MENDEZ-CABAN, Juan B.; '78 BA; 56 Sherdian Ave., Brooklyn, NY 11208, 718 743-5881.

MENDOLA, Philip L.; '83 BA; 274 1/2 22 St., Brooklyn, NY 11215, 718 768-7913.

MENDOLIA, Jeffrey; '98 BA; Claims Rep.; Reliance Ins., Hauppauge, NY 11788, 631 360-5920; r. 236 Thunder Rd., Holbrook, NY 11741, 631 472-3298; *Deborah.*

MENDOZA, Arcadio; '81 AS; 41-01 12th St., Long Island City, NY 11101, 718 626-1640.

MENDOZA, Esther C.; '99 BA; Paralegal; New York County Dist. Attorney's Ofc., One Hogan Pl., New York, NY 10013, 212 335-9000. e-mail

MENDOZA, Florance W.; '78 BA; Supervising Probation Ofcr.; NYC Dept. of Probation, 100 Center St., New York, NY 10013; r. 130 Fenimore St., Brooklyn, NY 11225; *Carlos;* Robin, Makeeda, Zaid. e-mail

MENDOZA, Joel; '95 BS; 810 North Ave. #3FL, Bridgeport, CT 06606.

MENDOZA, John; '96 BA; 2147 Starling Ave., Apt. 631, Bronx, NY 10462.

MENES, Yvette; '97 BA; 2609 Avenue D, Brooklyn, NY 11226.

MENKES, Andrew; '78 MA; 1464 E 35th St., Brooklyn, NY 11234, 718 338-6056.

MENNELLA, Concetta I.; '79 BA; JD CUNY Sch. of Law; Atty-at-Law/Prof.; 241 Sunrise Hwy., Rockville Centre, NY 11570, 516 536-9540; r. 83 Franklin Pl., Oceanside, NY 11572, 516 536-9540. e-mail

MENOS, Sedrys; '99; 153 Ludlow St. #4, New York, NY 10002, 212 677-7362.

MENOSCAL, Edward A.; '80 BS; 14419 78th Rd, Flushing, NY 11367, 718 380-6841.

MENSAH, Benjamin; '94 AS; 1250 5th Ave. Apt. 4l, New York, NY 10029.

MENSAH, Sylvester F.; '95 AS; 1250 5th Ave. # 4, New York, NY 10029.

MENSLER, Jeffrey; '96 BS; 54 Lincoln Ave., # 2, Poughkeepsie, NY 12601, 914 454-6325.

MENTUCK, Bazyk S.; '90 MA; 110 Scenic Dr., Horseheads, NY 14845.

MENTUCK, Edward M.; '76 AS; 8 Dogwood Pl., Massapequa, NY 11758.

MERCADO, Diana; '96 BS; 1641 Andrews Ave., Bronx, NY 10453, 718 409-4763.

MERCADO, Frances; '99 AS; Med. Receptionist; HIP New York Med. Grp., Bronx, NY 10451; r. 1406 Merriam Ave. 2E, Bronx, NY 10452, 718 538-5468; Keana. e-mail

MERCADO, Julio; '97 BA; 443 St.anns Ave., Bronx, NY 10455, 718 328-5439.

MERCADO, Lizbeth; '84 MA; 902 E 232nd St., Bronx, NY 10466, 718 328-5439.

MERCADO, Nancy; '91 BS; 3640 Bowne St. Apt. 1m, Flushing, NY 11354, 718 634-9029.

MERCADO, Raymond; '94 BS; 1717 Bryant Ave. # 2, Bronx, NY 10460.

MERCADO, Robert; '95 BS; Police Ofcr.; Port Authority Police, World Trade Ctr., New York, NY 10048, 212 435-3500; r. 8409 35th Ave., Jackson Hts., NY 11372, 718 507-4013; Daisy; Stephanie.

MERCADO, Robertson B.; '94 BA; 2 N. Pinehurst Ave., New York, NY 10033.

MERCADO, Wigberto; '95 BA; 1693 Linden St. # 2, Flushing, NY 11385, 718 634-9029.

MERCADO-ORTIZ, Luciano; '76 BS; 281 Balcom Ave., Bronx, NY 10465, 718 665-1130.

MERCED, Deborah; '90 MPA; 3120 Wilkinson Ave., Apt. 3B, Bronx, NY 10461.

MERCEDES, Wascar A.; '99 BA; 100 Overlook Ter. 610, New York, NY 10040, 212 795-7935.

MERCEDES, Wendy V.; '98 BA; Tchr.; r. 1 Audubon Ave. 3 l, New York, NY 10032, 212 544-9598; Wascar. e-mail

MERCER, C. W.; '91 MPA; 616 E 18th St. Apt. 3j, Brooklyn, NY 11226.

MERCER, Jacquelyn D.; '79 BS; 265 Cherry St. Apt. 13d, New York, NY 10002, 315 942-2015.

MERCILLIOTT, Frederic P., PhD; '74 MPA, PHD; MS Univ. of New Haven, PHD City Univ. of NY; Prof.; Chowan Clg., POB 1848, 200 Jones Dr., Murfreesboro, NC 27855, 252 398-6262; r. 108 Cove Point Dr., Suffolk, VA 23434, 757 538-0091; Barbara; Danielle. e-mail

MERCOGLIANO, Frank; '92 MA; 123 Mamaroneck Ave., # 5N, Mamaroneck, NY 10543, 914 670-5715.

MERENDA, Jean A.; '76 BS; 31 Chestnut Cir., Northport, NY 11768.

MERENDA, Stephen P.; '76 BS; 31 Chestnut Cir., Northport, NY 11768.

MEREUTA, Rodica D.; '98 BS; 19 10 Parsons Blvd. 5g, Whitestone, NY 11357.

MERO, John R.; '86 BA; 572 Pennsylvania Ave., Brooklyn, NY 11207.

MERO, Mildred; '97 BA; 85-32 90th St. 2, Woodhaven, NY 11421, 718 465-1463.

MERRIAM, Willard E.; '76 MA; 9 Northridge Dr., Coram, NY 11727.

MERRICK, Timothy; '95 AS, '97 BS; 4523 45th St. Apt. 2r, Long Island City, NY 11104, 718 335-3118.

MERRIFIELD, Lauri A.; '81 BS; 300 N Michigan Ave., Massapequa, NY 11758, 516 249-0097.

MERRITT, Douglas; '97, '98 BS; 18 Hirsch Ln., Staten Island, NY 10314.

MERRITT, Trica; '93 BA; 554 Powell St., Brooklyn, NY 11212, 718 485-0791.

MERRIWEATHER, Michelle L.; '98 BS; 259-03 147 Dr., Rosedale, NY 11422, 718 723-1996.

MERSHEIMER, Chris; '97 MA; 648 Central Park Ave., Scarsdale, NY 10583.

MERTZ, Mrs. Elizabeth H., (Elizabeth H. Tucker); '94 BA; Homemaker; r. 154 Martlang Ave., Tarrytown, NY 10591, 914 631-7617; Robert P.; David James, Ryan Tucker.

MESA, Nelson; '99 BA; Ins.; r. 79-25 150th St., D24, Flushing, NY 11367, 718 591-1721.

MESIBOV, David E.; '83 BA; City of NY Employee; r. 568 J Grand St., Apt. #1403, New York, NY 10002, 212 533-2744.

MESORANA, Carmen; '93 BA; 4002 Hickory Ct., Peekskill, NY 10566.

MESSAM, Carol R.; '85 BS; 136-05 Bennett Str, Jamaica, NY 11434.

MESSAM, Patrick; '80 MPA; 1600 16 St. NW #708, Washington, DC 20009.

MESSANA, Joseph; '88 BS, '96 MS; 6135 71st St. Apt. 1, Flushing, NY 11379.

MESSICK, Edna; '84 MPA; 444 Washington Blvd., Apt. 2331, Jersey City, NJ 07310.

MESSINA, Anthony L.; '81 BS; Retired Police Lt.; r. 90 Claypit Rd, # 2, Staten Island, NY 10309, 718 227-8883. e-mail

MESSINA, Camillo; '95 BS; 2373 83rd St., Brooklyn, NY 11214, 718 232-0144.

MESSINA, Camillo J.; '90 MPA; BA SUNY-Purchase; Retired Police Ofcr; NYPD; r. RR 1 Box 792, Dingmans Ferry, PA 18328, 570 828-1515; Brenda; Vincent, Lauren.

MESSINA, John J.; '99 MS; Lt.; New York Fire Dept., Mayor's Ofc. of Emergency Mngt, 7 World Trade Ctr., New York, NY 10048, 212 788-1502; r. 313 Sayville Blvd., Sayville, NY 11782, 631 563-8669; Erin; Matthew, Michael, Robert, Darcy. e-mail

MESZAROS-BRILLON, A.; '95 BS; 3236 Lafayette Ave., Bronx, NY 10465.

METAXAS, Alexander; '99 BS; Confidential Private Investigator; NYC Dept. of Investigations, New York, NY 10001, 212 306-4820; r. 33-18 28th St., Long Island City, NY 11106, 718 626-4692.

METAXAS, Mary; '92 BS; 587 16th St., Brooklyn, NY 11215.

METH, Jack; 445 W 59th St., New York, NY 10019.

METIVIER, Beverley A.; '95 BS; MS Brooklyn Clg.; Tchr.; PS 190, 590 Sheffield Ave., Brooklyn, NY 11207, 718 346-8780; r. 195 Underhill Ave., Apt. 2E, Brooklyn, NY 11238, 718 783-3904; Shavohn Osborne. e-mail

METIVIER, Margaret; '79 BS; 1077 NY Ave. #B4, Brooklyn, NY 11203.

METZGER, Robert; '77 BS; 10452 110th St., Jamaica, NY 11419, 718 848-1090.

METZLER, Arthur J.; '81 BS; Police Ofcr.; Hollywood Police Dept., 3250 Hollywood Blvd., Hollywood, FL 33021, 954 967-4357; r. 1450 S W 85th Ave., Pembroke Pines, FL 33025, 954 437-5614; Linda; Laura, Peter. e-mail

MEVORAH, Steven H.; '75 BS; 1225 Ocean Pkwy., Brooklyn, NY 11230, 718 338-5132.

MEYER, Kurt P.; '95 BS; 21-15 27th St., Astoria, NY 11105, 718 539-0100.

MEYER, Leonard A.; '76 BA; 106 Ft. Wash Ave. #6H, New York, NY 10032, 315 733-3678.

MEYER, Mitchell L.; '93 BA; 2080 Nechanel Ct. Apt. 3, Bend, OR 97701, 541 385-8048.

MEYERS, Cheryl-ann; '84 BA; 2300 5th Ave. #, New York, NY 10037, 315 733-3678.

MEYERS, George; '91 MPA; 42 Hudson Dr., New Windsor, NY 12553, 914 733-5282.

MEYERS, Glenn R.; '95 MA; 33 Dawson Cir., Staten Island, NY 10314, 718 761-5099.

MEYERS, Harold; '74 AA, '76 BA; Asst. Chief of Dept.; NYC Fire Dept., 9 Metro.Tech Ctr., Brooklyn, NY 11201, 718 999-2370; r. 57 Kingfisher Rd, Levittown, NY 11756, 516 796-5560; Cecelia; Harold, Michael, Dennis, Gregory.

MEYERS, John A.; '75 BS; 145-54 232nd St., Springfield Gardens, NY 11413, 516 746-2652.

MEYERS, Patricia C. '80 (See Otto, Ms. Patricia C.).

MEYERS, Robert J.; '73 BA; 1947 SW Stratford Way, Palm City, FL 34990, 561 220-8290.

MEYERS, Trishonna M.; '98 BA; 2011 Shore Blvd. 3C, Astoria, NY 11105, 718 626-0756.

MEYERS, Mrs. WillieEarl; '79 BS; Retired; r. 775 Concourse Vlg E, Apt. 7A, Bronx, NY 10451, 718 538-2310; Leroy Sr.; Deidra, Sheryn, Leroy Jr.

MEZA, Edgar E.; '97 BA; 1855 E Rose Ave., Apt. 28A, Orange, CA 92867, 714 761-0866.

MICELI, Peter S.; '77 BS; 156 Detroit Ave., Staten Island, NY 10312, 718 356-2708.

MICHAELIDES, Michael; '85 BS; 14617 Bayside Ave., Flushing, NY 11354, 718 961-5337.

MICHAELIDES, Vasilis; '90 BA; 30-01 Newtown Ave., Long Island City, NY 11102, 718 961-5337.

MICHAELS, Anne M., (Anne M. Dash); '83 BA; Homemaker; r. 2240 Burnett St. #6C, Brooklyn, NY 11229, 718 648-2551; Thomas; Thomas Jr, Joseph. e-mail

MICHAELS, Carol; '86 BA; Retired; NYC Human Resources Admin.; r. 5102 Sunnyvale Dr., Orlando, FL 32822, 407 273-5096; *George;* Mark Leon, Steven.

MICHAELS, Norman M.; '80 BS; 101-16 Avenue J, Brooklyn, NY 11218, 718 339-5988.

MICHAELSON, Estee M.; '99 BA; 1601 E 29th St. 2Fl, Brooklyn, NY 11229, 718 951-6781.

MICHEL, Nancy C.; '98 BA; 4823 Clarendon Rd, Brooklyn, NY 11203, 718 586-4555.

MICHEL, Olga E. '87 (See Michel-Martinez, Mrs. Olga).

MICHEL, Pierre H.; '92 BS; 24519A 76th Ave., Jamaica, NY 11426, 718 264-8855.

MICHEL, Pierre M.; '97 BA; Public Health Advisor; NYC Dept. of Health, 718 760-0962; r. 110 Lenox Rd #1A, Brooklyn, NY 11226, 718 693-5343. e-mail

MICHEL, Pierre R.; '98 BS; 236 Hudson Ave., Roosevelt, NY 11575, 718 264-8855.

MICHELAKOU, Sophie; '88 MA; 3162 35th St. Apt. 4, Long Island City, NY 11106, 718 204-1519.

MICHELL, Arthur N.; '75 MA; POB 1210, Massapequa, NY 11758.

MICHEL-MARTINEZ, Mrs. Olga, (Olga E. Michel); '87 BA; Caseworker; r. 600 W. 138th St., Apt. 44, New York, NY 10031, 212 368-7021; *Oscar Martinez;* Jacob, Michael.

MICKENS, Renee J.; '97 BA; Commercial Ins. Broker; Marsh USA Inc., 1166 Ave. of the Americas, 41st Fl., New York, NY 10036, 212 345-3074; r. 574 E. 163rd St., Apt. 5b, Bronx, NY 10456; Elliott. e-mail

MICKEY, Gregory; '83 BS; Supv.; City of NY, 718 963-5110; r. 3150 Broadway St., New York, NY 10027.

MICKULAS, Walter D.; '80 MPA; 84-50 85th Ave., Woodhaven, NY 11421.

MICUCCI, Frances E. '80 (See Kosowski, Mrs. Frances E.).

MIDDLETON, C. B.; '75 BS; 882-14k Colgate Ave., Bronx, NY 10473, 718 379-7146.

MIDDLETON, Karen A.; '99 BA; 4710 Avenue H, Brooklyn, NY 11234, 718 692-4681.

MIDDLETON, La-tonia B.; '96 BA; MA Fordham Univ.; Central Ofc. Technician; Bell Atlantic, 375 Pearl St., New York, NY 10028; r. 33 James St., Unit A, Washington Park, NJ 07102, 973 424-1195.

MIDDLETON, Ruth P.; '99 BA; 131-31 232nd St., Jamaica, NY 11413, 718 978-7525.

MIDDLETON, Sharon D.; '99 BS; Elem. Tchr.; P.S. 69 The New Vision Sch., 560 Threrlot Ave., Bronx, NY 10473; r. 1466 E Gun Hill Rd, Apt. 7C, Bronx, NY 10469, 718 324-2489. e-mail

MIELE, John E.; '78 BS; 55-09 Seabury St., Elmhurst, NY 11373.

MIELES, Christina M.; '98 BA; Admin. Asst.; Bear Stearns, 245 Park Ave., New York, NY 10167; r. 768 42nd St., Brooklyn, NY 11232, 718 853-0399.

MIER, Jodi L.; '80 BS; 17 Vesper Rd, Patterson, NY 12563.

MIGDAL, Sandra; '88 BA; 1175 York Ave. #2D, New York, NY 10021.

MIGHT, Francis E.; '80 BA, '83 MA; Retired; r. 765 Riverside Dr., New York, NY 10032, 212 568-6734.

MIGNANO, Michael J.; '94 BS; Intl. Equity Trader; Knight-Trimark, 525 Washington Blvd., 29th Fl., Jersey City, NJ 07310, 212 336-8843; r. 49 Skyline Dr., Warren, NJ 07059, 908 903-1606; *Denise.* e-mail

MIGNINI, Annmarie; '91 BA; 26 Mckinley Ave., Valhalla, NY 10595, 914 761-5289.

MIGNINI, Leonard; '87 BS; 507 Millard Way, Peekskill, NY 10566.

MIGUEL, Regina L.; '82 BS; 1415 Sterling Pl., Brooklyn, NY 11213, 718 953-3787.

MIHAILOS, Michele A.; '99 MA; 55 Seagate Rd., Staten Island, NY 10305, 718 720-7758.

MIHALAKELIS, Michael; '77 BS; Deportation Ofcr.; US Immigration & Naturalization Svc., Dept. of Justice, 26 Federal Plz., New York, NY 10278, 212 264-5854; r. 2247 29th St., Long Island City, NY 11105, 718 726-1686.

MIHALEK, Donald J.; '92 BS; 7 Hastings Dr., Ridge, NY 11961.

MIHOVICH, Anthony M.; '80 BS; 37 Princeton Dr., Syosset, NY 11791, 516 935-7004.

MIKOS, Ms. Nancy; '78 BS; Court Ofcr.; The Ofc. Ct. Admin., Staten Island, NY 10304; r. 92 Hatfield Pl., Staten Island, NY 10302.

MILA, Jennifer; '95 AS, '97 BS; 2512 University Ave. Apt. 3b, Bronx, NY 10468, 718 295-3124.

MILADINOV, Marija; '98 BA; 320 E. 23 St. #12m, New York, NY 10010, 212 475-2080.

MILADINOV, Mrs. Zora C., (Zora Cvijic); '96 BS; Paralegal; Hendricks & Hendricks, 73 Paterson St., New Brunswick, NJ 08901, 732 828-7800; r. 209 Cindy St., Old Bridge, NJ 08857, 732 679-0750; *Sima.* e-mail

MILEA, Daniel; '93 BS; 5939 60th Ave., Flushing, NY 11378.

MILEY, Gregory L.; '79 MA; 8323 248th St., Jamaica, NY 11426, 718 343-5131.

MILIEN, Patricia, (Patricia Sultan); '95 BA; MA Brooklyn Clg.; Fraud Investigator/Supv.; NYC Dept. of Social Svcs., 330 Jay St., Brooklyn, NY 11201, 718 237-5785; r. 717 E. 82nd St., Brooklyn, NY 11236, 718 968-7942; *Wiener.* e-mail

MILIONE, James M.; '74 BA; 40 E Figurea Ave., Staten Island, NY 10308.

MILLAN, Gregory; '82 BA; 276 Crescent St., Brooklyn, NY 11208, 718 574-6813.

MILLARD, Thomas G.; '81 BS; 150 Wifred Blvd., Hicksville, NY 11801.

MILLER, Amy B.; '89 BS; 50A Newark Way, Maplewood, NJ 07040.

MILLER, Ann M.; '99, MA; 8816 Harris, N. Ridgeville, OH 44039, 440 748-1001.

MILLER, Bobby; '91 AS; POB 122, Bronx, NY 10451, 718 293-2965.

MILLER, Carlos M.; '99 BA; Police Ofcr.; NYC Police Dept., New York, NY 10038; r. 194 Putnam Ave., Brooklyn, NY 11216, 718 230-4930. e-mail

MILLER, Chanell N.; '99 BS; AS; Fraud Investigator; NYC Dept. of Homeless Svcs.; r. 645 Magenta St., Bronx, NY 10467, 718 405-7078. e-mail

MILLER, Christine A.; '78 BS; 369 Mountainview Ave., Staten Island, NY 10314, 718 981-9844.

MILLER, Christopher A.; '95 BS; Detective-Investigator; NYC Police Dept., 1 Police Plz., New York, NY 10013, 212 374-5000; r. 7922 15th Ave., Brooklyn, NY 11228, 718 462-2814.

MILLER, Daniel; '88 BA; 27 Sunfield Ave., Staten Island, NY 10312.

MILLER, Dorothy J.; '83 BS; 67-12 Yellowstone, Forest Hills, NY 11375, 718 225-3053.

MILLER, Dwight D.; '97 BS; 326 S. 5th Ave., Mt. Vernon, NY 10550, 914 663-6068.

MILLER, Edward D.; '95 BS; 2111 23rd Dr., Long Island City, NY 11105, 718 224-6471.

MILLER, Eric C.; '90 BA; 177 Sussex Rd, Elmont, NY 11003, 516 775-7740.

MILLER, Gail E.; '89 BA, '93 MPA; Dir. of Prog. Devel.; John Jay Clg., 899 10th Ave., New York, NY 10019, 212 237-8653; r. 98-15 Horace Harding Expy. #11b, Corona, NY 11368. e-mail

MILLER, Georgetea A.; '97 BA; 707 E 224th St., Bronx, NY 10466, 718 881-3292.

MILLER, Gloria L.; '97 BS, '99; 257 Clinton St. #17, New York, NY 10002, 315 826-7272.

MILLER, Ivy C.; '98 BA; 98 Morningside Ave., New York, NY 10027, 212 864-1597.

MILLER, James J.; '85 BA; 1644 Corneilia St., Flushing, NY 11385, 718 932-2486.

MILLER, James O.; '94 BS; Billing Mgr.; Skytell; r. 229 Christie St., Apt. 4, Ridgefield Park, NJ 07660, 201 296-0463; *Freddie;* Asha.

MILLER, Jonathan D.; '76 BS; 61-45 Linden St., Ridgewood, NY 11385, 718 932-2486.

MILLER, Joseph; '77 BS, '90 BS; 139-25 31 Rd., Flushing, NY 11354, 718 932-2486.

MILLER, Judith A. '83 (See Butcher, Mrs. Judith A.).

MILLER, Kenneth L.; '79 BS; Real Estate Mgr.; NYS Div. of Housing & Community Renewal; r. 15 Highland Dr., Cortlandt Manor, NY 10567, 914 737-7090; *Patricia.*

MILLER, Kisha; '97 BA; 63-37 Austin St. 2, Rego Park, NY 11374.

MILLER, Lawrence; '85 MA; 438 W. Broadway, New York, NY 10012, 315 337-6595.

MILLER, Lee A.; '96 MPA; BS SUNY-Brockport; DC Loss Prevention Mgr.; Pep Boys, 3111 W. Alleghey Ave., Philadelphia, PA 19132, 914 469-6124; r. POB 2410, Middletown, NY 10940, 914 342-1021. e-mail

MILLER, Lionel R.; '79 BS; POB 80, New York, NY 10027, 315 337-6595.

MILLER, Lorraine E.; '82 MPA; 3456 Mickle Ave., Bronx, NY 10469, 718 796-1890.

MILLER, Louis J.; '96 BA; 460 Avenue Y, Brooklyn, NY 11223, 718 467-3251.

MILLER, Marion; c/o J.P. Wilson, 501 W. 156th St., New York, NY 10032, 315 826-7272.

MILLER, Melva; '96 BS; Paralegal; The Family Ctr., 66 Reade St., New York, NY 10007, 212 766-4522; r. 22715 137th Ave., Jamaica, NY 11413, 718 276-0719. e-mail

MILLER, Michael T.; '86 BS; 3 Rifton St., Elmont, NY 11003, 516 334-8690.

MILLER, Mousey S.; '93 BS; 359 W 54th St. Apt. 4fs, New York, NY 10019, 315 826-7272.

MILLER, Raymond C.; '92 BA; 3930 59th St. Apt. B1, Flushing, NY 11377, 718 672-6187.

MILLER, Robert; '93 AS; BS CUNY-JJC Campus; Detective; NYPD, 1 Police Plz., New York, NY 10038, 212 374-5000; r. 73 Fulton St., W. Babylon, NY 11704, 631 643-6931.

MILLER, Robert E.; '81 MA; Retired Secondary Educator; HS of Graphic Communications; r. 747 10th Ave. Apt. 24C, New York, NY 10019, 212 765-2494.

MILLER, Roy P.; '80 BA; 447 A State St. #1, Brooklyn, NY 11217.

MILLER, Scott K.; '94 BA; Police Ofcr.; NYPD; r. 4 Cedar Grove St. W, Patchogue, NY 11772.

MILLER, Steven G.; '81 MA; Personnel Analyst; Pennsylvania Dept. of Corrections, 251 Swope Rd, Bethel, PA 19507, 717 933-4012; r. same; *Linda;* Jane. e-mail

MILLER, Thomas J.; '82 MA; General Delivery, Otisville, NY 10963.

MILLER-DIAZ, Harriett; '83 BA; 107-01 Watson Pl., Jamaica, NY 11433, 718 262-8480.

MILLETT, John F.; '76 BS; 144 Sullivan St., Apt. 11, New York, NY 10012.

MILLEVOI, Frank; '96 BS; 3436 43rd St. Apt. 2l, Long Island City, NY 11101.

MILLIEN, Sabine M.; '84 BS; 11648 229th St., Jamaica, NY 11411, 718 978-7164.

MILLIEN, Tamara; '95 BA; 1655 Flatbush Ave., Apt. B1408, Brooklyn, NY 11210, 718 677-9535.

MILLMAN, Howard L.; '81 BS; 1 Magnolia Dr., Newtown, PA 18940, 215 497-0525.

MILLS, Aaron E.; '80 BS; 1747 Stein Dr., Bay Shore, NY 11706.

MILLS, Beverly A.; '93 BS; 794 Rogers Ave. # Pvt, Brooklyn, NY 11226, 718 345-5348.

MILLS, Charles M.; '76 BA; MPA Long Island Univ.; NYS Tax & Finance, 2 World Trade Ctr. 87-14, New York, NY 10048, 212 321-4582; r. 866 Broadway, Brentwood, NY 11717, 631 581-6352; *Marie;* Charles III, Adam, Alexander, Kari, John. e-mail

MILLS, James J.; '76 MPA; 3000 Alvin Ct., Oceanside, NY 11572, 516 536-6543.

MILLS, Lurline; '92 BA; 245 E. 57th St., Brooklyn, NY 11203, 718 345-5348.

MILNER, Michael C.; '98 BA MPA; 238 W. 106th St. #6C, New York, NY 10025, 212 864-1847.

MILONE, Debra D.; '78 BA; 2263 Edsall Ave., Bronx, NY 10463, 718 549-4485.

MILOVANOVIC, Dragan; '76 MA; 51-79 Manilla St., Elmhurst, NY 11373.

MIMMS, Pauline P.; '82 BA; 10444 210th St., Queens Vlg., NY 11429.

MIMMS, Yvette C., (Yvette C. Williams); '82 BS; JD Howard Univ., Washington; Cnslt.; r. 4662 Winterberry Ln., Oxon Hill, MD 20745; *Curtis;* Maurice. e-mail

MIMS, Venetia L.; '89 BA; Supv.; Manhattan, 600 E. 125th, New York, NY 10035; r. 3716 Rombouts Ave., Bronx, NY 10466, 718 654-2135. e-mail

MINACAPELLI, M.; '92 BS; 87-12 Liberty Ave., Ozone Park, NY 11417.

MINARA, Robert J.; '97 BA; 5002 Applewood, Carmel, NY 10512.

MINARDI, Rocco N.; '76 MPA; AS, BS; Retired; Police Dept./Bristol-Myers Squibb; r. 569 84th St., Brooklyn, NY 11209, 718 238-3866; *Beatrice;* Kathleen, Salvatore, Patricia, Peter, Michael.

MINAUSKAS, John A.; '75 MA; 1457 Astor Ave., Bronx, NY 10469.

MINAYA, Joselinne A.; '98 BA; Domestic Violence Couns.; Nuevo Amanecer/Dominican Women's Devel., 359 Ft. Washington Ave. #1G, New York, NY 10033, 212 740-1929; r. 701-03 W. 184th St., #4A, New York, NY 10033, 212 781-7916; Steven, Amy.

MINER, Juanita H.; '72 BA; 924 E 227 St., Bronx, NY 10466, 718 652-6418.

MINERVA, Dominick J.; '70 BS; 5 Peppermint Rd, Commack, NY 11725, 631 368-7487.

MINERVINI, Dominick; '93 MA; 299 Julianne Ter., Secaucus, NJ 07094, 201 348-0691.

MINES, Gerald E.; 178-14 Henley Rd., Jamaica, NY 11432.

MINGIONE, Ernest R.; '83 BS; 626 Washington St., Apt. 4B, New York, NY 10014, 212 627-2441.

MINGO, Alfred E.; '76 BA; CEO/Founder; Spec. In Security Cnsltg., AEM Security, 3363 Sedgwick Ave., Bronx, NY 10463, 718 601-3024; r. same. e-mail

MINIER, Mildred; '99 BA; 1334 Riverside Dr., New York, NY 10033, 212 781-3027.

MINOGUE, Edward T.; '75 MA; 27 Freezer Rd, Middletown, NY 10941, 914 692-4828.

MINORAS, Bert; '86 BA; 11918 235th St., Jamaica, NY 11411.

MINTO, James S.; '70 BS; 149 Springfield Ave., Staten Island, NY 10314.

MINTON, Kenneth W.; '84 MA; BS Univ. of Maryland; Deputy; Hillsborough Cnty. Sheriffs Ofc., POB 3371, Tampa, FL 33601, 813 247-0455; r. 603 Dali Dr., Brandon, FL 33511, 813 684-6378; *Elfrida;* Scott, Nicola. e-mail

MINTZ, Irwin; '75 BS; 2883 W. 12th St., Brooklyn, NY 11224, 718 339-0313.

MIR, Nancy J. '90 (See Mir-Elcik, Mrs. Nancy J.).

MIRABAL, Carolina; '99 BS; Law Student; Boston Univ. Sch. of Law; r. 350 Saint Ann's Ave. Apt. # 8-C, Bronx, NY 10454, 718 585-3929. e-mail

MIRALLA, Ms. Janet; '96 BS; AS BMCC; Paralegal; Martin Lassoff Esq, 160 Broadway, New York, NY 10038, 212 227-1350; r. 8 McKibbin Ct., Brooklyn, NY 11206, 718 366-8930. e-mail

MIRAND, Esther L.; '97 BA; 3021 Holland Ave., Bronx, NY 10467, 718 583-3078.

MIRANDA, Anthony R.; '92 BS; Sgt; NYC Police Dept., New York, NY 10001, 718 922-8001; r. 527 Willoughby Ave., Brooklyn, NY 11206, 718 599-4544; *Sylvia;* Antonio, Andres. e-mail

MIRANDA, Doreen; '95 BA; 115 8th Ave., Apt. 1, Brooklyn, NY 11215, 718 345-3682.

MIRANDA, Edwin R.; '93 BS; 3541 91st St., Jackson Hts., NY 11372, 718 956-5374.

MIRANDA, Georgina M.; '92 BA; 372 Dekalb Ave. Apt. 5c, Brooklyn, NY 11205, 718 345-3682.

MIRANDA, Sandra; '85 MA; 70 E 108th St. Apt. 8b, New York, NY 10029, 315 861-5784.

MIRANDA, Yvette M.; '89 BA; 17 La Salle Pl., Oakdale, NY 11769, 631 589-9225.

MIR-ELCIK, Mrs. Nancy J., (Nancy J. Mir); '90 BS; Paralegal; Law Offices of Stanley Teich, Esq, 14 S. Main St., New City, NY 10956, 914 634-4999; r. 10 Berry Ct., Congers, NY 10920; *James Elcik;* Samantha, James. e-mail

MIRO, Sandra M.; '90 BS; 411 Ridgewood Ave., Brooklyn, NY 11208, 718 499-5233.

MIRON, Lowell S.; '97 BS, 2000 MS; AS Kingsborough Comm Clg.; Food & Beverage Industry; r. 2329 E. 22nd St., Brooklyn, NY 11229, 718 769-4901. e-mail

MIRZA, Ashfa N.; '97 BA; AS Kingsborough Comm Clg.; Legal Secy.; r. 1025 E. 14 St., Apt. E 2, Brooklyn, NY 11230, 718 253-7431. e-mail

MISIANO, Eugene; '77; 1245 E 66th St., Brooklyn, NY 11234, 718 251-5607.

MISSON, George R.; '76 BA; MS Long Island Univ.; Police Capt.; Brookhaven Natl. Lab, Bldg. 50, Upton, NY 11973, 631 344-2238; r. 28 Pidgeon Ct., Manorville, NY 11949; *Veronica;* Suzanne, Michael, Jacqueline, Meryl.

MITCHELL, Anthony J.; '84 BA; Auto Glass Owner; Rim Traders, 142-10 Liberty Ave., Jamaica, NY 11433, 718 291-5932; r. 108-14 Sutphin St., Jamaica, NY 11433, 718 206-2875; Nuri, Abdul, Shakirah, Anthea.

MITCHELL, Barbara B.; '74 BA; 161-03 Baisley Blvd., Jamaica, NY 11434, 718 229-7885.

MITCHELL, Ms. Carolyn; '85 BA; Mgr.; Barnes&Noble.com, 100 Plaze Dr., Secaucus, NJ 07094, 201 272-3659; r. 2-C Dorado Dr., Morristown, NJ 07960, 973 539-8249. e-mail

MITCHELL, Charles A.; '97 BS, '99 BS; 1764 Stuart St., Brooklyn, NY 11229, 718 998-7551.

MITCHELL, Corey; '94 BS; Florida Hwy. Patrol Academy, Coral Springs, FL.

MITCHELL, Deborah; '97 BA; 484 Pennsylvania Ave., Brooklyn, NY 11207, 718 346-1416.

MITCHELL, Douglas J.; '83 MPA; Lieutenant Retired; r. 22 Cardinal Dr., Washingtonville, NY 10992, 914 496-3037. e-mail

MITCHELL, Gloria A.; '95 BS; 2802 Laflin Pl., Richmond, VA 23228, 804 784-5152.

MITCHELL, Harry J.; '78 BA; Retired-Police Ofcr.; r. 4832 Brighton Dr., Jacksonville, FL 32217, 904 636-5266. e-mail

MITCHELL, Jamell; '96 BS; 546 Concord Bridge Pl., Apt. 6l, Newark, DE 19702, 302 324-0191.

MITCHELL, James; '75 BA; 5202 Tilden Ave., Brooklyn, NY 11203, 718 773-6638.

MITCHELL, John M.; '77 BS; 185 Hall St. Apt. 813, Brooklyn, NY 11205, 718 773-6638.

MITCHELL, Kathleen G.; '80 BS; 579 61 St., Brooklyn, NY 11220, 718 348-9646.

MITCHELL, Kimberly A.; '98 BA; Corrections Ofcr.; NYC Dept. of Corrections; r. 1902 7th Ave. #3F, New York, NY 10026, 212 865-8725; Angel, Shavon.

MITCHELL, Leon A.; '78 BA; 223-29 113 Ave., Queens Vlg., NY 11429, 718 337-7219.

MITCHELL, Marianne; '90 BS; 10813 36th Ave., Flushing, NY 11368, 718 341-3018.

MITCHELL, Maureen; '95 BA; POB 900401, Far Rockaway, NY 11690, 718 341-3018.

MITCHELL, Napoleon; '77 MPA; 32 Greenvale Cir., White Plains, NY 10607, 914 682-8342.

MITCHELL, Natasha; '99 BA; 675 Lenox Rd., Brooklyn, NY 11203, 718 467-5513.

MITCHELL, Salahadine (Sal); '98 BA; Police Ofcr.; City of NY, 32nd Precinct, 250 W 135th St., New York, NY 10030, 212 690-6311; r. 548 Beach 65th St. PH, Arverne, NY 11692, 718 318-1050.

MITCHELL, Sharleen J.; '97; 652 Lafayette Ave., Mt. Vernon, NY 10552, 716 881-1638.

MITCHELL, Tracie-Ann N.; '98 BA; Caseworker; Little Flower Children's Svcs., 89-12-162nd St., Jamaica, NY 11432, 718 526-9150; r. 205-28 110th Ave., Hollis, NY 11412, 718 217-1084. e-mail

MITCHELSON, Thomas P.; '78 MPA; 104 Walt Whitman, Cherry Hill, NJ 08003.

MITESSER, Peter C.; '80 BS; AAB Nassau Community Clg.; Special Agt.; Drug Enforcement Admin., 8198 Terminal Rd, Lorton, VA 22079, 703 541-6967; r. 20807 Shy Beaver Ct., Ashburn, VA 20147, 703 858-0551; Marie; Christine, Stephanie, Marybeth.

MITKISH, John A.; '73 BS; 538 Summit Ave., Baldwin, NY 11510.

MITRA, Diditi; '91 BA; 123-05 Hillside Ave., Richmond Hill, NY 11418, 718 465-0696.

MITRCTASICS, Mrs. Catherine; '95 BS; 3184 35th St., Astoria, NY 11106; Chris.

MITRO, Edward J.; '81 BS; Retired; r. 712 Timbergate Ct., Millersville, PA 17551; Joyce; John, Edward Jr, Gregory, Lisa. e-mail

MITROTASIOS, Chris; '91 BS; 3229 35th St., Long Island City, NY 11106.

MITSINIKOS, Nikos J.; '99 BS. e-mail

MITTON, Herns; '97 BS; 115-23 237 St., Elmont, NY 11003, 516 867-4968.

MLADENOVIC, Goran B.; '93 MPA; 70 Pkwy. N. S, Yonkers, NY 10704.

MOBLEY, Ayanna T. '95 (See Castro, Mrs. Ayanna T.).

MOCK, Judy; '95 BS; 45 Allen St. Apt. 13c, New York, NY 10002.

MOCOMBE, John E.; '92 BS; 1142 E 35th St., Brooklyn, NY 11210.

MODAFFERI, Anne C.; '84 BS; 46 Lexington Rd, Tappan, NY 10983, 914 359-4169.

MODAFFERI, Peter A.; '76 MA; POB 186, Palisades, NY 10964.

MODAWAR, Faris A.; '77 BS; 346 Fawnridge St., Georgetown, TX 78628, 512 259-5780.

MODESTE, Elaine B.; '84 BA; 101 W 147th St. # 125, New York, NY 10039.

MOE, Richard; '78 AS, '79 BS; Retired NYPD; r. 2516 Hemlock Farms, Hawley, PA 18428, 570 775-6830.

MOEHRING, Thomas P.; '75 MA; 107 Fairview Ave., Oceanside, NY 11572, 516 536-0985.

MOELLER, Thomas R.; '80 BS; RR 2 Box 178, Cold Spring, NY 10516.

MOESER, Laura '73 (See Balcom, Mrs. Laura).

MOESER, Laura B.; 60 33rd St., Copiague, NY 11726, 631 789-0867.

MOESLINGER, Emma N.; '95 BS; 2223 Hermany Ave., Bronx, NY 10473.

MOFFATT, Maikov A.; '97 BS, '98 BS; Federal Correctional Officer; Federal Bureau of Prisons, 100 29th St., Brooklyn, NY 11232, 718 840-4200; r. 853 E. 49th St., Brooklyn, NY 11203, 718 284-3963. e-mail

MOFFETT, Anita; '95 BA; 106 Steuben St., Brooklyn, NY 11205, 718 789-8421.

MOFFETT, Melissa N.; '95 BA; Child Welfare Spec.; Admin. for Children Svcs., 185 Marcie Ave., Brooklyn, NY 11211, 718 218-6282; r. 575 Saratoga Ave., Brooklyn, NY 11212, 718 444-8437.

MOHAMMAD, Taj; '87 MA; 63-22 14th Ave., Brooklyn, NY 11219, 718 998-0054.

MOHAMMED, Hassim; '92 BS, '96 MS; Fire Protection Inspector; NYC Fire Dept., 9 Metrotech Ctr., Brooklyn, NY 11201; r. 1745 Eastburn Ave., Bronx, NY 10457, 718 792-3379.

MOHAMMED, Rijal; '97 BS; 119-17 Linden Blvd., S. Ozone Park, NY 11420, 718 323-1556.

MOHER, Jacqueline M.; '83 BA; 27 Hemlock Cir., Peekskill, NY 10566.

MOHLENHOFF, William R.; '79 BS; Ret. NYPD; Security St. Johns Univ.; r. 45 Greenleaf Ave., Staten Island, NY 10310, 718 273-2644.

MOHR, Michael; '90 BS, '96 MA; Spec., Agt.; ATF, 165 Passaic Ave., 3rd Fl., Fairfield, NJ 07004, 973 357-4065; r. 21 Bruce Ct., Milltown, NJ 08850; Laurie; Christopher, Nicholas. e-mail

MOHRMANN, Tina; '75 BA; Lt.; NYPD, One Police Plz. Rm. 1204, New York, NY 10038, 212 374-5330; r. 546 40th St. Apt. l, Brooklyn, NY 11232, 718 972-3833.

MOISE, Farah; '86 BA; 10800 SW 88th St. # 1, Miami, FL 33176, 305 688-7278.

MOJICA, Yolanda C.; '80 BA; 58-02 Myrtle Ave., Ridgewood, NY 11385, 718 337-5992.

MOJOCOA, Bibiana C.; '86 BA; 14140 25 Ave., Flushing, NY 11357.

MOLIGNANO, Nicole M.; '96 MA; BA Villanova Univ.; Account Mgr.; MapQuest.com, Denver, CO 80202, 303 312-0221; r. 135 E. 8th Ave., Denver, CO 80203, 303 861-5136. e-mail

MOLINA, Adnery; '84 BS; 88 16 St., Brooklyn, NY 11215, 718 765-1695.

MOLINA, Angelita; '99 BA; 877 Taylor Ave. 6E, Bronx, NY 10473, 718 842-9121.

MOLINA, Ariadne M.; '99 BA; Mktg. Mgr.; Roc-A-Blok Records, 519 Palisades Ave., Englewood Cliffs, NJ 07632, 201 569-1813; r. Teaneck, NJ 07666, 917 828-3622. e-mail

MOLINA, Bobby; '98 BA; 5316 3rd Ave. 3, Brooklyn, NY 11220, 718 492-3110.

MOLINA, Evelyn; '99 BA; 362 S. 2nd St. #1B, Brooklyn, NY 11211, 718 765-1695.

MOLINA, Maria T.; '88 BA; Probation Ofcr.; NYC; r. 595 Jefferson Ave., Brooklyn, NY 11221.

MOLINA, Oscar M.; '84 MA; 7 Dogwood Ave., Malverne, NY 11565, 516 488-4036.

MOLINA, Sandra M.; '99 BS; Legal Asst.; Platzer Forgeld LLP; r. 20-23 49th St., Astoria, NY 11105, 718 721-6499.

MOLINA, Sonia I.; '90 BA; 224 Saint Nicholas Ave., Brooklyn, NY 11237, 718 765-1695.

MOLINARO, Louis J.; '85 MA; Managing Dir.; Securities Industry Automation Corp., 2 Metro Tech Ctr., Brooklyn, NY 11201, 212 383-2067; r. 25 Barger St., Putnam Vly., NY 10579, 914 528-8695. e-mail

MOLINARO, Mario A.; '83 MA; Psychotherapist Prof. Couns.; Clinical Cnsltg. Ctrs., 1540 Pelham Pkwy. S., Bronx, NY 10461, 718 931-7496; r. 718 792-5588. e-mail

MOLINARO, Ms. Yvette; '87 BA; JD Southwestern Univ.; Atty.; Mitchell, Silberberg & Knupp LLP, 11377 W. Olympic Blvd., Los Angeles, CA 90064, 310 312-3297; r. 12325 Gorham Ave., Los Angeles, CA 90049. e-mail

MOLINELLI, James A.; '92 BS; 3 Old Orchard Way, Miller Place, NY 11764.

MOLLAGHAN, John T.; '96 BS; Lt.; NYCPD, 1 Police Plz., New York, NY 10038, 212 374-5000; r. POB 234, Shenorock, NY 10587, 914 248-5039; Kathleen; Bridget, Maggie, Marykate.

MOLLER, Kenneth C.; '96 BA; 91 Hanover Ave., Staten Island, NY 10309.

MOLLICA, Joseph C.; '80 MA; 17 Pioneer Ct., Trenton, NJ 08628, 609 818-0131.

MOLLOY, Patricia A.; '93 BS; 1640 E 35th St. Ph, Brooklyn, NY 11234, 718 375-3553.

MOLLOY, Patrick J.; '78 BS; 9209 Knights Branch St., Tampa, FL 33637, 813 985-1964.

MOLLOY, Sean E.; '75 MA; 1640 E 35th St., Brooklyn, NY 11234, 718 375-3553.

MOMENT, Keran M.; '79 BS, '81 MA; State Parole Ofcr./Recreation Thera; NYS Div. of Parole; r. 1281 Brooklyn Ave., Brooklyn, NY 11203, 718 462-4355.

MOMODU, Dove E.; '96 BA; 219 Miriam St., Bronx, NY 10458, 718 933-6144.

MONAGHAN, Luke; 91-22 90th St., Woodhaven, NY 11421, 718 820-0554.

MONAGHAN, William A.; '84 BA; 118 Bloomingdale Rd, Levittown, NY 11756.

MONAHAN, Charles M.; '74; 33 Jones Dr., Highland Mills, NY 10930, 914 928-6797.

MONAHAN, Thomas M.; '85 BS; JD Brooklyn Law Sch.; Atty. Commercial & Criminal; r. 216 Hwy. 18, E. Brunswick, NJ 08816, 732 745-9400; *Lori.*

MONCAYO, Frank J.; '95 BS; 160 S Gannon Ave., Staten Island, NY 10314, 718 494-2910.

MONCK, Robert F.; '85 BS; 20 Wyoming Dr., Huntington Sta., NY 11746.

MONDERSON, Frederick; '87 MPA; 102 Brooklyn Ave., Brooklyn, NY 11216, 718 756-2210.

MONEL, Barbara A. '81 (See Di Maggio, Barbara A.).

MONES, Denise; '94 AS; 18825f 71st Cres. # F, Flushing, NY 11365, 718 777-1308.

MONGAN, Heather A.; '77 BA; 97 Railroad Ave., Staten Island, NY 10305.

MONGE, Luis A.; '93 BA; Sr. Court Ofcr.; NYS Courts, 851 Grand Concourse, Bronx, NY 10451, 718 590-3704; r. 2420 Bronx Park E., Bronx, NY 10467, 718 652-7489.

MONGES, Abraham; '00 BS; 1655 Flatbush Ave., Brooklyn, NY 11210.

MONK, Marie; '99 BS; Syst. Analyst; Chase Manhattan Bank; r. 535 Livonia Ave., Apt. 3 D, Brooklyn, NY 11212, 718 922-5833.

MONNAY, Yves; '98 BA; Special Investigator; Brooklyn, NY 11201; r. 409 Hamilton St., Roselle, NJ 07203, 908 298-9371.

MONOKROUSOS, Dennis; '83 BS; 21-31 35th St., Astoria, NY 11105.

MONPLAISIR, Ms. Patricia D.; '98 BA; CERT New York Sch of Paralegal; Paralegal; r. 3456 DeKalb Ave. Apt. 4 A, Bronx, NY 10463, 718 432-0050.

MONROE, Alexis A.; '90 BA; 646 E 91st St., Brooklyn, NY 11236, 718 622-7189.

MONROE, Alisha J.; '93 BS; 1143 Anderson Ave., Bronx, NY 10452.

MONROE, Angeline E.; '96 BA; AS LaGuardia Comm. Clg.; Occupational Therapist; r. 201 W. 93rd St., Apt# 2l, New York, NY 10025, 212 678-0676.

MONSEGUE, Gail A.; '83 MA; MABISPED NYU; Special Educ. Tchr.; NYC Bd. of Educ., Home Instructions Programs, 2750 Lafayette Ave. Jhs101X, Bronx, NY 10465; r. 5016 Tilden Ave., Brooklyn, NY 11203, 718 922-4648.

MONSERRATE, Juan; '85 BS; 152 S 3rd St., Brooklyn, NY 11211.

MONTAGNA, Frank C.; '86 BS; 82 Florida St., Long Beach, NY 11561.

MONTAGUE, Angela R.; '89 MA; BA City Clg.; US Probation Ofcr.; US Courts; r. 2927 Turner Ave., Abington, PA 19001, 215 659-3651.

MONTAGUE, Kathleen B.; '99 BA; Police Ofcr.; NYPD, 26 Precient, New York, NY 10027; r. 3634 Tibbett Ave., Bronx, NY 10463, 718 884-3085.

MONTAGUE, Steven L.; '98 BA; 4402 Avenue K, Brooklyn, NY 11234.

MONTAGUE, William R.; '80 AS, '82 BS; Retired-Union Official; r. 62 Skymeadow Pl., Elmsford, NY 10523, 914 592-5213; *Marie.* e-mail

MONTALBANO, Gary F.; '84 BS; 836 50th St., Brooklyn, NY 11220.

MONTALBANO, John; '87 BA; 16223 14th Ave., Whitestone, NY 11357, 718 845-5519.

MONTALBANO, John P.; '76 BA; 14922 24th Ave., Whitestone, NY 11357, 718 845-5519.

MONTALBANO, Richard P.; '79 MPA; 255 Dahlgren Pl., Brooklyn, NY 11228, 718 238-8961.

MONTALI, Joseph R.; '86 AS; Private Investigator/Retired N.Y.C; r. 1229 Van Dale Ave., Spring Hill, FL 34608, 352 666-6470; *Cindy;* Michele, Rachel, Renee, Joseph, Kimberly. e-mail

MONTALVO, Juan; '95 BA; 3368 21st St. Apt. 14b, Long Island City, NY 11106, 718 545-1735.

MONTALVO, Oneida; '93 BA; Coord.-Caseworker; Cluster Inc., 20 S. Broadway, Yonkers, NY 10701, 914 376-0780; r. 161 Webster Ave., Yonkers, NY 10701; *Luis; Melanie.* e-mail

MONTANA, Paul J.; '99 BS; Firefighter; City of NY; r. 6216 12th Ave., Brooklyn, NY 11219, 718 232-3863.

MONTANEZ, Anna I.; '92 BA; MSW Hunter Clg.; Social Worker; Good Shepherd Svcs., 441 Fourth Ave., Brooklyn, NY 11205, 718 788-0666; r. 8116 5th Ave. Apt. 3F, Brooklyn, NY 11209.

MONTANEZ, Esteban; '87 BA; 280 9th Ave., New York, NY 10001.

MONTANEZ, Nellie; '93 BS; 1680 Vyse Ave. Apt. 5c, Bronx, NY 10460.

MONTANEZ, Shirley A.; '88 BA; 374 Pearl St. Apt. 16f, New York, NY 10038.

MONTARULI, Anthony M.; '80 BA; Lt.; Fire Dept. City of NY; r. 2541 Fortesque Ave., Oceanside, NY 11572; *Diane;* Mark, Dana, Matthew.

MONTAS, Roland; '81 BA; 11643 220th St., Jamaica, NY 11411, 718 525-8185.

MONTE, John J.; '77 BA; 523 Lorimer St., Brooklyn, NY 11211, 718 252-2150.

MONTECIER, Allison A.; '95 BA; 2020 E 41st St. Apt. 4f, Brooklyn, NY 11234.

MONTELEONE, Joseph C.; '76 BS; 3221 White Ibis Ct. Apt. B1, Punta Gorda, FL 33950.

MONTENEGRO, Richard (Rich), Jr.; '95 BS; Financial Planner; Liberty Financial, 60-20 Woodside Ave., Woodside, NY 11377, 718 899-8476; r. POB 843, Wading River, NY 11792; *Terri;* Jordan, Daniel. e-mail

MONTEVERDE, A.; '80 BS; 7100 SW 8th St., Plantation, FL 33317.

MONTGOMERY, Angela D.; '86 BA; Parole Ofcr.; NYS Div. of Parole, 97 Central Ave., Albany, NY 12206, 718 546-5876; r. 35 Cameron Ave., Hempstead, NY 11550; *Joaquin J. Nunez.* e-mail

MONTGOMERY, Dwayne K.; '84 BS; Capt.-NYC Police Dept.; r. 418 Central Park W, New York, NY 10025. e-mail

MONTGOMERY, Joann; '86 BA; Intensive Case Mgr.; State Ofc. of Mental Health, 681 Clarkson Ave., Brooklyn, NY 11203, 718 221-7646; r. 124 Forsyth St. Apt. 8, New York, NY 10002, 718 209-4664.

MONTGOMERY, Paul S.; '85 BA; 10943 191st St., Jamaica, NY 11412, 718 341-1867.

MONTGOMERY, Stephani; '97 BS; 9247 240th St., Bellerose, NY 11426.

MONTGOMERY, Victor; '89 AS; BS Empire State Clg. SUNY, MSW Univ. at Stony Brook; POB 2309, Mt. Vernon, NY 10551, 716 877-1618.

MONTI, Stanley P.; '79 BA; 407-1 Willow Rd Ea, Staten Island, NY 10314, 718 351-8886.

MONTICELLI, Mary '81 (See Monticelli Aivazis, Mrs. Mary).

MONTICELLI AIVAZIS, Mrs. Mary, (Mary Monticelli); '81 MA; BA Drew Univ.; Homemaker; r. 9805 Wintercress Ct., Vienna, VA 22182, 703 757-7316; *Elias Aivazis.*

MONTIJO, Jose; '91 BS; 1641 Madison Ave. Apt. 8d, New York, NY 10029.

MONTIJO, Maribel; '98 BA; 160 Stagg Walk, #4a, Brooklyn, NY 11206, 718 768-0478.

MONTOYA, Carlos A.; '99 BS; 150-15 95th St., Ozone Park, NY 11417, 718 205-3715.

MONTROSE, Sharon R.; '97 BA; Administrative Asst.; Lighthouse Intl., 111 E. 59th St., New York, NY 10022, 212 821-9565; r. 99-10 Metropolitan, Forest Hills, NY 11375, 718 793-9848. e-mail

MOODIE, Genevieve E.; '83 BS; POB 302, Yonkers, NY 10705.

MOODIE, Joyell T.; '98 BS; POB 302, Yonkers, NY 10705.

MOODY, Lee R.; '75 MPA; Govt. Analyst; r. 4104 Clark St., Washington, DC 20007, 301 420-2781.

MOODY, Ms. Sabrina R.; '92 BS; MSW Fordham Univ.; Social Work; Admin. for Children's Svcs., 150 Williams St., New York, NY 10038, 212 676-9957; r. 56 Van Buren St. #2, Brooklyn, NY 11221, 718 399-3885. e-mail

MOON, Charles C.; '97 BS; Trader; Bear Stearns, One Metrotech, Brooklyn, NY 11201, 212 272-0370; r. 375 Marlborough Rd, Cedarhurst, NY 11516, 516 374-1477. e-mail

MOONAN, Ravi N.; '99 AS; BA; Police Ofcr.; NYPD; r. 148-26 86th Ave., Jamaica, NY 11435, 718 526-4272.   e-mail

MOONEY, Martin C.; '76 MA; Rutgers Sch. of Law, MA Seton Hall Univ.; Burlington Cnty. Prosecutor; PO Box 6000, Mt. Holly, NJ 08060, 609 265-5637; r. 700 Thomas Ave., Riverton, NJ 08077, 856 786-8367; *Joanne; Martin, Lynn-Claudia.* e-mail

MOONEY, Richard (Moon Man) B.; '71 BA; MS ED Long Island Univ.; VP New York State-Nassau Cnty.; Parole Officers Assn.-Shop Steward PEF, New York State Division of Parole, 250 Fulton Ave., Hempstead, NY 11550, 516 485-2660; r. 25 Park Pl., Floral Park, NY 11001; *Gloria Jean; Melissa May, Melanie Marie.*

MOONEY, Richard P.; '80 MPA; 13 Hill St., Livingston, NJ 07039.

MOONEY, Thomas E.; '73 BS; 155 Devon Loop, Staten Island, NY 10314.

MOORE, Beverly A.; '77 BA; 890 Wallace Ave., N. Baldwin, NY 11510, 516 546-2738.

MOORE, Brigitte C.; '85 BA; 146-16 225 St., Springfield Gardens, NY 11413, 516 938-6109.

MOORE, Charles T.; 500 Harbison Blvd. Apt. 608, Columbia, SC 29212, 803 749-9418.

MOORE, Doreen; '95 BS; AA Borough of Manhattan Comm, BS; Contract Mgr. Auditor; Dept. of Social Svcs. Home Attendant, 109 E 16th St. New York NY 10003, Contract Services, New York, NY 10003, 212 835-7337; r. 8603 102nd St. Apt. 4e, Jamaica, NY 11418, 718 805-0494.

MOORE, Faryce B.; '80 BS; VP of Grievances & Legal Svcs.; Social Svc. Employees Union, Local 371, 817 Broadway, New York, NY 10003, 212 677-3900; r. 99 S. Portland Ave. #5, Brooklyn, NY 11217, 718 222-1245.

MOORE, Herman A.; '81 BA; 669 Schenck Ave., Brooklyn, NY 11207.

MOORE, Hukm; '96 BA; 177 Westwood Dr., Brentwood, NY 11717.

MOORE, James E.; '77 BS; 298 Travis Ave., Staten Island, NY 10314, 718 227-3405.

MOORE, James F.; '71 MPA; Prof. Emeritus; r. 8223 251st St., Bellerose, NY 11426, 718 343-4609; *Helen;* Joanne, James F., Brian.

MOORE, Janet M.; '83 BS; 1203 E 85th St., Brooklyn, NY 11236, 718 331-4803.

MOORE, Jason; '94 BS; 2311 5th Ave. Apt. 6gg, New York, NY 10037, 315 599-8879.

MOORE, Joseph; '79 AS; 119-26 225th St., Cambria Hts., NY 11411, 718 206-9430.

MOORE, Leon A.; '86 BS; 22129 104th Ave., Queens Vlg., NY 11429, 718 206-9430.

MOORE, Margaret M.; '82 BA; 250 1st Ave., New York, NY 10009, 212 533-5196.

MOORE, Nichole K.; '95 BS; 11 Bennett Ct., Copiague, NY 11726, 631 841-1593.

MOORE, Nilda J.; '86 BA; 1607 Prospect Pl., Brooklyn, NY 11233, 718 756-5996.

MOORE, Patricia K.; '81 BA; 1790 Bruckner Blvd., Bronx, NY 10473, 718 220-0023.

MOORE, Patrick; '99 BA; Martial Arts Tchr.; r. POB 159, Fishkill, NY 12524, 914 896-5953. e-mail

MOORE, Penelope A.; '87 MS; MED Temple Univ., BS Daemen Clg.; Principal Forensic Scientist; New Jersey State Police, Central Labatory Sierra Ofc. Park, 380 Scotch Rd., Ewing, NJ 08628, 609 671-0022; r. 536 Ryders Ln., E. Brunswick, NJ 08816, 732 257-8512.

MOORE, Sean; '92 BS; 1522 Park Pl. # 3, Brooklyn, NY 11213, 718 778-5524.

MOORE, Sherry R.; '88 BS; 829 Nostrand Ave., Brooklyn, NY 11225, 718 778-5524.

MOORE, Simone I. '94 (See Moore-Baker, Simone I.).

MOORE, Talitha; '99 BA; Child Protective Spec; The Admin. for Children's Svcs., 16515 Archer Ave., Jamaica, NY 11433; r. 20-39 Shore Blvd., Long Island City, NY 11105, 718 956-3876. e-mail

MOORE, Tanya M.; '89 BS; 217 Grant Ave., Brooklyn, NY 11208, 718 284-1317.

MOORE, William J.; '96 BA; 67 Peter Ave., Staten Island, NY 10306.

MOORE-BAKER, Simone I., (Simone I. Moore); '94 BA; JD Hofstra Univ.; Assoc.; Weil, Gotshal & Manges, LLP, 767 5th Ave., New York, NY 10153; r. 175-45 88th Ave., Jamaica, NY 11432; *Robert;* Kristan, Deja. e-mail

MOOREHEAD, Claude L.; '90 BA; 1810 Bruckner Blvd., Bronx, NY 10473.

MOOREHEAD, Norris E.; '76 BA; 1681 Townsend Ave., Bronx, NY 10453.

MOORER, Denise W.; '84 BS; 302 Bainbridge St., Brooklyn, NY 11233, 718 827-7181.

MOORER, Shannon; '92 BS; 170-42 130th Ave., Jamaica, NY 11434, 718 460-9520.

MOORES, Robert N.; '84 BS; POB 77192, Greensboro, NC 27417.

MOORHEAD, Henry A.; '89 BS; Retired Lt.; NYC; r. 100 Erskine Pl. # 16e, Bronx, NY 10475, 718 320-9528; *Marlene.*

MOORS, Gerald J.; 1927 Ryder St., Brooklyn, NY 11234.

MOQUETE, Cesar U.; '96 BS; Fraud Investigator; City of NY; r. 600 W. 165th St., Apt. 6-A, New York, NY 10032, 212 781-2908. e-mail

MORA, Felix; '95 AS, '97 BS; Correction Capt.; NYC Dept. of Corrections, 60 Hudson St., New York, NY 10036, 212 266-1000; r. 160 W 96th St. Apt. 12m, New York, NY 10025, 212 663-9287. e-mail

MORA, Jessica M.; '97 BA; Party Plng. Cnslt.; r. 3840 Orloff Ave., Apt. 2J, Bronx, NY 10463, 718 796-5292; *Carlos Estrella;* Isaiah. e-mail

MORA, Madeline C.; '97 BA; 405 E. 105th St., New York, NY 10029, 212 722-9186.

MORABITO, Douglas P.; '95 MA; BS Western CT State Univ., JD Quinnipiac Clg.; Atty.-Gen. Practice; US Courts, Judge Alan H. Navhs, Bridgeport, CT 06604, 203 579-5985; r. 675 Nichols Ave., Stratford, CT 06614, 203 377-2194; *Terri.* e-mail

MORADO, Calvin P.; '92 BA, '92 MA; MSW Hunter Clg.; Social Worker/Therapist; Cornell Univ.-Wiell Med. Clg., 56 W. 45th St., 9th Fl., New York, NY 10036, 212 764-5178; r. 1320 York Ave., Apt. 29V, New York, NY 10021, 212 737-9816. e-mail

MORALES, Aileen F. '93 (See Natale, Aileen F.).

MORALES, Alejandra; '89 MA; 4124 43rd St., Long Island City, NY 11104, 718 337-2309.

MORALES, Alejandro; 1637 Cornelia St., Flushing, NY 11385, 718 337-2309.

MORALES, Antonio; '77 BS; 21 Cedar Flats Rd, Stony Point, NY 10980.

MORALES, Auries M.; '96 BS; Legal Asst. Ofc. Mgr.; Robert Perlstein Atty-at-Law, 575 Lexington Ave., New York, NY 10022; r. 2460 28th St. Apt. 3A, Astoria, NY 11102, 718 545-5275.

MORALES, Benito; '86 BA; POB 350172, Jamaica, NY 11435, 718 706-7569.

MORALES, Bethzaida; '97 BA; MS Columbia Univ.; Prog. Coord.; CUNY Dispute Resolution Consortium, 555 W. 57th St., New York, NY 10019, 212 237-8686; r. 146 Weirfield St., Brooklyn, NY 11221, 718 452-5123. e-mail

MORALES, Carlos E.; '99 BS; Laboratory Technician; Westchester County Crime Laboratory, Forensic Biology Unit, Valhalla, NY 10595; r. 43 Westbrook Ave., Staten Island, NY 10303, 718 876-9804. e-mail

MORALES, Carlos R.; '93 AS, '95 BS, '99 MS; Loss Prevention Safety Supervisor; Kmart Corp. Logistics, 7373 Westside Ave., N. Bergen, NJ 07047, 201 854-5941; r. 535 Ellsworth Ave., Bronx, NY 10465, 718 597-6690. e-mail

MORALES, Cesar A.; '97 BS; Police Ofcr.; NYPD; r. 20 Freedom Ave., Staten Island, NY 10314, 718 761-6585. e-mail

MORALES, Charles W.; '88 BA; 1763 2nd Ave., New York, NY 10128, 315 826-7381.

MORALES, Hector; '97 BA; JHS Tchr.; r. 1005 Jerome Ave. Apt. D-51, Bronx, NY 10452, 718 537-6902. e-mail

MORALES, Indiana; '99 BS; Production Mgr.; Qad Graphics, New York, NY 10001; r. 600 W. 140 St. #5D, New York, NY 10031, 212 926-6410. e-mail

MORALES, Ingrid M.; '98 BS; 235 School St., Oyster Bay, NY 11771, 516 338-9177.

MORALES, Lucette; '82 BA; 301 E 143 St. #1C, Bronx, NY 10451, 718 231-6266.

MORALES, Marilyn; '95 BS; 2626 Homecrest Ave., Brooklyn, NY 11235, 718 257-1402.

MORALES, Nicholas F.; '90 BS; 17 Pleasant Ln., Levittown, NY 11756.

MORALES, Paola A.; '97 BA; 32-22 91st St. #1, E. Elmhurst, NY 11369, 718 760-1217.

MORALES, Rose; '83 BS; 704 Schenck Ave., Brooklyn, NY 11207, 718 387-1261.

MORALES, Sandra '75 (See Morales-De Leon, Sandra).

MORALES, Sara; '95 MPA; 799 Saint Anns Ave. Apt. A, Bronx, NY 10456, 718 325-6594.

MORALES, Wilfredo E.; '84 MPA; BS Pace Univ.; Program Director/Writer; Broward County Community Action Agency, 900 NW 31st Ave., Ft. Lauderdale, FL 33311, 954 327-8797; r. 6400 SW 181st Ln., Ft. Lauderdale, FL 33331, 954 680-2549; *Julia Manners-Morales; Wilfredo Jr, Nina, Eileen, Cesar, Xavier.* e-mail

MORALES, William; '92 BS; Security Supv.; Indian River Community Clg.; r. 595 SW Lake Charles Cir., Port St. Lucie, FL 34986, 561 879-7961.

MORALES, Yvette; '80 BA; 2744 Creston Ave., Bronx, NY 10468, 718 824-3602.

MORALES, Yvette; '95 BS; 8331 116th St., Richmond Hill, NY 11418, 718 337-2309.

MORALES, Ms. Yvonne, Esq.; '94 BS; JD Fordham Univ. Sch. of Law; Asst. DA; Kings Cnty. Dist. Attorney's Ofc., 350 Jay St., Brooklyn, NY 11201, 718 250-2533; r. 1502 Pondcrest Ln., White Plains, NY 10607, 914 421-0522; *Hugh R. Krzeminski.* e-mail

MORALES-DE LEON, Sandra, (Sandra Morales); '75 MA; BA City Clg.; Prof.; Hostos Community Clg.; r. 164 E 117th St., New York, NY 10035; *Robert; Adriana.* e-mail

MORALES-TORRES, Sandra E.; '95 BA; 514 Tinton ave. 7-S., Bronx, NY 10455, 718 409-5288.

MORAN, Brian K.; '97, '19 BS; Police Ofcr.; City of Yonkers, 104 S Broadway, Yonkers, NY 10701, 914 377-7900; r. 51 Liberty St., Hawthorne, NY 10532, 914 747-0414.

MORAN, Christopher J.; '86 AS; 6118 82nd St., Flushing, NY 11379, 718 848-7858.

MORAN, John A., III; '98 BS; Police Lt.; NYC Police Dept., 1 Police Plz., New York, NY 10038, 212 927-9441; r. 10 Skinner Ct., Tomkins Cove, NY 10986, 914 786-5030; *Karen.*

MORAN, John P.; '77 BS; 222 Bement Ave., Staten Island, NY 10310, 718 448-6864.

MORAN, Julia A.; '83 BA; 122-20 25th Ave., College Pt., NY 11356, 718 848-7858.

MORAN, Kendre M.; '99 BA; 138 45 Lloyd Rd, Jamaica, NY 11435.

MORASCO, Benjamin J.; '99 MA; BA Univ. of Northern Iowa, St. Louis Univ.; Grad. Student/Adjunct Instr.; St. Louis Univ. Dept. of Psychology, 221 N. Grand Blvd., Shannon Hall Rm. 201, St. Louis, MO 63103, 314 977-3686; r. 6820 Delmar Blvd., Apt. 511, St. Louis, MO 63130, 314 725-1664. e-mail

MORCELO, Domingo A.; '76 BA; MA Staton Island Clg.; Staten Island, NY 10314.

MORCIGLIO, Libertad E.; '79 BS; 300 N Broadway, Yonkers, NY 10701, 914 423-8863.

MOREIA, Fredrick M.; '98 BA; Police Ofcr.; NYC Police Dept., 1 Police Plz., New York, NY 10038, 212 374-3884; r. 36-45-30th St., Long Island City, NY 11106. e-mail

MOREIRA, Ms. Julie A.; BS, '99; Social Worker; Leke & Watts Svc, 463 Hawthorne Ave., Yonkers, NY 10703, 914 375-8632; r. 130-1 Glenwood Ave., Yonkers, NY 10703, 914 968-9824. e-mail

MORELL, Edward; '95 BS; 5210 Broadway # 14, Bronx, NY 10463.

MORELLI, Angelo M.; '78 MA; BS, JD Brooklyn Law Sch.; Deputy Dist. Atty.; Brooklyn Dist. Atty.; 350 J St., Brooklyn, NY 11201; r. 850 Howard Ave., Staten Island, NY 10301, 718 981-8305; *Ida.*

MORELLI, Joseph A.; '97 BS; 1954 Mulford Ave., Bronx, NY 10461, 718 822-4332.

MORENO, Ms. Evelyn; '88 BS CRJU; Protective Div. Security; NYU, 14 Washington Pl., New York, NY 10003; r. Apt. 31, New York, NY 10040, 212 304-4361; Rachel R. Azcui, Elise M. Azcui, Erik A. Azcui.

MORENO, Juan, Jr.; '88 BS; MS Hunter Clg. CUNY; Counseling/Teaching; Duval Jacksonville Bd. of Educ.; r. 13034 Viburnum Dr. N., Jacksonville, FL 32246, 904 821-0310; *Connie; Juan III, Nita, Shana.* e-mail

MORENO, Karla C.; '98 BS; 3118A Wilkinson Ave., # 2, Bronx, NY 10461, 718 409-9288.

MORENO, Miguel; '97 BA; 28 Helen St., St. Augustine, FL 32095.

MORENO, Thaimi; '98 BA; 1780 1st Ave., New York, NY 10128, 212 996-4190.

MOREY, Jose; '92 BS; 479 Montauk Ave., Brooklyn, NY 11208, 718 467-1441.

MOREY, Nadege; '88 BA, '92 MA; 163 President St., Brooklyn, NY 11231, 718 467-1441.

MORGAN, Bruce; '94 BS; 87-11 57th Ave. #2, Elmhurst, NY 11373.

MORGAN, Clarence; '86 BA; 12 George Pl., Mt. Vernon, NY 10550, 716 837-8846.

MORGAN, Diana; '92 BS; 82 Palmetto St., Brooklyn, NY 11221, 718 856-8134.

MORGAN, Donald L.; '86 BA; 5 Berkshire Rd, Park Ridge, NJ 07656, 201 391-2539.

MORGAN, James; '80 BA; 9307 Avenue A, Brooklyn, NY 11236, 718 602-1002.

MORGAN, John P.; '90 BS, '93 MA; Adjunct Prof. of Criminal Justice; Clg. of New Rochelle, Sch of New Resources, Notre Dame Hall, New Rochelle, NY 10805, 914 654-5528; r. 5706 Liebig Ave., Apt. 1, Bronx, NY 10471, 718 884-7269.

MORGAN, Kenneth; '91 BA; 112-30 Northern Bl #5G, Corona, NY 11368, 718 846-1036.

MORGAN, Robert F.; '74 BS; 172 Floral Ave., Plainview, NY 11803.

MORHMANN, Tina; 91-08 Colonieal RD #4F, Brooklyn, NY 11209.

MORIARTY, Edward P.; '98 MS; 31 Yorkshire Rd, Rockville Centre, NY 11570, 516 594-9167.

MORIARTY, Justine B.; '97 BA; Deputy US Marshal; r. Brooklyn, NY 11209.

MORIARTY, Robert C.; '99; 3067 Perry Ave., Bronx, NY 10467, 718 231-4062.

MORIARTY, Thomas M.; '75 BA; NYPD Retired Sgt.; r. 9 Richard St., Sloatsburg, NY 10974, 914 753-5526.

MORILLO, Luis R.; '89 BS; 671 W 193rd St. Apt. 2f, New York, NY 10040, 212 942-7014.

MORISANO, Anthony J.; '85 BS; 52 Winham Ave., Staten Island, NY 10306.

MORLE, Abena; '85 BS; 326 B 30 St., Far Rockaway, NY 11691, 718 454-0038.

MORLEY, Michael; '96 BS; Police Management Inst.; Deputy Inspector; NYC Police Dept., 1612 Mott Ave., Far Rockaway, NY 11691, 718 868-3408; r. Rockaway Park, NY 11694; *Susan; Michael.*

MORLEY, CAPT Susan; '92 AS, '95 BS; FBI Acad.; NYC Police Dept., 315 Hudson St., New York, NY 10013, 212 741-4613; r. Rockaway Park, NY 11694; *Michael;* Michael.

MORMAN, Cathy E.; '80 BS; 85 Navy Walk, Brooklyn, NY 11201.

MORMANDO, Joseph A.; '81 BS; 1681 65th St. Apt. C11, Brooklyn, NY 11204.

MORMINO, Bennett; '88 BS, '99; 30 S Railroad Ave., Staten Island, NY 10305.

MORNEL, Theodore B.; '97 BS; Theater Dir.; New York, NY 10001, 212 714-7102; r. 53 Terhune Ave., Jersey City, NJ 07305, 201 915-5204; *Marcia.* e-mail

MORO, Peter L.; '85 BS; AS Mercy Clg.; Detective 2nd Grade; NYPD, 1 Police Plz., New York, NY 10038, 212 694-3018; r. 93 S Harrison Ave., Congers, NY 10920, 914 268-2758; *Nancy; Christopher, Aileen, Kevin.*

MOROGEORGES, Tula; '82 BS; 32 Harmony Rd., Randolph, NJ 07869, 973 328-4295.

MORON, Robert D.; '79 BS; 25 Boerum St., Brooklyn, NY 11206, 718 388-1509.

MORONTA, Ana D.; '81 MA; 601 W 188th St. Apt. 3a, New York, NY 10040.

MORRA, Michael C.; '75 MA; Investigator; Daily News, New York, NY 10021, 212 681-3352; r. 12 Hunt Pl., Bethpage, NY 11714, 516 731-6978; Michael Thomas, Michele.

MORRETTA, Matthew G.; '92 BS; 3300 Radio Dr., Bronx, NY 10465.

MORRIS, Chasity L.; '99 MA; Clinical Supv.; r. 21-42 75 St., Jackson Hts., NY 11370, 718 267-2968.

MORRIS, Donna A. '96 (See Canady, Donna A.).

MORRIS, Elaine L.; '79 BS; 107-16 171 Pl., Jamaica, NY 11433, 718 461-1406.

MORRIS, John A.; '89 BS; AAS Dutchess Comm. Clg.; CEO; John Morris US Mail Contractors; r. 58 Hillcrest Dr., Poughkeepsie, NY 12603, 914 454-5746.

MORRIS, Keisha B.; '95 BS; 3400 Enslow Ave., Richmond, VA 23222, 804 422-6844.

MORRIS, Logan; '94 BS; 709 Bushwick Ave., Brooklyn, NY 11221, 718 443-2601.

MORRIS, Rhoda M.; '79 BA; 11414 167th St., Jamaica, NY 11434, 718 956-8534.

MORRIS, Susan M.; '86 BA; 8 Eastview Ave., White Plains, NY 10601, 914 245-3058.

MORRIS, Thomas; 520 Herzel Blvd., W. Babylon, NY 11704.

MORRIS, Vincent K.; '91 AS, '94 BS; State Correction Ofcr.; New York; r. 39 Spruce St., Poughkeepsie, NY 12601. e-mail

MORRIS, Walter A.; '95 MS; 34 Old Nyack Tpk., Monsey, NY 10952, 914 356-4590.

MORRIS-ALSTON, Sophi; '95; 3226 Hull Ave., Bronx, NY 10467, 718 590-4916.

MORRIS-ENGLISH, Patricia J.; '78 BA; 10286 Nightmist Ct., Columbia, MD 21044, 301 596-0935.

MORRISON, Benni S.; '78 MA; 24 5 Ave. #1117, New York, NY 10011.

MORRISON, Donald J., Jr.; '95 BA; Svc. Mgr.; Morning Star Ford; r. 1 Hoffman St., Poughkeepsie, NY 12601, 518 789-6770.

MORRISON, Joan E.; '91 BA; 916 E 34th St. # P, Brooklyn, NY 11210, 718 573-8033.

MORRISON, Steven J.; '89 BS; 341 W. 24 St., New York, NY 10011, 212 242-5741.

MORRISON BLACK, Charmaine; '85 BS; JD Rutgers Law Sch.; Atty.; NYU Supreme Ct.; r. 94 Princess Dr., North Brunswick, NJ 08902, 718 756-9342; *Conrad;* Conrad Jr.

MORRISSEY, Daniel F.; '75 BS; 416 Morris Ave., Rockville Centre, NY 11570, 516 764-1454.

MORRISSEY, Mary P.; '91 BA; Retired Detective; NYPD; r. 601 79th St. Apt. D8, Brooklyn, NY 11209, 718 680-9022.

MORRISSEY, Timothy K.; '99 BS; Anti-Money Laundering Unit; Prudential, 99 Water St., New York, NY 10005, 212 214-1224; r. 4 Lexington Ave. Apt. 3S, New York, NY 10010, 212 982-8409.

MORRISSEY, William J.; '67 BS; Brooklyn, NY 11209.

MORROW, William; '92 BS; 10744 126th St., Jamaica, NY 11419, 718 641-9782.

MORSE, Henry P.; 1 Police Plz. Rm 1406, New York, NY 10038, 315 732-1826.

MORSE, Henry R.; '75 MPA; JD New York Law Sch.; Asst. Prof.; John Jay Clg. of Criminal Justice, 212 237-8404; r. 7015 71st Pl., Glendale, NY 11385, 718 386-8319.

MORTEL, John R.; '85 BS; 1409 E 49th St., Brooklyn, NY 11234.

MORTELLARO, P.; '92 BA; 1644 71st St., Brooklyn, NY 11204.

MORTLEY, James L.; '85 BS; 4016 Avenue K, Brooklyn, NY 11210, 718 789-3313.

MORTON, Gerald T.; '81 MPA; 18-35 Corporal Ken, Bayside, NY 11360, 718 428-9853.

MOSBY, Edward A.; '91 BA; 160 Claremont Aven, New York, NY 10027, 212 749-9642.

MOSCA, Anthony M.; '79 MA; BA Clg. New Rochelle; Retired-Police Commissioner; r. 351 N 7th Ave., Mt. Vernon, NY 10550; *Carmen;* Anthony Jr., Roseanne, Rosemarie. e-mail

MOSCHELLA, Salvatore; '72 BA; 10 Rita Pl., Farmingdale, NY 11735, 631 249-2879.

MOSCHETTO, Andrew J.; '78 MA; 50-5 St. Joseph Blv, Lodi, NJ 07644.

MOSCOSO, Emilio C.; '97 BA; 2000 84th St., Brooklyn, NY 11214.

MOSELLE, Linda H.; '79 MA; 5 W 91st St. Apt. 6e, New York, NY 10024, 212 877-0844.

MOSER, Marian C.; '76 BA; 5 Primrose Ave., Floral Park, NY 11001.

MOSES, Deatra R.; '95 BS; 210-04 Hillside Ave., Queens Vlg., NY 11427, 718 468-8402.

MOSES, Herbert J.; '81 BS; 986 Centennial Ave., Baldwin, NY 11510, 516 466-1840.

MOSES, Puliti; '95 BS; 58 Fleet Walk Apt. 2e, Brooklyn, NY 11201, 718 342-5589.

MOSES, Stephanie M.; '93 AS, '95 BS; Police Ofcr.; NYC, New York, NY 10038; r. 168-10 127th Ave., Apt. 12 G, Jamaica, NY 11434.

MOSES, William (Bill) R.; '75 AS, '76 BS; MPA Marist Clg.; Intl. Police Monitor; OSCE, D.C. Metro Pd/NYPD Detective-24 Yrs, Retired-1993, Croatia; r. 4607 Whispering Hls, Chester, NY 10918, 914 469-7794; Stephanie, Kimberly, Mark.

MOSKOWITZ, Ari A.; '97 BA; Police Ofcr.; Town of Wallkill, 600 Rte. 211E, Middletown, NY 10941, 914 692-6757; r. POB 4764, Middletown, NY 10941; *Tamara.* e-mail

MOSLEY, Alicia M.; '85 BS; 11724 Nashville Blvd., Cambria Hts., NY 11411.

MOSLEY, Michelle J.; '87 BS; 133-03 160 St. PH, Jamaica, NY 11434, 718 945-2819.

MOSS, Cathy N.; '89 BS; Consumer Affairs Inspector; Dept. of Consumer Affairs, 42 Broadway, New York, NY 10004, 212 487-4325; r. 650 Lenox Ave. Apt. 4E, New York, NY 10037, 212 690-1438.

MOSS, Geoffrey; '96 MA; 194-25b 64th Ave., Fresh Meadows, NY 11365, 718 275-4684.

MOSS, Joel W.; '76 MA; Risk & Property Analysis; JM Family Enterpises Inc., 100 NW 12th Ave., Deerfield Bch., FL 33442, 954 429-2177; r. 2715 N. Ocean Blvd., Ft. Lauderdale, FL 33308, 954 561-3736; *Shelia.* e-mail

MOSS, Kathryn A.; '79 MA; Asst. to The Proj. Dir.; Ctr. for Employment Opportunity, 32 Broadway, New York, NY 10004, 212 422-4430; r. 30 East End Ave. # 7e, New York, NY 10028, 212 249-6688; *William;* Mary, Katy, Betsy, Amy, John, Gerry, Hugh, Quinn, Susan, Barbara.

MOSS, Kyna E.; '93 BS; 37 Broadway, Valley Stream, NY 11580, 516 897-4890.

MOSS, Raymond D.; '93 MA; 6060 59th Dr., Flushing, NY 11378.

MOSSA, Vincent A.; '89 BS; 708 Tudor Hl, Nanuet, NY 10954.

MOTA, Andrea; '94 BS; 2001 Morris Ave., Bronx, NY 10453, 718 933-2583.

MOTEN, Reva G.; '84 BS; Supervising Probation Ofcr.; NYC Dept. of Probation, 210 Jora Lemon St. 10th Fl., Brooklyn, NY 11201, 718 802-4564; r. 301 Sutter Ave. Apt. 11f, Brooklyn, NY 11212.

MOTISI, Meegan T.; '98 BS; Proj. Asst.; Battle Fowler LLP, 75 E. 55th St., New York, NY 10022, 212 856-7895; r. 71 Interlaken Ave., New Rochelle, NY 10801, 914 576-6903. e-mail

MOTTO, Robert A.; '91 BS; 36 Friend St., Congers, NY 10920, 914 268-3262; *Susan;* Steven.

MOULTRIE, Latoya Z.; '97 BS; Recruit in Police Acad.; r. 357 W. 115th St. # 43, New York, NY 10026, 212 749-7480.

MOUSADAKOS, Chrisoula; '96 BS; Special Investigator; Bur. Fraud Investigations, 250 Church St., New York, NY 10013, 212 274-6347; r. 495 W. 187th St. #5A, New York, NY 10033, 212 781-6365. e-mail

MOUTOPOULOS, Jimmy; '99 BS; 52-35 69th Pl., Maspeth, NY 11378, 718 779-4108.

MOWATT, Wendy A.; '97 BA; 3600 NW 21st St., Apt. 101, Lauderdale Lakes, FL 33311.

MOY, Sandra; '91 BS; 3934 58th St., Flushing, NY 11377, 718 441-1530.

MOY, Wing; '76 BS; 143 Mott St. Apt. 8, New York, NY 10013, 315 762-4896.

MOYA, Chico; '96 BS; 1309 5th Ave. # 2, New York, NY 10029.

MOYE, Michelle; '96 AS; BS; Asst. Benefits Examiner; Law Dept. Workers Compensation, 350 Jay St., Brooklyn, NY 11201, 718 222-2204; r. 1851 Fulton St., Brooklyn, NY 11233, 718 604-0372.

MOYE, Millicent L.; '95 BS; Fraud Investigator; Millicent Moye, 330 J St., Brooklyn, NY 11201, 718 237-0841; r. 10476 129th St., Jamaica, NY 11419.

MOYNIHAN, Thomas P.; '79 BS; POB 832, Floral Park, NY 11002.

MOZAFFAR, Ahson; '91 BS; 166 W 75th St. # 516, New York, NY 10023, 212 877-4056.

MOZIE, Edie D.; '96 BA; 3353 Ft. Independence St., Bronx, NY 10463, 718 549-8735.

MRAZ, Mrs. Leanne A.; '99 BS; Security Supv.; Johnson & Johnson, One Johnson & Johnson Plz., New Brunswick, NJ 08933, 732 524-2361; r. 18 Sycamore Ave., Edison, NJ 08817, 732 287-0011; *John L.* e-mail

MSHVELIDZE, Vadim; '99 BA; 2450 Haring St. #2B, Brooklyn, NY 11235, 718 891-8231.

MUAILLO, Leo; '79 MA; 8950 56th Ave. Apt. 4j, Flushing, NY 11373.

MUEGER, Warren; '85 MA; 136 Meyer Ave., Valley Stream, NY 11580.

MUELLER, Paul K.; '87 BS; Hc 67, Dingmans Ferry, PA 18328.

MUELLERS, Deborah L.; '92 BA; 923 N Greene Ave., Lindenhurst, NY 11757, 631 226-8773.

MUGNO, Richard E.; '81 MA; 8832 74th Pl., Jamaica, NY 11421, 718 335-8609.

MUHAMMED, Cornetta; '92 BS; 630 Ocean Ave. Apt. 11h, Brooklyn, NY 11226, 718 693-4291.

MUI, Michael S.; '95 BS, '96 CERT; 120 Avenue O, Brooklyn, NY 11204, 718 259-4510.

MUI, Yet C.; '80 BS; 137 E Broadway, New York, NY 10002, 212 233-8596.

MUIR, Harriette A.; '95 BA; MS Carnegie Mellon Univ.; Mgmt. Cnslt.; KPMG LLP, 345 Park Ave., 35th Fl., New York, NY 10154; r. 2125 St. Raymond Ave., Bronx, NY 10462; *David McQueen.*

MUJICA, Linda R.; '99 BS; Student; Police Acad., New York, NY 10014, 212 477-9721; r. 2010 Powell Ave. #6H, Bronx, NY 10472, 718 822-4562. e-mail

MULCAHY, Michele A.; '99; 1752 Hancock St., Hewlett, NY 11557, 516 593-2072.

MULDOWNEY, Linda M.; '90 BA; 11 Leeds Ln., N. Babylon, NY 11703, 631 667-6626.

MULE, Concetta M.; '99 BS; 801 N Broad St., Apt. 10K, Elizabeth, NJ 07208, 908 659-0208.

MULERO, George; '76 BS; Detective; Biscayne Park Police Dept., 640 NE 114 St., Biscayne Park, FL 33161, 305 893-7491; r. POB 545943, Surfside, FL 33154.

MULHALL, Brian; '84 BA; Samchuck Rd., Millerton, NY 12546, 518 789-3423.

MULHOLLAND, Patrick G.; '99 BA; 31 Sunny Ridge Rd, Spring Vly., NY 10977.

MULLADY, Joseph R.; '72 BA; 61 Hurtin Blvd., Smithtown, NY 11787, 631 265-1189.

MULLANE, Edward F.; '92 BS; 91 Oak St. Ph, Floral Park, NY 11001, 516 747-5387.

MULLEN-MORRIS, Veronica B.; '92 BS; JHS Tchr.-Math/Sci./Social Studies; Sch. Dist. 85, Brooklyn, NY 11225; r. 1103 Rutland Rd, Brooklyn, NY 11212, 718 756-9445; *Lerue Morris;* Shazara, Zakiya, Jelani.

MULLER, Deborah; '95 BS; Credit Analyst; Anheuser-Busch, 5501 Second St., Long Island City, NY 11101, 718 349-5151; r. 6061 Metropolitan Ave., Ridgewood, NY 11385; *Daniel Mehling;* Ashley.

MULLER, John K.; '95 MA; 16112 92nd St., Howard Bch., NY 11414, 718 651-9048.

MULLIGAN, Eleanor; '83 BA; 99 Macombs Pl., New York, NY 10039.

MULLIGAN, John P.; '77 BS; 29-50 137 St., Flushing, NY 11354, 718 358-6920.

MULLIGAN, Maritza; '90 BA; 16643 17th Rd, Whitestone, NY 11357, 718 446-2931.

MULLIGAN, Robert; '94 BS; 427 Maine Ave., Staten Island, NY 10314, 718 447-3561.

MULLIGAN, Thomas F.; '89 MPA; Retired Lt.; NYPD; r. 10 Christine Ln., E. Northport, NY 11731, 631 368-4193.

MULLIGAN, Thomas J.; '77 BS; 42 Morton St., Staten Island, NY 10306, 718 987-8163.

MULLIGAN, Thomas M.; '98 MS; BA City Clg. of NY; New York Fire Marshal; NYC, New York, NY 10001; r. 23 Oak Ave., Bronx, NY 10465, 718 822-6061.

MULLIGAN, Thomas P.; '78 BS, '99 MS; FDNY Lt. Operations; Fire Dept. City of NY, 9 Metro Tech Ctr., Brooklyn, NY 11201, 718 999-0281; r. 406 Philo St., New Windsor, NY 12553, 914 561-5354. e-mail

MULLIGAN, William; '77 BA; 1 Sullivan Ave., Farmingdale, NY 11735, 631 752-9377.

MULLIN, John H.; '97 BS; Police Ofcr.; Fulton Cnty. Police Dept., 7741 Roswell Rd, Atlanta, GA 30350, 770 551-7600; r. 3125 Monroe way, Alpharetta, GA 30004, 770 772-6280. e-mail

MULLINGS, Sandra V.; '78 BA; 1765 Albany Ave., Brooklyn, NY 11210, 718 693-2304.

MULLINS, Steven J.; '93 MA; 42-05 31 Ave., Astoria, NY 11103, 718 527-7515.

MULLINS, Theresa B.; '85 BA; BSN Lehman Clg.; RN; St. Cabrini Nursing Home, 115 Broadway, Dobbs Ferry, NY 10522, 914 693-6800; r. 56 Sedgewick Ave., Yonkers, NY 10705; *Michael;* Michael, Rebecca, Matthew.

MULRYAN, Joseph V.; '85 BA; 538 Bread & Cheese, Northport, NY 11768.

MULVANERTY, Daniel; '93 BS; 342 Beach 147th St., Far Rockaway, NY 11694, 718 634-8594.

MULVENA, James F.; '81 BS; 8937 85th St., Jamaica, NY 11421, 718 296-3595.

MULZAC, Henry; '91 BS; 393 Decatur St., Brooklyn, NY 11233, 718 455-6586.

MUMFORD, Ronald A.; '82 MA; Juvenile Probation Offc. Supv.; Florida Dept. of Juvenile Justice, 1600 NW 3rd Ave., Ste#69, Miami, FL 33136, 305 573-0000; r. 17321 NW 62nd Ct., Hialeah, FL 33015, 305 231-8998; *Angela;* Royce, Heiress. e-mail

MUNDO, Reymundo; '96 BS; 2786 Bainbridge Ave., Bronx, NY 10458, 718 410-9061.

MUNIZ, Mrs. Belinda; '95 BA; 612 Palisade Ave., Teaneck, NJ 07666, 201 287-1777. e-mail

MUNIZ, Eliu; '92 BA; Police Ofcr.; NYPD, 1 Police Plz., New York, NY 10038, 212 374-5410; r. 553 52nd St. # 3, Brooklyn, NY 11220, 718 854-3396. e-mail

MUNIZ, Eric R.; '82 MPA; 19 Yorkshire Dr., Toms River, NJ 08753, 732 255-2083.

MUNIZ, Inez; '83 BA; 145 Hicks St., Brooklyn, NY 11201, 718 996-5826.

MUNJACK, Joel A ; '82 MPA; 52-24 65th Pl., Maspeth, NY 11378.

MUNOZ, Antonio; '89 BS; 415 Helen St., Linden, NJ 07036.

MUNOZ, John; '89 BA; 3253 Glennon Pl., Bronx, NY 10465, 718 863-8973; *Laura.*

MUNOZ, Julio E.; '89 AS; POB 300, Bronx, NY 10457, 718 901-1977.

MUNOZ-SHIVERS, Rachel I.; '98 BS; 7424 20th Ave. #2nd Fl., Brooklyn, NY 11204, 718 256-0600.

MUNOZ-WILTSHIRE, Nelly; '91 BA; 20 W. 102nd St., New York, NY 10025.

MUNROE, Doris L.; '97 BS; 29 Washington St., Tuckahoe, NY 10707, 914 337-7961.

MUNROE, Simone A.; '99 BS; 930 Grand Concourse Apt. 9K, Bronx, NY 10451, 718 538-0803.

MURANELLI, Joel; '82 BS; 12 Hunter Ln., Apt. 3, Ossining, NY 10562, 914 923-3441.

MURATORE, Anthony; '67 AS, '68 BA, '69 MA; Chmn./Prof.; Orange Cnty. Community Clg., Criminial Justice Dept., Middletown, NY 10940, 914 341-4355; r. 4 Wilkin Ave., Middletown, NY 10940, 914 343-2679; *Marie;* Anthony Jr., Marie Jr., Dr. Elaina M. e-mail

MURAWSKI, Marianne; '93 BS; Detective; 25th Precinct Detective Squad, Nypd, 120 E 119th St., New York, NY 10035, 212 860-6536; r. 1552 Scriven Ave., N. Bellmore, NY 11710, 516 221-7644; *Anna Marie Buckley;* Theresa, Victoria.

MURAWSKI, Walter H.; '84 BS; 8015 Commonwealth Blvd., Bellerose, NY 11426.

MURCHISON, James; '94 BS; 1131 Forest Ave., Bronx, NY 10456, 718 295-7505.

MURDAUGH, Gale R.; '81 BS; 108 Christopher Ave., Brooklyn, NY 11212.

MURDOCK, Timothy P.; '86 MA; 11422 202nd St., Jamaica, NY 11412, 718 458-7602.

MURIEL, Marianela; '95 BS; 1664 Grove St. # 1r, Flushing, NY 11385, 718 932-6169.

MURILLO, Cynthia T.; '97 BS; 1560 Unionport Rd., Bronx, NY 10462, 718 597-5285.

MURILLO, Jose P.; '93 MA; 253 Sand Ln. # Bc, Staten Island, NY 10305.

MURILLO, Leo; '79 MA; 89-50 56th Ave., Elmhurst, NY 11373.

MURPHY, Brian C.; '96; 8823 Gettysburg St., Jamaica, NY 11426.

MURPHY, Brian J.; '99 MPA; 309 Retford Ave., Staten Island, NY 10312, 718 317-7333.

MURPHY, Charles M.; '94 MA; 45 Roundtree Ct., Beacon, NY 12508, 914 831-6107.

MURPHY, Colin W.; '79 BS; Inspector; US Marshals Svc., US Ct. of Intl Trade, 1 Federal Plz. Rm. 576, New York, NY 10007, 212 264-4715; r. USMS St. Andrews Pl., New York, NY 10007, 212 335-2612.

MURPHY, Daniel J.; '78 BS; 8281 Nadmar Ave., Boca Raton, FL 33434, 561 852-9860.

MURPHY, Daniel P.; '98 BA; Police Sergeant; NYC Police Dept., One Police Plz., New York, NY 10038; r. 7 Buttermilk Dr., New Windsor, NY 12553, 914 294-3481; *Barbara;* Erin, Daniel.

MURPHY, Donald R.; '79 BS; 2234 W Toledo Pl., La Habra, CA 90631, 949 729-1088.

MURPHY, Edwin E.; '79 MPA; 8020 258 St., Floral Park, NY 11004, 516 627-3418.

MURPHY, Eileen; '90 BS; 624 E. 20 St., New York, NY 10009, 212 674-7938.

MURPHY, James; '85 MPA; 1951 Mayflower Ave., Bronx, NY 10461, 718 824-6622.

MURPHY, John J.; '87 BS; Commanding Ofcr.; Organized Crime & Investigation Div., NYPD, One Police Plz., Rm. 1200, New York, NY 10038, 212 374-6640; r. 16 Furnace Tr., Greenwood Lake, NY 10925, 914 477-9458. e-mail

MURPHY, John T.; '70 BS, '70 AA; Pres.; Alliance Mortgage Bkg. Corp., 3601 Hempstead Tpk., Levittown, NY 11756, 516 520-4100; r. 3964 King Ct., Seaford, NY 11783, 516 731-0903; *Susan;* John, Brian, Elizabeth.

MURPHY, Joseph J.; '71 MA; 2944 163rd St., Flushing, NY 11358, 718 423-3301.

MURPHY, Joseph R.; 28 Nashua St. #1, Somerville, MA 02145, 617 267-8602.

MURPHY, Ms. Josephine A.; '99 BA; Police Ofcr.; NYC Police Force, 301 Gold St., Brooklyn, NY 11214; r. Brooklyn, NY 11214. e-mail

MURPHY, Kathleen E.; '99 MA; 1500 First Ave. #4A, New York, NY 10021, 212 628-2681.

MURPHY, Kenneth J.; '85 BS; AA Clg. of Aeronautics; Retired; r. 3524 204th St., Flushing, NY 11361, 718 423-4136.

MURPHY, Lisa; '97 BA; 157-10 Riverside Dr., New York, NY 10032, 315 735-3997.

MURPHY, Michael J.; '86 BA; 1055 53rd St., Brooklyn, NY 11219, 718 788-3585.

MURPHY, Michael J.; '61 MPA; 4 Harvard St., Port Jefferson Sta., NY 11776.

MURPHY, Patrick J.; '72 BS; 460 Durant Ave., Staten Island, NY 10308, 718 984-1639.

MURPHY, Patrick J.; '83 MA; BA; Detective; NYPD, 150-14 Jamaica Ave., Jamaica, NY 11432, 718 558-8822; r. 71 Huntington Rd, Garden City, NY 11530.

MURPHY, Patrick V.; '60 MPA; CN; Pat Murphy Assocs Inc.; r. 6403 Winston Dr., Bethesda, MD 20817; *Betty;* Betty, Patrick V. Jr, Eileen, Anne, Kevin, Gerard, Paul, Mark.

MURPHY, Paul E.; '78 BS, '96 MS; Mgr. of Business Devel.; American Express; r. 60 Dartmouth St., Rockville Centre, NY 11570, 516 766-4072; *Anne;* Christopher, Kevin, Julie Marie.

MURPHY, Robert E.; '72 BA; Retired; NYPD; r. 8 Lindquist Ln., Deer Park, NY 11729, 631 586-6908; *Maureen.* e-mail

MURPHY, Mrs. Rochelle M., (Rochelle M. Hill); '77 AS, '78 BA; Systs. Engr.; Bell Atlantic, 2 World Trade Ctr., New York, NY 10048, 212 390-9303; r. 1758 Troy Ave., Brooklyn, NY 11234, 718 377-2490; *Joseph;* Monique, Melanie. e-mail

MURPHY, Stephen F.; '81 MA; 522 61st St., Brooklyn, NY 11220, 718 462-6930.

MURPHY, Steven; '75 BS; 10711 115th St., Jamaica, NY 11419, 718 347-1269.

MURPHY, Thomas D.; '80 MPA; 156 Beach 134th St., Far Rockaway, NY 11694, 718 803-1294.

MURPHY, Thomas F.; '81 BS; 331 Grosvenor St., Flushing, NY 11363, 718 225-7218.

MURPHY, Thomas P.; '91 BS; 383 Colony Ave., Staten Island, NY 10306, 718 984-9252.

MURPHY, Timothy J.; '74 BS; Retired NYPD; r. 41 Amundsen Ln., New City, NY 10956, 914 634-9271.

MURRAY, Clyde E.; '74 BS; 102 Daleview Dr., Goldsboro, NC 27534.

MURRAY, Daniel F.; '95 BA; 8838 87th St., Jamaica, NY 11421, 718 322-4284.

MURRAY, Gregory L.; '90 MPA; 19 Sturbridge Dr., Dix Hills, NY 11746.

MURRAY, Gwendolyn; '92 BS; 11948 190th St., Jamaica, NY 11412, 718 740-6115.

MURRAY, James E.; '87 AS, '89 BS, '92 MPA; Sgt.; NYC Police, 179 Wilson Ave., Brooklyn, NY 11237, 718 573-5047; r. 874 72nd St., Brooklyn, NY 11228; *Linda;* Kelly. e-mail

MURRAY, John E.; '65 MPA; 3184 Ave. W, Brooklyn, NY 11229, 718 953-8550.

MURRAY, John J.; #8 Dellmar Ter., Long Valley, NJ 07853, 908 730-8733.

MURRAY, Lewis C.; '77 AS, '79 BS; Retired-Police Ofcr.; r. 650 SW 138th Ave., Pembroke Pines, FL 33027, 954 442-5695; Marie, Joyce, Janice, Vanessa.

MURRAY, Louis; '78 BA; 882 Blake Ave., Brooklyn, NY 11207, 718 485-2476.

MURRAY, Lucy; '76 BA; 240 E 93rd St. Apt. 16C, New York, NY 10128, 315 337-4185.

MURRAY, Lynne; '92 BS; 605 Louisiana Ave., Apt. 15A, Brooklyn, NY 11239, 718 336-6336.

MURRAY, Robert P.; '77 BS, '80 MPA; Retired Police Ofcr.; Retired Dir. of Safety for NYU; r. 20 Foxwood Rd, Lakewood, NJ 08701, 732 901-2253; *Mary.*

MURRAY, Sheila E.; '84 MPA; 880-8 Colgate Ave. #8F, Bronx, NY 10473, 718 798-8760.

MURRAY, Thomas K.; '83 BS; CEO; Innerstar Music, 195 Brown Ave., Hempstead, NY 11550, 516 489-1527; r. same.

MURRAY, William T.; '80 BS; 621 Lefferts Ave., Brooklyn, NY 11203, 718 469-2498.

MURRELL, Michelle C.; '92 AS, '94 BS; 16523 144th Dr., Jamaica, NY 11434.

MURRELL, Zenja J.; '95 BS; POB 1593, New York, NY 10026.

MURTAGH, James J.; '72 BS, '80 MPA; Deputy Chief; Fire Dept. of New York; r. 47 Paul Ct., Pearl River, NY 10965, 914 735-7558; *Fran.* e-mail

MUSARELLA, Mark; '85 BS; 25 Benjamin Dr., Staten Island, NY 10303, 718 494-9461; *Kathy;* Kristen, Victoria.

MUSMACHER, Robert J.; '81 BS; Retired Police Lt.; NYPD; r. 43 Lutz Dr., Valley Stream, NY 11580, 516 568-9604; *Ann Marie;* Dennis, Robert, Tara.

MWANGA, Frederick; '96 BS; 212-29 Hillside Ave., Queens Vlg., NY 11427.

MYERS, Ayanna C.; '93 BA; 325 E 143rd St. # 1, Bronx, NY 10451, 718 665-8098.

MYERS, Carol A.; '88 BS; Forensic Scientist; NYPD, 150-14 Jamaica Ave., Jamaica, NY 11432, 718 558-8792; r. 120 Carver Loop, #8A, Bronx, NY 10475, 718 671-7131. e-mail

MYERS, Cremston M.; '92 BS; 345 Dewitt Ave., Brooklyn, NY 11207, 718 789-0111.

MYERS, Debra A.; '80 BS; CERT. Ctr. for Montessori, CERT. Bible Church Theological; 1560 Grand Concourse Apt. 619, Bronx, NY 10457, 718 299-2043; Davon, LaRhonda, Jasmine, Anthony.

MYERS, Gregory; '92 AS, '94 BS; 10433 186th St., Jamaica, NY 11412, 718 454-3406.

MYERS, Joseph J.; '95 BS; 66-05 79th St., Middle Vlg., NY 11379, 718 740-7529.

MYERS, Lonnie; '89 MPA; POB 475, Brooklyn, NY 11211, 718 282-4889.

MYERS, Noah L.; '86 BS; 820 Colgate Ave., Apt. 8F, Bronx, NY 10473.

MYERS, Sayeeda; '99 BA; 325 E 163 St. 12F, Bronx, NY 10451, 718 665-8098.

MYERS, Victoria M.; '75 BS; Police Ofcr./Detective; NYCPD, 1 Police Plz., New York, NY 10038, 212 860-6536; r. 914 398-2030.

MYERS, Yvette '96 (See Myers-Punnette, Mrs. Yvette).

MYERSON, Wayne B.; '84 MA; 4702 Snyder Ave., Brooklyn, NY 11203.

MYERS-PUNNETTE, Mrs. Yvette, (Yvette Myers); '96 BS; Secy.; MB Furniture, 4459 Amboy Rd., Staten Island, NY 10312, 718 356-1900; r. 178 Lockman Ave., Apt. 2F, Staten Island, NY 10303, 718 698-7391; *Randy;* Randy Jr, Janaye.

MYLES, Miriam T.; '78 BS; 5457 NW 50th Ct., Coconut Creek, FL 33073.

MYLOTT, Robert H.; '98 MA; Polygraph Examiner; Applied Sci. Polygraph, Inc., 152 W Hoffman Ave. Ste. 10, Lindenhurst, NY 11757, 631 225-1578; r. 26 St. Marks Ln., Islip, NY 11751, 631 581-4037; *Linda.* e-mail

MYRIE, Antonio A.; 72 Weirfield St. #1, Brooklyn, NY 11221.

MYUNG, Ji-Man; '98 BA; 84 Irving Ave., Livingston, NJ 07039.

N

NABLE, Beth R.; '78 BS; 1546 E 18th St., Brooklyn, NY 11230, 718 375-9729.

NACHMANY, Etty; '95 BS; 2124 Avenue T, Brooklyn, NY 11229.

NACHTMAN, Iva; '98 BA; AA Nassau Community Clg.; Police Ofcr.; Fairfax Cnty. Police Dept., 6121 Franconia Rd., Alexandria, VA 22310; r. 16150 Taconic Cir., Dumfries, VA 22026, 703 590-5185; *Ramon Robertson.*

NACINOVICH, Ms. Diane M.; '98 BA; Administrative Asst.; Brown Bros. Harriman & Co., 63 Wall St., New York, NY 10005, 212 493-8398; r. 2459 E. 11th St., Brooklyn, NY 11235, 718 332-1866. e-mail

NACINOVICH, Mario; '77 BA; 26-03 9 St., Long Island City, NY 11102.

NADAL, Edwin M.; '84 BS; 62-60 99th St., Rego Park, NY 11374.

NADAL, Lucy; '86 BA; 1420 Amsterdam Ave., New York, NY 10027.

NADEL, David W.; '76 BSPS, '79 MA; Lt.; NYPD, 1 Police Plz., Ofc. of The Chief of Dept., New York, NY 10038, 212 374-0297; r. 24059 66th Ave., Douglaston, NY 11362; *Sharon;* Samantha, Daniel, Seth, Evan. e-mail

NADELBACH, Lisa M., (Lisa Mendez); '98 BS; Personnel Asst.; Local Initiatives Support Corp., 733 Third Ave. 8th Fl., New York, NY 10017, 212 455-9852; r. 118-18 Union Tpk. Apt. 6F, Kew Gardens, NY 11415, 718 544-7185; *Christopher.* e-mail

NADELLA, K.; '97 BS; 83-30 Vietor Ave., Elmhurst, NY 11373.

NAGASAR, Petamber; '93 AS; 9337 Vanderveer St., Queens Vlg., NY 11428, 718 465-6814.

NAHAR, Yesenia; '94 BA; 1554 Ocean Ave. #A, Brooklyn, NY 11230.

NAIGUS, Dede N.; '81 MA; 14 Washington Pl., New York, NY 10003.

NAKAO, Eric D.; '95 BS; POB 1054, New York, NY 10185.

NAMAN, Carol A.; '79 BS; 6821 61st Rd, Flushing, NY 11379.

NAMDAR, Gholam R.; '82 BS; 15324 77th ave., Flushing, NY 11367.

NAMOUR, Michael; '77 BS; 76-12 58 Rd, Elmhurst, NY 11373.

NANARTOWICZ, Carol; '82 BA, '85 MA; 318 Hett Ave., Staten Island, NY 10306.

NANDKISURE, Shawn; 91-56 111Street, Jamaica, NY 11418.

NANNA, Louis J.; '99 BS; Financial Cnslt.; Copeland & Co., E. Brunswick, NJ 08816, 732 514-2559; r. 207 Van Brackle Rd, Aberdeen, NJ 07747, 732 583-2707.

NANTON, Willena; '88 BS; JD Thurgood Marshall Sch Law; Deputy Counsel; NYC Civil Svc. Commission, 1 Centre St., Rm. 2300, New York, NY 10007, 212 669-2609; r. 1482 Needham Ave., Bronx, NY 10469, 718 798-9487. e-mail

NAPIER, Gregory M.; '97 BS; 212-23 Hollis Ave., Queens Vlg., NY 11429.

NAPIER, Raymond C.; '92 MPA; 35 Chase St., Hempstead, NY 11550.

NAPOLEON, Johnny L.; '98 BA; 636 Carlton Ave. #3, Brooklyn, NY 11238, 718 398-9387.

NAPOLI, George V.; '79 BA; 1129 E 98 St., Brooklyn, NY 11236, 718 376-5735.

NAPOLITANO, Ralph T.; '76 BS; 30-11 Astoria Blvd., Long Island City, NY 11102, 718 323-5981.

NAPOLITANO, Sal R.; '76 BA; 1635 Paulding Ave., Bronx, NY 10462, 718 829-9853.

NAPPI, Lori A.; '81 BS; Owner/Operator; Silver Plus-Sterling Silver and Jewelry; r. 119 Marsellus Pl., Garfield, NJ 07026, 973 340-5602. e-mail

NARDOZA, Michael J.; '75 BS; 521 E 14th Str., New York, NY 10009, 212 529-1927.

NARDOZA, Robert; '76; 300 1st Ave. Apt. 5e, New York, NY 10009.

NARDUCCI, Louis; '72 BA; 7 Valerie Ln., Patchogue, NY 11772.

NASA, Joseph; 135 Diana Ln., Mastic Bch., NY 11951.

NASH, Joseph F.; '73 BS; Retired Business Owner; r. 65 Western Concourse, Amityville, NY 11701, 631 842-2297; *Carole*. e-mail

NASH, Lois A.; '82 BS; 1151 Dean St., Brooklyn, NY 11216, 718 857-5731.

NASOFF, William J.; '76 BS; Retired; NYC Detective; r. 1123 Logan Rd, Wantagh, NY 11793.

NASS, Eric P.; '95 AS; 5724 8th Ave., Brooklyn, NY 11220, 718 377-5412.

NASSER, Sharifa M.; '99 BA; Student; Albany Law Sch., 6-26 161st St., Whitestone, NY 11357, 718 767-1785; r. 302 Washington Ave., Apt. 1F, Albany, NY 12203, 518 436-7449. e-mail

NASSOFER, Charles; '87 BA; 243 West End Ave., New York, NY 10023.

NATALE, Aileen F., (Aileen F. Morales); '93 BS; Intake Asst.; Christian Healthcare Ctr., 301 Sicomac Ave., Wyckoff, NJ 07481, 201 848-5869; r. 1189 Sycamore Ln., Mahwah, NJ 07430, 201 825-4648; *Giuseppe*; Giuseppe Jr.

NATALE, Marc J.; '98 BS; 1119 64th St. A-4, Brooklyn, NY 11219, 718 256-8980.

NATALE, Ralph A.; '83 AS; Captain Retired; NYC Dept. of Corrections, 60 Hudson St., New York, NY 10013; r. 298 Tulia Ave., Floral Park, Floral Park, NY 11001, 516 328-0052; *Teresa*; Jennifer Hill, Brian Ross.

NATH, Nirmala; '87 BS; 3124 Avenue I, Brooklyn, NY 11210, 718 499-6113.

NATHAN, Paul A.; '95 BA; BS; Flushing, NY 11355.

NATHANIEL, Nigel M.; '90 BA, '92 MA; Network Planner; NYC Admin. for Children Svcs., 150 William St., New York, NY 10038, 212 341-2913; r. 922 Wallace Ave., Baldwin, NY 11510, 516 867-5886.

NATOLI, Joseph J.; '79 BS; 73 Rumson Rd, Staten Island, NY 10314, 718 761-7954.

NATTA, Stephenie; '95 CERT; 300 W 55th St. # 14, New York, NY 10019.

NAU, Michael; '96 BS; Police Ofcr.; NYPD, 9720 Foster Ave., Brooklyn, NY 11236, 718 257-6211; r. 1761 Stuyvesant Ave., Merrick, NY 11566, 516 377-4309.

NAUGHTON, Thomas G.; '87 BS; 2245 33rd St., Long Island City, NY 11105, 718 204-7431.

NAVARRA, Angelo; '78 BS; 20 Andrews St., Cornwall on Hudson, NY 12520, 914 534-3567.

NAVARRO, Jose A.; '95 BA; 431 W 17th St. Apt. 4e, New York, NY 10011, 212 989-1435.

NAVARRO, Mario; '78 BS; 52 Sharon St., Brooklyn, NY 11211, 718 384-5314.

NAVARRO, William J.; '77 BS; 1061 Underhill Ave., Bronx, NY 10472, 718 585-7443.

NAVATTA, James A., '76 BS, 1417 141st St., Whitestone, NY 11357, 718 746-1657.

NAWROCKI, Mary-lynn; '87 BA; POB 158, Tappahannock, VA 22560.

NAYLOR, Howard C.; '79 BS; 227 Willow St., Massapequa Park, NY 11762.

NAZAIRE, Jacques; '93 BS; JD New York Law Sch.; Atty.; Law Ofc. of Jacques Nazaire PC, 118-50 193 St., Queens, NY 11412, 718 758-0366; r. 87-14 Homelawn St., Jamaica, NY 11432.

NAZAIRE, Magdala; '97 BS; 2859 W. 22nd St., Brooklyn, NY 11224, 718 602-0399.

NAZAIRE, Yvana; '97 BS; Media Researcher; r. 1300 Gates Ave., Brooklyn, NY 11221, 718 452-5026.

NAZAMY, Najib; '98 BS; 15437 27th Ave., Flushing, NY 11354.

NAZARIO, Francisco; '78 BA; Postal Worker; USPO; r. 1134 Stratford Ave., Bronx, NY 10472, 718 542-1319.

NAZARIO, John; '90 BS; Police Ofcr.; NYC Police Dept., 1 Police Plz., New York, NY 10038, 212 343-3795; r. 920 Ave. Saint John, Bronx, NY 10455, 718 402-1496; Brandon.

NAZARIO, Jose; '96 BS; 2260 Bronx Park E, Bronx, NY 10467, 718 320-4418.

NAZARZADEH, David R.; '99 AS; Grad. Student of Business; r. 38 Hemlock Dr., Paramus, NJ 07652.

NDREU, Firdez; '89 BS; 1020 Grand Concourse, Bronx, NY 10451, 718 538-7218.

NEAL, Sean M.; '98 BA; 1304 Midland Ave., Yonkers, NY 10704, 914 776-9246.

NEARY, Donna; '89 BA; PSYD Hofstra Univ., MS St. Johns Univ.; Sch. Psychologist; Massapequa Public Schs., 4925 Merrick Rd., Massapequa, NY 11758, 516 797-6090; r. 6700 192nd St., Apt. 805, Fresh Meadows, NY 11365, 718 454-4031. e-mail

NEARY, Kathleen T.; '70 BA; Proj. Mgr.; HDEP Intl., 1314 S King St., Honolulu, HI 96814, 808 591-2600; r. 1415 Victoria St. Apt. 1516, Honolulu, HI 96822, 808 537-3951; *Roger Hutchings*. e-mail

NEBLETT, Angela M.; '76; PSC Box 1105, APO, AE 09009.

NEBLETT, Annette; '96 BA; 555 Saratoga Ave., Brooklyn, NY 11212, 718 346-8486.

NEBLETT-FORD, Jillian A.; '85 BS; 364 5th St., Jersey City, NJ 07302, 201 418-8808.

NECKIN, Ian H.; '98 BA; 29 Croft Pl., Staten Island, NY 10314, 718 761-3992.

NEDD, Janine A.; '94 BS; Asst. Mgr. Quality Assurance; White & Case, 1155 Ave. of The Americas, New York, NY 10036, 212 819-7681; r. 33 Valley View Rd, Great Neck, NY 11021, 516 829-2412.

NEDDERMAN, Dionne A.; '97 BA; 10710 165th St., Jamaica, NY 11433.

NEDLIN, Marny B.; '95 MA; 4280 Galt Ocean Dr. Apt. 10A, Ft. Lauderdale, FL 33308.

NEDOS, William T.; '98 BS; AS Suffolk Community Clg.; Police Ofcr.; NYCPD, 1 Police Plz., New York, NY 10038; r. POB 244, Shoreham, NY 11786, 631 744-8187. e-mail

NEEDLEMAN, Ira J.; '89 MA; BA SUNY-Clg. at Old Westbury, JD CUNY-Queens Clg.; Staff Atty.; Northwestern Legal Svcs., 1031 Roemer Blvd., Farrell, PA 16121, 724 346-6112; r. 535 Dutch Ln., Apt. 17, Hermitage, PA 16148, 724 347-2751.

NEENAN, Kevin M.; '88 BA; POB 43, Greeley, PA 18425.

NEESON, Josephine A.; '81 BS; POB 86, Thompson Ridge, NY 10985, 914 361-5263.

NEGGIA, Thomas E.; '97 BS; Investigator Taxation; State of New Jersey Taxation Div., 124 Halsey St., Newark, NJ 07101, 973 648-4764; r. 82 Cedar Lake Rd, Blairstown, NJ 07825, 908 362-1455. e-mail

NEGLIA, Samuel R.; '82 BS; 3 E Logan Rd, Randolph, NJ 07869.

NEGRON, Diana; '90 BS; 789 S 8th St., Lindenhurst, NY 11757.

NEGRON, Larry; '96 BS; 156 E 37th St. 1D, New York, NY 10016.

NEGRON, Magaly; '93 BS; 641 E 13th St. Apt. 8f, New York, NY 10009.

NEGRON, Manuel A.; '91 BS; 86 Moore St., Brooklyn, NY 11206, 718 277-8213.

NEGRON, Maria E.; '98 BS; LICENSE Paralegal Inst.; Exec. Legal Secy.; Wilson Elser Moskowitz Edelman & Dicker, 150 E. 42nd St., New York, NY 10017, 212 490-3000; r. 170 Avenue C, #12G, New York, NY 10009, 212 529-9727; *Felipe; Michelle, Madeline.* e-mail

NEGRON, Peter; '98 BS; 175 W. 107th St. #5, New York, NY 10025, 212 678-1468.

NEGRON, Victor; '79 AS, '93 BS; 2855 Sampson Ave., Bronx, NY 10465, 718 409-3490.

NEGRONI, Deborah; '87 BS; 116 Mill St. #4C, Brooklyn, NY 11231.

NEGRYCZ, Raymond; '81 MPA; 779 Meadow Rd, Smithtown, NY 11787, 631 724-8488.

NEHAMA, Alan; '97 BS; 1950 59th St., Brooklyn, NY 11204.

NEIFELD, Robert; '72 AS, '73 BS; Security/Policeman; NYC Housing Authority/GEICO Ins.; r. 2 Poppy Ln., Levittown, NY 11756, 516 731-7458.

NEIL, Harold; '75 BA; 11021 Ascot Cir., Ph, Fredericksburg, VA 22407.

NEIL, Larold C.; '81 BS; Supervisory Spec. Agt.(SSA); FBI Baltimore Div., 7142 Ambassador Rd., Baltimore, MD 21244, 410 265-8080; r. 2604 Summer Hill Ct., Silver Spring, MD 20904, 856 456-9270; *SSA Faustina; Christina, Lorenzo.*

NEKRUTMAN, David R.; '97 BA; MSW Univ. of Pennsylvania; Legislative Analyst; City Council of New York, 92 24 Sutter Ave., Ozone Park, NY 11417, 718 843-5283; r. 1752 60th St., Brooklyn, NY 11204, 718 256-6753; *Kalanit.* e-mail

NELLIGAR, James E.; '95 BS; 3800 Waldo Ave. Apt. 11e, Bronx, NY 10463.

NELLY, Stabile; '96 BS; 31-65 29th St. #A6, Astoria, NY 11106.

NELMS, Luonel D.; '78 BS; 650 Rosedale Ave., Bronx, NY 10473.

NELSON, Anthony J.; '75 BS; 2111 60th St., Brooklyn, NY 11204, 718 693-2194.

NELSON, Claudette A., (Claudette Lloyd); '96 BS; AS NY Tech Clg.; Proj. Mgr.; Chase Manhattan Bank, 130 Belmont Dr., Somerset, NJ 08873, 732 563-8269; r. 2 Florence Ct., Jackson, NJ 08527. e-mail

NELSON, Debra A.; '97 MA; BA Hunter Clg.; Mitigation Spec./Investigator; NYS Capital Defender Ofc., 915 Broadway, New York, NY 10010, 212 780-5620. e-mail

NELSON, Denise '76 (See Freeman, Denise).

NELSON, Drew M.; '91 BS; 23115 87th Ave., Queens Vlg., NY 11427, 718 217-6915.

NELSON, Fitzroy R.; '97 BS; 4161 Bronxwood Ave., Bronx, NY 10466, 718 881-0952.

NELSON, Guerline; '96 BS; 82 Downing St., Brooklyn, NY 11238, 718 272-9402.

NELSON, Haneef; 2569 7th Ave., 17-1, New York, NY 10039, 315 826-7783.

NELSON, Lynda D.; '89 AS; 14b Earhart Ln., Bronx, NY 10475, 718 681-6535.

NELSON, Marcia '80 (See Baruch, Marcia L.).

NELSON, Mennie F.; '95 BS; 50 W 93rd St. # 5, New York, NY 10025, 315 826-7783.

NELSON, Noel N.; '89 BS; 4784 Boston Post Rd Apt. A43, Pelham, NY 10803.

NELSON, Nora A.; '87 BA; 369 W 116th St. Apt. 3d, New York, NY 10026, 315 826-7783.

NELSON, Troy; '91 BS; 217 W. 127th St., New York, NY 10027, 315 826-7783.

NELSON, Warren W.; '69 BS; 45 Monrovia Blvd., Tuckahoe, NY 10707, 914 779-4088.

NELSON, Yvens; '93 BA; 1504 Ocean Ave., Brooklyn, NY 11230.

NELSON, Yvonne '95 (See Lassiter, Yvonne).

NEMARA, Vanessa A.; '77 BA, '80 MA; Contracts Mgr.; USCG MLCA VPL1, 300 E Main St., Ste. 600 (VPL1), Norfolk, VA 23510, 757 628-4634; r. 2241 Willow Oak Cir., Apt. 204, Virginia Bch., VA 23451; *Sophia Marie.* e-mail

NEMORIN, James V.; '96 AS, '99 BS; Police Ofcr.; NYPD; r. 135-17 116th St., S. Ozone Park, NY 11420, 718 323-0982; *Rose; Stephen, Rudolphe.*

NEONAKIS, Alecsandro; '98 BS; Fed. Judiciary Ofcr.; US Bankruptcy Ct., White Plains, NY 10601, 914 390-4060; r. 31-19 98 St. #2, E. Elmhurst, NY 11369, 718 672-4425.

NESDILL, Patrick J.; '78 BS; Sr. Court Ofc.; NY State Ct., 262 Old Country Rd., Mineola, NY 11501, 516 571-2745; r. 71 Broadmoor Ln., Westbury, NY 11590, 516 997-2418.

NESENSOHN, Donald O.; '76 BA; 124 Sand Shore Rd, Budd Lake, NJ 07828.

NESFIELD, Dale D.; '89 BS; 310 Lenox Rd, Brooklyn, NY 11226.

NESMITH, Daron L.; '98 BS; Police Ofcr.; NYC Police Dept.; r. 2022 Monterey Ave. #4c, Bronx, NY 10457, 718 716-9530. e-mail

NESMITH, Phoebe R.; '95 BS; Child Protection Spec.; Admin. for Children Svcs., 150 Williams St. 2nd. Fl., New York, NY 10038, 212 676-6609; r. 119 W 129th St. Apt. 2A, New York, NY 10027, 212 722-1783; *Russell Lowery; Russell Jr.* e-mail

NESTOR, John T.; '95 BS; MOA Marist Clg.; Sgt; NYC, 2oth Trescent Detective Squad, 120 W 82nd, New York, NY 10024, 212 580-6414; r. 18 Woodridge Dr., Chester, NY 10918, 914 496-6352; *Cathleen; Sean, Daniel.*

NEUBORT, Betty; '79 BA; Retired Social Worker; Sr. Ctr.; r. 99 Hillside Ave., New York, NY 10040, 212 569-8970; *Emil; Simon.*

NEUFVILLE, Norris; '95 BS; Social Worker; St. Christopher's Inc., 1990 Westchester Ave., Bronx, NY 10462, 718 239-1610; r. 77R Locust Hill Ave. #304, Yonkers, NY 10701, 914 476-6276; *Kesha Glover;* Dajour.

NEUMANN, John; '91 BS; 15 Cliff Dr., Sag Harbor, NY 11963, 631 725-9111.

NEUMAYER, August F.; '75 BS; Retired Police Ofcr.; City of NY; r. 7545 Blackhawk Rd, Sebastian, FL 32976, 321 664-4777; *Charlotte;* Michael, Theresa, Glenn, Alexandra, Samantha, Anthony, Nicholas, Vincent, Amanda.

NEUMEYER, Donald G.; '75 BS; 8914 Desarc Rd, Jamaica, NY 11417.

NEUWIRTH-VREELAND, Denise; '98 MA; BA Hunter Clg.; VP; Sterling Protective Svcs. Inc., 1471 E. 63rd St., Brooklyn, NY 11234, 718 763-0206; r. same; *Nicholas Vreeland III.*

NEVAREZ, Ms. Melissa; '97 BA; Paralegal; r. 2058 W. 7th St., Brooklyn, NY 11223, 718 266-2495. e-mail

NEVILLE, John J.; 21 Stuyvesant Oval, New York, NY 10009, 212 673-8417.

NEWBERT, Robert M.; '76 BS; 199 Lexington St., Westbury, NY 11590, 516 333-6484.

NEWKIRK, Rosalind J.; '98 BS; Sergeant NYC Police Dept.; NYC; r. 1305 E 49 St., Brooklyn, NY 11234, 718 531-1908.

NEWKIRK, Tabitha; '95 MA; BA Univ. of Virginia; Dir., Social Svcs. Prog.; Help One Homeless Shelter, 515 Blake Ave., Brooklyn, NY 11207, 718 498-4002; r. 616 Halsey St. Apt. 3R, Brooklyn, NY 11233, 718 443-8545. e-mail

NEWMAN, James V.; '93 MA; 50 Hilltop Dr., N. Salem, NY 10560, 914 669-5045.

NEWMAN, Kim; '89 BA; Probation Ofcr.; NYC Dept. of Probation, 115 Leonard St., New York, NY 10013, 212 442-2960.

NEWMAN, Lisa N.; '85 BS; Sr. Probation Ofcr.; Bergen Cnty. Probation Dept., 133 River St., Hackensack, NJ 07601, 201 646-3677; r. 40 William St. # D3, Little Ferry, NJ 07643, 201 641-1621. e-mail

NEWMAN, Paul R.; '96 BA; Fire Capt.; City of Stamford, CT; r. 490 W. Hill Rd, Stamford, CT 06902, 203 353-8311. e-mail

NEWMAN, Roger K.; '80 BA; Asst. Commissioner; Dept. of Homeless Svcs., 33 Beaver St., New York, NY 10004, 212 361-0639; r. 96-08 57th Ave. #8D, Elmhurst, NY 11368, 718 699-5834; *Cheryle Stevens;* DeJon, Kevin, Autumn.

NEWSHAN, Bryan J.; '92 BS; 2117 Rene Ct., Flushing, NY 11385, 718 497-7080.

NEWSOME, Theodore; '78 BS; 53-01 92 St. 2Fl, Elmhurst, NY 11373.

NEWSON, Norman; '82 BS; 374 Pearl St. Apt. 13h, New York, NY 10038.

NEWTON, Cecil E.; 33 Lott Ave., Brooklyn, NY 11212, 718 531-5761.

NEWTON, Herold H.; '97 BS; 926 Wheeler Ave., Bronx, NY 10473, 718 861-6080.

NEWTON, Judy D.; '92 AS, '93 BA, 2000 MPA; Detective; NYPD; r. 1137 E 81st St., Brooklyn, NY 11236, 718 209-1299. e-mail

NEWTON, Samuel A.; '95 AS, '97 BS, '99 MPA; 525 Riverdale Ave. #7D, Yonkers, NY 10705, 914 376-7068.

NEWTON, Selassie A.; '74 BS; Retired Tchr.; Dept. of Educ. US Virgin Island; r. POB 2564, Frederiksted, VI 00841, 340 772-3382.

NEY, Beverly E.; '90 BS; 2366 Adam Clayton Powell Jr Blvd. #, New York, NY 10030.

NEZNANYJ, Taras P.; '83 BS; Security Hosp. Treatment Asst.; Mid-Hudson Forensic Psychiatric Ctr., Box 158, New Hampton, NY 10958, 914 374-3171; r. 6 Palmer Rd., Catskill, NY 12414.

NG, Anthony C.; '84 BS; Bldg. Mgr.; US Gen. Svcs. Admin., Peter W Rodino Jr Fed. Bldg., 970 Broad St., Newark, NJ 07102, 973 645-2413; r. 241 Seton Hall Dr., Freehold, NJ 07728, 732 409-0356. e-mail

NG, Frank K.; '89 BA; 954 E 12th St., Brooklyn, NY 11230, 718 230-8195.

NG, Grace; '77; 898 Washington Ave., Westwood, NJ 07675.

NG, Harry G.; '96 BA; Store Clerk; East West Books, 78 Fifth Ave., New York, NY 10011, 212 243-5994; r. 92-25 52nd Ave., Elmhurst, NY 11373, 718 271-4803.

NG, Molly C.; '90 BA; 125 Henry St. Apt. 2fw, New York, NY 10002, 315 336-6759.

NG, Phillip; '97 BS; Police Ofcr.; r. 2259 64th St., Brooklyn, NY 11204, 718 284-3527; *Neelam;* Joshua. e-mail

NG, Sukfong E.; '95 BS; 11 Sunshine Ln., Hopewell Jct., NY 12533, 518 789-4284.

NG, Tim; '89 BS; 110 Madison St. #12, New York, NY 10002, 315 841-3272.

NGADI, Francis B.; '91 BS, '93 MPA; 756 Vermont St., Brooklyn, NY 11207.

NGAI, Kenneth; '95 BS; 6 Rubenstein St., Staten Island, NY 10305.

NGAI, Lauren M.; '96 BS; Legal Asst.; Proskauer Rose, 1585 Broadway, New York, NY 10036, 212 969-4201; r. 50-45 Newtown Rd., Woodside, NY 11377, 718 545-8771. e-mail

NGAI-CRIM, Karin; '95 BA; 311 Washington Ave. Apt. C3, Brooklyn, NY 11205.

NGUYEN, Deidre; '99 BA; 109-14 Ascan Ave. 6C, Forest Hills, NY 11375, 718 263-5012.

NGUYEN, Huyen M.; '97 BS; 1473 Knapp St., Bronx, NY 10469, 718 671-7649.

NIAMONITAKIS, Steven; '87 BS; 1121 82nd St., Brooklyn, NY 11228.

NIBLOCK, Susan B.; '99 MPA; BA William & Mary; For. Svc. Ofcr.; Dept. of State, Eur Ex Rm. 5424, 21st & C St., Washington, DC 20520, 202 647-5977; r. 6100 Walhonding Rd., Bethesda, MD 20816, 301 263-9177; *Thomas Jr;* Victoria, Thomas III. e-mail

NICAJ, Vera; '98 BA; 3332 Hull Ave. 2, Bronx, NY 10467, 718 654-7573.

NICHOLAS, Ainsley; '95 BA; 22424 144th Ave., Jamaica, NY 11413.

NICHOLAS, Cyril W.; '93 BA; 853 Empire Blvd. # A, Brooklyn, NY 11213, 718 258-6181.

NICHOLAS, Florence M.; '84 BS; Supv.; Philadelphia Ofc.of The Housing Auth, 1101 Market St., Philadelphia, PA 19107, 215 684-8317; r. 515 C S. 10th St., Philadelphia, PA 19147. e-mail

NICHOLAS, Joanne C.; '81 BS; Ofc. Mgr.; Beth Israel Med. Ctr., 16th & 1st Ave., New York, NY 10003, 212 420-2487; r. 2921 Ericsson St., E. Elmhurst, NY 11369, 718 335-0115. e-mail

NICHOLAS, Joseph M.; '77 BS; 4213 247th St., Flushing, NY 11363.

NICHOLAS, Leslie-Ann; '92 BS; 1655 Flatbush Ave., Brooklyn, NY 11210, 718 493-8223.

NICHOLAS, Lester S.; '88 BA; 1655 Flatbush Ave., Brooklyn, NY 11210, 718 493-8223.

NICHOLS, Ferdinanda W.; '88 BA; Exec. Asst.; New York Hotel, 305 W. 44th St., New York, NY 10036; r. 201 Saint Pauls Ave. Apt. 15n, Jersey City, NJ 07306, 201 653-6543; Christopher, Ramik, Rajien.

NICHOLS, James J.; '98 MS; 6 Essex Ct., Washingtonville, NY 10992, 914 496-5729.

NICHOLSON, Conrad R.; '97 BS, '98 BS; 475 Carlton Ave., Brooklyn, NY 11238, 718 783-9897.

NICHOLSON, Tammy T.; '96 MA; 311 Utica Ave., Brooklyn, NY 11213, 718 443-0166.

NICHOLSON, Ms. Terry; '94 BS; NYC Police Ofcr.; NYC Police Dept., 480 Knickerbocker Ave., Brooklyn, NY 11237, 718 574-1605; r. 285 Classon Ave., Brooklyn, NY 11205, 718 789-6246.

NICHOLSON, Walter A.; '75 BS; Retired; r. 2533 Morningstar Rd., Manasquan, NJ 08736, 732 223-3905; *Patricia.* e-mail

NICKENS, Sheila '85 (See Nickens-Thomas, Sheila).

NICKENS- THOMAS, Sheila, (Sheila Nickens); '85 MA; Supv. Criminal Investigator; US Attys. Ofc., Southern District of New York, One St. Andrews Plz., New York, NY 10007, 212 637-2552. e-mail

NICKS, Alfonso M.; '97 BA; Fraud Investigator-Law Enforcement; NYC Ofc. of Revenue & Investigation, 260 11th Ave., New York, NY 10001, 212 630-9560; r. 5220 Glenwood Rd Apt. 1, Brooklyn, NY 11234, 718 251-2796. e-mail

NICOLA, Christos; '89 BS, '91 MA; BA Hunter Clg.; Sr. Investigator; NYS Dept. of Higher Educ., Ofc. of Professional Discipline, New York, NY 10001, 212 961-4369; r. Long Island City, NY 11103. e-mail

NICOLA, Maria E.; '96 BA; Analyst; City of NY Ofc. of The Comptroller, 1 Centre St., Ste. 1005, New York, NY 10007, 212 669-8211; r. 10 Richman Plz., Bronx, NY 10453, 718 716-4277; *Jonathan Strober.* e-mail

NICOLAOU, Carmen A.; '97 BA; Law Candidate-JD; Hofstra Law Sch.; r. 8803 Ridge Blvd., Brooklyn, NY 11209, 718 748-1421. e-mail

NICOLOSI, Joseph R.; '78 BS; 88 Foster Blvd., Babylon, NY 11702, 631 842-2651.

NICTAS, George J.; '83 BS; 11024 55th Ave., Flushing, NY 11368.

NIEMES, Monica C.; '96 BS; 143-02 Quince Ave., Flushing, NY 11355.

NIEMIEC, Theodore; '83 MA; 1246 Drumgoole Rd W, Staten Island, NY 10312.

NIERODA, Daniel W.; '86 MPA, '86 BA; 236 Edgewood Ave., Smithtown, NY 11787.

NIEVES, Angel; '85 BS; 418 Cathedral P'way, New York, NY 10025.

NIEVES, Carmen '92 (See Nieves-Cardenas, Mrs. Carmen).

NIEVES, Cynthia; '94 BA; 1011 E. 108th St., Brooklyn, NY 11236.

NIEVES, Dominick R.; '88 BS; 25 Linn Pl., Yonkers, NY 10705, 914 376-2905.

NIEVES, Gilbert; '77 BA; 18 De Sales Pl., Brooklyn, NY 11207.

NIEVES, Gloria E.; '99 BA; 4395 Broadway, New York, NY 10040, 212 740-6255.

NIEVES, Jaime; '89 AS, '91 BS; 456 41st St. # 5, Brooklyn, NY 11232, 718 372-3988.

NIEVES, Jose V.; '99 BA; Detective; NYC Police Dept.; r. 2387 Hoffman St. #1, Bronx, NY 10458, 718 584-0223.

NIEVES, Julie A.; '97 BA; Customer Svc.; Bell Atlantic, 375 Pearl St., New York, NY 10038, 212 285-7848; r. 2872 W. 19th St., Brooklyn, NY 11224, 718 372-3988; Tiana, Justin. e-mail

NIEVES, Linda R.; '98 BS; 2575 Steinway St., Astoria, NY 11103, 718 777-8059.

NIEVES, Ralph G.; '95 BS; 89 Shoreview Dr., Yonkers, NY 10710, 914 793-7702.

NIEVES, Samuel; '93 BS; 315 E 206 St. #2B, Bronx, NY 10467, 718 231-2881.

NIEVES-CARDENAS, Mrs. Carmen, (Carmen Nieves); '92 BS; MSED Univ. of PA; Clg. Instr. of Reading; Tidewater Community Clg., Virginia Bch., VA 23450, 757 321-7343; r. 1119 Foster Ave. # B, Brooklyn, NY 11230; *Michael E. Cardenas MD.* e-mail

NIGRO, Gregory; '86 BS; 449 Tupelo Dr., Naperville, IL 60540.

NIKAC, Maria; '94 BA; 87 Beacon St., Haworth, NJ 07641, 201 384-8987.

NIKITIN, Maxim; '99 BA; Student/Mgr of Operations; John Jay Clg/McCann & Surprises; r. 2775 E 12th St., Apt. 529, Brooklyn, NY 11235, 718 368-0485. e-mail

NIKOLOUDAKIS, Georgi; '96 BA; 1901 E. 17th St., Brooklyn, NY 11229, 718 375-4036.

NIMROD, Elvin G.; '78 MA; 574 Midwood St., Brooklyn, NY 11203.

NIMROD, Lloyd G.; '98 MPA; 200 E. 53rd St. #1, Brooklyn, NY 11203, 718 498-5578.

NINBURG, Svetlana; '97 BA; MPA NYU; Staff Analyst; 718 694-1931; r. 345 Webster Ave., Brooklyn, NY 11230, 718 851-2408. e-mail

NINOMIYA, Marilyn J.; '88 BA; MS Clayton Clg. of Natural, PHD American Inst of Hel Theo; Holistic Cnslt.; Marilyn J Ninomiya PhD, 40 E. 89th St. Apt. PHC, New York, NY 10128, 212 987-2662; r. 107 Forest Hill Dr., Palm Coast, FL 32137, 904 446-4362; *Eizo;* Mori, Renzo. e-mail

NISELY, Michelle S.; '96 MA; Psy Spec.; Prison Health Svcs., Miami, FL 33178, 305 592-9567; r. 4540 NW 79th Ave. Apt. 1d, Miami, FL 33166, 305 994-7769; David Santana, Athena Santana. e-mail

NISI, Anthony J.; '97 BS; MA Seton Hall Univ.; Probation Ofcr.; State of NJ/Passaic Cnty. Superior Ct, Probation Officer - Adult Services, Paterson, NJ 07504, 973 247-8700; r. 21Baron Rd, W. Milford, NJ 07480, 973 728-7812. e-mail

NISS, Oleg; '97 BA; CERT. New York Tech. & Bus.; Database Analyst/Asst. Prof.; John Jay Clg. Writing Ctr., 445 W. 59th St., New York, NY 10019, 212 237-8573; r. 250 Parkville Ave., Brooklyn, NY 11230, 718 859-1253.

NIXON, Henry E.; '99 BA; Law Student; Brooklyn Law Sch., Brooklyn, NY 11201; r. 1791 Bruckner Blvd#1G, Bronx, NY 10472, 718 589-5102. e-mail

NIXON, Sandra R.; '91 BS; Police; NYPD; r. POB 20209, New York, NY 10023.

NIXON, Staci E.; '85 BA; 1452 Carroll St., Brooklyn, NY 11213, 718 604-3250.

NIZZA, Joseph R.; '74 BS; 118-03 Sutter Ave., Jamaica, NY 11420, 718 738-0034.

NJOKU, Aloysius A.; '87 MPA; 332 Clinton Ave., Brooklyn, NY 11205.

NKRUMAH, Kafahni T., (Gerard T. Evans); '92 BS; JD Thurgood Marshall, TX; Staff Atty.; The Legal Aid Society, 49 Thomas St., #2014, New York, NY 10007, 212 298-5100; r. 1691 E. 174th St., Bronx, NY 10472, 718 617-3689; Christopher, Fishburn. e-mail

NNAMOCHA, Nestor U.; '79 MPA; Box 92 Umuahia, Imo, Nigeria.

NO, Steve; '98 BS; Police Ofcr.; Ft. Lee NJ Police Dept.; r. POB 2113, Ft. Lee, NJ 07024, 201 280-5820.

NOAILLES, Marie '96 (See Saint Cloux, Marie P.).

NOBILIONE, Joseph G.; '86 BA; 3290 Country Club Rd # 1, Bronx, NY 10465, 718 597-3262.

NOBLE, Janet C.; '86 BS; 790 Eldert Ln., Brooklyn, NY 11208, 718 444-4877.

NOBLE, Simone A.; '98 BS; 172-10 Linden Blvd., Jamaica, NY 11434, 718 784-7439.

NOBLES, Sharon V.; '97 BS; AS Borough Manahttan Clg.; Security Guard; Museum of Modern Art, 11 W 53rd St., New York, NY 10019, 212 708-9467; r. 40-13 10th St. #6D, Long Island City, NY 11101, 718 784-7439. e-mail

NOBLIN, Robert K.; '78 BS; 26 Eastover Dr., E. Northport, NY 11731.

NOCERA, Salvatore F.; 3132 Spenser Dr., Bronx, NY 10465.

NOCERA, Vito; '84 BS; 1552 74th St., Brooklyn, NY 11228, 718 331-1441.

NOCERINO, Thomas; '77 BS; 2nd VP of Claims Admin.; Security Mutual Life Ins. Co. of NY, 100 Court St., Binghamton, NY 13902, 607 723-3551; r. 903 Conklin Rd, Binghamton, NY 13903, 607 724-1883; Theresa; Trina. e-mail

NOCERO, Jeanne V.; '77 BA; BS Hunter Clg.; RN; Lenox Hill Hosp., 100 E. 77th St., New York, NY 10021; r. 520 E. 81st St. Apt. 7G, New York, NY 10028.

NOCK-DUDLEY, Joyce A.; '82 BS; 21-15 35 Ave., Long Island City, NY 11106.

NOEL, Beverly; '92 BS; 285 Aycrigg Ave. Apt. 10K, Passaic, NJ 07055.

NOEL, Desmond E.; '97 BS; 60 E. 55th St., Brooklyn, NY 11203, 718 498-4654.

NOEL, Gesner; '96 BS; Unique Systs. Operation & Admin.; ILX Systs., 212 384-8888; r. 197 E 32nd St., Brooklyn, NY 11226, 718 826-1986; Philippe. e-mail

NOEL, Kevin E.; '98 BA; 330 Lenox Rd #5p, Brooklyn, NY 11226, 718 462-8163.

NOEL, Samuel D.; '88 BS; Paralegal Spec.; US Atty's Ofc., 147 Pierre Pont Plz., Brooklyn, NY 11201, 718 254-6369; r. 409 E. 93rd St., Brooklyn, NY 11212, 718 485-1736. e-mail

NOEL, Sean S.; '98 AS, '99 BS; Law Enforcement; Fed. Govt., 150 Park Row, New York, NY 10007, 212 240-9669; r. 221-26 Murdock Ave., Queens Vlg., NY 11429, 718 479-3884.

NOLAN, Harold F.; 319 Sanilac St., Staten Island, NY 10306, 718 979-2399.

NOLAN, John E.; '82 MA; 23 Anderson Pkwy., Cedar Grove, NJ 07009.

NOLAN, Joseph J.; '77 BS; 109 Stevens Ave., Hempstead, NY 11550, 516 483-5989.

NOLAN, Wanda J.; '80 BA; 4779 Barnes Ave., Bronx, NY 10470.

NOLAN, William F.; '73 BS; AS NYC Community Clg.; Pres.; Connell, Nolan Assocs. Inc., 724 Hamilton Ave., Westhampton Bch., NY 11978, 631 288-3283; r. same; Melody; William, Kathleen, Kerry, Melody. e-mail

NOLASCO, Hector; '95 BS; 397 N. Broadway, Yonkers, NY 10701.

NOLASCO, Joseph; '81 BS; 85 Decker Ave., Staten Island, NY 10302.

NOLL, Harold W.; '73 BS; AA Seton Hall; Retired Exec. Ofcr.; US Customs Svc.; r. 19282 Meadowood Cir., Huntington Bch., CA 92648, 714 536-7932. e-mail

NONIS, Basil; '95 BS; Detective; NYPD, New York, NY 10001, 718 299-4119; r. 327 Pennyfield Ave., Bronx, NY 10465, 718 918-0548.

NOONAN, Peter; '78 BS; 1668 Central St., Yorktown Hts., NY 10598, 914 962-7688.

NORAT, Wigberto; '79 BS; Capt.; NYC Dept. of Corrections, New York, NY 10001, 718 579-4347; r. 7 Marion Ct., Middletown, NY 10941, 914 692-3906; Desiree I.

NORBERG, Scott; '95 BS; 37 Brandis Ln., Staten Island, NY 10312, 718 227-5174.

NORDEN, Paul A.; '96 BS; 247 Crown Ave., Staten Island, NY 10312.

NORDHAUG, Eric F.; '85 MPA; 400 Oak Ave., River Edge, NJ 07661, 201 262-7155.

NORFLETT, Ronald; '77 BA; 1724 Paulding Ave., Bronx, NY 10462.

NORGRIFF, Keith A.; '96 BA; 87 Remsen Ave. Ph, Brooklyn, NY 11212, 718 778-2488.

NORMAN, Kym R.; '86 BS; 1142 Belmont Ave., Brooklyn, NY 11208, 718 277-9323.

NORMIL, Chantal; '90 BS; 1292 Crestridge Ln., Riverdale, GA 30296, 770 991-0991.

NORMIL, Marie; '95 AS; 134-05 134 St., Jamaica, NY 11420.

NORRIS, Edward T.; '76 MA; AS Brooklyn Clg.; COO; New York Historical Society, 2 W. 77 St., New York, NY 10024, 212 873-3400; r. 1621 E. 51 St., Brooklyn, NY 11234, 718 253-5391; Catherine; Edward, Robert.

NORTON, Benjamin T.; '86 BA; POB 82, Ridgeland, SC 29936.

NORTON, Joseph M.; '91 BA; 7 Micieli Pl., Brooklyn, NY 11218, 718 680-7537.

NORTON, Keith J.; '95 BS; 321 E Clay Ave., Roselle Park, NJ 07204, 908 245-6361.

NORTON, William J.; '76 BA; 592 E 81 St. #3, Brooklyn, NY 11236, 718 627-2653.

NORVIO, Scott J.; '95 BS; 1461 Holiday Park Dr., Wantagh, NY 11793.

NORWOOD, Robert; '86 MPA; 7 Gerri Rd, E. Northport, NY 11731, 631 757-2517.

NOSEK, Frank R.; '87 BA; MBA St. Johns Univ.; Postal Police Ofcr.; USPO; r. 5 Southwind Dr., Cross River, NY 10518, 914 763-6129; Daryl; Kimberly.

NOSTRAMO, Thomas; '77 BS; 5826 61st St., Maspeth, NY 11378, 718 894-1807.

NOTTE, Daniel A.; '83 MA; 390 Thomas Ave., Lyndhurst, NJ 07071, 201 531-9734.

NOURAKIS, Ana C., (Ana C. Hernandez); '75 BS; MSW Fordham Univ.; Ret Asst. Supt. of Welfare Shelter; New York City; r. 11 Ft. George Hill, New York, NY 10040, 212 569-6742; Richard D.

NOUTSKY, Martin; '88 BA; POB 6948, New York, NY 10128.

NOVARRO, Santo F.; '76 MA; 15 Lyons Ave., Farmingdale, NY 11735, 631 694-9732.

NOVICK, David; '93 BS; 22 Leif Blvd., Congers, NY 10920.

NOVOA, Carmen M.; '77 BA; 320 W 47 St., New York, NY 10036, 212 247-7627.

NOWACOSKI, Michael; '93 BS, '95 MA; 1141 W Grace St., Apt. 3N, Chicago, IL 60613.

NOWAK, Dennis A.; '78 BA; 62-71 65 St., Middle Vlg., NY 11379, 718 426-4743.

NOWICKI, John F.; '80 MS; 8313 Portsmouth Dr. #B, Darien, IL 60561, 630 654-0657.

NOZINE, Josette M.; '98 BA; PO. Box 297202, Brooklyn, NY 11229, 718 385-3621.

NUCCIO, Anthony J.; '89 MA; 1505 3rd Ave., Asbury Park, NJ 07712.

NUGENT, Andrew G.; '78 BS; 218 Frederick Ave., Babylon, NY 11702, 631 321-7618.

NUGENT, Martha D.; '75 BA; 1595 Madison Ave., New York, NY 10029.

NUGENT, Michele D.; '95 MA; BA St. Johns Univ., MA; Social Worker; Gloucester Cnty. Dept. Social Svcs., POB 1390, Gloucester, VA 23061, 804 893-4031; r. 2830 Indian Creek Tr., Gloucester, VA 23061; Christopher. e-mail

NUGENT, Thomas; '87 BS; 727 Pine St., Roselle, NJ 07203, 908 298-1485.

NUNEZ, Claribel; '99 BA; Campus Peace Ofc.; Brooklyn Clg., 2900 Bedford Ave., Brooklyn, NY 11210, 718 951-5511; r. 116-30 Brewer Blvd. #8D, Jamaica, NY 11434, 718 525-7111. e-mail

NUNEZ, Elvin; '94 BA; 240 W. 65th St., New York, NY 10023.

NUNEZ, Hilda; '79 BA; 111 Montague St., Brooklyn, NY 11201, 718 624-5974.

NUNEZ, Janet F.; '97 BS; Dir. Asst.; Homeland Fndn., 230 Park Ave., Ste. 1528, New York, NY 10169, 212 949-4986; r. 733 Amsterdam Ave., Apt. 18J, New York, NY 10025. e-mail

NUNEZ, Janet F.; '97 BS; 920 Park Ave. #2, New York, NY 10028.

NUNEZ, Juan; '93 MPA; POB 765, Bronx, NY 10451, 718 466-5715.

NUNEZ, Miguel A.; '96 BS; 241 Woodbine St., Brooklyn, NY 11221, 718 443-5586.

NUNEZ, Noralee; '93 BA, '94 CERT; 681 W 193rd St. # 4, New York, NY 10040, 212 544-9873.

NUNEZ, Yohanna; '98 BA; 452 Lincoln Ave., Brooklyn, NY 11208, 718 235-5594.

NUNEZ-TORRES, Julie F.; '96 BA; 155 E 104th St. Apt. 5fw, New York, NY 10029, 212 427-2302.

NUNN, Jason A.; '96 BS; 515 Summit St., Ridgewood, NJ 07450, 201 444-8449.

NURSE, Henry E.; '96 BS; 3 W Decatur Rd, Mohegan Lake, NY 10547.

NURSE, Ingrid L. '85 (See Drakes, Ingrid L.).

NURSE, John·P.; '91 BS; Owner Store; r. 1275 Delmar Loop, Brooklyn, NY 11239, 718 642-1396.

NURSE, Scott; '85 MPA; 113-42 207th St., Jamaica, NY 11429, 718 723-7665.

NUSSER, Gary R.; '78 BS; 116-11 107 Ave., Richmond Hill, NY 11419.

NUZZI, Laurie A.; '97 MA; BA SUNY-Stony Brook; 20 Maine Ave., Staten Island, NY 10314, 718 727-9859. e-mail

NWAHIRI, Matthias; '91 MA; 785 E 211th St., Bronx, NY 10467.

NYLAND, Charles A.; '96 BS; 14 Shore Blvd., Slate Hill, NY 10973.

O

OAKLEY, Charlene S.; '97 BS, '98 BS; 30 Paerdegat 1st S, Brooklyn, NY 11236, 718 495-5582.

OBAROWSKI, Edward A.; '76 BS; 2054 E 28th St., Brooklyn, NY 11229.

O'BERG, Dennis J.; '76 BS; 1015 74th St., Brooklyn, NY 11228.

O'BOYLE, James M.; '96; 62 Hayrick Lang, Commack, NY 11725, 631 499-4952.

OBOYSKI, Victor; '77 BS; 14934 11th Ave., Whitestone, NY 11357.

OBREMSKI, Frank L.; '73 BS; MPS Long Island Univ.; Retired Deputy Chief; MTA Police Dept., New York, NY 10010; r. 7 Jayme Dr., N. Babylon, NY 11703.

O'BRIAN, Joseph J.; '78 MA; 62 Kirshon Ave., Staten Island, NY 10314.

O'BRIAN, Patrick J.; 43 Ainsworth Ave., Staten Island, NY 10308.

O'BRIEN, Dennis M.; '88 BS; Exec.; Park Ave. Security, 188-02 64th Ave., Fresh Meadows, NY 11365, 718 264-7749; r. 153 Wellington Rd, Mineola, NY 11501, 516 746-1929; *Joan.*

O'BRIEN, Hayden; '92 BS; 712 E. Gun Hill, Bronx, NY 10467.

O'BRIEN, Jeffrey S.; '90 BS, '95 MS, '98 MPA; 541 E. 20th St., New York, NY 10010, 212 475-1781.

O'BRIEN, John F.; '71 BS; 8211 259th St., Glen Oaks, NY 11004, 718 343-6569.

O'BRIEN, Joseph J.; '66 BS, '78 MA; Security Mgr.; McGraw-Hill, 1221 Ave. of The Americas, New York, NY 10020, 212 512-4202; r. 62 Kirshon Ave., Staten Island, NY 10314, 718 698-1196; *Margaret;* Joseph, Sean, Barry, Brendan.

O'BRIEN, Keri J.; '99 MA; 406 W. 46th St. #3C, New York, NY 10036, 315 724-8872.

O'BRIEN, Patricia A.; '75 BA; 431 Cumberland Ave., Teaneck, NY 07666.

O'BRIEN, Patrick J.; '80 BA; 1616 E 37th St., Brooklyn, NY 11234, 718 376-6567.

O'BRIEN, Patrick J.; '73 BS; 110 Kirshon Ave., Staten Island, NY 10314, 718 448-3073.

O'BRIEN, Patrick T.; '76 MA; 658 McCutchen St., Charleston, SC 29412, 843 971-1135.

O'BRIEN, Stephen P.; '91 BS; AS Sullivan Cnty. CC, CERT. FBI Natl. Acad.; Lt.; NYC DD Brooklyn North Investigations, 179 Wilson Ave., Brooklyn, NY 11237, 718 573-5045; r. 12 Sussex Ave., Massapequa, NY 11758, 516 798-4320; *Patricia;* Sean, Evan. e-mail

O'BRIEN, Thomas P.; '78 BA; 87-40 Francis Lewis, Queens Vlg., NY 11427, 718 706-8013.

OBRYAN, Diren D.; '85 BA; 4457 Murdock Ave., Bronx, NY 10466.

O'BRYAN, Rupert W.; '82 MPA; 4457 Murdock Ave., Bronx, NY 10466.

OBUCHOWSKI, Bart M.; '99 BA; AA Union Community Clg.; Deputy US Marshal; US Marshal, 500 Pearl St., New York, NY 10007; r. 10 Lucien Pl., Linden, NJ 07036, 908 587-1064.

O'BYRNE, Francis M.; '74 BS; 119 E 235th St., Bronx, NY 10470, 718 325-9143.

O'CALLAGHAN, Cormac D.; '95 BS; 15570 SW 105th Ln. Apt. 1716, Miami, FL 33169.

O'CALLAGHAN, Joseph; '97 BS; 24 Whiskey Rd., Coram, NY 11727.

OCAMPO, Julio; '90 BS, '93 MA; 70 Park Rd, Stony Point, NY 10980, 914 942-0727.

OCAMPO, Mayra D.; '93 BS; 1121 Morrison Ave., Bronx, NY 10472.

OCAMPO, Mrs. Melisa, (Melisa Almodovar); '96 BS; Police Ofcr.; NYPD, One Police Plz., New York, NY 10038, 212 374-5000; r. 70 Park Rd., Stony Point, NY 10980, 914 942-0727; *Julio A.;* Suleida, Scott, Brandon. e-mail

OCASIO, Carlos; '96 BS; 3555 Kings Clg., Bronx, NY 10467, 718 892-8707.

OCASIO, Jacqueline A.; '96 BA; Homemaker; r. 145 B George St., Brooklyn, NY 11237, 718 497-0734; *Edwin;* Edwin, Jaylene. e-mail

OCASIO, Roger; '87 BS; 57 Birchard Ave., Staten Island, NY 10314, 718 273-7078.

OCASIO, Yolanda M.; '83 BA; St. Johns Univ.; Dir. of Budget & Admin.; St. John's Univ. Sch. of Law, 8000 Utopia Pkwy., Rm. 4-52, Jamaica, NY 11432, 718 990-6046; r. 99 Park Ave. W, White Plains, NY 10607, 914 693-3349. e-mail

OCHS, Jeffrey J.; '99 MA; BA Assumption Clg.; FBI; r. 204 Burnside Ave., Cranford, NJ 07016, 908 272-4112; *Laura.*

OCHS, Scott A.; '83 MA; 341 S. Pascack Rd, Spring Vlly., NY 10977.

OCONNELL, Daniel V.; '98 AS; 41 Sutton St., Brooklyn, NY 11222, 718 389-5596.

OCONNELL, Edward T.; '95 BA; 17 Halstead Ave., Wallington, NJ 07057.

O'CONNELL, James H.; '77 BS; Retired; r. 3799 S. Banana River Blvd. #1005, Cocoa Bch., FL 32931, 321 779-3749.

O'CONNELL, Kevin J.; '76 MPA; 6 Northpark Ct., Garnerville, NY 10923.

O'CONNELL, Sean M.; '97 MA; BA St. Johns Univ.; Residential Psychologist; United Cerebral Palsy of Queens, Heartshare Human Services; r. POB 140011, Howard Bch., NY 11414, 718 323-3040. e-mail

O'CONNELL, Terrance; '81 BA; 79 W Clarkstown Rd, New City, NY 10956.

O'CONNOR, Catherine '95 (See O'Connor Wright, Catherine).

O'CONNER, Hilda N.; '89 BA; 680 Balcom Ave. Apt. 2g, Bronx, NY 10465.

O'CONNOLL, Thomas J.; 1495 Shore Dr., Bronx, NY 10465.

O'CONNOR, Andrew J.; '86 MA; 242A Brooklake Rd, Florham Park, NJ 07932, 973 377-8205.

O'CONNOR, Ms. Brigid; '95 BS; JD New York Law; Police Sergeant; NYC Police Dept., 1 Police Plz., New York, NY 10018; r. 193 Beach 127th St., Belle Harbor, NY 11694.

O'CONNOR, Edward G.; '73 BS; Chief; Fire Dept. of New York; r. 33 Brookfield Ave , Staten Island, NY 10308

O'CONNOR, James F.; '71 BS; Ret. Capt.; NYC Police Dept.; r. 148 Heights Dr., Yonkers, NY 10710.

O'CONNOR, Joanne M.; '76 BA; Police Lt.-Special Assignment; NYC Police Dept., 1 Lefarak City Plz. Rm. 1626, Corona, NY 11368, 718 760-7632; r. 121 Beverly Ave., Floral Park, NY 11001, 516 775-4460; *Frank Sclafani.*

O'CONNOR, John F.; '71 BS, '79 MPA; 4518 Arcadia Ln., Great Neck, NY 11020, 516 466-5871.

O'CONNOR, John J.; '75 BS; 10 Havervale Ln., Garnerville, NY 10923, 914 429-9252.

O'CONNOR, John J.; '76 BS; 6139 77th St., Flushing, NY 11379, 718 932-7017.

OCONNOR, John P.; '91 BA; 3220 Netherland Ave., Bronx, NY 10463, 718 884-7734.

O'CONNOR, Judy; '80 BS; 7448 45th Ave., Flushing, NY 11373, 718 672-6164.

O'CONNOR, Julie A.; '78 BS; 6 Westwood Dr. S, W. Orange, NJ 07052, 973 227-4180.

O'CONNOR, Karen; '88 MPA; 184 Pumpkin Ln., Clinton Corners, NY 12514.

O'CONNOR, Kevin M.; '89 MPA; 1 Horne Tooke Rd, Palisades, NY 10964, 914 359-6720.

O'CONNOR, Kevin R.; '78 AS, '89 BA; 105 Purcell St., Staten Island, NY 10310.

O'CONNOR, Michael J.; '81 BS; 6185 Hummingbird Dr., Mason, OH 45040, 513 459-0583.

O'CONNOR, Patricia A.; '78 BS; 109-37 120 St., S. Ozone Park, NY 11420, 718 932-7017.

O'CONNOR, Roderick J.; '74 BS; 19 Bay Ridge Pl., Brooklyn, NY 11209, 718 439-1532.

OCONNOR, Thomas J.; '98 BA; 74 Demarest Mill Rd, W. Nyack, NY 10994.

O'CONNOR, Thomas P.; '76 AS; 139 Kinkade Dr., Middletown, NJ 07748.

O'CONNOR, Valerie J.; '75; 147-50 Weller Ln., Rosedale, NY 11422.

O'CONNOR WRIGHT, Catherine, (Catherine O'Conner); '95 MA; BA C.W. Post Clg.; Support Staff Supv.; US Dept. of Justice, 147 Pierrepont St., Brooklyn Hts., NY 11201, 718 254-7000; r. 10 Tall Pines Ln., Nesconset, NY 11767, 631 585-7907; *Roy.* e-mail

OCTAVE, Colin; '99; 520 Madison St., Brooklyn, NY 11221.

ODABASHIAN, Ralph; '92 BS; 2360 28th St. # 2, Long Island City, NY 11105, 718 888-0654.

O'DANIELS, Tiffany L.; '95 BA; 177 Tweed Blvd., Nyack, NY 10960.

O'DAY, Joanne E.; '85 MA; 473 Central Park W, New York, NY 10025.

O'DELL, Jill C.; '97 MA; BA Western MI Univ.; Acct. Exec.; Prizm Com; r. 2400 N. Hampden Ct. Apt. 6E, Chicago, IL 60614, 773 529-7547. e-mail

ODITA, Pauline U.; '82 MPA; 2850 Decatur Ave., Bronx, NY 10458.

ODOM, Annie D.; '85 BA; 11592 229th St., Jamaica, NY 11411, 718 786-0090.

ODOM, Gwendolyn N.; '79 BA; 21608 117th Rd, Jamaica, NY 11411, 718 786-0090.

ODOM, Oscar, III; '83 BS; JD CUNY Law; Chief of Departments; NYC Sheriff's Ofc.; r. 341 A Grand Ave., Brooklyn, NY 11238, 718 398-6330.

O'DONNELL, Donald P.; '85 BS, '97 MA; MBA Wagner Clg.; Inspector; NYC Police, 154 Lawrence Ave., Brooklyn, NY 11230, 718 851-5516; r. 311 Edinboro Rd., Staten Island, NY 10306; *Peggy; Patrick.*

O'DONNELL, Eugene; '82 BS; 217 78th St., Brooklyn, NY 11209, 718 491-3810.

O'DONNELL, Irene M.; '87 BA; 4319 56th St. Apt. 3c, Flushing, NY 11377, 718 945-7295.

O'DONNELL, Lorraine J.; '75 MA; 166-05 Highland Ave. #5Q, Jamaica, NY 11432, 718 658-1146.

O'DONNELL, CAPT Steven; '99 BA; NYC Fire Dept., 9 Metrotech Ctr., Brooklyn, NY 11201, 718 430-0247; r. 40 Bay St., Bronx, NY 10464. e-mail

O'DONOGHUE, John P.; '78 BS; 21921 38th Ave., Flushing, NY 11361.

O'DOWD, Edward F.; '77 MA; 864 E Michigan Ave., Marshall, MI 49068, 616 781-9595.

O'DOWD, John W.; '79 BS; 1116 Greenbriar Rd, Cherry Hill, NJ 08034, 856 427-4119.

O'DOWD, Michael P.; '99 BA MPA; CUNY Administrative Asst.; John Jay Clg. of Criminal Justice, 445 W. 59 St., Ext. 2045, New York, NY 10019, 212 237-8874; r. 446 Senator St., Brooklyn, NY 11220, 718 238-3490; Lawrence. e-mail

ODOWD, Michael P.; '99 BA; Administrative Asst.; John Jay Clg. of Criminal Justice; r. 446 Senator St., Brooklyn, NY 11220, 718 238-3490. e-mail

ODUMS, Tanya S.; '95 BA; 2202 Linden Blvd. #, Brooklyn, NY 11207.

ODUSANYA, Abimbola; '85 BS; 958 E 43rd St., Brooklyn, NY 11210.

O'ESTRICHER, Marlo; '89 BS; 22215 101st Ave., Queens Vlg., NY 11429.

OETTINGER, Elizabeth '83 (See Elfeld, Elizabeth).

O'FLAHERTY, Donald M.; '76 BS; 7 Wildwood Ln., Hampton Bays, NY 11946.

O'GARA, William C.; '92 BS; 9025 212th St., Queens Vlg., NY 11428, 718 225-8024.

OGBARA, Jane; '82 BS; 1012 Ocean Ave. #6J, Brooklyn, NY 11226.

OGBENI, Felicia U.; '96 BS; 462a Chester St., Brooklyn, NY 11212.

OGORMAN, Marianne; '92 BS; 11 Dogwood Ln., Glen Head, NY 11545.

O'GRADY, Dermot; '81 BS; Deputy Atty. Gen.; New Jersey Div. of Criminal Justice, POB 085, Trenton, NJ 08625, 609 984-1446; r. 126 Ferry Rd, Flemington, NJ 08822, 908 806-0088; *Nancy.*

O'GRADY, Martin F.; '80 BS; Retired Security Dir.; r. 26 Weber Ave., Malverne, NY 11565, 516 593-5415; *Joan; Frank, Jean, Bernadette.*

OGUNADZ, Tamara; '96 BA; 410 W. 145 St., New York, NY 10031.

OH, Jong; '96 BS; 415 Beverley Rd., Brooklyn, NY 11218, 718 871-2832.

OHADOMA, Emmanuel O.; '98 BS; 909 E 220 St., Bronx, NY 10469.

OHAKAMNU, George N.; '92 BA; 3456 Mickle Ave., Bronx, NY 10469.

OHALE, Emmanuel U.; '96 BA; 805 Washington Ave., Brooklyn, NY 11238.

O'HALLORAN, Daniel; '86 BS; 635 73rd St., Brooklyn, NY 11209, 718 833-1086.

O'HALLORAN, Hugh M.; '84 MA; 11 Harper Ave., Montrose, NY 10548, 914 788-3821.

O'HANLON, Eugene C.; '72 BS; Retired; r. 15021 N 7th Dr., Phoenix, AZ 85023, 602 993-9364.

O'HARA, Brendan; '93 AS; 5713 Avenue M, Brooklyn, NY 11234, 718 234-6816.

O'HARA, Thomas P.; 8929 Lyman St., Queens Vlg., NY 11428, 718 464-2629.

O'HARE, Aileen; '87 AS; 3197 Giegerich Pl., Bronx, NY 10465, 718 828-5061.

O'HEIR, Thomas L.; '75 BS; 1536 Victoria St., N. Baldwin, NY 11510.

OJEDA, Gonzalo; '94 BS; 501 W 123rd St. Apt. 16b, New York, NY 10027, 212 666-1892.

OJEDA, Rosa E.; '80 BA; 201 W 93rd St. Apt. 18g, New York, NY 10025.

OJENA, Stephen; '72 MS; BSCHEM Univ. of California; Owner of Fingerprint, Crime Scene; Processing & Evidence Collection Materia, Forensic Spec.-Contra Costa Cnty., Sheriffs Crime Lab 1122 Escobar St., Martinez, CA 94553, 925 335-1600; r. 2429 Saybrook Pl., Martinez, CA 94553, 925 372-5863; *Jaylene; Benjamin.* e-mail

OKAFOR, Emeka D.; '97 BS; POB 672060, Bronx, NY 10467.

O'KANE, John J.; '76 MPA; MS SUNY Albany; Prof. Emeritus; Adirondack Community Clg., Bay Rd., Queensbury, NY 12804, 518 743-2221; r. 41 Heinrick Cir., Queensbury, NY 12804, 518 793-8053; *Theresa;* Patricia, Christine, John Jr. e-mail

O'KEEFE, Mary A.; '83 BS; 103-20 Alstyne Ave., Corona, NY 11368.

O'KEEFE, Patricia J.; '92 BA; Programmer Analyst; Chase Manhattan Bank, 4 Chase MetroTech Ctr., 16 Fl., Brooklyn, NY 11245, 718 242-3597; r. 3981 49th St., Long Island City, NY 11104, 718 396-2502; *Lester Logarta.* e-mail

OKEKE, James; '91 MA; 187-01 Liberty Ave., St. Albans, NY 11412.

OKHIKU, Ayo A.; '87 BS; 600 W 113th St., New York, NY 10025.

OKIN, Avery Eli; '79 MA, '79 BA; JD Brooklyn Law Sch., CAE Amer. Soc. of Assoc.Exec; Exec. Dir.; Brooklyn Bar Assn. & Fndn., 123 Remsen St., Mem Board of Gov. 100Yr Assoc.Of NY, Brooklyn, NY 11201, 718 624-0675; r. 217-06 85th Ave., Hollis Hls., NY 11427, 718 479-4340; *Lynn S.;* Evan Gilman, Zachary Dylan. e-mail

OKOSUN, Alexander E.; '99 BS; Juvenile Couns.; NYC Dept. of Juvenile Justice, 365 Broadway, New York, NY; r. 233 E. 176th St. #1B, Bronx, NY 10457, 718 583-4341. e-mail

OKRAH, Edward K.; '93 MA; BS Lehmann Clg. CUNY; Probation Ofcr.; NYC Dept. of Probation, 2-4 Nevins St., Brooklyn, NY 11217, 718 643-4881; r. POB 225, Baychester Sta., Bronx, NY 10469, 718 515-3223; *Geraldine;* Kwaku, Durell. e-mail

OLDS, Kevin D.; '83 BA; 231 Beach 127th St., Far Rockaway, NY 11694, 718 217-2293.

O'LEARY, Jeremiah J.; '76 MA; 443 Bement Ave., Staten Island, NY 10310.

O'LEARY, Joseph P.; '67 AS, '69 BS, '75 MPA; Ret. Lt./Supv. Investigative Svcs.; NYC Police Dept.-Internal Affairs Bur., Yonkers, NY 10702; r. 28 Alida St., Yonkers, NY 10704, 914 965-4349; *Concetta Ann;* Maureen A., Joseph A., Michael J., Michael A., Lisa A.

OLEKSA, James S.; '68 MS, '75 MPA; Dir. Security Florida; American Express Co., 3230 W. Commercial Blvd. #350, Ft. Lauderdale, FL 33309, 954 777-3201; r. 18229 103rd Tr. S, Boca Raton, FL 33498, 561 487-0579; *Helen.*

OLENDER, Dennis J.; '83 MA; 485 Darlington Ave., Staten Island, NY 10309, 718 317-1661.

OLENDER, Ronald W.; '75 MPA; 8328 Paseo Vista Dr., Las Vegas, NV 89128.

OLESKOWICZ, John F.; '83 BA; Special Agt.; US Dept. of Justice/Oig, 500 W. Madison, Ste. 3510, Chicago, IL 60661, 312 886-7050; r. 2524 Wild Timothy Rd., Naperville, IL 60564, 630 922-0206; *Deborah;* Daniel, Nicholas, Kathryn.

OLGA, Testa; 97-17 Eckford Ave., Ozone Park, NY 11417.

OLIJNYK, Steven A.; '95 AS; 22416 92nd Ave., Queens Vlg., NY 11428, 718 468-6871.

OLINTO, Luigi T.; '93 MA; 248 Graff Ave., Bronx, NY 10465.

OLIPHANT-CUMMINGS, H.; '82 BA; 1022 Barbey St., Brooklyn, NY 11207, 718 566-1861.

O'LIVARES, Elizabeth; '85 BS; 725 W. 172 St. #4, New York, NY 10032.

OLIVARES, Esther; '93 BS; 965 Tinton Ave. Apt. 18, Bronx, NY 10456, 718 617-9832.

OLIVARES, Flor E.; '98 BA; Correctional Ofcr.; Fed. Bur. of Prisons, 150 Park Row, New York, NY 10007, 212 240-9656; r. 1024 Walton Ave., 2D, Bronx, NY 10452, 718 588-2834.

OLIVER, Brenda L.; '84 BS; 1106 Prospect Pl., Brooklyn, NY 11213, 718 743-7643.

OLIVER, Cynthia A.; 2555 E 12th St. #3H, Brooklyn, NY 11235, 718 748-1333.

OLIVER, James H.; '76 BS; Retired; r. 1465 Hooksett Rd, #119, Hooksett, NH 03106, 603 485-2226.

OLIVER, Jennifer M.; '81 BA; 81 E 42 St., Brooklyn, NY 11203, 718 369-7976.

OLIVER, Paul S.; '95 BS; 13012 178th Pl., Jamaica, NY 11434, 718 341-4423.

OLIVER, Thompson; 7845 West Blvd., Inglewood, CA 90305, 310 532-0371.

OLIVERA, Tonia C.; '96 BA; 75 Hawthorne St., Apt. 4K, Brooklyn, NY 11225, 718 940-0416.

OLIVERAS, Mrs. Daisy I.; '95 BA; Mgr.; Clean Right Ctr., 48-03 69th St. Woodside, Woodside, NY 11377, 718 478-0690; r. 67-12 48th Ave., Woodside, NY 11377, 718 429-1335; *Raul;* Henry, Shaun, Adam, Tahlia. e-mail

OLIVERAS, Mary G.; '90 BS; 400 W 19th St. Apt. 2f, New York, NY 10011.

OLIVIERI, Richard; '73 BS; 29 Brookfield Ave., Staten Island, NY 10308, 718 356-0838.

OLIVO, Evelyn; '93 BS; 1631 67th St. N Apt. 340, St. Petersburg, FL 33710.

OLIVO, Jose; '97 BS; 1662 Parker St., Bronx, NY 10462, 718 716-3414.

OLIVO, Xavier F.; '68 BS; 10 Martense Ct., Brooklyn, NY 11226, 718 388-9398.

OLIVO-PEREZ, Sharon L.; '95 AS, '99 BA; Police Ofcr.; NYPD, 49th Precinct, Bronx, NY 10461, 718 918-2014; r. 7 Bernard Rd., Patterson, NY 12563, 914 278-6924.

OLLA, Philip A.; '79 BS; 3 Midland Gdns, Apt. 3H, Bronxville, NY 10708, 914 779-8214.

OLLEY, Donald E.; '82 BS; 14 Wilbur St., Yonkers, NY 10704.

O'LOANE, Daniel R.; '71 BA, '75 MA; Retired Financial Cnslt.; Metropolitan Life; r. 19 Branch Ln., Levittown, NY 11756, 516 433-6063; *Winford (Dec);* Diana, Daniel, Caroline.

O'LOONEY, Cara E. '92 (See Anastasopoulos, Mrs. Cara E.).

O'LOUGHLIN, Dennis; '87 MPA; 3 Crescent Pl., Monroe, NY 10950.

OLPE, Richard W.; '78 BS; 10 Shrub Hollow Rd, Roslyn, NY 11576, 516 747-3699.

OLSEN, Anton K.; '86 AS, '88 BA; 7915 154th St., Flushing, NY 11367, 718 229-4569.

OLSEN, Edward H.; '74 BA; 3840 Debra Ct., Seaford, NY 11783.

OLSEN, Dr. Francis B.; '74 BA; DDS SUNY at Stony Brook, MPA LIU CW Post Clg.; Sr. VP; Hip Health Plan, 7 W. 34th St., New York, NY 10001, 212 630-8642; r. 21 Oakfield Rd, St. James, NY 11780, 631 584-7313; *Angela;* Jeffrey, Ryan. e-mail

OLSEN, Gary J.; '76 BA; 40 Paladino Ave. Apt. 6c, New York, NY 10035, 212 534-2164.

OLSEN, Steven; '89 BS; 165 88th St., Brooklyn, NY 11209, 718 833-1592.

OLSEN, Thomas J.; '76 BA; 251 89th St., Brooklyn, NY 11209, 718 486-5799.

OLSSON, Christopher; '82 BS; 604 Oak St., Bellmore, NY 11710.

OLSSON, Eugene C.; '72 BS; 7 Acron Terrece, New City, NY 10956.

OLU-TALABI, Akinwole; '92 BS, '97 MPA, '99; 238-28 148th Dr., Rosedale, NY 11422.

OMAHONY, Brian E.; '91 BS; 42 Brighton 4th Co, Brooklyn, NY 11235, 718 871-1652.

OMAR, Abubakar O.; '87 MA; 647 S. Second S, Plainfield, NJ 07060.

OMOTAYO, Nixon O.; '84 BS; AA Bronx Community Clg.; Tax Fraud Investigator/Supv./IALEIA; NYC Dept. of Finance, 25 Elm Pl., 4th Fl., Fraud Investigation Bureau, Brooklyn, NY 11201, 718 260-0541; r. 665 E. 181st St., Apt. 2F, Bronx, NY 10457, 718 364-7145; Anuoluwapo. e-mail

O'NEIL, Robert F.; '70 BS, '71 MA; Cnslt.; r. 445 E. 14th St. Apt.#11, New York, NY 10009, 212 353-2225. e-mail

O'NEILL, Angelo L.; '97 BA, '98 BA; MSW NYU; MBA Candidate/Social Worker; Maimonides Med. Ctr., 979 48th St., Brooklyn, NY 11219, 718 283-8334; r. 625 E 2nd St., Brooklyn, NY 11218, 718 541-6396.

O'NEILL, Edward F.; '75 MPA; 255 No Ridge St., Port Chester, NY 10573, 914 273-3783.

O'NEILL, Eugene F.; '77 MA; PHD Fordham; Chief Hearing Ofcr.; New Jersey Dept. of Corrections; r. 402 Sharon Ct., Woodbridge, NJ 07095, 609 292-9240.

O'NEILL, James; '75 BS; 2466 Loft Ave., Baldwin, NY 11510, 516 378-3050.

O'NEILL, James P.; '88 BA, '93 MPA; NYPD, New York, NY; r. 10 Forestdale Ave., Monroe, NY 10950, 914 783-1020.

O'NEILL, John P.; '92 MPAIG, '98 MS; AAS, BS St. Francis Clg.; Sr. Court Ofcr.; NYS Supreme Ct., 60 Centre St. Rm. 542 Capt Ofc., New York, NY 10007, 212 374-8537; r. 419 E 93rd St. Apt. 1A, New York, NY 10128, 212 831-3488.

ONEILL, John P.; '91 MPA, '98 MS; AAS, BS St. Francis Clg.; Law Enforcement; New York State Supreme Ct, 60 Centre St., New York, NY 10007; r. 419 E. 93rd St. #1A, New York, NY 10128, 212 831-3488.

O'NEILL, John T.; '76; 1608 Third Ave., New York, NY 10028.

O'NEILL, Mark L.; '78 BS; 207 1/2 Elm Ave., # 2, Bogota, NJ 07603, 201 843-2419.

ONG, Johnny H.; '88 BS; Ten Confucius Plz., New York, NY 10002.

ONODU, Benjamin; '94 BA; MSW Adelphi Univ.; Domestic Violence Cnslt.; NYC Dept. of Social Svcs., New York, NY 10038, 212 331-4546; r. 97-05 Horace Harding Expy., Corona, NY 11368, 718 271-3289.

ONUFRAK, Stephen P.; '81 BS; 94 Nassau Ave., # 98, Brooklyn, NY 11222.

ONUKOGU, Ignatius J.; '91 BS; 11924 171st St., Jamaica, NY 11434.

ONWUCHEKWA, Chidinma '86 (See Mahamah, Chidinma).

ONWUKA, Nelson O.; '98 BA; Couns.; Metropolitan Jewish Health Syst.; r. 271 Putnam Ave., Brooklyn, NY 11216, 917 509-6234.

ONYEOBIA, Kelechi; '95 BA; Real Estate Rep.; Mid-State Mgmt., 97-77 Queens Blvd., Ste. 102, Rego Park, NY 11374, 718 575-4726; r. 2763 Reservoir Ave., Bronx, NY 10468, 718 601-1856. e-mail

O' OKPARA, Innocent; '96 MPA; 105-34 171Street Pl., Jamaica, NY 11433, 718 523-4537.

OPPEDISANO, Eileen C.; 67-09 61 Rd, Flushing, NY 11379.

OPPONG, Martin D.; '76 BS; POB 8666, Accra N., Ghana.

OQUEND, Madeline M.; '82 BS; 116-11 157 St. #1A, Jamaica, NY 11434.

OQUENDO, Olivet; '99 BS; Claims Asst.; SBLI Mutual Life Ins. Co. of NY, 460 W. 34th St., New York, NY 10001; r. 360 Neckar Ave., First Fl., Staten Island, NY 10304, 718 816-8478.

OQUENDO, Vivian L.; '93 BA, '97 MA; MA; Exec. Asst.; Morgan Stanley Dean Witter, 1585 Broadway, New York, NY 10036, 315 798-8895; r. 810 27th Ave. Apt. 109, Long Island City, NY 11102; *Carlos Rodriguez;* Racine Lee. e-mail

ORANGEO, Andrew D.; '75 BA; 855 Swinton Ave., Bronx, NY 10465.

ORDONEZ, Julio C.; '97 BS, '98 BS; 30-42 91st St., E. Elmhurst, NY 11369, 718 821-1990.

OREFICE, Michael L.; '75 BA; AA Staten Island Community; Retired-NYC Corrections Ofcr.; NYC Dept. of Corrections; r. 1578 83rd St., Brooklyn, NY 11228, 718 331-0567; *Rosanne;* Michael, Jennifer.

O'REILLY, John; '92 BA, '92 MPA; Bronx Bureau Commissioner; NYC Dept. of Sanitation, 800 E. 176th St., Bronx, NY 10460, 718 901-1295; r. 8 Mina Dr., Wappingers Falls, NY 12590; *Donna Maria;* Sean, Meaghan, Liam.

O'REILLY, John P.; '96 MAPUBAD; JD HON NY Law Sch.; Former NY Police Ofcr.; Atty.; r. 129 Main St. Unit B-12, Cornwall, NY 12518; Heather.

O'REILLY, Thomas C.; '76 MA; BA Kean Clg., AS Thomas Edison Clg.; Chief of Police Retired; Newark Police Dept., 31 Green St., Newark, NJ 07102; r. 161 Norman Rd, Newark, NJ 07106, 973 374-6767.

O'REILLY, Thomas V.; '76 BS; Retired Police; r. 2691 Runyon Cir., Orlando, FL 32837, 407 851-5661; *Frances.*

ORELLANA, Alfonso J.; '90 BS; 267 Grant Ave., Brooklyn, NY 11208, 718 235-2275.

OREN, Itzhak; '84 MA; 159 Longwood Ave., Brookline, MA 02446.

ORENDER, Patrick; 52 Quinlan Ave., Staten Island, NY 10314.

ORENDER, Patrick E.; '98 BS; US Customs Inspector; US Customs Dept. of Treas., Newark, NJ 07114; r. 52 Quinlan Ave., Staten Island, NY 10314. e-mail

ORGAN, Mrs. Miriam; '95 BA; AA NYI of Dietetics, MED Malcolm King Clg.; Owner; Organ Production, 90 Amsterdam Ave., New York, NY 10023, 212 247-3443; r. POB 231272, Ansonia, NY 10023, 212 757-7503; John, Denise, Tarvaris, Derrick, Tarsha, Miriam Jr., Michael.

ORGIAS, Peter D.; '94 BS; 22 E 58th St., Brooklyn, NY 11203, 718 346-5162.

ORICOLI, Anthony C.; 989 Grundy Ave., Holbrook, NY 11741.

ORLANDELLA, Sandra M., (Sandra M. Rodriguez); '95 BA; Police Ofcr.; New York Police Dept.; r. 65 Bogota St., Staten Island, NY 10314, 718 370-2166; *Michael;* Michael Jr. e-mail

ORLANDO, Dominic; '91 BS; 1433 74th St., Brooklyn, NY 11228, 718 331-2233.

ORLANDO, Robert A.; '95 MS; 428 Preston Ave., Staten Island, NY 10312, 718 948-3799.

ORLICH, Joseph A.; '73 BA; 49 Cord Pl., E. Norwich, NY 11732.

ORLICK, Harvey A.; '78 MPA, BS; Lt.; NYC Police Dept., 1 Edgewater Plz., Staten Island, NY 10305; r. 117 Rockville Ave., Staten Island, NY 10314, 718 698-6730; *Linda.* e-mail

O'ROURKE, Brian; '88 BS; 344 Roslyn Ave., Carle Place, NY 11514.

O'ROURKE, John J.; '75 BS; AA New York Technical Clg; Retired Chief of Dept.; New York Fire Dept.; r. 1892 Park Dr., Seaford, NY 11783, 516 679-8158.

OROURKE, Rosemarie K.; '99; 400 E. 20th St. Mc, New York, NY 10009, 212 460-9462.

O'ROURKE, Stacey M.; '98 BS; Police Ofcr.; Yonkers Police Dept., 104 S. Broadway, Yonkers, NY 10701, 914 377-7900; r. 58 Ramsey Ave., Yonkers, NY 10701, 914 963-2292. e-mail

O'ROURKE, Tara A.; '96 BS; JD Hofstra Univ. Sch. of Law; Atty. Labor & Employment; r. 36 Melrose Ave., E. Northport, NY 11731, 631 261-6499.

O'ROURKE, William J.; '67 BS, '71 MS; AA City Clg.; Ret. Asst. Prof., Criminal Justice; Cnty. Clg. of Morris/Secretary, Public Saftey-Govenors Cabinet; r. 614 Loveville Rd, Apt. D5D, Hockessin, DE 19707, 302 235-5859; *Mary;* Betty O. Sweet, Kathi O. Dalton, Kevin P., JacquelineAnson. e-mail

OROZCO, Odalis; '96 BS, 2000 MA; Clinician; Boro Med. Psych Treatment Svcs., 2920 Avenue R Ste. 240, Brooklyn, NY 11229, 718 646-6288; r. 3064 Bailey Ave. Apt. 22, Bronx, NY 10463, 718 884-1602. e-mail

ORR, Beverley B.; '93 BA; 224-09 145th Ave., Rosedale, NY 11422.

ORRIOLA, Victor M.; '76 AS, '79 BA; Health Care Admin.; Hollis Park Manor Nursing Home, 191-06 Hillside Ave., Hollis, NY 11423, 718 479-1010; r. 155 W. 68th St. Apt. 1012, New York, NY 10023, 212 769-2226; *Lisa;* Victor Jr. e-mail

ORTA, Aileen D.; '92 BS; 4821 Avenue O, Brooklyn, NY 11234, 718 265-1056.

ORTA, Harry H.; '79 BS; 20 Nevins St., Brooklyn, NY 11217, 718 265-1056.

ORTEGA, Corinne N.; '95 MA; 1025 A St. 1, Lincoln, NE 68502.

ORTEGA, Jessica; '99 BA; US Marshal; United States Marshals; r. 3418 Gates Pl. #5B, Bronx, NY 10467, 718 231-6917.

ORTEGA, Maritza; '99 BA; Secy.; St. Vincent Hosp./Rape Crisis Prog., 4151 University Pl. 9th Fl., New York, NY 10003, 212 609-8068; r. 428 W 26th St., New York, NY 10001, 212 255-3345.

ORTEGA, Mauricio; '92 BS; 164 Manhattan Ave., Brooklyn, NY 11206, 718 437-4839.

ORTEGA, Shirley L.; '99; 2841 Harrington Ave., Bronx, NY 10461, 718 901-2934; Julean Dejesus.

ORTEGA-VELIZ, Olga; '99 BA; 1042 45th Street#4A, Brooklyn, NY 11219, 718 851-4603.

ORTIZ, Alex; '98 BA; Private Investigator; Benchmark Intl., POB 12416, Hauppauge, NY 11788, 631 952-7070; r. 47 Tree Rd., Centereach, NY 11720, 631 981-8462.

ORTIZ, Amador P.; '96 BS; Police Ofcr.; NYCPD; One Police Plz., New York, NY 10038; r. 57-34 134th St., Flushing, NY 11355. e-mail

ORTIZ, Anne M.; '75 BA; RN; First Step of Sarasota; r. 4800 Rilma Ave., Apt. 138, Sarasota, FL 34234, 941 358-8803. e-mail

ORTIZ, Carlos E.; '97 BA; 2166 Frederick Douglass Blvd. Apt 4G, New York, NY 10026, 315 738-7044.

ORTIZ, Carolina M.; '95 MA; 209 Division Ave., Massapequa, NY 11758, 516 797-9305.

ORTIZ, Christopher W.; '97 BA; 1 Westfield Pl.Glen, Glen Cove, NY 11542.

ORTIZ, Dawn; '97 BS; 1690 Ralph Ave., Apt. 1B, Brooklyn, NY 11236, 718 243-2148.

ORTIZ, Edwin; '96 AS; 7967 68th Rd # 2, Flushing, NY 11379, 718 297-7325.

ORTIZ, Elizabeth; '85 BA; 225 Eastern Pkwy., Brooklyn, NY 11238, 718 235-1539.

ORTIZ, Janet; '96 BS; AAS Hostos Community Clg.; Paralegal; Gutman, Mintz, Baker, Sonnenfeldt PC, 813 Jericho Tpk., 1118 Grand Concourse, Bronx, NY 10456, 516 775-7007; r. 355 E 143rd St., Apt. 3E, Bronx, NY 10454, 718 402-4672; *Carols;* Carlos, Crystal, Christian. e-mail

ORTIZ, Johnny; '92 BS; 155 Wortman Ave. # 5, Brooklyn, NY 11207, 718 348-4571.

ORTIZ, Joseph A.; '89 BA; 2042 Webster Ave., Bronx, NY 10457, 718 239-2747.

ORTIZ, Maria; '98 BS; 138 Sneden Pl. W., Spring Vly., NY 10977, 914 425-4596. e-mail

ORTIZ, Marilyn; '90 BS; Prog. Supv.; Argus Community-Access II Prog., 760 E 160th St., Bronx, NY 10456, 718 401-5715; r. 3125 Park Ave. #5A, Bronx, NY 10451.

ORTIZ, Mario; '93 BA; 371a Union St. Bsmt, Brooklyn, NY 11231, 718 636-6229.

ORTIZ, Michael A.; '97 BS, '98 BS; 482 Pennyfield Ave., Bronx, NY 10465, 718 653-6366.

ORTIZ, Oscar J.; '93 BS; 1154 Elder Ave. # A1, Bronx, NY 10472, 718 933-4013.

ORTIZ, Raymond; '90 BA; 265 Livonia Ave. #2, Brooklyn, NY 11212, 718 694-0301.

ORTIZ, Col Rene P., USMC; '75 BS; MA Pepperdine Univ., MS Nav. Postgrad. Sch.; Pentagon, Washington, DC 20380, 202 703-6141; r. 1113 Richmond Ave., Stafford, VA 22554, 540 659-9492; *Michelle;* Paul, Stephanie. e-mail

ORTIZ, Ricardo L.; '97 BA; 805 Avenue O #D-1, Brooklyn, NY 11226, 718 694-0301.

ORTIZ, Silvia T.; '95 BA; 3215 79th St. Ph, Flushing, NY 11370, 718 835-4461.

ORTIZ, Yolanda; '99 BS MA; Therapist; Father Flanagan's Boys Town, 525 Dean St., Brooklyn, NY 11217, 718 636-3110; r. 473 Bayridge Ave. 3/Fl., Brooklyn, NY 11220, 718 748-4702; Carlos, Jessica. e-mail

ORTIZ, Yolanda R.; '87 BS; 1762 Story Ave. Apt. 5c, Bronx, NY 10473, 718 933-4013.

ORTIZ-BENJAMIN, Maira; '96 MPA; BA Neumann College; Fiscal Ofcr.; Kings Bridge Heights Community Ctr., 2851 University Ave., Bronx, NY 10463, 718 884-0700; r. same, 718 884-6773; Andres.

ORTIZ-CRUZ, Milagros; '89 BA; 1225 Fdr Dr. Apt. 2d, New York, NY 10009.

ORTIZ ORTIZ, Ana M.; '79 BA; JD Rutgers Law Sch.-Newark; Atty.; Smith & Abbott, New York, NY 10001; r. 1926 Obrien Ave., Bronx, NY 10473, 718 542-1496; Solangel, Sonali.

ORTLIEB, Robert J.; '89 AS, '91 BS; 2200 Connell Ter., Baldwinsville, NY 13027, 315 638-0849.

ORTMAN, Kathleen E.; '96 MA; 393 W 49th St., Apt. 5Nn, New York, NY 10019.

ORTOLANO, Lisa; '87 BS; JD New York Law Sch.; Asst. DA; Bronx Dist. Attorney's Ofc., 215 E. 161st St., Bronx, NY 10451, 718 590-2000; *John;* Kacey.

ORUKPE, Frank; '85 MA; 476 W 144th St., New York, NY 10031.

ORZILLO, Kelly S.; '99 BA; AA Union Cnty. Clg.; Paralegal Corp. Law; Cleary, Gottlieb, Steen & Hamilton, 1 Liberty Plz., New York, NY 10006, 212 225-3693; r. 215 Brightwood Ave., Westfield, NJ 07090, 973 751-8903. e-mail

OSAMWONYI, Joseph I.; '96 MA, '96 BS; PhD Walden Univ.; CEO/Pres.; Celebrity Investigative Agcy., 295 McLaws Cir., Ste. 3, Williamsburg, VA 23185, 757 258-5466; r. 100 Douglas Dr., Williamsburg, VA 23185, 757 258-3604; *Eleanor;* Adesuwa, Gibril, Precious, Kevin, LaChelle. e-mail

OSATTIN, Philip; '87 MA; 83-09 Talbot St., Kew Gardens, NY 11415.

OSBORNE, Kimberly M.; '99 BS, '99 AS; Protection Ofcr.; Fed. Reserve Bank of NY; r. 3571 Nostrand Ave., Brooklyn, NY 11229, 718 648-8399; Terrell Diggins, Tyree Bell.

OSBOURNE, Cherryann; '97 BS; 529 Beach 65th St., Arverne, NY 11692.

OSCHMANN, Edward J.; '81 AS; 4271 Kepler Ave., Bronx, NY 10470, 718 324-4317.

OSENI, Yetunde A.; '99 BS; POB 41, Brooklyn, NY 11224.

O'SHAUGHNESSY, Jeremiah; '87 MPA; 3804 Garden Ct., Peekskill, NY 10566, 914 736-3646.

O'SHEA, Kevin J.; '79 MA; 4 Ruth Pl., Glen Head, NY 11545.

O'SHEA, Thomas F.; '75 BA; 317 Beach 101st St., Far Rockaway, NY 11694, 718 897-8301.

O'SHEA, Timothy J.; '76 BS; 521 Woodbine Ln., Lakewood, NJ 08701, 732 905-5741.

OSIDELE, Solomon O.; '93 BS, '96 MPA; 1261 Schenectady A, Brooklyn, NY 11203.

OSLYN, Morris; '64 MA; 3308 22nd St. N, Arlington, VA 22201.

OSORIO, Theodore P.; '82 BA; 245 E Gunhill Rd, Bronx, NY 10467, 718 655-7224.

OSORIO, Uti; '94 BS; 301 Cathedral Park, New York, NY 10026.

OSPINA, Leonard; '91 MA; 13 Union St., Briarcliff Manor, NY 10510, 914 762-7319.

OSROFF, Peter H.; '81 BA, '83 MA; 337 Barwick Blvd., Mineola, NY 11501.

OSSA, Magda S.; '82 BA; 140-08 28 Rd #1C, Flushing, NY 11354.

OSSEN, Helen S.; '83 MPA; 2533 Batchelder St., Brooklyn, NY 11235.

OSSO, Gary; '82 BS; 18 Coe Pl., Huntington Sta., NY 11746.

OSSOHOU, Andre A.; '98 MA; MAS Columbia Law Sch.; Legal Coord.; NYC Dept. of Corrections, New York, NY 10001; r. POB 8001, New York, NY 10116, 212 743-7064; *Marie;* Andre Jr., Jessica Gonti.

OSTRANDER, Anthony (Tony) S.; '99 BS; US Bail Enforcement Agt.; Five Star Recoveries, POB 467, Poughkeepsie, NY 12602, 914 473-3809; r. 16 Pine Echo Dr., 118 Bermuda Blvd., Poughkeepsie, NY 12601, 914 473-1148; *Janaira Sosa-Ostrander.* e-mail

OSTROWSKI, Eugene; '78 BS; 5348 73rd St., Flushing, NY 11378.

OSTROWSKI, Greg T.; '97 BS; 102-18 81 St., Ozone Park, NY 11416.

OSUAGWU, Emeka; '90 BS; 9530 Kings Hwy., Brooklyn, NY 11212, 718 385-6754.

O'SULLIVAN, Christopher G.; '77 BS; Capt. Firefighter; FDNY; r. 4226 Napier Ave., Bronx, NY 10470, 718 994-2371.

O'SULLIVAN, Kevin M.; '99 BA; Law Student; St. John's Sch. of Law, 8000 Utopia Pkwy., Jamaica, NY 11439, 718 990-6403; r. 22-49 23 St., Astoria, NY 11105, 718 204-2352.

O'SULLIVAN, Marie; '94 BA; 828 E 228th St., Bronx, NY 10466, 718 863-9309.

O'SULLIVAN, Thomas F.; '75 BA; NYC Law Dept.; r. 52 Tudor City Pl., New York, NY 10017.

OTERO, Mildred; '94 BS; 2830 Briggs Ave. # 2, Bronx, NY 10458, 718 798-6731.

OTERO, Victor E.; '92 BS; Sergeant; NYC Police Dept., 1 Police Plz., New York, NY 10038, 212 374-5000; r. 319 W 35th St. Apt. 3e, New York, NY 10001, 212 947-2018.

OTIS, David B.; '79 MA; 1482 Crown St., Wantagh, NY 11793.

OTTEN, Kimberly A.; '96 BA; 102 Regis Dr., Staten Island, NY 10314, 718 983-9075.

OTTEY, Ms. Donna M.; '86 BA; Legal Asst.; Kings Cnty. Dist. Atty., 350 Jay, Brooklyn, NY 11201; r. 838 E 51st St., Brooklyn, NY 11203, 718 451-2441; Kiandra, Franklin.

OTTO, Ms. Patricia C., (Patricia C. Meyers); '80 BA MA; JD NYU; VP; SBC Communications, 480 E. Swedesford Rd., Wayne, PA 19087, 610 995-5811; r. 1011 Meadow Crest Dr., POB 682, Kimberton, PA 19442, 610 983-9556; *Darryl.* e-mail

OTTOMANO, Anthony R.; '78 MA; 846 Jean Pl., Seaford, NY 11783, 516 796-1167.

OUTAR, Beverley; '97 BA; 99-03 195th St., Hollis, NY 11423.

OUTAR, Gail A.; '91 MA; 39 Lincoln Ave., Brooklyn, NY 11208, 718 235-6504.

OUTSEN, Gregory J.; '82 BS; 673 Brian Ln., Seaford, NY 11783, 516 735-1024.

OVALLES, Mildred L.; '85 BA; Fed. Ofcr.; US Pretrial Svcs., New York, NY 10001, 917 457-5713; r. 36 Bulwer Pl., Brooklyn, NY 11207, 718 827-1142.

OVANDO, Percida R.; '88 BA; Social Worker Hospital; Columbia Presbyterian Hosp., 622 W 168th, Social Work Deprt., New York, NY 10032, 212 305-5926; r. 2810 Olinville, Bronx, NY 10467, 718 798-1695.

OVCOLI, Anthony C.; 968 Grundy Ave., Holbrook, NY 11741.

OWENS, Kelly E.; '99 BS; Correctional Ofcr.; r. 54 Boerum St., Brooklyn, NY 11206, 718 388-6999.

OWENS, Sharon '81 (See Owens-Duff, Sharon A.).

OWENS, Veronica M.; '96 BA; 14148 183rd St., Jamaica, NY 11413, 718 276-3780. e-mail

OWENS-DUFF, Sharon A., (Sharon Owens); '81 BA; MASTERS Brooklyn Clg.; Tchr.; Jamaica HS, Gothic Dr. & 168th St., Jamaica, NY 11434; r. 13219 157th St., Jamaica, NY 11434; *Johnny Duff;* Sonna Owens, Jason Duff, Jamila Duff, Yohance Duff.

OWIE, Edwin; '96 BA; Sr. Case Mgr.; Citizens Advise Bur., 2064 Morris Ave., Bronx, NY 10465, 718 293-0727; r. 1714 Crotona Pk.E, Bronx, NY 10460, 718 328-3980.

OYEDIRAN, Jacob O.; '95 BS; 97-30 57th Ave. #3, Corona, NY 11368.

OYEWAYO, Olusade; '99 AS; 1309 5th Ave. 16h, New York, NY 10029, 212 722-7085; Tiphani, Izea.

OYIBO-EBIJE, A.; '93 BA; POB 976, Bronx, NY 10451.

OZUNA, Maria J.; '98 BA; 328 W 53 St. 2b, New York, NY 10019.

OZZANDAR, Engin; '96 AS, '97 BA; 25-22 Steinway Str, Long Island City, NY 11103.

P

PABON, Karen K.; '99; 78 E. 119 St. #4S, New York, NY 10035.

PABON, Lisa; '92 BS; 1031 Lorimer St. Apt. 11, Brooklyn, NY 11222, 718 345-5398.

PACCIONE, Jack; '80 BA; Firefighter; NYC, 221 E 75st, New York, NY 10021, 212 650-1412; r. 803 Katan Ave., Staten Island, NY 10312, 718 227-9176; Jack, Jennifer.

PACE, David R.; '99 BA; AAS Schenectady Cnty. Comm Cl; Emergency Med. Tech.; NYC Fire Dept.; r. 260 91st. St., Brooklyn, NY 11209, 718 680-4629.

PACE, Geoffrey M.; '85 BS; 104 16 47th Ave., Flushing, NY 11368, 718 426-9518.

PACE, Paul A.; '84 BS; Detective; NYC Police Dept., 1 Police Plz., Woodside, NY 11377, 718 898-3556; r. 5617 43rd Ave., Flushing, NY 11377, 718 898-3556; *Renee';* Michele, Marisa, Megan, Paul Jr. e-mail

PACELLA, Thomas A.; '82 BS; 6818 Vista Pl., Brooklyn, NY 11220.

PACHECO, Brunilda; '80 MA; 835 Walton Ave. #2, Bronx, NY 10451, 718 933-0284.

PACHECO, Jose A., Jr.; '76 BA; Supv Investigator; Ofc. of The Dist. Atty. Kings Cnty., 350 Jay St., Brooklyn, NY 11201, 718 250-2766; r. 2343 Valentine Ave. #3A, Bronx, NY 10458.

PACHECO, Lizandro; '86 BA; 15224 Northern Blvd., Flushing, NY 11354, 718 426-6603.

PACHECO, M. Yvette, Esq.; '91 BA; JD CUNY Sch. of Law; Queens Mgr.; BQ Minority Business Opportunity Ctr., 120-55 Queens Blvd. Ste. 309, Kew Gardens, NY 11424, 718 263-0546; r. 6 June Walk, Long Beach, NY 11561, 516 432-6574.

PACHECO, Marilyn I.; '97 BA; 45 Surrey Way, White Plains, NY 10607, 914 289-0740.

PACHECO, Richard; '80 BA; 105 Baruch Dr. Apt. 7a, New York, NY 10002.

PACHECO, Shirley A.; '81 BS; 159 E 106 St., New York, NY 10029.

PACKER, Catherine; '97 BA; 50 Manhattan Ave., Brooklyn, NY 11206.

PACKMAN, Miriam A.; '97 BS; MS Univ. of New Haven; 185 Bronx River Rd, Apt. H4, Yonkers, NY 10704. e-mail

PADILLA, Alfonso; '99 BA; 3 W. Farms Square Pl. #18D, Bronx, NY 10460, 718 328-2493.

PADILLA, Anthony; '92 BS; 2019 Watson Ave., Bronx, NY 10472, 718 220-6089.

PADILLA, Eric; '93 BS; 535 W 135th St. Apt. 4c, New York, NY 10031.

PADILLA, Joseph A.; '86 AS, '92 BS; 2476 Cambreleng Ave., Bronx, NY 10458, 718 796-2637.

PADILLA, Margarita M.; '96 MA, '96 BA; Med. Rsch. Coord.; Columbia Univ./NYSPL, 722 W. 168th St. Box 126, New York, NY 10032, 212 543-5956; r. 3226 Randall Ave., Bronx, NY 10465, 718 597-8536. e-mail

PADRON, Ms. Linette; '99 BA; Benjamin Cardozo Law Sch.; Sr. Editor; Bear Stearns, 245 Park Ave., New York, NY 10167, 212 272-3895; r. 440 W 34th St. Apt. 9D, New York, NY 10001, 914 237-2642; *David Naar*. e-mail

PADULA, Louis J.; '94 AS; 1149 72nd St., Brooklyn, NY 11228.

PAGAN, Antonio; '86 MA; BA Univ. of Puerto Rico, JD Univ. of Puerto Rico Law; Commissioner of NYC of Employment; NYC Dept. of Employment, 220 Church St., New York, NY 10013, 212 442-2157; r. POB 1047 Cooper Sta., New York, NY 10276.

PAGAN, Edwin R.; '90 BA; 888 Grand Concourse, Bronx, NY 10451, 718 665-5195.

PAGAN, Eledier; '83 MPA; 6227 99th St., Flushing, NY 11374, 718 784-1898.

PAGAN, Michele D.; '91 BS; Detective; Palm Beach Police Dept., 345 S. County Rd., Palm Bch., FL 33480, 561 838-5470; r. 1928 Circle Dr., N. Palm Bch., FL 33408, 561 627-2362. e-mail

PAGAN, Neal; '83 BS; 6227 99th St., Flushing, NY 11374, 718 740-4255.

PAGAN, Tina-marie, (Tina Marie Deliz); '92 BA; Resident Advisor; Community Base Correctional Facility, 614 462-4600; r. 803 Windy Hill Ln., Galloway, OH 43119. e-mail

PAGANI, Donald P.; '84 BA; Lt. NY City Police Dept.; 6th Precinct 233, 233 W 10th St., New York, NY 10014, 212 741-4811; r. 69 Tinker Hill Rd., Putnam Vly., NY 10579, 914 528-2744; *Regina;* Regina Lynn, Gerard, Maria, Charles.

PAGANO, Bruce L.; '79 BS; 14302 Watery Mt Ct., Centreville, VA 20120.

PAGANO, Ms. Marci, (Marci Rickman); '85 BA, '89 MPA; Police Ofcr.; NYC Police Dept., 1 Police Plz., New York, NY 10038, 212 374-5000; r. 1257 78 St., Brooklyn, NY 11228, 718 238-2906. e-mail

PAGANO, Richard J.; '76 BS; 84-31 60th Ave., Elmhurst, NY 11373.

PAGE, Lauren S.; '97 BS; 3 Franklin Ct., Northport, NY 11768, 631 757-9785.

PAGE, Shawnee; '87 BA; 48 Wheeler Ave., Warwick, NY 10990, 914 774-2607.

PAGE, CW2 Wallace (Wally) B., Ret.; '77 BS; Retired Police Ofcr; r. 3648 Donna St., Port Orange, FL 32119, 904 788-9562; *Hwa Cha;* Sonja, Lan, Whinifred. e-mail

PAGE-OKHIRIA, Carolyn D.; '97 BA; 1475 Sheridan Ave., Bronx, NY 10457.

PAGLINO, Joseph R.; '97 MA; BS St. John's Univ.; Cnty. Detective; Monmouth Cnty. Prosecutors Ofc., 132B Jerseyville Ave., Freehold, NJ 07728, 732 409-7535; r. POB 304, Adelphia, NJ 07710. e-mail

PAGLIUGHI, Kathleen; '81 BS; Regional Dir. of Stores; Kids R Us, 333 N Central Ave., Hartsdale, NY 10530, 914 683-1270; r. 1552 Laurel Hollow Rd, Laurel Hollow, NY 11791, 516 662-6546.

PAHMAN, Marina; '99 BS; Paralegal; Law Offices of Alexis Ravitch, 1920 86th St., Brooklyn, NY 11214, 718 837-7747; r. 167 Pembroke St., Brooklyn, NY 11235, 718 646-3560.

PAIGE, Dorothy M.; '84 BS; Retired Postal Carrier; UPS; r. 85 Crooke Ave. Apt. 16, Brooklyn, NY 11226, 718 469-7550; Patricia, Michael, Lissette, Raven Olivia.

PAIGE, Jodi W.; '98 BS; Morgan Melhvish Monaghan, et al, 39 Broadway, 35th Fl., New York, NY 10006, 212 809-1111; r. 92 Vancortland Pk S., 9d, Bronx, NY 10463, 718 796-7604. e-mail

PAIGE, John J.; '77 MA; 306 Roosevelt Ave., Hasbrouck Hts., NJ 07604.

PAIK, Min K.; '96 BA; 327 Lincoln Ave., Ft. Lee, NJ 07024, 201 944-4259.

PAITAKIS, Terry; '92 BS; 13315 Hawtree St., Jamaica, NY 11417.

PAJOOH, Rudolph R.; '95 BA; 45 Overlook Ter. Apt. 6J, New York, NY 10033, 212 740-6533.

PALATNIK, Victoria D.; '97 BA; AA Kingsborough Comm. Clg.; Caseworker; Children's Svcs., 150 William St., New York, NY 10038, 212 341-3202; r. 1725 80th St., Brooklyn, NY 11214, 718 234-8766.

PALAU, Luis A.; '75 BS; 89-19 238th St., Bellerose, NY 11426.

PALAZZO, Thomas J.; '93 BS, '97 MA; AAS Queensborough Community; Dir. of Security; Bear Stearns, 245 Park Ave., New York, NY 10167, 212 272-4333; r. 45-05 Auburndale Ln., Flushing, NY 11358, 718 445-5806; Joanne, Peter. e-mail

PALAZZOLO, Florence F.; '78 BA; 2529 Newtown Ave., Long Island City, NY 11102.

PALAZZOTO, Diane; '80 BA; 339 W. 71st. St., Apt. #4, New York, NY 10023.

PALEGA, Paul K.; '97 BS, '98 BS; 3763 Dianne St., Bethpage, NY 11714, 516 735-8725.

PALERMO, Mario E.; '78 BA, '82 MA; 581 W Chester Ave., Bronx, NY 10455, 718 409-9243.

PALESANO, George J.; '91 BS; Lt.; NYC Police Dept., 1 Police Pl., New York, NY 10038; r. 7 F Signs Rd., Staten Island, NY 10314, 718 698-4499. e-mail

PALICIA, Deborah L.; '90 BS, '95 MA; US Pretrial Svcs. Ofcr.; US Pretrial Svcs., 50 Walnut St. Rm. 1018, POB 20240, Newark, NJ 07101, 973 645-2230; r. 146 Lincoln Park Rd, Pequannock, NJ 07440, 973 633-0953. e-mail

PALILLO, Ann '90 (See Palillo-Hoey, Ann).

PALILLO-HOEY, Ann, (Ann Palillo); '90 MA; Deputy Inspector Gen.; New York State Inspector General's Ofc., 1 Park Ave., New York, NY 10016, 212 447-1311; r. 4360 Douglaston Pk, Douglaston, NY 11363, 718 335-5976.

PALLADINO, James M.; '75 MPA; POB 141, Verona, NJ 07044.

PALLADINO, Marie A.; '95 BA; Licensed Dog Groomer/Animal Rescue; Marie A. Palladino, New York, NY 10011; r. 237 W. 14th St., New York, NY 10011, 212 242-0038. e-mail

PALLONETTI, John R.; '78 MA; BS Fordham Univ.; VP; C&C Catering Svcs., 7719 18th Ave., Brooklyn, NY 11214, 718 232-2800; r. 19 Mallow St., Staten Island, NY 10309, 718 356-1519.

PALMER, Donald E.; '73 BA, '76 MA; Prof.; Union Cnty. Clg., Criminal Justice, Cranford, NJ 07016, 908 709-7566; r. 54 Sherman St., Brooklyn, NY 11215, 718 499-9053; *Patricia;* Carolyn, Jennifer, Amy.

PALMER, Doreen O.; '97 BA; AA; Admin. Asst.; Interboro Inst., 450 W. 56th St., New York, NY 10019, 212 399-0091; r. 11125 Springfield Blvd., Queens Vlg., NY 11429, 718 479-1771.

PALMER, Eric T.; '85 BS; AS Nassau Comm Clg.; Union Carpenter; r. 2 Ridge Rd, Farmingdale, NY 11735, 516 433-5643.

PALMER, Lorrine R.; '98 BA; Fraud Investigator; NYC Dept. of Human Resources Admin.; r. 343 St. Nicholas Ave., Apt. 67, New York, NY 10027, 212 222-7923; *Carl;* Den White, Rosheda, Roshana. e-mail

PALMER, Nicole M.; '99 MA; 272 Ward Ave. #1F, Bordentown, NJ 08505, 609 452-7338.

PALMER, Robert A.; '84 BA; 677 Georgia Ave., Brooklyn, NY 11207, 718 462-2757.

PALMER, Virginia L.; '90 BS; Corrections Ofcr.; City of NY Corrections, 0909 Hazen St., E. Elmhurst, NY 11370, 718 546-2020; r. 215 Rochester Ave., Brooklyn, NY 11213, 718 756-1822.

PALMERI, LT Nicholas R.; '79 BS; Police Lt.; Baltimore Police Dept., 601 E. Fayette St., Baltimore, MD 21202, 410 396-2621; r. 3714 Parkhurst Way, Nottingham, MD 21236. e-mail

PALMISANO, Nicholas A.; '98 MA; 12 Fuller Ave., Piscataway, NJ 08854, 732 985-2523.

PALOZZOLA, Joseph R.; '90 AS, '91 BA; 212 W. 22 St., New York, NY 10011.

PALUMBO, Bill; '96 AS; CERT. Hofstra Univ.; Paralegal; Franchina & Giordano PC, 10001 Franklin Ave. Ste. 315, Garden City, NY 11530; r. 740 Pioneer Pl., W. Babylon, NY 11704. e-mail

PALUMBO, Peter J.; '77 AS; Retired Precinct Cdr.; NYC Police Dept.; r. 24 Balsam Ct., Wantagh, NY 11793, 516 221-6195; *Mildred.*

PALZA, Lyz '98 (See Collorafi, Mrs. Lyz S.).

PALZER, Lewis N.; 2756 Bouck Ave., Bronx, NY 10469, 718 882-3597.

PAN, Karen V.; '99 BA; 61-15 98th St. #10H, Rego Park, NY 11374, 718 592-8336.

PAN, Nanette; '90 BA; 6115 98th St. Apt. 10h, Flushing, NY 11374, 718 275-0504.

PANAGOPOULOS, Stilianos E.; '95 BS; 2056 26th St., Astoria, NY 11105.

PANAGOS, James W.; '91 BS; Actor (A.F.T.R.A.); r. 67-12 Yellowstone, Forest Hills, NY 11375, 718 897-0366.

PANAMA, Maritza B. '97 (See Quito, Mrs. Maritza B., NP).

PANARELLO, Gary R.; '76 BS; 111 Marshall Ave., Staten Island, NY 10314.

PANAZZOLO, Glenn P.; '84 BS; 138-71 St. #E9, Brooklyn, NY 11209.

PANCHAME, Allan G.; '94 BS; Police Ofcr.; Cobb Cnty. Police Dept., 140 N. Marietta Pkwy., Marietta, GA 30060, 770 499-3911; r. 2050 Austell Rd. Apt. Bb6, Marietta, GA 30008, 770 803-0267.

PANDOLFO, Edward P.; '79 AS, '80 BS; 4 Sagamore Ln., Dix Hills, NY 11746.

PANDOLFO, Peter J.; '78 BA; 6 Waterview Ln., Northport, NY 11768.

PANICO, Gene F.; '76 BS; 334 Singing Wood, Holbrook, NY 11741.

PANNELL, Derwin D.; '89 BA; 13030 Lefferts Blvd., Jamaica, NY 11420.

PANTHER, Shakira M.; '95 BA; 24210 131st Ave., Jamaica, NY 11422.

PANTING, Hilda C.; '94 BS; 611 W 156th St. Apt. 44, New York, NY 10032.

PANZARINO, Nicholas; '81 BS; 28 Putnam Ave., Valley Stream, NY 11580.

PAPACCIO, Charles J.; '80 BS; 3521 Ketha Hts., Festus, MO 63028, 636 937-1921.

PAPAGNI, Mary A.; '83 MA; 1586 208th Pl., Flushing, NY 11360, 718 224-3019.

PAPAMICHAEL, Norma; '86 BS; 6204 5th Ave., Brooklyn, NY 11220.

PAPAROZZI, Sandra M.; '82 BS; 3 Algonquin Dr., Cranford, NJ 07016.

PAPP, Robert J.; '97 BS; 509 Woodward Ave., Ridgewood, NY 11385, 718 386-2183.

PAPPALARDO, Vivian; '88 BA, '93 MPA; 604 College Ave., Staten Island, NY 10302.

PAPPAS, Chris L.; '81 MPA; S. Carrel Blvd., Oceanside, NY 11572, 516 678-4916.

PAPSON-ADAMS, David; '95 BS; MLS St. John's Univ., DIPLOMA Adelphi Univ.; Dir. of Info. Resources; Morrison, Cohen, Singer & Weinstein LLP, 750 Lexington Ave. 8th Fl., New York, NY 10022, 212 735-8815; r. 325 Westervelt Ave. Apt. 1l, Staten Island, NY 10301, 718 447-6996. e-mail

PAPURE, Gail; '85 MPA; 1559 E 3rd St., Brooklyn, NY 11230.

PARADISO, Michael; '98 BS; 74 Nelson Ave., Staten Island, NY 10308, 718 967-6876.

PARASKEVAS, Melissa; '88 BS; 45 Deppe Pl. Apt. C, Staten Island, NY 10303.

PARDESI, Guardial S.; '95 AS; 1374 York Ave., New York, NY 10021.

PAREDES, Graisy M.; '94 BA; 424 W 110th St. # 1, New York, NY 10025.

PAREDES, Josue; '76 AS; 9 Langdon St., Islip, NY 11751.

PAREDES, Ruth V.; '95 BA; Police Ofcr.; NYC; r. 225 Nichols Ave. Fl. 2, Brooklyn, NY 11208, 718 235-3018.

PARENTE, Richard A.; '79 BS; 4731 187th St., Flushing, NY 11358.

PARERA, Carolyn; '91 BS; 195 Victory Blvd. 3, Staten Island, NY 10301.

PARIKH, Pragati J.; '99 BS; 814 57 St. #2B, Brooklyn, NY 11220, 718 972-5308.

PARIS, David S.; '77 BS; 253-60 148 Rd, Rosedale, NY 11422, 516 483-8341.

PARIS, Jerome; '86 BS; 690 Prospect, Brooklyn, NY 11216, 718 398-5974.

PARISI, Domenico J.; '99 BS; AS Normandale Community Clg.; Paralegal; Kramer Levin Naftalis & Frankel, LLP; r. 10031 4th Ave. (#5H), Brooklyn, NY 11209, 718 491-0381.

PARK, Christine M.; '97 BA; 515 W. 59th St., New York, NY 10019, 315 896-6581.

PARK, Junkyu; '98 BS; 143-33 Sanford Ave. D4, Flushing, NY 11355, 718 353-0868.

PARK, Richard A.; '99 BS; Police Ofcr.; Prince William Cnty. Police Dept., POB 162, Aquebogue, NY 11931, 703 792-7200; r. 2901 Fox Lair Dr., Woodbridge, VA 22191, 703 441-8281. e-mail

PARKER, Calvin N.; '97 BS; Security Coord.; Clg. of New Rochelle Sr Co-op Campus, 755 Co-Op City Blvd., Bronx, NY 10475, 718 320-0300; r. 215 W. 2nd St., Mt. Vernon, NY 10550, 914 667-9885; Kevin, Gordon.

PARKER, Dieshia L.; '97 BS; Paralegal; McArter & English, One Riverfront Plz., Newark, NJ 07102, 973 622-7575; r. POB 101 Cathedral Sta., New York, NY 10025, 212 932-1769.

PARKER, George; '93 BS; 255 E 149th St. # 2, Bronx, NY 10451, 718 365-0085.

PARKER, James W.; '71 BA; 13033 229th St., Jamaica, NY 11413, 718 526-2074.

PARKER, Kim; '88 BS; 2021 Etting St., Baltimore, MD 21217.

PARKER, Lori V.; '90 BA; Administrative Mgr.; City of NY, Dept. of Human Resources, New York, NY 10001; r. 33 W. 130th St., New York, NY 10037, 212 690-1465.

PARKER, Matthew W.; '96 BA; 915 Surrey Dr., E. Meadow, NY 11554.

PARKER, Meryl L.; '86 BA, '93 MPA; 41 Newburgh St., Elmont, NY 11003, 516 223-2026.

PARKER, SGT Richard; '80 BA; 11826 225th St., Jamaica, NY 11411, 718 337-0911.

PARKER, Rodney K.; '82 BA; 13033 229th St., Jamaica, NY 11413, 718 337-0911.

PARKER, Sydney H.; '95 BA; 833 Penfield St., Bronx, NY 10470, 718 324-1696.

PARKER, Vanessa M.; '93 BA; 133 W. 138th St., New York, NY 10030, 315 733-5790.

PARKINS, Marcia D.; '97 BA; 3349 Dereimer Ave., Bronx, NY 10475.

PARKS, Bruce C.; '88 BS; POB 172, Keyser, WV 26726.

PARKS, Lanetta J.; '80 BA; 1535 University Ave., Bronx, NY 10453, 718 796-7905.

PARLANTI, Damiano; '94 BS; 2128 E. 8th St., Brooklyn, NY 11223, 718 336-7087.

PARLOW, James R.; '93 BS; 15 Herbert Ave., White Plains, NY 10606, 914 946-5520.

PARRA, Juan E.; '91 BS; Detective; NYPD, Police Plz., New York, NY 10038, 718 829-2690; Laura; Lauren, Andrea.

PARRA, Victoria E.; '93 BS; 4239 64th St., Flushing, NY 11377, 718 626-9807.

PARRALES, John T.; '96 BA; Investigator; r. 2732 Matthews Ave., Bronx, NY 10467, 718 519-9807.

PARRILLA, Steven J.; '78 BS; 133 Cortelyou Ave. Apt. 1-4, Staten Island, NY 10312, 718 398-6713.

PARRINELLO, Arthur J.; '76 BA; BS, AAS NYC Community Clg.; Deputy Chief; NYC Fire Dept., 1850 Clove Rd. Staten IInd 10304, 225 Broadway, New York, NY 10007, 212 293-9300; r. 12 Davis St., E. Rockaway, NY 11518, 516 593-3038; Helen; Arthur Jr., Lisa, Anthony, Gina. e-mail

PARRINO, Irene R.; '89 BS; 33 Woodhollow Rd, Albertson, NY 11507.

PARRINO, Joseph J.; '88 AS, '91 BS; 33 Woodhollow Rd, Albertson, NY 11507.

PARRIS, Cecilia G.; '89 BA; 1252 Chisholm St., Bronx, NY 10459, 718 652-5145.

PARRIS, Cherylann P.; '94 BS, '97 MA; Fraud Investigator; Ofc. of Revenue & Investigations; r. 130 Pelham Rd. 6f, New Rochelle, NY 10805, 914 235-7913.

PARRIS, Cyril J.; '84 BS; 1410 E 105th St. Apt. 1, Brooklyn, NY 11236, 718 209-4332.

PARRIS, David Mosa E.; '98 BA; 111-59 178th Pl., St. Albans, NY 11433, 718 949-6833.

PARRIS, Jerome R.; '86 BS; Proj. Estimator Engr.; Penguin Air Conditioning Corp., 26 West St., Brooklyn, NY 11222, 718 706-6500; r. 690 Prospect Pl. Apt. #5, Brooklyn, NY 11216, 718 398-8079.

PARRIS, Marie N.; '93 BS; Claim Mgr.; NYC Controllers Ofc., 1 Center St., New York, NY 10007; r. 130-02 130th St., S. Ozone Park, NY 11420, 718 760-2123; Dara.

PARRIS, Stacey A.; '94 BA; JD, MA Queens Clg.; 24 W Marshall Dr., Poughkeepsie, NY 12601, 914 471-8370.

PARRISH, David; '99 BS; AS Nassau Clg.; Loss Prevention Rep.; Greater New York Mutual Ins. Co., 200 Madison Ave., New York, NY 10016, 212 683-9700; r. 53 Atlantic Ave., Massapequa Park, NY 11762, 516 795-4273.

PARRISH, John F.; '76 BS; 33 1/2 Union Ave., E. Rutherford, NJ 07073.

PARRY, Lesroy T.; '98 BS; Police Ofcr.; NYPD, 2877 Berkley Ave., Bronx, NY 10465, 718 822-5411; r. 1252 W. Farms Rd #3d, Bronx, NY 10459, 718 991-1323. e-mail

PARSONS, Adrienne D.; '83 BS; 41-14 Vernon Blvd., Long Island City, NY 11101, 718 712-0399.

PARSONS, Ronald D.; '87 BA; 290 Clinton Ave. #3, Brooklyn, NY 11205, 718 492-4120.

PARSONS, Theodore; '73 BS; Regional Mgr.; Sutphen Corp., 1370 Plainfield Pike, Sterling, CT 06377, 860 564-2095; r. same; *Sheila;* Jennifer, Amanda, Theodore III. e-mail

PARTHEYMUELLER, Conrad; '77 BS; 4513 Avenue D, Brooklyn, NY 11203.

PARTRIDGE, Joseph; '97; 30 Pueblo Ct., Sayville, NY 11782.

PASCAL, Licet; '84 BS; 38 Herzl St. Apt. 12a, Brooklyn, NY 11212, 718 342-7404.

PASCALE, George; 16 Hidden Glen Ln., Monsey, NY 10952.

PASCALICCHIO, James; '71 BA; 1208 Pacific Ave., Beachwood, NJ 08722.

PASCHALL, Yvette M.; '90 BA; 135 W 115th St., New York, NY 10026.

PASCOCELLO, Anthony J., Jr.; '95 BA; Police Ofcr.; NYPD; r. 55 Warwick Tpk., Warwick, NY 10990, 914 988-9702. e-mail

PASCULLO, Anthony; '86 BS; Fireman; NYC; r. 52 Cara Dr., Pearl River, NY 10965, 914 735-1590.

PASICHOW, Jerome N.; '77 BA; 299 Kraemer Ct., E. Brunswick, NJ 08816, 732 238-8816.

PASICHOW, Steven A.; '78 BS; Asst. Commissioner; NYC Dept. of Investigation, 250 Broadway, Ste. 2800, New York, NY 10007, 212 306-3354.

PASINI, Roseann L.; '77 BA; 33-26 82 St., Jackson Hts., NY 11372.

PASSANESI, Dominick; '75 BS; 1530 Rosemont Dr., Clearwater, FL 33755, 727 588-9652.

PASSANO, Alexander; '76 MS; 18 Thunder Rd., Holbrook, NY 11741.

PASSERO, Robert J.; 24724 136th Rd, Jamaica, NY 11422.

PASSIKA, John I.; '77 BS; POB 1522, Big Pine Key, FL 33043.

PASTORE, Michael J.; '92 MA; 6 Farmers Ln., New Fairfield, CT 06812, 203 746-4666.

PASTRANA, Angel L.; '97 BA; Juvenile Couns.; Dept. of Juvenile Justice; r. 3514 Rochambeau Ave., Bronx, NY 10467, 718 882-1560. e-mail

PASTRANA, Joycelynne; '92 BS; 105 Baruch Dr., Apt. 8E, New York, NY 10002.

PASUIZACA, Carmen L.; '99 BA; Court Syst.; r. 41-96 Gleane St. #D-1, Elmhurst, NY 11373, 718 397-0119. e-mail

PATAKI, Steven; '87 BS; 2031 Palmetto St., Flushing, NY 11385.

PATANIA, John; '95 BS; 22 Meredith Rd, Edison, NJ 08817, 732 572-3326.

PATAO, Sonia; '81 BS; 445 E 5th St. #D5, Brooklyn, NY 11218.

PATEL, Kamlesh K.; '90 BS, '97 MPA, '98 MPA; 25 Pheasant Run, Scarsdale, NY 10583, 914 723-7588.

PATEL, Mayank R.; '89 BS; 252-03 82nd Rd., Bellerose, NY 11426, 516 333-2664.

PATINO, Michael F.; '85 BS; POB 140243, Brooklyn, NY 11214, 718 373-5529.

PATNETT-MILLER, Freddiemae; '93 BA; 9019 169th St. Apt. 2f, Jamaica, NY 11432.

PATRICE, Mic-arlem; '93 BS; Investigator for Human Resources; Ofc. of Revenue; r. 176 Dubois Ave., 2nd Fl., Staten Island, NY 10310, 718 720-8402; *Yasmine;* Kayla. e-mail

PATRICK, Michael A.; '84 MA; Special Agt.; Bur. of Alcohol, Tobacco & Firearms, 6 World Trade Ctr., Rm. 609, New York, NY 10048, 212 264-1061.

PATRISSI, John P.; '79 BS; 4123 57th St., Flushing, NY 11377, 718 343-1833.

PATRIZI, Dominick; '95 BS; 22426B Kingsbury Ave., Oakland Gardens, NY 11364.

PATRUNO, Cataldo; '96 BS; 51-23 65th St., Woodside, NY 11377.

PATTEN, Jennifer M.; '93 BS; Homemaker; r. 2149 Mapes Ave., Bronx, NY 10460, 718 584-3746; *Ronald;* Cirra, Ronald III.

PATTERSON, Erika P.; '95 MA; BA NC Central Univ.; Police Ofcr.; Kean Univ., 1000 Morris Ave., Union, NJ 07083, 908 527-2233; r. 1583 Leslie St., Hillside, NJ 07205, 973 923-1503. e-mail

PATTERSON, Germaine; '99 BS; 277 Stuyvesant Ave., Brooklyn, NY 11203, 718 464-3221.

PATTERSON, Ilani B.; '99 BA; 1272 Webster Ave. 10A, Bronx, NY 10456, 718 588-1930.

PATTERSON, Ison J.; '93 BS; 937 E 213th St. Ph, Bronx, NY 10469, 718 796-7198.

PATTERSON, Jeneva M.; '97 BA; 115-67 231 St., Cambria Hts., NY 11411, 718 297-3133.

PATTERSON, Rosezena; '96 BA; Police Ofcr.; NYPD, 25th Precinct, 120 E. 119th St., New York, NY 10035, 212 860-6526; r. 3315 Kingsland Ave., Bronx, NY 10469, 718 655-6456.

PATTERSON-DANDY, Creola; '90 BA; 88 Lewis Pl., Hempstead, NY 11550.

PATTI, Pasquale J.; '98 BA; Immigration Inspector; Dept. of Justice, Newark Int'l Airport Terminal B, Newark, NJ 07114, 973 645-3239; r. 1101 Stuart Pl., Linden, NJ 07036, 908 486-2360; Liliana. e-mail

PATTINSON, Mrs. Helen M., (Helen M. De Hart); '74 BS; Tax Auditor; IRS, 518 E. Main St., Riverhead, NY 11901, 631 851-4740; r. 23 Admiral St., Port Jefferson Sta., NY 11776; *Robert;* Lynn, Scott, Leigh. e-mail

PATTON, Brian V.; '80 BS; Lt.; NYC Police Dept., 1 Police Plz., New York, NY 10019, 212 374-0810; r. 8634 233rd St., Queens Vlg., NY 11427, 718 464-6365; *Eileen;* Vincent, Kieran.

PATTON, Marsha N.; '77 BA; 102-09 216th St., Queens Vlg., NY 11429.

PATTON, Ronda Y.; '96 BS; AS Nassau Community Clg.; Law Clerk; Blank Goolnick & Dittenhoefer, New York, NY 10013; r. 3043 Grand Ave., Baldwin, NY 11510, 516 867-3832. e-mail

PAUL, Mario; '99 BA; AS SUNY-Farmingdale; Fraud Investigator; Human Resources Admin. EVR, 30 Main St., Brooklyn, NY 11201, 718 260-7241; r. 3213 Snyder Ave. 7D, Brooklyn, NY 11226, 718 462-3797; *Ander.*

PAUL, Nigel; '99 BS; Law Enforcement; r. 347 489-5675. e-mail

PAUL, Yulonda J.; '98 BS; 1870 Lafayette Ave. #6G, Bronx, NY 10473, 718 542-3324.

PAULIK, John H.; '90 AS, '92 BS; 5922 Maspeth Ave., Flushing, NY 11378.

PAULINO, Jose P.; '99 BA; 1685 Toping #45, Bronx, NY 10457, 718 583-3439.

PAULINO, Reynaldo M.; '95 BS; Detective; NYC Police Dept., 1 Police Plz., New York, NY 10038, 212 258-2860; r. 3024 Kingsbridge Ave. # 5 E N, Bronx, NY 10463, 718 884-1038. e-mail

PAULK, Kim M.; '93 BS; 291 E. 143rd St., Bronx, NY 10451, 718 665-6174.

PAULS, Taisha; '92 BS; POB 454, Hartsdale, NY 10530, 914 235-9607.

PAULSEN, Maria E.; '81 MA; 16 Richlee Ct., Mineola, NY 11501.

PAULSON, Paul S.; '77 BS; 8 Kay Ct., Brooklyn, NY 11229.

PAUYO-SANZ, M.; '94 BA; 69-38 Kissena Blvd., Flushing, NY 11367, 718 721-4339.

PAVEGLIO, David J.; '76 MPA; 9 Evelyn Ct., Syosset, NY 11791.

PAVIA, Edward J.; '87 BS; 58 Berglund Ave., Staten Island, NY 10314.

PAWELCZAK, Peter; '75 BS; 42-09 23rd Ave., Astoria, NY 11105.

PAWLUK, William J.; '91 MPA; 11 Retford Ave., Staten Island, NY 10312.

PAYLAGO, Stanley U.; '91 BS; 11 Pheasant Run, Freehold, NJ 07728.

PAYNE, Andrea T.; '97 BS; Congressional Aide; US House of Reps, 196-06 Linden Blvd., Ofc. of Rep Gregory W Meeks, St. Albans, NY 11412, 718 949-5600; r. 111-49 180th St., Jamaica, NY 11433, 718 658-3026. e-mail

PAYNE, Jamil V.; '98 BS; Police Ofcr.; NYC Police Dept., 1000 Sutter Ave., Brooklyn, NY 11208, 718 827-3511; r. 230 E 123rd St. #2604, New York, NY 10035, 212 427-5070. e-mail

PAYNE, Jesse J.; '72 BA; POB 570318, Bronx, NY 10457, 718 585-4774.

PAYNE, Robert E.; '82 BS; Retired; r. POB 85, New York, NY 10031; *Deborah D.*

PAYUMO, Kenneth C.; '92 AS, '93 BS; RR 1 Box 209q, Cold Spring, NY 10516.

PEAKS, Harold A.; '82 BA; Criminal Investigator; Legal Aid Society, 718 243-6280; r. 13756 Laurelton Pkwy., Rosedale, NY 11422, 718 723-2172. e-mail

PEARCE, Donald; '93 BS; 91-13 217 St., Queens Vlg., NY 11428, 718 217-2702.

PEARCE, Edward; '75 BS; POB 404, Holbrook, NY 11741.

PEARCE, William; '88 BS; Massage Therapist/Owner; Massage Therapy Sports Medicine, 88-30 182nd St., Ste. 5 C, Jamaica, NY 11423, 718 739-5634; r. Jamaica, NY 11422.

PEARSON, Evelyn E.; '95 BS; Mgr./Corporate Security; Mastercard Intl., 2000 Purchase St., Purchase, NY 10577, 914 249-4621; r. 5900 Arlington Ave., Bronx, NY 10471, 718 796-7711. e-mail

PEARSON, Ida; '88 BS; Probation Ofcr.; King Family Ct., 283 Adam St., Brooklyn, NY 11201, 718 643-2216; r. 595 Marcy Ave. # 2, Brooklyn, NY 11206, 718 599-3628.

PEARSON, James T.; '76 BA; 12012 143rd St., Jamaica, NY 11436, 718 961-2288.

PEARSON, Joan E.; '75 MA; MSW SUNY-Stony Brook, BA Albany State Univ.; Retired, Sergeant & Social Worker; Police Officer-NYC Police Dept., SW-Private/Not For Profit; r. 7833 Ben Hogan Dr., Las Vegas, NV 89149, 702 655-1333.

PEARSON, Richard; POB 537, Red Lodge, MT 59068.

PEARSON, Timothy; '98 BS; 51 Teresa PL., Hempstead, NY 11550, 516 564-1823.

PEART, Annmarie B.; '95 BS; 58 Saint Francis St., Roosevelt, NY 11575, 516 505-0240.

PEART, Donaree Y.; '97 BA; Case Mgr.; Admin. for Children's Svcs., 150 Williams St., New York, NY 10038, 212 341-3154; r. 46 Paerdegat 13th St., Brooklyn, NY 11236, 718 209-7092; Taylor Fuller. e-mail

PEASAH, Joyce C.; '77 BA; 77 Columbia St., New York, NY 10002.

PEAY, Ms. Lisa D.; '99 BA; AS Borough of Manhattan CC; Youth Svcs. Spec.; NYC Police Dept., 1 Police Plz., New York, NY 10038; r. 287 S. 1st St. #3A, Brooklyn, NY 11211; Selina, Shaquenda. e-mail

PECORARO, Diana; '86 BS; Detective 2 Grade; NYPD-Bronx Narcotics Intelligence Unit, 1 Police Plz., New York, NY 10038, 718 378-8784; r. 55 Tumis Ave., Bronxville, NY 10708. e-mail

PECORARO, Robert H.; '83 BS; 40 Anderson St., Staten Island, NY 10305, 718 447-4866.

PECOU, Enrique A.; '83 AS; 280 Park Pl., Brooklyn, NY 11238, 718 638-4789.

PEDERSEN, Frank; '95 AS; 24848 88th Dr., Bellerose, NY 11426, 516 883-3539.

PEDONE, Riccardo; '77 BS; 7 Manor Dr., Marlboro, NJ 07746.

PEDRAZA, Evelyn; '89 BS; 127 Avenue X #2B, Brooklyn, NY 11223.

PEDRO, Hakeem A.; '95 BA; Fraud Investigator; HRA, 1716 Southern Blvd., Bronx, NY 10460, 718 617-8850; r. POB 570334, Bronx, NY 10457, 718 537-7067; *Latisat;* Ibrahim, Ahmed, Aminat. e-mail

PEELE, Ondra T.; '95 BS; Account Ofcr.-Stockbroker; TD Waterhouse, 4 Concourse Pkwy., Atlanta, GA 30328, 770 352-9999; r. 2766 Twin Brooks Dirve Apt. #6, Atlanta, GA 30319, 404 237-4297.

PEGO, Michelle M.; '89 BS; 42 Perri Cir., Middle Island, NY 11953, 631 205-0850.

PEGRAM, John A.; '76 BA; Retired; r. 920 Trinity Ave. Apt. 9f, Bronx, NY 10456, 718 993-8093; John Jr.

PEGRAM, John A.; '91 BA; 2707 Whispering Hls, Chester, NY 10918.

PEIFER, Ronald G.; '84 BA; 15 Jean Ln., Hartsdale, NY 10530.

PELAEZ, Armando L.; '75 BA; Sales Rep. Mgr.; American Airlines; r. 4550 170th St., Flushing, NY 11358, 718 762-5287.

PELISSIER, Junie; '99 MPA; 25-25 Mcintosh St., E. Elmhurst, NY 11369, 718 672-9376.

PELLE, James; '87 BS; 1690 President St., Brooklyn, NY 11213, 718 627-8543.

PELLETIER, Robert T.; '93 BS; 201 W. 109th St., New York, NY 10025.

PELLICANI, Stephen P.; '83 BS; Sr. Court Ofcr.; Nassau Cnty. Ct., 262 Old Country Rd., Mineola, NY 11501, 516 571-2621; r. 79 Derby St., Valley Stream, NY 11581, 516 791-2792.

PELLICANO, Donna M.; '93 MA; 612 Beekman Rd, Hopewell Jct., NY 12533, 914 227-5297.

PELLICANO, John M.; '89 MA; 138-29 Jewel Ave., Flushing, NY 11367.

PELLICCIO, Anthony; '92 MA; 238 Cherokee St., Ronkonkoma, NY 11779.

PELLINGER, Thomas G.; '80 MA; 134 Steele Rd #67, Ft. Tilden, Far Rockaway, NY 11695.

PELTON, Gwendolyn E.; '80 BA; 13022 N 38th Ave., Phoenix, AZ 85029, 602 547-1566.

PENA, Anthony; '98 BA; Community Worker; Covenant House Sch.-Based Prog., 1110 Boston Rd., Bronx, NY 10456, 718 991-5149; r. 74 W. 105 St., Apt. 5, New York, NY 10025, 212 749-2268.

PENA, Carmen L.; '95 BA PA; Caseworker; Cardinal McCluskey Family Svcs., Bronx, NY 10451; r. 2390 Creston Ave. Apt. B4, Bronx, NY 10468; Vamaler, Mariageli.

PENA, Eligia; '95 BS; 2785 University Ave., Bronx, NY 10468, 718 681-0310.

PENA, Erica; '99 BA; 1654 Grand Ave. 1st Fl., Bronx, NY 10453, 718 731-3579.

PENA, Esther; '99; 5008 Broadway Ave. #4I, New York, NY 10034, 212 569-4147.

PENA, Eva M.; '99; 20-70 26th St. #1A, Astoria, NY 11105, 718 639-9314.

PENA, Jenaro R.; '95 BS; Lt; NYPD-PBMN, 151 W 100 St. Rm. 405A, New York, NY 10025, 212 678-1836; r. 9 Tennis Ct., Plainview, NY 11803, 516 433-2210. e-mail

PENA, Joel; '94 BA; 503 W. 177th St., New York, NY 10033, 212 927-1252.

PENA, Julio; '95 BA; 615 W. 150th St., New York, NY 10031, 212 281-6989.

PENA, Leonel A.; '99 BA; 160 Stanton St. Apt. 3A, New York, NY 10002.

PENA, Lucas; '83 BS; 66-15 Wetherole St., Rego Park, NY 11374, 718 639-9314.

PENA, Ms. Marisel C.; '96 BS; Operations Mgr.; Thomson Financial, 1290 Ave. of The Americas, New York, NY 10104, 212 830-9366; r. 2314 E. 14th St., Brooklyn, NY 11229, 718 361-8940. e-mail

PENA, Marisol; '99 BA; Witness Aide; Manhattan Dist. Atty's. Ofc.; r. POB 110215, Brooklyn, NY 11211, 718 963-4177. e-mail

PENA, Miguel (Michael) A.; '84 BS, '90 MPA; AS San Antonio Clg.; Postal Inspector; US Postal Inspection Svc., 142-02 20Th. Ave., Flushing, NY 11351, 718 321-5600; r. 251 W. 87th St., New York, NY 10024.

PENDER, Patrick J.; '76 BS; Retired Deputy Fire Chief; NYC Fire Dept. FDNY; r. 9 Tall Pines Ln., Nesconset, NY 11767, 631 587-5314.

PENDER, Sylvia A.; '84 BA; 139 E 29th St., Brooklyn, NY 11226.

PENDERGAST, Teresa A.; '77 BS; 85 Livingston St., Brooklyn, NY 11201.

PENDOLA, Charles J.; 18 Guild Ct., Plainview, NY 11803, 516 681-1438.

PENN, Joseph C.; '95 BS; RR 1 Box 1103, Dingmans Ferry, PA 18328.

PENN, Marlon G.; '83 BS; 152 S 11th Ave., Mt. Vernon, NY 10550, 716 838-5357.

PENNA, Frederick, Jr.; '85 BS; Police Ofcr.; Nassau Cnty. Police, 1490 Franklin Ave., Mineola, NY 11501, 516 573-5340; r. 75 Intervale Ave., S. Farmingdale, NY 11735; *Marie;* Frederick III.

PENNES, Emilio; '86 BS; Asst. Deputy Warden; Correction Dept., 09-09 Hazen St., E. Elmhurst, NY 11370, 718 546-2128; r. 136-42 62nd Rd., Flushing, NY 11367, 718 461-9247; *Carolyn;* Brandon. e-mail

PENNETTI, Salvatore; '88 BS; 35 Raynor Rd, Ridge, NY 11961, 631 924-0874.

PENNISI, John A.; '68 BS; POB 139, Phoenicia, NY 12464.

PENON, David; '77 BS, '87 MPA; 55 E 99th St. Apt. 8e, New York, NY 10029.

PENTANGELO, Aniello A.; '80 BA; RR 1 Box 80, Shickshinny, PA 18655.

PEOPLES, Ms. Melissa; '95 BS; Paralegal/Real Estate Law; Parker Duryee Rosoff & Haft PC, 529 Fifth Ave., 8th Fl., New York, NY 10017, 212 599-0500; r. 56 W. 127th St., #4A, New York, NY 10027, 212 876-7961. e-mail

PEOPLES, Yasmeen (Yaszie) A.; '96 AS, '97 BS; PARACERT LIU; Paralegal; r. 2921 Tilden Ave., Brooklyn, NY 11226, 718 941-0470. e-mail

PEPE, Michael T.; '87 BS; 2061 Post St., E. Meadow, NY 11554, 516 796-8494.

PERALTA, Angelina R.; '83 BA; 5113 6th Ave., Brooklyn, NY 11220, 718 377-7835.

PERALTA, Omar J.; '97 BA; 189 Allen St., New York, NY 10002.

PERALTA, Vivian; '97 BS; 503 W.177th St., New York, NY 10033.

PERDOMO, Kevin A.; '98 BA; 15 Arden St. 41, New York, NY 10040.

PEREIRA, Laura; '98 BA; 135 E Main St., Apt. 2, East Islip, NY 11730.

PEREZ, Alicia; '96 BA; 337 55th St., Brooklyn, NY 11220, 718 439-3063.

PEREZ, Alida; '97 BS; 635 E.12th St. 4E, New York, NY 10009, 212 505-6299.

PEREZ, Anthony; '93 MPA; 4512 Belmont Rd, Great Neck, NY 11020, 516 487-0795.

PEREZ, Beatriz A.; '87 BA; 3681 Broadway Apt. 35, New York, NY 10031, 315 733-7931.

PEREZ, Bianca; '95 BS; 601 W 141st St Apt. 33, New York, NY 10031, 315 733-7931.

PEREZ, Carlos M.; '98 BA; Tchr.; HS for Leadership & Public Svc., 90 Trinity Pl., New York, NY 10006; r. 600 W. 136th St., New York, NY 10031, 212 491-1507. e-mail

PEREZ, Doreen; '92 BS; 3258 55th St. # 1st, Flushing, NY 11377, 718 821-3844.

PEREZ, Francisca; '90 BS; 2 N. Pinehurst, New York, NY 10033, 315 733-7931.

PEREZ, Gregory R.; '83 BS; 136 Cambridge Pl., Brooklyn, NY 11238, 718 385-2871.

PEREZ, Hiede; '93 BA, '93 CERT; 1050 Decatur St., Brooklyn, NY 11207, 718 453-2863.

PEREZ, Irma; '98 BS; Po. Box 6201, Bronx, NY 10451.

PEREZ, Ismael J.; '79 BA; 100-23 Elgar Pl. 23, Bronx, NY 10475, 718 379-9198.

PEREZ, Jaime A.; '99 BA; AA LaGuardia Community Clg.; Store Worker; John Jay Clg., 899 10th Ave., New York, NY 10019, 212 237-8763; r. 967 E 179th St., Bronx, NY 10460, 718 991-7769; *Martha; Giselle.* e-mail

PEREZ, John T.; '97 BS; 217-09 Spencer Ave., Queens Vlg., NY 11427, 718 205-5227.

PEREZ, Juan; '98 BS; 134 S. 4th St. #2, Brooklyn, NY 11211, 718 443-6349.

PEREZ, Juan A.; '89 BS; 427 Skyline Dr., Staten Island, NY 10304, 718 876-2680.

PEREZ, Lauro; '96 BS; 7 Carly Ct., Staten Island, NY 10309, 718 720-0748.

PEREZ, Leticia N.; '97 AS, '99; 117 Avenue C, Brooklyn, NY 11218, 718 492-2052.

PEREZ, Liduvina; '79 BS; 690 Saint Anns Ave., Bronx, NY 10455, 718 665-7559.

PEREZ, Lisbeth D.; '95 BS; 124 Bush St. # 4, Brooklyn, NY 11231, 718 492-2052.

PEREZ, Lizabeth (Lisa); '96 BA; AAS Fashion Inst. of Tech; Police Ofcr.; Co-op City Police Dept., 2049 Bartow Ave., Bronx, NY 10475, 718 320-3330; r. 2181 Wallace Ave., Apt. 4D, Bronx, NY 10462, 718 823-6308. e-mail

PEREZ, Lourdes M.; '97 AS, '98 BA, '98 BA; 129 E. 102nd St., New York, NY 10029, 315 733-7931.

PEREZ, Madeline; '86 BA; 4 Grand St., Wayne, NJ 07470, 973 772-0228.

PEREZ, Maria E. '87 (See Perez Y Gonzalez, Dr. Maria E.).

PEREZ, Maribel; '87 BA; 4729 47th St. Apt. 3r, Flushing, NY 11377, 718 278-0386.

PEREZ, Mario; '97 BS; Police Sergeant; NYPD, 116 Main St., Staten Island, NY 10306, 718 948-9306; r. 84 Stroud Ave., Staten Island, NY 10312, 718 948-1204.

PEREZ, Maritza, (Maritza Correa); '83 BS; Mortgage Banker; Republic Natl. Bank of New York, 2954 Aventura Blvd., Aventura, FL 33180; r. 4101 Garfield St., Hollywood, FL 33021, 954 964-2607; *Angel.*

PEREZ, Mayra E.; '97 BA; 465 E. 10th St., New York, NY 10009, 315 733-7931.

PEREZ, Melinda; '85 BA; 425 E 105th St. #8, New York, NY 10029, 315 733-7931.

PEREZ, Michelle, (Michelle Lemmonds); '89 BA, '94 MA; Secy. to Judge; Brooklyn Supreme Ct., 360 Adam St., Brooklyn, NY 11201, 718 643-5195; r. 3216 Griswold Ave., Bronx, NY 10465, 718 823-8931; *Bianca.* e-mail

PEREZ, Michelle; '97 BA, '98 BA; 25-26 89th St., Elmhurst, NY 11369, 718 268-1619.

PEREZ, Mike; '97 BS; 28-19 47th St. #3, Long Island City, NY 11103, 718 278-0386.

PEREZ, Milagros; '84 BA; 322 E 126 St. #7, New York, NY 10035, 315 733-7931.

PEREZ, Omar; '99, BA; Fed. Agt.; US Dept. of Health & Human Svc., 26 Federal Plz., New York, NY 10278, 212 264-1691; r. San Juan, PR 00923.

PEREZ, Rosa S.; '99 BS; 442 Lorimer Street#7, Brooklyn, NY 11206, 718 453-3573.

PEREZ, Sandra M.; '97 BA; 1265 Walton Ave., Bronx, NY 10452, 718 617-1588.

PEREZ, Sara L.; '90 BS; 611 W 177 St. #34, New York, NY 10033, 315 733-7931.

PEREZ, Vanessa; '96 BS; Claims Rep.; Social Security Admin., 3386 Fulton St., Brooklyn, NY 11208, 718 825-3864; r. 94-40 86 Ave., Woodhaven, NY 11421, 718 805-5579.

PEREZ, Victor M.; '95 BS; 230 Mendham Rd, Morristown, NJ 07960.

PEREZ, Vilma; '98 BA; 330 Est. 117 St. #8, New York, NY 10035, 315 733-7931.

PEREZ-RUIZ, Ines; '91 BA; 1684 Grand Concourse Apt. 1g, Bronx, NY 10457, 718 299-3033.

PEREZ Y GONZALEZ, Dr. Maria E., (Maria E. Perez); '87 BA MA; PHD Fordham Univ.; Prof.; Brooklyn Clg. CUNY, Dept of Puerto Rican & Latino Studi, 2900 Bedford Ave., Brooklyn, NY 11210, 718 951-5563. e-mail

PERFETTO, Robert M.; '95 MA; 461 Harrison Ave., Miller Place, NY 11764.

PERGAMO, Joseph J.; '76 BS; 418 Vanderbilt Ave., Brooklyn, NY 11238.

PERILLO, Lou B.; 1901 E. 17th St., Brooklyn, NY 11229.

PERINI, Bernard J.; '70 BS; Pres.; Worldwide Interactive Netlink Inc., 77 Arkay Dr., Hauppauge, NY 11788, 631 231-9225; r. 33 Caffrey Ave., Bethpage, NY 11714, 516 433-3868. e-mail

PERKINS, Charles T.; '83 BS; 13743 233rd St., Jamaica, NY 11422, 718 429-6993.

PERKINS, Christopher D.; 176-37 120 Ave., Jamaica, NY 11434, 914 855-3657.

PERKINS, Nicole S.; '96 BS; Paralegal; O'Sullivan, Graev, & Karbell, 212 728-5914; r. 1901 Gleason Ave., Apt. 5A, Bronx, NY 10472, 718 409-1922. e-mail

PERLLESHI, Luigi; '95 BS; Real Estate Mgr.; Metohija Realty Co., 16 Bedford Rd, Chappaqua, NY 10514, 914 238-6186; r. 16 Bedford Rd Ph, Chappaqua, NY 10514, 914 238-6186; *Aferdita;* Samantha, Sabrina, Linda. e-mail

PERLOV, Jane; '92 BS; 40 Tulip Ct., Nanuet, NY 10954, 914 356-8261.

PERLOV, Joshua M.; '95 BA; 4135 70th St., Flushing, NY 11377.

PERNICE, Louis R.; '87 MPA; 337 46th St., Brooklyn, NY 11220, 718 238-1173.

PERNO, John; '86 MPA; 370 Darlington Ave., Staten Island, NY 10312, 718 605-3510.

PERONNEAU, Ernest; '90 MPA; 100-18 A Dreiser Loop, Bronx, NY 10475.

PERRICONE, Gerard D.; '79 BS, '86 MA; 527 84th St., Brooklyn, NY 11209, 718 745-4352.

PERRIN, Heather K.; '93 MA; 23 Douglass St., Brooklyn, NY 11231, 718 376-2969.

PERRIN, Margaret B.; 51-01 39th Ave., Long Island City, NY 11104, 718 459-6821.

PERRINA, Enrico; '93 BS; MA Mercy Clg.; Tchr.; IS 220, Brooklyn, NY 11220; r. 1602 81st St., Brooklyn, NY 11214, 718 331-5658; *Joanne Gargin.*

PERRINE, John; 12 Karen Ct., Staten Island, NY 10310, 718 448-2639.

PERRITT, William J.; '99 BA MPA, '99 BS MPA; Assoc. Clerk; NYS Unified Ct. Syst., NYS Supreme Ct.-Bronx Cnty., 851 Grand Concourse, Bronx, NY 10451, 718 590-3802; r. 439 E 82nd St. 2B, New York, NY 10028, 212 861-5071; *Heidi.* e-mail

PERRONE, Diane; '86 BA; 21 Robin Hood Rd, Suffern, NY 10901, 914 369-0994.

PERROTTA, Fred J.; '76 BS; 25 Juana St., Tuckahoe, NY 10707, 914 793-0620.

PERROTTA, Michael J.; '98 BA; 96 N. Railroad Ave., Staten Island, NY 10304, 718 447-3570.

PERRY, Celeste M.; '84 AS; 162 Troy Ave. Apt. 11d, Brooklyn, NY 11213.

PERRY, Darlene L.; '92 MA; 45 Willard St., Apt. F, Hartford, CT 06105.

PERRY, Diane J.; '81 BS, '84 MPA; 148 Van Cortlandt, Yonkers, NY 10701, 914 944-4115.

PERRY, Elaine; '78 BS; 1194 New York Ave., Brooklyn, NY 11203.

PERRY, Gregory S.; '90 BS; 64 Rice Ave., Staten Island, NY 10314, 718 442-7396.

PERRY, Kevin; '95 BS; 2330 5th St., E. Meadow, NY 11554, 516 781-8363.

PERRY, Ofer J.; '98 BS; Financial Analyst; Wells Fargo; r. 1500 Plantation Oaks Dr., # 2802, Trophy Club, TX 76262, 817 491-3360. e-mail

PERRY, Patrick W.; '77 MPA; 85 Vista Ter. S, Mahopac, NY 10541, 914 628-5334.

PERRY, Robin; '93 BA; 8929 163rd St. Apt. 5m, Jamaica, NY 11432, 718 526-8474.

PERRY, Sandra; '82 BA; 933 Lafayette Ave., Brooklyn, NY 11221, 718 221-4424.

PERSAUD, Amanda J.; '99 BA; Treatment Coord.; Burkes & Salm, 875 Fifth Ave., New York, New York, NY 10021, 212 794-2007; r. 256 Schenck Ave., Brooklyn, NY 11207, 718 235-4007. e-mail

PERSAUD, Annette N.; '95 BS; 9218 213th St., Queens Vlg., NY 11428, 718 327-1863.

PERSAUD, Joseph M.; '90 BS; 290 Hemlock St., Brooklyn, NY 11208, 718 827-6235.

PERSAUD, Nalini; '98 BS; MIS Technical Support; Lyon Mercantile, New York, NY 10001, 212 967-6161; r. 104-17 123rd St., S. Richmond Hill, NY 11419, 718 738-2220. e-mail

PERSICO, Gerald C.; '93 BA, '96 MA; AA Borough Manhattan Comm.; 440 W. 20th St., None, New York, NY 10011, 212 807-0811; r. 440 W 20th St., Apt. 1, New York, NY 10011, 212 807-0811. e-mail

PERSINGER, Ms. Sherry L.; '95 BS, '99 MA; BS Indiana Univ.-SE; US Probation Ofcr.; r. Jackson, MO 63755.

PERSON, Brenda; '89 BS; 1242 Halsey St., Brooklyn, NY 11207, 718 452-5020.

PERSUAD, Annette; '95 BS; 9218 213th St., Queens Vlg., NY 11428, 718 738-4255.

PERVIS, Derrick; '86 MA; 11128 168th St., Jamaica, NY 11433.

PESANTE, Margarita, (Margarita Sanchez); '78 BS; US Probation Ofcr.; US Probation Dept. Eastern Dist., 75 Clinton St., Brooklyn, NY 11201, 718 254-7419; r. 4043 Seton Ave., Bronx, NY 10466; *Julio; Aramis, Ariel.* e-mail

PESCE, Frank J., Jr.; '71 BS; Retired Sgt.; r. 11616 Aspenwood Dr., New Port Richey, FL 34654, 727 856-5358; *Prudence;* Diane, Laura, Frank III. e-mail

PETER, John H.; '79 MPA; 1501 Catesby Cir., Virginia Bch., VA 23456, 757 495-5720.

PETER, Robert R.; 143-38 243 St., Rosedale, NY 11422, 516 933-7590.

PETERKIN, John W.; '77 MA; 8226 233rd St., Queens Vlg., NY 11427, 718 740-3353.

PETERKIN, Robert N.; '93 BS; 634 E. 221 St., Bronx, NY 10467, 718 220-1357.

PETERMAN, Jesse E.; '68 MPA; 33-47 14th St., Long Island City, NY 11106.

PETERS, Bernadette V., (Bernadette Duncan); '98 BA; Patient Rep.; New York Hosp., 520 E 7Oth St., New York, NY 10021, 212 746-3386; r. 699 Ocean Ave. #3b, Brooklyn, NY 11226, 718 462-6827; *Kelvon;* Delano. e-mail

PETERS, Calvin; '93 BS; 287 Rockaway Pkwy., Brooklyn, NY 11212, 718 469-7115.

PETERS, Claire E.; '98 BA; ROR Interviewer; NYC Criminal Justice Agcy., 16 Court St. Ste. 810, Brooklyn, NY 11241, 718 330-1500; r. 4000 Laconia Ave. #3c, Bronx, NY 10466, 718 515-0344.

PETERS, Clinton J.; '91 BS; Assoc.-Fire Protection-Insp; Fony, 9 Metro Tech Ctr., Brooklyn, NY 11201, 718 441-3717; r. 90 Wyona St., Brooklyn, NY 11207, 718 469-7115.

PETERS, Judy-lynne; '80 BA, '90 MPA; 1324 2nd Avo. Apt. 5b, New York, NY 10021, 315 737-0436.

PETERS, Kelly A.; '98 MA; 6485 Broadway #2k, Bronx, NY 10471, 718 547-6308.

PETERS, Marlene M. '74 (See Greene, Marlene M.).

PETERS, Petra P.; '99 BA; Tchr.; Dist. 17, Marlboro Rd., Brooklyn, NY 11216; r. 605 Louisiana Ave. Apt. 13E, Brooklyn, NY 11239, 718 642-1903; *Ronald Carter;* Matthew, Justin. e-mail

PETERS, Prestina D.; '93 BS; Ofc. Mgr.; Barnes & Noble, 160 E 54th St., New York, NY 10022, 212 829-1150; r. 2289 5th Ave. Apt. 14G, New York, NY 10037, 917 449-0950; Charles-Preston. e-mail

PETERS, Yule E.; '93 BA; 323 Wyona St., Brooklyn, NY 11207, 718 284-0667.

PETERSEN, Alan; '86 MA; BA Univ. of MA-Dartmouth; Student; SUNY New Paltz; r. 26 California Ave., Middletown, NY 10940, 914 344-1218.

PETERSEN, Eddy; '80 AS; Appraisal Ofcr.; Queens Cnty. Savings Bank, Flushing, NY 11358; r. 10-32 117th St., College Pt., NY 11356, 718 445-1077; *Helen;* Eric.

PETERSEN, Jacqueline; '97 BA; 140-23 Benchley Pl., Bronx, NY 10475, 718 671-4933.

PETERSON, Carrie L.; '80 BS; Paralegal; r. 119-11 200 St., St. Albans, NY 11412.

PETERSON, Claudette J. '79 (See Peterson-Kimborough, Mrs. Claudette J.).

PETERSON, Cynthia; '85 MA; 2 S End Ave. Apt. 8W, New York, NY 10280, 315 736-2014.

PETERSON, Daniel J.; '99 BS; 10 Scales Rd., W. Nyack, NY 10994, 914 623-1735.

PETERSON, Denise; '85 BS; 309 Lafayette Ave., Brooklyn, NY 11238, 718 495-1161.

PETERSON, Dennis J.; '79 BS; 1738 Copley Ct., Crofton, MD 21114, 410 721-1908.

PETERSON, Eugene, Jr.; '97 BS; New York City Police Ofcr.; 917 737-6009; r. 640 Ditmas Ave., Apt. 27, Brooklyn, NY 11218, 718 854-6094. e-mail

PETERSON, James J.; '81 BS; 17 Canterbury Ln., Colonia, NJ 07067, 732 388-8010.

PETERSON, Kevin C.; '79 BS; 9522 110th St., Jamaica, NY 11419, 718 322-5677.

PETERSON, Sandra; '95 BS; 33 Polk St., Freeport, NY 11520, 516 681-2427.

PETERSON, Sandra S.; '98 BA; 2406 8 Ave. #4C, New York, NY 10027, 315 736-2014.

PETERSON, Tania I.; '95 BS; Coord. of Court Operations; NYC TASC, 175 Remsen St., Ste. 505, Brooklyn, NY 11201, 718 237-9404; r. Flushing, NY 11367, 718 261-7795. e-mail

PETERSON, Thomas V.; '80 BS; 326 84 St., Brooklyn, NY 11209, 718 246-3779.

PETERSON-KIMBOROUGH, Mrs. Claudette J., (Claudette J. Peterson); '79 BS; Area Mgr.; Wackenhut Corp., 4000 E. Southport Rd., Ste. 30, Indianapolis, IN 46237, 317 784-6112; r. 5422 Nighthawk Way, Indianapolis, IN 46254, 317 347-8874; *Todd Kimbrough.*

PETITO, Thomas J.; '92 MPA; 481 Zadig St., Oceanside, NY 11572.

PETRACO, Nicholas; '79 MS; 220 Tyrconnell Ave., Massapequa Park, NY 11762.

PETRESKI, Toni; '96 BS; State Investigator; Div. of Criminal Justice NJ, 1 Appolo Dr., Whippany NJ 07981, 973 599-5968. e-mail

PETRICK, C.; '90 MA; 2714 Suburban Dr. R, Elmira, NY 14903, 607 562-8148.

PETRILLI, John A.; '78 BS; 1993 Debra Ct., Merrick, NY 11566.

PETRINC, Camille F. '96 (See Hughes, Mrs. Camille R.).

PETRIZZO, Joseph P.; '80 BA; 4 Glen Dr., Goshen, NY 10924, 914 615-1071.

PETROCELLI, Albert P.; '79 BS; 21 Presley St., Staten Island, NY 10308, 718 966-5088.

PETROCELLI, Dennis; '76 BS; 1750 Coleman St., Brooklyn, NY 11234, 718 934-9545.

PETRONE, Elizabeth; '83 BA; 25 Pinebrook Pl., # 25, Bay Shore, NY 11706.

PETROV, Aleksey; '95 BA; 2928 W 5th St., Apt. 9F, Brooklyn, NY 11224, 718 372-0836.

PETROVITCH, Diana; '90 BS; 9742 82nd St., Jamaica, NY 11416.

PETROVITS, John; '82 BS; 8820 Aubrey Ave., Flushing, NY 11385, 718 830-6212.

PETRUZZI, Dominick J.; '79 BA; 914 150th St., Whitestone, NY 11357, 718 767-2912.

PETTIGNANO, Charles; '82 MPA; 408 W. 57th St., New York, NY 10019.

PETTIGREW, Rose A.; '86 BA; 22314 114th Ave., Jamaica, NY 11411, 718 479-3417.

PETTIT, George J.; '99; 5231 Metropolitan Ave., Ridgewood, NY 11385, 718 939-2851.

PETTY, Bernard M.; '99 BS; 1153 86th St., Brooklyn, NY 11228, 718 965-2593.

PETTY, Camille B.; '89 MA; BS Hunter Clg.; Nursing Care Coord.; Bellevue Hosp., 27th St. & 1st Ave., New York, NY 10016, 212 562-4506; r. 972 Woodycrest Ave., Bronx, NY 10452, 718 410-7178. e-mail

PEZZO, Domenic; '75 BA; Dir. of Security; Date K Online, New York, NY 10005; r. 57 Fairway Ln., Manhasset, NY 11030, 516 365-4785. e-mail

PEZZULLO, Vito J.; '70 BS; 34 Northpark Dr., Garnerville, NY 10923, 914 429-4979.

PFADENHAUER, Peter T.; 146 Bengeyfield Dr., E. Williston, NY 11596.

PHANOR, Yves; '84 BS; 365 E. 25th St., Brooklyn, NY 11226.

PHELAN, Connie M.; '90 BS; 96 Trellis Ln., Wantagh, NY 11793, 516 785-9653.

PHILBERT, Donna-Marie; '99 BA; Sight Coord.; Kianga House.; r. 660 Empire Blvd. #7B, Brooklyn, NY 11213, 718 604-8170.

PHILIPS, Janet; '95 MA; Prog. Coordinator; Camba, 2211 Church Ave., Brooklyn, NY 11226, 718 282-0108; r. 190 Ward Ave. # B, Staten Island, NY 10304.

PHILIPS, Richard E.; '92 BS; 11148 159th St., Jamaica, NY 11433, 718 380-4583.

PHILIPS, Wilma, (Wilma Brown); '82 BA; Exec. Asst.-Asst. Commissioner; Admin. for Children Svcs., 150 Williams St., New York, NY 10038, 212 341-0958; r. 410 W. 149 St., New York, NY 10031, 212 234-2550; *Paul.* e-mail

PHILLIP, Arthur K.; '81 BS; 2950 W 35th St. # 52, Brooklyn, NY 11224, 718 265-0226.

PHILLIP, Charles; '92 BS, '95 MA; 10441 Springfield Blvd., Queens Vlg., NY 11429, 718 723-1836.

PHILLIP, Gayle D.; '99 BS; P.O.Box 1149, Bronx, NY 10466, 718 842-3128.

PHILLIP, Kyna W.; 193-17 100th Ave., Jamaica, NY 11423, 718 465-1197.

PHILLIPS, Anthony R.; '88 BS; 1435 Harrod Ave., Bronx, NY 10472, 718 681-6578.

PHILLIPS, Charles W.; '74 BS, '79 MPA; Ret Trng. & Devel. Spec.; US Postal Svc.; r. 160 W 97th St. Apt. 8C, New York, NY 10025.

PHILLIPS, Edward C.; '74 BS; Retired; r. 2 Bluebell Ct., Garden City, NY 11530, 516 294-8107.

PHILLIPS, Emily S. '98 (See Fisher, Emily P.).

PHILLIPS, Ernest G.; '99 BA; AS Kingsborough Clg.; Investigator; Dept. of Buildings, 11 Parkplace 2 Fl., New York, NY 10007, 212 442-2000; r. 1176 E 52 St., Brooklyn, NY 11234, 718 444-5131. e-mail

PHILLIPS, Ethel J.; '78 BA; 415 Lafayette Ave., Brooklyn, NY 11238, 718 257-4823.

PHILLIPS, George; 262 Central Park West #8D, New York, NY 10024, 315 361-4782.

PHILLIPS, Jennie R.; '86 BS; Retired Correction Ofcr.; r. 12033 147th St., Jamaica, NY 11436, 718 659-3877; Malik, Shukura, Derek, Jasmine, Armand, Shaheed.

PHILLIPS, Kevin D.; '91 BS; POB 97, Brooklyn, NY 11225, 718 857-2473.

PHILLIPS, Leon A.; '95 BS; 868 The Hideout, Lake Ariel, PA 18436, 570 488-6488.

PHILLIPS, Leon I.; '76 BS; 99 Hancock, Brooklyn, NY 11216, 718 789-5828.

PHILLIPS, Nickie D.; '98 MA; BS Belmont Univ.; PhD Student Criminal Justice; CUNY; r. 1015 8th Ave., # 4, Brooklyn, NY 11215, 718 788-6739. e-mail

PHILLIPS, Patrick A.; '97 BS; Territory Business Mgr.; Bristol-Myers Squibb, POB 4500, Princeton, NJ 08543, 800 838-4443; r. 91-14 210th Pl., Queens Vlg., NY 11428, 718 978-3528; Sierra.

PHILLIPS, Robert H.; '74 BA; MS Queens Clg.; Retired Sgt NYPD; History Tchr.; Southshore Christian Sch., Farmedge Rd., Levittown, NY 11756, 516 796-9301; r. 176 Beech St., Floral Park, NY 11001, 516 488-1365; Jodi; Matthew.

PHILLIPS, Stephen E.; '78 BA; 1547 64 St., Brooklyn, NY 11219, 718 259-3716.

PHILLIPS, Steven S.; '99 MPA; BS Northeastern Univ.; Claims Spec.; St. Paul Ins. Co., 516 949-2269; r. 35 W. 92nd #10G, New York, NY 10025, 212 665-0995. e-mail

PHILLIPS, Theresa A.; '88 BA; 267 Osborn St., Brooklyn, NY 11212, 718 453-8758.

PHILLIPS, Timothy F.; '98 AS, '99 BS; 80-23 159th St., Jamaica, NY 11432, 718 380-8454; Timothy Jr. e-mail

PHIPPS, Alfred L.; '80 BS; 118-40 234th St., Cambria Hts., NY 11411.

PHIPPS, Ms. April I.; '81 BA; Res. Mgr.; r. 9721 31st Ave., Flushing, NY 11369, 718 898-2690. e-mail

PHIPPS, Rocio; '95 BS; 170 Fenimore Stree, Brooklyn, NY 11225, 718 778-8905.

PHURCHPEAN, Kongkrit; '96 BS; 35-21 72nd St., Jackson Hts., NY 11372.

PIAGENTINI, Deborah; '93 BS; 373 Nicolls Rd, Deer Park, NY 11729.

PIAZZA, Anthony; '93 BS; 45a Village Ln., Staten Island, NY 10312, 718 815-0892.

PIAZZA, Karen L.; '96 BA; 15810 76th Ave., Apt. 2B, Flushing, NY 11366, 718 820-0248; John.

PICARDI, Richard; '92 BS; 304 E 92nd St., New York, NY 10128.

PICARELLO, Jodi A.; '90 BA; 171 Sunset Ave., Staten Island, NY 10314.

PICARILLO, Anthony P.; '83 BA; Security Admin.; Bulgari Corp. of America, 730 Fifth Ave., New York, NY 10019, 212 315-9700; r. 18-03 160 St., Whitestone, NY 11357, 718 746-5618; Lydia; Peter, Christine. e-mail

PICCERILL, Kenneth M.; '75 BA; 2821 W 12 St. #2A, Brooklyn, NY 11224.

PICCIARELLI, Patrick; '80 MA; 3251 92nd St., Flushing, NY 11369.

PICCIOCHI, Richard T.; '80 MS; 57 Rose Ave., Floral Park, NY 11001.

PICCIRELLA, Pasquale; '80 BS; 3531 10th St., Long Island City, NY 11106.

PICHARDO, Ana I.; '95 BS; 128 Ft.washington, New York, NY 10032.

PICHARDO, Fausto B.; '99 BA; Police Ofcr; City of NY; r. 132 Eldridge St. 3, New York, NY 10002, 212 925-3968.

PICHARDO, Francisca; '87 BA; 1010 Bryant Ave. #5, Bronx, NY 10459, 718 364-7224.

PICHARDO, Marcos; '97 BS; 87-05 78th St., Woodhaven, NY 11421, 718 418-1590.

PICHARDO, Maria F.; '95 AS, '97 BA; 547 W 142nd St. Apt. 30, New York, NY 10031.

PICKETT, John J.; '98 MA; Crisis Intervention Spec.; Newark Beth Israel Hosp., 201 Lyons Ave., Newark, NJ 07112, 973 926-7416; r. 603 River Renaissance, E. Rutherford, NJ 07073, 973 778-8244. e-mail

PICONE, Matilda; '78 MA; 210 Delaware Ave., Island Park, NY 11558.

PIECHOCKI, Mary T.; '80 BS; 5314 196th St., Flushing, NY 11365.

PIEDRA, Dennis; '92 BS; Sr. Investigator; HRA-ORI-EVR, 330 Jay St., Brooklyn, NY 11201, 718 237-6694; r. 67-38B 190th Ln., Fresh Meadows, NY 11365, 718 264-3125; Silvia. e-mail

PIEKARSKI-ROME, Cynthia; '89 BA; 9445 Lexington Cir. Apt. B, Charlotte, NC 28213.

PIEKLO, Eric J.; '96 BS; 244 4th St., South Amboy, NJ 08879.

PIERCE, Allison; '86 BS; 2832 University Ave., Bronx, NY 10468, 718 842-1556.

PIERCE, Bruce H.; BA; 3010 Clearview St., Yorktown Hts., NY 10598.

PIERCE, Latanya; '92 BA; 488a Chauncey St., Brooklyn, NY 11233, 718 485-0836.

PIERCEY, Melissa A.; '90 BS; 332 Senator St. Ph, Brooklyn, NY 11220.

PIERRE, Abel L.; '98 BA; 735 Bunker Rd, Valley Stream, NY 11581, 516 292-5487.

PIERRE, Bikens; '97 BS; Law; r. 694 Park Pl., Brooklyn, NY 11216, 718 230-5804. e-mail

PIERRE, Josephine; '97 MPA; BA Syracuse Univ.; Social Worker; Admin. of Social Worker NYC, New York, NY 10001.

PIERRE, Louicasse; '99 BA; CERT. NYC, CERT. Royal Canadian Mt. Police; CUNY Campus Peace Ofcr.; Hunter Clg., 695 Park Ave., New York, NY 10021, 212 772-4447; r. 250 Hawthorne St. #2B, Brooklyn, NY 11225, 718 756-5688; Ashley D. e-mail

PIERRE, Marylin; '87 BA; 8510 120th St. # 40, Kew Gardens, NY 11415.

PIERRE, Michael W.; '95 BA; 114 Prospect Pl., Brooklyn, NY 11217, 718 252-0098.

PIERRE, Taciana; '99 BA; 172-42 133rd Ave. #4G, Jamaica, NY 11434, 718 341-9054.

PIERRE-FRANCOIS, Wladimir; '98 BS; 34 Silver St., Elmont, NY 11003, 516 565-4733.

PIERRE-JACKSON, Paula; '89 BA; 572 Linden Blvd., Brooklyn, NY 11203, 718 919-9866.

PIERRE-JACQUES, Charles; '84 BA; Med. Analyst; Long Island Jewish Med. Ctr., New Hyde Park, NY 11040; r. 13021 235th St., Jamaica, NY 11422; Serge.

PIERRE-LOUIS, Ms. Audrey H.; '99 BA; POB 038342, Elmont, NY 11003, 718 481-6809; Asia Anderson. e-mail

PIERRE-LOUIS, M.; '92 BA; 88-40 173rd St. #C2, Jamaica, NY 11432.

PIERRELOUIS, Max; '97 BA, '98 BA; Sr. Accounts Payable Coord.; CUNY Rsch. Fndn.; r. 633 E 59 St., Brooklyn, NY 11234, 718 763-8528.

PIERRE-LOUIS, Wilson; '86 AS; 8824 188th St., Jamaica, NY 11423, 718 641-4005.

PIERRE PIERRE, Eddy; '89 BS; JD Nova Southeastern Univ.; Social Security Disability Atty.; Bindere & Binder, 315 Park Ave. S., Ste. 1600, New York, NY 10010, 212 677-6699; r. Jamaica, NY 11412.

PIERRI, Rocco J.; '99 BA; 1894 Willis Ave., Merrick, NY 11566, 516 546-7759.

PIETRZAK, Margaret M.; '98 MA; 234 Allen St., Lawrence, NY 11559, 516 239-0608.

PIGNATARO, SGT Anthony J.; '91 BS; Sergeant; NYPD, 1 Police Plz., New York, NY 10038, 718 482-6633; r. 129 Wicks Rd., Commack, NY 11725, 718 894-7601.

PIGNATARO, John V.; '89 BS; MS Brooklyn Polytech; Chief Tech. Ofcr.; Baltimore City Police Dept., 601 E Fayedtte St., Baltimore, MD 21202, 410 396-2568; r. 63 Lyle Ct., Staten Island, NY 10306; Perla. e-mail

PIGNATELLO, Robert; 18 Fieldstone Pl., Wayne, NJ 07470, 973 696-9354.

PIIL, Laura; '99 BA; 20 Astor Pl., Valley Stream, NY 11581, 516 872-1810. e-mail

PIJACA, John A.; '89 BA; Special Agt.; Bur. of Alcohol Tobacco & Firearms, 10 Causeway St., Boston, MA 02222, 617 565-7062; r. 40 Elliot Tr., Grafton, MA 01519, 508 839-3964; Patricia; Rose, Carmela. e-mail

PIKE, Linda A.; '83 MA; Family Svc. Spec.; DYFS, 140 Blvd. Ste. 3, Washington, NJ 07882, 800 531-1229; r. 290 Congress St., Phillipsburg, NJ 08865, 908 454-9789.

PILIERE, Roy E.; '77 BS; 165 Willow St., Floral Park, NY 11001.

PILIERO, Giuliano; '95 BA; 2180 47th St., Long Island City, NY 11105, 718 672-6314.

PILLION, George R.; '90 BA; Lt.; NYPD; r. 1031 N 6th St., New Hyde Park, NY 11040.

PILNY, Richard E.; '78 BS; 3218 Layton Ave., Bronx, NY 10465, 718 792-2855.

PIMENTA, Paul M.; '98 BS; 683 Palisade Ave., Yonkers, NY 10703, 914 965-5579.

PIMENTEL, Nelson E.; 164 E. 102nd ST., New York, NY 10029.

PIMENTEL, Rosa A.; '96 BS; 208 Huron St. #, Brooklyn, NY 11222, 718 336-8499.

PINCAR, Barbara, (Barbara McEvoy); '77 BS, '99 MA; MS Clg. of Staten Island; Tchr.; Notre Dame Acad., 76 Howard Ave., Staten Island, NY 10301, 718 273-9096; r. 68 Seaver Ave., Staten Island, NY 10306, 718 987-0345; *Martin;* Martin III, Stephanie. e-mail

PINCKNEY, Irene C.; '89 BS; 236-07 120 Ave., Cambria Hts., NY 11411.

PINCKNEY, Michael J.; '79 BS; 4360 Vireo Ave. 2Fl, Bronx, NY 10470.

PINCKNEY, Ramona J.; '84 BA; 2406 Frederick Douglass Blvd. Apt 6h, New York, NY 10027.

PINERO, Ismael J.; '80 BS; 2926 Brookhaven Ave., Far Rockaway, NY 11691, 718 545-8485.

PINETTE, Holly; '79 MA; 3610 SE 5th Ct., Cape Coral, FL 33904, 941 549-1346.

PINIZZOTTO, Anthony J.; '81 MA; Forensic Psychologist; FBI, Behavioral Science Unit, Quantico, VA 22135, 703 632-1141; r. POB 116, Stafford, VA 22555, 540 659-9433. e-mail

PINKHASOV, Mikhail; '99; 6141 Saunders Strett, Rego Park, NY 11374, 718 533-0953.

PINKNEY, Eddie P.; '82 MPA; BA Shaw Univ.; Retired; r. 27-32 Curtis St., E. Elmhurst, NY 11369; *Juanita;* Christopher.

PINKNEY, Tamela E.; '97 BS, '98 BS; 15 W 139th St., Apt. 16L, New York, NY 10037, 212 694-3251.

PINNISI, Daniel R.; '72 BS; 2314 West St., Brooklyn, NY 11223.

PINNOCK, Tania N.; '88 BS; 116 Hawthorne St., Brooklyn, NY 11225, 718 469-1193.

PINSENT, Clarenc M.; '73 BS; 40 Robert Cres., Stony Brook, NY 11790, 631 689-0173.

PINTI, Rosanne A.; '98 MA; BA Hofstra Univ.; Doctoral Student & Adjunct Prof.; Hofstra Univ., Hempstead, NY 11549; r. 681 Plato St., Franklin Sq., NY 11010, 516 483-9827. e-mail

PINTO, Christine M.; '96 BS; 8315 116th St., Jamaica, NY 11418, 718 760-7769.

PINTO, Giovanni V.; '96 BA; 17 Buffalo Ave., Apt. 62, Islip, NY 11751, 631 277-0796.

PINTOR, Felix E.; '92 BA; Doorman; UN Plaza Hotel, 1UN Plz., New York, NY 10017, 212 758-1234; r. 2321 84th St., Brooklyn, NY 11214, 917 553-4028; *Anne Wong-Pintor.*

PIOLI, Victor J.; '85 BS; 7211 60th Ave., Maspeth, NY 11378.

PIOTROWSKI, Michael; '78 MA; 527 Humboldt St., Brooklyn, NY 11222, 718 383-2563.

PIOTROWSKI, Ronald D.; '78 BS; 116 Park St., Staten Island, NY 10306.

PIRAINO, Joseph A.; '77 AS, '81 BS; Sergeant; NYC Police Dept., 1 Police Plz., New York, NY 10038, 212 374-6100; r. 98 Locust Ave., Staten Island, NY 10306.

PIRI, Ms. Maria A.; '92 BS; Police Sergeant; NYC Police Dept., Internal Affairs, 718 482-6899; r. 245 E 63rd St. Apt. 227, New York, NY 10021, 212 754-2239; Connor. e-mail

PISANE, Randolph (Randy); '72 BS; Retired Dir. of Public Safety; r. 4 Starlite Ct., Westfield, NJ 07090, 908 233-3320; *Rosalie;* Randy, Kimille.

PISANI, Angelo L.; '81 MA; 681 Yetman Ave., Staten Island, NY 10307, 718 979-1925.

PISANI, Michael T.; '88 MPA; POB 315, White Plains, NY 10603, 914 699-4222.

PISANO, Edward J.; '93 BA, '99 MA; AS Kingsborough Clg.; Asst. Mgr.; Commercial Bldg., 980 Maddison Ave., New York, NY 10021, 212 288-0626; r. 1919 8th Ave., Brooklyn, NY 11215, 718 768-3778.

PISARCZYK, Edyta; '97 BA; 32-13 47th St., Astoria, NY 11103.

PITRONE, Alberta J.; '90 MPA, BA; NYPD Detective; r. 453 Bard Ave., Staten Island, NY 10310, 718 273-5714; Dylan. e-mail

PITT, Christopher L.; '87 BA; 872 New York Ave., Brooklyn, NY 11203, 718 287-1032.

PITT, James R.; '99 BA; POB 2634, Brooklyn, NY 11202, 718 693-2480.

PITTELLI, Valerie G.; '76 BS; 8736 251st St., Jamaica, NY 11426, 718 347-1761.

PITTER, Violet M.; '95 MPA, '95 MS; 1194 Dr. Martin L King Jr Blvd., Bronx, NY 10452, 718 410-8337.

PITTINSKY, Leonard; '75 BS; Retired Lt.; NYC Police Dept.; r. 5 Stuyvesant Oval, #10A, New York, NY 10009.

PITTMAN, Yolanda R.; '97 BAGOVT; Social Worker; Victim Svcs., 3021 Atlantic Ave., Brooklyn, NY 11208, 718 827-4700; r. 102-21 Avenue J, Brooklyn, NY 11236, 718 649-5155; *William Ward;* William, Zachary, Josiah. e-mail

PITTS, Arthur A.; '82 BS; 250 E 178th St. Apt. 6c, Bronx, NY 10457, 718 294-7315.

PITTS, Jeffrey; '80 BA; 585 Blake Ave., Brooklyn, NY 11207.

PITTS, Stacey G. '90 (See Pitts-Williams, Stacey G.).

PITTS-WILLIAMS, Stacey G., (Stacey G. Pitts); '90 BA; Homemaker/ Grad. Student; r. 5 Collins Ave., Spring Vly., NY 10977, 914 425-1058; *Wayne.*

PIWOWARSKI, Joseph C.; '79 BS; 8966 218th Pl., Queens Vlg., NY 11427.

PIZARRO, Ramona; '88 BA; 920 Baychester Ave. # 19, Bronx, NY 10475, 718 860-1612.

PIZZANO, John; '76 BS; 8315 165th Ave. #2, Howard Bch., NY 11414.

PIZZI, Michael; '85 MA; 304 Bay 10th St., Brooklyn, NY 11228.

PIZZO, Dominick; '93 BA; 3276 Waterbury Ave., Bronx, NY 10465, 718 828-8224.

PIZZO, Vincent; '78 BS; Retired Chief of Detectives; Housing Police; r. 126 Roff Ave., Palisades Park, NJ 07650, 201 943-4324.

PIZZULLO, Victor; '93 BS; Police Ofcr.; KPF, 1 Police Plz., New York, NY 10038; r. 2026 W 5th St., Brooklyn, NY 11223, 718 373-9760; *Arlene;* Mathew.

PIZZY, Michael A.; '85 BA; 304 Bay 10th St., Brooklyn, NY 11228.

PLACIDO, Elizabeth J.; '99 BA; 610 Riverside Dr. 62, New York, NY 10031, 212 690-2645.

PLACKENMEYER, William; '75 BA; MS Hunter Clg.; Dir. of Safety & Security; Barnard Clg., 3009 Broadway, Retired Captain NYPD, New York, NY 10027, 212 854-3362; r. 400 Nicolls Rd, Deer Park, NY 11729, 631 242-3764; Kristy, Stacey. e-mail

PLADL, John R.; '80 BS; 355 Middle Rd, Hazlet, NJ 07730.

PLAIA, Vito; '95 BS; AAS Orange Cnty. Comm. Clg.; Correctional/Police Ofcr.; Orange Cnty. Sheriff Dept., Scotchtown, NY 10941; r. 127 Zoe St., Staten Island, NY 10305, 718 979-6756.

PLAMENCO, Roberto C.; '89 BS; San Jose State Univ., MA; Police Ofcr.; San Jose Police Dept., 201 W. Mission St., San Jose, CA 95110, 408 277-4631; r. 6147 Camino Verde #B, San Jose, CA 95119, 408 972-5636. e-mail

PLANT, Edward J.; '95 AS; 19 Hart Loop, Staten Island, NY 10306.

PLANTE, George J.; '75 MA; BA Richmond Clg.; Sr. Parole Ofcr.; NYS Div. of Parole, 10 Russell Rd, Albany, NY 12206, 518 459-3853; r. 422 Weatherwax Rd, Averill Park, NY 12018, 518 674-3811; George Jr, Rebecca, Matthew.

PLASENCIA, Dedie; '89 BS; 143 30th St. # 1, Brooklyn, NY 11232, 718 369-1955.

PLATAROTE, Karla B.; '91 BS; 59-12 Xenia St., Corona, NY 11368.

PLATIS, Anna C.; '96 MA; 10 Lyn Pl., W. Babylon, NY 11704.

PLAWNER, Thomas A.; '98 BS; Paralegal; Kronish Lieb Hellman & Weiner LLP, 1114 Ave. of The Americas, 44th Fl., New York, NY 10121, 212 307-7228; r. 21 Stuyvesant Oval #10F, New York, NY 10009, 212 677-6034. e-mail

PLAZA, Sandy N.; '96 BS; 69 Arlington Ave., Brooklyn, NY 11207, 718 834-9532.

PLEETER, Glenn R.; '87 BA; MTA; r. 2 Lancaster Ln., Monsey, NY 10952, 914 425-8831. e-mail

PLESNITZER, Edward J.; '76 MA; 85 Morris Ave. W, Malverne, NY 11565.

PLISNER, Sylvia '89 (See Seidman, Sylvia K.).

PLIVA, Alex; '99 BA; 651 W 171 St. #68, New York, NY 10032, 212 781-0967.

PLOUMES, Joanne; '92 MA; BA Queens Clg.; Criminal Rsch. Specialist; Social Security Admin., 212 264-3357; r. 122 Nugent St., New Hyde Park, NY 11040, 516 775-2234.

PLOVER, John; Naval Intel Nisra POB122, Pearl Harbor, HI 96860.

PLUCIENNIK, Thomas C.; '76 MA; BS, JD Seton Hall Univ.; Atty-at-Law Litigator; Thomas C. Pluciennik Esq., 11 Laurel Ln., Morris Plains, NJ 07950, 973 267-9182; r. same, 973 285-9027; *Maria Anne.*

POCCHIA, Barbara A.; '78 BS; 69-20 66th Pl., Glendale, NY 11385.

PODGORSKI, Robert B.; '78 BS; Correction Ctr. Asst.; NYS Dept. of Corrections, Rochester, NY 14608, 716 454-2280; r. 11 Sesqui Dr., Rochester, NY 14624, 716 247-0225.

POEJO, Victor A.; '91 BS; 1313 Waring Ave., Bronx, NY 10469, 718 547-6537.

POETTA, Charles; '80 AS; 1047 59th St., Brooklyn, NY 11219, 718 853-1707.

POGGI, John J., III; '95 MA; BA St. John Fisher Clg.; New York State Trooper; NYS Police, 25873 State Rte. 37, Watertown, NY 13601, 315 782-2112; r. 162 Haley St., Watertown, NY 13601, 315 786-8003; *Jennifer;* Andrew. e-mail

POGLODEK, Tina M.; '97 BS; 1416 Hollywood Ave., Bronx, NY 10461.

POINDEXTER, Lisa N.; '85 BA; 195 Willoughby Ave., Brooklyn, NY 11205, 718 342-3031.

POISELLA, Michael J.; 1720 Mayflower Ave., Bronx, NY 10461, 718 828-6364.

POITEVIEN, Eric; '92 BS; 3 Dahill Rd, Old Bethpage, NY 11804.

POJE, Leopold J.; '63 AA, '71 BS, '76 MA; Retired Capt.; NYC Police Dept.; r. 8461 251st St., Bellerose, NY 11426, 718 347-6930; *Virginia;* Leopold, Christopher, Karin.

POKA, John A.; '82 BA; 30 Steven Ct., Monroe, NY 10950.

POKORNY, Mrs. Cindy L., (Cynthia (Cindy) L. Winslow); '96 MA; BA Winona State Univ.; Commercial Account Analyst; Powercom Corp., 1807 N. Center St., Beaver Dam, WI 53916, 920 887-3148; r. 542 River Dr., Mayville, WI 53050, 920 387-1158; *Troy.* e-mail

POLAK, Simone C.; '82 AS, '89 BA; 1742 Broadway, New Hyde Park, NY 11040.

POLANCO, Alfa C.; '99 BS; 85-37 102nd St. #1Fl., Richmond Hill, NY 11418, 718 850-3665.

POLANCO, Lauvienska E.; '95 BS; POB 25360, Miami, FL 33102, 305 949-9302.

POLANCO, Miosotis; '94 BA; 225 Naples Ter., Bronx, NY 10463, 718 584-2815.

POLANCO, Veronica; '98 AS; 251-04 Memphis Ave., Rosedale, NY 11422, 718 341-4928.

POLAND, Jeremy M.; '97 BA; JD Brooklyn Law Sch.; Student; r. 669 E 7th St., Brooklyn, NY 11218, 718 871-6393. e-mail

POLENBERG, Carole; '92 BS; 645 Ocean Ave., Apt. A7, Brooklyn, NY 11226.

POLESEL, Steven L.; '75 BA; 2844 E. 197th St., Bronx, NY 10461.

POLEWAY, William P.; '75 BA; 4 Linda Ct., Nanuet, NY 10954, 914 356-0393.

POLIDORO Nunzia '93 (See McCabe, Mrs. Nunzia).

POLIN, Ms. Martha A.; '95 MA; BA American Univ., MA NYU; Asst. Principal; Simon Baruch Middle Sch. #104, 330 E 21st St., New York, NY 10010, 212 674-4545; r. 10910 Queens Blvd., Apt. 4C, Forest Hills, NY 11375, 718 793-8633. e-mail

POLIS, Stacy A.; '97 BS; 882 N.fletcher Ave., Valley Stream, NY 11580, 516 877-7223.

POLITANO, John; '92 BA, '92 MA; 1241 79th St., Brooklyn, NY 11228.

POLITIS, Steven, Esq.; '93 BS; JD Ohio Northern Univ.; Gen. Counsel/VP of Operations; PEO Svcs., Inc., 34-51 Vernon Blvd., Long Island City, NY 11106, 718 726-2000; r. 6530 75th Pl., Flushing, NY 11379. e-mail

POLLACK, Andrew B.; '95 MA; Prof./ Educator; Brookdale Community Clg./ Raritan HS, Lincroft, NJ 07738; r. 126 Harper St., Apt. 2a, Highland Park, NJ 08904, 732 565-9679; *Denise.* e-mail

POLLACK, Dan L.; '75 BS; 13-B Debs Pl., Bronx, NY 10475, 718 884-0336.

POLLARD, Melinda Y.; '79 BS; 138 Halsey St., Brooklyn, NY 11216, 718 493-6188.

POLLARD, Willette J.; '99 BA; Ofcr.; Fed. Govt.; r. 1296 Park Pl., Brooklyn, NY 11213, 718 221-1487.

POLLINI, Joseph A.; '92 BS, '95 MA; 70-25 Yellowstone, Forest Hills, NY 11375, 718 575-3110.

POLLY, Michael C.; '87 BS; 1454 Independence Ave., Brooklyn, NY 11228.

POLONETSKY, Lawrence; '94 MA; BA Queens Clg.; 110-21 73rd Rd., Forest Hills, NY 11375, 718 544-9715.

POLOVOY, John P.; '77 BA; 1545 E 36th St., Brooklyn, NY 11234, 718 338-4963.

POLTORAK, James T.; '77 AS; 6132 65th St., Flushing, NY 11379.

POLYAKOVA, Svetlana; '96 BA; JD Brooklyn Law Sch.; Legal Asst.; NY State Atty. Gen. Ofc., 120 Broadway, New York, NY 10271; r. 2840 Ocean Pkwy., Apt. 21 B, Brooklyn, NY 11235, 718 449-8411. e-mail

POLYE, Arlene M.; '83 BA, '85 MA; Volunteer & Aux Police Ofcr.; Midtown South-NYPD; r. 506 9th Ave., New York, NY 10018, 212 279-4412.

POMA, Ms. Patricia E.; '97 BA; City Carrier; US Postal Svc., 122-01 Jamaica Ave., Richmond Hill, NY 11418; r. 87-77 169St.,Apt. #C3, Jamaica, NY 11432, 718 291-5562.

POMALES, Jessica; '99 BA; Customer Svc. Rep.; HSBC Bank; r. 235 Brook Ave. #2B, Bronx, NY 10454, 718 292-5570.

POMALES, Mildred; '96 BS; AA NYC Technical Clg.; 3434 24th St., Apt. 1A, Long Island City, NY 11106, 718 482-7914; Michael.

POMERANTZ, Scot; '98 BS; Investigator/Disciplinary Unit; NYC Housing Preservation & Devel., 100 Gold St., New York, NY 10038, 212 863-5617; r. 1407 E. 100th St., Brooklyn, NY 11236, 718 968-1771.

POMPEY, Quwanna S.; '97 BA, '98 BA; 519 W. 151st St., New York, NY 10031.

PONDILLO, Anthony; '97 BS; 95-12 124 St., Richmond Hill, NY 11419.

PONTECORVO, Daniel M.; '83 BA, '90 MS; BS Pratt Inst.; Sr. Fire Protection Spec.; Con Edison, 4 Irving Pl., New York, NY 10003, 212 780-8618; r. 54 Redwood Ave., Staten Island, NY 10308, 718 356-4095. e-mail

PONTECORVO, Thomas J.; '98 BA; CERT. Nashaad Inst. of Tech; Tech. Support; Nabisco; r. POB 2006, Montauk, NY 11954, 631 725-5647. e-mail

PONZIO, William P.; '76 BS; Police Detective; NYCPD, Mastic, NY 11950; r. 215 Main Ave., Box 267, Mastic, NY 11950, 631 281-9178.

PONZO, Robert E.; '83 BS; 4141 N Henderson Rd Apt. 1007, Arlington, VA 22203, 703 527-3084.

POOLE, Florence K.; '80 MPA; 711 Amsterdam Ave. #23M, New York, NY 10025.

POOLE, Leslie; 711 Amsterdam Ave. #23M, New York, NY 10025.

POONAI, Roopnarine; '95 MA; BBA, MBA Pace Univ.; Supervising Probation Ofcr.; Dept. of Probation City of NY, 115 Leonard St., New York, NY 10013, 212 442-6132; r. 1505 Metropolitan Ave. Apt. 4B, Bronx, NY 10462, 718 931-9869; *Sreematti;* Kamminie, Wilfred, Kamala, Devika.

POPE, Thomas J.; '77 BA; 692 1st St., Secaucus, NJ 07094, 201 863-0910.

POPE, Winston L.; '98 BA; Police Ofcr.; NYPD, Brooklyn, NY 11201; r. 1373 Sterling Pl., Brooklyn, NY 11213, 718 467-4417.

POPLAVSKIY, Aleksandr A.; '98 BS; Fraud Investigator; Human Resources Admin., 330 Jay St., Brooklyn, NY 11201, 718 237-1741; r. 2237 81 St. #2a, Brooklyn, NY 11214, 718 232-7081. e-mail

POPOVIC, Jozef; '99 BS; 51 Lawrence Pl., Chestnut Ridge, NY 10977, 914 426-6327.

POPPE, John D.; '77 BS; 17 Homestead Ave., Staten Island, NY 10302.

POPPE, Matthew S.; '95 AS; 9 Woodcrest Rd, Staten Island, NY 10303.

POPPER, Alan H.; '86 BA; 3755 Henry Hudson, Bronx, NY 10463, 718 884-6292.

PORCELLI, Rita; '96 BS; 47-30 61st St., Woodside, NY 11377, 718 641-3190.

PORRAS, Patricio G.; '78 BA; 1097 Manhattan Ave., Brooklyn, NY 11222.

PORTELLI, Frank; '97 AS; 2255 Benson Ave., Apt. 6E, Brooklyn, NY 11214, 718 372-6778.

PORTER, A. Dashiell; '98 BS; Admin. Asst.; Samaritan Village, 144-10 Jamaica Ave., Jamaica, NY 11435, 718 206-1990; r. 356 Highland Blvd., Brooklyn, NY 11207, 718 827-6124; Tierra Syome.

PORTER, Elnora; '82 MA; 9725 147th Pl., Jamaica, NY 11435, 718 341-2110.

PORTER, Pamela S.; '90 AS, '95 BA, '96 CERT; 143-07 Sanford Ave., Flushing, NY 11355.

PORTER, Robert L.; '91 BS; 2076 Dean St. #, Brooklyn, NY 11233, 718 251-2306.

PORTER, Samuel A.; '97 BA; AAS Bronx Community; Teaching; Cooper City HS, 9401 Sterling Rd., Cooper City, FL 33328, 954 680-7200; r. 9540 Belaire Dr., Miramar, FL 33025, 954 438-3561; *Loraine;* Shadad, Latoya, Mariysa, Samuel, Brendan. e-mail

PORTER, Sandra; '81 BA; 9725 147th Pl., Jamaica, NY 11435, 718 341-2110.

PORTES, Francisco T.; '99 BS; 520 W 168 St. 6C, New York, NY 10032, 212 927-5916.

PORTORREAL, Ms. Yecenia; '98 BA; AS Kingsborough Comunity Clg; Police; NYPD, Brooklyn, NY 11201; r. 116 Bush St. Apt. #4B, Brooklyn, NY 11231, 718 625-1398.

PORTUONDO, Elaine L.; '78 BA; 1917 Cropsey Ave. Apt. 4g, Brooklyn, NY 11214, 718 996-6002.

POSAVETZ, Marilyn A.; '74 BS; MBA Florida Univ.; Sr. Financial Analyst; Perkin Elmer LLC, Norwalk, CT 06859, 203 762-6681; r. 61 Taylor Ave., Bethel, CT 06801, 203 744-7262.

POSELUZNY, Janis; '99 BA.

POSNIACK, Glenn; '95 BS; Security Mgr.; ADT Securities, Jacksonville, FL 32256, 877 202-0997; r. 7595 Baymeadow Cir. W, Apt. 2003, Jacksonville, FL 32256; *Shantil;* Austin. e-mail

POTTER, Hillary A.; '96 MA; BA Univ. of CO-Boulder; Asst. Prof.; Metropolitan State Clg. of Denver, Dept. of Criminal Justice, POB 173362 Campus Box 10, Denver, CO 80217, 303 556-3104; r. 1269 Logan St. Apt. 7, Denver, CO 80203, 303 837-9097. e-mail

POTTS, Janice P.; '97 BA; 293 Clinton Ave., Brooklyn, NY 11205.

POTUCEK, Daniel R.; '88 BS; 3832 S St. Rd, Marcellus, NY 13108, 315 673-1553.

POULIOT GRANT, Anne C.; '95 MA; 114 Park Pl., Brooklyn, NY 11217, 718 272-3030.

POULOS, Harry; '84 BA; Purchasing Agt. II/Furniture Buyer; NYC Bd. of Educ./O.P.M., 44-36 Vernon Blvd., Rm. 513, Long Island City, NY 11101, 718 361-3877; r. 8215 4th Ave., apt. D8, Brooklyn, NY 11209, 718 238-8964. e-mail

POULOS, James A.; '79 MA; 232 Lake St., Pleasantville, NY 10570, 914 337-5016.

POUNCIE, Ms. Amanda M.; '78 BA; MS Hostos Univ.; RN; Bd. of Educ., 110 Livingston St., Brooklyn, NY 11201, 718 320-1222; r. 3319 Fenton Ave., Bronx, NY 10469, 718 231-3199; Lillian, Roberta, Geraldine, Lance, Arrington.

POUST, Brian J.; '96 BA; 19 Oakwood Ter., Spring Vlly, NY 10977.

POVEROMO, Joseph; '85 BS; Detective; NYPD, New York, NY 10038; r. 3245 N Jerusalem Rd., Levittown, NY 11756, 516 731-8835; *Maria.*

POWELL, Alan C.; '81 BA; Dir. of Security; St. Mary's Regional Med. Ctr., 235 W 6th St., Reno, NV 89520, 775 770-3135; r. 4438 Highplains Dr., Reno, NV 89503, 775 746-2621; *Cynthia;* Michael, Nicole.

POWELL, Carol L.; '90 BS; 91-08 211 Pl., Queens Vlg., NY 11428.

POWELL, Clinton R.; '83 BS; 425 Central Park W, New York, NY 10025, 315 896-4740.

POWELL, Dalvanie K.; '87 BS; 120 Co Op City Blvd. Apt. 20j, Bronx, NY 10475.

POWELL, David F.; '85 BS; Probation Ofcr.; Rensselaer Cnty. Probation Dept., 403 Fulton St. Ste. #21, Troy, NY 12180, 518 274-9159; r. 10 Manor Blvd., Troy, NY 12180; *Nina.* e-mail

POWELL, Denise K.; '79 BS; 3214 Wilson Ave., Bronx, NY 10469, 718 881-6233.

POWELL, Gilbert R.; '77 BS; 96 Valdemar Ave., Staten Island, NY 10309.

POWELL, Hettie V.; '89 BS; 134-17 166 Pl., Jamaica, NY 11434, 718 322-6016.

POWELL, Howard G.; '76 BA; Retired 1st Grade Detective; N.Y.P.D.; r. 10919 192nd St., Jamaica, NY 11412, 718 468-7670; *Mattie;* Howard G., Stuart G.

POWELL, Hughlett O.; '85 BS; MSW Hunter Clg.; Doctoral Student; Norfolk State Univ.; r. 301 Elderwood Ct., Virginia Bch., VA 23462, 757 493-0304. e-mail

POWELL, Joseph S.; '74 BA; Retired-Police; r. 215 E 84th St. Apt. 2b, New York, NY 10028, 212 861-4296.

POWELL, Kerwin M.; '88 BA; CERT. POH Inst.; Unit Mgr./Youth Div. Couns.; State of NY, 170 E 21O St., Bronx, NY 10467, 718 798-6660; r. 10829 Fern Pl., Jamaica, NY 11433, 718 739-3619; *Katherina L.;* Fayola, Jamal, Keturah. e-mail

POWELL, Sandra C.; '85 BA; 114 Lexington Ave., Freeport, NY 11520, 516 564-4625.

POWELL, Shawnee '95 (See Powell-Phillips, Shawnee E.).

POWELL, Tanya G.; '77 BA; 401 Phillips Hill Rd, New City, NY 10956, 914 708-6072.

POWELL, Veronica D.; '99 BA; AAS Interboro Inst.; LWROR Interviewer/Substitute Tchr.; NYC Criminal Justice Agcy./NYC Pub. Schs, 52 Duane St., New York, NY 10007, 212 577-8777; r. 219-02 143 Rd., Springfield Gardens, NY 11413, 718 723-2395; *Willie;* Alicia, Carla, Shameka.

POWELL, Walter; '95 BS; MA, CERT. Univ. of Stony Brook; Ret. Correction Ofcr.; NY Dept. of Corrections; r. POB 158, Amityville, NY 11701, 914 356-8831; Walter Jr., Tiesha Forster.

POWELL, William M.; '77 BS; Ret. Police Ofcr.; r. 5517 Tabb Ave., Spring Hill, FL 34609, 352 688-6949; Adria, William II, Daniel. e-mail

POWELL-PHILLIPS, Shawnee E., (Shawnee Powell); '95 BS; Police Detective; NYCPD, 1774 3rd Ave., New York, NY 10029, 212 722-6277; r. 11 Laurie Rd, Cortlandt Manor, NY 10567, 914 528-8873; *William;* Rosa, Calvin, Maritza, Keisha, Keaunga, Jonathan.

POWER, Thomas J.; '76 BS, '81 MA; Retired; NYC Police Dept.; r. 166-35 Ninth Ave., Beechhurst, NY 11357, 718 767-7677; *Marilyn.*

POWERS, Derek L.; '89 AS, '92 BS; Commanding Ofcr. of Brooklyn; NYS, Brooklyn, NY 11201, 718 230-4461; r. 707 Beach 9th St. Apt. 3f, Far Rockaway, NY 11691, 718 471-7617. e-mail

POWERS, Robert; '89 AS; 667 Old Nichols Rd, Ronkonkoma, NY 11779.

POWLIS, Terrance; '82 BA; 115100 227th St., Jamaica, NY 11411.

POWMESAMY, Learie; '97 BS; Web/CD ROM Developer; Faulkner & Gray, 1110 Plz., New York, NY 10001, 212 631-1438; r. 260 Seaman Ave., Apt. E4, New York, NY 10034, 212 942-0521; Claire, Bridget. e-mail

POYERD, James D.; '94 MA; 345 Clinton Ave., Brooklyn, NY 11238.

POYNTER, Charles D.; '84 BA; 15 Halstead St., Clinton, NJ 08809.

PRADIEU, Caroline; '95 BS; 21-62 Crescent St., Long Island City, NY 11105.

PRAGER, Keith S.; '72 BS; Managing Dir.; Amsec Intl., 2977 Mcfarland Rd PH 5, Miami, FL 33133, 305 567-0029; r. 18933 NW 23rd Pl., Pembroke Pines, FL 33029, 954 431-7022; *Frances;* Hope, Joshua, Brian, Catherine, Tanya. e-mail

PRAHL, John F.; '76 BA, '87 MA; 70 Greenwich Ave. Box 295, New York, NY 10011.

PRASHAD, Dianna P.; '98 BA; 101-16 110th St., Richmond Hill, NY 11419, 718 641-7874.

PRATHER, Raymond B.; '77 AS; 807 Schenck Ave., Brooklyn, NY 11207.

PRAY, Randiolph P.; '78 BA; 1133 Ogden Ave., Bronx, NY 10452.

PREDDICE, Victoria A.; '99 MA; 141 Kersey Rd, Apt. B, Wakefield, RI 02879.

PREISS, George M.; '96 MPA; BS Jersey City State Clg.; Police Lt.; North Bergen Police Dept., 4233 JFK Blvd., N. Bergen, NJ 07047, 201 892-2141; r. 314 77th St., N. Bergen, NJ 07047, 201 869-6598; *Maureen.* e-mail

PRENDERGAST, Terri B.; '79 BS; Correction Ofcr.; NYC Dept. of Corrections, 225 Broadway, New York, NY 10007; r. 352 Richard Ct., Pomona, NY 10970.

PRENDERGAST, Yollette; '97 BA; Law Student; Thomas M. Cooley Law Sch., Lansing, MI 48901; r. c/o 160 W. 119th St., New York, NY 10026, 212 222-8508. e-mail

PRENTIS, Cheryle R.; '97 BA; 525 W. 156th St., New York, NY 10032.

PRESCOTT, Kay F.; '75 BA; Tchr.; North Shore Montessori sch., Stony Brook, NY 11790; r. 56 Summerwood Rd, Holbrook, NY 11741, 631 472-2986; *Maurice;* Brian.

PRESCOTT, Robert E.; '96 BS; 254 Seaman Ave., New York, NY 10034.

PRESSER, Allen; '75 MA; Mercer Co. Clg., Trenton, NJ 08690, 609 587-5416.

PRESSLEY, Sharon '83 (See Pressley-Collier, Sharon F.).

PRESSLEY-COLLIER, Sharon F., (Sharon Pressley); '83 MPA; BS South Carolina State Clg.; Supv.; HRA Protective Svcs. for Adults, Dept. of Social Services, 103 Clinton St., Brooklyn, NY 11201, 718 237-8377; r. 35 E 106th St. Apt. 9j, New York, NY 10029, 212 996-1655. e-mail

PRESTIA, Charles R.; '81 MPA; BS; Retired; r. 2645 Magnolia Park Ln., Apt. 201, Naples, FL 34109, 941 513-0051; *Elvira.* e-mail

PRESTIA, Michael; '89 BS; 124-02 23rd Ave., College Pt., NY 11356.

PRESTIA, Michael A.; '89 BS; 23 Rose Pl., Central Vly., NY 10917, 914 928-7747.

PRESTON, Alvin E.; '83 MPA; Retired Firefighter; NYC Fire Dept., Brooklyn, NY 11201; r. 8610 151st Ave. Apt. 6d, Jamaica, NY 11414, 718 848-4136; Sharon, Alan.

PRESTON, Thomas G.; '73 BS; MBA C W Post; Retired; r. 51 Rand Hill Rd, Morrisonville, NY 12962, 518 566-9739; *Viola (dec);* Jill Ann. e-mail

PRESUME, Thierry; '97 BS; AA Manhattan Community Clg.; Police Ofcr.; NYPD; r. 742 Lincoln Ave., Brooklyn, NY 11208, 718 827-2642. e-mail

PREVAL, Walter; '98 BS; 348 New Jersey Ave., Bay Shore, NY 11706.

PREVOST, Deborah A.; '93 BS; 14445 230th Pl., Jamaica, NY 11413.

PRIBETICH, John P.; '73 MA; 80 Skylark Dr., Holtsville, NY 11742.

PRICE, Fred E.; '78 MPA; JD Pace Sch. of Law; Retired Police Ofcr.; r. 17 Purdys Rd (rte 116), Somers, NY 10589, 914 277-2330; Stephen, Lauren. e-mail

PRICE, Henrimae; '99 BA; 590 Willoughby Ave. 1, Brooklyn, NY 11206, 718 782-7427.

PRICE, Laray; '95 BS, '95 CERT, '96 BA; AS; Cnsltg.; Social Svcs.; r. 1155 Grand Concourse Apt. 2g, Bronx, NY 10452; *Alwin.* e-mail

PRICE, Sherry V.; '79 BA; 20-65 29th St., Astoria, NY 11105, 718 357-3043.

PRICE, Vincent C.; '89 BS; 3471 Fenton Ave. # 4, Bronx, NY 10469, 718 671-8999.

PRICE, Warren J.; '83 BA; MSW Hunter Clg. Sch. Soc. Wk.; Social Worker; Jewish Bd. of Family & Children Svcs., 386 Park Ave. S, 4th Fl., New York, NY 10016, 212 481-2500; r. 3845 Sedgwick Apt. 6, Bronx, NY 10463, 718 543-6347; *Lynne;* Jabari.

PRICE-MOORE, Ms. Jennifer M.; '86 BS; Owner Recruitment & Staffing Co; Priceless Professional, 496 6th Ave., Brooklyn, NY 11215, 718 832-9892; r. Brooklyn, NY 11215. e-mail

PRIDE, Kasha L.; '98 BA; Admin. Asst./ Actress; Dept. of Justice, Community Relation Service Dept., 26 Federal Plz., New York, NY 10278, 212 264-0705; r. 578 Halsey St., Brooklyn, NY 11233, 718 443-3792. e-mail

PRIDE, Mashere V.; '76 BS; 15825 75th Ave., Flushing, NY 11366.

PRIETO, Juliza J.; '98 BA; MS CA State Univ.; Advt. Cnslt.; Harte-Hanks, 1325 Thousand Oaks Blvd., Thousand Oaks, CA 91360, 800 597-3669; r. 18307 Burbank Blvd. #129, Tarzana, CA 91356, 818 342-1109.

PRIGNANO, Roseann B.; '85 BA; 1779 2nd Ave. Apt. 3c, New York, NY 10128.

PRIME, Maria; '78 BS; AS; 218 Linden Blvd., #1D, Brooklyn, NY 11226; Mario Nimrod, Khadijah Nimrod. e-mail

PRIMIANO, John; '91 BS; 117 Reno Ave., Staten Island, NY 10306, 718 979-1566.

PRINCE, Daniel E.; '79 BS; Firefighter/ Hazmat Tech.; NYC Fire Dept., Brooklyn, NY 11201, 718 965-8276; r. 1933 Ryder St., Brooklyn, NY 11234, 718 692-1040; *Deborah;* Daniel, Heather.

PRINCE, Ernst; '95 BS; 13729 234th St., Jamaica, NY 11422, 718 978-3842.

PRINCE, Gilbert D.; '72 BA; 241 Medford St., Brentwood, NY 11717, 631 231-8116.

PRINCE, Mainert J.; '80 MA; 1046 President St., Brooklyn, NY 11225, 718 638-1450.

PRINCE, Mike K.; '93 BS; 20 E 127th St., New York, NY 10035.

PRINCIVIL, Rony; '90 BA; 108-05 227 St. PH, Queens Vlg., NY 11429.

PRINGLE, Hester V.; '78 AS, '80 BS; Correction Ofcr.-Retired; Variety Shop/ Albany NYS, Puzzle Freak 6337-Old Branch Ave., Camp Spgs., MD 20748, 301 449-6146; r. 831 E 215th St., 7712 Burnside Rd, Landover, MD 20785, 301 231-0924.

PRINZ, Ellen M.; '89 BA; 146-07 249 St., Rosedale, NY 11422, 516 922-5658.

PRIOLEAU, Catrina C.; '98 MPA; 2836 W. 23 St. #10n, Brooklyn, NY 11224, 718 363-1469.

PRIOLO, Charlene S.; '85 MA; 61 Frontier Way, Neptune, NJ 07753.

PRISCO, John J.; '87 BA; 455 Columbia Ave., Cliffside Park, NJ 07010.

PROCOPIO, Mary A.; '85 AS; 17 Poets Cir., Staten Island, NY 10312.

PROCTOR, Lillian N.; '82 BS; 4226 81st St. Apt. 7h, Flushing, NY 11373, 718 454-9357.

PROENZA-KLEIN, Jennifer E.; '99 MA; 76-19 Ditmars Blvd., Jackson Hts., NY 11370, 718 793-2403.

PROFETA, Susan L.; '84 BS; 31 W Walnut St., Farmingdale, NY 11735, 516 249-8406.

PRONMAN, Yonaton; '85 BS; 833 Central Ave. Apt. 6n, Far Rockaway, NY 11691, 718 327-4915.

PROPER, Diana E.; '99 MA; 25 Tudor City Pl. #422, New York, NY 10017, 212 953-5243.

PROPHETE, Marjorie; '90 BS; 10712 221st St., Queens Vlg., NY 11429, 718 776-6140.

PROSCIA, Thomas G.; '95 AS; 244 E. 196 Stree, Bronx, NY 10458.

PROSCIO, Charles J., Jr.; '99 BS; Police Ofcr.; NYC Police Dept., 1 Police Plz., New York, NY 10038; r. 1668 E. 4th St., Brooklyn, NY 11230, 718 645-5067. e-mail

PROSPER, Marlon R.; '95 BA; 470 Commonwealth Ave., Bronx, NY 10473, 718 295-6344.

PROST, Frank G.; '72 BS, '76 MPA; Dir. Safety & Sec.; South Nassau Communities Hosp., Oceanside Rd, Oceanside, NY 11572, 516 763-3974; r. 124 Widgeon Ct., Great River, NY 11739, 631 277-9695.

PROTAS, Roman; '99 BS; 1802 53 St. C2, Brooklyn, NY 11204, 718 234-3420.

PROTO, Rosa M.; '97 AS, '99 BA; Ford Investigator; City of NY; r. 250 Lake St., Brooklyn, NY 11223, 718 449-4013.

PROTONENTIS, Maria; '91 BS; 1095 Bordentown Ave., Parlin, NJ 08859.

PROVENZA, Charles S.; 124-08 Dearborn Dr., Bayonet Pt., FL 34667.

PROVIDENCE, Sharon; '87 BA; 5405 Snyder Ave., Brooklyn, NY 11203.

PRUITT, Denise L.; '95 BS; 231 Westwood Ave. #, Staten Island, NY 10314.

PRUSAK, Patricia R.; '78 BS; MS; Sr. Forensic Scientist; New Jersey State Police; r. 101 Mount Ln. 3, Manasquan, NJ 08736.

PRYCE, Genniveive O.; '96 BS; 3937 Monticello Ave., Bronx, NY 10466, 718 547-8815.

PRYJMAK, Myron W.; '84 BS; 78 Second Ave., New York, NY 10003, 212 254-3816.

PRYSOCK, Jeanine M.; '87 BA; 360 Bedford Ave., Uniondale, NY 11553, 516 486-3235.

PSAHOS, Theodoros (Ted); '95 BA; Inspector; Dept. of Justice, Jamaica, NY 11430, 718 553-0260; r. 2845 48th St., Long Island City, NY 11103, 718 932-4701; *Penny.* e-mail

PUCCI, Raymond; '72 BS, '77 MA; AAS CUNY; Retired; r. 437 101st St., Brooklyn, NY 11209, 718 745-6190. e-mail

PUCCIARELLO, Thomas R.; '78 BA; BA Stevens Clg.; Mgmt.; Lockheed; r. 28 Colonial Sq., Peterborough, NH 03458, 603 924-6262; Frisco.

PUELLO, Miguelina; '95 BA; Police Ofcr.; NYCPD; r. 885 E 169th St., Bronx, NY 10459, 718 893-5564; Eliza, Cynthia, Jennifer, Sean. e-mail

PUGH, Jason M.; '95 BS; 66-54 Myrtle Ave., Glendale, NY 11385, 718 525-8001.

PUGLIESE, Ferdinando; '91 BS; 428 N 16th St., Kenilworth, NJ 07033, 908 272-8460.

PUGLIESE, Naomi B.; '97 BA, '99 MA; Private Investigator; r. 346 Elwood Ave., Hawthorne, NY 10532, 914 773-9011. e-mail

PUJADAS, Gemma E. '99 (See Ribeiro, Gemma E.).

PULEO, Thomas A.; '93 BS, '98 MS; Security Coord.; Securities Industry Automation Corp., Brooklyn, NY 11201, 212 383-4365; r. 56-16 62 Ave., Maspeth, NY 11378, 718 366-7890. e-mail

PULGAR, Paula A.; '95 BA; Institutional Couns./Bilingual; Mercer Cnty. Correction Ctr., POB 8068, Trenton, NJ 08650, 609 989-6902; r. 231 Beal St., # 2, Trenton, NJ 08610, 609 584-8730.

PULICE, Ronnie; '97 BS; 1804 Muliner Ave., Bronx, NY 10462.

PULISIC, Zivko; '92 BS; 159-09 45th Ave., Flushing, NY 11358.

PUNCH, Amanda; '91 BA; 209-05B Hillside A, Queens Vlg., NY 11427.

PUNZI, Alfred M.; '76 BA; 147-05 Jasmine Ave., Flushing, NY 11355.

PUPIALES, Monica P.; '95 BS; 8564 144th St., Jamaica, NY 11435.

PUPINO, Joseph M.; '79 BS; Lt.; NYC Fire Dept., 4550 Riverdale Ave., Bronx, NY 10471, 718 430-0252; r. 16 S Cranford Rd, Nanuet, NY 10954.

PURCELL, Ralph J.; '83 AS; 7226 72 Ct., Brooklyn, NY 11209.

PURDIE, Yvonne W.; '98 MPA; 85 Ryerson St. #1, Brooklyn, NY 11205, 718 857-3450.

PURDY, Thomas J.; '86 BS; Police Ofcr.; NYCPD, 1 Police Plz., New York, NY 10038; r. 4 Kalvin Ter., Monroe, NY 10950, 914 782-0738; *Kathy;* Thomas. e-mail

PURPURA, Heather D.; '99 BA; 41 Sherman St., Huntington, NY 11743, 631 271-6412; *Roberto.*

PURTILL, Michael; '79 BA; 80 E 236th St., Bronx, NY 10470, 718 324-1112.

PYNE, Frederick F.; '90 BA; 3224 79th St., Flushing, NY 11370.

PYRONNEAU, Rose; '94 BS; 2525 Church Ave. # D, Brooklyn, NY 11226, 718 462-6214.

PYSARENKO, Katherine; '97 BA; Child Welfare Spec.; Admin for Children's Svcs., 150 William St., 8th Fl., New York, NY 10035; r. 3063 Godwin Terrance, Bronx, NY 10463, 718 432-9216.

Q

QADIRAH, Eleanor; '85 MA; BA North Carolina Central Un; Retired Bd. of Educ NYC; r. POB 176, Salisbury, NC 28145, 704 636-2811. e-mail

QIU, Hong; '92 MPA; 4803 5th Ave., Brooklyn, NY 11220.

QUAMINA, Michelle R.; '89 BA; Social Worker; Ofc. of Case Investigations, 186 Remsen St., Brooklyn, NY 11201, 718 260-8840; r. Freeport, NY 11520; *Anthony Reed.*

QUARANTO, Annette L.; '97 BA; AS Niagara Cnty. Community; Security Ofcr.; The Museum of Modern Art, 11 W 53rd St., New York, NY 10019, 212 708-9467; r. 301 E. 85th St., Apt. 11, New York, NY 10028, 212 517-2941. e-mail

QUARANTO, John C.; '88 BS; 43 Peninsula Blvd., Valley Stream, NY 11581, 516 791-5696.

QUARLES, Cheryl T.; '90 BS; 1021 E 233rd St. Apt. 2, Bronx, NY 10466.

QUARLESS, Tahaiwa V.; '97 BA; 350 E. 51st St., Brooklyn, NY 11203.

QUARTARA, Vita '95 (See Squillacioti, Vita).

QUARTIMON, Ronald L.; '93 BS; 1860 Grand Concourse, Bronx, NY 10457.

QUASHIE, Joy V.; '84 MA; 562 Albany Ave., Brooklyn, NY 11203, 718 385-8630.

QUASHIE, Thelma; 26 E 92nd St., Brooklyn, NY 11212, 718 385-8630.

QUATRONE, Rudolph S.; '76 BS; 1959 76th St., Brooklyn, NY 11214.

QUATTLANDER, Raymond; '91 BA; 1116 Hoe Ave. # 4, Bronx, NY 10459.

QUATTRUCCI, Elisa A.; '85 BS; 1837 Muliner Ave., Bronx, NY 10462, 718 863-5983.

QUETELL, Jennifer L.; '93 MA; 39 Raymond Pl., Yonkers, NY 10704.

QUEZADA, Alejandro; '97 BA; 1680 Grove St., # 2, Ridgewood, NY 11385.

QUICK, John W.; '76 BS; 152 Hawkins Rd, Centereach, NY 11720.

QUICK, Keri A.; '99 BA; 18B Labonne Dr., Patchogue, NY 11772, 631 289-6955.

QUIGLEY, Donald M.; '88 MPA; POB 192, Bronx, NY 10470, 718 231-5065.

QUIGLEY, John J.; '73 BA; 22 Great Circle Dr., Shelter Island, NY 11964.

QUIGLEY, M. F.; '78 BS; 2035 84th St., Brooklyn, NY 11214, 718 646-8736.

QUIJIJE, Kathy M.; '99 MPA; 233 Walker St., Cliffside Park, NJ 07010, 201 840-7904. e-mail

QUILL, Daniel J.; '60 AS; 9 Osage Ln., Staten Island, NY 10312.

QUINLAN, Ms. Casey E.; '94 MA; Investigator; State of NY, Attorney General's Ofc.; r. 520 Angola Rd, Cornwall, NY 12518, 914 534-3626.

QUINLAN, John F.; '80 BS; 8785 254th St., Jamaica, NY 11426, 718 347-2561.

QUINN, Dolores T.; '81 MPA; 21747 54th Ave., Flushing, NY 11364, 718 631-3263.

QUINN, Gerard M.; '77 BS; Capt.; NYC Fire Dept., 274 Hick St., Brooklyn, NY 11201, 718 965-8224; r. 15528 84th St., Jamaica, NY 11414, 718 641-3386.

QUINN, James C.; '80 BS; 51 Taunton St., Staten Island, NY 10306.

QUINN, James F.; '86 MA; JD St. Johns, BS PA State; Staff Judge Advocate; USA Military Traffic Mgmt. Cmd., 5611 Columbia Pike, Falls Church, VA 22041, 703 681-6580; r. 9214 Macswain Pl., Springfield, VA 22153, 703 455-8606. e-mail

QUINN, John F.; '76 BA; Chauffeur/Retired Policeman; Bell Atlantic; r. 16 Centennial Dr., Garnerville, NY 10923, 914 947-2453; *Eleanor;* Jeanne, Eleanor G., John J., Catherine, James, Elizabeth. e-mail

QUINN, John W., Esq.; '87 BA; JD Hofstra; Atty.; Perez & Furey, 333 Earl Ovington Blvd., Uniondale, NY 11553; r. 42 Maple Dr., New Hyde Park, NY 11040, 516 775-5493; *Arlene;* Jennifer, John Jr. e-mail

QUINN, Kevin A.; '76 BS; 16 Kreuz Dr., W. Nyack, NY 10994, 914 623-4021.

QUINN, Lawrence T.; '80 MPA; Retired; NYC Police Dept.; r. 161 Fifty Acre Rd. S., Smithtown, NY 11787, 631 724-0204; *Carol.*

QUINN, Michael B.; '76 MA; 709 W 169th St., Apt. 5C, New York, NY 10032, 315 724-3393.

QUINN, Michael R.; '84 BS; 1872 Batchelder St., Brooklyn, NY 11229.

QUINN, Paul G.; '72 BA; 66 Superior Rd, Floral Park, NY 11001, 516 437-7048.

QUINN, Robert J.; '72 BS; AA Baruch Clg.; Ret Security Profn; Exxon Co.; r. 7171 Kingston Cove Ln., Willis, TX 77318, 936 890-2843; *Janet;* Marianne, Carol, Robert Jr, Joseph. e-mail

QUINN, Terrence J.; '77 AS, '79 BS; 6239 59th Dr., Flushing, NY 11378, 718 416-2049.

QUINONES, Alma D.; '76 BS; 658 E. 156th St., Bronx, NY 10455, 718 824-9392.

QUINONES, Andrea; '99 BA; 807 Schenck Ave. 10B, Brooklyn, NY 11207, 718 649-1355.

QUINONES, Emanuel J.; 1253 Brunswick Ave., Far Rockaway, NY 11691, 718 896-6054.

QUINONES, Frances; '99 BS; 301 E. 156th St. #4E, Bronx, NY 10451, 718 401-6973.

QUINONES, Giselle; '95 BA; 1104 E Tremont Ave. Apt. 2d, Bronx, NY 10460, 718 824-9392.

QUINONES, Hector M.; '91 BA; MDIV Andrews Univ.; Minister; Seventh Day Adventist, Santa Fe, NM 87501; r. 825 Calle Mejia, Santa Fe, NM 87501. e-mail

QUINONES, Joann; '93 BA; 840 Grand Concourse Ofc. 5, Bronx, NY 10451, 718 325-2643.

QUINONES, Julio C.; '94 BS; 2194 Barnes Ave., Bronx, NY 10462, 718 892-0277.

QUINONES, Luis A.; '78 BS; 950 Underhill Ave., Bronx, NY 10473, 718 824-9392.

QUINONES, Mariluz; '88 BS; 391 Travis Ave., Staten Island, NY 10314, 718 720-4540.

QUINONES, Milagros; '97 BS; 784 Fox St., Apt. 4G, Bronx, NY 10455, 718 617-9644.

QUINONES, Monique; '99 BS; Fraud Investigator; Dept. of Homeless Svcs., 151 E 151st St., Bronx, NY 10451, 718 402-7080; r. 641 St. Marks Ave. #1H, Brooklyn, NY 11216, 718 735-4954.

QUINONES, Richard; '92 BS; 3455 Knox Pl. Apt. 2j, Bronx, NY 10467, 718 654-1424.

QUINONES, Zoraida; '97 BA; 1259 41 St. 3R, Brooklyn, NY 11218, 718 946-5306.

QUINTANA, Grisel; '97 BS; 89-06 102 Rd 1st, Ozone Park, NY 11416, 718 545-4247.

QUINTANA, Lydia C.; '91 BS; Legal Secy.; US Attorney's Ofc. S.D.N.Y., 1 St. Andrew's Plz., 9th Fl., New York, NY 10007, 212 637-1046; r. 1145 Morrison Ave. Apt. 2c, Bronx, NY 10472, 718 378-5411; Stacey Cherebin. e-mail

QUINTERO, Anthony; '85 BS; 1359 Noble Ave., Bronx, NY 10472, 718 589-6741.

QUINTERO, Marisol K.; '94 BS; Social Worker; Admin. for Children's Svcs., 350 St. Mark's Pl., 5th Fl., Staten Island, NY 10301, 718 720-2751; r. 4116 95th St., Flushing, NY 11373, 718 476-6929. e-mail

QUINTO, Donna M.; '85 BA; 39 Bedfield Rd., Island Park, NY 11558, 516 889-6109.

QUIRINDONGO, Eligio; '84 BS; 5554 Caithness Ct., Fairfax, VA 22032.

QUIROZ, Kathleen M.; '96 BA; 1365 74 St., Brooklyn, NY 11228, 718 398-2695.

QUITO, Mrs. Maritza B., NP, (Maritza B. Panama); '97 BA; Fraud Investigator; Lien & Recovery, 250 Church St., New York, NY 10008, 212 274-5557; r. 51-23 63rd St., Woodside, NY 11377, 718 478-3470; *Claudio;* Victoria, Cassandra.

QURAISHI, Zahid N.; '97 BA; Law Student; Rutgers Law Sch.-Newark, 123 Washington St., Newark, NJ 07102; r. 114 Woodland Ave., Fanwood, NJ 07023, 908 889-7154. e-mail

R

RABEL, Ilzee; '88 BS; Probation Court Ofcr.; Florida State Dept. of Corrections, 990 SW 1st St., Miami, FL 33130, 305 325-3531; r. 1316 NE 105 St. #103, Miami Shrs., FL 33138, 305 899-9363.

RABINOWITZ, M.; '75 BS; 5115 13 Ave., Brooklyn, NY 11219, 718 531-4571.

RABINOWITZ, Stacey M.; '89 BS; MS NYIT; Police Lt.; NYPD; r. 1171 Eastern Pkwy., Brooklyn, NY 11213, 718 382-5466.

RABSON, Mark J.; '77 BS; Asst. Dir.; Boy Scouts of America, 2208 Rte. 208 S., Fair Lawn, NJ 07410, 201 791-8000; r. 84 Upper Rainbow Tr., Denville, NJ 07834, 973 586-8352. e-mail

RACE, Robert R.; '70 BS; 300-26 Stevens St., Oceanside, NY 11572.

RACIOPPO, Ralph; '76 BS; Deputy Chief; NYC Fire Dept., 11 Metrotech, Brooklyn, NY 11201, 718 720-4141; r. 174 N Railroad St., Staten Island, NY 10312, 718 966-5230; *Arlene;* Jeff, Ellen. e-mail

RACKMILL, Stephen J.; 40 Jaffe St., Staten Island, NY 10314.

RADA, Frederick L.; '76 BS; 7571 183rd St., Flushing, NY 11366, 718 454-2147.

RADCLIFFE, Anna J.; '80 BA; Retired-Social Svcs. Coord.; r. 14A Debs Pl., Bronx, NY 10475.

RADER, Matthew; '79 MA; BA Long Island Univ.; Retired Social Worker; New York State Ofc. of Mental Health; r. 343 E 85th St. # 4F, New York, NY 10028, 212 879-9725.

RADKE, Henry; '75 BA; CW Post Clg., LIU; Ins. Fraud Cnslt.; POB 46, Cortland, NY 13045; r. 4572 Cosmos Hill Rd, Cortland, NY 13045, 607 749-2711.

RADOSLOVICH, Dario; '88 BS; 95 Cherry Ln., Hicksville, NY 11801.

RADZIEWICZ, Kathleen; '77 BS; 85-14 66 Rd, Rego Park, NY 11374.

RAEBURN, Phyllis S.; '98 BS; 1226 E. 51 St., Brooklyn, NY 11234.

RAFANIELLO, Helen M., (Helen M. Rapa); '91 MS, MA; BS St. Joseph's Clg.; Criminalist IV; Ofc. of Chief Med. Examiner of NYC, 520 1st Ave., New York, NY 10016, 212 447-2774; r. 99 McDonald Ave., Brooklyn, NY 11218, 718 436-6602; *Gary;* Carl Michael.

RAFFA, John J.; '77 BS; 21518 48th Ave., Flushing, NY 11364, 718 461-9424.

RAFFA, Matthew W.; '74 MA; 21518 48th Ave., Flushing, NY 11364, 718 461-9424.

RAFFERTY, Richard M.; '89 BS; POB 355, Stamford, CT 06904, 203 322-0277.

RAFFERTY, Thomas B.; '82 BS; 39-98 44th St., Sunnyside, NY 11104.

RAGGI, Michael L.; '79 BS, '91 MA; Special Agt.; US Dept. of Defense, Defense Criminal, Investigative Services, 1 Huntington Quadrangle Ste. 2c01, Melville, NY 11747, 631 420-4302; r. 4 Piedmont Ct., Centereach, NY 11720, 631 467-2385. e-mail

RAGGUETTE, Wayne; '91 AS, '93 BS; 820 Nostrand Ave., Brooklyn, NY 11216.

RAGIN, Kenya S.; '96 BS; Caseworker; Har Human Resource; r. 345 Livonia Ave., Brooklyn, NY 11212, 718 385-8018; Michael. e-mail

RAGLAND, Eric; '96 BS; 365 Clinton Ave. # 6, Brooklyn, NY 11238, 718 789-2271.

RAGO, Jodi J.; '87 BA; 131 Nassau Ave., Brooklyn, NY 11222, 718 389-9778.

RAGONESE, Lisa A.; '98 MA; Applied Behavioral Spec.; Developmental Disabilities Inst., 1 Scouting Blvd., Medford, NY 11763; r. 360 Deer Rd, Ronkonkoma, NY 11779, 631 737-3996.

RAGOONANAN, Ramcharan; '99 AAS; Security Guard Supv.; DA Riley Detective Bur. Inc., 232 Madison Ave., New York, NY 10016, 212 683-6020; r. 45-36 39th Pl. #1J, Sunnyside, NY 11104, 718 472-0741; *Bernadette C.;* Ryan N., Kester. e-mail

RAHAT, Mohamed; '95 AS; Supv. Guard; Lavoro Bank; r. 169-02 Gothic Dr., Jamaica, NY 11432, 718 658-6374.

RAHILL, Francis T.; '71 AA, '73 BS, '77 MPA; Retired Lt. CDS; NYPD/Manhattan North Homicide; r. 8301 63rd Ave., Middle Vlg., NY 11379, 718 651-4544; *Maureen;* Frank, Maureen, Kathleen.

RAHN, Robert H.; '81 MPA; Pres.; Hudson Valley Protective Svcs., 9 Boyd Rd, Monroe, NY 10950, 914 496-9364; r. same, 914 783-9272; *Patricia;* Robert, John. e-mail

RAICHLE, Carl J.; '76 BS; Sr. Forensic Document Examiner; US Postal Insp Svc. Forensic Lab, 90 Church St. Rm 400, New York, NY 10007, 212 330-5096; r. 630 Woodglen Rd., Glen Gardner, NJ 08826, 908 832-7633; *Martha Rigney-Raichle RN.* e-mail

RAIFORD, Louis G.; '77 BA; Retired; r. 2920 Sunstone St., Las Vegas, NV 89128, 702 256-3626; *Elois;* Bryan, Denise, Lance, Darryl.

RAILEY, James A.; '97 MA; 1295 5th Ave. 15E, New York, NY 10029.

RAINES, Alfonso D.; '88 BS; Tchr.; NYC Bd. of Educ., 65 Court St., Brooklyn, NY 11201, 718 935-4716; r. 11519 220th St., Jamaica, NY 11411, 718 276-1895; *Belle;* Judi, Mandi, Debra.

RAINES, Jonathan E.; '70 BS; Private Practice; r. 13165 227th St., Laurelton, NY 11413, 718 525-1640.

RAINEY, Eugene; '89 BS; Caseworker; City of NY, 212 835-7566; r. 2181 Madison Ave., New York, NY 10037, 212 690-7502.

RAINIS, Edward A.; '73 BS; MS CW Post; 225 Madrid Ct., Satellite Bch., FL 32937, 321 777-1330; *Linda;* Loralee, Carrie. e-mail

RAKOWSKY, Andrew R.; '82 BS, '91 MPA, '97 MPA; 1853 Haight Ave., Bronx, NY 10461, 718 824-1951.

RALDIRIS, Carlos J.; '89 BS; MA Columbia Univ.; Human Resources Business Partner; Dr. Pepper/7-Up Inc., Plano, TX 75024, 972 673-6433; r. 1504 Westmont Dr., Allen, TX 75013. e-mail

RALKO, Stephen E.; '77 BS; Weyhill Ln. 5441, Doylestown, PA 18901, 215 766-0586.

RALL, Charles E.; '76 BS; Maj.; USAR; r. 4504 E Fernwood Ct., Cave Creek, AZ 85331, 480 419-5000; *Patricia;* Daniel. e-mail

RAM, Chandrowtie; '96 BA; 8729 126th St., Jamaica, NY 11418, 718 264-6425.

RAMADAN, Mahmoud; '86 BA; 2 N Pinehurst Ave., New York, NY 10033.

RAMAN, Fredrick C.; '94 BS; 243 Jerusalem Ave., Massapequa Park, NY 11762, 516 795-4653.

RAMCHARAN, Praimadip; '84 BA; 446 Central Park W, New York, NY 10025.

RAMDEHOLL, Neville; '98 BA; 5605 4th Ave., Brooklyn, NY 11220, 718 492-4927; *Linda.*

RAMIREZ, Alexander; '75 BA; 1185 NE 134 St., N. Miami, FL 33161, 305 258-9488.

RAMIREZ, Alexis; '98 BS; Salesman; Healthfirst, 25 Broadway, New York, NY 10004, 212 801-6000; r. 533 E. 11th St., New York, NY 10009, 212 477-3155. e-mail

RAMIREZ, Anthony J.; '78 BS; 3021 Briggs Ave. #3A, Bronx, NY 10458, 718 561-5952.

RAMIREZ, Barry; '98 BA; Gen. Mgr.; TSC Foodservice Inc., 2140 Westchester Ave., Bronx, NY 10462, 718 409-6174; r. 1867 Hunt Ave., Apt. 7, Bronx, NY 10462, 718 319-1822.

RAMIREZ, Carlos; '88 BS; 2911 Barnes Ave. #1, Bronx, NY 10467, 718 295-7144.

RAMIREZ, Carlos; '93 BS; 11 Webster Pl., Brooklyn, NY 11215, 718 369-6715.

RAMIREZ, Debra L.; '99 BA; 2911 Barnes Ave., Bronx, NY 10467, 718 410-0521.

RAMIREZ, Edgar; '79 MA; 149-17 41 Ave., Flushing, NY 11355, 718 843-5076.

RAMIREZ, Eliud, Jr.; '85 BA, '98 MPA, '98 MPA; 264 Arlene St., Staten Island, NY 10314, 718 761-0325.

RAMIREZ, Ms. Elizabeth, (Elizabeth Rodriguez); '89 BS; MSW Hunter Clg.; Supervising Probation Ofcr.; NY Dept. of Probation, 1555 Linden Blvd., Brooklyn, NY 11212, 718 495-5695; r. 39-02 111 St. #R1D, Corona, NY 11368, 718 478-2629; Jonathan. e-mail

RAMIREZ, Giomar P.; '98 BA; 61 61 Woodhaven Blv 3g, Rego Park, NY 11374, 718 520-1405.

RAMIREZ, Hector V., Esq.; '92 BS, 2000 JD; Assoc. Atty.; r. 16012 Normal Rd, Jamaica, NY 11432. e-mail

RAMIREZ, Holli; '93 BS; Ofc. Mgr.; Ian Van Praagh, MD, 103 E. 86th St., New York, NY 10028, 212 427-5774; r. 405 E. 92nd St., New York, NY 10128, 212 722-0372.

RAMIREZ, Jessica D.; '98 BA; Correction Ofcr.; Rikers Island; r. 768 Brady Ave. #343, Bronx, NY 10462, 718 931-2826; Brianna.

RAMIREZ, Karen Y.; '96 BA; 11 Webster Pl., Brooklyn, NY 11215, 718 369-6715.

RAMIREZ, Lamberto; '98 BA; 602 W 137th St. 53, New York, NY 10031, 212 926-3810.

RAMIREZ, Lesbia '97 (See Villar, Leslie A.).

RAMIREZ, Lisandra; '86 BA; 72 Ridgewood Ave. Apt. B5, Brooklyn, NY 11207, 718 714-5641.

RAMIREZ, Manuel; '92 BA; JD Tulane Law Sch.; Atty.; Justice Dept., 701 Loyola, New Orleans, LA 70118, 504 589-3544; r. 508 9th Ave. Apt. 3rn, New York, NY 10018, 212 594-8849; *Virginie;* Andrea.

RAMIREZ, Reynaldo; '99 BS; CERT. Microsoft; Dir. of Info. Technology; Elektra Entertainment, 75 Rockefeller Plz., New York, NY 10019, 212 275-4442; r. POB 863603, Ridgewood, NY 11386, 718 386-6239.

RAMIREZ, Richard; '76 BS; 977 Valley Rd., Gillette, NJ 07933, 908 580-5167.

RAMIREZ, Robert; '98 BA; 275 Cherry 4G, New York, NY 10002, 212 227-3848.

RAMIREZ, Vernon; '98 BA; Owner; Vernon Is Hair, 1034 Union St., Brooklyn, NY 11225, 718 467-9852; r. 1546 St. Johns Pl. 1s, Brooklyn, NY 11213, 718 756-1203. e-mail

RAMIREZ, Vincent P.; '69 BS; Retired Capt./Dir. of Security; New Police Dept./ New York Racing Assn.; r. 39 Fieldhouse Ave., E. Setauket, NY 11733; *Carmen.*

RAMIREZ, Mrs. Virginie; '93 BA; Student; Tulane Law Sch., 6329 Froret St., New Orleans, LA 70125; r. 508 9th Ave., New York, NY 10018, 212 594-8849; *Manuel;* Andrea.

RAMJIT, Sheriffa; '93 BA; 1136 Metcalf Ave. Apt. 2r, Bronx, NY 10472.

RAMJOHN, Maria J.; '98 BA; 184 Castle Ave., Westbury, NY 11590, 516 997-2279.

RAMKARAN, Denyse; '91 BA, '91 MA; Dir. of Casting; r. 767 Whitehall Pl., Bronx, NY 10466, 718 994-9421.

RAMKISSOON, Ricardo; '96 BA; Police Ofcr.; NYC Police Dept., 1 Police Plz., New York, NY 10038, 917 825-1049.

RAMNARAIN, Kavita; '97 BA, '98 BA; 135-28 Kew Garden Rd, Richmond Hill, NY 11418, 718 465-1351.

RAMOS, Adrian; '75 BA; 8310 35th Ave., Apt. 2D, Jackson Hts., NY 11372, 718 739-1011.

RAMOS, Anthony J.; '76 MA; BBA, AAS Baruch Clg.; Retired; r. POB 347, Thiells, NY 10984.

RAMOS, Christopher L.; '85 BA; 91 Pine Rd, Mastic Bch., NY 11951.

RAMOS, Damaso; '99 BA; 1235 Morrison Ave., Bronx, NY 10472, 718 328-0322.

RAMOS, Denyse N. '89 (See Ramos-Sololongo, Denyse N.).

RAMOS, Elba I.; '86 BA; 10336 98th St., Jamaica, NY 11417, 718 347-2055.

RAMOS, Elvin; '77 BA; 9718 76th St., Jamaica, NY 11416, 718 347-2055.

RAMOS, Evelyn; '86 BA; 425 E. 102 St., New York, NY 10029.

RAMOS, Jack; '95 BS; 3059 82nd St. # 1, Flushing, NY 11370, 718 739-9488.

RAMOS, James J.; '99 BS; AS Kingsborough; Police Ofcr.; New York Police Dept.; r. 251 Carlton Ave., Brooklyn, NY 11205, 718 237-5993. e-mail

RAMOS, Jose; 50 Revere Cir., Washingtonville, NY 10992.

RAMOS, Julius; '77 BS; 1900 51st St. Apt. 1e, Brooklyn, NY 11204, 718 388-9134.

RAMOS, Laura; '97 BS; Account Analyst; HBO, 1100 Ave. of The Americas, New York, NY 10036; r. 820 Thieriot Ave., Bronx, NY 10473, 718 328-3132. e-mail

RAMOS, Magda; '93 BS; 3555 Olinville Ave., Apt. 1G, Bronx, NY 10467, 718 881-9169.

RAMOS, Manuel; '96 BS; 225 Nelson St., Allentown, PA 18103.

RAMOS, Maria; '92 BS; 5800 Arlington Ave. Apt. 21a, Bronx, NY 10471, 718 364-2288.

RAMOS, Marisol; '91 BA; 324 E 143rd St. Apt. 11c, Bronx, NY 10451, 718 364-2288.

RAMOS, Marlene (Mandy) M.; '96 BS; MASOWRK Adelphi; Admissions Couns.; FEGS Manhattan Counseling Cntr, 80 Van Dam St., New York, NY 10013, 212 366-8289; r. 3170 Broadway Apt. 6j, New York, NY 10027, 212 932-1635; *Errol O. Rodriguez.* e-mail

RAMOS, Mead S.; '97 BS, '98 BS; 551 Wales Ave. #511, Bronx, NY 10455, 718 364-2288.

RAMOS, Michael; '77 BA; 370 Marshall St., Oceanside, NY 11572, 516 536-8643.

RAMOS, Nestor; '99 BS MA; Investigator; NYS, 2 Penningfield Ave., Bronx, NY 10465, 718 637-4645; r. same, 718 319-5100; *Migdalia.* e-mail

RAMOS, Rafanzelin; '98 BA; 342 62nd ST., Brooklyn, NY 11220, 718 492-1934.

RAMOS, Ramonita; '96 BA; Legal Secy.; Tomen America Inc.; Grad. Student, John Jay Clg.; r. 54 Catherine St., New York, NY 10038, 212 285-1460; *Michael;* Savanah Adorno. e-mail

RAMOS, Rosemary; '80 BS; 542 Bergen St., Brooklyn, NY 11217, 718 272-2508.

RAMOS, Yolanda; '95 BS; Mutual Funds Admin.; The Bank of NY; r. 710 61st St. # 2f, Brooklyn, NY 11220, 718 492-6351. e-mail

RAMOS, Zenaida; '95 BA; 64 E 97th St. Apt. 5, New York, NY 10029.

RAMOS-SOLOLONGO, Denyse N., (Denyse N. Ramos); '89 BS; Correctional Probation Ofcr.; Dept. of Corrections State of FL, 12295 SW 133rd Ct., Miami, FL 33186, 305 234-2167; r. 16061 SW 152nd Ct., Miami, FL 33187, 305 233-1533; *Armando Sololongo;* Deanna, Aaron, Antonyo. e-mail

RAMOUTAR, Donny B.; '99 BS; Police Ofcr.; NYC Police Dept., New York, NY 10038; r. 461 51st St., Brooklyn, NY 11220.

RAMPIORAY, Kamini; '99 BS; Corporate Law Student; Hofstra Univ.; r. 103-61 102nd St., Ozone Park, NY 11417, 718 641-5261. e-mail

RAMPOLLA, Joseph J.; '94 MA; BA Ramapo Clg./Law & Society; Police Ofcr.; Park Ridge Police Dept., 55 Park Ave., Park Ridge, NJ 07656, 201 391-5400; r. 126 Center St., W. Milford, NJ 07480, 973 728-7625; *Pamela;* Stephen R. e-mail

RAMPOLLA, Mrs. Pamela A., (Pamela A. Hawley); '94 MA; BS Old Dominion Univ.; Social Worker; Div. of Youth & Family Svcs., 60 State St., Hackensack, NJ 07601, 201 996-8900; r. 126 Center St., W. Milford, NJ 07480, 973 728-7625; *Joseph;* Stephen. e-mail

RAMSARAN, Ramcharita; '96 BS; 1457 E 101st St., Brooklyn, NY 11236, 718 968-1758.

RAMSAY, Cherylann G.; '83 BS; 332 E 53rd St., Brooklyn, NY 11203, 718 735-4621.

RAMSAY, Elcah; '98 BA; Administrative Asst.; JP Morgan, 345 Park Ave., New York, NY 10017; r. 309 Lafayette Ave., Apt. 6 A, Brooklyn, NY 11238, 718 638-2891.

RAMSAY, Margaret; '95 BS; NYC Tax Investigator; NYC Dept. of Finance, 100 Adam St., New York, NY 10017, 718 881-4200; r. 1315 E 224th St., Bronx, NY 10466, 718 515-5819; Tristan Nelson. e-mail

RAMSAY, Rhona H.; '85 BS; 860 E. 55 St., Brooklyn, NY 11234, 718 735-4621.

RAMSAY, Walter J.; '94 MPA; 12 Alva Ln., Monticello, NY 12701.

RAMSEY, Charles E.; '72 AAS, '80 BA; Retired, Police Ofcr.; NYC Police Dept., 205 923-2817; r. 1136 15th Pl. SW, Birmingham, AL 35211, 205 923-7785; *Juanita;* Averil.

RAMSEY, Claude C.; '93 BS; Bay Shore, NY 11706.

RAMSEY, Danette; '90 BS; 773 Concourse Village, Bronx, NY 10451, 718 294-4875.

RAMSEY, Darryl M.; '95 BS; 352 W 117th St. Apt. 2f, New York, NY 10026.

RAMSEY, Keitha Y.; '80 BS; 2119 Claire Ct., Sugar Land, TX 77478, 281 494-7767.

RAMSEY, Richard M.; '85 BS; 192-16 119 Ave., St. Albans, NY 11412, 718 268-6297.

RAMSEY, Waltis, Jr.; '75 BA, '79 MA; Operations Mgr. Security Dept.; The Mt. Sinai Med. Ctr., One Gustave L Levy Pl., New York, NY 10029, 212 241-1220; r. 312 Beechwood Ln., Yorktown Hts., NY 10598, 914 245-5259; Natalie.

RANAGHAN, Eric; 80-18 85th Dr., Woodhaven, NY 11421.

RANCIC, Valentino; '95 BS; 50 Anderson Ave. Apt. 3, Fairview, NJ 07022.

RANDALL, Calvin P.; '79 BS; 23010 139th Ave., Jamaica, NY 11413.

RANDALL, Francis E.; '75 BA; CPCU Clg. of Ins.; Asst. Mgr.; TM Claims Svc. Inc. (Marine Ins.), 101 Park Ave., New York, NY 10178, 212 297-6752; r. 207 Clinton Ave., Staten Island, NY 10301, 718 442-2854; *Linda;* Melanie. e-mail

RANDALL, Keron K.; '92 DS; 6 Fox Hill Rd, Spring Vly., NY 10977.

RANDAZZO, Gary G.; '88 BS; 61 Gates Ave., Malverne, NY 11565.

RANDAZZO, Jason; '85 BS; Special Agt., F.B.I.; FBI, 26 Federal Plz., New York, NY 10278, 212 384-1000; r. 8724 115th St. Apt. 6j, Jamaica, NY 11418, 718 846-1516.

RANDAZZO, Leonard; '77 BA; 166 Wyckoff Ave., Brooklyn, NY 11237, 718 680-3882.

RANDAZZO, Todd; '78 BS; Police Ofcr.; Village of Lynbrook, Lynbrook, NY 11563; r. 485 Ocean Ave., Lynbrook, NY 11563, 516 599-1825; *Kay;* Ryan, Sean, Kathryn Skye.

RANDLE, Kevin M.; '95 BA; 25 Boerum St. Apt. 17f, Brooklyn, NY 11206, 718 388-6667.

RANDO, Gregory J.; '76 BS; 265 Mountview Ave., Staten Island, NY 10314.

RANDOLPH, Kirk A.; '93 BA; 3200 Broadway, New York, NY 10027.

RANDOLPH, Wanda; '91 BS; 861 E 219th St., Bronx, NY 10467, 718 547-9063.

RANGER, Hazel G.; '82 BA; 139 11 227 St., Laurelton, NY 11413, 718 298-6078.

RANIERI, Joseph N.; '99 MA; 531 E. 78th St. 3H, New York, NY 10021, 212 744-7584.

RANIOLA, John; '76 AS; 1232 Barry Dr. S # S., Valley Stream, NY 11580.

RANKIN, Ms. Louise M.; '98 BA; Intl. Civil Svc.; United Nations; r. 15 Exeter Ln., Manhasset, NY 11030, 516 627-0651.

RANKINE, Denise; '95 BS; 74 Sterling Rd, Elmont, NY 11003.

RAO, Anthony J.; '77 BS; 76-18 Glenmore Ave., Ozone Park, NY 11417, 718 459-9354.

RAPA, Helen M. '91 (See Rafaniello, Helen M.).

RAPALE, Sandra, '92 BS; 95 Richmond St., Brooklyn, NY 11208.

RAPHAEL, Giselle L.; '97 BA; Admissions Couns.; Ultrasound Diagnostic Sch., 4780 N State RD 7 Launderdale Lakes, Ft. Lauderdale, FL 33317, 954 733-8900; r. 10206 Harbor Inn Pl., Coral Springs, FL 33071; Ritchie Franks; Nilah, Michai.

RAPP, Edward J.; '79 BS; 2644 E 26th St. # 1fl, Brooklyn, NY 11235, 718 851-9008.

RAPTIS, Stacy; 300 Pelham Rd., New Rochelle, NY 10805, 914 576-1676.

RAPTIS, Thomas N.; '89 BS; Police Ofcr.; New Rochelle Police Dept., 475 North Ave., New Rochelle, NY 10801, 914 654-2300; r. 283 Mile Square Rd., Yonkers, NY 10701, 914 963-2864; Stephanie. e-mail

RASENBERGER, Joseph; '92 BS; 266 90th St. # 2, Brooklyn, NY 11209.

RASHBAUM, Maurice; BA Yale, LLB New York U Sch. of Law; Adjunct-Assoc. Prof.; John Jay; r. 139 E. 35th St., New York, NY 10016.

RASSO, Louis J.; '95 BS; 25 Spruce Ln., Staten Island, NY 10309.

RATCLIFFE, Robert G.; '78 AS; 8 Demartini Pl., Waldwick, NJ 07463.

RATNEY, Alyson D.; '97 BA; 692 Cleveland St. #1F, Brooklyn, NY 11208. e-mail

RATTIGAN, Wilfred S.; '81 BS; 608 Alabama Ave., Brooklyn, NY 11207, 718 363-2928.

RAUCH, Richard S.; '88 BS; 43-08 28th Ave. #8, Astoria, NY 11103, 718 897-9655.

RAUCHET, Joseph L.; '78 BS; Deputy Chief; NYS Organized Crime Task Force, 101 E. Post Rd., White Plains, NY 10601, 914 422-8777; r. 24 Waimer Pl., Staten Island, NY 10312, 718 966-3751.

RAVALGI, Julienne (See Salzano, Dr. Julienne).

RAVALGI, Patrica M.; '76 BA; 2168 E 13th St., Brooklyn, NY 11229.

RAVELO, Ms. Mercedes; '91 AS; BSBA City Univ. of NY, JD New York Law Sch.; Sr. Asst. Dir.; Hofstra Univ.-Public Safety, 17 Hofstra Info. Ctr., Hempstead, NY 11549, 516 463-7712. e-mail

RAVENELL, Jason; '96 BA; BS; Child Protective Spec.; Admin. for Children's Svcs., 150 William St., New York, NY 10038, 212 676-7211; r. Bronx, NY 10468. e-mail

RAVENS, Carl; '68 MPA; BBA, AAS City Clg.; Retired Asst. Chief; NYC Police Dept.; r. 2029 Ainlie #B, Boca Raton, FL 33434, 561 483-0805; Lillian; Eileen, Maxine, Michael. e-mail

RAVER, Deidre M.; '98 BS, '98 MA; Assoc.; Blackrock, New York, NY 10022, 212 409-3266; r. 118-66 Metropltn. Ave./6j, Kew Gardens, NY 11415, 718 849-9780. e-mail

RAWLES, Melba; '76 BS, '78 MS; Svc. Coord.; Canaan Housing Devel., 161 W 116th St., New York, NY 10026, 212 222-5445; r. 2289 Fifth Ave., New York, NY 10037, 212 926-8262; CJ Daniels.

RAWLINGS, Karen V.; '99 BA; 823 Marcy Ave. #1, Brooklyn, NY 11216, 718 638-6712.

RAWLS, Shanell; '96 BA; 148 W 142 St., New York, NY 10030, 315 839-5659.

RAY, Donald L.; '99 MA; BA Univ. of OK; Adjunct; John Jay Clg. of Criminal Justice, 4445 W 59th St., New York, NY 10019, 212 237-8934; r. 9-02 27th Ave., Astoria, NY 11102, 718 267-7260. e-mail

RAY, Robert J.; '74 BS; 152 72nd St., Brooklyn, NY 11209, 718 342-7276.

RAY, Thomas B.; '95 MPA; 8915 Metropolitan Ave. # 2r, Flushing, NY 11374, 718 275-2893.

RAY, Vern; '93 MPA; MA NJ City Univ.; Investigator-Child Protection; City of NY-Admin. for Children Svcs., 1274 Bedford Ave., Brooklyn, NY 11216; r. 216 Main St., Spotswood, NJ 08884; Judith. e-mail

RAYFIELD, Peter T.; '77 BS; Production Control Planner; r. 21 Larry Dr., Commack, NY 11725, 631 499-5775; Mary; Michael, Kenny, William, Christina, Maria, Cory. e-mail

RAYFORD, James C.; '95 BA; 1411 Linden Blvd. # 12d, Brooklyn, NY 11212.

RAYMOND, Catherine '85 (See Raymond-Bitz, Catherine, RN).

RAYMOND, Edward P.; '79 MPA; 24 Gallatin Dr., Dix Hills, NY 11746.

RAYMOND, Sherly; '99 BS; 2110 Beeekman St., Brooklyn, NY 11225, 718 875-2943.

RAYMOND, Woody; '98 BS; Network Admin.; Lissner & Lissner, 250 W 57th St. Ste. 615, New York, NY 10107; r. 817 E 21st St., Brooklyn, NY 11210, 718 421-4153. e-mail

RAYMOND, Zulma B.; '79 BS; 8 Fairgreen Ct., Cortlandt Manor, NY 10567, 914 271-2803.

RAYMOND-BITZ, Catherine, RN, (Catherine Raymond); '85 MA; BLA Lehman Clg., RN LICH Sch. of Nursing; Asst. Chief; NYC Dept. of Corrections, E. Elmhurst, NY 11370; r. 8736 Little Neck Pkwy., Floral Park, NY 11001; Randolph.

RAYNOR, David N.; '95 BA; 247 Eastwood Ave., Deer Park, NY 11729, 631 667-1696.

RAZACK, Sakhawat; '90 BS; 10023 92nd Ave., Jamaica, NY 11418, 718 850-8984.

RAZUKAS, Matthew D.; '93 BS; 8011 New Colony Ct., Severn, MD 21144.

RAZZI, Dana L.; '99, MA; 402 Benson Ave., Glenolden, PA 19036, 610 532-4670.

RAZZORE, Annmarie; '93 BA, '93 CERT; Med. Secy.; Barton Nisonson MDPC, 130 E 77th St., New York, NY 10021; r. 35 May Ave., Staten Island, NY 10314; John; Alexa.

REALE, Alan P.; '76 BA; 5117 48th St., Flushing, NY 11377.

REALE, Ronald G.; '85 BS; Detective Sgt; Union Cnty. Prosecutors Ofc., 32 Rahway Ave., Elizabeth, NJ 07202, 908 527-4500; r. 440 Shearer Ave., Union, NJ 07083, 908 353-5188.

REARDON, Katherine B.; '87 MA; 2 Byron Ln., Larchmont, NY 10538.

REARDON, Norbert J.; '70 AA, '71 BS; Retired; r. 50 Mahogany Dr., Naples, FL 34108, 941 597-8262.

REATEGUI, David; '92 BS; 25619 86th Ave., Floral Park, NY 11001.

REAVES-BEY, Leroy; 149 Cornelia St., Brooklyn, NY 11221, 718 338-4971.

REAVIS, Piar N.; '85 MA; 88 Long Pond Ln., Staten Island, NY 10304, 718 448-6780.

REBOYRAS, Jessica M.; '99 BA; 250 E.176Th St. Apt. 3G, Bronx, NY 10457, 718 294-2063.

RECHENBERG, Jan M.; '76 BA; Owner; Golden Spike Intl., 1700 Grand Concourse, Bronx, NY 10457, 718 294-1614; r. same. e-mail

REDDICK, Euphemia S.; '96 BA; 62 E 92nd St. # 6, New York, NY 10128.

REDDIN, James P.; '81 BA; 44 S Evergreen Dr., Selden, NY 11784, 631 696-8311.

REDDING, Assunta S.; '99 BA; Marist Clg. Grd. Sch.; Supervising Administrative Law Judg; Traffic Violations Bureau-DMV, Brooklyn, NY 11201; r. 2504 85 St., Brooklyn, NY 11214.

REDDINGTON, Francis; '82 MA; 140 Essex St., Jersey City, NJ 07302.

REDICAN, Joseph E.; '79 BS; 3436 Roxbury Ave., Wantagh, NY 11793; Maryann; Joseph.

REDMAN, Stacy L.; '96 BS; 21 Lamont Ct., Brooklyn, NY 11225, 718 604-0976.

REDMAN, Stephanie C. '84 (See Redman-Modeste, Stephanie C.).

REDMAN-MODESTE, Stephanie C. (Stephanie C. Redman); '84 BS; MS Brooklyn Clg.; Child Protective Spec.; Admin. of Children Svcs., 150 Williams, New York, NY 10019; r. 591 Ocean Ave., Brooklyn, NY 11226, 718 462-2482.

REDMOND, Benjamin J.; '71 MPA; 278 Taft Ct., River Edge, NJ 07661.

REDMOND, Robin L.; '94 MA; BA CW Post; Dir. of Social Svcs.; Flatbush Devel. Corp., 1616 New Kirk Ave., Flatbush, NY 11226, 718 859-3800; r. 20807 Bayside, Breezy Pt., NY 11697, 718 474-4508.

REDMOND, Thomas J.; '79 BS; AVP/ Corp. Security; Merrill Lynch, WFC S. Twr. 6fl NewYork NY, New York, NY 10080, 212 236-3738; r. 201 Earl St., E. Williston, NY 11596, 516 741-8471; Florence; Alison, Kathryn.

REED, Anthony; '86 BS; 242 Vernon Ave., Brooklyn, NY 11206, 718 222-1201.

REED, Jasmine M.; '99 BA; Paralegal; Brecher Fishman Law Firm, 222 Brodway, New York, NY 10038, 212 341-7952; r. 1066 Walton Ave., Apt. 2, Bronx, NY 10452, 718 681-1060; Daniel. e-mail

REED, Marylin '81 (See Borquàye, Marylin).

REED, Rachel A.; '99 BA; 8 Prospect St.(#N2), Caldwell, NJ 07006, 973 226-6315.

REED, Robert; '82 BS; 68 Villa Nova St., Staten Island, NY 10314.

REED, Shelley, Jr.; '77 AS, '80 BS, '82 MPA; Real Estate/Ins. & Securities; Century 21, 4226 White Plains Rd, Bronx, NY 10466, 718 994-7300; r. Yonkers, NY 10701. e-mail

REEKIE, Robert; '76 MA; Detective Sgt; NYPD, New York, NY 10007; r. 8 Apollo Ct., Nanuet, NY 10954, 914 623-6334. e-mail

REEKIE, Robert; '99 BS; AS SUNY-Cobleskill; NYC Police Ofcr.; Mounted Unit; r. 4 Brookside Ave., New City, NY 10956.

REEN, Shaun M.; '98 MS; 540 Beach 136th St., Belle Harbor, NY 11694, 718 474-3020.

REERS, Richard L.; '75 BS; 153 Park Ave., Williston Park, NY 11596.

REESE, Lavinia; '79 BA; 75 Park Ter. E Apt. D30, New York, NY 10034, 212 569-3532.

REEVES, Lee; '82 BS; Sergeant; NYPD, New York, NY 10038; r. 14 Moffat Rd, Washingtonville, NY 10992; *Mary Ellen;* Kaleigh, Kristen. e-mail

REFUTO, George J.; '77 BA; 19 Locust Ave., Staten Island, NY 10306.

REGALADO, Ana R.; '97 BA; 11 Stagg St. #1, Brooklyn, NY 11206.

REGAN, Charles E.; '77 BS; Ret. Sgt; NYC Police Dept.; r. 36 Shadow Ln., Staten Island, NY 10306, 718 667-5645.

REGAN, James K.; '78 MA; Uniformed Court Ofcr.; Ct. Security Svcs.-Bronx Civil Ct, 851 Grand Concourse-RM.B119, Bronx, NY 10451, 718 590-3609; r. 91 Christopher St. Apt. 2, New York, NY 10014, 212 989-5707.

REGAN, John M.; '77 BS, '81 MPA; Capt.; NYPD, Police Plz., New York, NY 10038, 718 797-1845; r. 2257 E 65th St., Brooklyn, NY 11234, 718 251-3632; *Joan;* Denise, Jennifer. e-mail

REGAN, Kevin J.; '78 MA; BBA St. Johns Univ.; Deputy Commisioner; Town of Hempstead, 350 Front St., Hempstead, NY 11550, 516 489-5000; r. 28 Chase Ln., Levittown, NY 11756, 516 731-5016; *Joann;* Dierdre, Kevin Jr, Erin.

REGAN, Patrick J.; MA SUNY-Geneseo, Sullivan Co. Comm; Clg. Prog. Dir.; GNNY State Div. Criminal Justice, US 4 Tower Pl., Albany, NY; r. 7 Wooddale Dr., Ballston Lake, NY 12019; *Margaret;* Erin, Brenda. e-mail

REGESTER, Mrs. Kimberly, (Kimberly Hardy); '99 AS; Correction Ofcr.; NYC Dept. of Corrections, 60 Hudson St., New York, NY 10013, 212 266-1000; r. 1270 E. 51st St., Brooklyn, NY 11234, 718 241-1886; *Anthony;* Jada Krystine. e-mail

REGINA, Croswell '92 (See Turner, Mrs. Regina).

REGIS, Ms. K. F.; '95 BS; Probation Ofcr.; NYC Dept. of Probation, 115 Leonard St., New York, NY 10013, 718 876-5696; r. 827 Beverly Rd., Brooklyn, NY 11218, 718 854-5858. e-mail

REGLER, John W.; '82 BA; 140 Cornwell Ave., Williston Park, NY 11596.

REGO, Simon A.; '95 MA; PSYM Rutgers Univ.; Grad. Student-Doctoral Candidate; Rutgers Univ., New Brunswick, NJ 08901; r. 72 D'Arcy Magee Cres., West Hill, ON, Canada M1C 2T5. e-mail

REGUS, Judith G.; '97 BS; 39-62 64th St., Woodside, NY 11377.

REHAL, Joseph G.; '89 BS, '94 MA; BS, MA JJC; Probation Ofcr.; NYC Probation Dept., 100 Centre St., New York, NY 10013, 212 442-9672; r. 30 Osage Ct., Coram, NY 11727, 631 474-9864; *Tureka Ray;* Joseph III, Jaelisa.

REIBEL, Denise L.; '99 BA; 130 Spruce St., Freehold, NJ 07728, 732 577-9345.

REIBSCHEID, Mark A.; '99 BA; Social Worker-Foster Care; New York Foundling Hosp., 11-43 47th Ave., Long Island City, NY 11101, 718 784-4422; r. 1940 Ocean Ave. 3G, Brooklyn, NY 11230, 718 339-2537. e-mail

REICHENBACH, Robert W.; '77 BS; 59-35 156 St., Flushing, NY 11355.

REID, Anne E.; '99 BA; 475 Mill Rd, Staten Island, NY 10306, 718 979-6045.

REID, Antoinette M.; '97 BA; 115 Eastern Pkwy., Brooklyn, NY 11238, 718 622-1395.

REID, Arlene J. '75 (See Foubister, Arlene J.).

REID, Armando E.; '77 BA; 286 E 40 St., Brooklyn, NY 11203, 718 455-0069.

REID, Deborah E.; '87 BS; 1620 E. 12th St. #3C, Brooklyn, NY 11229, 718 627-0254.

REID, Diana M.; '95 BS; 706 Soundview Ave., Bronx, NY 10473, 718 325-6821.

REID, Diane P.; '86 MA; BA Univ. of Texas; Cnslt.; Forensic Jury Rsch., 4124 Ballard Tr., The Colony, TX 75056, 972 625-5622.

REID, Mrs. Dorothy L.; '79 BA; Retired-Deputy Supt. of Security; NYS Dept. of Correctional Svcs.; r. 457 Lily Pond Rd, Granville, NY 12832, 518 642-2338; *Luther;* Kenyatta Lambie.

REID, Dyke O.; '97 BA, '98 BA; 2613 Avenue D # 1b, Brooklyn, NY 11226, 718 703-4977.

REID, Elenor; '93 BS; 172-10 133rd Ave., Jamaica, NY 11434, 718 835-5645.

REID, Ethan E.; '84 BS; 63 7th St., Pelham, NY 10803, 914 271-9352.

REID, Gloria M.; '80 BA; Plant Mgr.; US Postal Svc., 1050 Forbell St., Brooklyn, NY 11256, 718 348-3100; r. 156 Marvin Ave., Uniondale, NY 11553, 516 485-2385. e-mail

REID, Hattie; '95 BA; 8800 Shore Front, Far Rockaway, NY 11693.

REID, Howard; '90 BA; 1291 Givan Ave., Bronx, NY 10469, 718 324-9232.

REID, Jennifer J. '94 (See Arroyo, Jennifer R.).

REID, Jermaine; '96 BS; 797 Schenck Ave. #1A, Brooklyn, NY 11207, 718 251-3647.

REID, Julanne L.; '78 BS; MS Baruch Univ.; Dir.; Medger Evers Clg., Brooklyn, NY 11225, 718 270-6474; r. 610 Empire Blvd., Brooklyn, NY 11213, 718 756-2872. e-mail

REID, Karlene; '90 BS; 114 Hempstead Rd, Spring Vly., NY 10977.

REID, Keith L.; '94 BS; JD Rutgers Univ.; Mgr. of Customer Svc.; US Postal Svc., 2101 Rte. 27, Edison, NJ 08817, 732 287-4311; r. 1405 Sabrina Ln., Piscataway, NJ 08854, 732 819-8487; *Kim C.*

REID, Kenneth; '89 BS; 55 Austin Pl. # 5, Staten Island, NY 10304.

REID, LaLisa; '89 BS; 120 Casals Pl. # 16, Bronx, NY 10475; Tarice, Latrel.

REID, Lorna P.; '95 BA; 602 Hegeman Ave., Brooklyn, NY 11207, 718 444-2629.

REID, Luther; '79 BA; Retired-Trng. Lt.; NYS Dept. of Correctional Svcs.; r. 457 Lily Pond Rd, Granville, NY 12832, 518 642-2338; *Dorothy;* Brian, Martin, Calvin.

REID, Nora A.; '85 CERT; 240 Chattanooga St. Apt. 28, San Francisco, CA 94114, 415 695-0383.

REID, Shaun C., Esq.; '95 BS; JD Fordham Law Sch.; Atty.; Grotta Glassman & Hoffman, 125 W. 55th St., New York, NY 10019, 212 315-3510; r. 278 E 55th St., Brooklyn, NY 11203, 718 209-6677. e-mail

REID, Thomas P.; '68 BS; 4060 New York Ave., Seaford, NY 11783, 516 501-0612.

REID, Trevor M.; '84 MPA; 38 Foster Ave., Valley Stream, NY 11580.

REIDER, Lester; '74 BS; 698 Sherman Ct., Westbury, NY 11590, 516 997-4334.

REID-WALSTON, Barbara; '93 BS; 835 Willoughby Ave., Brooklyn, NY 11206, 718 599-5897.

REILL, Mary V. '77 (See Lessner, Mrs. Mary V.).

REILLY, Andrew J.; '78 BS; 140 Vermilyea Ave. Apt. 2a, New York, NY 10034, 212 567-9830.

REILLY, Edward; '96 BS; 23 Leslie Ln., Massapequa, NY 11758.

REILLY, James P.; '75 MA; FBI Special Agent; 1600 Golf Rd, Rolling Meadows, IL 60008, 847 290-0525; r. 1036 E Jules St., Arlington Hts., IL 60004, 847 398-7538. e-mail

REILLY, Janet S., (Janet Schulte); '76 BA; Underwriter; The Travelers Ins. Grp., 1000 Legion Pl., Orlando, FL 32801, 407 649-3735; r. 4717 Chardonnay Ln., Port Orange, FL 32119, 904 761-4475; *Paul;* Paul Jr, Erin, Andrea.

REILLY, John T.; '75 BA, '77 MA; 325 Hampton Pl., Bluffton, SC 29910, 843 705-3406.

REILLY, Joseph A.; '75 MA; 204 Gruber Ct., W. Hempstead, NY 11552, 516 822-0665.

REILLY, Michael; '96 BS; 53 Camport Blvd., Staten Island, NY 10305, 718 605-9562.

REILLY, Nancy A.; '80 BA; 1493 Ericson Pl., Bronx, NY 10461, 718 823-2107.

REILLY, Paul J.; '76 BS; Pres.; PJR Foods Inc., 4050 S. Ridgewood Ave., Port Orange, FL 32127, 904 761-2181; r. 4717 Chardonnay Ln., Port Orange, FL 32119, 904 761-4475; *Janet; Paul Jr., Erin, Andrea.* e-mail

REILLY, Peter J.; '88 BS; 4356 Martha Ave., Bronx, NY 10470, 718 994-5473.

REILLY, Rupert A.; '82 AS, '83 BS; 178 Prospect Park, Brooklyn, NY 11215, 718 331-3545.

REILLY, Theresa M.; '94 BA; 10210 66th Rd Apt. 19k, Flushing, NY 11375, 718 204-9852.

REILLY, Thomas J.; '78 MA; 1060 Park Ave. #7A, New York, NY 10128, 315 339-0143.

REILLY, Thomas W.; '74 BS; MS CW Post; Retired Lt./Security Mgr.; NYC/Piser Inc.; r. 89 Village Line Rd, Babylon, NY 11702, 631 587-9758. e-mail

REILLY, William F.; '75 BS; 93 Landing Rd, Miller Place, NY 11764.

REILLY, William G.; '77 BA; 29 Abeel St. Apt. 4a, Yonkers, NY 10705, 914 423-4476.

REIMAN, Kenneth R.; '81 MPA; Ret. Supv.; NYC Police Dept. Organized Crime Control, Bureau/Narcotics Div./Brooklyn, Trustee For 1013 Organization; r. Brooklyn, NY 11234, 718 252-3749.

REIMANN, Elsbeth; '76 AA, '77 BA, '79 MPA; Community Liaison; Assembly Member Pete Grannis, 1672 First Ave., New York, NY 10128, 212 860-4906; r. 222 E 93rd St. Apt. 38h, New York, NY 10128, 212 427-3702.

REINERT, Mendoza L.; '98 MA; 4060 Bermuda Dunes Pl., Bonita, CA 91902, 619 267-8657.

REINGOLD, Michael; '96 BA; 511 E. 80th St., New York, NY 10021.

REINHARDT, Richard; '96 BA; 93 Neptune Ave., Neptune, NJ 07753, 732 536-5277.

REINHARDT, Ronald R.; '77 AS; 1729 Bay Ridge Pkwy., Brooklyn, NY 11204.

REINHARDT-O'BRIEN, Mary E.; '86 BA; 39 S Portland Ave., Brooklyn, NY 11217, 718 855-3361.

REINKE, John J.; '80 BS; 692 9th St., Secaucus, NJ 07094, 201 865-5045.

REINKING, Robert F.; '90 BS; 525 Grand Blvd., Long Beach, NY 11561.

REINOSO, Rafael A.; '88 MPA; 47 Ft. Washington Ave. Apt. 3, New York, NY 10032.

REIS, Thomas C.; '99 BA; 6 Celestial Way, Newburgh, NY 12550, 914 856-7256.

REISMAN, Barbara; '86 MA; MSED, BS Hunter Clg.; Dir. of Transportation Svcs.; American Red Cross, Greater New York; r. 5609 15th Ave. Apt. 6c, Brooklyn, NY 11219, 718 851-2031. e-mail

REISS, Gary; '89 BS; Capt.; New York Police Dept., I Police Plz., New York, NY 10001, 212 374-5000.

REITANO, Anthony; '77 BA; 3810 Chesterfield Dr., Mohegan Lake, NY 10547.

REITKOPF, Patricia B.; '86 MA; 250 E. 87th St., New York, NY 10128, 212 534-4926.

RELLO, John J.; '98 BS; Sheriff Ofcr.; Essex Cnty. Sheriff Dept., 50 Nelson Pl., Newark, NJ 07102, 973 621-4097; r. 62 St. Charles Ave., W. Caldwell, NJ 07006, 973 882-1319.

REMICE, Yvette T.; '81 BA; 137-29 173rd St., Jamaica, NY 11434.

REMON, Malena C.; '95 BS; Paralegal; Sullivan, Papain, Block, McGrath, Cannavo, 120 Broadway, New York, NY 10271, 212 732-9000; r. 9232 43rd Ave., Elmhurst, NY 11373, 718 335-5585. e-mail

RENAUD, Jacqueline '89 (See Rivera, Jacqueline).

RENDA, Eugene; '88 BS; 1416 74th St., Brooklyn, NY 11228, 718 252-7828.

RENDEIRO, Alfred P.; '78 MA; 19 Shotwell Ave., Staten Island, NY 10312, 718 356-4249.

RENNER, Nils; '99 BA; Healthcare Provider; Long Head Injury, 65 Austin Blvd., Commack, NY 11725, 631 543-2245; r. 147 Walter Ave., Hauppauge, NY 11788, 631 979-6981; *Ann Marie Sheehan-Renner.* e-mail

RENOIS, Paul J.; '79 MA; 205 Reflections Dr., San Ramon, CA 94583.

RENSCH, Laura; '95 BA; 664 Blueridge Dr., Medford, NY 11763.

RENTON, Benjamin E.; '77 BS; POB 237, Larchmont, NY 10538.

RENTZ, Tracy D.; '91 BA; MSED Dowling Clg.; Special Educ. Tchr.; Central Islip UFSD, O'Neill Elem Sch., 50 Wheeler Rd, Central Islip, NY 11722, 631 348-5061; r. 1136 Nugent Ave., Bay Shore, NY 11706, 631 242-6970; Malik N. e-mail

RENZ, Peter H.; '77 MPA; BA Long Island Univ.; Analyst; NYS Higher Educ.; r. 6 W. Bayberry Rd, Glenmont, NY 12077, 518 478-0335. e-mail

RENZULLO, Vittoria; '82 BS; 320 Jessamine Ave., Yonkers, NY 10701.

REPACI, Richard; '92 MA; 2025 82nd St., Brooklyn, NY 11214.

REPETTO, Tom; Citizen's Crime Commission, New York, NY 10176.

RESKO, Ronald J.; '99 BS; Police Ofcr.; NYPD, 1 Police Pl., New York, NY 10025, 212 258-2840; r. 166 W. 75th St., Apt. 918, New York, NY 10023, 212 579-8985.

RESKOW, Kristin E.; '94 BA; 3337 29th St., Long Island City, NY 11106.

RESTO, Hipolito; '76 BS; 44 Metropolitan Wl, Bronx, NY 10462, 718 590-6793.

RESTO, Lourdes; '85 BA; 960 E 163rd St. # 3, Bronx, NY 10459, 718 590-6793.

RESUA, Ronald; '80 MS; 41 Dickson St., Inwood, NY 11096.

RESZETYLO, Karen; '99 BA; 523 E 85 St. #5A, New York, NY 10028, 212 535-0424.

REUBEN, Ernest M.; '95 BS; 121 Parkside Ave. Apt. 24, Brooklyn, NY 11226, 718 851-8181.

REYES, Alida; '78 BS; 1723 Cornelia St., Flushing, NY 11385, 718 386-2977.

REYES, Alma T.; '85 BA; 65-10 108 St., Forest Hills, NY 11375.

REYES, Ana A.; '99 BA; Paralegal Workers Compensation; Brecher Fishman Pasternack Poposh et al, Livingston St. 22nd Fl., Brooklyn, NY 11201, 718 643-8300; r. 2676 Morris Ave. #21, Bronx, NY 10468, 718 933-1954; *Juan Carlos Henriquez;* Juan Carlos Jr. e-mail

REYES, Donna; '84 BS; MS North Carolina A&T; Couns.; Moses Cone Behavioral Health Ctr., 700 Walter Reed Dr., Greensboro, NC 27403, 336 852-4821; r. 3219 Regents Park Ln. Unit F, Greensboro, NC 27455, 336 545-6530.

REYES, Frank M.; '94 BS; 205 W. 103 St., New York, NY 10025.

REYES, Gloria; '96 BS; 102-01 134th St., Richmond Hill, NY 11419, 718 845-5527.

REYES, Henry; '97 BA; 521 W. 185th St., New York, NY 10033.

REYES, Jacayra C.; '99 BS; 88 Saratoga Ave., Yonkers, NY 10705, 914 709-9266.

REYES, Javier; '85 BS; 185 Audubon Ave. #4, New York, NY 10033.

REYES, Jose; '96 BA; 236 Mott St. 6, New York, NY 10012.

REYES, Joselyne A.; '99 BA; Social Worker; Talbot Perkins, 116 W. 32nd St., New York, NY 10001, 212 736-2510; r. 3045 Godwin Ter. #4K, Bronx, NY 10463, 718 884-0894. e-mail

REYES, Josephine; '83 BA; 14142 78th Ave., Flushing, NY 11367, 718 278-7126.

REYES, Kimberly; '91 BA; 720 E 39th St., Brooklyn, NY 11203, 718 435-8315.

REYES, Leila T.; '92 BA; 360 E 55th St., Apt. 3C, New York, NY 10022.

REYES, Lina E.; '98 BA; 510 W. 184 St. #2, New York, NY 10033, 212 795-2103.

REYES, Moses; '97 BA; 511 W 167th St., New York, NY 10032.

REYES, Olga; '95 BA; Social Ins. Spec.; Social Security Admin., Brooklyn, NY 11207, 718 485-7085; r. 150 Jerome St. # 1st, Brooklyn, NY 11207, 718 827-2723. e-mail

REYES, Rachel; '89 BS; MSED Hunter Clg., Boston Clg.; Sergeant; New York Police Dept.; r. 10 Morris Ave., Florida, NY 10921, 914 651-1048.

REYES, Sudhey; '99 BA; Mgr.; New York Business Ctrs., 811 7th Ave., New York, NY 10019, 212 841-6777; r. 550 53 St., Brooklyn, NY 11220, 718 439-7072. e-mail

REYES, Victor L.; '78 BA; 193 Schermerhorn S, Brooklyn, NY 11201, 718 625-5994.

REYES, William; '79 BS; 320 E 103rd St. #6A, New York, NY 10029.

REYES, William M.; '87 AS; 5416 152nd St., Flushing, NY 11355.

REYES, Yahayra; '99 BS; Corporate Paralegal; Windels Marx Lane & Mittendorf, LLP, 156 W. 56th St., 23rd Fl., New York, NY 10019, 212 237-1188; r. 88 Saratoga Ave., Yonkers, NY 10705, 914 966-1593. e-mail

REYNA, Yocasta; '86 BA; 63 Post Ave. #51, New York, NY 10034.

REYNOLDS, Bertrand A.; '88 BA; 584 Northern Pkwy., Uniondale, NY 11553, 516 565-2095.

REYNOLDS, George F.; '95 AS; Retired Police Sergeant; NYC Police Dept.; r. 21 Garland Ct., Brooklyn, NY 11229, 718 332-1263. e-mail

REYNOLDS, Gertrude; '82 BA; 417 St. Johns Pl., Brooklyn, NY 11238, 718 759-0275.

REYNOLDS, Linda-Keisha M.; '80 MA; BA Hampton Univ.; Chief Dept. Sheriff Scoff Patrol; NYC Sheriff's Ofc., 550 W. 59th St., New York, NY 10019, 212 397-8724; r. 300 Cathedral Pkwy., Apt. 9A, New York, NY 10026, 212 932-8789. e-mail

REYNOLDS, Patrick; '85 MPA; BA William Paterson Clg.; Chief; Maywood Police Dept., Maywood, NJ 07607, 201 845-8800; r. 194 Desoto Ave., Maywood, NJ 07607, 201 845-2926; *Barbara*. e-mail

REYNOLDS, Sandra M.; '93 BS; 599 E 80th St., Brooklyn, NY 11236, 718 759-0275.

REYNOLDS, Stephen; '89 BS, '95 MA; 385 Lathrop Ave., Staten Island, NY 10302.

REYNOSO, Alexa J.; '99 BA; Pre-Employment Instr.; Alianza Dominicana, Inc., 2410 Amsterdam Ave., New York, NY 10033, 212 740-7600; r. 56 W 180th St. #4E, Bronx, NY 10453, 718 716-3901. e-mail

REYNOSO, Edgar; '92 BA; 1427 Wythe Pl. Apt. 6c, Bronx, NY 10452, 718 537-0642. e-mail

REYNOSO, Florinda; '95 BA; 130 W 228th St. Apt. 5f, Bronx, NY 10463, 718 367-8196.

REZOAGLI, Frank; '79 MA; BA Wagner Clg.; Supreme Criminal Term; Supreme Ct. of New York; r. 135 Kelvin Ave., Staten Island, NY 10306, 718 667-5342. e-mail

RHEES, Alma; '84 AS; POB 452075, Kissimmee, FL 34745, 407 846-7389.

RHEM, Karen B.; '83 BS; CERT. Adelphi Univ.; Train Dispatcher & Mgr.; NYC Transit Authority, 370 Jay St., Brooklyn, NY 11201, 718 243-3000; r. 526 Linwood St., Brooklyn, NY 11208, 718 277-1364.

RHETT, Sheila A.; '83 BA; Housing Mgr.; NYC Housing Authority, New York, NY 10001; r. 322 Old Forge Dr., Bath, PA 18014, 610 837-6416.

RHODEN, Audrey E.; '89 BA; 616 E. 37th St. P, Brooklyn, NY 11203, 718 968-8710.

RHODEN, Horace; '87 BS; 1007 Sutter Ave., Brooklyn, NY 11208, 718 968-8710.

RHODES, Frank J.; '89 MA; 2243 Harris Hill Rd, Elmira, NY 14903, 607 732-3078.

RHODES, Onesia S.; '98 BS; Customer Svc.; Seamen's Furniture, 300 Crossways Park Dr., Woodbury, NY 11797, 516 496-9560; r. 218-12 112 Ave., Queens Vlg., NY 11429, 718 465-5954; Damon Scott Jr.

RHODES, Rebecca; '75 MA; 1037 Annapolis St., Far Rockaway, NY 11691, 718 471-8306.

RHONDA, Harris L.; '98 BA; 522 Westgate Ave., Edison, NJ 08820.

RIAZ, Aneerah '93 (See Ali, Mrs. Aneerah R.).

RIBAUDO, Mark A.; '82 BA; 135-35 122 St., Jamaica, NY 11420, 718 279-1049.

RIBEIRO, Gemma E., (Gemma E. Pujadas); '99 BA; Community Assoc.; Kings Cnty. Dist. Atty., 350 Jay St., Brooklyn, NY 11201, 718 250-2080; r. 87-42 126th St. #3, Richmond Hill, NY 11418, 718 805-1187; Carla, Stephan. e-mail

RICALDE, Russell J.; '89 BA; 402 Argyle Rd, E. Meadow, NY 11554.

RICARDO, Myrilin U.; '72 BS; 524 NW San Remo Cir., Port St. Lucie, FL 34986, 561 878-6142.

RICARDO, Pilar E.; '81 BS; 78 Post Ave. Apt. 1m, New York, NY 10034.

RICCARDI, Kenneth P.; '76 BS, '89 MPA; Archivist/Public Svcs. Librarian; Laguardia Community Clg., 31-10 Thomson Ave., Long Island City, NY 11101, 718 482-5434; r. 39-27 44th St., Sunnyside, NY 11104, 718 729-6460.

RICCI, Carmen M.; '95 BS; 2809 Tilden Ave., Brooklyn, NY 11226, 718 856-5881.

RICCIO, Arthur P.; '80 AS; Retired-Computer Prog.,Police Offic; NYC Police Dept.; r. 16030 99th St., Howard Bch., NY 11414, 718 835-9563; *Angela; Michelle, Arthur.*

RICCIO, Joseph P.; '78 MA; BA St. Johns Univ.; Supv/Special Agt.; Nav. Criminal Investigative Svc., 8901 Wisconsin Ave., Bethesda, MD 20889, 301 295-0570; r. 1276 N Wayne St. Ph 18, Arlington, VA 22201, 703 243-0846.

RICCIUTO, Michael; '77 MA; 39 Stratford Dr., Englishtown, NJ 07726.

RICCOBONO, Salvatore; '77 AS; 3332 12th Ave., Brooklyn, NY 11218.

RICE, Damon E.; '99 BS; 205 Harry S Truman Dr. Apt. 33, Largo, MD 20774, 301 216-9884.

RICE, James T.; 55-01 31st Ave., Woodside, NY 11377, 718 217-5007.

RICE, Robert D.; '73 BA; 67 Park Pl., Staten Island, NY 10301.

RICE, Sharnik; '96 BS; 3423 Wickham #2, Bronx, NY 10469, 718 590-5895.

RICEVUTO, Anthony R.; '91 BS; 1084 Morris Park Ave., Bronx, NY 10461.

RICH, Cecelia; '96 BS; 137-20 45th Ave. #2, Flushing, NY 11355, 718 341-6778.

RICH APPELBERG, Lori; '85 MA; 9 Edgewood Rd., Monroe, CT 06468, 203 261-9767.

RICHARDS, Andrea N.; '97 BA; 31-25 98th St., E. Elmhurst, NY 11369, 718 454-9427.

RICHARDS, Emanuel (Manny) H., Jr.; '86 BS; US Postal Clerk/NY Dept. Corr. Ret; US Postal Svc., General Processing/Dist. Ctr., 1905 S I 85 Service Rd., Charlotte, NC 28228, 704 393-4480; r. 9431 Arborview Ct., Charlotte, NC 28269, 704 599-1805; *Gloria Y.; Emanuel H. III, Gia R. Byrd.* e-mail

RICHARDS, Felicia A.; '92 BA; 130 Bristol St. #1F, Brooklyn, NY 11212.

RICHARDS, Holly; '92 BA; 21 Birchwood Rd, Coram, NY 11727, 631 736-9865.

RICHARDS, Jeannette R.; '99 BA; 2278 Atlantic Ave., Brooklyn, NY 11233, 718 498-6412.

RICHARDS, Jodi J.; '87 MA; 772 E El Conquistador, Palm Spgs., CA 92262, 760 322-0134.

RICHARDS, Kimberly A.; '96 BA; 22 Freedom Rd., Pleasant Vly., NY 12569, 518 789-3528.

RICHARDS, Lorraine; '95 BA; 1333 C St., Elmont, NY 11003, 516 326-3275.

RICHARDS, Luis A.; '84 AS; 1070 Lafayette Ave., Brooklyn, NY 11221, 718 467-7021.

RICHARDS, Nadege; '99 BS; 32 Nicholas Ave. 1 Fl., Brooklyn, NY 11208, 718 647-3511.

RICHARDS, Stephne; '93 BS; 1526 New York Ave., Brooklyn, NY 11210, 718 756-5836.

RICHARDSON, Barbara; '90 BA; 285 E 35th St., Brooklyn, NY 11203, 718 363-9150.

RICHARDSON, Brenda, (Brenda Bernard); '85 BS; 18902 64th Ave., Apt. 11J, Fresh Meadows, NY 11365, 718 217-1012; *Bobby;* Jelesa.

RICHARDSON, Bruce A.; '99 BS; 958 E 102St., Brooklyn, NY 11236, 718 363-9150.

RICHARDSON, Cheryl J.; '87 BS; 2130 Quimby Ave., Bronx, NY 10473, 718 671-5353.

RICHARDSON, D. O.; '76 BA; 128-35 226 St., Jamaica, NY 11413, 718 476-5966.

RICHARDSON, Ernest V.; '90 MA; 2955 Randall Ave., Bronx, NY 10465, 718 798-9511.

RICHARDSON, Homer W.; '76 BA; 740 Miller Ave., Brooklyn, NY 11207, 718 209-0897.

RICHARDSON, Joanne A. '89 (See Richardson Anthony, Joanne A., Esq.).

RICHARDSON, Joseph R.; '76 BS; 11837 219th St., Jamaica, NY 11411.

RICHARDSON, June L.; '81 BS; 279 Lincoln Ave., Roosevelt, NY 11575, 516 681-0954.

RICHARDSON, Kevin S.; '88 BS; 629 A Madison St., Brooklyn, NY 11221, 718 209-0897.

RICHARDSON, Maureen G.; '86 BS; 13 Timber Trce, Ballston Spa, NY 12020, 518 882-9855.

RICHARDSON, Randall; '76 MPA; 25 N Wickom Dr., Westfield, NJ 07090, 908 233-5080.

RICHARDSON, Steven J.; '79 BS; 596 E 7th St., Brooklyn, NY 11218, 718 346-3538.

RICHARDSON, Thomas; '99 BS; Lt.; NYPD; r. 531 N. Corona Ave., Valley Stream, NY 11580. e-mail

RICHARDSON, Yanicke; '99 BA; 254 Stanley Ave., Brooklyn, NY 11207, 718 927-0106.

RICHARDSON ANTHONY, Joanne A., Esq., (Joanne A. Richardson); '89 BS; JD Benjamin Cardozo Law Sch.; Atty.; Thomas & Anthony LLP, 299 Broadway, New York, NY 10007, 212 385-4840; r. 13720 223rd St., Laurelton, NY 11413, 718 723-1137. e-mail

RICHBURG, Lionel; '76 BS; Firefighter Capt.; NYC Fire Dept., 9 Metro Tech, Brooklyn, NY 11201; r. 427 Holly Pl., W. Hempstead, NY 11552, 516 764-5242.

RICHIEZ, Irving G.; '99 BA; Admin. Asst./Cnslt.; T.H. Family Inc.; r. 75 W. End Ave. #C16H, New York, NY 10023, 212 582-6693.

RICKMAN, Marci '85 (See Pagano, Ms. Marci).

RIDDICK, Robert R.; '85 BS; 119 Hickory Rd, Somerset, NJ 08873, 732 247-4332.

RIDGES, Thomas C.; '95 BA; 824 Park Ave. #7, Brooklyn, NY 11206, 718 453-1453.

RIDGWAY, Donald L.; '79 MA; 257 Brenrich Cv N, Memphis, TN 38117.

RIDLEY, Cathy L.; '90 BS; 135 Ocean Pkwy. Apt. 4p, Brooklyn, NY 11218.

RIDLEY, Grace E.; '89 AS, '92 BS; Sergeant; NYC Police Dept., 1 Police Plz., New York, NY 10038; r. POB 350522, Central Sta., Jamaica, NY 11435, 718 529-3643; Leroy, Shawn.

RIDLEY, Sandra O.; '95 BA; Staff Analyst; NYC Police Dept., New York, NY 10021, 212 477-9768; r. 1020 Grand Concour, Bronx, NY 10451, 718 538-4437. e-mail

RIDRIGUEZ, Alice; '91 BS; 11404 Liberty Ave. # 1l, Jamaica, NY 11419.

RIEDEL, Dale B.; '83 BS; 8535 239th St., Jamaica, NY 11426.

RIEDINGER, Guy E.; '88 BA; Sgt.; City of Beacon Police, Beacon, NY 12508, 914 831-4111; r. RR 4 Box 379, Hopewell Jct., NY 12533, 914 226-4562.

RIEDY, William F.; '69 BS, '75 MA; AAS Brooklyn Clg.; Asst. Prof. Emeritus; Westchester Community Clg.; r. 36 Wells Ave., Croton-on-Hudson, NY 10520, 914 271-9267; Mary E.

RIEHL, Alfred P.; '76 BA; 7829 68th Ave., Flushing, NY 11379, 718 894-3735.

RIGGINS, Diane; 427 E 140th St., Bronx, NY 10454.

RIGGIO, Michael; '94 BA; 2413 Kingsland Ave., Bronx, NY 10469, 718 892-9080.

RIGNEY, James C.; '73 BS; CERT. Harvard-JFK Sch. of Govt; Retired Dir. of Tax Investigation; NYS; r. 3850 Galt Ocean Dr., Ft. Lauderdale, FL 33308, 954 564-5887.

RIGNEY, James R.; '94 BS; 112-08 103 Ave. #PH, Richmond Hill, NY 11419.

RIGONO, Gabriel; '93 BA; Principal Administrative Assoc.; NYC Police Dept., 1 Police Plz., New York, NY 10038; r. 99 Saint Marks Pl. Apt. 6d, New York, NY 10009; Barbara.

RIGOULOT, John P.; '79 BS; 4340 S Tom Ave., Inverness, FL 34452, 352 637-1665.

RIKER, William A.; '79 AS; 9231 Gettysburg St., Jamaica, NY 11426, 718 347-4970.

RIKOON, Elizabeth J.; '87 MA; BA Oakland Univ.; Mental Health Spec; Rikers Island; r. 118-2A Cooper Dr., New Rochelle, NY 10801.

RILEY, Dawn M.; '97 BA; 126 E. 89th St., Brooklyn, NY 11236, 718 485-3281.

RILEY, James B.; '75 MA; BA St. John's Univ.; Real Estate; Industry One Realty Corp., 707 Broad Hollow Rd., Farmingdale, NY 11735, 631 694-3500; r. 149 John St., Levittown, NY 11756, 516 731-1159; Loretta; Timothy, Mary Ellen, Daniel, Patricia, John.

RILEY, John F.; '76 BA; 8012 89th Ave., Jamaica, NY 11421, 718 476-0995.

RILEY, Laura D.; '90 BS; 10115 160th Ave., Jamaica, NY 11414, 718 358-0726.

RINALDI, Joseph; '90 MPA; RR 2 W. End Rd., Wappingers Falls, NY 12590.

RINALDI, Noel A.; '99 MS; 100 Brooklyn Ave. #1D, Freeport, NY 11520, 516 887-7328.

RINALDI, Patrica M.; '75 BS; 15747 92nd St., Jamaica, NY 11414, 718 846-8521.

RINALDI, Yolanda M.; '78 BS; 15747 92nd St., Jamaica, NY 11414, 718 846-8521.

RING, Brian; '96 BS; 433 Mansfield Ave., Levittown, NY 11756, 718 204-2674.

RING, William; '79 BA; 83-43 258 St., Floral Park, NY 11004, 516 829-2607.

RIOJAS, G. H.; 1991 Troy Ave. 2Fl., Brooklyn, NY 11234, 718 377-1251.

RIOLLANO, Miriam; '79 BS; 1265 Gerard Ave. #3, Bronx, NY 10452.

RIORDAN, Patricia A.; '92 BS; 220 Manhattan Ave., New York, NY 10025.

RIOS, Diana; '88 BS; 80-13 Myrtle Ave., Glendale, NY 11385, 718 418-4247.

RIOS, Donald; '92 BS; Police Ofcr.; NYC Police Dept., 1 Police Plz., New York, NY 10038, 718 287-3231; r. 22 Paerdegat 11th St., Brooklyn, NY 11236, 718 763-2209. e-mail

RIOS, Edwin; '77 BS; 114-34 E 122nd St., New York, NY 10035.

RIOS, Ferdinand J.; '81 BS; 85-15 Main St., Jamaica, NY 11435, 718 396-5438.

RIOS, George J.; '75 MPA; BA Hunter Clg., PHD Mercy Clg.; Commissioner-Public Admin./Trustee; D.O.R.I.S./CUNY, 31 Chambers St., New York, NY 10007, 212 788-8607; r. 2665 Netherland Ave., Bronx, NY 10463, 718 601-3566; Nydia Negron-Rios; George, David.

RIOS, Jennery; '95 AS; 1695 Foster Ave., Schenectady, NY 12308.

RIOS, Juan R.; '98 BA; JD Harvard Law Sch.; 845 Forest Ave., Bronx, NY 10456, 718 585-0213. e-mail

RIOS, Nilsa M.; '94 BS; 165 E. 112 St., New York, NY 10029.

RIOS, Ruben; '93 BS; 2455 Cruger Ave., Apt. 2E, Bronx, NY 10467, 718 881-7656.

RIPANDELLI, Alphonse; '76 BA; 61-57 69th La, Middle Vlg., NY 11379.

RIPPS, Carol A.; '80 MA; BA CUNY-Queens Clg.; Sr. Administrative Asst.; Brooklyn Clg., Dept. of Continuing Education, 2900 Bedford Ave., Brooklyn, NY 11210, 718 951-4141; r. 135 Amersfort Pl., Brooklyn, NY 11210; Melissa. e-mail

RIQUELME, Peter L.; '96 BA; 352 Bleecker St., Brooklyn, NY 11237, 718 497-9130.

RISO, Edward T.; '97 BS; 104-21 91Street, Richmond Hill, NY 11418, 718 961-4147.

RISTENBATT, R.; '90 MS; 2431 Seymour Ave., Bronx, NY 10469.

RISTER, Esther S.; '79 MA; 5622 14th Ave., Brooklyn, NY 11219, 718 435-7110.

RITCHIE, John D.; '75 MA; 4628 243rd St., Flushing, NY 11362, 718 229-2789.

RITCHIE, Kerri; '98 MA; 320 E. 34th St. #5a, New York, NY 10016, 212 573-1633.

RITONDO, Marcello; '93 BA; Principal LAN Admin; NYC Civil Ct., 111 Centre St., New York, NY 10013, 212 374-8020; r. 7210 11 Ave., Brooklyn, NY 11228, 718 680-1753; Josefina; Amanda, Alex, Marcello. e-mail

RITTENHOUSE, John P.; '82 BS; 105 Newel St., Brooklyn, NY 11222, 718 383-2730.

RIVAS, Alejandro J.; '96 BS; 504 W. 139 St., New York, NY 10031.

RIVAS, Fradis; '96 BA; Asst. Fraud Investigator; The NYC Dept. of Homeless Svc., 151 E 151st St., Bronx, NY 10451, 718 402-8889; r. 45 Fairview Ave. #7F, New York, NY 10040, 212 942-3970. e-mail

RIVAS, Linda Y.; '94 BS; 279 Lincoln Rd., Brooklyn, NY 11225, 718 941-6041.

RIVELA, Steven M.; '79 BA; 7 Brighton 4th Pl., Brooklyn, NY 11235.

RIVERA, Andrew A.; '84 BS; 46 Adrian Ave., Bronx, NY 10463, 718 295-2217.

RIVERA, Angel M.; '83 BS; 37 Washington Ave., Brentwood, NY 11717.

RIVERA, Brenda; '95 BA; 810 Pacific St. # 8l, Brooklyn, NY 11238.

RIVERA, Carmen; '95 BS; 578 Marcy Ave. Apt. 4r, Brooklyn, NY 11206, 718 338-7887.

RIVERA, Cesar J.; '95 AS, '99 BA; City of New York/USAR; Fraud Dept. of Homeless Svcs., 151 E 151st St., Bronx, NY 10451, 718 402-6272; r. 947 Rockaway Ave., Brooklyn, NY 11212. e-mail

RIVERA, Cynthia M.; '99 BA; 2725 Creston Ave., Apt. 503, Bronx, NY 10468, 718 295-1166.

RIVERA, Dana E.; '99 BA; Versace, 815 Madison Ave., New York, NY 10021, 212 744-6868; r. 950 Evergreen Ave., Bronx, NY 10473, 718 589-6838. e-mail

RIVERA, Daniel; '79 BS; 40 E. 98th St., New York, NY 10029.

RIVERA, David; '80 BS; POB 717, New York, NY 10116.

RIVERA, David; '97 BA; Police Ofcr.; NYPD, One Police Plz., New York, NY 10001; r. 553 Warwick St., Brooklyn, NY 11207, 718 277-7217. e-mail

RIVERA, Denise; '98 BS; 1735 Barnes Ave. Apt. 4, Bronx, NY 10462, 718 299-1633.

RIVERA, Eduardo; '95 BS; 234 W 21st St. Apt. 74, New York, NY 10011.

RIVERA, Eduardo; '97 MA, '98 MA; Sr. Supv. Advocate; Assigned Counsel Svcs., 175 Remsen St., Brooklyn, NY 11201, 718 637-6560; r. 79 Seigel St., Brooklyn, NY 11206. e-mail

RIVERA, Elba; '97 BS; 400 Rugby Rd. #L1, Brooklyn, NY 11226.

RIVERA, Elisha S.; '98 MA; 95-18 40th Rd., Elmhurst, NY 11373, 716 665-4758.

RIVERA, Elizabeth; '95 BA; 686 E 79th St., Brooklyn, NY 11236.

RIVERA, Eric; '97 BS; 623 Underhill Ave., Bronx, NY 10473, 718 231-7204.

RIVERA, Estela L.; '92 BS; 10226 134th St., Jamaica, NY 11419, 718 558-5568.

RIVERA, Evelyn; '90 BA, '96 CERT; 1939 Grand Concourse, Bronx, NY 10453, 718 231-7204.

RIVERA, George; '91 BS; 920 Metcalf Ave. # 2, Bronx, NY 10473, 718 589-0244.

RIVERA, George A.; '81 BS; 2695 Briggs Ave., Bronx, NY 10458, 718 292-5297.

RIVERA, Grace M.; '93 BA; 1244 Clay Ave., Apt. 4A, Bronx, NY 10456, 718 292-5297.

RIVERA, Herman; '93 BS; Soc. Svc./ Outreach Coord.; r. 1700 Metropolitan Ave., Apt. MG, Bronx, NY 10462, 718 794-1313; *Brunilda Davila.*

RIVERA, Hilda; '81 BS; 700 Saint Anns Ave., Bronx, NY 10455, 718 401-4390.

RIVERA, Iris M.; '96 BS; 248 Centre Ave., New Rochelle, NY 10805, 914 526-3205.

RIVERA, Ivette; '92 BA; 1071 Elder Ave. Apt. 5j, Bronx, NY 10472, 718 542-9749.

RIVERA, Ivette M.; '90 MPA; 159-64 Harlem River, New York, NY 10039.

RIVERA, Jacqueline, (Jacqueline Renaud); '89 BA; Process Server Court Clerk; Stroock Stroock Lauan, 180 Maiden Ln., New York, NY 10038, 212 806-5784; r. 146 Coffey St., Brooklyn, NY 11231, 718 596-0685; *Alex;* Jocelyn, Ashby.

RIVERA, Jalika; '96 BA; MA Univ. of New Haven; Crime Scene Tech.; City of Mesa Police Dept.; r. 265 Cherry St., Apt. 24 E, New York, NY 10002, 212 469-7440; *Krif Korsmo.* e-mail

RIVERA, James; '76 BA; 16311 Foch Blvd. Apt. 6a, Jamaica, NY 11434, 718 296-4824.

RIVERA, Javier A.; '90 BS; 628 E 20th St. Apt. 3A, New York, NY 10009, 212 529-0554.

RIVERA, Jo Anne; '94 BS, '94 CERT; Gary John Dmoch & Assocs., 171-22 Northern Blvd., Flushing, NY 11358; r. 2140 Seward Ave. #, Bronx, NY 10473, 718 295-1461.

RIVERA, Joey S.; '99; 223 Betts Avenues, Dronx, NY 10473, 718 295-1461.

RIVERA, John G.; '96 BA; 149 Marine Ave., Apt. 6S, Brooklyn, NY 11209, 718 491-2969.

RIVERA, Jonathan M.; '97 BA; 258 20th St., Brooklyn, NY 11215, 718 266-0803.

RIVERA, Jorge W.; '75 AS; 549 Riverside Dr. Apt. 3B, New York, NY 10027, 315 733-8757.

RIVERA, Jose; '96 BS; 3440 Broadway 3E, New York, NY 10031.

RIVERA, Jose A.; '98 BS; 57-25 Mazeau St., 2nd Fl., Maspeth, NY 11378, 718 296-4824.

RIVERA, Julie A.; '97 BS; 838 N Kearney St., Allentown, PA 18103, 610 776-0487.

RIVERA, Karen E.; '98 BA; 4809 4th Ave. #1L, Brooklyn, NY 11220, 718 346-5201.

RIVERA, Loyda E.; '91 BS; 178 Ocean Pkwy., Brooklyn, NY 11218, 718 422-7864.

RIVERA, Luz A.; '96 BS; P.O.Box 110-800, Brooklyn, NY 11211, 718 422-7864.

RIVERA, Manuel S.; '99 BS; 72-12 51 Ave. 2 Fl., Woodside, NY 11377, 718 647-8853.

RIVERA, Maria F.; '86 BA; 112 E. 96th St., New York, NY 10028.

RIVERA, Maria P.; '83 BS; 105 E 177 St., Bronx, NY 10453, 718 239-0557.

RIVERA, Maria R.; '95 BA; 45 Rutgers St. Apt. 12b, New York, NY 10002.

RIVERA, Marilyn; '92 BS; 503 56th St. # 3f, Brooklyn, NY 11220, 718 272-6015.

RIVERA, SGT Mario L.; '92 BS; Narcotics Supv.; Bronx Narcotics OCCB, 500 Abbot St. Bronx NY, Bronx, NY 10470, 718 653-7068; r. 2 Cambridge Ct., Washingtonville, NY 10992, 914 496-6578; *Patricia E.;* Samantha, Candice. e-mail

RIVERA, Marta; '84 BA; 1210 Hancock St., Brooklyn, NY 11221, 718 272-6015.

RIVERA, Mary M.; '82 BS; 1840 Sedgwick Ave. #6E, Bronx, NY 10453, 718 239-0557.

RIVERA, Michael; '81 BA; 1332 Thieriot Ave., Bronx, NY 10472, 718 239-0557.

RIVERA, Michael E.; '99 BA; Grad. Student/Forensic Psychology; Drug & Alcohol Counselor/John Jay Clg.; r. 5 Andover Rd., Old Bridge, NJ 08857, 732 254-7317.

RIVERA, Michelle; '95 BA; 85 Montrose Ave., Brooklyn, NY 11206, 718 272-6015.

RIVERA, Nicholas; '76 BS; 645 Water St. Apt. 5a, New York, NY 10002.

RIVERA, Nickcole D.; '98 BS; 99 Heberton Ave., Staten Island, NY 10302, 718 442-5768.

RIVERA, Onix; '95 BS; 326 60th St. # 1, Brooklyn, NY 11220, 718 622-5027.

RIVERA, Pedro, Sr.; '99 AS; Correction Ofcr.; Queens, NY 11412; r. 134-47 166 Pl. #1B, Jamaica, NY 11434, 718 712-4022; Pedro Jr. e-mail

RIVERA, Peter; '99 BS; Police Ofcr.; NYC Police Dept., 33rd Precinct, New York, NY 10032; r. 3636 Fieldston Rd #2D, Bronx, NY 10463, 718 432-8873. e-mail

RIVERA, Pio; '92 BS; 285 E 138th St. # 6, Bronx, NY 10454, 718 220-8725.

RIVERA, Robert O.; '97 BS; 950 E. 4 Walk 5e, New York, NY 10009.

RIVERA, Roberto; '97 BA; Correction Ofcr.; NYC Dept. of Corrections; r. 4809 4th Ave. #6, Brooklyn, NY 11220. e-mail

RIVERA, Rosa E.; '83 BA; 308 E 145th St. Apt. 9d, Bronx, NY 10451, 718 432-1275.

RIVERA, Russell T.; '93 BA; 185 Wortman Ave. # 3, Brooklyn, NY 11207, 718 241-8331.

RIVERA, Samari; '76; 4118 Vernon Blvd. Apt. 2c, Long Island City, NY 11101, 718 471-3258.

RIVERA, Sandra; '85 BS; 80 N. Moore St., New York, NY 10013.

RIVERA, Selenia; '97 BS; 603 Sheffield Ave., Brooklyn, NY 11207, 718 345-2579.

RIVERA, Sergio T.; '83 BA; 111 Atlantic Ave., Brooklyn, NY 11201, 718 345-2579.

RIVERA, Steven; '96 BS, 2000 MS; Criminal Investigator; NY State, 2 World Trade Cntr, Ste. 8714, New York, NY 10048, 212 321-4613; r. New York, NY 10016, 212 679-9322. e-mail

RIVERA, Teresita F.; '95 BA, '96 BA; 344 E 28th St. Apt. 23b, New York, NY 10016, 212 779-3871.

RIVERA, Valerie; '91 BA; 2300 Bronx Park E., Bronx, NY 10467, 718 402-1327.

RIVERA, Victor L.; '96 BA; 400 E.Mosholu Pkwy., Bronx, NY 10458, 718 562-3143.

RIVERA, Walter; '92 BS; 277 Franklin Ave., Brooklyn, NY 11205.

RIVERA, Wanda L.; '90 BA; 2256 33rd St. # 3, Long Island City, NY 11105, 718 776-1344.

RIVERA, Wilfredo; '89 BS; 155 Heritage Dr., Glastonbury, CT 06033.

RIVERA, Yvonne; '95 BA; AA LaGuardia Community Clg.; US Probation/ Parole Ofcr.; Fed. Courthouse, New York, NY 10001; r. 11 Fountain Dr. Apt. #1, Lakewood, NJ 08701, 732 730-0076.

RIVERO, Lisandra; '95 BA; 10222 62nd Rd, Forest Hills, NY 11375, 718 803-1775.

RIVERS, John J.; '82 MA; Dir. of Public Safety; Oracle Corp., 517 Rte. One S., Ste. 4000, Iselin, NJ 08830, 732 726-2504; r. 26 Whispering Hills, Annandale, NJ 08801, 908 735-2797; *Susan;* Matthew, John IV. e-mail

RIZZO, Brian J.; '93 MPA; BAPSYC Muhlenburg Clg., MACJ SUNY-Albany; Sergeant, Police Dept.; 1 Police Plaza, New York, NY 10038; r. 35 Clinton Pl., Staten Island, NY 10302.

RIZZO, Joseph M.; '85 BA; 8 E. 2nd St., Brooklyn, NY 11218.

RIZZO, Kevin; '95 BS; 17 Grand Teton Ave., Howell, NJ 07731, 718 236-7777.

RIZZO, Leonard I.; '97 BA; 75-22 62nd St., Glendale, NY 11385, 718 545-6353.

RIZZO, Raymond; Retired Prof.; John Jay Clg.; r. 40 Earle Pl., New Rochelle, NY 10801; *Betty.*

RIZZUTO, Zoe C.; '99 BA; Investigator; C.C.R.B, New York, NY 10006. e-mail

ROACH, Erle S.; '95 MPA; BA Ohio Univ.; Housing Devel. Spec.; NYC Housing Authority, New York, NY 10038; r. 2802 Bruner Ave., Bronx, NY 10469; *Pearl;* Alonzo, William, Irving, Kyle. e-mail

ROACH, Eugene J.; '79 BS; 82 Warren Ave., Ronkonkoma, NY 11779.

ROACH, Kairis J.; '97 AS, '99; 28 Monroe St. L, Brooklyn, NY 11238, 718 399-8963.

ROBERSON, Irene; '79 MPA; POB 21, Staten Island, NY 10314.

ROBERSON, Lakeisha A.; '99 BA; Customer Svc. Rep.; Bell Atlantic, 237 Pearl St., Brooklyn, NY 11221; r. 254 Woodbine St., Brooklyn, NY 11221, 718 919-4289; Tyriq.

ROBERSON, Margie; '91 BA; Probation Ofcr.; NYU Dept. of Probation; r. 950 Underhill Ave., Apt. 12d, Bronx, NY 10473.

ROBERSON, Shawanda '98 (See Wright, Shawanda).

ROBERSON, Toni V.; '83 BA; 1768 Popham Ave., Bronx, NY 10453, 718 299-9070.

ROBERSON, William C.; '99 BA; Police Ofcr.; Housing Police Dept.; r. New Windsor, NY 12553. e-mail

ROBERTS, Alston L.; '82 BA; 221-08 120 Ave., Jamaica, NY 11411, 718 539-1543.

ROBERTS, Cheri A.; '80 BS, '83 MPA; Paralegal; Rodriguez & Leid PC, 3274 Boston Rd, Bus Ext:125, Bronx, NY 10469, 718 547-3800; r. 1140 Burke Ave. Apt. 4d, Bronx, NY 10469, 718 798-6653; John E. Garnett, Euraiya Garnett.

ROBERTS, Cheryl L.; '94 BS; 910 Thieriot Ave., Apt. 5G, Bronx, NY 10473, 718 378-5719.

ROBERTS, Diana C.; '85 BS; Probation Ofcr.; NYC Dept. of Probation, 210 Joralemon St., Brooklyn, NY 11226, 718 802-4363; r. 180 Lenox Rd, Brooklyn, NY 11226, 718 462-9084.

ROBERTS, Jewel F.; '85 BS; 1016-4E Bronx Park, Bronx, NY 10460, 718 617-3884.

ROBERTS, Linda; '97 BA; 47-55 39th Pl., Long Island City, NY 11104, 718 776-7746.

ROBERTS, Matthew A.; '97 BS, '98 BS; 735 E 26th St. 1Rr, Brooklyn, NY 11210, 718 443-3674.

ROBERTS, Pamela T.; '98 BS; 2340 Mott Ave. #1d, Far Rockaway, NY 11691, 718 471-7953.

ROBERTS, Richard H.; '78 MPA; Assoc. Commissioner; NYC Dept. of Probation; r. 503 Summit St., Ridgewood, NJ 07450, 201 444-7293; *Betty Ann;* Sean, Garrett.

ROBERTS, Sherman S.; '98 BS, MA; Fed. Police Ofcr./Fed Protector Svc; Gen. Fed. Svcs. Admin., 26 Federal Plz., New York, NY 10021, 212 264-3443; r. 1833 Amsterdam Ave., New York, NY 10031, 212 491-3420. e-mail

ROBERTS, Mrs. Sonya, (Sonya Davis); '89 BA; Corrections Investigator; NYC Dept. of Corrections, 60 Hudson St., New York, NY 10013, 212 266-1955; r. 98-11 Northern Blvd., Corona, NY 11368, 718 479-0971.

ROBERTSON, Bruce A.; '95 MPA; BA NYIT; Adjunct Lecturer; John Jay Clg., Dept. of Law & Police Sceince, 899 10 Th Ave., New York, NY 10019, 212 237-8658; r. 2815 Hobart St., Woodside, NY 11377, 718 278-1530; *Deirdre;* Brian, Heather.

ROBERTSON, Erin N.; '99 MA; BA Hood Clg.; Crime Analyst; Baltimore Cnty. Police Dept., 700 E Joppa Rd, Baltimore, MD 21286, 410 887-2245; r. 6421 Hazelwood Ave., Baltimore, MD 21237, 410 866-3922. e-mail

ROBERTSON, Roy; '88 BS; 400 Cozine Ave., Brooklyn, NY 11207, 718 332-2229.

ROBERTSON, Ms. Sallie A.; '97 BA; AOS Interboro Institute; Acad. Advisor; Interboro Inst. Jr. Clg., 450 W. 56th St. 3rd Fl., New York, NY 10019, 212 399-0019; r. 240 W. 112th St., Apt. #5e, New York, NY 10026, 212 662-1415; Francine, Frank, John, Tracey, Yvette.

ROBERTSON, Sean J.; '99 MS; BA Adelphi Univ.; Fire Inspector; NYC Fire Dept., 9 Metrotech Ctr., Brooklyn, NY 11201, 718 999-2894; r. 16 W. 16th St. #2Ps, New York, NY 10011, 212 741-2233.

ROBERTSON, Stanford B.; '97 AS, '99 BA; 170 S. Portland #10F, Brooklyn, NY 11217, 718 857-4780.

ROBILLARD, Michelle; '97 MA; 1334 South Ave. B, Apt. 188, Yuma, AZ 85364.

ROBIN, Latasha B.; '99 BA; Counseling; Magellan Behavioral Health, 120 Bethpage Rd, Hicksville, NY 11801, 516 938-6627; r. 12 E. Garfield St. #1A, Bay Shore, NY 11706, 631 969-3422; *Darien Geames.* e-mail

ROBINSON, Alvin M.; '80 BS; 1390 Dean St., Brooklyn, NY 11216, 718 363-7370.

ROBINSON, Angela M.; '95 MPA, '95 MS; 121 La Salle St., Apt. 10, New York, NY 10027, 315 245-1439.

ROBINSON, Barbara E.; '92 BS; AA Manhattan Comm. Clg., MS Iona Clg.; Social Caseworker; West Chester Cnty. Dept. of Social Svcs., 270 North Ave., New Rochelle, NY 10801, 914 637-5941; r. 254 Martine Ave. Apt. Bw, White Plains, NY 10601.

ROBINSON, Benjamin E.; '79 BS; 530 Second St., Brooklyn, NY 11215, 718 230-0494.

ROBINSON, Charles; '79 MA; 11729 225th St., Jamaica, NY 11411, 718 470-6453.

ROBINSON, Christopher; '81 BS; Commanding Ofcr.; 50 Precinct New York Police Dept., Detectives Division, New York, NY 10038, 718 543-6134; r. 29 Frederick St., Garnerville, NY 10923. e-mail

ROBINSON, Cynthia (Cyndy); '95 BA; Proj. Mgmt.; Sponsors for Educational Opportunities, 23 Grammercy Park S., New York, NY 10003, 212 979-2040; r. 235 West End Ave. #15C, New York, NY 10023, 212 873-2495. e-mail

ROBINSON, Daniel T.; '99 BA; 2156 Linden Blvd. #5A, Brooklyn, NY 11207, 718 272-2597.

ROBINSON, Dawn M.; '99 BA; 84 Frost Ln., Mahwah, NJ 07430, 201 848-8382.

ROBINSON, Donna; '91 BS; 11819 201st Pl., Jamaica, NY 11412, 718 264-7604.

ROBINSON, Dwight C.; '98 BS; Unit Mgr.; Montefiore Med. Ctr., 111 E 210th St., Bronx, NY 10467, 718 920-4118; r. POB 689, Bronx, NY 10467, 718 654-4085; Dwight, Haley. e-mail

ROBINSON, Edward S.; '90 BA; 54 Wildey St. Apt. 10, Tarrytown, NY 10591, 914 923-0233.

ROBINSON, Hamilton; '72 BS; 2404 Stemwell Blvd., Richmond, VA 23236, 804 675-0929; *Irma Jean.*

ROBINSON, John A.; '77 MA; BS, MA; Police Ofcr.; City of East Orange, 61 N. Munn Ave., E. Orange, NJ 07019, 973 266-5000; r. 45 Fulton St., E. Orange, NJ 07017, 973 675-5282; *Rita B.;* Karriem, Canaan, Kimberly.

ROBINSON, Koy E.; '95 BA; 11149 139th St., Jamaica, NY 11435, 718 327-6385.

ROBINSON, Ms. Lillian W., (Lillian W. Weir); '77 BA; Retired Safety Ofcr.; NYS; r. 1156 Tuxedo Sq., Teaneck, NJ 07666, 201 837-6783; *John R. Morales;* Gerard, Shavona.

ROBINSON, Marilyn C.; '85 BS; Columbia Univ.; Atty.-Tax Law; r. 4280 Grove Ct., Virginia Bch., VA 23462, 757 495-9594.

ROBINSON, Michelle D.; '98 BS; 3685 Eastchester Rd., PH, Bronx, NY 10466, 718 430-6858.

ROBINSON, Neil H.; '99 AS; Security Ofcr.; Museum of Modern Art, 11 W. 53St Ny Ny 10019, New York, NY 10019, 212 708-9467; r. 172-33 Amelia Rd., Jamaica, NY 11434, 718 276-7657.

ROBINSON, Philip E.; 203 Lakeland Ave., Apt. 3B, Sayville, NY 11782.

ROBINSON, Roberto I.; '98 BA; 4623 6 Ave. 3a, Brooklyn, NY 11220, 718 647-4855.

ROBINSON, Sheila E.; '78 BS; 1285 Washington Ave., Bronx, NY 10456, 718 325-4255.

ROBINSON, Timolin C.; 142-21 Spring Blvd., Jamaica, NY 11413, 718 937-1056.

ROBINSON, Walter A.; '83 MA; BA Kean Univ.; Retired-Police; Twp. of Union, New Jersey; r. 6 Emily Ave., Vauxhall, NJ 07088, 908 687-3738; *Otelia.*

ROBINSON, Yolanda D.; '85 BS; 301 Cathedral Pkwy. Apt. 10g, New York, NY 10026, 315 245-1439.

ROBINSON, Zandra; '99 BS; Law Student/Homemaker; r. 88-60 76th St., Woodhaven, NY 11421, 718 521-1530; Deirdre. e-mail

ROBLES, Jose E.; '95 AS; 200 Teneyck walk, Brooklyn, NY 11206, 718 642-0312.

ROBLES, Laurel; '73 BA; 605 W 170 Pl. #3B, New York, NY 10032.

ROBLES, Nelson A.; '98 BS; 41 23 Newtown Rd, Astoria, NY 11103, 716 881-0592.

ROBLES-NUNEZ, Julia E.; '94 BA; 187 Laing Ave. #R1, Clymer, PA 15728, 724 357-8710.

ROBLEY, Vanessa; '90 BS; 2 Stoddard Pl.,, Brooklyn, NY 11225, 718 495-0765.

ROBOTTI, Carlo; '93 BS; 452 Hillside Ave., Allendale, NJ 07401, 201 236-3874.

ROBSON, Robert (Bob) J.; '78 BS, '80 MA; AA Queensborough Community; Owner; Farmers Ins., 381 N Arizona Ave., Chandler, AZ 85225, 480 786-0809; r. Chandler, AZ 85225; *Dawna;* Daniel, Bobby.

ROCA, Randall S.; '84 BS; Detective; NYPD, Manhattan S. Homicide Squad, 230 E 21st St., New York, NY 10010, 212 477-7474; r. POB 301, Bronx, NY 10471.

ROCCARO, Rosario J.; '76 BA; 90 Titus Ave., Staten Island, NY 10306, 718 761-9556.

ROCCHIO, Peter A.; '72 BA; 103 Pell Pl., Bronx, NY 10464, 718 885-1850.

ROCCO, Janet N., (Janet N. Rosenbach); '94 BS; Secy.; NYC Police Dept., 1 Police Plz., New York, NY 10038, 212 374-5000; r. 3025 Ocean Ave., Brooklyn, NY 11235, 718 891-1203.

ROCCO, Kenneth B.; '98 BS; Police Ofcr.; New York Police Dept, 24-17 86th St., Jackson Hts., NY 11369; r. 20 Juniper Dr., Cedar Knolls, NJ 07927, 973 267-9695.

ROCCOMBOLI, Teresa; '94 BS; 42-15 164 St., Flushing, NY 11358.

ROCHE, Edward J.; '79 BA; MA Long Island Univ.; Retired; r. 5 Church Twrs Apt. 6 K, Hoboken, NJ 07030, 201 963-7011; *Theresa;* Eve, Theresa, Natalie.

ROCHE, Grace V.; '84 BA; 61 Huntting Dr., Dumont, NJ 07628.

ROCHFORD, Edward V.; '72 BS; Cnty. Sheriff; Morris Cnty. Sheriff's Ofc., Courthouse, POB 900, Morristown, NJ 07963, 973 285-6600; r. POB 108, Convent Sta., NJ 07961, 973 361-8988; *Diana.* e-mail

ROCK, Allen C.; '88 BS; 657 E. 94 St., Brooklyn, NY 11236, 718 389-7163.

RODGERS, Karen P.; '87 BS; 1355 E 51st St., Brooklyn, NY 11234, 718 209-5765.

RODGERS, Lamont K.; '98 BS; Law Student; St. John's Univ. Sch. of Law; r. 698 Ralph Ave. Apt. 1E, Brooklyn, NY 11212, 718 953-4762. e-mail

RODGERS, Sherrice T.; '99 BA; 2045 Rockaway Pkw 1A, Brooklyn, NY 11236, 718 629-3937.

RODRIGUES, John; '92 BA; 1577 Fenimore St., N. Bellmore, NY 11710.

RODRIGUES, Maurice; '94 BS; 261 Lefferts Ave., Brooklyn, NY 11225, 718 234-5036.

RODRIGUEZ, Abigail; '98 BS; 114-16 103 Ave. #2, Jamaica, NY 11419, 718 845-7185.

RODRIGUEZ, Adrienne J.; '99 BS; 1739 Pilgrim Ave. #5L, Bronx, NY 10461, 718 823-9515. e-mail

RODRIGUEZ, Alba L.; '97 BS; CUNY Sch. of Law; Couns./Law Student; Immigrant Ctr., New York, NY 10001, 212 650-6620; r. 221 W. 233rd St. Apt. #5I, Bronx, NY 10463, 718 432-9316; *Neftali Betances.* e-mail

RODRIGUEZ, Albania; '85 MA; 657 W. 161st St., New York, NY 10032, 315 735-1759.

RODRIGUEZ, Andres E.; '93 BS; Criminal Investigator; NYS Petroleum & Tobacco Bur., 2 World Trade Cntr., Ste. 87-14g, New York, NY 10048, 212 321-4636; r. 339 Concord Ave., Bronx, NY 10454. e-mail

RODRIGUEZ, Andrew W.; '99 BA; Performance Mgmt. Analyst; ASCAP, 1 Lincoln Plz., New York, NY 10023, 212 621-6053; r. 1126 Evergreen Ave., Apt. 4-A, Bronx, NY 10472. e-mail

RODRIGUEZ, Angela E.; '98 BS; 638 E. 2nd St. #5d, Brooklyn, NY 11218, 718 853-2067.

RODRIGUEZ, Antonio R.; '90 BA; 61 Audubon Ave. Apt. 4n, New York, NY 10032, 315 735-1759.

RODRIGUEZ, Araceli; '95 AS; 2149 Harmon St., Apt. B2, Ridgewood, NY 11385, 718 271-1586.

RODRIGUEZ, Awilda; '86 BA; 104-20 Queens Blvd., Forest Hills, NY 11375, 718 271-1586.

RODRIGUEZ, Barbara M.; BS; 107-11 80th St., Ozone Park, NY 11417, 718 739-8233.

RODRIGUEZ, Belinda; '97 BA; 803 Beverley Rd #1, Brooklyn, NY 11218, 718 266-4303.

RODRIGUEZ, Betty; '93 BS; JD New York Law Sch.; Asst. Dist. Atty.; Kings Cnty Dist. Attorney's Ofc., 350 Jay St., Brooklyn, NY 11201, 718 250-2000; r. 10426, 125th St., Jamaica, NY 11419, 718 843-6731. e-mail

RODRIGUEZ, Bolivar M.; '76 BA; 2325 Hermany Ave., Bronx, NY 10473, 718 402-8941.

RODRIGUEZ, Braulio; '99 BS; 1365 St. Nich Ave. 20J, New York, NY 10033, 315 735-1759.

RODRIGUEZ, C.; '95 BS; 20 Miami Ct. P.h, Brooklyn, NY 11225, 718 467-5441.

RODRIGUEZ, Charles; '76 BA; 13283 Bedford Mews Ct., W. Palm Bch., FL 33414, 561 792-9324.

RODRIGUEZ, Claudia; '95 BA; Couns.; Beth Israel Med. Ctr., 245 E 17th St., Third Fl., New York, NY 10003, 212 420-2034; r. 135-20 Hoover Ave. 5J, Kew Gardens, NY 11435, 718 849-4198; *Sean Cameron.* e-mail

RODRIGUEZ, Damian A.; '98, '99; 1849 Sedgwick Ave. #11 A, Bronx, NY 10453, 718 239-5556.

RODRIGUEZ, Denise; '93 BA; 200 E Mosholu Pkwy., Bronx, NY 10458, 718 882-6008.

RODRIGUEZ, Eddie; '97 BS; 2703 W. 33rd St., Brooklyn, NY 11224, 718 238-7128.

RODRIGUEZ, Edward N.; '83 MPA; 25-58 127 St., College Pt., NY 11354, 718 417-1595.

RODRIGUEZ, Elizabeth '89 (See Ramirez, Ms. Elizabeth).

RODRIGUEZ, Errol O.; '96 MA; PHD CCNY; Counseling Psychotherapist:Prvt Prc; Inter-Care, 51 E 25th St. Ste. 400, New York, NY 10010, 212 532-0303; r. 3170 Broadway #6J, New York, NY 10027, 212 932-1635; *Mandy Ramos.* e-mail

RODRIGUEZ, Estela; '92 DG; 45 Overlook Ter., New York, NY 10033, 315 735-1759.

RODRIGUEZ, Ms. Fiordaliza A., (Flordaliza A. Alba-Gil); '93 BA; MA New Sch. for Social Rsch., JD CUNY Sch. of Law; Atty.; Admin. for Children Svcs.; Bronx Family Ct., 900 Sheridan Ave. 6B-12, Bronx, NY 10451, 718 590-5438; r. 2090 Barnes Ave., Apt. 6 D, Bronx, NY 10462, 718 823-9730. e-mail

RODRIGUEZ, Franklin; '84 BA; 9028 Sutphin Blvd., Jamaica, NY 11435, 718 229-9223.

RODRIGUEZ, Franklin Delano; '83 BSCJ; MSPA; Freight Operator; S.L. Green, 420 Lexington Ave., New York, NY 10170, 212 995-8165; r. New York, NY 10009; *Luz E. Urrutia;* Marilyn.

RODRIGUEZ, Gilbert; '89 BS; Supv. Delivery Svc.; US Postal Svcs., 21-17 Broadway, Long Island City, NY 11106, 718 932-4235; r. 14 Madison Ave., Deer Park, NY 11729. e-mail

RODRIGUEZ, Gloria M.; '80 BA; 140-22 Asch Loop Apt. 22-C, Bronx, NY 10475, 718 320-9707.

RODRIGUEZ, Hector; '94 BA; Regional VP; Primerica Financial Svcs., 5 Beekman St. Ste. 820, New York, NY 10038, 212 385-9854; r. 253 20th St., Brooklyn, NY 11215; *Joann;* Marc Anthony.

RODRIGUEZ, Iris J.; '95 CERT; 110 Forsyth St. Apt. 15, New York, NY 10002, 315 735-1759.

RODRIGUEZ, Isabella; '95 BA; 125 Willow Bend Dr., Apt. 3A, Owings Mills, MD 21117, 410 825-7068.

RODRIGUEZ, Ivan J.; '97 BS; 91 Jefferson St., Brooklyn, NY 11206, 718 403-0411.

RODRIGUEZ, Jacqueline; '91 BS; 2059 E 14th St., Brooklyn, NY 11229, 718 346-2292.

RODRIGUEZ, James; '76 BA; 11538 Royal Tee Cir., Cape Coral, FL 33991, 941 283-9217.

RODRIGUEZ, Mrs. Jeannette, (Jeannette Ferreira); '97 BA; 3447 Edenwood Cir., Virginia Bch., VA 23452; *Andy Sr.;* Andy Jr.

RODRIGUEZ, Jeffrey; '97 BS; 322 W. 17th St., New York, NY 10011, 315 735-1759.

RODRIGUEZ, Jhoel; '99 BA; 390 E. 162 St. 1A, Bronx, NY 10451, 718 293-0907.

RODRIGUEZ, Jimmy; '96 BA; Tchr.; P.S. 46, 279 E 196th St., Bronx, NY 10458, 718 584-4450; r. 754 Brady Ave. Apt. 503, Bronx, NY 10462, 718 409-1307.

RODRIGUEZ, Joey; '97 BA; 135-24 226th St., Laurelton, NY 11413, 718 297-2594.

RODRIGUEZ, Jose A.; '90 AS; 210 E. 181 St., Bronx, NY 10457, 718 293-0907.

RODRIGUEZ, Jose J.; '81 BS; Retired; r. 170 Barbey St., Brooklyn, NY 11207, 718 277-2925; *Sylvia.* e-mail

RODRIGUEZ, Jose M.; '83 BS; 564 W 188 St. #1F, New York, NY 10040, 212 927-2452.

RODRIGUEZ, Juan C.; '95 BS; Investigator; W Chester Cnty. Dist. Atty's. Ofc.; r. 190 State St. GF, Brooklyn, NY 11201; *Thu Nguyen.* e-mail

RODRIGUEZ, Juan C.; '97 BA; Marine Ofcr.; r. 1941 Andrews Ave., Bronx, NY 10453, 718 716-3834.

RODRIGUEZ, Julio; '95 BS; 142 Wilson Ave., Brooklyn, NY 11237, 718 497-9357.

RODRIGUEZ, Kenneth M.; '84 BS; Supervising Investigator; King Dist. Atty.; 350 Jay St., Brooklyn, NY 11201, 718 250-3325; r. Yonkers, NY 10704.

RODRIGUEZ, Lina B.; '95 BS; 149-45 Northern Bl, Flushing, NY 11354, 718 446-0043.

RODRIGUEZ, Lisa; '96 BS; 136 Shepherd Ave., Brooklyn, NY 11208, 718 277-1650.

RODRIGUEZ, Lizette; '98 BA; Health Educ.; Grand St. Settlement, 80 Pitt St., New York, NY 10002, 212 674-1740; r. 663 Eagle Ave., Bronx, NY 10455, 718 585-5169. e-mail

RODRIGUEZ, Louis; '91 BS; POB 658, New York, NY 10163, 315 735-1759.

177

RODRIGUEZ, Louis I.; '95 BS; 3420 74th St. Apt. 4a, Flushing, NY 11372, 718 446-0043.

RODRIGUEZ, Lourdes N.; '97 BA; 288 Maple St., Brooklyn, NY 11225, 718 821-6108.

RODRIGUEZ, Luis D.; '99 BA; EMT-D Spec Level 1; NYC Fire Dept., 9 Metro Tech Plz., Brooklyn, NY 11238, 718 999-2000; r. 1188 Sheridan Ave. 4D, Bronx, NY 10456, 718 537-2850. e-mail

RODRIGUEZ, Luis R.; '92 BS; 1761 3rd Ave. Apt. 8D, New York, NY 10029, 315 735-1759.

RODRIGUEZ, Marcos A.; '99 BA; 803B Union Ave., Bronx, NY 10459, 718 231-8668.

RODRIGUEZ, Maria; '96 BA; 505 W. 183 St., New York, NY 10033, 315 735-1759.

RODRIGUEZ, Maribel; '96 BS; Case Mgr., Social Worker; Northern Manhattan Improvement Corp., 76 Wadsworth Ave., New York, NY 10033, 212 822-8330; r. 565 E 39th St., Brooklyn, NY 11203, 718 469-1695. e-mail

RODRIGUEZ, Marilyn; '82 BA; 72 Wadsworth Ter., New York, NY 10040, 315 735-1759.

RODRIGUEZ, Marilyn D.; 115-59 208 St., Cambria Hts., NY 11411, 718 264-1099.

RODRIGUEZ, Mashea M.; '98 BS; 3475 Bivona St. #9j, Bronx, NY 10475, 718 671-6310.

RODRIGUEZ, Michael; '91 BS; 24542 77th Cres., Bellerose, NY 11426, 516 483-0358.

RODRIGUEZ, Michelle; '95 MA; 140 De Kruif Pl. Apt. 7f, Bronx, NY 10475, 718 231-8668.

RODRIGUEZ, Migdalia; '80 BS; 8811 132nd St., Jamaica, NY 11418, 718 264-1099.

RODRIGUEZ, Ms. Migdalia A.; '78 AS; '80 BA; '87 MA; Detective; NYC Police Dept., One Police Plz., New York, NY 10003, 212 533-2041; r. 496 S. 4th St., Lindenhurst, NY 11757. e-mail

RODRIGUEZ, Milagro; '92 BS; 213 67 St., Brooklyn, NY 11220, 718 221-5685.

RODRIGUEZ, Miriam M.; '98 BA; 50 Est 102 St. #4E, New York, NY 10029, 315 735-1759.

RODRIGUEZ, Morahina; '96 BA; 624 W 176 St., New York, NY 10033, 315 735-1759.

RODRIGUEZ, Myrza M.; '95 BS; 409 E. 81st St., New York, NY 10028, 315 735-1759.

RODRIGUEZ, Nelson; '95 BS; 45 Rutgers St. Apt. 12b, New York, NY 10002, 315 735-1759.

RODRIGUEZ, Nemesio; '90 AS; 1565 Odell St. Apt. 12f, Bronx, NY 10462, 718 861-0460.

RODRIGUEZ, Nicholas; '97 BA; Controlman; Village of Chester Police, Chester, NY 10918, 914 469-4681; r. 719 North St., Middletown, NY 10940, 914 341-0477. e-mail

RODRIGUEZ, Olgania; '86 BS; 1267 Sheridan Ave., Bronx, NY 10456, 718 829-9051.

RODRIGUEZ, Rafael; '92 BS, '95 MA; '97 MPA; 1516 W 10th St., Brooklyn, NY 11204, 718 237-9791.

RODRIGUEZ, Rebecca; '95 BS; 1260 Gates Ave. # 1, Brooklyn, NY 11221, 718 237-9791.

RODRIGUEZ, Regino; '93 AS, '95 BS; 1055 Walton Ave. # 2, Bronx, NY 10452, 718 733-9299.

RODRIGUEZ, Ricardo; '81 BS; 7924 154th St., Flushing, NY 11367, 718 337-0817.

RODRIGUEZ, Ruth M.; '88 BS; 1918 Linden St. # 3l, Flushing, NY 11385, 718 337-0817.

RODRIGUEZ, S.; '95 BS; 2010 Bruckner Blvd., Bronx, NY 10473, 718 792-3158.

RODRIGUEZ, Sandra; '99 BS; 2552 University Ave. Apt. 55N, Bronx, NY 10468, 718 220-4140.

RODRIGUEZ, Sandra M. '95 (See Orlandella, Sandra M.).

RODRIGUEZ, Servando; '97 BA; 43 Burhans Ave., Yonkers, NY 10701.

RODRIGUEZ, Sylvia; '97 MA; BA Kean Univ.; Forensic Spec.; St. Mary's Hosp., 211 Pennington Ave., Passaic, NJ 07055, 973 470-3025; r. 245 Passaic Ave., Apt. C9, Passaic, NJ 07055, 973 471-9198. e-mail

RODRIGUEZ, Tanya I. '91 (See Rodriguez-Barros, Tanya I.).

RODRIGUEZ, Ms. Veronica; '97 BA; Human Resources Admin.; Universal Music Grp., 825 Eighth Ave., New York, NY 10019, 212 333-8407; r. 18 Pleasant Ct., Staten Island, NY 10304, 718 447-6933. e-mail

RODRIGUEZ, Victor M.; '83 BS; Police Ofcr.; Transit; r. 74 S Main St., Spring Vly., NY 10977, 914 426-6819; *Raysa; Victoria, Stephanie, Jasmine.*

RODRIGUEZ, Wanda '95 (See Rodriguez-Aviles, Wanda).

RODRIGUEZ, William; '80 BS; 314 E 143rd St. Apt. 2c, Bronx, NY 10451, 718 829-9051.

RODRIGUEZ, Yara; '98 BA; Security Supv.; Guardsmark, New York, NY 10036, 212 522-3547; r. 1005 E 179 St. 4h, Bronx, NY 10460, 718 328-2706; Ciara. e-mail

RODRIGUEZ, Yolanda; '95 BS; Correction Ofcr.; NYC Dept. of Corrections, 60 Hudson St., New York, NY 10001, 718 417-2300; r. 8211 Atlantic Ave., Woodhaven, NY 11421, 718 296-6136; Cayla. e-mail

RODRIGUEZ, Yvonne; '98 BA; 136 W 168th St. #3c, Bronx, NY 10452, 718 992-5868.

RODRIGUEZ-AVILES, Wanda, (Wanda Rodriguez); '95 BA; Sr. Profn. Conduct Investigator; Ofc. of Professional Discipline, 163 W. 125th St., New York, NY 10027, 212 961-5835; r. 1613 Bogart Ave., Bronx, NY 10462, 718 892-9275; *Daniel;* Arleen, Ashleigh, MarcAndrew. e-mail

RODRIGUEZ-BARROS, Tanya I., (Tanya I. Rodriguez); '91 BA; Chief Mental Health Unit; St. Barnabas Hosp., Rikers Island Correctional Facility, Mental Health Unit, Elmhurst, NY 11373; r. 951 Fenwood Dr., #2, Valley Stream, NY 11580, 516 285-4991; *Wolfgang Barros;* Alexis Nicole.

RODRIGUEZ-KANEYASU, Peter; '93 BS; 212 W 91st St., New York, NY 10024, 212 873-2000.

RODRIQUEZ, Fernando; BS; Tech.; Yonkers Police Dept., Yonkers, NY 10702; r. 621 W. 171th St. #bsmt, New York, NY 10032, 212 928-1731.

RODRIQUEZ, Julissa; '90 BS; 643 Saint Lawrence Ave., Bronx, NY 10473, 718 328-5943.

RODRIQUEZ, Odanis; BS; 320 W 86street, New York, NY 10024.

RODRIQUEZ, William, Jr.; '99 BS; Accounts Receivable Coord.; Primedia Special Interest Publications, 260 Madison Ave., New York, NY 10016, 212 726-4391; r. 1127 Commonwealth Ave. Apt. 1, Bronx, NY 10472, 718 892-3725. e-mail

ROE, Julie; '92 BS; 706 Central Ave., Apt. A, San Francisco, CA 94117, 415 749-1503.

ROEDELL, Kristen; '99 MA; 376 Bowler Ct., Piscataway, NJ 08854.

ROGASKI, John; '95 BS; 27-24 23rd St. Apt. 2F, Astoria, NY 11102.

ROGDAKIS, Constantine; 35 Princeton Dr., Syosset, NY 11791, 516 938-2492.

ROGERS, Burl L.; '91 BA, '97 MPA; MA SUNY at Albany; Sgt. Investigator; NYS Police, 99 10th Ave., New York, NY 10011, 212 620-4950; r. 2835 Webb Ave., Bronx, NY 10468, 718 601-8690.

ROGERS, Charles L.; '78 BS; 1108 Dean St., Brooklyn, NY 11216, 718 857-6834.

ROGERS, Gerard J.; '79 BS; 330 Clermont Ave., Brooklyn, NY 11205, 718 783-5591.

ROGERS, James; '93 BS; MPA Marist Clg.; Capt.-Ofc. of The Chief of Dept.; NYC Police Dept., 1 Police Plz., Rm 1300, New York, NY 10038, 212 374-6710; r. 132 Hilltop Rd, Monroe, NY 10950; *Catherine; James.* e-mail

ROGERS, Jaton; '91 BS; 930 Belmont Ave., Brooklyn, NY 11208, 718 623-8552.

ROGERS, Jennifer L.; '88 BS; Probation Ofcr.; NYC Dept. of Probation, 215 E. 161th St., 5th Fl., Bronx, NY 10451, 718 590-3102; r. 130 Gale Pl., Apt. 5B, Bronx, NY 10463, 718 884-3965; Erica. e-mail

ROGERS, Katherine C.; '92 BS; Assoc. for The Investigator; Ofc. of Revenue & Investigation, 260 11th Ave., New York, NY 10011, 212 630-9730; r. 2976 Marion Ave. # Pt3f, Bronx, NY 10458, 718 295-2174.

ROGERS, Lakesha; '96 BA; 118 W. 139 St., New York, NY 10030, 315 964-2154.

ROGERS, Sharon L.; '85 BA, '93 MPA; 168-32 127th Ave., Jamaica, NY 11434, 718 268-4570.

ROGERS, Timothy L.; '87 BA; 25 Kenneth Stuart Blvd. Apt. A, Mohegan Lake, NY 10547, 914 378-1606.

ROGERS, William D.; '79 BS; 4 Ridge Rd, Wheatley Hts., NY 11798, 631 491-4651.

ROGERS, William J.; '76 BS; 54-08 Nurge Ave., Maspeth, NY 11378, 718 268-4570.

ROGERS-GRINAGE, Debra; '83 BA; MS Adelphi Univ., PD C.W. Post; Educator; r. 13549 227th St., Laurelton, NY 11413. e-mail

ROGNON, Rudolph G.; '95 BS; Deputy Inspector; New York Police Dept., 1 Police Plz., New York, NY 10038, 718 558-5400; r. 123 Berkley St., Valley Stream, NY 11581, 516 791-4973; *Carol; Melissa, Jennifer.*

ROHAN, James; '87 BA; 2232 3rd St., E. Meadow, NY 11554, 516 794-6876.

ROHAN, Kevin; '87 BS; Retired Inspector; NYC Police Dept.; r. 299 Carnation Ave., Floral Park, NY 11001, 516 488-1953; *Claire;* Kieran, Julia, Maryanne, Regina, Cecilia, Timothy.

ROHAN, Robert V.; '77 BS; Private Investigator; r. 205 Woodhampton Dr., White Plains, NY 10603, 914 428-3767; *Denise;* Megan, Siovhan, Robert III.

ROHLFING, Herbert V.; 402 Jackson Ave., Mineola, NY 11501, 516 248-6005.

ROHRBERG, George J.; 10 Southern Ln., Warwick, NY 10990, 914 986-3432.

ROJAS, David; '93 BS; 1236 Elder Ave., Bronx, NY 10472.

ROJAS, Inez M.; '96 BS; 2405 1st Ave., Apt. 8H, New York, NY 10035.

ROJAS, Lee Y.; '87 BA; 615 W. 150 St., New York, NY 10031, 212 694-9342.

ROJAS, Luis E.; '98 BS; 319 W 47 St. 5r, New York, NY 10036, 212 265-8451.

ROJAS, Paola R.; '99 BS; Clg. Asst.; John Jay Library, New York, NY 10019; r. 1351 Park Ave. Apt. 1-B, New York, NY 10029, 212 987-7049. e-mail

ROJAS-DYKES, Carol; '77 BA; 3312 Emily Dr., Plano, TX 75093, 972 612-1777; *Raymond;* Deborah, Karen, Susan.

ROJEWSKI, Robert; '97 BA; 115 Stanton Ave., Piscataway, NJ 08854, 732 752-5744.

ROLDAN, Mrs. Eleanor J., (Eleanor Wawa); '96 BA; AS BMCC; Social Worker; Social Security Admin., 85 Delancey St., 3rd Fl., New York, NY 10002, 212 674-8701; r. 8550 Forest Pkwy., Apt. 2D, Woodhaven, NY 11421, 718 521-0669; *James.* e-mail

ROLLA, Peter J.; '99 BA; AA SUNY-Farmingdale Univ.; Case Mgr.; EAC, Hempstead, NY 11550; r. 23 Balfour Dr., Bethpage, NY 11714, 516 731-5561.

ROLLE, Robert J.; '84 MPA; BS Herbert H. Lehman Univ.; Sr. Ct. Ofcr.; r. Central Islip, NY 11722.

ROLLOCK, Roderick; '89 BS; Med. Coord.; Pius 12, 188 W 230th St., Bronx, NY 10451, 718 562-7855; r. 11568 220th St., Cambria Hts., NY 11411, 718 978-9327. e-mail

ROLON, Miriam; '98 BS; Client Victims Coord.; Self-Help; r. 96-10 57 Ave., Apt. L, Flushing, NY 11368, 718 271-1934.

ROLON, Nicholas; '91 BS; 820 76th St., N. Bergen, NJ 07047.

ROLSTON, Felisia G.; '93 BS; 345 E 55th St., Brooklyn, NY 11203.

ROMAGNOLI, Michael; '89 BA; Police Ofcr.; Suffolk Cnty.; r. 30 Aberdeen Dr. Ext., Hampton Bays, NY 11946, 631 728-8144.

ROMAIN, Mario; '88 BS; 41 Winfield Ave., Mt. Vernon, NY 10552, 914 668-6435.

ROMAN, Ana J.; '87 AS; Records Mgmt. Spec.; Port Authority of NY & NJ, 1 World Trade Cnter, New York, NY 10048, 212 435-8420; r. 430 E. 105th St., Apt. 6 C, New York, NY 10029, 212 722-4729. e-mail

ROMAN, Angel L.; '89 BS; 423 Baltic St. #13B, Brooklyn, NY 11217, 718 234-1504.

ROMAN, Aracelio; '82 AS; 2 Haven Plz., New York, NY 10009, 315 867-2178.

ROMAN, Carmen; '83 MA; 1502 White Plns Rd #2, Bronx, NY 10462, 718 823-2562.

ROMAN, Edwin; '95 BA; MS Queens Clg.; Tchr.; Cornell Univ., 16 E. 34th St., New York, NY 10016, 212 340-2900; r. POB 342, New York, NY 10034, 212 569-3022. e-mail

ROMAN, Hector L.; '76 MPA; 9 Chiswell Dr., Melville, NY 11747.

ROMAN, Ms. Janet; '92 BS; 425 W. 25th St. Apt. 17D, New York, NY 10001, 315 867-2178.

ROMAN, Jenny; '99 BA; Community Assoc.; NYC Housing Authority, 340 Georgia Ave., Brooklyn, NY 11207, 718 495-4252; r. 232 Metropolitan Ave. 3D, Brooklyn, NY 11211, 718 387-9335.

ROMAN, Linda S.; '88 BS; 360 S. First St., Brooklyn, NY 11211, 718 253-0242.

ROMAN, Lisa; '97 BS; 314 25th St., Union City, NJ 07087.

ROMAN, Marian C.; '95 BS; CERT.; Peace Ofcr.; NY Presbyterian Hosp., 622 W. 168th St., New York, NY 10032, 212 305-2222; r. 350 Ft. Washington Ave. Apt. 1b, New York, NY 10033, 212 568-6119; Aryel. e-mail

ROMAN, Matilde L.; '93 BA; 205 Sunnyside Ave., Brooklyn, NY 11207, 718 277-1309.

ROMAN, Robert; '86 BA; 286 South St. Apt. 22a, New York, NY 10002, 315 732-6520.

ROMAN, Vivian; '98 MA; BA Syracuse Univ.; Youth Div. Couns.; NYS Ofc. of Children & Family Svcs., 163 W. 125th St. Rm. 209, New York, NY 10027, 212 961-4370; r. 1955 2nd Ave. #7c, New York, NY 10029, 212 876-5868. e-mail

ROMAN, Yvette; '82 BS; 167 Jefferson St., Brooklyn, NY 11206, 718 456-2927.

ROMANI, C.; '75 MA; 726 Spring Valley Rd., Maywood, NJ 07607.

ROMANI, Mark A.; '70 AS, '72 BS; Retired Lt.; Substitute Tchr.; Mamaroneck Village Police Dept.; r. 516 Hunter St., Mamaroneck, NY 10543, 914 698-4912; *Irene;* Nanci, Julie.

ROMANO, Christopher; '95 BA; JD St. John's Univ.; Atty.; r. 6365 72nd St. # 3, Flushing, NY 11379, 718 969-6668.

ROMANO, Frank J.; '75 BS; Supv.; Town of Goshen, 41 Webster Ave., Goshen, NY 10924, 914 294-6996; r. 1 Sunrise Hts., Goshen, NY 10924, 914 294-4735.

ROMANO, George A.; '85 BS; 127 Thorne Dr., Bethpage, NY 11714, 516 488-2912.

ROMANO, Gina M.; '94 BS; 1640 Tomlinson Ave., Bronx, NY 10461, 718 518-0783.

ROMANO, Hogla T.; '78 MA; 5814 5th Ave., Brooklyn, NY 11220, 718 449-9434.

ROMANO, Mrs. Lisa M., (Lisa M. Adanski); '95 BA; Technical Asst. Claims Analyst; Folksamerica Grp., Liberty Plz. 19th Fl., New York, NY 10006, 212 312-2610; r. 3 Jamie Ct., Staten Island, NY 10314, 718 983-6322; *Charles.* e-mail

ROMANO, Raymond; '83 BS; 7738 160th St., Flushing, NY 11366, 718 591-8685.

ROMANO, Robert P.; 282 Carroll St., Brooklyn, NY 11231, 718 836-5153.

ROMANO, Susan D.; '85 BA; 9528 126th St., Jamaica, NY 11419, 718 423-0594.

ROMERO, Angela; '96 BS; 3946 27th St. Apt. 3, Long Island City, NY 11101, 718 729-2625.

ROMERO, Benita A.; '95 BA; 437 Morris Park Ave., Bronx, NY 10460, 718 798-3141.

ROMERO, Heriberto; '90 BA; 712 Fox St. Apt. 4a, Bronx, NY 10455, 718 409-1271.

ROMERO, Jose A.; '77 BS; 1523 Glover St., Bronx, NY 10462, 718 320-8794.

ROMERO, Orestes R.; '81 BS; 568 83rd St., Apt. 2R, Brooklyn, NY 11209, 718 230-3141.

ROMERO, Palmira; '81 MPA; 25 Elizabeth St. Apt. 2m, Farmingdale, NY 11735.

ROMERO, Xaviera E.; '96 BA; 320 Beach 100th St., Far Rockaway, NY 11694, 718 261-6101.

ROMERO, Yenia J.; '98 BA; MSW Hunter Clg.; Social Worker; r. New York, NY 10029. e-mail

ROMM, Barry L.; '74 BA; Assn. Dir.; NYC Dept. of Buildings, 11 Park Pl., New York, NY 10007, 212 442-2000; r. 2285 Ocean Ave. Apt. 2m, Brooklyn, NY 11229, 718 998-3828.

RONDINA, Frederick E.; '77 BS; CERT. Cornell Univ.; Retired Detective New York City; Special Investigator, Medicaid Fraud, NY State Attorney General's Ofc., 120 Broadway, New York, NY 10271, 212 417-4024; r. 59 E Olive St., Long Beach, NY 11561, 516 431-2292; *Virginia.*

RONDON, Julia M.; '89 BS; 610 W 152nd St. Apt. 54, New York, NY 10031, 212 283-6164.

RONDON, Natasha J.; '96 BA; 4 Sunset Ave., Staten Island, NY 10314.

RONELLI, Danielle A.; '97 BA; 43-42 45th St., Sunnyside, NY 11104.

RONNING, Steve O.; '76 BS; 4 St. Anne Dr., New Windsor, NY 12553.

RONZO, Louis; '77 MA; 53 Oak Crest Rd, W. Orange, NJ 07052, 973 736-5106.

ROONEY, Joseph E.; '76 BS; 6433 60th Ave., Flushing, NY 11378, 718 326-1867.

ROONEY, Thomas F.; '75 MA; 7 Hemlock Dr., Glen Head, NY 11545, 516 626-5359.

ROONEY, William; '74 MPA; 171 Fremont St., Harrison, NY 10528, 914 835-0149.

ROOS, Denise; '71 BA; 1046 Wintergreen Ter., Rockville, MD 20850.

ROPER, Kenneth A.; '87 MA; Supervisory Special Agt.; FBI, 935 Pennsylvania Ave., NW, Washington, DC 20535, 202 324-3825; r. 634 E 233rd St. Apt. E, Bronx, NY 10466, 718 231-5848. e-mail

RORIE, Scott F.; '97 BS; Fraud Investigator; Human Resources Admin., 330 Jay St., Brooklyn, NY 11201; r. 1144 Lenox Rd. #3, Brooklyn, NY 11212.

RORKE, Charles V.; '71 BS; 19 Beach 222nd St., Far Rockaway, NY 11697, 718 634-5248.

ROSA, Confesor; '99 BS; 190 Brown Pl. #15, Bronx, NY 10454, 718 299-1757.

ROSA, Evelyn; '90 BS; 180 South St., New York, NY 10038.

ROSA, Gualberto; '92 BS; 263 Nichols Ave., Brooklyn, NY 11208, 718 372-5973.

ROSA, Justo; '97 BA; 1671 Vyse Ave., Bronx, NY 10460, 718 220-4061.

ROSA, Migdalia; '83 BA; 1430 Parkchester Rd Apt. 6d, Bronx, NY 10462, 718 549-1732.

ROSA, Rolando A.; '85 BS; 600 W. 165 St. #2D, New York, NY 10032, 315 734-0153.

ROSA, Rosemarie; '76 MA; 681 Crtlnd Ave. #11F, Bronx, NY 10451, 718 561-5857.

ROSA, Vapaira M. '99 (See Liranzo, Mrs. Yahaira M.).

ROSA, Yadira; '90 AS, '92 BS; 236 8th St. # 4r, Brooklyn, NY 11215, 718 349-6829.

ROSADO, Alfredo; '82 MA; 91-44 114th St., Richmond Hill, NY 11418, 718 949-0429.

ROSADO, Annette; '91 BS; 1562 Ocean Ave. Apt. 3f, Brooklyn, NY 11230, 718 383-0439.

ROSADO, Aracelis; '91 BS; 444 Fountain Ave. 2, Brooklyn, NY 11208, 718 383-0439.

ROSADO, Carmen; '99; 1823 Second Ave. S5, New York, NY 10128.

ROSADO, Christine; '96 BS; 13915 83rd Ave., Apt. 101, Jamaica, NY 11435, 718 949-0429.

ROSADO, Concepcion P.; '80 BS; 184 Chestnut Ave., Staten Island, NY 10305, 718 815-6435.

ROSADO, Jacqueline; '97 BA, '98 BA; 1100 Grand Concourse, Bronx, NY 10456, 718 538-5356.

ROSADO, Jose; '91 AS, '96; 340 Rte. 210, Stony Point, NY 10980.

ROSADO, Leslie M. '91 (See Vargas, Leslie M.).

ROSADO, Lisette; '91 BA; 2530 Independence Ave., Apt. 6E, Bronx, NY 10463, 718 829-2330.

ROSADO, Mercedes; '87 BS; 830 Columbus Ave., New York, NY 10025, 315 734-0153.

ROSADO, Lt Col Samuel A., USAF(Ret.); '75 BS; MS Nova Southeastern Univ.; 2515 Hillview Ave., Dayton, OH 45419, 937 298-8533; *LtCol Nyvia;* Keila, Samuel, Alexander. e-mail

ROSA-JIMENEZ, Anna; '90 BS; 2 Thayer St. Apt. 4d, New York, NY 10040.

ROSARIO, Cynthia A.; '99 BA; 414 Baltic Street#9C, Brooklyn, NY 11217, 718 643-1640.

ROSARIO, Donna M. '92 (See Saviano, Mrs. Donna M.).

ROSARIO, Fernando; '96 BA; 60-14 72nd St., Maspeth, NY 11378, 718 381-0099.

ROSARIO, Georgette; '89 BA; 622 E 23rd St., Brooklyn, NY 11210, 718 748-9069.

ROSARIO, Juan; '97 BS; 216 E Tremont Ave. 8, Bronx, NY 10457, 718 364-2561.

ROSARIO, Luisa J., (Luisa J. Taveras); '95 BS; 106-24 Corona, Flushing, NY 11368, 718 699-0224; *John;* Genesis. e-mail

ROSARIO, Manuel D.; '75 BA; 749 Azores Cir., Baypoint, CA 94565, 925 685-4547.

ROSARIO, Maria D. '83 (See Rosario-Dixon, Maria D.).

ROSARIO, Miguel; '92 BS; 515 W 174th St., Apt. 2C, New York, NY 10033.

ROSARIO, Moises; '97 BA; 2608 Creston Ave., Bronx, NY 10468, 718 364-0211.

ROSARIO, Percida; '89 BS; AS Hostos Community Clg.; Correctional Ofcr.; RMAC, 1919 Hazen St., E. Amherst, NY 14051; r. 25914 Craft Ave., Rosedale, NY 11422, 718 712-1037.

ROSARIO, Phaedra; '94 BS; 20943 Whitehall Ter., Queens Vlg., NY 11427, 718 381-0099.

ROSARIO, Rafael; '98 BA; Fraud Investigator; City of NY, Human Resources Admin., 250 Church St. 3rd Fl., New York, NY 10013, 212 274-4901; r. 539 W 163 St. 31, New York, NY 10032, 212 795-8713.

ROSARIO, Victor M.; '98 BS; Indep. Special Investigations; 914 720-5676; r. 40 Lincoln Ave., New Rochelle, NY 10801, 914 235-3580; Alejandro. e-mail

ROSARIO-DIXON, Maria D., (Maria D. Rosario); '83 BA; Homemaker; r. 1108 Landing Meadows Dr., Henderson, KY 42420; *Jerome;* Kyle.

ROSATI, Daniel J.; '98 MA; 3607 Avenue L, Brooklyn, NY 11210, 718 252-3489.

ROSATO, Lindy M.; '91 BA; 61 Daniel Ave., Rutherford, NJ 07070.

ROSE, Brigitte; '87 BS; 385 E. 143 St., Bronx, NY 10454, 718 597-1834.

ROSE, Dulcie D.; '82 BA; 588 Saint Marks Ave., Brooklyn, NY 11216, 718 756-0704.

ROSE, Jack N.; '73 MA; 129 East St., Oneonta, NY 13820, 607 433-7644.

ROSE, Jacqueline A.; '85 BA; Investigator; Metropolitan Transportation, 130 Livinston St., Brooklyn, NY 11201, 718 694-3410; r. 154 Rockaway Pkwy., Brooklyn, NY 11212.

ROSE, Joyce H.; '79 BA, '82 MA; MS Lehman Clg.; Psychologist Spec.; Charlotte Correctional Inst., Punta Gorda, FL 33955, 941 575-2828; r. 1402 Terry Ave., Port Charlotte, FL 33980, 941 624-0366.

ROSE, Kim D.; '83 BS; 968 54th St., Brooklyn, NY 11219, 718 436-8609.

ROSE, Lynn; '77 BAH; Accounts Receivable/Finance; Middle Atlantic Prods.; r. 1 Cannonball Rd, Pompton Lakes, NJ 07442, 973 839-4628.

ROSE, Michael J.; '77 BS; 22 Dover Pkwy., Stewart Manor, NY 11530, 516 773-3526.

ROSE, Richard A.; '85 MA; Detective Lt.; Morris Cnty. Prosecutor Ofc.; r. 34 Radcliffe Dr., Succasunna, NJ 07876, 973 252-9695; *Janet.*

ROSE, Rodney J.; '96 BA; 322 Bainbridge Str, Brooklyn, NY 11233, 718 856-6824.

ROSE, Ronald M.; '81 MPA; MPA SUNY Albany; Lt.; NYC Police Dept., Police Plz., New York, NY 10038, 212 314-6640; r. 573 Lincoln Blvd., Long Beach, NY 11561, 516 432-8487.

ROSEN, David B.; '83 MA; 377 Rector Pl. #6C, New York, NY 10280, 315 732-0781.

ROSEN, Marie; '82 BA; 405 W. 57th St., New York, NY 10019, 315 732-0781.

ROSEN, Penny; '93 MA; 128 2nd St., Mahwah, NJ 07430.

ROSEN, Warren; '79 BS; 2701 Sunrise Lakes Dr. E # Bl10-2o7, Sunrise, FL 33322, 954 747-0828.

ROSENBACH, Janet N. '94 (See Rocco, Janet N.).

ROSENBAUM, Frances; '72 MPA; Assoc. Staff Analyst; NYC; r. 328 W. 15 St., New York, NY 10011, 212 989-6385.

ROSENBAUM, Meredith; '84 MA; 26 Dobbs Ter., Scarsdale, NY 10583, 914 472-6794.

ROSENBERG, Linda S.; '80 BA; Bus. Owner; Black Tie Stationers, 1831 E. 2nd. St., Brooklyn, NY 11223, 718 645-5496; r. 1831 E 2nd St., Brooklyn, NY 11223, 718 645-5496; *Allan;* Sari L. Setton, Gabriel Lesser, Yve Massre. e-mail

ROSENBERG, Michelle L.; '98 BS; 101 Robin Hood Ln., W. Nyack, NY 10994, 914 638-2837.

ROSENBERG, Susan B.; '77 MA; 868 E. 55 St., Brooklyn, NY 11234, 718 436-1780.

ROSENBERGER, Joseph N.; '98 BS; 10 Winchester Ave., #2a, Yonkers, NY 10710.

ROSENBERGER, Michael; '96 BA; 183 W. 238th St., Bronx, NY 10463, 718 543-1912.

ROSENFELD, Marcia C.; '86 BA; 141 Dutchess Tpk., Poughkeepsie, NY 12603, 914 471-4320.

ROSKE, Daniel; '95 BS; 61 Main Bayway, Toms River, NJ 08753, 732 349-0150. e-mail

ROSLAN, Gary J.; '81 MPA; 6523 165th St., Flushing, NY 11365, 718 445-7858.

ROSS, James; '79 BS, '81 AS; Detective; NYC Police Dept., 718 383-8456; r. 13309 Sitka St., Jamaica, NY 11417, 718 641-9244.

ROSS, James D.; '71 BA; Inspector Police Ofcr.; NYC Police Dept. Housing Bur., New York, NY 10038; r. 799 Planders Ave., Uniondale, NY 11553, 516 489-1162; *Julia;* David, Adam, Paul. e-mail

ROSS, Jennifer '89 (See Ross Shapiro, Jennifer S.).

ROSS, Richard M.; '80 BS; 3730 Inverrary Dr. Apt. 1c, Lauderhill, FL 33319, 954 485-4019.

ROSS, Stanley; '97 BS; Correction Ofcr.; NYC Dept. of Corrections; r. 257-55 148th Dr., Rosedale, NY 11422, 718 527-8039; *Brenda;* Keeana. e-mail

ROSSELLO, Manuel; '97 BS; Police Ofcr.; City of NY; r. 5965 60th Ln., Maspeth, NY 11378, 718 821-4417.

ROSSI, David; '91 BS; 499 Fashion Ave., #3, New York, NY 10018, 315 826-5425.

ROSSI, Dennis J.; '81 AS; 4923 166th St., Flushing, NY 11365, 718 539-8719.

ROSSI-ROSEN, Renee M.; '96 MA; 14 Longfellow Dr., Colonia, NJ 07067, 732 574-9634.

ROSS SHAPIRO, Jennifer S., (Jennifer Ross); '89 MA; BA Univ. of WI Madison; Assist. Finance Dir.; Chicago Fire Dept., 121 N LaSalle, Chicago, IL 60602, 312 744-9229; r. 5960 N Neva Ave., Chicago, IL 60631, 773 775-2161; *Jonathan;* Jacob, Julia. e-mail

ROTH, Joan L.; '86 MA; 345 Eighth Ave., New York, NY 10001, 315 738-1682.

ROTH, Paul P.; '95 BA; 6053 76th St., Flushing, NY 11373, 718 424-8265.

ROTHANG, Robert A.; '74 BS; AS SUNY at Farmingdale; Surgical Technologist; Veterans Admin., Northport, NY 11768; r. 140 Parkwood Dr., Shirley, NY 11967, 631 281-7410.

ROTHENBERG, Bruce A.; '83 MPA; Clerk; US Postal Svc.; r. 6348 Lansdowne Cir., Boynton Bch., FL 33437, 561 742-8064. e-mail

ROTHENBERG, Daniel S.; '99 MS; BA Univ. of Pennsylvania; Forensic Scientist; Westchester Cnty.; r. 15 Old Lyme Rd., Scarsdale, NY 10583. e-mail

ROTHENBERG, Jackie; '95 MA; BS Univ. of Arizona; Journalist; r. New York, NY 10021.

ROTHLEIN, Steve; '74 BA; Police Chief; Miami-Dade Police Dept., 9105 NW 25 St., Miami, FL 33172, 305 471-2350; r. 6220 Plymouth Ln., Davie, FL 33331, 954 680-1710. e-mail

ROTHLEIN GOLDSTEIN, Mary; VP; John Jay Clg. of Criminal Justice, 899 10th Ave., New York, NY 10019, 212 237-8624; r. 50 Sutton Pl., 6H, New York, NY 10022, 212 644-9775.

ROTHMAN, Flora; '78 MA; 1708 215th St., Flushing, NY 11360, 718 423-3542.

ROTHMAN, Peter L.; '76 MA; 253-42 147 Ave., Rosedale, NY 11422, 516 747-2143.

ROTHMANN, Scott F.; '91 BS; 326 E 74th St. Apt. 1, New York, NY 10021.

ROTHNAGEL, Meredith; '93 BS; 117-01 Park Ln. S, Kew Gardens, NY 11418.

ROTTKAMP, William J.; '75 BS; 768 Silver Lake Pl., Baldwin, NY 11510.

ROUGH, Thomas C.; '85 BS; POB 219, Poughquag, NY 12570.

ROULHAC, Teresa; '97 BA, '98 BA, '99; 577 Fdr Dr. #5a, New York, NY 10002, 212 677-6249.

ROULSTON, Tammy L.; '94 BS; Police Ofcr.; US Capitol Police, 119 Northeast St., Washington, DC 20515; r. 610 Northwest St. Apt. 505, Alexandria, VA 22314.

ROUNDS, Thomas E.; '70 BS; Zone Sergeant; New York State Police; r. 10 Cornish Ave., Binghamton, NY 13901, 607 723-9259; *Rosemary;* Eric, Dennis, Michael.

ROUSE, Evelyn; '99 BA; Paraprofn.; Cassidy Cataloguing Svcs., 111 Frank E. Rodgers Blvd. S., Harrison, NJ 07029, 973 481-0900; r. 618 E 9 St. Apt. 3E, New York, NY 10009, 212 995-9524. e-mail

ROVIRA, Catherine; 27 Purdue St., Staten Island, NY 10314.

ROWAN, Edward T., Sr.; '77 MA; BS JJCCJ; Dir. of Security for The Lottery; 1 Broadway Ctr., POB 7500, Schenectady, NY 12301, 518 388-3475; r. 47 Brookline Dr., Country Knolls W., Clifton Park, NY 12065, 518 877-6213; *Bonnie C.;* Linda, Edward Jr, Shawn, Glenn, Scott. e-mail

ROWE, John M.; '97 MS; BA Boston Clg.; Mgr. of Investigations; Health & Hosp. Corp.-Inspector Gen., 346 Broadway Ste. 500, New York, NY 10021, 212 676-0895; r. 1416 York Ave., Apt. C, New York, NY 10021, 212 535-5681. e-mail

ROWE, Leonard A.; '72 AA, '76 BA; Retired Police Ofcr.; r. POB 350965, Palm Coast, FL 32135, 904 446-5775.

ROWE, Thomas P.; '91 BS; 135 Willow St., Elmwood Park, NJ 07407, 201 797-0549.

ROWLAND, Eileen; Prof. Emerita; John Jay Clg. of Criminal Justice; r. 5 Leach Hollow Rd, Sherman, CT 06784, 860 354-6064.

ROWLAND, John; '76 BA; 4854A Dovewood Cir., Boynton Bch., FL 33436.

ROWLAND, Tamesha Q.; '79 BA; 1720 Bedford Ave. Apt. 13a, Brooklyn, NY 11225, 718 694-0838.

ROY, Christine M.; 2326 Esplanade, Bronx, NY 10469, 718 547-8307.

ROYCE, Kevin J.; '95 BS; 5 3rd St., Wayne, NJ 07470, 973 696-4963.

ROYER, Gary; '86 MPA; 22 Edgewater Rd, Cliffside Park, NJ 07010.

ROYER, Helena C.; '98 BS; 98 Park Ter. E. #4a, New York, NY 10034, 212 544-7090.

ROZIER, Christopher; '97 BA; Paralegal; r. 2186 Strauss St., Brooklyn, NY 11212, 718 346-1322. e-mail

ROZON, Xiomara A.; '94 BS; 75 La Salle St., New York, NY 10027.

RUANE, James P.; '84 MPA; 317 77th St., Brooklyn, NY 11209, 718 788-7395.

RUBAN, Ms. Carlyne S.; '92 BS, '98 MPA; AA Manhattan Comm Clg.; Asst. to The Chief; NYC Dept. of Parks & Recreation, Arsenal North, 1234 5th Ave., New York, NY 10029, 212 360-2796; r. 993 President St., Apt. 1H, Brooklyn, NY 11225, 718 735-0463. e-mail

RUBEN, Scott P.; '84 BS; AA NYC Tech Clg.; Supv. Dist. Adjudications/SE; US Immigration Svc., 26 Federal Plz., Rm. 700, New York, NY 10278, 212 204-1631; r. 457 F.D.R. Dr., New York, NY 10002, 917 691-5359. e-mail

RUBENSTEIN, Hy D.; '77 BA; JD Brooklyn Law Sch.; Atty.; Hale and Door LLP, 1455 Pennsylvania NW, Washington, DC 20004, 202 942-8472; r. 3915 Pinkney Rd, Baltimore, MD 21215, 410 358-9920. e-mail

RUBERO, Kenneth; '99 BS; Detective; NYC, Box 881, Bronx, NY 10473; r. P.O.Box 881, Bronx, NY 10473, 718 518-9162. e-mail

RUBI, Connie M.; '77 BS; POB 647, Bronx, NY 10459.

RUBINO, Arthur S.; '92 BS; POB 490, Thiells, NY 10984, 914 429-7007.

RUBINO, Charles J.; '83 BA; MSW Hunter Clg.; Sch. Social Worker; Martin Deporres Sch., 136-25 218th St., Springfield Gardens, NY 11413, 718 525-3414; r. 107 Milton St., Brooklyn, NY 11222, 718 383-2979.

RUBINSON, Scott H.; '91 BS; 160 Broadway, Massapequa Park, NY 11762.

RUBIROSA, Natasha; '95 BA; 120 2nd Ave. #3b, New York, NY 10003.

RUCK, Songa L.; '88 BS; 49 E 10th St., Brooklyn, NY 11218, 718 944-8278.

RUDAWITZ, Edward M.; '76 BS; 47-34 190 St., Flushing, NY 11358.

RUDD, Alexis H.; '93 MA; BA Cornell Univ.; Law Student; Santa Clara Univ., Santa Clara, CA 95053; r. 130 Barneson Ave. #9, San Mateo, CA 94402, 650 357-7914. e-mail

RUDDEN, John; 25 Sherman Rd, Old Bethpage, NY 11804, 516 694-7348.

RUDDER, Carol A.; '81 BS; 952 E 224th St., Bronx, NY 10466, 718 231-9245.

RUDDOCK, Ethelbert; '84 MA; 11559 217th St., Jamaica, NY 11411.

RUDERMAN, Harriet; '81 BS; Retired Asst. Registrar; r. Jamaica, NY 11421.

RUDOLPH, Deandre D.; '91 BS; POB 20458, Newark, NJ 07101, 973 371-4727.

RUDOLPH, Gary J.; '97 AS; 225 W. Olive, Long Beach, NY 11561, 516 872-0871.

RUDOWITZ, Bruce S.; '88 BS; Probation Ofcr.; NY Dept. of Probation, 44 Worth St., New York, NY 10013, 212 676-1834; r. 102-28 Park Ln. S., Richmond Hill, NY 11418, 718 441-1867; *Frances;* Brian. e-mail

RUDSHTEYN, Yuriy; '99 BS FISC; Fire Safety Tech.; Fire Safety Co.; r. 1525 W 11th St., Apt. 8A, Brooklyn, NY 11204, 718 331-7612; *Lana.*

RUDZIANIS, Patricia; 5825 220 St., Flushing, NY 11364.

RUE, Sheena R.; '98 AS; 73 Lott Ave., # 11, Brooklyn, NY 11212, 718 498-5415.

RUEDA, Zoila N.; '88 BA; 265 Cherry St. #4, New York, NY 10002.

RUFF, Michelle N.; '99 BS; Admin. Asst.; Rochdale Securities Corp., 570 Lexington Ave., 8th Fl., New York, NY 10022, 212 588-3410; r. 130-12 109th Ave., S. Ozone Park, NY 11420, 718 529-0867. e-mail

RUFFINOTT, Robert R.; '84 BS; 6244 82nd Pl., Flushing, NY 11379, 718 457-0169.

RUFFO, Robert; '74 AA, '76 BA, '82 MA; Police Ofcr.; Veterans Admin., 423 E. 23rd St., New York, NY 10017; r. 5 Keeley St., Staten Island, NY 10305, 718 981-1736; *Victoria;* Annette Marie, Thomas Anthony.

RUFINO, Annette L.; '99 BA; Teacher; Adam Clayton Powell IS #8, 2240 690-5873; r. 947 Columbus Ave. Apt. #2A, New York, NY 10025, 212 749-6106; *Carlos Ferreiras;* Heather, Karla Ferreiras.

RUGGERI, Ronald X.; '71 BA; Air Traffic Mgr.; Fed. Aviation Admin., New York International AFSS, 150 Arrival Ave., Ronkonkoma, NY 11779, 631 471-7181; r. 202 Erik Dr., Setauket, NY 11733, 631 642-2399. e-mail

RUGGIERO, Anthony; '95 BS; 2118 74th St. Apt. 1, Brooklyn, NY 11204, 718 373-0389.

RUIZ, Ada; '99; 505 E. 120th St., New York, NY 10035, 315 339-2924.

RUIZ, Angel L.; '84 BS; 308 E. 145 St., Bronx, NY 10451.

RUIZ, Bernadette; '95 BS; 8401 89th Ave., Jamaica, NY 11421, 718 848-5802.

RUIZ, Ivelisse; '93 BS; 302 E 151st St., Bronx, NY 10451, 718 378-1188.

RUIZ, Judy; '96 BA; Social Worker; Salvation Army, 1420 Bushwick Ave., Ofc. 222, Brooklyn, NY 11207, 718 574-0129; r. 93 Lewis Ave., Apt. 11G, Brooklyn, NY 11206, 718 453-9843; Dorcine Rodgers. e-mail

RUIZ, Nydia '95 (See Ruiz-Velez, Mrs. Nydia).

RUIZ, Pedro J.; '95 BS; 2010 Bruckner Blvd., Bronx, NY 10473, 718 792-9110.

RUIZ, Peggy E.; '83 BS; 1905 Second Ave., New York, NY 10029, 315 339-2924.

RUIZ, Vicki L.; '96 BA; 1363 Merry Ave., Apt. 1, Bronx, NY 10461.

RUIZ-BASQUEZ, Luisa E.; '87 BA; Sr. Claims Approval Rep.; Grp. Health Inc, 442 Ninth Ave., New York, NY 10001, 212 615-0414; r. 587 Riverside Dr. Apt. 1g, New York, NY 10031, 212 234-2014. e-mail

RUIZ-VELEZ, Mrs. Nydia, (Nydia Ruiz); '95 BS; Legal Asst.; Law Ofc. of Edward H Rosenthal, 125-10 Queens Blvd., Kew Gardens, NY 11415, 718 520-1100; r. 88-28 86th St., Woodhaven, NY 11421, 718 296-4256; Ignacio Velez. e-mail

RULLO, Antonia; '80 MA; 21217 42nd Ave. Apt. 2a, Flushing, NY 11361.

RUMBERG, Alan R.; 211-65 23rd Ave., Bayside, NY 11360.

RUMELL, William N.; '99 MA; BS LaSalle Univ.; Primary Therapist, FIR Prog.; Northeast Treatment Ctrs., Spring Garden Counseling Ctr., 497 N. 5th St., Philadelphia, PA 19123, 215 451-7100; r. 21 Willis Ave., Cherry Hill, NJ 08002, 856 317-5727; Carolyn; Liam David, Adia Shea.

RUMPF, William R.; '81 MA; 50 Glenwood Ave., Staten Island, NY 10301, 718 273-2699.

RUMPH, Richard; '78 MPA; 112 Chauncey Ave., New Rochelle, NY 10801.

RUOCCO, Dante; '96 BA; 27 Battle Ridge Tr., Totowa, NJ 07512.

RUOTOLO, Joseph C.; '96 BS; 24 Vanderbilt Ave., Babylon, NY 11704.

RUSH, Vilethia; '96 BA; AA Borough of Manhattan CC; 3628 215th St., Bayside, NY 11361, 718 229-7890.

RUSHTON, Denise A.; '85 BS; 1659 Parkview Ave., Seaford, NY 11783, 516 221-2061.

RUSSEL, Patrick O.; '99; 17 Ferndale Dr., Hicksville, NY 11801, 516 377-3826.

RUSSELL, Brenda M.; '99 MA; BA Cornell Univ.; Student; r. 531 W. 49th St. #3W, New York, NY 10019, 212 307-6288. e-mail

RUSSELL, Jessica K.; '96 BA; 410 Williams Ave., Brooklyn, NY 11207, 718 646-8654.

RUSSELL, Marsha Natasha; '95 BS; MA CCNY, Univ. of North London; Info. Technology Profn./Cnslt.; r. Jamaica, NY 11423. e-mail

RUSSELL, Michael L.; '95 BS; 234 E 87th St. # P, Brooklyn, NY 11236, 718 646-7012.

RUSSELL, Michel M.; '87 BS; D-1/1 ADA Box 1189, APO, AE 09123.

RUSSELL, Roslyn; '91 BA; 3815 Birchwood Ct., North Brunswick, NJ 08902, 732 422-2203.

RUSSELL, Sara; '99 MPA; 264 Water St. #4D, New York, NY 10038, 212 406-0671.

RUSSO, Dello A.; '91 BA, '91 MA; 44 Churchill Rd, Cresskill, NJ 07626, 888 529-0011.

RUSSO, Dora; '89 BA; 852 Revere Ave., Bronx, NY 10465, 718 863-4975.

RUSSO, Elizabeth; '85 BA; 111 Mulberry St. 50, Newark, NJ 07102.

RUSSO, Franco; '83 BS; 1572 82nd St., Brooklyn, NY 11228, 718 259-0934.

RUSSO, John; '81 BS; Investigator; Keyspan Energy Corp., One Metrotech Ctr., Brooklyn, NY 11201, 718 403-3178; r. 350 65th St. Apt. 12m, Brooklyn, NY 11220, 718 238-7437; Patricia; Gary. e-mail

RUSSO, Joseph J.; '78 BS; 1462 E. 3 St., Brooklyn, NY 11230, 718 968-1507.

RUSSO, Joseph P.; '89 MA; 498 Willow Rd W, Staten Island, NY 10314, 718 979-4593.

RUSSO, Lucia; '87 BA; 2213 63rd St., Brooklyn, NY 11204, 718 331-3293.

RUSSO, Philip A.; '95 BA; 180 S 6th St., Lindenhurst, NY 11757.

RUSSO, Robert M.; '93 BS; 46 Penn Ave., Staten Island, NY 10306, 718 273-6443.

RUSSO, Stacey A.; '97 BS; Child Welfare Spec.; NYC Admin. for Children's Svcs., 150 William St., New York, NY 10038, 212 341-3307; r. 2120 Mapes Ave., Bronx, NY 10460, 718 562-5227; Christopher.

RUSSWURM, John C.; 69-03 66 St., Glendale, NY 11385.

RUSZNAK, Richard C.; '90 BS; 16 George St., Bayonne, NJ 07002, 201 339-0112.

RUTHERFORD, Chauncey A.; '99 BA; 100 Winthrop St. 3F, Brooklyn, NY 11225, 718 287-2243.

RUTIGLIANO, Serafina; '84 BS; 3412 Tibbett Ave., Bronx, NY 10463, 718 543-2847.

RUVOLO, Anthony P.; '79 BS; 59-04 Fresh Pond Rd, Maspeth, NY 11378.

RYALL, Jeremiah J.; '93 BS; 258 Irving Ave., Deer Park, NY 11729.

RYAN, Allen G.; '73 BS; 31 Garden Blvd., Hicksville, NY 11801, 516 822-7487.

RYAN, Christopher; '95 BS; 12 71 St. Bayridge, Brooklyn, NY 11209, 718 346-7220.

RYAN, Daniel; '67 MPA; 245-13 133rd Rd, Rosedale, NY 11422, 516 594-8539.

RYAN, Denis P.; '79 BS; 1799 Seminole Ave., Bronx, NY 10461, 718 548-8163.

RYAN, Edward J.; '74 BS; Retired Police; r. 1386 E 17 St., Brooklyn, NY 11230, 718 339-1387.

RYAN, Edward J.; '73 BA; 11 Huntsman Ln., Belle Mead, NJ 08502.

RYAN, Francis M.; '70 BS; Retired Tchr.; r. 12 Mildred Rd, Danvers, MA 01923.

RYAN, Fred C.; '92 BA; POB 104h, Scarsdale, NY 10583.

RYAN, James J.; '76 BS; 4114 Foster Ave., Brooklyn, NY 11203, 718 759-9617.

RYAN, John F.; '78 BA, '79 BS; POB 4743, Sunnyside, NY 11104, 718 657-1208.

RYAN, John P.; '98 BA; NYC Police Ofcr.; r. 5709 7 Ave., Brooklyn, NY 11220, 718 492-4314.

RYAN, Kenneth J.; '80 MA; 102 Oberlin St., Staten Island, NY 10305, 718 981-0286.

RYAN, Kim; '95 BS; Sr. Investigator; Dept. of Buildings Investigation Unit, New York, NY 10001; r. 58-58 Catalipa Ave., Ridgewood, NY 11385, 718 821-4852.

RYAN, Laura J.; '93 BS; 448 45th St. # 2, Brooklyn, NY 11220, 718 287-1276.

RYAN, Martin J.; '76 BA; 64-38 65 Ln., Middle Vlg., NY 11379, 718 634-7236.

RYAN, Maureen C.; '80 BS; 1902 E 38 St., Brooklyn, NY 11234, 718 368-4431.

RYAN, Michael; '78 BS; POB 769, Mahopac, NY 10541, 914 968-3633.

RYAN, Michael P.; '94 BS; 1267 California Rd, Eastchester, NY 10709, 914 968-3633.

RYAN, Patricia A.; '84 BS; Criminalist; Ofc. of Chief Med. Examiner, NYC, New York, NY 10016, 212 447-7511; r. 440 Senator St., Brooklyn, NY 11220, 718 745-3084.

RYAN, Patrick J.; '84 BA; 1902 E 38th St., Brooklyn, NY 11234, 718 346-7220.

RYAN, Richard J.; '75 BS; 9 Lakeland Ave., Congers, NY 10920, 914 268-3730.

RYAN, Robert T.; '97 BS; 27 Burbank Ave., Staten Island, NY 10306, 718 273-2664.

RYAN, Ronald J.; '78 BS; 25 E Gulf to Lake Hwy., Lecanto, FL 34461.

RYAN, Capt Stephen J.; NYARNG; '92 MPA; BA St. Johns Univ., MPA; Police Ofcr.; Nassau Cnty. Police Dept., Broadway & Sheridan, Hewlett, NY 11557, 516 573-6400; r. 1013 78 St., Brooklyn, NY 11228, 718 836-1797.

RYAN, Theresa A.; '99, MA; 36739 Stevens Blvd., Willoughby, OH 44094, 216 941-4361.

RYAN, Thomas; '75 BS; 31 Jersey St., Hicksville, NY 11801, 516 433-8602.

RYAN, Thomas P.; '77 MPA; AS Baruch Clg., BS; Retired Dep. Chief; NYC Police Dept., New York, NY 10003; r. 57 Dogwood Ln., Hewitt, NJ 07421, 973 728-3816; Barbara; Patricia, Barbara.

RYAN, William G.; '75 MA; 12 Fremont Ave., Nanuet, NY 10954, 914 623-5853.

RYAN, William J.; '78 BS; 842 Huasna Rd, Arroyo Grande, CA 93420, 805 473-3871.

RYBACKI, Laureen A.; '91 BA, '94 MA; 6241 69th St., Flushing, NY 11379, 718 835-0591.

RYDEN, Carolyn Y.; '89 BA; 1677 85th St., Brooklyn, NY 11214.

RYLEY, Thomas; '90 BA; 566 Rose Blvd., N. Baldwin, NY 11510.

RYNIAK, William A.; '89 MA; Parole Ofcr.; State of New Jersey, 66 Hamilton St. 2nd Fl., Paterson, NJ 07505, 973 977-4217; r. 24 Highland Ave., Bloomingdale, NJ 07403, 973 492-5629. e-mail

RYNNE, John; '81 BS; 4362 247th St., Flushing, NY 11363, 718 229-6208.

RYNNE, John P.; '85 BA; 34 Hickory Ln., Garnerville, NY 10923, 914 354-2561.

RYNNE, Thomas M.; 6 Hickory Ln., Garnerville, NY 10923, 914 354-3754.

RYNNE, Thomas M.; 6020 Delafield Ave., Bronx, NY 10471, 718 549-5722.

S

SABALA, Maritza; '78 BS; 555 W 156th St. #5H, New York, NY 10032.

SABATER, Barbara M.; '93 BA, '95 MA; Case Mgr.; Westchester Cnty., 112 E. Post Rd., White Plains, NY 10601, 914 285-3033; r. 4 Georgetown Oval, New City, NY 10956, 914 639-0048. e-mail

SABATINI, Karen; '90 BS; 28-05 206 St., Bayside, NY 11360.

SABATINO, Ludwig V.; '73 MS; Retired NYC Det. Crime Lab; New York, NY 10001.

SABB, Jamal M.; '98 BS; Child Protective Specialist; City of NY, 718 579-9458; r. 4535 Hoxie St., Bronx, NY 10470, 718 325-7550.

SABEL, Raymond P.; '78 BS; 6930 44th Ave., Woodside, NY 11377.

SACACCIO, Michael J.; '81 BS; 33-B Katan Loop, Staten Island, NY 10308, 718 317-1588.

SACCHERI, Paula A.; '82 BA; 51-43 Codwise Pl., Elmhurst, NY 11373.

SACCO, Dominick A.; '74 MPA; PHD Fordham Univ.; Retired Tchr. PT; Suffolk Community Clg., 516 451-4336; r. 94 Lyncliff Rd., Hampton Bays, NY 11946, 631 728-9630.

SACCO, Ilene; '91 MA; 84-25 Elmhurst Ave., Elmhurst, NY 11373.

SACIPI, Bujar B.; '97 BS; BBA Kingsborough Comm. Clg.; Security Guard; GMSC, 11 Pen Plz., New York, NY 10001; r. 484 McDonald Ave., Brooklyn, NY 11218, 718 853-2186.

SACK, Nichole L.; '99 BA; Asst. Mgr.; Diamond Hallmark, New York, NY 10020; r. 206 E 139th St. Basement, Bronx, NY 10454, 718 585-4348.

SACKEL, James H.; '82 BS; Capt.; NYC Police Dept., 140 58th St., Ste. 6 B, Brooklyn, NY 11220, 718 765-4316; r. 586 College Ave., Staten Island, NY 10302, 718 442-8111; *Rita;* James Jr, Talia. e-mail

SACKMAN, David W.; 39 Terry Ln., Commack, NY 11725, 631 499-0899.

SACKS, Barbara K.; '70 MA; MPA NYU; City Mgr.; Fair Lawn, 8-01 Fair Lawn, Fair Lawn, NJ 07410, 201 794-5310; r. 303 Scotland Rd., S. Orange, NJ 07079, 973 763-5759.

SACKS, Bruce E.; '80 BS; 2670 Colby Ct., Brooklyn, NY 11223, 718 769-7010.

SADOVSKIY, Yevgeniy; '97 BA; 2044 21st Dr., Brooklyn, NY 11214.

SADOWSKI, Cecilia A. '82 (See Torres, Mrs. Cecilia A.).

SADRAKULA, Michael P.; '76 AA, '78 BA, '80 MA; Police Ofcr.; NYC Police Dept.; r. 77 Hickory Ln., Bedford, NY 10506, 914 234-9671; *Cindy;* Elizabeth.

SAENGER, Patricia A.; '79 BA; 34-13 11th St., Long Island City, NY 11106.

SAFFORD, Carl E.; '82 BS; POB 470088, Brooklyn, NY 11247.

SAFFORD, Simone S.; '94 BA; 1519 Pacific St., Brooklyn, NY 11213, 718 493-7135.

SAFRAN, Leo; '70 MPA; 15050 Booth Memorial Ave., Flushing, NY 11355.

SAGET, Marie P.; '96 BS; AAS NYC Technical Clg.; Probation Ofcr.; Florida State Dept. of Corrections, 915 NW 10th Ave., Ft. Lauderdale, FL 33311, 954 467-4267; r. 240 Commodore Dr. Apt. 1117, Plantation, FL 33325, 954 916-5142.

SAHDALA, Ambiorix A.; '97 BA, '98 BA; 5160 Post Rd # 2, Bronx, NY 10471.

SAHLBERG, Fred J.; '78 MPA; 32 Merritt Ave., Bergenfield, NJ 07621.

SAI, Nancy M.; '93 BS; 63-03 Wetherole St., Rego Park, NY 11374.

SAIGO, Shondell A.; '95 BS; MA Brooklyn Clg.; Tchr.; Bd. of Educ. PS 249, 18 Marlborough Rd., Brooklyn, NY 11226, 718 282-8828; r. 1110 E. 38th St., Brooklyn, NY 11210, 718 258-5653; *Elly Walters;* Troy. e-mail

SAINT CLOUX, Marie P., (Marie Noailles); '96 BS; MS Brooklyn Clg.; POB 260030, Brooklyn, NY 11226, 718 859-0080. e-mail

SAINT-FLEUR, Johanne A.; '98 BS; Child Protective Spec.; Admin. for Children Svcs.; r. POB 20486, Columbus Cir., New York, NY 10023. e-mail

SAINTIL, Naomi M.; '96 BS; 4404 Avenue K #2, Brooklyn, NY 11234, 718 444-0206.

SAINTJULIEN, Emilio; '84 BS; 1799 Nostrand Ave., Brooklyn, NY 11226, 718 421-5696.

SAINT VICTOR, Lewis; '97 BA; 220-21 99th Ave., Queens Vlg., NY 11429.

SAKELHIDE, Keith A.; '80 BAPA; JD Hofstra U. Sch. of Law; Attorney-Worker's Comp.; Employers Ins. Co. of Nevada, 1700 W. Charleston, Las Vegas, NV 89126, 702 671-7154; r. 7220 Painted Shadows Way, Las Vegas, NV 89149, 702 396-7893; *Jeanette.* e-mail

SALA, Eva M.; '93 BA; 740 Newcastle Dr., # Unta, Schererville, IN 46375.

SALA, John A.; '78 BS; 30 Horizon Farms Rd, Warwick, NY 10990, 914 258-3663; *Helen;* Jessica, Thomas, John.

SALA, Joseph J.; '76 BS; 43 Knickerbocker Rd, Manhasset, NY 11030, 516 365-1913.

SALADINO, Frank N.; '82 BS; 632 Townline Rd, Hauppauge, NY 11788.

SALAHUDDIN, Shaifah; '96 BA; Tchr.; Bd. of Educ. JHS 149, 360 E 145 St., Bronx, NY 10454, 718 292-2221; r. 707 Jerome St., Brooklyn, NY 11207, 718 927-4349; Asha Robinson.

SALAMO, Michael R.; '76 BA; 2426 E 23rd St., Brooklyn, NY 11235, 718 853-6585.

SALAMON, Carmelita J.; '79 BS; 102-02 63 Rd, Forest Hills, NY 11375, 718 591-9485.

SALAMONE, John A.; '75 BS; MPS Sch. for Social Rsch.; Retired-Hosp. Admin.; r. 3842 Cir. Lake Dr., W. Palm Bch., FL 33417, 561 471-1913; *Rosemarie;* Barbara, John Jr, James.

SALAMONE, Vincent; '95 BA; 3835 Richmond Ave., Staten Island, NY 10312, 718 273-7689.

SALAMY, Joseph M.; '89 BS; Special Agt.; US Dept. of Transportation, 22690 Cactus Ave., Ste. 250, Moreno Vly., CA 92553, 909 653-2299; r. 1126 Plz. Miraleste, Chula Vista, CA 91910. e-mail

SALANE, Douglas; 44-09 196th St., Flushing, NY 11358.

SALAS, Ivan; '88 AS, '92 BA; 6723 Roosevelt Ave., Flushing, NY 11377, 718 446-4120.

SALAS, Julius O.; '98 BS; Fraud Investigator; Fleet Credit Card Svcs., 550 Blair Mill Rd., Horsham, PA 19044; r. 103 Lampeter Ct., Exton, PA 19341, 610 524-5717. e-mail

SALAZAR, Marcelo; '94 BS; MS Long Island Univ.; Valenzuela Capital Partners, 1270 Ave. of the Americas, New York, NY 10020; r. 2125 E 13th St., Brooklyn, NY 11229. e-mail

SALAZAR-ATIAS, Ms. Camila D.; '99 BA; BA; Rsch. Assoc.; Street Org. Proj., 445 W 59th St. Sociology Dep, New York, NY 10019, 212 237-8694; r. 324 1/2 E. 8th St. # 1b, New York, NY 10009, 212 375-0488. e-mail

SALCEDO, Felix M.; '99 BA; 45 Thayer #1B, New York, NY 10040, 212 569-6234.

SALCEDO, Yadira I.; '99 BS; Customer Svc. Supv.; Chase Manhattan Bank, 42nd & Lexington Ave., New York, NY; r. 510 E 142nd, Bronx, NY 10454, 718 585-3570. e-mail

SALDANA, N. Antonio; '92 BS; Probation Ofcr.; Suffolk Cnty., 631 853-5637; r. POB 5183, Day Shore, NY 11706. e-mail

SALDIVAR, Philip D.; '87 BA; 719 E 218th St., Bronx, NY 10467, 718 547-7219.

SALERNO, Joseph J.; '76 BS; Retired Capt.; NY City Police Dept.; r. 1156 Trails End, Prescott, AZ 86303, 520 717-9904. e-mail

SALGADO, Luis A.; '78 BS; 1451 Leland Ave., Bronx, NY 10460, 718 918-2170.

SALGADO, Nelida; '97 BS; 6405 Kennedy Blvde # A3, W. New York, NJ 07093.

SALGUERO, Elcida; '95 BS; 3334 75th St., Flushing, NY 11372.

SALIM, John R.; '84 BA; 192 Cambridge Ave., Englewood, NJ 07631, 201 569-9363.

SALIM, Said; '95 BS; 670 W 193rd St. Apt. 1b, New York, NY 10040.

SALIM, Zameena '92 (See Salim-Rasheed, Bibi Zameena).

|

SALIM-RASHEED, Bibi Zameena, (Zameena Salim); '92 BS; PARALEG NYU; Workers Compensation Rep./Paralegal; Docs Physician, Bimc, 465 Columbus Ave., Valhalla, NY 10595, 914 749-6551; r. 2028 Anthony Ave., Bronx, NY 10457, 718 861-3870; *Feroze Rasheed;* Asif Rasheed. e-mail

SALINAS, Liz K.; '98 BA; Police Ofcr.; NYPD; r. 156 W. 9th St., First Fl., Brooklyn, NY 11231, 718 643-2657. e-mail

SALISBURY, Robert; '92 BS; 11025 195th St., Jamaica, NY 11412.

SALLEMI, Ralph; '96 BA; 1428 E. 5th St., Brooklyn, NY 11230.

SALLEY, Jacqueline M.; '85 BA; 31-25 49 St., Woodside, NY 11377, 718 529-1058.

SALMON, Horace S.; '97 BS; 146-07 119th Ave., Jamaica, NY 11436, 718 978-4755.

SALMON, Philip E.; '85 BS; 267 Beach 136th St., Far Rockaway, NY 11694.

SALOMON, Myrna I.; '94 BS; MA Adelphi Univ.; Tchr.; NYC Bd. of Educ.; r. 83-43 118th Apt. 1H, Kew Gardens, NY 11415, 718 268-4166.

SALTENBERGER, Otto H.; '68 MPA; 317 Santa Ynez Way, Sacramento, CA 95816, 916 452-1648.

SALUMN, Joseph C.; '80 BA; Sr. Court Clerk; Bronx Criminal Ct., Bronx, NY 10451; r. 19 Fieldstone Dr. Apt. 162, Hartsdale, NY 10530, 914 428-7068; Chris, Thomas.

SALVADOR, Selene; '98 BS; NYU; Customer Svc.; Michael Anthony Jewelers, 115 S. MacQuesten Pkwy., Mt. Vernon, NY 10550, 914 699-0000; r. 1041 Pugsley Ave. 4-H, Bronx, NY 10472, 718 822-3437.

SALVATORE, Lawrence F.; '79 BS; MS Kean Univ.; I.T. Dir.; Lucent Technologies, 283 King George Rd., Warren, NJ 07059, 908 559-8450; r. 73 W Springtown Rd, Long Valley, NJ 07853, 908 876-4855; *Deena;* Matthew, Phillip. e-mail

SALVO, Vlasta K.; '80 MA; 13328 126th St., Jamaica, NY 11420, 718 575-0945.

SALZANO, Dr. Julienne, (Julienne Ravalgi); MA, EDD Columbia Univ.; Intelligence Analyst; Drug Enforcement Admin., 175 Pinelawn Rd Ste. 205, Melville, NY 11747, 516 420-4545; r. 15 Tappen Dr., Melville, NY 11747; *Lawrence;* Lawrence. e-mail

SAMA, Anthony M.; '85 BS; 1984 E 19th St., Brooklyn, NY 11229, 718 836-5142.

SAMA, Jessica; '99 BA; New York Presbyterian Hosp., 622 W. 168th St., New York, NY 10032; r. 1 Arden St. 512, New York, NY 10040, 212 942-7658. e-mail

SAMBULA, Anthony L.; '97 AS, '98 AS, 2000 BS; Mech.; US Postal Svc., 558 Grand Concourse, Bronx, NY 10451, 718 402-7481; r. 269 Lewis Ave., Brooklyn, NY 11221, 718 455-1443. e-mail

SAMBULA, Violeta A.; '93 BA; 1350 Washington Ave. Apt. 15a, Bronx, NY 10456, 718 590-6185.

SAMEDI, John F.; '99 BA; Claim Rep./Tchr.; Social Security/PS9; r. 225 E 53rd St., Brooklyn, NY 11203, 718 385-1323; Benjamin. e-mail

SAMHAN, Ahmad; '93 BS; 147 Vanderbilt Ave., Brooklyn, NY 11205, 718 237-4273.

SAMIDE, Erik C.; '99 BS; Mgr.; Cafe Lugana; r. 64 21 Woodbine St., Flushing, NY 11385, 718 456-9304.

SAMPEL, James J.; '75 BA; 270 Oakwood Ave., Staten Island, NY 10301, 718 761-5843.

SAMPLES, Mrs. Carole R., (Carole R. Benjamin); '86 BA; MPA Long Island Univ., MSW Stony Brook Univ.; Clinic Social Worker; The Ctr. for Rapid Recovery, 352 Greenwich Ave., Hempstead, NY 11550, 516 292-4449; r. 1470 Motor Pkwy., Hauppauge, NY 11788, 631 234-9249; Darius, Deandre.

SAMPSON, Darryl C.; '80 BA; 536 W 150th St. #3, New York, NY 10031.

SAMPSON, Frank C.; '76 MA; 1545 Union Port Rd, Bronx, NY 10462, 718 861-7506.

SAMPSON, Ingrid E.; '86 BA; 553 Saratoga Ave., Brooklyn, NY 11212, 718 485-6458.

SAMPSON, Marcia E.; '87 BS, '92 MA; 125 Lake Valhalla, E. Stroudsburg, PA 18301, 570 424-0894.

SAMROCK, Walter P.; 157-42 101 St., Howard Bch., NY 11414.

SAMSONOV, Aleksandr; '98 BS; 2313 Avenue Y #2C, Brooklyn, NY 11235, 718 769-7896.

SAMUEL, Glenn P.; '91 MA; 29 Hampton Pl., Brooklyn, NY 11213, 718 629-2159.

SAMUEL, Gracita R.; '99 BA; Child Protective Spec.; NYC Dept. of Admin. for Children Svcs., 150 Williams St., New York, NY 10038, 212 363-2275; r. 411 Legion St. 2nd Fl., Brooklyn, NY 11212, 718 385-7782; *Livingston Languedoe;* Leshaun.

SAMUEL, Kenroy; '94 BA; 3987 Carpenter Ave., Bronx, NY 10466, 718 652-7495.

SAMUELS, Bradshaw; '96 BS; Constr. Worker; r. 465 W 157th St. Apt. B, New York, NY 10032, 212 368-8738.

SAMUELS, Jason S.; '98 BA; Customs Inspector; U.S. Customs Svc., Jamaica, NY 11430; r. 43-17 48 St., Sunnyside, NY 11104, 718 533-7030. e-mail

SAMUELS, Levi E.; '89 BS; 7652 Kimberly Blvd., N. Lauderdale, FL 33068, 954 720-1824.

SAMUELS, Lisa; '93 BS; 1233 Wheeler Ave., Bronx, NY 10472, 718 842-4247.

SAMUELS, Sandra E.; '95 BS; Fashion Designer; r. 325 Nostrand Ave., Brooklyn, NY 11216, 718 398-6077; Annmarie Foster, Belen Kelly.

SAMUELS, Sheila A.; '82 BA; 1919 McGraw Ave. #6C, Bronx, NY 10462, 718 798-3866.

SAMUELS, Sheila Y.; '97 BA; Student; Pace Univ. Sch. of Law; r. 4611 Murdock Ave., Bronx, NY 10466, 718 994-2004. e-mail

SAMUELS, Susan R.; '96 MA; BA Univ. of Southern CA; Free-lance Writer; r. 340 E. 74th St., New York, NY 10021, 212 628-3387. e-mail

SANABRIA, Deborah; '98 BA; 976 Leggette Ave. 5b, Bronx, NY 10455, 718 402-9317.

SANABRIA, Mark A.; '94 BS; Chief Investigator; NYC Dept. of Buildings, Invest Unit, 11 park Pl. 2nd Fl., New York, NY 10007, 212 442-2000; r. 35-05 87th St. #1C, Flushing, NY 11372, 718 478-9107; *Aida.*

SANBORN, Laurel; '96 BA; 36 Gramercy Pk.East, New York, NY 10003.

SANCHEZ, Angelica; 535 Bergen St. #2L, Brooklyn, NY 11217, 718 622-0949.

SANCHEZ, Anna S.; '98 BA; Social Worker; Abbott House Family Svcs., 100 N. Broadway, Irvington, NY 10533, 914 591-7300.

SANCHEZ, Baldemiro; '98 BA; BA CITY College; Caseworker; HRA, 260 E.161st St., Bronx, NY 10457; r. 500 W 174 St. 2b, New York, NY 10033, 212 740-2589; *Sandra Nunez;* Alan, Isabel, Vladmir.

SANCHEZ, Carlos M.; '95 BS; Postal Police Ofcr.; Postal Inspection Svc., 142-Ozone Park 20th Ave., Flushing, NY 11351, 718 990-1091; r. 1628 Rosalind Ave., Elmont, NY 11003, 516 352-7380; *Lorraine;* Carlos III, Bianca, Melissa. e-mail

SANCHEZ, Castalia; '97 BA; 3442 Cannon Pl., Bronx, NY 10463, 718 828-2455.

SANCHEZ, Catherine L.; '97 MA; 5350 Paragon St., Rocklin, CA 95677.

SANCHEZ, Constanza; '96 MPAIG; BSCJ St. Johns Univ.; Special Agt.; Dept. of Justice, US Immgration & Naturalization Svc., 26 Federal Plz. 9th Fl. Inv., New York, NY 10278, 212 264-5400; r. 102-30 Queens Blvd. Apt. 4N, Forest Hills, NY 11375, 718 896-2353.

SANCHEZ, Diana; '95 BS; 487 Carlton Ave., Brooklyn, NY 11238, 718 622-8829.

SANCHEZ, Enrique; '99 BA; Youth Service Officer; State of Connecticut, Long Lane School, Middletown, CT 06457, 860 344-2897; r. 23-13 24th Ave., Apt. 3R, Astoria, NY 11102, 718 278-5578; *Jacqueline;* Ricardo, Vincent, Alex. e-mail

SANCHEZ, Felipe A.; '95 BS; Police Ofcr.; NYPD, 6840 Austin St., Forest Hills, NY 11375; r. 8138 102nd Ave., Jamaica, NY 11416; *Marilyn;* Ashley.

SANCHEZ, Felix R.; '98 BA; 45 12 97 Pl. Apt.2c, Corona, NY 11368, 718 335-6532.

SANCHEZ, Irene '98 (See Marshall, Mrs. Irene).

SANCHEZ, Ivonne D.; '93 BS; 10443 46th Ave., Flushing, NY 11368, 718 335-6532.

SANCHEZ, John; '80 BS; 1628 Hancock St., Flushing, NY 11385, 718 458-1464.

SANCHEZ, John; '92 MPA; 350 63rd St., Brooklyn, NY 11220, 718 218-7114.

SANCHEZ, Johnny; '85 BS; 790 11th Ave. Apt. 22b, New York, NY 10019, 315 734-0377.

SANCHEZ, Joseph (Joie) R.; '95 BA; Hunter Clg.; Supv.; Park West HS; r. 11 Broadway Ter., New York, NY 10040, 212 942-6337. e-mail

SANCHEZ, Juan P.; '77 BA; 6 Oberman Ln., Monmouth Jct., NJ 08852, 732 297-7066.

SANCHEZ, Julie; '99 BA; Flight Attnd.; Delta Air Lines; r. 266 Bedford Park Blvd., Bronx, NY 10458, 718 584-3384. e-mail

SANCHEZ, Lissette; '91 BA; Deputy US Marshal; Newark, NJ 07102; r. 50 Walnut St., Rm#2009, Newark, NJ 07102, 973 645-2017.

SANCHEZ, Margarita '78 (See Pesante, Margarita).

SANCHEZ, Michael J.; '93 BA; 5 Ensign Dr., Massapequa, NY 11758.

SANCHEZ, Milagros; '89 BS; 541 Van Nest Ave., Bronx, NY 10460, 718 892-9654.

SANCHEZ, Milton J.; '92 BS; 14181 SE 36th Ave., Summerfield, FL 34491, 352 245-9004.

SANCHEZ, Natasha H.; '97 BA; 44-15 43rd Ave., Sunnyside, NY 11104, 718 776-5381.

SANCHEZ, Sandra P.; '97 BA, '98 BA; 212-76 16th Ave. 1fl, Bayside, NY 11360, 718 528-8001.

SANCHEZ, Valerie; '92 BA; 108 Harrison Pl. Apt. 3, Brooklyn, NY 11237, 718 855-5815.

SANCHIRICO, Paul M.; '76 BS; 3529 Ropes Ave., Bronx, NY 10475, 718 994-6889.

SANCLEMENTE, Erlinda; '93 BA; 108 Sagamore Rd, Tuckahoe, NY 10707.

SAND, Valerie S.; '71 BA; Tchr.; Saddleback Valley, Laguna Hls., CA 92654; r. 932 A. Avenida Majorca, Laguna Hls., CA 92653, 949 586-8744. e-mail

SANDBERG, Vilma B.; '82 MA; 12 Pequa Ln., Commack, NY 11725.

SANDELLI, Wendy L.; '97 MA, '99; 281 Windsor Pl.#9, Brooklyn, NY 11218.

SANDERFER, Gale R.; '83 BS; 2714 Cannon Ave., Chattanooga, TN 37404.

SANDERS, Antoinette; '95 BS; Caseworker; Human Resources Admin., 505 Fulton St., Brooklyn, NY 11201, 718 488-5691; r. 165 Rockaway Pkwy., Apt. 1 E, Brooklyn, NY 11212, 718 498-5784; Dorian, Ashley, Jeremy.

SANDERS, Elaine M.; '93 BA; 2955 Frederick Douglass Blvd. Apt 22, New York, NY 10039, 315 841-8793.

SANDERS, Evelyn C.; '78 BS; 159-20 115 Rd., Jamaica, NY 11434, 718 723-3657.

SANDERS, Gregory L.; '90 BA; 11310 209th St., Queens Vlg., NY 11429, 718 723-3657.

SANDERS, Mrs. Jeanne F.; '99 BA; Registrar; St. Luke's Roosevelt Hosp., 212 523-2843; r. 3415 Knox Pl. 4C, Bronx, NY 10467, 718 655-6729; James.

SANDERS, Joann; '78 BA; POB 732, New York, NY 10027, 315 841-8793.

SANDERS, Liliana M.; '91 MAFS; MSCD Pace Univ.; Doctorate Student; Pace Univ.; r. 1619 Bay Blvd., Atlantic Bch., NY 11509, 516 239-7749; Sanford Drob; Amarila, Martin. e-mail

SANDERSON, Paul M.; '76 BA; MA Long Island Univ.; Retired Police Ofcr.; NYC; r. 13746 225th St., Jamaica, NY 11413; Marian; Paul, Lynne, Carlen. e-mail

SANDIFORD, Jerry A.; '98 BA; 41-24 50th St. #1D, Woodside, NY 11377.

SANDIN, Eric J.; '91 BS; Data Base Admin.; O'Melveny & Myers LLP, 400 S Hope St. Ste. 1500, Los Angeles, CA 90071, 213 430-6000; r. 112 Ninth St., Apt. #5, Huntington Bch., CA 92648, 714 658-8041. e-mail

SANDSETH, Thomas R.; '86 BS; Lt.; NYC Police Dept., Vice Enforcement Division, 1 Police Plz., New York, NY 10038; r. 125 Malone Ave., Staten Island, NY 10306, 718 979-6432; Deborah; Tracy, Eric. e-mail

SANDY, Denise M.; '99 MA; 2007 Portland Ave., Scotch Plains, NJ 07076.

SANES, Anthony; '89 BS; 14629 SW 104th St., Miami, FL 33186.

SANFILIPPO, Debra A., (Debra A. Zambito); '90 MA; BA San Diego State Univ.; Homemaker; r. 84 Fox Chapel Dr., Orchard Park, NY 14127, 716 662-2100; Charles; Charlotte, Christopher, Charles. e-mail

SANFILIPPO, Monica L.; '98 BA; 2449 Riverside Dr., Wantagh, NY 11793, 516 781-6504.

SANFORD, Wexler; 230 E. 12th St., New York, NY 10003, 315 732-1889.

SANG, John L.; '80 MS; Forensic Document Examiner; John L Sang, 1 Harbour Ln., Glen Head, NY 11545, 516 656-0443; r. 1 Harbor Ln., Glen Head, NY 11545, 516 674-0881. e-mail

SANG, Suiling; '95 BA; 67 Eldridge St. Apt. 11, New York, NY 10002, 315 724-0295.

SANGIORGIO, Maryann; '90 BA; POB 65, Bovina Ctr., NY 13740.

SANGIOVANNI, Louis; 6210 80th St., Flushing, NY 11379.

SANKEY, John P.; '75 MA; 3325 Barker Ave., Bronx, NY 10467.

SANNI, Musliu; '86 MPA; 790 Eldert Ln., Brooklyn, NY 11208, 718 647-3229.

SANNI, Thomas G.; '84 MPA; 790 Eldert Ln. # 1, Brooklyn, NY 11208, 718 647-3229.

SANON, Farrah; '96 BS; 55 W. 100 St., New York, NY 10025.

SANSARRAN, Nirmala; '95 BS; Supv.; Medicaid, 330 W. 34th St., 6th Fl., New York, NY 10001, 212 630-1228; r. 159 Hemlock St., Brooklyn, NY 11208, 718 235-8382.

SANSO, Andre; '75 BA; 119 Ridgewood Ave., Farmingville, NY 11738.

SANSONE, Salvatore J.; '73 BS; MBA NY Inst. Tech; Ret Deputy Asst Chief; NYC Fire Dept.; r. 13 Fruitwood Ln., Commack, NY 11725; Eileen. e-mail

SANTA, James M.; '83 BS; Police Ofcr.; 90th Precinct, 211 Union Ave., Brooklyn, NY 11210; r. 19 Roydon Dr. W., N. Merrick, NY 11566, 516 826-5745.

SANTA, Maria S.; '85 BS; 1154 E 88th St., Brooklyn, NY 11236, 718 251-3842.

SANTA, Robert C.; '98 MA; 35 Charleston Ave., Staten Island, NY 10309, 718 356-4070.

SANTA ANA, Richard; '84 BA; MPA NYU; Supervisory Special Agt.; US Drug Enforcement Admin., 99 Tenth Ave., New York, NY 10011, 212 337-1777; r. 99 Tenth Ave., 99 Tenth Ave., New York, NY 10011, 212 337-1777. e-mail

SANTANA, Alberto; '89 BS; 2800 Marion Ave. Ph, Bronx, NY 10458, 718 822-1310.

SANTANA, Felicia A.; '95 BS; 44 Butler Pl., Apt. 3J, Brooklyn, NY 11238.

SANTANA, Gilbert; '79 BS; 16029 79th Ave., Flushing, NY 11366, 718 738-2958.

SANTANA, Maribel; '95 BA; 286 Schaefer Stree, Brooklyn, NY 11237, 718 399-0171.

SANTANA, Ricardo; '96 BA; 174 17th St. # 1, Brooklyn, NY 11215, 718 399-0171.

SANTANA, Sixto J.; '76 BA; 2686 Bailey Ave., Bronx, NY 10463, 718 220-6358.

SANTANA MARTUEZ, Odalis; '99 BS; Tchr.; Bronx, NY 10456, 718 822-5133; r. 1149 Stratford Ave. Apt.K, Bronx, NY 10472, 718 328-5781; Juan C. e-mail

SANTANGELO, Antoinett; '84 BA; MSN Fordham Univ.; Social Work Coord.; Staten Island University Hosp., 375 Segvine Ave., Staten Island, NY 10312, 718 226-2440; r. 14 Monterey Ave., Staten Island, NY 10312, 718 967-5317; Louis G.; Louis, Tomas.

SANTANGELO, Frank; '79 MPA; Retired Dir. of Security; United Bank of Switzerland; r. 43 Fulling Mill Ln., Ridgefield, CT 06877, 203 438-9070; Dagmar; Lisa.

SANTIAGO, Anna P.; '98 BA; Civil Servant; City of NY, New York, NY 10001; r. 223 S. Brookside Ave., Freeport, NY 11520, 516 867-8218.

SANTIAGO, Annette; '89 BA; 365 Ford St. # 2a, Bronx, NY 10457, 718 367-3598.

SANTIAGO, Carmen; '92 BA; 1155 Grand Concourse, Bronx, NY 10452, 718 992-4382.

SANTIAGO, Carmen L.; '85 BA; 1261 Evergreen Ave., Bronx, NY 10472, 718 220-6786.

SANTIAGO, Darren B.; '94 BS; 2385 Barker Ave., Bronx, NY 10467, 718 328-6040.

SANTIAGO, David; '85 BS, '95 MA; 673 E. 140 Street#4A, Bronx, NY 10454, 718 328-6040.

SANTIAGO, Edwin; '80 BS; 1050 Soundview Ave. Apt. 1e, Bronx, NY 10472, 718 588-6432.

SANTIAGO, Frances; '99 BS; NYC PO; City of NY, Bronx, NY 10467; r. 57 Rosedale Ave., Carmel, NY 10512, 914 228-0049. e-mail

SANTIAGO, George L.; '94 BA; 218 Desoto Pl., Cliffside Park, NJ 07010.

SANTIAGO, Ivette; '85 BS; 10715 Lefferts Blvd., Jamaica, NY 11419.

SANTIAGO, Jackeline; '99 BA; Family Case Planner; Puerto Rican Family Inst.-ACS, 545 Broadway, Brooklyn, NY 11206, 718 387-5200; r. 2332 Tiebout Ave. 9F, Bronx, NY 10458, 718 584-5495. e-mail

SANTIAGO, Jeanette; '99 BS; Legal Asst.; Friedman & Friedman, 401 Broadway, Ste. 808, New York, NY 10013, 212 267-0380; r. 983 Home St., Bronx, NY 10459, 718 842-9291; Ashley Jeanette, Andrew Nicholas. e-mail

SANTIAGO, Jeffrey; '85 BS; 41-51 Kenmare St. Apt. 16, New York, NY 10012, 315 733-2902.

SANTIAGO, Jessica; '98 AS; 184-07 Jamaica Ave., Hollis, NY 11423, 718 736-8365.

SANTIAGO, Jose A.; '94 BS; Peace Ofcr.; Morningside of Housing Corp., 80 La Salle St., New York, NY 10027, 212 222-1752; r. 1718 Purgy St. Apt. 6E, Bronx, NY 10462, 718 918-2464; Miriam Torres-Santiago; Crystal. e-mail

SANTIAGO, Jose L.; '99 BA; 137 Bleecker St., Brooklyn, NY 11221, 718 453-3010.

SANTIAGO, Lisette; '97 BA; 2386 Walton Ave., Apt. 5D, Bronx, NY 10468, 718 367-8943.

SANTIAGO, Luz D.; '99 BA; 950 E 4 Walk 1A, New York, NY 10009, 315 733-2902.

SANTIAGO, Marc A.; '94 AS, '95 BS; Dir. of Security; The Wiz, 2045 Lincoln Hwy., Edison, NJ 08817, 732 650-3806; r. 209 Center Ave., Keansburg, NJ 07734. e-mail

SANTIAGO, Mariano; 3101 Eastchester Rd, Bronx, NY 10469, 718 364-0555.

SANTIAGO, Melissa S.; '96 BA; Claims Rep.; Social Security Admin., Park Pl. 3rd Fl., Peekskill, NY 10566, 914 739-1984; r. 270 Carpenter Ave., Newburgh, NY 12550, 914 568-3490; Heriberto; Tristan, Gigianna. e-mail

SANTIAGO, Nellie Q.; '81 BA; 15630 80th St., Jamaica, NY 11414, 718 418-7336.

SANTIAGO, Publio; '92 BS; 203 Bergen St., Brooklyn, NY 11217.

SANTIAGO, Raymond (Ray) S., Esq.; '96 BS; JD CUNY Sch. of Law; Assistant DA; Nassau County District Attorney's Office, 99 Main St., 3rd Fl., Hempstead, NY 11550, 516 572-2078; r. 2081 E. 61st St., Brooklyn, NY 11234, 718 763-5083. e-mail

SANTIAGO, Ricardo N.; '64 AS, '68 BS; Retired; r. POB 847, Goldenrod, FL 32733, 407 671-6491; Florence. e-mail

SANTIAGO, Richard; '90 BS; 1466 Shore Dr., # 3, Bronx, NY 10465, 718 518-1124.

SANTIAGO, Rose M.; '76 BA; 108 Taylor St., Staten Island, NY 10310, 718 317-8991.

SANTIAGO, Ruth M.; '93 BA; 599 W 177th St. Apt. 52, New York, NY 10033, 315 733-2902.

SANTIAGO, Mrs. Sueleyba; '98 AS; Correction Ofcr.; Dept. of Corrections, 11-11 Hazen St., E. Elmhurst, NY 11370; r. 1234 E. 82nd St. Unit 75, Brooklyn, NY 11236, 718 531-9536; Joseph Williams. e-mail

SANTIAGO, Tina M.; '96 AS, '99 BA; 1817 Himrod St., Ridgewood, NY 11385.

SANTIAGO, William; '99 BA; 383 Livonia Ave. #4A, Brooklyn, NY 11212, 718 495-4731.

SANTIAGO, Zoraida; '98 BA; 100-14 89th Ave. #2, Richmond Hill, NY 11418, 718 805-8864. e-mail

SANTIMAYS, Alice V.; '79 BA; AA; Retired Police Ofcr. & Detective; NYC; r. 186 Acacia Ave., Staten Island, NY 10308; Norman (Dec).

SANTO, Ronald H.; '75 MA; 2211 149th St., Whitestone, NY 11357, 718 463-2298.

SANTORA, Alexander; '74 BS, '79 MPA; Fire Chief; NYC Fire Dept., 9 Metro Tech Ctr., Brooklyn, NY 11201, 718 430-0207; r. 21-25 34th Ave., Long Island City, NY 11106, 718 626-4215; Maureen. e-mail

SANTORA, Matthew A.; 80 Autumn Ave., Brooklyn, NY 11208.

SANTORO, Charles S.; '87 BS, '93 MPA; 8 Francis St., Nesconset, NY 11767.

SANTORO, Thomas D.; '88 BS; 2502 E 23rd St., Brooklyn, NY 11235, 718 436-3896.

SANTOS, Edwin; '84 BA; 40 Waterside Plz., New York, NY 10010, 212 689-7459.

SANTOS, John J.; '78 BS; 76-66 Austin St., Forest Hills, NY 11375, 718 291-3588.

SANTOS, Jose J.; '95 BS; 4 Stanford Dr. Ph, Highland Mills, NY 10930, 914 726-4360.

SANTOS, Josefina; '77 BA; 114 E 57 St., Brooklyn, NY 11203, 718 599-2620.

SANTOS, Margaret A.; '81 BA; 13137 Clock Tower Pkwy., Hudson, FL 34667, 727 862-1029.

SANTOS, Nancy; '89 BA; 100-27E Benchley P, Bronx, NY 10475, 718 299-1758.

SANTOS, Omar R.; '88 BS; 2160 Anthony Ave., Bronx, NY 10457, 718 665-1792.

SANTOS, Sharon E.; '92 BA; Davis 57 Lorraine, Mt. Vernon, NY 10553, 716 837-1678.

SANTOS, Tyrone S.; '97 BS; Police Ofcr.; Metropolitan Transportation Police Dept., State of NY, 347 Madison Ave., New York, NY 10017; r. 559 50th St. #2, Brooklyn, NY 11220, 718 435-1632; Logan.

SANTUCCI, Jennifer S.; 87-09 Santigo St., Holliswood, NY 11423, 718 217-5276.

SANZONE, Augustine; '85 BS; 392 Arlene St., Staten Island, NY 10314, 718 761-9149.

SAPIO, Donald J.; '78 BS; 360 W. 22 St., New York, NY 10011.

SAPRAICONE, Jane T.; '79 BS; 2053 Brook Ln., Seaford, NY 11783.

SAR, Steve N.; '93 MA; BS Syracuse Univ.; Deputy Sheriff; NYC Sheriff's Ofc., 550 W 59 St., New York, NY 10019, 212 397-0354; r. 2044 62 St. #2F, Brooklyn, NY 11204, 718 621-1903; Soma; Jasmine.

SARACENI, Frank M.; '98 BA; 1302 82nd St., N. Bergen, NJ 07047, 201 662-1905.

SARACH, Omar J.; '87 BS; Peace Ofcr./Special Investigator; NYC Dept. of Investigation; r. 81 Columbia St., New York, NY 10002, 212 533-8068. e-mail

SARCONE, Richard; '85 MPA; POB 275, Croton-on-Hudson, NY 10520.

SARDISCO, Salvatore; '99 BA; Police Ofcr.; NYC Police Dept., 1 Police Plz., New York, NY 10038; r. 225 Curtin Ave., W. Islip, NY 11795, 631 321-8006.

SARDONE, John R.; 8643 15th Ave., Brooklyn, NY 11228, 718 851-4995.

SARFO, Solomon; '95 BA; 1763 Fulton Ave., Bronx, NY 10457.

SARGEANT, Mark A.; '95 BS, '97 MS; 391 Rockaway Pkwy., Brooklyn, NY 11212, 718 763-0189.

SARGENT, Douglas L.; '83 BS; 52 Hempstead Ave., Staten Island, NY 10306.

SARITSON, Anthony R.; '93 BS; 505 W 162nd St. Apt. 208, New York, NY 10032, 212 568-4518.

SARKUS, LT Peter J.; '72 BS; MS C.W. Post; NYC Police Lt.; NYC Police Dept.; r. 47 79th Ave., New Hyde Park, NY 11040, 516 775-7066; Lucy; Michael, Darren, Jasmyne.

SARNATARO, Geoffrey L.; '80 BS; Collector; Info. Builders Inc., Two Penn Plz., New York, NY 10121; r. 2951 167th St., Flushing, NY 11358, 718 359-0651. e-mail

SARNO, Henry C.; '82 BS; 754 Shore Walk, Lindenhurst, NY 11757.

SARNO, Lisa D.; '99 BA; Couns.; Parsons JHS, Flushing, NY 11352; r. 5 Willard Way, Dix Hills, NY 11746, 631 427-1865.

SARRANTONIO, Lana; '78 MA; Probation Ofcr.; Arlington Cnty. Bd., 1425 N. Courthouse Rd., Fifth Fl., Arlington, VA 22201; r. 605 Crestwood Dr., Alexandria, VA 22302. e-mail

SARRO, Peter J.; '99 MPA; BA Wagner Clg.; Inspector; Trade Waste Commission, 253 Broadway, 10th Fl., New York, NY 10007, 212 676-6276; r. 7802 10th Ave., Brooklyn, NY 11228, 718 745-4066. e-mail

SARTER, Leonard; '75 BA; Captain/Police Commnagi; NYPD 46 Precinct, 2120 Ryer Ave., Bronx, NY 10457, 718 220-5205; r. 18 Hollywood Dr., Plainview, NY 11803, 516 938-4188. e-mail

SARTI, Annmarie; '90 BA; 67 Sullivan St. #6, New York, NY 10012.

SARYIAN, Paul D.; '90 BS; Lt.; NYPD; r. Staten Island, NY 10309.

SASSO, Jill E.; '99; 145 Willow Ave., Stratford, CT 06615.

SASSON, Dina J.; '92 BS; MSW Yeshiva Univ.; Sr. Case Mgr.; Brooklyn AIDS Task Force, 465 Dean St., Brooklyn, NY 11217, 718 783-0883; r. 643 Warren St., Apt. 1F, Brooklyn, NY 11217, 718 230-9148. e-mail

SASSONE, Joseph; 26 Cres. Beach Dr., Huntington, NY 11743, 631 423-1715.

SATCH, Steven; '81 MA; 26 Auburn Rd, Parsippany, NJ 07054.

SATCHELL, Sonia E.; '98 MPA; 367 Est 45th St. #03, Brooklyn, NY 11203, 718 469-7540.

SATIRO, Raymond; '88 MA; 1273 North Ave. Bld, New Rochelle, NY 10804.

SATRIANA, Peter; '96 BS; 1970 E.15th St., Brooklyn, NY 11229.

SATTERFIELD, Charles; '79 BS; 836 Tilden St. Apt. 6b, Bronx, NY 10467.

SATTERFIELD, Kevin; '87 MA; 119-03 232 St., Cambria Hts., NY 11411, 718 712-4110.

SAULNIER, Richard; 300 E. 85th St., New York, NY 10028.

SAUNDERS, Arconza; '76 BA; 530 Louisiana Ave., Brooklyn, NY 11239, 718 235-8327.

SAUNDERS, Kathyann C.; '97 BS; 216 Rockaway Ave., Brooklyn, NY 11233, 718 385-0161.

SAUNDERS, Leroy N.; '82 BS; 11 Stuyvesant Oval # M-O, New York, NY 10009, 315 855-4264.

SAUNDERS, Louvinia; '96 BS; Assoc. Fraud Investigator; NYC Dept. of Homeless Svcs., 161 Williams St., New York, NY 10038, 718 402-7080; r. 1370 St.Marks Ave., Brooklyn, NY 11233, 718 778-6024.

SAUNDERS, Michael R.; '78 BA; 725 Riverside Dr., New York, NY 10031, 315 855-4264.

SAUNDERS, Phillip M.; '82 MPA; 17014 130th Ave. # Bld9c-1d, Jamaica, NY 11434, 718 481-9087.

SAUNDERS, Xavier A.; '83 BA; 208 St. Marks Ave., Brooklyn, NY 11238, 718 235-8327.

SAVAGE, Mark J.; '79 BA; VP of Operations; OCS Grp., 99 Madison Ave., 15th Fl., New York, NY 10016, 212 277-9600; r. 10 Cheyenne Tr., Branchburg, NJ 08876, 908 704-8805.

SAVAGE, Patricia D.; '87 BS; 8738 Marengo St., Jamaica, NY 11423, 718 740-7643.

SAVAGE, Patrick J.; '98 MS; BS Oneonta State; Firefighter; FDNY, 718 965-8229; r. 516 Bch. 136 St., Belle Harbor, NY 11694, 718 474-3820. e-mail

SAVARESE, Gabriel M.; '95 BS; 7922 16th Ave., Brooklyn, NY 11214, 718 259-6364.

SAVATTERI, Stephine; '99 MA, '99 BA; AA The Way Clg. of Emporia; Couns.; r. POB 1614, Cranford, NJ 07016, 908 759-1284. e-mail

SAVIANO, Mrs. Donna M., (Donna M. Rosario); '92 BS; NY City Police Ofcr.; NY City, 333 65th St., Brooklyn, NY 11220, 718 439-4211; r. 239 Corona Ave., Staten Island, NY 10306; *Anthony;* Anthony Jr, Christian. e-mail

SAVOIA, Michael F.; '82 BS; 307 Prospect Ave. Apt. 9c, Hackensack, NJ 07601.

SAVOPOULOS, Emmanuel; '96 BA; 87-53 138 St., Jamaica, NY 11435.

SAWANGNETR, Somchart; '83 MA; Royal Thai Emb 190, Washington, DC 20088.

SAWINA, Gregory; '90 BA; 66 Daniel Rd S, Massapequa, NY 11758, 516 735-3290.

SAWRUK, Gary R.; '81 BS; 20 Eldorado Ct., Rochelle Park, NJ 07662.

SAWTELL, Edward; '93 BS; 5203 92nd St., Flushing, NY 11373, 718 592-7585.

SAWYER, Genqunic R.; '99 MPA; 2800 University, Bronx, NY 10468, 718 841-1408.

SAWYER, James W.; '76 BS; 2540 Red Hbscs Blvd., Delray Bch., FL 33445.

SAWYER, William F.; '84 BA; 226-09 135th Ave., Laurelton, NY 11413, 718 592-6509.

SAXBY, Michele W.; '98 BA; 930 Grand Concourse, #10f, Bronx, NY 10451, 718 654-6563.

SAXE, Susan N.; '95 BS; 1428 Lexington Ave. Apt. 3A, New York, NY 10128, 315 858-1283.

SAYAD, Karim; '75 BS; 43 86th St., Brooklyn, NY 11209.

SAYERS, Donna C.; '76 BA; 160 W 97th St. Apt. 14a, New York, NY 10025.

SAYERS, Sylma C.; '88 BS; 496 Thatford Ave., Brooklyn, NY 11212, 718 346-0284.

SCAFIDI, Marie A.; BA; 1223 42nd St., Brooklyn, NY 11219.

SCAGLIONE, Dominic J.; '76 MA; 534 No 3rd St., E. Newark, NJ 07029.

SCALA, Richard A.; '97 BA; 7718 20th Ave., Brooklyn, NY 11214, 718 256-0875.

SCALICI, Joseph; '96 MA; BBA Pace Univ.; Immigration Inspection; INS, JFK Intl. Airport, New York, NY 10278, 718 553-1688; r. 122-C Donley Ave., Staten Island, NY 10305, 718 815-1311.

SCALLY, Tina M.; '95 MPA; BS Mercy Clg.; Probation Ofcr.; Westchester Cnty.; r. 410 Foxrun Ln. Rr6, Carmel, NY 10512, 914 225-5403. e-mail

SCALZO, Charles; '97; 1792 E 54th St., Brooklyn, NY 11234.

SCALZO, Ronald G.; '95 BA; Retired; NYC Police Dept., 1 Police Plz., New York, NY 10038; r. 278 Ave. s, # A, Brooklyn, NY 11223, 718 375-8927; *Mary Lyn;* Ronald, Paula. e-mail

SCANLON, Frances E.; '78 BS; Atty.; 718 762-4980; r. 14065 Beech Ave. Apt. 7e, Flushing, NY 11355, 718 706-8719. e-mail

SCANLON, Kevin J.; '94 BS, '99 MS; Battalion Chief; NYC Fire Dept.; r. 3242 159th St., Flushing, NY 11358, 718 353-9649. e-mail

SCANTERBURY, Renee S.; '79 BS; c/o Weeks, 626 Troy, Brooklyn, NY 11203.

SCARABINO, Virginia; '84 AS; 48 Mulberry Ave., Staten Island, NY 10314.

SCARBOROUGH, Stacey; '88 BA; 200 W. 147th St., New York, NY 10039.

SCARBOROUGH, Thomas; '78 BS; 17210 133rd Ave. Apt. 10f, Jamaica, NY 11434.

SCARMALIS, Barbara K.; '87 BA; 1496 Bass Cir., Ft. Myers, FL 33919, 941 433-3178.

SCARPONE, Leonardo; '94 BA; Business; San Panino; r. 158 Dahlia St., Staten Island, NY 10312, 718 966-1237. e-mail

SCAVELLI, Guy V.; '95 AS; 13217 83rd St., Jamaica, NY 11417.

SCEUSA, Peter S.; '79 AS, '89 BS; 12 Crown Ave., Staten Island, NY 10312.

SCHAAFF, Henry G.; '75 BS, '77 MPA; MA SUNY Albany; Police Inspector; NYC Police Dept., One Police Plz., New York, NY 10038, 212 741-8430; r. 6 Revere Dr. W., Floral Park, NY 11001, 516 352-9614; *Annette;* Lisa Patwell, George, Joseph.

SCHACHINGER, Mildred C.; '76 MPA; PHD Fordham Univ.; Probation Ofcr. Ret; r. 110-20 71 Ave., Forest Hills, NY 11375, 718 261-3498.

SCHACHT, Laurence C.; '70 BS, '75 MPA; Security Cnslt.; United Security, 4295 Arthur Kill Rd., Staten Island, NY 10309, 718 967-6820; r. 3150 Perry Ave., Bronx, NY 10467, 718 515-8494; *Mary (Dec);* Laurence Jr, Kathleen.

SCHACHTER, Lisa; '95 BA; Homemaker; r. 1163 E. 10th St., Brooklyn, NY 11230, 718 372-1790.

SCHADE, Joseph; '85 MPA; 12418 5th Ave., Flushing, NY 11356, 718 461-5247.

SCHAEFER, Deborah, (Deborah Afanador); '91 BA, '93 MPA; Prog. Chairperson; HS for Arts & Business, 105-25 Horace Harding Expy., Corona, NY 11368, 718 271-8383; r. 17 Miller Blvd., Syosset, NY 11791, 516 921-2799; *Thaddeus.* e-mail

SCHAEFER, Lawrence; '80 BA; 653 Correll Ave., Staten Island, NY 10309, 718 273-8216.

SCHAEFER, Richard W.; '83 AS, '84 BS; Dir. of Workers Compensation; Keyspan Energy, 100 E. Old Country Rd, Hicksville, NY 11801, 516 545-6172; r. 129 Bregman Ave., New Hyde Park, NY 11040; *Joan;* Kristen, Richie, Julianne, Kerri. e-mail

SCHAEFFER, Joseph J.; '81 BA; 185 W. End Ave., New York, NY 10023.

SCHAFFER, Robin F.; '82 BS; 83-35 116th St. #5B, Kew Gardens, NY 11418, 718 969-0549.

SCHAFFER, Scott L.; '74 BS; Dir. of Sales; Ultralife Batteries Inc.; r. 119 Forrestal Ave., Staten Island, NY 10312, 718 948-8045. e-mail

SCHAN, Robin A.; '76 BA; Brooklyn, NY 11226.

SCHANIL, Robert; '90 BA; MA Manhattanville Univ.; Police Ofcr.; Harrison Police Dept.; r. 20 Collier Dr. E, Carmel, NY 10512, 914 228-0108; *Marlene;* Ashlyn, Robert, Jason. e-mail

SCHATZ, John E.; '79 BS; 77-03 86th St., Glendale, NY 11385, 718 520-8242.

SCHATZBERG, Rufus; '81 MA; MPH, PHD CUNY; Retired Detective 1st Grade; of Dir. Phd Alumni Assn.; r. 21 B Cooper Pl., Bronx, NY 10475, 718 379-2352; *Sarah E.;* Carol Ann. e-mail

SCHATZLE, Kevin P.; '84 BS; 9369 Vanderveer St., Jamaica, NY 11428.

SCHAUFFERT, R. C.; '76 BA; 173 Stafford Ave., Staten Island, NY 10312.

SCHECHTER, Marvin; '68 BA, '75 MA; Retired Law Enforcement; NYPD/US Govt.; r. 328 Concord Ave., Oceanside, NY 11572, 516 678-5504.

SCHECTER, Robert J.; '88 BS; 1928 80th St., Brooklyn, NY 11214, 718 252-1261.

SCHEER, Paul J.; '79 BS; 5034 202nd St., Flushing, NY 11364, 718 224-8757.

SCHEINER, Adam; '90 BS; 28 Lark Ave., Old Bethpage, NY 11804.

SCHELLHASS, Kenneth J.; '83 BS; Asst. Mgr.; American Express, 200 Vesey St., New York, NY 10285, 212 640-3886; r. 1646 E 36th St., Brooklyn, NY 11234, 718 375-4063; *Antonia.* e-mail

SCHEMBRI, Anthony J.; '77 MA; JD Pace Univ. Sch. of Law; Atty.; r. 562 San Remo Cir., Inverness, FL 34450, 352 726-4789.

SCHENCK, Ginette N.; '79 BS; 199 Avenue A Apt. 5, New York, NY 10009.

SCHENKER, Stephen; '79 MA; CEO; Long Island Exterminating Co. Inc., 800 734-3939; r. 64 Barry Ln. E, Old Bethpage, NY 11804, 516 694-9200. e-mail

SCHEPER, Frederick W.; '76 BS; Electronic Equip. Spec.; Gen. Svc. Admn., FPSD, 26 Federal Plz., New York, NY 10278; r. 9512 161st Ave., Howard Bch., NY 11414, 718 634-7845.

SCHIAVONE, Vincent; '82 BS; 164 35th St., Brooklyn, NY 11232, 718 788-7478.

SCHICK, Raymond W.; '79 BS; Fraud Prevention Ofcr.; Chase Manhattan Bank, 52 Broadway-15 Fl., New York, NY 10004, 212 701-5330; r. 6061 59th Dr., Flushing, NY 11378, 718 326-2827.

SCHIECK, William J.; '76 BA; 22025 75th Ave., Flushing, NY 11364.

SCHIELER, Jean M.; '86 BA; 1045 116th St., Flushing, NY 11356.

SCHIFFER, Herbert J.; '76 BS; 261 E. 236 St., Bronx, NY 10470.

SCHIFINI, Thomas A.; '95 BS; JD Univ. of Akron Law Sch.; US Border Patrol Agt.; US Border Patrol INS DOJ, POB 194 Hwy. 85 Ee, Carrizo Spgs., TX 78834, 830 876-3557; r. 1518 Garner Field Rd Apt. 902, Uvalde, TX 78801. e-mail

SCHILD, Alexandra H.; '98 BA; 111 Second St., Brooklyn, NY 11231, 718 771-0470.

SCHILD, Stephanie V.; '98 BA; 111 Second St., Brooklyn, NY 11231, 718 858-8240.

SCHILLING, Francis L.; '76 MPA; 25515 85th Ave., Floral Park, NY 11001, 516 794-5945.

SCHILLINGER, Robert; '81 BS, '99; 1916 23rd Rd, Astoria, NY 11105.

SCHIRALDI, Vito; '85 BS; 85 Chicago Ave., Massapequa, NY 11758, 516 541-9863.

SCHIRALLI, Anthony M.; '88 BS; Operation Mgr.; r. 100 Sunset St., Dumont, NJ 07628, 201 384-7793.

SCHISSEL, Alan R.; '82 BS; 305 Madison Ave., New York, NY 10165, 212 362-3488.

SCHLETTER, Donna L.; '89 BS; Narcotics Investigator; NYC Housing Authority, 212 776-5080; r. Flushing, NY 11379. e-mail

SCHLITT, Robert W.; '83 BS; 199 Crystal Ave., Staten Island, NY 10302.

SCHLOSSER, Kevin; '81 BA; JD Hofstra Law Sch.; Atty./Partner; Ruskin, Moscou, Evans & Faltischek, PC, 170 Old Country Rd., Mineola, NY 11501, 516 663-6515; r. 43 Parkview Dr., Searingtown, NY 11507, 516 484-0378. e-mail

SCHLOTON, Joy E.; '77 BS; 123 87 St., Brooklyn, NY 11209.

SCHMIDT, John; '95 BA; 46 Summit Rd., Oak Ridge, NJ 07438, 973 697-1789.

SCHMIDT, Margaret J.; '97 BS; 326 Centre Ave., Secaucus, NJ 07094.

SCHMIDT, Michael; '95 BS; 62-27 108 St. #, Forest Hills, NY 11375, 718 805-1456.

SCHMIDT, Wayne F.; '76 BS; 2 Lafayette St. #500, New York, NY 10007, 315 724-7611.

SCHMIDT, William; '90 BS; 2 Equestrian Ct., Farmingville, NY 11738, 631 698-5931.

SCHMITZ, William J.; '98 BS; Dir. of Public Safety; Borough of Manhattan Community Clg., 199 Chambers St., Rm. S-202, New York, NY 10007, 212 346-8872; r. 122 Holland Ave., Floral Park, NY 11001, 516 354-6786; *Geryl Pecora; Sam.* e-mail

SCHMOLLINGER, Justine M.; '99 MA; Proj. Coord.; Samhsa Comm Action Grant, 212 992-9702; r. 205 W 103 St. #3B, New York, NY 10025, 212 749-6993. e-mail

SCHMUCKER, Walter M.; '70 BS; 35-21 90 St., Jackson Hts., NY 11372.

SCHNEIDER, David; '91 BS; 2239 Troy Ave., Brooklyn, NY 11234, 718 258-2071.

SCHNEIDER, Gertrude; CUNY Grad. Clg., Alumni Ofc., New York, NY 10021.

SCHNEIDER, Guy A.; '84 BS; 5 Halesite Dr., Sound Bch., NY 11789.

SCHNEIDER, James T.; '79 BS; AA Union Cnty. Clg.; Police Lt.; Westfield Police, 425 E. Broad St., Westfield, NJ 07090, 908 232-1000; r. 28 Inwood Ave., Colonia, NJ 07067, 732 388-5742; *Diane; Todd, Stephen.*

SCHNEIDER, Joseph E., Jr.; '78 MPA; AAS Clg. of Aeronautics; Principal Investigator; New York State Organized Crime Task forc, 142 Grand St., White Plains, NY 10601, 914 422-8700; r. 2640 Willard Ave., Baldwin, NY 11510, 516 889-0805; *Noreen; Joseph, Kristen, Katie.*

SCHNEIER, Steven; '75 BS; 446 Beach 65th St., Far Rockaway, NY 11692.

SCHNELL, Barry A.; '99 BS; 75-26 Bell Blvd. #5B, Bayside, NY 11364, 718 850-9044.

SCHNELL, George L.; '76 BS; 200 Lemon Tree La, Ormond Bch., FL 32174, 904 677-5218.

SCHNELL, Jeanine; BA; 609 Columbus Ave., New York, NY 10024, 212 724-6355.

SCHNELL, Nina A.; '82 BA; MA Columbia Univ Teacher Clg; Account Mgr.; r. 1763 2nd Ave., New York, NY 10128, 212 410-2969.

SCHNITZER, Shirley R., PhD; PHD CUNY; Retired Assoc. Prof. of English; John Jay Clg.; r. 430 E. 86th St., New York, NY 10028, 212 772-3249; *Raymond; Michael.* e-mail

SCHNUPP, Jerome E.; '75 BA; Security Spec.; r. 7943 78th Ave., Glendale, NY 11385; *Kathleen; Michael, Patricia.*

SCHOELLER, Dennis M.; '94 BS; 110 Pearsall Dr. Apt. 1a, Mt. Vernon, NY 10552, 914 664-6230.

SCHOEN, Richard M.; '87 BS; Police Communications Tech.; Communications Div. Tape & Records Unit, #1 Police Plz., New York, NY 10038, 212 374-6778; r. 168 Camden Ave., Staten Island, NY 10309, 718 227-5444; *Annette; Jenna.*

SCHOLL, Charles M.; '84 BS; Police Capt.; NYCPD; r. 814 59th St., Brooklyn, NY 11220, 718 854-5355.

SCHRADER, Richard A.; '71 BS; MA Univ. of Virgin Islands; Retired Prison Warden; Author; r. POB 39, Kingshill, VI 00851, 340 778-0477; *Slaubette;* Richard Jr, Patricia, Joseph, Claudia.

SCHRAUD, Louis; '90 AS, '96 BS; Sgt/ Sr. Court Ofcr.; Bronx Supreme Ct., Bronx, NY 10451, 718 590-3704; r. 2018 Caesar Pl., Bronx, NY 10473, 718 931-3381; *Cristobalina;* Rosalina, Alicie.

SCHREIBER, Robert; '93 AS; Police Ofcr.; NYPD, 1 Police Plz., New York, NY 10038; r. Fresh Meadows, NY 11365. e-mail

SCHREINER, John A.; '76 AS; 251-03 86 Ave., Bellerose, NY 11426.

SCHREPEL, Raymond J.; '86 BS; 52 Elinor Pl., Yonkers, NY 10705, 914 968-7708.

SCHRETTNER, Joseph; '81 MPA; 21 Sparkill Ave., Tappan, NY 10983.

SCHRIER, Leonard S.; '76 MA; 6656 Winding Lake Dr., Jupiter, FL 33458, 561 743-7127.

SCHROEDER, Donald J.; '73 MPA; 1799 166th St., Whitestone, NY 11357, 718 352-3229.

SCHROEDER, Fredric; '73 BA; MPA Long Island Univ.; Asst. Dir. of Security; Pratt Inst.; r. 139 Tanners Pond Rd., Garden City, NY 11530.

SCHROEDER, Lizette; '81 BS; 1799 166th St., Whitestone, NY 11357, 718 352-1814.

SCHROEDER, Thomas; '98 BS; Ofcr.; Park Ridge PD; r. 72 Mountain Ave., Park Ridge, NJ 07656, 201 573-1919.

SCHRYVER, Harold; '67 AS, '73 BS; Retired Asst. Chief Police; NYC Police Dept., 1 Police Plz., 38 Belmont Ave., Plainview, NY 11803, 561 433-6276; r. 325 No. Causeway. Apt. E101, New Smyrna Bch., FL 32169, 904 428-5171; *Edith; Kenneth, Debra.*

SCHUBERT, Kristin; '95 BA; 108 Stack Dr., Staten Island, NY 10312, 718 984-5354.

SCHUCHMAN, Robert W.; '74 BS, '85 MA; Sr. Probation Ofcr.; Suffolk Cnty., NY, Yaphank, NY 11980, 631 852-5047; r. 3 Celia St., E. Patchogue, NY 11772, 631 475-7443.

SCHUHMANN, Mrs. Dorothy P.; (Dorothy Higgins); '79 BS; Sergeant-NYPD Retired; NYCPD; r. 2041 E 29 St., Brooklyn, NY 11229, 718 646-0269.

SCHULHOFF, Pamela; '99 BA; 2328 Esplanade, Bronx, NY 10469, 718 655-0213.

SCHULTE, Janet '76 (See Reilly, Janet S.).

SCHULTZ, Conrad J.; '77 BS; 243 Mcdonald Ave. Apt. 3h, Brooklyn, NY 11218, 718 871-7442.

SCHULTZ, John A., Jr.; '97 BS; MS American Univ.; Doctoral Student/Teaching Asst.; Temple Univ.; r. 525 Reese St., Philadelphia, PA 19147, 215 925-4608. e-mail

SCHULTZ, Philip R.; '93 BS; 3438 Ella Rd, Wantagh, NY 11793, 516 781-3776.

SCHULZ, Dr. Dorothy M.; '73 MA; BA, PHD NYU; Assoc. Prof.; John Jay Clg. of Criminal Justice, 899 10th Ave., New York, NY 10019, 212 237-8405; r. New York, NY 10024; *David.* e-mail

SCHULZE, Raymond; '76 MA; 42 Kulick St., Clifton, NJ 07011.

SCHUMACHI, Anthony; 320 Logan Ave., Bronx, NY 10465.

SCHUMANN, Robert A.; '78 BS; 3 Celia St., E. Patchogue, NY 11772.

SCHUPP, Elizabeth; '93 MA; 19 Commerce St. Apt. 14, New York, NY 10014, 212 627-6360.

SCHUPPERT, Ronald; '77 BS; CEO; Linden Security Assocs Inc., POB 276, New York, NY 10044, 212 583-0426; r. 531 Main St. Apt. 923, New York, NY 10044, 212 308-9863; *Jennifer; Alexandra, Margaret.* e-mail

SCHURR, John F.; '91 BS; POB 1476, Rocky Point, NY 11778.

SCHUSTER, Kenneth G.; '76 BS; 223-44 56 Ave., Bayside, NY 11361.

SCHWARTZ, Edward H.; '80 BS; 239 Dogwood Dr., Bridgeport, CT 06606.

SCHWARTZ, Ellen R.; '84 BA; 8 Wooleys Ln. Apt. B1, Great Neck, NY 11023.

SCHWARTZ, Eric S.; '85 MA; 1230 Bergen Ave., Brooklyn, NY 11234, 718 332-6440.

SCHWARTZ, Kenneth M.; '82 BA; Correction Officer; City of NY Correction Dept., 17-17 Hazen St., E. Elmhurst, NY 11370, 718 546-1396; r. 20 Veteran Cir., Monroe, NY 10950, 914 782-8675; *Susan; Adam.* e-mail

SCHWARTZ, Lawrence; '73 BA; 12470 SW 11 Ct., Davie, FL 33325.

SCHWARTZ, Louis; '81 BS; 15217 Lakes of Delray Blvd. #117, Delray Bch., FL 33484, 561 496-3562.

SCHWARTZ, Milton; '75 MA; COO; Triumph Security Corp., 65 E. 55 St., New York, NY 10022, 212 644-1200; r. Apt. A1611, New York, NY 10021, 212 988-9530; *Arlene Wolff.* e-mail

SCHWARTZ, Ned E.; '77 AS, '78 BS; JD New York Law Sch.; Spec. Agt. in Charge, Reg. II; US Dept. Trans Ofc. of Insp Gen., 26 Federal Plz. Rm. 3134, New York, NY 10278, 212 264-8700; r. Wantagh, NY 11793; *Betty; Adam.*

SCHWARTZ, Robert I.; '70 BS; 156 Bridgetown St., Staten Island, NY 10314, 718 351-1532.

SCHWARTZ, Robert T.; '94 BA; Guid. Couns.; Kennedy HS, Somers, NY 10589; r. 49 Halcyon Ter., New Rochelle, NY 10801, 914 636-2782.

SCHWARTZ, Stuart E.; '79 MA; 21417 15th Ave., Flushing, NY 11360, 718 465-5994.

SCHWARTZ, Thomas P.; '99 BA; AS Passaic Cty Community Clg, PHD Fairleigh Dickinson Univ.; Research/Clinical Assoc.; Kessler Institute for Rehab., 240 Central Ave., E. Orange, NJ 07018, 973 414-4700; r. 103 Willow St., Bloomfield, NJ 07003, 973 748-0372. e-mail

SCHWARTZ, Dr. Tony; Communications Spec.; Tony Schwartz, 455 W 56th St., New York, NY 10019, 212 581-5025; r. same; *Reenah.*

SCHWARTZMAN, Leon; '77 BA; Chief Investigator; NYC Ofc. of Spec Narcotics, 80 Centre, New York, NY 10013, 212 815-0496; r. same. e-mail

SCHWARZ, Eric E.; '80 MA; 21-66 33 Rd., Long Island City, NY 11106, 718 776-9266.

SCHWARZ, Gunter G.; '76 MA; BA NYC Clg.; Sr. Probation Ofcr.; City of NY; r. 8335 139th St. Apt. 1d, Jamaica, NY 11435, 718 805-6968.

SCHWEIBINZ, Paul J.; '75 BS; 122 Forest Tr., Port Richey, FL 34668.

SCHWEITZER, William; '97 BS; 1136 Brunswick Ave., Far Rockaway, NY 11691, 718 740-6459.

SCHWENZER, Roseann; '99 BA; 207 At The Fls, Bushkill, PA 18324, 570 424-5503.

SCHWIMMER, Claudia; '93 MA; 2 Links Dr., Great Neck, NY 11020, 516 482-1950.

SCI, Paul R.; '75 BA; 949 Ivory Rd., Rio Rancho, NM 87124, 505 892-6470.

SCIANDRA, Joseph R.; '80 BS, '86 MA; MA; Mgr., Security; Hoffmann-La Roche Inc., 340 Kingsland St., Nutley, NJ 07110, 973 235-2265; r. 60 Old Rd, Sewaren, NJ 07077; *Jan;* Stephanie. e-mail

SCIARINI, Charles K.; 436 Saint Luke Pl., Franklin Sq., NY 11010.

SCIARRINO, S.; '93 BS; 115 Decker St., Valley Stream, NY 11580.

SCLAFANI, Cara J. '99 (See Vaill, Mrs. Cara J.).

SCLAFANI, Joseph C.; '84 BS; Police Ofcr.; NYS, 973 593-3000; r. 7 Meadowview Ave., Succasunna, NJ 07876, 973 584-1792; *Vivian;* Carrie, Billy, Susanne, Marybeth, Katie, Sara. e-mail

SCLAFANI, Leonard A.; '74 BA; 3336 167th St., Flushing, NY 11358, 718 357-3340.

SCOLARO, John F.; '87 BA; 2942 171st St., Flushing, NY 11358.

SCONFIETTI, James; '90 MA; Asst. Prof.; Finger Lakes Community Clg., 4355 Lakeshore Dr., Canandaigua, NY 14424, 716 394-3500; r. 19 Modelane, Rochester, NY 14618, 716 461-2169. e-mail

SCONZO, Rachel L.; '99 BA; AS Essex Cnty. Clg.; VP of Sales; Bowles Corp. Svcs., 673 Clifton Ave., Clifton, NJ 07011, 973 773-0699; r. 50 28 W Lindsley Rd, Cedar Grove, NJ 07009, 973 812-6539. e-mail

SCORDATO, Matthew; '96 BA; 44L Glen Keith Rd, Glen Cove, NY 11542.

SCOTT, Andrea; '96 BS; 7540 Bell Blvd. # 2, Flushing, NY 11364, 718 528-4879.

SCOTT, Ann T.; '89 BA; 1015 Barbey St., Brooklyn, NY 11207, 718 467-4104.

SCOTT, August J.; '79 BS; 665 New York Ave. Apt. 2g, Brooklyn, NY 11203, 718 467-4104.

SCOTT, Bertram A.; '85 BA; 355 E. 48th St., Brooklyn, NY 11203, 718 302-1450.

SCOTT, Cleve M.; '85 BS; 231 Hudson Ave., Hopatcong, NJ 07843, 973 770-1866.

SCOTT, Edward S.; '89 BA; 6101 16th St. NW, Apt. 518, Washington, DC 20011.

SCOTT, Edythe; '95 BS; 288 Maple St., Apt. 5C, Brooklyn, NY 11225, 718 363-0456.

SCOTT, Emily E.; '96 BA; Child Protective Spec.; Admin. for Children's Svcs., 192 E 151st St., Bronx, NY 10451, 718 579-9364; r. 2094 Boston Rd., Bronx, NY 10460, 718 328-6463.

SCOTT, Mrs. Gladys A.; '98 BA; AA Borough of Manhattan Comm; Police Ofcr.; NYC Police Dept., 2951 W 8th St., Brooklyn, NY 11231, 718 946-3311; r. 269 Von Huenfeld St., Massapequa Park, NY 11762; *Ira;* Kailyn, Alexis. e-mail

SCOTT, Irving J.; '79 BA; 154 Decatur St., Brooklyn, NY 11233, 718 243-1277.

SCOTT, Ivory L., (Ivory L. Jackson); '86 BS; Supv.; HRA-MAP-HOME Care, 109 E 16th St., New York, NY 10003, 212 835-7395; r. 150 W 225 St., Apt. 17a, Bronx, NY 10463, 718 563-2340; *Karim L.;* Kyle J. e-mail

SCOTT, Karim L.; '84 BS; Probation Ofcr.; Warrant Div. NYC, 115 Leonard St., New York, NY 10013, 212 442-4541; r. 150 W. 225th St., Bronx, NY 10463, 718 563-2340; *Ivory Lynn;* Kyle J.

SCOTT, Lezlie A.; '95 BS; 121 Wake St., Bridgeport, CT 06610, 203 338-8280.

SCOTT, Mable; '79 BS; Social Worker; Tuscaloosa Cnty. Dept. of Human Resource, POB 70100, 3716 12th Ave., Tuscaloosa, AL 35405, 205 554-3300; r. 1229 Canterbury Rd., Tuscaloosa, AL 35405, 205 759-1536; David.

SCOTT, Marjorie; '87 BA; 190 E. 38th St., Brooklyn, NY 11203, 718 342-0169.

SCOTT, Monica; '95 BA; 1611 Foster Ave., Brooklyn, NY 11230, 718 342-0169.

SCOTT, Monica; '99 BS; Police Ofcr.; State of NY; r. 142-23 253rd St., Rosedale, NY 11422, 917 576-1543. e-mail

SCOTT, Nichole R.; '99; 160 St. Marks Ln., Islip, NY 11751, 631 205-1375.

SCOTT, Rosalyn; '86 BA; 14539 115th Ave., Jamaica, NY 11436, 718 659-7487.

SCOTT, Thorance A.; '99 BS, '99 CERT; Probationary Police Ofcr.; NYC Police Dept; r. 1190 Park Pl., Brooklyn, NY 11213, 718 467-7987. e-mail

SCOTTI, Salvatore; '76 BS; 2440 83rd St., Brooklyn, NY 11214.

SCOTTO, Anthony F.; '90 BS, '95 MS; 40 Figurea Ave., Staten Island, NY 10312, 718 668-9496.

SCOTTO, Joseph M.; '98 MS; 135 William Ave., Staten Island, NY 10308, 718 948-1359.

SCOTTO-LAVINO, T.; '95 MA; JD New York Law Sch.; Atty; The Admin. for Children Svcs., New York, NY 10013; r. 170 Devon Loop Apt. 7, Staten Island, NY 10314, 718 984-3663; *Joseph Liss.* e-mail

SCOTT-WILSON, Nichole; '95 BA; 110 Cardinal Ln., Islip, NY 11751, 718 935-1057.

SCREEN, Crystal L., (Crystal L. Biggers); '86 BA; Sergeant; New York Police Dept., 1 Police Plz., New York, NY 10015, 212 374-5000; r. 859 Seaman Ave. E, Baldwin, NY 11510.

SCREEN AGUILAR, Cynthia A.; '80 BA; Staff Analyst; NYC, 109 E. 16th St., New York, NY 10003, 212 835-7285; r. 2727 Yates Ave., Bronx, NY 10469, 718 654-7696; *Tony;* Christopher.

SCRIBANI, Santo A.; '93 BS; 511 Main St., Staten Island, NY 10307.

SCRUBB, Michelle A.; '92 BA; 173-06 109 Ave., Jamaica, NY 11433.

SCUDDER, Ivy; '93 BS; Dubois Walk 85E, Englewood, NJ 07631.

SCUDERI, Mary L.; '78 AA, '82 BS; Sergeant Retired; New York Police Dept.; r. 1418 212th St., Flushing, NY 11360, 718 224-9383.

SCULLEY, Maryanne; '95 BA; 551 Hudson St. Apt. 5, New York, NY 10014.

SCUMACI, Anthony J.; 29 Hamlet Rd, Levittown, NY 11756.

SEABROOK, Larry; '74 BA; POB 302, Bronx, NY 10454, 718 681-1189.

SEABROOK, Reginald K.; '96 AS, '97 BS; MPA Wilmington Clg.; Juvenile Justice; State of DE, 959 Centre Rd, Wilmington, DE 19805, 302 993-3810; r. 4007 Christiana Meadows, Bear, DE 19701, 302 326-1527. e-mail

SEABROOK, Stephanie; '89 BS, '93 MPA; 1276 Rev James A Polite Ave., Bronx, NY 10459, 718 893-6456.

SEABURY, Major C.; '85 BA; 2 Victoria Cir., E. Patchogue, NY 11772.

SEAFORTH, Zolton; '92 BS; 575 E 18th St., Brooklyn, NY 11226, 718 451-0197.

SEALES, Paul J.; '75 BA; POB 110109, Cambria Hts., NY 11411.

SEALY, Curtis V.; '81 BA; 20611 100th Ave., Queens Vlg., NY 11429.

SEALY, Grantley M.; '81 MPA; 185 Lefferts Ave., Brooklyn, NY 11225, 718 604-8996.

SEALY, John; '82 BS; Retired Microfiche Operator; Gundal Corp.; r. 13147 232nd St., Springfield Gardens, NY 11413, 718 712-9021; *Valentine (dec);* Janet, Karline, Anthony, Michael, Jacqueline.

SEALY, Wendell L.; '98 MPA; 226 Atkins Ave., Brooklyn, NY 11208, 718 604-8996.

SEARS, Joanne; 8617 103rd Ave., Jamaica, NY 11417, 718 446-7654.

SEAY, Rholanda R.; '95 BS; 208-09 100th Ave., Queens Vlg., NY 11429.

SEBRO, Kathy; '97 BA; 179-29 136th Ave., Jamaica, NY 11434.

SEBRO, Sherwin K.; '95 BA; Conductor; NYC Transit Auth, 370 Jay St., Brooklyn, NY 11201; r. 10914 217th St., Queens Vlg., NY 11429, 718 217-1769; Justin, Shenyse. e-mail

SECOR, Bruce M.; '97 BS, '98 BS; 28 Ridge Rd., Coram, NY 11727, 631 331-4033.

SECRETO, James A.; '80 BA; Deputy Inspector; Commander 28th Precinct, New York, NY 10027; r. 11304 219th St., Queens Vlg., NY 11429, 718 217-2514; *Yvonne;* Chanel, Kiesha, Shamieka, Allure, Ajile.

SECTER, Charles W.; '79 MA; 192 Elton Rd, Stewart Manor, NY 11530, 516 437-1958.

SEDA, Sandy; '99 BA; 25 76 45 St., Astoria, NY 11103.

SEDUTTO, Joseph; 103 Benedict Ave., Staten Island, NY 10314.

SEEBARAN, Darsan; '84 BS; 615 45th St., Brooklyn, NY 11220.

SEEDMAN, Albert A.; '62 MPA; BBA CUNY-Baruch; Retired Chief of Detectives; NYPD, 561 737-0105; r. 5513 Lakeview Mews Ter., Boynton Bch., FL 33437, 561 737-6286; *Henny;* Dr Barry, David. e-mail

SEEDMAN, Elizabeth; '89 BA; 19 Panorama Dr., Huntington, NY 11743.

SEEGOPAUL, B.; '88 BS; 35-15 34 St. #A24, Long Island City, NY 11106.

SEELIG, George W.; '80 BS; Database Mgr.; Lockheed Martin, 300 Robbins Ln., Syosset, NY 11791, 516 349-2100; r. 9 Putnam Ct., Commack, NY 11725, 631 499-7944; *Barbara;* Bryan, Jennifer. e-mail

SEELIG, William (Billy); '97 MS; BA NY Inst. of Tech; Fireman; NYC, New York, NY 10001; r. 53-14 Bell Blvd., Flushing, NY 11364, 718 428-3766.

SEESTEDT, Tad H.; '87 BA; 84-10 129 St. #5W, Kew Gardens, NY 11415.

SEGAL, Susanne; '83 MA; 300-914 Winston Dr. #914, Cliffside Park, NJ 07010.

SEGALINI, George L.; '79 BS; 3417 Little Neck Pkwy., Flushing, NY 11363.

SEGAR, Yvonne; '96 BS; POB 834, Hardeeville, SC 29927, 718 933-0691.

SEGARRA, Elsie; '92 BA; Parole Ofcr.; NYS Div. of Parole, 97 Central Ave., Albany, NY 12206, 518 473-5572; r. 150 Troy Schenectady Rd, #B5-G, Watervliet, NY 12189, 518 271-2509. e-mail

SEGARRA, Juan; '85 BS; 3015 Roberts Ave., Apt. 6A, Bronx, NY 10461.

SEGREE, Wilbur R.; '80 BS; 11136 132nd St., Jamaica, NY 11420.

SEGUR, Webb; '87 MPA; Internet Developer; Capital, New York, NY 10017; r. 433 W 54th St. Apt. 20, New York, NY 10019, 212 582-7899.

SEIBERT, Eleanore; '97 BS; Biochemistry Grad. Student; Mt. Sinai Sch. of Medicine, New York, NY 10001; r. 59 E. 98th St., # 9-D1, New York, NY 10029, 212 722-3262; *Kevin C. Bynum.* e-mail

SEIDE, Nadege; '97 BS; 88-16 Burdette Pl., Jamaica, NY 11432, 718 458-8935.

SEIDMAN, Sylvia K., (Sylvia Plisner); '89 BS; Homemaker; r. 209 Calyer St., Brooklyn, NY 11222, 718 389-0339; *Steve;* Courtney, Samantha.

SEIGNIOUS, Lisa A.; '84 BA; 206-07 46 Ave., Bayside, NY 11361.

SEIGNIOUS, Patricia; 206-07 46th Ave., Bayside, NY 11361.

SEIGNIOUS, Robert; '75 MA; 206-07 46th Ave., Bayside, NY 11361.

SEKESAN, Maria; '93 BS; POB 776, Mineola, NY 11501.

SELIP, Raena A.; '99; 200 E 94th St., New York, NY 10128, 212 410-6489.

SELKOWITZ, Richard; 1016 Cassel Ave., Bay Shore, NY 11706.

SELKOWITZ, Steven A.; '87 BA; 100 Dreiser Loop # 23, Bronx, NY 10475, 718 671-5143.

SELL, Angela M.; '97 MA; BS Kutztown Univ.; Proj. Mgr.; Professional Security Bur., Philadelphia, PA 19104; r. 1002 Foxmeadow Rd, Royersford, PA 19468, 610 792-9225. e-mail

SELLERS, Terence C.; '86 BA; POB 188, Abiquiu, NM 87510, 505 699-2096.

SELOVER, Joan; '92 BS; 2545 Lefferts Pl., Bellmore, NY 11710.

SELTZBERG, Mark S.; '81; BS, MA Brooklyn Clg.; Physical Educ. Tchr./Coach; William Grady HS, Brighton Forth Rd., Brighton, NY 11235, 718 332-5000; r. 74 Ramabo Ave., Staten Island, NY 10309, 718 966-3765; Michael, Heather. e-mail

SELVAGGI, Anthony; '95 BS; 68 Hemlock Rd, Briarcliff Manor, NY 10510.

SELZNER, Jennifer L.; '95 BS; 223 N Cedar St., Massapequa, NY 11758, 516 541-6140.

SEMETIS, Arthur J.; '78 BA; 35 N. Brook Ln., Irvington, NY 10533, 914 591-1316.

SEMEXANT, Biel; '95 AS; 1842 SE Floresta Dr., Port St. Lucie, FL 34983, 561 340-4672.

SEMPLE, Darryl M.; '79 BS; 122 Lamport Blvd., Staten Island, NY 10305.

SENA, James P.; '78 BS; 4019 Warner Ave. A3, Landover Hls., MD 20784.

SENA, Nino D.; '97 BS; 258 Carteret St., Staten Island, NY 10307, 718 317-1532.

SENERCHIA, Anthony G.; '79 BA; 420 Stewart Ave., Staten Island, NY 10314.

SENEY, Jeannette V.; '95 BS; 10443 108th St. # 2, Jamaica, NY 11419.

SENISE, John B.; 24-53 28th St., Astoria, NY 11102.

SENITT, Melissa V. '72 (See Vigder, Melissa V.).

SENS-CASTET, Robert; '78 BS; 23 Villa Rd, Pearl River, NY 10965.

SENTOUKTSI, C.; '91 AS, '95 BA; 400 W. 19 St. #6D, New York, NY 10011, 212 929-6106.

SEPP, Karen; '92 BS; 151-40 18th Ave., Whitestone, NY 11357.

SERAFINO, John M.; '85 BA; Disc Jockey; r. 34 Cabot Rd. W., Massapequa, NY 11758, 516 797-6713; *Donna.* e-mail

SERANO, Frank R.; '78 BA; 1814 Himrod St. #2R, Ridgewood, NY 11385.

SERASPE, Danilo; '95 MS; Engrg. Proj. Mgr.; US Electric Corp.; r. 239 E 3rd Ave., Roselle, NJ 07203, 908 241-6403; *Rebecca;* Rachael Lee, Darryl Spencer. e-mail

SERE, Edward C.; '77 MPA; 13555 126th St., Jamaica, NY 11420, 718 457-2718.

SEREMETIS, Michael; '93 BS; Special Agt.; US Secret Svc., Rm. 295, Oeob, Washington, DC 20502, 202 757-4800; *Maria.* e-mail

SERES, Harvey; 1159 E. 100 St., Brooklyn, NY 11236.

SERGE, Victor J.; '96 BS; 50 Gouverneur St., New York, NY 10002.

SERGI, Frank; '80 MA; Assoc Med. Dir.; Introspect of BuxMont, 215 997-3600; r. 309 Mapple Ave., Wyncote, PA 19095, 215 572-5860. e-mail

SERGIO, Alice E.; '73 AA; BA California State Univ.; 15040 71st Ave., Kew Gardens, Flushing, NY 11367.

SERLING, Latonja F.; '97 BA, '98 BA; 218 W 112th St. #7b, New York, NY 10026, 212 749-3464.

SERMET, Carmen M.; '89 BS; 12 Schiller Ave., Huntington Sta., NY 11746.

SERNAQUE, Janet; '97 BA; 2818 San Pedro St., Apt. A, Austin, TX 78705.

SERNIAK, Walter R.; '81 BS; 138 Sunset, Farmingdale, NY 11735.

SERRA, Raphael; '98 BA; 24717 89th Ave., Bellerose, NY 11426.

SERRANO, Ana S.; '97 BS; 1956 W. 13 St., Brooklyn, NY 11223, 718 627-7808.

SERRANO, Estella; '95 BA; 2137 23rd St. # 3rd, Long Island City, NY 11105, 718 479-0055.

SERRANO, Francine; '99 BA; Residential Advisor; The Woodstock Job Corps, Baltimore, MD 21203, 800 949-9401; r. 51 Aven Way, Baltimore, MD 21236, 410 882-2756.

SERRANO, Jose; '96 BS; Student; Fordham Univ. Law Sch.; r. Brooklyn, NY 11206. e-mail

SERRANO, Linda C.; '94 BS; 235 Cheltenham Rd, W. Babylon, NY 11704.

SERRANO, Michelle O.; '96 BA; 431 W. 17 St., New York, NY 10011.

SERRANO, Millie; '98 BS; Labor Standards Investor; NYS Dept. of Labor, 345 Hudson St., New York, NY 10014, 212 352-6018; r. 250 Clinton St. #15-G, New York, NY 10002, 212 732-6393; Victoria Sotoma.

SERRANO, Samantha; '95 BS; 50 W 97th St. Apt. 2j, New York, NY 10025.

SERVIS, Anthony; '88 BA; JD Seton Hall Law Sch.; Atty-at-Law; Law Offices of Susan Servis, 504 Sunset Ter., Ridgefield, NJ 07657, 201 313-8600; r. 668 Virgil Ave., Ridgefield, NJ 07657; *Patricia;* Susan, Anthony Jr. e-mail

SERVISS, Barbara A. '85 (See Belasco, Mrs. Barbara A.).

SETHER, Andrew G.; '74 BS; 427 100th St., Brooklyn, NY 11209.

SETOUTE, Sonel; '83 BS; 213 Nichols Ave., Brooklyn, NY 11209.

SETTER, George, Jr.; '76 BS; Retired Firefighter; NY; r. 3 Ashford Dr., Lake Grove, NY 11755, 631 467-4898.

SETTLES, Hannah; '85 MA; 16010 89th Ave. 4J, Jamaica, NY 11432, 718 739-6278.

SEUBERT, Robert J.; '78 BS; 6420 60th Rd, Flushing, NY 11378, 718 821-0928.

SEVASTYANOV, Vladimir; '97 BS; Programmer; PDI, 10 Mountainview Rd, Upper Saddle River, NJ 07458, 201 258-8510; r. 13404 Jewel Ave. # 2L, Flushing, NY 11367, 718 575-0084. e-mail

SEVERIN, David A.; 101 Gilmore Blvd., Floral Park, NY 11001, 516 488-3214.

SEVERINO, Solangel A.; '96 BS; 25-02 Cres. Str, Astoria, NY 11102.

SEVOS, John; '85 BA; 5 Bogert Ave., White Plains, NY 10606.

SEWARD, James D.; '84 MA; 346 Paoli Woods, Paoli, PA 19301, 610 644-2278.

SEWELL, Keechant L.; '99 BS; 82-08 135 St. 4M, Kew Gardens, NY 11435, 718 956-0228.

SEWER, Enrique D.; '92 BS; AS Nassau Community Clg.; Sheriff's Ofc.; Nassau Cnty Sheriff's Dept., 100 Carmen Ave., E. Meadow, NY 11554; r. 239 Hudson Ave., Roosevelt, NY 11575, 516 868-3938. e-mail

SEWNARAIN, Prabha; '92 BS; 212-76 Whitehall T, Queens Vlg., NY 11427.

SEXTER, Jay; 341 Furnace Dock Rd #22, Cortlandt Manor, NY 10567.

SEXTON, William A.; '80 MA; POB 2115, Venice, FL 34284, 941 918-8390.

SGANGA, Richard F.; '76 BS; 45 Rugby St., Brentwood, NY 11717.

SHACK, Robert C.; '81 AS, '87 BS; Probation Ofcr.; Fulton Cnty. Juvenile Ct., 136 Pryor St., Atlanta, GA 30303, 404 335-2759; r. POB 832, Clarkston, GA 30021, 404 299-1388; Selena K., Nicole M., Robert Jr. (D).

SHACK, SGT Stanley; MS; MS Queens Clg., NY; Retired Sgt; NYPD/Transit; r. 52-28 Leith Pl., Little Neck, NY 11362, 718 428-2414; *Nancy;* Abraham, Victoria. e-mail

SHAH, Jignesh; '99; 48-19 43rd #4B, Flushing, NY 11377, 718 426-7165.

SHALEESH, LT William; '89 BS; NYPD, Organised Crime Investigation Div., 1 Police Plz., New York, NY 10038, 212 374-6640; r. 2325 Knapp St., Brooklyn, NY 11229. e-mail

SHALOM, Marietta; '79 MA; 25-04 83rd St., Jackson Hts., NY 11370.

SHALVEY, Edward P.; '76 BA; 65 Roxbury Dr., Yonkers, NY 10710.

SHAMSUNDAR, Jaso; '99 BA; Case Mgr.; Concord Home Svcs. for The Elderly, Brooklyn, NY 11221; r. 4219 18 Ave. D5, Brooklyn, NY 11218, 718 871-8311. e-mail

SHANNON, Doris; '93 BA; Case Mgr.; CEVSI; r. 1239 Stanley Ave. Apt. 6d, Brooklyn, NY 11208, 718 647-8757.

SHANNON, Michael; '92 BS; 14229 223rd St., Jamaica, NY 11413, 718 476-3163.

SHANNON, Michael P.; '85 BS; POB 110335, Jamaica, NY 11411, 718 476-3163.

SHANNON, Shiann; '97 BA; 21136 99th Ave. # 2, Queens Vlg., NY 11429, 718 592-7878.

SHANNON, Valerie; '91 BA; 1959 76th St., Brooklyn, NY 11214, 718 389-6207.

SHAPIRO, Eric M.; '84 MA; Pres.; Indoor Air Quality Solutions, 233 London Ct., Egg Harbor Twp., NJ 00234, 609 640-5455; r. POB 618, 233 London Ct., Egg Harbor Twp., NJ 08234, 609 646-5455.

SHAPIRO, Janet L.; '85 MA; 1062 E. 4th St., Brooklyn, NY 11230, 718 382-4159.

SHAPIRO, L. P. '80 (See Smith, L. P.).

SHAPIRO, Ruth B., PhD; BA Univ. of MI, PHD NYU; Assoc. Prof. Psychology/ Dept Chair; John Jay Clg.; r. 185 E 85th St., New York, NY 10028, 212 348-2439; *Dr Robert;* Ann Scherzer, Naomi Langer.

SHAPIRO, Stanley; '70 BS; 528 W. Hudson St., Long Beach, NY 11561, 516 825-2287.

SHARK, Anthony; '92 BS; Police Ofcr.; NYC Police Dept., 1 Police Plz., New York, NY 10038, 212 570-4746; r. 29 Adrian Ave. Apt. D6, Bronx, NY 10463, 718 365-5724.

SHARK, Ricardo A.; '84 BA; 2661 Decatur Ave., Bronx, NY 10458, 718 237-5667.

SHARKEY, Daniel M.; '92 AS; 21 Apollo St., Brooklyn, NY 11222.

SHARON, Elihu; '95 BS; 1428 Webster Ave., Bronx, NY 10456, 718 293-9619.

SHARON, Isaac; '95 BS; 2473 E 22nd St., Brooklyn, NY 11235, 718 382-4485.

SHARPE, Dolores K.; '86 BS; 10439 165th St., Jamaica, NY 11433.

SHARPE, Ryan R.; '96 BS; JD Benjamin N. Cardozo Law; Student; r. 146-04 224th St., Rosedale, NY 11413, 718 341-0503. e-mail

SHARPIRO, Jerry; 39 Seminole Ct. E, Royal Palm Bch., FL 33411.

SHATTUCK, John; US Dept. of State, Washington, DC 20520.

SHAVERS, Donna L.; '97 BA; AS BMCC; Tech.; Bell Atlantic, New York, NY 10001; r. 15 W. 139th St., Apt. 16A, New York, NY 10037, 212 491-7668. e-mail

SHAW, Mrs. Alexandria, (Alexandria Altes); '95 BS; Paralegal; Edelman & Goldstein, PC, 11 Park Pl. Ste. 1802, New York, NY 10007, 212 349-2181; r. 126 E 53rd St., Apt. A2, Brooklyn, NY 11203, 718 778-1895; *Jasper;* Justin F., Matthew A. e-mail

SHAW, Cil M. '82 (See Shaw-Brewer, Cil M.).

SHAW, Jacqueline '83 (See Walters, Ms. Jacqueline M.).

SHAW, La-shonda V.; '96 BS; 99 Metropolitan Ave., Bronx, NY 10462, 718 239-1290.

SHAW, Michelle M.; '95 BS; 1049 E 99th St., Brooklyn, NY 11236, 718 968-7568.

SHAW, Rudolph A.; '82 MA; BA Queens Clg., MA NYU; Exec. Dir.; Caribbean American Reperatory Theater, 98-23 Horace Harding Expy., Rego Park, NY 11368; r. 98-23 Horace Harding Expy., Apt. 18M, Rego Park, NY 11368, 718 271-3248; *Rubina.* e-mail

SHAW, Yolanda L.; '96 BS; 170 Avenue C #5G, New York, NY 10009, 315 822-3428.

SHAW-BREWER, Cil M., (Cil M. Shaw); '82 BA; JD Western New England Clg.; Atty.; Law Offices of Cil M. Shaw-Brewer, 26-53 30th St., Astoria, NY 11102, 718 932-3962; r. 2653 30th St., Long Island City, NY 11102, 718 932-3962.

SHAYNE, Alan F.; '72 BS; 6041 Marathon Pkwy., Flushing, NY 11362.

SHAZEL, Everett; Researcher; Sutton Reed & Croft Svcs., 5330 Headdress Ct., Virginia Bch., VA 23464.

SHEA, Cornelius P.; '75 BA; 5505 Newhall Ct., Centreville, VA 20120, 703 998-4022.

SHEA, Edward M.; '74 BS; 2421 US Rte. 9W, Ravena, NY 12143, 518 383-9468.

SHEA, James; '95 BS; 68 Weygant Hl, Highland Mills, NY 10930.

SHEA, John W.; '77 BS, '80 MA; Dir. of Operations; The Galleria at Crystal Run, One Galleria Dr., Middletown, NY 10941, 914 692-5757; r. 374 Black Meadow Rd, Chester, NY 10918, 914 469-5579; *Jean;* John, Jennifer, Jeanne, James. e-mail

SHEA, Kathleen C.; '96 BA; 2344 63rd St., Brooklyn, NY 11204, 718 833-6457.

SHEA

SHEA, Nicola D., (Nicola M. Duda); '94 MS; BIOLOGY UC-Riverside; Sr. Forensic Scientist-DNA; Forensic Analytical Specialties, 3777 Depot Rd Ste. 409, Hayward, CA 94545, 510 887-8828; r. 1744 Pierce St., San Mateo, CA 94403, 650 341-7901; John; Michael. e-mail

SHEA, Patrick J.; '98 BS; 84-37 248th St., Bellerose, NY 11426.

SHEARD, Paige C.; '98 BA, '99 MA; Horizon Hls #4B, Middletown, NY 10941, 914 692-0231. e-mail

SHEARD, Sandra Y.; '81 MA; 438 E 141st St., Bronx, NY 10454, 718 742-1742.

SHEARER, Kimberley; '97 MA, '98 BA; 4332 164th St., Flushing, NY 11358, 718 461-4083.

SHEARIN, John D.; '95 BS; 1611 John F Kennedy Blvd., Jersey City, NJ 07305.

SHEBO, David J.; '81 BS; 13720 45th Ave. Apt. 7b, Flushing, NY 11355.

SHEDDEN, Jennifer L., (Jennifer L. Vazquez); '89 BS; Exec. Legal Secy.; Whitman Ransom, Met Life Bldg., New York, NY 10002; r. 6 Dreyer Ave., Staten Island, NY 10314; Stephen; Loren Ashley, Leanne Alison. e-mail

SHEDDEN, Stephen B.; '89 BA; 106 Laredo Ave., Staten Island, NY 10312.

SHEDRICK, Jimmy; '74 BS; 738 Bradford St., Brooklyn, NY 11207.

SHEEHAN, Brian; '84 BA, '98 MS; Capt.; r. 52 Hamlin Rd., Mahopac, NY 10541, 914 628-8138. e-mail

SHEEHAN, Eileen J.; '90 BA; 6947 181st St., Flushing, NY 11365, 718 591-9751.

SHEEHAN, Francis X.; '80 BS; Lecturer of Chemistry Criminalistic; John Jay Clg.; r. 1 Essex Pl., Hartsdale, NY 10530, 914 693-1344.

SHEEHAN, Gerald J.; '75 MPA; 1950 Htcnsn Riv Py, Bronx, NY 10469, 718 549-2226.

SHEEHAN, John; '96 AS; 7401 Ridge Blvd. #4, Brooklyn, NY 11209, 718 743-0469.

SHEEHAN, John P.; '73 BA; Developer/Owner; Skyline Properties, 993 Morris Park Ave., Bronx, NY 10462, 718 597-5660; r. 53 The Neck, Manhasset, NY 11030, 516 365-1408.

SHEEHAN, Raymond A.; '80 BS; 15814 Cross Island Pkwy. Apt. 2, Whitestone, NY 11357, 718 456-6897.

SHEEHAN, Vincent J.; '79 BS; MA Ohio State Univ.; Ret Law Enforcement Instr.; Ohio Peace Officer Trng. Acad.; r. 980 Holly Hill Dr., Columbus, OH 43228, 614 276-1010. e-mail

SHEEHEED, Wadeedah; '93 BA; 306 W 138th St., New York, NY 10030.

SHEEHY, John K.; '72 BS; RFD #1, Epsom, NH 03234.

SHEELER, Daniel H.; '71 BS; 6 Cat Hollow Rd, Bayville, NY 11709, 516 628-3746.

SHEENAN, Timothy M.; 14 Don Ln., Hauppauge, NY 11788.

SHEERIN, Brendan; '85 BS, '97 MA; Capt.; NYC Police Dept., 1 Police Plz., New York, NY 10038, 718 299-4314; r. 86 Westbury Ave., Plainview, NY 11803, 516 931-2305; Carrie; Danielle, Amanda. e-mail

SHEFF, Bonnie M.; '93 BS; 6565 Wetherole St. Apt. 2g, Flushing, NY 11374, 718 459-1541.

SHEINKOPF, Henry A.; '79 MA; 170 E 79th St. # 8-B, New York, NY 10021, 212 580-8122.

SHEINMAN, Ilana; '78 BSCJ, '80 MA; Handwriting Expert Polygraph; Veritas Assoc. Inc., 3100-47th Ave., Long Island City, NY 11101, 718 391-7400; r. 20 W. 64th St. #15N, New York, NY 10023.

SHELLEY, Charles J.; '78 BS; 1389 Shore Pkwy., Brooklyn, NY 11214, 718 266-3486.

SHELLEY, Marilyn M.; '79 BS; 72 Adelphi St., Brooklyn, NY 11205, 718 266-3486.

SHEPARD, Frederick A.; '94 BS; Dir. of Labor Relations; NY Health & Hosps. Corp., 3424 Kossuth Ave., Bronx, NY 10454; r. 2160 E Tremont Ave. Apt. 1d, Bronx, NY 10462, 718 931-4965; Bernice; Frederick W. Jr.

SHEPPARD, Kinsey O.; '84 BA; Correction Ofcr.; NYC Dept. of Corrections; r. 24 Windsor Pkwy., Hempstead, NY 11550; Kim Carr; Kinsey Ryan.

SHERGALIS, Joseph A.; '76 BS; Retired Also NYC Police; NYC Police Dept. & Forbes Inc.; r. 7 Cane Ln., Westbury, NY 11590; Julia.

SHERK, Edgar F.; '78 MA; 7034 RFD, Mundelein, IL 60060.

SHERLOCK, Bernard F.; 2896 Court St., N. Bellmore, NY 11710.

SHERLOCK, Gerald; '98 MPA; 91 Van Cortlandt Ave. W. #3F, Bronx, NY 10463, 718 601-8667.

SHERLOCK, Ralph M.; '90 BS; 4761 Broadway Apt. 2p, New York, NY 10034.

SHERMAN, Antoine; '93 BS; 8710 34th Ave., Apt. 5D, Jackson Hts., NY 11372, 718 396-9519.

SHERMAN, Barbara J.; '79 BA; 263 6th Ave., Brooklyn, NY 11215, 718 921-2808.

SHERWIN, Lenore K.; '85 BS; 232 Dean St. Apt. 3, Brooklyn, NY 11217.

SHERWOOD, Christopher; '91 MPA; Basic Sch. Coord.; Rockland Police Acad., Pomona, NY 10970, 914 364-8700; r. 305 Chestnut Ave., New Windsor, NY 12553, 914 496-5973; Lynn; Theresa, Margaret, Dorothy.

SHERWOOD, Raymond G.; '74 BS; 24 Lambeth St., Holbrook, NY 11741, 631 589-8195.

SHERWOOD, Roxanne M.; '96 BA; Paralegal; Brian Cave, 245 Park Ave., New York, NY 10036; r. 212 Seaman Ave. # 3C, New York, NY 10034, 212 544-2404.

SHERWOOD, William C.; '98 BA; 24 Third St., New City, NY 10956, 914 639-6760.

SHEWNARAIN, Maya; '95 BA; MA, EDM Columbia Univ.; Higher Educ. Profn.; Columbia Clg. Chicago, 600 S Michigan Ave., Chicago, IL 60605, 312 663-1600; r. 1224 W Farwell Ave. Apt. 2 S, Chicago, IL 60626, 773 973-7187. e-mail

SHEY, Jeff; '80 BA; 36 Maple Rd, Cornwall on Hudson, NY 12520.

SHIELDS, Diana L.; '97 BS; 216 W. 62nd St. 1D, New York, NY 10023, 315 339-5115.

JOHN JAY COLLEGE

SHIELDS, Eugene G.; '75 MA; Retired-Lt.; NYC Police Dept.; r. 330 Fingerboard Rd, Staten Island, NY 10305; Gladys; Dorothy, Timothy, Juliet, Adriana, Megan.

SHIELDS, James S.; '80 MPA; 6 Steven Ct., Mt. Sinai, NY 11766.

SHIELDS, Joseph G.; '90 MA, '90 BS; Substitute Teacher; Wallkill Central Sch. Dist.; r. 19 Waterbury Rd, Warwick, NY 10990, 914 986-6810; Mary. e-mail

SHIELDS, Phillip A.; '81 BS; PSC 470 Box Cus, FPO, AP 96534.

SHIELDS, Richard C.; '77 MPA; BA Univ. of Pittsburgh; Special Agt.; Drug Enforcement Admin., DEA Ofc. of Training, Quantico, VA 22134, 703 632-5162; r. 3809 Raynold Ct., Fredericksburg, VA 22407, 540 786-6157.

SHIELDS, Roger L.; '77 BS; Prog. Mgr.; Dept. of The Army, POB 469, Ben Franklin Sta., Washington, DC 20044, 703 695-3520; r. 5801 Summerlake Way, Centreville, VA 20120, 703 263-0538.

SHILENSKY, Michael D.; '69 MPA; POB 457, Roslyn Hts., NY 11577.

SHILLINGFORD, Wilford P.; '78 BS; Ret Police Sgt; NYC Police Dept.; r. 10610 227th St., Queens Vlg., NY 11429, 718 217-4034; Agnes; Sandra, Peter, Kim.

SHINABA, Jumoke D.; '89 BA; Social Worker; Family Support Syst., 1749 Grand Concourse, Bronx, NY 10453, 718 716-6000; r. 646 Adee Ave. # 2, Bronx, NY 10467; Niyi; Aseev, Razak, Kazeem, Seliat.

SHINAUL, Sherrisse; '86 BS; 269 W 113th St., New York, NY 10026.

SHINNICK, Edward (Ed) J.; '77 BS; Corp. Security; Exxon Mobile Corp., 5959 Las Colinas Blvd., Irving, TX 75039, 972 444-1028; r. 1117 Winding Creek Dr. W, Grapevine, TX 76051, 817 481-6800.

SHIVA, Andrew; '97 MA; 40 Riverside Dr., New York, NY 10023.

SHIVERS, Lashonne L.; '99 BA; Admin. Asst.; Arrow Electronics; r. 121 W Bartlett Rd, Middle Island, NY 11953, 631 736-1829; Hafiz Shakur; Devonte.

SHKOLNIK, Albina; '96 BS; 2898 W 8th St., Apt. 5K, Brooklyn, NY 11224.

SHLAPAK, Beverly; '94 BA; 345 W 58th St. Apt. 9r, New York, NY 10019, 212 541-9883.

SHLAPAK, Myron; 345 W. 58th St. Apt. 9R, New York, NY 10019, 212 541-9883.

SHOEMAKER, Douglas; '93 BS; 16 Bay 8th St., Brooklyn, NY 11228.

SHOENFELD, Samuel; '91 BS; 48 6th Ave., Cedarhurst, NY 11516, 516 371-2217.

SHOMION, Carol A., (Carol A. Corcoran); '75 BA; MSW Florida State Univ.; Social Worker; 210 681-2197; r. 9223 Oxted, San Antonio, TX 78250, 210 681-2197; Stephen; Stephanie, Stacey, Natalie. e-mail

SHORE, Arnold; '77 BS; Retired; r. 1820 Ave. W, Brooklyn, NY 11229, 718 332-1013.

SHORT, Eugene A.; '76 BA; 7316 Blythwood Ln., Charlotte, NC 28227, 704 552-1038.

SHORTELL, Michael E.; '90 BS; Deputy Inspector; NYPD, 450 Cross Bronx Expy., Bronx, NY 10454, 718 299-4314; r. 52 Forest Ave., Pearl River, NY 10965. e-mail

SHORTELL, Robert E.; '75 MPA; AS; Retired Capt. NYPD; r. 390 Jeremiah Dr. Apt. A, Simi Vly., CA 93065, 805 584-2303; Robert, David, John, Jeanne, Daniel.

SHOVLIN, John P.; '72 BS; Retired; r. 543 73rd St., Brooklyn, NY 11209, 718 836-7880.

SHPRITZER, Felicia; '61 MPA; AB Hunter Clg., MA Univ. of MI; Retired Tchr./ Police Lt.; John Jay Clg.; r. 446 E 20th St., Apt. 6F, New York, NY 10009, 212 228-4742.

SHTINO, Gani; '76 AS; 2099 Saddle Path, Seaford, NY 11783.

SHTULL, Penny R.; '84 MA; MPH, PHD City Univ. NY; Prof.; Trinity Clg., 208 Colchester Ave., Burlington, VT 05401, 802 846-7000.

SHTURMINA, Marina; '95 BS; 1445 Shore Pkwy., Brooklyn, NY 11214, 718 449-2579.

SHU, Howard; '97 BS; 5615 211th St., Flushing, NY 11364, 718 463-3446.

SHUEMATE, Melissa A.; '98 BA; 413 Decatur St., Brooklyn, NY 11233, 718 604-2222.

SHUFORD, Keisha R.; '97 BA; 60 Gouverneur St., New York, NY 10002.

SHULMAN, Ronnie J.; '84 MA; 143-17 38 Ave., Flushing, NY 11354.

SHULTERBRON, Johanna; '95 BA; 2059 Davidson Ave., Bronx, NY 10453.

SHULTERBRON, Luz M.; '98 BA; AS Borough Manhattan CC; Operations Asst.; DEA, 99 10th Ave., New York, NY 10011, 212 337-1810; r. 2170 University Ave. #4T, Bronx, NY 10453, 718 561-3554; *Theodore;* Chanel.

SHUSTER, Galina V.; '99 BS; Programmer; Oven Digital, 440 Lafayette St. 5th Fl., New York, NY 10003, 212 253-2100; r. 370 Ft. Washington Ave. Apt412, New York, NY 10033, 212 781-6356. e-mail

SHUSTER, Irina V.; '99 BS; Programmer; Oven Digital, 440 Lafayette St., New York, NY 10003, 212 253-2100; r. 370 Ft. Washington Ave. Apt412, New York, NY 10033, 212 781-6356. e-mail

SHVARTSMAN, Alexander; '99 BA MA; 1549 E. 96th St., Brooklyn, NY 11236, 718 251-4880.

SHVARTSMAN, Maria T.; '98 MA; Care Mgr.; The Apt Fndn., New Haven, CT 06511, 203 426-3344; r. 3 Huntington Ct., Bethel, CT 06801, 203 744-2609.

SIBBLIES, Lauri S.; '89 BA; 1292 E 49th St. Ph, Brooklyn, NY 11234, 718 636-4808.

SICA, Richard J.; '74; 667 Handwerg Dr., River Vale, NJ 07675.

SICCARDI, Vincent F.; '75 BA, '81 MA; JD Touro Law Sch.; Private Practice; 11929 80th Rd, Kew Gardens, NY 11415, 718 261-7660; r. 133-21 85th St., Ozone Park, NY 11417, 718 848-0108. e-mail

SICHLER, George D.; '76 BS; 241 Revere Ave., Bronx, NY 10465.

SICILIA, Frank G.; '80 BS; AS SUNY-Farmingdale; Owner/Process Server; Serve-All Process Svc., POB 1538, Mineola, NY 11501, 516 409-5711; r. 2520 Oak Ct., Seaford, NY 11783, 516 409-5711.

SICURELLI, Karen A.; '95 MA; 3864 Avoca Ave., Bethpage, NY 11714, 516 681-5875.

SIDBERRY, Christina; '96 BS; 1618 Benson St., Bronx, NY 10461.

SIDERS, Yolanda C.; '90 BA; 755 Whittier St. # 16, Bronx, NY 10474.

SIDMAN, Jerry R.; '96 BS; Student; Brooklyn Clg.; r. 1619 W. 9th St., Brooklyn, NY 11223, 718 266-9652. e-mail

SIEBENKAS, Joseph C.; '91 AS, '93 BS; 6844 Burns St. Apt. F1, Flushing, NY 11375.

SIEGEL, Heather; '94 BA; 200 E. 57th St., New York, NY 10022, 315 797-4813.

SIEN, Tjia (Chito) T., Jr.; '96 BS; Police Ofcr.; NYPD; r. 66 Autumn Ave., Brooklyn, NY 11208, 718 235-5230. e-mail

SIERP, Robert W.; '81 BS; 1 Chalfonte Dr., Lebanon, NJ 08833.

SIERRA, Jennifer G.; '99 BA; 769 Lenore Ln., Elmont, NY 11003, 516 568-2031.

SIERRA, Lesly; '83 MA; 3960 54th St., Apt. 6U, Woodside, NY 11377, 718 539-3157.

SIERRA, Martin, Jr.; '93 AS, '95 BS; Operations Supv.; Social Security Admin., 55 W. 125th St., New York, NY 10027, 212 860-6148; r. 154-156 Broome St., New York, NY 10002, 212 614-1289; *Carmen;* Joseph, Damaris, Martin. e-mail

SIGNORILE, Michael V.; '80 BS; 1223 E 45 St., Brooklyn, NY 11234.

SIHAGA, George E.; '93 BA; 7518 62nd St. # 1, Flushing, NY 11385.

SILBERZWEIG, Lorraine '79 (See Waxman, Mrs. Lorraine).

SILVA, Catherine C.; '84 BS; 221-02 Breezy Pl. B, Breezy Pt., NY 11697, 718 631-8437.

SILVA, Maria J.; '95 BA; MSW Hunter Sch. Social Work; Dir. Sr. Programs; East Side House Settlement, 372 E. 152St, Bronx, NY 10455, 718 665-2280; r. 40 Harrison St. Apt. 34I, New York, NY 10013, 212 233-8704; Barbara M. e-mail

SILVA, Martin; '95 BS; 58 Hausman St., Brooklyn, NY 11222, 718 642-4401.

SILVA, Roberto, Jr.; '95 BA, 2000 MPA; Clerical Supv.; Sheltering Arms, 122 E. 29th St., Phone Ext. 810, New York, NY 10016, 212 679-4242; r. 169 Cypress Ave. Apt. 8c, Bronx, NY 10454, 718 665-5356. e-mail

SILVA, Wendy; '86 BA; 3840 Orloff Ave., Bronx, NY 10463, 718 796-0145.

SILVA, Yahaira; '96 BS; 548 53rd St., Brooklyn, NY 11220, 718 642-4401.

SILVER, Alan L.; '78 BS; 151-20 88 St., Howard Bch., NY 11414, 718 229-3072.

SILVER, Daniel S.; '86 BA; 37 Cobalt Ln., Westbury, NY 11590, 516 767-1506.

SILVER, Sherrelle M.; '96 BS; Investigator; Dept. of Justice, 26 Federal Plz., New York, NY 10278, 212 384-1000; r. 161 Ocean Ave., Valley Stream, NY 11580.

SILVER, Sibyl J.; 54 Duffield Dr., S. Orange, NJ 07079.

SILVERA, Colleen; '90 BS; 1800 Albermarle Rd, Brooklyn, NY 11226, 718 771-5174.

SILVERA, Sashika T.; '98 BA; 135-34 Dennis, Jamaica, NY 11434, 718 525-7302.

SILVERIO, Elizabeth '93 (See Espina, Elizabeth, Esq.).

SILVERMAN, Alex; '72 AS, '75 BS; Retired Deputy Inspector; NYCPD; r. 21 Wood Sorrel Ln., E. Northport, NY 11731; *Gloria;* Howard M., Richard D., Douglas R.

SILVERMAN, Barry P.; '80 BA; 500A Grand St., New York, NY 10002.

SILVERMAN, Neal; 415 W 23 St., New York, NY 10011.

SILVERMAN, Susan W., PhD; '93 MA; Psychologist; Jacobi Med. Ctr., Pelham Pkwy., Bronx, NY 10461, 718 918-4600; r. 64 Little Town Ln., Bedford, NY 10506, 914 244-3464. e-mail

SILVERS, Renee; '84 BA; 1363 61 St., Brooklyn, NY 11219, 718 625-0412.

SILVERSTEIN, Andrew; '99 BS; Mutual Fund Trading; TD Waterhouse; r. 570 Westminster Rd. D22, Brooklyn, NY 11230, 718 282-0147. e-mail

SILVERSTEIN, Karen; '85 MA; 1673 E 16th St., # 181, Brooklyn, NY 11229, 718 236-9685.

SIMANDUYEVA, Juliya; '97 BA; MA The Azerbaijan State Univ; Fraud Investigator; Dept. of Homeless Svcs., 151 E. 151 St., Bronx, NY 10451, 718 402-6279; r. 650 Water St., Apt. 5-E, New York, NY 10002, 212 619-1323.

SIMENAUER, David; '96 BS; 140 Cabrini Blvd., New York, NY 10033.

SIMEON, Esther; '93 BA; 1638 Brooklyn Ave., Brooklyn, NY 11210.

SIMION, Nicolae; '98 BA; 67-08 64th Pl. #2nd Fl., Glendale, NY 11385.

SIMMOND, John J.; '92 BS; 425 Prospect Pl. #1, Brooklyn, NY 11238, 718 272-1993.

SIMMONS, Buffie; '94 BA; Brooklyn, NY 11203.

SIMMONS, Cathy; '92 BS; 843 N Clinton Ave., Lindenhurst, NY 11757, 631 226-8501.

SIMMONS, Cheryl '92 (See Simmons-Broadbelt, Cheryl D.).

SIMMONS, Clifford L.; '99 BS; 508 E 54th St., Brooklyn, NY 11203, 718 349-7693.

SIMMONS, Denise L.; '82 MA; 1520 Sedgwick Ave. Apt. 8b, Bronx, NY 10453.

SIMMONS, Karen L.; '90 MPA; BA Duke Univ., LAW CUNY Law; Dir.; Bronx Treatment Ct., 215 E. 161st St., Bronx, Bronx, NY 10451, 718 537-5063; r. 37 Theatre Ln., Staten Island, NY 10304, 718 720-3130.

SIMMONS, Melodi K.; '98 BA; Tchr./ Volunteer; r. 117-47 223 St., Cambria Hts., NY 11411, 718 276-2612. e-mail

SIMMONS, Melvin; '92 MPA, '92 BA; JD New York Law Sch.; Atty.-Detective; NYC Police Dept., One Polcie Plz.-Rm. 1400, New York, NY 10038, 212 374-5410; r. 16 Ellington Way, Spring Vly., NY 10977; *Theresa;* Erin.

SIMMONS, Mia; '99; 380 E. 143rd St., Bronx, NY 10454, 718 562-2682.

SIMMONS, Yvonne; '95 BA; 94 Moffat St. # 2, Brooklyn, NY 11207.

SIMMONS-BROADBELT, Cheryl D., (Cheryl Simmons); '92 BS; Legal Secy.; Wachtell, Lipton, Rosen & Katz, 51 W. 52nd St., New York, NY 10019, 212 403-1716; r. 16911 Sayres Ave., Jamaica, NY 11433, 718 262-8899; *Arthur Broadbelt.* e-mail

SIMMS, Clarence J.; '87 AS; Sta. Supv.; NYCTA, 370 Jay St., Brooklyn, NY 11201, 718 243-3925; r. 2486 W. 29th, Brooklyn, NY 11224, 718 946-1797.

SIMMS, Jacqueline; '93 BA; MS ED Fordham; 7th Grade Math Tchr.; NYC Bd. of Educ., 188 Rochester Ave., Brooklyn, NY 11213, 718 756-3164; r. 10801 Flatlands 8th St., Brooklyn, NY 11236, 718 209-2983; *Howard; Darnell, Jarvis.* e-mail

SIMMS, John; '81 BA; 328 Flatbush Ave. #239, Brooklyn, NY 11238, 718 444-0484.

SIMON, Barry; '97 MA; 350 W. 51st St., New York, NY 10019, 315 336-4575.

SIMON, Catherine G.; '84 BA; 78 Manhattan Ave., New York, NY 10025, 315 858-0569.

SIMON, Gregory D.; '83 BA; 2044 1st Ave., San Diego, CA 92101, 619 297-5430.

SIMON, Jacqueline L.; '93 MA; MA Duquesne Univ., PSYD Miami Inst. of Tech; Psychologist; r. 509 78th St., N. Bergen, NJ 07047, 201 869-0884. e-mail

SIMON, Lennox J.; '76 BS; 50 Hawaii Ave. NE #204, Washington, DC 20011.

SIMON, Michael; '98 BA; Assoc.; Deutsche Bank Corporate Security; r. 1569 E 91st St., Brooklyn, NY 11236, 718 377-4228.

SIMON, Michelle R.; '98 BA; Paralegal; Lumberg; r. 487 Prospect Pl., Brooklyn, NY 11238, 718 398-2252.

SIMON, Stacey; '94 BA; 563 E 53rd St., Brooklyn, NY 11203, 718 451-2475.

SIMON, Tyrone K.; '97 BS; MS Polytech Univ.; Investigator; NYC Dept. of Investigation, 80 Maiden Ln. 17 Fl., New York, NY 10038, 212 825-6822; r. 174 E. 54th St., Brooklyn, NY 11203.

SIMONE, Allen; '80 MA; 1125 65th St., Brooklyn, NY 11219, 718 451-2475.

SIMONETTI, Joseph J.; '92 BS; 211 Meagher Ave., Bronx, NY 10465.

SIMONETTI, Joseph J.; '91 BS; 106 Winchester Ave., Staten Island, NY 10312.

SIMONETTI, Tosano J.; '76 MA; 276 Fairbanks Ave., Staten Island, NY 10306, 718 987-3289.

SIMONS, Basilio A.; '83 BA; Detective; NYCPD, 1154 E. 100th St., Brooklyn, NY 11236, 718 230-4414; r. 1154 E 100th St., Brooklyn, NY 11236, 718 209-3666.

SIMONS, Emily; '79 BA; 40-19 155 St., Flushing, NY 11354, 718 639-3708.

SIMONS, Lee L.; '75 BA; 135 Avenue P, Brooklyn, NY 11204, 718 857-2595.

SIMORELLA, Paul; '88 BA; 258 Rintin St., Franklin Sq., NY 11010, 516 328-6862.

SIMPSON, Alicia; '97 BA; 663 E.223rd St., Bronx, NY 10466, 718 798-4063.

SIMPSON, Gerald C.; '96 BA; 8418 52nd Ave., Flushing, NY 11373, 718 712-8780.

SIMPSON, Nicole D.; '97 BS; AOS Interboro Jr. Clg.; Admin. Asst.; Exec. Corporate, 295 Madison Ave., 18th Fl., New York, NY 10017, 212 972-0350; r. 220-49 138 Ave., Springfield Gardens, NY 11413.

SIMPSON, Paula M.; '79 BA; 4701 Snyder Ave., Brooklyn, NY 11203, 718 284-5387.

SIMPSON, Rhoda; '91 BA; 45-03 23rd St., Long Island City, NY 11101, 718 291-5740.

SIMPSON, Shelaine; '95 BS, '98 MPA; 1075 Grand Concourse #3o, Bronx, NY 10452, 718 681-3878; *Vanessa, Donell Lynzette.* e-mail

SIMPSON, Thomas G.; 389 Oak Branch Rd., Charleston, SC 29401, 803 552-9067.

SIMPSON, William; '71 BA; Amer Embassy DEA, APO, AP 96346.

SIMSOVITS, Rachel; '97 BA; 1138 E 27th St., Brooklyn, NY 11210.

SIMUNOVIC, Nikola; '85 BS; 7826 75th St., Flushing, NY 11385.

SINATRA, Francis A.; '89 MPA; 7417 62nd St., Flushing, NY 11385.

SINATRA, James K.; '75 MA; 9 Hobart St., Ridgefield Park, NJ 07660, 201 641-6774.

SINATRA, Patricia M.; '75 BS; POB 7392, Newburgh, NY 12550.

SINCLAIR, Amanda J.; '85 BS; 1376 E 51st St., Brooklyn, NY 11234, 718 253-1904.

SINCLAIR, Andrene S.; '88 BS; 264 Weequahic Ave., Newark, NJ 07112, 973 483-5698.

SINCLAIR, Brian; '93 BS; 91 Myers Ave., Hicksville, NY 11801, 516 420-0797.

SINCLAIR, Darryl; '93 BS; 340 Georgia Ave. 5H, Brooklyn, NY 11207, 718 253-1904.

SINCLAIR, Melody A.; '94 BA; 485 Ocean Ave., Brooklyn, NY 11226, 718 421-3181.

SINCLAIR, Michael C.; '87 BS; 2067 Pitman Ave., Bronx, NY 10466.

SINCLAIR, Pablo F.; '96 BS; 172 Roquette Ave., Elmont, NY 11003, 516 326-2670.

SINDAB, Rosalind A.; '83 BS; POB 301, Brooklyn, NY 11206.

SING, Deonarine; '92 BS; Police Ofcr.; NYC Police Dept.; r. 1918 Cortelyou Rd, Brooklyn, NY 11226, 718 856-9281.

SINGER, Donald L.; '76 MA; 74 Cordwood Rd, Cortlandt Manor, NY 10567, 914 739-2427.

SINGER, Michael R.; '76 BS; 2422 E 26th St., Brooklyn, NY 11235, 718 646-7694.

SINGH, Andrei Y.; '96 BA; 107-71 109th St., Jamaica, NY 11419, 718 262-0667.

SINGH, Christina; '99 BS; 190 Saint Nicholas Ave., Brooklyn, NY 11237, 718 417-6931.

SINGH, Esther A.; '96 BS; 910 E 83rd St., Apt. 1, Brooklyn, NY 11236, 718 417-6931.

SINGH, Krishna S.; '97 BS; ROR Interviewer; NYC Criminal Justice Agcy., 125-01 Queens Blvd., Kew Gardens, NY 11415, 718 286-3147; r. 145-74 220th St., Rosedale, NY 11413, 718 978-0061.

SINGH, Lata; '92 AS; 2443 90th Pl., Flushing, NY 11369, 718 565-5633.

SINGH, Nandkumar; '91 BS; DCO 2/72 Armor Battalion, Camp Casey, APO, AP 96224.

SINGH, Priya; '97 BS; 93-36 205 St., Hollis, NY 11423, 718 217-4282.

SINGH, Rajdai D.; '91 BS; 10750 116th St., Jamaica, NY 11419, 718 296-1051.

SINGH, Ramkumar; '83 BS; Atty.; Law Ofc. Ray R. Singh, 1301 Dudle Dr., Carrollton, TX 75007; r. 1301 Dudley Dr., Carrollton, TX 75007, 972 394-0292; *Damini; Sasha, Satya.*

SINGH, Rubi K.; '96 MA; 31 E. 12th St., New York, NY 10003.

SINGH, Sugrim; '91 MPA; 1808 Grand Concourse, Bronx, NY 10457.

SINGLETARY, Charles R., Jr.; '90 BS; BS CJ; Correctional Ofcr.; NC Dept. of Corrections, Central Prison, 1300 Western Blvd., Raleigh, NC 27606, 919 733-0800; r. 714 Old Barn Ave., POB 11543, Durham, NC 27704, 919 477-1859; *Barbara; Christina, Catherine, Charles III.*

SINGLETARY, S.; '94 BA; 2123 Boston Rd #2N, Bronx, NY 10460, 718 901-3581.

SINGLETON, Janice; '87 BA; 1 Prospect Park S., Brooklyn, NY 11215, 718 768-9793.

SINGLETON, Ms. Latanya M.; '96 BA; MS Mercy Clg.; Educ. Tchr.; NYC Bd. of Educ.; r. 120 Bellamy Loop Apt. 7b, Bronx, NY 10475, 718 671-3419. e-mail

SINGLETON, Mrs. Maureen V.; '92 AS; Correction Capt.; NYC Dept. of Corrections; r. 21736 109th Ave., Queens Vlg., NY 11429, 718 723-9372.

SINGLETON, Michelle; '96 BS; Tchr.; Francisco Oller Elem. Sch., Bronx, NY 10460; r. 945 E 174 St., Bronx, NY 10460.

SINGLETON, Thelia L.; '99 BA; 340 Hudson Walk 1F, Brooklyn, NY 11201, 718 522-4756.

SINGLETON, Virginia; '86 BA; 2305 Bedford Ave., Brooklyn, NY 11226, 718 693-8040.

SINNOTT, George P.; '80 MA; MA Baruch Clg., BS Villanova Univ.; Contract Admin.; US Govt., 207 New York Ave., Staten Island, NY 10305, 718 390-1045; r. 8624 Ft. Hamilton Pkwy., Brooklyn, NY 11209.

SINNOTT, Thomas G.; '96 BS; Seton Hall Univ.; Correctional Ofcr.; The Fed. Bur. of Prison, Fci-Ft. Dick; r. 23 Fern Dr., Little Egg Harbor Twp., NJ 08087.

SIOTKAS, John; '79 BS, '89 MPA; Asst. Dir. of Public Safety; CUNY-Baruch Clg., 17 Lexington Ave., New York, NY 10010, 212 802-3007; r. 63 Jamaica Ave., Plainview, NY 11803. e-mail

SIOTKAS, John; '78 BS; 8211 25th Ave., Flushing, NY 11370, 718 639-5490.

SIRECI, Gerard; '76 BS; 2036 Bergen St., Bellmore, NY 11710.

SIRICO, Michael G.; '77 BS; 1675 York Ave. Apt. 23h, New York, NY 10128, 212 996-8902.

SIRLIN, Jill; '78 MA; 353 Maryland Ave., Freeport, NY 11520, 516 377-1716.

SIROKA, Andrew L.; '75 BA; 5526 84th St., Flushing, NY 11373.

SISCO, Edward R.; '78 BS, '85 MA; 9128 90th St., Jamaica, NY 11421, 718 777-5268.

SISO, Frank; '90 BS; 20415 42nd Ave., Flushing, NY 11361, 718 229-7084.

SITA, Joseph M.; '80 BS; Mgr. Manufacturing Operations; Steck-Vaughan Publishing, 4515 Seton Ctr. Pkwy., Ste. 300, Austin, TX 78759, 512 343-8227; r. 13109 Highpark Dr., Austin, TX 78729, 512 250-0779; *Marjorie;* Victoria, Craig. e-mail

SIVLER, Les I. '75 (See Gallo-Silver, Les I.).

SJOBLOM, Andreas E.; '99 BA; 84th E. 2 St., New York, NY 10003.

SKEETE, Samuel; '80 BA; POB 274, New York, NY 10268.

SKEETER, Raymond S.; '96 BS; 1376 York Ave. #3B, New York, NY 10021, 212 734-1309.

SKEETER, Shireene D.; '85 BA; 1310 Noble Ave., Bronx, NY 10472, 718 328-9391.

SKELLY, John F.; '69 MPA; BS LIU; Police Cdr.-Retired; NYPD; r. 4 Hillside Ter., Nanuet, NY 10954, 914 623-4067; *Ellen.*

SKELLY, John G.; '77 BA, '79 MA; Adjunct; Troy State Univ.; r. 4072 Soundpointe Dr., Gulf Breeze, FL 32561, 850 934-5686; Sean, Shannon. e-mail

SKELLY, Patrick J.; '80 BS; Retired Lt.; 110th Precinct; r. 9 Sybil Pl., Smithtown, NY 11787, 631 979-8541; *Anne;* Monica, Patrick, Anne.

SKINNER, Elizabeth; '93 MPA; 6167 Reservoir Ct., Granite Bay, CA 95746.

SKLYUT, Olga; '98 BA; 1711 E. 15th St. Apt. 2c, Brooklyn, NY 11229, 718 376-0266.

SKOLNICK, Paul; 161-55 Jewel Ave., Flushing, NY 11365, 718 321-1267.

SKOLNIK, Mrs. Anita D., (Anita D. Stashin); '77 BS, '79 MA, AS; Retired Communications; NYPD, 1 Police Plz., New York, NY 10036, 212 374-5000; r. 310 E. 90th St. 4D, New York, NY 10128, 212 831-9654; *Walter;* Martha Stashin, Albert Stashin, Deirdre Stashin, Avi, Dorea, Gabe.

SKOPIN, Raymond P.; '75 BS; Lt.; Metropolitan Authority Police, 345 Madison Ave., New York, NY 10017; r. 35 Vails Gate Hts., New Windsor, NY 12553, 914 562-5762; *Grace;* Rachale, Shaina. e-mail

SKOVERA, Anne F.; POB 128, Nesconset, NY 11767.

SKRYPKUN, Meg E.; '98 MA; 9338 S Leavitt St., Chicago, IL 60620, 773 239-8161.

SKUBISZ, Peter; '90 BA; Sales; CTA; r. 423 77th St., N. Bergen, NJ 07047.

SKULUDIS, Theodora; '87 BS; 2027 43rd St., Long Island City, NY 11105.

SLACK, Beverly D.; '80 BS; 106 E 57th St., Brooklyn, NY 11203, 718 349-7184.

SLADE, Howard M.; '95 MS; 11 Schenck Ave. Apt. 3d, Great Neck, NY 11021, 516 487-5188.

SLAGG, John J.; '80 BS; 6432 79th St., Flushing, NY 11379, 718 894-0090.

SLANE, William G.; '92 BS; 37 Birch Ave., Farmingdale, NY 11735, 516 694-3363.

SLATER, Roxanne Y.; '99 MPA; BA VA State Univ.; Human Resources Coord.; NY Cruise Lines, Pier 81 W 41st St. & 12th Ave., Times Square, NY 10036, 212 630-8135; r. 1223 E. 39th St., Brooklyn, NY 11210, 718 253-6924. e-mail

SLATTERY, Joseph F.; '72 BS; Retired Law Enforcement/Feds; NYPD; r. 235 Kings Hwy., Congers, NY 10920, 914 268-9206.

SLATTERY, Joseph W.; '89 BS; VP Admin; L.C. Security Cnsltg. Grp. Inc., 7706 17Ave, Brooklyn, NY 11214, 718 331-7400; r. 1892 Willoughby Ave., Flushing, NY 11385, 718 381-8245; Joseph, John. e-mail

SLATTERY, Robert J.; '77 BS; 11158 Willow Dr., # C, Bealeton, VA 22712.

SLAUGHTER, Kathy L.; '83 MA; 815 Howard Ave., Brooklyn, NY 11212, 718 922-4521.

SLAUGHTER, Wayne C.; '93 BS; 4689 Sweetmeadow Cir., Sarasota, FL 34238, 941 921-6629.

SLAVIN, Dennis F.; '78 BA; 2485 Martin Ave., Bellmore, NY 11710.

SLEVIN, Edward F.; '81 BS; 248 Harvest Ave., Staten Island, NY 10310, 718 981-0732.

SLEVIN, John J.; '97 AS, '98 AS; 136 E. 208 St., Bronx, NY 10467, 718 882-4704.

SLEZAK, Alice '95 (See Jaworsky, Alice).

SLIGH, Ms. Geneva L.; '92 BS; Supv. of Info. Mgmt.; Justice Dept., 26 Federal, New York, NY 10278, 212 324-2000; r. 100 La Salle St., New York, NY 10027, 212 222-0945.

SLUKA, Keith; '90 BS; 61 Oleander Way, Clark, NJ 07066, 732 821-9310.

SMALL, Christine J.; '95 BS; 1231 S Argonne Cir., Aurora, CO 80017.

SMALL, Cynthia A.; '96 BA; 206 Prospect Pl., Brooklyn, NY 11238, 718 257-4089.

SMALL, Darnloy E.; '78 BA; NYPD; Retired; r. 133 E 46th St., Brooklyn, NY 11203, 718 774-4234; Thomas, Eric.

SMALL, Dona S.; '96 BA; 3150 99th St. Ph, Flushing, NY 11369, 718 723-4364.

SMALL, Erona R.; '95 BS; 1315 E 224th St., Bronx, NY 10466, 718 324-6133.

SMALL, Karen S.; '95 BS; Long Island Univ.; Life Skills Educator; The Hope Prog., 157 Montague St., 3rd Fl., Brooklyn, NY 11201, 718 852-9307; r. 334 Beach 12th St., Far Rockaway, NY 11691, 718 337-1710. e-mail

SMALL, Kimberly O.; '99 BA; Songwriter; r. 1280 Croton Loop 13G, Brooklyn, NY 11239, 718 642-8006. e-mail

SMALL, Kwame O.; '95 BS; 230 Ocean Pkwy., Brooklyn, NY 11218, 718 287-4306.

SMALL, Oral B.; '79; 920 Vermont St., Brooklyn, NY 11207, 718 346-5661.

SMALLS, Curtis; '76 BA; 108-03 Fern Pl., Jamaica, NY 11433.

SMALLS, Jessie; '86 BS; 147-10 120th Ave., Jamaica, NY 11436, 718 527-5629.

SMALLS, Larue C.; '96 BS; Security Supv.; First Security, 219 W 50th St., New York, NY 10019, 212 725-3330; r. 216-W 64th St./5B, New York, NY 10023, 212 765-2994; Brianna. e-mail

SMALLS, Shameka; '98 BA; 219 W. 144th St., #51, New York, NY 10030.

SMALLWOOD, Lee N.; '99 MA; BA SUNY at Albany; 8 Woodland Ter., Yonkers, NY 10701, 914 963-6927. e-mail

SMALLWOOD, William K.; '83 BS; 68-24 53 Rd., Maspeth, NY 11378.

SMATLICK, Richard P.; '85 BS; 300 Amsterdam Ave., # 607, New York, NY 10023, 212 873-5506.

SMIGIELSKA, Katarzyna P.; '98 BS; 286 Woodhull Ave., Port Jefferson, NY 11776, 631 928-4756.

SMIKLE, Conrad M.; '89 BS; 4140 Digney Ave., Bronx, NY 10466.

SMIT, Christie M.; '95 AS, '96 BS; 80 La Salle St. Apt. 13H, New York, NY 10027, 315 858-0167.

SMIT, W. R.; 711 Amsterdam Ave., New York, NY 10025.

SMITH, Allen J.; '80 AS; Dir. of Security & Fire Safety; Bedford Stuyvesant Restoration Corp., 1368 Fulton St., Brooklyn, NY 11216, 718 636-6928; r. 16024 119th Ave., Jamaica, NY 11434, 718 712-2407; *Elizabeth;* Lynette, Eric, Kimberly. e-mail

SMITH, Alma D.; '84 BA; 147 W. 5th St., Mt. Vernon, NY 10550, 716 831-0906.

SMITH, Arlene A.; '89 BS; 598 Halsey St., Brooklyn, NY 11233, 718 443-3296.

SMITH, Arthur C.; '78 MPA; 31 Pondview Ave., Congers, NY 10920.

SMITH, Bettina J.; '99 BA; AA Borough of Manhattan CC; CUNY Ofc. Asst.; Brooklyn Clg., 2900 Bedford Ave., Brooklyn, NY 11210, 718 951-5095; r. 334-F Chester St., Brooklyn, NY 11212, 718 922-1247; Natifah. e-mail

SMITH, Bonita E.; '90 BS; 455 Carlton Ave. # 9, Brooklyn, NY 11238, 718 622-6553.

SMITH, Catherine H.; '75 MPA; 305 6th Ave. Apt. 3c, Pelham, NY 10803, 914 738-8138.

SMITH, Cheryl D.; '84 BS; 250 Covert St., Brooklyn, NY 11207, 718 277-7184.

SMITH, Christopher; '96 BS; Police Ofcr.; NYPD; r. 9148 111th St., Jamaica, NY 11418, 718 481-7157.

SMITH, Clarence, Jr., Esq.; '84 BA; JD Fordham Univ. Sch. of Law; Atty.; US Dept. of Justice Immigration, 26 Federal Plz. 14th Fl., New York, NY 10278, 212 264-5916; r. 95 Park Ter. E., Apt. 2c, New York, NY 10034, 212 569-2395. e-mail

SMITH, Corlis Y.; '86 BS; 686 Park Pl., Brooklyn, NY 11216, 718 277-7184.

SMITH, Courtney; '95 BA; 245-36 147th Ave., Rosedale, NY 11422, 516 868-0499.

SMITH, Cynthia R.; '86 BS; 440 State St., Brooklyn, NY 11217.

SMITH, Daniel J.; '98 BS; Bus Operator; NYC Transit Authority; r. 200 Rector Pl., Apt. 19 H, New York, NY 10280, 212 786-0877.

SMITH, Deborah '91 (See McGraw, Deborah S.).

SMITH, Denise B.; '95 BA; 1144 Lydig Ave. Apt. 6E, Bronx, NY 10461, 718 320-7778.

SMITH, Derrick A.; '98 BS; 616 E 18th St., Apt. 5L, Brooklyn, NY 11226, 718 253-7765.

SMITH, Donald V.; '71 BS; Retired; r. 790 Becker Ave., NE, Palm Bay, FL 32905, 321 727-7412; *Doris (dec.);* Donald, Jr., Douglas Albert.

SMITH, Eugene F.; '75 MA; 362 Senator St., Brooklyn, NY 11220, 718 257-6271.

SMITH, Farah A.; '98 BS; 4360 Baychester Ave., Bronx, NY 10466, 718 994-9268.

SMITH, Florita E.; '86 BS; Sr. Court Clerk; Ofc. of Ct. Admin., 80 Centre St., New York, NY 10013, 718 590-2920; r. 975 Walton Ave., Apt. 4F S, Bronx, NY 10452, 718 992-1434.

SMITH, Francis X.; '96 AS, '97 BS; 191 Floral Blvd., Floral Park, NY 11001.

SMITH, Gail Y.; '85 BS; 3615 Eastchester Rd, Bronx, NY 10469, 718 798-1868.

SMITH, Glenn A.; '80 BA; 192 E 8th St., Apt. 1E, Brooklyn, NY 11218, 718 230-3904.

SMITH, Harry, CPP; '73 BS; Pres.; Harry Smith, C.P.P. Security Cnslt., 56 Jefferson Pl., Massapequa, NY 11758, 516 541-9120; r. same, 516 795-5753; *Bobbi; John, Jacqueline.* e-mail

SMITH, Hayden R.; '90 BA; 803 E 35th St., Brooklyn, NY 11210, 718 485-2305.

SMITH, Henry G.; '80 MPA; BA Grad. Ctr.; Electronic Data Processing Assoc.; The NY Times, 229 W 43 St., New York, NY 10036, 212 556-1234; r. 167-24 Northern Blvd., Flushing, NY 11358, 718 297-5866. e-mail

SMITH, Jacqueline D.; '98 BS; 1902 Beverly Rd/2f, Brooklyn, NY 11226, 718 235-2124.

SMITH, James A.; '81 BS, BA; 12 W. 119th St. #2, New York, NY 10026, 212 369-9868.

SMITH, James F.; '76 BS; 3333 201st St., Flushing, NY 11361, 718 205-4358.

SMITH, James R.; '78 BA; 2931 W 29 St., Brooklyn, NY 11224, 718 235-2124.

SMITH, James W.; '76 BS; 733 Emerald Lake D, Virginia Bch., VA 23455, 757 487-5290.

SMITH, John R.; '76 BA; 11246 207th St., Queens Vlg., NY 11429, 718 205-4358.

SMITH, John W.; 42 Broadway, Bayonne, NJ 07002.

SMITH, Joyce E.; '97 BA; Fraud Investigator I; Human Resources Admin., 180 Water St., New York, NY 10038, 212 630-9756; r. 258 E 125th St. #4B, New York, NY 10035, 212 348-5920; *Priscilla Brown.*

SMITH, Karen K.; '97 BS; 1931 Bergen St., Brooklyn, NY 11233, 718 783-8084.

SMITH, Kundora, (Kundora Wright); '95 BA; Social Worker; The Salvation Army Social Svcs., 89-31 161st St. rm401, Jamaica, NY 11432, 718 558-4486; r. 451 Kingston Ave., Brooklyn, NY 11225, 718 363-9415; *Rodney; Julia, Khalil.*

SMITH, L. P., (L. P. Shapiro); '80 BS; Cocktail Waitress; Fremont Hotel, Fremont St., Las Vegas, NV 89101; r. 1003 Hollowbluff Ave., N. Las Vegas, NV 89031, 702 657-0699; *Russell.* e-mail

SMITH, Launcelott; '74 BA, '76 MA; Proj. Dir.; John Jay Clg. CUNY, 555 W. 57th St. Ste. 605, New York, NY 10019, 212 237-8572; r. 1170 Ossipee Rd, W. Hempstead, NY 11552, 516 764-9327. e-mail

SMITH, Lawrence C.; '76 BS; Retired Police Detective & Tchr.; NYPD; r. 1 Folcroft Ln., Palm Coast, FL 32137, 904 447-5400; Keith L., Howard M.

SMITH, Leo E.; '75 MA; 8 Clove Lake Pl., Staten Island, NY 10310, 718 420-0795.

SMITH, Leon; '79 BS; 344 E 59th St., Brooklyn, NY 11203, 718 235-3546.

SMITH, Leroy G.; 1730 Maxwell Ct., Yorktown Hts., NY 10598, 914 423-1957.

SMITH, Mrs. Lesley B., (Lesley Borden); '95 BA; Aide to Boston City Council; Boston City Council, One city Hall Plz., 5th Fl., Boston, MA 02201, 617 635-3200; r. 17 Franklin St., #2, Charlestown, MA 02129, 617 242-8443. e-mail

SMITH, Leslie C.; '79 BS; 256 Erie Rd, W. Hempstead, NY 11552, 516 338-1652.

SMITH, Ms. Lillian B.; '77 BS; Clerical Assoc.; NYC Dept. of Sanitation, 343 E. 99th St., New York, NY 10029, 212 369-6414; r. 55 W 100th St. Apt. 3a, New York, NY 10025, 212 531-4116; Denyse, Donya, Damon, Donnia, Demetrius, Dedrick, Dedra, Derric, Delaney, Dominique.

SMITH, Lorraine E.; '91 BS; 3958 Marilyn Dr., Seaford, NY 11783.

SMITH, Maria L.; '93 BA; Supv. Social Services; Human Res. Admin.-Fraud Investigation, 260 11th Ave., New York, NY 10001, 212 630-9752; r. 1920 Union St. Apt. 1G, Brooklyn, NY 11233, 718 778-8129.

SMITH, Marjorie (Mardie) W.; '79 MA; MSED Pace Univ.; Sch. Psychologist; Springs Sch., 48 School St., East Hampton, NY 11937, 631 324-0144; r. 216 Two Holes Water Rd, East Hampton, NY 11937, 631 324-8557; *J. Dana;* Hannah, Simon. e-mail

SMITH, Matthew R.; '76 BA; 21 Endor Ave., Staten Island, NY 10301, 718 273-0575.

SMITH, Melba L.; '95 BA; 1687 Vyse Ave., Bronx, NY 10460, 718 991-0453.

SMITH, Melinda G.; '97 BS, '98 BS; Sr. Acquisitions Spec.; Ford Ford Fndn.; r. 708 9th Ave. 2R, New York, NY 10019, 212 765-6857; Kyle. e-mail

SMITH, Michael S.; '95 BS; 417 52nd St. # 2, Brooklyn, NY 11220, 718 252-8276.

SMITH, Michelle D.; '95 BA; Psychology Asst.; The Brooklyn Sch. for Special Children, 376 Bay 44th St., Brooklyn, NY 11214, 718 946-9700; r. 126 Vanderbilt Ave., Staten Island, NY 10304, 718 448-7649.

SMITH, Michelle S.; '95 BA; 1036 E 85th St., Brooklyn, NY 11236, 718 241-3415.

SMITH, Pamela D.; '95 AS; 660 Saint Ann's Ave., Bronx, NY 10455, 718 324-8322.

SMITH, Peter G.; '75 BS; 235 Barbara St., Staten Island, NY 10306, 718 980-2776.

SMITH, Raquel L.; '93 MPA; 213-31 112th Ave., Queens Vlg., NY 11429, 718 352-8611.

SMITH, Richard C.; 611 Prescott Pl., Valley Stream, NY 11581, 516 791-4852.

SMITH, Robert A.; '82 BS; Detective Sergeant; New Rochelle Police Dept., 475 North Ave., New Rochelle, NY 10801, 914 654-2334; r. 77 Country Ridge Rd, Scarsdale, NY 10583; *Diane Cassara-Smith.* e-mail

SMITH, Robert C.; '80 BS; 3018 Murray St., Flushing, NY 11354, 718 352-8611.

SMITH, Roberta L.; '97 BS; Intake Clerk II; State Atty. Ofc., 201 SE 6th St., Ft. Lauderdale, FL 33301, 954 831-8026; r. 6600 Landings Dr. #212, Lauderhill, FL 33319, 954 486-5028; Imani. e-mail

SMITH, Robin; '96 BA; 10822 Ditmars Blvd., Flushing, NY 11369, 718 956-6609.

SMITH, Rodney; '95 BA; Parole Ofcr.; NYS Div. of Parole, 92-36 Merrick Blvd., Jamaica, NY 11432, 718 558-5150; r. Brooklyn, NY 11225; *Kundora;* Julia, Khalil.

SMITH, Ronald G.; '95 BS; 201 Breezewood Ct., Mt. Airy, MD 21771.

SMITH, Rose; '79 BS; 314 E Clinton Ave., Roosevelt, NY 11575, 516 482-8264.

SMITH, Russell; '90 BS; Detective; r. 22221 Edmore Ave., Queens Vlg., NY 11428, 718 776-4047; David.

SMITH, Ms. Ruth D.; '78 BS; MA Fordham Univ., MSW Hunter Clg.; Dir. of Residential Svcs./Trng.; VIP Community Svcs.-Social Svc. Agcy., 1790 Clinton Ave., Bronx, NY 10457, 718 583-3233; r. 4103 Bronxwood Ave., Bronx, NY 10466, 718 547-2224. e-mail

SMITH, Sabrina; '97 BA; 755 W Hancock Ave., Athens, GA 30601, 706 369-9247.

SMITH, Sarah A.; '85 BS; MAHUSRV Sch. of Busn/Technology, Webster Univ.; Human Svc. Coord. II; South Carolina Dept. of Corrections, 4344 Broad River Rd, Columbia, SC 29210, 803 896-1481; r. 585 Rosemont Dr., Orangeburg, SC 29115, 803 772-1517; William V. Alex, Ender Jr, Henry E., Jr. e-mail

SMITH, Saundra; '96 CERT; 60 Hamilton Ave. Apt. 1a, Staten Island, NY 10301, 718 273-4135.

SMITH, Shelley; '90 BS; 1031 E 81st St., Fl. 1, Brooklyn, NY 11236, 718 221-5454.

SMITH, Sidney; '78 BS; 10741 Van Wyck Expy., Jamaica, NY 11435, 718 206-9110.

SMITH, Steven A.; '89 BA; Sgt. NYPD; New York, NY 10001, 718 972-7111; r. 13214 157th St. # Pvt, Jamaica, NY 11434; *Lydia;* Steven Jr.

SMITH, Steven D.; '89 BS; 2215 Bronxwood Ave., Bronx, NY 10469, 718 515-8743.

SMITH, Susanne M.; '79 BS; Merchandise Mgr./Bookkeeper; New York Exch. for Women's Work, 212 753-2330; r. 571 FDR Dr., New York, NY 10002, 212 982-7266. e-mail

SMITH, Sylvia M.; '79 BA; 78 E 119 St.-5 S., New York, NY 10035, 315 337-8796.

SMITH, Teresa; '78 BA; 808 Charles James Cir., Ellicott City, MD 21043, 410 575-7559.

SMITH, Tina P.; '98 BA; 10 swo 15th Ave. #18, Mt. Vernon, NY 10550, 716 564-0070.

SMITH, Walter D.; '75 BA; Minister; Believers In Faith House of Prayers; r. 3 Abingdon Way, Durham, NC 27713, 919 544-7249; *Virginia;* Walter V.

SMITH, Wayne J.; '87 BS; 10 Franklin Dr., Smithtown, NY 11787, 631 265-3808.

SMITH, William G.; '80 BS; AS Hudson Valley Community C; Retired 2nd Grade Detective; City of Newburgh Police Dept., 55 Broadway, Newburgh, NY 12550, 914 561-3131; r. 4527 High Grove Ct. NW, Acworth, GA 30102, 770 590-1877; *Sharon;* Maurice, William. e-mail

SMITH, Yvonne C.; '93 BA; 542 Essex St., Brooklyn, NY 11208.

SMITHER, Mrs. Melissa; '91 MPA; Owner; Bistros Inc., Main Exchange, West Point, NY 10996, 914 446-2168; r. 421a Bailey Loop, West Point, NY 10996, 914 446-2709; *Robert;* Greyson. e-mail

SMOKE, Clinton H.; '85 BA; 100 Oxford Rd., Westwood, MA 02090.

SMOLENSKY, Glen D.; '96 BA; Police Ofcr.; NYPD; r. New York, NY 10003.

SMOLOWITZ, Barry M.; '79 BS; JD Touro Law Sch.; Atty.; Law Ofc. of Barry M. Smolowitz, 7 Marilyn Dr., Kings Park, NY 11754, 631 544-0759; r. same. e-mail

SMOLUCH, Joseph E.; '77 BS; 185 Wyckoff St., Brooklyn, NY 11217.

SMORTO, Ivette; '83 BA; Businesswoman; r. 5007 Surf Ave., Brooklyn, NY 11224, 718 373-8104. e-mail

SMRCKA, Peter G.; '85 BA; 2525 33rd St., Long Island City, NY 11102.

SMULCZESKI, Richard; '99 MS; BA Queens Clg.; Lt.; NYC Fire Dept., Engine 274, Flushing, NY 11355; r. 92 New Hwy., Commack, NY 11725, 631 864-2374. e-mail

SMULLEN, Margaret; '97 BA; 2923 La Sallo Avo., Bronx, NY 10461.

SMYTH, Kerry M.; '85 BS; Ins. Investigator; INChubb & Son, 12 Vreeland Rd, Florham Park, NJ 07932; r. 55 Garden Ct., Succasunna, NJ 07876; *Christine.* e-mail

SNEED, Karen; '88 BA; 830 Columbus Ave. #, New York, NY 10025.

SNELL, Gerald J.; '76 BA; 14210 Holly Ave., Flushing, NY 11355, 718 461-4888.

SNELLA, Mark A.; '88 BA, '91 MPA; 525 Marlborough Rd, Brooklyn, NY 11226.

SNYDER, Bruce E.; '78 BS; 225-10 141 Ave., Laurelton, NY 11413, 718 932-2071.

SNYDER, Heather T.; '96 MA; Ph.D. Candidate/Adjunct Lecturer; Fordham Univ./Lehman Clg.; r. 44-14 Newtown Rd. Apt. 3M, Astoria, NY 11103, 718 274-6049. e-mail

SNYDER, Kimberly S.; '93 BA; Security Mgr.; McDonald's Corp., 1 Crossroads Dr., Bldg. A, Bedminster, NJ 07921, 908 658-4100; r. 1 Westway, Clinton, NJ 08809, 908 238-0075.

SNYDER, Teresa M.; '79 BA; 1289 Union St., Brooklyn, NY 11225.

SO, George; '93 BS; 2701 Harway Ave., Brooklyn, NY 11214, 718 241-9204.

SO, Hoi-ming; '88 BA; 100 Ocean Pkwy., Brooklyn, NY 11218, 718 375-3332.

SO, Hong Min; '96 BS; 53-01 Seabury St., Elmhurst, NY 11373.

SOARES, Scott A.; '93 MA; 1 Muscoot Rd W, Mahopac, NY 10541, 914 376-1004.

SOBOTOR, Bonnie G.; '78 BS; 203 Ficus St., Celebration, FL 34747, 407 566-9146.

SOCCI, Michael F.; '78 BS; 15240 SW Teal Blvd. #C, Beaverton, OR 97007.

SOGHOMONIAN, Christine A.; '99 MA; BA Boston Univ.; Rsch. Asst.; Yai Natl. Inst. for People W/DD, 39 W. 34th St., New York, NY 10001, 212 273-6239; r. 426 Graham Ave. #2F, Brooklyn, NY 11211, 718 383-7113. e-mail

SOHAN, C.; '90 BS; Acctg.; Auto Parts, N. Palm Bch., FL 33403, 561 622-0101; r. 14647 Heights Blvd., Jupiter, FL 33458, 561 622-8293; *Steve;* Mark, Julie. e-mail

SOKOL, Louise J.; '80 MA; MSW Adelphi Univ.; CISW License; Merit Behavorial Care; r. 38065 N Cave Creek Rd, Cave Creek, AZ 85331, 480 595-9841; Carol. e-mail

SOLANA, Iris E.; '78 BA; 57 Park Ter. W, New York, NY 10034.

SOLANKE, Yetunde O.; '86 BS; 958 E 43rd St., Brooklyn, NY 11210.

SOLANO, Elsa E.; '94 BS; 155 Dahlia Dr., Mastic Bch., NY 11951.

SOLANO, Joseph L.; '76 MPA; 60 Kathleen Dr., Syosset, NY 11791.

SOLANO, Silvia M.; '95 BA; 357 Bedford Ave. # 2, Brooklyn, NY 11211, 718 599-6818.

SOLER, Diana L.; '95 BS; 13 Fairview Ave., Nanuet, NY 10954.

SOLER, Doris; '91 BA; 811 Courtlandt Ave., Bronx, NY 10451, 718 294-6086.

SOLER, Luis; '82 BS; Deputy Dir.; NYC Housing Authority-Dept. Comm. Ope, 433 Lafayette Ave., Brooklyn, NY 11238; r. 336 E 4th St. Apt. 4b, New York, NY 10009, 212 475-2010; *Rosita;* Luis Jr., Miguel.

SOLER, Rafael; '85 BS; CERT. NYS P.I. License; Ret. NYPD Det.; 84th Precinct, 301 Gold St., Brooklyn, NY 11201; r. 12 Beryl St., Farmingdale, NY 11735, 516 249-0346; *Evedaisy;* Jenine, Krystal, Michael. e-mail

SOLER-LUGO, Maria; '95 BA; 1116 Hoe Ave. Apt. 1b, Bronx, NY 10459, 718 562-3444.

SOLESKY, Edward J.; '82 MPA; 307 Hazel St., Clifton, NJ 07011.

SOLEYN, Verrol E.; '91 BA; 640 Empire Blvd., Brooklyn, NY 11213, 718 531-3177.

SOLGAN, Christopher J.; '97 BS; Law Candidate-JD; New York Law Sch.; r. 42 Pinelawn Ave., Farmingville, NY 11738, 631 736-1906. e-mail

SOLIS, John E.; '94 BS; Tchr. of Bilingual Educ./Student; Bd. of Educ./ Fordham Univ.; r. 6 W. Farms Sq., Bronx, NY 10460, 718 842-8369; Elijah J.

SOLIS, Sandra; '84 BA; 226 Revere Ave., Bronx, NY 10465, 718 796-5260.

SOLIS, Susana M.; '93 BS; 89-07 34th Ave., Jackson Hts., NY 11372, 718 899-4377.

SOLLITTO, James R.; '76 BS; 316 W Jamaica Ave., Valley Stream, NY 11580, 516 825-3865.

SOLOMON, Frederick; '92 BS; 2301 5th Ave. # 6d, New York, NY 10037, 212 862-2234.

SOLOMON, Osbert K.; '99 BS MA; POB 310250, Brooklyn, NY 11231, 718 382-7742.

SOLOMON, Sharon R.; '76 MA; 205 Bedford Ave., Brooklyn, NY 11211, 718 382-7742.

SOLOMONS, William H.; '93 BA; POB 5465, North Branch, NJ 08876, 908 689-8435.

SOLORZANO, Sandra; '89 BS; 68 Ferris Pl., Ossining, NY 10562, 914 686-7169.

SOMERSALL, Tara S.; '96 BA; 2800 Heath Ave., Bronx, NY 10463.

SOMERSTEIN, Ilyse R.; '95 BA; 10 Orchard St., Elmwood Park, NJ 07407, 201 794-8338.

SOMERVILLE, Deborah A.; '79 BS; 412 4th Ter., Palm Bch. Gardens, FL 33418.

SOMMER, William J.; '76 BS; 13 Columbine Ave. S, Hampton Bays, NY 11946.

SOMMERS, Barry M.; '75 MPA; 203 Lewiston St., Staten Island, NY 10314.

SON, Keith; '96 BS; 9972 66th Rd Apt. 3z, Flushing, NY 11374, 718 392-5144.

SONNETTA JOYNER, Tisa; '95 BA; 445 New Lots Ave., Brooklyn, NY 11207, 718 287-5845.

SOO-HOO, William; '88 BA; JD Brooklyn Law Sch.; Atty. Gen. Practice; William Soo-hoo Esq., Brooklyn, NY 11201.

SORANNO, Carlo C.; '76 BA; Lt.; NYFD, New York, NY 10001; r. 5733 157th St., Flushing, NY 11355, 718 939-6431.

SORCI, Frank X.; '77 BS; JD Univ. of Tulsa; Mgr. of Delta Vacations; Delta Air Lines, 1030 Delta Blvd., Atlanta, GA 30320, 404 715-5283; r. 110 Benjamin Ct., Fayetteville, GA 30214, 770 461-6051; *Susan;* Sacha, Elena. e-mail

SORDI, Joseph C.; '96 BS; 1867 Marine Pkwy., Brooklyn, NY 11234.

SORENSEN, Bo N.; '98 BS; Kattehalevez 45, 3460 Birkerod 450, Denmark, 2129899221.

SORENSON, James G.; '78 BS; Fire Safety; World Trade Ctr., 1 Wtc, New York, NY 10048, 212 435-7505; r. 4008 Clarendon Rd, Brooklyn, NY 11203, 718 629-0002.

SORGE, Glenn W.; '87 BS; 326 Stoughton Ave., Cranford, NJ 07016, 908 272-6762.

SORGE, Richard; '85 MPA; 6299 Chasewood Dr. Apt. H, Jupiter, FL 33458.

SORGENTI, Josephine; '85 MPA; 1138 Lawn Ct., Brooklyn, NY 11235.

SORIA, Katterine I.; '95 BA; 168 Ash St., Valley Stream, NY 11580, 516 565-4429.

SORIANO, Anthony; '91 AS; 6236 99th St., Flushing, NY 11374, 718 397-3310.

SORIANO, Christina; '95 BS; 1611 E 23 St., Brooklyn, NY 11229, 718 964-0064.

SORMANI, Christopher; '76 BA; 1025 71st St., Brooklyn, NY 11228.

SOROKIN, Jill; '93 BS; 160 S Virgil Ave., Apt. 337, Los Angeles, CA 90004.

SORRENTINO, Frank; '83 BS; 6927 66th Rd, Flushing, NY 11379, 718 848-9412.

SOSA, Juanita; '79 BS; 490 Lincoln Ave. #2, Brooklyn, NY 11208, 718 456-1193.

SOSA, Ms. Kilsie; '97 BS; Ofc. Mgr.; John Jay Clg. Alumni Assoc., 899 Tenth Ave., New York, NY 10019, 212 237-8548; r. 1420 Wood Rd. #8D, Parkchester, NY 10462. e-mail

SOSA, Stephanie A.; '97 BA; POB 41, Highland Mills, NY 10930.

SOSIN, Alexander; '97 BA, '98 BA; Fraud Investigator; HRA, 330 Jay St., Brooklyn, NY 11201, 718 237-7636; r. 3311 Shore Prkw Apt. 4m, Brooklyn, NY 11235, 718 368-9558; *Zlata.*

SOSNOWIK, Daniel E.; '96 BS; MPA Harvard Univ.; Lt., NYPD; NYC Police Dept., One Police Plz. Rm. 1408, New York, NY 10038; r. Brooklyn, NY 11230; *Ester.* e-mail

SOTERO, Robert F.; '93 BS; 11 N Cambridge St., Malverne, NY 11565.

SOTO, Barbara M.; '80 BS; 420 W 19th St. Apt. 13c, New York, NY 10011.

SOTO, David; '97 BA; AS Southern Cnty Comm.-NY; Tech. Support Operator; ADP-Automatic Data Processing, Jersey City, NJ 07303; r. 1565 Odell St., Apt. 12D, Bronx, NY 10462, 718 239-0826; Errol. e-mail

SOTO, Denice C.; '99 MPA; 24 Third Ave., Paterson, NJ 07524, 973 279-0039.

SOTO, Diana; '84 BA; Retired Police Ofcr.; r. 11167 W Almeria Rd, Avondale, AZ 85323.

SOTO, Eleuterio; '76 AS; 335 Grand St., Brooklyn, NY 11211, 718 388-2212.

SOTO, Evangelina; '95 BS; 720 Riverside Dr., Apt. 3C, New York, NY 10031, 212 283-6564; Andres, Athena, Carlos, Yvette. e-mail

SOTO, Francisco; '90 BS; Police Ofcr.; r. 552 E Mountain Rd S, Cold Spring, NY 10516, 914 265-9627; Francisco Jr, Natalie, Milton. e-mail

SOTO, Grace M.; '99 MA; BAS Adelphi Univ.; 30 Wallace St., Freeport, NY 11520, 516 546-9412. e-mail

SOTO, Javier; '88 BS; 2085 Lex Ave. #6D, New York, NY 10035, 212 807-3416.

SOTO, Michelle C. '98 (See Garcia, Michelle C.).

SOTO, Suesette; '99 BS; Police Ofcr.; NYC, 62nd Precinct, New York, NY 10001; r. 215 27 St., Brooklyn, NY 11232, 718 832-2694; Christopher.

SOTO, Tareva L.; '99 BS; 23-06 21St. 3D, Astoria, NY 11105, 716 885-3168.

SOTOLONGO, Pedro; '95 BA; 1345 Pennsylvania Ave. Apt. 2, Miami Bch., FL 33139.

SOTOMAYOR, Ana R.; '99 BA; 900 Fox St. #2C, Bronx, NY 10459, 718 409-4167.

SOTOMAYOR, Carmen L.; '84 BS; 8510 151st Ave. Apt. 5l, Jamaica, NY 11414.

SOTOMAYOR, Celia; '78 BS; 87 Columbia St. Apt. 5h, New York, NY 10002.

SOTOMAYOR, John P.; '90 BS; Computer Assoc.; Dept. Citywide Admin. Svcs., 1 Centre St., 15th Fl. S., New York, NY 10007, 212 669-4160; r. 87-24 Apt. 2a Pitkin Ave., Jamaica, NY 11417. e-mail

SOTTILE, Marion; '86 MA; 261 N 7th St., Lindenhurst, NY 11757.

SOTTOLANO, Steven M.; '77 BS; 118-07 14th Ave., College Pt., NY 11356.

SOUFFRANT, Reginal; '92 BA; POB 2021, New York, NY 10025.

SOULES, Christopher; '91 BA; JD Pace Univ. Law; Police Ofcr.; Greenwich Police Dept., 11 Bruce Pl., Greenwich, CT 06830, 203 622-8000; r. 42 Sheridan Ave. 4G, Mt. Vernon, NY 10552, 914 668-9655; *Hope;* Ashley. e-mail

SOUSA, Robert; '87 BS; Concierge; PRC Management, New York, NY 10025, 212 772-1108; r. 2819 Schley Ave., Apt. 3, Bronx, NY 10465, 718 824-6116. e-mail

SOUTHARD, Richard C.; '93 BS; 6713 19th Ave. Apt. H2, Brooklyn, NY 11204.

SOUTHERLAND, Gilbert A.; '76 BA; Property Mgmt.; HPD, 100 Gold St., New York, NY 10038; r. 745 E 180th St., Bronx, NY 10457; *Loretta;* Gil Jr, Briana. e-mail

SOUTHWELL, Anthony I.; '96 BS; Tchr.; P.S. 184, 778 Forest Ave., Bronx, NY 10456; r. 1283 Rosedale Ave., Bronx, NY 10472.

SOUVENIR, Latoya V.; '99 BA; 503 Powell St., Brooklyn, NY 11212, 718 345-1290.

SOUVENIR-BRICE, Mrs. Cassandra Y., (Cassandra Y. Brice); '95 BS; CERT. Adelphi Univ.; Grad. Student Education; Dowling Clg., Long Island City, NY 11101; r. 45 Camp Rd, Massapequa, NY 11758, 516 795-3093; *Alexandre J. Brice;* Alexander III, Arielle. e-mail

SOVULJ, Josip; '81 BS; 56-07 31st Ave. #5C, Woodside, NY 11377.

SOW, Ms. Cynthia B., (Cynthia Banks); '81 BS; MS Adelphi Univ.; Early Childhood Educator; NYC Bd. of Educ., 65 Court St., Brooklyn, NY 11226, 718 368-5151; r. 3714 Polar St., Brooklyn, NY 11224, 718 265-7193; Aissa. e-mail

SOWAH, Ayeley; '97 BS; 650 Lenox Ave., # 7G, New York, NY 10037.

SOWAH, Ayiteh; '99 BS; Paralegal/ Constr.; LAC, 212 577-7900; r. 475 Prospect Pl. #2R, Brooklyn, NY 11238, 718 636-5662.

SOWAH, Mawuli; '95 BA; 86 Chestnut St. Apt. 7, Rutherford, NJ 07070, 201 804-8174.

SPACCARELLI, Roy J.; '76 BA; 1850 82nd St. #1B, Brooklyn, NY 11214.

SPADAFORA, Ronald R.; '86 BS; BA Queens Clg. CUNY, MA CW Post LIU; Fire Chief; Fire Dept. NYC, 9 Metro tech, Brooklyn, NY 11201, 212 570-4334; r. 20 Horn Ln., Levittown, NY 11756, 516 579-8038; *Marie.*

SPADY, Sonya A.; '98 BA; Youth Court Clerk; City of New Rochelle; r. 16 Keogh Ln., Apt. 1B, New Rochelle, NY 10805, 914 633-6781.

SPAGNOLA, Carmen T.; '96 MA; BA Moravian Clg.; Special Agt.; Fed. Bur. of Investigation, Bridgeport, CT 06604, 203 333-3512; r. 15 Shadowood Ln., Trumbull, CT 06611, 203 380-2704; *Robin.* e-mail

SPAGNOLI, Dominick A.; 31 Rogers Pl., Floral Park, NY 11001.

SPAIER, Matthew H.; '95 BS; 9914 59th Ave., Apt. 6A, Corona, NY 11368.

SPAIN, Pauline; '78 BA, '80 MA; AA Bergen Com Clg., MA Jersey City State Clg.; Head Tchr.; Montclair Child Devel. Ctr., 272 Baldwin St., Glen Ridge, NJ 07028; r. 1846 Longview Ct., Teaneck, NJ 07666, 201 837-1365; *Richard;* Debra, Diana, Vincent. e-mail

SPALLIN, John J.; '81 BS; 120 E 238th St., Bronx, NY 10470.

SPANN, Anita; '81 BS; 437 Bainbridge St., Brooklyn, NY 11233, 718 453-3137.

SPANN, Cassaundra; '92 BS; Contract Spec.; Gen. Svcs. Admin., 26 Federal Plz., New York, NY 10278; r. 171 Old Bergen Rd, Jersey City, NJ 07305. e-mail

SPANN, Kim A.; '94 BS; 112 E 128th St. # 126, New York, NY 10035, 212 996-3959.

SPANN, Regina M.; '86 BS; 437 Bainbridge St., Brooklyn, NY 11233, 718 469-2082.

SPANO, Albert; '92 BA; 875 S. Decatur St., Denver, CO 80219, 303 623-5837.

SPANOWER, Michael J.; '89 BS; 234 Old Sylvan Lake Rd, Hopewell Jct., NY 12533.

SPARLING, Daniel E.; '75 BS; 103 Warwick Rd, Elmont, NY 11003.

SPARRO, Michael R.; '92 BA; Financial Analyst; ADT, Jersey City, NJ 07303, 201 714-3000; r. 245 96th St., Brooklyn, NY 11209, 718 833-1994; *Tatiana;* Gabrielle. e-mail

SPARROW, James T.; '98 BA; 5 19 Ave., Bay Shore, NY 11706, 631 968-1764.

SPARROW, Rodney B.; '93 BS; 328 Malcolm X Blvd., Brooklyn, NY 11233.

SPATARO, James A.; '93 MPA, '96 MS; BA Brooklyn Clg.; Tchr. HS Social Studies; St. Joseph By The Sea HS, 5150 Hylan Blvd., Staten Island, NY 10312, 718 984-6500; r. 235 Armstrong Ave., Staten Island, NY 10308, 718 967-7274.

SPAULDING, James P.; '80 BA; 158-09 76 Rd, Flushing, NY 11366, 718 263-5560.

SPAUN, Gregory (Greg) J.; '86 BA, '96 MA; JD Brooklyn Law Sch.; Atty.; r. 3329 208th St., Fl. 2, Bayside, NY 11361. e-mail

SPEARMAN, Larry D.; '79 BA; 611 W 148th St. Apt. 67, New York, NY 10031.

SPECHT, John F.; '90 BA; 3995 Marilyn Dr., Seaford, NY 11783.

SPECTOR, Abraham M.; '79 BA; 11 Greaves Ct., Staten Island, NY 10308.

SPEIDEL, Philip G.; '84 MPA; 33-17 29th St., Astoria, NY 11106, 718 323-1013.

SPELLMAN, Kenneth M.; '87 BS; 348 Broadwell Ave., Union, NJ 07083.

SPENCE, Dawn M.; '83 BS; 47 Mc Keever Pl., Brooklyn, NY 11225, 718 485-5477.

SPENCE, Maurice A.; '97 BS; 3411 Gunther Ave., Bronx, NY 10469, 718 402-0282.

SPENCE, Robert J.; '77 AS; 65 Woodvale Ave., Staten Island, NY 10309.

SPENCER, Anna-Maria '82 (See Urrutia, Anna-Maria).

SPENCER, Dahlia L.; '96 BS; 17009 143rd Rd, Jamaica, NY 11434, 718 657-2515.

SPENCER, Janine M.; '93 BS; 845 Blake Ave. Apt. 3a, Brooklyn, NY 11207, 718 951-6273.

SPENCER-DEJESUS, Jesusa T.; '99 BA; Intake Coord.; Victim Svcs., 2 Lafayette St., New York, NY 10016, 212 577-8235; r. 2910 Wallace Ave. #10C, Bronx, NY 10467, 718 654-4056; *John;* Michael, Madison. e-mail

SPERA, David N.; '87 BS; 6 Messina Ave., Center Moriches, NY 11934.

SPERANZA, Joseph A.; '85 BS; 1429 Shore Dr., Bronx, NY 10465.

SPIEGEL, Jack; '76 MA; Ret Capt.; NYC Police Dept.; r. 6051 La Palma Ln., Delray Bch., FL 33484, 561 499-3155; *Ruth;* Robert (dec), Mark, Kenneth (dec).

SPIEGEL, Matthew; '97 BA; 250 Central Ave., Lawrence, NY 11559, 516 239-3361.

SPINELLA, Raymond; '98 BS; 55 Starlight Ln., Levittown, NY 11756, 516 735-1577.

SPINELLI, Michael; '96 BA; 36-12 21st Ave., Astoria, NY 11105.

SPINOSO, Thomas D.; '83 MA; 50-41 Newtown Rd, Woodside, NY 11377.

SPIRITOSANTO, Anton; '89 BS; 26 Shepherd Ln., Levittown, PA 19055.

SPISTO, Brian N.; '81 BS; Firefighter; NYC, 65 Harbour Rd, Engine Co. 158, Staten Island, NY 10310; r. 749 Pelton Ave., Staten Island, NY 10310, 718 442-8010.

SPITZBARTH, Robert; '95 BS; 213 Adelaide Ave. # P, Staten Island, NY 10306.

SPIVEY, Leroy; '77 BS; Retired NYCPD; r. 4114 Avenue I, Brooklyn, NY 11210, 718 241-7822; Talaaba, Crystal, Dawn, Leroy C., Nicole.

SPOONER, William M.; '81 BA; 11732 165th St., Jamaica, NY 11434, 718 276-3789.

SPRAGUE, Robert F.; '72 BS; MS Long Island Univ.; Security Mgr.; First Security Svcs. Corp., 200 W. 50 St., New York, NY 10019, 212 872-3499; r. 18 Peg Ct., Hicksville, NY 11801, 516 681-5719; *Viann;* Robert Lee, Toni.

SPRAGUE, Steven J.; '76 BS; 262B Richmond Blvd., Ronkonkoma, NY 11779.

SPREEN, Johannes F.; '66 BS, '68 MPA; ABD PHD Wayne State Univ.; Ret Police Commissioner/Clg. Instrt; NYC Police Dept.; r. 8093 River Rd, Cottrellville, MI 48039, 810 765-8662; *Sallie;* Betty.

SPRIGGS, Jeffrey; '96 BA; Investigator; Dept. of Homeless Svc., Bronx, NY 10451, 718 402-6484; r. 920 Trinity Ave. Apt. 3a, Bronx, NY 10456, 718 401-0088. e-mail

SPRIGGS, Lashunn; '95 BS; 11531 126th St., S. Ozone Park, NY 11420.

SPRINGER, Laurana M.; '99 MPA; 642 Park Ave#1B, Brooklyn, NY 11206, 718 952-8984.

SPRINGER, Louis G.; '74 BS; 370 Chesterton Ave., Staten Island, NY 10306, 718 815-6260.

SPRINGER, Richard L.; '76 BA; MS CW Post; Fed. Investigator; Drug Enforcement Admin.; r. 120 Iris Ave., Floral Park, NY 11001, 516 328-1422.

SPRINGETT, Linda; '80 BS; 8 Deane Ct., Norwalk, CT 06853.

SPRINGLE, Stephen V.; '93 BS; JD St. Thomas Univ. Sch. Law; Atty.; r. 1476 Sutter Ave., Brooklyn, NY 11208, 718 827-0342. e-mail

SPYNTIUK, Stephen P.; '91 BS, '98 MA, '98 MA; Police Ofcr.; New York Police Dept., New York, NY 10004; r. 3746 Ferndale Dr., Wantagh, NY 11793, 516 735-0144.

SQUARCINO, Dawn M. '84 (See Lo Braico, Mrs. Dawn M.).

SQUASSONI, Laura C.; '79 BS; Administrative Fire Protection Insp; Fire Dept. City of NY; r. 22 Honey Ln., Staten Island, NY 10307. e-mail

SQUILLACIOTI, Vita, (Vita Quartara); '95 MA; BA Wagner College; Probation Ofcr.; US Probation Dept., 75 Clinton St., Brooklyn, NY 11201, 718 254-7380; r. 168 Bay 26 St., Brooklyn, NY 11214, 718 266-8312; *Elwis.*

SQUIRES, Bobby E.; '82 BA; 197 Hart St., Brooklyn, NY 11206, 718 693-4247.

SQUIRES, Ronald W.; '99 BS; Front End Supv.; Home Depot, 530 Mount Pleasant Ave., Dover, NJ 07801, 973 442-0101; r. 37 Valley Tr., Oak Ridge, NJ 07438, 973 697-6156. e-mail

SRIBNIK, Steven; '91 MPA; 26-80 30th St. #3B, Long Island City, NY 11102.

SROKA, Annette M.; '87 BS; 1811 E 15th St., Brooklyn, NY 11229.

ST, Jules G.; '83 MA; POB 184, Brooklyn, NY 11216, 718 855-0769.

STAAB, Ryan R.; '96 BS; Police Ofcr.; FBI Hdqrs., Washington, DC 20535; r. 13673 Bent Tree Cir. Apt. 403, Centreville, VA 20121. e-mail

STACK, John J.; '83 MA; Retired Sr. Counselor; NYS Dept. of Correctional Svcs.; r. 435 Seguine Ave., Staten Island, NY 10309; *Thelma E.*

STACK, Maurice J.; '88 BS; 266 Beach 138th St., Far Rockaway, NY 11694, 718 945-4123.

STAGNARI, John M.; '75 BA; 3417 Bell Blvd., Flushing, NY 11361.

STAHL, Doris A.; '74 MA; BA St. Johns Univ.; Councilwoman, Supv. Tax Compliance; Town of Carmel, New York Tax Dept., Mcalpin Ave., Mahopac, NY 10541, 914 933-2309; r. Shear Hill Rd, Mahopac, NY 10541, 914 628-7533. e-mail

STAHL, John P.; '75 BS; 4313 64th St., Flushing, NY 11377, 718 651-9479.

STAHL, John R.; '76 BS; 34 Hawley Ter., Yonkers, NY 10701, 914 969-4646.

STAHL, Lowell L.; '81 BS; 440 Cortelyou Ave., Staten Island, NY 10312.

STAINES, Alex; '96 BA; 1 Beach 105th St., Apt. 10P, Rockaway Park, NY 11694.

STAINES, Edmund T.; '76 BS; 428 Penn Est, E. Stroudsburg, PA 18301.

STAKIAS, Ellen S.; '95 BS; 1254 152nd St., Whitestone, NY 11357, 718 767-4025.

STAMATELOS, Danny S.; '77 BS; Police Ofcr.; Yorktown Police Dept., 2281 Carompond Rd, Yorktown, NY 10598, 914 962-4141; *Lisa;* Michelle, Melissa.

STANCIL, Barbara A.; '86 BA; 89 Audubon Ave., Jersey City, NJ 07305.

STANDARD, Deborah; '92 BS; 216 Acorn Ave., Central Islip, NY 11722.

STANDEL, Marie; '92 MA; 16 Arbor Ridge Ln., S. Setauket, NY 11720, 516 681-5774.

STANEK, Thomas; '90 BA; 2552 Standish Ave., Union, NJ 07083.

STANFORD, William G.; 8 Kingswood Dr., Orangeburg, NY 10962.

STANIEK, Magdalena; '95 BA; Fraud Investigator; City of NY, Water St., New York, NY; r. 6702 Ridge Blvd., Brooklyn, NY 11220, 718 836-3029; *Rastislav Lim.*

STANIS, Mary E.; '75 BA; Customer Svc. Rep.; r. 32-40 92nd St., Apt. 509, E. Elmhurst, NY 11369.

STANISLAUS, Franklyn; '78 BS; 190 E 38 St., Brooklyn, NY 11203.

STANISZEWSKI, Thaddeus W.; 160 Earl Pl. E., E. Meadow, NY 11554.

STANLEY, Alonzo; '76 BS; 2569 Adam Clayton Powell Jr Blvd., Apt11i, New York, NY 10039, 212 663-9351.

STANLEY, Dora L.; '76 BS; MS SUNY Albany; Dir. of Rehab.; NYS Crime Victims Bd., 845 Central Ave., Albany, NY 12206, 518 457-9032; r. 1/2 Meadow Ln., Saratoga Spgs., NY 12866, 518 587-3226; *William;* Eboni, Amber, Kamaai, Jesse, Antuan. e-mail

STANLEY, Lynnette; '98 BA; 34-15 12th St., Long Island City, NY 11106, 718 634-8446.

STANTON, John P.; '77 BA; 20 Norwich Ave., Lynbrook, NY 11563, 516 599-3155.

STANTON, Katherine A.; '84 BS; 67 Stonecutter Rd, Levittown, NY 11756, 516 933-6156.

STANTON, Mary; '85 MPA; 60 Nolans Point Rd., Lake Hopatcong, NJ 07849.

STANTON, Matthew S.; '87 BS; 1362 Estelle Ct., Seaford, NY 11783, 516 221-9103; *Terri-Anne.*

STANTON, Sam M.; '97 BA; 150 W. 97th St., New York, NY 10025, 315 363-6884.

STANULIS, Mary W.; '70 BS; 14849 61st Rd, Flushing, NY 11367.

STANULIS, Robert J.; 382 Charles Ave., Massapequa Park, NY 11762.

STAPLES, Sharon A.; '96 BS; 85-29 114 St., Richmond Hill, NY 11418.

STAPLETON, James J.; '79 BS; 209 Van Duzer St., Staten Island, NY 10301, 718 720-8612.

STAPLETON, James W.; '72 AS, '73 BS, '91 MPA; Ret Deputy Chief/VP Admin. & Sec.; Housing Authority Police Dept., The NY State Battery Park Authority; r. 313 Kassik Cir., Orlando, FL 32824, 407 438-8524; *Fredonia;* Laurelle, Victoria, Annette, Vanessa, Marissa. e-mail

STAPLETON, Mary A.; '95 BA; Broadway Theatre; r. 520 W 56th St. Apt. 9L, New York, NY 10019, 212 664-0087; Jennifer, Robert, John.

STARACE, Theresa K.; '99 BS; 203 Richart Ct., Pomona, NY 10970, 914 354-2474.

STARK, Ms. Carmen C.; '97 BA; Court Ofcr.; Manhattan Criminal Ct., New York, NY 10013, 212 374-3054; r. 201A Linden Blvd., Brooklyn, NY 11226, 718 469-0476; Christina. e-mail

STARK, Linda A.; '78 MA; JD Brooklyn Law Sch.; Atty. Partner; Molod Spitz Desantis & Stark PC, 1140 Ave. of Americas, New York, NY 10036, 212 869-3200; r. 245 E 54th St. Apt. 24g, New York, NY 10022, 315 732-6318; Edward Conroy.

STARK, Robert M.; '95 MS; BA Brooklyn Clg.; Real Estate; Ryan & Walace, Long Beach, NY 11561, 516 897-5909; r. 430 Shore Rd # B7j, Long Beach, NY 11561, 516 889-0512. e-mail

STARKES, Tommie C.; '95 MA; 515 E 143rd St., Apt. 2A, Bronx, NY 10454.

STASHIN, Anita D. '77 (See Skolnik, Mrs. Anita D.).

STASIO, Marie R.; '83 BA; 2128 23rd St., Astoria, NY 11105, 718 721-7143.

STATHOPOULOS, E.; '80 BS; 2814 Astoria Blvd., Long Island City, NY 11102.

STATON, Keith; '95 AS; 120 Grant Ave. # Pvt, Peekskill, NY 10566.

STAWCHANSKY, Donna; '84 BA; 61 Loring Ave., Staten Island, NY 10312.

STAYMENTS, Bruce; '89 MA; Sgt. Town of Elmira Police; Partnership for Responsible Fathering/CE; r. 87 Redfield Dr., Elmira, NY 14905, 607 734-6537; Brittany, Eianca, Mollie, Shawna.

ST. BERNARD, Shari; '94 BA; 145-65 220th St., Springfield Gardens, NY 11413, 516 484-4217.

ST. CLOR, Wagner P.; '95; 1688 E 55th St., Brooklyn, NY 11234, 718 604-3075.

STEELE, David N.; '77 BA; 174-09 128 Ave., Jamaica, NY 11434, 718 470-6324.

STEELE, Edward J.; '91 MPA; BA Hunter Clg.; Police Ofcr.; NYC Police Dept., One Police Plz., New York, NY 10038; r. 93 Bismark Ave., Valley Stream, NY 11581.

STEELE-BAIRD, Svetlana; '96 BS; CERT. Baruch Clg.; Paralegal; Kroll Rubin & Fiorella, 520 Madison Ave., New York, NY 10022, 212 223-9400; r. 16978 144th Rd, Jamaica, NY 11434, 718 341-5291; Royston Baird; Osric.

STEER, Joan M.; '85 BA; 966 1/2 Bergen St., Brooklyn, NY 11216, 718 382-6163.

STEETS, Vanessa C.; '96 BS; Child Abuse Investigator; ACS, 150 Williams St., New York, NY 10038, 212 676-6449; r. 31 Grange St., Huntington, NY 11743, 631 754-0629.

STEETS, William R.; '95 BSCJ; Detective-Property Crimes; VA Beach Police Dept., 840 Kempsville Rd., Virginia Bch., VA 23464, 757 474-8500. e-mail

STEFANESE, Anthony C.; '85 BA; 2515 Glebe Ave. Ph, Bronx, NY 10461.

STEFANICK, Richard A.; '84 BS; 602 Leanora St., Brick, NJ 08723, 732 920-2651.

STEFANIDIS, Stavros; '90 BS; 2053 33rd St., Long Island City, NY 11105.

STEIGMAN, Arnold L.; MPA; 1194 Godfrey Ln., Schenectady, NY 12309, 518 381-1100.

STEIGMAN, Heidi J.; '98 MA; 2384 24th St., Apt. 2A, Astoria, NY 11105.

STEIMKE, Tara; '97 BA; POB 552, New City, NY 10956.

STEIN, Brian; '92 BA; 30 W 60th St. # 12, New York, NY 10023, 212 265-4282.

STEIN, Eugene P.; '88 BS; JD St. Johns Univ.; Atty.; Shearman & Sterling, 599 Lexington Ave., New York, NY 10022, 212 848-4000; r. 3641 211th St., Bayside, NY 11361, 718 428-8435.

STEIN, Heather J.; '95 MS; 90 1/2 Crescent Ave., Buffalo, NY 14214, 716 862-0731.

STEIN, Richard E.; BS; 44 Rockwood Ter., New City, NY 10956, 914 942-2462.

STEIN, Sherry; '82 BS; Police Ofcr.; New York Police Precinct 66, Brooklyn, NY 11204, 718 851-5600; r. 2807 Kings Hwy., Brooklyn, NY 11229.

STEINBERG, Martin S.; '80 BS; 10 Park Ln., Nanuet, NY 10954, 914 624-2511.

STEINERT, Rosa M.; '79 BA; 135-16 134 St., S. Ozone Park, NY 11420.

STEINFELD, Mark D.; '78 BS, '81 MA; Police Ofcr.; NYC Police Dept., 127 Utica Ave., Brooklyn, NY 11213, 718 735-0611; r. 1180 Midland Ave. 2b, Bronxville, NY 10708, 914 961-5626.

STEINHAUSER, Ina; '87 CERT; 360 E. 57 St., New York, NY 10022.

STEINMANN, Robert W.; '91 BA; 112 Coventry Ave., Albertson, NY 11507.

STELLA, Jason M.; '96 BS; 91 Franklin St., E. Rockaway, NY 11518, 516 887-4324.

STELLA, John F.; '76 BS; 6 Stonewall Ct., Westwood, NJ 07675.

STELLING, Barbarann; '88 BS; 65 High Ridge Rd, Monroe, NY 10950, 914 783-2627.

STELMACH, Joanne; '99 MA; 272 Ward Ave. #1F, Bordentown, NJ 08505, 609 324-7868.

STELMASHUK, Joseph; '76 BS; 10 Circledale Ln., Holbrook, NY 11741.

STEN, Brian C.; '96 BS; 924 N Victoria Park Rd, Ft. Lauderdale, FL 33304.

STEO, Frank; '96 MA; 1433 2nd Ave. #2, New York, NY 10021.

STEPHEN, Joyce A.; '81 BS; 29 Pomander Dr., White Plains, NY 10607, 914 923-1965.

STEPHENS, Eric; '95 BS; 1173 E. 229th St., Bronx, NY 10466, 718 293-7808.

STEPHENS, Gary; '97 BA; 271 Rosemont Pl., Englewood, NJ 07631.

STEPHENS, Leslie A.; '76 BS; 1 Spruce St., Garnerville, NY 10923.

STEPHENS, Sukeena M.; '99 MPA; BA Syracuse Univ.; Law Enforcement Ofcr.; Inspector Generals Ofc.; r. 9613 Avenue B, Brooklyn, NY 11236, 718 498-2713; Kimberley. e-mail

STEPHENSON, Beverley; '92 MA; Clg. Prof.; Monroe Clg./Lehman Clg., Bronx, NY 10451; r. 965 E 220th St., Bronx, NY 10469, 718 515-9324; Shanlander, Samantha. e-mail

STEPHENSON, Michelle; '91 BS, '91 CERT; 1365 St. Nicholas A, New York, NY 10033.

STEPHENSON, Oscar L.; '95 BS; Tchr.; Bd. of Educ.; r. 350 Lenox Rd, Apt. 4H, Brooklyn, NY 11226, 718 826-1182; Dawn O.; Dale. e-mail

STEPNIEWSKI, Mark S.; '76 BS; 15612 97th St., Jamaica, NY 11414.

STERLING, Donna; '81 BS; 609 Willoughby Ave. Apt. 4a, Brooklyn, NY 11206, 718 237-0031.

STERLING, Kenneth; '92 BS; 76 Sunnyside Ave., Brooklyn, NY 11207, 718 348-6858.

STERN, Barry P.; '89 MA; BA Clg. of Emporia KS; Sr. Corrections Ofcr.; State of New Jersey Dept Of Corrections, 8 Production Way Avenel Nj, Avenel, NJ 07001, 732 574-2250; r. 26 M Westminster Blvd., South Amboy, NJ 08879, 732 727-5667; Shira B. Daves, Brandon G, Karissa R.

STERN, Helen A.; '95 MA; 2232 SW 33rd Way, Ft. Lauderdale, FL 33312.

STERN, Lee R.; '80 BS; 738 Willowbrook Rd., Staten Island, NY 10314, 718 761-4111.

STERN, Martin; '76 BS; 3858 Rivers Run Trce, Acworth, GA 30101, 770 966-9120.

STERNBLITZ, Paul S.; '76 BS; Principal Police Communications Tec; NYCPD; r. 3085 Brtn 13th St., Brooklyn, NY 11235, 718 743-0791. e-mail

STETSON, Ms. Eleanor L.; '89 BA; Court Clerk Spec.; Kings Cnty. Supreme Ct., 360 Adams St. Rm 850, Brooklyn, NY 11201, 718 643-5075; r. 3 Sheridan Sq., Apt. 15C, New York, NY 10014.

STETTNER, Charles P.; '68 AA, '71 BA, '75 MA; Retired Chief of Hosp. Police; r. 4 Roxbury Ct., Oakdale, NY 11769, 631 567-6465; Patricia; Richard, Janine. e-mail

STEUERER, John; '97 MS; BA Fordham Univ.; 131 E. 83rd St., 3E, New York, NY 10028, 212 628-7205. e-mail

STEUERMAN, Michael; 700 Columbus Ave. Apt. 6j, New York, NY 10025.

STEVENS, Gloria J.; '81 BA; 4150 Bronxwood Ave. # 2r, Bronx, NY 10466, 718 231-2725.

STEVENS, Gordon F.; '72 BS; JD St. John's Univ.; Inspector; Nassau Cnty. New York Police Dept., 1490 Franklin Ave., Mineola, NY 11501, 516 573-7210; r. 196 Lincoln Pl., Brooklyn, NY 11217, 718 783-6958; Gislaine Jouanneau. e-mail

STEVENS, Patricia; '91 BS; 427 Washington Ave., Brooklyn, NY 11238.

STEVENS, Tamika S.; '98 BA; 115-42 220th St., Cambria Hts., NY 11411, 718 525-7705.

STEWARD, Dominique K.; '87 BA, '94 MPA; Supr. Probation Ofcr.; NYC Dept. of Probation, 555 Bronx River Rd., # 4 N, Yonkers, NY 10704, 718 590-3178; r. 555 Bronx River Rd., Yonkers, NY 10704, 914 237-5086.

STEWART, Ann M.; '80 BS; 287 Rutland Rd, Brooklyn, NY 11225, 718 257-4029.

STEWART, Carol M.; '89 CERT; 13 Cheshire St., Huntington Sta., NY 11746, 631 271-3440.

STEWART, Deirdre N., (Deidre Griggs); '94 MA; 117-23 197th St., St. Albans, NY 11412, 718 481-6220; *Horace;* Ciara, Chanel. e-mail

STEWART, Delisia R.; '98 BA; 204 Schmidts Ln. #5e, Staten Island, NY 10314, 718 370-7572.

STEWART, Frank A.; '76 BS; 4122 Avenue P, Brooklyn, NY 11234, 718 257-4029.

STEWART, Hazel L.; '87 BA; JD Fordham Law Sch.; Captain New York City Police; 1 Police Plz., New York, NY 10038, 914 965-7509; r. 86 Durst Pl., Yonkers, NY 10704, 914 965-7509. e-mail

STEWART, Janet S.; '95 BA; MS Lehman Clg.; Elem. Tchr.; Richard R. Green Middle Sch., Bronx, NY 10451; r. 1056 E 211th St., Bronx, NY 10469, 718 547-8858; *Sylvester CPA;* Brynette, Janelle. e-mail

STEWART, Jeffrey; '93 BS; 5921 State Rte. 167, Little Falls, NY 13365, 315 855-4126.

STEWART, John E., Esq.; '80 MPA; BA Glassboro Clg., JD Widener Univ.; Atty.; John E Stewart Atty-at-Law, 1205 N Kings Hwy., Cherry Hill, NJ 08034, 856 428-8880; r. 128 E Partridge Ln., Cherry Hill, NJ 08003, 856 428-8880; *Marlene;* Michael, Sean.

STEWART, Juanita M.; '99 BA; 2055 Anthony Ave. #4F, Bronx, NY 10457, 718 299-2873.

STEWART, Karen D.; '98 BA; 249-08 Weller Ave., Rosedale, NY 11422, 718 297-9316.

STEWART, Lenore O.; '97 BS; Investigator; NYC State Dept. of Taxation & Finance; r. 8915 Parsons Blvd., Apt. 7D, Jamaica, NY 11432, 718 297-2412. e-mail

STEWART, Lisa M.; '99 MA; Grad. Student; The Fielding Inst., Santa Barbara, CA 93105; r. 2536 Dwight St., San Diego, CA 92104, 619 298-5404. e-mail

STEWART, Louisia; '79 BA; Case Mgr.; Human Resources Assoc., 180 Water St., New York, NY 10038, 212 331-4579; r. 22-30 Mott Ave., Apt. 50, Far Rockaway, NY 11691, 718 327-0858.

STEWART, Marie A.; '99 BS; Child Protective Spec.; City of NY, New York, NY 10038, 212 676-7693; r. POB 350710, Jamaica, NY 11435, 718 845-1854.

STEWART, Michelle D.; '91 BA; 34-05 12th St. #5H, Long Island City, NY 11106, 718 945-3221.

STEWART, Paul L.; '84 MA; 7304 Treehills Pkwy., Stone Mtn., GA 30088, 404 286-2068.

STEWART, Shannon E.; '95 MA; 5418 W Genesee St., Camillus, NY 13031, 315 468-0621.

STEWART, Vivienne; '85 BS; 18 Neptune Ave., Jersey City, NJ 07305, 201 435-8522.

STEWART, Mrs. Wendy A., (Wendy Guerrier); '95 BS; Mortgage Loan Ofcr./ Real Estate; Lendmor Mortgage Bankers, Paralegal/Title Closing/, 300 Garden City Plz., Garden City, NY 11530, 516 741-1177; r. 15 Harvard St., Valley Stream, NY 11580, 516 285-5144.

ST. FIRMIN, Bertrand; '84 BA; 241 W 62nd St., New York, NY 10023, 315 797-1983.

STFIRMIN, Gyna M.; '99 BA; Asst. Acct. Exec; Thesco Benefits, LLC, 320 W. 57th St., New York, NY 10019, 212 603-0298; r. 241 W. 62nd St. #2A, New York, NY 10023, 212 586-6702.

ST-FIRMIN, Wenda I.; '90 BA; 241 W 62nd St. Apt. 2a, New York, NY 10023.

ST. FORT, Lina; '98 BS; 1023 Remsen Ave., Brooklyn, NY 11236, 718 783-6349.

ST. GEORGE, Joyce; '74 BA; POB 146, New Kingston, NY 12459, 914 647-5640.

STICKEVERS, John J.; '78 AS, '79 BS; Owner; J. Stickevers Investigations, 156-33 100th St., Howard Bch., NY 11414, 718 843-2335; r. same; *Eleanor;* John III. e-mail

STICKNEY, Charles; 800 West End Ave., New York, NY 10025.

STILLER, Marla K.; '95 MA; 3 Gabriel Ct., Greenlawn, NY 11740, 631 262-0761.

STILLIE, Elizabeth; '96 BA; 103-06 117 St., Richmond Hill, NY 11419.

STILLWELL, Nisha R.; '99 BS; 206 Jay St. 1st Fl., Albany, NY 12210, 518 462-3531.

STIMPHIL, Kathy K.; '98 BA; Domestic Violence Unit Coord.; Victim Svcs. Domestic Viol. Prevention P, 103 Rd Precint, 168-02 91st Ave., Jamaica, NY 11432, 718 739-6561; r. 507 Westminster Rd, Brooklyn, NY 11218. e-mail

STINSON, William M.; '77 BS; Ret-Sgt #2 Put Investigations; NYCPD Eastern Investigative, Nycpd Nyc, 190 S. Broadway, White Plains, NY 10605, 914 997-9693; r. 898 Cooley Rd., Parksville, NY 12768, 914 292-0340.

STITH, Theodore; '80 BA; 364 Montauk Ave., Brooklyn, NY 11208.

STIVALA, Rachel D.; '95 BA; 2531 6th Ave., E. Meadow, NY 11554, 516 221-6469.

ST. JEAN, Fritz; '96 BA; Public Servant; r. 2197 Troy Ave., Brooklyn, NY 11234, 718 253-8672; *Martine;* Daniel, David, Ariana. e-mail

ST. JOHN, Daniel; '83 BA; Queens Clg.; Fire Safety Dir.; Local 32 B&J, 101 6th Ave., New York, NY 10013, 212 388-3001; r. 92-07 95th St., Woodhaven, NY 11421, 718 441-4710; *Susan;* Kristiana, Erica.

ST. LEGER, Lucie; '81 BA; MA Hunter Clg., AS BMCC; LPN/Head Nurse/Supv. Retired; Bellevue Hosp., Brooklyn, NY 11201; r. 331 E 29th St. Apt. 5A, New York, NY 10016, 212 689-2566.

STOCK, Edward J.; '93 BS; 88-13 Rutledge PH, Glendale, NY 11385, 718 459-7855.

STOCK, Louis; '76 MA; 73 Riverview, Port Ewen, NY 12466, 914 339-2236.

STOCKHAUSEN, Scott; '97 BA; 560 Ellsworth Ave., Bronx, NY 10465.

STOCKMAN, Lavelle; '94 BA; Sanitation Supv.; NYC Sanitation Dept.; r. 380 Mountain Rd, Union City, NJ 07087, 201 866-3447.

STOKER, John; 2925 Schurz Ave., Bronx, NY 10465.

STOKLEY, Hope B.; '98 BA; 1491 Grand Concourse #1D, Bronx, NY 10452, 718 992-5508.

STOKLEY, Madlyn; 116 Cambridge Pl., Apt. 4C, Brooklyn, NY 11238.

STONE, Carl J.; '97 BA; 5 Sprat St., Medford, NY 11763.

STONE, Lada, (Lada Zagorodnyuk); '98, '98 BA; MSW Yeshiva Univ.; Social Worker; SADC, 9517 Avenue J, Brooklyn, NY 11236, 718 272-5913; r. 2038 Bay Ridge Ave. #2F, Brooklyn, NY 11204, 718 259-5386; *Oleg;* Olga, Katherine.

STONE, La-Toya T.; '99 BS; 129-12 131 St., S. Ozone Park, NY 11420, 718 529-0608.

STONE, Marianne E.; '77 BS; 135 Kenosha St., Albany, NY 12209, 518 463-8503.

STONE, Pandora; '95 BA; 2300 5th Ave. Apt. 5f, New York, NY 10037, 315 822-3456.

STONE, Richard E.; '81 MA; POB 360, New York, NY 10159, 315 822-3456.

STONE, Robert; '76 MA; 23 State St., Brooklyn, NY 11201, 718 624-1395.

STONE, LTC Wayne A., USA; '82 BA; MS Long Island Univ.; Lt. Col.; Pentagon, Washington, DC 20310, 703 614-9049; r. 2896 Chalet Ct., Woodbridge, VA 22192, 703 670-2848; Brian, Stephen. e-mail

STONIS, Richard V.; '78 BS; 95-04 118th St., Richmond Hill, NY 11419.

STOPLER, Michael J.; '95 BS; 34 Heritage Dr. Apt. B, New City, NY 10956.

STORCH, Arthur S.; '77 MA; 7 Styvesant Ave. 10 B, New York, NY 10009.

STORCH, Jerome E.; '75 MA; MED, EDD Columbia Univ.-Teacher's; Prof. Emeritus; John Jay Clg. of Criminal Justice; r. 9100 W Flamingo Rd Unit1043, Las Vegas, NV 89147, 702 314-4134; Allysen, Aaron. e-mail

STORTZ, Herbert A.; '87 BS; 31 E 2nd St., Freeport, NY 11520.

STOUT, Donald R.; '80 BS; Staff Ofcr.; US Dept. of the Army, HQDA, ODCS for Intelligence, 2511 Jeff Davis Hwy., Ste. 9300, Arlington, VA 22202, 703 601-1596.

STOUTE, Jacqueline; '84 MPA; 10926 172nd St., Jamaica, NY 11433.

STRACCI, Joseph R.; '82 BA; 3288 Agar Pl., Bronx, NY 10465.

STRACHAN, Miriam E.; '87 BA; 18725 Rome Dr., Jamaica, NY 11412, 718 949-4054.

STRACK, Walter T.; '81 BS; 8003 101st Ave., Jamaica, NY 11416.

STRACKER, Cassandra L.; '99 MPAIG; BA Seton Hall Univ.; Fraud Analyst; US Postal Inspection Svc., POB 509, 2 Fed. Sq., 5th Fl., Newark, NJ 07101; r. 1 Wheeler Rd., Chester, NJ 07930, 908 879-5574. e-mail

STRAFELLA, Kim M.; '97 BA; 48-14 170th Pl., Flushing, NY 11365.

STRANAHAN, Fred; '92 BA; 33 Farview Rd, Hopewell Jct., NY 12533.

STRAUB, Jacqueline; '82 BS; 40 Mildred Ave., Staten Island, NY 10314, 718 698-5494.

STRAUB, R. F.; '89 MA; 1 John Alexander Dr., Cortlandt Manor, NY 10567, 914 736-5548.

STRAUSS, Walter; '78 MA; 9882 Erica Ct., Boca Raton, FL 33496.

STRAYHORN, Ms. Michelle; '98 BA; Mktg. Rep.; Madison Square Garden, 2 Penn Plz., New York, NY 10121; r. 1646 Anthony Ave. #4A, Bronx, NY 10457, 718 583-8183.

STRAZZULLO, Salvator; '97 BA; 244 Bay 13th St., Brooklyn, NY 11214.

STREBER, Kathleen I.; '82 BA; 15 W Beech St., Long Beach, NY 11561.

STREETE, Tenneshia S.; '99 BA; 340 E 91 St., Brooklyn, NY 11212, 718 769-8598.

STREFFACIO, Patrick; '92 BS; 7343 71st St. # 2, Flushing, NY 11385.

STREGER, Matthew R.; '96 BA; MPA Clemson Univ.; Paramedic; Greenville Cnty. Ems; r. 218 Cross Field Rd, Greenville, SC 29607, 864 987-0904; *Marian.* e-mail

STRICKLAND, Annette; '95 BS; 580 E 17th St. Apt. 1j, Brooklyn, NY 11226.

STRICKLAND, Jeane L.; '81 BA; 1520 Sedgwick Ave., Bronx, NY 10453, 718 294-7131.

STRICKLAND, Justin C.; '78 BS; 8401 Pan American Frwy. #34, Albuquerque, NM 87113, 505 828-0987.

STRICKLAND, Robert; '85 MPA; 111 Cambridge Pl., Brooklyn, NY 11238.

STRINGER, Judith L.; '97 BA; 474 Windermere Ave., Mt. Arlington, NJ 07856.

STROBL, Staci E.; '99 MA; BA Cornell Univ.; US Probation Ofcr.; Fed. Dist. Ct., 111 Livingston St., Brooklyn, NY 11201, 718 254-7421; r. 30-91 Cres. St. #1J, Astoria, NY 11102, 718 726-4047. e-mail

STROCCO, Allison M.; '85 BA; 3738 29th St., Long Island City, NY 11101, 718 786-7153.

STROH, Christopher M.; '99 BA; 5 Barney St., Yonkers, NY 10710, 914 969-3510.

STROMAN, Vivian N.; '82 BS; 305 Livonia Ave., Brooklyn, NY 11212, 718 498-5941.

STRONG, Kevin L.; '95 AS; 10929 Lefferts Blvd., Bsmt, Jamaica, NY 11420.

STRONG-BANKS, Yvette; '83 BA; 13048 229th St., Jamaica, NY 11413, 718 341-2363.

STROUP, Timothy; POB 105, Annandale-on-Hudson, NY 12504.

STRUBBE, Maureen; '97 BA; 104-55 112th St., Richmond Hill, NY 11419.

STRUBE, Edward W.; '75 BS; Sr. Parole Ofcr.; Dept. of Corrections, POB 237, Bedford, VA 24523, 540 586-7920; r. 147 Coffee Rd, Lynchburg, VA 24503, 804 384-0468. e-mail

ST. SURIN, Mietta; '96 BS; 101-10 223 St., Queens Vlg., NY 11429, 718 464-6483.

STUART, Calvin; '95 AS; Correction Ofcr.; NYC Dept. of Corrections; r. 552 E 83rd St., Brooklyn, NY 11236, 718 209-9407; Kalena. e-mail

STUART, Linnea; '92 BS; JD CUNY Law School; Adjudications Ofcr.; Dept. of Justice; r. 6125 97th St. Apt. 1 E, Rego Park, NY 11374, 718 271-0134.

STUDWOOD, Joyce E.; '82 BS; 3204 Holland Ave., Bronx, NY 10467.

STUGER, Lavern N.; '96 BA; Police Ofcr.; NYC Police Dept.; r. Brooklyn, NY 11203.

STUHLER, Joanne; '80 BS; 352 Bay Ridge Ave., Brooklyn, NY 11220.

STUIS, Charles F.; '80 BS; 66 Lincoln Ave., Wood-Ridge, NJ 07075, 201 935-3058.

STUKES, Ms. Ernestine T.; '95 BS; Correction Ofcr.; NYC Dept. of Corrections, 10-10 Hazen St., E. Elmhurst, NY 11370; r. 2515 Glenwood Rd #, Brooklyn, NY 11210, 718 434-3839; Tyesha, Paul.

STUMP, William P.; '73 BA, '76 MA; Pres.; SSI Programs, POB 4, New Rochelle, NY 10804, 914 637-8343; r. 44 Beechmont Dr., New Rochelle, NY 10804, 914 636-7456. e-mail

STURMAN, Mitchell; '76 BS; MS New York Inst. of Tech.; Mgr. EEO; US Postal Svc.; r. 458 Neptune Ave. Apt. 9p, Brooklyn, NY 11224, 718 372-0213. e-mail

ST. VICTOR, Lewis; '97 BS; 220-21 99th Ave., Queens Vlg., NY 11429, 718 337-3755.

SUAREZ, Christopher; '93 BS; 117 Rutland Rd. P, Brooklyn, NY 11225, 718 437-9699.

SUAREZ, Felix; '96 BS; 617 E.Fordham Rd., Bronx, NY 10458, 718 892-9126.

SUAREZ, Jose; '85 BA; 107-12 107 Ave., Ozone Park, NY 11417, 718 463-2398.

SUAREZ, Judith '96 (See Suarez-Figueroa, Judith).

SUAREZ-FIGUEROA, Judith, (Judith Suarez); '96 CERT, '96 BA; AS Bronx Comm Clg.; POB 5052, S. Hackensack, NJ 07606, 917 737-3835; *Michael.*

SUAREZ-SERAFIN, J.; '94 MA; 202 Washington Ave., Clifton, NJ 07011.

SUBACH, Robert J.; '76; 5955 57th Dr., Flushing, NY 11378.

SUDOL, Richard W.; '92 MS; 132 Waverly Ave., Apt. 1, Mamaroneck, NY 10543, 914 381-3783.

SUGARMAN, Stacy; '98 BA; 21 Hull Ave., Staten Island, NY 10306, 718 816-1535.

SUGHRUE, Daniel F.; '75 MPA; BA Boston Clg.; Retired FBI; r. POB 179, Concord, NH 03302, 603 228-3751.

SUIDZAK, Victor J.; 165 Greenleaf Ave., Staten Island, NY 10310.

SUKRA, Brian; '90 BS; 3921 New Utrecht Ave., Brooklyn, NY 11219.

SULFARO, George V.; '93 BS; 35 Stuart Dr., Syosset, NY 11791.

SULLIVAN, Allison M.; '90 BS; RR 3 Box 3326, Saylorsburg, PA 18353, 570 646-3252.

SULLIVAN, Angela D.; '85 BA; 60 First Ave., New York, NY 10009, 315 732-1194.

SULLIVAN, Brien P.; '96 BA; Couns. Substance Abuse; St. Luke's Roosevelt Hosp., 324 W 108th St., New York, NY 10025, 212 678-6342; r. 14653 26th Ave., Flushing, NY 11354, 718 353-2933; *Dr. Ann;* Stephen, Jessica. e-mail

SULLIVAN, Claudia; '89 MA; 7550 Bell Blvd., Flushing, NY 11364.

SULLIVAN, Daniel F.; '68 MPA; 59 E Raliegh Ave., Staten Island, NY 10310, 718 987-1419.

SULLIVAN, Elizabeth; '90 MPA; 315 Avenue C Apt. 7c, New York, NY 10009, 212 982-4899.

SULLIVAN, James F.; '80 BS; 25 Vandermeer Dr., Basking Ridge, NJ 07920, 908 306-0642.

SULLIVAN, James J.; '75 MPA; 197 Lafayette Ave., Staten Island, NY 10301, 718 987-6329.

SULLIVAN, Jennifer C.; '98 MA; 38 Miller Ave., Floral Park, NY 11001, 516 766-5397.

SULLIVAN, John J.; '86 BS; 555 Broadway, Dobbs Ferry, NY 10522, 914 764-8704.

SULLIVAN, John M.; '81 BS; Sergeant Brooklyn North Homicide; 211 Union St., Brooklyn, NY 11231, 718 963-5373; r. 3565 Naomi Pl., Seaford, NY 11783.

SULLIVAN, Joseph; '97 BA; 128 India St., Brooklyn, NY 11222, 718 748-0288.

SULLIVAN, Kathy; '90 MA; 9396 SE Cornell Rd, Port Orchard, WA 98366, 360 871-2729.

SULLIVAN, Kevin L.; '89 MA; 2111 Murray St., Whitestone, NY 11357, 718 726-0126.

SULLIVAN, Michael K.; '87 BA; 21 S Dorado Cir., Apt. 2H, Hauppauge, NY 11788.

SULLIVAN, Nancy G.; '99 BA; Couns.; Odyssey House, 212 987-5193; r. 116 Pinehurst Ave. Apt. J25, New York, NY 10033, 212 928-7743.

SULLIVAN, Patrick F.; '75 BS; Sr. Special Agt.; GAO-Ofc. of Special Investigations, 441 G St. NW, Washington, DC 20548, 202 512-7472; r. POB 102, Mc Lean, VA 22101, 703 326-0698. e-mail

SULLIVAN, Raymond J.; 437 Beach 132nd St., Far Rockaway, NY 11694, 718 945-2993.

SULLIVAN, Terrence C.; '95 BS; 448 Beach 143rd St., Far Rockaway, NY 11694, 718 956-1619.

SULLIVAN, Thomas F.; 528 Beach 134th St., Far Rockaway, NY 11694, 718 956-1619.

SULLIVAN, Timothy J.; '72 BS, '80 MA; 12 Rosewood Dr., Stony Point, NY 10980, 914 786-3387.

SULLIVAN, Vincent T.; '73 BS; 159 Norwood Ave., Port Jefferson Sta., NY 11776, 631 473-1056.

SULLIVAN, William T.; '75 BS, '83 MPA; 70 Ceder, Cocoa Bch., FL 32931.

SULTAN, Patricia '95 (See Milien, Patricia).

SULTANA, John G.; '76 BS; 5 Primrose Ave., Floral Park, NY 11001.

SUMMERLIN, Gale P.; '78 BS; 13234 41st Ave., Flushing, NY 11355.

SUMMERLIN, Gregory P.; '75 BS; PARALGL Long Island Univ.; Substance Abuse Couns.; Elmcor Youth & Adult Activities, 107-20 Northern Blvd., Corona, NY 11368, 718 651-0096; r. 13234 41st Ave., Flushing, NY 11355, 718 762-8966; *Velisa;* Jonathan, Chaz, Geronimo.

SUMMERS, Cheryl A.; '85 MA; 325 E. 112th St., New York, NY 10029.

SUMMERS, Melody Y.; '99 BS; 151 Richards 2B, Brooklyn, NY 11231, 718 237-1689.

SUMMERS, William F.; '73 MA; 31 Avalon Rd, Garden City, NY 11530, 516 489-7183.

SUMNER, Joan M.; '79 MA; 7 Beech St., Garden City, NY 11530.

SUMNER, Sally L.; '89 MA; 6156 Rte. 79 POB 7, Mecklenburg, NY 14863, 607 564-7311.

SUMPTER, Michelle T.; '97 BA; 1074 Bacall Rd, Jacksonville, FL 32218, 212 348-1078.

SUMTER, Antoinette; '97 MPA; '97; BS York Clg.; Health Sciences Coord.; York Clg., Jamaica, NY 11451, 718 262-3875; r. 119-29 130 St., S. Ozone Park, NY 11420, 718 322-1173. e-mail

SUNDHEIM, Irina H.; '99 BA; 78-36 147 St. 1D, Flushing, NY 11367, 718 969-0199.

SUPONITSKIY, Serge; '97 BS, '99 MS; QA Engr.; Scholastic Inc., 1290 Wall St., Lyndhurst, NJ 07071, 201 372-2478; r. 12 Koenig Ct., Fair Lawn, NJ 07410, 212 982-2605. e-mail

SUPPA, Christina; '98 BA; 719 Pelhamdale Ave., Pelham, NY 10803, 914 738-7218.

SURGEON, Clarence M.; '77 BA; MPA Long Island Univ.; Retired Detective; r. 44 Rochester Ave., Brooklyn, NY 11233, 718 774-7768. e-mail

SURIEL, Julissa A.; '97 BS; 1512 Townsend Ave., Bronx, NY 10452.

SURIN, Fredly; '92 BA; 240 E 18th St. Apt. 5j, Brooklyn, NY 11226.

SURLESS, James M.; '89 BS; 2448 Hudson St., E. Meadow, NY 11554.

SURPHLIS, Kimberly; '92 BA; 140 Elgar Pl. #9, Bronx, NY 10475.

SUSINO, Joseph; '98 BS; 1441 38 St., Brooklyn, NY 11218, 718 686-9717.

SUSS, Charles L.; '73 BS; 14 Lamont Rd, Ridge, NY 11961.

SUTHERLAND, Carla H. '96 (See Sutherland-Simpson, Carla H.).

SUTHERLAND, Sharon; '90 BA; 3 White Birch Dr., Ossining, NY 10562.

SUTHERLAND-SIMPSON, Carla H., (Carla H. Sutherland); '96 BA; Parole Ofcr.; NYS Parole, 119 W. 31st St., New York, NY 10001, 212 736-9759; r. 1091 Dekalb Ave., Brooklyn, NY 11221, 718 453-3324; *Brian Simpson;* Cabria.

SUTLEY, Steven L.; '85 BS; 6 Coolidge Rd, Hampton Bays, NY 11946.

SUTTON, Carl; '92 BS; 190 Willoughby St., Brooklyn, NY 11201, 718 266-8255.

SVANE, Stella; '79; 204 Donaldson Ave., Rutherford, NJ 07070, 201 438-5481.

SVEC, Kimberley '88 (See Ackerson, Kimberley, PhD).

SVENDSEN, Bruce J.; '76 BA; 94-26 57th Ave., Elmhurst, NY 11373.

SVENDSEN, Christian; '77 BS; 2943 201st St., Flushing, NY 11360.

SVETLOV, Victoria; '96 BS; 1021 Ave. W, Brooklyn, NY 11223, 718 627-2858.

SWABY, Harris D.; '83 BS; Police Acad.; Police Acad.; r. N. Miami, FL 33181.

SWAIN, Connie; '95 AS; 11001 62nd Dr., Apt. 5L, Forest Hills, NY 11375.

SWAIN, Michael; '96 BS; AS; Detective; NYC Police Dept., 7th Precinct Detective Squad, 19 1/2 Pitt St., New York, NY 10002, 212 477-7671; r. Bronx, NY 10461, 718 824-4707. e-mail

SWAIN, Quinton E.; '79 MPA; 8 Arlington St., Westbury, NY 11590, 914 856-3993.

SWAIN, Warren; '99 AS; NYC Dept. of Corrections, 1606 Hazen St., E. Elmhurst, NY 11370, 718 546-4191; r. 86-72 208th St. Apt. #2-F, Queens Vlg., NY 11427, 718 464-4195. e-mail

SWANNO, Gerard F.; '86 BA; 188 31st St., Brooklyn, NY 11232, 718 768-1901.

SWANSTON, James E.; '86 AS; Security Supv.; CBS Columbia Broadcasting Syst., 51 W 52nd St., New York, NY 10019, 212 975-5200; r. 21528 Murdock Ave., Queens Vlg., NY 11429, 718 468-0394; *Sadie.*

SWARM, Edward; '83 AS; 480 Union Valley Rd, Mahopac, NY 10541, 914 628-3462.

SWARTOUT, Peter J.; '78 BA; 116 Jackson Ave., Staten Island, NY 10305.

SWASEY, Arthur M.; '89 MA; 190 Willoughby #6l, Brooklyn, NY 11201.

SWAYNE, Patricia '74 (See Koenig, Patricia A.).

SWEEN, Bodden; '90 BA; 2098 Matthews Ave., Bronx, NY 10462, 718 549-2174.

SWEENEY, Gerard F.; '76 BS, '79 MPA; 38 Parma Rd, Island Park, NY 11558, 516 431-3148.

SWEENEY, Joseph M.; '76 BS; 4550 Auburndale Ln., Flushing, NY 11358, 718 945-1098.

SWEET, Roslyn E.; '78 BA; 632 Meade St., Bronx, NY 10460, 718 320-3031.

SWEETING, Soyini T.; '95 BS; Police Ofcr.; NYPD, 81st Precient 30 Ralph Ave., Brooklyn, NY 11221, 718 574-0411; r. 790 Eldert Ln., Apt. 1H, Brooklyn, NY 11208; *William Cooper;* Nailah Cooper. e-mail

SWIATOCHA, Donald J.; '85 BS; 65-07 79 Pl., Middle Vlg., NY 11379.

SWIERZOWSKI, Christi; '92 BS; 85 Rocky Ridge Rd, Amsterdam, NY 12010, 518 842-2145.

SWINDELL, Darryl A.; '88 BS; 25 Huntington, Ste. 520, Boston, MA 02116, 718 467-8456.

SWINTON, Darlene; '95 BS; Trade Svc. Rep.; Citigroup, 111 Wall St., New York, NY 10005, 212 657-6935; r. 375 56th St. Apt. 3f, Brooklyn, NY 11220, 718 439-7401. e-mail

SWINTON, Luther; '79 BS; 13329 229th St., Jamaica, NY 11413, 718 723-5474.

SWINTON, Victor; '97 AS, '98; 375 56th St. #3, Brooklyn, NY 11220, 718 439-7401.

SWIRSKY, Sheldon; '76 MA; BS Long Island Univ.; Ret. Field Parole Ofcr.; NYS Div. of Parole; r. 412 Arbuckle Ave., Cedarhurst, NY 11516, 516 295-4344; *Linda;* Michael, Robert.

SYDELMAN, Lesley J.; '89 BS; 176 Pembroke St., Brooklyn, NY 11235.

SYED, Ghazali A.; '95 BA; 9211 48th Ave., Flushing, NY 11373, 718 271-5158.

SYLVER, Peter T.; '94 BS; 60 Howard Dr. # J, Bergenfield, NJ 07621, 201 387-0339.

SYLVESTER, Alpher K.; '92 MPA; 2664 Pitkin Ave., Brooklyn, NY 11208, 718 778-9867.

SYLVESTER, Glen A.; '81 MA; BA Brooklyn College; Warden; Correctional Ctr. for NY; r. 1285 Village Ave., N. Baldwin, NY 11510, 516 538-2615; *Eslyn;* Nadeje, Amilcar.

SYLVESTER, John; '90 BS, '95 MS; 9502 Church Ave. # 2f, Brooklyn, NY 11212, 718 498-5323.

SYLVESTER, Philip; '85 MA; Tchr.; NYC Bd. of Educ.; r. 1324 E. 56th St., Brooklyn, NY 11234, 718 531-0542; Philip Jr, Simone. e-mail

SYLVESTER, Rukiya A.; '99 BA; 579 E. 29th St., Brooklyn, NY 11210, 718 338-0475.

SYMOLON, Kelly M.; '99 MA; BS Charleston Southern Univ.; Social Worker; State of CT Public Defenders Ofc., New Britain, CT 06050; r. 162 Fox Run, Southington, CT 06489, 860 621-9261.

SYMON, Gordon J.; '77 BS; Battalion Chief; NYC Fire Dept.; r. 125 Norfolk St., Brooklyn, NY 11235.

SYMPI, Bernard; '81 BS; 41-11 Elbertson St., Flushing, NY 11373.

SYSAK, Paul J.; '75 BA; Production Mgr.; Searle, 119 W 40th St., Midtown, NY 10018, 212 730-7717; r. 227 Westchester Ave., Thornwood, NY 10594, 914 747-1247; *Carole;* Paul, Andrew.

SZALL, Barbara M.; 1230 Pennsylvania A #3E, Brooklyn, NY 11239.

SZARAWARSKI, Michael; '79 MA; Constr. Contractor; 732 446-7931; r. 146 County Rd. 522, Englishtown, NJ 07726, 732 446-4796; *Carollee;* Charles, Michael, Nicholas. e-mail

SZCZERBA, Eugenia; '77 BS; 92-19 54 Ave., Elmhurst, NY 11373.

SZUKALSKI, Henry S.; '78 BS; 941-78 St., Brooklyn, NY 11228.

SZYMBORSKI, Leo J.; '76 BA; 16 Diamond St., Brooklyn, NY 11222, 718 383-7133.

T

TABACHNICK, Carrie R.; '97 MA; Proj. Dir.; Kings Cnty. Dist. Atty. Ofc., Brooklyn, NY 11201, 718 250-3045; r. 315 Seventh Ave., Brooklyn, NY 11215, 718 832-2119. e-mail

TABB, James L.; '75 BA; 61 1st Ave., Medford, NY 11763.

TABB, Ms. Yolanda; '98 MPA; BS SUNY at New Paltz; 149 Lafayette Ave. #3a, Brooklyn, NY 11238, 718 802-9604. e-mail

TABOADA, Maria F.; '91 MA; 222 B Daller Dr., New Milford, NJ 07646.

TABOADA, Yelitza C.; '98 BS; 112 Haven Ave. 16, New York, NY 10032, 212 795-0814.

TABONE, Michelle; '94 BA; 43-13 41st St., Sunnyside, NY 11104.

TABOR, Violet; '99; 245 Parker Ave., Maplewood, NJ 07040.

TABRIZI, Ms. Monica N.; '95 MA; BA PSYCH CA State-San Bernardino; Pharmaceutical Sales Rep.; AstraZeneca Pharmaceutical Co., Long Beach, CA 90814; r. 5005 Twilight Canyon Rd, Long Beach, CA 90814.

TADDEO, Jack; '76 BS; Fire Capt.; FDNY, 29 Vermilyea Ave., Inwood, NY 10034, 212 570-4295; r. 367 Fulle Dr., Valley Cottage, NY 10989, 914 353-0199; *Patricia;* Eric, Sara, Nicholas, Christopher. e-mail

TADROS, Oudeh M.; '86 BS; 325 95th St. # 1, Brooklyn, NY 11209.

TAGARELLI, Nicholas A.; '79 MA; Police Sergeant; Port Authority NY NJ, Lincoln Tunnel, 201 617-8540; r. 111 Briar Way, Neshanic Sta., NJ 08853, 908 369-8106; *Irene;* Tiffany. e-mail

TAGLIAFERRO, Jennifer; '93 BS, '99; Import Spec.; US Customs Svc.; r. 20 Broadway Ter., New York, NY 10040.

TAHANY, John M.; 116-10 103 Ave., Richmond Hill, NY 11419.

TAI, Shuk-Yu; '99 BS; Criminalist; Ofc. of Chief Med. Examiner, 520 First Ave., New York, NY 10016; r. 89-23 86th St., Woodhaven, NY 11421, 718 441-0698.

TAIBBI, Patricia A.; '77 BA; 12 Paxton St., Staten Island, NY 10301.

TAIN, Valerie '92 (See Tain-Slater, Mrs. Valerie).

TAIN-SLATER, Mrs. Valerie, (Valerie Tain); '92 BA, '95 MPA; Sr. Case Coordinator; Jewish Care Svcs. of Long Island, 97-45 Queens Blvd., Ph, Rego Park, NY 11374, 718 459-7805; r. 2700 Grand Concourse, Apt. #511, Bronx, NY 10458, 718 295-6285; *Glen Slater;* Jacqueline.

TAKEUCHI, Michael; '97 BA; Old Post Rd, Bedford, NY 10506.

TALAMAS, Jacqueline C.; '99 BA; Grp. Leader; Concourse Day Care Ctr., 100-120 Mount Eden Ave., Bronx, NY 10452, 718 583-9664; r. 103 Hawkstone St. D2, Bronx, NY 10452, 718 901-4206. e-mail

TALAMO, John; '81 BS; 2080 E 55th St., Brooklyn, NY 11234.

TALAMO, Peter M.; '79 BS; 18-05 150th St., Whitestone, NY 11357, 718 278-6287.

TALBOT, Richard J.; '79 BS; 9281 Shore Rd, Brooklyn, NY 11209.

TALISSE, Richard G.; '82 BS; 656 10th St., Brooklyn, NY 11215, 718 768-9642.

TALLENT, Thomas P.; '89 BS; POB 526oad, Armonk, NY 10504.

TALLON, LT Kenneth A.; '76 BS; Police Lt.; Port Authority NY NJ Police, World Trade Ctr., New York, NY 10048; r. 771 Willard St., N. Bellmore, NY 11710. e-mail

TALTON, Simone M.; '95 BA; Clinical Social Worker; r. 875-7 Boynton Ave., Bronx, NY 10473.

TALTY, Edward J.; '76 BA; 150-79 Village Rd, Jamaica, NY 11432, 718 937-3188.

TALTY, Richard B.; '75 MA; 0-53 Fair Lawn Pkwy., Fair Lawn, NJ 07410, 201 797-3731.

TAM, Joemy C.; '82 AS, '92 BS, '99 MBA; MD Arabian Sch. of Medicine; Police Ofcr.; NYPD, New York, NY 10038; r. 734 King Ave., Bronx, NY 10464, 718 885-0676. e-mail

TAMAI, Julianne Sumiyo; '95 BS; JD Univ. of Miami-Law; Law Legal Svcs.; r. New York, NY 10029, 212 426-0213. e-mail

TAMARO, Loring; '96 MA; BA NYU; Dept. of Justice, 26 Federal Plz., New York, NY 10278, 212 384-1000; r. 5355 Henry Hudson Pkwy., # 8B, Bronx, NY 10471, 718 548-8361. e-mail

TAMBORINO, Michael; '93 BA; 355 Broadway Ph, Massapequa Park, NY 11762, 516 797-5625.

TAMPARO, William L.; '76 MPA; 927 E 38 St., Brooklyn, NY 11210.

TAN, Lolito T.; '79 BS; 451 E 14th St. # Apt., New York, NY 10009, 315 738-9522.

TANAKA, Daniel S.; '99; 21 Creek Bend Rd., Hopewell Jct., NY 12533, 914 227-2453.

TANCO, Jenny; '94 BS; 246 E 119th St. Apt. 3b, New York, NY 10035.

TANCULA, Aldona; '95 BS; .80-08 135th St., Kew Gardens, NY 11435.

TANELLA, Gerard M.; '98 BA; 1976 E 24 St., Brooklyn, NY 11229, 718 627-4014.

TANG, Linda Y.; '99; 400 Eldert Ln., Brooklyn, NY 11208, 718 856-2837.

TANKARD, Reginald; '94 AS; 2048 Blackrock Ave., Bronx, NY 10472.

TANNER, Melinda; '93 BS; 484 W 43rd St., Apt. 33N, New York, NY 10036.

TANSIL, Julie A.; '91 BA; 607 Essex St., Brooklyn, NY 11208.

TAORMINA, Peter F.; '78 AS; Retired; r. 1011 SW 16th St., Boynton Bch., FL 33426, 561 732-8881.

TA'PENZIERI, Charles; '77 BA; 66-07 Gray St., Middle Vlg., NY 11379.

TAPIA, Arturo A.; '96 BS, '97 CERT; CERT. Cesda Technical Inst.; Transportation; Metropolitan Hosp., 1901 1st Ave., Ext. 7523, New York, NY 10029, 212 423-8045; r. 154 W. 129th St., Apt. 3b, New York, NY 10027, 212 961-1781; *Antonia;* Osvaldo, Sony T. Mercado.

TARAS, Joseph G.; '88 MPA; 5811 60th St., Flushing, NY 11378.

TARAS, Lorelle S.; '96 MA; 2109 Broadway #10, New York, NY 10023, 315 733-5967.

TARASEWICH, Thomas A.; '76 BA; 221 Armstrong Ave., Staten Island, NY 10308.

TARPEY, Terence M.; '69 MPA; 21-07 Murray St., Whitestone, NY 11357.

TART, Angela L.; '95 BS; 8826 Lincoln St., Savage, MD 20763, 718 596-5335.

TARVER, Dionne E.; '98 BA; 42-20 Kissena Blvd. #E7, Flushing, NY 11355, 718 539-7481. e-mail

TARWACKI, Robert E., Sr.; '93 BS; Sr. Rackets Investigator; NY Cnty. Dist. Attorney's Ofc., One Hogan Pl., New York, NY 10013, 212 335-3744; r. 103 Commerce St., Staten Island, NY 10314. e-mail

TASSY, Joseph G.; '91 BS; 464 Linden Blvd. # 1s, Brooklyn, NY 11203.

TATAR, Paul A.; '83 BS; 7 Firth Rd, Staten Island, NY 10314, 718 370-8371.

TATE, Michael; '78 BA; 140 Einstein Loop # 8, Bronx, NY 10475, 718 584-9273.

TAUBLIB, Allan M.; '75 BS; 537 Loughton Ln., Arnold, MD 21012, 410 757-9497.

TAUCKUS, Peter J.; '83 AS; 11 Calvin St., Lynbrook, NY 11563.

TAVARES, Ana M.; '96 BS; 1571 Vyse Ave. #1A, Bronx, NY 10460.

TAVARES, Karen C.; '93 BS; 107-28 132rd St. Bs, Richmond Hill, NY 11419, 718 533-7393.

TAVAREZ, Guilda; '92 BS; 308 E 209th St. Apt. 5d, Bronx, NY 10467, 718 329-1046.

TAVAREZ, Juan; '92 BS; 355 S. 2nd St., Brooklyn, NY 11211, 718 599-9527.

TAVAREZ, Merrybet; '97 MA; 105 Lynch St. #1, Brooklyn, NY 11206, 718 827-2656.

TAVERAS, Elvis; '90 BS; Case Mgr.; US Dist. Ct., Eastern District of NY, 225 Cadman Plz. E, Brooklyn, NY 11201, 718 260-2328; r. 61 W. 104th St., New York, NY 10025, 212 665-8110; *Sherry;* Alexis, Jessica. e-mail

TAVERAS, Jacqueline; '89 BS, '98 MPA; Assoc. Staff Analyst; NYC Dept. of Homeless Svcs., 33 Beaver St., New York, NY 10004; r. 59-45 155th St., Flushing, NY 11355, 718 460-2719.

TAVERAS, Juan A.; '90 BS; 59-45 155th St., Flushing, NY 11355, 718 460-2719.

TAVERAS, Luisa J. '95 (See Rosario, Luisa J.).

TAVERAS, Seny; '95 BS; 260 Audubon Ave. Apt. 21f, New York, NY 10033.

TAVERAS, Wendy; '97 BS; 87 Rockland Ln., Spring Vly., NY 10977.

TAVERNA, Ignazio; '75 AA, '77 BS; Retired New York Police; r. 75 Selden Blvd., Centereach, NY 11720, 631 698-9663.

TAVERNI, Robert E.; '75 MA; 7571 184th St., Flushing, NY 11366, 718 454-5037.

TAVITIAN, Lucy G.; '95 MA; 3911 210th St., Flushing, NY 11361.

TAYLOR, Aisha J.; '99 BA; Tech.; Bell Atlantic, 375 Pearl St., New York, NY 10038, 212 890-2100; r. 1895 2 Ave. 13 G, New York, NY 10029, 212 410-7286.

TAYLOR, Albert; '88 MPA; POB 363, Cocoa, FL 32923, 321 504-3988.

TAYLOR, Ms. Ann L.; '97 AS, '99 BS; Master Tutor; John Jay Clg Student Enrichment Prog, 555 W. 57th St., Ste. 600, New York, NY 10019, 212 237-8254; r. 240 W.73rd St. 1303, New York, NY 10023, 212 362-7564.

TAYLOR, Arlene V.; '92 BS; 3152 Hull Ave. A5, Bronx, NY 10467, 718 548-0454.

TAYLOR, Arthur; '80 BA; 129 Sportsman Ave., Freeport, NY 11520, 516 867-4393.

TAYLOR, Deserie; '97 BA; AAN Kingsborough; Homemaker; r. 259 Euclid Ave., Brooklyn, NY 11208, 718 235-2980; *Dean;* Kearah, Vision, Amber.

TAYLOR, Donnell; '97 BA; 3045 Ave. W #3C, Brooklyn, NY 11229, 718 252-8196.

TAYLOR, Du R.; '76 BA; 156-20 RSD W #7E, New York, NY 10032, 315 724-3388.

TAYLOR, Heidi M.; '98 MA; 114 E. Radcliffe Dr., Claremont, CA 91711, 858 483-2761.

TAYLOR, Hilton T.; '95 MA; 2754 Grand Concourse Apt. 4j, Bronx, NY 10458.

TAYLOR, Jamal; '97 BS; 188 E.39th St., Brooklyn, NY 11203, 718 241-1043.

TAYLOR, Jeanette R.; '80 BS; Assoc. Staff Analyst; NYC Dept. of Corrections, Manhatten Detention Complex, 125 White St., New York, NY 10013, 212 225-1346; r. 167 Adelphi St., Brooklyn, NY 11205, 718 237-2302.

TAYLOR, Jennifer A.; 739 E. 182 St. #4C, Bronx, NY 10457, 718 548-0454.

TAYLOR, Joseph F.; '77; 15 Goodrich St., Williston Park, NY 11596, 516 741-1796.

TAYLOR, Junior P.; '96 BS; Tchr.; Board of Educ., Brooklyn, NY 11226; r. 1120 Lenox Rd., Brooklyn, NY 11212, 718 385-3203; Tonya. e-mail

TAYLOR, Kevin L.; '96 AS; 665 Westchester Ave. Apt. 4B, Bronx, NY 10455, 718 231-8214.

TAYLOR, M. L.; '94 BA; Criminalist; r. 1603 Lincoln Pl. Apt. 2, Brooklyn, NY 11233, 718 467-3881; Taneisha, Tiasha, Tye Roberts, Trevor Roberts.

TAYLOR, Olive; '92 BS; 344 Chester St. B, Brooklyn, NY 11212.

TAYLOR, Pasey N.; '97 BS; 511 E. 5th St., Mt. Vernon, NY 10553, 716 895-1148.

TAYLOR, Richard F.; '75 BA; 1192 St. Marks Ave., Brooklyn, NY 11213, 718 237-1549.

TAYLOR, Robert F.; '83 BA, '83 MPA; Assoc. Prof.-Political Sci.; Montgomery Clg., 3200 Hwy. 242 W., Conroe, TX 77384, 936 273-7324; r. 119 E. Sundance Cir., The Woodlands, TX 77382, 281 363-4317; Maryanne; Christopher, Matthew, Patrick. e-mail

TAYLOR, Robert G.; '93 BA; Sr. Couns.; NYC Dept. Corrections, 1515 Haven St., Gmbc Sad, E. Elmhurst, NY 11370; r. 114-95 180th St., St. Albans, NY 11434, 718 297-9274; Ashley, Gregory, Jean.

TAYLOR, Rosemarie; '95 BS; 226 Jefferson Ave., Apt. 2, Brooklyn, NY 11216, 718 237-1549.

TAYLOR, Sandra L.; '72 BS; MA Montclair State Clg.; Admin.; Jefferson Cnty. Public Schs., 7862 W. Mansfield Pkwy., Denver, CO 80235, 303 987-4578; r. 1148 S Rifle Cir., Aurora, CO 80017, 303 306-0784; Guy, Gary. e-mail

TAYLOR, Ms. Shernill; '97 BS; AA Kingsborough Comm College; Admission Coord.; Baruch Clg.; r. 3421 Avenue K, Brooklyn, NY 11210, 718 338-2791. e-mail

TAYLOR, Steven M.; '83 BS; 123-07 Newport Ave., Belle Harbor, NY 11694, 718 529-8119.

TAYLOR, Tonya, (Tonya Lewis); '93 BA; Substance Abuse Couns.; Board of Educ., Brooklyn, NY 11212, 718 345-4957; r. 1120 Lenox Rd, Brooklyn, NY 11212, 718 385-3203; Jr. e-mail

TAYLOR, Tyrone; '85 BS; 116-11 157 St. #1A, Jamaica, NY 11434, 718 206-4299.

TAYLOR, Virginia; '87 BS; Police Ofcr.; 90th Precinct, 211 Union Ave., Brooklyn, NY 11211, 718 963-5363; r. 1239 Lincoln Pl., # 2, Brooklyn, NY 11213, 718 778-6570; Ronnet Miller. e-mail

TAYLOR, William; '78 BS; 6115 Avenue T, Brooklyn, NY 11234.

TEACHEY, George A.; '81 BS, '99 MA; BS, MPA; Capt.; NYC Dept. of Corrections; r. 184 Evergreen Dr., Westbury, NY 11590. e-mail

TEDINO, Gabriel; '91; 655 Blauvelt Dr., Oradell, NJ 07649, 201 265-6221.

TEEL, Taneka S.; '96 BS; 278 Amboy St., Brooklyn, NY 11212.

TEELIMIAN, Henrik; '98 BS; Police Ofcr.; NYPD, One Police Plz., New York, NY 10038, 212 374-5000; r. 97-50 Queens Blvd., Rego Park, NY 11374, 718 896-5765. e-mail

TEJADA, Jorge L.; '97 BS; 561 W. 175th St., New York, NY 10033, 212 923-6635.

TEJADA, Marianela; '98 BA; 57-52 Xenia St. #3, Corona, NY 11368, 718 592-1383.

TEJADA, Ripcary; '97 BA; MBW Yeshiva Univ.; Social Worker; Bd. of Educ. NYC, 4360 Broadway, New York, NY 10033; r. 88 Seaman Ave.2B, New York, NY 10034.

TEJADA, Rosa; '86 BA; 1011 E 29 St., Brooklyn, NY 11210, 718 647-0093.

TEJEDA, Miguel A.; '84 BA; 674 Academy St. Apt. E4, New York, NY 10034.

TEJERA, Manuel; '92 BA; 2412 Webster Ave., Bronx, NY 10458.

TEJERA, William; '92 BA; 2412 Webster Ave., Bronx, NY 10458.

TELESCA, John; '74 BA; 1410 Hobart Ave., Bronx, NY 10461, 718 863-0678.

TELESCO, Christina B.; '99 BS; Assoc.; r. 4396 Baldwin Ave., Mariners Point 79, Little River, SC 29566, 843 281-2526; Jesse Garcia.

TELESCO, Grace A.; '87 BS, '91 MA; ABD Fordham Univ.; Chairperson Behavioral Sci.; NYPD Police Acad. Lieutenant, Adjunct Prof-Crisis Intervention, John J Clg., New York, NY 10003, 212 477-9217; Kris Drumm. e-mail

TELESFORD, Janelle R.; '94 BS; Paralegal; Emmet, Marvin & Martin, LLP, 120 Broadway, New York, NY 10271, 212 238-3244; r. 7607 Glenwood Rd., Brooklyn, NY 11236, 718 241-8823. e-mail

TELFER, Michael A.; '99 BS; Police Sergeant; City of NY, 3016 webster Ave., Bronx, NY 10467, 718 220-5841; r. 4186 Murdock Ave., Bronx, NY 10466, 718 325-1952; Marilyn; Kimberlye, Mischa, Sacha, Mandisa, Mekisha. e-mail

TELFORD, Ken; '97 BA; 100 E 21st St., Brooklyn, NY 11226, 718 209-4936.

TELLEFSEN, Laurie J.; '94 BA; Ofc. of Victim Witness Advocacy; Bergen Cnty. Prosecutor's Ofc.; r. Staten Island, NY 10305. e-mail

TELLERIA, Alberto F.; '95 BA; 1529 Leland Ave. # 1a, Bronx, NY 10460.

TELLIS, Allison; '93 BA; 1237 Leland Ave., Bronx, NY 10472.

TEMPESTA, Michael F.; '76 BS; 126 Terrace Pl., Brooklyn, NY 11218.

TEMPLIER, Pierrette; '99 BS; Paralegal; r. 3204 Calibre Creek Pkwy., Roswell, GA 30076, 770 993-2441. e-mail

TENCZA, Adam S.; '78 AS; MS FBI Natl. Acad.; Retired Mgr. of Security; Hoffman La Roche Pharmaceutical; r. 14 Wesley St., Clifton, NJ 07013, 973 458-9341; Jean; Kathleen.

TENCZA, Ronald A.; '70 BA; 99 N. 7 St., Brooklyn, NY 11211, 718 387-3792.

TENNANT, Denise M.; '99 BA; AA NYC Tech Clg.; Fed. Correctional Official; NDC Brooklyn, 129th St., Brooklyn, NY 11232, 718 840-4200; r. 980 E 106 St., Brooklyn, NY 11236, 718 649-2878.

TENNELL, Henrietta; '85 BA; 219-04 Murdock Ave., Queens Vlg., NY 11429.

TENNENT, Wayne A.; '83 MPA; 2333 Fifth Ave., New York, NY 10037, 212 926-4651.

TENZER, Mitchell R.; '79 BS; 78 Dent Rd, Staten Island, NY 10308.

TERILLI, Michael; '88 MPA; 28th Tran Det Box 146, APO, AE 09159.

TERIO, Stephen; '91 BA; 24-02 92nd St., E. Elmhurst, NY 11369.

TERRANOVA, Susan '83 (See Foley, Ms. Susan).

TERRELL, David R.; '90 BS; 130-05 160th St., Jamaica, NY 11434.

TERRIBILE, Joseph S.; '83 BS; 1555 W 6th St., Piscataway, NJ 08854, 732 968-4124.

TERRILL, Cletus D.; '78 BS; 31 Kilburn Rd, Garden City, NY 11530, 516 873-1248.

TERRY, Lera T.; '85 BA; 2086 2nd Ave. Apt. 5b, New York, NY 10029, 315 733-6473.

TERRY, Walter P.; '75 MA; 25512 61st Ave., Flushing, NY 11362, 718 224-7522.

TERRY, William L.; '80 BA; 1630 Undercliff Ave., Bronx, NY 10453, 718 583-9684.

TERSIGNI, Christopher T.; '87 BS; Special Agt.; DEA, 300 International Pkwy., Heathrow, FL 32746, 407 333-7000; r. 512 Eastbridge Dr., Oviedo, FL 32765, 407 366-6243.

TESFAMARIAM, Bernice; 400 Chalfont St., Pittsburgh, PA 15210.

TESORIERO, Thomas J.; '86 BS; Fed. Employee & Writer; US Postal Svc.; r. 7011 11th Ave., Brooklyn, NY 11228, 718 680-6051; Grace; Joseph, Anthony, Angelica.

TESSA, Hackett '79 (See Hackett-Viera, Tessa I.).

TESTA, Lawrence W.; '98 MA; BS Brooklyn Clg.; Asst. Mgr.; Lechters Housewares, 2173 86th St., Brooklyn, NY 11204, 718 372-4488; r. 2402 65th St. #F12, Brooklyn, NY 11204, 718 627-6457.

TESTA, Olga; 97-17 Eckford Ave., Ozone Park, NY 11417, 718 456-0426.

TEXIDOR, Jose L.; '82 BA; 2264 Virgil Pl., Bronx, NY 10473, 718 863-3993.

TEXLER, Misty; '98 AS; 2935 W. 5th St. Apt. 3B, Brooklyn, NY 11224, 718 372-6865.

THEARD, Jacques E.; '82 BA; 94-25 57th Ave., Elmhurst, NY 11373.

THEILE, Jane; 100 08 Ascan Ave., Forest Hills, NY 11375.

THEODORE, Leticia S.; '95 BA; 788 Bergen St. Apt. 1, Brooklyn, NY 11238, 718 282-8560.

THOMANN, Joseph S.; '76 MPA; 1746 Remsen Ave., Merrick, NY 11566, 516 379-7701.

THOMAS, Alisa J.; '98 BA; Fraud Investigator; NYC; r. 669 Eagle Ave., Bronx, NY 10455, 718 665-3035.

THOMAS, Andrew; '90 BA; 635 Jerome St., Brooklyn, NY 11207, 718 649-0694.

THOMAS, Caran C.; '99 BA; 70 2nd Ave., Gloversville, NY 12078, 518 725-4152.

THOMAS, Carl; '99 BA; 87-85 191 St., Holliswood, NY 11423, 718 291-3536.

THOMAS, Carolyn; '90 BA; 183 Nassau Ln., Island Park, NY 11558, 516 431-5006.

THOMAS, Danny T.; '96 CERT; 15319 111th Rd, Jamaica, NY 11433, 718 217-6062.

THOMAS, Darrell E.; '95 BA; 3 Birchwood Dr., Valley Stream, NY 11580, 516 432-9745.

THOMAS, Denise S.; '96 BS; 1256 E. 83 St., Brooklyn, NY 11236, 718 235-6102.

THOMAS, E.; '79 BS; 820 Colgate Ave. #1, Bronx, NY 10473, 718 561-4241.

THOMAS, Edmund; '86 BS; 353 Beach 57th St. #2K, Arverne, NY 11692, 718 634-0866.

THOMAS, Francis C.; '78 BA; 281 Avenue C, New York, NY 10009, 212 677-4391.

THOMAS, Gary E.; '88 BS; 1632 Carroll St., Brooklyn, NY 11213, 718 856-8450.

THOMAS, Jennifer N.; '99; 177 Rogers Ave., Brooklyn, NY 11216, 718 377-0356.

THOMAS, Joan P.; '79 BS; 1556 Fulton St., Brooklyn, NY 11216, 718 221-8495.

THOMAS, Joy E.; '95 MA; BA SUNY-Geneseo; Community Coord.; NY Bd. of Educ., New York, NY 10009, 212 979-3351; r. 50 Parkview Rd, Elmsford, NY 10523, 914 592-5664.

THOMAS, Judy C.; '95 BS; 435 Bristol St., Brooklyn, NY 11212, 718 221-8495.

THOMAS, Keith B.; '95 BS, '98 MS; Adjunct. Lecturer; John Jay Clg.; r. 500 St. Johns Pl. #6C, Brooklyn, NY 11238, 718 638-9343; *Avril;* Akeiva, Keril, Keivanna. e-mail

THOMAS, Kristal L.; '99 BA; Social Worker; St. Vincent's Svcs., 205 Montague St., Brooklyn, NY 11201, 718 522-3700; r. 105 St.Felix St., Brooklyn, NY 11217, 718 237-1858.

THOMAS, Lawrence A.; 137-04 172 St., Jamaica, NY 11434, 718 276-2717.

THOMAS, Linda P.; '83 BS; AAS UMDNS-Newark; Dental Hygienist; Today's Dental, 263 Central Ave., E. Orange, NJ 07018, 973 675-1799; r. 31 S Willow St., Montclair, NJ 07042.

THOMAS, Lisa M.; '91 BS; 3946 Barnes Ave. #2, Bronx, NY 10466, 718 547-4695.

THOMAS, Lorna M.; '87 BS; 730 Linden Blvd. # 6, Brooklyn, NY 11203, 718 246-5999.

THOMAS, Marie-Maud '94 (See Dupoux, Mrs. Marie-Maud).

THOMAS, Melinda D.; '99 BS; 145-51 180th St., Jamaica, NY 11434, 718 712-6324.

THOMAS, Natacha; '97 BA; 104-20 199th St., Jamaica, NY 11412.

THOMAS, Peter L.; '87 BS; Emer Dept. Coord.; Mary Immaculate Hosp., 152-11 89th Ave., Jamaica, NY 11432, 718 558-2115; r. 92-33 245th St., Bellerose Terrace, NY 11001, 516 488-3599; *Wanda;* Melanie, Megan.

THOMAS, Rebecca A.; '78 BA; 149 W 140 St. #45, New York, NY 10030.

THOMAS, Regina P.; '84 BA; 652 Bauer Ct., Elmont, NY 11003, 516 327-2492.

THOMAS, Richard; '69 BS; 179-35 Anderson Rd, Jamaica, NY 11434, 718 318-0678.

THOMAS, Richard G.; '77 BA; 107 Great Oaks Ln., Roswell, GA 30075, 770 518-1781.

THOMAS, Robert J.; '81 BS; 7911 270th St., New Hyde Park, NY 11040, 516 771-4272.

THOMAS, Roxanne D.; '98 BS; 328 E 57 St., Brooklyn, NY 11203, 718 209-6969.

THOMAS, Trevor A.; '89 MPA; 1029 Rutland Rd Apt. 2-r, Brooklyn, NY 11212, 718 363-1211.

THOMAS, Umberto P.; '80 BS; 231 N Brookside Ave., Freeport, NY 11520.

THOMAS, Yvonne; '92 BS; 44-10 Ketcham St., Elmhurst, NY 11373, 716 789-3325.

THOMASON, Tamika; '99 BS; Housing Asst.; NYC Housing Authority; r. 144 W. 144 St. #5D, New York, NY 10030, 212 281-3536; Tanajah.

THOMPSON, Adam; '85 BA; Lawyer; Law Offices Adam M Thompson PC; r. 5 Beekman St. Rm 310, New York, NY 10038, 212 267-2424. e-mail

THOMPSON, Cecilia E.; '92 BA; 944 Nostrand Ave., Brooklyn, NY 11225, 718 452-2667.

THOMPSON, Donald E.; '79 BS; 47 E 58 St., Brooklyn, NY 11203, 718 857-7020.

THOMPSON, George C.; '82 BA; 2333 100th St., Flushing, NY 11369, 718 464-8270.

THOMPSON, Gregg W.; '93 BS; 374 Midwood St. # 4, Brooklyn, NY 11225, 718 642-4004.

THOMPSON, Janet A.; '85 BS; 2302 Strauss St., Brooklyn, NY 11212, 718 265-9553.

THOMPSON, Ms. Joan F.; '99 BA; Fraud Investigator; HRH/ORI, 30 Main St., Brooklyn, NY 11201; r. 631 E. 77th ST., Brooklyn, NY 11236.

THOMPSON, Julia E.; '83 BS; 831 W Payson Pkwy., Payson, AZ 85541, 520 474-4052.

THOMPSON, Kenneth; '89 BA; JD NYU; Fed. Prosecutor; US Attys. Ofc. Eastern Dist. NY, Brooklyn, NY 11201, 718 254-6459; r. Bronx, NY 10475. e-mail

THOMPSON, Kenneth V.; 909 Wheatridge Dr., Tucson, AZ 85704, 520 743-4192.

THOMPSON, Kristal Y.; '91 BA; 13419 166th Pl. Apt. 2g, Jamaica, NY 11434, 718 393-1125.

THOMPSON, Madelyn, (Madelyn Diotallevi); '81 BA; Regional Oper. Mgr.; Zurich American Ins., Chicago, IL 60606, 312 496-9010; r. 1485 Spero Ct., Wheaton, IL 60187, 630 588-1336; *Harold Sr;* Harold, Michael. e-mail

THOMPSON, Michele C.; '95 BS; 1314 Fteley Ave. # Fl.2, Bronx, NY 10472, 718 671-5498.

THOMPSON, Nedra A.; '99 BS; 368 Eastern Pkwy. 2C, Brooklyn, NY 11225, 718 493-0731.

THOMPSON, Rhonda D.; '81 BA; 116-51 157 St., Jamaica, NY 11434, 718 393-1125.

THOMPSON, Robert A.; '83 AS; 299 Foster Rd, Staten Island, NY 10309, 718 984-5406.

THOMPSON, Rory S.; '86 BA; 23-33 100th St., Flushing, NY 11369, 718 429-5596.

THOMPSON, Sally A.; '91 BS; 5 Red Mill Rd, Cortlandt Manor, NY 10567, 914 524-8380.

THOMPSON, Shirleen; '79 BS; 4033 De Reimer Ave., Bronx, NY 10466, 718 994-3065.

THOMPSON, Tanya N.; '78 BA; 11834 192nd St., Jamaica, NY 11412, 718 461-5190.

THOMPSON, Theda A.; '79 BS; 371 E 52 St., Brooklyn, NY 11203, 718 774-9283.

THOMPSON, Thomas J.; '85 BA; 3529 204th St., Flushing, NY 11361, 718 423-1350.

THOMPSON-CARVELLI, Amy E.; '93 BS; 118 S. Bridge St. #129, Rye Brook, NY 10573. e-mail

THORBS, Carlene O.; '89 BA; MA St. Johns Univ.; Retired Police Ofcr.; r. 145-01 116th Ave., Jamaica, NY 11436, 718 529-6424.

THORNTON, Craig C.; '93 BS; 8953 221st St., Queens Vlg., NY 11427, 718 726-2453.

THORNTON, Jenell; '97 BS; Caseworker; Admin. for Children's Svcs., City of New York; r. 544 Stone Ave., 1A, Brooklyn, NY 11212, 718 345-5772; Timothy, Shanita, Tyequane, Sa'Briyana, Winston. e-mail

THORPE, Geraldine G.; '82 MPA; 195 Willoughby Ave., Brooklyn, NY 11205, 718 797-2622.

THORPE, Jennifer J. '95 (See Jones-Thorpe, Jennifer J.).

THORPE, Leslie P.; '80 MA; 241 Lamberts Mill Rd, Westfield, NJ 07090.

THORPE, Richard W.; '84 MPA; 125 Russell St., Cornwall, NY 12518, 914 534-4007.

THORSON, Steven J.; '85 BA; MA Webster Univ.; Sr. Engr.; Camber Corp., Arlington, VA 22202; r. 1219 Poplar Rd, Stafford, VA 22554, 540 752-1814. e-mail

THOUPOS, Thomas; '85 MA; 2175 West St., Brooklyn, NY 11223.

THREAT, Reginald W.; '76 BS; 470 Malcolm X Blvd. Apt. 11c, New York, NY 10037.

THURNEAU, Robert D.; '76 AS; 9126 219th St., Queens Vlg., NY 11428, 718 740-4817.

TIBALDI, Thomas J.; '77 BS; 1325 Adee Ave., Bronx, NY 10469.

TIBBATTS, Eddie J.; '93 BS; 19b Edgewater Park, Bronx, NY 10465.

TIBURCIO, Rolando A.; '91 BS; 60 Division Ave. Apt. 6c, Brooklyn, NY 11211.

TICE, Harry A., III; '74 AS, '77 BS; Retired; r. 19 Crescent St., Bayville, NY 11709, 516 628-1877; *Garaldine.*

TIEDEMANN, LT James R.; '83 MPA; Lt.; West Chester Cnty. Police, Saw Mill River Pkwy., Hawthorne, NY 10532, 914 741-4400; r. POB 320, Hawthorne, NY 10532, 914 741-4400. e-mail

TIEFENWERTH, Thomas J.; '83 MA; MPS Long Island Univ., MPA Univ. of TX-Tyler; Psych/Admin.; UTMB-TDCJ Correctional Mang. Care, Skyview Psych Ctr., Hwy. 69, Rusk, TX 75785, 903 683-5781; r. 26 Woodbox Estates, Henderson, TX 75652, 903 657-3424; *Jana.* e-mail

TIERNEY, James M.; '78 MPA; 390 1st Ave. Apt. 13f, New York, NY 10010, 212 673-5489.

TIERNEY, Michael N.; '82 BS; Retired Police Sgt.; r. 17 Willow Ln., Irvington, NY 10533, 914 591-9744. e-mail

TIGHE, Michael R.; '87 MA; 672 Priscilla Pl., Seaford, NY 11783, 516 735-5142.

TILLETT, Vincent A.; '93 BA; Social Worker; Admin. for Children Svcs., 210 Jorlemon St., Brooklyn, NY 11201, 718 802-2301; r. 530 Parkside Ave., Brooklyn, NY 11226, 718 856-1184; *Julito, Gianni.*

TILLMAN, Robin '83 (See Baicher, Robin M.).

TIMONEY, Gavin J.; '78 BA; Court Ofcr.; NYS Courts, New York, NY 10001; r. 6660 80th St. Apt. 302, Apt. 302, Flushing, NY 11379, 718 326-4884.

TIMONEY, John F.; '74 BA; 225 S 18th St., Apt. 1008, Philadelphia, PA 19103.

TIMOTHY, John E.; '70 BS; 173 Beach 129th St., Far Rockaway, NY 11694.

TIMS, Claude D.; '75 BA; 191-02 110th Rd, Hollis, NY 11412.

TINGLIN, Morris C.; '85 BA; CEO; SNN News, 490 E. 28th St., Brooklyn, NY 11226, 718 230-7821; r. 490 E 28th St., Brooklyn, NY 11226, 718 230-7821; *Barbara;* Deanna, William.

TINSLEY, Clayton M.; '95; 151 W 75th St., Apt. D, New York, NY 10023.

TINSLEY, Wanda A. '91 (See James, Wanda A.).

TIPALDO, Joseph P.; '84 AS; 8653 24th Ave., Brooklyn, NY 11214.

TIPLITSKY, Steven T.; '78 BS; 800 Ocean Pkwy., Brooklyn, NY 11230.

TIRADO, Carol L.; '83 BS; 186 Claremont Ave., New York, NY 10027.

TIRADO, Donna; '84 MA; 8024 19th Ave., Brooklyn, NY 11214.

TIRADO, Lydia; '79 BS; 95-05 Jamaica Ave., Woodhaven, NY 11421, 718 296-5253.

TISCHLER, Jeffrey I.; '80 BA; MA Long Island Univ., MS Polytechnic Univ.; 2662 W 2nd St., Apt. 2A, Brooklyn, NY 11223, 718 648-6081. e-mail

TISDALE, Kristine A.; '96 BS; 166 Claremont St., Deer Park, NY 11729.

TITTERTON, James; '81 BA; 712 Premier Blvd., New Hyde Park, NY 11040.

TITUANA, Luis; '96 BS; 41-50 46th St. 2B, Sunnyside, NY 11104.

TITUS, Serina E.; '95 BA; 13726 159th St., Jamaica, NY 11434.

TJERIKO, Zelna; '90 BS; 2807 Sedgwick Ave., Bronx, NY 10468.

TOAL, Brian J.; '88 BA; 544 61st St., Brooklyn, NY 11220.

TOAL, Joseph V.; '76 BS; Pres.; Sergeants Benevolent Assn., 35 Worth St., New York, NY 10013, 212 226-2180; r. 1927 Gerritsen Ave., Brooklyn, NY 11229, 718 376-3394; *Joan.* e-mail

TOBIN, Eileen M.; '85 BA; Branch Ofc. Mgr.; Off-Track Betting; r. 3505 Decatur Ave., Bronx, NY 10467, 718 882-7646.

TOBIN, Erla; '94 MA; 310 Riverside Dr., New York, NY 10025.

TOBIN, James J.; '76 BS; Retired Detective; NYC Police Dept.; r. 265 Lyndale Ave., Staten Island, NY 10312.

TOBIN, John W.; '72 BS; 13621 N 51st Pl., Scottsdale, AZ 85254, 602 996-6192.

TOBIN, Joseph X.; '87 BA; 899 Union St., Brooklyn, NY 11215, 718 622-0537.

TOBIN, Patricia E.; '80 BS; 1421-42nd St., Brooklyn, NY 11219, 718 435-5837.

TOCCI, Daniel L.; '98 BS; 42 Wilstan Ave., Patchogue, NY 11772, 631 758-9688.

TOCCI, Steven C.; '91 BS; 560 73rd St., Brooklyn, NY 11209, 718 748-6075.

TOCCO, Stephen M.; '96; 54 Hitchcock Ave., Staten Island, NY 10306, 718 667-5868.

TOCKER, Leonard H.; '83 BS, '92 MA; Paralegal Cert.; Sr. Investigator; NYS Ins. Fraud Bur., 25 Beaver St., New York, NY 10004, 212 480-5893; r. 550 G Grand St., #1F, New York, NY 10002; *Dena;* Benjamin, Daniel, Ruth. e-mail

TODD, Michael A.; '84 BA; 3531 Kingsland Ave., Bronx, NY 10469, 718 405-5863.

TODD, Myra; '81 BS, '85 MA; 1625 President St. Apt. 3f, Brooklyn, NY 11213, 718 748-2220.

TODOROVA, Yeleina V.; '98 BS; Paralegal; r. 468 Avenue Y, 3rd Fl., Brooklyn, NY 11223, 718 336-6667.

TODOROVIC, Jelica; '96 BA; Exec. Svc. Coord.; The New York Palace, 455 Madison Ave., New York, NY 10022, 212 303-7768; r. 1583 Crescent Dr., Tarrytown, NY 10591, 914 333-0188. e-mail

TODRAS, Jay P.; '81 BA; 92 Stebbins Ave., Tuckahoe, NY 10707.

TOLEDO, Pedro; '93 BS; 601 40th St. Apt. A10, Brooklyn, NY 11232, 718 567-7185.

TOLEDO, Richard; '93 BS; 601 40th St. Apt. A10, Brooklyn, NY 11232, 718 567-7185.

TOLENTINO, Thomas N.; '71 BS; 453 Emory Rd, Mineola, NY 11501.

TOLER, Theodore E.; '76 BA; Box 51, Comstock, NY 12821.

TOLIVER, Vonda; '96 BA; 77 Riverdale Ave., Brooklyn, NY 11212, 718 498-7760.

TOMALA, Jeannette; '96 BA; 600 W.204th St., New York, NY 10034, 212 567-4081.

TOMASHOSKY, Eugene; '95 BS; 6660 Lino Rd, Venice, FL 34286.

TOMASSI, Garrett P.; '76 BS; 8415 60th Ave., Elmhurst, NY 11373.

TOMASSO, Nicholas F.; '75 BS, '81 MPA; Court Ofcr.; Nassau Cnty. Ct., 262 Old Country Rd., Mineola, NY 11501, 516 571-2745; r. 208 Walnut St., Lynbrook, NY 11563, 516 596-0138.

TOMBACK, Daniel M.; '99 BA; Fraud Investigator; HRA City of NY, 180 Water St., New York, NY 10038, 212 630-9756; r. 1765 E 19th St., Brooklyn, NY 11229, 718 336-0469. e-mail

TOMCZAK, Jill; '89 BS; 474 48th Ave., Long Island City, NY 11109.

TOMLIN, Sheila M.; '93 BA; 902 Drew St., Apt. 355, Brooklyn, NY 11208, 718 235-7781.

TOMLINSON, Mrs. Beatrice E.; '77 BA; Assoc. Court Clerk; New York State Supreme Ct. First Dept., 60 Center St., New York, NY 10007; r. 29 Moore St. Apt. 13t, Brooklyn, NY 11206; Michael, Nikki. e-mail

TOMLINSON, Camille E.; '96 BS; AA Queensborough Comm Clg.; Caseworker; HRA, 89-61 162nd St., Jamaica, NY 11432, 718 297-5702; r. 77 Seymour Ln., Medford, NY 11763, 631 732-4559; Kennedy Kerr. e-mail

TOMLINSON, Jodi L.; '97 BA; 36 John St., Patchogue, NY 11772.

TOMLINSON, Kenneth; '95 BS; 1326 142nd St., Whitestone, NY 11357.

TOMPKINS, Gail H.; '77 BA; PHD North Central Univ., CERT MA The City Clg. of NY; Psychologist-Sch.; G.H. Tompkins Cnsltg. Svc., PO B 151, Beacon, NY 12508, 914 440-0390; r. POB 151, Beacon, NY 12508. e-mail

TONER, Vincent E.; '75 BA; 82-29 Pettit Ave., Elmhurst, NY 11373.

TONG, Patrick Y.; '90 BS, '93 MPA; 86-05 58th Ave., Elmhurst, NY 11373.

TOOHEY, John J.; '82 BS; Ret Chief of Fire Prevention; City of NY, New York City Fire Dept.; r. 4 Barbara Rd, New City, NY 10956; *Mary;* Maryann M., Kathleen R.

TOOLSEE, Drupatie R. '98 (See Ganpat, Mrs. Drupatie R.).

TOORIE, Paula A.; '91 BS; 254 E Fulton Ave., Roosevelt, NY 11575.

TOORIE, Trudy A.; '88 BS; 254 E Fulton Ave., Roosevelt, NY 11575.

TOPP, Viviane M.; '94 CERT; 170 W. End Ave., New York, NY 10023.

TOPPIN, Douglas J.; '95 BS; 1050 Decatur St. Apt. 2, Brooklyn, NY 11207, 718 940-9752.

TORLISH, Helena; '97 BA, '99 BS; 37 Thompson St., Raritan, NJ 08869.

TORNETTI, Frank J.; '95 AS; Police Ofcr.; New York Police Dept., Brooklyn, NY 11235, 718 946-3311; r. 178 Bay 28th St., Brooklyn, NY 11214, 718 449-1345.

TORO, Eric; '84 BA; MS New Sch. Univ., CRFP Yale Sch. of Mgmt.; Pres. & Partner; E. Toro & Assocs., 1968 Ellis Ave., Bronx, NY 10472, 718 828-4674; r. same; *Rebecca;* Adam, Lauren. e-mail

TORO, Miriam; '96 BA; 130 W. 228th St., Bronx, NY 10463, 718 792-2176.

TORO, Salvador; '89 BS; 114-20 Queens Blvd., Forest Hills, NY 11375, 718 721-0899.

TORO, Zacarias; '95 BA; 573 Grand St. Apt. 707, New York, NY 10002, 315 797-9123.

TORRENCE, Lorna Y.; '77 BS; 835 Riverside Dr., New York, NY 10032, 212 927-2182.

TORRENCE, Sandra E.; '96; 420 E. 111 St., New York, NY 10029.

TORRENS, Mark A.; '95 BA; 8400 Blvd. E Apt. 2A, N. Bergen, NJ 07047.

TORRES, Advendizo; '91 BS; 186 Richards St., Brooklyn, NY 11231, 718 253-3088.

TORRES, Alejandra, (Alejandra Trigo); '95 BS; Tchr.; r. 7242 61st St., Flushing, NY 11385, 718 381-3186; *Humberto;* Roxanna, Steven, Bryan. e-mail

TORRES, Allison; '97 BS; 3296 Perry Ave.2A, Bronx, NY 10467, 718 328-3921.

TORRES, Ana D.; '86 BS; JD CUNY Law Sch.; Atty.; Catholic Guardian Society, 1990 Westchester Ave., Bronx, NY 10462, 718 828-0300; r. 1969 McGraw Ave. Apt. 7D, Bronx, NY 10462, 718 931-1922; Samantha.

TORRES, Anibal; '81 BA; MS SCSU; Supervisory Criminal Inv.; ATF, USCH BATF Rm. 607, Philadelphia, PA 19106, 215 597-7266; r. 5 Tidewater Ln., Marlton, NJ 08053, 609 723-4940; *Tammy;* David, Natalie, Nelson.

TORRES, Candy; '93 BS; 80 E 110th St. # 10, New York, NY 10029, 212 427-6649.

TORRES, Mrs. Cecilia A., (Cecilia A. Sadowski); '82 BS; Security Operations Mgr.; SN Apparel, a Div. of Jag USA Inc., 11201 Armour Dr., El Paso, TX 79935, 915 633-0056; r. 3400 Hickman St., El Paso, TX 79936, 915 595-0348; *Javier.* e-mail

TORRES, Daisy '98 (See Lopez, Daisy).

TORRES, Damaris E.; '97 BS; 50 Avenue D 13F, New York, NY 10009, 212 387-7775.

TORRES, David; '86 BA; 21 Deepdale Dr., Brentwood, NY 11717.

TORRES, Dennisa A.; '94 BS; Atty.; The Legal Aid Society, Livingston St., Brooklyn, NY 11201, 718 243-6896; r. 1865 Gates Ave., Ridgewood, NY 11385, 718 456-2492. e-mail

TORRES, Donald; '72 MA; 4 Montgomery, Montville, NJ 07045.

TORRES, Eduardo; '87 BS; 4134 Wickham Ave., Bronx, NY 10466, 718 992-7762.

TORRES, Elizabeth; '97 BA; 34 Ray St., Freeport, NY 11520.

TORRES, Eriberto; '94 AS; 154 Highland Blvd., Brooklyn, NY 11207, 718 277-5059.

TORRES, Ernest; '77 BS; 13 Beach St., Mt. Vernon, NY 10550, 716 839-2597.

TORRES, Evelyn '93 (See Torres-Parks, Mrs. Evelyn).

TORRES, Fernando; '99 BA; 33-37 154St #2, Flushing, NY 11354, 718 323-0374.

TORRES, Frank P.; '81 BA; 779 Riverside Dr., New York, NY 10032.

TORRES, Gerardo; '99 BA; 50 Davenport Ave#2C, New Rochelle, NY 10805, 914 278-9315.

TORRES, Hector L.; '95 AS, '97 BA; 2287 Mott Ave. Apt. 4b, Far Rockaway, NY 11691, 718 471-2058.

TORRES, Ivette; '91 BS; 681 Courtlandt Ave., Bronx, NY 10451, 718 329-9809.

TORRES, Jeanette; '82 BS; 310 5th Ave., Brooklyn, NY 11215, 718 238-0727.

TORRES, Jeanette F.; '92 BS; 21810 103rd Ave., Queens Vlg., NY 11429, 718 205-6725.

TORRES, Jesus; '75 AS; 2150 Crestn Ave. #6A, Bronx, NY 10453, 718 328-0903.

TORRES, Jesus; '95 BS; 25-46 89th St., Jackson Hts., NY 11369, 718 205-6725.

TORRES, Katherine; '96 BS; 1 Maplewood Rd, Hartsdale, NY 10530, 914 278-9315.

TORRES, Lissette; '95 AS, '97 BS; 261 E. Kingsbridge, Bronx, NY 10458, 718 515-1071.

TORRES, Manuel; '91 BS; 27 Demarest Ave., W. Nyack, NY 10994, 914 627-0604.

TORRES, Marybell; '82 BS; 50 Manhattan Ave. #6G, Brooklyn, NY 11206, 718 439-5349.

TORRES, Michelle; '89 BA; 3231 202nd St., Flushing, NY 11361, 718 939-9363.

TORRES, Milly '96 (See Mendez, Mrs. Milly).

TORRES, Nelson; '88 BA; 13 Morris Rd., Garrison, NY 10524.

TORRES, Peter E.; '82 BA; Atty.; 12 E. 23rd St., Ste. 500, New York, NY 10010, 917 312-3169; r. 2241 1st Ave. # 1, New York, NY 10029.

TORRES, Ricardo; '98 BA; MSW Hunter Grad. Sch. SW; Sch. Social Worker; NYC Bd. of Educ., New York, NY 10001; r. 145 Fourth Ave. #12 L, New York, NY 10003, 212 505-1759; *Elvera Carrera;* Mario.

TORRES, Talia C., (Talia C. Cruz); '99 BS; AA Hostos Community Clg.; Youth Employment Dir.; Madison Square Boys & Girls Club, 1665 Hoe Ave., Bronx, NY 10460, 718 328-3900; r. 1933 Daly Ave. #51, Bronx, NY 10460, 718 860-2921; *Wilfredo;* Wilfredo Jr. e-mail

TORRES, Tanya I.; '99 BA; 762 Brady Ave. Apt. 521, Bronx, NY 10462, 718 547-6549.

TORRES, Vilma T.; '81 BS; MSW Hunter Clg. Sch. of SW; Prog. Mgr.; Victims Svcs., 210 Joralemon St., Brooklyn, NY 11201, 718 834-6688; r. 33-45 Murray St., Flushing, NY 11354.

TORRES-HERNANDEZ, Maritza; '98 BA; 443 51 St. 2, Brooklyn, NY 11220, 718 492-2502.

TORRES-PARKS, Mrs. Evelyn, (Evelyn Torres); '93 BS; Probation Ofcr.; Rockland Cnty. Probation Dept., 11 New Hempstead Rd, New City, NY 10956, 914 638-5514; r. 3 Albacon Rd, Nanuet, NY 10954, 914 426-1478; *Michael Parks;* Jazmin, Chelsea.

TORRETTA, Michael V.; '80 BS; 1412 31st Ave., Long Island City, NY 11106, 718 932-1721.

TORTORA, Joseph; '88 MPA; 6 Willow Rd, Beacon, NY 12508, 914 831-7658.

TORUN, Aydin N.; '84 BA; Clerk; The Strand Book Store, 828 Broadway, New York, NY 10003, 212 473-1452; r. 98-30 67th Ave. Apt. 6-S, Flushing, NY 11374, 718 896-5225.

TOSADO, Mariveila; '88 BA; MSED Hunter Clg.; PhD Candidate; SUNY Albany; r. 2568 Western Ave. #3-18, Altamont, NY 12009, 518 355-2582. e-mail

TOSCANO, Daisy E.; '85 BS; 1039 86th St., Brooklyn, NY 11228, 718 384-5567.

TOSCANO, Stephen M.; '85 BA; 1039 86th St., Brooklyn, NY 11228, 718 384-5567.

TOULON, Anthony S.; '85 AS; 800 Concourse Vill, Bronx, NY 10451.

TOUSSAINT, Barbara; '99 BS; Student; Long Island Univ.; r. 135 Ocean Ave. 4D, Brooklyn, NY 11225, 718 282-1564; *Claudy Brutus;* Melissah Brutus.

TOUSSAINT, Emmanuel; '99 BA; 193-14 100th Ave., Hollis, NY 11423, 718 740-8522. e-mail

TOUSSAINT, Leveque; '91 BS; Law Clerk/JD Candidate; Naimark & Tannenbaum, 169-95 137th Ave., Jamaica, NY 11434, 718 528-3700; r. 138-02 90th Ave., Jamaica, NY 11435, 718 658-5290. e-mail

TOUWSMA, Geo J.; '62 MPA; 383 Andrews Rd, Mineola, NY 11501, 516 294-6920.

TOW, Dean O.; '89 MA; 160 Front St. Apt. 3D, New York, NY 10038, 315 839-5161.

TOW, Jonathan L.; '94 BA; Mgr.; Aamco Transmissions, 200 E Merrick Rd., Valley Stream, NY 11580, 516 872-8122; r. 31 Skyview Pl., Melville, NY 11747, 631 425-5944; *Laurie.*

TOWNER, Andrew T.; '75 BS; 80 Pearsall Pl., Deer Park, NY 11729.

TOWNS, Henry; '92 AS; 1540 E 102nd St. Apt. 6d, Brooklyn, NY 11236.

TOWNS, Suzanne; '96 BA; Student; r. 3083 44th St. Apt. 3, Astoria, NY 11103, 718 278-0677.

TOWNSEND, Michael C.; '93 BA, '97 MA; Quality Assurance Coord.; Gateway Counseling Ctr., 4500 Furman Ave., Bronx, NY 10470, 718 325-5021; r. 12227 26th Ave., Flushing, NY 11354, 718 461-6109. e-mail

TOZZI, Thomas J.; '85 BS; 42 Colling Ave., Rochelle Park, NJ 07662, 201 843-1489.

TOZZO, James J.; 42-39 191 St., Flushing, NY 11358.

TRACY, John C.; '92 BA HON; AS Palm Beach Jr. Clg.; Correctional Ofcr.; NYS, Staten Island, NY 10314; r. 83 Canton Ave., Staten Island, NY 10312, 718 967-2334.

TRACY, Peter; '85 BS; 100 Junard Dr., Bay Shore, NY 11706.

TRAGER, Leonard; '75 BS; 3124 Messick Ave., Oceanside, NY 11572, 516 536-6181.

TRAIL, Robert L.; '98 BA; US Pretrial Svcs. Ofcr.; US Pretrial Svcs. Agcy., 500 Pearl St., New York, NY 10007, 212 805-4146; r. 6 Sealy Ave., #3f, Hempstead, NY 11550.

TRAINOR, Patrick J.; '95 MPA; BA Fordham Univ.; Special Agt.; DEA, 600 Arch St., Philadelphia, PA 19106, 215 861-3474; r. 1815 John F Kennedy Blvd., Apt. 1619, Philadelphia, PA 19103, 215 761-9023.

TRAKAS, Arthur G.; '77 MA; BA SUNY-Stony Brook, JD Univ. of Bridgeport; Atty.; Arthur G Trakas & Assoc., 34-19 Broadway Lic, Long Island City, NY 11106, 718 721-7171; r. 47 Shortridge Dr., Mineola, NY 11501, 516 248-0636; *Karen;* Andrew, Lauren. e-mail

TRAMONTANA, G.; '96 BS; 157-54 95 St. #, Jamaica, NY 11414.

TRAMUTO, Mrs. Andrea E., (Andrea E. Deceilio); '98 MA; Sr. Forensic Caseworker; Chautauqua Cnty. Dept. of Mental Health, 7 N. Erie St., Mayville, NY 14757, 716 753-4550; r. 35 Castile Dr., Fredonia, NY 14063; *Jeffrey.* e-mail

TRANCHINA, Gregory; '92 MA; 60 Kilburn Rd # S., W. Hempstead, NY 11552, 516 742-5973.

TRAUSE, Victoria; '97 MA; BA Montclair State Univ.; Substance Abuse Couns.; Straight & Narrow, 508 Straight St., Paterson, NJ 07503, 973 345-6000; r. 442 Ridgewood Blvd. N., Westwood, NJ 07675, 201 664-5494. e-mail

TRAUTMANN, S.; '95 MA; 165 Twin Arch Rd., Rock Tavern, NY 12575, 914 355-2184.

TRAVERS, Richard A.; '73 BS; 50 Jerusalem Ave., Levittown, NY 11756, 516 731-3870.

TRAVIS, Jody A.; '97 MA; P.O.Box 214, Ilion, NY 13357.

TREACY, Daniel J.; 1834 New York Ave., Brooklyn, NY 11210, 718 377-7480.

TREANOR, William P.; '74 BA; AAS Bronx Comm. Clg.; Dispatcher; NYCFD, 1129 E 180th St., Bronx, NY 10461, 718 430-0200; r. 98 Bay St., Bronx, NY 10464, 718 885-0648; *Bridget;* William Jr., Michael, Steven.

TREIBLE, Roy D.; '89 BA; 50 Noblehurst Ave., Pittsfield, MA 01201.

TRELLES, Henry X.; '99 BA; Police Ofcr.; NYPD; r. 348 48th St., Brooklyn, NY 11220, 718 439-5172; *Francesca,* Alexis. e-mail

TRENCA, Michael P.; '96 BS; 302 Elbow Rd, Syracuse, NY 13212.

TRENT, Rachel S.; '99 BA; POB 1081, Chatham, NJ 07928, 973 635-2127.

TRENTACOSTA, Dena M. '95 (See Trentacosta-Rosado, Dena M.).

TRENTACOSTA-ROSADO, Dena M., (Dena M. Trentacosta); '95 BS; Correctional Ofcr.; Fed. Bur. of Prisons, Metropolitan Detention Ctr., 100 29th St., Brooklyn, NY 11232, 718 840-4200; r. 24 Mystic Cir., Bay Shore, NY 11706, 516 429-2568.

TREPPIEDI, Rocco N.; '75 BS; 5008 W Navaho Ave., Spokane, WA 99208, 509 466-7415.

TREVELLIAN, Christine; '96 BS; 244 Decatur St. # 3, Brooklyn, NY 11233.

TREYVUS, Kira; '99 BA; Student; Brooklyn Law Sch.; r. 2325 Ocean Ave. 3G, Brooklyn, NY 11229, 718 645-3573.

TRIARSI, Emmanuel; '80 BA; 29 Pouch Ter., Staten Island, NY 10305.

TRICARDO, Dominick; '96 BA; 125 Dahlgren Pl., Brooklyn, NY 11228.

TRICE, Leona '91 (See Trice Williams, Ms. Leona).

TRICE WILLIAMS, Ms. Leona, (Leona Trice); '91 MPA; Probation Ofcr.; NYC Dept. of Probation, 162-24 Jamaica Ave., Jamaica, NY 11432, 718 658-5323; r. 197 Swalm St., Westbury, NY 11590, 516 334-8258; *Michael;* Komieko.

TRICOMI, Carolyn; '71; 200 E 89th St., New York, NY 10128.

TRIEBE, Michael; '90 BA; 8419 55th Rd, Flushing, NY 11373.

TRIEBEL, Erika M.; '98 BS, '98 BA; 2375 Ocean Ave., #5g, Brooklyn, NY 11229.

TRIEBWASSER, Jonah, Esq.; '71, '72 BS; AA, JD New York Law Sch.; Sr. Atty.; NYS Dept. of Environ. Conservation, 21 S. Putt Corners Rd., New Paltz, NY 12561, 914 256-3030; r. 85 Manor Rd, Red Hook, NY 12571, 914 758-8206; *Ellen;* Thomas, Alison. e-mail

TRIFFON, George E.; '97 BS, '98 BS; 155 W. 81 St. #5j, New York, NY 10024, 212 877-4914.

TRIGNANO, Marcia V., (Marcia Vergillo); '78 MA; Technology Spec. in Ins.; Traveler Ins. Grp.; r. 17 Jaqui Ave., Morris Plains, NJ 07950, 973 539-1765; *William;* Marc. e-mail

TRIGO, Alejandra '95 (See Torres, Alejandra).

TRILLO, Ismael; '78 BS; Park Ranger; City of Ft. Lauderdale, 1200 Gh Martin Dr., Ft. Lauderdale, FL 33304, 954 468-1634; r. 12196 Quilting Ln., Boca Raton, FL 33428, 561 451-2894. e-mail

TRINIDAD, Evelyn; '98 BA; Student; Hunter Clg.; r. 390 E. 162 St., #2b, Bronx, NY 10451, 718 402-7992.

TRINIDAD, Linda M.; '98 BS; Researcher; CCH Corsearch, 28 W. 23rd St., New York, NY 10010, 212 627-0330; r. 960 E. 163rd St. #4B, Bronx, NY 10459, 718 542-8785. e-mail

TRIOLA, Michael; '89 BS; 300 Kirkman Ave., Elmont, NY 11003.

TRIOLO, Bobbi A.; '95 MA; 33 Leonhard Dr., Haledon, NJ 07508.

TRIPI, Anthony F.; '88 BS; Owner; Message Therapy Ctr., Healthy Bodyworks, 911 Union St., Brooklyn, NY 11215, 718 230-7933; r. 223 Berkeley Pl., Brooklyn, NY 11217, 718 622-0974. e-mail

TRIPP, Peter G.; '89 BA; Lt.; NY City Fire Dept.; r. 3 Strong Ave., Babylon, NY 11702, 631 669-2968.

TRIPPEDO, Donna M.; '99 BS; 501 Pelham Rd., New Rochelle, NY 10805, 914 633-4137.

TRIPPLIN, Crystal L.; '87 BS; 11027 196th St., Jamaica, NY 11412.

TROIS, Robert F.; '99 AS; 280 Rte. 303N, Congers, NY 10920, 914 268-9693.

TROISI, Alfred R.; '74 MA; 2951 W 8 St. 60 Pct, Brooklyn, NY 11224.

TRONOLONE, Susan L.; '85 BA; 1017 74th St., Brooklyn, NY 11228.

TROTMAN, Deborah '77 (See Kinnebrew, Deborah).

TROTTER, John; 10438 93rd Ave., Jamaica, NY 11418.

TROTTER, Lee E.; '83 BS; 8815 Ashford St., Queens Vlg., NY 11427, 718 736-1435.

TROUPE, William D.; '170-20 130 Ave., Jamaica, NY 11434.

TROVILLOT, Claude; '99 BS; 200 W. 81st St. #52, New York, NY 10024.

TROY, Jacqueline D.; '99; 81 Park St., Centereach, NY 11720.

TROYANSKY, Eugene; '96 BA; Police Detective; r. 25 Market St., POB 085, Trenton, NJ 08611, 609 984-6500.

TRUITT, James F.; '96 BS, '99 MPA; AAS Dutchess Community Clg.; Police Ofcr.; Town of Poughkeepsie Police Dept., 19 Tucker Dr., Poughkeepsie, NY 12603, 914 485-3666; r. 161 Roosevelt Rd., Hyde Park, NY 12538, 914 229-2303. e-mail

TRUITT, John; '85 MA; BED Univ. of Miami; Retired; r. POB 141772, Coral Gables, FL 33114, 305 232-7354; *Nancy;* Gregory H., John A. (Dec.), Victoria R., Teresa Timmons.

TRULLI, Christine; '92 BS, '94 MA; 75 Clinton St., Brooklyn, NY 11201.

TRUMMER, Brian J.; '85 BS; 11 Lakeview Dr., N. Salem, NY 10560.

TRUONG, Dan; '96 BS; 233 Henry St. #, New York, NY 10002.

TRUSTY, Beshon; '96 AS, '98 BA, '98 BA; 14-10 New Haven Ave. #R103, Far Rockaway, NY 11691, 718 291-7592.

TRUTA, John J.; '69 MPA; 14423 Charter Rd, Jamaica, NY 11435, 718 591-2515.

TRUZZOLINO, John W.; 586 Lincoln Ave., W. Hempstead, NY 11552.

TSAI, Jeffrey; '95 BA; 3416 148th St., Flushing, NY 11354, 718 888-9553.

TSANG, David; '93 BS, '97 MPA; Fraud Investigator; City of NY, Ofc. of Revenue & Investigations, 330 J St., Brooklyn, NY 11201, 718 237-6407; r. 41-18 Bedford Ave. 1Fl., Brooklyn, NY 11229, 718 769-7320.

TSANG, Hitomi T.; '99 BA; 2 Eldridge St., New York, NY 10002, 212 925-3581.

TSANG, Wing C.; '97 BS. e-mail

TSEKOURAS, Fay F.; '98 BA; 193 06 42 Ave., Flushing, NY 11358, 718 357-7805.

TSENG, Chih H.; '95 BS; 1239 Avenue V, Brooklyn, NY 11229.

TSEVDOS, Stefanos; '95 BA; BA, AAS KCC; Sales Mktg Mgr ; Bells Security Inc , 501 fifth Ave. Ste. 501, New York, NY 10017, 212 867-7500; r. 7306 Ridge Blvd., Brooklyn, NY 11209, 718 491-3106. e-mail

TSIAMES, Nicholas B.; '93 BS; 3074 50th St., Flushing, NY 11377, 718 274-5095.

TSO, Yee B.; '86 BA; 664 4th Ave., Brooklyn, NY 11232, 718 965-1397.

TSUJI, Marian E.; '83 MA; BA Long Island Univ.-CW Post; Deputy Dir. for Corrections; State of Hawaii, Dept. of Public Safety, 919 Ala Moana Blvd., Honolulu, HI 96814, 808 587-1340; r. 1001 Wilder Ave. Apt. 702, Honolulu, HI 96822, 808 524-2629; *David.* e-mail

TTLEY, Sheila A.; '97 BS; 841 Gates Ave., Brooklyn, NY 11221.

TUASON, Aleli P.; '98 BA; 70 Bevan St., Jersey City, NJ 07306, 201 795-3027.

TUBRIDY, Daniel J.; 15-05 Cross Bay Blvd., Broad Channel, NY 11693.

TUCCIARONE, Theodore; 13 4 Ave., Massapequa Park, NY 11762.

TUCK, Christopher C.; '96 BS; 2400 E Las Olas Blvd., # 326, Ft. Lauderdale, FL 33301.

TUCK, Stephen J.; '80 BA; MA Queens Clg.; Tchr.; IS125, 46-02 47th Ave., Woodside, NY 11377, 718 937-0320; r. 7716 86th St., Glendale, NY 11385, 718 850-3108. e-mail

TUCKER, Amber R.; '94 BA; POB 704, Bronx, NY 10469, 718 293-3759.

TUCKER, Bonita C.; '76 BS; CERT Nat Inst. Paralegal Trn; Property Mgr.; Dekalb Cnty. Housing Authority, 3218 Tobie Cir., Scottdale, GA 30079, 404 292-2400; r. 1422 Kelsworth Cir., Atlanta, GA 30349, 770 907-9512; Dana. e-mail

TUCKER, Darlene; '97 BS; Paralegal; AIG, 70 Pine St., New York, NY 10270, 212 770-6546; r. 2045 Story Ave. #4, Bronx, NY 10473. e-mail

TUCKER, Elizabeth H. '94 (See Mertz, Mrs. Elizabeth H.).

TUCKER, Julia E.; '75 MA; 77-61 78th St., Glendale, NY 11385, 718 591-1642.

TUCKER, Thomas A.; '82 MA; 78 Ditmars Ave., Trenton, NJ 08648.

TUDORIU, Opritsa E.; '99 BS; 3390 Wayne Ave. #G31, Bronx, NY 10467, 718 652-5773.

TUFFEY, Thomas V.; '89 MPA; JD Brooklyn Law Sch., BA Iona Clg.; Sergeant NYC Police Dept. & Atty.; NYC Police Dept., 1 Police Plz., New York, NY 10038, 212 374-5400; r. 50-48 245th St., Douglaston, NY 11362, 718 224-2516; Diane; Claire, Michael.

TULLER, James; '79 BS; 8901 87th St., Jamaica, NY 11421, 718 850-6948.

TULLEY, Dionne; '97 BS; Business Owner; We Manifest Productions, Brooklyn, NY 11201, 718 302-0309; r. 30 Montrose Ave. #4-T, Brooklyn, NY 11206, 718 302-1906; Tajh Danielle, Koyami Saiyd.

TULLO, James T.; '82 BS; Retired Police Ofcr.; N.Y.P.D.; r. 846 59th St. Apt. 2, Brooklyn, NY 11220, 718 438-0531.

TULLOCH, Macola A.; '99 BA; Security Ofcr.; Mandel Security, 29-28 41st Ave., Attn Security Ext. 101, Long Island City, NY 11101, 718 349-9100; r. 97-29 106th St. 2nd Fl., Ozone Park, NY 11416, 718 846-8169.

TULLOCH, Natalie T.; '98 BA; 191 50 114 Dr., St. Albans, NY 11412, 718 465-6985.

TULLOCH, Taneese T.; '99 BS; 3747 Olinville Ave., # 1, Bronx, NY 10467, 718 231-1182.

TULLY, Joanne M.; '78 BS; 140-22 Poplar Ave., Flushing, NY 11355, 718 224-8886.

TULLY, Rachel; '97 BA; Tchr.; Our Lady of Refuge, E 196 Briggs Ave., Bronx, NY 10461; r. 675 E. 234th St. 1-H, Bronx, NY 10466, 718 324-2659; Angel Lopez.

TULY, Beth M.; '96 BA; 19 Oakwood Ter., Spring Vly., NY 10977.

TUMASAR, Diane M.; '97 BA; Ofc. Mgr.; Standard Intl. Grp., 730 Fifth Ave., Ste. 900, New York, NY 10019, 212 307-3167; r. 115-21 114 Pl., S. Ozone Park, NY 11420, 718 843-9702. e-mail

TUNCA, Ms. Yasemin N.; '96 BA, '99 MA; Child Protection Spec.; Westminster Station for Children's Svcs., 425 Adams St., Brooklyn, NY 11201, 718 522-8236; r. 2 Webster Ave. Apt. 3g, Brooklyn, NY 11230, 718 854-0919.

TUNG, Nelson; '91 BS; 715 Elo St., Brooklyn, NY 11230, 718 256-3651.

TUOHY, Patrick; '97 BS; 20 Drake Ln., Kings Park, NY 11754.

TURBEE, Patricia A.; '80 BA; MA Polytech; Retired; r. 10990 200th St., Jamaica, NY 11412, 718 740-0491; Frederic; Frederic Jr, Michael Andrew.

TURBETT, William F.; '77 BS; 836 S Park Ave., Linden, NJ 07036, 908 486-5431.

TURBIAK, Robert J.; '78 BA; 299 Lamberts Ln., Staten Island, NY 10314, 570 685-4323.

TURCIC, Stefanie; '90 BS; 1509 Westervelt Ave., Baldwin, NY 11510, 516 379-9024.

TURCO, Angelo J.; '72 BS; 51 Burns Pl. #3C, Briarcliff Manor, NY 10510, 914 241-7694.

TURKIYA, Vladimir A.; '96 BS; 759 E. 10th St., Brooklyn, NY 11230.

TURNAGE, Tywanna C.; '99 BS; 1419 Shakespeare Ave. 2H, Bronx, NY 10452, 718 293-1782.

TURNBULL, Berris A.; '82 BS; Police Ofcr.-Retired; r. 1511 Brook Hollow Dr., Orlando, FL 32824, 407 859-1594; Mattie; Jacqueline, Ogaard, Tisha.

TURNER, Al; '70 MPA; Treasury F.L.E.T.C, Glynco, GA 31520, 912 265-1120.

TURNER, Andrea L.; '91 BS; 1384 Pacific St. # B, Brooklyn, NY 11216, 718 735-3933.

TURNER, Andrew C.; '99 MA; 413 E 81st St., Apt. 3A, New York, NY 10028, 315 336-5989.

TURNER, Candia; '97 BA; 138-16 232nd St., Jamaica, NY 11413, 718 276-8726.

TURNER, Gerard; '96 BA; 19 W 76th St. Apt. 1bw, New York, NY 10023.

TURNER, Joseph A.; '97 BA; 2968 Perry Ave. 5E, Bronx, NY 10458, 718 881-6931.

TURNER, Joseph P.; '75 BS; AS BS, MPA C.W. Post; Retired Sergeant; NYC Police Dept., 1 Police Plz., New York, NY 10038; r. 25117 Meriweather Rd, Leesburg, FL 34748, 352 326-4096.

TURNER, Michele; '97 BS; 46 Marian Ct. Ph, Warwick, NY 10990, 914 557-6392.

TURNER, Michelle A.; '95 BS; 10111 Remington St., Jamaica, NY 11435, 718 739-2650.

TURNER, Mrs. Regina, (Croswell Regina); '92 BS; Bus Operator; Mabstoa, 370 Jay St., Brooklyn, NY 11210, 800 367-2884; r. 663 Howard Ave. Apt. 1B, Brooklyn, NY 11212, 718 922-5218; Alvin; Ladrius. e-mail

TURNER, Tinaddine N.; '96 BA; Hunter Clg.; Caseworker; Admin. for Children's Svcs., 150 Williams St., New York, NY 10038, 212 676-7249; r. 1554 E. 45th St., Brooklyn, NY 11234, 718 258-4863.

TURSCHMANN, Michelle '98 (See Villani, Michelle T.).

TUSA, Paul; '78 BA; 195 St. Nicholas, Brooklyn, NY 11237.

TUSA, Philip P.; '82 BA; 6723 14th Ave. #2R, Brooklyn, NY 11219.

TUTANI, Sidney; '95 BS; 98-23 Horace Hrdng, Corona, NY 11368.

TUTINO, Barbara J.; '90 BS, '96 MA; 2068 27th St. Apt. 3a, Long Island City, NY 11105, 718 224-9720.

TWINAME, John J.; '81 BS; 1 Mars Ct., Smithtown, NY 11787.

TWOMEY, Dennis; '85 MPA, '85 BA; JD CUNY Law Sch Queen's Clg.; Asst. DA; Queens Cnty. New York, Kew Gardens, NY 11415; r. 14739 16th Rd, Whitestone, NY 11357.

TWU, Yu-jeng; '94 MA; 3455 Crescent St., Long Island City, NY 11106.

TYLER, Brian D.; '95 MPA; 331 E 188th St., Bronx, NY 10458.

TYLER, Edward J.; '70 MPA; RD 3, E. Harwich, MA 02645.

TYLER, Trent S.; '85 BA; 131 Lincoln Rd #3F, Brooklyn, NY 11225, 718 782-1653.

TYNES, Harcourt A., III; '88 BS; Sch. Safety Agt.; New York Police Dept. Sch. Safety Div., E 60th. St., New York, NY 10006; r. 19 S Lawrence Ave., Elmsford, NY 10523, 914 592-7675; Camilla; Joi.

TYRE, Iasia A.; '98 BA; Yeshiva Univ.; Caseworker/Social Work Intern; NYC Admin. for Children Svcs., 19 Grant Sq., Brooklyn, NY 11216, 718 264-4656; r. 3571 Nostrand Ave. #5D, Brooklyn, NY 11229, 718 615-1223; Kaiim Vieira. e-mail

TYRRELL, Edward; '82 MPA; BS City Clg. of NY; Deputy Administrative Ofcr.; US Atty's Ofc., New York, NY 10007, 212 637-2269; r. 17 Pond Rd, Ridgefield, CT 06877, 203 438-4049; Carol; Nancy. e-mail

TYSON, Genine G.; '92 BS; 410 St. Nicholas Ave., New York, NY 10027, 212 491-8137.

TYTELL, Harold; '68 BS, '70 MA; Retired Asst. Prof.; Rutgers State Univ. New Jersey; r. 301 NE 14th Ave. Apt. 701, Hallandale, FL 33009, 954 456-3924; Arlyne; Lon, Wayne. e-mail

TYTELL, Peter V.; '95 BA; Forensic Document Examiner; Forensic Rsch., 188 Broadway, New York, NY 10038, 212 233-3822; r. 207 W. 106th St., New York, NY 10025, 212 222-4911; Tikva. e-mail

TZIAZAS, Pilar; '86 BS; 78-07 N Conduit Ave., Ozone Park, NY 11417.

U

UBELLI, Michael A.; '78 BA; 24-50 29 St., Astoria, NY 11102.

UBERTI, Arthur A.; '82 BS; 358 Clinton Ave., Cedarhurst, NY 11516.

UBWA, Hilary A.; '81 MA; 138-46 Northern Bl, Flushing, NY 11354.

UCELLI, Monique S., (Monique Browning); '97 BS; Customer Svc.; Bell Atlantic Phone Co., 1625 Forest Ave., Staten Island, NY 10302. e-mail

UDE, Jude M.; '95 BS; 626 Riverside Dr., New York, NY 10031, 212 283-3950.

UFFER, Roselyn; '99 BA; 111 Hicks St., #21K, Brooklyn, NY 11201, 718 246-4735.

UHLMANN, Dennis P.; '83 BS; MPA Marist Clg.; POB 4724, New Windsor, NY 12553, 914 561-3884; *Lorraine;* Christina, Dennis, Jennifer. e-mail

UHNAK, Dorothy; '68 BS; 37 Nostrand Ave., Shelter Island, NY 11964.

UKE, Evaristus U.; '95 BS; Police Ofcr.; City of NY, Bronx, NY 10472, 718 253-7511; r. 1314 Croes Ave., Bronx, NY 10472, 718 328-5216; Unimke. e-mail

ULIANKO, John A.; '77 BS; 22 Weatherhill Way, Dayton, NJ 08810.

ULRICH, Eileen '76 (See Commike, Eileen A.).

ULRICH, Michael; '92 BS; 425 Sunset Ave., Haworth, NJ 07641, 201 384-6298.

ULRICH, Thomas L.; '98 BS; 10 Woodcliff Ave. 2a, N. Bergen, NJ 07047.

ULSAMER, John J.; '77 BA; 311 Oak Ave., Staten Island, NY 10306; *Angela;* John Jr, Daniel, Marissa, Dana, Meghan.

UMAR, El-farouk; '97 BS; 1562 Vyse Ave. 3B, Bronx, NY 10460.

UMAR, Warith-Deen; '85 BA; MS Grad. Sch.; Ministerial Prog. Coord./Pres.; NYS Dept. of Correctional Svcs., National Association of Muslim, Chaplains, Albany, NY 12206, 518 457-8106; r. 520 Feura Bush Rd, Glenmont, NY 12077, 518 439-8409; *Islah Waliah;* Muhammad, Kauthar, Saheer, Khalid, Rafiq, Tajah, Jannah, Alaudeen. e-mail

UMSTETTER, Susan M.; '79 BS; 8428 90th St., Jamaica, NY 11421.

UNDERWOOD, James S.; '80 MA; BA Seton Hall Univ., MBA Fairleigh Dickinson Univ.; Retired, Law Enforcement; r. 237 Madison Dr., Naples, FL 34110, 941 597-1139; *Joan;* Mary Kate, James Jr.

UNDERWOOD, Mark; '90 MA; 1931 Market St. # C, Harrisburg, PA 17103, 717 233-4505.

UNGARINO, Peter J.; '95 AS; 8105 149th Ave., Howard Bch., NY 11414.

UNGER, Robert E.; '93 MPA; 260 Arleigh Rd, Flushing, NY 11363.

UPSHER, Denise; '97 AS; 572 Warren St. 2K, Brooklyn, NY 11217.

UPSHUR, Roderick W.; '75 BA; POB 555, Jamaica, NY 11411, 718 712-4207.

UR, Joseph; '86 MPA; Lt.; East Brunswick Twp., 1 Civic Center Dr., E. Brunswick, NJ 08816; r. 409 Dunhams Corner Rd, E. Brunswick, NJ 08816; *Kelly.* e-mail

URBAEZ, Eliet; '96 BS; 232 Metropolitan Ave., Brooklyn, NY 11211.

URBAN, Daniel E.; '84 BA; 18-07 121 St., College Pt., NY 11356, 718 945-9552.

URENA, Gustavo; '99 BS; 161 06 Grand Cent Pkway, Jamaica, NY 11432, 718 291-5668.

URENA, Haydee; BA; 1822 Woodbine St#1R, Ridgewood, NY 11385, 718 456-5861.

URGO, John F.; '76 BA; 97 Village Loop Rd, Pomona, CA 91766.

URIA, Maria; '96 BA; 163 Eastern Pkwy., Brooklyn, NY 11238.

URIBE, Brian S.; '99 MA; 333 E. 43rd St., New York, NY 10017, 212 370-1963.

URPRASAD, Deodat; '92 MPA; BA York Clg./CUNY; Sgt; NYC Police Dept., Brooklyn, NY 11201; r. 4542 220th St., Bayside, NY 11361, 718 631-4712.

URRUTIA, Anna-Maria, (Anna-Maria Spencer); '82 BS, '93 MA; Tchr.; John Bailey Elem.; r. 30 Muriel Ave., N. Providence, RI 02911, 401 233-9680; *Robert;* Elaina Jones, Jordan, Marinda. e-mail

URRUTIA, Julio E.; '79 BS; 4588 Ashfield Ter., Syracuse, NY 13215, 315 498-4020.

URSO, Robert M.; '82 BA; 8 Glow Ln., Hicksville, NY 11801, 516 938-6939.

URTEAGA, Ana M.; '98 BA; Social Worker; St. John's Home for Boys, Rockaway Bch., NY 11693, 718 945-2800; r. 19310 45th Ave., Flushing, NY 11358, 718 357-6130.

URVANT, Marvin D.; 2503 Antigua Ter. Apt. B4, Coconut Creek, FL 33066, 954 974-5552.

USERA, Jessica, (Jessica Gonzalez-Usera); '97 BS; Counseling Coord.; John Jay Clg. of Criminal Justice, 445 W. 59th St. #3140N, New York, NY 10019, 212 237-8112; r. 2910 Seymour Ave., Bronx, NY 10469, 718 547-4914; Jamie. e-mail

UTSEY, Robert E.; '95 MA; NYPD-Lt.-Retired; r. 504 Blue Mountain Lake, E. Stroudsburg, PA 18301, 570 424-9273. e-mail

UTTARO, Raymond J.; '75 BS; 34 Brookside Dr., Smithtown, NY 11787.

UTTENDORFSKY, M.; '90 BS; 118 Highland Ave., Maybrook, NY 12543.

UVEGES, Michael J.; '99 BA; Child Protective Spec.; Admin. for Children's Svcs., 192 E. 151 St., Bronx, NY 10451, 718 579-9209; r. 765 Midland Ave., Yonkers, NY 10704, 914 968-2886; *Sandra.* e-mail

UWAGUE, Nelson; '97 BS; 3425 Kingsbridge, Bronx, NY 10463.

UWA-OMEDE, Tonnie; '92 BS, '97 MS; MPA; Adjunct Prof.; Clg. of New Rochelle, John Cardinal O'Connor Campus Bronx, E 149 Th, Bronx, NY 10451, 718 665-1310; r. 1200 E. 53rd St., 2G, Brooklyn, NY 11234, 718 251-1121; *Eugenia;* Efosa, Osazee. e-mail

UWASOMBA, Dominic; '81 MPA; 2430 Morris Ave. Apt. 44a, Bronx, NY 10468.

UWUIGBE, Wilfred; '90 BS; 267 Winthrop St., Brooklyn, NY 11225.

UZCATEGUI, Robert E.; '95 BA, '95 MA; Sergeant; NYPD, Bronx District Attorney's Ofc., 161st St. & Grand Concourse, Bronx, NY 10451, 718 590-2080; r. 90 Claremont Ave., Rye, NY 10580.

V

VACCARELLI, Robin A.; '77 BS; 409 Port Au Peck Ave., Oceanport, NJ 07757, 732 870-9263.

VACCARELLO, Maria J.; BA; 208A No Boston Ave., N. Massapequa, NY 11758, 516 454-9147.

VACCARO, Joseph A.; '77 BA; 386 Mayfair Dr. S, Brooklyn, NY 11234, 718 522-7089.

VAHER, Kristi L.; '99 BA; 39 Clafford Ln., Melville, NY 11747, 631 421-2078.

VAHEY, Josephine E.; '82 BS; 3307 Hull Ave., Bronx, NY 10467, 718 882-8551.

VAILL, Mrs. Cara J., (Cara J. Sclafani); '99 MA; BA Univ. of MD; Child Care Provider; St. Mary's Children & Family Svc.; r. 59-A Shirra Ave., Staten Island, NY 10314, 718 698-4224; *Richard.*

VAILS, Dawn; '88 BA; 120 Asch Loop Apt. 23f, Bronx, NY 10475.

VAIRO, SGT Daniel; '74 AS; Sr. Court Ofcr. Admin. Sgt; NYS Courts, 111 Dr. Martin Luther King Blvd., White Plains, NY 10601, 914 285-3020; r. 142 Cottage Rd., Carmel, NY 10512, 914 225-2724; *Lisa;* Ashley.

VALCARCEL, Carmen E.; '99 BA; Outreach Worker; William F. Ryan Comm. Health Ctr., New York, NY 10025; r. Bronx, NY 10455. e-mail

VALDES, Connie B.; '93 BA; 10632 79th St., Jamaica, NY 11417, 718 323-2121.

VALDES, Elena M.; '83 BS; 418 W 17th St. Apt. 6d, New York, NY 10011.

VALDES, Jesus M.; '90 BS, '93 MA; Police Detective; Nassau Cnty. Police Dept., 1490 Franklin Ave., Mineola, NY 11501, 516 573-6353; r. 3662 Park Ave., Apt. 2M, Wantagh, NY 11793, 516 826-4767. e-mail

VALDEZ, Esteban; '81 BA; 426 Himrod St., Brooklyn, NY 11237, 718 852-0245.

VALDEZ, Rafaela A.; 165 W. 76th St., New York, NY 10023.

VALDEZ, Rosa E.; '91 BA; 525 Neptune Ave. # 11, Brooklyn, NY 11224, 718 852-0245.

VALDEZ, Rosanna Y.; '96 BS; 108-78 42 Ave. #, Corona, NY 11368, 718 296-5492.

VALDINOTO, Frank W.; '76; 7622 11th Ave., Brooklyn, NY 11228, 718 745-5719.

VALE, Carmen R.; '92 BA; Sch. Psychologist; Village Child Devel. Ctr., 334 E 14th St., New York, NY 10003, 212 260-7440; r. 3520 101st St., Flushing, NY 11368, 718 776-2508. e-mail

VALENCIA, Armando; '79 MA; 9 Badger St., Spring Vly., NY 10977.

VALENTE, Joseph F.; '77 BA; 1419 Mill Ave., Brooklyn, NY 11234, 718 209-5053.

VALENTI, Philip J.; '75 BA; USS Rath Burne FF1057, FPO, AP 96677.

VALENTIN, Elliot; '93 BA; 855 Wyckoff Ave. # 1, Flushing, NY 11385, 718 507-1687.

VALENTIN, Julio A.; '96 BS; Police Ofcr.; NYC Police Dept., 212 477-9715; r. 7 Seabird Ave., Spring Vly., NY 10977, 914 352-9041.

VALENTIN, Luis A.; 70-08 66th St., Glendale, NY 11385, 718 380-0929.

VALENTIN, Miguel A.; '77 BS; Retired Detective; Detective Squad In Queens; r. 6 Waterview Ave., Ronkonkoma, NY 11779, 631 588-6102; *Elizabeth;* Michael, Oscar. e-mail

VALENTIN, Pablo; '92 BS; 1260 E 105th St., Brooklyn, NY 11236.

VALENTIN, Patricia J.; '78 BA; 101 St. Marks Pl., New York, NY 10009, 212 260-7729.

VALENTIN, Ruben; '82 BS; 3691 Secor Ave., Bronx, NY 10466.

VALENTIN, Sheila S.; '84 BS; 91-06 91st Ave., Woodhaven, NY 11421, 718 529-1629.

VALENTINE, Christine; '86 BS; 945 Saratoga Ave., # 1R, Brooklyn, NY 11212, 718 624-0190.

VALENTINE, Hillel J.; 100-33 Elgar Pl., Bronx, NY 10475, 718 379-4849. e-mail

VALENTINE, Rudolph N.; '76 BA; MA, MS Long Island Univ.; Adjunct Prof. Monroe Clg.; Monroe Clg., Bronx, NY 10468, 718 796-9022; r. 2739 Claflin Ave., Bronx, NY 10468, 718 796-9022; Chesne.

VALENTINE, William C.; '75 MA; 209 Tulip Ave., Floral Park, NY 11001, 516 489-8820.

VALENTINO, Michael; '91 BS; Park Enforcement Police; NYC Parks Dept., New York, NY 10001; r. 23 Berkley St., Staten Island, NY 10312, 718 605-4626.

VALENZANO, Michael D.; '79 BS; 165 Park Row, New York, NY 10038, 315 732-5685.

VALERA, Magalys; '95 BA; Co-Mgr.; Rite Aid Pharmacy, 86 St. Lexington Ave., New York, NY 10028, 212 878-0600; r. 2790 Grand Concour, Bronx, NY 10458, 718 292-6169; Bryan Saldana, Michael Saldana.

VALERIO, Peter; '97 AS, '99 BA; 1959 59th St., Brooklyn, NY 11204, 718 331-8882.

VALLDERUTEN, Fabiola; '95 BS; 1515 N Nicholas St., Arlington, VA 22205.

VALLE, Frank V.; '75 BS; 2823 45th St., Long Island City, NY 11103, 718 672-8813.

VALLE, Nelson; '95 BA; 4830 40th St., Apt. 5B, Sunnyside, NY 11104, 718 672-8813.

VALLECILLO, Gonzalo A.; '93 BS; JD Pace Law Sch.; Atty.; Dept. of Treas., 1111 Constitution Ave., Washington, DC 20224, 202 622-4068; r. 5260 Duke St., Alexandria, VA 22304, 703 823-9228.

VALLEJO, Fanny; '95 BS; 362 Wadsworth Ave. Apt. 23, New York, NY 10040.

VALLES, LT Evelyn; '76 BA; MED Fordham Univ.; Lt.-Police Ofcr.; Broward Cnty. Police Dept., Dept. of Ins. Fraud, Plantation, FL 33317, 954 327-6020; r. POB 938716, Margate, FL 33093, 954 970-0845; Thomas Tam. e-mail

VALLUZZI, Frank S.; '93 BS, '96 MA; 6 Tiptop Ln., Hicksville, NY 11801.

VAMVOUKAKIS, Patricia A.; '99 BS; 504 W. 44th St., New York, NY 10036, 212 736-5516; Angelo; George, Christina, Mary, Stephanie.

VAN, Benschoten W.; '75 MA; 325 Gretna Hill, Pleasant Vly., NY 12569, 518 789-3070.

VAN, Hien D.; '99 BA MA; 200 Central Park S. 14Q, New York, NY 10019, 212 262-9275.

VAN, Nostrand P.; '89 BS; 96 Monitor St., Brooklyn, NY 11222, 718 349-6160.

VANAGER, Kenneth; '81 BA; 54-15 Beach Channel, Rockaway Bch., NY 11692.

VAN ARSDEL-CHIMKA, Alison M.; '99 MA; 224 Country Club Dr., Titusville, FL 32780, 321 267-2574.

VANBUCKLEY, Hilburn; '77 BS; 1362 Ocean Ave. #3J, Brooklyn, NY 11230.

VANDEMARK, Maurice T.; '85 AS; 44 Grandview Ave., Kingston, NY 12401, 914 626-2573.

VAN DENBERG, Gregory C.; '94 MA; 53 Harth Dr., New Windsor, NY 12553, 914 346-4639.

VANDERBURGH, Thomas; '87 BS; 310 Outwater Ln., Garfield, NJ 07026.

VANDERLEE, Cynthia S.; '95 MA; BA SUNY Brockport; Prevention Svcs. Spec.; Canandaigua City Sch. Dist., 1 Academy Cir., Canandaigua, NY 14424, 716 396-3859; r. 117 High St., Apt. 3, Fairport, NY 14450, 716 377-1902. e-mail

VANEGAS, John J.; '91 BS; 7106 32nd Ave., Flushing, NY 11370.

VAN LOON, Gary; '83 MA; 133 Birchwood Dr., Elmwood Park, NJ 07407.

VANN, Keith K.; '91 BA; Clerk; Dept. of Corrections, 611 Edgecomb Ave., New York, NY 10032, 212 923-2575; r. 326 Mckinley Ave., Brooklyn, NY 11208, 718 348-1688. e-mail

VANNATA, Janice M.; '93 BS; Retired Police Ofcr./Cnslt.; r. 6911 Caldwell Ave., Flushing, NY 11378, 718 426-8234. e-mail

VANNATA, Stephen L.; '76 BS; 6911 Caldwell Ave., Flushing, NY 11378, 718 426-8234.

VANOFSKY, Michael; '79 MA; 24-07 86th St., Flushing, NY 11369.

VANPUTTEN, Archie; '93 BS; 3544 Wayne Ave., Bronx, NY 10467.

VAN RONDA, Joann; '90 BS; 10 Pratt St., Mt. Vernon, NY 10550, 716 941-9058.

VANROSSEM, Charles V.; '82 BS; 156-35 99 St., Howard Bch., NY 11414.

VANTERPOOL, Arthur E.; '76 BA; 4361 Murdock Ave., Bronx, NY 10466.

VANZANT, Rhonda; Medgar Evers Clg., Alumni Ofc., Brooklyn, NY 11225.

VARA, Lisa; '99 MA; 2263 Whittier St., Rahway, NJ 07065, 732 388-3945.

VARADARAJAN, K.; '81 MA; 666 Grove St., Ridgewood, NJ 07450.

VARANELLI, Andrew; '82 MS; POB 528, Center Moriches, NY 11934.

VAREAM, Richard; '87 AS, '91 BA; 145-01 20th Ave. #, Whitestone, NY 11357, 718 746-0731.

VARELA, Anthony F.; '98 BA; 1 Eagle Rock Vlg, Apt. 3B, Budd Lake, NJ 07828.

VARELA, Lillian; '96 BA; 1 Georgia Ave. Apt. 4f, Bronxville, NY 10708.

VARELA, Mauricio; '79 BS; 14710 Coolidge Ave., Jamaica, NY 11435.

VARELA, Mildred; '85 BA; 651 48th St., Brooklyn, NY 11220, 718 234-5412.

VARELA, Wilson; '93 BS; 651-48th St., Brooklyn, NY 11220, 718 234-5412.

VARGA, Donna M., (Donna Battaglia); '81 BS, '90 MA; Detective; NYC Police Dept., One Police Plz., New York, NY 10038, 212 374-6960; r. 70 Harvard Ave., Rockville Centre, NY 11570, 516 764-1005; Stephen J.

VARGA, Stephen J.; '80 BS, '91 MPA; Sergeant; NYC Police Dept., One Police Plz., New York, NY 10038, 212 374-4274; r. 70 Harvard Ave., Rockville Centre, NY 11570, 516 764-1005; Donna. e-mail

VARGAS, Adriana; '99 BA; 1641 Madison Ave. #20G, New York, NY 10029, 212 369-2743.

VARGAS, Ariel; '99 BS; Field Supv.; r. 609 W 174th St., New York, NY 10033, 212 740-4417.

VARGAS, Bernabe; '99 BA; Police Ofcr.; NYC Police Dept., 145th & Saint Nicholas Ave., District #3, New York, NY 10030, 212 281-5303; r. 819 F.D.R. Dr. #7B, New York, NY 10009, 212 777-6846. e-mail

VARGAS, Dayana; '95 BS; 4255 Colden St. # 1, Flushing, NY 11355, 718 459-4002.

VARGAS, Dayanara J.; '98 BA; 3300 Bailey Ave., Apt. E3, Bronx, NY 10463, 718 329-5455.

VARGAS, Howard R.; '93 BA; 5017 Broadway Apt. 2a, Flushing, NY 11377, 718 392-1223.

VARGAS, Jeffrey (Jeff); '95 BS; E-mail Admin.; Morgan Stanley Dean Witter, 2 World Trade Ctr., New York, NY 10048, 212 392-7020; r. 1115 Fdr Dr. Apt. 9h, New York, NY 10009, 212 473-1688. e-mail

VARGAS, Mrs. Jennifer L.; '91 BS; 108 Horton St., Williamston, SC 29697, 864 847-1690; Ivan; Sierra, Lucas. e-mail

VARGAS, Jose; '97 BA; 400 E 147th St., Bronx, NY 10455, 718 994-1822.

VARGAS, Leslie M., (Leslie M. Rosado); '91 BA; US Probation Ofcr.; r. 77 Fulton St., New York, NY 10038; Alex. e-mail

VARGAS, Miriam; '78 BS; 452 Buchanan Ave., Staten Island, NY 10314, 718 983-9852.

VARGAS, Shirley W.; '97 BA; AAS Hostos Community Clg.; Youth Div. Aide; The Ofc. of Children & Family Svcs.; r. 870 Elsmere Pl., Apt. 4C, Bronx, NY 10460, 718 589-0091.

VARGAS, Susana; '81 BA, '93 MPA; 446 W 26th St. Apt. 6e, New York, NY 10001.

VARGAS-GONZALEZ, Ana; '90 BS, '97 MPA, '98 MPA; 2085 Amsterdam Ave., New York, NY 10032, 315 337-1752.

VARGHESE, Vinod; '96 BA; Gov; r. 7 Kamda Blvd., New Hyde Park, NY 11040, 516 616-4396; Grace Vinod. e-mail

VARLACK, Charleswort; '75 BA; 120-01 143rd St., Jamaica, NY 11436.

VARNELL, Mary Allen B.; '98 MA; 800 Burke St., Mc Comb, MS 39648, 601 684-9435.

VARNEY, Lillian; '78 BA; 24601 Harbor View Dr. Unit A, Dana Point, CA 92629.

VARSAMAS, Tommy A.; '98 BS; 20 06 18 St., Astoria, NY 11105.

VARSHAVSKIY, Yevgeniy; '99 BS; 470 Ocean Prwy #b7, Brooklyn, NY 11218, 718 253-1250.

VARTABEDIAN, Darryl; '95 MA; BS Kutztown Univ.; Loss Prevention Investigator; TJ Maxx, 34 E Ridgewood Ave., Paramus, NJ 07652, 201 444-3955; r. 10-07 Morlot Ave., Fair Lawn, NJ 07410, 201 791-6660. e-mail

VASAPOLLO-D'AUGUSTA, Barbara; '92 MPA; Homemaker; r. 20 Hunters Pointe, N. Middletown, NJ 07748, 732 495-3772. e-mail

VASILE-DAVILA, Fern; '96; 125-10 Queens Blvd., Kew Gardens, NY 11415, 718 723-4032.

VASQUEZ, Ms. Daisy; '96 BA; Financial Analyst; Patterson Beiknap Webb & Tyler LLC, 1133 6th Ave., New York, NY 10036, 212 336-2593; r. 337 Hendrickson Ave., Valley Stream, NY 11580, 516 825-7182; *Eladio;* Jasmine. e-mail

VASQUEZ, Julio E.; '98 BA; 96-13 Alstyne Ave., Corona, NY 11368, 718 848-3135.

VASQUEZ, Maria I.; '99 BA; Social Worker; Family IMC, 728, Ste. 1A, Bronx, NY 10453, 718 716-6000; r. 108-28 38 Ave. #4H, Flushing, NY 11368, 718 505-1033.

VASQUEZ, Michael J.; '98 BA; 82-05 134th St., Jamaica, NY 11435.

VASTI, Thomas; '79 MA; 1622 Hone Ave., Bronx, NY 10461, 718 904-1474.

VATEL, Wileen; '99 BA; Admin. Asst.; Haragone Sporting Goods, 867 Broadway, New York, NY 10003, 212 255-8036; r. 200 Winthrop St. #B7, Brooklyn, NY 11225, 718 941-1241.

VAUGHAN, Sheila M.; '94 BS; Chief of Mgmt. & Plng.; NYC Dept. of Corrections, Ryker's Island Complex; r. 162-01 Powells Cove Blvd. #2D, Beechhurst, NY 11357, 718 767-5009; *James T.* e-mail

VAUGHAN, Susan; '75 MA; 249 E 7th St. Apt. 11, New York, NY 10009.

VAUGHAN, Terry; '82 BS; 901 W 19th St., Wilmington, DE 19802, 302 594-9016.

VAUGHN, Robbie; '96 BA; Police Ofcr.; NYPD, 77th Precinct; r. 2703 W.33rd St. #4, Brooklyn, NY 11224, 718 373-7288. e-mail

VAUGHN, Sean; '95 BS; 333 Patchen Ave. Apt. 3E, Brooklyn, NY 11233, 718 221-5714.

VAUGHN, Staci C.; '86 BS; 345 Clinton Ave., Brooklyn, NY 11238, 718 488-9108.

VAZ, Fernando P.; '98 MA; 9716 Liverpool St., Jamaica, NY 11435, 718 526-1893.

VAZQUEZ, Anodel; '91 BS; 1926 Holland Ave., Bronx, NY 10462, 718 824-1511.

VAZQUEZ, Blanca '84 (See Gary, Ms. Blanca I.).

VAZQUEZ, Carlos E.; '92 BS; Deputy Sheriff; City of NY, 212 565-2030; r. 1115 Woodycrest Ave., Apt. 1b, Bronx, NY 10452.

VAZQUEZ, Daniel M.; '99 BS; 1834 Colden St., Bronx, NY 10462, 718 824-1511.

VAZQUEZ, Edward A.; '84 BS; Juvenile Cnty.; 22nd Judicial Circuit Ct., 929 N. Vandeventer, St. Louis, MO 63108; r. 6544 Oleatha Ave., St. Louis, MO 63109, 314 645-6061; *Ann;* Christina, Zachary, Louisa. e-mail

VAZQUEZ, George N.; '89 BA; MS Long Island Univ., CERT. Hofstra Univ.; Paralegal; Koeppel Martone Leistman & Herman, 155 First St., Mineola, NY 11501, 516 747-6300; r. 1669 Westmoreland Rd, Merrick, NY 11566, 516 771-6569.

VAZQUEZ, George P.; '76 BS; 3444 92nd St., Flushing, NY 11372, 718 296-5417.

VAZQUEZ, Gwendolyn; '85 BS; 1545 Archer Rd Apt. Tg, Bronx, NY 10462, 718 824-1511.

VAZQUEZ, Janette; '87 BS; 452 Shepherd Ave., Brooklyn, NY 11208, 718 638-1008.

VAZQUEZ, Jennifer L. '89 (See Shedden, Jennifer L.).

VAZQUEZ, Jose R.; '96 AS, '97 BA; 22 E. 103rd St., New York, NY 10029.

VAZQUEZ-RODRIGUEZ, Freddie; '95 BA; EDS Lincoln Recovery Inst.; Grad. Student-Audrey Cohen Clg.; Counseling Svc.-Substance Abuse Couns., 384 E 149th St., Ste. 200, Bronx, NY 10455, 718 292-4221; r. 8816 89th Ave., Jamaica, NY 11421, 917 523-8785.

VECCHI, Louis; '76 BA; 65 Cyanamid Dr., Wayne, NJ 07470.

VECCHIARELLI, Dennis; '83 MA; 21 Edstone Dr., Staten Island, NY 10301.

VECCHIO, Jack; '74 AA, '76 BA; AS George Brown Clg.; Mgr. of Securities; The Royal Ontario Museum, 100 Queens Park, Toronto, ON, Canada M5R 2C6, 416 586-5508; r. 20 Prince Arthur Ave., 20, Toronto, ON, Canada M5R 1B1, 416 924-3576; *Oriole;* John, Richard. e-mail

VECCHIO, Thomas J.; '89 BS; 10712 106th St., Jamaica, NY 11417, 718 849-3480.

VECCHIONE, Deborah A.; '76 BA; 72 Nottingham Rd, Malverne, NY 11565, 516 599-0690.

VEDRAL, Chris J.; '84 BA; 150-08 33 Ave., Flushing, NY 11354.

VEGA, Carmen M.; '95 MPA; BS SUNY Clg.-Old Westbury; Mgr.; Worldwide Pricing & Contracts, American Express, 140 Broadway, New York, NY 10005, 212 640-6361; r. 45 S. Elliot Pl. #4, Brooklyn, NY 11217, 718 330-0462.

VEGA, Ernan, Jr.; '87 AS, '93 BS; Detective; NYPD 120 Pct., 78 Richmond Ter., Staten Island, NY 10301, 718 981-2714; r. 25 Grandview Ave., Staten Island, NY 10303, 718 448-8007; *Jeanette;* Ernan III, Steven Ray, Christopher.

VEGA, Javiel; '99 BA; Dir. Case Mgmt.; CASES, 346 Broadway, New York, NY 10013, 212 553-6323; r. 888 Grand Concourse #3M, Bronx, NY 10451, 718 401-1498. e-mail

VEGA, Jose R.; '95 AS; Sergeant; NYC Police Dept.; r. 180 29th St., Copiague, NY 11726, 631 841-3871.

VEGA, Kevin J.; '93 BS; 825 Caton Ave., Brooklyn, NY 11218.

VEGA, Mario; '81 BS; 194 McKinley Ave., Brooklyn, NY 11208, 718 497-5133.

VEGA, Michael A.; '99 BS, '99; Ofc. Svcs. Supv.; Nautica Enterprises, 40 W. 57th St., New York, NY 10019, 212 841-7178; r. 751 E 161st Street#5B, Bronx, NY 10456, 718 585-1376. e-mail

VEGA, Nanette '97 (See Aridas, Mrs. Nanette).

VEGA, Ronald; '80 BS; Police Ofcr./Sgt Military Police; Maryland Natl. Capitol Park Police, Pg Cnty. Div, 6700 Riverdale Rd, Riverdale, MD 20737, 301 459-9088; r. 3307 Delpha Ct., Parkville, MD 21234, 410 665-8197; *Deborah;* Antonia Frances.

VEGA, Thomas; '84 BS; NYS Parole Ofcr.; NYS Div. of Parole, 260 E. 161st St., Bronx, NY 10451, 718 292-7273; r. 135 W. 225th St., Bronx, NY 10463; *Victor L. Santiago.* e-mail

VEGA, Thomas R.; '94 BS; 672 Grand Ave., Lindenhurst, NY 11757.

VEIGL, Eugene E.; '91 BA; 255 Jamaica Blvd., Carle Place, NY 11514, 516 333-7410.

VEILSON, Martin; '92 BS; Private Investigator; r. 6010 47th Ave. # 12H, Woodside, NY 11377, 718 779-0213; *Noreen;* Lisa, Susan. e-mail

VELA, Bianca M.; '98 BA; Pres.; Collins Constr., Brooklyn, NY 11215, 718 369-9024; r. 410 16th St., Brooklyn, NY 11215, 718 499-7082; *Stephen Collins Jr.;* Justin Collins, Erika Valerio. e-mail

VELARIDES, Anastasios; '89 MA; 111 Thornwood Dr., Marlton, NJ 08053, 856 985-8127.

VELASQUEZ, Carmen R.; '84 BA; JD Temple Univ. Sch. of Law, CERT. Univ. of Athens Law Sch.; Criminal Defense Atty.; Carmen Velasquez Law Ofc., 3732 75th Street; Ste. 301, Jackson Hts., NY 11372, 718 446-8188; r. 3732 75th St. Ste. 301, Jackson Hts., NY 11372, 718 803-6321; Jessica. e-mail

VELASQUEZ, Edwin; '97 BA; 930 Hart St. #3, Brooklyn, NY 11237, 718 252-4117.

VELASQUEZ, Katty; '98 BA, '98 CERT; Fraud Investigator; HRA, 260 11th Ave., New York, NY 10001, 212 630-9503; r. 483 Columbus Ave. #1B, New York, NY 10024, 212 595-3037. e-mail

VELASQUEZ, Yanina; '96 BA; The Paralegal Inst.; Paralegal; Mandel & Mandel PC, 1931 Mott Ave., Far Rockaway, NY 11691, 718 471-0100; r. 60 Munro Blvd., Valley Stream, NY 11581, 516 792-2404. e-mail

VELAZQUEZ, Felix J.; '95 AS; 100-22 Erdman Pl. 22-B, Bronx, NY 10475, 718 537-3767.

VELAZQUEZ, Liz; '99 BA; Exec. Sec.; New York Presbyterian Hosp., 525 E. 68th St., Box 156, New York, NY 10021; r. 400 E. 20th St., New York, NY 10009, 212 777-1704. e-mail

VELAZQUEZ, Pedro L.; '89 BS; 1001 Jerome Ave. Apt. 7g, Bronx, NY 10452, 718 588-1678.

VELEZ, Alex; '84 BS; 308 Brielle Ave., Bayville, NJ 08721.

VELEZ, Cindhia; '96 BA; Elem. Sch. Tchr.; NYC Bd. of Educ, PS 143; r. Flushing, NY 11377, 718 267-2644. e-mail

VELEZ, David A.; '97 BA; AA Clemson Univ.; Police Ofcr.; NYC, 1 Police Plz., New York, NY 10001, 212 374-5000; r. 70 Ledgewood Dr., Smithtown, NY 11787, 631 543-2468; *Mary.*

VELEZ, Donato; '98 BS; 84 Minuteman Cir., Orangeburg, NY 10962, 914 359-7076.

VELEZ, German J.; '96; 116 Levit Ave., Staten Island, NY 10314, 718 556-2483.

VELEZ, Glorialee; '96 BS; JD NYU; Atty.; Krupnick & Campbell et al, 850 SE 3rd Ave., Ft. Lauderdale, FL, 954 763-8181; r. 9001 SW 142 Ave., #1332, Miami, FL 33186, 305 380-8771; *Randolph Bremer;* Desiree, Michael. e-mail

VELEZ, Martha S.; '99 AS; Data Entry; GE Financial Assurance, New York, NY 10001; r. 2227 Stillwell Ave., Brooklyn, NY 11223, 718 333-1142; Kassandra.

VELEZ, Ramon; '85 MPA; 326 Swinton Ave., Bronx, NY 10465.

VELEZ, Rosendo P.; '95 MA; Lt. Police Ofcr.; NYC Police Dept., One Police Plz., New York, NY 10038, 212 741-8443; r. 773 Concourse Vlge E, Apt. 17 L, Bronx, NY 10451, 718 293-0194; *Zaida;* Brandon, Christopher, Catherine. e-mail

VELEZ, Theresa L.; '95 MA; AS Johnson & Wales Univ., BS Johnson & Wales; Events Admin. Mgr.; KBA Mktg. Grove, 520 Broadway 9th Fl., New York, NY 10012, 212 274-9970; r. 522 N Maple Ave., Apt. C4, Ridgewood, NJ 07450, 201 488-5049.

VELEZ-CRUZ, Margaret R.; '83 BA; Financial Svc. Rep./Ins. Broker; Fidelity Fed. Bank, Rancho Palos Verdes, CA 90275; r. 5710 Dairy Ave., Long Beach, CA 90805, 562 423-4227; Melissa, Tobias, Rafael, Taina, Mario, Margaret. e-mail

VELILLA, Angel E.; '99 BA; Deputy Sheriff; NYC Sheriff's Ofc., 550W 59 St., New York, NY 10019, 212 397-0509; r. 2933 Grand Concourse #B5, Bronx, NY 10468, 718 329-5014. e-mail

VELIZ, Giovanni; '92 BS; POB 1350, Flushing, NY 11370.

VELJANOVSKA, Marija; '98 BA; Investigator; HLA; r. 334 W 37 St. 3a, New York, NY 10018, 212 736-7629.

VELLUCCI, Frank R.; '79 MA; Sr. Court Clerk; NYS Supreme Ct. Criminal Branch, 100 Centre St., New York, NY 10013; r. 978 Drumgoole Rd W, Staten Island, NY 10312, 718 984-7662.

VELOZ, Ramon; '98 BA; 1044 Fox St. 14, Bronx, NY 10459.

VENDETTO, Janine '94 (See Geschwinder, Janine).

VENDITTO, Anthony M., Esq.; '87 BA, '90 JD; Atty.; Gordon & Silber; r. 33 Virginia Ave., Dobbs Ferry, NY 10522.

VENEZIANO, Salvatore; '80 BS; Sgt.; N.Y.P.D., New York, NY 10007; *Rita;* Kathleen. e-mail

VENKERSAMMY, Mark; '86 BA; 104-48 124 St., Richmond Hill, NY 11419.

VENN, Magadlene; '93 AS; 9022 208th St., Queens Vlg., NY 11428, 718 776-6491.

VENTIMIGLIA, Vincent; '74 BA; AA Kingsborough Community Cl; Supv.; Social Security Admin., 10 Bouck Ct., Brooklyn, NY 11223, 718 627-7062; r. 7403 11th Ave., Brooklyn, NY 11228, 718 680-9185; *Margaret;* Christine, Vincent. e-mail

VENTO, Frank J.; '81 BS; 19 Knoll Ct., Matawan, NJ 07747.

VENTRICE, Tinamarie '84 (See Bliach, Tinamarie).

VENTURA, Frank P.; '73 BA; 115 Alexander Dr., Red Bank, NJ 07701, 732 842-8976.

VENTURA, Rosanny J.; '99 BA; 501 W 170th St. 51, New York, NY 10032, 212 568-7643.

VENTURA-ROSA, Rafael; '79 BA; 36 Monroe St. # Di9, New York, NY 10002, 315 734-0153.

VENUTI, Christine M.; '99 MA; BS Florida Intl.; Sr. Case Mgr.; The Dome Proj. Inc., 486 Amsterdam Ave., New York, NY 10024, 212 724-1780; r. 18 Butler Pl., Northport, NY 11768, 631 261-1196. e-mail

VERA, Ana A.; '94 BA; 224 E 13th St. Apt. 10, New York, NY 10003, 212 614-9308.

VERA, Sharon L.; '99 BA; Events Coord.; NYU, 11 W 42nd. St., New York, NY 10036; r. 2332 Walton Ave. 4, Bronx, NY 10468, 718 824-7119. e-mail

VERBITSKY, Bruce; '75 BS; 86 Vermont St., Brooklyn, NY 11207.

VEREEN, Beverly F.; '88 BA; 22 Metropolitan Oval Apt. 9h, Bronx, NY 10462, 718 583-2673.

VERGILLO, Marcia '78 (See Trignano, Marcia V.).

VERICKER, Robert W.; '78 MA; 874 Dillingham BLvd., Honolulu, HI 96817, 808 845-9227.

VERNAZZA, Laurel A.; '98 BS; 297-101 Kinderkamack Rd. Suite#194, Oradell, NJ 07649, 201 594-0139.

VERNON, Patrice A.; '94 BS, '97 MA; 619 S 5th Ave., Mt. Vernon, NY 10550, 716 649-2509.

VERSACI, Brian J.; '89 BS; 415 S Lexington Ave., White Plains, NY 10606.

VERWOERT, Brian G.; '82 BS; 31 Argow Pl., Nanuet, NY 10954, 914 623-6189.

VERWOERT, John A.; '77 MPA; BBA Baruch; Retired; Police Dept.; r. 484 W Clarkstown Rd., New City, NY 10956, 914 627-2455; *Alice;* John S., Brian G.

VERWOERT, John S.; '81 BS; Detective Sergeant; r. 484 W Clarkstown Rd, New City, NY 10956, 914 627-2455; *Melinda;* Alexis, Alyssa.

VESSIO, Nicholas P.; '76 BA, '83 MPA; Supv. Investigator; New York Cnty. Dist. Attys Ofc., 1 Hogan Pl., New York, NY 10013, 212 335-9000; r. 16211 9th Ave., Apt. 5A, Whitestone, NY 11357, 718 767-0198. e-mail

VESSUP, Earl L.; '79 MPA; 11726 123 St., S. Ozone Park, NY 11420.

VETERE, Lisa M.; '95 BA; 191 Bellmore St., Floral Park, NY 11001.

VEYVODA, Joseph F.; '76 MPA; BS MN Long Island Univ.; Retired; r. 738 Hunt Ln., Manhasset, NY 11030, 516 627-0373; *Isabelle;* Gerald Joseph, Alice Lorraine.

VIALVA, Kelson B.; '82 AS; 3322 Clarendon Rd, Brooklyn, NY 11203.

VICCICA, Charles J.; '80 MA; 9599 130th Ave., Largo, FL 33773.

VICENS, Carol; '83 BS; 1986 Westover Ln. NW, Kennesaw, GA 30152.

VICENTE, Milagros; '99 BS; Asst. Dir.; Coalition for Economic Devel., 185th St., New York, NY 10033; r. 215 E. 164th St. #C, Bronx, NY 10456, 718 992-5088; Rafael, Tony.

VICKERIE, Dana A.; '90 AS, '93 BS; 20-25 Seagirt Blvd., Far Rockaway, NY 11691.

VICKERIE, Natasha P.; '97 BA; 3002 Surf Aveune, Brooklyn, NY 11224.

VICKERS, Maxine T.; '99 BS; Sch. Safety Agt.; NYC Police Dept., 1 Police Plz., New York, NY 10038; r. 1405 Brooklyn Ave., Apt. 5B, Brooklyn, NY 11210, 718 693-7202; Nyasia, Nikima.

VICKS, Leah D.; '88 BS; 10819 Rhodenda Pl., Upper Marlboro, MD 20772.

VICTOR, Chilov; '87 BS; 1641 Brooklyn Ave., Brooklyn, NY 11210, 718 265-6125.

VICTOR, David; 66-11 Park Dr. E., Flushing, NY 11367, 718 639-7735.

VICTOR, Philson J.; '97 BA; RR 8, Stroudsburg, PA 18360, 570 595-2172.

VIDAL, Edwin C.; '80 BS; 170-30 130 Ave., Jamaica, NY 11434.

VIDAL, Nellie R.; '79 BS; 131 Broome St., New York, NY 10002.

VIDAL, Raquel E.; '92 BS; 10139 133rd St., Jamaica, NY 11419.

VIDAL-ROMERO, Elida; '97 BS; MSW Baruch Clg.; Social Worker; Human Resources Admin., Dept. of Social Services, New York, NY 10038, 718 901-0227; r. POB 746, New York, NY 10032, 718 863-5898. e-mail

VIELOT, Marshka M.; '98 BA; Child Protective Spec.; Admin. for Children's Svcs., 19 Grant Sq., Brooklyn, NY 11216; r. 1043 E 81st, Brooklyn, NY 11236, 718 251-5272.

VIGDER, Melissa V., (Melissa V. Senitt); '72 BA, '72; Tchr.; PS 188, 3314 Neptune Ave., Brooklyn, NY 11224; r. 2940 Ocean Pkwy., Brooklyn, NY 11235, 718 996-6007; *Howard;* David.

VIGGIANI, Catherine; '82 BS; 20934 33rd Rd, Flushing, NY 11361.

VIGGIANO, Doreen M.; '87 BA; 108 Jefferson Ave., Deer Park, NY 11729.

VIGGIANO, Paul M.; '84 MPA; 90 Gold St., New York, NY 10038.

VIGIANO, John T.; '83 BS; 318 W 24th St., Deer Park, NY 11729.

VIGILANCE, Fitzroy; '96 BA; Police Ofcr.; r. Flushing, NY 11365; Darien.

VIGLIONE, Albert J.; '76 BA; 90-25 Shore Pkwy., Howard Bch., NY 11414; *Concetta;* Robert, Alan.

VIGNALI, Frank R.; '77 BS; Lt. Firefighter; Fire Dept. City of NY, Ladder 51 3446 E. Chester Rd., Bronx, NY 10469, 718 430-0238; r. 1915 Narragansett Ave., Bronx, NY 10461, 718 931-6581; *Debra;* Christopher, Brian.

VILFORT, Nedgine; '95 CERT; 13204 131st Ave., Jamaica, NY 11420.

VILLACORTA, Adriel W.; '97 BS; 9716 Metropolitan Ave., Forest Hills, NY 11375.

VILLADA, Arturo; '76 BA; 142-03 130th Ave., Jamaica, NY 11436.

VILLAFANE, Awilda; '75 BA; 1221 Saint Lawrence Ave., Bronx, NY 10472.

VILLALOBOS, Christine '92 (See Francois, Mrs. Christine).

VILLANI, Michelle T., (Michelle Turschmann); '98 BS; PC LAN Tech; MITEQ. Inc., 320 Oser Ave., Hauppauge, NY 11788, 631 439-9349; r. 9 Tulip St., Nesconset, NY 11767, 631 851-4434; *Michael A. Jr.*

VILLANI, Elizabeth; '80 BS; 73 Monitor St., Brooklyn, NY 11222, 718 383-4835.

VILLANO, Valerie F.; '79 BS; 27 Sea Gate Rd, Staten Island, NY 10305, 718 720-6643.

VILLANUEVA, David; '95 AS; 10717 86th St. # 1, Jamaica, NY 11417, 718 932-5239.

VILLANUEVA, Hector M.; '98 BS; Police Ofcr.; Los Angeles Police Dept., Los Angeles, CA 90086, 213 485-5245; r. 333 First St. A120, Seal Bch., CA 90740, 562 493-9248. e-mail

VILLANUEVA, Nilda; '92 BS; 840 Grand Concourse, Bronx, NY 10451.

VILLAR, Leslie A., (Lesbia Ramirez); '97 BS; Legal Asst.; Law Offices of Sergio Vilavede, 718 220-1400; r. 37 Payson Ave., Apt. 5l, New York, NY 10034, 212 569-6943; Chelsia K.

VILLARREAL, Paul H.; 157 Beach 121st St., Far Rockaway, NY 11694, 718 595-1702.

VILLEGAS, Lliana; '97 BS; Tech. Educ. Coord.; Enterprise Engrg., 55 Broad St. 7th Fl., New York, NY 10004, 212 742-2225; r. Middle Vlg., NY 11379; *Johnny Ortiz;* Justin Brian. e-mail

VILME, Jeannette; '87 AS, '91 BS; MS Staten Island Clg.; Elem. Sch. Tchr.; NYC Public Sch. Teacher, PS 22, Brooklyn, NY 11238, 718 857-4503; r. 972 Rogers Ave., Brooklyn, NY 11226, 718 693-9762; *Renold;* Elisabeth, Glen.

VINAS, Paul; '94 AS; 174 Bark Ave., Central Islip, NY 11722.

VINCENT, Nadienne K.; '80 BS; 28-23 42nd St., Astoria, NY 11103, 718 529-7323.

VINCENT, Wayne A.; '94 MA; 343 Waverly Ave. Apt. 2, Brooklyn, NY 11238, 718 467-9185.

VINCENZI, Victor A.; '81 MA; 352 Cedar Hill Rd, Fishkill, NY 12524.

VINCES, Rev. Edgar J.; '82 BA; MDIV Alliance Theological Semi; Fiscal Ofcr.; Admin. for Children Svcs., 150 William St. 1039, New York, NY 10038, 212 676-9056; r. 4610 102nd St. # 1, Flushing, NY 11368, 718 426-0650; *Blanca;* Jeremy, Jennifer, Christine. e-mail

VINCI, Mrs. Catherine A., (Cathy A. Juers); '92 BS; AS Natl. Clg., MA NYU; Assoc. Publisher; Thomson Publishing/ Faulkner & Gray, 11 Penn Plz., New York, NY 10001, 212 967-7000; r. POB 411, Shenorock, NY 10587, 914 248-4833; *Mark.* e-mail

VINCI, Donald S.; '94 MA; 30 Amsterdam Ave., Staten Island, NY 10314.

VINCK, Agustin D.; '78 BA; 7601 10th Ave., Brooklyn, NY 11228.

VINDICE, Vincent; '90 MA; 2376 85 St., Brooklyn, NY 11214.

VINEIS, Steven S.; 208 Birch Dr. #7, Brick, NJ 08723.

VINES, Bernard A.; '95 BS; POB 366, Bronx, NY 10456.

VINSON, Deborah D.; '88 BA; 443 Marcus Garvey #21, Brooklyn, NY 11216, 718 769-0277.

VINTON, Jeanette, (Jeanette Hirschberg); '85 BS; CERT. UNH-Manchester; Deputy Town Clerk; Town of Mount Vernon, 1 S. Main St., POB 444, Mont Vernon, NH 03057, 603 673-9126; r. POB 366, Mont Vernon, NH 03057, 603 672-4595; *Drury;* Joseph Ochs, Timothy, Louis.

VIOLLIS, Paul M., Sr.; '83 BS, '89 MPA; VP; Kroll, 900 3rd Ave., New York, NY 10022, 212 226-8577; r. 3580 Big Pine Rd, Melbourne, FL 32934, 321 733-0773; *Karen;* Jennifer, Paul M. Jr. e-mail

VIRGILIO, Thomas M.; '81 MPA; 41 12 52 St., Woodside, NY 11377.

VIRZERA, Victor L.; '75 MPA; BA, AA Kingsborough Comm Clg.; Publisher/ Musician; VVI Publishing, 21 Wilton St., New Hyde Park, NY 11040, 516 354-4322; r. same; *Evelyn;* Jon, Dave.

VISHNUDAT, Mrs. Indira D.; '95 BS; Police Ofcr.; 43rd Precinct, 900 Steley Ave., Bronx, NY 10472, 718 542-0888; r. 170-49 Cedar Croft Rd, Jamaica Estates, NY 11432, 718 291-1886; *Asis.* e-mail

VISKUP, Milly A.; '80 BS; Legal Asst.; Gruntal & Co. LLC, New York, NY 10001; r. 5900 Arlington Ave. Apt. 8t, Bronx, NY 10471, 718 549-8211.

VISTOSO, Julio M.; '91 BS; 3775 Ardsley Ct., Marietta, GA 30062.

VITALE, George E.; '79 AS, '84 BS, '97 MA; Sr. Investigator; NYS Troopers, Governor's Ofc., 633 3rd Ave. 38th Fl., New York, NY 10017, 212 681-4813. e-mail

VITALE, Tammy; '97 BA; Police Ofcr.; NYPD; r. 60 Jamie Ln., Staten Island, NY 10312, 718 605-6437.

VITALIANO, Anthony J.; '77 BS; 1596 Waring Ave., Bronx, NY 10469.

VITOLE, Jeffrey M.; '88 BA; MA William Harrison Univ.; Special Agt.; US Dept. of Defense, Defence Security Service; r. 290 High Mountain Rd, N. Haledon, NJ 07508, 973 304-0738.

VITOLO, John J.; '96 BS; 2250 E. 4th St., Brooklyn, NY 11223.

VITOLO, Marco A.; '80 BS; 1955 Williamsbridge, Bronx, NY 10461, 718 931-2458.

VITOLO, William (Billy) R.; '87 BS; Sergeant; US Park Police, Dept. of Interior; r. 65 Pemberton Pl., Freehold, NJ 07728; *Annika;* Logan.

VITUCCI, Frank; '77; 1679 Harold Ave., Wantagh, NY 11793.

VIVIECA, Adriana; 6440 65th Ln. # 2, Middle Vlg., NY 11379.

VIVO, Robert F.; '88 BS; 1677 43rd St. # 2, Brooklyn, NY 11204, 718 854-2926.

VIXAMAR, Berenice; '89 BA; 2045 Schenectady Ave., Brooklyn, NY 11234.

VIZCAINO-LAMBRIGHT, '93 BS; 443 Greene Ave., Brooklyn, NY 11216.

VLAD, Cristian A.; '98 BS; NYU; Senior Tech. Analyst-Window NT; Bank of New York, 101 Barclay St., New York, NY 10286, 212 815-4534; r. 98-25 64th Rd., Rego Park, NY 11374, 718 897-8058. e-mail

VO, Chau; '95 BS; Police Ofcr.; NYPD; r. Bronxville, NY 10708, 914 793-2044; *Joyce;* Isabella.

VODDE, Robert F.; '81 MA; 1062 Lafayette Ave. Ext., Hawthorne, NJ 07506.

VOGEL, Bruce J.; '96 BS; 12 Floral Blvd., Floral Park, NY 11001.

VOGLESONG, Daniel P.; '92 MPA; 320 Walnut Ave., New Windsor, NY 12553.

VOGT, Julie A.; '96 MA; 165 Patrice Ter., Williamsville, NY 14221, 716 632-3786.

VOLIN, Howard J.; '82 MA; BS NY Tech, MSW Hunter Clg.; Social Worker/ Retired, Sgt.; The Bronx Medical Ctr./NYC Police, Inpatient Cronic Psyc Unit, 130 W Kingsbridge Rd, Bronx, NY 10468, 718 584-9000; r. 30 Devine St., Lynbrook, NY 11563; *Karen.*

VOLKERTS, Joanne; '90 BS; 112-06 221 St. PH, Queens Vlg., NY 11429.

VOLLMER, D. J.; Rochester Institute of Tech, 1 Lomb Memorial Dr., Rochester, NY 14623.

VOLLMER, Paul; '77 MPA; 12 Campagnoli Ave., Copiague, NY 11726.

VOLMAR, Gary P.; '95 BA; 146 E. 52 St. Ph, Brooklyn, NY 11203, 718 771-0671.

VOLMAR, Marc A., Jr.; '98 BA; Case Planner; Edwin Gould Svcs. for Children, 41 E. 11th St., New York, NY 10003, 212 876-0367; r. 149-77 254 St., Rosedale, NY 11422, 718 712-3952; *Keashawn.* e-mail

VOLPE, Anthony; '76 BS; Fire Chief; Veteran Affairs Fire Dept., Middleville Rd., NYCity Fire Dept-Retired Lieutenant, Northport, NY 11768, 631 754-7915; r. 41 Larry Dr., Commack, NY 11725; *Gloria;* Michael, Richard. e-mail

VOLPE, Frank J.; 1331 80th St., Brooklyn, NY 11228.

VOLPE-WASSERMAN, Catherine M.; '80 BS; 66 Ochard Hill Rd., Monroe, NY 10950.

VOLPI, Ms. Jennifer M.; '98 BA; Human Res. Mgr.; r. 233 Kings St., Staten Island, NY 10312, 718 948-1042; *Shawn Barco.*

VOLYNETS, Anatoliy; '98 BA; 2416 64th St., 1fl., Brooklyn, NY 11204.

VON, Dietsch; '95 BS; 367 Washington Ave., Pleasantville, NY 10570, 914 332-0995.

VONBARGEN, Philip H.; '75 BA; Retired Police Sgt.; r. 309 Twin Ln. S # S., Wantagh, NY 11793, 516 826-3205.

VOSMUS, James F.; '95 BS; 2350 Broadway # 930, New York, NY 10024.

VOUTHAS, Spiros; '96 AS; 6616 52nd Dr., Flushing, NY 11378.

VRANA, Denise L.; '82 BS; 48-26 44 St., Woodside, NY 11377.

VRANA, Dennis; '79 BS; 508 E. 78th St., New York, NY 10021.

VRANA, Kenneth J.; '76 BS; 4150 Kings Hwy., Brooklyn, NY 11234.

VRANTSIDIS, Dorothea; '91 MA; BA, BED Univ. of Windsor; New Model Parts Analyst Mopar; Daimler Chrysler Motors Corp., 2450 Chrysler Ctr., POB 1621, Windsor, ON, Canada N9A 4H6, 519 973-2915; r. 219 Elm Ave., Windsor, ON, Canada N9A 5G9, 519 256-2075. e-mail

VREDENBURGH, E.; '95 MA; Probation Ofcr.; NYC Dept. of Probation, 340 Bay St., Staten Island, NY 10301; r. 85 Cebra Ave., Staten Island, NY 10304, 718 273-3464.

VREDENBURGH, Robert P.; '74 BS; MSED SUNY New Paltz; Special Educ. Tchr.; New York Inst. for Special Educ.; 999 Pelham Pkwy., Bronx, NY 10469, 718 519-7000; r. 25 Sunset Ter., Highland Mills, NY 10930, 914 928-6383. e-mail

VREELAND, Nicholas F.; '86 BA; 26 Pacific Ave., Staten Island, NY 10312.

VROOM, Charles C.; '76 BA; 2 Fabian St., Staten Island, NY 10312, 718 984-4128.

VU, Mimi; '99 BA; 8703 57th Road2nd Fl., Elmhurst, NY 11373, 716 484-6499.

VU, Peter; '94 BS; 141-03 Union Turnp, Flushing, NY 11367, 718 274-3596.

VYAS, Ashwin G.; '76 MA; 140-37 Ash Ave. #604, Flushing, NY 11355.

W

WACHTER, Mark T.; '97 BS; Police Ofcr.; NYC Police Dept.; r. 64-74 80th Ave., Glendale, NY 11385, 718 634-1633. e-mail

WADE, Lori H.; '96 BA; 715 Noble Ave. #, Bronx, NY 10473, 718 378-3791.

WADE, Ryeburn A.; '74 BA; 11579 237th St., Elmont, NY 11003.

WADIS, William A.; '78 BS; 53 Devon St., Malverne, NY 11565.

WAFULA, Bramwell; '86 MPA; 168 Harrison Ave. Apt. 23, Jersey City, NJ 07304.

WAGENSTEIN-VEGA, Carla; '87 MA; 729 W. 186 St. #6E, New York, NY 10033, 315 831-3118.

WAGER, Tracy A.; '96 MA; 33 Steves Ln., Gardiner, NY 12525.

WAGNER, Colette A.; '79 MPA; Asst. Dean; CUNY Ofc. of Computing & Info. Svcs., 212 541-0319; r. 14547 6th Ave., Whitestone, NY 11357, 718 767-8872. e-mail

WAGNER, Harold A.; '86 MPA; Security Cnslt.; r. 2 Normandy Village #5, Nanuet, NY 10954, 914 624-8948.

WAICHMAN, Herbert L.; '79 BS; Atty.; Parker & Waichman, 111 Great Neck Rd., Great Neck, NY 11021, 516 466-6500; r. 163 W. 95th St., New York, NY 10025.

WAITE, Dahlia L.; '95 MA; 9511 Caribbean Blvd., Miami, FL 33189, 305 866-0419.

WAITE-CARSON, Gloria; '87 BA; Licensing Coord.; The Ayco Co., 1 Wall St., Albany, NY 12205, 518 464-2428; r. 102 Patroon Dr. Apt. 11, Guilderland, NY 12084, 518 452-8614. e-mail

WAITE-SHULER, Yvette M.; '97 AS, '98 BA; Child Protective Spec.; Admin. for Children's Svcs., 150 William St., New York, NY 10038, 212 676-6475; r. 35-21 21st St., Apt. 5 H, Long Island City, NY 11106, 718 706-7886; *Romel Shuler;* Anthony, Thomas, Precious.

WALCOT, Marlene A.; '78 BA; 228 E 93rd St., Brooklyn, NY 11212, 718 342-5372.

WALCOTT, Alliston; '90 BS; 861 Saratoga Ave., Brooklyn, NY 11212, 718 345-6026.

WALCOTT, Howard E.; '79 BS; 541 E 52nd St., Brooklyn, NY 11203, 718 455-6453.

WALCOTT, Kama E.; '97 MPA, '99; 48 Sterling St., Brooklyn, NY 11225, 718 756-8330.

WALDEN, Kevin J.; '86 BS; MA Brooklyn Clg., CERT. NYPD Acad.; Retired Asst. Mgr./Guest DJ KISSFM; N.Y.C.H.A., Battery Park City, NY 10007; r. 40 Waterside Plz., New York, NY 10010, 212 686-1818. e-mail

WALDEN, Moises J.; '94 AA, '96 BS; Correction Ofcr.; NYS Dept. of Correctional Svcs., Albany, NY 12201; r. 155-A Riverdale Ave., Brooklyn, NY 11212, 718 346-9314. e-mail

WALDON, Hon. Alton R., Jr.; '68 BS; JD New York Law Sch.; Judge; NYS Ct. of Claims-Suite 8339, 5 World Trade Ctr., New York, NY 10048, 212 775-0100; r. 115-103 222 St., Cambria Hts., NY 11411, 718 723-6136; *Barbara;* Alton, Dana, Ian, Alton III, Kyle Carbucia.

WALDRON, John F.; '98 MA; Police Ofcr.; The City of Sayreville, Sayreville, NJ 08872; r. 10 Green Leaf Way, Holmdel, NJ 07733, 732 264-0298. e-mail

WALDROND, Debra Y.; '78 BA; 11926 144th St., Jamaica, NY 11436.

WALFISH, Karen T. '93 (See Kaj, Karen T.).

WALKER, Adrienne J.; '99 BS; 42 Oakland Ave., Mt. Vernon, NY 10552, 914 969-4911.

WALKER, Ann Marie '94 (See Walker-Rivera, Ann-Marie).

WALKER, Brian H.; '93 BS; Police Ofcr./Secret Svc. Agt.; 120 Balentine Ave., Lake Ronkonkoma, NY 11779, 516 721-4308; r. 120 Balaton Ave., Ronkonkoma, NY 11779. e-mail

WALKER, Ms. Chenyear A.; '97 BS; Case Mgr.; Dept. of Juvenile Justice; r. 1425 Amsterdam, New York, NY 10027, 917 641-1371. e-mail

WALKER, Dana R.; '99 BS; 1010 Sherman Ave. 1E, Bronx, NY 10456, 718 562-7484.

WALKER, Darrell; '76 BA; Capt.; NYC Dept. of Corrections, New York, NY 10001; r. 1791 E 91st St., Brooklyn, NY 11236, 718 763-3568; *Linda;* Elizabeth, Dorian. e-mail

WALKER, David; '99 BA; Child Protective Spec./Student; City of NY/John Jay Clg.-Sch. Pub. Mgmt.; r. POB 20017, Brooklyn, NY 11202.

WALKER, Donna M.; '79 BS; 35 E 106th St. Apt. 4k, New York, NY 10029, 315 336-9377.

WALKER, Edward; '94 BS; Security Coord.; Scudder Kemper, 345 Park Ave., New York, NY 10154; r. 46 Beebe Ave., Hempstead, NY 11550, 516 292-8317.

WALKER, Everlina; '94 BS; 415 Argyle Rd., Brooklyn, NY 11218, 718 771-9521.

WALKER, Heather G.; '93 BS; 766 Crown St., Brooklyn, NY 11213, 718 773-0507.

WALKER, Ms. Hillery G.; '83 BS; Special Agt.; US Customs Svc., 8075 NW 53rd St., Miami, FL 33166, 305 597-6000. e-mail

WALKER, Latanya L.; '86 AS, '87 BA; 17210 133rd Ave. # 11, Jamaica, NY 11434, 718 712-6498.

WALKER, Lisa L.; '97 BS; 515 E 156th St. A, Bronx, NY 10455, 718 893-1167.

WALKER, Mala D., (Mala D. Bentley); '78 BA; Dir./Pres. & CEO; NY Life Ins. Co./Darcel Unlimited; r. 60 Howard Ave., Brooklyn, NY 11221, 718 574-6437. e-mail

WALKER, Marcus R.; '91 BA; 12237 Lakeview Ln., Jamaica, NY 11434, 718 217-0827.

WALKER, Marsha; '90 BA; 496 Linden Blvd., Brooklyn, NY 11203, 718 235-0585.

WALKER, Michael J.; '96 BS; Detective; NYPD; r. 21 3rd Pl., Roosevelt, NY 11575, 516 223-7750. e-mail

WALKER, Pammi (See Hayes, Mrs. Pammi M.).

WALKER, Reginald A.; '92 AS, '95 BS; NYC Transit Police Retired; r. 91-08 32 Ave. Apt.607, E. Elmhurst, NY 11369; Tammy.

WALKER, Robert C.; '79 BS; Admission Coord.; Addictive Disease Svc., 2601 Ocean Pkwy., Brooklyn, NY 11235, 718 616-5615; r. 1213 Avenue Z Apt. D41, Brooklyn, NY 11235, 718 934-9409; Kelly.

WALKER, Sharlisa M.; '97 BS; 49 Granada Ave., Roosevelt, NY 11575, 516 333-6534.

WALKER, Shidina L.; '98 BA; 13422 222nd St., Bsmt, Laurelton, NY 11413, 718 835-7622.

WALKER, Shirley E.; '88 BA; 473 Canterbury St., Westbury, NY 11590, 516 333-6534.

WALKER, Susan M.; '82 BS; MS Chapman Univ.; Stockbroker; Morgan Stanley Dean Witter, 3281 Guasti Rd., Ontario, CA 91761; r. 740 La Cumbre St., Corona, CA 92879, 909 278-3642.

WALKER, Theodore, Jr.; '77 BS; Court Clerk; NYS Supreme Ct. Criminal, 111 Centre St., New York, NY 10013, 212 374-8036; r. 38 Jewell Mckoy Ln., Brooklyn, NY 11213, 718 221-0134.

WALKER, Thomas J.; '77 MPA; 25b Broun Pl., Bronx, NY 10475, 718 994-4522.

WALKER-RIVERA, Ann-Marie, (Ann Marie Walker); '94 BS; Event Specialist; Nasdaq; r. Bronx, NY 10467; *Eddie.*

WALL, Richard; '92 BS; 348 Bauer Pl., Mineola, NY 11501, 516 594-1126.

WALLACE, Adrian N.; '76 BA; Ret. NY Police Dept.; r. 3000 Holiday Dr., Unit. 1604, Ft. Lauderdale, FL 33316, 954 523-6737.

WALLACE, Amanda L.; '95 MA; JD NYU; Atty.; Jones Day Reavis Pogue, 599 Lexington Ave., New York, NY 10022, 212 326-3469; r. 450 Clinton St., Apt. 1B, Brooklyn, NY 11231, 718 596-7322.

WALLACE, April L.; '82 BA; 7534 162nd St., Flushing, NY 11366, 718 977-1228.

WALLACE, Evelyn; '93 BS; 700 Park Ave., Uniondale, NY 11553, 516 489-0812.

WALLACE, John J.; '91 BS; Capt. of The Police Dept.; NYC Police Dept.; r. 8777 254th St., Jamaica, NY 11426.

WALLACE, Patrick J.; '79 BS; Mgr.-in-Charge; Guardsmark Inc., 1290 E. Main St., Stamford, CT 06902, 203 356-0000; r. 31 Brewer Rd, Monsey, NY 10952. e-mail

WALLACE, Roxanne S.; '98 BA; 4137 Wickham Ave., Bronx, NY 10466, 718 716-5616.

WALLACE, Sandra E. '82 (See Higgins, Mrs. Sandra E.).

WALLACE, Stanley; '90 MPA; 3314 Huntley Square Dr., Temple Hills, MD 20748.

WALLACE, Wayne E.; '81 BA; 921 Jefferson Ave., Brooklyn, NY 11221, 718 443-7760.

WALLAWACH, Liane C.; '99 BA; POB 223, Hastings-on-Hudson, NY 10706, 914 478-0521.

WALLE, Brenda; '87 BA; 668 Broadway, Brooklyn, NY 11206, 718 388-8553.

WALLEN, Pamela; '91 BS; 321 E 153 St. #7E, Bronx, NY 10451, 718 601-6414.

WALLEN, Richard J.; '95 BA; 20 Fischer Graduate Res, Apt. 2A, Notre Dame, IN 46556, 219 872-4693.

WALLER, Henry; '85 BS; 114-09 175th Pl., St. Albans, NY 11434, 718 847-0549.

WALLER, Nicole; '93 AS; 225 Wortman Ave. # 8, Brooklyn, NY 11207, 718 266-5030.

WALLIN, Dennis; 17 Elkhart Dr., E. Northport, NY 11731.

WALLS, Bradley J.; '83 BS; 6482 82nd Pl., Flushing, NY 11379, 718 845-1474.

WALLS, Jeanne M.; '83 BA; 512 W 134th St., New York, NY 10031; Hosea, Angela.

WALSH, Ann; '94 AS; 546 Foster Rd, Staten Island, NY 10309, 718 668-0801.

WALSH, Declan J.; '96 MA; Asst. to Pres. John Jay Clg.; John Jay Clg. of Criminal Justice, 899 10th Ave., New York, NY 10019; r. 76 Remsen St. # B, Brooklyn, NY 11201, 718 624-2418. e-mail

WALSH, Dennis J.; '80 BS; Administrative Lt.; NY Police Dept., 1 Police Plz., New York, NY 10038, 212 477-7834; r. 390 Madison Ave., W. Hempstead, NY 11552, 516 483-6483.

WALSH, George J.; '75 BA; Appraiser; Accurate Appraisals, 1018 Post Ave., Staten Island, NY 10302, 718 815-2020; r. 253 Crystal Ave., Staten Island, NY 10302, 718 816-5467; *Katherine;* Logan. e-mail

WALSH, James G.; '93 BS; 169 Read Ave., Tuckahoe, NY 10707.

WALSH, James J.; '76 BA; 1215 81st St., Brooklyn, NY 11228, 718 434-6734.

WALSH, Jeanne M.; '88 BS; 1727 Andrea Rd, E. Meadow, NY 11554.

WALSH, John J.; '76 BS; NYC Detective; NYC Police Dept., 94th Precinct, 100 Meserole Ave., Brooklyn, NY 11222, 718 383-8456; r. 193 Bromleigh Rd., Garden City, NY 11530; *Marylou;* Meagan, Marybeth, Thomas.

WALSH, Joseph C.; '79 BA; 314 W 1st St., W. Islip, NY 11795, 631 277-3324.

WALSH, Lawrence G.; '87 MA; 15110 35th Ave. Apt. 3h, Flushing, NY 11354, 718 634-4635.

WALSH, Martin F.; '78 BS; 1751 E 29th St., Brooklyn, NY 11229, 718 837-8923.

WALSH, Matthew T.; '95 BA; 53 S Grove St., Valley Stream, NY 11580, 516 825-6441.

WALSH, Michael J.; '73 BS; 2260 Burnett St. # Ik, Brooklyn, NY 11229, 718 332-8725.

WALSH, Patricia M.; '80 BS; 9808 Ft. Hamilton Pkwy., Brooklyn, NY 11209, 718 836-2173.

WALSH, Paul; '92 AS; Police Ofcr.; NYC Police Dept., Long Pl. Plz., New York, NY 10001; r. 3530 Henry Hudson, Bronx, NY 10463, 718 549-4858; *Bridget;* Terrence, Katie.

WALSH, Thomas B.; '98 BS; 3 Hickory Hill Rd., Newburgh, NY 12550, 914 564-6393.

WALSH, Thomas J.; 811 52nd St., Brooklyn, NY 11220, 718 768-6902.

WALSH, Thomas P.; '74 BS; 568 Bement Ave., Staten Island, NY 10310, 718 447-5232. e-mail

WALSH, William T.; '78 BS; 83-15 98 St., Woodhaven, NY 11421, 718 634-4635.

WALSH-WRIGHT, Carlene; '93 BS; 650 Baltic St., Brooklyn, NY 11217, 718 230-8051.

WALTER, Bruce W.; '75 BS; MBA CW Post; Pres.; RTWB Ltd., Laudry Services, Bethpage, NY 11714, 516 794-7509; r. 1696 Coral Rd, E. Meadow, NY 11554, 516 794-7509; *Lorraine;* Jeffrey, Janet, Brian. e-mail

WALTERS, Eustace; '79 BS; 106-09 Glenwood Rd, Brooklyn, NY 11236, 718 625-8649.

WALTERS, Ms. Jacqueline M., (Jacqueline Shaw); '83 BS; Investigator; State Inspector Gen. Ofc., 61 Broadway, 12th Fl., New York, NY 10006; r. 494 Kirkman Ave., Elmont, NY 11003, 516 437-4899; *Roy;* Roy Jr.

WALTERS, Mark; '93 BS; 1233 Wheeler Ave., Bronx, NY 10472, 718 515-3396.

WALTERS, Paul A.; '83 BS; 3400 Tiemann Ave., Bronx, NY 10469, 718 655-4768.

WALTERS, Veronica; '76 BA; 22015 118th Ave., Jamaica, NY 11411.

WALTHER, Derek G.; '95 BS; 4240 Hutchinson R., Bronx, NY 10475.

WALTHER, Jennifer '96 (See Levitz, Jennifer).

WALTON, Joyce W.; '90 BA; 218 W. 112 St., New York, NY 10026, 315 839-5342.

WALZ, Thomas M.; '76 BS; Supv.; NYC Dept. Sanitation; r. 666 45th St., Brooklyn, NY 11220, 718 633-7358.

WAN, Chung N.; '87 BS; 239 Bay Ridge Ave., Brooklyn, NY 11220, 718 965-1685.

WANIGASINGHE, Sarath; '90 BS; 54 W. 74 St., New York, NY 10023, 212 799-0555.

WARD, Clayton; '81 BA; 175 Ardsley Loop Apt. 12e, Brooklyn, NY 11239, 718 221-1329.

WARD, Clifford; '97 BS, '98 BS; 1249 E 39th St., Brooklyn, NY 11210, 718 221-1329.

WARD, Donella; '79 BA; 1370 New York Ave., Brooklyn, NY 11203, 718 856-1699.

WARD, Edward C.; '79 BS; 55 Wyona Ave., Staten Island, NY 10314, 718 448-2610.

WARD, Esther L.; '80 BS; Police Ofcr.; NYC Police Dept.; r. Brooklyn, NY 11238. e-mail

WARD, Florence V.; '86 BS; Customer Svc. Agt.; Northwest Airlines, Inc., Corporate Headquarters, 5101 Northwest Dr., St. Paul, MN 55111, 612 726-2206; r. 154 Hidden Hill Cir., Odenton, MD 21113, 410 672-4148. e-mail

WARD, Jacqueline A.; '99 BA; 628 E 95th St.2nd Fl., Brooklyn, NY 11236, 718 257-3015. e-mail

WARD, John J.; '74; 188 Beach 122nd St., Far Rockaway, NY 11694, 718 634-7609.

WARD, John W.; '74 BA; Retired-Police Capt.; NYC Police Dept.; r. 117 Berkeley Pl., Massapequa, NY 11758, 516 795-6287.

WARD, Joseph R.; '75 BS; 421 S W 2nd St., Boca Raton, FL 33432, 561 395-6479.

WARD, Kevin; '91 BA; 566 74th St., Brooklyn, NY 11209, 718 282-0085.

WARD, Kevin M.; '79 BS; Police Ofcr.; New York Port Authority, New York, NY 10004.

WARD, Ms. Linda M.; '95 BA; Technical Coord. for Projects; Skadden Arps Slate Meagher & Flom LLP, 4 Times Sq., #36328, New York, NY 10022, 212 735-2317; r. 547 Hillside Ter., W. Orange, NJ 07052. e-mail

WARD, Orson R.; '98 BS; 906 Jefferson Ave., Brooklyn, NY 11221, 718 453-9359.

WARD, Richard H.; '68 BS; MCRIM Univ. of CA-Berkeley, DCRIM Univ. of CA Berkeley; Dean; Clg. of Criminal Justice, Sam Houston State Univ, Huntsville, TX 77341, 936 294-1632; r. POB 1140, Huntsville, TX 77342; *Michelle;* Jeanne, Jonathan. e-mail

WARD, Rodney C.; '80 BA; JD Jacobs Fuchsberg Univ.; Atty.; Rodney Ward, 774 Manor Rd., Staten Island, NY 10314, 718 698-8176; r. 178 Devoe Ave., Spotswood, NJ 08884, 732 251-6345; *Catherine;* Rodney IV, Jeanne Martin.

WARD, Roger; '97 BA, '97 MPA; Asst. Dean of Students; Kingborough Community Clg., Brooklyn, NY 11235; r. 90-21 204th St., Hollis, NY 11423, 718 776-8437. e-mail

WARD, Thomas J., DPA; DPA Nova Southeastern Univ.; Dir. Criminal Justice Prog.; St. John's Univ., 8000 Utopia Pkwy., Jamaica, NY 11439, 718 990-6110; r. 22 Ohio Ave., Massapequa, NY 11758, 516 799-2044; *Patricia;* Thomas. e-mail

WARD, Yvette A.; '97 BS; Sgt.; NY Police Dept., 718 520-9367; r. 985 Pierce Ave., Bronx, NY 10462. e-mail

WARGO, Albert J.; 23 Midwood Rd., W. Babylon, NY 11704.

WARGO, Catherine M.; '99 MA; Family Therapist; Catholic Charity, Bridgewater, NJ 08807; r. 46 Village Green Apt. P, Budd Lake, NJ 07828, 973 448-0757; *Robert Oates.* e-mail

WARGO, Jennifer; '98 MA; 25-55 42nd St. #1, Astoria, NY 11103, 718 267-0964.

WARLEY, Raquel-Maria; '93 BA, '95 MA; Rsch. Assoc.; Natl. Devel. & Rsch. Institutes, 2 World Trade Ctr., 16 Fl., New York, NY 10048, 212 845-4539; r. 1735 Fulton Ave. Apt. 2A, Bronx, NY 10457; *Gerald Goodwin;* Royale. e-mail

WARNE, Kenneth C.; '75 BS; 530 Dubois Ave. Apt. 3c, Valley Stream, NY 11581, 516 481-3312.

WARNER, Mary L.; '78 BA; 245 Lefferts Ave., Brooklyn, NY 11225, 718 921-0858.

WARNER, Philip R.; '85 BS; Client Svc. Mgr.; Burns Intern. Security, 29 John St., New York, NY 10038, 212 312-1900; r. 874 W. Broadway, B3, Woodmere, NY 11598, 516 569-5854. e-mail

WARNER, Rupert R.; '77 BA; 245 Lefferts Ave., Brooklyn, NY 11225, 718 789-5969.

WARNER- LYONS, Mrs. Elyse Y.; '94 AS; Administrative Asst.; Mendes & Mt., LLP, 750 Seventh Ave., New York, NY 10019, 212 261-8369; r. 4100 Hutchinson River Pkwy. E, Apt. 12G, Bronx, NY 10475, 718 320-9812; *Patrick Lyons.* e-mail

WARNQUIST, David G.; '76 AS; 207 Seeley Ave., Kearny, NJ 07032.

WARREN, Gerald; '97 BA; 139 E. 150th St., Bronx, NY 10457, 718 671-1903.

WARREN, Glenn E.; '96 BS; 2800 Heath Ave., Bronx, NY 10463.

WARREN, Michael A.; '94 BS; 15076 Village Rd Apt. B, Jamaica, NY 11432, 718 657-7962.

WARREN, Robert C., Sr.; '76 AS; Retired Personal Inspection Svc.; r. 12243 Long St., Jamaica, NY 11434, 917 901-5937.

WARREN, Sondra J.; '95 BA; 631 Beach 9th St. Apt. 4j, Far Rockaway, NY 11691, 718 746-1419.

WARREN, Sophia D.; '95 BS; 1273 E 85th St., Brooklyn, NY 11236, 718 237-0096.

WARREN-LEVANT, Cassandra '91 (See Levant, Cassandra D.).

WARSAW, Harmon; '90 BS; 245 Lenox Rd Apt. 3e, Brooklyn, NY 11226.

WARTHEN, Rodney; '98 BS; 1040 E. 92nd St., Brooklyn, NY 11236, 718 649-7812.

WASHINGTON, Archie; '97 BS; Sergeant; NYPD, 1 Police Plz., New York, NY 10038; r. 440 Warburton Ave., Yonkers, NY 10701, 914 969-4796.

WASHINGTON, Bernetha; '98 BS; 40 W 135th St., Apt. 2L, New York, NY 10037.

WASHINGTON, David L.; '82 BS; 11846 221st St., Jamaica, NY 11411, 718 848-3646.

WASHINGTON, Dawn C.; '92 BS; 540 Louisiana Ave., Apt. 3Fl, Brooklyn, NY 11239, 718 573-7683.

WASHINGTON, Dennise Y.; '90 BA, '97 MPA, '98; Asst. Court Analyst; 60 Lafayette Street Suite 6B9, New York, NY 10013, 212 374-0165; r. 137-40 45th Ave. #1C, Flushing, NY 11355, 718 359-7870. e-mail

WASHINGTON, Genesis; '87 MA; 920 Co Op City Blvd. # 3, Bronx, NY 10475.

WASHINGTON, Juanita; '79 MPA; 284 Park Pl. #2, Brooklyn, NY 11238, 718 252-1556.

WASHINGTON, Kim; '88 BS, '95 CERT; 462 Miller Ave., Brooklyn, NY 11207, 718 348-5763.

WASHINGTON, Kurt M.; '78 BS; 20516 113th Rd, Jamaica, NY 11412, 718 465-6878.

WASHINGTON, Leona; '85 MPA; 2010 Bruckner Blvd., Bronx, NY 10473, 718 829-1436.

WASHINGTON, Oliver J.; '83 BS; POB 110084, Jamaica, NY 11411, 718 353-6697.

WASHINGTON, Reginald; '90 BS; 74 Sugarloaf Mt. R, Chester, NY 10918.

WASHINGTON, Rudy; '76 BA; 116-36 148th St., Jamaica, NY 11436, 718 353-6697.

WASHINGTON, Thalia; '84 BS; 3303 Foster Ave., Brooklyn, NY 11203, 718 388-2548.

WASHINGTON, Theresa M.; '99 BA; 329 Archer, Freeport, NY 11520, 516 771-6123.

WASHINGTON, Vermell; 2144 Lacombe Ave., Bronx, NY 10473, 718 562-7987.

WASHINGTON-GOELOE, Stephanie; '95 AS, '97 BS; 712 E 95th St., Brooklyn, NY 11236, 718 485-8402.

WASSELL, Michael M.; '89 MA; 62-23 Asquith Cres., Rego Park, NY 11374.

WASSERMAN, David; '87 BS; Metrology Coordinator Chemist; Pfizer Inc., Eastern Point Rd., Groton, CT 06340, 860 441-1329; r. 12 Hem St., E. Haddam, CT 06423, 860 873-2743. e-mail

WASSERMAN, Mitchell; '82 BS; 2820 Ocean Pkwy., Brooklyn, NY 11235, 718 435-8090.

WASZCZUK, Wieslaw; '98 BA; Confidential Investigator; r. 190 Russell St., Brooklyn, NY 11222, 718 389-3942. e-mail

WATENBERG, Mark; '82 BS; Police Lt.; NYC Police Dept.; r. 60 Charing Cross, Lynbrook, NY 11563; *Carol;* Amanda, Michael. e-mail

WATERMAN, Georgina L.; '96 BA; 93 E 45th St., Brooklyn, NY 11203, 718 237-9389.

WATERS, Sean H. T.; '97 MPA, '98 MS; BA Iona Clg.; Spec.; Fed. Emergency Mgmt. Agcy., 26 Federal Plz., 13th Fl., New York, NY 10278.

WATERS, Therese M.; '95 MA; POB 6, Mt. Laurel, NJ 08054.

WATFORD, Gregory J.; '85 BS; 140 Einstein Loop # 21, Bronx, NY 10475, 718 542-1261.

WATKINS, John S.; '89 MA; 53 Plymouth Rd, White Plains, NY 10603, 914 592-9334.

WATKINS, Ms. Tracey L.; '85 BA; Logical Provisioner; Northpoint Communications, 5858 Horton St., Emeryville, CA 94608, 510 985-6700; r. 802 Hancock St., Apt. 602, Hayward, CA 94544, 510 733-2153. e-mail

WATLINGTON, James L.; '88 BS; Probation Ofcr.-Warrant Div.; NYC Dept. of Probation, 2-4 Nevins St., Brooklyn, NY 11217, 718 643-4603; r. 11488 225th St., Jamaica, NY 11411.

WATSON, Alwyn; '87 BS; Legal Cnslt.; Admin. for Children's Svcs.; r. 1155 Grand Concourse, Apt. 2g, Bronx, NY 10452; *Laray Price.*

WATSON, Gerard; '81 BS, '87 MPA; 10 Stratford Rd Apt. 5a, Brooklyn, NY 11218, 718 968-0297.

WATSON, Roosevelt A.; '83 BA; 288 E 54th St., Brooklyn, NY 11203, 718 282-7413.

WATT, Robert E.; '81 BS; 74 Lansing St., Staten Island, NY 10305, 718 984-5493.

WATTS, Timothy D.; '91 BS; 216 Cascade Dr., Athens, AL 35611.

WAWA, Eleanor '96 (See Roldan, Mrs. Eleanor J.).

WAWRZONEK, Matthew; '75 AS; 8960 215th St., Queens Vlg., NY 11427, 718 465-7208.

WAXENBERG, Sheldon; Prof of Psychology; John Jay Clg. of Criminal Justice; r. 175 Riverside Dr. # 14f, New York, NY 10024, 212 787-4324.

WAXMAN, Mrs. Lorraine, (Lorraine Silberzweig); '79 MA; Homemaker; r. 325 Sinclair Ct., Morganville, NJ 07751, 732 617-2405; *Allan;* Gregory, Matthew, Jonathan. e-mail

WAYE, Jane; '85 BA; Retired Police Ofcr.; r. POB 20794, Cleveland, OH 44120.

WAYMER, Connie R.; '79 BA; 108 Grafton St., Brooklyn, NY 11212.

WAYNE, Reva R.; '83 MPA; 5135 66th St., Flushing, NY 11377.

WAZETER, Edward J.; '78 BS; 19 Franklin Ln., Apt. B, Staten Island, NY 10306.

WEAVER, David; '77 AS; 13149 226th St., Jamaica, NY 11413, 718 634-4137.

WEAVER, Ronald; '77 BS; POB 159, Carmel, NY 10512, 914 225-9499.

WEBB, Amir; 401 E. 89th St., Apt. 9G, New York, NY 10128, 315 363-5205.

WEBB, Elizabeth V.; '82 BS, '85 MPA; 100 Bellamy Loop Apt. 23c, Bronx, NY 10475, 718 329-2956.

WEBB, Hillary D.; '99 BA; CUNY Grad. Ctr.; Rsch. Asst/Grad. Student; Ctr. for Advanced Study In Educ., New York, NY 10001, 212 817-1847; r. 50 W. 97 St. Apt. 10 T, New York, NY 10025, 212 865-3769. e-mail

WEBB, Karen A.; '93 BS; 2846 W. 31st St., Brooklyn, NY 11224, 718 253-3933.

WEBB, Ruth H.; '99 MA; Student; Illinois Sch. of Profn. Psych. Chicago; r. 12826 Hickory Ct., Clive, IA 50325, 515 221-1009.

WEBB, Shaun D.; '99 BA; Investigator; EVR HRA Agcy., New York, NY 10001; r. 226 Fountain Ave. 1, Brooklyn, NY 11208, 718 277-1258. e-mail

WEBBER, Leroy M.; '97 BS; 1st Grade Tchr.; Bd. of Educ.; r. 3308 Kingsland Ave., Bronx, NY 10469, 718 231-1415.

WEBER, Herschel; '96 BA; MA Tchrs. Clg.; Staff Analyst/Technical Recruiter; NYC Dept. of IT & Telecommunications, New York, NY 10001; r. 773 E 2nd St., Brooklyn, NY 11218, 718 436-3961.

WEBER, John; '72 BS; Police Ofcr.; Town of Haverstraw, 1 Rosman Rd, Garnerville, NY 10923, 914 354-1500; r. 33 Summit Ave., Tappan, NY 10983, 914 359-0526.

WEBER, Robert D., Jr.; '96 MA; Retired Police Lt.; Briarcliff Manor Police Dept.; r. 72 Burning Bush Dr., Palm Coast, FL 32137, 904 445-2005. e-mail

WEBER, Thomas K.; 7101 69th Pl., Flushing, NY 11385, 718 544-7955.

WEBER, William J.; '75 MPA; 25 S Serven St., Pearl River, NY 10965, 914 735-8913.

WEBER, William P.; '81 BS; 3879 Ralph St. S, Seaford, NY 11783.

WEBLEY, Karen R.; '97 BS; 1154 E 56th St., Brooklyn, NY 11234, 718 443-6645.

WEBSTER, Noel W.; '78 BS; Retired Lt. NYPD; r. 235-40 148th Ave., Rosedale, NY 11422, 718 723-6010; *Monica;* David, Elizabeth.

WEDIN, Frederick H.; '76 BS; 32 Keen Ct., Brooklyn, NY 11229.

WEEDEN, Thomas A.; '86 BS; 2966 Avenue R, Brooklyn, NY 11229.

WEEEKS, Donnetta; '98 BA; 143-08 Glassboro Ave., Jamaica, NY 11435, 718 291-4578.

WEEMS, Betty P.; '93 BS; Security Cnslt.; 718 857-3507; r. 325 Clinton Ave., Apt. 9A, Brooklyn, NY 11205. e-mail

WEEMS, Scott C.; '95 BA; 22 Ellicott Ave., Batavia, NY 14020.

WEGMAN, James L., CPP; '80 BS, '80 AS; Literary Cnslt.; 9217 E. Coopers Hawk Drive, Sun Lakes, AZ 85248, 480 883-1538; r. 9217 E Coopers Hawk Dr., Sun Lakes, AZ 85248, 480 883-1538; *Regina;* Maryellen, Allyson.

WEHYE, Prince M.; '86 BS; 1311 Dean St., Brooklyn, NY 11216.

WEIDENFELD, Alan I.; '97 BA, '98 MA; 135 96th St., Brooklyn, NY 11209.

WEILER, Edward; '89 BS; Dist. Supv.; Wise Recycling, 2312 Senic Hwy., Baton Rouge, LA 70812, 800 820-9473; r. 3804 Morriswood Dr., Harvey, LA 70058, 504 341-0897; Shawndra. e-mail

WEINBAUM, Nathan; '74 BA; MA NYU; HS Social Studies Tchr.; NYC Public Schs.; r. 100 Beekman St. Apt. 26k, New York, NY 10038, 212 571-1319; *Carol B.* e-mail

WEINBERG, Blair; '93 BS; 710 West End Ave., New York, NY 10025.

WEINBERG, Jeffrey; '87 BS; 807 Inwood Ter., Ft. Lee, NJ 07024.

WEINBERG, Paul; '92 BS; 501b Surf Ave. Apt. 23m, Brooklyn, NY 11224, 718 968-1928.

WEINER, Alan R.; '70 MPA; BBA CUNY, MLS Pratt Inst.; Retired Prof.; CUNY; r. 3 Markham Dr., Morganville, NJ 07751, 732 536-3090; *Margo;* Frances, Daniel.

WEINER, Barry J.; '78 BA; 142 15 Franklin Ave., Flushing, NY 11355, 718 739-8277.

WEINSHALL, Ilene; '93 BA; 8855 Bay Pkwy., Brooklyn, NY 11214.

WEINSTEIN, Jay A.; '71 BS; MS Columbia Univ.; Supv.; City of NY, 275 Bergen St., Brooklyn, NY 11217, 718 694-8759; r. 303 Beverley Rd Apt. 2a, Brooklyn, NY 11218, 718 633-2286. e-mail

WEINSTOCK, Margot; '93 MA; Lawyer; r. 180 East End Ave. Apt. 14E, New York, NY 10128; *Alexander.* e-mail

WEIR, Jacqueline M.; '79 MA; 8402 4th Ave., Brooklyn, NY 11209, 718 748-8698.

WEIR, Lillian W. '77 (See Robinson, Ms. Lillian W.).

WEIR, SGT Seamus P.; '91 BS; Sergeant; NYPD Midtown North Detective Squad, 306 W. 54th St., New York, NY 10019, 212 767-8415; r. Goshen, NY 10924; *Jessica;* Seamus Jr., Megan, Kathryn, Brian. e-mail

WEIS, Richard; '85 MA; BS New York Inst. of Tech; Sr. Court Ofcr.; NYS Ofc. of Ct. Admin.; r. 60 Deer Lake Dr., N. Babylon, NY 11703, 631 586-9263.

WEISBERG, Daniel M.; '89 BS; JD Pace Univ. Sch. of Law; Police Sergeant; Town of Clarkstown Police Dept, 20 Maple Ave., New City, NY 10956, 914 639-5800; r. 97 Burda Ave., New City, NY 10956. e-mail

WEISBERG, Elyse J.; '90 MPA; Network Data Security; City of NY Admin. Children's Svc., 150 Williams St., New York, NY 10038, 212 616-8668; r. 9323 Shore Rd, Apt. 5F, Brooklyn, NY 11209, 718 759-0888. e-mail

WEISENFELD, Marc D.; '95 BA; Special Investigator; NYC Dept. of Investigation; r. 132 W. 71st. #4, New York, NY 10023, 212 579-8206.

WEISFUSE, Irene W.; '81 MA; 3087 Hickory St., Yorktown Hts., NY 10598.

WEISS, Deborah J.; '78 BS, '88 MA; 3057 Brighton 4th St., Brooklyn, NY 11235, 718 859-4160.

WEISS, Jason H.; '96 BS; 35 Edward St., Demarest, NJ 07627, 201 767-3946.

WEISS, Kenneth D.; '80 MA; 2953 Ardsley Rd, Wantagh, NY 11793, 516 826-5838.

WEISS, Rudolf; '85 MPA; 6731 73rd Pl., Flushing, NY 11379, 718 279-9174.

WEISSMAN, David E.; '75 BA; 506 1/2 N Genesee, Los Angeles, CA 90036, 323 650-6232.

WEISWASSER, David; '97 BA; 60 E.8th St. 21E, New York, NY 10003, 212 777-4047.

WEKARSKI, Stanley P.; '78 AS; 188 W Prospect St., Waldwick, NJ 07463, 201 670-9129.

WELCH, Edward J.; '93 MA; 152 Cleveland Dr., Croton-on-Hudson, NY 10520.

WELCH, James A.; 14 Reed Dr., Deer Park, NY 11729, 631 586-4936.

WELCH, Nicole D.; '93 BS; Acctg.; Cadwalader, Wikersham & Taft, 100 Maiden Ln., New York, NY 10038, 212 504-6791; r. 2045 Story Ave., Apt. 3E, Bronx, NY 10473; *Kenny;* Justin. e-mail

WELCH, Sylvia P.; '82 BA; AA NYCC; Supv; US Dept. of Justice-Immigration, Naturalization Service, Arlington, VA 22203, 202 307-1667; r. 16915 Toms River Loop, Dumfries, VA 22026, 703 221-7694; Michele, Janine, Rodolfo Jr., Tamaris, Janiesha.

WELCOME, Bryan N.; '92 BA; 426 E. 35th St., Brooklyn, NY 11203.

WELLENKAMP, Susan A.; '82 MA; 457 81st St., Brooklyn, NY 11209.

WELLINGTON, Jacqueline; '91 BA; 17 Marietta Dr., Westbury, NY 11590, 516 334-7724.

WELLS, Angie Y.; '81 BA; Confidential Investigator; Dept. of Investigations, 180 Water St., New York, NY 10038, 212 331-3015; r. 15620 Riverside Dr. W Apt. 5M, New York, NY 10032, 212 923-4052.

WELLS, Charles J.; '78 AS; BS; 262 Delafield Ave., Staten Island, NY 10310, 718 442-5932.

WELLS, Marianne E.; '99 MA; Unit Therapist; MA Treatment Ctr., Bridgewater, MA 02324; r. 230 Willard St., Quincy, MA 02169, 617 479-7649. e-mail

WELLS, Roderick C.; '84 MPA; 135 Eastern Pkwy., Brooklyn, NY 11238, 718 375-0627.

WELLS, Rory J.; '92 BA; 21 Clinton St., Belleville, NJ 07109, 973 751-3593.

WELLS, Ruth A.; '78, '80 BS; 10938 Guy R Brewer Blvd., Jamaica, NY 11433, 718 526-3071.

WELLS, Tara; '92 BA; 345 Cypress Ave. # 3, Bronx, NY 10454, 718 515-0006.

WELLS, William E.; '75 AS; 13412 155th St., Jamaica, NY 11434, 718 341-3149.

WELSH, Christopher; '88 BA; 2 5th Ave. Apt. 12p, New York, NY 10011, 212 533-5021.

WELSH, James L.; '93 MPA; 3232 Bears Den Rd, Youngstown, OH 44511, 330 995-0112.

WELSH, John J.; '79 BS; 423 Bert Rd, Far Rockaway, NY 11693, 718 429-4745.

WELSH, Katherine W.; '80 MA; BS SUNY-New Paltz, Southern CT State Univ.; Special Educ. Supv.; Danbury HS, 43 Clapboard Ridge Rd, Danbury, CT 06811, 203 790-2868; r. 4 Claremont Ave., Danbury, CT 06810, 203 744-2183. e-mail

WELSH, Lawrence J.; '95 BA; AAS Bronx Community Clg.; Sr. Couns. Addiction Treatment; Dept. of Corrections, 1010 Haven St., E. Elmhurst, NY 11370, 718 546-6297; r. 11842 197th St., St. Albans, NY 11412, 718 712-4425; *Thomasina.*

WELSH, Mrs. Venesia A., (Venesia Crooks); '94 BS; Claims Examiner; Grp. Health Inc., 441 Ninth Ave., New York, NY 10116, 212 615-0100; r. 348 Levinsohn Pl., Englewood, NJ 07631, 201 871-9303; *Clyde;* Clyde Jr. e-mail

WELSH-SHIRLEY, Joyce L.; '97 BS; Portfolio Support Analyst; Scudder Kemper Investments, 345 Park Ave., New York, NY 10154, 212 326-6459; r. 1320 E. 224th St., Bronx, NY 10466, 718 325-5031; *Clifton Shirley.*

WELT, Carey A.; '89 BS; AAS SUNY-Farmingdale; Fire Marshal/Div. Supv.; Nassau Cnty., 899 Jerusalem Ave., Uniondale, NY 11553, 516 572-1038; r. 57 Myles Ave., Levittown, NY 11756, 516 681-7912; *Deborah;* Sarah, Adam, David, Rachel. e-mail

WEMPE, Raymond H.; '81 BS; Detective; Suffolk Cnty. Police Dept., 30 Yaphank Ave., Yaphank, NY 11980, 631 852-6000; r. 226 Sears Rd, W. Islip, NY 11795. e-mail

WENDLE, Thomas A.; '73 BA; AS Westchester Community Clg; Mgr.; Axa Financial Inc., 1290 67th Ave., New York, NY 10104, 212 314-2684; r. 171 N. Washington St., Sleepy Hollow, NY 10591, 914 332-0648; Katie, Lily. e-mail

WENDOLSKI, Peter P.; '75 BS; 246 Stone Ave. # 3, Yonkers, NY 10701, 914 965-8840.

WENDRUFF, Lorrie; 117 Hudson St., Lakewood, NJ 08701, 732 363-0152.

WENSTROM, Erika M.; '99 BA; 925 S Wolfe Rd Apt. 76, Sunnyvale, CA 94086.

WENTHE, Leah A.; '93 MA; 526 Pacific Ave., Apt. 2407, Atlantic City, NJ 08401, 609 345-4040.

WENZ, Maura; '83 BS; 20 S. First St., New Hyde Park, NY 11040, 516 656-0123.

WERBKAY, Victor R.; '75 BA, '78 MA; Retired Deputy Inspector; NYC Police Dept.; r. 613 Marcellus Rd, Williston Park, NY 11596, 516 294-0136; *Jacqueline;* Karen, Steven, Christopher.

WERMUTH, Ezra C.; '77 BS; 680 West End Ave., New York, NY 10025.

WERNER, Edward C.; '83 MA; 60 Haven Ave., Valley Stream, NY 11580, 516 285-8159.

WERNLY, Robert P.; '78 MPA; 92-09 101 Ave., Ozone Park, NY 11416.

WERTKIN, Stephen L.; '75 MA; Asst. Deputy Commissioner; Ofc. Chief Med. Examiner, 520 1st Ave., New York, NY 10016; r. 1561 E 17th St., Brooklyn, NY 11230, 718 375-8063.

WESBY, Darryl K.; '86 BS; 13133 133rd St., Jamaica, NY 11420, 718 322-1289.

WESLEY, George E.; 12933 154th St., Jamaica, NY 11434, 718 712-2544.

WESLEY, Lois A.; '76 BA; Retired Library Asst.; r. 2201 Amsterdam Ave., New York, NY 10032.

WESSOLOCK, Robert E.; '81 BS; 1243 Todt Hill Rd, Staten Island, NY 10304.

WEST, Clifford W.; '89 MA; 109 Jennings Rd, Horseheads, NY 14845.

WEST, Deborah, (Deborah George); '83 BS, '85 MPA; Child Welfare Spec./ Ofc.Base Traine; Admin. for Child Svcs., 150 Williams St., New York, NY 10038, 212 676-7083; r. 289 Marion St., Brooklyn, NY 11233; *Whitfield;* Whitney, Tiffany.

WEST, Donna M.; '89 BS; 150 Dreiser Loop, Apt. 14E, Bronx, NY 10475.

WEST, Felicia A.; '99 BA; 98-30 57th Ave. #11Dd, Rego Park, NY 11368, 718 699-5242.

WEST, Janice Y.; '81 BS; Sr. Court Clerk; r. 9 Park 200 Apt., Clifton Park, NY 12065, 518 348-0333; *Nigel;* Xavier, Christopher.

WEST, Valerie; '95 BA; 708 W 171st St., Apt. 44B, New York, NY 10032, 315 361-1799.

WESTCOTT-MARSHALL, Darryl A.; '78 BA, '93 MA; Couns. Academic Advisor; John Jay Clg. of Criminal Justice, 445 W. 59th St. Rm. 3137n, New York, NY 10019, 212 237-8304; r. Apt. 1K, Bronx, NY 10451, 718 893-8803.

WESTFALL, Julius M.; New York, NY 10001.

WESTON, Denise M.; '97 BS; Police Ofcr.; NYPD; r. 32-45 88th St., Jackson Hts., NY 11369, 718 468-7256. e-mail

WESTRENEN, Jack; '78 BS; 330 Mosel Ave., Staten Island, NY 10304, 718 273-8034.

WETZEL, Tracey P.; '95 BS; 15825 97th St., Jamaica, NY 11414, 718 843-1936.

WEXLER, Jason D.; '93 BS; 153 Arbutus Ave., Staten Island, NY 10312.

WHALEN, Joseph W.; '76 BS; 258 Rugby Rd, Brooklyn, NY 11226, 718 462-0019.

WHARTON, Arnetha N.; '99 BS; 758 E 219 St. 18E, Bronx, NY 10467, 718 881-7085.

WHEATLE, Kerensa C.; '98 BS; 602 Midwood Ave., Brooklyn, NY 11203, 718 774-0007.

WHEELER, James J.; '80 MA; 18 Stuyvesant Oval Apt. 9h, New York, NY 10009, 212 217-2854.

WHEELER, Jo; Sales Mgr.; Stutts Advt. Agcy., 1016 Collection Creek Way, Virginia Bch., VA 23454.

WHEELER, Thomas J.; '80 MPA; 431 E. 20th St., New York, NY 10010, 212 477-6108.

WHELAN, Francis J.; '64 MPA; 8789 95th St., Jamaica, NY 11421, 718 380-1845.

WHELAN, William E.; '79 BS; 10 Eisenhower Rd, Centereach, NY 11720.

WHINFIELD, Dennis; '86 BS; 3524 Avenue K, Brooklyn, NY 11210, 718 852-3877.

WHITAKER, M. Katrina; '86 BS; PARALEG. Long Island Univ., MEDIAT. LI Univ.; Hosp. Care Investigator; King Cnty. Hosp. Cntr.; r. 960 Sterling Pl., Apt. 1 J, Brooklyn, NY 11213, 718 493-4377.

WHITAKER, Thelma J.; '81 BS; Retired Safety Ofcr.-Sergeant; State of NY; r. 138-70 Elder Ave., Flushing, NY 11355, 718 961-3366.

WHITE, Aleda J.; '80 BS; 679 E 78th St., Brooklyn, NY 11236.

WHITE, Andre L.; '94 BS; 169-12 Brinkerhoff Ave., Jamaica, NY 11433, 718 533-0444.

WHITE, Brenda L.; '89 BS; 3419 Irwin Ave. #15, Bronx, NY 10463, 718 655-8373.

WHITE, Caleb J.; '99 BA; 35 Ethelridge Rd, White Plains, NY 10605, 914 948-1373.

WHITE, David W.; '76 BA; 2137 Avalon Dr., Sumter, SC 29154.

WHITE, Debra; '94 BS; 14541 Foch Blvd., Jamaica, NY 11436.

WHITE, Debra G.; '83 BS; 129-18 158th St., Jamaica, NY 11434, 718 533-0444.

WHITE, Douglas; '75 BA; 104 3rd St., New City, NY 10956, 914 358-4556.

WHITE, Geneva A.; '80 BS; 19611 100th Ave., Hollis, NY 11423, 718 276-8730.

WHITE, Gregory A.; '83 BA; 98-23 H. Harding E, Rego Park, NY 11368, 718 276-8730.

WHITE, James; '83 BS; Correction Ofcr.; NYC Dept. of Corrections, 335 Broadway, New York, NY 10013, 212 740-7800; r. 1425 Amsterdam Ave. Apt. 2c, New York, NY 10027, 212 234-8995; *Stacy;* Shakera, James, Kyle, Kaori.

WHITE, James J.; '87 MA; 546 High St., Monroe, NY 10950, 315 423-3663.

WHITE, Janet E. '74 (See Jordan, Ms. Janet E.).

WHITE, Jennifer J.; '93 BS; 1712 Longfellow Ave., Bronx, NY 10460, 718 931-9583.

WHITE, John H.; '76 BS; Personal Financial Analyst; John White & Assocs., 10000 600 Northwest Frwy., Houston, TX 77092, 713 956-1246; r. 2510 Golden Rd, Highlands, TX 77562, 281 843-3385; *Barbara;* Kia, Tony Atwood. e-mail

WHITE, Joseph B.; '99 BA; 420 E 111 St. 2901, New York, NY 10029, 315 363-9080.

WHITE, Joseph M.; '95 BA; 66 Harvey Ave., Staten Island, NY 10314, 718 477-0858.

WHITE, Karen; '95 BA; 3420 Gunther Ave., Bronx, NY 10469, 718 519-7671.

WHITE, Letecia J.; '97 BA; 456 Schenectady Ave., Brooklyn, NY 11203, 718 237-0746.

WHITE, Lisa M.; '93 BA; Public Svc.; Kings Cnty. Criminal Ct.; r. 224 W 122nd St., Apt. 4B, New York, NY 10027, 212 531-9270; Jasmine.

WHITE, Marilyn; '94 MA; 415 Greene Ave., Brooklyn, NY 11216, 718 522-1522.

WHITE, Michael W.; '87 MA; 2912 Tulip Ave., Baldwin, NY 11510, 516 379-6275.

WHITE, Monique L.; '96 BA; 1350 Webster Ave., Bronx, NY 10456, 718 231-0640.

WHITE, Norman K.; '98 BA; 1411 Linden Blvd. 7k, Brooklyn, NY 11212.

WHITE, Pamela S.; '81 BS; 35 Riverside Ave., Mastic Bch., NY 11951.

WHITE, Patrick C.; '97 BA; Astoria, NY 11102.

WHITE, Pearl E.; '73, '74 BA; Retired NYC Youth Bd.; r. 309 Lafayette Ave. 14N, Brooklyn, NY 11238, 718 783-2169; Lynette.

WHITE, Reginald H.; '83 BS; Indep Rep.; American Communications Network, 516 486-5351; r. 609 Lincoln Ave., W. Hempstead, NY 11552, 516 486-5351; *Joyce.* e-mail

WHITE, Ricky L.; '84 BA; 385 Argyle Rd, Brooklyn, NY 11218, 718 522-1318.

WHITE, Robert; '80 BS; 2838 Ford St., Brooklyn, NY 11235, 718 522-1318.

WHITE, Robert L.; '95 AS, BS; 40 Waterside Plz. #, New York, NY 10010, 212 213-4291.

WHITE, Robin L.; '96 MA; 7722 Hanover Pkwy., Apt. 301, Greenbelt, MD 20770.

WHITE, Sharlene; '93 BS; 323 Macdonough St., # 2, Brooklyn, NY 11233, 718 488-9296.

WHITE, Stephanie; '86 MA; 70 Eddy Rd., Roosevelt, NY 11575, 516 739-3849.

WHITE, Valerie; '96 BA; 11236 209th St., Queens Vlg., NY 11429, 718 533-0444.

WHITE, Woodrow; '90 BS; 2534 Gilmore St., Flushing, NY 11369, 718 533-0444.

WHITED, Daniel F.; '78 MA; 738 Bayard St., Teaneck, NJ 07666, 201 837-2139.

WHITEHEAD, Sarita C.; '91 BS; 966 Montgomery St., Brooklyn, NY 11213, 718 237-1193.

WHITELY, Donald H.; '82 MPA; 16 Mechanics Ave., Tarrytown, NY 10591, 914 631-0067.

WHITELY, Marcia A.; '94 AS, '95 BS; Police Ofcr.; r. 982 E 92nd St., Fl. 2, Brooklyn, NY 11236, 718 287-3577; *Aggrey Dechinea;* Ayodele, Amari.

WHITESIDE, Lisa; '97 BA, '98 BA; 45 Twin Pines Dr., Brooklyn, NY 11239, 718 642-9132.

WHITESIDE, Scott L.; '96 BS; 165 Landford Dr., Elmont, NY 11003.

WHITFIELD, Mrs. Allison J.; '99 BA; Child Protective Spec.; Admin. for Children's Svcs., 1360 Fulton St., Brooklyn, NY 11216, 718 399-8237; r. 235 E. 91st St., Brooklyn, NY 11212, 718 346-3320; *William;* Nichollas, Nia Chelsea.

WHITFIELD, Camille; '95 BA; 21654 113th Dr., Queens Vlg., NY 11429.

WHITFIELD, David; 20 Kellum St., Lindenhurst, NY 11757.

WHITFIELD, Fred L.; '85 BA; Sole Proprieter-Business Owner; Fred's Tasty Treats, 290 Broadway, New York, NY 10007; r. 135 W. 23rd St. Apt. 501, New York, NY 10011, 212 924-7568. e-mail

WHITFIELD, Kimberly; '91 BA; MSW Fordham Univ.; 2045 Story Ave. Apt. 10c, Bronx, NY 10473.

WHITING, John W.; '93 BS; Sr. Systs. Engr.; Unified Technologies, 10 Plz., New York, NY 10119; r. 1013 E 229th St., Bronx, NY 10466, 718 882-5338. e-mail

WHITLOCK, Michael J.; '83 BS; 53 Essex Depot Pz, Andover, MA 01810.

WHITLOCK, Toyea B.; '93 AS; 18845 114th Dr., Jamaica, NY 11412.

WHITNEY-SHULER, Wanda D.; '87 BS; 147 Washington Ave., Brooklyn, NY 11205.

WHITT, Kimberly D.; '96 MA; 805 Giles Ct., Virginia Bch., VA 23456, 757 468-2086.

WHITTAKER, Franklin J.; '98 BA; 528 E. 51st St., Brooklyn, NY 11203, 718 498-6895.

WHITTAKER, George F.; '93 BS; 366 Ave. W, Brooklyn, NY 11223, 718 339-3511.

WHITTAKER, Ikiesha T.; '97 BS; 5525 98th Pl., Apt. 2A, Corona, NY 11368, 718 507-8764.

WHITTED, Frank N.; '93 MPA; 771 E 229th St., Bronx, NY 10466.

WIATER, Frank F.; 340 Ellicott St., Batavia, NY 14020.

WICKER, Jason A.; '95 BS; Tech. Recruiter; Lucent Technology; r. 369 18th Ave., Brick, NJ 08724, 732 840-2023. e-mail

WICKLUND, Jill P.; '99 BA; 886 Sound Shore Rd, Riverhead, NY 11901, 631 722-8023.

WICKS, Gwynne, (Gwynne Berkowitz); '91 MA; MSW Yeshiva Univ.; Social Worker Pres.; Chelsea Creative Cnsltg. Corp., 490 Main St., Northport, NY 11768, 631 754-1204; r. 2 Cedar Ln., Lloyd Neck, NY 11743; *Stephen;* David. e-mail

WIDNICK, Steven M.; '76 MPA; BS CCNY; Special Agt.; USDOJ OIG, 1 Texas Commerce Ctr., Mc Allen, TX 78501, 956 618-8145; r. POB 4641, Mc Allen, TX 78502, 956 682-6635; *Alida;* Steve Jr, Matthew. e-mail

WIEDEMANN, Paul M.; '82 BS; Sgt.; NYPD, 2 Lafayette St. Fifth Fl., New York, NY 10007, 212 374-2536; r. 659 College Ave., Staten Island, NY 10302.

WIEGAND, Robert W.; 177 Katan Ave., Staten Island, NY 10308.

WIENER, Lorin; '98 MA; BA Binghamton Univ.; Public Info. Coord.; The State Senate Minority Conference, 270 Broadway, 18th Fl., New York, NY 10007, 212 298-5585; r. 216 6th Ave., Apt. 3-B, Brooklyn, NY 11215, 718 230-3221. e-mail

WIENER, Norman; '60 MPA; 2510 E. 24th St., Brooklyn, NY 11235, 718 258-3385.

WIENER, Paul T.; '71 MPA; Virginia Bch., VA 23455.

WIERL, Christopher; '95 MA; BA SUNY Albany; Mgr.-in-Charge; Guardsmark Inc., 90 Madsion Ave. Ste. 700, Denver, CO 80206, 303 388-2800; r. 2073 N Fork Dr., Lafayette, CO 80026, 303 926-5467; *Stacey A.* e-mail

WIERZBICKI, Stanley; '87 AS; 48 Nevada St., Hicksville, NY 11801.

WIETING, Ernest F.; Retired; r. 47 Winthrop Dr., Cortlandt Manor, NY 10567, 914 528-5408; *Eleanor;* Steven.

WIGGIN, Matthew J.; '96 BS; POB 20735, New York, NY 10023.

WIGGINS, Angela E.; '94 BS; 1166 Rogers Ave., Brooklyn, NY 11226, 718 756-6380.

WIGGINS, Cathy; '94 BS; MA Brooklyn Clg.; Sch. Secy.; Brooklyn Clg. Acad., 350 Coney Island Ave., Brooklyn, NY 11218, 718 853-6184; r. 3215 Avenue H, Brooklyn, NY 11210.

WIGGINS, Dionne R.; '99 BS; 174-48 128th Ave., Jamaica, NY 11434, 718 977-9266.

WIGGINS, Robert G.; '88 BS; Assoc. Fraud Investigator; The NYC Dept. of Homeless Svcs., 151 E. 151 St., Bronx, NY 10451, 718 402-8866; r. 218 E 93rd St., Brooklyn, NY 11212, 718 756-6380; *Marsha;* Robert, Aaron.

WILBER, BethanyAnne '99 (See Gianusso, BethanyAnne).

WILDAY, Robert D.; '77 BS; AAS Brooklyn Clg.; Retired; NYFD; r. 5 Rhett Ave., Staten Island, NY 10308, 718 356-2509; *Kathryn;* AnnMarie, Robert J., Sharon. e-mail

WILDER, Cornell L.; '93 BS; 198 W. 134th St., New York, NY 10030, 212 862-6190.

WILDSTEIN, Harold M.; 107-38 92nd St., Ozone Park, NY 11417.

WILEY, Denise T.; '96 BA; 2010 Bruckner Blvd., Bronx, NY 10473, 718 860-2770.

WILFRID, Joanne; '76 BA; 16 Forest Ave., Plymouth, MA 02360.

WILKANOWSKI, Barbara; '84 BS; 26-27 Francis Lewis Blvd., Flushing, NY 11358.

WILKERSON, Walter P.; '95 BS; AS BMCC; Paralegal; Raskin, Kremins LLP, 160 Broadway, New York, NY 10038, 212 587-3434; r. 333 Beach 32nd St. 10 A, Far Rockaway, NY 11691, 718 868-0793. e-mail

WILKINS, Clarinda; '81 MA; 909 Sheridan Ave., Bronx, NY 10451, 718 590-0549.

WILKINS, Michael R.; '99 BS; Computer Spec.; Shareholder Communication, Jersey City, NJ 07303; r. 34 E. 42nd St., Brooklyn, NY 11203, 718 953-0469. e-mail

WILKINSON, Denise; '96 MA; 199 Remsen Ave., Brooklyn, NY 11212, 718 241-6457.

WILKINSON, Thomas C.; '79 BS; Capt.; NYC Fire Dept., 9 Metrotech, Brooklyn, NY 11201; r. POB 236, Sparkill, NY 10976.

WILKMAN, Robert A.; '76 BS; 408 Beach Rd, Staten Island, NY 10312, 718 356-0482.

WILLE, Diana '98 (See Zagariello, Mrs. Diana S.).

WILLIAM, Julius; '93 BS; 12118 155th St., Jamaica, NY 11434, 718 205-0306.

WILLIAMS, Albert D.; '77 BA; Maj. Account Exec.; Sprint PCS, 1545 Rte. 206 Ste. 2000, Bedminster, NJ 07921, 732 979-5505; r. 2 London Dr., Jackson, NJ 08527, 732 367-8399; *DaJuan;* Danielle, Darrielle. e-mail

WILLIAMS, Alecia S.; '99 BA; Benefits Coord.; The New York Public Library; r. 19429 111th Rd # 2, St. Albans, NY 11412, 718 465-0319. e-mail

WILLIAMS, Alfred; '79 BA; Retired Police Sergeant; PSA7; r. 1862 O'Brien Ave., Bronx, NY 10473, 718 991-8368.

WILLIAMS, Alvin L.; '77 BS; 56-53 Van Cleef St., Flushing, NY 11368, 718 262-0768.

WILLIAMS, Alwin R.; '95 BS; Detective; NYC Police Dept., 1 Police Plz., New York, NY 10038, 718 677-8332; r. 715 Saint Marks Ave. # 4D, Brooklyn, NY 11216, 718 363-1352. e-mail

WILLIAMS, Andel G.; '88 BS LGST; MBA Redlands Univ.; Financial Svc. Advisor; Advanta Natl. Bank, 10790 Rancho Bernardo Rd, San Diego, CA 92127, 858 676-3099; r. 4443 Kansas St., Apt. 2, San Diego, CA 92116. e-mail

WILLIAMS, Angela; '97 BA; Administrative Asst.; Mentmore Holdings Corp., 680 Fifth Ave., 8th Fl., New York, NY 10019, 212 931-5209; r. 252 E.92nd St., Brooklyn, NY 11212, 718 342-3286. e-mail

WILLIAMS, Anthony M.; '79 BS; 445 W 48 St. #2A, New York, NY 10036, 315 363-2652.

WILLIAMS, Anthony R.; '95 BS; 114-15 169th St., Jamaica, NY 11434, 718 262-0768.

WILLIAMS, Arthur R.; '81 MPA; 10215 Farmers Blvd., Jamaica, NY 11423, 718 262-0768.

WILLIAMS, Avis; '96; 11028 174th St., Jamaica, NY 11433, 718 262-0768.

WILLIAMS, Barbara A.; '97 BS; 904 Williams Ave., Brooklyn, NY 11207, 718 398-9449.

WILLIAMS, Brenda G.; '92 BA; 50 W 93rd St. Apt. 3M, New York, NY 10025, 315 734-9507.

WILLIAMS, Bridget L.; '87 BS, '91 MA; Shift Supv.; NYC Criminal Justice Agcy., 215 E 161 St., Rm.# M29, Bronx, NY 10451, 718 681-3600; r. 1166 Burke Ave. Apt. 5g, Bronx, NY 10469, 718 881-2974. e-mail

WILLIAMS, Calvin C.; '80 BS; 489 Park Pl., Brooklyn, NY 11238, 718 221-0116.

WILLIAMS, Chester; '90 BS; 680 Linwood St., Brooklyn, NY 11208, 718 221-0116.

WILLIAMS, Cornelia M.; '96 BA; 146-18 123 Ave., Jamaica, NY 11436, 718 206-4939.

WILLIAMS, Cynthia; '88 BA; Computer Tchr.; NYC Bd. of Educ., New York, NY 10001; r. 21603 115th Rd., Cambria Hts., NY 11411, 718 481-9536.

WILLIAMS, David; '86 MA, '86 BA; US Probation & Parole Ofcr.; Eastern Dist. of New York, 75 Clinton St., Brooklyn, NY 11201, 718 254-7440; r. 14 Rutgers St., Maplewood, NJ 07040, 973 313-1981; *Jill;* Jonah, Aaron.

WILLIAMS, Deborah E.; '97 BS; Recruiter; Govt.; r. 1205 Summerbrook Dr., Atlanta, GA 30350.

WILLIAMS, Deborah M.; '81 BA; 10242 221st St., Queens Vlg., NY 11429, 718 740-3888.

WILLIAMS, Deborah R.; '95 BS; 771 Grote St. #, Bronx, NY 10460, 718 299-7637.

WILLIAMS, Debra A.; '91 BS; 183 Stone St., Elmont, NY 11003, 516 378-5283.

WILLIAMS, Demetrius; '96 BS; 140-23A Donizetti, Bronx, NY 10475, 718 299-7637.

WILLIAMS, Donald G.; '85 BS; 311 Grove St., Brooklyn, NY 11237, 718 221-2109.

WILLIAMS, Donna A.; '80 MA; MA Long Island Univ.; Staff Analyst Level II; NYC Housing Authority, 90 Church St., New York, NY 10007, 212 306-8143; r. 1026 Saint Johns Pl., Brooklyn, NY 11213, 718 221-2109.

WILLIAMS, Donna M.; '94 BS; 4374 Edson Ave. Ph, Bronx, NY 10466, 718 299-7637.

WILLIAMS, Douglas L.; '79 BS; 115104 230th St., Jamaica, NY 11411, 718 525-8851.

WILLIAMS, Elizabeth; '93 BS; 189 New Dover Rd, Colonia, NJ 07067, 732 381-9668.

WILLIAMS, Euclyn A.; '97 BS, '98 BS; 115-79 Springfield, Jamaica, NY 11411, 718 276-6748.

WILLIAMS, Fay D.; '83 BA; 285 E. 35th St., Brooklyn, NY 11203, 718 258-1439.

WILLIAMS, Fernard M.; '76 BS; 195 Glenwood Ave., E. Orange, NJ 07017, 973 678-3685.

WILLIAMS, Frank C.; '70 BS; 26 Avebury Pl., Somerset, NJ 08873, 732 537-8299.

WILLIAMS, Geraldo A.; '85 BS; Admin. Spec. Sr.; VA Dept. of Motor Vehicles, 2300 W Broad St., Richmond, VA 23220, 804 367-2350; r. 6232 Binns Ave., Richmond, VA 23225, 804 745-1367; *Gabrielle.* e-mail

WILLIAMS, Gordon; '95 BS; 14 Helene Rd, Warwick, NY 10990.

WILLIAMS, Grace M.; '98 BS; 2080 Barnes Ave., #1c, Bronx, NY 10462, 718 367-9844.

WILLIAMS, Gregory G.; '80 BA; 1041 Barbey St., Brooklyn, NY 11207, 718 287-9370.

WILLIAMS, Hubert; '68 AA, '70 BA; JD Rutgers Sch. of Law, FELLOWSH Harvard; Pres.; Police Fndn., 1201 Conniticut Ave., Washington, DC 20036, 202 833-1460; *Annette.*

WILLIAMS, Ibikunle A.; '85 BS; 1875 University Ave. #6G, Bronx, NY 10453.

WILLIAMS, Ivy C. '88 (See Williams-Carr, Ivy C.).

WILLIAMS, James O.; '75 BA, '79 MPA; Registered Mortgage Broker/Ret. Sgt; NYS Bkg. Dept./NYPD, POB 690116, E. Elmhurst, NY 11369, 718 523-9057; r. POB 116, Flushing, NY 11369, 718 523-9057.

WILLIAMS, Jeffery L.; '90 AS, '91 BS; 675 Walton Ave. Apt. 1e, Bronx, NY 10451, 718 231-5593.

WILLIAMS, Jesse N.; '78 BA; 11811 223rd St., Jamaica, NY 11411, 718 528-0581.

WILLIAMS, Jewel; '88 BS; 116-12 121 St., S. Ozone Park, NY 11420, 718 205-0306.

WILLIAMS, Joanne '94 (See Williams-Borden, Joanne L.).

WILLIAMS, Johnnymae; '87 BS; 289 Blake Ave., Brooklyn, NY 11212, 718 209-9022.

WILLIAMS, Jose A.; '86 BA; 44 5th Ave. # 206, Brooklyn, NY 11217, 718 209-9022.

WILLIAMS, Katrina J.; '98 BS; Fraud Investigator; NYC Dept. of Homeless Svcs., Bronx, NY 10451; r. 1170 Walton Ave., Bronx, NY 10452, 718 293-0528.

WILLIAMS, Kenneth R.; '88 BA; Caseworker Investigator; Bur. of Child Support Enforcement, 115 Chyrstie St.-5th Fl., New York, NY 10002, 212 334-7615; r. 1468 Bushwick Ave., Apt. 3R, Brooklyn, NY 11207.

WILLIAMS, Kenwyn S.; '86 BA; 455 Linden Blvd., Brooklyn, NY 11203, 718 287-2203.

WILLIAMS, Kevin A.; '98 BS; Police Ofcr.; r. 98-25 Horace Harding Expy. #9m, Corona, NY 11368, 718 699-3039.

WILLIAMS, Keyla N.; '98 BA; Child Protective Spec.; Admin. for Children Svcs.; r. 740 E 243rd St., Apt. 4H, Bronx, NY 10470, 718 324-5493.

WILLIAMS, Kimberly; '92 BA; Police Ofcr.; NYCPD, New York, NY 10038; r. 518 Berriman St., Brooklyn, NY 11208, 718 922-1373; Kiana.

WILLIAMS, L.; '80 BS; 947 Grant Ave. # 3, Bronx, NY 10456, 718 538-4321.

WILLIAMS, La K.; '95 BA; 11529 200th St., Jamaica, NY 11412, 718 712-6738.

WILLIAMS, Lauren E.; '77 BA; 414 W 149th St., New York, NY 10031, 315 822-1126.

WILLIAMS, Le'roy C.; '86 BA; 325 E 143rd St. Apt. 3f, Bronx, NY 10451, 718 538-4321.

WILLIAMS, Lillian; '99 BS; Child Protective Spec.; r. 766 Brady Ave. 435, Bronx, NY 10462, 718 823-7355; *Godfrey.*

WILLIAMS, Ms. Linda, (Linda Cardwell); '76 BS; Assoc. Staff Analyst; NYC Police Dept.; r. 515 W 59 St. #20K, New York, NY 10019, 212 262-0551. e-mail

WILLIAMS, Lisa A.; '96 MA; BA Mt. St. Mary Clg.; Sr. Rsch. Asst.; Butler Hosp. & Brown Univ., 345 Blackstone Blvd., Providence, RI 02906, 401 455-6480; r. 73 Messenger St. Apt. 203, Plainville, MA 02762, 508 699-9463.

WILLIAMS, Lloyd C.; '91 BS; AS Regents Clg.; Corrections Ofcr.; NYS Dept. of Correctional Svcs., Fishkill Correctional Facility, POB 307, Beacon, NY 12508, 914 831-4800; r. POB 16, Glenham, NY 12527, 914 831-0852; *Elsie;* Antonio, Neil A., Richard A., Travis P., Hortensie A., Christopher, Christina, Jacqueline. e-mail

WILLIAMS, Loise L. '75 (See George, Loise L.).

WILLIAMS, Lucille; '80 BA; 2926 W. 25th St. #1205E, Brooklyn, NY 11224, 718 230-5697.

WILLIAMS, Madonna S.; '94 MA; BS St. Francis Clg.; Assoc.-Welfare Fraud Investigations; Dept. of Social Svcs., Brooklyn, NY 11201; r. Brooklyn, NY 11210; Sigmund, Shannon. e-mail

WILLIAMS, Marissa D.; '89 BS; 705 President St., Brooklyn, NY 11215, 718 253-9653.

WILLIAMS, Marlon V.; '90 BS; 990 President St., Brooklyn, NY 11225, 718 253-9653.

WILLIAMS, Marva L.; '80 MA; 21918 113th Dr., Jamaica, NY 11429, 718 776-7768.

WILLIAMS, Mary A.; '78 BS; 220 Wadsworth Ave., New York, NY 10033, 315 337-5333.

WILLIAMS, Migdalia; '78 BA; 1219 Beach Ave., Bronx, NY 10472, 718 220-3746.

WILLIAMS, Myron S.; '96 BS; Security Ofcr.; Garrison Protection Svc., 790 Austin St., Queens, NY 11412; r. 1170 Nameoke #2B, Far Rockaway, NY 11691, 718 327-5459.

WILLIAMS, Nakesha L.; '97 BA; MS Long Island Univ.; Job Retention Spec.; Covenant House NY, 346 W 17th St., New York, NY 10011, 212 727-4034; r. 5220 Glenwood Rd, Brooklyn, NY 11234, 718 251-2797. e-mail

WILLIAMS, Nathaniel; '84 BS; 1116 Halsey St., Brooklyn, NY 11207, 718 257-1021.

WILLIAMS, Norman L.; 14446 167th St., Jamaica, NY 11434, 718 268-8341.

WILLIAMS, Olin T.; '95 BA; 186 Bond St. Apt. 1c, Brooklyn, NY 11217.

WILLIAMS, Patricia H.; '97 MA; 249 Bedford Park, Bronx, NY 10458, 718 671-8690.

WILLIAMS, Randy E.; '82 BS; 2039 E 41st St. Ph, Brooklyn, NY 11234, 718 209-7107.

WILLIAMS, Raphael W.; 720 St. Marks Ave., Brooklyn, NY 11216, 718 209-7107.

WILLIAMS, Ravannah; '83 BS; 785 Quincy St., Brooklyn, NY 11221, 718 602-2311.

WILLIAMS, Rhonda Y., JD; '95 BAGOVT; JD Benjamin Cardozo Law Sch.; Political Cnslt.; r. 4613 Foster Ave., Brooklyn, NY 11203, 718 451-0337. e-mail

WILLIAMS, Richard R.; '87 BA; Detective Sgt.; City of Passaic Police Dept.-Train & Pla, Passaic, NJ 07055; r. POB 9312, New York, NY 10006.

WILLIAMS, Richelle; '88 BA, '91 MA; MA Psychologist; St. Barnabas Hosp., Rikers Island Associate, 18-18 Hazan St., E. Elmhurst, NY 11370; r. 3235 Emmons Ave. Apt. 605, Brooklyn, NY 11235, 718 332-2555. e-mail

WILLIAMS, Robert L.; '95 BA; AA Univ. of Maryland; Substance Abuse Couns., Supv.; St. Luke's Roosevelt Halfway House, 306 W 102nd St., New York, NY 10025, 212 678-6317; r. 409 W 145th St. Apt. 305, New York, NY 10031, 212 368-7728.

WILLIAMS, Roderick M.; '99 MPA; BA Univ. at Albany; Policy Analyst; City of NY, New York, NY 10001, 917 719-2908. e-mail

WILLIAMS, Roland H.; 130-28 227 St., Laurelton, NY 11413, 718 276-3146.

WILLIAMS, Roxanne; '93 BS; 109 E 130th St. # 29, New York, NY 10037, 212 694-0037.

WILLIAMS, Samuel W.; '88 BA; 3811 Avenue H, Brooklyn, NY 11210, 718 235-6962.

WILLIAMS, Sandra; '84 BS; 105 Lincoln Rd Apt. 5h, Brooklyn, NY 11225, 718 235-6962.

WILLIAMS, Sonya Y.; '97 BS; 1981 Sedgwick Ave., Apt. 4B, Bronx, NY 10453.

WILLIAMS, Suzette S.; '98 BS; 1188 Sheridan Ave., #5e, Bronx, NY 10456, 718 324-2004.

WILLIAMS, Theresa M.; '85 AS, '91 BA; POB 7792, Flushing, NY 11373, 718 264-7485.

WILLIAMS, Thomas; 1128 E. 32 St., Brooklyn, NY 11210, 718 345-1961.

WILLIAMS, Tonya V.; '94 BA; 323 Lincoln Pl. Apt. 4l, Brooklyn, NY 11238, 718 345-1961.

WILLIAMS, Van D.; '90 MS; 582 Decatur St., Brooklyn, NY 11233, 718 493-9898.

WILLIAMS, Vanessa E.; '99 BA; 1030 President St., Brooklyn, NY 11225, 718 493-9898.

WILLIAMS, Wade; '78 BS; 22820 114th Ter., Jamaica, NY 11411, 718 525-0971.

WILLIAMS, Winsome O.; '99 BA, '99 CERT; Dispute Resolution Cert.; CPS Investigator; Admin. for Children's Svcs., 165-15 Archer Ave., Jamaica, NY 11433, 718 481-6034; r. 118-36 196th St., St. Albans, NY 11412, 718 712-2153.

WILLIAMS, Yvette C. '82 (See Mimms, Yvette C.).

WILLIAMS, Yvonne; 2075 2nd Ave., New York, NY 10029, 315 363-2652.

WILLIAMS-BORDEN, Joanne L., (Joanne Williams); '94 MA; BS Queens Clg.; Prog. Dir.; r. 68-16a 136th St., Flushing, NY 11367, 718 268-5221; *Phillip; Amber Borden.*

WILLIAMS-CARR, Ivy C., (Ivy C. Williams); '88 BA; MS Long Island Univ-Brooklyn; Special Educ. Tchr/Child Protective; Bd. of Educ NYC/Admin. for Children Svcs; r. 497 Elton St., Brooklyn, NY 11208; *Bruce; Christina, Angela.*

WILLIAMSON, Flavia M.; '98 BS; 147-71 Edgewood St., Rosedale, NY 11422, 718 341-5972.

WILLIAMSON, Stacie; '96 BA; 4357 De Reimer Ave., Bronx, NY 10466.

WILLINGHAM, Brenda; '94 BS; 5016 31st Ave. Apt. 3c, Flushing, NY 11377.

WILLIS, Melvin H.; '69 BS; 2363 207th St., Flushing, NY 11360, 718 352-0691.

WILLIS, Wayne; '82 BA; 177 Woodruff Ave., Brooklyn, NY 11226, 718 240-0237.

WILLIS, Yvonne A.; '89 BS; Supv.; Dept. of Probation; r. 79-09 162nd St. ., Flushing, NY 11366, 917 817-8874; *Odis.* e-mail

WILLSON, Robert H.; '83 BA; 103 Franklin Ct., Decatur, GA 30030.

WILSON, Aaron; '95 MPA, '95 MS; 4303 Fairway View Ter., Apt. 309, Upper Marlboro, MD 20772, 301 449-7234.

WILSON, Andrew J.; '86 CERT; JD Queens Clg., MA CCNY; Atty.; 5 Doyers St., New York, NY 10036, 212 876-1034; r. 420 E. 111th St., Apt. 3204, New York, NY 10029.

WILSON, Annette G.; '97 BS; AA LaGuardia Community Clg.; Retired; r. 119-57 224th St., Cambria Hts., NY 11411; Gregory, Jeffrey.

WILSON, Cleveland F.; '79 BS; 10131 223rd St., Queens Vlg., NY 11429, 718 393-0771.

WILSON, Mrs. Cynthia E.; '81 BA; Caseworker; Admin. for Children's Svcs.; 150 Williams St., New York, NY 10038; r. 1468 Eastern Pkwy., Brooklyn, NY 11233, 718 498-5728.

WILSON, Desiree T.; '81 BS; 1195 E 229th St., Bronx, NY 10466, 718 652-0242.

WILSON, Dolores M.; '76 BA; POB 60, Bronx, NY 10466, 718 652-0242.

WILSON, Fertima; '97 BS; 296 5th St., Jersey City, NJ 07302.

WILSON, Francine; '94 BS; Fed. Correction Ofcr.; r. 23 Miami Ct., Brooklyn, NY 11225, 718 778-2083.

WILSON, Gary J.; '78 BS; 85-16 125 St., Kew Gardens, NY 11415, 718 468-0457.

WILSON, James D.; '77 BS; MSW Hunter Clg.; NYS Parole Ofcr.; NYS Div. of Parole, 82 Washington St., Rm. #102, Poughkeepsie, NY 12601, 914 452-0620; r. 8 Darlene Dr., Poughkeepsie, NY 12601, 914 449-9871; James D., David M.

WILSON, James H.; '76 BA; Policeman Retired; r. 32 Weberfield Ave., Freeport, NY 11520, 516 546-0242; *Marnzella;* Teresa Sadylott, Eleanor, James Jr., Lakiesha. e-mail

WILSON, John E.; '76 MPA; 21 Gaby Ln., New Rochelle, NY 10804, 914 633-9271.

WILSON, Kathleen M.; '85 BS; 9140 220th St., Queens Vlg., NY 11428, 718 468-8850.

WILSON, Keryon T.; '99 BA; Administrative Asst.; Brown Raysman Millstein Felde & Steiner, 120 W. 45th St., New York, NY 10036, 212 944-1515; r. 631 S. 8 Ave., Mt. Vernon, NY 10550, 914 665-6834. e-mail

WILSON, Larry E.; '81 BS; 1563 President St., Brooklyn, NY 11213, 718 258-0662.

WILSON, Luana A.; '89 BS; AS NYC Tech. Comm. Clg.; Administrative Asst.; Lehman Bros., 200 Vesey St., New York, NY 10285, 212 526-2225; r. 140 Clarkson Ave. #4G, Brooklyn, NY 11226, 718 284-7334. e-mail

WILSON, Marsha M.; '94 BA; 17 Clovelly Dr., Valley Stream, NY 11580, 516 671-1137.

WILSON, Ms. Myrna; '93 BA; MS Columbia U Sch Soc. Work; Psychiatric Couns.; Svcs. for The Underserved, 25 Chapel St. 10th Fl., Brooklyn, NY 11201, 718 852-0587; r. 714 Halsey St., Brooklyn, NY 11233, 718 574-7561. e-mail

WILSON, Nina M., (Nina Binford); '91 BS; Paralegal Supv.; NYC Law Dept., 89-14 Parsons Blvd., Jamaica, NY 11432, 718 658-0500; r. 231-08 128 Rd., Laurelton, NY 11413, 718 978-8175; Niaren Binford, Alyssa Netto.

WILSON, Patricia B.; '83 BA; 233 E 56th St., Brooklyn, NY 11203, 718 284-2949.

WILSON, Ramlka; '95 BA; 4114 10th St. Apt. 2c, Long Island City, NY 11101, 718 206-1009.

WILSON, Regina D.; '97 BA; 472 E. 55th St., Brooklyn, NY 11203, 718 257-1372.

WILSON, Richard P.; '98 MS; BA Manhattan Clg.; Security Mgr.; Salomon Smith Barney, 250 West St. 1st Fl., New York, NY 10013, 212 723-4000; r. 1580 E. 34th St., Brooklyn, NY 11234, 718 951-6558; *Patricia;* Richard, Christopher. e-mail

WILSON, Robert; '81 MPA; 11516 170th St., Jamaica, NY 11434, 718 206-1009.

WILSON, Robert A.; '95 MPA; '95; 28 Cedar Rd, Dumont, NJ 07628, 201 385-8155.

WILSON, Sharon; '96 BA; 782 Hendrix St., Brooklyn, NY 11207, 718 455-5569.

WILSON, Tillie L.; '74 BS; 869 Flushing Ave. Apt. 6e, Brooklyn, NY 11206, 718 257-0359.

WILSON, Yolanda; '84 MA; 2908 East Ave., District Hts., MD 20747, 301 552-4742.

WILSON-HOWARD, Terri; '99 BA; AA LaGuardia Clg.; Caseworker; Pius XII Youth And Family Services, 188 W. 230 St., Bronx, NY 10463, 718 562-7855; r. 984 Ashford St., Brooklyn, NY 11207, 718 649-3962; *John Howard.* e-mail

WILTSHIRE, Ms. Cheryl M.; '95 BA; JD Cleveland-Marshall; 2200 Prospect Ave. E, Apt320, Cleveland, OH 44115, 216 623-0314. e-mail

WILTSHIRE, Heather '92 (See Woolfolk, Heather).

WIMBERLY, Sheila A.; '97 BA; Police Ofcr.; Nassau Cnty. Police Dept., 1490 Franklin Ave., Mineola, NY 11501, 516 573-7210; r. 163-45 130th Ave., Apt. 2 A, Jamaica, NY 11434, 718 949-2722. e-mail

WIMBISH, Patsy; '79 BS; 1480 Popham Ave., Bronx, NY 10453, 718 716-4092.

WINCELOWICZ, Michael; '75 BS; 143 Roe St., Staten Island, NY 10310.

WINDSOR, Pedro J.; '99 BA; Law Student; Univ. of Iowa Sch. of Law, Iowa City, IA 52242; r. New York, NY 10029. e-mail

WINDUS, James E.; '81 BS; 2329 Quimby Ave., Bronx, NY 10473.

WINFIELD, Karen M.; '99 BA; Correction Ofcr.; Queensboro Correctional Facility, 47-04 Van Dam St., Long Island City, NY 11101, 718 361-8920; r. 55-01 31st Ave., Apt. 2A, Woodside, NY 11377. e-mail

WINFIELD, Lillian B.; '75 BS; 18915 120th Ave., St. Albans, NY 11412, 718 527-9141.

WINGATE, Gregory; '82 MPA; 129 E 87th St., Brooklyn, NY 11236, 718 629-2526.

WINN, Mrs. Martha D.; '87 BA; Dir. of Computer Systs. Mgmt.; City of NY, 156 William St., New York, NY 10038, 212 442-0949; r. 618 Osborn St., Brooklyn, NY 11212, 718 385-0338. e-mail

WINSKI, Debra L.; '95 MA; 102 Glenwood Rd., Glenwood Landing, NY 11547.

WINSLOW, Cynthia (Cindy) L. '96 (See Pokorny, Mrs. Cindy L.).

WINSLOW, James G.; '92 BS; Lt.; New York Police Dept.

WINSLOW, James P.; '82 BS; 470 11th St., Brooklyn, NY 11215.

WINSTON, Oscar S.; '81 MPA; 800 Concourse Vlg W Apt. 5d, Bronx, NY 10451.

WINTER, Dawn A.; '84 BA; 751 E 45th St., Brooklyn, NY 11203, 718 339-6008.

WINTERS, Alan J.; '79 BS; 42 Greencrest Dr., # 42, Middletown, NY 10941, 914 386-2134.

WISE, Edwina R.; '78 BA; 4214 Edson Ave., Bronx, NY 10466, 718 294-3875.

WISE, Francis S.; '92 BS; 97-05 Spring Field, Queens Vlg., NY 11429.

WISE, Lashanda M.; '99 BS; 1461 Hicks St. 3, Bronx, NY 10469, 718 549-9182.

WISE, Lauren A.; '75 BS; JD NY Law Sch.; VP; Columbian Mutual Life Ins. Co., 4704 Vestal Pkwy. E, Binghamton, NY 13902, 607 724-2472; r. 2191 E Hampton Rd, Binghamton, NY 13903, 607 772-6691. e-mail

WISEMAN, Kenneth F.; '72 BA; 2918 Chippewa Ave., Simi Vly., CA 93063, 805 649-1985.

WISLAR, Margaret E.; '96 BS; 34 W 69th St. Apt. 4B, New York, NY 10023.

WISOTSKY, Amy '77 (See Wisotsky-Burt, Ms. Amy T.).

WISOTSKY-BURT, Ms. Amy T., (Amy Wisotsky); '77 BS; MSED Univ. of Louisville; Mgr.-Human Resources; Brown-Forman Distillery Co., 850 Dixie Hwy., Louisville, KY 40210, 502 774-7276; r. 5210 Moccasin Tr., Louisville, KY 40207, 502 896-2357; *Henry Burt;* Ashley, Terri. e-mail

WISSERT, Theresa A.; '95 BS; 711 Iris St., Franklin Sq., NY 11010.

WITKOWICH, Michael F.; '78 BS; 3436 N Deerfield Ave., Yorktown Hts., NY 10598, 914 245-6271.

WITT, Olin T.; '86 BA; Supv.; Dept. of Homeless Svcs., 33 Beaver St., New York, NY 10004; r. 611 Wythe Ave., Apt. 8K, Brooklyn, NY 11211, 718 782-0126; *Cheryl;* Shanelle, Antoinette, Olin Jr. e-mail

WITTICH, Mark H.; '78 BS; Sergeant; Freeport Police Dept., 40 N Ocean Ave., Freeport, NY 11520, 516 377-2433; r. 258 S Brookside Ave., Freeport, NY 11520; *Linda;* Daniel, Richard. e-mail

WITTROCK, William G.; '76 BS; Security Mgr.; Holiday Inn, 49 W. 32 St., New York, NY 10001, 212 736-3800; r. 16 Carrolton Pl., Malverne, NY 11565, 516 887-2691; *Doris;* Billy, Kimberly.

WITTY, Marina I.; '98 BS; 30 E. Clarke Pl. #4c, Bronx, NY 10452, 718 538-2099.

WITTY, Sandra D.; '90 BS; 5210 Broadway Apt. 7b, Bronx, NY 10463, 718 562-3185.

WLADICH, Richard; '77 MA; POB 9191, Daytona Bch., FL 32120.

WNUK, Kazimierz S.; '99 BS; Police Ofcr.; NYC, (Residence Mailing Address), POB 1743, Long Island City, NY 11101; r. Brooklyn, NY 11222.

WODARSKI, Joseph P., Jr.; '86 BA MPA; CERT. Police Mgmt. Inst.; Retired Deputy Inspector; NYC Police Dept.; r. 792 Candlewood Lake Rd. S., New Milford, CT 06776, 860 350-8808; *Sui;* Joseph III, Kevin, Christina, Michael. e-mail

WOESSNER, Eileen M.; '96 BS; 2100 N. Scottsdale Rd. Apt. B412, Tempe, AZ 85281.

WOHLFIEL, Allison E.; '98 MA; 15983 S. Woodson Dr., Ramona, CA 92065, 760 789-0068.

WOHLLEB, Joanne; '85 MPA; RR#1 Benjamin St., Wading River, NY 11792.

WOJCIK, Jerry H.; '97 BS; 2495 Hunterbrook, Yorktown Hts., NY 10598, 914 739-5345.

WOJTACH, Christophe J.; '97 BS; Police Ofcr.; Hopatong Police Dept., 111 River Styx Rd., Hopatcong, NJ 07843, 973 398-5000; r. 2 Duck Hawk Ct., Hackettstown, NJ 07840.

WOJTACH, Susan E.; '99 BS; Front Desk Mgr.; Lisa Bonaventura, 2345 Lamington Rd Ste. 104, Bedminster, NJ 07921, 908 781-9661; r. 712 N Washington Ave., Dunellen, NJ 08812, 732 968-2661; *Christian Gonzalez.* e-mail

WOLF, John B.; 18 Sunrise Dr., Morris Plains, NJ 07950.

WOLF, John H.; 125 Park Ave., Deer Park, NY 11729.

WOLFE, Joseph G.; '78 BS; 9285 SW 19 Ave., Ocala, FL 34476, 561 278-2508.

WOLFE, Timothy E.; '99 BS; AA SUNY-Farmingdale; 476 Village Oaks Ln., Babylon, NY 11702, 631 376-0917.

WOLFMANN, Monik H.; '88 BA; POB 207, Stanfordville, NY 12581.

WOLFSON, David B.; '86 BS; 0000000000000000, Brooklyn, NY 11229, 718 998-4059.

WOLINSKI, Thomas P.; '78 BA; Retired; r. 47 Old Pine Dr., Manhasset, NY 11030.

WOLMER, Steven M.; '81 BS; 30 Woodbine Dr. S., Hicksville, NY 11801.

WOLOSZYN, Jeanette O.; '76 MA; 8717 80th St., Jamaica, NY 11421, 718 296-7542.

WOLOWSKI, Richard C.; '74 BS; Retired NYPD & CMB; Cnslt.; 176 Cottage Blvd., Hicksville, NY 11801, 516 681-2698; r. 12 Sea Raven Ter., Ormond Bch., FL 32176, 904 441-0390. e-mail

WOLSTENCROFT, John M.; '80 MA; 251 Townline Rd, W. Nyack, NY 10994.

WOMBLE, Geraldine; '78 BA; 695 St. Nicholas Ave., New York, NY 10030, 212 234-2833.

WON, Shawn W.; '89 BS; 630 77th St., Brooklyn, NY 11209, 718 369-6002.

WONG, Fidel A.; '97 BA; 7 Aljan Dr., Brentwood, NY 11717.

WONG, Geoffry; '79 BS; 133-36 244 St., Rosedale, NY 11422.

WONG, Kenneth; '83 BS; 30-84 47 St., Astoria, NY 11103, 718 268-8973.

WONG, Ms. Mareen S.; '93 BS; Admin. Asst.; Hunter Clg., 212 772-4395; r. 7419 85th Rd, Jamaica, NY 11421, 718 296-3936.

WONG, Peter; '91 AS; 102-09 62nd Dr., Forest Hills, NY 11375, 718 268-8973.

WONG, Rachel; '96 BA; 3510 150th St., Apt. 2N, Flushing, NY 11354, 718 793-5557.

WONG, Rose; '95 BS; 135 Eldridge St. Apt. 14, New York, NY 10002.

WONG, Selwyn M.; '98 BA; BA Baruch, MS Long Island Univ.; Tchr.; PS 75; r. 506 Rugby Rd., Brooklyn, NY 11226, 718 284-8243.

WONG, Vincent M.; '78 BA; 8821 53rd Ave., Flushing, NY 11373, 718 268-8973.

WONNUM-GAINES, Lora; '82 BA, '86 MPA; 124 Torpedo Rd, Manahawkin, NJ 08050, 609 698-6226.

WOO, Stanley W.; '78 BA; Correction Ofcr.; The City of NY, New York, NY 10001; r. 11114 76th Ave., Apt. 412, Forest Hills, NY 11375, 718 357-8089.

WOOD, David J.; '85 BS; 510 6 St., E. Northport, NY 11731.

WOOD, Joseph D.; '96 BS; 253 Oak Ave., Shirley, NY 11967, 631 395-5987.

WOOD, Raymond; '82 MA; Traveling Prof.; Univ. of Virginia; r. POB 485, New York, NY 10024.

WOODARD, Chrystal; '95 BS; 10 Lamont Pl., W. Babylon, NY 11704.

WOODARD, Richard; '75 MS; 16030 English Ave. # Bld-c, Bowie, MD 20716, 301 982-0625.

WOODBERRY, Corey; '95 BS; Administrative Asst.; Cornell Univ. Med. Clg., New York, NY 10021, 212 746-1034; r. 475 Hancock St. Apt. 8, Brooklyn, NY 11233, 718 443-9290.

WOODBYNE, Maurice C.; '99 BS; AA BMCC; Criminalist Forensic; Med. Examiners Dept., 520 1st Ave., New York, NY 10016, 212 447-2655; r. 3947 Wilder Ave., Bronx, NY 10466, 718 994-3981. e-mail

WOODLEY, Charles T.; '83 BA; 910 Bedford Ave., Brooklyn, NY 11205, 718 573-5905.

WOODLEY, Janeth F.; '80 BA; 904 Westwind Pl., Virginia Bch., VA 23452.

WOODROFFE, Dawn C.; '89 BA; 110-08 204th St., St. Albans, NY 11412.

WOODRUFF, Nancy; '93 AS; 56 Willowbrook Ct., Staten Island, NY 10302.

WOODS, Arthur C.; '70 BS; 6321 77th St., Flushing, NY 11379, 718 474-5066.

WOODS, Gail D.; '85 BS; 1155 Grant Ave., Bronx, NY 10456, 718 992-1158.

WOODS, Gregory A.; '91 BS; 135 Hawthorne St., Brooklyn, NY 11225, 718 856-8893.

WOODS, Ms. Sheila; '95 AS; Corrections Ofcr.; Queens Detention Complex, Queens Blvd., Queens, NY 11412; r. 538 Putnam Ave. # 3, Brooklyn, NY 11221, 718 574-7523.

WOOLASTON, Denise P.; '77 BA; 187-05 Brnkrhf Ave., St. Albans, NY 11412.

WOOLFOLK, Heather, (Heather Wiltshire); '92 BS; Legal Asst.; State Ins. Fund, New York, NY 10021, 212 312-9172; r. 742 Putnam Ave., Brooklyn, NY 11221, 718 573-2219; Norman.

WOOLWARD, Sharon; '96 BS; Paralegal; Criminal Courts; r. 108-27 Union Hall, Jamaica, NY 11433, 718 739-4212.

WOOTEN, Antoinette M.; '85 BS; 235 Arlington Ave., Brooklyn, NY 11207, 718 625-2035.

WORLEY, Donna J.; '86 BS; 1554 Unionport Rd Apt. 6a, Bronx, NY 10462.

WORTH, John T.; '74 BA; 7 Norwich St., Staten Island, NY 10314.

WORTHAM, Robert; 129 W 147th St. # 133, New York, NY 10039.

WORTHY, Patricia A.; '93 AS; Correction Ofcr.; Brooklyn Correctional Facility, 136 Flushing Ave., Brooklyn, NY 11205, 718 802-3341; r. 204-15 Foothill Ave., Hollis, NY 11423, 718 468-1076; Roderick, Rashad. e-mail

WOSELEY, Hollis M.; '88 BS; 19726 90th Ave., Jamaica, NY 11423.

WRAY, Raimundo A.; '82 BS; 751 E 52nd St., Brooklyn, NY 11203, 718 940-2500.

WRAY, Tasha V.; '91 BS; 100 Alcott Pl. # 13, Bronx, NY 10475.

WREN, William; '78 BS; 4707 Beverly Rd, Brooklyn, NY 11203, 718 488-0085.

WRIGHT, Andrea A.; '97 BA; 2242 Bragg St., Brooklyn, NY 11229, 718 646-1604.

WRIGHT, April A.; '95 BS; Asst. Mgr.; r. 537 E. Thirteenth St., Apt. #1-A, New York, NY 10009, 212 254-5480; Johnny Lugo.

WRIGHT, Charmone; '97 BS, '98 BS; 1833 7th Ave. #1e, New York, NY 10026, 315 861-2092.

WRIGHT, Floyd A.; '83 BS; 270 Van Siclen Ave., Apt. 4B, Brooklyn, NY 11207, 718 935-0169.

WRIGHT, Fred; '79 BS; 87 E 53 St., Brooklyn, NY 11203, 718 935-0169.

WRIGHT, Garnet C.; '90 BS; 23 Birchwood Dr., Goshen, NY 10924, 914 346-0049.

WRIGHT, Kundora '95 (See Smith, Kundora).

WRIGHT, Mrs. Kyristel P., (Kyristel P. Koontz); '96 MA; BA Hunter Clg. CUNY; Dir. of Social Svcs.; Food First, Inc., 1469 Bedford Ave., Brooklyn, NY 11216, 718 623-2737; r. 4228 Bruner Ave., Bronx, NY 10466; Shawn; Isaiah Jarryd.

WRIGHT, Pamela G.; '91 BS, '92; JD Univ. of Miami Sch. Law; Atty.; Legal Aid Society of Palm Beach Cnty., 423 Fern St., Ste. 200, W. Palm Bch., FL 33401, 561 655-8944; r. 868 Troy Ave., Brooklyn, NY 11203, 718 941-3833.

WRIGHT, Pamelia K.; '90 AS; 31 Leonard St., Apt. 15J, Brooklyn, NY 11206, 718 348-0220.

WRIGHT, Rochelle T.; '99 MA; BA Bradford Clg.; Supv. Level 2; The City Agcy. to Protect Children, The Admin. For Children's Servs., 55 6th Ave., New York, NY 10013, 212 966-8000; r. 122 Ashland Pl., Brooklyn, NY 11201, 718 852-1770. e-mail

WRIGHT, Roy J.; '95 MA; BS State University of NY; Deputy US Marshal; US Marshal Svc., 225 Cadman Plz. E., Brooklyn, NY 11201, 718 254-6700; r. 10 Tall Pines Ln., Nesconset, NY 11767, 631 585-7907; Catherine. e-mail

WRIGHT, Sharnickqua O.; '99 BA; AS Berkeley Clg.; Tchr.; Peshin Avenue Univ. Prep., 433 Peshin Ave., Newark, NJ 07112, 973 750-3890; r. 3111 Heath Ave. 62A, Bronx, NY 10463, 718 601-2131; Zahkiya.

WRIGHT, Sharon L.; '89 BA; 11421 201st St., Jamaica, NY 11412, 718 932-1831.

WRIGHT, Shaulene; '97 BA; NYC Police Ofcr.; NYC Police Dept., 718 735-0611; r. 21317 Nashville Blvd., Queens Vlg., NY 11429, 718 776-8825; Umar; Adam, Kevin.

WRIGHT, Shawanda, (Shawanda Roberson); '98 BS; AS Westchester Community Clg; New York, NY 10027.

WRIGHT, Teresa A.; '86 AA, '87 BS; CA3; NYC Dept. of Corrections; r. 1140 Woodycrest Ave., Bronx, NY 10452, 718 538-6131; Doreen.

WRIGHT, Theresa V.; '97 BA; 118-44 Marsden St., Jamaica, NY 11434, 718 276-6147.

WRIGHT, Tiffany E.; '95 BS; 2025 Seward Ave. # 3, Bronx, NY 10473, 718 325-1433.

WRIGHT, Vivene G.; '96 BS; 11420 173rd St., Jamaica, NY 11434, 718 776-6219.

WRIGHT, Wayne R.; '97 BA; 275 Autumn Ave., Brooklyn, NY 11208, 718 348-9660.

WRYNN, James J.; 1 Coventry Ct., Ridge, NY 11961.

WRYNN, Mrs. Maura A., (Maura Foley); '82 BS; MA St. John's Univ.; Tchr.; r. 8 Hillside Ave., Douglaston, NY 11363, 718 229-6089; James; Katie, James III, Kevin. e-mail

WULACH, James; 30 Park Rd, Maplewood, NJ 07040, 973 763-4588.

WUNDERLICH, Donald S.; '75 MA; 308 Parkwood St., Ronkonkoma, NY 11779.

WUNSCH, John A.; '75 BS; 2731 167th St., Flushing, NY 11358.

WURZBACH, Stephen J.; '82 BS; 103-04 109 Ave., Ozone Park, NY 11417.

WURZEL, Glenn J.; '89 BA; 6411 Madison St., Ridgewood, NY 11385, 718 418-5480.

WUSTEFELD, Janet L.; '97 BS; AA Union Cnty. Community Clg; Civil Investigator; Div. of Criminal Justice OIFP, Whippany, NJ 07981; r. 435 Sycamore Ave., Scotch Plains, NJ 07076, 908 322-5265.

WYATT, Antoinette C.; '97 BA; 69 W.225th St., Bronx, NY 10463, 718 562-8461; Andre.

WYATT, Paul A.; '85 MPA; 92 S. Oraton Pk, E. Orange, NJ 07018.

WYATT-DIAZ, Lisa; '88 MA; 230 Jay St. Apt. 14a, Brooklyn, NY 11201, 718 452-8467.

WYRE, Marcus L.; '78 BS; 133-35 131st St., S. Ozone Park, NY 11420.

WYSOCKA, Anita; '99 BA; 71 02 Grand Ave. 3F, Maspeth, NY 11378, 718 894-0998.

X

XAVIER, Canisius R.; '97 BS; 146-31 58th Rd., Flushing, NY 11355.

XENAKIS, Helen; '99 BS; Paralegal; r. 120 09 26 Avo., Collogo Pt., NY 11356, 718 461-8730. e-mail

XEPOLITOS, Constance; '82 BS; 22-06 38th St., Astoria, NY 11105.

Y

YABLOKOFF, Robin J.; '83 MA; 3552 Bedford Ave., Brooklyn, NY 11210, 718 252-0037.

YACOOB, Azimoon N.; '99 BA; 94-16 241st St., Bellerose Terrace, NY 11001, 516 488-1799; Christopher. e-mail

YAGUAL, Magali E.; '87 BS; 200 Dominion Park Dr., Apt. 1708, Houston, TX 77090.

YAGUAL, Rick W.; '90 BA; 4756 45th St. Apt. 5d, Flushing, NY 11377.

YAM, Serena J.; '95 BS; 148-02 35 Ave. #2, Flushing, NY 11354, 718 358-3546.

YAMADA, Stella; '96 BA; 315 W.70th St. #5, New York, NY 10023.

YAN, Hon-man; '97 BS, '98 BS; 3355 60th St., Woodside, NY 11377, 718 446-1999.

YANARELLA, Maryann; '77 MA; Larchmont Acr 811B, Larchmont, NY 10538.

YANCEY, Davina R.; '96 BS; 467 Stratford Rd, Brooklyn, NY 11218.

YANES, Francisco J.; '89 BS, '99; 430 W 205th St. Apt. 1C, New York, NY 10034, 315 735-7443.

YANG, Yinhui; '90 MPA; 11 Dock Ln., Great Neck, NY 11024, 516 431-4576.

YANIS, Ricardo A.; '99 BS; Police Ofcr.; Twp. of Jackson, 102 Jackson Dr., Jackson, NJ 08527, 732 928-1111; r. 967 E. Veterans Hwy., Jackson, NJ 08527, 732 367-5352. e-mail

YANOFSKY, Barbara I.; '79 BS, '82 MPA; Investigator; DEA, 99 Tenth Ave., New York, NY 10011, 212 337-1590; r. 150-10 79th Ave. Apt. 5F, Flushing, NY 11367. e-mail

YANOFSKY, Michael A.; '79 MA; BA Richmond Clg.-SI NY; Retired Capt., Correction; NYC Dept. Corrections, 60 Hudson St. NYC, New York, NY 10013; r. 24-07 86th St., Flushing, NY 11369, 718 779-5835; Marc, Jaime, Stephanie.

YANOLATOS, Michael D.; '76 BA; Retired; r. 270 Shore Rd, Apt. 51, Long Beach, NY 11561, 516 889-5921. e-mail

YARDE, Margarette R.; '81 BS; 362 E 58 St., Brooklyn, NY 11203, 718 826-1874.

YASSO, Michael; '75 BA; 31 Grissom Ave. # 2, Staten Island, NY 10314.

YASSO, Michael; '90 AS, '92 BS; 4709 Bell Blvd., Bayside, NY 11361.

YATES, Genithia; '98 BA; Student Business; Temple Univ.; r. 8500 Lindbergh Blvd., Apt. 2302, Philadelphia, PA 19153, 215 365-7710. e-mail

YEARWOOD, Lisa E.; '95 BA; 645 Shepherd Ave. # P, Brooklyn, NY 11208, 718 346-3832.

YEATES, Smith L.; '92 BS; 157 Weirfield St., Brooklyn, NY 11221.

YEBOAH, Stephen F.; '89 BA; 57 Lincoln Rd Apt. B55, Brooklyn, NY 11225, 718 856-7610.

YEE, Arthur; '95 BS; 4365 Bowne St., Flushing, NY 11355, 718 886-5965.

YEE, Peter J.; '93 BA; AAS Borough of Manhattan Comm; Clerical Assoc.; Human Resources Admin., 109 E. 16th St., New York, NY 10003; r. 58 Mott St. # 1, New York, NY 10013, 212 431-4506. e-mail

YEE, William; '77 BS; 773 Concourse Vlg E Apt. 12d, Bronx, NY 10451, 718 892-9718.

YEE, Yu S.; '98 BS; Sgt.; NYPD, 19 Elizabeth St., New York, NY 10013, 212 334-0711; r. same. e-mail

YEN, Chih-Chung; '99 MS; 17315 Stark Ave., Cerritos, CA 90703, 562 865-8543.

YERA, John; '88 BA; 38556 Millstone Dr., Purcellville, VA 20132.

YEUN, Ray B.; '95 BS; 1230 E 36th St., Brooklyn, NY 11210.

YEVOLI, Peter A.; '78 AS, '79 BS; Sr. Security Ofcr./Spec. Svcs. Unit; United Nations, United Nations Headquarters, New York, NY 10017, 212 963-9341; r. 24228 90th Ave., Bellerose, NY 11426, 718 343-1395; *Edwina Dayao-Yevoli;* Michael, Michelle, Adrian.

YHUN, Suk-han; '96 BA; Law Sch. Student; New York Law Sch.; r. 14945 14th Ave., Whitestone, NY 11357, 718 767-9532; *Hojin;* Christopher, Benjamin.

YIM, Steven S.; '94 BS; 11214 Edson Park Pl., # 13, Rockville, MD 20852, 301 231-5325.

YOCH, Marchelle R.; '99 MA; 5912 Cove Landing Rd Apt. 304, Burke, VA 22015.

YOO, John; '99 BS; Claims Investigator; Inphoto Surveillance, 103 Center Blvd., Marlton, NJ 08053, 888 822-8804; r. 149-49 Ash Ave., 2nd Fl., Flushing, NY 11355, 718 461-4412. e-mail

YORIO, James V.; 98 Cedar Dr., Farmingdale, NY 11735, 631 756-0863.

YOSHIZAKI, Takuji; '99 MA; 28 Caryl Ave., Yonkers, NY 10705, 914 928-0420.

YOUNG, Adrienne M.; '81 BS; MASTERS Lehman Clg., MASTERS Hunter Clg.; Educ.-Tchr.; NYC Bd. of Educ., P588 1340 Sheridan Ave., Bronx, NY 10456, 718 681-6220; r. 1113 Findlay Ave. Apt. 1E, Bronx, NY 10456, 718 992-5151; Amar, Dominique. e-mail

YOUNG, Antonia R.; '98 BA; Student; r. 77 Bronx River Ro 5b, Yonkers, NY 10704, 914 776-0592.

YOUNG, David F.; '88 BS; 14342 222nd St., Jamaica, NY 11413, 718 525-8381.

YOUNG, Dawn; '87 BS; 5981 59th Pl., Flushing, NY 11378, 718 454-4544.

YOUNG, Dennis M.; '97 BS; 300 Cathedral Pkway, New York, NY 10026, 315 964-2903.

YOUNG, Don; '83 BS; 21239 Gary Dr., Apt. 209, Castro Vly., CA 94546, 949 458-3813.

YOUNG, Edwin A.; '77 BA, '80 MPA; BA; Adjunct Instr./Inspector; John Jay Clg./NYC Police Dept., 1 Police Plz., New York, NY 10038, 212 374-5072; r. 2550 Independence Ave., Bronx, NY 10463, 718 543-1921; *Joan;* Edward, Susan, Christine, Dara Franks.

YOUNG, Felicity A.; '97 BA; 3521 Farragut Rd, Brooklyn, NY 11210, 718 235-5954.

YOUNG, Gail; '95 BS; Tchr.; r. 100 Terrace Ave., Apt. 252, Hempstead, NY 11550, 718 565-5167.

YOUNG, Harold C.; '77 BS; AS Queens Clg.; Battalion Chief-Retired; NY Fire Dept.; r. 8043 89th Ave., Woodhaven, NY 11421.

YOUNG, John C.; '91 BA; 4406 Martha Ave. # 4, Yonkers, NY 10704, 914 631-2301.

YOUNG, John W.; '77 BA; Firefighter Retired; r. 81 David St., Staten Island, NY 10308, 718 317-1918; *Geraldine;* Lori, John, Kerry L.

YOUNG, Marcia; '91 BA; 10113 Northern Blvd., Flushing, NY 11368, 718 712-2765.

YOUNG, Michael G.; '78 BS; 174 Queen St., Staten Island, NY 10314, 718 494-0948.

YOUNG, Natalia S.; '90 MPA; 45 Overlook Ter., # Te5G, New York, NY 10033, 315 964-2903.

YOUNG, Robert E.; 6319 Silvermoon La, Lake Worth, FL 33463, 561 795-0617.

YOUNG, Robert J.; '79 AS; POB 231, Carmel, NY 10512.

YOUNG, Rodney; '92 BS; 1110 E 81st St., Brooklyn, NY 11236, 718 241-2461.

YOUNG, Rodney D.; '93 BS; 23 Lexington Ave., Poughkeepsie, NY 12601.

YOUNG, Shnequa A.; '98 BA; Correction Ofcr.; NYC Dept. of Corrections, 718 575-5387; r. 145-37 231 St., Springfield Gardens, NY 11413, 718 528-9591.

YOUNG, Trent J.; '93 BA; 467 Crescent St., Brooklyn, NY 11208, 718 773-6582.

YOUNG, Virgil L.; AA City Clg of San Francisco, CERT. The New Sch. Social Res; Nursing Coord.; Cabrini Med. Ctr.; r. 401 W 56th St. # 2g, New York, NY 10019, 212 757-7221.

YOUNGBLOOD, Schwanna; '95 BA; 1370 5th Ave. Apt. 14f, New York, NY 10026.

YOUNGS, Chance R.; '98 BS; 89 Coleridge Pl., Greenlawn, NY 11740.

YOUNGS, Michael A.; '87 BA; 555 Pacific St. Apt. 4r, Brooklyn, NY 11217.

YOUSSEF, Magdi H.; '77 BS; 66 Bay 11th St., Brooklyn, NY 11228, 718 238-8816.

YU, Andy; '88 BS; 6221 19th Ave., Brooklyn, NY 11204, 718 769-5279.

YUEN, Hon; '97 BS; 606 W. 137th St., New York, NY 10031.

YUHASZ, Paula J.; '80 MA; 657 E 26 St. #6M, Brooklyn, NY 11210.

YUNEMAN, Thomas E.; '79 BA; 5823 81 St., Flushing, NY 11373, 718 478-8089.

YURCHAK, Karyn; '94 BA, '94 MA; 7 North Ln., # 11, Bayonne, NJ 07002.

YURMAN, Robert J.; '81 BS, '98 MA, '98 MA; 191 Cebra Ave., Staten Island, NY 10304, 718 448-1558.

YURUS, William; '89 MA; 45 Victor St., Yonkers, NY 10701, 914 969-3241.

YUSUF, Mohamed S.; '95 BA; 400 Brook Ave., Bronx, NY 10454.

Z

ZABIELSKI, Henry S.; '81 BS; 1833 Norman St., Flushing, NY 11385.

ZABORAS, John S.; '79 BS; 6325 71st St., Flushing, NY 11379.

ZACCARO, Anthony R.; '76 MPA; 2815 Barkley Ave., Bronx, NY 10465.

ZACHARY, William E.; '76 BS; 8 Kent Pl., Amity Harbor, NY 11701.

ZADOROZNY, Maureen M.; '75 BA; 4 3rd Ave., Ossining, NY 10562.

ZAGARIELLO, Mrs. Diana S., (Diana Wille); '98 MPA; Account Mgr.; Empire Blue Cross Blue Shield; r. 2336 Birch St., N. Merrick, NY 11566, 516 771-0216; *Michael.* e-mail

ZAGORODNYUK, Lada '98 (See Stone, Lada).

ZAHARKO, Stephen P.; '78 BS; 67 Woodhail St., Long Beach, NY 11561.

ZAHARUK, Joseph P., Jr.; '78 BS; Special Agt.; US Environ. Protection Agcy., New York, NY 10007; r. 1698 Forest Hill Rd, Staten Island, NY 10314, 718 698-8840; *Laurie.* e-mail

ZAIDENBERG, Nidia; '97 BA; 611 Banner Ave. Apt. 5E, Brooklyn, NY 11235, 718 934-2152.

ZAIDMAN, Esther; 183 Dover Grn, Staten Island, NY 10312.

ZAINO, James R.; '79 BS; 120 Erskine Pl. # 17, Bronx, NY 10475.

ZAJICEK, Renee M.; '98 BA; 310 Holmes Dr., Fairborn, OH 45324.

ZALEPA, Robert P.; '75 BA; 6530 78th St., Flushing, NY 11379.

ZAMBITO, Debra A. '90 (See Sanfilippo, Debra A.).

ZAMBRANO, Bethsave; '97 BS; 70 Amsterdam Ave., New York, NY 10023.

ZAMBRANO, Victor H.; '94 BA; 487 Amsterdam Ave., New York, NY 10024.

ZAMERINSKY-LUSSIER, Randy; '80 MA; Therapist; r. POB 1506, Bemidji, MN 56619, 218 759-2538.

ZAMOR, Marie; '94 BS; 762 Saint Marks Ave., Apt. 6C, Brooklyn, NY 11216, 718 940-7339.

ZAMORN, Esperanza; '96 BS; 655 E. 228th St. #, Bronx, NY 10466.

ZAMPIERON, Paul W.; '92 BA; MS Hunter Clg.; Intensive Case Magr.; 50 Clinton Strret, Hempstead, NY 11550, 516 505-7113; r. 146 Fawn Ln. E., S. Setauket, NY 11720, 631 928-2064.

ZANDY, Matthew P.; '96 MA; BS Univ. of Scranton; Police Ofcr.; Binghamton Police Dept., Binghamton, NY 13901; r. 1157 Talan Dr., Endwell, NY 13760, 607 748-2932; *Michelle;* Emily. e-mail

ZANI, Daniel J.; '79 MA; 1467 81st St., Brooklyn, NY 11228.

ZAPPULLA, Barbara J.; '79 MA; 111-39 76th Rd, Forest Hills, NY 11375.

ZARAGOZA, Deserie M.; '89 BS; 3 Bradley St., Brentwood, NY 11717.

ZARATE, Sandra L.; '85 BA; Private Co.; r. 15 Dorothy Pl., Lynbrook, NY 11563, 516 599-3894.

ZAREK, Edward T.; '84 MPA; BS St. Francis Clg.-Bklyn, AS St. Francis College-Bklyn; Police Captain Retired; NYC Transit Police Dept., 370 Jay St., Bro, Brooklyn, NY 11201; r. 36 Steeds St., Smithville, NJ 08201, 914 624-0391; Barbara, Karl, Thomas. e-mail

ZARETSKY, Kathie L.; '77 BS; 22528 88th Ave., Queens Vlg., NY 11427, 718 464-1225.

ZARILLA, Anthony J.; '79 BS; 211 N Madison St., Knob Noster, MO 65336.

ZARO, Ines A.; '99 BA; Fraud Investigator/Forensic Psych.; NYC, 180 Water St., New York, NY 10007; r. 1895 University Ave. #4D, Bronx, NY 10453, 718 716-7552; Ilene Maracallo, Bryant Garcia. e-mail

ZARRILLO, Tina; '87 BA; MSW NYU; Psychotherapist; St. Mark's Place Mental Health Inst., 57 St. Marks Pl., New York, NY 10003; r. 6518 10th Ave., Brooklyn, NY 11219; *Stephen King.* e-mail

ZARTMAN, Brian B.; '95 BS; 5555 Lake Park Way, # 36, La Mesa, CA 91942.

ZAVALA, James E.; '98 BS; Fraud Investigator; HRA-Bur. of Fraud Investigation, 250 Church St., 4th Fl., New York, NY 10013, 212 274-4883; r. 33-48 72nd St., Jackson Hts., NY 11372, 718 457-0283. e-mail

ZAVELOFF, Sarah H.; '98 MA; Criminal Investigator; Bur. of Fraud Investigation, 250 Church St., New York, NY 10013, 212 274-4893; r. 68-38 Yellow Stone Blvd., Forest Hills, NY 11375, 718 896-2062. e-mail

ZAVISTOSKI, Robert; '93 BS; MPA Columbia Univ.; Detective Police Ofcr.; Piscataway Twp. Police Dept., 555 Sidney Rd, Piscataway, NJ 08854, 732 562-1100; r. 67 College Dr., Edison, NJ 08817, 732 248-9242. e-mail

ZAYAS, Japhet J.; '80 BA; 93-42 Francis Lewis, Jamaica, NY 11428, 718 651-0283.

ZAYAS, John; '79 BA; 2850 Claflin Ave., Bronx, NY 10468, 718 862-8862.

ZAYAS, Victor L., Jr.; '99 BS; Legal Coord.; NYC Dept. of Corrections, 1600 Hazen St., E. Elmhurst, NY 11370, 718 546-6436; r. 1409 E. 88th St., Brooklyn, NY 11236, 718 531-3823. e-mail

ZAYERZ, Agueybana; '95 BA; NYS Assembly; r. 25 Montgomery St. Apt. 14b, New York, NY 10002, 212 732-0792. e-mail

ZAZECKIE, William J.; '86 BA; 111 Hickory St., Port Jefferson Sta., NY 11776.

ZAZZERO, Paul W.; '84 BS; Detective; NYC Police Dept., 3280 Broadway, New York, NY 10027; r. 280 Farm 2tl Market Rd., Brewster, NY 10509; *Dee;* Nicole, Michelle, Christopher.

ZAZZI, Marie L.; '72 BA, '78 MA; Tariss Mgr.; Alitalia Airline, 666 5th Ave., New York, NY 10103, 212 903-3472; r. 16640 Powells Cove Blvd., Apt. 5a, Whitestone, NY 11357, 718 767-9641. e-mail

ZEBELEIN, John R.; '76 BA; 149 E. 96 St., Brooklyn, NY 11212.

ZECCA, Joseph M.; '77 BA; 6 Bleakley Dr., Peekskill, NY 10566.

ZEDECK, Deborah S.; '91 BA; Day Care Provider; r. 420 Shore Rd Apt. 5k, Long Beach, NY 11561, 516 431-3181.

ZEF, Aleksandr; '97 BS; Investigator; Northern Intelligence Agcy.; r. 3090 Voorhies Ave., Brooklyn, NY 11235, 718 891-6392.

ZEIDEIA, Bajes M.; '96 BS; 4746 45th St. Apt. 3, Flushing, NY 11377.

ZEIGLER, Douglas; '75 MA; 13322 Inwood St., Jamaica, NY 11436.

ZEIGLER, Neldra M., Esq.; '76 MA; BA Temple Univ., JD New York Law Sch.; Deputy Commisioner; 1 Police Plz., New York, NY 10038, 212 374-5330; r. 13322 Inwood St., Jamaica, NY 11436.

ZELAYA, Theresa M., (Theresa M. Esposito); '95 BA; MS Fordham Univ.; Case Mgmt. Supv.; Ctr. for Children & Families, 1931 Mott Ave., Far Rockaway, NY 11691, 718 471-6818; r. 255-34 147th Dr., 1st Fl., Rosedale, NY 11422, 718 528-0694; *Elmer A.* e-mail

ZEMAN, John; 93-13 244th St., Bellerose, NY 11426.

ZENA, Carlos W.; '84 BS; 16 Sky Ln., Levittown, NY 11756.

ZENDZIAN, Craig A.; '73 MA; 476 Flanders St., Southington, CT 06489.

ZENTENO, Antonio; '99 BA; 109 4th Ave. Apt. 3, Brooklyn, NY 11217.

ZEPF, Darin R.; '96 BA; 12 Denoyelles, Garnerville, NY 10923.

ZEPHIRIN, Nadege L.; '97 BA; 777 E 31st Apt. 5M, Brooklyn, NY 11210, 718 434-3319.

ZERBARINI, John P.; '83 BA; Accident Investigator Postal Svc.; r. 110 Grand Ave., Middletown, NY 10940, 914 341-0489; *Dede;* John, Liza.

ZERELLA, Denise; '89 AS, '94 BS; MS NY Inst. of Technology; Police Ofcr.; NYC Police Acad., 235 E. 20 St., New York, NY 10003; r. 11860 Metropolitan Ave. Apt. 3e, Kew Gardens, NY 11415, 718 846-4566. e-mail

ZERNER, Jeffrey; '91 BA; 9712 63rd Dr. Apt. 11A, Rego Park, NY 11374.

ZERNITSKY, Jeremy D.; 548 Hudson St. #2, New York, NY 10014.

ZEVON, Robert J.; '95 BS; POB 354042, Palm Coast, FL 32135.

ZHANG, Hui; '99 BS; 149-22 45th Ave., Flushing, NY 11355, 718 898-8408.

ZHUKOVSKY, Alexander; '99 BA; Intern; r. 8721 Bayparkway 6J, Brooklyn, NY 11214, 718 714-5302.

ZIAS, Joanne; '78 BS; 61 Tioronda Ave., Beacon, NY 12508.

ZICCARDI, John R.; 5123 58th Pl., Flushing, NY 11377.

ZICHETTELLO, Thomas; '85 BS; 17 Roberts Dr., Staten Island, NY 10306.

ZICUIS, Paul; '97 BA; 19-22 23rd Ave.#2, Long Island City, NY 11105.

ZIEDE, Gwen; '89 BA; 357 79 St., Brooklyn, NY 11209.

ZIEGLER, Jay E.; '86 BA; 50 Davis Dr., Bergenfield, NJ 07621.

ZIELINSKI, Peter; '98 BS; Investigator; r. 13 Russell St. #2, Brooklyn, NY 11222, 718 383-0971.

ZIETEK, Stanley J.; '78 BA; Police Ofcr.; NYPD; r. 9334 43rd Ave., Flushing, NY 11373, 718 899-1743.

ZIMMER, Marianne E.; '78 MA; 2513 Valleyview Ave., Holladay, UT 84117.

ZIMMERMAN, Peter S.; '97 BA; Actor; r. 1410 Ave. S, Apt. 3D, Brooklyn, NY 11229, 718 339-3995.

ZIMMERMAN, Richard E.; '86 MA; 88-29 155 Ave., Howard Bch., NY 11414, 718 847-9530.

ZIMMERMAN, Sidney; '76 BS; 60-10 47 Ave., Woodside, NY 11377, 718 847-9530.

ZIMMERMAN, Wheeler L., Jr.; '95 BA; Ins. Rep.; NYU, 726 Broadway, New York, NY 10003; r. Bronx, NY 10467.

ZIMMERMANN, William J.; '77 BS; 3 Grassy Ln., Smithtown, NY 11787.

ZINNEL, Michael G.; '92 BA; 78 Spring Ln., Levittown, NY 11756, 516 579-3074.

ZINNERMAN, Alva; '87 MPA, '87 BA; 11714 196th St., Jamaica, NY 11412.

ZINNO, Lorrie A.; '89 BS; AS Nassau Comm Clg.; Paralegal; The Queens Cnty. Dist. Attys Ofc., 125-01 Queens Blvd., 80-02 Kew Gardens Rd 8th Fl., Kew Gardens, NY 11415, 718 286-5817; r. 1 E Broadway Apt. 6a, Long Beach, NY 11561, 516 897-9231; Anthony, Riva.

ZLOCHOWER, Sol; '72 BS; 676 Blackhawk Dr., Colorado Spgs., CO 80919.

ZLOTNICK, Jack; 1984 E 23rd St., Brooklyn, NY 11229.

ZOLLNER

ZOLLNER, Martin; '86 BA; 15224 10th Ave., Whitestone, NY 11357, 718 767-8629.

ZORN, Andrew G.; '88 BS; 8122 Washington St., Niles, IL 60714, 847 698-6387.

ZORRILLA, Agatha N.; '99 BS; 47-05 48 St., Woodside, NY 11377, 718 789-7755.

ZORRILLA, Yngrid E.; '96 BS; 674 49th St. #2, Brooklyn, NY 11220.

ZOSKOVITZ, Mark; 225 W 23 St. Apt. 20, New York, NY 10011.

ZOUFALY, Thomas M.; '77 BS; 17a Union Corners Rd, Warwick, NY 10990.

ZOUHBI, Faisal; '98 BA; Correction Ofcr.; NYC, E. Elmhurst, NY 11370; r. 114 E. 98th St. 3r, New York, NY 10029, 212 410-4749.

ZUCCARELLO, Mina S.; '78 BS; 26-07 29 St., Astoria, NY 11102.

ZUCKER, Marc T.; '99, MA; BA Lynn Univ.; PhD Student; Nova Southeastern Univ.; r. 6781 College St., Davie, FL 33317, 954 382-1799. e-mail

ZUMMO, Annette M.; '79 BS; Administrative Ofcr.; Fed. Govt., Dept. of Justice; r. 4279 Katonah Ave., Bronx, NY 10470, 718 324-1390.

ZUMMO, Michael A.; '77 BS; 8914 210th St., Queens Vlg., NY 11427.

ZUMMO, Michael A.; '77 BS; JD St. Johns Univ. Law, AA Queensborough Comm Clg.; Assoc. Court Atty.; Criminal Ct. of The City of NY, Law Dept. Rm. Me 37, 125-01 Queens Blvd., Kew Gardens, NY 11415, 718 520-8131; r. 101 Arizona Ave., Long Beach, NY 11561, 516 897-1825. e-mail

ZUNIGA, John; '90 AS; 154-16 Bayside Ave., Flushing, NY 11354, 718 337-6142.

ZUNIGA, Martin; '95 BS; 180 Bay 32nd St. # B, Brooklyn, NY 11214.

ZUPKA, Barbara J.; '92 AS, '93 BS; POB 687, New York, NY 10272, 315 736-4304.

ZUPKA, Jeanette '84 (See Hentze, Jeanette M.).

ZUPKA, Paul W.; '85 BS; 65-05 Yellowstone, Forest Hills, NY 11375.

ZURITA, Barbara; '97 BS; 20-36 24th St., Astoria, NY 11105, 718 738-6477.

ZURITA, Charles N.; '95 BS; 280 E 10th St. Apt. 15, New York, NY 10009, 212 477-2357.

ZWARYCZUK, William; '80 BS; 206 E 6th St., New York, NY 10003, 212 674-0594.

ZWEIBEL, Patrick; '87 BS; 104-75 112 St., Richmond Hill, NY 11419.

ZWERLING, Gayle B.; '98 BS; Paralegal; Kral Clerkin Redmond Ryan Perry & Girvan, 69 E. Jerico Tpk., Mineola, NY 11501, 516 742-6240; r. 25 Boat Ln., Levittown, NY 11756, 516 735-7914.

ZWICKEL, Randi D.; '99 BS; Police Ofcr.; NYC Police Dept., 84 Precinct, 301 Gold St., Brooklyn, NY 11201, 718 875-6811; r. POB 22458, Brooklyn, NY 11202, 917 740-4667; Diandra, Macario.

ZWICKER, Jay L.; '77 BS; Dir. of Campus Safety; Marymount Clg., 100 Marymount Ave., Tarrytown, NY 10591, 914 332-8393; r. 709 Ardsley Rd, Scarsdale, NY 10583, 914 693-9049. e-mail

ZYTA, Richard E.; '94 BS; Detective; NYPD, 1 Police Plz., New York, NY 10007, 212 374-5000.

CLASS YEAR SECTION

1942
Howard, Frances L., NY

1958
Bincarowsky, George, NY

1959
O'Neill, John J.*

1960
Cordella, Robert H.**
Gannon, John F., PA
Murphy, Patrick V., MD
Quill, Daniel J., NY
Wiener, Norman, NY

1961
Chess, Abraham P.*
Murphy, Michael J., NY
Shpritzer, Felicia, NY
Stalzer, Benjamin*

1962
Berryman, John H., NY
Calzerano, Joeph P., NY
Defranco, Edward J., NY
Fedorschak, Leonard, NY
Neary, Matthew J.**
Pomarico, John A.*
Seedman, Albert A., FL
Touwsma, Geo J., NY

1963
Bosco, Vicent I., NY
Boyle, John F., SC
Hildebrand, James A.*
Kelly, Martin A., NY
La Barbera, Salvator*
Meehan, James B., NY
Poje, Leopold J., NY
Reiter, Sidney*
Rybak, Edward A.*
Wease, Bernard D.*

1964
Brown, James M., NJ
Dempsey, Lawrence J.*
Hamilton, Lander C.*
Jones, Ernest K., NY
Leonard, Gerald M., NY
Loughrey, Leo C., NY
Mc Partland, Matthew*
O'Brien, Kevin P.*
Oslyn, Morris, VA
Peterson, Lloyd*
Santiago, Ricardo N., FL
Whelan, Francis J., NY

1965
Burke, Robert F., NY
Cunningham, Joseph J., NY
Herman, Albin A., NJ
Lavoie, Edgar S.*
Lipson, Hyman*
Luisi, Charles A.*
Mc Donald, James E.*
Mc Guire, Peter A., NY
Murray, John E., NY

1966
Baiardi, Vincent P.*
Barry, John J., NY
Baumert, Robert (Boomer) J., NY
Blumenstein, Harry*
Clancy, William C., NJ

Clark, William R., NY
Cosgrove, William F.*
Fleming, Roger, NY
Gabos, Mario, NY
Gallagher, Walter, NY
Hill, Arthur B., NY
Kenneally, James J., NY
Kirschner, Milton I., NY
Melchiona, Diane B., NY
O'Brien, Joseph J., NY
Schneider, Arnold J.*
Spreen, Johannes F., MI

1967
Adams, Charles J., NY
Barron, Joseph J.*
Blake, Dr. Henry E. E., TX
Boye, Robert F.*
Burnicke, Leonard E.*
Casey, James J., NY
Cunneen, William A., NY
De Phillips, Alfred P., NY
Derenowski, John C., AZ
Duignan, Ms. Mary T., NY
Foran, Philip J., FL
Forbell, Michael P., FL
Green, James J.*
Grimes, John J., Esq., NY
Gyss, Henry F., NJ
Haas, John J., NY
Keane, Timothy J., NY
Luchuf, Michael**
Marano, Joseph C., NY
Mc Cullough, William, NY
Mc Loughlin, Hubert*
Mc Nevin, Arthur J., NY
Morrissey, William J., NY
Muratore, Anthony, NY
O'Leary, Joseph P., NY
O'Rourke, William J., DE
Ryan, Daniel, NY
Schryver, Harold, FL

1968
Albano, Anthony J.**
Athanasidy, Nicholas*
Behan, Cornelius (Neil) J., MD
Blom, Henry*
Bolz, Francis A., Jr., NY
Bouza, Anthony V., NY
Brandt, William J., DE
Brennan, James J., NJ
Brennan, John P., NY
Bussert, Loren*
Davis, Andrew R., NJ
DeMarest, John*
Dignon, Frederick L., FL
Donovan, Thomas J.*
Fandel, Samuel**
Fogarty, James P., NY
Forman, Morrey A., NY
Gambino, Anthony S.**
Giammarino, Michael, NY
Glynn, James J., NY
Hussey, Robert F., NY
Irish, Carleton P., NY
Jenkins, Anthony*
Jenkins, Edward*
Katzman, Stuart*
Kelly, William P., NY
Kenny, Raymond J., NY
Krivitzky, Marvin H., NY
Leo, Frank R.**
Malapero, Raymond, NY
Mc Namara, Joseph D., CA
Murphy, James J.*

Oleksa, James S., FL
Olivo, Xavier F., NY
Pennisi, John A., NY
Peterman, Jesse E., NY
Ravens, Carl, FL
Reid, Thomas P., NY
Ryan, Edward S.*
Saltenberger, Otto H., CA
Schechter, Marvin, NY
Stettner, Charles P., NY
Sullivan, Daniel F., NY
Tytell, Harold, FL
Uhnak, Dorothy, NY
Waldon, Hon. Alton R., Jr., NY
Ward, Richard H., TX
Whalen, John J.*
Williams, Hubert, DC
Woods, Ulysses*

1969
Adams, Robert W., NY
Babb, Harry N., NY
Bamrick, Kenneth G., FL
Benson, Irving, FL
Blumenthal, George, AZ
Brady, Michael J., NY
Brancella, Silvano, NY
Briscoe, Harold P., NY
Brownstein, Herbert, FL
Callas, George S., NJ
Carlo, John R., NY
Clement, Timothy J.*
Confusione, Michael J., NY
Connolly, John J., NY
Cronin, Kathleen V., CA
Cusack, William E.*
Daig, Edwin M.*
Danielson, Eugene C.*
Depierro, Joseph M., NY
Donnelly, Stephen J., NY
Ellis, Norton*
Ericson, Marvin F., FL
Erikson, James M.*
Fey, Alfred, NY
Fischer, Stephen F., NY
Guthrie, Thomas J., NY
Hoover, Herbert B., CA
Hughes, Francis J., NY
Kelly, Thomas J., FL
Kolodny, Nathan, NY
Kornblum, Allan, DC
Kostanoski, John I., NY
Marcus, Marvin*
Maurer, Richard H.*
Mc Cann, Terence, NY
Mc Crystal, Harry J., NY
Mc Cutcheon, Charles*
Mc Dowell, Charles P.*
Mc Gary, William*
McGourty, Michael J., NY
Mc Leod, Donald K., NY
Minnis, Leroy*
Moore, Joseph J.*
Morreal, Julius*
Muller, Raymond R.*
Nelson, Warren W., NY
Nolan, William P.*
O'Rourke, Charles J.**
Powers, William F.*
Ramirez, Vincent P., NY
Riedy, William F., NY
Rostow, Leo*
Scheiner, George H.*
Shilensky, Michael D., NY
Skelly, John F., NY
Tarpey, Terence M., NY

Thomas, Richard, NY
Truta, John J., NY
Willis, Melvin H., NY

1970
Alves, Hibert M.**
Bland, John H.*
Bracco, Michael P.*
Brennan, Dennis P.*
Brown, Arthur M., NY
Burke, Francis D., NY
Carvino, James J.*
Casarino, Carmine J., FL
Coiro, Vincent M.*
Constantino, Ralph V., PA
Cooper, Neil J., NY
Costales, Frederico*
Costantino, Saverio T.**
Cretella, Joseph V.*
Crowley, Charles S.*
Daly, CAPT Francis J., NY
Davis, Jay E., NY
Dellabella, Joseph J.*
Didonato, Anthony R., NY
Dobranski, William J.*
Dolan, Michael F., NY
Donelan, Arthur G.*
Downes, Thomas A., NY
Drakos, Nickolas D.*
Epstein, Trevor J., PA
Eymer, John A.*
Fishbaum, Ari*
Fitzgerald, John W., NY
Fredericksen, Robert, NY
Gaeta, Dominic J., NY
Garber, Joseph G., NY
Gillespie, Bernard M., NY
Greenberg, Martin A., NY
Haag, Edward C., NY
Hague, George T., PA
Higgins, Albert T., NY
Higgins, Malachy T., NY
Horan, Francis J., NY
Horvath, Robert J., NY
Hughes, Patrick J.*
Iadanza, Charles, NY
Jackson, Harvey, NY
Johansen, Erling*
Jones, John A.*
Kelleher, William J., NY
Kenney, Wilson C., NJ
Kern, Lewis F.*
Kessler, Dennis, NY
Killerlane, James J., NY
Koren, John, NJ
Kraus, Andrew E., NY
Kretschmann, George, NY
Kurtz, Robert T., NY
Lepkowski, Edward M.*
Locke, Robert A.*
Lynch, Richard T., NY
Maddalena, Leopold, NY
Maltese, Hon. Joseph J., NY
Mangus, Denise, NY
Mannino, Paul, FL
Masiulanis, Ryszard*
Mc Gill, John J., VA
Mc Mahon, John P., NY
Mc Manus, Pierce B., NY
Mc Nicholas, Eveann V., NJ
Mercer, Charles E.*
Mermel, Harold*
Minerva, Dominick J., NY
Minto, James S., NY
Mondovano, Jeanne A.*
Mosiello, Alfred R.*

Murphy, John T., NY
Napoli, Salvatore J.**
Neary, Kathleen T., HI
O'Neil, Robert F., NY
Perini, Bernard J., NY
Pezzullo, Vito J., NY
Pogrebin, Mark*
Pultorak, Edward K.*
Race, Robert R., NY
Raguso, Joseph P.*
Raines, Jonathan E., NY
Reardon, Norbert J., FL
Romani, Mark A., NY
Rothman, Irving*
Rounds, Thomas E., NY
Ryan, Francis M., MA
Sacks, Barbara K., NJ
Safran, Leo, NY
Schacht, Laurence C., NY
Scharf, Emanuel**
Schilling, Herbert H.*
Schmucker, Walter M., NY
Schwartz, Robert I., NY
Shapiro, Stanley, NY
Slattery, Richard*
Stanulis, Mary W., NY
Stauber, Hyman*
Stoller, William*
Sullivan, Neil W.*
Tencza, Ronald A., NY
Timothy, John E., NY
Turner, Al, GA
Tyler, Edward J., MA
Wallace, Arthur J.*
Waters, Noel P.*
Weiner, Alan R., NJ
Weingart, Michael R.*
Williams, Frank C., NJ
Woods, Arthur C., NY
Yander, Michael W.*

1971

Allen, Beryl R., NY
Anisowicz, George, GA
Armiento, Michael J., NY
Aulbach, Philip E., NY
Barr, Leroy, NY
Battel, Patrick J., NY
Blackshear, Cornelius, NY
Boyle, John J., NY
Browne, Robert J., NY
Burgess, Mrs. Marjorie L., NJ
Burnett, Byron K., NY
Busacco, Angelo, NJ
Busch, Robert E.*
Campbell, Robert E., NY
Casaburi, Joseph A., NY
Cawley, Donald F., NY
Chiappetta, Gennaro (Jerry), NY
Chimento, William F., NY
Connolly, John J., NY
Corr, John F., NY
Cossu, Stephen*
Cotter, Warren N.*
Creighton, Rober J., NY
Crichton, Alva H.*
D'agostino, Michael, NY
D'amato, Michael, NY
Daniel, George G., NY
Davis, Ray*
Dearman, William, NY
DeVito, Louis J., NY
Di Liberto, Joseph J.*
Dillion, Richard, NY
Donleavy, William P., PA
Dowling, Edward J., NY
Draghi, Paul, NY
Dunne, Joseph A., FL
Eberhardt, Ruth A., NY
Elmore, Allan F., MD
Fagan, Kenneth F., FL
Fauci, Richard A., NJ
Flynn, John J., NC
Francis, Richard W., NY
Fyfe, James, NJ

Gaston, Arnett W., MD
Gorsuch, Robert P., NY
Gotay, Albert, NY
Hair, Robert A., NY
Harrison, Henry A., NY
Hogan, Robert A., NJ
Hommel, Richard W.**
Johnson, Bernard, NY
Johnson, Bernard A., NY
Joyce, William D., NJ
Kapinos, Thomas S., NY
Kaplan, Leonard A., NY
Keenan, Joseph P., NY
Kendall, Walter J.**
Kenny, Michael J., NJ
Konopka, Edward A., NY
Kost, Martin L., NY
Kotz, Donald V.*
Kreuzkamp, Paul J.*
Krutys, Edward J., NY
Lande, John, NY
Langellotti, Phillip, NY
Latarski, Sigmund J., NY
Leask, William M., NY
Lightfoot, Jerome, NY
Mc Carthy, Timothy J., FL
McCarthy, William F., NY
Mc Donald, James T.*
Mc Givney, John A., NY
Mc Glinchey, Ms. Catherine, NY
Mooney, Richard (Moon Man) B., NY
Moore, James F., NY
Murphy, Joseph J., NY
O'brien, John F., NY
O'Connor, James F., NY
O'connor, John F., NY
O'Loane, Daniel R., NY
Parker, James W., NY
Pascalicchio, James, NJ
Pesce, Frank J., Jr., FL
Psota, Edward W.*
Rahill, Francis T., NY
Redmond, Benjamin J., NJ
Roos, Denise, MD
Rorke, Charles V., NY
Ross, James D., NY
Ruggeri, Ronald X., NY
Sand, Valerie S., CA
Schrader, Richard A., VI
Sheeler, Daniel H., NY
Simpson, William, AP
Smith, Donald V., FL
Somerville, Stuart R.*
Tolentino, Thomas N., NY
Torres, Henry M.*
Tricomi, Carolyn, NY
Triebwasser, Jonah, Esq., NY
Weinstein, Jay A., NY
Wiener, Paul T., VA

1972

Albertus, Alfred J., NY
Alers, Benjamin, NY
Alonso, Michael, NY
Askin, John P., NY
Baribault, Richard, NY
Bartoszek, Peter C., NY
Beatty, Gerard V., CA
Becker, Lester, NY
Becker, Robert L., NY
Behlmer, Harold F.*
Bergeron, John D., MA
Boston, Denver G., NY
Brady, Sylvia T., VI
Campbell, John J., NY
Canal, Eugene, NY
Capponi, Louis J., NY
Carney, William F., PA
Carroll, Patrick J., NY
Cerullo, Vincent, NY
Clarke, Winston M., NY
Clavell, Louis F., NY
Cockburn, George A., NY
Collins, Michael J., NY

Conlon, Peter J., PA
Conlon, Richard V., NY
Connolly, William J., NY
Cooke, Abraham*
Coticelli, Neal, NY
Cronin, John J.**
Cunningham, Walter J.*
Czajkowski, Richard J., NJ
Darcey, Lawrence G., NY
Darcy, Thomas J., NY
De Candia, Domenic, NY
Deery, Patricia M.*
Delahanty, Lt Neal C., NY
Dempsey, John S., NY
Derenthal, Frederick E., NY
Di Marco, Andre N., NY
Donovan, Edwin J., PA
Donovan, Gerald J., NY
Doran, Richard J.*
Duncan, Abraham D., NY
Dunne, Richard A., NY
Dwyer, Frank J.*
Edwards, Sam L., NY
Ehrlich, Sidney, NY
Evangelista, Albert Z.**
Fernandes, Francis C.*
Fink, Joseph**
Fisher, Joseph R.*
Fitzmaurice, Robert*
Flanagan, Leonard, NY
Foley, Thomas B., ACP, DC
Fonde, LTC Philip, USA(Ret.), NJ
Fortino, Richard J., NY
Galiano, Richard H., NC
Gallagher, Kevin E.*
Gallagher, Thomas E., NY
Garcia, Julio G., NY
Germano, Erasmo A., NY
Gerrity, William J.**
Hall, David E., NJ
Hanrahan, Joseph J., MA
Hassett, Jean M., CA
Herron, Francis R., NY
Hershman, Michael, VA
Hopkins, Warner V., NY
Jacobs, Lawrence W., AZ
Jensen, Paul V., NY
Jirak, Milton, NY
Keenan, Jane, NY
Kelly, Gerard W., NY
Kelly, Henry J.**
Kelly, Joseph A., IL
Kelly, Stephen P., IN
Kelly, William M.*
Kern, Neil E., NY
Koehler, Karl F., NC
Kummer, William F.*
Kupiec, Joseph, NY
Lambert, Edwin F., NY
Lee, Dr. Henry C., CT
Leibowitz, Morton J., VA
Liede, James M., NY
Linden, Jack, SC
Lopez, Gabriel R., NY
Loughlin, Michael, MA
Loughman, Robert P., NY
Luongo, John D., NY
Marchese, Joseph J., NY
Maroney, Robert D.*
Martin, Angela, GA
Maughan, William F., FL
Mazen, Aaron*
Mc Caffrey, Raymond A.*
Mc Coy, Henry, NY
McDevitt, James P., CA
Mc Gee, Peter P., NY
Mc Kenzie, John H.*
Mc Kissic, Aaron, NJ
Mc Knight, Thomas J., NY
Mc Veety, James A., NY
Meeks, John A., NJ
Miner, Juanita H., NY
Moschella, Salvatore, NY
Muhlin, Gregory**
Mullady, Joseph R., NY

Mullooly, William F.*
Murphy, Patrick J., NY
Murphy, Robert E., NY
Murray, Peter P.**
Murtagh, James J., NY
Nagle, Brian C.*
Narducci, Louis, NY
Neifeld, Robert, NY
Oberle, Robert P.*
O'hanlon, Eugene C., AZ
O'Hara, Patrick*
Ojena, Stephen, CA
Olsson, Eugene C., NY
Panzera, Stephen C.*
Payne, Jesse J., NY
Pilner, Thomas F.*
Pinnisi, Daniel R., NY
Pisane, Randolph (Randy), NJ
Pitlivka, John**
Plant, Philip*
Prager, Keith S., FL
Prince, Gilbert D., NY
Prost, Frank G., NY
Pucci, Raymond, NY
Quinn, Paul G., NY
Quinn, Robert J., TX
Ramsey, Charles E., AL
Ricardo, Myrilin U., FL
Robinson, Hamilton, VA
Rocchio, Peter A., NY
Rochford, Edward V., NJ
Rosenbaum, Frances, NY
Rowe, Leonard A., FL
Sarkus, LT Peter J., NY
Senitt, Melissa V., NY
Shayne, Alan F., NY
Sheehy, John K., NH
Shovlin, John P., NY
Silverman, Alex, NY
Slattery, Joseph F., NY
Sprague, Robert F., NY
Stapleton, James W., FL
Stevens, Gordon F., NY
Stuart, Robert A.**
Sullivan, Timothy J., NY
Tabert, Frank J.*
Taylor, Sandra L., CO
Tobin, John W., AZ
Torres, Donald, NJ
Turco, Angelo J., NY
Walsh, Thomas**
Weber, John, NY
Wiseman, Kenneth F., CA
Zazzi, Marie L., NY
Zlochower, Sol, CO

1973

Aguilar, Robert P.*
Albright, Eugene T., NY
Amaker, Larry*
Antab, Vaughn, NY
Aquino, Donald D., NY
Assante, Philip J., VA
Assenheimer, Carl F., NJ
Bachorik, Edward S., NY
Baker, Harold C., NJ
Balcom, MAJ Jerome (Jerry) K., NY
Bannon, John W., FL
Benton, F. W., NY
Berns, Lewis A.*
Berzins, Gunars*
Bochette, Louis R., NY
Bond, Keith A.*
Bryant, Victor E.*
Burger, James, NJ
Byrd, Paul H., NY
Cadogan, Darwin D., AP
Calhoun, James J., NY
Carroll, John J., NY
Carroll, Thomas R., NY
Casey, Bernard T.*
Cassagne, Rene A.*
Catalano, Thomas, IL
Christman, SGT Dennis L., NY
Cline, James, NJ

Coakley, Daniel P., NY
Colgan, John J.*
Colon, Robert G., NY
Corcoran, Michael T., NY
Costabile, Michael J., NJ
Cotty, Edward, NY
Cronin, George P.*
Davis, Gideon, NY
Delong, Joseph, NY
Dicker, Benjamin R.**
Dicker, Stanley M.*
Dodenhoff, Peter C.*
Donnellan, Roger W., NY
Dorfman, Abraham, NY
Dos Santos, Richard D., NY
Drogalis, John J., NY
Duncan, Mrs. Louise L., NY
Erickson, John*
Farrell, John R., CT
Fillyaw, Leonard D., NY
Finn, Brian T., NY
Ford, Christina E., NY
Forni, Mario T., CA
Frierson, Tom E., NY
Fucito, Michael J., NY
Fullam, Robert F., NY
Gabora, Herman R., NY
Gannon, James F., NY
Garbarini, Andrew J.*
Giddings, Robert J., NY
Goldstein, Patricia, NY
Gould, Edward*
Gramlich, Ronald W., FL
Gray, Thomas E., NY
Grieve, Daniel P., NY
Grode, George F., PA
Grosso, Joseph D., NY
Hamilton, Carl, NY
Henderson, Joseph M., FL
Howell, Grover D.*
Hulsmann, Robert N., NY
Jones, George E., NY
Jones, Joseph L., NY
Jordan, Robert R., NY
Juris, John R., NY
Kaecker, Richard J., NY
Keelan, James G., NJ
Kerton, Ervin (Ernie), FL
Knaplund, Virginia, NY
Koehler, Richard J., JD, NJ
Korman, Arnold I., Esq., NY
Kushner, Abraham, NY
Latimer, George A., NY
Lawrence, Brent L., NY
Lazansky, George, NY
Littlejohn, Robert F., NY
Loughery, Michael J., NY
Lubomski, CAPT Joseph E., NY
Maillard, William L., FL
Mangano, Louis, NJ
Marshall, Joseph, NY
Matera, Michael A., NY
McCabe, John P., NY
Mc Keegan, John J., NY
Mc Nally, Francis J.*
Medalion, Jonny M.*
Meyers, Robert J., FL
Mitkish, John A., NY
Moeser, Laura, NY
Mooney, Thomas E., NY
Morgan, Robert L.*
Nash, Joseph F., NY
Nolan, William F., NY
Noll, Harold W., CA
Obremski, Frank L., NY
O'Brien, David J., NY
O'Connor, Edward G., NY
Olivieri, Richard, NY
Orlich, Joseph A., NY
Palmer, Donald E., NY
Parsons, Theodore, CT
Pinsent, Clarenc M., NY
Preston, Thomas G., NY
Pribetich, John P., NY
Prunty, John M.*

Pucillo, Linda A.*
Quigley, John J., NY
Rainis, Edward A., FL
Rice, Robert D., NY
Rigney, James C., FL
Roberts, Vincent*
Robles, Laurel, NY
Rose, Jack N., NY
Ryan, Allen G., NY
Ryan, Edward J., NJ
Sabatino, Ludwig V., NY
Sansone, Salvatore J., NY
Schroeder, Donald J., NY
Schroeder, Fredric, NY
Schulz, Dr. Dorothy M., NY
Schwartz, Lawrence, FL
Schwartz, Sylvia*
Sedefian, Dickran*
Sergio, Alice E., NY
Sheeham, John P.*
Sheehan, John J., NY
Smith, Harry, CPP, NY
Stump, William P., NY
Sullivan, Vincent T., NY
Summers, William F., NY
Suss, Charles L., NY
Torres, Joseph*
Travers, Richard A., NY
Tyler, Juanita W.*
Ventura, Frank P., NJ
Walsh, Michael J., NY
Wanderman, Phillip J.*
Wendle, Thomas A., NY
White, Pearl E., NY
Zendzian, Craig A., CT

1974

Agosto, Patricia M.*
Albright, Frederick*
Anschick, Robert H., NY
Arinoldo, Carlo G.*
Barrett, John J., NY
Bashen, John C.*
Belgrave, Reginald, NY
Bibla, Raymond A.*
Bielski, Chester W., PA
Blige, Slater S., GA
Bonner, Edward J., NY
Bonner, John W.*
Borgstrand, Margaret A., NY
Brathwaite, LeRoy L., NY
Bratton, James G., NY
Breslin, Ethel T., NY
Bridgewater, Joel A., NJ
Bunch, Robert L., NJ
Burke, William J., NY
Buscemi, Salvatore, NY
Calvanese, Jerry F., NY
Campion, Edmund J., AZ
Campion, John D., NY
Cardillo, Joseph L., NY
Clausen, Vincent J., TX
Clinton, Brian J., FL
Cohen, Jeffrey L., NY
Cooper, Edwin B., FL
Corcoran, James P., NY
Crosby, Walter V., NY
Cruz, Raul, NY
Cullen, John J., FL
Cunningham, D., CT
Curran, Eleanor A., NY
Curran, Matthew F., NY
Cutler, Lynn, NY
Dagnello, Rudy J., NY
Daly, David, NY
D'Amato, George R., NY
Danese, Elizabeth Anne, NJ
Darpoh, Tetteh S.*
De Hart, Helen M., NY
Dillon, Edward J., NY
Diver, Hugh J., NY
Doda, Eleanor*
Donadio, Francis X., NY
Donnelly, Gerald M., NY
Donnley, Eleanor T., NY
Dorsett, Floyd W., NY

Doughney, Joseph C., NY
Doyle, Arthur, NY
Dunican, Thomas A., NC
Dunn, William H.*
Dunne, Francis X.*
Edwards, Bernard E., NY
Edwards, James W., NY
Eiler, Louis G.*
Ellis, Donna R.*
Esposito, Frances, NY
Fagan, Harry J., NY
Faro, James J., NY
Farrell, Kevin P., NY
Farrelly, Francis J., NY
Ferrara, Toni A., NJ
Flaherty, Richard J., NY
Foley, MAJ Thomas P., NY
Frankel, Robert R., NY
Freeman, Theodore R., NY
Fuchsman, Alan, NY
Galante, Carol*
Galante, Paul G.*
Galchus, Frank M., NY
Gallagher, Thomas, NY
Gannon, Thomas H., NJ
Garvey, James T., Jr., NY
Gazzola, Anthony J., NY
Geil, Terrence G., NY
Gellman, Harold, NY
Giaime, Vincent*
Gibbons, John M., NY
Goff, Richard, CA
Goldman, Robert*
Goldstein, Arthur, NY
Gotlob, Henry*
Grant, Kenneth G., FL
Greco, CAPT Carl J., NY
Gross, Solomon, CT
Guyet, Allan R., TN
Hackett, Catherine*
Harris, Bishop Robert W., NY
Healy, Patrick J., NY
Hendrickson, Avis, NY
Henrich, Paul C.*
Hettler, Kenneth R., NY
Heyward, Louis*
Holder, Gloria I., VA
Holder, Winthrop A., NY
Hollenbeck, Bruce A.*
Hopp, Philip M., NY
Horn, Martin F.*
Huscilowitc, Walter M.*
Kallas, Leo, PA
Katz, Marvin A., NJ
Keck, Joseph F.*
Keegan, Timothy F., NY
Kelly, John E., NY
Kelly, Leonard, NY
Kimlicka, Daniel E., NY
Knox, Charles, PA
Kolodkin, Richard R.*
Kuhn, Donald A., NY
Kurau, William R., Jr., PA
Laird, Donald (Don) A., CFE, FL
Laperuta, Domenick A., NY
Mari, Daniel J., NY
Marks, John G., NY
Marlovitch, Elaine A., NY
Marra, Anthony J., Esq., NY
Marsh, Warren S., NY
Martens, Frederick T.*
Marzoli, Joseph L., NY
Mattiace, Christopher, NY
Mc Cormick, Daniel, NY
McEniry, John A., NY
Mc Glone, Jim, NY
Mc Gowan, Edgar*
Mc Hugh, Edward C., NY
Mc Keon, Joseph D., NY
Mc Nally, Patrick M., NY
Mc Sweeney, Dennis F., NY
Mercilliott, Frederic P., PhD, VA
Merkel, Roy F.*
Meyers, Harold, NY

Milione, James M., NY
Miller, Jon I.*
Mitchell, Barbara B., NY
Monahan, Charles M., NY
Morgan, Robert F., NY
Murphy, Timothy J., NY
Murray, Clyde E., NC
Murray, James M.*
Murrell, Hubert*
Newborn, Harry*
Newton, Selassie A., VI
Nizza, Joseph R., NY
Nowacki, Michael M.*
O'byrne, Francis M., NY
O'connor, Roderick J., NY
Olsen, Edward H., NY
Olsen, Dr. Francis B., NY
Palmiotto, Michael J.*
Peters, Marlene M., FL
Phillips, Charles W., NY
Phillips, Edward C., NY
Phillips, Robert H., NY
Posavetz, Marilyn A., CT
Powell, Joseph S., NY
Profeet, Thelma Y.*
Radden, Melvin*
Raffa, Matthew W., NY
Ray, Robert J., NY
Reider, Lester, NY
Reilly, Thomas W., NY
Rogan, John F.*
Romm, Barry L., NY
Rooney, William, NY
Rothang, Robert A., NY
Rothlein, Steve, FL
Ruffo, Robert, NY
Ryan, Edward J., NY
Sacco, Dominick A., NY
Santora, Alexander, NY
Schaffer, Scott L., NY
Schechner, Lester S.*
Schuchman, Robert W., NY
Sclafani, Leonard A., NY
Seabrook, Larry, NY
Sether, Andrew G., NY
Shea, Edward M., NY
Shedrick, Jimmy, NY
Sherwood, Raymond G., NY
Sica, Richard J., NJ
Smith, Launcelott, NY
Springer, Louis G., NY
Stahl, Doris A., NY
St. George, Joyce, NY
Swayne, Patricia, NJ
Telesca, John, NY
Tice, Harry A., III, NY
Timoney, John F., PA
Treanor, William P., NY
Troisi, Alfred R., NY
Vairo, SGT Daniel, NY
Vecchio, Jack, Canada
Ventimiglia, Vincent, NY
Verde, Silverio B.*
Vredenburgh, Robert P., NY
Wade, Ryeburn A., NY
Walsh, Thomas P., NY
Ward, John J., NY
Ward, John W., NY
Ward, Robert C.**
Weinbaum, Nathan, NY
White, Janet E., NJ
Wilson, Tillie L., NY
Wolowski, Richard C., FL
Worth, John T., NY

1975

Abolsky, Stuart D.*
Abraham, George C., NY
Abramson, Rebecca D., NY
Acevedo, Cruz, AP
Acosta, Willie R., NY
Adelson, Arthur, FL
Agterberg, Elaine M.*
Aiello, Frank P., NY
Alber, Donald L.*
Allen, Allen B., NY

Allen, Richard E., NY
Anderson, Charles P., FL
Anderson, Ivil*
Anderson, Dr. Melody M., NY
Andujar, Michael, NY
Aponte, Miguel*
Appelman, Andrea S.*
Argent, Holly B., NY
Arzberger, Robert M., NY
Atkinson, Donald, MD
Atlas, Gary, NY
Atlas, Thomas A., NY
Attiyat, Abdulrahman*
Augustus, Sondra R., PA
Auleta, Kent R., NY
Austin, Reginald A., NY
Ayari, Abderrahman B., NY
Baird, Ernest, NY
Baney, James M., NY
Banzer, Frederick K.*
Baran, Ilona M.*
Barba, Maria E., VA
Barbieri, Ellen B., CA
Barna, John A., NY
Barnathan, Jack**
Barr, Charles S., CPP, CFE, NY
Barry, Kevin B., NY
Bashir, Benjamin M., NY
Batt, Jerome P., NY
Battle, Charles E.*
Beauchaine, David J., AR
Bell, Benjamin R.*
Benedetto, Anthony S., NY
Benjamin, Edward, CA
Berdan, Warren C., NY
Bernstein, Myron E.*
Best, George M., NY
Bianchi, Joseph A., NY
Bile, Robert S.*
Birbiglia, Joseph M., NY
Birk, Stuart E.*
Bodkin, John E., NY
Boltman, George A.*
Bonacum, William T., NY
Bonaparte, Henry, NY
Borman, Charles J., NY
Borman, William G., NY
Borruso, Mariano, NY
Bowes, Vincent, NY
Boyce, Audrei T., NY
Braff, Jeraldine, NY
Braithwaite, R. L.*
Braithwaite, Reginald, Esq., NY
Bramble, Elvira T., NY
Brennan, Daniel K., NY
Brennan, Michael J., NY
Brennan, Thomas F., FL
Brito, Evelyn G.*
Broadhurst, William, NY
Brophy, Edward J., NY
Brown, Alan R., NY
Browne, James, NY
Bruno, Anthony A.*
Bryan, Ernest A.*
Buchalter, Steven, NJ
Buell, Joseph T.*
Butterworth, William*
Byrnes, John P., NY
Caban, Wilfred, Sr., NY
Callahan, Michael P., NY
Cama, Pasquale A., NY
Camera, Andrew M.*
Campagnola, Alfonso, NY
Campbell, Michael W.*
Canaii, Angel B., NY
Cantwell, Thomas J.*
Carbin, Bernard J., NY
Carlson, Richard D., Jr., NJ
Carr, Robert J., NY
Carreras, Ralph, NY
Carrington, Frederic, NY
Catalfumo, Michael, NY
Cavanagh, Charles W., NY
Chaffee, David J., CO

Chimenti, Frank J., NY
Christensen, Jarl H., NJ
Cinti, John A., PA
Clancy, James P.*
Claps, Arthur V.*
Clark, Dennis P., NY
Clark, Joseph F., NJ
Clark, Paul V.*
Cohen, Ralph J.*
Cohen, Samuel, NJ
Coker, Marilyn V.*
Colligan, Mary E., NY
Collins, Gail M., NY
Collins, Thomas**
Colucci, Jooann, NJ
Conlon, Joseph, NY
Connolly, Raymond J.*
Console, Dominick J.*
Conti, Nicholas A., NY
Cooper, Stuart H.*
Corcoran, Carol A., TX
Cordova, Alfred*
Cornwall, Robert J., NY
Cottam, Gerard J., NY
Cotter, Joseph P., NY
Cotter, William J., NY
Creaney, Anthony P., NY
Cregan, Michael, NY
Crepeau, Louis J., NY
Cruz, Elizabeth T.*
Cuccio, Rocco J., NY
Cuomo, Anthony, FL
Curas, Sophia, NY
Curtiss, George R.*
Czarnecki, Anthony, NY
Danckwerth, Edward T., NJ
Danielson, Eskil S., NJ
Daubman, Arthur G., NY
Davis, Margaret M.*
Dean, James M.*
Defina, Joseph F., NY
Defina, Louise M., NY
DeGiovine, Arthur M., SC
Deitel, Abraham, NY
Deltoro, Jose R.*
De Luca, Fortunato J., NY
Demaggio, John M., NY
Dempsey, Robert*
Dennis, Gustina M., NY
Detres, Richard M., NY
Detres, Ronald*
Devlin, John F., NJ
Diamond, Sharon C.*
Diaz, Raymond J., NY
Diecidue, Charles J., FL
Diegnan, John J., NY
Dielensnyder, George, NY
Doherty, James P., NJ
Dolan, Edward G., NY
Donnelly, Edwin R.*
Donohue, Patrick T., NY
Donovan, Arundell (Tony) A., NY
Doran, Eileen A.*
Dorans, Edward T., NY
Doucet, Robert J.*
Dougherty, Vincent J., NY
Dowling, Richard J., NY
Drucker, Mitchel E., NY
Duane, William D., NY
Dubanevich, Denis*
Duff, James P., NY
Dumas, Peter R., NY
Dunham, Willard W.*
Dunne, Jay C., NY
Eanes, Ms. Barbara A., NY
Edwards, Theresa A., CA
Egan, John J., NY
Eilen, Howard S.*
Einsel, Craig D.*
Eisenberg, Mark C., NY
Eisenberg, Sally*
Elio, Michael F., NY
Elkin, Denise R., FL
Ellison, Henry J., NY
Ellson, James P., NY

Enright, John J.*
Epstein, Joel*
Escobar, Louis, NY
Esposito, Carlo R.*
Esteves, Carmen*
Evans, Jonathan, NY
Fagan, Richard G.*
Falvey, Lynn R., CA
Falvey, Stephen J., CA
Familgietti, Louis M.*
Farrell, Walter D., NY
Farry, Richard D., NY
Feeley, Jayne P.*
Feffer, Lawrence, NY
Fennell, Gerard, NY
Fenrich, Ronald J., NY
Ferdenzi, Joseph N., NY
Ferrante, Carol A., NY
Finamore, Daniel J., NY
Finkel, William P.*
Finley, Woodrow R.*
Finnerty, Thomas W., NY
Fiore, Anthony M., NY
Fiore, Nicholas S., NJ
Flanagan, Richard Y., PA
Fleming, William, NJ
Flood, James E., NY
Flynn, Eugene W., MA
Flynn, Hugh P., NY
Foley, Michael O., PhD, NY
Ford, Robert H.*
Franks, Robert J., NY
Fraser, Walter W., NY
Frawley, James M.**
Frohberg, John H., NY
Gadry, Albert J., MS
Gagatch, Robert P., NY
Gallagher, Michael G., NY
Gallmon, William*
Gallo, Joan, NY
Gault, Wendell*
Gelfman, George, NY
Genes, George J.*
Genna, Robert E.*
Gerardi, Domenick R.*
Gerhold, Lawrence R., NY
Gest, Richard W.*
Gibson, Alfred E.*
Giglio, Andrew M.*
Gildea, Michael O., NY
Gillner, George E.*
Gimlett, Brian F., DE
Giordano, Liz*
Girolamo, Anthony, NY
Goeddeke, D. T.*
Goetz, John F., PA
Goldberg, Joel A.*
Goldberg, Steven B.*
Goldstein, Burton S., NY
Gonzalez, Reinaldo, NY
Gooden, Herman, NY
Goodstein, Mark A.*
Granelli, Lawrence V.*
Grant, Michael G., NY
Grant, Michael J., NJ
Graziano, Frank A.*
Green, Lawrence E., NY
Greenberg, George, NY
Greene, Matthew L., FL
Greene, Ronell*
Griffith, Stanford A., NY
Griffiths, Robert P., NY
Guarco, Anthony, NY
Guido, John, NY
Hadley-Bailey, Cynthia, NJ
Halliday, Georgette*
Hamblin, Desmond M., CA
Hankinson, Golphin*
Hannigan, James R., NY
Hanold, George M., NY
Hanson, Charles J., NY
Hardy, Nicholas J.**
Harris, Gene R., NY
Harris, John R., Sr.*
Hart, Peter M.*
Hassa, Vincent J., NJ

Hatton, Kenneth R., NY
Hatton, Laurence F., NY
Healy, James T.*
Heineman, Frederick K., NC
Helmus, Harry H., NY
Hennessy, Gloria A.*
Henry, Conrad V., NY
Henry, Newton D., NY
Hernandez, Ana C., NY
Hess, Harold J., FL
Higgins, Kathryn, NY
Hill, Georgiana P.*
Hinnrichs, Jeffery K., KY
Hirschhorn, Lawrence*
Hodge, Laverna T., NY
Hogan, Brian F., NY
Hogan, Virginia M., NY
Holvik, Thor, NY
Horan, James J., NY
Horowitz, Lawrence J., NY
Howard, Catherine, NY
Hoy, Patrick J., NY
Hudson, John J., NY
Hughes, Martin J., NY
Humber, Charles M., NY
Hunt, Marvin S., FL
Hunter, John M.*
Iannaco, Vincent T., NY
Iannotta, Richard A., NY
Ilardi, Arthur, NY
Imparato, Michael G., NY
Irvine, Geraldine M.*
Iuliano, Stefano, NY
Jackson, Al*
Jackson, Barrett, NY
Jacubovics, Robert S., NY
Jefferson, Leo**
Jenkins, Samuel N., NY
Jeselnik, Joseph J., NY
Johannessen, Frank A.**
Johnsen, David P., TX
Johnson, Donald F., NY
Johnson, Joseph, NY
Jones, Theresa R.*
Julian, Michael A., NY
Kalisky, Bernard*
Karpusiewicz, S., FL
Kaufman, Mitchell J., NY
Kayton, John J., NY
Keeshan, Edward J., NY
Kelley, Eugene R.*
Kelly, Austin P., NY
Kelly, Dennis E., NY
Kelly, John P.*
Kelly, Margo F., IN
Kelly, William M., NJ
Kennedy, Richard J., NY
Kerins, Gerard J., NY
Killeen, Thomas P.*
Killorin, Stephen V.**
King, John T., NY
King, Joseph F., PhD, NY
Kinsella, William F., NY
Kirk, Edward J., NY
Kissane, Thomas P., NY
Klar, Marc E., NJ
Klink, Gunther J., NJ
Klinkenberg, William (Bill) H., FL
Koch, Robert P., NY
Koepfer, Stephen*
Kormendi, Robert, NY
Korzekwinski, Jack T., NY
Kosoff, Edward, NY
Kravath, Pauline, NY
Krueger, Edward O.*
Kurz, Edward A., FL
Laine, Frank C.*
Landers, Thomas J.*
Landis, James L., NJ
Lang, Paul A.*
Lathan, Rosemyer, NY
La Veglia, Anthony J., NY
Laveglia, Joseph A., NY
Lebron, Israel*
Lee, Richard, NY

Lefkowitz, Abraham Z., NY
Lehan, Joseph A.**
Leiker, David C., NC
Lekach, Jakub, PA
Leonard, Robert S.*
Levi, Barbara, NY
Levin, Erica*
Levine, Leslie J.*
Levinsky, Ronald F.*
Levy, Nelson S.*
Lichtenstein, Barry J., NY
Linder, Myril I., NY
Lipper, George D., NY
Liptak, Thomas J., NY
Lisogorsky, Michael N., NY
Locadia, Janet B., NY
Lomascolo, Frank J., NY
Lombardo, Blase D., NY
Lombardo, Frank A., NY
Lombardo, Michael D., NY
Lopez, Raymond J., NY
Love, Archie C., NY
Love, Shelly B.*
Lustberg, Robert M., NY
Lutkenhouse, Nancy E., NY
Lyons, Hester, NY
Mac Kay, Donald R., NY
Maher, James M., NY
Mahoney, Richard A., NY
Maillard, James H., NY
Malast, John*
Malcolm, Valerie V., NY
Malfi, Ronald D.*
Malone, Daniel E., NY
Mandarine, Joseph J.*
Maney, Michael A.*
Mangano, Edward J.*
Manning, Robert T.*
Marchak, George*
Mark, Lowell L.*
Marlin, Susan E., NY
Marrow, Gail M.*
Martin, Robert A., NJ
Martin, Robert P.*
Martinez, Joseph, NY
Martinicci, Pasquale*
Matteis, Salvatore, NY
Maurer, Barbara J.*
Maurer, Robert T., NY
Mazzella, John A.*
Mc Ardle, Richard A.*
Mc Cabe, Gregory R., PA
Mc Cabe, James J., NY
Mc Cann, James F.*
Mc Cann, Michael F., NY
Mc Carthy, Vincent, NY
Mc Clane, Kershaw C., NY
Mc Conney, Christine, NY
Mc Covery, Diane Y., NY
Mc Elroy, Andrew C., NY
McGahan, George E., NY
Mc Garry, MAJ Frederick S.,
   USA(Ret.), NY
Mc Govern, Patrick J., FL
Mc Gowan, Martin J., NY
Mc Guinness, Francis, NY
Mc Innis, Ronald P., NY
Mc Intyre, John F., NJ
McIver, Errol*
Mc Kay, John J., NJ
Mcmahon-Carroll, Suzanne,
   NY
Mc Parland, Thomas A., NJ
Mc Williams, John J., NY
Meara, Charles E., NY
Mevorah, Steven H., NY
Meyers, John A., NY
Michell, Arthur N., NY
Middleton, C. B., NY
Mims, Sharron E.*
Minauskas, John A., NY
Minogue, Edward T., NY
Minor, Clifford J.*
Minsky, Martin*
Mintz, Irwin, NY
Mitchell, James, NY

Moehring, Thomas P., NY
Mohrmann, Tina, NY
Molloy, Sean E., NY
Monahan, Arthur F.**
Montgomery, Ogden K.*
Moody, Lee R., DC
Moore, Raymond E.*
Morales, Sandra, NY
Moriarty, Thomas M., NY
Morra, Michael C., NY
Morrissey, Daniel F., NY
Morse, Henry R., NY
Moses, William (Bill) R., NY
Moss, Louis M.*
Murphy, Steven, NY
Myers, Victoria M., NY
Nardoza, Michael J., NY
Neil, Harold, VA
Nelson, Anthony J., NY
Neumayer, August F., FL
Neumeyer, Donald G., NY
Nicholson, Walter A., NJ
Nieves, Eliud*
Nostramo, Benjamin*
Nugent, Martha D., NY
O'brien, Patricia A., NJ
O'Connor, John J., NY
O'Connor, Valerie J., NY
O'Donnell, Lorraine J., NY
O'hagan, John T.**
O'heir, Thomas L., NY
O'Leary, Clifford B.*
O'Leary, John M.*
Olender, Ronald W., NV
O'Neill, Edward F., NY
O'neill, James, NY
Orangeo, Andrew D., NY
Orefice, Michael L., NY
Oreszczyn, Stephen A.*
O'Rourke, John J., NY
Ortiz, Anne M., FL
Ortiz, Col Rene P., USMC, VA
O'shea, Thomas F., NY
Osterreich, Martin G.*
O'sullivan, Thomas F., NY
Overton, Eric*
Palau, Luis A., NY
Palermo, Frank J.*
Palladino, James M., NJ
Panvini, Joann*
Parshall, Mary A.*
Pascal, Dave*
Passanesi, Dominick, FL
Pawelczak, Peter, NY
Pearce, Edward, NY
Pearson, Joan E., NV
Pelaez, Armando L., NY
Perkins, William J.*
Perrlno, Peter E.*
Peters, George L.*
Pezzo, Domenic, NY
Piccerill, Kenneth M., NY
Piper, Herbert*
Pittinsky, Leonard, NY
Plackenmeyer, William, NY
Plante, George J., NY
Polesel, Steven L., NY
Poleway, William P., NY
Pollack, Dan L., NY
Prescott, Kay F., NY
Presser, Allen, NJ
Rabinowitz, M., NY
Radke, Henry, NY
Ramirez, Alexander, FL
Ramos, Adrian, NY
Ramsey, Waltis, Jr., NY
Randall, Francis E., NY
Reers, Richard L., NY
Reid, Arlene J., NY
Reilly, James P., IL
Reilly, John T., SC
Reilly, Joseph A., NY
Reilly, Lillian P.*
Reilly, William F., NY
Rhodes, Rebecca, NY
Rice, George A.*

Riley, James B., NY
Rinaldi, Patrica M., NY
Riordan, Michael J.*
Rios, George J., NY
Ritchie, John D., NY
Rivera, Jorge W., NY
Rivera, Nestor*
Rizzo, Joseph P.*
Robins, Randall S.*
Rock, Barry*
Rodriguez, George*
Roman, George N.*
Romani, C., NJ
Romano, Frank J., NY
Ronan, Francis J.*
Rooney, Thomas F., NY
Rosado, Lt Col Samuel A.,
   USAF(Ret.), OH
Rosario, Manuel D., CA
Rose, Theodore*
Ross, Mark M.*
Rottkamp, William J., NY
Ryan, Richard J., NY
Ryan, Thomas, NY
Ryan, William G., NY
Salamone, John A., FL
Sampel, James J., NY
Samuels, Yvonne M.*
Sanchez, Victor A.*
Sankey, John P., NY
Sanso, Andre, NY
Santana, Josefina*
Santo, Ronald H., NY
Santoli, Joseph J.*
Sarter, Leonard, NY
Sasson, Lionel A.*
Sattelberger, Alfred*
Sayad, Karim, NY
Sbrocchi, Louis A.*
Schaaff, Henry G., NY
Schneier, Steven, NY
Schnupp, Jerome E., NY
Schoenberg, Karen*
Schoepe, Peter A.*
Schwartz, Milton, NY
Schweibinz, Paul J., FL
Sci, Paul R., NM
Scott, Andre K.*
Scretching, Ralph O.*
Seales, Paul J., NY
Seignious, Robert, NY
Seubert, Anthony J.*
Shanley, Robert C.*
Shareef, Jaffer*
Shea, Cornelius P., VA
Sheehan, Gerald J., NY
Shelton, Anthony*
Shields, Eugene G., NY
Shortell, Robert E., CA
Shury, C.*
Siccardi, Vincent F., NY
Siegel, Natanya*
Silverman, Kenneth M.*
Simons, Lee L., NY
Sinatra, James K., NJ
Sinatra, Patricia M., NY
Siroka, Andrew L., NY
Sivler, Les I., NY
Skopin, Raymond P., NY
Smartt, George D.*
Smith, Albert J.*
Smith, Catherine H., NY
Smith, Eugene F., NY
Smith, Leo E., NY
Smith, Peter G., NY
Smith, Richard*
Smith, Walter D., NC
Sommers, Barry M., NY
Spandorf, Neil D.*
Sparkman, William D.*
Sparling, Daniel E., NY
Stagnari, John M., NY
Stahl, John P., NY
Stanis, Mary E., NY
Staten, Charles A.*
Stepinski, Catherine*

Stoecker, Frank R.*
Storch, Jerome E., NV
Strojnowski, Joseph*
Strube, Edward W., VA
Sughrue, Daniel F., NH
Sullivan, James J., NY
Sullivan, Patrick F., VA
Sullivan, William T., FL
Summerlin, Gregory P., NY
Sysak, Paul J., NY
Tabb, James L., NY
Talty, Richard B., NJ
Taublib, Allan M., MD
Taverna, Ignazio, NY
Taverni, Robert E., NY
Taylor, Richard F., NY
Terhune, John S.*
Terry, Walter P., NY
Tims, Claude D., NY
Tomasso, Nicholas F., NY
Toner, Vincent E., NY
Torres, Jesus, NY
Towner, Andrew T., NY
Tozzo, Charles W.*
Trager, Leonard, NY
Treppiedi, Rocco N., WA
Troini, Mary V.*
Tucker, Julia E., NY
Turner, Joseph P., FL
Twyford, Thomas E.**
Upshur, Roderick W., NY
Uttaro, Raymond J., NY
Valenti, Philip J., AP
Valentine, William C., NY
Valentino, Vincent*
Valle, Frank V., NY
Van, Benschoten W., NY
Varlack, Charleswort, NY
Vastola, Anthony*
Vaughan, Susan, NY
Verbitsky, Bruce, NY
Villafane, Awilda, NY
Virzera, Victor L., NY
Vonbargen, Philip H., NY
Walsh, George J., NY
Walter, Bruce W., NY
Ward, Joseph R., FL
Warne, Kenneth C., NY
Wasiluk, Harry*
Wawrzonek, Matthew, NY
Weber, William J., NY
Weidenbaum, Paul T.*
Weinert, George P.*
Weissman, David E., CA
Wells, William E., NY
Wendolski, Peter P., NY
Werbkay, Victor R., NY
Wertkin, Stephen L., NY
Whipple, Lois*
White, Douglas, NY
Whyte, James J.**
Wickham, Denis*
Williams, James O., NY
Williams, Loise L., NC
Wilson, Alfred L.*
Wilson, Joseph R.**
Wincelowicz, Michael, NY
Winetzky, Rochelle*
Winfield, Lillian B., NY
Wise, Lauren A., NY
Wood, Joseph L.*
Woodard, Richard, MD
Woods, Frank J.**
Wunderlich, Donald S., NY
Wunsch, John A., NY
Yasso, Michael, NY
Zadorozny, Maureen M., NY
Zalepa, Robert P., NY
Zeigler, Douglas, NY
Zurer, Erica*
Zwerdling, Seymour*

1976

Aboulafia, Sandy*
Abraham, Robert, NY
Acevedo, CW4 Efrain, NY

Adams, David T.*
Adolfsson, Boyd, NY
Agosta, Felice J.*
Ahlers, Kenneth W., NY
Albanese, Philip P., NY
Albano, Daniel J., NY
Alberga, Jeanna M.*
Albury, Nicholas A., NY
Alibrande, Donald, NY
Alifano, Charles*
Allen, Alton D., FL
Allen, Carl, NY
Allen, Christine V., NY
Allen, James T., NY
Allessandro, James, NY
Almedina, Joseph A., NY
Alvarez, Charles*
Alveranga, Glanvin*
Amato, Edward J., NY
Amereno, Bernice O., NY
Anderson, Greta, NY
Anderson, Paul M., NY
Andrews, Peter, NY
Andricosky, John J., NY
Angley, Richard J., HI
Annucci, Anthony J., NY
Antisz, Stephen*
Anziani, Victor, NY
Aponte, Victor M., Italy
Appelbaum, Jed, NY
Arestie, Martin J., TX
Argiento, Ralph, NY
Ash, Sylvia G., Esq., NY
Augello, Angelo J., NY
Austin, Karen F., NY
Bach, Robert R., NY
Backof, Richard W., NY
Baez, Henry, NY
Bagley, Reginald N., NY
Bagnall, Gerald*
Bailey, Stephen H., NY
Baker, John M.*
Baker, Roberta R.*
Bala, James W., ME
Baldwin, Robert M., NY
Ballerini, Jeffrey A.*
Bank, Maurice H., NY
Banks, Hermon J., NY
Barreyre, Raymond, NY
Bartlett, Thomas W., NJ
Bauer, Richard C., PA
Bauman, David L.*
Baumann, Kevin P., NY
Bayard, Marie-denise, NY
Bedor, Paul M.*
Beirne, Margaret, NY
Belanich, M. S.*
Bellamy, Doris J., NJ
Benedisuk, Mary R., NY
Benes, Kenneth J., NY
Bennardo, Andrew N.*
Bennett, Robert B.*
Benson, Elizabeth*
Benson, Rodney B., NY
Bergersen, John R., NY
Bergstrom, Carl D.*
Bernstein, Richard W., NY
Betty, Melvin L., NY
Bianco, Aniello R., NY
Bianculli, Frank C., NY
Biberaj, Hasan, NY
Biesty, William F., NY
Billings, Robert P., NY
Bines, Joseph G., NY
Birnbaum, Benjamin*
Blackwood, Laurence*
Bleiberg, Michael S., NY
Bodigheimer, Edward*
Bole, Nicholas, NY
Bonacchi, Eugene, NY
Borfitz, Irving E., NY
Boutineau, Robert G., NY
Boyer, John C.*
Boyko, Kevin E., ND
Brady, Joseph J.*
Brady, Noreen P.*

Bragg, Joseph L., NY
Brandi, Daniel J., NY
Bree, John P.*
Breen, Patrick F.*
Bretton, Ronald, HI
Brigandi, Douglas, NY
Brill, John J., NY
Brogan, Ronald J.*
Brosnan, Donald P., NY
Brosnan, William P.*
Brown, Angela L.*
Brown, Louis, NY
Brown, Ralph J., NY
Brown, Raymond M., NY
Brown, Ronald E., GA
Bruschi, Mario J., NY
Bruthanz, Walter R.**
Burger, Frederick (Fred) R., NY
Burger, William C., NY
Burke, Clifford P.*
Burke, Jeremiah M., NY
Burns, Michael J.*
Burrell, William D., NJ
Bursey, Bruce A.*
Byrne, John T., NY
Byrnes, Robert M., NY
Cagna, Delores*
Calcagni, John R.*
Caldararo, John V., NJ
Caldarelli, John L., NY
Calhoun, William F., NY
Calkin, Ronald F., NY
Callahan, Robert M., NY
Cambria, Frank M.*
Cameron, Peter F., NJ
Cammallere, M. J., NY
Campbell, John F.*
Campbell, Robert, NJ
Campbell, Wilfrid R., NY
Campion, Terrence J.*
Canelo, Juan, FL
Canfield, Dennis V., PhD, OK
Cannella, Joseph D., NY
Capece, Daniel*
Capella, Ms. Jeanette, NY
Capobianco, John J., NY
Caracola, John A., NY
Carberry, George M., NY
Carbo, Joseph A.*
Cardwell, Linda, NY
Carey, Gary T., NY
Carrigan, Richard M., NY
Carroll, Ellen M., NY
Carson, Andrew F., NY
Carter, James E., NY
Carter, Owen, NY
Casey, Dennis R., NY
Casper, Rene E., NY
Cassano, Salvatore J., NY
Cassidy, John J., NY
Cassidy, Patrick E., NY
Castagna, Anthony R.*
Caulfield, Hugh J., NY
Cavoto, Anthony, NY
Cederholm, Allan A.*
Celardo, George A.*
Cerami, Victor S., NY
Cerato, John*
Cersosimo, Liana*
Cestare, John, NY
Chandler, Debora*
Cheatham, Leroy R., NY
Chimienti, Alexander, NY
Chin, Rose, NY
Chisholm, Elizabeth, NY
Chugerman, Jacob E., NY
Chung, George, NY
Ciccone, Joseph F., NY
Citron, Mary, NY
Clancy, James T., NY
Clarke, James G., NY
Clarke, Thomas J., NY
Clendening, John P.*
Cleveland, Alfonzie, NY
Cocozzo, Harry B.*
Coffman, Gerald R.*

Cohen, Marcia B.*
Cohen, Michael J., NY
Cohen, William J.*
Coleman, William E., NY
Collins, Eileen M.*
Colon, Juan*
Concepcion, Angel, NY
Condiotti, Irving, NY
Condon, Robert A., NY
Confredy, John W.*
Conlin, Eugene A.*
Connolly, Charles P., NY
Connolly, Francis P.*
Conroy, Gary P., NY
Convery, James H., NJ
Copeland, Geraldine*
Coschignano, John J.*
Costello, Edward T.*
Cotto, Gerald*
Could, Luwyana C.*
Counce, Carole A.*
Cousar, Johnny*
Coyne, James, NY
Crawford, Arthur J., NY
Creegan, John I., NY
Creelman, Thomas C., NY
Cregan, Dennis J., NY
Cregan, Robert J., NY
Crice, Carroll B.*
Crimmins, John D., NY
Crippen, James H.*
Crosby, Delois, NY
Cruz, Louis A., Esq., NY
Culvert, Romano, NJ
Cummings, James P., NY
Cunningham, Dennis J., NY
Curran, John T., NY
Curry, Thomas J.*
Curry, Thomas P., NY
Cusanelli, Thomas*
Czajkowski, Raymond, NY
Dacenay, Yvonne A.*
D'Adamo, John*
Dailey, Andrew G.*
Daley, Robert E., NY
Dalton, John J.*
Daly, William J., NY
D'ambrosio, Louis J., NY
D'Amico, Joseph*
Danaher, James L., NY
Danik, Mark D., NJ
D'antonio, Steven A., NY
Dantschisch, Andrew*
Dargan, Thomas J., NY
Dascoli, Francis, NJ
Davis, Dominique, NY
Davis, Elaine M.*
Davis, Ronald J., NY
Day, Thomas M., FL
De Canio, Camille M., NY
De Cluitt, Gerald C., NY
Deery, Edward, NY
Degering, Steven V., NY
Deignan, George N.*
De John, Gregory G., NY
Delano, Donald F., NJ
De Paulo, Peter A., NY
De Rario, Liberio J.*
Desantis, Francesco, NJ
De Santis, Nicholas, NY
De Vita, Michael J.*
Dickerson, Joeann M., NY
Dier, Dennis M.*
Di Gaetano, Alcide V., NY
Di Gaudio, Patricia*
Di Giaro, Sam R.*
Dignon, Francis T., NY
Doherty, CAPT Michael J., NY
Donelan, Michael J., MA
Downing, Charles*
Dragonett, Carimine*
Drayton, Kenneth R., NY
Druss, Philip M., NY
Du Brino, Joseph F.*
Duda, Joseph (Joe) T., NY
Duggan, Frank, CT

Durando, Doanld M., NY
Durnack, Robert (Bob) P., NY
Durr, Johershey, NY
Ears, Joannee, NY
Egan, Patrick J., NY
Egan, Thomas P., NY
Eklund, Thomas**
Ellsworth, Thomas, IL
Emanuelo, Michael S.**
Eschenbacher, Bill*
Eschenberg, Conrad J., IV, NY
Esko, Jeffrey*
Esnard, Richard, NY
Ezell, Willie L.*
Facilla, Theresa M., NY
Fackner, Robert E., NY
Fahy, John W.*
Fallon, John G., NY
Fallon, Thomas W., IL
Farkas, Howard G., NY
Farrell, James M., NY
Farrell, Michael F.**
Fassnacht, Irene E., NY
Fealey, Joseph C., NY
Feeley, Matthew M.*
Feeley, Warren J., NY
Feeney, Mary D., NJ
Feminella, Ralph J., FL
Ferguson, Charles J., NY
Ferguson, James G., AP
Ferguson, Phyllis D.*
Ferrara, Albert A., NY
Fetonti, Paul J., NY
Fevelo, John F., NY
Finan, Edward J.*
Finneran, John J.*
Fitzgibbons, Marie E., NY
Fitzpatrick, Thomas G., NY
Flaherty, John H., NY
Fleming, Arthur J., NY
Fleming, Laqueth, NY
Flemings, Elmer W., NY
Flemmings, Lamont S., NC
Flowers, Leon A., NY
Flynn, Edward A.*
Flynn, Thomas J., NY
Forner, Michael S., NY
Fornino, Gerald C.*
Franceschini, Remo*
Fredericks, Walter F., NY
Frein, Laurence*
Frye, Dale G.*
Fuchs, Pearl M.*
Fuentes, Dainery M.*
Fuentes, Gustavo*
Fumai, John H., NY
Fumai, Joseph F., NY
Gafford, Hazel V., NY
Gaioni, Robert J., NY
Galarza, Iris*
Galasso, Rocco A., NY
Galea, John A., NY
Galfy, James T., NJ
Gallagher, Edward*
Gallagher, G. J.*
Gallagher, Harold D., MD
Gallagher, William J.*
Galletta, Cyrus B., NY
Gamber, Mark E., NY
Gamble, James R.*
Gannon, Walter E., NY
Garcia, Isabel M., NY
Garvey, Thomas D., NY
Gaskin, Bill R., NY
Gasser, Rosemary, NY
Gaton, Errol C., NY
Geary, Howard C., NY
Gersbeck, Joseph T., NY
Gervasio, Louis A., NY
Gianatiempo, Peter S.**
Giannasio, Martha B.*
Gibbons, John W., FL
Gildea, Edward J., NY
Gilgan, Gerald P.*
Gillen, Brian J., NY
Gilmartin, John F., NY

Glenn, Gary F., NY
Glynn, Francis P.**
Goldsmith, Jay K.*
Goldstein, Morton J.*
Gomez, Alfredo S.*
Goodman, Alan Z., NY
Goodman, Gail H.*
Goods, Samuel E., NY
Goodwin, Bruce K., NY
Gore, Barbara H., NY
Gorman, James P., NY
Gottlieb, Paul, NY
Goudie, David W., NY
Grant, Alphonzo S., NY
Grant, Sharon D., NY
Grattan, Walter W., NY
Graziano, Michael A., NY
Greaves, Eustace L., NY
Green, Esther*
Green, Herman L., NY
Grennan, Sean A., PhD, NY
Grice, Richard G., NY
Griffith, Stephen C.*
Griggs, Kenneth L.*
Grimes, Joann E., NY
Groger, Kathleen M., NY
Grubert, Arthur C.*
Guarino, Nicholas E., NY
Guest, Gerard A., NY
Guido, William J., NY
Gulinello, Joseph J., NJ
Gundersen, William, NC
Gunn, Josephine T.*
Gunn, Robert (Bob), NY
Gurry, Michael J.*
Hackett, George A., NY
Hahn, Harold, NY
Hall, James R., NY
Hanley, Samuel, NY
Hanna, George J., NY
Hanna, Patrick J., NY
Hannon, Timothy J.*
Hansen, Gerard T.*
Hantman, Michael*
Harding, Rev. Curtis T., Jr., NY
Hardy, Ernest T., NY
Harrington, Kevin M., NY
Harris, Arthur J., NY
Harris, Marilyn J., NY
Hart, Adolph W.*
Harvey, Edmund P., NY
Harvey, Stephen F.*
Hastings, Joseph**
Hawkins, Wallie E., NY
Hayes, Edward A.*
Hazelhurst, Bernice, NY
Heavey, Michael F., NY
Hegarty, Catherine M.*
Hennig, George D., NY
Henry, Kenneth D., NY
Hepburn, Lawrence P.*
Hering, Robert K., NY
Herting, Edward C., NY
Higgins, Daniel P., NY
Higgins, Harry F., NY
Higgins, Patrick H.*
Hill, Charles*
Hill, Thomas*
Hinchey, Arthur F., NY
Hinkson, Kenmore I., NY
Hochbaum, Charles H.*
Hoehl, Allan H., NY
Hoffman, Howard A., NY
Hoffman, Joseph C., NY
Holden, McThaddeus, NY
Holland, Michael, NV
Holland, Ronald P., NY
Holloway, Harold T., NJ
Holmes, Michael*
Holsten, Harold F.*
Hopkins, Steven B., NJ
Howell, George A., NY
Hudson, Charles T., NY
Huggins, Eddie C., NY
Huggins, Ms. Jocelyn, NY
Hughes, Ellsworth K., NY

Hughes, Shirley E.*
Hughes, Timothy P., CA
Hussey, Robert, NY
Hussey, Robert J., NY
Hyde, Phillip E., PA
Israel, Gary G., NY
Jackson, M. B.*
Jackson, Marilyn G.*
Jacobs, Harold, NY
Jacobson, Benjamin, NJ
James, Preston*
Janousek, Stanislav, NY
Janssen, Ronald P., NY
Jenkins, Michele, NY
Jernigan, Sherry A.*
Johnson, Charlie L., NY
Johnson, Francis R., NY
Johnson, Herbert R., NY
Johnson, Richard A.*
Johnson, Roger J., NY
Johnston, Robert J.*
Jones, Charles F.*
Jones, Otis M., NY
Jones, Seymour A., GA
Jones, Ursilla E., NY
Kaecker, Ernest A.*
Kahlon, Tejindar S., NY
Kalmar, Roberta, NY
Karback, William S.*
Katz, Robert G., NY
Kavanagh, John P., NY
Kaye, Allan H., NY
Kaye, Mrs. Marion, NY
Kealy, Thomas J., FL
Kehoe, James P.**
Kehoe, William J., NY
Kelaher, Peter E., NY
Kelly, James F., NY
Kelly, John J., NY
Kelly, Kevin J.*
Kelly, Kevin P.*
Kemly, Ronald H., NJ
Kennedy, Patrick C., NY
Key, Kenneth*
Kilfoyle, Margaret*
King, David W., NY
King, Hilarey A.*
King, Kenneth L., NY
King, Martin J., NY
King, R., NY
Kirk, Michael, NY
Kirkman, Edward J., NY
Kittrell, John E., NY
Klaman, Richard, NY
Klein, Fredric C., NY
Klein, Leon E., NY
Knox, James W.*
Kolman, David O., NY
Koltun, Andrew*
Kovic, Martin J.*
Kowsky, Frederick P.*
Kozel, Joseph D., NY
Kramer, William, NY
Kruesi, Arthur W., NY
Kupper, Donald F., NJ
Kurtz, Michael J., NY
Kutcher, Raymond, NY
Lambdin, George C., NY
Lambkin, John J., NY
Lane, Edward B., NY
Lane, Henry L., NY
Lane, James E.*
Lanning, Paul J.*
Lara, Joseph J.*
Larberg, Stephen M.*
Laskowski, Michael*
Latham, Kevin J.*
Ledee, Robert, NY
Lee, Melvin C.*
Leggio, Vito J.*
Leibowitz, Harold, NY
Lembo, Stephen J., NJ
Lenahan, Thomas A.*
Lenoci, Nicholas P.*
Leonard, Thomas J.*
Lester, Denise F.*

Levinsky, Mitchell A.*
Lewandowski, S. J., NY
Lewis, Emanuel*
Lewis, Heather D.*
Lifshutz, George, NY
Lipschitz, Stephen, NY
Lock, Linda C., AE
Loeffler, Raymond W., NY
Loewe, Frederick H.*
Lopez, Jose I., NY
Lowe, John P., NY
Luby, John D.*
Lucarelli, Modestino, NY
Luis, Hector, NY
MacDougall, John, NY
Machowsky, Barton*
Maddox, Charles, NY
Madsen, Theodore S., NY
Mahabir, Anthony F.*
Mahon, John F., NY
Mahoney, Patrick D., NV
Maione, Fortune*
Majeski, William J., NJ
Malcan, Jay W., VA
Maldonado, Rose, NY
Maloney, John F., NY
Mancuso, Peter J., PA
Mandelbaum, Marvin H., CA
Mangus, Peter J., NY
Manning, George J., NY
Mar, Marie A., NY
Marchetta, Stephen B.*
Marcus, James A., NY
Marino, Vincent D., NY
Marion, Mary A., NY
Markey, John F., NY
Marousek, Frank W.*
Marron, James P.*
Marsh, Joannie*
Martell, Maurice J.**
Martin, Jules A.*
Martin, Patrick J., NY
Martinkovic, J. Y.*
Martino, Angelo, NY
Martino, Steven J., NY
Martocci, Rocco A., NY
Mason, William J.*
Mateo, Richard E., NY
Mattson, Gary A.*
Maurer, Michael J., NY
Mauro, Thomas A., NJ
Maybury, Kevin C., NY
Maycock, Neville G., NY
Mayer, John J.*
Mayfield, Gwendolyn*
Mazza, Cajetan, NY
Mazza, Frank, NY
Mazza, Salvatore*
Mc Aleer, James T.*
Mc Aree, Anne M., NY
Mc Cann, Michael D., NY
Mc Carthy, Donald F., FL
Mc Carthy, Edward V.*
Mc Carthy, Eugene F., NY
Mc Cormack, Burchell*
Mc Coy, Felix J., CA
Mc Coy, Michael G., NY
Mc Dermott, Thomas, NY
Mc Donald, Doretha*
Mc Donald, John E., NY
Mc Donnell, Robert, PA
Mc Elroen, Lawrence*
Mc Gary, Roger A., MD
Mc Ginnis, Robert D., NJ
Mc Gorty, Martin*
Mc Greal, James J., NY
Mc Hugh, Edward, NY
Mc Kay, John, NY
McKeon, James E., NY
Mc Kie, Herman, NY
Mc Knight, Walter D., NY
Mc Loughlin, Robert, NY
Mc Mahon, Daniel F., NY
McMickens, Jacqueline*
Mc Mickens, Jacqueline M.*
Mc Mnmon, Dennis, NJ

Mc Nally, Joseph P.*
Mc Naughton, Robert*
Mc Neal, Harry E., NY
Mc Nicholas, James F., NY
Mc Queen, Gerald T.*
Mc Rae, Guy H.*
Mc Sherry, Martin M., NY
Meadow, Howard S., NV
Mealia, Robert M., NY
Meaney, Edna M.*
Mecir, Thomas B., NY
Medeiros, Michael, NY
Meehan, Robert E.*
Melone, John E., NY
Mendel, Alan, NJ
Mendez, Miguel A.*
Mentuck, Edward M., NY
Mercado-Ortiz, Luciano, NY
Merenda, Jean A., NY
Merenda, Stephen P., NY
Merriam, Willard E., NY
Meyer, Carl N.*
Meyer, Leonard A., NY
Miao, Myron K.*
Miller, Jonathan D., NY
Miller, Mark B.*
Miller, Thomas E.*
Miller, Vincent J.*
Miller, William S.*
Millett, John F., NY
Mills, Charles M., NY
Mills, James J., NY
Mills, Mary A.*
Milovanovic, Dragan, NY
Minardi, Rocco N., NY
Mingo, Alfred E., NY
Misson, George R., NY
Modafferi, Peter A., NY
Moncure, Linda B.*
Monfasani, Neil L.*
Montalbano, John P., NY
Monteleone, Joseph C., FL
Mooney, Martin C., NJ
Moore, Dennis*
Moorehead, Norris E., NY
Morcelo, Domingo A., NY
Moser, Marian C., NY
Moss, Joel W., FL
Moy, Wing, NY
Mulero, George, FL
Mullen, Brian G.*
Mulryan, Austin P.*
Muniz, Gary S.*
Murphy, Bruce O.*
Murphy, Jeremiah J.**
Murray, Carolyn M.*
Murray, Lucy, NY
Myers, Robert*
Nadel, David W., NY
Napolitano, Ralph T., NY
Napolitano, Sal R., NY
Nardoza, Robert, NY
Narkiss, Shmuel*
Nasoff, William J., NY
Navatta, James A., NY
Neblett, Angela M., AE
Nelson, Denise, NY
Nelson, Samuel**
Nesbit, Robert D.*
Nesensohn, Donald O., NJ
Nevarez, Hector*
Newbert, Robert M., NY
Newfeld, Mark L.*
Niemeyer, Charles J.*
Nixon, Rene*
Noa, Albert*
Noonan, Edward S.*
Norris, Edward T., NY
Norton, William J., NY
Novarro, Santo F., NY
Obarowski, Edward A., NY
O'berg, Dennis J., NY
O'Brien, Patrick T., SC
O'Connell, Kevin J., NY
O'Connor, Darrell*
O'Connor, Joanne M., NY

O'connor, John J., NY
O'connor, Thomas P., NJ
O'flaherty, Donald M., NY
O'Kane, John J., NY
O'keefe, James F.*
O'leary, Jeremiah J., NY
Oliver, James H., NH
Olsen, Gary J., NY
Olsen, Thomas J., NY
O'Neill, John T., NY
Oppong, Martin D., Ghana
O'Reilly, John E.*
O'Reilly, Thomas C., NJ
O'Reilly, Thomas V., FL
Orriola, Victor M., NY
O'shea, John F.*
O'Shea, Timothy J., NJ
Pacheco, Jose A., Jr., NY
Pagano, Richard J., NY
Panarello, Gary R., NY
Panettie, Margaret M.*
Panico, Gene F., NY
Paredes, Josue, NY
Parrinello, Arthur J., NY
Parrish, John F., NJ
Passano, Alexander, NY
Patterson, Duval H.*
Paveglio, David J., NY
Pearson, James T., NY
Pearson, Leonard B.*
Pegram, John A., NY
Pender, Patrick J., NY
Pergamo, Joseph J., NY
Perrotta, Fred J., NY
Peterson, Daniel V.**
Petrocelli, Dennis, NY
Philip, Emile*
Phillips, Leon I., NY
Phipps, Samuel**
Pierre, Thomas K.*
Pisani, Ernest*
Pittelli, Valerie G., NY
Pizzano, John, NY
Plesnitzer, Edward J., NY
Pluciennik, Thomas C., NJ
Polland, Hugh*
Ponzio, William P., NY
Powell, Howard G., NY
Power, Thomas J., NY
Prahl, John F., NY
Price, Carroll B.*
Pride, Mashere V., NY
Prince, Donald J.*
Punzi, Alfred M., NY
Quatrone, Rudolph S., NY
Quick, John W., NY
Quinn, John F., NY
Quinn, Kevin A., NY
Quinn, Michael B., NY
Quinones, Alma D., NY
Racioppo, Ralph, NY
Rada, Frederick L., NY
Raffa, Gerald T.*
Raichle, Carl J., NY
Raiser, George D.*
Rall, Charles E., AZ
Ramirez, Richard, NJ
Ramos, Anthony J., NY
Rando, Gregory J., NY
Raniola, John, NY
Ravalgi, Patrica M., NY
Rawles, Melba, NY
Reale, Alan P., NY
Rebelein, John R.*
Rechenberg, Jan M., NY
Reekie, Robert, NY
Reilly, Paul J., FL
Reimann, Elsbeth, NY
Remsen, John M.*
Resto, Hipolito, NY
Reyes, Lourdes*
Rhodes, Richard L.*
Riccardi, Kenneth P., NY
Rice, Ronald L.*
Rice, William D.*
Richardson, D. O., NY

Richardson, Homer W., NY
Richardson, Joseph R., NY
Richardson, Laurence*
Richardson, Randall, NJ
Richburg, Lionel, NY
Riehl, Alfred P., NY
Riley, John F., NY
Ripandelli, Alphonse, NY
Rivera, Euclid*
Rivera, James, NY
Rivera, Nicholas, NY
Rivera, Samari, NY
Roccaro, Rosario J., NY
Rodriguez, Antonio*
Rodriguez, Bolivar M., NY
Rodriguez, Charles, FL
Rodriguez, James, FL
Rogers, William J., NY
Roman, Hector L., NY
Ronning, Steve O., NY
Rooney, Joseph E., NY
Rosa, Rosemarie, NY
Rosas, Michael A.*
Rosen, Helen M.**
Rosenthal, Richard P.*
Rothman, Peter L., NY
Rowland, John, FL
Rowland, William J.*
Rudawitz, Edward M., NY
Runco, Anthony M.*
Ryan, James J., NY
Ryan, John F.*
Ryan, Martin J., NY
Sadrakula, Michael P., NY
Sala, Joseph J., NY
Salamo, Michael R., NY
Salerno, Joseph J., AZ
Sampson, Frank C., NY
Sanchirico, Paul M., NY
Sanderson, Paul M., NY
Santana, Sixto J., NY
Santiago, Rose M., NY
Satin, Fred L.*
Saunders, Arconza, NY
Savage, Rose M.*
Sawyer, James W., FL
Sayers, Donna C., NY
Scaglione, Dominic J., NJ
Schachinger, Mildred C., NY
Schaefer, Robert B.*
Schan, Robin A., NY
Schauffert, R. C., NY
Scheper, Frederick W., NY
Schieck, William J., NY
Schiffer, Herbert J., NY
Schilling, Francis L., NY
Schmid, Joseph J.*
Schmidt, Vincent R.*
Schmidt, Wayne F., NY
Schnell, George L., FL
Schreiner, John A., NY
Schrier, Leonard S., FL
Schulte, Janet, FL
Schulze, Raymond, NJ
Schuster, Kenneth G., NY
Schwarz, Gunter G., NY
Scott, Neil D.*
Scotti, Salvatore, NY
Setter, George, Jr., NY
Sganga, Richard F., NY
Shalvey, Edward P., NY
Sharkey, Arthur*
Shergalis, Joseph A., NY
Shore, Jeffrey A.*
Short, Eugene A., NC
Shtino, Gani, NY
Shugrue, James E.**
Sichler, George D., NY
Sieber, Robert J.*
Simmonds, Samuel G.*
Simon, Lennox J., DC
Simonetti, Tosano J., NY
Simorelli, Vincent*
Singer, Donald L., NY
Singer, Michael R., NY
Sireci, Gerard, NY

Sloan, James M.*
Slowick, Daniel W.*
Small, Justin W.*
Smalls, Curtis, NY
Smith, Daniel*
Smith, James F., NY
Smith, James W., VA
Smith, John H.*
Smith, John R., NY
Smith, Judith H.*
Smith, Lawrence C., FL
Smith, Matthew R., NY
Smith, Philip J.*
Snell, Gerald J., NY
Sokolow, Nechama*
Solano, Joseph L., NY
Sollitto, James R., NY
Solomon, Sharon R., NY
Sommer, William J., NY
Soranno, Carlo C., NY
Sormani, Christopher, NY
Soto, Eleuterio, NY
Southerland, Gilbert A., NY
Spaccarelli, Roy J., NY
Spencer, Cecile B.*
Spiegel, Jack, FL
Sprague, Steven J., NY
Springer, Richard L., NY
Stahl, John R., NY
Staines, Edmund T., PA
Stanley, Alonzo, NY
Stanley, Dora L., NY
Stella, John F., NJ
Stelmashuk, Joseph, NY
Steneck, Wayne P.*
Stephens, Leslie A., NY
Stepniewski, Mark S., NY
Stern, Martin, GA
Sternblitz, Paul S., NY
Sternesky, Leonard*
Stevens, Veronica M.*
Stewart, Frank A., NY
St. Fort, Guy J.*
Stock, Louis, NY
Stone, Robert, NY
Stopherd, Cynthia J.*
Sturman, Mitchell, NY
Subach, Robert J., NY
Sultana, John G., NY
Svendsen, Bruce J., NY
Swan, Laura L.*
Sweeney, Gerard F., NY
Sweeney, Joseph M., NY
Swirsky, Sheldon, NY
Szymborski, Leo J., NY
Taddeo, Jack, NY
Tallon, LT Kenneth A., NY
Talty, Edward J., NY
Tamparo, William L., NY
Tanner, Bernice**
Tarasewich, Thomas A., NY
Taylor, Du R., NY
Tedesco, Paul J.*
Tempesta, Michael F., NY
Terenzi, Elaine*
Thomann, Joseph S., NY
Thomson, William D.*
Threat, Reginald W., NY
Thurneau, Robert D., NY
Toal, Joseph V., NY
Tobin, James J., NY
Toler, Theodore E., NY
Tomassi, Garrett P., NY
Trautwig, Kenneth*
Tucker, Bonita C., GA
Turner, Charles J.*
Ulrich, Eileen, NJ
Unger, Robert M.*
Urgo, John F., CA
Valdinoto, Frank W., NY
Valentin, Frank*
Valentine, Rudolph N., NY
Valles, LT Evelyn, FL
Vannata, Stephen L., NY
Vanterpool, Arthur E., NY
Vazquez, George P., NY

Vazza, Nora A.*
Vecchi, Louis, NJ
Vecchione, Deborah A., NY
Vessio, Nicholas P., NY
Veyvoda, Joseph F., NY
Viglione, Albert J., NY
Villada, Arturo, NY
Vlack, Stanley*
Vladescv, Manuela*
Volpe, Anthony, NY
Vrana, Kenneth J., NY
Vroom, Charles C., NY
Vyas, Ashwin G., NY
Walker, Darrell, NY
Wallace, Adrian N., FL
Walsh, James J., NY
Walsh, John J., NY
Walsh, Joseph T.*
Walters, Veronica, NY
Walz, Thomas M., NY
Warnquist, David G., NJ
Warren, Robert C., Sr., NY
Warren, Teresa E.*
Washington, Rudy, NY
Weber, Frank J.*
Wedin, Frederick H., NY
Weintraub, Mark S.*
Wesley, Lois A., NY
Whalen, John R.*
Whalen, Joseph W., NY
White, David W., SC
White, John H., TX
White, Joseph A.*
White, Tom*
Widnick, Steven M., TX
Wilfrid, Joanne, MA
Wilkman, Robert A., NY
Williams, Fernard M., NJ
Williams, James A.*
Wilson, Dolores M., NY
Wilson, James H., NY
Wilson, John E., NY
Wincelowicz, Vincent*
Wisniewski, Richard*
Wittrock, William G., NY
Wollman, Jane*
Woloszyn, Jeanette O., NY
Wondrack, Kenneth F.*
Wooten, Mary E.*
Yanolatos, Michael D., NY
Yates, Alfredo V.*
Yurgel, Thea L.*
Zaccaro, Anthony R., NY
Zachary, William E., NY
Zebelein, John R., NY
Zeigler, Neldra M., Esq., NY
Zimmerman, Sidney, NY

1977

Abdullah, Aysha*
Acerra, Lucy A.*
Acevedo, Luz A., NY
Acosta, Jose R.*
Acosta, Luis, NY
Adamson, Edgar A.*
Alaimo, Frank A., NY
Albanese, William F.**
Alexander, Jaems I.*
Allen, Theresa L., NY
Andros, Frances S., NY
Ann, Ryan L., NY
Aponte, Cesar, NY
Aquilone, Samuel*
Archer, Ralph T.*
Arias-Klein, Marta, FL
Ash, Barbara A.*
Ashcroft, Courtland H.*
Augustynowicz, Richard, CT
Auletta, Richard N., NY
Babb, Randolph, NY
Babiscko, Stephen G., FL
Babnik, Andrew, NY
Badamo, Robert T., NY
Bailey, Alban O., CA
Baker, Jimmie R., GA
Ballero, Hilda E., NY

Band, Nora H., NY
Baron, Serge C.*
Barrett, Calvin A., NY
Barry, Charles P., NY
Basile, Daniel A.*
Bayley, George A., NY
Bazazian, Dennis G., NY
Becker, Cynthia, NY
Becker, John J., NY
Bell, Valerie P.*
Bender, John R., NY
Benedict, Clare T., NY
Benson, Michael J., NY
Biggins, Patrick N., NY
Birch, Judith E., NY
Birmingham, Dennis E.*
Black, Daniel G.*
Bloom, Dennis*
Bocian, Stephen J., NJ
Bocon, John M.*
Bon, Johnny, NY
Borman, Gary M., NY
Bourquin, Peter E., NY
Bowler, William T., NY
Boyle, Donald J., NY
Boyle, James J., NY
Bozzi, Elissa, NY
Brady, COL Edward T.,
  USA(Ret.), NC
Brady, James S., NY
Braithwaite, George F., NY
Branch, Robert L., NY
Brangman, Philip H., NY
Brennan, Kenneth D., NY
Brennan, Patrick D.*
Breslin, Daniel E., NY
Brewer, Denize, NY
Britton, John J., FL
Brooks, Eugene W.*
Brosokas, Victor J., NY
Brown, Belviana A., NY
Brown, Iris D., NY
Brown, Thomas P.*
Brown, Valerie L., NJ
Brown, William D.*
Brownstein, Daniel, NY
Bruder, William J., NY
Bruno, Joan, CA
Buckley, William*
Buono, Joseph F., NY
Burke, James J., NY
Burke, Robert M., NY
Burkhalter, Gerald, NY
Burns, Christopher A., NY
Burns, Robert F.*
Butler, Tyrone T., NY
Cabrera, Stanley*
Cadicamo, Maria, FL
Cahill, Donna M., NY
Calabro, Andrew J., NY
Calderon, Angel, NY
Califano, John J., NY
Cancel, Blanca I., NY
Cannata, Augustine M., NY
Cantirino, William J.*
Cappello, Edward, NY
Carrington, Charlotte, NY
Caserta, Joseph M., NY
Cassano, Vito M., NY
Castro, Robert J., NY
Cavanagh, Joseph G., NY
Chamorro, Sol M., NY
Chany, Christopher P., NY
Charla, Stephen P., MI
Chavkin, Robert M.*
Cheatham, James E.*
Cherry, James C., NY
Cherry, Patrick J., NY
Cherwak, Walter, NY
Chiara, Frank J., NY
Chiarini, George J., CA
Chin, James M., NY
Chisolm, Elouise J., NY
Christiano, Michael J., NY
Chung, Victor L., NY
Cilla, Peter A., NY

Cintron, Yvonne, NY
Cisneros, Albert E., CA
Ciuzio, Maria, FL
Clark, Gerard R.*
Clark, John B., NY
Clark, John L., NY
Clarke, Kathleen O., NY
Clarke, Lois G., NY
Cohen, Seymour I., NY
Coleman, James J., NY
Coll, Thomas F., NY
Collins, James K.*
Collins, Maurice J.*
Colon, Norma I., NY
Colon, Reinaldo, NJ
Columby, Thomas W.*
Comperiati, Joseph A., NY
Confort, Richard K., NY
Conlon, James T., NY
Connolly, Peter J.*
Connor, Gregory L., NY
Conroy, Edward A., FL
Conry, Terry L., NY
Conti, Salvatore*
Cooper, Kenneth, AZ
Corbin, Christian H., NY
Corcoran, John K.*
Cordes, Joseph G.*
Correa, Felix L., NY
Corringham, Brian W.*
Corsey, Priscilla, NY
Cosenza, Bernard S., NY
Cotter, Daniel J., NY
Coyle, John W.*
Craig, Victor B.*
Crosby, Linda D.*
Crouzilhat, Gerard J.**
Cruz, Louis H.*
Cuebas, Edwin, NY
Cuomo, Vincent F., FL
Da Corta, Elaine, NY
Dames, Kenneth A.*
Dana, Robert J., NY
D'Aquino, Anthony*
Dasilva, Gioia, NY
David, Yves A., NY
Dawson, Benjamin*
Deans, Corinthia*
Debany, Barry P.*
Debany, Beatrice F.*
De Caprio, Angelo, NY
Delaney, Brian P.*
De Laura, James V.*
Dellicarpini, Joseph, NY
Delmore, John G., NY
Delnevo, Louis J.*
De Maio, Joseph, NY
De Martini, Joseph, NY
Demayo, Alphonso J.*
Dennelly, Lawrence E., NY
Denny, Jeff T.*
De Nunzio, Steven M., NY
Deppert, Dennis M.*
Desurmeaux, Paul E., MA
Deutcsh, Arthur V.*
Devlin, Patrick J., NY
Diaz, Raymond*
Dieckmann, Martin W., NY
Di Matteo, Philip J., NY
Dimura, Gerard J.*
Di Raimondo, Carl A., NY
Dittman, Frank W.*
Dolan, Bernard A., NY
Domingo, Joel J., NY
Donovan, John J., NY
Dowd, Charles F., NY
Dowling, Jack F., PA
Doyle, Lawrence J.*
Duchaine, Nina S., NY
Dunn, Michael F., PA
Duran, Dixon A.*
Durisin, George G., NJ
Durnin, Thomas A., NY
Edwards, Joseph B., NY
Egl, Anthony E., NY
Eich, Thomas J., NY

Eng, Kenneth J.*
Etuk, William U.*
Eyman, Buster D., NY
Faherty, Donald J., NY
Farber, Eric*
Farrell, John, NY
Farrell, John J.*
Farrell, Marianne J., NY
Farrell, Thomas F.*
Farruggia, Charles F.*
Feehan, Jeremiah K., NY
Feely, Francis J.*
Feely, Thomas J., NY
Feldman, Irene, NY
Feldmann, Dalia, NY
Ferrone, Joseph*
Filipponi, Dominick, FL
Finnerty, Frederick C., NY
Fiorillo, Anthony R., NY
Fiscina, Michael J., NY
Fitzgerald, Loretta E., NY
Flohr, Gyora Y.*
Flynn, Dennis J., NY
Flynn, Michael P., NY
Fogarty, Michael P.*
Forest, Vicki J.*
Forrester, Vincent P., NY
Forte, Leonard L., NY
Fortunato, Richard V., NY
Fountain, Belinda M., NY
Fox, Edward L., NY
Fox, Lawrence J., NY
Francis, Joan C., NY
Francisci, Bruno M., NY
Freund, Charles G., NY
Fried, Robert A.*
Fruscella, Paul D., NY
Fry, James W., NY
Gallo, James E., NY
Gargiulo, John A., NY
Garside, James H., NY
Gelaj, Maria, NY
Geoghan, Dennis P., NY
Gerrish, John P., NY
Gibbs, James H., PA
Giegerich, Joseph F.*
Gilmartin, James J., IL
Gilmore, Maudelle E.*
Gilmore, Robert W., NY
Gimlett, Kevin L., NY
Gimlett, Linda, DE
Giorgio, Rocco*
Giovinazzo, Michael*
Glynn, Martin P., NY
Glynn, Michael P., NY
Goldberg, Steven E.*
Gonzalez, Francisco, NY
Goode, Gail M., NY
Gorton, Michacl J., NY
Governale, Joseph M., NY
Grayson, Patricia W.*
Green, Norman H.*
Greene, Edmund J.*
Greene, Stephen, NY
Gross, Roger A., VA
Grossman, Martin, NY
Grunski, Alexander F., CA
Guarnieri, Rosemarie, NY
Gurley, Joyce*
Hackett, Joseph E., NY
Hackford, Donald E., NY
Hade, Patrick J., NC
Hagin, Karen M., NY
Haines, James V., NY
Halback, Richard A.*
Halfpenny, Peter, NY
Hargrove, James, FL
Harley, Thomas D.*
Harrigan, John J., NY
Hartigan, George T., NY
Hartnett, Michael J., NY
Harvey, Brian F., NY
Haviken, John J., NY
Haynes, Marjorie P., NY
Hemby, Patricia L.*
Hemrick, James F., NY

Henao, Rosa E., NY
Henriques, Marie, CA
Herlihy, Patrick F., NY
Hibbler, Louise, MD
Hickson, Robert L.*
Higgins, Michael J., PA
Higginson, Michael*
Higgs, Ruth, NY
Hill, Rochelle M., NY
Hillery, Joseph F., NY
Hoffman, Charles, CA
Holder, Lynnette N., NY
Holland, Daniel J., NY
Homer, Eva L.*
Howard, George E., NY
Howard, Gerard A., NY
Howley, Mary E., NY
Hubert, Frank J., NY
Huller, Thomas P., NY
Hunt, Kathleen T., NY
Igleasias, Rosa*
Ignaciuk, Stanley, NY
Ilkiw, Michael E.*
Ippolito, Michael J., NY
Jackson, Rodney J.*
Jakubowski, Thomas R., NY
Jascewsky, George E., NY
Jefferson, Oubey L., NY
Jenkins, Alexander D., NY
Jenkins, Ida F., NY
Jensen, Glenn A., MA
Jeselnik, Margaret, NY
Jetter, David A., NY
Johnson, Frank J., NY
Johnson, Martin C., NY
Johnson, Robert C., NY
Jones, Richard, NY
Jones, Roger, GA
Jones, Saundra L.*
Jones, Shirley A.*
Josephs, Sandy L., NY
Joyce, James L.*
Juliana, Richard F.*
Kalmikoff, Larry*
Kamine, Daniel F.*
Kane, James A., NY
Kane, Peter J., NY
Kastava, Paul*
Kauangh, Patrick J.*
Kearney, Michael J.*
Keefe, Dennis C., MA
Kelly, James F., NY
Kennedy, Katherine, NY
Kiernan, Gary J.*
Kiernan, Henry, NY
King, Edward J., NY
King, John E.*
King, Vera L., FL
Kinyatti, Mrs. Njoki W., NY
Kirschner, Robert D., NY
Kleinheidt, William, NY
Kobyra, Raymond E., FL
Koscinski, Robert, NY
Kozma, John F., NY
Kozma, Mariann E., NY
Krebbs, Joseph*
Kunkis, Robert, NJ
Kwapinski, Martin E.*
La Barbera, Dennis, NY
La Bette, Charles R.*
La Covara, Margaret M., NY
Laferrera, Anthony F., NY
La Franco, Wayne E.*
La Malfa, James J., NY
Lamb, James S., NY
La Mont, Olivia E., CA
Lampinstei, Edward S., NY
Land, Johannie, NY
Laporta, Annmarie*
Lawrence, Veryan E.*
Leader, Martin L., NY
Leather, Joseph J., NJ
Lee, James C., NY
Lennek, Robert N.*
Lettieri, Peggy C., NY
Levine, Fran N., NY

Levy, Shoshana*
Linzer, Tamara*
Livingston, Phyllis E.*
Livingstone, Lennox, NY
Lock, Clifford A., GA
Lockwood, May R., NY
Loesch, Lawrence F., NY
Loewenstein, Paul E.*
Lombardo, Joseph A., NY
Longobardi, Alfred C., NY
Lopez, Manuel W., NY
Lore, Joseph M., NY
Loria, Nicholas J.*
Loscalz, Peter J.*
Louden, Dr. Robert J., NJ
Lovett, Joseph, NY
Lowe, Rudolph E., NY
Lubove, Diane*
Lynch, Theresa B.*
Lyons, Thomas, NY
Maccone, Joseph, NY
Mack, Robert J., CA
Madden, Dennis J., NY
Magid, Stephen H., NY
Mahoney, Daniel P., NY
Mahoney, Edward D., NY
Maldon, Annie P.*
Manessis, Barbara J.*
Manus, Raymond P., NY
Manzolillo, Carmine, NY
Marchina, John E., NY
Marchisello, Geralyn, NY
Martella, Joseph, NJ
Martin, Angelique P., NY
Martinez, Eugene, NY
Martinez, William, NY
Martini, John F., NY
Martino, Bruce F., NY
Mathews, Frank J., NJ
Matthews, Kevin E., FL
Mattiasich, Fabio L., NY
Maxcy, Nilda D.*
Mazzacano, Paul J.*
Mc Carthy, Daniel J.*
McCarthy, Margaret G., NY
Mc Clain, Joseph, NY
Mc Clellan, John J., NY
Mc Cray, Gabriel*
Mc Creary, Joanne L., NY
Mc Darby, Frank, NY
Mc Dermott, John P., NY
Mc Devitt, Joseph G.**
Mc Eneaney, Kevin J.*
McEvoy, Barbara, NY
Mc Fadden, George R.*
Mc Geown, James R., NY
Mc Govern, Kevin M., NY
Mc Grath, Kevin J., NY
McInerney, Robert (Bob) X.,
  CPP, NJ
Mc Kenna, Daniel J., NY
Mc Kenna, Peter, NY
Mc Kernan, Patrick J.*
Mc Kinney, Joyce F., NY
Mc Leod, James, NY
Mc Mahon, Lawrence M.*
Mc Menemon, Thomas P., NY
Mc Nulty, James E., NY
Mc Queen, George W.*
Mc Quillan, Matthew A., NY
Mecca, Stephanie C.*
Menard, Earl J., Jr., NY
Messinger, Rachel C.*
Metzger, Robert, NY
Miceli, Peter S., NY
Mihalakelis, Michael, NY
Miller, Joseph, NY
Misiano, Eugene, NY
Mitchell, John M., NY
Mitchell, Napoleon, NY
Mitsch, George*
Modawar, Faris A., TX
Mongan, Heather A., NY
Monte, John J., NY
Moore, Beverly A., NY
Moore, James E., NY

Moore, William C.*
Morales, Antonio, NY
Moran, John P., NY
Moriarity, Brian T.*
Morrison, William*
Mulligan, John P., NY
Mulligan, Thomas J., NY
Mulligan, William, NY
Murawski, Henry W.*
Murray, Lewis C., FL
Murray, Robert P., NJ
Nacinovich, Mario, NY
Nagle, David F.**
Najdek, Robert T.*
Namour, Michael, NY
Nassisi, Richard T.*
Navarro, William J., NY
Neff, April L.*
Nemara, Vanessa A., VA
Ng, Grace, NJ
Nicholas, Joseph M., NY
Nienhuis, Marleen*
Nieves, Gilbert, NY
Nixon, Willie R.*
Nocerino, Thomas, NY
Nocero, Jeanne V., NY
Nofi, Anthony P.*
Nolan, Joseph J., NY
Norflett, Ronald, NY
Nostramo, Thomas, NY
Novoa, Carmen M., NY
Oboyski, Victor, NY
O'Connell, James H., FL
Odell, Robert B.**
O'dowd, Edward F., MI
Ohawan, Parmod*
Olender, Dennis J.*
O'neill, Eugene F., NJ
O'Sullivan, Christopher G., NY
Pacht, Seymour S.*
Pagan, Rita E.*
Page, CW2 Wallace (Wally) B.,
  Ret., FL
Paige, John J., NJ
Pall, Harriet*
Palumbo, Peter J., NY
Paris, David S., NY
Partheymueller, Conrad, NY
Pasha, Wali K.**
Pasichow, Jerome N., NJ
Pasini, Roseann L., NY
Passika, John I., FL
Patterson, Berman W.*
Patton, Marsha N., NY
Paulson, Paul S., NY
Peasah, Joyce C., NY
Pedone, Riccardo, NJ
Pellegrino, Donald A.*
Pendergast, Teresa A., NY
Penon, David, NY
Perry, Patrick W., NY
Peterkin, John W., NY
Pierce, Raymond M.*
Piliere, Roy E., NY
Piraino, Joseph A., NY
Plaza, Frank J.*
Polovoy, John P., NY
Poltorak, James T., NY
Pope, Thomas J., NJ
Poppe, John D., NY
Powell, Gilbert R., NY
Powell, Johnette C.*
Powell, Tanya G., NY
Powell, William M., FL
Power, James C.*
Prather, Raymond B., NY
Presley, Harrell E.*
Prince, Shelia*
Pruitt, Alberta*
Puszka, Mary*
Quigley, Thomas M.*
Quinn, Ellin M.*
Quinn, Gerard M., NY
Quinn, Terrence J., NY
Rabson, Mark J., NJ
Radziewicz, Kathleen, NY

Raffa, John J., NY
Raiford, Louis G., NV
Ralko, Stephen E., PA
Ramos, Elvin, NY
Ramos, Julius, NY
Ramos, Michael, NY
Randazzo, Leonard, NY
Rao, Anthony J., NY
Rayfield, Peter T., NY
Reed, Shelley, Jr., NY
Refuto, George J., NY
Regan, Charles E., NY
Regan, John*
Regan, John M., NY
Reichenbach, Robert W., NY
Reid, Armando E., NY
Reill, Mary V., NY
Reilly, William G., NY
Reinhardt, Ronald R., NY
Reitano, Anthony, NY
Renton, Benjamin E., NY
Renz, Peter H., NY
Ricciuto, Michael, NJ
Riccobono, Salvatore, NY
Rios, Edwin, NY
Rivera, Octavio*
Rizzo, Thomas V.*
Robinson, John A., NJ
Rohan, Robert V., NY
Rojas-dykes, Carol, TX
Romero, Jose A., NY
Rondina, Frederick E., NY
Ronzo, Louis, NY
Rooney-costin, G. A.*
Rose, Lynn, NJ
Rose, Michael J., NY
Rosenberg, Andrew L.*
Rosenberg, Susan B., NY
Rothman, Ellen R.*
Rowan, Edward T., Sr., NY
Rubenstein, Hy D., MD
Rubi, Connie M., NY
Russo, Carmine F.*
Ryan, Joseph F.*
Ryan, Thomas P., NJ
Ryerson, Robin A.*
Sanchez, Juan P., NJ
Santos, Josefina, NY
Schembri, Anthony J., FL
Schinasi, Michael*
Schindler, Leonard S.*
Schiotis, James J.**
Schlomowitz, Lois H.*
Schloton, Joy E., NY
Schnaars, Gerard R.*
Schultz, Conrad J., NY
Schuppert, Ronald, NY
Schwartz, Ned E., NY
Schwartzman, Leon, NY
Scire, Robert L.*
Scolaro, John S.*
Sealy, Percival P.*
Sere, Edward C., NY
Shea, John W., NY
Sheehan, Lawrence J.*
Sheehan, Martin M.*
Sheilds, Roger L.*
Shields, Richard C., VA
Shields, Roger L., VA
Shinnick, Edward (Ed) J., TX
Shore, Arnold, NY
Sirico, Michael G., NY
Skelly, John G., FL
Slattery, Robert J., VA
Smith, Ms. Lillian B., NY
Smith, Madeline*
Smith, Sonia P.*
Smoluch, Joseph E., NY
Sorci, Frank X., GA
Sottolano, Steven M., NY
Spence, Robert J., NY
Spinozzi, Joseph*
Spivey, Leroy, NY
Stamatelos, Danny S., NY
Stanton, John P., NY
Stashin, Anita D., NY

Steele, David N., NY
Stern, Jo E.*
Stinson, William M., NY
Stone, Marianne E., NY
Storch, Arthur S., NY
Sulzer, Albert J.*
Surgeon, Clarence M., NY
Svendsen, Christian, NY
Sweeney, Patricia C.*
Sylvester, Ronald*
Symon, Gordon J., NY
Szczerba, Eugenia, NY
Taibbi, Patricia A., NY
Ta'Penzieri, Charles, NY
Taylor, Joseph F., NY
Telesford, Alec G.*
Thomas, Earle B.*
Thomas, Preston W.*
Thomas, Richard G., GA
Tibaldi, Thomas J., NY
Tobia, Michael A.*
Tomlinson, Mrs. Beatrice E.,
  NY
Tompkins, Gail H., NY
Torrence, Lorna Y., NY
Torres, Ernest, NY
Trakas, Arthur G., NY
Trotman, Deborah, CT
Tucker, Benjamin B.*
Turbett, William F., NJ
Ulianko, John A., NJ
Ulsamer, John J., NY
Vaccarelli, Robin A., NJ
Vaccaro, Joseph A., NY
Valente, Joseph F., NY
Valentin, Miguel A., NY
Vanacore, Michael J.*
Vanbuckley, Hilburn, NY
Vasquez, Edwin M.*
Velkovich, Helen M.*
Verwoert, John A., NY
Vestermark, Neil A.*
Vignali, Frank R., NY
Vitaliano, Anthony J., NY
Vitucci, Frank, NY
Vollmer, Paul, NY
Waldman, Michael*
Walker, Theodore, Jr., NY
Walker, Thomas J., NY
Walsh, Kenneth J.*
Warner, Rupert R., NY
Weaver, David, NY
Weaver, Ronald, NY
Weir, Lillian W., NJ
Wermuth, Ezra C., NY
Wilday, Robert D., NY
Williams, Albert D., NJ
Williams, Alvin L., NY
Williams, Lauren E., NY
Wilson, James D., NY
Wisotsky, Amy, KY
Wladich, Richard, FL
Wolfert, Marc S.*
Woolaston, Denise P., NY
Wright, Phyllis P.*
Yanarella, Maryann, NY
Yee, William, NY
Young, Edwin A., NY
Young, Harold C., NY
Young, John W., NY
Youssef, Magdi H., NY
Zajac, Mary C.*
Zamist, Ida**
Zaretsky, Kathie L., NY
Zecca, Joseph M., NY
Zimmermann, William J., NY
Zion, Myriam*
Zoufaly, Thomas M., NY
Zummo, Michael A., NY
Zummo, Michael A., NY
Zwicker, Jay L., NY

1978

Abarca, Celia J., NJ
Abolade, Wasiu A., NY
Abrams, Robynn L.*

Abramson, Neal G., TX
Acevedo, Lawerence A.*
Ackerman, Elaine R.*
Acosta, Galo F., CA
Actie, Winnifred, NY
Adams, Dennis A., NY
Adams, Partick H., NY
Adefope, Adebayo S.*
Adum-Bawdah, Hana, PhD, NY
Ahern, Dennis J., NY
Alarid, Victoria B.*
Alford, Donald S.**
Alston, Barbara A., NY
Alvarez, Margarita, NY
Amorese, Sam A., NY
Amplo, Anthony J., NY
Anderson, Harold T., NY
Anderson, Otis C., NY
Andrades, John, Jr., NY
Ansaldi, Angela, NY
Antoine, Phyllis A., NY
Antomez, SGT Herbert, NY
Appelt, Peter J., NY
Arce, Michael H., UT
Arciniaco, Joyce*
Argenti, Karen M., NY
Arons-Schultze, Janet A., CA
Arrington, Otis W., NY
Ashwood, Carlos A., NY
Attard, Linda*
Austin, Evelyn G., NY
Ayala, Francisco, Jr., NY
Barattini, Peter F., NY
Barbato, Ben R.*
Barber, Glenn M., VA
Barclay, Donald N.*
Barros, Anna M., FL
Barry, Patrick T., NY
Barry, Rupert V., NY
Bartley, Glenn*
Battaglia, Eugene F., MD
Baxter, Katherine, NY
Beberaggi, Ralph, NY
Beekman, Mary E., NY
Beiro, Benjamin W.*
Belfon, Joyce P., NY
Bell, Jymie W.*
Bellamy, Charlie M., NY
Beneri, Fred P., NY
Benevento, John F.*
Bennett, Margaret G., NY
Bentley, Mala D., NY
Bercaw, Robert*
Bernard, Ronald P., PA
Bert, Therese*
Beveridge, Alvin J., NJ
Birstein, S. J.*
Blair, Dwight A., NY
Blakely, Andrea*
Bleeker, Stanley W., NY
Bluett, Esther T.*
Bodigheimer, Charles*
Bolton, Judy L., NY
Bonderow, I. A.*
Boresky, Peter J., NY
Bortone, Susanna V.*
Bove, John D., NY
Bowens, Hermine E., NY
Boyd, William S., NY
Boykin, Thomas, OH
Boylan, Michael P., NY
Bradshaw, William J.*
Brady, Brian J.*
Bramson, Joy A., NY
Brant, Clifford E., NY
Brant, John J., NY
Bratman, Sandra T.*
Brennan, John J., NY
Brigliadoro, Richard*
Brobbey, Godfrey K.*
Brock, La F.*
Bronkhurst, Frank X., NY
Brooks, Robert A., FL
Brown, Gene A., NY
Brown, Gloria J.*

Brown, James D.*
Brown, Leslie C., NY
Buda, Richard, NY
Bugge, Brian K., NY
Bundy, Hyder G.*
Bunyan, Michael C., NY
Buonpane, Angelina, NY
Burke, Glenn E., NY
Burke, Marie A.*
Burke, Richard T.*
Burnett, Guy E.*
Burns-Lemp, Patricia, NY
Bursuk, Paulette R., NY
Byrne, William J.**
Byrnes, James E., NY
Cade, David W., NY
Cahill, Patrick, NY
Calichio, Frank J., NY
Callanan, Maureen F., NY
Calle, Washington R., NY
Calo, Nancy*
Camacho, Marta*
Campbell, Robert J., NY
Campbell, Steven T., NJ
Campisi, Charles V., NY
Camuti, Marie J.*
Canavan, Francis P., NY
Carbuccia, Julio C., NY
Cardillo, Bob J., NY
Carillo, Joseph A., NY
Casserly, Michael, NY
Castaneda, Jose A.*
Castineiras, Fernando, NY
Castro-Gonzalez, Wilf, NY
Cavuto, Michael T., NY
Chabrier, Evelyn*
Chao, Kang*
Charles, Rulolph N., NY
Cheeks, Karen N.*
Cheeks, Roy C.*
Cherena-Pacheco, Yvonne, TX
Chern, Gail S.*
Chomiak, Robert H., NY
Christiansen, Janet E., NY
Christie, Jerome G.*
Christman, William C., NC
Christopher, Lola C., NY
Chung, Foon C.*
Ciccarello, Linda F., NY
Cinquemani, Joseph, NY
Ciuzio, Richard G., FL
Clark, James, NY
Clark, John W., NY
Clause, Smyrna E., NY
Clifford, Elizabeth M.*
Cohen, Bonny A., NY
Colitti, Madeline, NY
Collier, Darnell S.*
Collins, Charloc C.*
Collins, Theodore R.*
Colon, Lourdes M.*
Colon, Richard P.*
Concannon, John P., NY
Condon, Richard J., NY
Connors, Patrick F.*
Conti, Jack, NY
Conze, Yves S.*
Cooper, Alfonso A., NY
Cooper, Gavin A., NY
Coppola, Ralph M.*
Cortellino, Gary J., GA
Costello, Vivian, NY
Cosumano, Robert L., NY
Cotter, Robert T., NY
Courtney, William M.*
Cowan, James T., NY
Cox, Stephanie A., NY
Crabtree, Gerard W.*
Craig, Kenneth A., NY
Crawbuck, Charles R., NY
Crawford, Audrey D., NY
Crawford, Bobby G., GA
Crawford, Douglas T., NY
Criscuolo, Louis, NY
Croce, Bruce W., NY
Croker, Austin D.*

Crowe, Thomas P.*
Cuesta, George M., NY
Cuff, Patrick K., NY
Cummings, Gerard M.*
Cunningham, Francis T.*
Curley, John E., NY
Curran, Charles J.*
Curran, James E., NY
Dallara, Mark A., NY
Daly, Roger A.*
D'Amato, Frank E.*
Dancy, Ernest A., NY
Daniel, William A., NJ
Dantzler, John L.*
Davan, Robert J., NY
David, Denis P., NY
David, Harley, GA
Davis, Mrs. Eleanor, PhD, NY
Davis, Ethel V.*
Davis, Londel, NY
Davis, Stephen P., NY
Dawber, Mary I., NY
Dawber, Mary J., NY
Dawson, Darlene D., NY
De Garcia, Carmen M., NY
De Jesus, Fernando A.*
De Jesus, Joel L.*
De Jesus, Juan A., NY
De Matas, Robert P., NY
Demmerle, George E.*
Dennis, Jose J., CA
Derosario, Leonard*
Devine, James J., NY
Devine-Molin, Carol, NY
Devlin, William P.*
Diaczuk, Peter J., NY
Diaz, Juan M., NY
Dicks, Garry S., GA
Dielensnyder, Fred J., NY
Di Mango, Domenick, NY
Di Mauro, Antoinette*
Dinon, George R.*
Doerrbecker, George, NY
Dominguez, Shirley*
Donahue, Daniel J., NY
Donnay, Joseph C.*
Donohue, Patricia M., NY
Dougherty, John T.*
Douglas, John F.*
Dowd, Timothy M., NY
Downs, Maureen F., NY
Draffin, Beverly H., KY
Drielak, Steven C., NY
Dubois, Maryjude*
Dulberg, Barbara A.*
Duran, Wilfredo*
Durham, Elaine C., NJ
Dwyer, Brian C.*
Earlcy, Patrick J.*
Ebner, Theodore*
Edwards, Brian W.*
Elmore, William (Bill) L., NY
Encarnacion, Felicito, NY
Engel, Diana**
Ertrachter, Gail R.*
Esposito, Robert*
Esposito, Vincent P., NY
Fahey, John W., NY
Falletta, Louis A.*
Fallon, Margaret A.*
Farrell, Edward J., NY
Farrell, Franklin H., NY
Farrell, John J., CT
Favara, Anthony J., NY
Feit, Harvey D., NY
Feliciano, Charles S.*
Feltham, Edward A.*
Felton, Ronald, NY
Fergerson, Jean C.*
Fioricia, Lynne M.*
Fischer, William R., NY
Fishman, Howard (Howie) L., CA
Flagg, Richard D.*
Flanagan, Doreen M., NY
Flanagan, Edward J., NY

Fleming, Donald L., NY
Fleming, Edward J., NY
Flood, William F., NY
Flowers, Marie Y.*
Floyd, Joseph M., NY
Flynn, Joseph E., NY
Folmer, Gary M., NY
Fonfrias, Edna, NY
Ford, Matthew C., NJ
Foti, Anthony G., NY
Fountain, Roscoe E., NY
Fox, Morris J.*
Foxx, John H., NY
Frank, Neal R.*
Franke, Patricia D., NY
Fratter, Jeffrey, VA
Fredrickson, Kenneth*
Frey, Richard A.*
Froman, Gerald A., NY
Fulton, Audrey M., NY
Fusaro, Michael J., NY
Gaffney, Kevin A.*
Gallagher, Kevin R., NY
Gambardella, Vincent, NY
Gantt, Larry, NY
Garcia, Luis J., NY
Garcia, Michael A.*
Gargin, John J., NY
Garrity, Thomas J., NY
Gasparino, Anthony J.*
Gates, Edward T.*
Gaughan, Edward T., NJ
Gecewicz, Edward T., NY
Geisendorfer, Ann E.*
Genovese, Ronald J.*
Gentile, Anthony L., NY
Georges, Pierre R.*
Gesualdi, Anthony*
Giacobbe, Joseph A., NY
Giannuzzi, Thomas A., NY
Giglio, Charles J., NY
Gilbert, Rubin B.*
Gilroy, Terence J., NY
Gives, Tillman W., NY
Glasser, Michael A., NY
Gleberman, Fredric P., NY
Gloria, Joseph R.*
Glosson, Muriel C., NY
Goldbach, George A., CO
Golding, William D., NY
Goldrick, Thomas J., NY
Goldstein, Bruce, NJ
Goldstein, Steven E.*
Gomez, Blanca L.*
Goodwin, Patrick J., NJ
Gordon, Frances C.*
Gorgia, John*
Granstrand, Brian M.*
Crasberger, Thomas Γ.*
Grau, Bernard*
Greco, Joseph P., NY
Greenberg, Harry, NY
Greene, Wilma*
Greenfield, Howard*
Greenfield, Myrna*
Gretih, Anthony L., NY
Grey, Edward I., NY
Grom, Peter J., NY
Gross, Daniel, NY
Gross, Kenneth D., MD
Grosso, Thomas P.*
Gural, Gary P., NY
Guzman, Wilma*
Gyapong, Enid H.*
Hagan, Andrew A., NY
Hall, Yvonne*
Hammond, Avis, NY
Harper, Leonard, NC
Harris, Jonas R.*
Harris, Winston E.*
Hartt, Kevin J., NY
Harvey, George D.*
Hayden, Patricia M., NY
Hedderich, Robert F., NY
Hehir, Joseph J., NY
Henderson, David R., NY

Henderson, Robert A., NJ
Hennessey, Richard E., NY
Henry, James W., NJ
Henry, Mark A., NY
Hernandez, William*
Hetrick, John G., NY
Heyward, Richard, NY
Hickman, John J., NY
Hillen, Brian J.*
Hines, James R., NY
Hinrichs, Robert J.*
Holihan, John W., NY
Holst, Irma R., NY
Holub, Peter W., NY
Hom, Diane, NY
Honan, Robert F.*
Hope, Kenmore*
Horowitz, Robert B., NY
Horwitz, Braham*
Houston, Bernard P., NY
Howard, Timothy F.*
Howley, Maureen A., NY
Hrusovsky, John*
Hudson, Henry L.*
Hughes, John R.*
Hummel, Janet J.*
Iannace, Arthur B., NY
Igneri, Patrick N., NY
Indimine, Lawrence F., NY
Innace, Thomas E., NY
Israel, Richard*
Ivory, Patrick V., NY
Izzo, Anthony J., NY
Jacoutot, Alfred, NY
Javorsky, Stephen M., NY
Johansen, Louis H.*
Johnson, Doris W., NY
Johnson, Lucinda, NY
Johnston, James J.**
Jones, Osie C.**
Jones, Robert H., Sr., NY
Joseph, Ingrid, NY
Joyner, Betty A.*
Jung, Eleanor J., NY
Kalankiewicz, Edward*
Kaltenmeier, John W., NY
Katz, William A.*
Kearns, John P.*
Keniry, Jeanne F., NY
Kenny, William J., NY
Kerzner, Barbara H.*
Kettering, William N., VA
Kiessling, William J.*
King, Susan M.*
Kirschner, Edward, NY
Kisling, Arnol F., NY
Kitz, Alfred F., NY
Knight, Katherine M.*
Knox, Blanche M., NY
Kopycinski, David H.*
Koulombinis, Nicholas, NY
Kowalinski, Richard G.*
Kuceluk, Joseph R., NY
Kuehnle, William A., NY
Kuras, Thomas J., NJ
Kuss, Russell A.*
Kuttler, George P., NY
Laird, Molly*
Lamanna, Thomas*
Lamberti, Anthony J., NY
Lambertis, Ronald B.*
Langley, Lola H., NY
Latour, William J., NY
Lattimore, Gloria J.*
Lawrence, Michael G., NY
Lawrence, Pansey G.*
Leahy-Edwards, Arbara*
Lekos, Ronald N., NY
Lemons, Henry, NY
Lenahan, William R., NJ
Lenihan, Mary D.*
Lett, John A., NY
Lett, Lorraine, NY
Levin, David J., NY
Lewis, Alden T.*
Lewis, Ms. Annamarie, NY

Lewis, Bernice, NY
Lewis, Michael, NY
Lewis, Richard*
Lidz, Linda M.*
Linden, Scott L., NY
Lindsay, Howard*
Liscouski, Robert P., AE
Llano, Robert J., NY
Lohnes, Robert C., NY
Lombardi, Louis E.*
Lopez, Richard*
Loughlin, Bernard E., NY
Luna, Petra M.*
Lundy, Barry*
Luongo, Vincent R.*
Lynah, Henrietta*
Lyons, John R., NY
Magliaro, Joseph L., NJ
Maher, John P., NY
Mahon, Edward T., NY
Mahoney, Joseph R.*
Mainieri, Christopher*
Maltz, Barbara K., NY
Mammano, Richard A., NY
Mandzik, Philip J., NY
Manzi, Thomas J.*
Markgraf, Kenneth P.*
Marshall, Luis R., NY
Martin, Betty J., LA
Martinez, Esperanza, NY
Martir, Kirby, NY
Martorano, Thomas A., NY
Matheson, Gerard J., NY
Maxwell, James M.*
Maxwell, John F.*
May, Larry R.*
May, Lena*
Mc Allister, Daniel J.*
Mc Andrew, Paula L., NY
Mc Bride, Eugene T.*
Mc Bride, Hugh J., NY
Mc Bride, Richard H., NY
Mc Cabe, Robert K., NY
Mc Caffrey, Daniel X., NY
Mc Carren, Charles J., NY
Mc Carthy, Gerard F., CA
Mc Carthy, Robert A., NY
Mc Ganney, Mary L., NY
Mc Gowan, Kenneth T., NJ
Mc Guire, John P.*
Mc Guire, Patricia*
Mc Inerney, John P.*
Mc Intosh, James C.*
Mc Kinley, Ronald R., TX
Mc Lean, Carol A., NY
Mc Leod, Kendall, NY
Mc Quillen, Joseph T., NY
Meagher, Brian C., NY
Meenan, Patrick J., NY
Mehaffey, Paul R., NJ
Melendez, Aida L., DC
Melendez, David*
Melrose, Valerie L., NY
Mendez-Caban, Juan B., NY
Mendoza, Florance W., NY
Menkes, Andrew, NY
Meyer, Frank X.*
Miele, John E., NY
Mikos, Ms. Nancy, NY
Miletti, Robert N.*
Miller, Christine A., NY
Miller, Gina M.*
Miller, Janet R.*
Miller, Martin*
Miller, Terri R.*
Milo, Barbara*
Milone, Debra D., NY
Mirza, Barkat A.*
Mitchell, Harry J., FL
Mitchell, Leon A., NY
Mitchelson, Thomas P., NJ
Moe, Richard, PA
Molloy, Patrick J., FL
Monaghan, Thomas L.*
Moore, Patricia A.*
Morelli, Angelo M., NY

Morris-english, Patricia J., MD
Morrison, Benni S., NY
Morrison, Shirley E.*
Moschetto, Andrew J., NJ
Moseley, Sharmon*
Moultak, John C.*
Mulligan, Thomas P., NY
Mullings, Sandra V., NY
Murphy, Daniel J., FL
Murphy, John D.*
Murphy, Paul E., NY
Murray, Louis, NY
Murray, Michael J.*
Myles, Miriam T., FL
Nable, Beth R., NY
Natal, Catherine*
Navarra, Angelo, NY
Navarro, Elia I.*
Navarro, Mario, NY
Nazario, Francisco, NY
Nelms, Luonel D., NY
Nesdill, Patrick J., NY
Nesmith, Nathaniel*
Newsome, Theodore, NY
Nicolosi, Joseph R., NY
Nimrod, Elvin G., NY
Noblin, Robert K., NY
Noon, Ann P.*
Noonan, Peter, NY
Nowak, Dennis A., NY
Nowak, George J.*
Nugent, Andrew G., NY
Nusser, Gary R., NY
O'brian, Joseph J., NY
O'Brien, Thomas P., NY
O'Connor, Joseph P.*
O'connor, Julie A., NJ
O'connor, Kevin R., NY
O'Connor, Patricia A., NY
O'donoghue, John P., NY
O'Keefe, David G.*
Olpe, Richard W., NY
O'Mara, Robert T.*
O'neill, Mark L., NJ
Orlick, Harvey A., NY
Ostrowski, Eugene, NY
Ottomano, Anthony R., NY
Padilla, Michael A.*
Pagan, Richard*
Page, Harriet C.*
Pajooh, Rachel P.*
Palazzolo, Florence F., NY
Palermo, Mario E., NY
Pallonetti, John R., NY
Pandolfo, Peter J., NY
Panzenbeck, John M.*
Paolicelli, Anthony*
Parks, Michael J.*
Parrilla, Steven J., NY
Pascarella, Richard*
Pasichow, Steven A., NY
Paulits, Rita M.*
Peeples, William H.*
Perez, Efrain*
Perez, Gloria*
Perillo, Theresa A.*
Perry, Elaine, NY
Peters, Austin*
Petrilli, John A., NY
Phillips, Ethel J., NY
Phillips, Stephen E., NY
Picone, Matilda, NY
Pilny, Richard E., NY
Pineiro, Pedro J.*
Piotrowski, Michael, NY
Piotrowski, Ronald D., NY
Pizzo, Vincent, NY
Pocchia, Barbara A., NY
Podgorski, Robert B., NY
Porras, Patricio G., NY
Portuondo, Elaine L., NY
Pouncie, Ms. Amanda M., NY
Power, John F.*
Powers, Jay H.*
Pray, Randiolph P., NY
Price, Fred E., NY

Prime, Maria, NY
Pringle, Hester V., MD
Prusak, Patricia R., NJ
Pucciarello, Thomas R., NH
Quigley, M. F., NY
Quinones, Luis A., NY
Raimindi, Louis J.*
Ramirez, Anthony J., NY
Ramirez, Frances*
Ramos, Luz D.*
Randazzo, Todd, NY
Ratcliffe, Robert G., NJ
Rauchet, Joseph L., NY
Regan, James K., NY
Regan, Kevin J., NY
Reid, Julanne L., NY
Reilly, Andrew J., NY
Reilly, Thomas J., NY
Rendeiro, Alfred P., NY
Reyes, Alida, NY
Reyes, Victor L., NY
Riccio, Joseph P., VA
Riley, Edward P.*
Riley, Englow*
Rinaldi, Yolanda M., NY
Rivera, James*
Rivera, Joseph*
Robbins, Eileen H.*
Roberts, Lorraine M.*
Roberts, Richard H., NJ
Robinson, Sheila E., NY
Robinson, Stephanie A.*
Robson, Robert (Bob) J., AZ
Rodriguez, Alfred*
Rodriguez, Ms. Migdalia A., NY
Rogers, Charles L., NY
Romano, Hogla T., NY
Romo-Leroux, Lillian*
Rooney, Thomas N.*
Rosenthal, Loree E.*
Rosenwald, Mark**
Rothman, Flora, NY
Rougeux, Peter F.*
Rudolph, Sa*
Ruggeri, Lucille C.*
Ruiz, Marilyn I.*
Rumph, Richard, NY
Russo, Joseph J., NY
Russo, Lawrence M.*
Ryan, John F., NY
Ryan, Michael, NY
Ryan, Ronald J., FL
Ryan, William F.*
Ryan, William J., CA
Sabala, Maritza, NY
Sabel, Raymond P., NY
Sahlberg, Fred J., NJ
Sala, John A., NY
Salgado, Luis A., NY
Salpeter, Jay S.*
Sammartano, Joseph P.*
Sanchez, Luis A.*
Sanchez, Margarita, NY
Sandbank, Stephanie*
Sanders, Evelyn C., NY
Sanders, Joann, NY
Santiago, Fred*
Santos, John J., NY
Sapio, Donald J., NY
Sarrantonio, Lana, VA
Sather, Ralph E.*
Saunders, Michael R., NY
Scanlon, Frances E., NY
Scarborough, Thomas, NY
Schmidt, Robert J.*
Schneider, Joseph E., Jr., NY
Schumann, Robert A., NY
Scuderi, Mary L., NY
Selassie, Haile*
Semetis, Arthur J., NY
Sena, James P., MD
Sens-castet, Robert, NY
Serano, Frank R., NY
Seubert, Robert J., NY
Shane, Todd M.*
Shannon, Edward J.*

Shannon, James E.**
Shea, Michael E.*
Sheinman, Ilana, NY
Shelley, Charles J., NY
Sherk, Edgar F., IL
Shields, Michael P.*
Shillingford, Wilford P., NY
Silver, Alan L., NY
Silverman, Irwin*
Siotkas, John, NY
Sirlin, Jill, NY
Sisco, Edward R., NY
Skae, Robert**
Slavin, Dennis F., NY
Small, Darnley E., NY
Smith, Arthur C., NY
Smith, James R., NY
Smith, Patricia O.*
Smith, Ms. Ruth D., NY
Smith, Sidney, NY
Smith, Teresa, MD
Snyder, Bruce E., NY
Sobotor, Bonnie G., FL
Socci, Michael F., OR
Solana, Iris E., NY
Sommer, Harold R.*
Sorenson, James G., NY
Sotomayor, Celia, NY
Spain, Pauline, NJ
Spaleny, Rosemary T.*
Spencer, Roderick*
Springer, John E.*
Stanislaus, Franklyn, NY
Stark, Linda A., NY
Stein, Marvin*
Steinfeld, Mark D., NY
Stenson, Albert F.*
Stickevers, John J., NY
Stonis, Richard V., NY
Strauss, Walter, FL
Strickland, Justin C., NM
Summerlin, Gale P., NY
Swartout, Peter J., NY
Sweet, Roslyn E., NY
Szukalski, Henry S., NY
Taormina, Peter F., FL
Tappan, Mark S.*
Taranto-Riveron, C.*
Tate, Michael, NY
Taylor, Barbara A.*
Taylor, Saturina A.*
Taylor, William, NY
Tencza, Adam S., NJ
Terrill, Cletus D., NY
Thomas, Francis C., NY
Thomas, Rebecca A., NY
Thompson, Tanya N., NY
Thomson, Andros X.*
Thousand, Charles*
Tierney, James M., NY
Timoney, Gavin J., NY
Tiplitsky, Steven T., NY
Toone, David S.*
Torres, Nellie*
Torres, Yevette*
Trainor, Francis J.**
Trani, Frank*
Triggs, Cheryl F.*
Trillo, Ismael, FL
Tully, Joanne M., NY
Turbiak, Robert J., NY
Tusa, Paul, NY
Ubelli, Michael A., NY
Valentin, Patricia A., NY
Vargas, Miriam, NY
Varney, Lillian, CA
Velasquez, Francisco*
Velazquez, Miguel A.*
Vera, Peter J.*
Vergillo, Marcia, NJ
Vericker, Robert W., HI
Vinck, Agustin D., NY
Vodvarka, Anton*
Wadis, William A., NY
Walcot, Marlene A., NY
Waldrond, Debra Y., NY

Waleski, Chester A.*
Walsh, Martin F., NY
Walsh, Thomas J.**
Walsh, Thomas M.*
Walsh, William T., NY
Warner, Mary L., NY
Washington, Kurt M., NY
Washington, Marlene*
Waterman, Steven E.*
Wazeter, Edward J., NY
Webster, Noel W., NY
Weekes, Dana*
Weidner, Brian G.*
Weiner, Barry J., NY
Weiner, Steve*
Weinman, Beth A.*
Weiss, Deborah J., NY
Weiss, Frances M.*
Wekarski, Stanley P., NJ
Wells, Charles J., NY
Wells, Ruth A., NY
Welters, Beatrice W.*
Wernly, Robert P., NY
Westcott-Marshall, Darryl A., NY
Westrenen, Jack, NY
Whitaker, Susan A.*
White, Edward J.*
Whited, Daniel F., NJ
Wieda, Richard J.*
Wiedemann, Barbara E.*
Williams, Cheryl A.*
Williams, Elaine*
Williams, Jesse N., NY
Williams, Mary A., NY
Williams, Migdalia, NY
Williams, Shirley B.*
Williams, Vinicio*
Williams, Wade, NY
Wilson, Gary J., NY
Winkfield, Colette E.*
Wise, Edwina R., NY
Witkowich, Michael F., NY
Wittich, Mark H., NY
Wolfe, Joseph G., FL
Wolinski, Thomas P., NY
Womble, Geraldine, NY
Wong, Vincent M., NY
Woo, Stanley W., NY
Woods, Richard E.*
Wren, William, NY
Wyre, Marcus L., NY
Yevoli, Peter A., NY
Young, Michael G., NY
Zaharko, Stephen P., NY
Zaharuk, Joseph P., Jr., NY
Zappia, Anthony F.*
Zias, Joanne, NY
Zietek, Stanley J., NY
Zimmer, Marianne E., UT
Zimmermann, Roger J.*
Zuccarello, Mina S., NY

1979

Acevedo, Gladys*
Acha, Beraldine L., NY
Adade, Dr. Aaron Y., MD
Adanga, Ignatius U.*
Addison, Jeanette D., NY
Adler, Harvey L., VA
Ahern, Liam G., NY
Aivazis, Elias K., VA
Alexander, Samuel, NY
Ali, Na'imah A., NY
Allen, Pauline L., NY
Amandola, Joseph J., NY
Amato, Rosemarie A., NY
Anderson, Linda M., NY
Antalek, Sharon W.*
Anthony, Tyrone, NY
Antoine, Wayne A., NY
Antrobus, Jennifer B., NY
Aponte, Myriam, VT
Aponte, Olga A.*
Armet, Thomas F., NY
Artesani, Joanne A., NY

Audinot, Leila B., NY
Auer, John G.*
Austin, Barbara J., NY
Ayers, Charles E., NY
Bailey, Belinda A., NY
Baker, Michael L.*
Balaschak, Susan F.*
Ballard, Michael A., NY
Balliraj, Ramjit, NY
Banks, Demorris J., NJ
Barbosa, Jose M.*
Bargebuhr, Nancy E., NY
Barrett, Michael F.*
Barry, Kevin P.*
Barton, Johnny M.*
Basso, Richard N.*
Baxter, George T., NJ
Beckett, Michael L., NY
Beckford, Failey M.*
Beja, Zachary, NY
Belfiore, Thomas E., NY
Belluardo, Joseph B., NY
Bender, Daniel T.**
Bendetson, Robert, NY
Bennett, Margaret M., NY
Bennett, Sylvia L., NY
Bermudez, Michael, NY
Bertolami, Richard P.*
Betsch, Robert E.*
Betso, Philip R., NY
Beyer, Howard L., NJ
Bieling, Christopher, MD
Bilello, Anthony, AZ
Bility, Moses M.*
Black, Anne, NY
Black, Irwin M.*
Black, Judett R.*
Blois, James H., NY
Bluszcz, Frank J., NY
Bogovic, Anthony P., NY
Bonelli, Basil A., NY
Boody, Steven F.*
Booker, Walter L., NY
Booker, Wayne R., NY
Borchers, Henry J., NY
Borrego, Dalila*
Bowman, Kenneth F.*
Boyd, Tracey, VA
Brady, Matthew E., SC
Brandofino, Elaine M., NY
Brennan, Eileen M., NY
Bresnihan, Jeremiah P.*
Brewer, Howard, NY
Britan, Judith S., MA
Britt, Deborah L., NY
Brody, Bonnie*
Brogan, Francis J., NY
Brown, Charles L., NY
Brown, Patricia R., NY
Brown, Robin T.*
Bruning, Howard A., NY
Bryant, Kevin J., NY
Buckley, Mary E.*
Buluro, Tope S.*
Burgess, SGT Irving, Jr., FL
Burgess, Thomas S., NC
Burks, Ishmon F.*
Burton, Lisa L., NY
Burton, Sheffield*
Calby, Paula M., NY
Calderoli, Carlos H.*
Calderone, Vincent A., NJ
Callahan, Gerard R.*
Cantalino, Carmine C., NY
Caparco, Randy M., NY
Capasso, Geraldine C., NY
Cappello, Mary G., NY
Carey, John J., NY
Carey, William G., NY
Carolan, John J., NY
Carpanini, Nancy M., NY
Carter, Luis A., NY
Carter, Willie M.*
Casano, Angelo P.*
Cashin, John G., NY
Castillo, Luis R., NY

Castillo, Virginio*
Cavanagh, James P., NY
Cervino, Anthony R., NY
Chabrier, Lydia I., FL
Chagrin, Jay W., NY
Chappelle, Roger G.*
Charles, Marie M., NY
Chin, George W., NJ
Chin, Jane*
Chisholm, Marvin A., NY
Cintron, Angela, NY
Clark, Edward F.*
Clifford, Timothy J., NY
Cody, John C.*
Cofer, Sherlene L., NY
Cohane, Miriam B., NY
Cohen, Donna M., NY
Cohen, Ronald, TX
Colarusso, Richard M.*
Colavita, Maria A., NJ
Colgan, George J., CT
Colicci, Gerald P., NY
Collazo, Jesus T.*
Colon, Aris D.*
Colon, Carlos J., NY
Connolly, Thomas E.*
Cook, William J.*
Coombs, Cyril F.*
Cooper, Michael M.*
Copps, Maria A.*
Corcoran, William C., NY
Corney, Raymond J., NY
Correa, Miguel A., TX
Corrigan, William J.*
Cortese, Frank, NY
Coyle, James G., NJ
Coyne, Edward J., NY
Crawford, Ollie A., FL
Crescente, Pedro R., FL
Crimmins, Martin E., NY
Criscuolo, Ann L., NY
Cromer, Brenda S.*
Crotty, Peter J.*
Cruz, Lourdes R.*
Cruz, Margarita, NY
Cruz, Orlando, NY
Cunningham, Darrow, NY
Cunningham, Edmund P., NY
Curtis, Terri L., NY
Custus, Saundra M.*
Cutrone, Felix P., NY
Dallatorre, Elaine B., NY
D'andrilli, Stephen L.*
Dane, Edward C.*
Danziger, Benjamin H.*
D'Aquila, Maureen, NY
Darby, Mildred E., NY
Davidson, Mark E., OR
Davis, Edward R.*
De Acosta, Emilio*
De Angelo, Ronnie J., NY
De Bernardo, Joseph A.*
De Castro, Teri*
De Jesus, Esther*
Del, Preore S., NJ
Della, Torre T., NJ
Del Preore, Salvatore, NY
Delrusso, Christopher, NJ
Deluca, Anthony E., NY
De Luca, Guy D.*
Dempsey, Dennis J., NJ
De Rosa, Vincent P., NY
Deshazo, Clant E., NY
Deshong-Busby, Iseult*
Destefano, Michael, NY
Devlin, Kevin G., NY
Deyubero, Candida L., NY
Diaz, Angelica, NY
Diaz, Mercedes, TX
Didonato, Vincent, NY
Di Gaetano, Tullio*
Di Martino, Steven J., NY
Dinwiddie, Harman B., CT
DiPasquale, Robert J.*
Dolan, Maureen A., NY
Domanski, George M.*

Donahue, Kevin D., NY
Donnelly, Matthew T., NY
Dooley, Bradford O., PA
Dooley, Patricia K.*
Dorsinville, Yolande, NY
Douge, Max, NY
Douglas, Glenda E., NY
Dour, Daniel F., NJ
Douse, Patricia A., NY
Doyle, Edward J.**
Droner, Gerard P., NY
DuFresne, Raymond K., WY
Duke, Daniel L., NY
Dunphy, Timothy G., NY
Durant, Portia R., NY
Dwyer, Lawrence T., NY
Dymant, Terry J.*
Dziardziel, Heidi W.*
Eaton, Desmond B.*
Edison, Mel, NY
Eichhorn, Barbara L., NJ
Ellis, Stephen N.*
Emert, David M.*
Enaw, John E.*
Eng, Lorna, NY
Ernst, James T., NJ
Ervin, Minnie G., NY
Espinosa, Jose C.*
Everett, Hilda W., NY
Faison, Alma J., NY
Falley, Roy B., TX
Farago, Stephen T., NY
Farkas, Judith P.*
Fauvell, Alfred J.*
Fedor, Chester, NY
Feeley, William F., NY
Feinstein, Alan H.*
Feldman, David A., FL
Feldstein, Kenneth I., MA
Ferguson, Janice L.*
Ferman, Yolanda D., NY
Fermon, Yolanda D.*
Fernandez, Ferdinand*
Fiorella, Dominic A.*
Fish, Elizabeth N.*
Fitzgerald, Daniel J., NY
Fitzgerald, Patrick J., NJ
Fletcher, Pauline V.*
Flores, Andre, NY
Flores, Miguel A.*
Foley, Elizabeth A., NY
Fonseca, Miriam*
Ford, Jeffrey M.*
Foresta, Jody A., NY
Forster, Larry M.*
Forsythe, Farris B., NY
Foss, John R., SC
Frangos, Victoria H., NY
Frasco, Leonard W., NY
Fredricks, Charles J.*
Freeman, Cynthia, NY
Frey, Maureen B.*
Frost, David, NY
Fuller, William, NY
Gaffney, Kathleen V.*
Galup, Alice S.*
Gandolfo, Lucian J.*
Garavito, George E., NY
Garbow, Bruce, NY
Garcia, Hilda E.*
Garcia, Nonato, NY
Garcia, Victoria*
Geaney, Laura A.*
Gerry, Joseph A.*
Gilligan, Deborah K.*
Gillooly, Margaret, NY
Gione, Gary J., NY
Giordano, Jack J., NY
Gleason, Patrick J.**
Gleason, Richard J., NY
Glovack, Joseph J.*
Gluck, Robert A.*
Gmelch, Eileen F.*
Godino, Joseph, NY
Goings, Alvin, NY
Golden, Beth A.*

Goldsmith, Alan R.*
Goldstein, Robin L.*
Gomez, Angelina, NY
Gonzalez, Luis M., NY
Gonzalez Jimenez, Ramona
　G., NY
Gooden, Elsa G., NY
Goodloe, Chet*
Gorman, Michael J., NY
Grabin, Scott D., NY
Gray, Albert P., NY
Gray, Carol A.**
Gray, Donald R., NY
Grays, Marguerite, NY
Graziano, Paul W., NY
Greaney, John J., NY
Grechanik, Carolyn A., NY
Green, Linda M.*
Green, Vincent E., NY
Gregg, Tommy L., NY
Gregory, Raymond W., NY
Grobluski, George F., NY
Gross, Jeffrey*
Grossberg, Sanford R.*
Guadagno, Carmine, NY
Guarino, John M., NY
Gunn, Madeline M.*
Gustafson, Linda A., NY
Guzman, Paul N., NY
Haar, Barry M., NY
Hagan, Thomas, NY
Hagan, William P., NY
Hahn, John J., NY
Hallen, Joseph T., NY
Handman, Stuart W., NY
Hartman, Donna M., NY
Hayde, William P., NY
Hayes, Dorsey L., NJ
Hayes, James J., NY
Hayes, Raymond*
Heller, Kenneth C., NY
Hemrick, Henry J., FL
Hennen, Christopher G., NY
Henry, Shirley M., NY
Hercules, Keith F., NJ
Heym, Eugene, NY
Hickman, Virgil*
Higgins, Dorothy, NY
Hill, Willie G., NY
Hillegass, Christine*
Hochberg, Ian P., NY
Hochfeld, Richard P., NY
Hodge, Patricia I., NY
Hodges, Warren A., NJ
Hoeneveld, Robert J., NY
Hoffman, Neil, NJ
Hoffman, Walter G.*
Hopkins, Emma J.*
Hopkins, John K., NY
Howard, Harold**
Hubbard, April R., NY
Hubert, Richard B., NY
Hughes, Brian J., NY
Hyams, Laurie, NY
Ippolito, Steve, NY
Jackson, Eugene P.*
Jackson, Vicki D., NY
Jacobellis, Anthony C.*
Jacobs, Arthur W., NY
Jaffe, Joanne, NY
James, Tyrone L., NY
Jefferson, Clarett, NY
Jenkins, Garlien*
Jeru-Ahmed, Yejide M.*
Johnson, Jeanne, NY
Johnson, Joni S., NY
Johnson, Lynhurst M.*
Johnson, Patricia L.*
Johnson, Roby F.*
Johnson, Samuel M., NY
Johnson, Stepahnie, NY
Johnson, Walter E., NY
Johnston, Eileen R.*
Joiner, Joyce R., NY
Jones, Thomas M.*
Jordan, Carol A., NY

Joseph, Jane*
Joseph, Richard T., NY
Joyner, William L., NY
Junco, Jorge N., DC
Kanacki, Gaye D., NY
Kania, Gabrielle A.*
Kaplan, Neil J., NY
Katz, Linda*
Katz, Michael R., NY
Katzr, Bette*
Kearney, Karen E.*
Keller, Jean M.*
Kelly, James P., NY
Kelly, Thomas F., NY
Kemenczy, John L., NJ
Kende, George**
Kessler, Marlene D.*
Kilcullen, Kevin J., NY
King, John J., NY
King, Raymond F., NY
King, Stephen J., III, NY
Kissinger, Charles T.**
Klein, Martha E., NY
Klie, Nancy H.*
Klimas, Jeffrey W., NY
Klingener, Lawrence J., NY
Klink, John H., NY
Knott, Clare A., NY
Kolarik, Timothy D., NY
Konczynin, Maria V., NY
Konig, Eric L., NY
Konig, Norman, NY
Kosko, Joseph M.*
Kramer, Karen L.*
Krane, Thomas W., NY
Kress, Robert J., NY
Kriegsman, Jeffrey, NY
Kristofic, Anton*
Kristofic, Jo-ann*
Kump, Erwin, NY
Kwiatkowski, Joseph F.*
Lagathels, Lucy T.*
Lagoda, Anthony A., NY
Lambe, Joan S., NY
Lambe, John J.*
Landers, William C.*
Lane, Betty A., NY
Lang, William B.*
Langer, Robert B.*
Lantier, William X.*
Laporte, Angel L., NY
Larkin, James J.*
La Sala, Stephen F., NY
Laub, George W., NY
Laverpool, Frederick*
Layne, Frederick R., NC
Lebowitz, Raymond, FL
Lee, John F.*
Lee, Philip W., NY
Lee, Theresa, NY
Leibowitz, Gail D., NY
Lejbzon, Mimi, NY
Leon, Flor*
Lesniak, Thomas*
Leto, Teresa A., NY
Levine, Jonathan*
Levy-Lee, Karen*
Lewis, Satia M., NY
Lewis, William E.*
Lichtenstein, Arthur*
Lidondici, Robert*
Limitone, Anthony V., NJ
Lindsey, Wayne, NY
Lipari, Anthony J., NY
Liu, George, NY
Loboda, Henry J., VA
Locker, Martin, NJ
Logan, Benjamin, NY
Logan, Jeffrey J.*
Lohse, Joseph R.*
Longarello, Michael J.*
Lopez, Eric, NY
Lopez, Lopez C.*
Lopez, Luis A., NY
Lopez, Michael*
Lopez, Veronica D.*

Lopez-Rivera, Pedro, NY
Lord, Spencer*
Losak, Raymond J., NY
Losi, Stephen H., NY
Louttit, Robert J., NY
Ludwig, William J., NY
Lugo, Nelson J., NY
Lustig, Marsha L., NJ
Lynch, Michael P.*
Lyons, Ronald C., NY
Mack, Alice, NY
Mack, John B., NY
Madden, James A.*
Maguire, John T., CT
Mahoney, Francis J., NY
Maloney, Dennis R.*
Maloney, Eileen A., NY
Mandia, John F.**
Manisero, Thomas R., NY
Mansky, Orin, NJ
Marchetta, Raymond A., CA
Marcial, Luis A.*
Marcos, Maria E., NY
Marcotrigiano, James, NY
Marcune, Patrick, NY
Mario, John R., CT
Markman, Russell P.*
Markowitz, Thomas, NY
Marolda, William G., NY
Marone, Anne L., NY
Marotta, Michael G., NY
Marra, John M.*
Marron, John F.*
Martin, Jacqueline*
Martinez, George A., NY
Martinez-Garcia, M.*
Marucci, Barbara A., NY
Mastronardy, Michael, NJ
Matias, Luis A.*
Matysiak, Daniela S., WA
Maxey, Naomi T.*
Mayer, Mark F.*
Mayo, Roger J.*
Mc Allister, Justice, NY
Mc Andrew, Lois J., NY
Mc Cabe, Joseph T., NY
Mc Carron, Lawrence B.*
Mc Carthy, Kenneth M.*
Mc Cay, Ralph E.*
McDonald, Clarence (Chris),
　FL
Mc Donald, Thomas T., NY
Mc Ewan, Felix F.*
Mc Grath, Henry J., NY
Mc Intosh, Cheryl E., NY
Mc Kenna, V.*
Mc Leod, Gloria Y.*
Mc Loughlin, James F., NY
Mc Mahon, Peter D.*
Mc Manus, Elizabeth G., NY
Mc Namara, Patrick, NY
Mc Nulty, Daniel J., NY
Mc Pherson, Dianne, NY
Medina, Andres*
Melendez, Eugenio, NJ
Menendez, Carlos*
Mennella, Concetta I., NY
Mensah, Samuel A.*
Mercer, Jacquelyn D., NY
Metivier, Margaret, NY
Meyers, Mrs. WillieEarl, NY
Miano, Anthony G.*
Miley, Gregory L., NY
Miller, Kenneth L., NY
Miller, Lionel R., NY
Mitchell, Dennis N.*
Mohlenhoff, William R., NY
Moitt, Susan L.*
Moment, Keran M., NY
Moncada, Marlene S.*
Mondi, Darlene*
Montalbano, Richard P., NY
Montanez, Jose E.*
Monti, Stanley R., NY
Moore, Joseph, NY
Morciglio, Libertad E., NY

Morley, Christopher D.*
Moron, Robert D., NY
Morris, Elaine L., NY
Morris, Rhoda M., NY
Morris, Valeria L.*
Mosca, Anthony M., NY
Moselle, Linda H., NY
Moses, Renee M.*
Moss, Kathryn A., NY
Moynihan, Thomas P., NY
Muaillo, Leo, NY
Mullgrav, Susan B.*
Murillo, Leo, NY
Murphy, Colin W., NY
Murphy, Donald R., CA
Murphy, Edwin E., NY
Naar, Robin A.*
Naman, Carol A., NY
Napoli, George V., NY
Narbut, Richard*
Natoli, Joseph J., NY
Naughton, Mary T.*
Naylor, Howard C., NY
Negron, Angelina*
Negron, Victor, NY
Neilan, Thomas H.**
Nesmith, Eugene*
Neubort, Betty, NY
Newson, Eula M.*
Ng, Fay*
Nichols, Glenda J.*
Niedzielski, George*
Nnamocha, Nestor U., Nigeria
Norat, Wigberto, NY
Nunez, Hilda, NY
O'Brien, William J.*
Odom, Gwendolyn N., NY
O'dowd, John W., NJ
O'Keefe, Cornelius*
Okin, Avery Eli, NY
Oli, Sampson I.*
Olla, Philip A., NY
Orta, Harry H., NY
Ortiz Ortiz, Ana M., NY
Osazuwa, Frank O.*
O'Shea, Kevin J., NY
Osorio, Benedict*
Osuna, Miriam*
Otero, Abisai*
Otis, David B., NY
Pagano, Bruce L., VA
Palmeri, LT Nicholas R., MD
Pandolfo, Edward P., NY
Parente, Richard A., NY
Parisien, Elianne*
Parker, Thomas*
Patrissi, John P., NY
Pauline, Gerard T.*
Perez, Ismael J., NY
Perez, Liduvina, NY
Perez, Salvador*
Perricone, Gerard D., NY
Peter, John H., VA
Peterson, Claudette J., IN
Peterson, Dennis J., MD
Peterson, Kevin C., NY
Petraco, Nicholas, NY
Petrocelli, Albert P., NY
Petruzzi, Dominick J., NY
Piazza, Pete*
Piccirilli, Roger A.*
Pinckney, Brenda J.*
Pinckney, Michael J., NY
Pinette, Holly, FL
Piwowarski, Joseph C., NY
Plantamura, Toni H.*
Planzos, Sotirios A.*
Plourde, Yolande R.*
Pollard, Melinda Y., NY
Poppe, Christine M.*
Poritz, Michael J.*
Poulos, James A., NY
Powell, Denise K., NY
Prato, Barbara A.*
Prendergast, Terri B., NY
Price, Sherry T., NY

Price, Wayne H.*
Prince, Daniel E., NY
Prince, Gerald B.*
Pupino, Joseph M., NY
Purtill, Michael, NY
Rader, Matthew, NY
Raggi, Michael L., NY
Rakowsky, George B.*
Ramirez, Edgar, NY
Ramos, Elise*
Randall, Calvin P., NY
Raphael, John L.*
Raphael, Marlene*
Rapp, Edward J., NY
Raymond, Edward P., NY
Raymond, Zulma B., NY
Redican, Joseph E., NY
Redmond, Thomas J., NY
Reese, Lavinia, NY
Reeves, Dorothy M.*
Reid, Mrs. Dorothy L., NY
Reid, Luther, NY
Reid, Vonnie E.*
Reilly, William T.*
Renaghan, Sheila G.*
Renois, Paul J., CA
Reyes, William, NY
Rezoagli, Frank, NY
Richardson, Deborah O.*
Richardson, Steven J., NY
Ridgway, Donald L., TN
Rigoulot, John P., FL
Riker, William A., NY
Riley, Lucky*
Ring, William, NY
Riollano, Miriam, NY
Rister, Esther S., NY
Rivela, Steven M., NY
Rivera, Daniel, NY
Rivera, Denise*
Roach, Eugene J., NY
Roberson, Irene, NY
Robertson, Sheryl D.*
Robinson, Benjamin E., NY
Robinson, Charles, NY
Roche, Edward J., NJ
Rodriguez, Edwin*
Rogers, Gerard J., NY
Rogers, William D., NY
Rosario, Daniel B.*
Rose, Joyce H., FL
Rosen, Warren, FL
Ross, James, NY
Roth, Jeffrey H.*
Rowland, Tamesha Q., NY
Rubin, Stacey*
Rubinkowski, Irene S.*
Ruiz, Teresita*
Rundle, Pamela M.*
Ruvolo, Anthony P., NY
Ryan, Denis P., NY
Saenger, Patricia A., NY
Salaman, Bernardo*
Salamon, Carmelita J., NY
Saltz, Abby R.*
Salvatore, Lawrence F., NJ
Sanchez, Georgina E.*
Santana, Gilbert, NY
Santangelo, Frank, CT
Santiago, Edward*
Santimays, Alice V., NY
Sapraicone, Jane T., NY
Satterfield, Charles, NY
Savage, Mark J., NJ
Savidis, Paul*
Scanterbury, Renee S., NY
Sceusa, Peter S., NY
Schatz, John E., NY
Scheer, Paul J., NY
Schenck, Ginette N., NY
Schenker, Stephen, NY
Schick, Raymond W., NY
Schmucker, Paul W.*
Schneider, James T., NJ
Schultz, Harold S.*
Schwartz, Stuart E., NY

Sciarabba, Nicholas J.*
Scott, August J., NY
Scott, Irving J., NY
Scott, Mable, AL
Secter, Charles W., NY
Seeger, William J.*
Sefcik, John F.*
Segalini, George L., NY
Semple, Darryl M., NY
Senerchia, Anthony G., NY
Sepulveda, Eva*
Seta, Richard V.*
Shalom, Marietta, NY
Shamblee, Cheryl A.*
Shapiro, Jerome*
Shaw, Lindore E.*
Sheehan, Vincent J., OH
Sheinkopf, Henry A., NY
Shelley, Marilyn M., NY
Sherman, Barbara J., NY
Signorile, William V.*
Silberzweig, Lorraine, NJ
Simons, Emily, NY
Simpkins, Donna*
Simpkins, Lillian*
Simpson, Paula M., NY
Siotkas, John, NY
Sira, Ronald B.*
Small, Oral B., NY
Smith, Leon, NY
Smith, Leslie C., NY
Smith, Marjorie (Mardie) W., NY
Smith, Rose, NY
Smith, Susanne M., NY
Smith, Sylvia M., NY
Smolowitz, Barry M., NY
Snyder, Teresa M., NY
Somerville, Deborah A., FL
Sosa, Juanita, NY
Spearman, Larry D., NY
Spector, Abraham M., NY
Spinelli, Philip C.*
Squassoni, Laura C., NY
Stapleton, James J., NY
Steinert, Rosa M., NY
Stephens, Violet M.*
Stewart, Louisia, NY
Sumner, Joan M., NY
Svane, Stella, NJ
Swain, Quinton E., NY
Swinton, Luther, NY
Szarawarski, Michael, NJ
Tabman, Michael H.*
Tagarelli, Nicholas A., NJ
Takas, Vincent*
Talamo, Peter M., NY
Talbot, Richard J., NY
Tan, Lolito V., NY
Taylor, Mildred C.*
Tenzer, Mitchell R., NY
Tessa, Hackett, NY
Texidor, Armanda*
Theodore, Inginac*
Thomas, E., NY
Thomas, Joan P., NY
Thomas, Leroy W.*
Thomas, Robert M.*
Thomas, Roland W.*
Thompson, Clyde W.*
Thompson, Donald E., NY
Thompson, Shirleen, NY
Thompson, Theda A., NY
Tirado, Lydia, NY
Torres, Julia*
Towns, James H.*
Trefcer, Frank A.*
Trotman, George L.*
Trotman, Sam V.*
Tuller, James, NY
Umstetter, Susan M., NY
Upton, Robert W.*
Urrutia, Julio E., NY
Valencia, Armando, NY
Valenzano, Michael D., NY
Van, Aken R.**

Vanofsky, Michael, NY
Varela, Mauricio, NY
Vasti, Thomas, NY
Velez, Julio L.*
Velez, Luis E.*
Vellucci, Frank R., NY
Venditelli, Grazyna*
Ventura-rosa, Rafael, NY
Vessup, Earl L., NY
Vidal, Nellie R., NY
Villano, Valerie F., NY
Villar, Miriam I.*
Vitale, George E., NY
Vrana, Dennis, NY
Wagner, Colette A., NY
Waichman, Herbert L., NY
Walcott, Howard E., NY
Walker, Barbara L.*
Walker, Charles A.*
Walker, Donna M., NY
Walker, Robert C., NY
Wallace, Patrick J., NY
Walsh, Joseph C., NY
Walters, Eustace, NY
Ward, Donella, NY
Ward, Edward C., NY
Ward, Kevin M., NY
Washington, Juanita, NY
Washington, Yvette V.*
Waymer, Connie R., NY
Wechsler, Mark*
Weintraub, Lary M.*
Weir, Jacqueline M., NY
Welsh, John J., NY
Whelan, William E., NY
White, Edith*
Wilkinson, Thomas C., NY
Williams, Alfred, NY
Williams, Anthony M., NY
Williams, Douglas L., NY
Wilson, Cleveland F., NY
Wilson, Theodore*
Wimbish, Patsy, NY
Wing, Dennis J.*
Winters, Alan J., NY
Wong, Geoffry, NY
Wood, John A.*
Wright, Fred, NY
Yanofsky, Barbara I., NY
Yanofsky, Michael A., NY
Young, Robert J., NY
Yuan, Judy*
Yuneman, Thomas E., NY
Zaboras, John S., NY
Zaino, James R., NY
Zani, Daniel J., NY
Zappulla, Barbara J., NY
Zarilla, Anthony J., MO
Zayas, John, NY
Zucker, Samuel M.*
Zummo, Annette M., NY

1980

Aaron, Grantley W., NY
Abbott, Milton N., NY
Abdullah, Ms. Doris T., NY
Abrams, Fay A., NY
Abreu, Arnold, NY
Acevedo, Ramon, NY
Acosta, Milvian*
Adinolfi, Thomas R., NY
Aguero, Maggie, PA
Aguirre, Esperanza M.*
Aiosa, Claire J., NY
Akalonu, Rosalyn B., NY
Alaimo, William N., NY
Albert, Philip J., NY
Albino, Jose E.*
Alexander, Eileen R.*
Alexander, Walter, NY
Allan, Colin P., CA
Allen, John J., NY
Aloi, Carole A., NY
Aloisio, Sal, NY
Alswang, Scott B., NJ
Alvarez, Rene*

Al-zahra, Hakimah*
Ambrosio, Ralph V., NY
Andruszkewicz, Phillip M., NY
Annarumma, Thomas P., NY
Annina, Ralph, WI
Anobile, John J., NY
Anshanslin, James B., AZ
Appel, Michael A., NY
Armatti, Linda, NY
Armstrong-morales, Yette*
Arnold, Henry C., FL
Arsenakos, Stella, JD, NY
Arthur, Easlyn C., NY
Asamoah, Benoni A., CT
Astrizky, Beatrice N., NY
Augustine, Clyde L., NY
Avery, Earl, NY
Bacchus, Garvin W., NY
Bachmann, Peter J., NY
Balgovind, Satya D.*
Baratta, Anthony, NY
Barclay, Keith G., NJ
Barnes, Bray, NJ
Barnes, Charles E., NY
Barnes, Enobia E., NY
Barrett, Kevin J., NJ
Barrett, Thyrone V., NY
Barry, Edward P., NJ
Barton, Wade J., NY
Batista, Carmelo, NY
Batista, Ruth, NY
Bauer, Michael, NY
Baumgart, Edward W., NJ
Beck, Marianne*
Bednarik, Jane P.*
Bellamy, Beverly J., NY
Bellejambe, Melanie, NY
Benassi, Joann V.*
Ben-Rubin, Linda G.*
Bergman, Jay B.*
Berman, Merrily A., NY
Bierling, John J.*
Bills, Sylvester, NY
Bioh, Joseph K.*
Bitsimis, Jeffrey, NY
Blackman, Michael J., MD
Blair, Bernardo R., NY
Bleiberg, Bruce A., NY
Bohrer, Philip, NY
Bonanno, Stephen*
Borakov, Fred S., NY
Boresky, George M., NY
Borgia, Donald D., NY
Boris, Elizabeth, NY
Boritza, Ms. Patricia A., TX
Boswell, Joseph A., NY
Botte, Dominick, Jr., NY
Boudiette, Charles T., NY
Boyle, Sheila A., NY
Bracht, Margarita J.*
Brandon, John, NY
Brennan, Thomas D.*
Brennan, Thomas H., NY
Brogan, Michael P., NJ
Bromley, Stephen T., NY
Brooks, Eurita, NY
Brown, Elizabeth A., NY
Brown, Herbert, NY
Brown, Joyce C., NY
Brown, Leonetta M., NY
Brown, Patrick J., NY
Brush, Gerard C.*
Bryan, Egan E., NY
Buckley, Maurice, NY
Bullaro, Marc J., NY
Buntin, Mark M., CT
Burrows, Winston A., NY
Caffrey, James D., CO
Caines, Angela V.*
Caldarola, Anthony E., NY
Calderone, William D., NY
Cali, Richard J., AZ
Callan, Cesar A., NY
Calle, Juan G., NY
Calouro, Joseph, NY
Campbell, Rita, NY

Campisi, Ronald P., NY
Canals-rosa, Mildred C., NY
Canavan, Andrew J., NJ
Canning, Thomas P., MA
Carbone, Richard J.*
Cardiello, Patrick*
Cardone, Robert A., NY
Carey, William J., NY
Castellano, John, NJ
Castellanos, Angeles*
Castro, Giselle, NY
Catalano, Daniel J., NY
Cates, Denise S.*
Cazzoli, Ubaldo, NY
Celella, Carolyn C., NY
Chamble, Benjamin S., NY
Champagne, Nancy F., NY
Channell, Warren T., FL
Che, Atanga J.*
Chong, LT David E., NY
Choudhry, Muhammad Y.*
Ciepierski, Joseph R., NY
Ciorciari, David J., NY
Clark, Kevin M., NY
Clark, Rhonda C., NY
Clarke, Lynn A., NY
Clarke, Thomas M., NY
Cleary, Michael J., NY
Clerico, Lucien T., NY
Clinton, Linda M., FL
Clive, Laurence E., NY
Cohen, Amy B., NY
Cohen, Fern, NY
Cohen, Steven M., NY
Colangelo, Robert**
Cole, Karen E., NY
Cole, Michael A.*
Coleman, Charles E., NY
Colon, Camille, NY
Colon, Nelson, NY
Colon-Ramos, CAPT Miguel
  A., NY
Comadore, Alberta, NY
Comastri, Harold N., NY
Connelly, Robert T., PA
Cook, Robert A., NY
Cooper, Charles D., NY
Cooper, Iris A., NJ
Coppolo, James A., NY
Corcoran, Frank E., NY
Corke, Kathleen M., NY
Corneh, Varney M., NY
Corsentino, Anthony P., NY
Corson, Randi L., PA
Cosentino, Louis A., NY
Cosenza, Joseph, NY
Costa, Richard, NY
Costas, Yvette-Marie, NY
Courtney, William D., NJ
Cousins, Thomas D., MD
Crenshaw, Frank D., NY
Criscuolo, Carol, NY
Cronnelly, John J., NY
Crowley, John M., NY
Cruz, Heriberto, NY
D'agostino, John, NY
D'Agostino, Joseph A.*
Daly, Daniel, NY
Daniel, Ralston, NY
Daniel, Weston S.*
Davenport, John J.*
Davids, Joseph Z., NY
Davila, Jeannette*
Davis, Anthony W., NY
Davis, Hildegarde B., NY
DeCastro, Janet L., NY
De Filippo, Michael, NY
de Holczer, Lauren J., NY
De Luca, Lawrence J., NY
De Marino, Vincent A., NY
Denardo, Jeffrey J., NY
Denton, Karen L.*
De Paolo, Steven M., NY
De Quatro, Joseph C.*
De Rosa, James*
Desiderio, Richard A., NY

Desire, Yves C., NY
De Vergee, Winston W.*
Devine, Edward W., NY
De Vito, Dennis W., NY
De Vito, Michael J., NY
De Vivo, Francis (Frank) W.,
  NJ
Devlin, Philip G.*
Diamond, Theresa A., NY
Di Meglio, Ciro P., NY
Dionne, John M.*
Ditto, Robbin A., NY
Dogan, Walter R., NY
Donadio, Randall J., NY
Donato, Elsie I.*
Donohue, John D.*
Doria, Margaret T.*
Dotzler, Paul P., NY
Dowd, Dennis G.*
Dowd, Kenneth W.*
Doyle, Robert E.*
Doyle, William H.*
Dudash, Stephen, NY
Dudley, George S.**
Dunbar, Andrew*
Dunigan, Bryan P., NY
Durando, Donald M., NY
Dyshanowitz, Mark*
Dzumyk, Anna M.*
Edwards, Rev. Michael, NY
Enoch, Lisa A.*
Espanol, Joseph L., FL
Evans, Madeline C., NY
Ewald, William E., NY
Faith, Francis L., NY
Falcone, Loretta T., NY
Fanning, Margaret M.*
Farngalo, Rosemarie H.*
Farrell, John F., NY
Farrell, Patrick J., FL
Farrell, Patrick R., NY
Farrell, Peter G.*
Featherstone, Aubrey, NY
Felix, Joan P.*
Ferguson, Lisa A., NY
Ferrell, John*
Figueroa, Jimmy*
Finamore, Sandro, NY
Fisch, Roberta, NY
Fischer, Maureen J., NY
Fisher, William E., NY
Fitzpatrick, Eugene*
Fleming, Sibyl L., NY
Flynn, David T.*
Flynn, Raymond J., NV
Foody, Liam J., NY
Forde, Ivy D., NY
Forker, Edward C., NJ
Francis, Mildred L., NY
Frank, Kathryn K., NY
Fraser, Kenneth A., NY
Frazier, William E., NY
Freeman, Thomas G., NY
Fryce, Deborah A.*
Fuller, Myrtle*
Furcillo, Jane*
Furr, Angela R., NY
Gaby, Thomas R., NY
Gaffikin, Gerard P.*
Gannon, John J., NY
Garay, Edna E., NY
Garcia, Annie*
Gardella, Ronald G., NY
Geller, Patricia A., EdD, MA
Genova, Alfred F., NY
Gentile, John R., NY
Gil, Mark*
Gilchrist, John T., NY
Gill, William B., NY
Gillette, Phyllis B.*
Giordano, Susan E., NY
Girard, Sheila T.*
Goldbeck, Erik H.*
Goldfinger, Mary Ann, NY
Golding, Bridget D.*
Gonzalez, Janet, NY

Goral, Helen, NY
Gordon, Barbara R.*
Gorrasi, Joseph R., NY
Gottesman, Marjorie*
Goulbourne, Marilyn R., NY
Gower, Susan-jo*
Grant, Barbara V., NY
Granville, Alfonso M., NJ
Gray, Philburn W., NY
Greenberg, Marc D.*
Grefe, Lynn S.*
Gregory, Helen A., AL
Grossman, David L., NY
Guadalupe, Miriam A.*
Guarino, Anthony J.*
Guerra, Ismael*
Guerriero, Douglas G., NY
Gurney, Francis W.*
Guss, Bertram C.*
Haggerty, James J., NJ
Halbohn, Donald F., NY
Hall, Thomas F.*
Hallahan, Thomas R., NY
Halloran, Frank H., NJ
Hammel, Manuela M., NY
Hannan, Louis G.*
Hannibal, Louise, NY
Hansen, Glenn J., CT
Hargrave, Rhonda T., NY
Harman, Patrick J.*
Harris, Anette R.*
Harris, Rodney C., NY
Harrison, Alicia M., NY
Harrison, Olivia F., NY
Harrison, Sheridan*
Harrison, Willie, NY
Hart, Keith R., NY
Haskins, Roberta H., NY
Healy, John E., NY
Helfman, Michelle, NY
Hemmings, Frank E., NY
Hempfield, Linda D., NY
Henry, Florence D., NY
Hernandez, Nancy M., NY
Hickson, Wilibelle, NY
Higgins, William J., NY
Hill, Marilyn E., NY
Hirsch, Karl W., FL
Hochberg, Stephen H.*
Hochstadt, Marc M., FL
Hochstadt, Yolanda P., FL
Holcroft, George J.*
Holian, Kevin M., NY
Holman, Jeffrey M., NY
Holmes, George R., NY
Honore, Michelle M., NY
Hotz, Karl A.*
Howkins, James O., NY
Igartua, Julie A.*
Indelicato, C.*
Inducci, Craig G., PA
Ingellis, Daniel A., NY
Ithier, Walma*
Iyoha, Friday E., NJ
Jackson, Alena R., NY
Jackson, David*
Jacob, George N., NJ
James, Arthur, NY
Jenik, Alice J., NY
Jermin, Cyril E., NY
Johannes, Brian J.*
Johnson, Dean L., NY
Johnson, Ellen C.*
Johnson, Gloria, NY
Johnson, James, Jr., NY
Johnston, Stephen F.*
Jones, Clarissa A., NY
Jones, Innie*
Jones, Solomon, NY
Jones, William, NY
Jordan, Robert W.*
Joseph, Essy A., FL
Joseph, Lola*
Kahan, Robert*
Kaminski, Dennis J., NY
Kananowicz, Eugene G., NY

Kanterman, Ronald E., NJ
Kantrowitz, Steven H., NJ
Kaplan, Robert, NY
Kappler, Richard*
Karalis, Patricia R., NY
Kast, Frederick P.*
Katz, Geoffrey B.*
Katz, Lawrence, MD
Kelly, Robert J., NY
Kendrick, John V., HI
Keogh, Dennis F., NY
Kiernan, Dean T.*
Killela, James*
Kilmer, Joseph F., FL
Kipp, Edward C., NY
Kirk, John J., NY
Kirk, Thomas A., NY
Kirkland, Alma W.*
Konig, Irving, NY
Kraemer, Richard E., NJ
Krinick, Norman, NY
Kucinski, James E.*
Kuhne, Gary R.*
Kulesa, LT Edward J., NY
LaBarbera, Sandra*
Lamorte, Lisa, NY
Laniado, Elliot J., NY
Lanzilotti, Carlo J., NY
Largo, Alfred E., NY
La Rosa, Mickey, NY
Latawiec, Robert F., NY
Lauda, Edward C., FL
La Vaughn, Deanna A., SC
Lebron, Nancy, NY
LeDee, John*
Ledford, Kathleen T., NY
Lee, James G.*
Leitgeb, Edward C., NJ
Lentini, Michael D.*
Levine, Kenneth H., NY
Levine, Morris, NY
Lewis, Kevin, NY
Lewis, Roslyn R., NY
Liga-Colon, Ilyna*
Linares, Antonio, NY
Lindo, Chelcea O., NY
Lindsay, Clive B., NY
Lobet, Esther M.*
Lopez, Daisy, NY
Lopez, Lucy C., NY
Lora, Alba*
Lukasavage, Francine*
Lynch, Alan B.*
Lynn, William J., NY
Lyons, Phyllis S.*
Lytle, Emanuel, NY
Lyttle, John P., NY
Maccarone, Virginia, NY
Maglione, Diane C., NJ
Mahone, Robert L., NY
Mahoney, Edward J., NY
Maier, George J.*
Maini, John, NY
Major, Lee H.*
Mallory, Randolph C.*
Malloy, William*
Mandarino, Michael A., NY
Mangual, William P., NY
Manners, Julia C., FL
Manns, Olivien D., NY
Marchia, Ms. Theresa, NY
Marino-Palermo, Esthr*
Markman, Michael, NY
Markowitz, Nathan*
Marotta, James A., NY
Marquez, Miguel A., MD
Martin, Dennis E., NY
Martin, Richard A., NY
Martinez, Jose B., NY
Matalon, Victor C., NY
May, Jonathan B.*
Mazza, Dolores R., NY
McCann, Robert H., NY
Mc Cants, Robert J.*
Mc Cormick, James J.*
Mc Daniel, Glenda E.*

Mc Gee, Denise D.*
Mc Ghee, Denise-Ann, NY
Mc Grath, Eugene T.*
Mc Hugh, Robert A., NY
Mc Junkin, William M., NY
McLaughlin, John P., NY
Mc Nerney, Christine*
Mc Nish, Clarence L.*
Meine, Manfred F., PhD
  CGFM, FL
Mendelsohn, Clifford*
Mendez, Angel, NY
Mendez, Felix R., NY
Menoscal, Edward A., NY
Messam, Patrick, DC
Meyers, Patricia C., PA
Michaels, Norman M., NY
Mickulas, Walter D., NY
Micucci, Frances E., NY
Mier, Jodi L., NY
Might, Francis E., NY
Mihovich, Anthony M., NY
Miller, Roy P., NY
Mills, Aaron E., NY
Mills, Tani P.*
Millsaps, Carl*
Mitchell, Kathleen G., NY
Mitesser, Peter C., VA
Moeller, Thomas R., NY
Mojica, Yolanda C., NY
Mollica, Joseph C., NJ
Montague, William R., NY
Montalvo, Agnes*
Montaruli, Anthony M., NY
Monteverde, A., FL
Mooney, Richard P., NJ
Moore, Faryce B., NY
Moore, Mark A.*
Morales, Yvette, NY
Moran, James J.*
Morgan, James, NY
Morman, Cathy E., NY
Morrongiello, Michael*
Mui, Yet C., NY
Munford, Julianne*
Murdock, Vicki L.*
Murphy, Thomas D., NY
Murray, William T., NY
Myers, Debra A., NY
Natal, Catherine M.*
Nelson, Frank E.*
Nelson, Marcia, NJ
Newman, Roger K., NY
Ng, Henry W.*
Nolan, Wanda J., NY
Norman, Lewis A.*
Normoyle, William T.*
Nowicki, John F., IL
Obeng-Dompreh, L.*
Obremski, Gerald F.*
O'brien, Patrick J., NY
O'connor, Judy, NY
O'Grady, Martin F., NY
Ojeda, Rosa E., NY
Oliver, Gwendolyn L.*
Omar, Jemela G.*
O'Neill, Michael P.*
Ortiz, Nilda N.*
Pabon, Hector L.*
Paccione, Jack, NY
Pacheco, Brunilda, NY
Pacheco, Richard, NY
Palazzoto, Diane, NY
Palmer, Joseph*
Pantoja, Isabel*
Paoloni, John K.*
Papaccio, Charles J., MO
Parker, SGT Richard, NY
Parks, Lanetta J., NY
Patton, Brian V., NY
Pellinger, Thomas G., NY
Pelton, Gwendolyn E., AZ
Pentangelo, Aniello A., PA
Perry, William J.**
Peters, Judy-lynne, NY
Petersen, Eddy, NY

Peterson, Carrie L., NY
Peterson, Thomas V., NY
Petrizzo, Joseph P., NY
Phipps, Alfred L., NY
Picciarelli, Patrick, NY
Picciochi, Richard T., NY
Piccirella, Pasquale, NY
Piechocki, Mary T., NY
Piecoro, Susan M.*
Piliere, Kevin*
Pinero, Ismael J., NY
Pitts, Jeffrey, NY
Pladl, John R., NJ
Poetta, Charles, NY
Pogeweit, Harold J.*
Pollowitz, Scott R.*
Poole, Florence K., NY
Popovic, Ljiljana K.*
Post, Ephraim R.*
Praino, Vincent J.*
Prince, Mainert J., NY
Quinlan, John F., NY
Quinn, James C., NY
Quinn, Lawrence T., NY
Radcliffe, Anna J., NY
Ramos, Rosemary, NY
Ramsey, Keitha Y., TX
Raspante, Dominick F.*
Reid, Gloria M., NY
Reilly, Nancy A., NY
Reinke, John J., NJ
Rempy, Robert E.*
Resua, Ronald, NY
Reynolds, Linda-Keisha M., NY
Riccio, Arthur P., NY
Rios, Angela*
Ripps, Carol A., NY
Rivas, Julio R.*
Rivera, David, NY
Roberson, Sharen K.*
Roberts, Cheri A., NY
Robinson, Alvin M., NY
Rodriguez, Angel S.*
Rodriguez, Gloria M., NY
Rodriguez, Israel J.*
Rodriguez, Luz M.*
Rodriguez, Migdalia, NY
Rodriguez, William J., NY
Rosado, Concepcion P., NY
Rosario, Evelyn*
Rosenberg, Linda S., NY
Ross, Richard M., FL
Rowinski, John A.*
Rudloff, Robert W.*
Rullo, Antonia, NY
Ruocco, Domenick F.*
Ryan, Charles E.*
Ryan, Kenneth J., NY
Ryan, Maureen C., NY
Sacks, Bruce E., NY
Sakelhide, Keith A., NY
Salumn, Joseph C., NY
Salvo, Vlasta K., NY
Sampson, Darryl C., NY
Sanchez, John, NY
Sanford, Miriam*
Sang, John L., NY
Santiago, Edwin, NY
Sarnataro, Geoffrey L., NY
Saulnier, Ana*
Schaefer, Lawrence, NY
Schroepfer, Bruce C.*
Schwartz, Edward H., CT
Schwarz, Eric E., NY
Sciandra, Joseph R., NJ
Screen Aguilar, Cynthia A., NY
Scurti, Stephen G.*
Secreto, James A., NY
Seelig, George W., NY
Segree, Wilbur R., NY
Sergi, Frank, PA
Serrant, Joseph H.*
Sexton, William A., FL
Shanley, Kevin O.*
Shapiro, L. P., NV
Sheehan, Francis X., NY

Sheehan, Raymond A., NY
Shey, Jeff, NY
Shields, James S., NY
Sicilia, Frank G., NY
Sierra, Peter*
Signorile, Michael V., NY
Silverman, Barry P., NY
Simone, Allen, NY
Simpson, Annette*
Simpson, John*
Sinnott, George P., NY
Sita, Joseph M., TX
Skeete, Samuel, NY
Skelly, Patrick J., NY
Slack, Beverly D., NY
Slagg, John J., NY
Smith, Allen J., NY
Smith, Glenn A., NY
Smith, Henry G., NY
Smith, Joan B.*
Smith, Mary L.*
Smith, Robert C., NY
Smith, William G., GA
Sokol, Louise J., AZ
Soto, Barbara M., NY
Soto, Ernie*
Soto, Richard*
Spaulding, James P., NY
Spinrad, William*
Springett, Linda, CT
Stathopoulos, E., NY
Steinberg, Fred E.*
Steinberg, Martin S., NY
Stern, Lee R., NY
Stewart, Ann M., NY
Stewart, John E., Esq., NJ
Stigliano, Gerard*
Stith, Theodore, NY
Stout, Donald R., VA
Stuhler, Joanne, NY
Stuis, Charles F., NJ
Sullivan, James F., NJ
Sullivan, Judith A.*
Tabor, Rowena G.*
Taylor, Arthur, NY
Taylor, Jeanette R., NY
Taylor, Reginald*
Terry, William L., NY
Thomas, Umberto P., NY
Thornton, Patricia**
Thorpe, Leslie P., NJ
Tirado, Harry**
Tischler, Jeffrey I., NY
Tobin, Patricia E., NY
Tohidi, Mohamad E.*
Torretta, Michael V., NY
Triarsi, Emmanuel, NY
Tuck, Stephen J., NY
Turbee, Patricia A., NY
Tyber, Edward F.*
Udell, Debra J.*
Underwood, James S., FL
Urbino, Jacinto*
Varga, Stephen J., NY
Vassilalcos, Elliot J.*
Vega, Ronald, MD
Velez, Harry*
Veneziano, Salvatore, NY
Viccica, Charles J., FL
Vidal, Edwin C., NY
Villano, Elizabeth, NY
Villareal, Carlos L.*
Vincent, Nadienne K., NY
Viner, Linda B.*
Viskup, Milly A., NY
Vitolo, Marco A., NY
Volpe-Wasserman, Catherine
  M., NY
Walicki, John R.*
Wallace, Lloyd O.*
Walsh, Dennis J., NY
Walsh, Mary A.*
Walsh, Patricia M., NY
Ward, Esther L., NY
Ward, Rodney C., NJ
Watterson, William E.**

Wegman, James L., CPP, AZ
Weiss, Kenneth D., NY
Welsh, Katherine W., CT
Werter, James S.*
Wheeler, James J., NY
Wheeler, Thomas J., NY
Whelan, Edmund P.*
White, Aleda J., NY
White, Collis*
White, Geneva A., NY
White, Robert, NY
White, Shirley F.*
Williams, Calvin C., NY
Williams, Donna A., NY
Williams, Floyd A.*
Williams, Gail E.*
Williams, Gregory G., NY
Williams, L., NY
Williams, Lucille, NY
Williams, Marva L., NY
Wilson, Cynthia D.*
Wilson, John*
Winter, Janet F.*
Wolstencroft, John M., NY
Woodley, Janeth F., VA
Yeboah, George K.*
Yuhasz, Paula J., NY
Zagami, Bartholomew N.*
Zamerinsky-lussier, Randy, MN
Zayas, Japhet J., NY
Zayerz, Helen M.*
Zoecklein, Carl G.*
Zuk, Olga M.*
Zundel, Joseph F.*
Zwaryczuk, William, NY

1981

Abruzzi, Raymond J., NY
Acevedo, Louis, NJ
Acosta, Elvis*
Acosta, Elvy*
Adams, C. J., NY
Adams, Vernice E.*
Adorno, Carmen I.*
Aitken, John J., FL
Alamo, Ildefonso L., CA
Alexander, Angela F.*
Alexandre, Carl, NY
Allen, Brenda R., NY
Allen, Cynthia Y.*
Alverio, Daisy M., NY
Amador, Doris, NY
Amato, Ronald J., NY
Armorer, Ayshia Y.*
Aronoff, Mark D.*
Arroyo, Miriam E., NY
Arthur, Mario, VA
Astor, Kevin R., NC
Ayala, Carmelo, NY
Badaracco, Charles R.*
Bailey, Patricia A., DE
Banks, Celia B., NY
Banks, Cynthia, NY
Barajas, Robert J., NJ
Barracato, Joseph L.*
Barrett, Daniel J., NY
Barrett, Junior A.*
Barry, Karl S., NJ
Bastian, Gladys M.*
Battaglia, Donna, NY
Bauer, Richard B., PA
Bauso, Louis J., NY
Behrmann, Rachelle M.*
Bellomo, Richard C.*
Belviso, Lawrence M., VA
Benitez, Emilio*
Berry, BG Robert W.,
    USA(Ret.), CO
Bertolini, Vinicio, NY
Bibiloni, Angela I.*
Bilous, Stephen R., NJ
Birdling, Pur W.*
Bishun, Peter R., NY
Blanks, Juanita D., NY
Blaszcyk, Theodore W., NY
Blount, Danny H., PA

Bogdanowicz, Kathleen, NY
Bolger, John P., NY
Bonita, Thomas J., NY
Bosio, Franklin J., NY
Bosko, George M., FL
Boutsikakis, Margrte, NY
Brady, Alicia D.*
Brender, Ronald J.**
Brindisi, Frank A., NY
Brody, Stephen D., NY
Brogan, Edward J.*
Brooks, Lorraine K., NY
Brousseau, Joseph O., NY
Brown, Annette M., NY
Brown, Debra E., NY
Brown, Melvin R., NY
Browne, Vivian C., NY
Burge, John S., NY
Burgois, John M., NY
Burke, Redmond P., NY
Burns, Junious L., NY
Burruano, Vivian S., NJ
Caines, Bruce*
Calamia, Thomas A.*
Calvosa, Ronald P., NY
Campbell, Rosalie G.*
Cantone, Anne M.*
Cappelia, Albert M., NY
Carias, Marco T.**
Carlson, Karen F., NY
Carmona, Jaime*
Carter, Mary A., SC
Carter, Wylene Y., PA
Casadevall, Alberto*
Castricone, John A., TX
Catalano, Domenick, NY
Catanzaro, Joseph, CA
Centamore, Ronald J., FL
Chahalis, Constance, NY
Chamberlain, Cathleen*
Chambers, Hewitt L., Jr., NJ
Chason, Neil S., NY
Cheesman, Marguerite, NY
Chicolo, Mary E., NY
Chicolo, Michael, NY
Chow, Julianne T., NY
Christensen, James, CA
Cilla, Veronica M., NY
Cimorelli, Gary H., NJ
Clancy, Edward C.*
Clarke, Michelle Y., NY
Clarke, Sheena D., NJ
Claytor, Kenneth*
Clements, Shirley, NY
Codispoti, Michael, NY
Cole, Leslie, CPP, NJ
Colon, Walter, NY
Confino, Sherry L., NY
Conway, Gerard F.*
Conway, Michael A., NJ
Cook, Steven W., NY
Cookingham, Vincent P., NY
Coor, Floyd*
Corey, James A., NY
Coribello, Linda, NY
Cortes, Nelson, NY
Cotto, Wilfredo, NY
Cox, Thomas P., NY
Crawley, William J., NY
Crichlow, Tracy, NY
Crinnion, George E.*
Cristiani, Christine, NY
Crosby, Karen P., AZ
Crudup, Eartha L., NY
Cruz, Roberto D., NY
Cuciti, Nicholas S., NY
Cuddeback, Douglas*
Culver, Arden*
Curry, Anthony, NY
Cusmano, Maureen A.*
Cuyler, Julius T., NJ
Dalton, Christopher, NY
Dalton, Robert B., FL
Daniels, Eugene R.*
David, Edwin A.*
Davies, Charmaine A., NY

Davis, James M.*
Davis, Jeannette M., MA
Davis, Veronica*
De Jesus, Nestor R., NY
Del, Vecchio F., NY
Delaney, Ann, NY
De La Pena, Mario, NY
Delio, Jaime V.*
De Maio, Anthony V., NY
De Naro, Robert J., NY
De Serio, Joseph M., NY
Dettmann, Edmund P., NY
Devine, Leo T.*
Diaz, Miguel A., NY
Di Blasi, Philip A., NY
Di Donato, Steven, NY
Dietz, Andrew C.*
Dillinger, Kathryn*
Diotallevi, Madelyn, IL
Di Paolo, Alfred J., NY
Di Stefano, Bill P.*
Doering, Christine E.*
Donato, Donna A., NY
Dorell, Eugene N.*
Dorritie, Raymond J., NY
Doyle, James J.*
Drewal, Roger F., NY
Duffy, Bernard J.*
D'ulisse, Carl, NY
Dure, Archeline*
Durkin, Jane*
Dybdal, George M.*
Earle, Thomas, NY
Edward, Selvin F., NY
Edwards, Joyce A., NY
Effrece, Frank P., NY
Egger, Stephen L., NY
Eghaghe, James O., NY
Egner, Elizabeth, NY
Elliott, Sandra E., GA
Evans, Vernon J.*
Fabrizio, Ralph A., NY
Fanelli, Ronald J., NY
Fatone, Anthony P., NY
Ferreyra, Orlando F., Jr., NY
Fidanque, Claudia S., NY
Fields, Joyce P.*
Figueroa, Ivan F., NY
Fisk, Karen B., NY
Flanagan, Leon E., NY
Fleisher, David S., NY
Fleming, Maureen, NY
Floyd, Ruth*
Fontana, John P., NJ
Ford, Melvin, NY
Fragapane, V., NY
Franko, Philip*
Franz, Robert J.*
Fraza, Louise J., NY
Frazier, Linda J.*
Freeman-Robinson, C.*
Freundlich, Jeffrey, NY
Friedlander, William*
Fuchs, Deborah, NY
Gaffney, Kevin J., CT
Gagliardi, Michael J., NY
Gale, John D., NY
Garcia, Christopher*
Garcia, Esteban*
Gardner, Virginia C., NY
Gaynor, Michael*
George, Steven N., NY
Gerchak, Ralph E., NY
Giambrone, John J., NY
Gibbs, Phyllis A.*
Gill, LeRoi L., NY
Gillen, Michael J., NY
Gillis, James R., NY
Gilmartin, Kerri A., NY
Girardi, James J., NY
Girimonte, Albert (Al) W., NY
Glenn, Christine*
Glover, Elliott P., VA
Glupposo, Anne M.*
Goldhaber, Martin H.*
Goldstein, Richard A.*

Gollob, Steven J.*
Gomez, Marina A., NY
Goodloe, Alice T.*
Gordon, Gail M., NY
Gordon, Wayne, NY
Gracia, Jorge J., NY
Grant, Calvin, NY
Grant, John C., NY
Grasty, Hope L.*
Graves, Gerald T.*
Greenidge, Reginald F., NY
Gregorovic, Peter S.*
Griffith, Liddon, NY
Griles, Victor A., NY
Guarino, Kevin S.*
Guy, Yvette D., NY
Haimes, Raymond C.*
Hall, Cheryl A., NY
Halliday, William R.*
Hampton, Barbara H.*
Hanson, Diane R., NY
Harmon, Michael P., NY
Harper, Bennie, NY
Harper, James*
Harris, Belinda L.*
Hart, Angelette*
Hazel, Amelia E., NY
Hecker, Peggyanne M., NY
Hecker, William A., NY
Hector, David A., NY
Hendrick, John S., TX
Henry, Andre B., NY
Hernandez, Michael A., NY
Herskovitz, Marian, NY
Hill, Madlyn S., NY
Hill, Susan*
Hines, Vera D., NY
Hobbs, Elray T.*
Holder, Wayne A., NY
Holmes, Anthony, NJ
Holmes, Sabrina, NY
Housel, Barry E.*
Howell, Elestine S.*
Hoyt, Robert M., NY
Hunce, Joseph D., NY
Iacopelli, Lisa, NY
Iacopelli, Thomas A., NY
Intervallo, Francis*
Irizarry, Joseph*
Izevbizua, Godwin O.*
Jackson, Archie V., NY
Jackson, Derek A., NY
Jackson, James H.*
Jackson, Stephen C., NY
Jacob, Thomas P., NY
Jacobs, Cynthia D., NY
Jacobs, Sarah*
Jaeger, Judith*
Jakubowski, Steven, NJ
James, Peter G., NY
James, Spencer L., NY
Jensen, Cheryl M.*
Jessie, Mary L.*
Jewell, Robert G.*
Johnson, Anthony L., NY
Johnson, Geronia G., NY
Johnson, Keith M., NY
Johnson, Pamela A., NY
Johnston, David C., NY
Johnston, Gordom M., NY
Jolly, Terry E., NY
Jones, Donnie*
Jones, Gregory, CA
Jones, Lois M., NY
Joyner, Harry, NJ
Jurain, Ronald S., NY
Kadluboski, Linda*
Kaplan, Mercedes M., NY
Kashimer, Irene, NY
Kaufman, Bessie*
Kellebrew, Ida L., NY
Keller, Thomas*
Kelly, Karen M., FL
Kelly-mixon, Brenda A.*
Kende, Miriam M.*
Kennedy, Stephen R., NY

Kim, Hak K.*
King, Emma C., NM
Kleiner, Richard L., CO
Kolarik, Sean, NY
Konesky, Karilyn, NY
Koppelmann, Barbara*
Kornbluh, Beatrice C.*
Kotterheidt, Walter C., NY
Kramer, David A., NJ
Kramer, Kathleen M., NY
Krus, Carol A., NY
Kurtz, Gary S., NY
La Bozzetta, Victor, NY
Lacondre, Earl, NY
Lai, Laura, NY
Lampert, Donna L., NY
Landsberg, Barry, NY
Latora, Vincent, NY
Lattimore, James F.*
Learperl, Alnando H.*
Lemon, Lorna T.*
Lennon, Hugh P.*
Leonard, Michael M., NY
Leung, Rose, NY
Levinson, Sara-ann*
Lewis, Diane, TN
Lewis, Robert S.*
Lewis, Terry J.*
Libock, Lawrence J.*
Licitra, Joseph, NY
Lieberman, Ira*
Lieff, John C., NY
Lizzio, Peter J., NY
LoCascio, Salvatore, NJ
Logan, Mary A., NY
Lopez, Lorraine, NY
Lopez-Sirvent, Fernando, NY
Loschen, Wayne D.*
Lotierzo, James D., NY
Low, Timothy J., NJ
Lynch, John S., NY
Machin, Annette M., NY
Mahone, Ernest, NY
Maieli, Mark S., NY
Manigaulte, Steven C.*
Marchesano, Neil, NJ
Marooney, Margaret A., NY
Martinez, Carlos E., NY
Mascia, Joseph, NY
Mastorides, George F., NY
Mateo, Josue, NY
Mathews, Achoy O., NY
Mc Carthy, Kevin M., NY
Mc Coy, Carl L., NY
Mc Coy, Richard E., NY
Mc Donald, Elizabeth, NY
Mc Donnell, Kathleen, NY
Mc Elligott, Peter, NY
Mc Elroy, Patrick J., NJ
Mc Geady, Robert J., NY
Mc Ginn, Timothy M.*
Mc Gorry, Thomas A.*
Mc Kee, Barry*
Mc Kenize, Reginald, NY
Mc Kenzie, Andrew O., NY
Mckenzie, Reginald R., NY
Mc Leod, Jacqueline*
Mcmanamon, Michael, NY
Mc Manus, Deborah A., NY
Mc Nulty, Kathryn B., NY
Me, Delson-berko*
Mehlig, George G.*
Mendoza, Arcadio, NY
Merrifield, Lauri A., NY
Messina, Anthony L., NY
Mestey, Anita*
Metzler, Arthur J., FL
Meyers, William E.*
Milgram, Ruth S.*
Millard, Thomas G., NY
Miller, Raymond A.*
Miller, Robert E., NY
Miller, Steven G., PA
Millman, Howard L., PA
Mirabella, Michael*

Mitchell, Andrew R.*
Mitro, Edward J., PA
Monel, Barbara A., NJ
Montas, Roland, NY
Monticelli, Mary, VA
Moore, Herman A., NY
Moore, Patricia K., NY
Mormando, Joseph A., NY
Moronta, Ana D., NY
Morton, Gerald T., NY
Moses, Herbert J., NY
Mugno, Richard E., NY
Mulroy, John P.*
Mulvena, James F., NY
Muniz, Helen*
Murdaugh, Gale R., NY
Murphy, Stephen F., NY
Murphy, Thomas F., NY
Musmacher, Robert J., NY
Naigus, Dede N., NY
Nappi, Lori A., NJ
Neeson, Josephine A., NY
Negrycz, Raymond, NY
Neil, Larold C., MD
Nicholas, Joanne C., NY
Nolasco, Joseph, NY
Novogrod, R. J.*
O'connell, Terrance, NY
O'connor, Michael J., OH
O'Grady, Dermot, NJ
Oliver, Jennifer M., NY
Onufrak, Stephen P., NY
Oschmann, Edward J., NY
Osroff, Peter H., NY
Ostrow, Lynn C.*
Owens, Audrey L.*
Owens, Sharon, NY
Pabon, Maria S.*
Pacheco, Shirley A., NY
Pagliughi, Kathleen, NY
Palermo, Stephen J.*
Panzarino, Nicholas, NY
Pappas, Chris L., NY
Patao, Sonia, NY
Paulsen, Maria E., NY
Pawlikowski, Mary C.*
Pecorino, Charles R.*
Penn, Julian*
Pentangelo, Joseph M.*
Perez, Robinson*
Perry, Diane J., NY
Peterson, James J., NJ
Pfeiffer, Richard F.*
Phillip, Arthur K., NY
Phillips, Genevieve*
Phipps, Ms. April I., NY
Pinizzotto, Anthony J., VA
Pisani, Angelo L., NY
Porcaro, Mary J.*
Porter, Sandra, NY
Portnoy, Carol*
Powell, Alan C., NV
Prestia, Charles R., FL
Quinn, Dolores T., NY
Rahn, Robert H., NY
Ramirez, Elizabeth A.*
Ramirez, Nivia*
Rattigan, Wilfred S., NY
Reddin, James P., NY
Reed, Marylin, NY
Reid, Marilyn M.*
Reiman, Kenneth R., NY
Remice, Yvette T., NY
Rendos, Edward C.*
Ricardo, Pilar E., NY
Rice, Ronald G.*
Richardson, June L., NY
Rios, Ferdinand G., NY
Rivera, Elizabeth*
Rivera, George A., NY
Rivera, Hilda, NY
Rivera, Michael, NY
Robinson, Christopher, NY
Rodriguez, Abraham*
Rodriguez, Jose J., NY
Rodriguez, Ricardo, NY

Roldan, Alana J.*
Romero, Orestes R., NY
Romero, Palmira, NY
Rose, Ronald M., NY
Rosenberg, Michael L.*
Roslan, Gary J., NY
Rossi, Dennis J., NY
Rubenstein, Richard*
Rudder, Carol A., NY
Ruderman, Harriet, NY
Rumpf, William R., NY
Russo, John, NY
Rynne, John, NY
Sacaccio, Michael J., NY
Salumn, Deborah A.*
Santiago, Nellie Q., NY
Santos, Margaret A., FL
Satch, Steven, NJ
Sawruk, Gary R., NJ
Scala, Peter P.*
Schaeffer, Joseph J., NY
Schatzberg, Rufus, NY
Schillinger, Robert, NY
Schlosser, Kevin, NY
Schrettner, Joseph, NY
Schroeder, Lizette, NY
Schwartz, Louis, FL
Sealy, Curtis V., NY
Sealy, Grantley M., NY
Seltzberg, Mark S., NY
Senno, Henry J.*
Sepulveda, Roberto*
Serniak, Walter R., NY
Shack, Robert C., GA
Sheard, Sandra Y., NY
Shebo, David J., NY
Shields, Phillip A., AP
Shuler, Ann F.*
Sierp, Robert W., NJ
Simms, John, NY
Simpson, Nathaniel W.*
Slevin, Edward F., NY
Small, Stanley F.*
Smith, James A., NY
Smith, Karen V.*
Smith, Lynnette S.*
Smith, Timothy E.*
Soll, Cynthia*
Solomon, Claude J.*
Sovulj, Josip, NY
Spallin, John J., NY
Spann, Anita, NY
Spisto, Brian N., NY
Spooner, William M., NY
Srour, Louis M.*
Stahl, Lowell L., NY
St. Clair, Gerald J.*
Stefanidis, Chris N.*
Stephen, Joyce A., NY
Sterling, Donna, NY
Stevens, Gloria J., NY
Stirrup, Vani E.*
St. Leger, Lucie, NY
Stone, Edward*
Stone, Richard E., NY
Strack, Walter T., NY
Strickland, Jeane L., NY
Suarez, Valentin*
Sullivan, John M., NY
Sweeney, William E.*
Sylvester, Glen A., NY
Sympi, Bernard, NY
Talamo, John, NY
Taub, Evette S.*
Teachey, George A., NY
Thaete, Katherine G.*
Thomas, Robert J., NY
Thompson, Rhonda D., NY
Titterton, James, NY
Todd, Myra, NY
Todras, Jay P., NY
Torres, Anibal, NJ
Torres, Frank P., NY
Torres, Vilma T., NY
Toussaint, Sharon P.*
Tucker, Bobbie J.*

Twiname, John J., NY
Ubwa, Hilary A., NY
Urbina, Ruben V.*
Uwasomba, Dominic, NY
Vader, Michael*
Valdez, Esteban, NY
Vanager, Kenneth, NY
Varadarajan, K., NJ
Vargas, Susana, NY
Vazquez, Lloyd A.*
Vazquez, Priscilla*
Vega, Mario, NY
Velez, Luis W.*
Vento, Frank J., NJ
Verwoert, John S., NY
Viggiani, Anthony V.*
Vincenzi, Victor A., NY
Virgilio, Thomas M., NY
Vodde, Robert F., NJ
Wallace, Wayne E., NY
Ward, Clayton, NY
Washington, Jennifer*
Watson, Gerard, NY
Watt, Robert E., NY
Weber, William P., NY
Weisfuse, Irene W., NY
Wells, Angie Y., NY
Wempe, Raymond H., NY
Werdann, George J.**
Wessolock, Robert E., NY
West, Janice Y., NY
West, Katherine A.*
Whitaker, Thelma J., NY
White, Pamela S., NY
Wiacek, Josephine*
Wilkins, Clarinda, NY
Williams, Arthur R., NY
Williams, Birdena*
Williams, Deborah M., NY
Williams, Mary-lou*
Wilson, Mrs. Cynthia E., NY
Wilson, Desiree T., NY
Wilson, Larry E., NY
Wilson, Robert, NY
Windus, James E., NY
Winston, Oscar S., NY
Wittine, Dianne J.*
Wolmer, Steven M., NY
Wood, Janice*
Yagoda, Steven A.*
Yarde, Margarette R., NY
Young, Adrienne M., NY
Yurman, Robert J., NY
Zabielski, Henry S., NY
Zambrana, Jean*
Zelman, Julia A.*
Zimbardo, Barbara*

1982

Abramchik, Trudy, NY
Adams, Rafael D., NY
Adesky, Neil*
Aiken, Daniel, NY
Aikens, Denise G.*
Almenares, Maria T.*
Alston, Harry T., NY
Alston, Samuel, NY
Alvarado, Wilberto*
Anaipakos, George P., FL
Anderson, Margaret R., NY
Archibald, Emanuel, NY
Arneman, Barbara A., NY
Arocho, Belinda A., NY
Arrieta, Frank J., NY
Arrieta, Marcela R., NY
Astrinidis, Stavros*
Attmore, Alyce E.*
Aufiero, Gelasio*
Bailey, William S., NY
Baker, Henry R.*
Ball, Robert, NY
Ballantine, Jean M., NY
Bandik, Mark G., AA
Banks, Shaundra L., NY
Baran, James S.**
Barfield, Miriam, NY

Barmore, Ellen J., NY
Barrett, Katherine E., NY
Bartlett, Glen E., NY
Beadle, Errol*
Bello, Muhammad A., NY
Benzan, Lourdes M., NY
Berrios, Miguel*
Berzins, Loida*
Bianchino, Diane*
Biberaj, Mus*
Billy, Joseph, NJ
Bishop, John H., NY
Blackett-Gould, Gwendolyn*
Blamo, Cecilia M.*
Blank, Dorothea, NY
Bobb, Hamilton E., FL
Boggio, Linda M., NY
Bolds, Sharon E.*
Bolt, Ronald G., NY
Bonanno, Douglas A., NY
Bondor, Stephen A., NY
Bonello, Casper M.**
Borelli, Anthony M., NY
Bostick, Denise G., NC
Boyle, Charles F.*
Brady, John J., NY
Brady, Richard J., Esq., NJ
Bronfman, Eben M.*
Brown, Arline D., NY
Brown, Beverley M., NY
Brown, Francisco A., NY
Brown, Richard W., NY
Brown, Wilma, NY
Browne, Samuel A., NY
Bruno, Frank W., NY
Bucci, Joseph R., NY
Burke, Thomas, FL
Burns, John W., NY
Burns, Robert T., NY
Burton, Cynthia J.*
Bush, Carole*
Byrd, Vanessa A., NY
Caballero, Ricardo M., NY
Caban, Edwin*
Calderbank, Gina M.*
Calhoun, Roy L., NY
Callahan, Leon P.**
Calvo, Ramon, NY
Cameron, Bradner S.*
Cammallere, Catherine, NY
Campbell, Duncan, NY
Campbell, Isaac J., NJ
Campbell, Sandra L.*
Cantaves, Elaine, NY
Carillo, C., NY
Carlson, Stephanie R.*
Carr, Danielle M., NY
Castro, Gloria A.*
Cedeno, Jaime, NY
Cepeda, Ivan A., NY
Chan, Agnes, NY
Charan, Shamla M., NY
Chester, Rochelle, NY
Chiriani, Daniel T., NY
Chisholm, Delores, NY
Christofides, Angela*
Cicenia, Gail C.*
Clabby, William F., NY
Cody, Gayle L., NY
Coleman, Eunice, NY
Coleman, Philip W., NY
Collier, Dyral, NY
Colon, Evelyn*
Colon, Gary M.*
Connelie, William G., NY
Contino, Jeffrey J., NY
Cooper, Ava A., NY
Corbett, Glenn P., NJ
Corr, Dennis G.*
Corrigan, Michael J., NY
Cozzi, Henry J.**
Creque, Romelia Y., NY
Crociata, Thomas A., NY
Cross, Barnard J.*
Cuccia, Frances E., NY
Culkin, Margaret A., OK

Cunningham, Thomas P., NY
Cutler, Robin A., NJ
D'Amato, Jeannine*
Darconte, Bruce M.*
Daughtry, Veda D., NY
Davis, Richard A., NJ
Delgado, Benny, NY
Dennis, Thomas L.*
De Santo, Joseph A., PhD, NY
Diamint, Claudio J., NY
Diaz, Joanne M.*
Diaz, Lenny P.*
Dipaolo, Paul J., NY
Disken, Timothy J., NY
Docekal, Paul G., NY
Dolan, Brendan M., NY
Donahue, Steven J., NY
Donohue, Brian A., CT
Doolittle, Timothy, CT
Downs, Thomas J.*
Doyle, Thomas M., NY
Driscoll, Elizabeth K., NJ
Drucker, Alan N.*
Duarte, Anthony C., NY
Duesterdick, Kurt A., NJ
Dunbar, Kevin F.*
Dunn-Jones, Felicia G.*
Dure, Jacques P., FL
Eckhoff, Karen, NY
Eisner, Judy, NY
Elliott, Johnathan R., NY
Ellman, Louis M., NY
Enright, Mary E., NY
Erhunmwunsee, Isaac, NY
Esoff, Donald J., NY
Espinosa, Patricia, NY
Fagan, Rochelle G.*
Farkas, Ted C.*
Fazzari, Carmine F.*
Fenkel, Robert I., NJ
Ferguson, Craig D., CA
Figueroa, Luis A., PA
Foley, Maura, NY
Forte, Louis (Lou), NJ
Fraioli, Joyce A., NY
Francis, Lois E., NY
Frank, Alicia S.*
Frank, Rudolph A., NJ
Friaglia, Richard A., NY
Fried, Howard, NY
Frisik, David J., NY
Gander, Edward F., PA
Garcia, Alan F., NY
Gargano, Mark D., NY
Gedajlovic, Sara H.*
Gee, Leslie, NY
Ghedina, John R.*
Gibbs, Faye V., NY
Gniazdowski, William*
Godun, Barbara A.*
Goldman, Stanley, NY
Gormley, Ann V., NY
Grant, Virginia L., NY
Greeme, Harold S.*
Greenberg, Gwynneth, NY
Greenidge, Doreen T., NY
Gregorin, Dr. David, PA
Griffith, Dorothy R., NY
Grimes, William P., FL
Grygier, Amelia*
Guella-dury, Catherine*
Guerra, Denitor*
Gunning, Jeanne B., NY
Gustie, Michael A.*
Hamilton, Allan R.*
Hansen, Robert C., NY
Haran, Patricia, NY
Harper, Yvonne, NY
Harriatte, Cheadrick*
Harrigan, Thomas M., NY
Hart, Davis B., AP
Hartnett, Donald F.*
Hartnett, Sharon M., NY
Hawkins, Carol L., NY
Hay, Douglas J., NY
Hellthaler, F. W., NY

Helton, Juanita*
Hernandez, Hugo F., NY
Hernandez, Jose A., NY
Herzberg, Edward M., NY
Hicks, Theresa, NY
Hill, Prince W.*
Hoelldobler, Frank*
Hoffman, Robert J., NY
Holder, Laura M., NY
Holladay, Dorothy E., NY
Holmes, Clennan W.*
Hooper, Julian C., NY
Horansky, Joan R.*
Houston, Leonard W., PhD, NY
Huggins, Pamela L.*
Hughes, Joanne P., NY
Hunt, Edward J.*
Iadisernia, Philip*
Iannella, Nicholas J.**
Ibezim, David, NY
Infante, Almando*
Irizarry, Sylvia E., NY
Iwarimie-Jaja, D.*
Jackson, Ava B.*
Jackson, Gail A.*
Jackson, Renee M., NY
Jaffee, Sharon B.*
James, Edwina*
Jarvis, Venetta E., NY
Jenkins, Frederick V., NY
Joe, Chuck F.*
Johnson, Robert, NY
Johnson, William*
Jones, Cynthia E.*
Jones, Rodney S., Sr., NY
Jones, Stephanie*
Jordan, Lucille*
Jorge, Marcelo, NY
Joseph, Jennifer M., NY
Joseph, William, NY
Joyce, Kevin P., NY
Joyner, Wilmon E.*
Kalogeras, Eleni, NY
Kamienski, Kevin**
Kane, Keith*
Karayiannes, John G., CT
Kenny, Robert E., CCA, CA
Kicki, Michael E., NJ
Kid, John R.*
Kinard, Brussell*
Kirkpatrick, Michael, NY
Klimek, Katherine A., NY
Kmech, William G.*
Knight, Roger V., NY
Kolega, Lorraine, NY
Kopstein, Jay I., NY
Kortright, Jerry*
Koski, Richard A., NJ
Kroll, Irwin S., NY
Ku, Jara-na-ayut W., NY
Kuberski, Richard S., NY
Kupfer, James R., NJ
Lamb, Owen H., NY
LaMothe, Michael F., MD
Langelle, Eugene A.*
Larkin, Cheryl A., NY
Lauer, Deborah A., NY
Laurence, Oscar, NY
Laurendi, Domenick A., NY
Lavagna, Peter J., NJ
Lavin, Michael B., NY
Leadem, Susan A.*
Leavey, Marion A., NY
Lennon, Madeline D., NY
Le Page, Robert J., NY
Levine, David A., NY
Levine, Harriett J., NY
Levine, Susan, NY
Lewis, Dora M., NY
Liendo, Luis E., NY
Linn, Edith, NY
Lopez, Diana*
Lopez, Jose L., Sr., CT
Lucas, Carl, NJ
Ludvigsen-Jennings, M.*
Lynch, George T.*

Lynch-Ivins, Ellen P., NY
Lynn, Gary D.*
Mackey, Elayne S., NY
Maher, John W., NY
Mahoney, Robert E., NJ
Mahoney-Gardner, J.*
Majette, Minnie, VA
Malcolm, Sedrick, NY
Malpica, Betzaida, NY
Mangual, Perla E.*
Manich, Elisabeth A.*
Manning, Roger V.*
Mapp, Andrew W.*
Mapp, Hazel O.*
Marchello, Charles J., NY
Margulies, Randy B., NY
Marinoff, Gary A., NY
Mark, Irma L.*
Marrone, Gerald H., NJ
Marti, Lauren B., NJ
Martin, Kim D.*
Martin, Nina L.*
Martin, LCDR Vertel T., NY
Masella, Richard P., NJ
Masucci, James J., NY
Matesich, Susan M., NY
Mayer, Kathleen R.*
Mazur, Robert P.*
McAliney, Kevin P., NY
Mc Cabe, Edward G.*
Mc Cray, Tracey C., NY
Mc Dermott, Raymond T., NY
McGarrell, Bonnie, NY
Mc Geary, Joseph T., NY
Mc Govern, James J.*
Mc Grath, Coleen M.*
Mc Kinzie, Linda M., NY
Mc Loughlin, Kevin, NY
Mc Sharry, Talbot, KY
Medina, Hector A.*
Meggett, Cynthia Y., NY
Melendez, Luis E., NY
Miguel, Regina L., NY
Millan, Gregory, NY
Miller, Gary*
Miller, Lorraine E., NY
Miller, Thomas J., NY
Milligan, Kenneth A.*
Mimms, Pauline P., NY
Minnock, Kathrynn H.*
Modest, Virginia C.*
Monell, Julio*
Moore, Lloyd W.*
Moore, Margaret M., NY
Moore, Pamela A.*
Morales, Lucette, NY
Moreno, Alcides*
Moriarty, Paul J.*
Morogeorges, Tula, NJ
Morrison, Billy R.*
Moss, Marjorie N.*
Mumford, Ronald A., FL
Muniz, Eric R., NJ
Munjack, Joel A., NY
Munn, Kathleen*
Muranelli, Joel, NY
Murphy, John C.*
Nall, Marilyn A.*
Namdar, Gholam R., NY
Nanartowicz, Carol, NY
Nash, Lois A., NY
Neglia, Samuel R., NJ
Negron, Aracelis*
Nestoros, Costas*
Newson, Norman, NY
Nock-Dudley, Joyce A., NY
Nolan, John E., NJ
O'bryan, Rupert W., NY
Odita, Pauline U., NY
O'Donnell, Eugene, NY
O'Donnell, Neil*
Ogbara, Jane, NY
Oliphant-Cummings, H., NY
Olley, Donald E., NY
Olsson, Christopher, NY
Oquend, Madeline M., NY

Ortega, Hector M.*
Osansky, Arnold*
Osorio, Theodore P., NY
Ossa, Magda S., NY
Osso, Gary, NY
Outlar, Gerald*
Outsen, Gregory J., NY
Pacella, Thomas A., NY
Pagan, Orlando*
Palleja, Sandra L.*
Panza, Narcelle R.*
Paparozzi, Sandra M., NJ
Pardo, Carolyn*
Parker, Rodney K., NY
Payne, Robert E., NY
Peaks, Harold A., NY
Perez, Joe*
Perez, Lydia*
Perez, Samuel*
Perry, Michael A.*
Perry, Sandra, NY
Petrovits, John, NY
Pettignano, Charles, NY
Phinn, Pamela L.*
Pinkney, Eddie P., NY
Pitts, Arthur A., NY
Plunkett, Kenneth J.*
Poe, Connie J.*
Poka, John A., NY
Polak, Simone C., NY
Pon, Tommy*
Porter, Elnora, NY
Powlis, Terrance, NY
Proctor, Lillian N., NY
Rafferty, Thomas B., NY
Rakowsky, Andrew R., NY
Ramirez, Edwin*
Ramirez, Evelyn*
Ranger, Hazel G., NY
Rattray, Michele*
Reddington, Francis, NJ
Reed, Robert, NY
Reeves, Lee, NY
Regler, John W., NY
Reilly, Ann M.*
Reilly, Rupert A., NY
Reimer, Stanley A.*
Renzullo, Vittoria, NY
Reynolds, Gertrude, NY
Ribaudo, Mark A., NY
Richardson, Karon*
Rifkind, Leslie*
Rittenhouse, John P., NY
Ritter, John M.*
Rivera, Jorge L.*
Rivera, Mary M., NY
Rivera, Miguel*
Rivera, William P.*
Rivers, John J., NJ
Rizzo, Joseph T.*
Roberts, Alston L., NY
Robinson, Eugene*
Robles, Ruth D.*
Rodriguez, Dalila*
Rodriguez, Marilyn, NY
Roman, Aracelio, NY
Roman, Edfra C.*
Roman, Yvette, NY
Rosado, Alfredo, NY
Rosado, Carmen M.*
Rose, Dulcie D., NY
Rose, May A.*
Rosen, Marie, NY
Ross, Deborah A.*
Rotholc, Alec*
Rountree, Rodney M.*
Ryan, Sharon Y.*
Saccheri, Paula A., NY
Sackel, James H., NY
Sadowski, Cecilia A., TX
Safford, Carl E., NY
Saladino, Frank N., NY
Salyga, Joseph R.*
Samuels, Sheila A., NY
Sanabria, Abraham*
Sanabria, Steven P.*

Sanchez, Diana*
Sanchez, Jorge*
Sanchez, Mercedes*
Sandberg, Vilma B., NY
Santoni, Lewis A.*
Sarno, Henry C., NY
Saunders, Leroy N., NY
Saunders, Phillip M., NY
Savoia, Michael F., NJ
Savvas, Anthony P.*
Schaffer, Robin F., NY
Schiavone, Vincent, NY
Schissel, Alan R., NY
Schmidt, Steven M.*
Schnell, Nina A., NY
Schwartz, Kenneth M., NY
Sealy, John, NY
Semegran, Paul E.*
Shapiro, Rhonda E.*
Shaw, Cil M., NY
Shaw, Rudolph A., NY
Simmons, Denise L., NY
Sipp, Andrea P.*
Smith, Robert A., NY
Soler, Luis, NY
Solesky, Edward J., NJ
Sosa, Daisy I.*
Spencer, Anna-Maria, RI
Squires, Bobby E., NY
Stanley, Mary A.*
Stein, Sherry, NY
Stevens, Allen R.*
Stone, LTC Wayne A., USA, VA
Stracci, Joseph R., NY
Strange, John C.*
Straub, Jacqueline, NY
Streber, Kathleen I., NY
Stroman, Vivian N., NY
Studwood, Joyce E., NY
Sugrue, Timothy J.*
Tabone, John M.*
Talisse, Richard G., NY
Tam, Joemy C., NY
Tam, Pik Y.*
Tarquinio, Doris A.*
Tello, Bolivar*
Texidor, Jose L., NY
Theard, Jacques E., NY
Thompson, George C., NY
Thorpe, Geraldine G., NY
Tierney, Michael N., NY
Toohey, John J., NY
Torres, Charles*
Torres, Jeanette, NY
Torres, Linda S.*
Torres, Marilyn*
Torres, Marybell, NY
Torres, Peter C., NY
Townsend, Vera R.*
Tucker, John J.*
Tucker, Thomas A., NJ
Tullo, James T., NY
Tunnock, Terrence J.*
Turnbull, Berris A., FL
Tusa, Philip P., NY
Tyrrell, Edward, CT
Uberti, Arthur A., NY
Urso, Robert M., NY
Vahey, Josephine E., NY
Valentin, Ruben, NY
Vanrossem, Charles V., NY
Varanelli, Andrew, NY
Vargas, Rosanne M.*
Vasquez, George E.*
Vaughan, Terry, DE
Verna, Diana L.*
Verwoert, Brian G., NY
Vialva, Kelson B., NY
Viggiani, Catherine, NY
Vilches-marano, Vilma R.*
Vinces, Rev. Edgar J., NY
Volin, Howard J., NY
Vrana, Denise L., NY
Walker, Susan M., CA
Wallace, April L., NY

Wallace, Sandra E., NY
Washington, David L., NY
Wasserman, Mitchell, NY
Watenberg, Mark, NY
Wayser, Myra E.*
Webb, Elizabeth V., NY
Webster, Charles E.*
Webster, Patricia O.*
Weinstein, Rissa*
Welch, Sylvia P., VA
Wellenkamp, Susan A., NY
Weston, Richard J.*
Whelan, Michael W.*
Whitely, Donald H., NY
Wiedemann, Paul M., NY
Wilkins, Rodney S.*
Williams, Barbara E.*
Williams, Randy E., NY
Williams, Yvette C., MD
Willis, Wayne, NY
Wilson, Michael F.*
Wingate, Gregory, NY
Winslow, James P., NY
Wonnum-gaines, Lora, NJ
Wood, Raymond, NY
Wray, Raimundo A., NY
Wright, Theadore E.*
Wurzbach, Stephen J., NY
Xepolitos, Constance, NY
Yee, Gin T.*
Zagreda, Franco*
Zeoli, Jerry G.*
Zwillich, Ira**

1983

Abdul-Muntaqim, Sayeed, NY
Abney, Deborah C.*
Adamiak, Alan B., NJ
Adamo, Robert A.*
Adams, Farrell M., VA
Agrapides, Peter, NY
Aimone, Paul J., NJ
Akukwe, Bernard E.*
Alexander, Saundra, NY
Alford, Regine L.*
Algarin, Henry M.*
Amengual, Margie, NJ
Anderson, Greer M.*
Annis, Nancy L.*
Antwi-adjei, Frank A.*
Aramino, Sandra L., NJ
Araneo, Suzanne, NJ
Austin, James**
Ayrovainen, Thomas, NY
Babakitis, Paul G., NY
Babbini, Patricia A., NJ
Baptiste, Wilfred E., NY
Barfield, Patricia V.*
Barrett, Doreen A., NY
Bartolone, Maria, NY
Batnick, Christie J., NY
Belgrave, Carl C., NJ
Bentham, Colin H., NY
Benton, Stephanie G., NY
Berman, Florence R.*
Berman, Stacey, NY
Bernstein, Ms. Leslie, NY
Bernstein, Stuart L., NY
Berrios, Carmen M., CA
Berrios, Laura M., NY
Bethel, Cassandra V., NY
Bittles, Richard J., NY
Blake, David K.*
Blueford, Helen J., NY
Boatright, Gina E., NY
Bobo, Inez M.*
Bolling, Charise M., NY
Bona, Alan J., NY
Bonano, Gregory, NY
Borders, Delisa Y., NY
Bowman, Tanya G.*
Bowman, William D., NY
Boyle, Edward R., TX
Brady, Neil J.*
Brennan, Joseph R., NJ
Brinson, Allyson C., NY

Brook, Jonathan A., TX
Brown, Carol N., NY
Brown, James D., NY
Brown, Joanna U., NY
Brown, Julia C., NY
Brumer, Steven N., GA
Bryan, Anita, NY
Bryan, Annmarie L., NY
Bullock, Doris K., NY
Butcher, Margaret P., MD
Butler, Colleen A.*
Byrnes, John W.*
Caban, Juan A., NY
Cadet, Yves, NY
Cairl, Brian D., NY
Calathes, Dr. William, NY
Camacho, Sarita, NY
Cangro, Frank F., NY
Canzoneri, Leah A., NY
Carey, Vincent M., NY
Carle, William R., FL
Carollo, Anthony M., NY
Casatelli, Joseph A., NY
Cash, Charisse R., NY
Cassidy, Kevin A., NY
Castro, Cristine D., NY
Cecere, Michael A., NJ
Chamagua, Iris E., FL
Channell, Albert M., NJ
Chiesa, Nicholas P.*
Cho, Jody, NJ
Ciampo, Michael N., NY
Cini, Robert A., NY
Cinnamo, Vincent, NY
Civello, Joseph S., NY
Clayton, James O., NY
Cohen, Stefan T.*
Coiro, Robert M., NY
Cole, Opal M., NY
Colon, Mary, NY
Colon, Nancy, NY
Concha, Hugo J., FL
Cooper, Sylista M.*
Corrales, Nancy*
Correa, Maritza, FL
Corredine, Roger A.*
Cotton, Gloria B., NY
Crane, Ernest, NY
Crespi, Ralph M., NY
Crespo, Evelyn, NY
Cruz, Angel, NY
Culpepper, Karen*
Cunneen, Judith A., NY
Cunningham, Thomas F., NY
Cusack, Nancy M., NY
Dacken, Diane A., NY
D'alessandro, Paul V., NY
D'Ambrosio, Jaime, NY
D'Angclo, Edna K.*
Daniels, Renee L., NY
Darcy, Christopher F., NY
Dash, Anne M., NY
Davis, David, NY
Davis, Jerome, NY
Davis, Xiomara D., NY
DeGregorio, Deborah*
Dehlinger, Alfred, NJ
De Jesus, Fernando A.*
De Jesus, Jose R., NY
Denicolo, Anna*
Dennett, Phyllis D., NY
Deravin, MAJ Eric H., USAR(Ret.), NY
Devia, Lydia M., NY
Digiacomo, Nancy F., FL
Diprenda, Daniel, NY
Dirocco, Dana L., NY
Divino, Marie R.*
Dobbins, William J., NY
Dolan, Steven*
Dolcimascolo, Jeffrey A., NY
Dombrowski, Michael, NY
Dotterell, Monica H., NY
Drzewiecki, Helena D., NY
Duncan, Jennifer J.*
Durham, John P.*

Durney, William C., NY
Dussek, Philippe R., NY
Earle, Winston S., NY
Eason, Rufus J., GA
Echols, Phyllis A., NY
Eddington, Mark, NY
Edelman, Bernard L.*
Edwards, Gail L.*
Edwards, Martin W., NY
Ellington, Shelia*
Elliott, Stacie M.*
Ellison, Larry*
Erb, Kenneth G., NY
Ertischek, Tamie*
Esposito, Gerald A., NY
Estrada, Jose, NY
Ettinger, Dorit*
Farmer, Clezel D., NY
Faucher, Jean F.*
Faustin, Brigette, NY
Feldstein, Robert A., NY
Felix, Allyson*
Figueroa, Annette M., NY
Figueroa, Saul, NY
Filipiak, Paul J., NY
Fisher, Todd A.*
Fitzpatrick, Brian R., NY
Foley, Stephen P., NJ
Fox, Daniel J., Esq., NJ
Francis, Robert H., NY
Fullerton, Khalfani O., TX
Furman, Stephen*
Gaillard, Leroy, NY
Galdi, Joseph M., NY
Gamble, Gloria*
Garvin, Deborah A., NY
George, Deborah, NY
George, Sandy D.*
Geraghty, Christopher, NY
Giammarinaro, Andrea, NY
Gladston, Lewis F., NY
Gleason, Joseph P.*
Golfinopoulos, Kostas, NY
Gomez, Angelita, NY
Gomez, Cecilio, NY
Gomez, Elizabeth, NY
Gonzalez, Nancy, NY
Goodin, Carolyn P.*
Gordon, Edward J.**
Gordon, Winston A., NY
Green, Edith A.*
Greene, Bobby**
Gudat, John F., NY
Guerrero, June A., NY
Hailey, Cathy L., NY
Hajisava, John, NY
Hammer, David S., NY
Hammer, Frank K.*
Hanley, Gary T., NY
Hardy-major, Gloria, NY
Hare, Ruby E., NY
Harper, Lisa S., NY
Harris, Adrienne R., NY
Harris, Cynthia R., NY
Harrison, Pamela P.*
Harvin, David B.*
Hastings, Kevin M., NJ
Haynes, Kenneth, NJ
Hazzard, Rev. Carrie L., FL
Hemphill, Stephanie, NY
Henderson, Audrey, NJ
Henshaw, George V., NJ
Herbert, John D., NY
Hernandez, Ana E., NY
Herrera, Edwin, NY
Hickey, L. F., CA
Highsmith, Susan*
Hill, Barbara G., NY
Hill, Shirley R., NY
Hodgins, Joseph A., NY
Holland, Lawrence D.*
Holly, Jacqueline R., NY
Hom, Tak J., NY
Horne, Marion R., NY
Houlihan, Maureen A., NY
Howard, Linder A., NY

Hynes, Walter G., NY
Ierardi, Andrew J., NY
Iglesias, Rosa E., FL
Jackman Brown, Pam B.*
Jackson, Cecile, NY
Jackson, Mertol, NY
Jackson, Robert A., VA
Jallow, Ahmat A.*
Jay, Catherine, NY
Jefferson, Stephen M., FL
Jenkins, Michael A., NY
Joel, Kenneth W., CO
Johnson, Marion, NY
Johnson, Sandra*
Jones, Lamont J., NY
Jones, Leona*
Jordan, Sherryl D., NY
Joyner, Joann, NY
Juzefyk, Susan M., NJ
Karl, Peter M.*
Kelly, Diane Y.*
Kelly, Timothy P., NY
Kelson, Cuthbert*
Kerik, Reuven*
Kian, Tammy E.*
Kiely, Mary A., NY
King, Dorothy J., NY
King, Edith I., NY
Kippins, Susan A., NY
Kishlicky, Eric K., NY
Klapakis, Diana M., NY
Koshak, William, NY
Krajci, Stephen C., NY
Krakue, Lawrence A.*
Kramer, Arthur*
Kruger, Henry J., NY
Kukaj, Mustafa M., NY
Labrenz, Bettyann M., NY
Laffey, John J., NY
Lance, Deborha A., NY
Lange, Douglas M.*
Lanza, James J., NY
Larson, Allan G., NY
Lascano, Mercy, NY
Laskin, Edward S., NY
Latorre, Thomas*
Lauther, Beverly, NY
Lawrence, Denise A., NY
Lawrence, Gustave J., NY
Lawrence, Janet M., NY
Lee, David, NJ
Lee, Pamela, NY
Lettis, Paul M., NY
Lewis, April A., FL
Lewis, Arnold C., NY
Lewis, Marian R., NY
Limaco, Grace*
Linton, Bobby K.*
Lipuma, John P., NJ
Little, Lynn M.*
Lombardy, Michael J.*
London, George B.*
Long, Demosthenes, NY
Lopez, David R., NY
Lopez, Eugenia, NY
Loriston, Verlena D.*
Lowenstein, Bruce H., NY
Lucas, Robert J.*
Lynch, Rodolfo R., NY
Mackie, Dawn R., NY
Magadia, Paul, NY
Mahfood, Jad P., NY
Mallory, Debra A., NY
Mancuso, Jo-Anne, NY
Mandel, Philip, NY
Marengo, Christopher, NY
Mariette, Yvonne M., NY
Marrero, Jose N., NY
Marrero, Leticia L., NY
Martinez, Alma E., NY
Maselli, John M., CA
Mathis, Harvey L.*
Matos, Angel, NY
Matthews, Cecil A.*
McAndrew, Joseph*
Mcbarnette, Wilfred, NY

Mccarthy, Richard A.*
McDougal, Shirleen A.*
McDougal, Sonya B., NY
McEwan, Valdene S.*
Mcgill, Richard K., NY
Mcgrath, Michael P., NY
McGreevey, Joan A.*
McInerney, Joseph, NY
McKenna, Hugh*
McKenna, Stephen P.*
Mcketney, Edwin C.*
McKetney, L., NY
McKoy, Barbara S., NY
McLaughlin, Debra F.*
Mclees, Mark J., NY
Mcmahon, Michael, NY
Mc Nair, Robert L.*
McPhaul, Sharon*
Meadowcroft, James J., NY
Medina, Jose L.*
Mendez, Lourdes A., NY
Mendola, Philip L., NY
Mesibov, David E., NY
Messios, Soteris*
Miceli, Frank J.*
Mickey, Gregory, NY
Miller, Dorothy J., NY
Miller, Judith A., NY
Miller-Diaz, Harriett, NY
Mingione, Ernest R., NY
Mitchell, Douglas J., NY
Mohan, Edward C.*
Moher, Jacqueline M., NY
Molinaro, Mario A., NY
Monahan, Jayne F.*
Monokrousos, Dennis, NY
Monsegue, Gail A., NY
Moodie, Genevieve E., NY
Moore, Janet M., NY
Moore, Lisa*
Morales, Rose, NY
Moran, Julia A., NY
Mosaphir, Nalini T.*
Mulligan, Eleanor, NY
Muniz, Inez, NY
Murphy, Michael B.*
Murphy, Patrick J., NY
Murray, Thomas K., NY
Narvaez, Diana*
Natale, Ralph A., NY
Natoli, Marianne*
Nedd, Cicely B.*
Nelson, Reginald*
Neznanyj, Taras P., NY
Nictas, George J., NY
Niemiec, Theodore, NY
Notte, Daniel A., NJ
Nowak, Izabel A.*
Ocasio, Yolanda M., NY
Ochs, Scott A., NY
Odom, Oscar, III, NY
Oettinger, Elizabeth, NY
O'Keefe, Mary A., NY
Olds, Kevin D., NY
Olender, Dennis J., NY
Oleskowicz, John F., IL
Olivier, Jose A.*
Oreskovich, Robert B.*
Ortiz, Shari K.*
Orzo, Thomas M.*
Ossen, Helen S., NY
O'Toole, Deborah F.*
Padilla, Felix A.*
Pagan, Eledier, NY
Pagan, Neal, NY
Papagni, Mary A., NY
Parsons, Adrienne D., NY
Paulin, Gregory M.*
Pecoraro, Robert H., NY
Pecou, Enrique A., NY
Pellicani, Stephen P., NY
Pena, Lucas, NY
Penigian, Richard*
Penn, Marlon G., NY
Peralta, Angelina R., NY
Perez, Gregory R., NY

Perkins, Charles T., NY
Petrella, Maria*
Petrone, Elizabeth, NY
Phillips, John E.*
Picarillo, Anthony P., NY
Pifling, Arlene J.*
Pike, Linda A., NJ
Planter, Clarice J.*
Plasencia, Anthony*
Pokoluk-Brady, Lisa*
Policare, Ronald T.*
Polye, Arlene M., NY
Pontecorvo, Daniel M., NY
Ponzo, Robert E., VA
Portillo, Miriam L.*
Powell, Clinton R., NY
Powlis, Alvin*
Pressley, Sharon, NY
Preston, Alvin E., NY
Price, Warren J., NY
Purcell, Ralph J., NY
Purdue, Philip J.*
Quick, Denise Y.*
Ramsay, Cherylann G., NY
Remsen, William P.*
Renneman, Matthew S.*
Reyes, Josephine, NY
Rhem, Karen B., NY
Rhett, Sheila A., PA
Rich, Jennifer S.*
Riddick, Ruth*
Riedel, Dale B., NY
Rinaldi, Richard A.*
Rivera, Angel M., NY
Rivera, Maria P., NY
Rivera, Raymond L.*
Rivera, Rosa E., NY
Rivera, Sergio T., NY
Roberson, Toni V., NY
Robinson, Delano M.*
Robinson, Frankie*
Robinson, Walter A., NJ
Robinson, Yvonne W.*
Rodgers, Tearence L.*
Rodriguez, Edward N., NY
Rodriguez, Franklin Delano, NY
Rodriguez, Jose M., NY
Rodriguez, Victor M., NY
Rogers-Grinage, Debra, NY
Rolon, Melinda*
Roman, Carmen, NY
Roman, Rosemary*
Romano, Raymond, NY
Rosa, Migdalia, NY
Rosario, Maria D., KY
Rose, Kim D., NY
Rosen, David B., NY
Rothenberg, Bruce A., FL
Rubel, Jorge A.*
Rubino, Charles J., NY
Ruiz, Peggy C., NY
Russo, Franco, NY
Sago, Angela R.*
Sanderfer, Gale R., TN
Santa, James M., NY
Santana-Gerrish, P.*
Santiago, Ivan*
Santiago, Maribel*
Sargent, Douglas L., NY
Saunders, Xavier A., NY
Sawangnetr, Somchart, DC
Schaefer, Richard W., NY
Schellhass, Kenneth J., NY
Schlitt, Robert W., NY
Schwindel, Kirk J.*
Segal, Susanne, NJ
Sekulla, Natasha*
Senior, Veda*
Setoute, Sonel, NY
Shaw, Jacqueline, NY
Shoot, Laura L.*
Sierra, Lesly, NY
Simon, Gregory D., CA
Simons, Basilio A., NY
Sindab, Rosalind A., NY

Singh, Ramkumar, TX
Slaughter, Kathy L., NY
Smallwood, William K., NY
Smorto, Ivette, NY
Solivan-haspil, Udith*
Sorrentino, Frank, NY
Spalding, Bruce W.*
Speese, Ebonii J.*
Spence, Dawn M., NY
Spern, Robin*
Spinoso, Thomas D., NY
St, Jules G., NY
Stack, John J., NY
Stasio, Marie R., NY
St. John, Daniel, NY
Strong-banks, Yvette, NY
Sullivan, John P.*
Summers, Keith*
Swaby, Harris D., FL
Swarm, Edward, NY
Sykes, Steve M.*
Tatar, Paul A., NY
Tauckus, Peter J., NY
Taylor, Robert F., TX
Taylor, Steven M., NY
Tennent, Wayne A., NY
Terranova, Susan, NJ
Terribile, Joseph S., NJ
Thomas, Laverne E.**
Thomas, Linda P., NJ
Thomas, Towana*
Thompson, Andrea*
Thompson, Julia E., AZ
Thompson, Robert A., NY
Thompson, Suzanne Y.*
Tiedemann, LT James R., NY
Tiefenwerth, Thomas J., TX
Tillman, Robin, NJ
Tirado, Carol L., NY
Tocker, Leonard H., NY
Torrellas, Barbara L.*
Trotter, Lee E., NY
Tsuji, Marian E., HI
Tucker, Shirley L.*
Uhlmann, Dennis P., NY
Valdes, Elena M., NY
Valentin, Dalma*
Van Loon, Gary, NJ
Varrone, John*
Vasquez, Helen*
Vecchiarelli, Dennis, NY
Vega, Waleska*
Velez-cruz, Margaret R., CA
Vicens, Carol, GA
Vigiano, John T., NY
Viollis, Paul M., Sr., FL
Viskoc, Thomas E.*
Walker, Ms. Hillery G., FL
Walker, Leslie R.*
Walker, Minyoun C.*
Walls, Bradley J., NY
Walls, Jeanne M., NY
Walters, Paul A., NY
Washington, Oliver J., NY
Watson, Anne*
Watson, Roosevelt A., NY
Wayne, Reva R., NY
Webb, Toussaint S.*
Wenz, Maura, NY
Werner, Edward C., NY
West, Helene M.*
White, Debra G., NY
White, Gregory A., NY
White, James, NY
White, Reginald H., NY
Whitlock, Michael J., MA
Williams, Fay D., NY
Williams, John E.*
Williams, Kenneth M.*
Williams, Ravannah, NY
Willson, Robert H., GA
Wilson, Patricia B., NY
Wong, Kenneth, NY
Woodley, Charles T., NY
Wright, Floyd A., NY
Wright, Rose M.*

Yablokoff, Robin J., NY
Young, Beverly A.*
Young, Don, CA
Zapata, Kimberly L.*
Zavala, Bertha*
Zerbarini, John P., NY
Ziccardi, Maxine B.*

1984
Abreu-lotz, Yosmari M., NY
Aiello, Raymond A.*
Allen, Katherine B.*
Almodovar, Steven A., FL
Almonor, Max N.*
Almonte, Nidia*
Alonzo, Barber, NY
Alvarez, Elvin, NY
Alvarez-Black, Sharon*
Anderson, Henry, NY
Anderson, Monroe R.*
Anderson, Robert J., NJ
Anderson, Sandra M.*
Appel, Kenneth P., NY
Applewhite, Elsie, NY
Arthur, Terri E., VA
Ashley, Jo-an G., NY
Attanasio, Linda*
Aviles, Victor, NY
Avramidis, Georgios, NY
Aweeky, Peter A., NY
Baez, Benjamin, NY
Banko, Ellen, NY
Banner, Sonia*
Barbato, Ralph A., NY
Barrett, James*
Barry, Gail L., NY
Barton, Kenneth L., NY
Bassett, Patricia A., NY
Bassinger, Deborah N., OH
Battiste, Denise, NY
Baumann, Ms. Deborah C., NY
Baxter, Deborah M.*
Bell-morris, Bonita*
Beneby-plaza, Cathy, NY
Berisha, Xhavid, NY
Berry, Joseph S., NY
Bifulco, Frank J., NY
Billups, Leeanna, NY
Blatt, Barry A., NY
Bokser, Deborah L.*
Booker, Eric G., NJ
Boosquet, Juliette*
Bornmann, Ines C., NY
Bottiglieri, Mona L.*
Bowman, Debra, NY
Bowman, Jeffrey H., NY
Bowry, Letitia R., NY
Boyce-el, Emanuel J.*
Boyle, William M., MA
Braithwaite, Elise D.*
Brasero, Rever, NY
Brett, Veronica E., NJ
Brockway, Mary Z., NY
Brooks, Conchita*
Brown*
Brown, Carla S., NY
Brown, Victoria L.*
Brown-Cathey, Ms. Gertrude, NJ
Bullock, Stephen R.*
Bunis, Joy, NY
Burdi, Michael J., NY
Butler, Joanne L., NJ
Byrne, Therese M., PA
Cali, Jack, NY
Camacho, Edgar M., NY
Caminske, Russell L., NY
Campbell, Caswell E.*
Camper, Deborah F., Esq., MD
Cankat, Johnny A., NY
Caputo, Rosemarie, NY
Carruthers, Bevan, NY
Caruana, Vincent J., NY
Cerami, Joseph*
Chandler, Edna L.*
Chandler, Sybil A.*

Chapman, Marva M.*
Chazan, Barbara A., NY
Chetta, Michael D.*
Cohen, David L., NJ
Collins, Jeremiah, NY
Collins, Timothy K., NY
Comuniello, Richard*
Concepcion, Melissa, NY
Connelly, Karen T., NJ
Conway, Patricia M., NY
Cook, Caudieu, NY
Cook, Ida M., FL
Cooper, Anthony, NY
Cooper, Karl M., NY
Crawford, Michelle D., NY
Crowley, Colin, NY
Crowley, Denis F., NY
Crum, Melvin*
Cruz, Tirza A.*
Cuadrado, Mary*
Cuebas, Tonia Y., NY
Cummings, Vernessa, NY
Curro, Isabella, NY
Daidone, Anthony, NY
Daniels, Hilda B., NY
Danjer, Marcq J.*
Dash, Randolph C., NY
David, Rupert A.*
Davis, Adrian C., NY
Davis, Thurston G.*
De, Filippo M.*
De Jesus, Sandra*
Del Castillo, Vincent, NY
De Leon, Rafael A., NY
Demeo, Teresa A., NY
Demera, Carlos A.*
Derac, Yves P., CA
Dever, John A., NJ
Difede, Michele A.*
Di Scala, Helen M., NY
Dixon, Alexandreena, NY
Domenech, Edgar A., NY
Dotson, Allen, NY
Dougherty, Anthony D.*
Dougherty, Roger B., NY
Douglas, Randolph G.*
Dourmas, Georgia, NY
Downing, Christopher*
Draper, Norma*
Drobny, Charlene, Israel
Drysdale, Althea E.*
Echenique, Patricia S., NY
Ehigiegba, Paul O.*
Emanuel, Michael L., NJ
Engel, Peter W., NY
Engleton, Lena D., NY
English, Eleanor A., NY
Enright, Joseph G.*
Estrada, John*
Evans, Anderson*
Fafoutis, Nicholas A., NY
Falkenhainer, William, NY
Farmer, Flossie S.*
Farnes, Milagros, NY
Felder, Calvin L., NY
Felton, Karen G., NY
Fennell, Ivory*
Ferguson, Wanda, NY
Fernandez, Vicky*
Ferrer, Awilda, NY
Field, Heather L., NY
Fleming, Dolores*
Folsom, Norman, KY
Ford, Vanessa D., NY
Forster, Linda J.*
Fortune, Patricia, NY
Fox, Susan H.*
Frabasile, Carmelo, NY
Franzese, Paul N., NY
Frazier, Elizabeth P.*
Frierson, Lue B.*
Frisco, Nick M., NY
Fuller, Stanley*
Fusco, Filomena J., IA
Gagliardo, Diane M., NY
Garcia, Anaire R., NY

Garcia, Publio A., NY
Garrick, Paula A., NY
Garrison, Wayne W., NY
Gaud, Juan R., NY
Geise, Edward*
Ghermezian, Lily, NY
Gillen, Mary E.*
Giustra, Salvator, NY
Goines, Michael A.*
Golden, Lois J.*
Gomes, Valerian*
Gonzalez, Jo A., NY
Gonzalez, Jose R.*
Gonzalez, Sylvia, NY
Gonzalez, William*
Goodman, Karen*
Gorman, Albert J., NJ
Gotsopoulis-blum, Mary, NY
Grandstaff, Glenn, NJ
Grant, E. G., NY
Greene, Martine B.*
Gregoric, Maximilian, UT
Griffin, Richard M., NY
Griffin, Uriel, NY
Grogan, Lorna A., GA
Grossman, Jack, NY
Grosso, Ralph, PA
Gurielov, Shalva, NY
Gutierraz, Raisa, PA
Gutierrez, Eugene R.*
Hairston, Debra R., NY
Hammond, Gregory C., NJ
Hamperian, Joseph M.*
Hanlon, James O., NY
Harden, Sheryl D., NY
Harper, Deborah A., NY
Harris, Deidre*
Hatzis, Alexander C., TX
Hayes, Susan L.*
Hegarty, James, NY
Henderson, Richard T., NJ
Hercules, Martineau, NY
Herrera, Julian, NY
Hillman, Mary E.*
Hinds, Marcia R., NY
Hoffmann, James A., NY
Holder, Desiree A., NY
Hollingsworth, Jerald, NY
Horne, Geri C.*
Ho-shing, Viodelda C.*
Hosking, Carlos*
Houghton, Richard M., NJ
Hudson, Sharen D., NY
Hung, Fu-chin, Taiwan
Hussey, Brian P., NY
Hymowitz, Alan J., NJ
Insardi, Philip J.*
Iqbal, Nelly R., NY
Jackson, Falinyi D., NY
Jackson, Sheryl R.*
Jaffe, Lawrence B., NY
James, Laurie M.*
James, Pamela A.*
Jean, Francklin N.*
Johnson, Charles L.*
Johnson, Phyllis R., NY
Jones, Shirley D., NY
Jordan, Rafael*
Joyner, Valerie K., NY
Julia, Veronica A., NY
Juliano, Richard P., NY
Jusino, Jenny*
Kapitan, Gary A., NJ
King, Barbara, NY
King, Elizabeth L.*
Kobel, Richard T., NY
La, Barbera I., NY
Laboy, Luis, NY
Lalonde, Marie, NY
Lamot, Michael D., NY
Lasack, Ian N., NY
Latty, Gregory C., NY
Laughlin, Paula, PA
Le, Brew V., NY
Le, Page R.*
Lecoin, Serge*

Lee, Chak Y., NJ
Lee, James M., NY
Lee, Kin, NY
Lennon, James, NJ
Leong, Lai L., NY
Lesser, Debra E., NY
Lewis, Ellen R., NY
Lewis, Ingrid P., NY
Liesdek, Felitia E.*
Lieske, Donald G., NY
Linehan, Edward T., NY
Livingstone-pucci, Ann M.*
Locantro, James C., NY
Locicero, Alfio*
Logan, Mark R., FL
Logie, Mason, NY
Lopez, Dina M.*
Lopez, Jonathan M.*
Lopez, Lucy, NY
Lopez-Coriano, C. L., NY
Love, William A., NY
Love-fox, Chris, NY
Lui, Alan S., NY
Lydick, Fred S.*
Macchiaroli, Joseph, NJ
Macdowell, Kenneth M., NY
Mackesy, Richard, PA
Magnus, Connie L., NY
Maldonado, Thomas L.*
Manasse, Gigi R., NY
Manning, Delores H., NY
Manning, Joni R., NY
Marino, Carmine L., FL
Marks, Debbie A., NY
Martin, Michael A., NY
Martorana, John*
Martos, Mrs. Elena L., NY
Mascoll, Carolyn P., NY
Massaro, Patricia*
Maute, Lora L., NY
May, Paul D., NY
Mayer, Michael J., NY
Mc, Corkle D., NJ
McCaffrey, James P., NY
Mcclean, Sonia P., NY
McDonnell, C.*
McDuffie, Robert, NY
McEachin, Anthony J., NY
Medina, Moraima, NY
Melbourne, Phyllis M., NY
Melekwe, Augustina M., NY
Mercado, Elizabeth*
Mercado, Lizbeth, NY
Messick, Edna, NJ
Meyers, Cheryl-ann, NY
Millien, Sabine M., NY
Mills, Joseph A.*
Minton, Kenneth W., FL
Mitchell, Anthony J., NY
Modafferi, Anne C., NY
Modeste, Elaine B., NY
Molina, Adnery, NY
Molina, Oscar M., NY
Monaghan, William A., NY
Montalbano, Gary F., NY
Montgomery, Dwayne K., NY
Moore, Kieyasten K.*
Moorer, Denise W., NY
Moores, Robert N., NC
Morales, Wilfredo E., FL
Morton, Gary K.*
Moten, Reva G., NY
Muhlert, Beth A.*
Mulhall, Brian, NY
Muraca, Felice J.*
Murawski, Walter H., NY
Murray, Sheila E., NY
Myerson, Wayne B., NY
Nadal, Edwin M., NY
Naglieri, Frank J.*
Nazario, Lourdes*
Ng, Anthony C., NJ
Nicholas, Florence M., PA
Nieves, George*
Nocera, Vito, NY
Ocasio, Minerva*

Ocasio, Sandra*
O'Connell, Paul E.*
O'Halloran, Hugh M., NY
Oliver, Brenda L., NY
Olugboroko, Anthony*
Omotayo, Nixon O., NY
Oren, Itzhak, MA
Ortiz, Maria L.*
Pace, Paul A., NY
Pagani, Donald P., NY
Paige, Dorothy M., NY
Palmer, Robert A., NY
Panazzolo, Glenn P., NY
Parker, Andrew D.*
Parris, Cyril J., NY
Pascal, Licet, NY
Patrick, Michael A., NY
Peifer, Ronald G., NY
Pena, Miguel (Michael) A., NY
Pender, Sylvia A., NY
Perez, Maritza*
Perez, Milagros, NY
Perry, Celeste M., NY
Petris, Philip*
Pettaway, Christopher*
Phanor, Yves, NY
Pierre-Jacques, Charles, NY
Pinckney, Ramona J., NY
Pizzola, Peter A.*
Poulos, Harry, NY
Poynter, Charles D., NJ
Pradhan, Shrikant*
Profeta, Susan L., NY
Pryjmak, Myron W., NY
Puco, Angela B.*
Quashie, Joy V., NY
Quinn, Michael R., NY
Quirindongo, Eligio, VA
Ramcharan, Praimadip, NY
Ramcharitar, Asha D.*
Ramos, Jose L.*
Redman, Stephanie C., NY
Reid, Ethan E., NY
Reid, Trevor M., NY
Reyes, Donna, NC
Rhees, Alma, FL
Richards, Luis A., NY
Richburg, Rogina W.*
Rick, Freddie*
Rivera, Andrew A., NY
Rivera, Marta, NY
Rivera, Wilfredo*
Robergeau, Marise*
Roca, Randall S., NY
Roche, Grace V., NJ
Rodriguez, Delia*
Rodriguez, Franklin, NY
Rodriguez, Kenneth M., NY
Rolle, Robert J., NY
Romanoff, Kim H.*
Rosenbaum, Meredith, NY
Ruane, James P., NY
Ruben, Scott P., NY
Ruddock, Ethelbert, NY
Ruffinott, Robert R., NY
Ruiz, Angel L., NY
Rutigliano, Serafina, NY
Ryan, Patricia A., NY
Ryan, Patrick J., NY
Saintjulien, Emilio, NY
Salim, John R., NJ
Sanni, Thomas G., NY
Santa Ana, Richard, NY
Santangelo, Antoinett, NY
Santiago, Joseph A.*
Santos, Edwin, NY
Sapolsky, Sharon P.*
Sawyer, William F., NY
Scarabino, Virginia, NY
Scelfo, Gloria A.*
Schaefer, Dennis H.*
Schaefer, Jacqueline*
Schatzle, Kevin P., NY
Schneider, Guy A., NY
Scholl, Charles M., NY
Schwartz, Ellen R., NY

Sclafani, Joseph C., NJ
Scott, Karim L., NY
Seebaran, Darsan, NY
Seignious, Lisa A., NY
Seward, James D., PA
Shapiro, Eric M., NJ
Shark, Ricardo R., NY
Shear, David S.**
Sheehan, Brian, NY
Sheppard, Kinsey O., NY
Sheppard, Leslie*
Shtull, Penny R., VT
Shulman, Ronnie J., NY
Silva, Catherine C., NY
Silvers, Renee, NY
Simon, Catherine G., NY
Simpson, Cheryl D.*
Smith, Alma D., NY
Smith, Cheryl D., NY
Smith, Clarence, Jr., Esq., NY
Smusz, Margaret A.*
Soba, Yvette*
Solis, Sandra, NY
Soto, Diana, AZ
Sotomayor, Carmen L., NY
Speidel, Philip G., NY
Spellman, Alan G.*
Squarcino, Dawn M., NY
Squire, Cid C.*
Stanton, Katherine A., NY
Stawchansky, Donna, NY
Stefanick, Richard A., NJ
Stewart, Paul L., GA
St. Firmin, Bertrand, NY
Still, Curtis M.*
Stoute, Jacqueline, NY
Sukhan, Premwati*
Tejeda, Miguel A., NY
Terry, Debora D.*
Thomas, Regina P., NY
Thorpe, Richard W., NY
Tipaldo, Joseph P., NY
Tirado, Donna, NY
Todd, Michael A., NY
Toro, Eric, NY
Torun, Aydin N., NY
Urban, Daniel E., NY
Valdez, Herbert M.*
Valentin, Sheila S., NY
Vargas, Mencia J.*
Vazquez, Blanca, NY
Vazquez, Edward A., MO
Vedral, Chris J., NY
Vega, Richard*
Vega, Thomas, NY
Velasquez, Carmen R., NY
Velez, Alex, NJ
Velez, Eric H.*
Ventrice, Tinamarie, FL
Vicente, Agustin*
Viggiano, Paul M., NY
Wakschal, Stephen J.*
Washington, Thalia, NY
Weaver, James M.*
Weekes, Harold W.*
Weinberg, Kenneth J.*
Wells, Roderick C., NY
White, Henry*
White, Ricky L., NY
Wilkanowski, Barbara, NY
Williams, Annie E.*
Williams, George*
Williams, Nathaniel, NY
Williams, Sandra, NY
Wilson, Yolanda, MD
Winter, Dawn A., NY
Yahaya, Bashari S.*
Zarek, Edward T., NJ
Zayas, Luis A.*
Zayas, Maggie R.*
Zazzero, Paul W., NY
Zena, Carlos W., NY
Zupka, Jeanette, VA

1985

Abbott, Fern A., NY

Abdallah, Adib, NY
Abdul-Kareem, Sanah, NY
Abraham, Michael B.*
Abrams, Robert, NY
Acevedo, Jasmine T.*
Acosta-hancock, Dora, NY
Adams, Martha M., NY
Adams, Sabrina T., NY
Adler, Morton N., NY
Ahaneku, Ike I.*
Akerman, John M., NY
Akinsiku, Frederick, NJ
Alvarez, Denise*
Alvarez, Judith A., NY
Ambert, Ms. Arlene, NY
Amelio, Anthony, NY
Anderson, Claudette*
Anderson, Esther G., NY
Anthoine, Robert, NY
Arias, Flora, NY
Arrington, Oscar P., NY
Ashoory, Bracha, NY
Austin, Timothy*
Austria, Crisanta H., NY
Ayres, Richard, VA
Badillo-Martinez, Fe*
Bailey, April, NY
Bakare, Bello*
Baker, James, WA
Balogun, Raheem, NY
Banner, Jocelyn A.*
Barbour, Ms. Susan M., NY
Barth, Christine, NY
Beatty, Cephus J., NY
Bell, Miriam C.*
Bellamy, Myra D., NY
Beltranena, Michael*
Benitez, Janet*
Benton, Delores, NY
Bernard, Brenda, NY
Betty, June E.*
Betz, William, NY
Bilski, Frank A.*
Blake, Micheryl R., NY
Bliss, Stuart, NY
Blumlein, Michael, NY
Boatright, Sarah E.*
Bolen, Thomas J., NY
Bologna, Joe, NY
Bonilla, Jose L., NY
Bonilla, Nilda, NY
Booker-Williams, Lois*
Borchers, James E., NJ
Borges, Cibella R., NY
Bossong, Denise, NY
Boyeson, Warren, SC
Brady, Robert M.*
Braithwaite, Deborah, NJ
Branch, Joseph, PA
Brantley, Donnell*
Bren, Fern M., NY
Brezny, Charles G., MA
Briant, Anita K., NY
Brindisi, Thomas A.*
Broderick, Harold T., NY
Brogan, Thomas M., NY
Brosnan, David J., NY
Brown, Allen E.*
Brown, Desiree, NY
Brown, Myrtle M., NY
Buckley, Anna M., NJ
Burchett, Mildred*
Byrne, Lawrence P., NY
Cadet, Pascal*
Caffrey, Ronald, NJ
Campbell, Edison A.*
Campbell, Sheilah N., NY
Candelaria, Gladys, NY
Cannizzo, Enzo F., NY
Cannon-Woodson, Jean*
Caputo, Joseph, NY
Carmichel, Debora L., NY
Carrasqillo, Myriam, NY
Carroll, James W., NJ
Carr-sheppard, Kim D., NY
Carter, Dawn E., NY

Carter, Kim, NY
Caruso, Rosemary, NY
Catella, Paul W.**
Cennamo, John E., NY
Cerreta, Kenneth, NY
Chabla, Patricia A., NY
Chambers, Taryn B.*
Charalambous, T.*
Chase, Garel S., NY
Chen, Jose, NY
Chow, Frederick R., NY
Christiano, Steven A., NY
Christman, Thomas V., NY
Chudhabuddhi, Pichai, NY
Cichon, Michael, NY
Clark, Gerald C., Jr., OH
Clarke, Adolphus*
Clarke, John, NY
Claudio, Rafael*
Clay, Eugene S., NY
Clemons, Cecelia*
Cohen, Maxine*
Colden, Michael A.*
Coleman, Edmond D., NY
Coleman, Kevin G.*
Collins, Cassandra L., NY
Colon, Edwin*
Cooper, Donna M., NY
Cordero, Victor, NY
Corrica, Jerome S., NY
Corseri, Alessandra, NY
Cosenza, Charles*
Costantino, Regina, NJ
Cox, Andrea, NY
Crespo, Porfiro, NY
Crooks, Sonia E., NY
Cruz, Evelyn*
Daley, Thomas J., NY
Daly, William, NJ
Dangler, Donald J., NJ
Daniels, Owen O.*
Davenport, Charles H.*
Davies, Latonia D.*
De, Holzer L., NY
De, Nigris B., NY
Decuir, Donna M., NY
Defreitas, Ewald, NY
Degnan, Brian A., NY
Degraffenreid, Adella, NY
Degroot, Daniel R., NJ
Delaney, Melvin, NY
Delapaz, Jose M.*
Delgado, Jose L., NY
Demirkaya, Yalkin, NY
De Urquiza, Enrique*
Deychman, Igor*
Dezenzo, Gerald A.*
Di, Donato L.*
Diaz, Michelle A., NY
Diaz, William, NY
Diesel, Dennis*
Diomede, Vito S., NY
Dockery, Dawn M.*
D'Onofrio, Mary T.*
Duncan, Jennifer*
Duncan, LT Robert W., NY ,
Dunlop, Winston I., FL
Early, Kimberly M., NY
Eason, Marcus, NY
Echevarria, Daliza E., NY
Ejemai, Michael*
Ekenezar, Napoleon O.*
Eley, Regina E., NY
Epps, Shirley A., NY
Erdy, Janet*
Esposito, Ralph A., NY
Essig, Frank, NY
Eyma, Patrick*
Ezeobi-Ekwueme, Comf*
Fairconeture, Stace, NY
Falzon, Jean*
Fanara, Anthony P.*
Farmer, Rube*
Farngalo, Gregory N.*
Fereance, Jacqueline*
Figueroa, Cynthia L., NY

Flateau, Andrea, NY
Florkowski, Thomas, NY
Flynn, Alexander A., NY
Flynn, Brian P., NY
Fofana, Unisa A., NY
Follett, Mary R., NY
Fong, Wayne M., NY
Foster, Wanda A.*
Fournillier, Brian F., NY
Foy, Lawrence B., NY
Foy, Rena*
Frederick, Dennis*
Fret, Jeanette, NY
Funiciello, Linda A.*
Funk, Joanna*
Gaddy, Karen C.*
Gallo, Richard, NY
Gambrell, Vivian R., NY
Garcia, Margie*
George, Patrick F., NY
Gershfeld, Sharon*
Gibbs, Gail M., NY
Giblin, John F., NY
Gillen, Thomas C.*
Giordani, Anthony G., NY
Goldstein, Merrill*
Gonzalez, Grisselle, NY
Gordon, Henry, NY
Gordon, Vivian A., FL
Goris, Damaris T., NY
Gorman, Nina, PA
Goulbourne, Norval, NY
Grant, Joan, NY
Graves, Daisy P.*
Gray, Edward B., NY
Green, Eunice H., NY
Greene, Rita D., NY
Griffith, Todd A., NJ
Grillo, Richard S., NJ
Guagenti, Alfonso P., NY
Guardino, Deborah, NY
Guerrero, Adolfo*
Gurierrez, Geraldine, NY
Haggerty, Michael C., PA
Hahn, Robert J.*
Hall, Bertrand M.*
Hardy, Kevin A., NY
Harrigan, Justin, VI
Harris, Adrienne L., NY
Harrison, Patricia M., NY
Hashimi, Muhammad, NY
Hawxhurst, Patricia, NY
Haynes, Vincent, NY
Hazel, Melford J.*
Healy, James, NY
Hee, Jackson, CA
Held, Sharon Z., NY
Hendricks, Allona*
Hendricks, Garfield, NY
Hennessey, Michael J.*
Herman, Michele A., NY
Herring, John, NY
Hewitt, Russell, NY
Heywood, Angela B., NY
Hicks, Bruce, NY
Hill, Mercedes S., NY
Hinds, Randolph A., NY
Hirschberg, Jeanette, NH
Ho, Jon, NY
Hobbs, Tammy*
Hogarth, Emmanuel J., CA
Holland, Nelson K., NY
Holloway, Cecelia T., NY
Holt, Kevin T., NY
Houston, Gwendolyn*
Howard, Theodora E., NY
Hudyma, Amie, NJ
Hyman, April J., NY
Idiart, George J., NY
Ingram, James*
Iovino, James, NY
Irobunda, Claralee, NY
Isaac, Joeletha*
Izzo, Angelo, NY
Jackson, Edward, NY
Jackson, Gail H.*

Jackson, Hardy, NY
Jackson, Yvonne C., NY
Jadusingh, Carlene*
James, Derek A.*
Jarratt, Kent D., NY
Jawad, Naim, NY
Jean, Carlo, NY
Jeffers, Yana L.*
Jefferson, Alicia, NY
Jefferson, Marvella, NY
Jenkins, Sandy R.*
Johannesen, Richard, NY
Johnson, Alfred K., NY
Johnson, Christine*
Johnson, Edward J., NY
Johnson, Granville, NJ
Johnson, Jessica F.*
Johnson, Willie B., NY
Jones, Darrell R., NY
Jones, Leroy*
Jordan, Percival A., NY
Jordan, Thomas J., NY
Joseph, La V.*
Juliano, Maria A., NJ
Jusino, Ismael, NY
Kallimanis, George, NY
Karageorge, Basil A., NY
Karmazin, Nancy, NY
Kashinsky, Alan J., NY
Kaufman, Steven, NY
Kaufmann, Kevin J., NY
Kaye, Daniel*
Keeney, Brendan W., NY
Kehrer, Jeffery R.*
Kelly, Frank A.*
Khan, Nezam, NY
Kiely, Deirdre, NY
King, Anthony B., NY
Knight, Lorraine*
Knight, Thaddeus A., FL
Kobayashi, Beatriz, NY
Kostolni, Vincent P., NY
Kouzoujian, Gary B., NY
La Fauci, Jack*
Langdon, Antonio C.*
Lara, Jose A.*
Lartigaut, Sandra, NY
Lasalle, Jeffrey J., PA
Latham, John F., NJ
Lathrop, Gary*
Lauria, Michele A., FL
Lauriano, Robert*
Lawrence, Robert M., NY
Lawrence, Yvonne J., NY
Leary, Jeremiah J., NY
Lee, Chang-Ming, NY
Leibman, Faith, PA
Levers, Leona, NY
Levinson, Peter A., NY
Levy, Amir, NY
Lewis, Ms. Deidre Y., NY
Liou, Choa-po, NY
Littles, Willette C., NY
Livingston, Gregory, NY
Lombardo, Richard, NY
Lopes, James, NY
Lopez, Dolores A.*
Lopez, Jose E.*
Lopez, Juan A.*
Lopez, Leardo L.*
Lorenzini, Michael V.*
Louis, Barbara L.*
Lowery, Lee R., FL
Lupinetti, Laura J.*
Lurry, Mary L., NJ
Lyons, Daphony P., NY
Mack, Bernard A.*
Mackey, Daniel, NY
Malinowski, Christop*
Malone, Patrick A., NY
Maltese, Barry*
Mangual, Sylvia*
Marcel, Jean, NY
Marinaro, Michael V., PA
Markey, Peter, NY
Marquez-Drew, Felix, NY

Martzinek, Carol*
Marus, James L., NY
Matheis, Jean, NY
Matias, Awilda, NY
Matos, Nelson-Ness, NY
Mayers, Joshua B.*
Mazzone, Gregory, NY
Mc, Donald R., NY
Mc, Donnell Z.*
McCray, Michelle E., NY
McDowell-Satterfield, Laci D.*
Mceneaney, Catherine, NY
Mcevoy, Peter J.*
McGinniss, Debra A., NY
Mc Gorty, Donald J., NJ
Mcgotty, Thomas J., NJ
Mc Lain, Jeffrey L.*
McMain, Shelley*
McManus, Robert A.*
Mc Millan, Bonnie L., NY
McMorrow, James O.*
Mcqueeney, Patrick, MI
McRae, Elizabeth A., NY
Mead, Judith D.*
Meighan, Litna, NY
Meilleur, Leslie M., NY
Melican, Michael*
Melita, Gregory V., NY
Messam, Carol R., NY
Michaelides, Michael, NY
Miller, James J., NY
Miller, Lawrence, NY
Minor, Lisa M.*
Miranda, Sandra, NY
Mitchell, Ms. Carolyn, NJ
Molinaro, Louis J., NY
Molinelli, Barbara*
Monahan, Thomas M., NJ
Monck, Robert F., NY
Mondiello, Philip*
Monserrate, Juan, NY
Montero, Hector*
Montes, Grace*
Montgomery, Paul S., NY
Moore, Brigitte C., NY
Morales, Antonio P.*
Morisano, Anthony J., NY
Morle, Abena, NY
Moro, Peter L., NY
Morrison Black, Charmaine, NJ
Mortel, John R., NY
Mortley, James L., NY
Moskal, Joanne*
Mosley, Alicia M., NY
Mueger, Warren, NY
Mulholland, Sean*
Mullins, Theresa B., NY
Mulroney, Edward A.*
Mulryan, Joseph V., NY
Murphy, Anne M.*
Murphy, Earl R.*
Murphy, James, NY
Murphy, Kenneth J., NY
Murray, Antoinette D.*
Musarella, Mark, NY
Nadkarni, Lavita*
Neblett-ford, Jillian A., NJ
Negron, Gladys*
Newman, Lisa N., NJ
Nickens, Sheila, NY
Nieves, Angel, NY
Nixon, Staci E., NY
Noble, Lisa G.*
Nordhaug, Eric F., NJ
Nurse, Ingrid L., NY
Nurse, Scott, NY
Obryan, Diren D., NY
O'Day, Joanne E., NY
Odom, Annie D., NY
O'Donnell, Donald P., NY
Odusanya, Abimbola, NY
Ogunbadejo, Safi E.*
Okoro, Isaac N.*
O'Livares, Elizabeth, NY
Olmo, Hipolito*
Olomo, Solomon*

Ortega, Alejandro*
Ortiz, Elizabeth, NY
Orukpe, Frank, NY
Osorio, Edwin*
Ovalles, Mildred L., NY
Owens, Ronald*
Owens Skrodanes, Loren J.*
Pace, Geoffrey M., NY
Palmer, Eric T., NY
Papure, Gail, NY
Paras, Kenneth J.*
Patino, Hilda H.*
Patino, Michael F., NY
Patterson, Cynthia*
Penna, Frederick, Jr., NY
Perez, Melinda, NY
Peterson, Cynthia, NY
Peterson, Denise, NY
Phillip, Beverly L.*
Pioli, Victor J., NY
Pizzi, Michael, NY
Pizzy, Michael A., NY
Plottner, Mary P.*
Poindexter, Lisa N., NY
Poveromo, Joseph, NY
Powell, David F., NY
Powell, Hughlett O., VA
Powell, Sandra C., NY
Prignano, Roseann B., NY
Priolo, Charlene S., NJ
Procopio, Mary A., NY
Pronman, Yonaton, NY
Puckett, Bonnie L.*
Qadirah, Eleanor, NC
Quattrucci, Elisa A., NY
Quintero, Anthony, NY
Quinto, Donna M., NY
Ramirez, Eliud, Jr., NY
Ramos, Carmen S.*
Ramos, Christopher L., NY
Ramsay, Rhona H., NY
Ramsey, Richard M., NY
Randazzo, Jason, NY
Rasmussen, Michelle*
Raymond, Catherine, NY
Reale, Ronald G., NJ
Reavis, Piar N., NY
Reid, Nora A., CA
Remauro, Richard*
Resto, Lourdes, NY
Reyes, Alma T., NY
Reyes, Javier, NY
Reynolds, Patrick, NJ
Rich Appelberg, Lori, CT
Rickman, Marci, NY
Riddick, Robert R., NJ
Riha, Wendy L.*
Rivera, Sandra, NY
Rizzo, Joseph M., NY
Roberson, Gary*
Roberts, Diana C., NY
Roberts, Jewel F., NY
Robinson, Doris C.*
Robinson, Marilyn C., VA
Robinson, Yolanda D., NY
Robles, Robert A.*
Rodriguez, Albania, NY
Rogers, Sharon L., NY
Romano, George A., NY
Romano, Susan D., NY
Rosa, Paula I.*
Rosa, Rolando A., NY
Rose, Jacqueline A., NY
Rose, Richard A., NJ
Rosenthal, Scot R.*
Rough, Thomas C., NY
Rushton, Denise A., NY
Russo, Elizabeth, NJ
Rynne, John P., NY
Sachelari-blackman, Regina A.*
Salley, Jacqueline M., NY
Salmon, Philip E., NY
Sama, Anthony M., NY
Sanabria, Elsie*
Sanchez, Johnny, NY

Santa, Maria S., NY
Santiago, Carmen L., NY
Santiago, David, NY
Santiago, Ivette, NY
Santiago, Jeffrey, NY
Santory, Michael*
Sanzone, Augustine, NY
Sarcone, Richard, NY
Saunders, Derek E.*
Scahill, Marilyn F.*
Schade, Joseph, NY
Schiraldi, Vito, NY
Schliesmann, Barry*
Schmidt, Robert E.*
Schrader, Steven R.*
Schwartz, Eric S., NY
Scott, Bertram A., NY
Scott, Cleve M., NJ
Scott, Lionel F.*
Seabury, Major C., NY
Segarra, Juan, NY
Serafino, John M., NY
Serviss, Barbara A., NY
Settles, Hannah, NY
Sevos, John, NY
Shannon, Michael P., NY
Shapiro, Janet L., NY
Sheerin, Brendan, NY
Sherwin, Lenore K., NY
Shinn, Frederick W.*
Siew, Zanifa*
Siino, Rose*
Silverstein, Karen, NY
Simmons, Marthena L.*
Simunovic, Nikola, NY
Sinclair, Amanda J., NY
Singh, Karan*
Skeeter, Shireene D., NY
Slater, Dennis*
Smatlick, Richard P., NY
Smith, Gail Y., NY
Smith, Sarah A., SC
Smoke, Clinton H., MA
Smrcka, Peter G., NY
Smyth, Kerry M., NJ
Sokoloff, Maxine I.*
Soler, Rafael, NY
Solomon, Harry A.**
Sorge, Richard, FL
Sorgenti, Josephine, NY
Speranza, Joseph A., NY
Sprague, Richard C.*
Stanton, Mary, NJ
Steer, Joan M., NY
Stefanese, Anthony C., NY
Stephenson, Barbara*
Stewart, Alexandra M.*
Stewart, Christophe*
Stewart, John*
Stewart, Michael*
Stewart, Vivienne, NJ
Stone, Michele*
Strickland, Robert, NY
Strocco, Allison M., NY
Suarez, Jose, NY
Sullivan, Angela D., NY
Summers, Cheryl A., NY
Sutley, Steven L., NY
Sweeney, William J.**
Swiatocha, Donald J., NY
Sylvester, Philip, NY
Taaffe, Edward*
Tanks, Wanda Y.*
Taylor, Tyrone, NY
Tennell, Henrietta, NY
Terry, Lera T., NY
Thomas, Gloria G.*
Thompson, Adam, NY
Thompson, Janet A., NY
Thompson, Thomas J., NY
Thorson, Steven J., VA
Thoupos, Thomas, NY
Tinglin, Morris C., NY
Tobin, Eileen M., NY
Toscano, Daisy E., NY
Toscano, Stephen M., NY

Toulon, Anthony S., NY
Tozzi, Thomas J., NJ
Tracy, Peter, NY
Tronolone, Susan L., NY
Truitt, John, FL
Trummer, Brian J., NY
Tucker, Jan*
Twomey, Dennis, NY
Tyler, Trent S., NY
Umar, Warith-Deen, NY
Vaccarino, Guy T.*
Vandemark, Maurice T., NY
Vanmeter, Yvonne D.*
Varela, Mildred, NY
Vargas, Alvin**
Vaughn, Eric*
Vazquez, Gwendolyn, NY
Velez, Carlos A.*
Velez, Ramon, NY
Waller, Henry, NY
Warner, Philip R., NY
Warren, Regina L.*
Washington, Leona, NY
Washington, Ricky*
Watford, Gregory J., NY
Watkins, Ms. Tracey L., CA
Waye, Jane, OH
Webb, Vance S.*
Weber, Cynthia J.*
Weis, Richard, NY
Weiss, Rudolf, NY
Whitfield, Fred L., NY
Wihlborg, William T.*
Williams, Donald G., NY
Williams, Geraldo A., VA
Williams, Ibikunle A., NY
Williams, Pauline E.*
Williams, Theresa M., NY
Wilson, Kathleen M., NY
Wilson, Tyrone E.*
Wohlleb, Joanne, NY
Wood, David J., NY
Wooden, Renata D.*
Woods, Gail D., NY
Wooten, Antoinette M., NY
Wyatt, Paul A., NJ
Zarate, Sandra L., NY
Zichettello, Thomas, NY
Zupka, Paul W., NY

1986

Acevedo, Marcos A., FL
Adeosun, Bolanle*
Agosta, Michelle*
Agugliaro, John P., NY
Aguiar, Yvette, NY
Ahern, Kevin, NY
Aiello, Michael, NJ
Alexander, Lorna V., NY
Alfred, Rosa A., NY
Allen, Matthew C., VA
Alvarez, Gil Q.*
Alvarez, Osiris*
Anand, Srikala, India
Angelakis, Kaliope, NY
Angilletta, Joseph A., NY
Anglin, Brian, NY
Animashaun, Morufu A.*
Antonicello, Giacomo, NJ
Aracena, Angela A.*
Arneja, Mindy C., NY
Arzuaga, Rudy*
Ashton, Cornelius M., NY
Baker, Teresa, NY
Banach, Paul F., NJ
Baranello, James P., NY
Barriteau, Gemma M., NY
Batista, Jane*
Batista, Julio, NY
Beckett, Lori J.*
Belin, Thelma, NY
Benjamin, Carole R., NY
Bennett, Reginald*
Bentley, Mary F.*
Bermudez, Iris E., NY
Berry, Stephen D., PA

Bettman, Michael, Canada
Biggers, Crystal L., NY
Billie-Cosby, Bridget, NY
Bishop, William B., NY
Boeru-Vlas, Caius*
Borruso, Martin*
Brennan, Barbara A.*
Brieba, Lorenzo A., NY
Broomfield, Arthur, FL
Brown, Marie B., NY
Brownbill, Susan, NY
Brownlee, Michelle, NY
Brownstein, Brian J., FL
Bryant, Brenda A., NY
Buffaloe, Kenneth S., NY
Burnette, Lebro C., NY
Buska, Richard M., NJ
Butterfield, Anna, NY
Cadet, Darley, NY
Calle, Ana Maria, NY
Calzadilla, Esme M., FL
Camarda, Susan A., NY
Campbell, Carol G., NY
Campos, Susan*
Cantave, Alexandra M., NY
Caraballo, Judith*
Carmona, Amada, NY
Carr, Quanda H.*
Carroll, William J., NY
Carvajal, Rita M., NY
Carver, Dorothy A.*
Cavagnetto, Lawrence, NY
Cendagorta, Louis M., NY
Chandler, Jana, NY
Chanin, Ann*
Charles, Deryck, NY
Chastain, Douglas*
Chypre, Richard L., NY
Clark, Damaris X., NY
Clarke, Frank G.*
Coates, John R., Jr., NY
Collins, Dayna*
Colon, Sophie M., NY
Concepcion, David*
Concepcion, Grace*
Connaughton, Kenneth, NY
Connelly, Susan, TX
Connolly, Maryann, NY
Cooper, Tonya, NY
Copeland, Cynthia R.*
Cornish, Michael J., CT
Corpening, La'tanya, NY
Cosme-satina, Sandra M., NY
Crespo, Sylvia, NY
Crosby, Peter A.*
Crosby, Willie*
Cruz, Elbert, FL
Cruz, Lillian, NY
Cucciniello, Steven*
Cullum, Christopher, NY
Daniels, Karen*
Daniels, Yvonne, NY
David, Wilfred, NY
Deane, Eric, NY
Decanditis, Neil, NY
Delaney, Katharine, NY
Delprino, Robert, NY
Deow, Nadira, NY
Derienzo, Mari*
Devito, Diane, NY
Dewell, Wayne, NY
Diaz, Nestor H., NY
Diehl, William T., NY
Dipasquale, Tommy O., NY
Dixon, Shellese, NY
Dodds, Dwayne M., TX
Donaldson, Irving F., NY
Doyle, Catherine, NY
Drucker, Leslie, NY
Earle, Lynda E., MD
Ekpenyong, Florence*
Enright, Mary M.*
Enriquez, Evelyn, NY
Ertrachter, Jana G., NY
Espinosa, Gadelia I.*
Fegan, Ewart, NY

Felix, Lesly, NY
Felton, Crystal Y., NY
Fernandez, Robert*
Ferrigno, Mario, NJ
Fimiano, Anthony J.*
Fisher, Michael A., NY
Fleming, John M., NY
Flores, Yvonne E., NY
Fontanez-Vega*
Francis, Alvin D., NY
Frank, Laura, NY
Fuentes, Jack*
Furey, John, NJ
Gallagher, Kieran M.*
Garcia, Maria*
Gardner, Marva, NY
Garvin Huntley, Lynn M., PhD, IL
Gayle, Carol R.*
George, Farid H., NY
George, Glenroy*
George, Hector A., NY
Gera, Mary E., NY
Giacobbe, Nicholas, NY
Giesinger, Marie A., ND
Gilford, Valerie J., NY
Gill, Alyson J., NY
Gill, Americus*
Giustra, Robert, NY
Glenn, Dwight, NY
Glynn, James M., NY
Goldstein, Harold M.*
Gonzalez, Nancy L., NY
Good, Carlton, NY
Gore, Elissa, NY
Gorman, Joan*
Gorritz, Maria G.*
Graham, Harry W., NY
Grant, Vanessa, NY
Granville, Stromme J., Sr., NY
Green, Eliot, MA
Green, Vanessa M., SC
Greene, Lillian A.*
Gregov, Drago*
Griffith, Anthony, AZ
Guerrier, Michele P., NY
Gugel, William H., NY
Gutierrez, Shamaine, NY
Hallman, Carol D.*
Hargrow, Peggy J.*
Harper, Renee Y., NY
Harrington, James J., NJ
Hernandez, Anthony P., NY
Hernandez, Nancy*
Hernandez, Rosalia, NY
Heyward, Derrick*
Hillowe-Donahue, C., NY
Hodge, Lisa A.*
Hofmeister, Brian, NJ
Hood, Melody E., CO
Howard, Eugene H.*
Howell, Kathy A.*
Hunte, Ruthven G., NY
Hurley, William T., NY
Hylton, Yvette*
Iacono, Richard M., NY
Ibrahim, Husaini, NY
Immesberger, Eric T.*
Jackson, Cecile L.*
Jackson, Hazel L., NJ
Jackson, Ivory L., NY
Jackson, William P., NY
Jacquitte, Ernst M.*
James, Carol A., NY
Jenkins, Andre H., NY
Jerez, Mercedes C., NY
Jinks, Veronica, NY
Jones, Diane*
Jones, Donna*
Jones, Frances M., NY
Jones, Joyce K.*
Jones, Robert L., NY
Jordan, Kathleen C., NY
Jose, Gail A., FL
Juris, David, NY
Karam, Anthony A., PA

Karloszczuk, Monique, NY
Kearney, Kevin, NJ
Kennedy, Donald P., NY
Kershaw, Eugene, Jr., NY
Kim, Yongjin*
Kirkman, Lisa A., NY
Kirton, Donna C., NY
Knox, Theresa J., NY
Ko, Ivan, NY
Koval, Robert, NY
Kozlow, Mary, NY
Kronenfeld, Jeffrey, NJ
Krouslis, William J., NY
Lambert, John*
Lampasso, Albert J., NY
Langer, Rosalind*
Lauria, James, NY
Leahey, John G., NY
Lebron, Azalea*
Lee, Franklin, NJ
Lent, Michael J.*
Lepore, Silvano, NY
Levy, Baron O., NY
Levy, Joel*
Lieber, Stewart A.*
Loox, Michael J., CA
Lopez, Deborah*
Lopez, Michelle B., NY
Lora, Maria*
Lorquet, Lionel*
Luftman, Lance J., KS
Lynam, David S., NY
Lynch, Kevin*
Lyttle, Judith, NY
Maccou-Young, Aisy*
Madan, Jorge I.*
Maghan, Jess, IL
Malloy, Annette M.*
Malone, Victor E., Jr., NY
Mannix, Delia*
Marcus, Edward, NY
Marquez, Elizabeth, NY
Martinez, Desiree C., NY
Martinez, Jeannette*
Matiz, Judith A., NY
Matthews, Tracy S., NY
Mbugua, Francis*
Mc, Nulty I., NY
McCabe, William T.*
Mcclelland, Laura D., NY
Mcfarlane, Elaine C., NY
Mcleod, William A.*
McRae, Sue E.*
McShall, Florence I., NY
Meade, Lyndia F., NY
Melamed, Joel S., NY
Mero, John R., NY
Mesias, Wilda A.*
Michaels, Carol, FL
Miller, Michael T., NY
Minoras, Bert, NY
Moise, Farah, FL
Mojocoa, Bibiana C., NY
Montagna, Frank C., NY
Montali, Joseph R., FL
Montanez, Danny*
Montgomery, Angela D., NY
Montgomery, Joann, NY
Moore, Leon A., NY
Moore, Nilda J., NY
Morales, Benito, NY
Moran, Christopher J., NY
Morgan, Clarence, NY
Morgan, Donald L., NJ
Morris, Susan M., NY
Muccio, Anthony*
Murdock, Timothy P., NY
Murphy, Michael J., NY
Myers, Noah L., NY
Nadal, Lucy, NY
Nelson, Rosa A.*
Nieroda, Daniel W., NY
Nigro, Gregory, IL
Nobilione, Joseph G., NY
Noble, Janet C., NY
Norman, Kym R., NY

Norton, Benjamin T., SC
Norwood, Robert, NY
O'connor, Andrew J., NJ
O'halloran, Daniel, NY
Okello, Jane*
Olsen, Anton K., NY
Onwuchekwa, Chidinma, NY
Ortiz, Felicito*
Otero, Antonio*
Ottey, Ms. Donna M., NY
Pacheco, Lizandro, NY
Padilla, Joseph A., NY
Pagan, Antonio, NY
Panton, Charles*
Papamichael, Norma, NY
Paris, Jerome, NY
Parker, Meryl L., NY
Parris, Jerome R., NY
Pasculla, Anthony, NY
Pecoraro, Diana, NY
Pennes, Emilio, NY
Perez, Carmen A.*
Perez, Madeline, NJ
Perno, John, NY
Perrone, Diane, NY
Pervis, Derrick, NY
Petersen, Alan, NY
Pettigrew, Rose A., NY
Phillips, Jennie R., NY
Phillips, Michael*
Pierce, Allison, NY
Pierre-louis, Wilson, NY
Popper, Alan H., NY
Potter, Howard*
Price-Moore, Ms. Jennifer M., NY
Puma, Janis C.*
Purdue, Philip*
Purdy, Thomas J., NY
Quailey, Merville*
Quinn, James F., VA
Ragusa, Rose M.*
Ramadan, Mahmoud, NY
Ramirez, Lisandra, NY
Ramos, Elba I., NY
Ramos, Evelyn, NY
Ray, Lisa A.*
Reed, Anthony, NY
Reid, Diane P., TX
Reinhardt-O'brien, Mary E., NY
Reisman, Barbara, NY
Reitkopf, Patricia B., NY
Reyna, Yocasta, NY
Rice, Yvette*
Richards, Emanuel (Manny) H., Jr., NC
Richardson, Martin L.*
Richardson, Maureen G., NY
Rivera, Daisy*
Rivera, Juanita M.*
Rivera, Maria F., NY
Robinson, Dorothy H.*
Robinson, Willie M.*
Roca, Ronald*
Rodriguez, Awilda, NY
Rodriguez, Olgania, NY
Rodriguez, Rosita*
Roman, Robert, NY
Rosa, Norma E.*
Rosario, Pedro*
Rosenfeld, Marcia C., NY
Roth, Joan L., NY
Royer, Gary, NJ
Ruiz, Jaime*
Russo, Frank P.*
Sampson, Ingrid E., NY
Sandseth, Thomas R., NY
Sanni, Musliu, NY
Sanpietro, David*
Saxton, Wanda D.*
Scanlan, Eileen P.*
Scelta, Gina*
Schieler, Jean M., NY
Schrepel, Raymond J., NY
Scott, Rosalyn, NY
Sekulla, Christina*

Sellers, Terence C., NM
Sharpe, Dolores K., NY
Shinaul, Sherrisse, NY
Silva, Wendy, NY
Silver, Daniel S., NY
Singer, Mark D.*
Singh, Bhimdath*
Singleton, Virginia, NY
Smalls, Jessie, NY
Smith, Corlis Y., NY
Smith, Cynthia R., NY
Smith, Florita E., NY
Sohmer, Robin A.*
Solanke, Yetunde O., NY
Soto, Franklin G.*
Sottile, Marion, NY
Souffrant, Georges M.*
Soukup, Leslie A.*
Spadafora, Ronald R., NY
Spann, Regina M., NY
Spaun, Gregory (Greg) J., NY
Squires, William G.*
Stacy, Jesse*
Stancil, Barbara A., NJ
Stokley, Elly M.*
Stringer, Scott M.*
Sullivan, John J., NY
Sullivan, Paul F.*
Sussman, Laurel W.*
Swan, Eileen F.*
Swanno, Gerard F., NY
Swanston, James E., NY
Tadros, Oudeh M., NY
Tavernier, Tony A.*
Tejada, Rosa, NY
Tesoriero, Thomas J., NY
Thomas, Edmund, NY
Thompson, Chester*
Thompson, Rory S., NY
Tinney, Beverly L.*
Torres, Ana D., NY
Torres, David, NY
Torres, Elizabeth*
Torres, Maria*
Torres, Olga L.*
Tso, Yee B., NY
Tucci, Anthony*
Tziazas, Evagoras*
Tziazas, Pilar, NY
Ur, Joseph, NJ
Urzola, Giovanni J.*
Valentine, Christine, NY
Vaughn, Staci C., NY
Venkersammy, Mark, NY
Villani, Frances*
Vreeland, Nicholas F., NY
Wafula, Bramwell, NJ
Wagner, Harold A., NY
Walden, Kevin J., NY
Walker, Latanya L., NY
Walker, Marvin A.*
Waltman, Michael*
Ward, Florence V., MD
Watson, Georgianna*
Weeden, Thomas A., NY
Wehye, Prince M., NY
Wesby, Darryl K., NY
Whinfield, Dennis, NY
Whitaker, M. Katrina, NY
White, Stephanie, NY
Wildstein, Michael S.*
Williams, David, NJ
Williams, Della L.*
Williams, Jose A., NY
Williams, Kenwyn S., NY
Williams, Le'roy C., NY
Wilson, Andrew J., NY
Wilson, Michael*
Witt, Olin T., NY
Wodarski, Joseph P., Jr., CT
Wolfson, David B., NY
Worley, Donna J., NY
Wright, Joi M.*
Wright, Teresa A., NY
Zazeckie, William J., NY
Ziegler, Jay E., NJ

Zimmerman, Richard E., NY
Zollner, Martin, NY

1987

Abramowitz, Michael, NY
Acevedo, Javier J., NY
Addo-lobo, Kate, NY
Adkins, Lewis W., OH
Aiken, Avril A., NY
Almonor, Danielle**
Amann, Gloria D., NY
Ameen, Bola A.*
Amellio, Renee M.*
Andaluz-scher, Maria, NY
Aniello, Nicholas A., NY
Aptacker, Steven I., NY
Archer, Mable L., NY
Arroyo, Nydia*
Auerbach, Alan R., NY
Ayala, Robert, NY
Ayers, Manford G., NJ
Bailey, Lisa, NY
Baker, Michele C., NY
Barclay, Melina*
Barile, Peter J.*
Barlowe, Brian K., NY
Barrett, C.*
Beckles, Arlene D., NY
Belford, Mary J., NY
Bennie, Michele C.*
Bermann, Julia, NJ
Bernard, Diane M., NY
Bernardez, Carmen L.*
Bernstein, Robert G.*
Bialick, Yifah*
Bittar, Robert N., NY
Boakye-yiadom, Kwame, NY
Bolden, Denise, NY
Boodram, Natalie, NY
Boylan, Mary B.*
Bradley, Donna M., NY
Brady, Gerard D., NY
Brancato, Gregory R., NJ
Brockway, Alvin J., NY
Brooks, Gloria, NY
Brown, Charlane O., NY
Brown, Cheryl A.*
Brown, Herman, NY
Brown, Ian L., NY
Bryan, John*
Burke, Donald H., NY
Burke, Michael N., NY
Cabrera, Daniel, NJ
Calderon, Jose, NY
Cato, Kenrick F., NY
Ceballos, Alba L.*
Chalmers, Trudy O., NY
Chan, Wai H., NY
Chapman, Doris, NY
Chatman, Zemender, VA
Chiarantano, Daniel, NY
Chin, Tin Y., NY
Claro, Brian K., NY
Clouden, George, NY
Codrington, Randolph, NY
Colas, Clotaire*
Cole, Donald M., NY
Colon, Jacqueline, NY
Conry, Steven, NY
Cook, James F.*
Coombs, Kirk*
Cooper, Christopher, NY
Corey, Jessica E., CPP, NY
Cox, Patricia A., NY
Cozens, Mark P., NJ
Crawford, Sheryl*
Cresciullo, Frank*
Cross, Darrell, NY
Crudup, Roslyn S., NY
Cruz, Sylvia*
Culpepper, Steven A., NJ
Curcio, John J.*
D'Angelo, Anthony J.*
D'angelo, Edward, NJ
D'Aponte, Alice*
Davila, Jacinto, GA

Davis, George C.*
Davis, Johnny E., NY
Davis, Kelceda A., NY
Davis, Tarik*
Dawson, Robin D.*
D'Chavez, Nestor*
Desnoyers, Hans N., NY
Detore, Susan*
Diaz, Geneva, NY
Diaz, Gloria, NY
Diaz, Veronica*
Dietz, Michael*
Di Giacomo, Anthony M., NY
Dilone, Rafael, NY
Dipasquale, Catherine*
Dobson, Dexter A., NY
Dodrill, Christopher A., NY
Draffen, Karla J., NY
Dzielski, Michael, NY
Eanniello, Andrew, NY
Eastman, Kenneth N., NY
Ebanks, Norman A., NY
Eddy, Eric, NY
Edwards, Evelyn M., NY
Egbujor, Maryanne*
Eisenstein, Roslyn*
Eng, Thomas, NY
Evans, Elsa, NY
Feliciano, Evelyn, NY
Feliciano, George, NY
Ference, Thomas J., NY
Fernandez, Odalys, NY
Ferraioli, Steven J., NJ
Few, Terry R., NY
Figueroa, Lucinda, NY
Figueroa, Luz I., NY
Finkelstein, Eric L., NY
Finney, John H., NY
Flickstein, Madelon*
Flood, Linda P., NY
Forbes, Carla M., NY
Forsthoff, SGT Roger A., NJ
Fradella, Margaret, NJ
Franqui, Mary A., NY
Frazer, David, NY
Fuller, Leslie G.*
Gaiotti, Helaine J., VT
Gansrow, Ruth, TX
Garcia, Evelyn M., NY
Garcia, Jose L.*
Garcia, Pedro C., NY
Garden, Felix*
Genna, Jay*
Gentil, Mark, NY
Giaccio, William G., NY
Gibson, Robert*
Giordano, David*
Gisors, Roselyne, NJ
Goldson, Kenneth A., NY
Golombek, Leonard, NY
Gonzalez, David*
Gonzalez, Miriam*
Goodloe, Edward O.*
Gordon, Sharon M., NY
Gorman, John, NY
Grant, Colleen, NY
Gray, Antoinette*
Gray, Boima, NY
Green, James, NY
Greenberg, Howard*
Griffin, Osie L., TN
Griffith, Cheryl L., NY
Grimsley, Bernard*
Gross, Arthur, NJ
Gruspier, Charles G., NY
Guerra, Cynthia, NY
Guglielmi, Anthony R., NY
Guttenplan, Sheldon, NY
Hall, Alaric*
Halterman, Carl R.*
Hammie, Keith D., NY
Hancock, Stephen C., NY
Harding, Michael L., NJ
Harrison, Emile R., NY
Hasin, Jill M.*
Hayes, Stephanie D., NY

Heller, Valerie*
Henderson, Sheila*
Henesy, Robert J.*
Hernandez, Hyda D., NY
Hernandez, Jesus J., NY
Herrera, Linda, NY
Heskin, Kathryn F., NY
Hetzel, Maureen A., NY
Hill, Octavia D.*
Hisiger, Kerri I.*
Hoag, Bridget A.*
Hodges, Judith L., NY
Hoffman, Xena H.*
Holt, Sharon P.*
Hopkins, Kevin M., NJ
Horne, Peter, NJ
Howard, Bradley D., NY
Hsueh, John K., NY
Hughes, Karen, NY
Hurley, Jennifer D., NY
Hyde, Dorrel A., NY
Iacovou, Jack, NY
Illas, David, NY
Ilori, John K.*
Intrieri, Dominick D., NY
Jackson, Amanda K.*
Jackson, Katherine L., NY
Jackson, Raymond, NY
Jameson, Luxmore P.*
Jamieson, Peta-gaye, NY
Jarosch, Richard A., NY
Jefferson, Shirley E.*
Jelcic, Thomas A., NY
Jenik, Peter K., NY
Jia, Zongshu*
Jimenez, Linda J., NY
Johnson, Clinton, NY
Johnson, Michael K., NY
Johnson, Patricia R., NY
Jones, Gertrude E., MD
Jones, Vernesa, NY
Kallash, Anas M., NY
Kaplan, Renee E., NY
Kaza, Gandhi*
Kennedy, Angela, FL
Key, Cheryl V., NY
Kieserman, Veronica*
King, John, NY
Kirschner, Kenneth*
Ko, Susan*
Koumides, Steve, NY
Krieger, Brenda T.*
La, Rose M., NY
La, Sala D.*
Ladson, Brenda*
Lam, Alfred, CA
Lamark, Mary R.*
Lashley, Michelle L., NY
Lawton, Kim R., NY
Leach, Preston*
Leader, David K., NY
Leinweaver, Kenneth*
Lennon, Gerard M., NY
Le Pugh, Rosa L.*
Lessner, Lee, NY
Lew, Lisa A., NY
Lewinski, Shari*
Lewis, Michael D.*
Lighty, Michael, NY
Lipari, Donna M., NJ
Litvin, Lawrence H., FL
Lockhart, Colleen M., NY
Longobardi, Ms. Josephine A., NY
Lorde, Deirdre*
Luland, Jane*
Lustgarten, Adam, NY
Maldonado, Ebelia, NY
Maldonado, Elvira*
Maniscalco, Raymond, NY
Mannix, William R., NJ
Mariette, Roberto, NY
Marino, Thomas J.*
Marro, Elizabeth A., NY
Martinez, Annette, NY
Martinez, Robert*

Martino, Victor J., NY
Martins, Colin A.*
Masotti, Alexander, NY
Mathis, Caliph T., NY
Matos, Wendy*
Maysonet, Ana*
Maysonet, Manuel*
Maze, Kathleen*
Mc, Alister K., NY
Mc, Anoff K., NY
Mc, Nally L., NY
McCarthy, Marianne T.*
McCole, Peter, AK
Mcdaniel, Carol D., NY
McField, Mary A.*
McGeehan, Deborah J.*
McKee, John R.*
Mc Kenna, Michael, NY
Mc Leod, Kirk, NY
Meagher, Dr. Patrick B., NJ
Mejias, Edgar, NY
Melendez, Michael J., NY
Mendez, Jorge A., CT
Michel, Olga E., NY
Mignini, Leonard, NY
Mohammad, Taj, NY
Mojica, Kevin*
Molinaro, Ms. Yvette, CA
Monderson, Frederick, NY
Montalbano, John, NY
Montanez, Esteban, NY
Moore, Penelope A., NJ
Mosley, Michelle J., NY
Mueller, Paul K., PA
Mullgrav, Sandra E.*
Murphy, John J., NY
Murphy, Merilee A.*
Murray, James E., NY
Nassofer, Charles, NY
Nath, Nirmala, NY
Naughton, Thomas G., NY
Nawrocki, Mary-lynn, VA
Negron, Luis*
Negroni, Deborah, NY
Nelson, Nora A., NY
Niamonitakis, Steven, NY
Nieves, Antonio*
Nieves, Mayra*
Njoku, Aloysius A., NY
Nnorom, Gladys*
Nosek, Frank R., NY
Nota, Yicel*
Nugent, Thomas, NJ
Ocasio, Roger, NY
O'donnell, Irene M., NY
O'hare, Aileen, NY
Okhiku, Ayo A., NY
O'loughlin, Dennis, NY
Omar, Abubakar O., NJ
Ortiz, Herb A.*
Ortiz, Yolanda R., NY
Ortolano, Lisa, NY
Osattin, Philip, NY
O'shaughnessy, Jeremiah, NY
Page, Shawnee, NY
Parker, Jackie T.*
Parsons, Ronald D., NY
Pataki, Steven, NY
Patterson, Corenthia*
Patterson, Richard*
Pavia, Edward J., NY
Paz, Juan C.*
Pelle, James, NY
Pepe, Michael T., NY
Perez, Beatriz A., NY
Perez, Jose L.*
Perez, Maria E., NY
Perez, Maribel, NY
Perez, Sandra*
Perez, William*
Pernice, Louis R., NY
Pescatore, Michael M.*
Petcharak, Ekprawat*
Pichardo, Francisca, NY
Pierre, Marylin, NY
Pitt, Christopher L., NY

Planas, Evelyn*
Pleeter, Glenn R., NY
Plunkett, Gavin N.*
Polly, Michael C., NY
Powell, Dalvanie K., NY
Priester, Myron*
Prisco, John J., NJ
Providence, Sharon, NY
Prozeller, Andrew*
Prozeller, Rachel W.*
Prysock, Jeanine M., NY
Quarino, Lawrence A.*
Quinn, John W., Esq., NY
Rago, Jodi J., NY
Ramirez, Jose*
Ranieri, John**
Ray, Bernard*
Reardon, Katherine B., NY
Reid, Deborah E.*
Reyes, William M., NY
Rhoden, Horace, NY
Richards, Jodi J., CA
Richardson, Cheryl J., NY
Rikoon, Elizabeth J., NY
Rivera, Maritza*
Rivera, Zenaida*
Robles, Rosa E.*
Rodgers, Karen P., NY
Rodriguez, Joanne*
Rogers, Timothy L., NY
Rohan, James, NY
Rohan, Kevin, NY
Rojas, Lee Y., NY
Roman, Ana J., NY
Roper, Kenneth A., NY
Rosado, Mercedes, NY
Rose, Brigitte, NY
Ruiz-Basquez, Luisa E., NY
Russell, Michel M., AE
Russo, Lucia, NY
Saldivar, Philip D., NY
Sampson, Marcia E., PA
Sanchez, Richard T.*
Sanchirico, Susan M.*
Santoro, Charles S., NY
Sarach, Omar J., NY
Satterfield, Kevin, NY
Savage, Patricia D., NY
Scarmalis, Barbara K., FL
Schnitzler, Fran E.*
Schoen, Richard M., NY
Scolaro, John F., NY
Scott, Marjorie, NY
Seestedt, Tad H., NY
Segur, Webb, NY
Selkowitz, Steven R., NY
Sigelakis, Dolores A.*
Simms, Clarence J., NY
Sinclair, Michael C., NY
Singer, David A.*
Singleton, Janice, NY
Skuludis, Theodora, NY
Smith, Wayne J., NY
Sorge, Glenn W., NJ
Soto, Jacqueline*
Sousa, Robert, NY
Spellman, Kenneth M., NJ
Spera, David N., NY
Sroka, Annette M., NY
Stanton, Matthew S., NY
Steinhauser, Ina, NY
Steward, Dominique K., NY
Stewart, Hazel L., NY
Stortz, Herbert A., NY
Strachan, Miriam E., NY
Sullivan, Michael K., NY
Taveras, Mayra*
Taylor, Virginia, NY
Telesco, Grace A., NY
Tersigni, Christopher T., FL
Thomas, Lorna M., NY
Thomas, Peter L., NY
Thomas, Rosalind Y.*
Thompsen, Linda L.*
Thorpe, Evelyn*
Tierney, Matthew T.*

Tighe, Michael R., NY
Tobin, Joseph X., NY
Toledo, Lorenzo*
Torres, Eduardo, NY
Tripplin, Crystal L., NY
Ulm-singleton, Sharon C.*
Van, Wygerden P.*
Vanderburgh, Thomas, NJ
Vanegas, Louis*
Vaream, Richard, NY
Vazquez, Janette, NY
Veesart, Dawn C.*
Vega, Ernan, Jr., NY
Velez, Victor*
Venditto, Anthony M., Esq., NY
Venegas, Margarita*
Victor, Chilov, NY
Viggiano, Doreen M., NY
Vilme, Jeannette, NY
Vitolo, William (Billy) R., NJ
Wagenstein-Vega, Carla, NY
Wahab, Naeem M.*
Waite-carson, Gloria, NY
Walcott, Sonja M.*
Walker, Elizabeth Y.*
Wallace, Lanora*
Walle, Brenda, NY
Walsh, Lawrence G., NY
Wan, Chung N., NY
Washington, Genesis, NY
Washington, Sheldon*
Wasserman, David, CT
Watson, Alwyn, NY
Watson-tucker, Robin*
Weinberg, Jeffrey, NJ
White, Gilbert O.*
White, James J., NY
White, Michael W., NY
Whitney-shuler, Wanda D., NY
Wierzbicki, Stanley, NY
Williams, Bridget L., NY
Williams, Janice V.*
Williams, Johnnymae, NY
Williams, Paulette M.*
Williams, Richard R., NY
Winn, Mrs. Martha D., NY
Wint, Anthony O.*
Woodburn, Antonette*
Yagual, Magali E., TX
Young, Dawn, NY
Youngs, Michael G., NY
Zarrillo, Tina, NY
Zinnerman, Alva, NY
Zweibel, Patrick, NY

1988

Abimbola, Ayetigbo C., NY
Acevedo, Carmelo, NY
Addie-kennedy, Darlene L.*
Agatstein, Phyllys, NY
Ajah, Efut, FL
Aleman, Kleber E., NY
Alleva, Nicholas, NY
Alvarez, Adam*
Alvarez, Ana A., NY
Alvear, Mrs. Bonnie S., NY
Amaya, Allan F., NY
Ambrosio-dey, Maria, NY
Ando, Scott M., LA
Andreasen, Michele*
Ayetigbo, Abimbola*
Baaske-Rodriguez, Anna*
Baddoo, Juliana, NY
Bahna, Alfred M., NY
Bailey, Kathy F.*
Bakare, Raheem*
Barclay, Roosevelt*
Barnswell, James N.*
Beacco, Joseph M., NY
Bergner, Kevin, VA
Bermudez, Yvette, NY
Billitteri, Christina, FL
Bink, Melissa L.*
Bongiovanni, R., NY
Borsilli, Mildred O., NY
Boston, Karen, NY

Bottoms, Joy L.*
Boyce, Duwayne*
Braff, Neil S., NY
Branic, Doretha, NY
Braxton, Melvin*
Brill, Adam H., NY
Brisbane, Joyce L., NY
Brown, Robin, NV
Brown, Shanteil, NY
Brown, Valerie A.*
Brun, Gina, NY
Burch, Felicia, NY
Burd, Dr. Marc A., NY
Buscaglia, Joann, NY
Butkiewicz, Susan, NY
Butler, Robert E., NY
Cafarelli, Michael L., NJ
Canacoo, Seth, NY
Caputo, John, NY
Carradero, Wilfredo, NY
Ceballos, Amelia A., NY
Chambers, Debra L.*
Chaparro, Hiram, NY
Chillo, Generoso A., NY
Chisolm, Karen A., SC
Chong, Gayle E., NY
Christman, Donald*
Chung, Judy Y., NY
Ciringione, Frank J., NJ
Clark, Georganna, NY
Clarke, Denise L., NY
Clements, Lavonda D., NY
Collazo, Diana, NY
Conlon, Paul J.*
Cooke, Phylis B.*
Cranford, Charles, Jr., NY
Crimmins, James P.*
Cruz, Nancy, NY
Cuevas, Ana V.*
Cuffari, Josephine, NY
Darsillo, Francis, NY
Davis, Edward A.*
Davis, Lynette, NY
De, Vertevil S., NY
De Jesus, Anna M.*
Deleon, Marcia*
Delgado-rios, Lisa, NJ
Demeo, Steven*
Dey, William F., NY
DiBrizzi, Michael A., Esq., NY
Dinkel, Ross E.*
Dixon, Sharon H., NY
Douglas, Laura V., NY
Douthit, Teresa M., MD
Duncan, Darryl*
Dunn, Thomas J., NY
Durham, Bette L., NY
Dwyer, Douglas R., NY
Elcik, James J., NY
Elliott, Sean M., NY
Elmore, Ronald*
Emanuel, Peter S., NY
Erosa, Manuel L., NY
Etkins, Margaret R.*
Falk, Selwyn*
Farquharson, Paul, NY
Farrar, Deborah R., NY
Feinblatt, Barbara*
Felix, Suzanne, PA
Fernandez, Carlos J.*
Ferrara, Vivian, MD
Figueroa, Miguel A., NY
Fisher, Steven A., NY
Fitzgerald, John K., NY
Fitzgibbon, John, NY
Forestieri, Paul J., NY
Frazier, Gloria D., NY
Freeman, Aldric, NY
Fujawa, Andrea*
Garcia, Julie M.*
Garland, Daniella, NY
Garvey, Eileen P., NY
Gayle, Armena D., NY
Genovese, Dominic A., NY
Gilchrest, Cheryl L.*
Girau, Rosalie*

Glover, Damon A.*
Goicochea-Bonilla, S., NY
Gonzalez, Angel L., NY
Gonzalez, Carlos M.*
Gonzalez, Frances*
Gonzalez, Gregory*
Gotay, Beverly A.*
Gousse, Sonhita, FL
Grant, Jule A., NY
Gray, Teresina*
Graziani, Noel E., NY
Greenwood, Deidra, NY
Greer, Michele A., NY
Greer, Stephanie E., NY
Groody, John M.*
Hall, Valrie C.*
Harmon, Adrienne*
Hayes, Clarence E., NJ
Healy, Michael F., NY
Hemming, Norman*
Hendrick, Carl, NY
Henry, Adrienne A.*
Hernandez, Ivelisse*
Hernandez, Mercedes*
Heyward, Tina M., NY
Ho, Jei-fu, NY
Hobson, Kendall G., NY
Hodges, Phyllis, NY
Holland, Linda J., NJ
Holliman, Jeffrey, NY
Holloman, G. B., NY
Holmes, Ronald K.*
Huber, Paul, WV
Hughes, C.*
Hunter, Lydia A.*
Hynes, Stephen D., NY
Indelicato, James, NJ
Indio, Sylvia*
Ingram, Garrett, NY
Iscen, Nebahat S.*
Jalaf, Gabi G., NY
James, Claudia L., NY
James, Michael G., NY
James, Sherwyn*
Janzekovich, Robert, NJ
Jeffrey, Clinton G.*
Jensen, Donna*
Jimenez, Sergio*
Jochim, Myron W., NY
Johnson, Evelyn, NY
Johnson, Ophelia T., NY
Jolly, Andrea P., NY
Jones, Carolyn M., NY
Jones, Lisa K.*
Joseph, Dominique*
Kadir, Maqsood U., PhD, CT
Kanrich, Susan, NJ
Katz, Richard, FL
Kaufman, Benjamin, NY
Kawalec, Lisaann*
Keleman, Robert, NY
Kelly, Eileen*
Kelly, Robert T.*
Kerr, Barbara*
Khan, Imran E., NY
Kiely, Gregory, NY
Kiggins, Rebecca*
Kinney, Susan, NY
Kinsey, Barbara, NY
Kirst, Kevin, NJ
Klein, Debra*
Kleman, Maryline E., NY
Klug, Kenneth C., NY
Knoblich, James P., NY
LaChanas, Christiano, NY
Laureano, M. M.*
Lawrence, Darcel Y., NY
Lawson, Cecelia B., NY
Lee, Monique L., NY
Leone, Steven C., NY
Lerner, Steven A., NY
Levine, Aaron J.*
Levins, Thomas W.*
Libretti, Lisa*
Linares, Virginia, NY
Long, David S., NY

Lopez, Carmen L., NY
Lorimer, Philip, CPM, NJ
Lugo, Jose A., NY
Lynch, Elda M., NY
MacDowell, Rick W., NY
Maillard, Patricia L., NY
Major, Livingstone R., NY
Makahon, James R., NY
Marcano, Maribel V., NY
Maria, Manuela*
Marshall, Mauline A., NY
Martin, Annette M., NY
Martin, Duane, NY
Mascari, John C., NY
Mathis, Stacey O.*
Matos, Miguel A.*
Maysonet, Elsie*
Mazzella, James, NY
McClean, Monique D., NY
Mcnamara, Joan B., NY
Melian, Octavia A., NY
Messana, Joseph, NY
Michelakou, Sophie, NY
Migdal, Sandra, NY
Miller, Daniel, NY
Molina, Maria T., NY
Monroig, Madeline*
Montanez, Shirley A., NY
Moore, Sherry R., NY
Morales, Charles W., NY
Moreno, Ms. Evelyn, NY
Moreno, Juan, Jr., FL
Morey, Nadege, NY
Mormino, Bennett, NY
Moss, Corey B.*
Murphy, Timothy I.*
Murray, June A.*
Myers, Carol A., NY
Nanton, Willena, NY
Neenan, Kevin M., PA
Nicholas, Lester S., NY
Nichols, Ferdinanda W., NJ
Nieves, Dominick R., NY
Nieves, Luis F.*
Ninomiya, Marilyn J., FL
Nixon, Stephanie R.*
Noel, Samuel D., NY
Noutsky, Martin, NY
O'Brien, Dennis M., NY
Ochrym, Lois C.*
O'Connor, Karen, NY
Ogiste, Christopher*
O'Keefe, William J.*
O'Neil, Lysheka L.*
O'neill, James P., NY
Ong, Johnny H., NY
O'rourke, Brian, NY
Ortego, Alan*
Ovando, Percida R., NY
Pagan, Luz C.*
Page, Denise*
Pappalardo, Vivian, NY
Paraskevas, Melissa, NY
Parker, Kim, MD
Parks, Bruce C., WV
Parrino, Joseph J., NY
Pearce, William, NY
Pearson, Ida, NY
Pellegrino, Michael*
Pennetti, Salvatore, NY
Phillips, Anthony R., NY
Phillips, Lorraine*
Phillips, Theresa A., NY
Piggott, Margaret*
Pinnock, Tania N., NY
Pisani, Michael T., NY
Pizarro, Ramona, NY
Potucek, Daniel R., NY
Powell, Kerwin M., NY
Priola, Leo V.*
Quaranto, John C., NY
Quigley, Donald M., NY
Quinones, Mariluz, NY
Rabel, Ilzee, FL
Radoslovich, Dario, NY
Raines, Alfonso D., NY

Ramirez, Carlos, NY
Randazzo, Gary G., NY
Ranieri, Nicholas*
Rauch, Richard S., NY
Reid, Sharon*
Reilly, Peter J., NY
Reinoso, Rafael A., NY
Renda, Eugene, NY
Reynolds, Bertrand A., NY
Richardson, Kevin S., NY
Riedinger, Guy E., NY
Rios, Diana, NY
Robertson, Roy, NY
Rocco, Michael J.*
Rock, Allen C., NY
Rodriguez, Lissette*
Rodriguez, Ruth M., NY
Rogers, Jennifer L., NY
Romain, Mario, NY
Roman, Linda S., NY
Rosario, Reynaldo*
Rose, Fitzerrol*
Ruck, Songa L., NY
Rudowitz, Bruce S., NY
Rueda, Zoila N., NY
Russo, Daniel R.*
Salas, Ivan, NY
Sambor, Shelley*
Sandoval, Janet*
Santoro, Thomas D., NY
Santos, Omar R., NY
Satiro, Raymond, NY
Sayers, Sylma C., NY
Scarborough, Stacey, NY
Schecter, Robert J., NY
Schiralli, Anthony M., NJ
Scrimenti, Doreen R.*
Seegopaul, B., NY
Servis, Anthony, NJ
Silfen, Moses*
Simone, Annette T.*
Simorella, Paul, NY
Sinclair, Andrene S., NJ
Sneed, Karen, NY
Snella, Mark A., NY
So, Hoi-ming, NY
Soo-hoo, William, NY
Soto, Javier, NY
Sowell, Tanya*
Stack, Maurice J., NY
Stein, Eugene P., NY
Stelling, Barbarann, NY
Stengel, Meredith L.*
Sturges, Nancy B.*
Sullivan, Lisa*
Sullivan, Stephen D.*
Svec, Kimberley, AL
Swindell, Darryl A., MA
Taras, Joseph G., NY
Taylor, Albert, FL
Taylor, Dina*
Terilli, Michael, AE
Thomas, Gary E., NY
Toal, Brian J., NY
Toorie, Trudy A., NY
Torres, Ivonne*
Torres, Nelson, NY
Tortora, Joseph, NY
Tosado, Mariveila, NY
Tripi, Anthony F., NY
Turner, Colon L.*
Tynes, Harcourt A., III, NY
Vails, Dawn, NY
Vasseghi, Fereydun*
Vaughn, Carmella*
Veloz, Migdalia E.*
Vereen, Beverly F., NY
Vicks, Leah D., MD
Vinson, Deborah D., NY
Vitole, Jeffrey M., NJ
Vivo, Robert F., NY
Walker, Shirley E., NY
Walsh, Jeanne M., NY
Washington, Kim, NY
Watkins, Keith*
Watlington, James L., NY

Wells, Anthony G.*
Welsh, Christopher, NY
White, Elaine*
Wiggins, Robert G., NY
Williams, Andel G., CA
Williams, Cynthia, NY
Williams, Ivy C., NY
Williams, Jewel, NY
Williams, Kenneth R., NY
Williams, Richelle, NY
Williams, Samuel W., NY
Wilson, William*
Wolfmann, Monik H., NY
Woseley, Hollis M., NY
Wyatt-diaz, Lisa, NY
Yaghdjian, Vicken*
Yera, John, VA
Young, David F., NY
Yu, Andy, NY
Zorn, Andrew G., IL

1989
Abarca, Elizabeth*
Abdallah, Jimmy*
Abreu, Maria T., NY
Acevedo, Nancy, NY
Ahmed, Abdul M., NY
Alerte, Gary C., FL
Alexander, Beverly J., NY
Alicea, Ana*
Alkhayat, A.*
Ally, Sydney*
Alvarez, Cathy, NY
Amezquita, Michael*
Ancrum, Alberta, NY
Anderle, Joseph W., NY
Andrews, Joy A., NY
Anduze, Kenneth R., NY
Antoine, McFredy, NY
Antonelli, Ralph, NY
Aponte, Gina, NY
Arce, Jose M., NY
Argentine, Michele, NY
Armstrong-barrows, Valerie F., NY
Arroyo, David, NY
Arzola, Elizabeth, NJ
Asad, Jamal M., NY
Avallone, Carolann, NY
Avila, Douglas E., NY
Ayala, Judith M.*
Ayala, Maria, NY
Ayala-devito, Linda, NY
Bacon, Cynthia, GA
Bailey, Christine, NY
Balunas, William E., NY
Barkley, Darlene, NY
Barnes, Carrol D.*
Barnes, Wallace, NY
Baron, Sherry C.*
Bartiromo, Michael, NY
Barton, Jeffrey A., NV
Batista, Manuel L., NY
Bauza, Lourdes*
Baylor, Charlene, NY
Been, Monette L., NY
Beers, Albert S., NJ
Behlin, Charlotte E., NY
Belle, Franklin D., NY
Bello, Joseph J., NY
Benedetto, George, NY
Berkley, Denise, NY
Besse, Marysa J.*
Best, William S., NY
Blake, T. K.*
Blum, Steven*
Bonds, Charles W., MD
Bonds, Cheryl D., NY
Boone, Vernette L., NY
Bossa, Anna L., NY
Bostic, Lydia A.*
Bota, Heidi, NY
Bouccara, Martine J.*
Bouillon, Stephen, NY
Bourdon, Martha L., NY
Bovea, Liana, FL

Boylan, Joan, NY
Boyle, Christopher*
Braun, Eileen E., NY
Britton, Lyria K., NY
Brooks, Michele, NY
Brown, Angela R., CA
Brown, Brian K., NY
Brown, Charles R., NY
Brown, Delroy, NY
Brown, Lashawn*
Brunson, Sharon B., NY
Buccino, Peter J., NY
Buckley, Christopher*
Burns, Jeanette*
Burton, Charlane*
Burwell, Louise M., NY
Cabral, Raymond, NY
Cabrera, Leslie C.*
Calvo, Jenny M., NY
Candia, Fernando A., NY
Cantone, Michael D., NJ
Capers, Cheryl E.*
Caputo, James M., NY
Carey, James P., NY
Carpio, Marcus, NY
Carr, Alicia A.*
Carr, Autuam D., NY
Carrington, Keith B.*
Casanova, Veronica, NY
Casey, Michael P., NY
Cashin, Margarette, NY
Cassidy, Susan E., NY
Castagna, Alfred R., NY
Castillo, Karla C., NY
Castria, Frank A.*
Castro, Debra, NY
Castro, Deron R., NY
Casul, Efrain*
Cates, Bernice, NY
Cerven, James F., NY
Chadwick, Keith, NY
Chambers, Robert F., NY
Chan, William, NY
Charles, Victor D.*
Chaves, Gladys J.*
Cheatham, Anthony, NY
Chernick, Steven M., NY
Cherry, Tyrone, NY
Chille, Edward, NY
Chin, David*
Chodakiewicz, Thomas, NY
Chorzewski, Robert, NY
Church, Robin A., NY
Ciavarella, Joanne, NY
Clark, Jeffrey W., NJ
Clark, William D., NY
Clarke, Selwart R., NY
Clemente, Dionne D.*
Clemente, Michael A., NY
Cobb, Michael A., NY
Coffey, Thomas K., NY
Colasuonno, Dominick, NY
Colon, Diana A., NY
Concepcion, Idaly, NY
Conlon, Brian*
Connor, Steven, AR
Corbin, Marguerita*
Corrado, Vincent J., NY
Cortes, Nelida, NY
Coveleski, Joyce E., NY
Creary, Michael C., NY
Crocilla, Daniela*
Crockett, Timothy A.*
Cruz, Gloria C., NY
Cuevas, Doris M., NY
Cumberbatch, Anita*
Cutchin, Steven D.**
Cyran, Paul, NY
Dampeer, Sherrie F.*
Dare, Joseph O.*
David, Fredrick D., NY
David, Joycelyn P., NY
Davila, Sandra M., NY
Davis, Sonya, NY
Degen, Daniel W.*
Deluca, Henry, NY

Delvalle, Carlos, NY
Demby, Janice, NJ
D'Erasmo, Maria L., NY
Desbiens, Gregory M.*
Desio, Frances M., NY
Desousa, Neil, NY
Dewberry, Valerie M., NY
Diaz, Carmen I., NY
Diaz, Conception M., NY
Difiglia, Samuel J., NY
Dillon, Frank, NJ
Dingal, Wilfredo R.*
Disarno, Michael T., NJ
D'meza, Ruth, NY
Dolan, Christine, NY
Donaldson, Michelle, NY
Donlon, John L., NY
Donohue, Luisa M., NY
Dooley, Joan T., NY
Doolittle, Nancy L.*
Dorogoff, Paul A., NY
Dougherty, William, NY
Douglas, Gibbon E., NY
Dove, Darlene C., NY
Dowd, Lorraine E., NY
Dreyfuss, Caron D.*
Driscoll, John G., NY
Dubois, Charmian E., NY
Dudley, Celeste*
Duncan, Garfield S., NY
Dundon, Reilly J., NJ
Duprey, Richard*
Durkin, Mary A., NY
Edreira, Anna-marie, NY
Edwards, F. M.*
Edwards, Patrick L., NY
Edwards, Randy M., NY
Eichner, Andrew J., NY
Eilbeck, Jean C., NY
Ekstrom, Charles A., CT
Erazo, Elliot, NJ
Etheridge, Crystal*
Evans, Ann M.*
Fahy, Michael*
Faison, Sylvia, NY
Falero, Joseph*
Fannon, Richard P., NY
Farrell, Thomas, NY
Farrice, Edward P., NY
Fay, Catherine, VT
Fenty, Michael A.*
Ferguson, Lois G.*
Ferguson, Terry A., NY
Fernandez, Australia, NY
Fernandez, Mercedes, NY
Figueroa, Alexander*
Figueroa, Blanche, NY
Figueroa, Luis A., NY
Figueroa, Monica P., NY
Fischer-Long, J., NY
Flores, Arsenio, NY
Flores, Jimmy, NY
Forde, Angela E., NY
Fortune, Christine*
Fray, Harold J., NY
Frazier, David H.*
Freed, Lesly W., NY
Fusco, Peter*
Ganu, Komla S., NY
Garcia, Aixa J., NY
Garcia, Claire M., NY
Garcia, Gonzalo*
Garris, Tanya J., MD
Gasparino, John J., NY
Gee, Peter, NY
Gegrin, Rhonda L.*
George, Ann M.*
Gianfrancesco, Paul, PA
Gilkes, Kathy A.*
Gill, Adonica E., NY
Gillen, Laurie A.*
Girault, Marie, NY
Giscome, Mario, NY
Gomez, George, NY
Gonzalez, Anthony, NY
Gonzalez, Emilio, NY

Gonzalez, Luis A.*
Goodman, Mary B., NY
Gordon, Davina S., NY
Gorman, Timothy P., NY
Gormley, Paula E., NY
Graham, Janet A., NY
Grant, Lillie, NY
Grant, Vivienne J., NY
Gravesandy, Colin S., NY
Green, Valerie M., NY
Greenberg, Jonathan F., FL
Greenspan, Lisa*
Griffin, Dennis M., NY
Griffin, Thomas M.*
Grossi, Roxana I.*
Grullon, Mario E., NY
Gudowitz, Peter M., CO
Guerrero, Daniel G., NY
Guzman, Neida V., NY
Hackle, Kirk D., NY
Hagerty, Brian D., NY
Halecki, Krzysztof, NY
Halpern, Samuel B., NY
Halsey, Sylvia R.**
Hanney, Thomas V., NY
Harfmann, Lawrence, NY
Harris, Hugh A., NY
Harris, Will C., III, NY
Hart, Susin B., NJ
Haskins, Kimberley A., NY
Hawkins, Michael L., NY
Head, Sidney W., Sr., NY
Hemingway, Richard C., NY
Herencia, Craig, NY
Hernandez, Virginia, NY
Hess, Donna A., NY
Hill, Kenneth O.*
Hill, Mozell S.*
Hill, Renee C., NY
Hinds, Barry M., NY
Hobson, Richard, NY
Hodge, Marie A.*
Holder, Eleanor*
Holder, Lorna I., NY
Holder, Maxcine R.*
Holland, Sandra A.*
Holland, William G.*
Holmes, Ian*
Horace, Sara J., MI
Hough, Deborah J.*
Howard, Keith S., NY
Howard, Timothy, CT
Huang, Yi, NY
Hugee, Angela L., NY
Hughes, James D., NY
Hutchinson, J., GA
Hutchinson, Nikki*
Idowu, Frances A., NY
Iloka, Samuel C., NJ
Irvine, Raymond*
Isaacs, Waymond Q., NY
Iyalla, Tina A., NY
Jackson, Gwendolyn*
James, Melissa A., NY
James, Walter A., NY
Janneck, Walter F., NJ
Jaudon, Gerald J., NY
Jean-Baptiste, C., NY
Jenkins, Patricia, NY
Jennings, Charles R., NY
Jn-Marie, Monique*
John, Jacqueline D., NY
Johnson, Ramona C., NY
Johnston, Deanna M., NY
Jones, Bobby R., NY
Jones, Cassandra D., CA
Kalisky, Alan M., NY
Karlovitch, Jay, FL
Kelly, Cheryl R., NY
Kelly, Joi C., NY
Kennedy, Henry W., NY
Kerr, Frederic G.*
Kersellius, Gavin I., NY
Keyes, James D.*
Khan, Salima J., NY
Kiggins, Timothy J.*

King, Eric D., AZ
Kinley, Kevin, NY
Kiyat, Aycan*
Klein, Richard J., NY
Klein, Robert E., NJ
Kleinman, James R.*
Knights, Robert A., NY
Krumholtz, Cindy*
Kulyrych, Lubomyr P., NY
Kuszel, Philip, NY
Kwakye-Berko, B., NY
Lacassagne, Monica, NY
Lagano, Christopher, CT
Laikhram, Sharmila*
Lam, David*
Lang, Pamela D., NY
Lavin, Christopher, NY
Lee, Amy R., NY
Lee, M. J., NY
Lemmonds, Michelle, NY
Lenz, Tracy, NY
Leonard, Sean R., NJ
Lewis, Shalleter*
Lewis, Yolanda Y., NY
Lindgren, George A., NJ
Lo, Eliza, NY
Lopez, Antonio E., NY
Lopez, Carlos A.*
Lopez, Mayra, NY
Loresto, Emil J., NY
Loughlin, Terence A., NY
Lovell, Brian I., CT
Low, Elvis T., NY
Luffman, John P.*
Luna, Sandra, NY
Lunn, Joyanne E., NY
MacFarlane, Lavinia*
Madgett, Brian, CO
Mahany, Annemarie, FL
Majette, Jeffrey T.*
Maldonado, Patricia A., NY
Maley, James E., Jr., NY
Manahan, William F., NY
Mandile, Frank A., NY
Maner, Benjamin, GA
Manfredy, Anna A., NY
Manning, Lisa D.*
Manning, Trevor E., NY
Marion, Dorothy M., NY
Markowitz, Paul B., NY
Marshall, Vanessa M., MD
Marti, John L., NY
Martin, Sherly M., NY
Martinez, Jose M.*
Martinez, Kendall, NY
Martinez, Marlene, NY
Martinez, Miriam C.*
Masiello, Samuel J.*
Masterson, Kevin M., NY
Mateo, Octavio C.*
Matias, Jose*
Mauro, Patrick, NY
Maynard, Carol R., NY
Mayo, Charles*
Mazyck, Burnetta F.*
Mazzola, Joseph C.*
Mcfarlane, Barbara, NY
Mcghee, Liza, NY
McGrann, Joseph P., NY
McGuinness, Hugh, NC
McLeod, Andrea M., NY
McManus, John J., NY
Mcnally, Terence E., NY
McNulty, John K.*
Mead, Dianne J., NY
Medina, Luis A., NY
Medows, Deborah, NY
Meier, Patricia M., NY
Melendez, David, NY
Mellado, Cristina B., NY
Mendez, Zenaida, NY
Miller, Amy B., NJ
Miller, Gail E., NY
Mims, Venetia L., NY
Miranda, Lizette*
Miranda, Yvette M., NY

Mohammed, Elton B.*
Molligo, Wilma*
Monaghan, John G.*
Montague, Angela R., PA
Montgomery, Victor, NY
Moore, Tanya M., NY
Moorhead, Henry A., NY
Morales, Alejandra, NY
Moran, Eucaris C.*
Morillo, Luis R., NY
Morris, John A., NY
Morris, Linda C.*
Morrison, Steven J., NY
Moss, Cathy N., NY
Mossa, Vincent A., NY
Mulligan, Thomas F., NY
Mullings, Sandra G.*
Munoz, Antonio, NJ
Munoz, John, NY
Munoz, Julio E., NY
Murphy, Anne M.*
Murro, John*
Myers, Lonnie, NY
Ndreu, Firdez, NY
Neary, Donna, NY
Needleman, Ira J., PA
Nelson, Lynda D., NY
Nelson, Noel N., NY
Nesfield, Dale D., NY
Newman, Kim, NY
Ng, Frank K., NY
Ng, Tim, NY
Nicholas, Clinton*
Nicola, Christos, NY
Nieves, Ana M.*
Nieves, Jaime, NY
Nuccio, Anthony J., NJ
Nyameme, Helen*
O'conner, Hilda N., NY
O'Connor, Kevin M., NY
Oechsler, George P.*
O'estricher, Marlo, NY
Olsen, Steven, NY
Onufurko, Neoni*
Ortiz, Joseph A., NY
Ortiz-cruz, Milagros, NY
Ortlieb, Robert J., NY
O'Shaughnessy, John*
Pabon, Enrique*
Pagan, Desiree L.*
Pannell, Derwin D., NY
Parrino, Irene R., NY
Parris, Cecilia G., NY
Patel, Mayank R., NY
Pedraza, Evelyn, NY
Pego, Michelle M., NY
Pellicano, John M., NY
Pena, Juan D.*
Perez, Juan A., NY
Person, Brenda, NY
Peterson, Ilayne N.*
Petty, Camille B., NY
Piekarski-rome, Cynthia, NC
Pierre-jackson, Paula, NY
Pierre Pierre, Eddy, NY
Pignataro, John V., NY
Pijaca, John A., MA
Pinckney, Irene C., NY
Plamenco, Roberto C., CA
Plasencia, Dedie, NY
Plisner, Sylvia, NY
Pollydore, Wanda*
Powell, Hettie V., NY
Powers, Derek L., NY
Powers, Robert, NY
Prestia, Michael, NY
Prestia, Michael A., NY
Price, Vincent, NY
Prinz, Ellen M., NY
Quamina, Michelle R., NY
Quinata, Alice E.*
Rabinowitz, Stacey M., NY
Rafferty, Richard M., CT
Railey, Robert*
Rainey, Eugene, NY
Raldiris, Carlos J., TX

Ramos, Denyse N., FL
Raptis, Thomas N., NY
Rehal, Joseph G., NY
Reid, Kenneth, NY
Reid, LaLisa, NY
Reiss, Gary, NY
Renaud, Jacqueline, NY
Reyes, Anthony*
Reyes, Rachel, NY
Reynolds, Stephen, NY
Rhoden, Audrey E., NY
Rhodes, Frank J., NY
Ricalde, Russell J., NY
Riccio, Rose M.*
Richardson, Joanne A., NY
Ridley, Grace E., NY
Rivera, Wilfredo, CT
Rodriguez, Elizabeth, NY
Rodriguez, Gilbert, NY
Rodriquez, Yvonne*
Rogan, Daniel J.*
Rollock, Roderick, NY
Romagnoli, Michael, NY
Roman, Angel L., NY
Ronda, Anthony*
Rondon, Julia M., NY
Rosado, Rocky*
Rosario, Georgette, NY
Rosario, Percida, NY
Ross, Jennifer, IL
Rowser, Helene*
Russo, Dora, NY
Russo, Gina A.*
Russo, Joseph P., NY
Ryant, Regina P.*
Ryden, Carolyn Y., NY
Ryniak, William A., NJ
Sabeti-kolahi, Shahra*
Salamy, Joseph M., CA
Salvatto, Candace L.*
Samuels, Levi E., FL
Sanchez, Maria M.*
Sanchez, Milagros, NY
Sanes, Anthony, FL
Santana, Alberto, NY
Santiago, Annette, NY
Santos, Nancy, NY
Santos-hatoum, Mayra*
Schirtzer, Robert*
Schletter, Donna L., NY
Schwarz, Daniel*
Scott, Ann T., NY
Scott, Edward S., DC
Scully, James J.**
Seabrook, Stephanie, NY
Seedman, Elizabeth, NY
Seidel, Michael J.*
Seney, John F.*
Sepulveda-tusa, Vivian*
Sermet, Carmen M., NY
Shaleesh, LT William, NY
Shedden, Stephen B., NY
Shinaba, Jumoke D., NY
Sibblies, Lauri S., NY
Simmons, Glynice L.*
Sinatra, Francis A., NY
Sitaras, K.*
Slattery, Joseph W., NY
Smikle, Conrad M., NY
Smith, Arlene A., NY
Smith, Henry C.*
Smith, Linda M.*
Smith, Steven A., NY
Smith, Steven D., NY
Soler, Hiram*
Solorzano, Sandra, NY
Soto, Jose J.*
Spanower, Michael J., NY
Sparovich, Gustavo*
Spencer, Jeri-lyn*
Spiritosanto, Anton, PA
Spodek, Amy*
Stallworth, Diane L.*
Stayments, Bruce, NY
Stern, Barry P., NJ
Stetson, Ms. Eleanor L., NY

Stewart, Carol M., NY
Straub, R. F., NY
Stroman, Sharon A.*
Stuart, Tara A.*
Sullivan, Claudia, NY
Sullivan, Kevin L., NY
Sumner, Sally L., NY
Surless, James M., NY
Swasey, Arthur M., NY
Sydelman, Lesley J., NY
Tallent, Thomas P., NY
Tansey, Karen*
Tavarez, Julie*
Taveras, Jacqueline, NY
Tejada, Kelly O.*
Theophanous, T.*
Thomas, Trevor A., NY
Thompson, Kenneth, NY
Thorbs, Carlene O., NY
Tomczak, Jill, NY
Toner, Lisa J.*
Toro, Salvador, NY
Torres, Michelle, NY
Tow, Dean O., NY
Treible, Roy D., MA
Trial-O'Neil, Annette S.*
Triola, Michael, NY
Tripp, Peter G., NY
Tuffey, Thomas V., NY
Valbrun, Ingrid*
Valentin, Carlos*
Van, Nostrand P., NY
Vazquez, George N., NY
Vazquez, Jennifer L., NY
Vecchio, Thomas J., NY
Vega, Jose M.*
Velarides, Anastasios, NJ
Velazquez, Pedro L., NY
Versaci, Brian J., NY
Viera, Lydia*
Vixamar, Berenice, NY
Vlah, Kimberly R.*
Vojvodich, Thomas*
Wang, Victor*
Wassell, Michael M., NY
Watkins, John S., NY
Weiler, Edward, LA
Weisberg, Daniel M., NY
Welt, Carey A., NY
West, Clifford W., NY
West, Donna M., NY
White, Brenda L., NY
Williams, Marissa D., NY
Williams, Willie F.*
Willis, Yvonne A., NY
Wilson, Donna M.*
Wilson, Luana A., NY
Wilson, Rochelle L.*
Won, Shawn W., NY
Woodroffe, Dawn C., NY
Wright, Sharon L., NY
Wurzel, Glenn J., NY
Yanes, Francisco J., NY
Yeboah, Stephen F., NY
Yurus, William, NY
Zaragoza, Deserie M., NY
Zayas, Iris J.*
Zerella, Denise, NY
Ziede, Gwen, NY
Zinno, Lorrie A., NY

1990

Acevedo, Rene, NY
Acosta, Gilbert*
Adams, Elke, NY
Adams, James A., NY
Adeniran, Adeyinka, NY
Aiken, Norman F., NY
Alexander, Dawn L., NY
Alexis, Andy E.*
Algarin, Dwayne D., NY
Allende, Rosanna L.*
Alleyne, Peter, NY
Allman, Crystal C., NY
Aloia, Augustine C., NY
Amplo, Anthony S., NY

Andrews, Benjamin (Ben), NY
Anduze, Lisa M., FL
Anton, Robert W., NJ
Anyansi, James O., NY
Aponte, Ana, NY
Arce, Nancy, NY
Arroyo, Henry, NY
Atweh, Mahmoud M.*
Azzolini, John, NY
Ball, Raymond H., NY
Ballard, Faye G.*
Barnett, Denise E., FL
Barreto, Amelia R., FL
Barron, Michael*
Barta, Randolph*
Bartlett-Josie, Mrs. Christine, CT
Barton, Lisa M., NY
Basic, Antonella*
Beamon, Tanya J., NY
Beauvais, Reginald, NY
Beckenstein, Cheryl*
Becker, Frederick J.*
Benfatti, Kristeine, NY
Benjamin, Irvin*
Bennetti, Joseph J., NY
Benson, Marshall*
Benson, Wendy*
Bentsen, Robert C.*
Bess, Ruth*
Besthoff, Eric A., NY
Bifulco, Anthony P., NY
Billups, Phyllis L.*
Birnbaum, Lewis R., NY
Bishop, Barbara A., NY
Black, Sally E., NY
Blackman, David B., NY
Blake, Claire*
Bolivar, Matilde, NY
Boyd, Arlene F.*
Braithwaite, Ken M.*
Brassil, Gail*
Brassington, Michael, NY
Brathwaite, CAPT Rafael, NY
Breen, Susan L., NY
Brignoni, Amy B., NY
Brock, Beverly W., NY
Brooks, Ms. Marvie B., NY
Brown, Clifford E., NY
Brown, Doslyn V., NY
Brown, Elizabeth M.*
Brown, Renelle, NY
Brown, Tara C., NY
Browne, Albert*
Browne, Cleo-renee, NY
Buie, Deborah L., NY
Burgos, Brenda, NM
Buttaro-sanchez, Joann, NY
Caccavale, Andrew C., NY
Caffrey, James, NY
Callistro, Cynthia Y., NY
Cameron, Rosalind R., NY
Campbell, Bradley S., NY
Campbell, Gina M.*
Campbell, Hopeton A., NY
Cannon, Austin E., NY
Capon, Joseph, NY
Cappiello, James T., NJ
Caragiulo, Dominic, NY
Carcaterra, Salvatore F.*
Cardoza-Heyward, Debra*
Carley, Joseph, NY
Carolan, Edward, NY
Carpenter, Scott, NY
Carroll, George T.*
Carthon, Arlene, CA
Caserma, Louis J.*
Casiano, Miguel A., FL
Casley, Sabrina*
Caso, Luis, NY
Castillo, Ernesto (Pete) A., Jr., CFE, NY
Catalano, John M., NY
Chambers, Crystal M.*
Chapman, James L., NY
Charest, Mark F., NY

Charles, Isabelle, NY
Cody, Thomas E., NY
Cohen, Faith M., NY
Coleman, Joseph W., NY
Coley, Anthony G., NY
Collado, Olga, NY
Collins, Kevin P., NV
Collins, Michael, NY
Conklin, Denise A.*
Connolly, Delano E.*
Cook, Alice J.*
Cook, Pamela B.*
Cordero, James A., NY
Cordova, Leonor, NY
Correa, Rosa M., NY
Correa, Sonia, NY
Cotto, Jose L., NY
Court, Eric, NY
Coyne, Thomas R., NY
Coyne, William P., NY
Cozzoli, John M.*
Cuccia, Anthony J., NY
Cuevas, Sonia*
Currao, Thomas J., NY
Cusumano, Charles, NY
Dale, Thomas V., NY
Daly, Daren S., NY
Daniel, L'tanya G.*
David, Lafleur, NY
Davidson, Leslie-Ann, NY
Davila, Angela M.*
Davis, James R., NY
De, Jesus M., NY
De Jesus, Edwin*
De Jesus, Julio*
De Jesus-Rodriguez, Blanqui I., NY
Delpin, Pedro, NY
Derring, Tremell, NY
Desmond, Frances, NY
Detzel, Thomas M.*
Dockery, Maria, NY
Dodson, Toshia E., NY
Donato, Roberto, NY
Donnadio, John G.*
Donnelly, James E., NY
Dozier, Shaunda, NY
Drucker, Eric G., NY
Druker, Courtenae, NY
Duarte, Delilah S., NY
Dunlap, Daniel, NY
Echevarria, Mabel, NY
Edmonds, Joan F.*
Edwards, Richard A.*
Elcock, Erskine L., NY
Elisson, Chris, NY
Emerson, James C., NY
English, Christopher, NJ
Enriquez, Jorge, NY
Espada-Waite, M., NY
Esparza, Christopher, NY
Faison, Thomas A., NY
Farah, Lyes, NY
Farley, Thomas*
Febus, Enid*
Ferdinand, David, NY
Ferris, Lauraine E., NC
First, Jeffrey D., NJ
Fisher, Bobby, NY
Fleming, William J., NY
Flynn, John, NJ
Foster, Dianne M.*
Foy, Raymond G., NY
Francois, Marlene, NY
Friedman, Bruce*
Gager, Philip A., NY
Gagne, Christopher*
Gallagher, Brian, NY
Garcia, Daniel J.*
Garcia, Daysi, NY
Gardner, Michael L., NY
Garnier, Joubert, NY
Giambrone, Alphonse, NY
Gill, Arleen A., NY
Giordano, Julie A.*
Givens, Sinclair N.*

Golaszewski, Henry, NY
Goncalves, Alvaro, NJ
Gonzalez, Georgina, NY
Gonzalez, Jimmy A., NY
Gonzalez, Lourdes, NY
Gonzalez, Norma I.*
Graham, Patricia, NY
Grant, Ian W.*
Granum, Denise L., NY
Grasso, John F.*
Gravitch, Daniel J., NY
Green, Cynthia A., NY
Gretsinger, Charles*
Grinage, David F., NY
Groody, Patricia A.*
Gualtiere, Robert**
Gulbin, Robert D.*
Haber, Edward, NY
Haberfeld, Maria M., NJ
Hamilton, H. S., NY
Hamilton, Smallwood, NY
Haney, Stephen M., NY
Harley, Beverly D., NY
Harrison, Scott H.*
Harrison, Tonya, NY
Hart, James R., NY
Hawthorne, Latonya, NY
Hayes, Emogene S., NY
Hayes, Tracy L., NY
Healy, Craig C., NY
Healy, Regina A., NY
Heinbach, Mark*
Heine, Susan K., NY
Heres, Ana M., NY
Hernandez, Elsa, NY
Hernandez, Luisa, NY
Hernandez, Michelle*
Hewitt, Darryl F., NY
Hiler, Edmund G., NY
Hill-McMichael, S.*
Hizme, Joshua A.*
Hodge, Loretta E., NY
Hodges, Rodney R., NY
Holly, Glavdia*
Holmes, Ms. Gloria, NY
Hope, Quinzelle, NY
Horan, Michael, NY
Horn, Lukas, NY
Hurley, Paul T.*
Hussey, Douglas*
Indar, Dennis K., NY
Iocco, Luigi G., NY
Isaacs, Paul K., NY
Jablons, David N., NY
Jackson, Kim A., NY
Jackson, Luis A.*
James, Ainsworth, NY
James, Marcia L., NY
Jamindar, Swatl P., NY
Jaundoo, Madeleine, CA
Jean, Pierre Y., NY
Jean-Philippe, Herro, NY
Jennings, Hon. Allan W., Jr.,
  NY
Jennings, Rubin L., NY
Johnson, Larry, NY
Johnson, Roy F.*
Jones, Brian T., NY
Jones, Melissa S., NY
Jones, Shelanda R., AL
Joseph, Nancy J.*
Jules-Louis, C., NY
Jusino, Elizabeth*
Kane, Timothy, NY
Kane, Veronica A., NY
Kearns, Margherita, NJ
Keegan, Scott J., NY
Keenan, Christopher*
Kennedy, Karen M., MD
Kennedy, Sean P.*
Kennedy, Toqui V.*
Kenny, John B., NY
Kitchens, Leyla, NY
Klaus, William A., NY
Kmetz, Thomas R., NY
Kordick, Mark R.*

Krukin, Ms. Avalon S., NY
Kuczinski, Gregory*
Kulis, Ivan*
Kurtyka, George F., CT
Ladson, Anthony M., NY
L'amour, Mousslin, NY
Langone, Darin, NY
Lanier, Louis I., NY
Larrymore, Cynthia, NY
Lavin, John F., NY
Lee, Mrs. Karen B., NY
Lee, Lisa, NY
Lee, Robert, NY
Lee, Shashana R., NY
Leicht, Paul F., NY
Leopold-hooke, Fred L., NY
Levine, Lenore H., NY
Lew, Steven, NY
Lewis, Anthony, NY
Lindner, LT Peter M., NY
Linkletter, David P., NY
Little, Brian R., NY
Littleberry, Dorothy, NY
Livanis, John*
Llaurado, Heriberto*
Lloyd-Sealey, Michele, NY
Logrande, Antonino, WI
Lopez, Charles, NY
Lopez, Esteban*
Lopez, Israel, NY
Lopez, Wanda L., NY
Louis-Jeune, K.*
Lugo, William, NY
Luncheon, Pedro O., NY
Lundquist, James M., NJ
Lyons, John J., NY
Macdougall, Michael, NY
Macfarlane, Maria L., FL
Mackey, George R.*
Macolino, Eric J., NY
Madera, Brenda, PA
Madison, Darryl*
Magrino, Robert, NY
Mahoney, Dawn, NY
Malcolm, Carl*
Marcus, Steve A., NY
Marone, Dominic J., NY
Marslow, Margaret, NY
Martinez, Agnes*
Martin-Washington, A.*
Matusiak, William, NY
Mc, Call T., NY
Mc, Quade M., NY
McCarthy, Daniel, NY
McCutcheon, James H.*
Mc Gee, Kathy, NY
Mchugh, Bridget M.*
Mckenzie, Patricia*
McLain, Darrell, NY
McLamore, Samuel N.*
Mcloughlin, Thomas, NC
Mcmichael, Marty*
Medintz, Igor, NY
Meire, Eduardo*
Melendez, Cruz V.*
Mentuck, Bazyk S., NY
Merced, Deborah, NY
Messina, Camillo J., PA
Meyer, Thomas F.*
Michaelides, Vasilis, NY
Miller, Eric C., NY
Mir, Nancy J., NY
Miro, Sandra M., NY
Mitchell, Angela T.*
Mitchell, Marianne, NY
Mitchell, Richard D.*
Mohr, Michael, NJ
Molina, Sonia I., NY
Monahan, James F.*
Moncrief, Frances F.*
Monges, Abraham, NY
Monroe, Alexis A., NY
Moorehead, Claude L., NY
Mora, Blanca D.*
Morales, Nicholas F., NY
Morgan, John P., NY

Moye, Evelyn*
Muldowney, Linda M., NY
Mulligan, Maritza, NY
Murphy, Eileen, NY
Murray, Gregory L., NY
Nathaniel, Nigel M., NY
Nazario, John, NY
Negron, Diana, NY
Ney, Beverly E., NY
Ng, Molly C., NY
Ngomassock, D.*
Njoku, Clifford N.*
Normil, Chantal, GA
Nunez, Javier*
Obong, Solomon A.*
O'Brien, Jeffrey S., NY
Ocampo, Julio, NY
O'Donnell, Gerard*
Ogboe, Kelly E.*
Ojeda, Evelyn*
Oliveras, Mary G., NY
Orellana, Alfonso J., NY
Ortiz, Marilyn, NY
Ortiz, Raymond, NY
Ortiz, Vincent*
Osuagwu, Emeka, NY
Ozoa, Brunilda*
Pagan, Edwin R., NY
Palicia, Deborah L., NJ
Palillo, Ann, NY
Palmer, Virginia L., NY
Palozzola, Joseph R., NY
Pan, Nanette, NY
Pao, John T.*
Parker, Lori V., NY
Paschall, Yvette M., NY
Patel, Kamlesh K., NY
Patterson-Dandy, Creola, NY
Paulik, John H., NY
Perez, Francisca A., NY
Perez, Myrna*
Perez, Sara L., NY
Peronneau, Ernest, NY
Perry, Gregory S., NY
Persaud, Joseph M., NY
Petrick, C., NY
Petrovitch, Diana, NY
Phelan, Connie M., NY
Piazza, Robert*
Picarello, Jodi A., NY
Piercey, Melissa A., NY
Pillion, George R., NY
Pitrone, Alberta J., NY
Pitts, Stacey G., NY
Porter, Pamela S., NY
Powell, Carol L., NY
Princivil, Rony, NY
Prophete, Marjorie, NY
Pyne, Frederick F., NY
Quarles, Cheryl T., NY
Radeljic, Hughes L.*
Ramos, David*
Ramos, Lyvia*
Ramsey, Danette, NY
Razack, Sakhawat, NY
Reid, Howard, NY
Reid, Karlene, NY
Reinking, Robert F., NY
Reynolds, Ronald*
Richardson, Barbara, NY
Richardson, Ernest V., NY
Ridley, Cathy L., NY
Riley, Laura D., NY
Rinaldi, Joseph, NY
Ristenbatt, R., NY
Rivera, Elba I.*
Rivera, Evelyn, NY
Rivera, Frances R.*
Rivera, Ivette M., NY
Rivera, Javier A., NY
Rivera, Wanda L., NY
Roberts, Yvonne O.*
Robinson, Edward S., NY
Robinson, Tijon*
Robley, Vanessa, NY
Rodriguez, Antonio R., NY

Rodriguez, Jose A., NY
Rodriguez, Manuel*
Rodriguez, Nemesio, NY
Rodriquez, Julissa, NY
Rogers, Laura*
Romero, Ada*
Romero, Heriberto, NY
Rosa, Evelyn, NY
Rosa, Yadira, NY
Rosado, Alexander*
Rosa-jimenez, Anna, NY
Rosario, Enid*
Rusznak, Richard C., NJ
Ryley, Thomas, NY
Sabatini, Karen, NY
Sanders, Gregory L., NY
Sangiorgio, Maryann, NY
Sanoguet, Jeffrey*
Santiago, Richard, NY
Santos, Nora*
Sarti, Annmarie, NY
Saryian, Paul D., NY
Sawina, Gregory, NY
Schanil, Robert, NY
Scheiner, Adam, NY
Schmidt, Jeffrey A.*
Schmidt, William, NY
Schneider, John S.*
Schraud, Louis, NY
Scienski, Larry*
Sconfietti, James, NY
Scotto, Anthony F., NY
Selwyn, Steven*
Sheehan, Eileen J., NY
Sheeler, Gregory R.*
Sherlock, Ralph M., NY
Shields, Joseph G., NY
Shortell, Michael E., NY
Siders, Yolanda C., NY
Sierra, Luis M.*
Silvera, Colleen, NY
Simmons, Karen P., NY
Simpson, Da R.*
Singletary, Charles R., Jr., NC
Sirotko-Turner, M.*
Siso, Frank, NY
Skubisz, Peter, NJ
Sluka, Keith, NJ
Smallwood, Dawn T.*
Smith, Bonita E., NY
Smith, Hayden R., NY
Smith, Karen A.*
Smith, Russell, NY
Smith, Shelley, NY
Smith-Rawlins, Raul G.*
Sohan, C., FL
Soto, Francisco, NY
Sotomayor, John P., NY
Spain, Polly*
Specht, John F., NY
Stanek, Thomas, NJ
Stannish, Matthew**
Stefanidis, Stavros, NY
St-firmin, Wenda I., NY
St. Louis, Gregory*
Strong, Eric D.*
Suddler, Carlton*
Sukra, Brian, NY
Sullivan, Allison M., PA
Sullivan, Elizabeth, NY
Sullivan, Kathy, WA
Sutherland, Sharon, NY
Sween, Bodden, NY
Sylvester, John, NY
Taveras, Elvis, NY
Taveras, Juan A., NY
Taylor, Richard A.*
Terrell, David R., NY
Thomas, Andrew, NY
Thomas, Carolyn, NY
Tjeriko, Zelna, NY
Tong, Patrick Y., NY
Torres, Edward J.*
Toussaint, Patrick*
Triebe, Michael, NY
Trotman, Grace P.*

*Address Unknown **Deceased

Turcic, Stefanie, NY
Turner, Seneca*
Tutino, Barbara J., NY
Underwood, Mark, PA
Uttendorfsky, M., NY
Uwuigbe, Wilfred, NY
Valdes, Jesus M., NY
Vallejo, Francisco*
Van Ronda, Joann, NY
Vara, Anthony J.*
Vargas-Gonzalez, Ana, NY
Vickerie, Dana A., NY
Viglione, Roseann*
Vindice, Vincent, NY
Volkerts, Joanne, NY
Walcott, Alliston, NY
Walker, Marsha, NY
Wallace, Stanley, MD
Walters, Lauren R.*
Walton, Joyce W., NY
Wanigasinghe, Sarath, NY
Warren, Jeanette T.*
Warsaw, Harmon, NY
Washington, Dennise Y., NY
Washington, Reginald, NY
Weisberg, Elyse J., NY
Wheatley, Hillaire C.*
White, Woodrow, NY
Wilkins, Bryan L.*
Williams, Chester, NY
Williams, Jeffery L., NY
Williams, Marlon V., NY
Williams, Stephanie*
Williams, Van D., NY
Witty, Sandra D., NY
Wizeman, Marguerite*
Wong, Honver*
Wright, Delores*
Wright, Garnet C., NY
Wright, Gwendolyn*
Wright, Pamelia K., NY
Yagual, Rick W., NY
Yang, Yinhui, NY
Yasso, Michael, NY
Young, Natalia S., NY
Zambito, Debra A., NY
Zephir, Aaron J.*
Zhang, Yurong*
Zimmerman, Maurice*
Zuniga, John, NY

1991

Abdul-Baseer, Nailah*
Adebiyi, Christina, NY
Adesanya, Oluwatoyin, NY
Adesina, Mufutau A., NY
Afanador, Deborah, NY
Aguero, Arnulfo M.*
Aguilera, Emily, NY
Aiken, Iris A., VA
Aikhoje, Monday O.*
Akpan, Obong F.*
Alberti, Leonardo L., NY
Aldrich, Alicia, SC
Alma, Gilbert J., NY
Alston, Yvonne, NY
Alvarado, Gloria M., NY
Alvarez, Lucrecia, NY
Amadu, Onoriode P., NY
Amaro, Marta, NY
Anderson, Carlos F.*
Anderson, Martha C., VA
Anfiteatro, Andrea, NY
Annitto, Paul E., NY
Aupont, Frederic*
Bacon, Levora L.*
Baird-alleyne, Arlene, NY
Bak, Robert*
Baker, Candiace V., NY
Banks, Linda, NY
Barrett, Kevin, CA
Barriere, Wilfred M., NY
Bavaro, Nicholas, NY
Bayuelo, Claudia S., NY
Bellomee, Cynthia*
Beltrez, Manuel, NY

Benjamin, Lesley V., NY
Bennett, Curtis L., NY
Berkowitz, Gwynne, NY
Berroa, Ms. Janice, RN, NY
Bila, Anthony, NY
Binford, Nina, NY
Block, James B., NY
Blugh, Eneida A., NY
Bohack, Susan, NY
Bohigian, Valerie, NY
Bolger, Barbara, NY
Bolger, William J., NY
Bonacorsa, Michael F., NY
Bonanno, Patsy, NY
Bond, Lonnie H.*
Boselli, Denise M., NY
Bottarini, Carlos, NY
Bourdon, Edwin L., NY
Bowen, Fielding W., NY
Braxton, Aubrey S., NY
Briggs, Renee, NY
Briscoe, James J., NY
Broady, Michelle*
Brock, Ralph E., NY
Broderick, Mark*
Brogli, Maria C., NY
Brown, Ms. Janet L., NY
Broyard, Sharon*
Bruen, Noel F., NY
Bruneau, Johanne, NY
Bruno, Richard F., NY
Bruzzichesi, William, NJ
Budenas, John M., NJ
Burgos, Mata A.*
Burrell, Tracey, PhD, CA
Burwell, Shawna M., NY
Bussanich, Lisa M.*
Bute, Jessica A., NY
Buylding, Douglas W., NY
Byrne, Daniel C., NY
Cadot, Marie M., NY
Cantarella, Elena*
Carbone, Carol A.*
Cardona, Michael A., NY
Carozza, John P., FL
Carroll, Thomas J., NY
Carter, Arnold, NY
Carter, Melvin R., NY
Cassidy, Stephen J.*
Castillo, Alfredo, NY
Castillo-rosado, V. S.*
Cavalier, Dorothy P., NY
Cavendish-sosinski, Elizabeth*
Cepeda, Luis, Jr., NY
Chametzky, Steven A., NY
Chan, Patrick, NY
Chandler, Annie*
Chang, Mrs. Josephine, Esq., NY
Chaparro, Miriam E.*
Chase, Audrey, NY
Chavis, Malcolm L., NY
Chin, Theresa*
Chuenvong, Bolt*
Ciccotelli, Richard, NY
Cintron, Diana*
Clarke, Patrick J.*
Coleman, Linda C., NY
Collazo, Antonio, NY
Collins, Elliot, NJ
Colon, Helen, NY
Colon, Rubina, NY
Coney, Angela D.*
Conforti, Paul J., NY
Connick, Kathleen, NY
Cooper, Peter J., NY
Cornell, Richard R., NY
Corredor, Leonel F., FL
Corrigan, Thomas F., NY
Crespo, Luisa E., NY
Cross, Michelle I., DC
Crugnola, Charles K., NJ
Crummell, Donna, NY
Cruz, Jeanette, NY
Cruz, Onassis M.*
Cummings-Moran, Michelle*

Curry, John A., Esq., NY
Cyrille, Celia*
D'amicantonio, Thomas, NY
Dandridge, Antoine*
Daniels, Alethia*
Daugherty, Cassandra, NY
Davidson, Craig R., NJ
Davidson, James*
Davis, Eaton, NY
De, Noyers N.*
Debellis, Michael A., NY
DeCastro, Lydia, NY
Decocq, Michael E., NY
DeJesus, Maudi I.*
Delince, Jean R.*
Delma, Nadege, NY
Del Vicario, Robert E., NY
Demers, Martha, CA
Denoyers, Nicole M.*
Desvarieux, Camille*
Deteskey, Henry R., NY
Devlin, Maria M., NY
Diaz, Abed N.*
Diaz, LT Arthur, JD, NY
Diaz, Fanny A., NY
Diaz, Jessica*
Diaz, Lisa A.*
Dickson, Paul, NY
Dipierro, Paul, NY
D'Isselt, Lauren, NY
Dongo, Marsha M., NY
Dressler, Marcella, NJ
Dumois, Jesus, NY
Dunbar, Ramon*
Duncan, Charles A., NY
Duru, Athanasius O., NY
Edlam, Lionel, NY
Edwards, Carla, NJ
Eng, Thomas*
Epstein, Jonathan L.*
Ervin, Irene E., NY
Esguerra, Martin I.*
Estrella, Anthony*
Evans, Robert, NY
Fagan, Jay R.*
Fajardo, Edward, NY
Febus, Vivian E.*
Feinberg, Mark S., NY
Ferguson, Brian, NY
Fernandez, Jeffrey J., NY
Figurski, Susan A., NY
Finn, Sean P., NY
Finn, Timothy H.*
Fisher, Deborah A.*
Fitzpatrick, Barbara*
Fitzpatrick, Oona M., NY
Fonseca, Ms. Lisa A., NJ
Forte, Jennifer M., NY
Francis, Sandra O.*
Freckleton, Lloyd J., FL
Freeman, Ronald A., NY
Fuentes, Joseph, NJ
Gaddy, James, NY
Gaetano, Gregory, NY
Gagliardo, Robert*
Gallagher, Joseph E., NY
Galloway, Robin L., NY
Gamory, Thaddeus D.*
Garcia, Clarisa E.*
Garcia, Raymond, NY
Garvey, Martin V., NY
Geist, Mitchell, NY
Gelfand, Jeremy, VA
Gheta, Barbara A., GA
Giangrasso, F., NY
Gillespie, Jane*
Giordani, Christina*
Gittens, Constantino, NY
Gittleman, Cynthia*
Glavey, Edward, NY
Gomez, Henry J., NY
Gomez, Maria E.*
Gonzalez, Antonio, NY
Gonzalez, Enrique, FL
Gonzalez, Felipe*
Goodman, Milton, NY

Gordon, Abby R., KY
Gordon, Charmaine*
Graf, Margaret M., NY
Graham, Kenneth, NY
Grajales, Ednah, NY
Granelle, Anja E., NY
Griffin, Robin L., NY
Griffith, Rodney F., NY
Grippi, Ada, NY
Gruenstrass, Steven, NY
Guastella, Maria, NY
Gustave, Grevirlene, NY
Haas, Keith*
Hahn, Robert, NY
Hairston, Lucinia, NY
Hale, Altina M., NY
Hall, Ami*
Hallett, Sarah J., AZ
Hamel, William, NY
Hankins, Michael, NY
Harb, Rifat A., NY
Hardy, Kurt*
Harinski, James, NY
Harp, Jeffrey D., NY
Harrington, Dennis, NY
Harris, Latonia*
Harris, Terrence H., NY
Harrison, Julie*
Harvilla, Joseph, NY
Hazel, Ms. Kim R., FL
Hennigan, Jill*
Hernandez, John*
Hernandez, Josefina, NY
Hilaire, Livingstone, NY
Hinds, Opal S.*
Hoffmann, LT Russlan D., NY
Hogans, Mrs. Robin K., NY
Holman, Gregory R., NY
Holmes, Ms. Angela A., NY
Honovic, John*
Huber, Johanna*
Hunt, Nicole D., FL
Hurst, Veta P., MI
Hutchinson, Minerva, NY
Hutchinson, Thomas, GA
Hyiamang, Bossman*
Ierardi, Peter A., NY
Ithier, Carmen, NY
Jackson, Collette A., NY
Jacobs, Jerry L., NY
Jaghroo, Hilary, NY
James, John G.*
James, Michelle R., NY
Jasmin, Lude, NY
Jeffrey, Bridget A.*
Jenkins, Gary, NY
Jiggetts, Raymond R., NY
Jochim, Angela*
Johnson, Erious, NY
Johnson, Laurie J., NY
Jones, Floyd*
Jones, Lasalle, NY
Jones, Ronnie A., NY
Jones, Theresa*
Jones, Tracey L., NY
Jordan, Gwendolyn, NY
Jordan, Robbin M., NY
Joseph, Michael R., NY
Julien, Heather J., NY
Kamara, Samuel M., NJ
Katz, Jeffrey F.*
Keegan, Mark*
Kelly, Angela D., NY
Kelly, Gloria J.*
Kelly, Kiely, NY
Kennedy, Lori, CT
Kenny, Marie, NY
Kiapokas, Theodora, PA
King, Michael A., NY
King, Sabrina*
Kiravanich, T.*
Kisala, Stanley M., NJ
Klein, Thomas N., NY
Kluft, Elizabeth R., NJ
Kokis, Peter W., NY
Kornreich, Bessie*

Kouloumbinis, N., NY
Kowalewski, Steven A., NJ
Kravitz, Leslie*
Kudry, Joseph S., NY
Kurnatowski, C., NY
Kyle, Patricia M.*
Lake, Ms. Deborah (Debbie) R., NY
Lamb, Jerry D., NY
Langer, Catherine*
Langevin, Guy, ME
La Pietra, Louis C., NY
Lara, Antonio L., NY
Laruffa, Erik*
Lavelle, Joseph T., NY
Lawrence, Andrea L., NY
Lawson, James, NY
Lee, Ruthsana M., NY
Lee, Sharon*
Lee, Sun, NY
Leonardi, Angela, NY
Levinton, Judith*
Levy, Patrick, NY
Li, Xin*
Liberatore, Benedett, NY
Liddie, Michael A., NY
Lizardi, Joseph, NY
Lloyd-Bey, Ridwana, NY
Lombard, Alexander, NY
Lopez, Anthony, NY
Lopez, Lisa J., NY
Lopez, Luis M., NY
Lopez, Madeline*
Lopez, Miguel, NY
Lopez, Stanley, NY
Loughran, Keith R.*
Louis, Jean R., NY
Lukula, Audrey, NY
Luquis, Annette, NY
Luyando, Elizabeth, NY
Lynch, John*
Machulski, Edward R.*
Mack, Gregory I.*
Magerkurth, Valarie*
Maggiacomo, Eddie M., NY
Magill, Melanie R.*
Maldonado, Jose*
Malenka, Elliot, NY
Maloney, Eugene*
Manco, Robert E., NY
Manios, Louis N., NY
Markert, Anthony, CT
Martin, Dejannie*
Martinetti, Tatiana, NY
Martinez, Delfin, NY
Martinez, Lucy, NY
Martinez, Margaret, NY
Martucci, June R., NY
Mateo, Leticia M.*
Mathless, Scott*
Matobo, Mawela*
Matrisciano, Joan, NY
Matthew, Raymond T., VA
Matthews, Elaine*
Maxson, Cree L., NY
McCabe, Patrick M., NY
Mccarthy, Geryl, NY
Mcclure, Steven M., NY
McCorkle, Emma, NY
Mccue, Frank T., NY
Mc Glincy, Hugh J., PA
Mcguinness, Charles, NY
Mcguire, George J., NY
Mckenna, Siobhan H., NY
McKenzie, Laura, VA
McKenzie, Maribel E., NY
Mcknight, Margaret, NY
Mckoy, Lynette Y.*
Mcnamara, Eugene, NY
Mcnamara, Thomas G., NY
Medina, Ms. Marianella, NY
Mehr, Thomas P.*
Mele, Mary G., NY
Mendez, Gloria Z.*
Mendez, Irma E., NY
Mercado, Nancy, NY

Mercedes, Pilar R.*
Mercer, C. W., NY
Meyers, George, NY
Mignini, Annmarie, NY
Miller, Bobby, NY
Miralla, Sylvette*
Mitchell, Yvonne M.*
Mitra, Diditi, NY
Mitrotasios, Chris, NY
Montijo, Jose, NY
Morgan, Kenneth, NY
Morris, Sophia M.*
Morris, Tabbetha T.*
Morris, Vincent K., NY
Morrison, Joan E., NY
Morrissey, Mary P., NY
Morton, Cynthia E.*
Mosby, Edward A., NY
Motto, Robert A., NY
Moy, Sandra, NY
Mozaffar, Ahson, NY
Mulonda, Mwitwa*
Mulzac, Henry, NY
Munoz-Wiltshire, Nelly, NY
Murphy, Thomas P., NY
Murray, Karen A.*
Nasta, Stephen*
Negron, Manuel A., NY
Nelson, Drew M., NY
Nelson, Troy, NY
Neumann, John, NY
Ngadi, Francis B., NY
Nieves, Esther*
Nixon, Sandra R., NY
Norton, Joseph M., NY
Nunez, Michell*
Nurse, John P., NY
Nwahiri, Matthias, NY
O'Brien, Stephen P., NY
Oconnor, John P., NY
Ogrady, Patrick E.*
Okeke, James, NY
Olatunji, Rita*
Omahony, Brian E., NY
Oneill, John P., NY
Onukogu, Ignatius J., NY
Orlando, Dominic, NY
Ospina, Leonard, NY
Otero, Jorge L.*
Outar, Gail A., NY
Pacheco, M. Yvette, Esq., NY
Pagan, Angel L.*
Pagan, Michele D., FL
Palesano, George J., NY
Panagos, James W., NY
Parera, Carolyn, NY
Parkins, Carlos A.*
Parks, Joyce A.*
Parra, Juan C., NY
Parris, Brian C.*
Pastorella, Richard*
Paul, Marla*
Pawluk, William J., NY
Paylago, Stanley U., NJ
Pean, Mary D.*
Pegram, John A., NY
Pena-davis, Sky L.*
Pereira-Figueroa, Ma*
Perez, Marco A.*
Perez-ruiz, Ines, NY
Peters, Clinton J., NY
Phillips, Kevin D., NY
Philogene, Jackie J.*
Pignataro, SGT Anthony J., NY
Platarote, Karla B., NY
Poejo, Victor A., NY
Pomante, Robert*
Porter, Robert L., NY
Primiano, John, NY
Protonentis, Maria, NJ
Pugliese, Ferdinando, NJ
Punch, Amanda, NY
Quattlander, Raymond, NY
Quinones, Hector M., NM
Quintana, Lydia C., NY
Ragguette, Wayne, NY

Ramkaran, Denyse, NY
Ramos, Lissette*
Ramos, Marisol, NY
Ramos, Orlando*
Rancic, Angela*
Randolph, Wanda, NY
Rapa, Helen M., NY
Ravelo, Ms. Mercedes, NY
Reid, John R.*
Rentz, Tracy D., NY
Reyes, Kimberly, NY
Ricevuto, Anthony R., NY
Ridriguez, Alice, NY
Rijos, Yvonne*
Riotto, Joseph*
Rivera, George, NY
Rivera, Loyda E., NY
Rivera, Valerie, NY
Roberson, Margie, NY
Robinson, Donna, NY
Rodriguez, Jacqueline, NY
Rodriguez, Louis, NY
Rodriguez, Michael, NY
Rodriguez, Nelly Y.*
Rodriguez, Richard*
Rodriguez, Tanya I., NY
Rodriguez, Zoila*
Rogers, Burl L., NY
Rogers, Jaton, NY
Roller, Colleen A.*
Rolon, Kenneth*
Rolon, Nicholas, NJ
Rosado, Annette, NY
Rosado, Aracelis, NY
Rosado, Jose, NY
Rosado, Leslie M., NY
Rosado, Lisette, NY
Rosato, Lindy M., NJ
Rossi, David, NY
Rothmann, Scott F., NY
Rowe, Thomas P., NJ
Rubinson, Scott H., NY
Rudolph, Deandre D., NJ
Ruff, Kenneth*
Russell, Roslyn, NJ
Russo, Dello A., NJ
Rybacki, Laureen A., NY
Sacco, Ilene, NY
Samuel, Glenn P., NY
Sanchez, Lissette, NJ
Sanders, Liliana M., NY
Sandin, Eric J., CA
Santos, Pamela*
Santos, Rodney*
Scala, Jeanne*
Schneider, David, NY
Schurr, John F., NY
Sentouktsi, C., NY
Shannon, Valerie, NY
Sherwood, Christopher, NY
Shoenfeld, Samuel, NY
Siebenkas, Joseph C., NY
Sierra, Sandra*
Silvestri, Robert L.*
Simmons, Kenya D.*
Simonetti, Joseph J., NY
Simpson, Rhoda, NY
Singh, Nandkumar, AP
Singh, Rajdai D., NY
Singh, Sugrim, NY
Smalls, Douglas E.*
Smith, Deborah, CA
Smith, Lorraine E., NY
Smith, Opal J.*
Smither, Mrs. Melissa, NY
Snyder, David*
Soler, Doris, NY
Soleyn, Verrol E., NY
Soriano, Anthony, NY
Souder, Shelley*
Soules, Christopher, NY
Speller, Michelle*
Spiegelberger, Julie*
Springer, Kim S.*
Spyntiuk, Stephen P., NY
Sribnik, Steven, NY

Steele, Edward J., NY
Steinmann, Robert W., NY
Stephenson, Michelle, NY
Stevens, Patricia, NY
Stewart, Carmen H.*
Stewart, Michelle D., NY
St. Laurent, Arthur*
Stravalle, Charles*
Strockbine, Susan*
Sullivan, Sheelah E.*
Taboada, Maria F., NJ
Tansil, Julie A., NY
Tassy, Joseph G., NY
Tedino, Gabriel, NJ
Tejada, Jimmy J.*
Terio, Stephen, NY
Tesler, William H.*
Thomas, Lisa M., NY
Thompson, Kristal Y., NY
Thompson, Sally A., NY
Tiburcio, Rolando A., NY
Tiedemann, Eric H.*
Tinsley, Wanda A., NY
Tirado, Lori M.*
Tocci, Steven C., NY
Tomsky, Ross*
Toorie, Paula A., NY
Torres, Advendizo, NY
Torres, Ivette, NY
Torres, Manuel, NY
Toussaint, Leveque, NY
Trice, Leona, NY
Troyd, Steven M.*
Tung, Nelson, NY
Turner, Andrea L., NY
Udin, Francine*
Vaccaro, Richard*
Valdez, Rosa E., NY
Valentine, Valerie*
Valentino, Michael, NY
Vallon, Obeniste*
Vanegas, John J., NY
Vann, Keith K., NY
Vanterpool, Hattie*
Vargas, Mrs. Jennifer L., SC
Vargas, Marilyn*
Vazquez, Anodel, NY
Veigl, Eugene E., NY
Velazquez, Maritza*
Vistoso, Julio M., GA
Vrantsidis, Dorothea, Canada
Walker, Marcus R., NY
Wallace, John J., NY
Wallen, Pamela, NY
Ward, Kevin, NY
Warren-Levant, Cassandra, NY
Washington, David J.*
Watts, Timothy D., AL
Weir, SGT Seamus P., NY
Wellington, Jacqueline, NY
Whitehead, Sarita C., NY
Whitfield, Kimberly, NY
Williams, Debra A., NY
Williams, Lloyd C., NY
Wiltshire, Clarence*
Wingate, Donald*
Wong, Peter, NY
Wong, Yue*
Woods, Gregory A., NY
Wray, Tasha V., NY
Wright, Pamela G., NY
Yearwood, Davey R.*
Young, John C., NY
Young, Marcia, NY
Zedeck, Deborah S., NY
Zerner, Jeffrey, NY
Zimmerman, Howard J.*
Zulu, Nubian*

1992

Abbatepaolo, Lisa M., NY
Abdelhady, Zamyra, NY
Abednego, David A.*
Adams, Bernard S., NY
Agiri, Iyabo, MD
Airola, Kay*

Akerele, Gabriel A., NY
Alanis, Kevin, NY
Albanese, James J., NY
Alejandro, Byanca, NY
Alexander, Lavern K., NY
Alexis, Kathyann*
Allen, Tonya, NY
Allen, Wayne A., NY
Alonso, Vivian*
Altagracia, Zobeida*
Alwill, Gale A., NJ
Amatore, Alfred, NY
Amodeo, Lenny*
Amoruso, William M., NY
Anderson, Erik J., NY
Andino, Eddie, NY
Annis, Christopher, NY
Anzola, Jorge E.*
Appleton, Althea*
Archer-Joefield, Shellyann M., NY
Arcuri, Gary, NY
Arnold, Sharol A., NY
Arp, Ronald N.*
Arthur, Kent, NY
Arzuaga, Juan J., NY
Auerbach, Alice, NY
Aviles, LT Edwin R., NY
Aviles, Norma, NY
Aviles, Victor R., NY
Ayala, Manuel D., NY
Ayetiwa, Theresa F.*
Azeglio, Anna M., NY
Badillo, Anderson, NY
Bahan, Mildred, NY
Baierlein, Raymond*
Baires, Xenia C.*
Balfour, Joshua H., NY
Banjoko, Arewa A.*
Barbera, Joseph, NY
Baricelli, Patrick C., NY
Barnwell, James B.*
Barquin, Armando X., NY
Barreto, Samuel, NY
Barrios, Leonthe, NY
Barriteau, Marsha A., NY
Barrow, Audra J., NY
Barry, James P., NY
Bartolotta, John, NY
Bax, Wayne F., NY
Bayne, Melvin, NY
Beard, Darryl, NJ
Beauzile, Tamara M., NY
Bell, Christopher, NY
Benitez, Gustavo, NY
Benshafrut, Ronnie*
Berger, Richard, NY
Bermudez, Rosa A., NY
Bernardez, Mirtha C., NY
Beswick, David G.*
Biggers, Thomas P.*
Billik, Philip A., NY
Bishop, Robert J., NY
Blackman, Salena M., NY
Blake, Ms. Vera A., NY
Blanch, Gary T.*
Boisrond, Marie-Fran, NY
Bologna, Anthony (Tony) V., NY
Bonaparte, Jessie C.*
Bonet, Deborah H., NY
Bonilla, Sandra G., NY
Bosco, Michael, NY
Bottino, Roland, NY
Bourdon, Ana M., NY
Bowen, Gerard, NY
Boyce, Karentessa D., NY
Brady, Oral W., NY
Bratcher, Illene, NY
Bridges, Rhonda, NY
Broach, Myra K., PA
Broadnax, Cassandra*
Brown, Candra L., NY
Brown, Marcia S., NY
Brown, Mary A.*
Brown, Scott D.*

Browne, Amy (Amelia), NY
Browning, Darlene, NY
Bruckenstein, K., NY
Bryan-piper, Hannah, NY
Budnick, Jason*
Buie, Teresa, NY
Burke, Derek, NY
Burnside, Robert W., NY
Burton, Robert, FL
Butler, Sandra, NY
Byer, Charles, NY
Byrne, James F., NY
Cacciatore, Robert J., NY
Cadena, Jeanette*
Cadet, Marie*
Cahoon, Alexis Y.*
Callender, Colette D., NY
Camp, Nicole, NY
Cannady, Terri, NY
Capone, Peter, NY
Cardichon, D., NY
Carew, Ademola*
Carlson, Mary, Canada
Carlson, Todd S., NY
Carpenter, Jeffrey S., NY
Carroll, Steven*
Carter, Corynne D., NY
Carter, Michael R., CT
Casola, Anthony, NY
Cassidy, Sharon E., NY
Cebic, Svetlana, NY
Cedeno, Mariela, NY
Celedonio, Leonin, NY
Centoducati, Dena M., NJ
Cerasoli, Justine M., NY
Cesarz, Christopher, NY
Cethoute, Guy J., NY
Chambers, Darrell, NY
Chan, Danny, NY
Chan, Kalung, NY
Chappell, Christian*
Chen, Changqin*
Chernjawski, Nicholas, NY
Chisolm, Kim A.*
Chow, Patty Y., NY
Chun, Min J.*
Cioffi, Christopher*
Clark, Kevin P., NY
Clark, Mark, NY
Claudio, Luis E., NY
Clermont, Maxim, NY
Codd, Maria E.*
Coker, Showole A.*
Collins, Kellis, NY
Colon, Bernardo, NY
Colon, Monique, NY
Colonnello, Karen A., NY
Conboy, Raymond C., NY
Concepcion, Dr. Lydia, NY
Conlon, Patricia A., NY
Connor, Charles, NY
Conway, Gary F., NY
Cooper, William C., NY
Cornelius, Eric J., NY
Correale, Mark, NY
Cort, Martha R., NY
Costello, Mary C., NY
Cote, Raymond A., NY
Cox, Daniel H., NY
Crosby, Trevor, NY
Cruz, Carlos M., NY
Cruz, Judy, NY
Cruz, Monica C., NY
Cruz, Nelly, NY
Curylo, Christopher J., NJ
Cusumano, Patricia (Tricia), NY
Daniels, Joseph R., NY
D'aquino, Madelyn*
Darby, Anthony G., NY
Davis, Cheryann, NY
Davy, Christopher S., NY
Dawkins, Leslie V., NY
De, Hermandez*
Deliz, Tina Marie, OH
DeMagistris, Scott J., NJ

Dembrosky, Jacquelin*
Dement, William, NY
Dennigan, Paul R., NY
Denzler, Thomas A., NY
Derienzo, Thomas, NJ
Desandies, Mark L.*
Desimone, Andrew, NY
Desir, Nadine (Nadia) O., NY
Desrouilleres, Jean, NY
Devonish, Claudette, NY
D'fora, Fred, NY
Diaz, Jose R., NY
Diaz, Zulma, NY
Dilan, Ivan, NY
Dixon, Roxann T., NY
Doherty, Danielle*
Donohue, Patrick J., NY
Douglas, Cornelius J., NY
Downey, John R., NY
Drain, Cheri*
Drayton, Sabrina R., NY
Duffy, Kevin*
DuFresne, Roserita, WY
Duncan, Clarence, NY
Duncan, Donald G., NY
Duncan, Kathy, NY
Dundon, John W., NY
Dunleavy, Sean, NY
Dunlop, Winston I., NY
Durant, Richard*
Durugordon, Shariff*
Duvil, Jack P., NY
Dwyer, Donna M., NY
Dziekonski, Barbara, NY
Eddy-McArthur, J.*
Edelstein, Jonathan*
Edmondson, Gregory*
Edwards, Nicole R., NY
Egan, Christopher*
Ellis, Rodney*
Ellis, Sean*
Emilio, Frederico*
Erickson, Kathleen, NY
Esperto, Patti-jo, NY
Espino, Nadiana A.*
Evans, Gerard T., NY
Evans, Robert C., NY
Facey, Julia C., NY
Falcone, Joseph H.*
Fantauzzi, Douglas, NY
Farrell, Daniel*
Fearon, William G., NJ
Feigenbaum, Daniel, NY
Felder, Venitia, NY
Ferebee-Dingle, V.*
Ferguson, Adriane, NY
Ferguson, Anselma, NY
Fernandez, Alexis V., PR
Fernandez, Michael, NY
Feuer, Jason L.*
Fischer, Lauren J., NJ
Fitzmaurice, M., NJ
Flanigan, Sean R., NY
Fleury, Andre, NY
Fodera, Robert F., NY
Fogg, Harry, NY
Fontana, Susan, NY
Fossum, Carl R.*
Fosu, Louis K.*
Fournier, Marissa A.*
Francis, Yolanda A.*
Franklin, Kim, NY
Franzese, Peter J., NY
Frazer, Linden C.*
Frazier, Marguerite, NY
Freder, Drew F., NY
Frederick, Ondie L., NY
Freeze, Christopher*
Fremaint, Julissa*
Fung, Kit T., NY
Furtick, Anna E., NY
Gagliano, Allene, VA
Gaines, Dionne E., NY
Gamble, Derick, NY
Garbutt, Sylvia*
Garcia, Carmen I.*

Garcia, Daniel, NY
Garcia-Guzman, Mrs. Elizabeth, NY
Gardella, Mark D., NY
Gelina, Jeffery A., NY
George, Dick, NY
Georges, Marcelle M., NY
Germain, Gislaine*
Germosen, Wilson*
Gholson, Leigh L., NY
Giambalvo, Deborah, NY
Gibbons, Eugenia F.*
Gibson, Sherry A., NY
Giordano, Joseph*
Gleason, Evelyn E.*
Glover, Alicia F., NY
Glover, Elemenia*
Glover, Valoyd R.*
Goddard, Jill A.*
Goddard, Mayfield, NY
Goico, Noemi, NY
Gomez, Freddy A., NY
Goncalves, Paula, NY
Gonzalez, Madeline, NY
Goode, Anna R., NY
Gordon, Hal S.*
Gordon, Karen, NY
Gorey, Frank*
Gouin, Martine*
Graham, Wendy, NY
Granata, Robert, NY
Gray, John H., NY
Greenaway, David R.*
Greene, Tryphena, NY
Griffiths, William, NY
Grogan, Dennis, NJ
Grooms, Cordell, NY
Guillebeaux, Kiesha, NY
Guillouette, Darlay, NY
Gumbs, Douglas J., NJ
Hagan, Stephen*
Hale, Thomas M., NY
Hall, Vincent D.*
Halpern, Mitchell, NY
Hampleton, Jerome*
Hance, Ms. Rachel, NY
Harilal, Kaitnarine*
Harvey, Patrick J.*
Hatzis, Gregory S., NY
Hawkins, Crystal, NY
Haymes, Keith B.*
Hazim, Gladys M., NY
Hazlewood, Gloria, NY
Henri, Claudine L., NY
Henry, Lashawn O.*
Henvill, Winston C.*
Hernandez, Jenny, NY
Hernandez, Victor, NY
Hernandez, Yvette, NY
Herrera, George P., NY
Hewitt, Althea E., NY
Hicks, Keith E., NY
Hidalgo, Joanne E., FL
Higgins, Patrick (Pat) J., NJ
Hill, Calvin B., NY
Hill, Suzanne A., NY
Hillier, Regina M.*
Hoitsma, Camille L.*
Holmes, Reginald, NY
Hope, Jennifer, NY
Howard, Regina*
Hudson, Richard, NY
Hughes, Holly B.*
Hughes, Isabel, NY
Humphrey, Jaleel*
Hunt, Obie, NY
Hunter, George A., VA
Hunter, Gloria E., NY
Ingram, Margaret, NY
Irizarry, Jose A.*
Irizarry, Richard*
Iyalla, T., NY
Jablonsky, William, NY
Jack, David*
Jacknow, Jayson K., NY
Jackson, Albert A., NY

Jackson, Karen M., NY
Jacob, Lisa G., NY
Jaime, Alfred L.*
James, Richard L., NY
James, Sharon, NY
Jean-felix, Marie*
Jefferson, Gregory, NY
Jeremie, Yves A., NY
Johannes, Eleanor*
John, Clayton P., NY
Johnson, Anne T., NY
Johnson, Bruce, NY
Johnson, Darryl A., PA
Johnson, Kathryn*
Johnson, Kristel A., NY
Jones, Beverly V., GA
Jones, David A., NY
Jones, Kimberly A., NY
Jones, Robin M., NY
Jones-scott, Vena, NY
Joseph, Andrea M., NY
Juers, Cathy A., NY
Jules, Wisner, NJ
Kaestle, Kathryn, NY
Kearse, Russell L., NY
Kelly, Patrick H., NY
Kelly, Paul J., NY
Kennedy, Lillian, NY
Kennedy, Thomas*
Killeen, Michael K., NJ
King, Edwina J., NY
King, Gillian L., NY
Kirby, Thomas H., NY
Kirkman, Scott J., NY
Klein, Stacey J.*
Klimoski, Frank, NY
Klotko, Steven G., NY
Koenderman, Kevin*
Kolbeck, David A., NY
Kontoleon, Anthony*
Kosseim, Amin, NY
Kostner-armato, Michele, NY
Kovacs, John, NJ
Krieg, Barry M., NY
Kuhn, Ann, NY
Kurzawa, Matthew C.*
Laguna, Milagros*
Lamont, Naeemah, NY
Lamperti, Edward P., NJ
Landais, Martine, NY
Lansing, Amy E.*
Lau, Ricardo C., NY
Laudisi, Craig D.*
Lebron, David*
Lee, Fei, NY
Lee, Jyung K.*
Lee-Wyss, Mrs. Helen, NY
Lejuez, Kim M., NY
Lennek, Christopher, NY
Leon, Margarita, NY
Levy, William E.*
Lewis, Derrick L., NY
Lewis, Georgene L., NY
Lewis, Sandra Y., NY
Liburd, Evelyn S.*
Lindsay, Cordelia, NY
Liu, Mark A.*
Logozzo, Allison, NY
Lopez, Della L., NY
Lopez, Lisa L., NY
Luces, Antoinette, NY
Lugo, Olga I., NY
Luther, Jodell L.*
Lynch, Donna M.*
Lyudmir, Alex, NY
Maffettone, Dennis, NY
Magnuson, Ms. Leah, NY
Mahoney, Matthew, CA
Major, Sharon, NY
Maldonado, Edwin, NY
Malichek, Steve*
Malysz, Josephine, NY
Mancuso, John J., NJ
Manson, James E., NY
Marcus, Gary B.*
Marinakos, Demos E., NY

Marmol, Julie, NY
Marmolejos, Winston, NY
Marrero, Andy, NY
Mars, Emmanuel, NY
Marshall, David, NY
Marshall, Edward S., CO
Marshall, Glenn T., NY
Marshall, Vernon D., NY
Marsicovetere, Louis, NY
Martinez, Maria*
Martinez, Theresa, NY
Martinez-Claudio, Mi*
Marvelli, Albert J., NY
Mateo, Carlos*
Matterson, Eric, NY
Maurice-Matthews, D., NY
Maynard, Reuben W., ME
Mayushan, Avram M., NJ
Mcbain, Michael, NY
Mccarthy, Justin M., NJ
McDonald, Jeannette, NJ
Mcdonald, John, NY
Mcdonnell, Patrick, NY
Mcelligott, Thomas M.*
McGehean, Donna G., OH
McGinn, LT Timothy R., NY
McGlinchey, Ms. Anne T., NY
Mcgreal, Edward J., NY
Mckenna, Thomas, NY
Mckenzie, Roger A., NY
Mclaughlin, Deborah, NY
Mcmahon, Patrick J., NY
McMullen, Mark F., NY
Mcneill, Denise L., NY
Mcpherson, Clint A.*
Mecea, Robert, NY
Medina, Deborah, NY
Mena, Eda L., NY
Mendelsohn, David, NY
Mendez, Luz E.*
Mendez, Maria, NY
Mengel, Thomas A.*
Mercogliano, Frank, NY
Merolle, George*
Metaxas, Mary, NY
Michel, Pierre H., NY
Mignone, Anthony*
Mihalek, Donald J., NY
Miller, Raymond C., NY
Mills, Lurline, NY
Minacapelli, M., NY
Miranda, Anthony R., NY
Miranda, Georgina M., NY
Mixon, Thomas E.*
Mocombe, John E., NY
Mohammed, Hassim, NY
Molinelli, James A., NY
Montanez, Anna I., NY
Moody, Ms. Sabrina R., NY
Moore, Sean, NY
Moorer, Shannon, NY
Morado, Calvin P., NY
Morales, William, FL
Morey, Jose, NY
Morgan, Diana, NY
Morley, CAPT Susan, NY
Morretta, Matthew G., NY
Morris, Joseph*
Morrow, William, NY
Mortellaro, P., NY
Moy, Harold C.*
Moye, Laurita*
Muellers, Deborah L., NY
Muhammed, Cornetta, NY
Mulchinski, Edward C.**
Mullane, Edward F., NY
Mullen-Morris, Veronica B., NY
Muniz, Eliu, NY
Murillo, Rudy*
Murphy, Patricia*
Murray, Gwendolyn, NY
Murray, Lynne, NY
Murrell, Michelle C., NY
Murton, Mark*
Muschett, Elita*
Myers, Cremston M., NY

Myers, Gregory, NY
Napier, Raymond C., NY
Navarro, Alexander*
Newshan, Bryan J., NY
Newton, Judy D., NY
Nicholas, Leslie-Ann, NY
Nieves, Carmen, NY
Noel, Beverly, NJ
Nolan, William M.*
Obioha, Louis N.*
O'brien, Hayden, NY
Odabashian, Ralph, NY
O'gara, William C., NY
Ogorman, Marianne, NY
Ohakamnu, George N., NY
O'Keefe, Patricia J., NY
O'looney, Cara E., NY
Olu-Talabi, Akinwole, NY
O'Neill, John P., NY
O'Reilly, John, NY
Orta, Aileen D., NY
Ortega, Mauricio, NY
Ortiz, Johnny, NY
Osemwengie, Charles*
Otero, Victor E., NY
Owens, Darrell N.*
Pabon, Lisa, NY
Padilla, Anthony, NY
Paitakis, Terry, NY
Pastore, Michael J., CT
Pastrana, Joycelynne, NY
Pauls, Taisha, NY
Payumo, Kenneth C., NY
Pelliccio, Anthony, NY
Perez, Doreen, NY
Perlov, Jane, NY
Perry, Darlene L., CT
Petito, Thomas J., NY
Philips, Richard E., NY
Phillip, Charles, NY
Picardi, Richard, NY
Piedra, Dennis, NY
Pierce, Latanya, NY
Pierre, Avron*
Pierre-louis, M., NY
Pintor, Felix E., NY
Piri, Ms. Maria A., NY
Ploumes, Joanne, NY
Poitevien, Eric, NY
Polenberg, Carole, NY
Politano, John, NY
Pollini, Joseph A., NY
Pulisic, Zivko, NY
Qiu, Hong, NY
Quinones, Michelle L.*
Quinones, Richard, NY
Ramirez, Hector V., Esq., NY
Ramirez, Manuel, NY
Ramos, Maria, NY
Randall, Keron K., NY
Randolph, Valerie*
Rante, Brenda A.*
Rapale, Sandra, NY
Rasenberger, Joseph, NY
Reategui, David, NY
Reed, Bryan J.*
Regina, Croswell, NY
Reid, Alicia J.*
Reissman, Stephan*
Renna, Thomas*
Repaci, Richard, NY
Restrepo, De*
Reyes, Leila T., NY
Reynoso, Edgar, NY
Richards, Felicia A., NY
Richards, Holly, NY
Rico, Nancy L.*
Riordan, Patricia A., NY
Rios, Donald, NY
Rivera, Estela L., NY
Rivera, Ivette, NY
Rivera, Marilyn, NY
Rivera, SGT Mario L., NY
Rivera, Pio, NY
Rivera, Rolando R.*
Rivera, Walter, NY

Rivera-Silva, E.*
Robinson, Barbara E., NY
Rodrigues, John, NY
Rodriguez, Estela, NY
Rodriguez, Jeannette*
Rodriguez, Luis R., NY
Rodriguez, Milagro, NY
Rodriguez, Rafael, NY
Roe, Julie, CA
Rogers, Katherine C., NY
Roman, Ms. Janet, NY
Rosa, Gualberto, NY
Rosario, Donna M., NY
Rosario, Miguel, NY
Ross, April D.*
Ruban, Ms. Carlyne S., NY
Rubino, Arthur S., NY
Russell, Patricia A.*
Ryan, Fred C., NY
Ryan, Capt Stephen J., NYARNG, NY
Sahm, Katherine E.*
Saldana, N. Antonio, NY
Salim, Zameena, NY
Salisbury, Robert, NY
Sanchez, John, NY
Sanchez, Milton J., FL
Sanchez, Valerie, NY
Santiago, Carmen, NY
Santiago, Publio, NY
Santos, Sharon E., NY
Saravia, Sara M.*
Sasson, Dina J., NY
Schulze, Paul W.*
Scrubb, Michelle A., NY
Seaforth, Zolton, NY
Segarra, Elsie, NY
Selover, Joan, NY
Sepp, Karen, NY
Sewer, Enrique D., NY
Sewnarain, Prabha, NY
Shannon, Michael, NY
Shark, Anthony, NY
Sharkey, Daniel M., NY
Simmond, John J., NY
Simmons, Cathy, NY
Simmons, Cheryl, NY
Simmons, Melvin, NY
Simonetti, Joseph J., NY
Sing, Deonarine, NY
Singh, Lata, NY
Singleton, Mrs. Maureen V., NY
Slane, William G., NY
Sligh, Ms. Geneva L., NY
Smith, Alphonso H.*
Smith, Royal*
Smith, Vergion J.*
Solano, Javier*
Solomon, Frederick, NY
Sotelo, Ricio*
Souffrant, Reginal, NY
Spann, Cassaundra, NJ
Spano, Albert, CO
Sparro, Michael R., NY
Standard, Deborah, NY
Standel, Marie, NY
Stein, Brian, NY
Stephenson, Beverley, NY
Sterling, Kenneth, NY
Sterrett, Duray D.*
Stranahan, Fred, NY
Straun, Avernel D.*
Streffacio, Patrick, NY
Stuart, Linnea, NY
Sudol, Richard W., NY
Sullivan, Joseph E.*
Sumter, Delia A.*
Surin, Fredly, NY
Surphlis, Kimberly, NY
Sutton, Carl, NY
Sweeney, Robert J.*
Swierzowski, Christi, NY
Sydney, Frantz*
Sylvester, Alpher K., NY
Tain, Valerie, NY

Taussi, Joseph*
Tavarez, Guilda, NY
Tavarez, Juan, NY
Taylor, Arlene V., NY
Taylor, Olive, NY
Tejera, Manuel, NY
Tejera, William, NY
Thomas, Yvonne, NY
Thompson, Cecilia E., NY
Thompson, Dorleen D.*
Tinsley, Derrick L.*
Toomey, Regina*
Torres, Jeanette F., NY
Towns, Henry, NY
Tracy, John C., NY
Trail, Laura A.*
Tranchina, Gregory, NY
Trevino, Leonides*
Trulli, Christine, NY
Tyson, Genine G., NY
Ulrich, Michael, NJ
Urprasad, Deodat, NY
Uwa-Omede, Tonnie, NY
Vale, Carmen R., NY
Valentin, Lydia*
Valentin, Pablo, NY
Vasapollo-d'Augusta, Barbara, NJ
Vazquez, Carlos E., NY
Vega, Betty*
Vega, Widesmina*
Veilson, Martin, NY
Veliz, Giovanni, NY
Vidal, Raquel E., NY
Villalobos, Christine, NY
Villanueva, Nilda, NY
Voglesong, Daniel P., NY
Walker, Reginald A., NY
Wall, Richard, NY
Walsh, Paul, NY
Washington, Dawn C., NY
Webb, Albertina*
Weeks, Kathina*
Weinberg, Paul, NY
Weiner, Dennis*
Welcome, Bryan N., NY
Wells, Rory J., NJ
Wells, Tara, NY
Widofsky, Brenda F.*
Wilkinson, M.*
Williams, Brenda G., NY
Williams, Deborah P.*
Williams, Delores*
Williams, Kimberly, NY
Williams, Owen E.*
Williams, P.*
Wilson, Lynette F.*
Wilson, Maxine*
Wiltshire, Heather, NY
Winslow, James G.
Winstock, Richard*
Wise, Francis S., NY
Yeates, Smith L., NY
Young, Rodney, NY
Zampieron, Paul W., NY
Zinnel, Michael G., NY
Zupka, Barbara J., NY

1993

Abdur-Rashid, Sabura, NY
Abodunrin, Felix O.*
Abrams, Jonathan A., NY
Abreu, Maria A., NY
Acevedo, Socrates, NY
Adams, Julia V., FL
Aglietti, C., NY
Agosto, Barbara, FL
Ahel, Sabine, NY
Akapolawal, Wasiu A., NY
Alava, Tricia, NY
Alba-Gil, Flordaliza A., NY
Aldrich, Darcy M., AZ
Aledo, Elymar E.*
Alexander, Algernon, NY
Alexander, Guerlande*
Aleyne, Aida M., NY

Aliaga, Vanessa J.*
Allen, Jerome, NY
Alleyne, Pauline A., NY
Almanzar, Sandra*
Alphonso, Errol A., NY
Al-qadiri, Talla, NY
Altman, Sedric D., NY
Alvarado, Darlene, NJ
Alvarado, Jose A.*
Alvarez, Betsaira, NY
Alvez, Christina M.*
Amarutsanon, Kittisak, VA
Amedee, J., NY
Anderson, Timothy T., NY
Andiarena, Wilfredo, NY
Andrews, Jewel D.*
Andujar, Diana, NY
Angeletti, Debra, CA
Annetts, Paul D., NY
Anthony, Wade D., NY
Aponte, Cindy*
Applyrs, Stanley D.*
Archie, Michelle J., NY
Armorer, Sharifa J., NY
Armstrong, Lenore, NY
Arp, Christopher*
Artis, Michelle*
Asbery, Joseph, NY
Audiffred, Jesus, NY
Autera, Marysusan D., NY
Avila, Gil, NY
Ayala, Alex*
Bacchus, Roseema S., NY
Baierlein, Elizabeth, NY
Bailey, Michele D.*
Bain, Geneva T.*
Balcombe, Marcelle, NY
Balsamo, Patricia, NY
Barbato, Michael, NY
Barnett, Rodney A., NY
Barr, Heather E.*
Barrios, Diane*
Barrows, Alleen A., NY
Barton, Shari L., LA
Bates, Colleen M.*
Batista-Delacruz, Erika A.*
Battle, Lisa M., NY
Battle, Robyn*
Bauza, Luis N., NY
Beato, Marino, NY
Bell, Tasmiya J., NY
Benedetto, Michael, NY
Benfanti, Louis A., NY
Benjamin, Candace E., NY
Bernard, Joseph, NY
Berrios, Frank J., NY
Bhojwani, Manny, NY
Bieniewicz, Linda M., NY
Billings, Saiheme, NY
Bird, Edwin T., NY
Biscuti, Anthony J., NY
Bitkower, Amy J., NY
Bittar, Dennis, NY
Blackwell, Darius S., NY
Blake, Richard A., FL
Blassingame, Paul, NY
Blugh, Michael, NY
Boldin, Teresa S., NY
Bolton, Garfield L., NY
Borzotta, David R., NJ
Bovell, Donna A., NY
Brady, John J., NY
Brady, Matthew, NJ
Bramble, Michael P., NY
Bramble, Rachel, CA
Bresnan, Eilish B., NJ
Brissett, Jacqueline, NY
Brivett-Hill, Andrene*
Broker, Edward J.*
Brown, Ms. Estelle A., NY
Brown, Henry*
Brown, Rodney W., NY
Brown, Stevelle M., NY
Bruce, Tommy, NY
Brusco, Lisa, NY
Bucaj, Alfons, NY

Burbridge, Adero, NY
Burcea, Corina M.*
Burrows, Kenneth A., NY
Busby, Kathryn M.*
Bustillos, Norma I., NY
Cabrera, Maritza, NY
Cabrera, Marjorie, NY
Cadet, Bella C., NY
Cadet, Myrtelle, NY
Cadet, Robinson, NY
Calabria, Michael, NY
Calabro, Dennis P., NY
Calderon, Peter, NY
Callahan, Patricia, NY
Callan, Kathleen A., NY
Campbell, Courtney*
Cangelosi, Robert S., NY
Canto, Salvatore, NY
Capaobianco, Sr. Carmela, NY
Cardet, Carolyn, NY
Carela, Wanda, NY
Carney, Raymond J., NY
Carolina, Tanya L., NY
Carrera, George, NY
Carrion, Luis A., NY
Carter, Melvina M., NY
Castillo, Elizabeth, NY
Castro, Jacqueline, NY
Chan, Steven, NY
Charles, Ronald, NY
Chavies, Phyllis A., NY
Cheski, Philip M., NJ
Chong, Renee H., NY
Chou, Alice M., NY
Chow, Richard, NY
Chung, Jane, NY
Ciavarella, Louis S.*
Ciccone, Frank, NY
Cihan, Nerkiz, NY
Cilione, Jeffery, NY
Cisek, Mary T., NY
Clarke, Barry R., NY
Clarke, Deborah*
Clarke, Joan B., NY
Clarke, Nuria E., NY
Cleaton, Larry C., NY
Clement, Carol E.*
Coaxum, Teresa (Teri), NY
Cocoros, Denise, NY
Cohen, Richard A., NY
Collazo, Desiree, NJ
Collins, Ruby A., NY
Colon, Licelyn, NY
Colon, Ms. Luz, NY
Comerford, Barry*
Concannon, Joseph R., NY
Coniglio, Kenneth J., OH
Conversano, Victor M., NJ
Cooper, Juan R.*
Cora -Lundquist, Marissa, NY
Corchado, Maribel, NY
Cordero, Yolanda*
Correa, Jose M., NY
Cotton, Eddie, NY
Craven, Cheryl V., NY
Creary, Jemal D., NY
Crespo, Gladys L., NY
Crusoe, Irvin, NY
Cruz, Annette, NY
Cruz, Rafael A.*
Cuello, Francisca, NY
Cugliandro, Pasquale, NY
Cunningham, Sheila, NY
Cusack, Eva M.*
Cusher, Devin, NY
Dahlberg, Cathrin M.*
Daley, Carlton A., NY
Daly, Peter J., NY
Damon, Theadora P., NJ
Danna, Yvette M.*
D'Arpe, Gene, NY
David, Lori L.*
Davis, Sharise*
Davis, Vameershala, NY
Davis, Vanessa*
Davodowich, Erek G., FL

Davy, Andrea M.*
Decicco, Dominick, NY
Decoteau, Mark F.*
De Dona, Natalie, NY
Delaney, Ernest S., NY
Delaney, James T., NY
Demaio, Vincent, NY
Desensi, Darren T.*
DeSimone, Andrew J., NY
Devito, James M., NY
Diaz, Fatima, NY
Diaz, Mildred M., NY
Dicks, Daniel M., NY
Dier, Daniel, NY
Difusco, Andrew F., NY
Dimmock, James A., NY
Dinnall, Michael A.*
Dixon, Paulette, NY
Dobro, Stuart, TN
Doenges, April*
Donnery, Mary C., NY
Dorch, Joyce M., NY
Dormi, Edward J., NY
Dougall, Angela K., NJ
Duffy, David, NY
Duignan, Daniel, NY
Dula, Eva M., NY
Dutes, Ronald, NY
Dyer, Mark, CT
Eason, Pansy, NY
Ebrahim, Linda, NY
Edokpolo, James O., NY
Eisenhauer, Letty, NY
Elg, Christopher*
Espinal, Elida, NY
Esposito, Dorothy F.*
Evans, Jasseth M., NY
Evans, Telora, NY
Ewang, Kenneth E.*
Fabozzi, Michael, NY
Fahje, Donald, NY
Faison, Venessa, NY
Fana, Fermin E., NY
Farino, Thomas, NY
Feliz, Tanya*
Ferber, Eric M., NY
Ferguson, Deborah A., NY
Fernandez, Evelyn, NY
Fernandez, Theodore (Ted), NY
Ferrson, Norita, VA
Fetus, Patrick, NY
Fields, Bernadette (Michelle), NY
Figueroa, Lisset, NJ
Findlay-Paul, S., NY
Firpo, Andrea*
Fitzgerald, James J., NY
Fleming, Patrice A., NY
Fletcher, Daniel A., NY
Flor, Lourdes C.*
Floroiu, Elena*
Fludd, Tracy K.*
Flynn, Kevin C., NY
Folan, John B., NY
Forteau, Clement, NY
Fox, Bonnie R., NY
Fox, Kevin M., NY
Francis, Mario J., NY
Francis, Noel C.*
Frazier, Eric W.*
Freire, Richard J., NY
Fullard, David A., NY
Funtow, Alexander*
Furr, Katherine M.*
Fuster, Adam, NY
Gaddist, Valerie, NY
Gaynor, Rabiah M., NY
Gentile, Janene M., NY
Gentry, Devin P.*
Gerald, Jason*
Gerardi, Richard R.*
Ghaly, Ayman N., NY
Giannoutsos, K., NY
Gilchrist, J., NY
Giovinazzo, Alise, NY

Glidden, Ariana M., NY
Gluck, Geri H., NY
Glynn, Keith A., NY
Goldberg, Abigail S., NY
Goldsmith, Andrea M., NY
Gomez, Victor R., NJ
Gonin, Daniel O., NY
Gonsalves, B., NY
Gonzalez, Marlene*
Gonzalez, Robert A., NY
Gonzalez, Rodney, NY
Goode, Laleatha, VA
Goon, William, NY
Gordon, Troy A., NY
Gowins, Ruthlee, NY
Grasso, John P., NY
Graves, Tywana E., NY
Gray, Golda, NY
Green, Carlyn D., NY
Green, Lorraine*
Green, Margaret A., NY
Green, Mark A., NY
Green, Markus*
Green, Michelle, NY
Greene, Elizabeth P., NY
Greene, Jeanique, NY
Griffin, Gilbert A.*
Griffiths, Marcia J., NY
Grossman, Steven H., NY
Guarnotta, Jacqueline R., NY
Guayama, Juanita R., NY
Guerrier, Marline, NY
Haberstock, John G., NY
Hackett, Michelle A., NY
Hadjidemetriou, George, NY
Hall, MSgt Everett M., USAFR, NY
Hall, Lesley A., NY
Hall, Tyson W., NY
Halley, Ms. Stacey A., GA
Hamilton, Steve N.*
Harding, Clive D., NY
Harlow, Petal A.*
Harmon, Teon, NY
Harrington, Edward*
Harris, Darice B., NY
Harris, Sheila A., NY
Harrison, Judith A.*
Harvey, Beverly, NY
Haynes, Steven*
Henry, Chaka A.*
Henry, Hopeton H., NY
Henry, Sonya M., NY
Hermida, Mercedes, NY
Hernandez, Jorge E.*
Hernandez, Robert, NY
Herrera, Jose, NY
Hibbert, Marcia A., NY
Hickman, Lynn B., NY
Higuchi, Rika*
Hill, Siobhan, NY
Hill, Veronica S., NY
Hills, Tonya S., NY
Hockler, Terry M., NY
Hodges, Billieannett, NY
Holder, Tonya, NY
Holtzman, Cynthia R., NJ
Horan, John F.*
Horan, Robert G.*
Hosein, Richard A., NY
Hoyt, Ms. Yvette C., NY
Hughes, Leola M., NC
Hum, Julia S., NY
Humphreys, Beverly, NY
Hurley, Michael J., NY
Hutchinson, Marla, FL
Hyde, Tucker, NY
Hylton, Iline M.*
Hyppolite, Nadia*
Indrathaher, Wahyudi, NY
Isang, David Y.*
Iyer, Seema*
Jackson, Patrice M., NY
James, Jannes A.*
Jarecki, Jane M., NY
Jawad, Naeil, NY

Jay, Henry, Jr., NY
Jemmott, Norman A., NY
Jenkins, Ernestine, NY
Jenkins, Nicole, NY
Jinenez-Francis, Els, CA
Jirak, Donald J., NY
Johnson, Ava Y., NY
Johnson, Halsey J., NY
Johnson, Kesha Y., NY
Johnson, Sonia R.*
Johnson, Tara*
Johnston, Steven C.*
Jones, Alonzo J.*
Jones, Cheryl M., NJ
Jones, Heather D., NY
Jones, Kevin, NY
Jones, Melissa R., NY
Joseph, Carlas, NY
Joseph, Carol P.*
Joseph, Kisha C., NY
Joseph, Sheila, NY
Juliano, Albert T., NY
Kamara, Alex T., NY
Kanne, James A., NY
Kantor, Nancy*
Karira, Raj J., MD
Kassai, Michael D., NJ
Keating, Robert P., NY
Keitt, Veronica, NY
Kelleher, Kenneth*
Keller, Kurt L.*
Kenner, Marvin L., NY
Keymer, Mary M., NY
Kiely, Jeremiah T.*
King, Jemma F., NY
Klyde, Catherine H., NY
Krueger, Robert W., NY
Kurka, Jeffrey S., NY
Kurtzberg, Jared, NY
Kyei, Patricia C., NY
Laffey, Christopher, NJ
LaForgia, Madeline*
Laljie, Vishnu D., NY
Lambert, Joseph M., NY
Landin, Rudolph, NY
Lane, Tammie T.*
Langston, Sandra D., NY
LaRosa, Anthony, NY
Lassen, Joseph, NY
Lautenberger, R., NY
Laverde, Jacqueline, NY
Lawlor, Jason A., NJ
Leacock, Colleen E., NY
Leah, Magnuson, NY
Lee, Annette M.*
Lee, Jacinto M.*
Lee, Tiemei*
Leitch, Noel E., NY
Leonard, John J., NY
Levy, Sarah*
Lewis, Kerry P.*
Lewis, Steven R., NY
Lewis, Tonya, NY
Lin, Ching-Hua, Taiwan
Liquori, Maureen A., NY
Long, William F., III, NY
Longo, Steven, NY
Longsworth, Patrick, NY
Lopez, Albertina F., NY
Lopez, Cuahutemoe, NY
Lopez, Wanda*
Louison, Arleigh K.*
Love, Jason C., NJ
Lucher, Lasean, NY
Luciano, Ana V., NY
Luis, Marvin, NY
Lyons, Robert T., NY
Mack, Gerard C., NY
Mahipat, Premmattie*
Mahoney, Sheila, NY
Mai, Herbert L., NY
Mairanda, Adriana, NY
Maisano, Michael P., NY
Majestic, C., NY
Maldonado, Annette, NJ
Maldonado, Aristides, NY

Malhotra, Ravi, NY
Maloney, Joeann D.*
Malool, Paul G., NJ
Manges, Alison C.*
Marchello, John A., NY
Marines, Henry, NY
Marks, Bettina R., NY
Marrero, William, FL
Martin, Jeanne E., NY
Martin, Teresa R., NY
Martinez, Bryant, NY
Martinez, Deborah, NY
Martinez, Duandie, FL
Martinez, Irving, NY
Martinez, Santiago, NY
Massaro, Joseph**
Matheson, Alethia A., NY
Matthews, Joy V.*
Mauro, Mario F., NY
Maxim, Ana, GA
Maxim, Ilie, GA
Maynard, Lonene C.*
Mazyck, Marshall, NY
Mc Gowan W., NY
McCallum, Sonya L., NY
McCann, Patricia J., NY
McCarey, Colleen A., NJ
Mccarthy, Timothy, NY
Mccauley, Chris, CT
Mcfarlane, C., NY
McGill, Steven J., NJ
McInerney, SGT Brian G., NY
Mcloughlin, John*
McMillan, Bridgett, NY
McMillan, Ralph E., NY
Mc Nichols, Keith B., NY
Mcrae, Denise A.*
Mctursh, Rachel, NY
Medina, Jaime, NY
Medina, Jose M., NY
Meeres, Victoria, NY
Mejias, Desiree, NY
Mele, Elizabeth A., NY
Mendez, Omar A., NY
Merritt, Trica, NY
Mesorana, Carmen, NY
Meyer, Mitchell L., OR
Meyers-Wedden, N.*
Milea, Daniel, NY
Miller, Mousey S., NY
Miller, Robert, NY
Mills, Beverly A., NY
Minervini, Dominick, NJ
Miranda, Edwin R., NY
Mladenovic, Goran B., NY
Molloy, Patricia A., NY
Monge, Luis A., NY
Monroe, Alisha J., NY
Montalvo, Oneida, NY
Montanez, Nellie, NY
Montgomery, James D.*
Morales, Aileen F., NJ
Morales, Carlos R., NY
Morales, Daniel*
Morales, Denise I.*
Morales, Jose M.*
Moreno, Walker R.*
Moses, Stephanie M., NY
Moss, Kyna E., NY
Moss, Raymond D., NY
Moya, Cristian*
Mullen, Steven M.*
Mullins, Steven J., NY
Mulvanerty, Daniel, NY
Murawski, Marianne, NY
Murillo, Jose P., NY
Myers, Ayanna C., NY
Nagasar, Petamber, NY
Nazaire, Ivy*
Nazaire, Jacques, NY
Negron, Magaly, NY
Neil, Brian*
Nelson, Yvens, NY
Newman, James V., NY
Nicholas, Cyril W., NY
Nieves, Samuel, NY

Nixon, Colin G.*
Norman, Janella*
Novick, David, NY
Nowacoski, Michael, IL
Nunez, Juan, NY
Nunez, Noralee, NY
Nunez-Dunn, Genoveva*
Obando, Milagros*
Obinyan, Gregory V.*
Ocampo, Mayra D., NY
O'hara, Brendan, NY
Okrah, Edward K., NY
Olinto, Luigi T., NY
Olivares, Esther, NY
Olivo, Evelyn, FL
Oquendo, Vivian L., NY
Orr, Beverley B., NY
Ortiz, Mario, NY
Ortiz, Oscar J., NY
Ortiz, Rosemary*
Osidele, Solomon O., NY
Oyibo-Ebije, A., NY
Padilla, Eric, NY
Palazzo, Thomas J., NY
Parker, George, NY
Parker, Vanessa M., NY
Parlow, James R., NY
Parra, Victoria E., NY
Parris, Marie N., NY
Pascal, Woody*
Pascarella, Joseph*
Patnett-miller, Freddiemae, NY
Patrice, Mic-arlem, NY
Patten, Jennifer M., NY
Patterson, Ison J., NY
Paulk, Kim M., NY
Pearce, Donald, NY
Peavy, Emma D.*
Pelletier, Robert T., NY
Pellicano, Donna M., NY
Perez, Anthony, NY
Perez, Hiede, NY
Perez, Michele*
Perrin, Heather K., NY
Perrina, Enrico, NY
Perry, Robin, NY
Persico, Gerald C., NY
Peterkin, Robert N., NY
Peters, Calvin, NY
Peters, Prestina D., NY
Peters, Yule E., NY
Pfeffer, David J.*
Piagentini, Deborah, NY
Piazza, Anthony, NY
Piedra, Sandra*
Pisano, Edward J., NY
Pizzo, Dominick, NY
Pizzullo, Victor, NY
Polanco, Carmen*
Polidoro, Nunzia, NY
Politis, Steven, Esq., NY
Porras, Carolyn M.*
Pralgo, David S.*
Prevost, Deborah A., NY
Prince, Mike K., NY
Puleo, Thomas A., NY
Quartimon, Ronald L., NY
Quetell, Jennifer L., NY
Quinones, Joann, NY
Quintana, Suzette*
Ramirez, Carlos, NY
Ramirez, Holli, NY
Ramirez, Mrs. Virginie, NY
Ramjit, Sheriffa, NY
Ramos, Magda, NY
Ramsey, Claude C., NY
Randolph, Kirk A., NY
Rathan, Suzanne*
Ray, Vern, NJ
Razukas, Matthew D., MD
Razzore, Annmarie, NY
Reid, Elenor, NY
Reid-joseph, Vivia*
Reid-walston, Barbara, NY
Reynolds, Sandra M., NY
Riaz, Aneerah, MI

Richards, Stephne, NY
Rigono, Gabriel, NY
Rios, Ivan*
Rios, Ruben, NY
Ritondo, Marcello, NY
Rivera, Agosto B.*
Rivera, Grace M., NY
Rivera, Herman, NY
Rivera, Isabel*
Rivera, Russell T., NY
Rizzo, Brian J., NY
Robotti, Carlo, NJ
Rocco, Aldo N.*
Rodriguez, Andres E., NY
Rodriguez, Betty, NY
Rodriguez, Blanca N.*
Rodriguez, Denise, NY
Rodriguez, Joe L.*
Rodriguez, Regino, NY
Rodriguez-kaneyasu, Peter, NY
Rogers, James, NY
Rojas, David, NY
Rolston, Felisia G., NY
Roman, David A.*
Roman, Marcia P.*
Roman, Matilde L., NY
Rosado, Kathlyn A.*
Rosario, Nancy M.*
Rosen, Penny, NJ
Rothnagel, Meredith, NY
Rubin, Jodi*
Rudd, Alexis H., CA
Ruiz, Ivelisse, NY
Russo, Robert M., NY
Ryall, Jeremiah J., NY
Ryan, Laura J., NY
Sabater, Barbara M., NY
Sai, Nancy M., NY
Sala, Eva M., IN
Salek, Vladimir P.*
Sambula, Violeta A., NY
Samhan, Ahmad, NY
Samuels, Lisa, NY
Sanchez, Ivonne D., NY
Sanchez, Michael J., NY
Sanclemente, Erlinda, NY
Sanders, Elaine M., NY
Sanders, Thomas*
Santiago, Keysha A.*
Santiago, Ruth M., NY
Santos, Rita*
Sar, Steve N., NY
Saritson, Anthony R., NY
Sawtell, Edward, NY
Schreiber, Robert, NY
Schultz, Philip R., NY
Schultze, Joan D.*
Schupp, Elizabeth, NY
Schwartz, Jason B.*
Schwimmer, Claudia, NY
Sciarrino, S., NY
Scribani, Santo A., NY
Scudder, Ivy, NJ
Sekesan, Maria, NY
Selby, Cassandra*
Seremetis, Michael, DC
Shannon, Doris, NY
Shao, Min*
Sheeheed, Wadeedah, NY
Sheff, Bonnie M., NY
Sherman, Antoine, NY
Shields, Veronica*
Shimshi, David S.*
Shoemaker, Douglas, NY
Sierra, Martin, Jr., NY
Sihaga, George E., NY
Silverio, Elizabeth, NY
Silverman, Lisa A.*
Silverman, Susan W., PhD, NY
Simmons, Tarvatta S.*
Simms, Jacqueline, NY
Simon, Jacqueline L., NJ
Sinclair, Brian, NY
Sinclair, Darryl, NY
Skinner, Elizabeth, CA

Skinner, Terrence J.*
Slaughter, Wayne C., FL
Smalls, Helena*
Smith, Cynthia E.*
Smith, Janice*
Smith, Maria L., NY
Smith, Nicole B.*
Smith, Raquel L., NY
Smith, Yvonne C., NY
Snyder, Kimberly S., NJ
So, George, NY
Soares, Scott A., NY
Solis, Susana M., NY
Solomons, William H., NJ
Sorokin, Jill, CA
Sotero, Robert F., NY
Southard, Richard C., NY
Sparrow, Rodney B., NY
Spataro, James A., NY
Spencer, Janine M., NY
Spengel, Linda S.*
Springle, Stephen V., NY
Squires, Claudette*
Stack, Nancy*
Stewart, Elisa J.*
Stewart, Jeffrey, NY
Stock, Edward J., NY
Suarez, Christopher, NY
Suarez, Gricel*
Sudol, Robert*
Sulfaro, George V., NY
Suter, Desiree*
Tagliaferro, Jennifer, NY
Tamborino, Michael, NY
Tannenbaum, Rodney*
Tanner, Melinda, NY
Tarrats, Emily*
Tarwacki, Robert E., Sr., NY
Tavares, Karen C., NY
Taylor, Robert G., NY
Tellis, Allison, NY
Thompson, Gregg W., NY
Thompson, Marcy R.*
Thompson-Carvelli, Amy E., NY
Thornton, Craig C., NY
Thorsten, Myungsun J.*
Tibbatts, Eddie J., NY
Tillett, Vincent A., NY
Toledo, Pedro, NY
Toledo, Richard, NY
Tomlin, Sheila M., NY
Torres, Candy, NY
Torres, Evelyn, NY
Townsend, Michael C., NY
Tsang, David, NY
Tsiames, Nicholas B., NY
Tuggle, Freddie*
Tulloch, Matalie*
Unger, Robert E., NY
Utter, Laura T.*
Valdes, Connie B., NY
Valentin, Elliot, NY
Vallecillo, Gonzalo A., VA
Valluzzi, Frank S., NY
Vannata, Janice M., NY
Vanputten, Archie, NY
Varela, Pedro*
Varela, Wilson, NY
Vargas, Howard R., NY
Vasquez, Fernando*
Vega, Kevin J., NY
Vega, Lillian*
Velilla, Manuel H.*
Venn, Magadlene, NY
Ventura, Arlene C.*
Villegas, Gloria*
Vizcaino-Lambright, NY
Walfish, Karen T., NY
Walker, Brian H., NY
Walker, Heather G., NY
Walker, Tunesia*
Wallace, Evelyn, NY
Waller, Nicole, NY
Walsh, James G., NY
Walsh-wright, Carlene, NY

Walters, Mark, NY
Walters, Tanya M.*
Walton, Vanessa L.*
Warley, Raquel-Maria, NY
Washington, Alicia F.*
Washington, C.*
Waters, Tania*
Watkins, Tony*
Webb, Karen A., NY
Wedlock, Thomas J.*
Weems, Betty P., NY
Weinberg, Blair, NY
Weinshall, Ilene, NY
Weinstock, Margot, NY
Welch, Edward J., NY
Welch, Nicole D., NY
Welch, Zonela A.*
Welsh, James L., OH
Wenthe, Leah M., NJ
Wexler, Jason D., NY
White, Jennifer J., NY
White, Lisa M., NY
White, Sharlene, NY
White, Shelby*
Whiting, John W., NY
Whitlock, Toyea B., NY
Whittaker, George F., NY
Whitted, Frank N., NY
Wilder, Cornell L., NY
William, Julius, NY
Williams, Elizabeth, NJ
Williams, Mary*
Williams, Michael P.*
Williams, Roxanne, NY
Wilson, Ms. Myrna, NY
Wong, Ms. Mareen S., NY
Woodruff, Nancy, NY
Worthy, Patricia A., NY
Yeatts, William G.*
Yee, Peter J., NY
Young, Rodney D., NY
Young, Trent J., NY
Zavistoski, Robert, NJ

1994

Abrams, Deon S., NY
Acevedo, Edward T., FL
Adolphe, Marsiste, NY
Adrien, Viola*
Aleman, Jose L., NY
Alexander, Cheryl P., NY
Alexander, Paul H.*
Alexis, Monica, NY
Allen, Jennifer J.*
Allen, Neil G., NY
Almeida, Esther M., NY
Alvarez, Mercedes*
Alvarez, Ronald J., NY
Anders, Scott, NY
Anderson, Kevin G., NY
Anthony, Ceredo F., NY
Appadoo, Ruth S., NY
Arellano, Fabiola H.*
Armas, Margie, NY
Artman, Lindella*
Ayangbesan, Paul*
Babalola, Sikiru, NY
Baez-felix, Eileen, FL
Bailey, Alex T., NY
Balducci, Frank, NY
Banatte, Carline, NY
Bankovic, Milan, NY
Barrington, Nichelle, NY
Beatty, Pamela Y., NY
Beecher, Evelyn, NY
Beers, Lisa M., NY
Beldo, Gina, NY
Belenky, Dmitry, NY
Benitez, Juan A.*
Benjamin, Gilda E., NY
Benjamin, Yvonne E., NY
Bennett, Deborah E.*
Bennett, Keren M., NY
Bermudez, Carlos R., NY
Bernstein, Faye K., MN
Best, Jennifer A., NY

Black, Sylvia C., NY
Blaize, Desmond*
Bluethgen, Jane M., NY
Bobb, Ms. Irma Diane, Esq., NJ
Bodden, Juana, NY
Boggiano, Daniel, NY
Bonilla, Cesar A., NY
Boone, Bruce A., NY
Bowens, Lynn*
Bowens, Renita D., NY
Bowles, Leslie M., NY
Bravo-reid, Sandra*
Breslin, Michael D., NY
Brideson, Dawn M., NY
Brooks, Ronald*
Brown, Annie D., NY
Brown, Cathy, NJ
Brown, Jonathan G.*
Bucca, Maria, NY
Burrows, Jonathan, RI
Butler, Jason L., NY
Byrd, Derrick W.*
Caicedo, Astrid, NY
Callender, Cynthia, NY
Camilleri, Michele, NY
Campbell, Yolan, NY
Carattini, Esteban, NY
Carey, Charee A.*
Carpenter, Taurina, NY
Cartagena, Hector, NY
Caruso, Michael L., NY
Cazeau, Beatrice, NY
Chacon, Mario E., NY
Chamaki, Ramella*
Chan, Lai F., NY
Chatterjee, Sheila, NY
Chau, Tony K., NY
Cherry, Julie, NY
Christophe, Joseph, NY
Chung, Christina J., NY
Chung, Thomas H., NY
Cintron, Yvette, NY
Clark, Veronica V., NJ
Clarke, Charmaine, NY
Clarke, Harold C.*
Codrington, Paula A., NY
Cohen, Rachel L., MA
Colletti, C., NY
Colon-posniack, Glenda D.*
Colvin, Bernard W., NY
Comans, Chantay*
Conley, Nora, NY
Conroy, Sharon A., NJ
Cooper, Janet, NY
Cotham, Jeffrey D., TX
Cox, Ayoka, NY
Coyne, Stephen M.*
Crawford, Derek, NY
Crawford, Todd L., NY
Creamer, Jeanet E., NY
Cregin, Matthew T., NY
Crooks, Venesia, NJ
Crosse-Williams, P.*
Curtis, Keith H.*
Daouphars, Jean Y., NY
Davis, Matthew, NY
Davis, Michelle*
Dejesus, Nelly J., NY
De La Cruz, Ramon, NY
DeLuca, Lorayn, NY
Denesopolis, John, NY
Desaussure, Ms. Martha, NY
Diaz, Theresa Y.*
Dineen, William F., NJ
Donnelly-Brinkley, Virginia, NY
Donohue, Eileen, NY
Dore, John*
Dougherty, Shawn M., NY
Dowtin, Ronda, CT
Doyle, Maureen E.*
Drakes, Imogene, NY
Dubose, Kenneth E., VA
Duda, Nicola M., CA
Duffy, Craig T., NJ
Edwards, Latisha, NY

Egoavil, Linda M.*
English, James A.*
Eromosele, Henry J.*
Estrada, Mario B., NJ
Evans, Doris P., NY
Evans, Stacy*
Facciponti, Ronald, NY
Fares, Ali, NY
Feeney, Kathleen, NY
Feliciano, Gloria, NY
Ferguson, Brian P., NY
Ferrer, Jorge M., NY
Ferris, Andrew P., NY
Fiskaa, Thomas E.*
Fitzpatrick, Paul J., NY
Fleetwood, Yancy, NY
Flynn, Michael, NY
Flynn, William J., NJ
Fonseca, Reinaldo*
Fortino, Denise M., NY
Foti, Frank G., NY
Francis, John W., NY
Francis, Willie W., NY
Frazer, John H., NJ
Fred, Jacqueline*
Fuller, Jane, NY
Gala, Michael F., NY
Galvez, Alexander J., NY
Gantt, Jeffrey, NY
Gatewood, June Y.*
Gaughan, John M., NY
Gentles, Andrea V., NY
Geritano, Lenore, NY
Gestring, Brian J., NJ
Giantelli, Patricia, NY
Gibbs, Rose A.*
Glover, Trevor R., NY
Gomez, Ana M.*
Gonzalez, Ivette*
Gonzalez, Jose A., NY
Goodman, Janet*
Graham, Deborah A., NY
Grajales, Ananias, NY
Grant, Cheryl M., NY
Greaux, Roslyn A., NY
Green, James M., NY
Green, Monique, NY
Green, Tracy V.*
Greenberg, Hal D.*
Grier, John E., NY
Griggs, Deidre, NY
Grossman, Lisa, NY
Gualberto, Edgar M., NJ
Guarino, Jerry C., NY
Gyenes, Albert R., Jr., NJ
Halka, Jill A., NY
Ham, Gustavo, NY
Hanrahan, Claire T., NY
Harris, Clotilde M., NY
Harris, Gabriella, NY
Harris, Joseph*
Harris, Karen D.*
Harrison, Sharlene, NY
Hartley, Wayne, NY
Hawley, Pamela A., NJ
Haynes, Robert M., NY
Headen, Cherese*
Healey, Peter B.*
Held, Kenneth L., NY
Hermenegildo, Luis*
Hernandez, Iris, NY
Hernandez, Petronio, NY
Hilliman, Charlyn A., NY
Holloway, Anthony, NY
Hosten, Heston*
Housen, Faith D., NY
Huggins, Laurel, NY
Hughes, Denita R., NY
Hurrey, Ayanna I., NY
Iannone, Barbara A., NY
Ingoglia, John V., NY
Ingram, Carlean N., NY
James, Debra A.*
James, Dina M., NY
Jarrett, E. C., PA
Jean, Reginalde D.*

Jefferson, John A., NY
Jimperson, Mary, NY
Johnson, Crystal M., NY
Johnson, Franceska, NY
Johnson, Ms. Nykelle S., NJ
Johnson, Shandel, NY
Jones, Phillip*
Jones-knight, Helen, DE
Joseph, Clayton, NY
Kahn, Christina K.*
Karczmer, Aaron S., NY
Karras, Andrea I., NJ
Kay, Paul, NJ
Keating, Rian T., NY
Keys, Robin N.*
Khemai, Kamlapatie, NY
Kissel, John S., NY
Kornfeld, Mitchell, NY
Kosciusko, Charles, FL
Krasnov, Felix, NY
Krawec, Victor*
Kroncher, Alex T., CO
Kunin-Savinon, L.*
Lam, Alan, NY
Langlan, Diane M., CT
Lao, Jorge L., NY
Lara, Manuel E., NY
Larkins, Gregory*
Lastra, Christopher J.*
Laville-Wilson, Debra, VA
Lawrence, Barbara J., NY
Lawson, Desiree T.*
Layne, Christopher, NY
Ledgister-dennis, Carla, NY
Lee, Brenda, NY
Lee, Wai H.*
Leone, Michael J., NY
Leung, Chiu H., NY
Leventon, Douglas C., NY
Levin, Michael, NY
Lewis-Short, Verna, NY
Liebowitz, David A., NY
Linares, Boris, NY
Longo, Dolores A., AZ
Lopez, Erik C., NY
Lopez, Judith, NY
Lukowski, Fred J., PA
Lynch, Claudia P.*
Macchia, Anthony P., NY
Maddux, Davina P., NY
Mais, Byran R., NY
Malvasio, Sylvia S., NY
Mandel, Michael J., NY
Manibo, Joel R., NJ
Mann, Kevin C., NY
Manning, Carl E., NY
Mannino, Salvatore O., FL
Mars, Nadeige, NY
Marte, Carmen, NY
Marte, Sandra, NY
Martin, Cecelia, NY
Martin, Michael J.*
Martinez, Richard, NY
Matos, Willie, NY
Matsuoka, Andrew H., NY
Maynard, Heather E., NY
Mcallister, Stephen, NY
Mccaffrey, Sean P., MN
McCain, Jamaine, NY
McCoy, Robert N., NY
McGowan, Hugh M., NY
Mckinney, Tracy, NY
Mckoy, Marcia, NY
McPherson, Tony*
Melidor, Avmart, NY
Menardy, Jasmine, NY
Mendell, Jonathan, NY
Mendez, Lucitania B., NY
Mendez, Rafael, NY
Mendoza-Nasser, Jose*
Mensah, Benjamin, NY
Mercado, Raymond, NY
Mercado, Robertson B., NY
Micalizzi, Paul C.*
Mignano, Michael J., NJ

Miller, James O., NJ
Miller, Scott K., NY
Mitchell, Corey, FL
Mitchell, Ryan J.*
Mones, Denise, NY
Moore, Jason, NY
Moore, Simone I., NY
Morales, Ms. Yvonne, Esq., NY
Morgan, Bruce, NY
Morris, Logan, NY
Mota, Andrea, NY
Mulligan, Robert, NY
Murchison, James, NY
Murphy, Charles M., NY
Nahar, Yesenia, NY
Nannery, Kevin P.*
Naveo, Sadie E.*
Nedd, Janine A., NY
Nicholson, Ms. Terry, NY
Nieves, Cynthia, NY
Nikac, Maria, NJ
Nunez, Elvin, NY
Oderinde, Alexander*
Ojeda, Gonzalo, NY
Onodu, Benjamin, NY
Orgias, Peter D., NY
Osorio, Uti, NY
O'sullivan, Marie, NY
Otero, Mildred, NY
Padula, Louis J., NY
Panchame, Allan G., GA
Panting, Hilda C., NY
Paredes, Graisy M., NY
Parlanti, Damiano, NY
Parris, Cherylann P., NY
Parris, Stacey A., NY
Pauyo-Sanz, M., NY
Pena, Joel, NY
Perlleshi, Luigi*
Pineda, Rumaldo*
Polanco, Miosotis, NY
Polonetsky, Lawrence, NY
Pomerantz, Russell*
Poyerd, James D., NY
Pyronneau, Rose, NY
Quinlan, Ms. Casey E., NY
Quinones, Julio C., NY
Quintero, Marisol K., NY
Raman, Fredrick C., NY
Ramdhany, Joseph K.*
Rampolla, Joseph J., NJ
Ramsay, Walter J., NY
Redmond, Robin L., NY
Reid, Jennifer J., NY
Reid, Keith L., NJ
Reilly, Theresa M., NY
Reskow, Kristin E., NY
Reyes, Evelyn*
Reyes, Frank M., NY
Reynolds, Rebecca L.*
Riggio, Michael, NY
Rigney, James R., NY
Riley, Michele A.*
Rios, Nilsa M., NY
Rios-pris, Denine M.*
Rispoli, Melinda J.*
Rivas, Linda Y., NY
Rivera, Jeanette*
Rivera, Jo Anne, NY
Rivera, Lucia*
Rivera, Paul R.*
Roberts, Cheryl L., NY
Robles-nunez, Julia E., PA
Roccomboli, Teresa, NY
Rodrigues, Maurice, NY
Rodriguez, Arelis J.*
Rodriguez, Hector, NY
Rolen, Linda F.*
Romano, Gina M., NY
Romero, Thomas D.*
Rosario, Phaedra, NY
Rosenbach, Janet N., NY
Roulston, Tammy L., VA
Rozon, Xiomara A., NY
Ruane, Matthew P.*
Ryan, Michael P., NY

Safford, Simone S., NY
Saintilaire, G.*
Salazar, Marcelo, NY
Salomon, Myrna I., NY
Samuel, Kenroy, NY
Sanabria, Mark A., NY
Santiago, Darren B., NY
Santiago, George L., NJ
Santiago, Jose A., NY
Santiago, Marc A., NJ
Scanlon, Kevin J., NY
Scarpone, Leonardo, NY
Schlesinger, Jill*
Schoeller, Dennis M., NY
Schwartz, Robert T., NY
Scibelli, Philip*
Sealy, Juliette Y.*
Serrano, Linda C., NY
Seymour, Lisa M.*
Shepard, Frederick A., NY
Sheppard, Victoria*
Shlapak, Beverly, NY
Siegel, Heather, NY
Simmons, Buffie, NY
Simon, Stacey, NY
Sinclair, Melody A., NY
Singletary, S., NY
Smalls, Shawn M.*
Smith, Keisha*
Smith, Tara F.*
Smyth, Dan J.*
Solano, Abelardo*
Solano, Elsa E., NY
Solis, John E., NY
Spann, Kim A., NY
Stockman, Lavelle, NJ
Suarez-Serafin, J., NJ
Sylver, Peter T., NJ
Tabone, Michelle, NY
Tanco, Jenny, NY
Tankard, Reginald, NY
Taylor, M. L., NY
Telesford, Janelle R., NY
Tellefsen, Laurie J., NY
Thomas, Marie-Maud, NY
Tineo, Leticia M.*
Tobin, Erla, NY
Topp, Viviane M., NY
Torres, Dennisa A., NY
Torres, Eriberto, NY
Torres, Josefina*
Tow, Jonathan L., NY
Tucker, Amber R., NY
Tucker, Elizabeth H., NY
Twu, Yu-jeng, NY
Van Denberg, Gregory C., NY
Vaughan, Sheila M., NY
Vega, Thomas R., NY
Velez, Marla E.*
Vendetto, Janine, NY
Vera, Ana A., NY
Vernon, Patrice A., NY
Villanueva, M.*
Vinas, Paul, NY
Vincent, Wayne A., NY
Vinci, Donald S., NY
Voss, Donna*
Vu, Peter, NY
Walden, Moises J., NY
Walker, Ann Marie, NY
Walker, Edward, NY
Walker, Everlina, NY
Wall, Melissa J.*
Walsh, Ann, NY
Warner- Lyons, Mrs. Elyse Y., NY
Warren, Michael A., NY
Waterhouse, Jessica L.*
White, Andre L., NY
White, Debra, NY
White, Marilyn, NY
Whitely, Marcia A., NY
Wiggins, Angela E., NY
Wiggins, Cathy, NY
Williams, Donna M., NY
Williams, Joanne, NY

Williams, Joseph V.*
Williams, Madonna S., NY
Williams, Tonya V., NY
Willingham, Brenda, NY
Wilson, Francine, NY
Wilson, Marsha M., NY
Witty, Julia*
Xu, You*
Yim, Steven S., MD
Yurchak, Karyn, NJ
Zambrano, Victor H., NY
Zamor, Marie, NY
Zavaglia, R.*
Zyta, Richard E., NY

1995

Abamwa, Osaka M., NY
Abdul, Christine A., GA
Abensur, Peggy*
Accardi, Nicole M.*
Acsay, Gyongyi*
Acuna, George A., NY
Adams, Charice Y., VA
Adamson, Evette C., NY
Adanski, Lisa M., NY
Adegbamigbe, Adedeji, NY
Adeshchenko, Alexand*
Adjaero, Alphonsus A., NY
Adler, Scott J., NY
Agrusti, Craig D., NJ
Agueda, Juan A.*
Ahmad, Shiraz, NY
Akrivos, Jimmy, NY
Akselrod, Steve, NY
Alaji, Omar U., CA
Alban, Donna A., NY
Albino, Diane*
Aleman, Tania E., NY
Aleo, Vito V., NY
Alexandre, Jphilippe, NY
Ali, Fyza D., NY
Ali, Shakawat, NY
Alicea, Elliott J., NY
Allamby, Kevin, NY
AllBright, Nicole, NY
Allen, Jacinta, NJ
Alleva, Michael, NY
Almodovar, Michele Y., NY
Alongi, Michael R., NY
Alpa, Yalcin, NY
Altes, Alexandria, NY
Alzandani, Mansoor, NY
Amaro, Margarita, NY
Amato, Peter J., NY
Ambris, Marcia C., NY
Anderson, Luke E., NY
Anderson, Vanita M., NY
Antoine, Yamille*
Apolinario, Marcia, NJ
Apolito, Ingrid M.*
Aponte, Bianca M., NY
Arce, Nelson, NY
Arellano, Jose, NY
Arevalo, Yesenia M., TX
Argaluza, Roberto, NY
Arias, Milagros A., NY
Armstead, David, NY
Arroyo, Anthony, NY
Arroyo, Jose A., NY
Aruz, Steve A., NY
Asad, Abdalla M., NY
Avella, Tracey E., NY
Averett, Darryl*
Avila, Patricio, NY
Avinger, Denise, NY
Ayari, Dalinda C., NY
Ayers, Rashida, NY
Aylward, John, NY
Aziz, Amina, NY
Baca, Lizette*
Baerga, Venus*
Baez, Eileen, NY
Baez, Gerardo*
Baez, Tina M., NY
Bailey, Nigel R., NY
Baird, Babara A.*

Baird, Omadeli S., NY
Baker, Janice L., NY
Bambach, John*
Bapiste, Gail T.*
Barbetta, Mary T., NY
Barbieri, William T., NY
Barbot-Antoine, Yous*
Bargelini, Gionata M., NY
Barker, Cathy-anne O., NY
Barnett, Robert, NY
Barry, Billjeanna A., NY
Bartlett, Ms. Judith R., NY
Basil, John, NY
Batanus, John, NY
Bateman, Marsha N.*
Batista, Nelsa, NY
Beal, Susan, NY
Beckenstein, Michal*
Beharry, Mark A.*
Beichner, Karen R., NJ
Bellaflores, Jamari, NY
Bello, David*
Beltre, Gustavo A., NY
Benitez, John J., NY
Beritan, Jorge L., NY
Berke, Marshall L., NY
Berkley, Desiree M., NY
Bermudez, Leyla V., NY
Berridge, Heather, NY
Berrios, Rafael, NY
Bert, Richard A., Netherlands
Berthley, Maria D., NY
Bess, Tara S., NJ
Betts, Steven D., NY
Blackman, Clayton*
Blackman, Evette A.*
Blackman, Michelle, NY
Blackthorne, Brian*
Blaha, Richard, NY
Blomquist, Bryan D., NY
Boggio, Marco A., NY
Borden, Lesley, MA
Borgella, Lisa F.*
Borwornthammarat, A., NY
Boshell, Kevin M., NY
Bowles, Aries, NY
Braccini, Stefano A., NY
Bradford, Selena*
Bradley, Kevin, NJ
Brathwaite, Sheron, NY
Brea, Lizette, NY
Breder, Donald J., NY
Brenord, Celius, NY
Brice, Cassandra Y., NY
Brickwood, Dale, NY
Brien, William E., NY
Brienza, Jeffrey T., NY
Briggs, Errol, NY
Brinadze, Anna, NY
Brisbane, Kamber L.*
Brito, Michael J., FL
Brodack, Jeffrey, NY
Broner, Jeffrey W.*
Brown, Agnes*
Brown, Colin R., NY
Brown, Deborah L., NY
Brown, Isaac L., NY
Brown, Janean A., NY
Brown, Sherise N., IL
Brown, Valerie A., NY
Brown, Van, NY
Brown, Yvette E., NY
Brumbelow, Cameron*
Bruno, Daniel J., NY
Bruntel, Doris H., NY
Bryant, Nicole, NY
Buckner, Martha, NY
Bueno, Josner, NY
Bugros, Michelle, NY
Buhrmeister, Robert K., NY
Bulter, Bernard P., NY
Burchenson, Kaye A.*
Burgess, Mia*
Burton, Ines V., NY
Burwell, Tyese L.*
Busby, Dyedra P., NY

Buser, Robert J., CFE, NY
Bush, Christopher P., PA
Bushelon, Jennifer, NY
Busreth, Marjorie*
Butler, Raymond M., NY
Bynum, Kevin C.*
Byrnes, Robert G., NY
Caballero, Nester J., NY
Caban, Wilfred, NY
Cabrera, Yokasta, NY
Caceres, Elisabeth, NY
Caceres, Silvia*
Caddle, Carolyn A., NY
Caesar, Tessa V., NY
Cagliuso, Nicholas, NY
Cajigas, Veronica, NY
Calabrese, Christine A.*
Calixte, Nevelus*
Callahan, William J., NJ
Calle, Maria I., NY
Camacho, Christine*
Camacho, Gabriel, NY
Campanile, Anthony, NY
Campbell, Morven A., NY
Campbell, Patricia A., NY
Cannon, Edward T., NY
Cano, Jeanette, NY
Canty, Maria A., NY
Caola-oskin, Courtney B., NY
Capelli, Robert, NY
Capparelli, Madeline C., NY
Carbonell, Elisa M., NY
Caro, Shirley, NY
Carr, Dietrich M., NY
Carr, Monica*
Carrasco, Edward, NY
Carrington, Eric, NY
Carroll, Donna-Jean**
Caruth, Godson R., NY
Carvajal, Ibethe*
Carvajal, Patricia, NY
Carvajal, Xiomara G., NY
Casey, Michael J., NY
Cassagnol, Nikole, NY
Cassidy, Michael A., NY
Cassillo, Theresa M.*
Castagna, John J., NY
Castanza, James, NY
Castiglione, Steven, NY
Castillo-mullings, Glynnis, NY
Castro, Fermin, NY
Castro, Hildi*
Catanese, Joseph J., NJ
Catlyn, Dasha V., NY
Cavaliere, Christopher, NY
Cayetano, Olga, VA
Cerda, Maria C., NY
Cesarano, Anthony, NY
Chabran, Jennifer, NY
Chan, David, NY
Chandler, Kinya, NY
Charles, Alice, NY
Charles, Joseph, NY
Charles, Rose M., NY
Chatman, Mayai N., NY
Chavis, Rosezina, NY
Chavis, Shawn, NY
Checo, Christina, NY
Checo, Manuela E., NY
Cheeks, Robert, NY
Chen, Hang, NY
Cheregotis, Peter J., NY
Chester, Shonette A., PA
Chico, Ivelisse, NY
Chin, Frank, NY
Chin, Howard F.*
Chinchilla, Maria M., NY
Chittick, Diane A., MD
Chorney, Tonya L., NY
Chow, Lynette S., IL
Christian, Elmo E., NY
Chung, Michael, NY
Church, William J., NY
Cintron, Aracelis, NY
Cintron, David, NY
Cintron, Edna I.*

Cipri, Anthony J., NY
Civitano, Danielle L., NY
Clapp, Michelle D., NY
Clarke, Justin H., NY
Claudio, Roberto, NY
Clough, Francis, NY
Clue, Denese A., NY
Coakley, Lorianne, NY
Cobb, Mrs. Mamie O., NY
Cobia, Reuben T., NY
Cocchi, John A., NY
Codling, Omar, NY
Coffran, William J., NY
Cohen, Karen, NY
Cohen, Steven A., NY
Coley, Helen, NY
Colon, Belinda*
Colon, Hector E., NJ
Colon, Mirna E., NY
Colon, Monica, NY
Colon, Yesenia, NY
Comenzo, Craig, NY
Commerford, Donald A., NJ
Connolly, Daniel, NY
Conroy, Francis A.*
Conway, Edward F.*
Cooper, Dermot A., NY
Corbett, Ms. Heather A., NY
Corbin, Stephen, NY
Corchado, Diana A., NY
Corona, Edwin R., NY
Correa, Tula J., NY
Corry, Lorraine, NY
Cortes, Albert S.*
Cortes, Denise, NY
Costanzo, Elizabeth*
Courtney, Diane T., NY
Covil, Mathieu*
Cowick, Gary L., NY
Cox, Julie A., GA
Craig, Sara Elizabeth, PA
Crandell, Xavier O., NY
Crosby-Greene, Lee, NY
Cucaj, Xhevat, NY
Culver, Tanya L., NY
Cunneen, Joseph F., NY
Cunningham, Eric D., NY
Cunningham, Maureen, NY
Curran, Catherine C., NY
Curry, Heather M., NJ
Curry, Warren P., NY
Curti, Ms. Jennifer, NY
Cus, Stefanie M., NY
Dabkowski, Liza E.*
Daise, Cerita E., NY
Damato, Victor V.*
Dames, Fatima C., CT
Daniel, David C., NY
Daniel-Hurry, Nadine N., NY
Daniels, Deborah M.*
Daniels, Thomas L., NY
Danjer, Marco V., CA
Dardzinski, Lisa A., NY
Dautaj, Ylli, NY
Davidson, Walter*
Davies, Christopher J., NJ
Davila, Jose, NY
Davis, Diane L., NY
Davis, Judie, NY
Davis, Lawrence R.*
Davis, Roshawn B., NY
Davis, Teresa A., PA
Davis, Veronica*
De, Stefano, NY
Dean, James C., NY
Decambre, Brenda, NY
De Cicco, Donna M., NY
De Cicco, Timothy J., NY
DeConinck, David A., NY
Deegan, Kevin T., NY
Deen, Mohamed, NY
Deetjen, Marie J.*
DeFina, Bernice, NY
Deixler, Lonnie*
De Jesus, Evelyn A., NY
Dejesus, Lillian*

De Jesus, Lisa, NY
Dejohn, Regina M., NY
Delapaz, Frank C., NY
Deleon, Anna M., NY
Delerme, Stevenson, NY
Delgado, Ms. Fatima A., CO
Delorenzis, Ellis R., NY
De Mastri, Gregory S.*
Derrick, Jasmine C.*
Desir, Pierre E.*
Detres, Cynthia, NY
Devins, Brian M., NY
Devonish, Sharon, NY
Diaz, Andres F., NY
Diaz, Diana, NY
Diaz, Janice, NY
Diaz, John M., NJ
Diaz, Juan*
Diaz, Solangel R.*
Diaz, Valdez, NY
Dietz, John S., NY
Diez, Angela M., NY
Digirolomo, Nicholas, NY
Di Iorio, Jeannette, NY
Dillon, Andrea D.*
Dillon, Michael P., NJ
Dimarco, Christine*
Dingui, Yessenia*
Dirkin, Walter J., Esq., NJ
Di Stefano, Vincent M., NY
Ditoro, Mark S.*
Dixon, John H., NY
Dixon, Nora, NY
Dominguez, Thomas, NY
Donleavy, William C.*
Donohue, Brian E., NY
Dorvil, Rommelle T., NY
Dowie, Heather M., NY
Dudley, Shawn L., NY
Duffy, Charles P., NY
Dugas, Anne F.*
Dummett, Dexter C., NY
Dunn, Hayley, NY
Durante, Eugene G., NY
Duro, Christopher M., NY
Dwyer, Karen, NY
Dzieniszewska, Ewa, NY
Eagle, Tanya M., NY
Eason, Erica M., NY
Easterling, Dolores L., NJ
Eastman, Elkan H., NY
Edelman, Steven P., NY
Egan, Mary, NY
Eisenberg, Scott, NY
Ekiziah, Stephen K., NY
Elder, Velma, NY
Embden, David R., DC
Engel, William, NY
English, David J., NY
Entler, Michele M.*
Epstein, Bonnie, NY
Erb, Justin C., NJ
Ergun, Halime, NY
Esposito, Theresa M., NY
Espreo, Jose A.*
Ess, Tanya L.*
Esteban, Ricardo, NY
Estrada, Orlando, NY
Estrella, Yojaida, NY
Evans, Cherisse T., NY
Evelyn, Spencer E., NY
Fabian, Raymond, NY
Fairley, Norman S., NY
Faison, Yolanda B.*
Falcon, Mercedes, NY
Falebita, Diane E.*
Faraone, Ms. Teri, NY
Fares, Kassem*
Farias, Jeanine V., NY
Farley, James F., NY
Fatsis, Kyriakoula, NY
Faulk, Alisa, NY
Faustino, Allison, NY
Fealy, Michael D., NY
Federici-LaFargue, Ms.
　Marietta, NY

Fee, Christopher J., NY
Feiler, Christopher, NY
Feinholtz, Leslie, NJ
Feldman, Felix P., NY
Feliz, Yokasta*
Fell, Scott E.*
Feneque, Samuel, NY
Ferrall, Christopher T., NY
Ferrante, Victor, NY
Fertullien, Kenia Y.*
Fex, George T., NY
Fields, Jennifer A., NY
Figueroa, Carmelo J., NY
Figueroa, Melissa, NY
Figueroa, Paul A., NY
Fillie-Faboe, G.*
Fine, Barbara J., NY
Finlayson, Thomas C., Jr., NY
Fiore, Albert J., NY
Fisch, Daniel G., NY
Flaherty, John P., NY
Fletcher, Ali A., NY
Flores, Allan T.*
Flores, Victor H., NY
Foley, William J., NY
Fontnel, Monique A., NY
Forbes, Candace T., NY
Forshay, Karen, NY
Foster, Cherie S., NY
Four, Rebeka*
Fowler, Kareem, NY
Frances, Miguel A., NY
Francillon, Joanne, NY
Francis, Charles R., NY
Franco, Robert J., NJ
Francois, Mrs. Marie M., NY
Franks, William*
Frederick, Darrell, NY
Fredericks, Andrew A., NY
Freeman, James H., NY
Friedman, Jenna, NY
Fries, Timothy, NY
Fuller-bey, Tayhlia, NY
Furelli, Gianfranco, NY
Furman, Cynthia, NY
Gabbin, Catherine P., NY
Galarza, Maria E., NY
Galbreath, Lauren M., NY
Gallagher, James W.*
Gallup, Tamara, NY
Gambichler, Edward F., NY
Garcia, Deborah S., NY
Garcia, Jason K., NY
Garcia, Jose F.*
Garry, Thomas M., NY
Garvey, Michael J., Sr., NY
Gaudet, Eugene C., NY
Gaviria, Janeth M., NY
Gay, Joseph B., Jr., NY
Gayle, Janet E., NY
Gellard, Douglas, NY
Genovese, Alexander V., MD
Georges, Nadine E.*
Geraghty, Susan P.*
Gerald, Ira, NY
Germosen, Otto, NY
Gerstheimer, Pamela, NY
Gesualdi, Frank J., NY
Geter, Leon T.*
Gibbs, Eugene, NY
Gilbert, Kenroy B., NY
Gilbert, Miguelina, NY
Gill, Michelle R., NY
Gilmore, Robert, NY
Ginyard, Lyvone*
Giron, Juan C., NY
Giwa-osagie, Yesuf*
Glazer, Sheindel, NY
Goddard, Alson D., NY
Godi, Mihai, NY
Goeden, Jolene A.*
Goldman, Howard F., NY
Goldman, Robert M., NY
Goldsby, Shannell D.*
Goldsmith, Michelle, NY
Golino, Michael J., NY

Gomez, Anibal, NY
Gomez, Carmen M., NY
Gomez, Maribel A.*
Gomez, Orlando N., NY
Gondry, Nicole, NY
Gonzales, Burt R., FL
Gonzalez, Hector, NY
Gonzalez, Kenneth A., NY
Gonzalez, Manuel, NY
Gonzalez, Oscar E.*
Gonzalez, William A.*
Gordon, Benjamin A., NJ
Gordon, Blanche M., NY
Gordon, Linda, NY
Gottlieb, Cara, NY
Granata, George M., NY
Graney, Heidi, NY
Grant, Anne C., NY
Grant, Anthony A.*
Grattan, Lori*
Gray, Earl E., NY
Greaves, June S., NY
Green, Andrew, NY
Green, Andrew P., NY
Green, Stephanie, NY
Griffin, Cheryl E., NY
Griffin, Romania A., NY
Griffith, Samantha, NY
Grimm, Matthew B., NY
Grisancich, Anna M.*
Gudino, Sheila D., NY
Guerra, Josefina*
Guerrero, Isaida I.*
Guerrier, Wendy, NY
Guillen, Mencia*
Guinyard, Freddie, SC
Gunerard, Gabrielle R., NY
Guneraro, Gabrielle R., NY
Gustavsen, Kjell S.*
Gutkin, Jonathan M., NJ
Guzman, Jose A., NY
Guzman, Rosa E., NY
Hadley, David C., NY
Hajaree, Sabita, NY
Halkias, John E., NY
Hall, Debra L., NY
Halton, Darreiel A., NY
Hamilton, Natalie D.*
Hancock, Nikki*
Handy, Mitzu E.*
Hanover, Scott W., NY
Harcourt, Kimberly, NY
Hargett, Lori A.*
Hargrave, Abdula R., NY
Harnett, Michael, NJ
Harper, Christa J., NJ
Hart, Robert, NY
Hart, Todd J., NY
Harvey, Charmaine P., NY
Hasan, Samiuddin, NY
Hasso, Lisa S., NY
Hastings, Mark E., WI
Haugk, Charles J., NY
Hauptman, Eric J., NY
Haussermann, Angela, NY
Hawking, Andrew*
Hawkins, Shelly-ann L., NY
Hayes, Philip L., NY
Haynes, Unelda*
Hazel, William B., III, CT
Helzner, Daniel M.*
Henderson, Thomas W.*
Henry, Carline M.*
Herlihy, Terance T.*
Hernandez, Amarilyz, NY
Hernandez, Virginia*
Herrera, Juan, NY
Herring, Mattie R.*
Hicks, Frances E., NY
Hicks, Netoya S., NY
Hilario, Dilcia Y., NY
Hill, Donna, NY
Hind, David V., NY
Hinds, Elizabeth C., NY
Hoch, Joseph B., NY
Holder, Giovanna, NY

Holley, James D., NY
Hopkins, Farrell J., NY
Horton, Edward, NY
Hospedales, Jared M.*
Howe, Lawrence, NY
Huang, Melody C., NY
Hults, Carol D., NY
Humes, Gilbert C., NY
Imbasciani, Theodore*
Ingman, Matthew A., NY
Irizarry, Yolanda, NY
Isles, Samantha, NY
Israel, Ruth L., NY
Isroe, Karyn E., NY
Jablonska, Beata, NY
Jabouin, Alain S., NY
Jack, Bryan A., NY
Jackson, Hellouise*
Jackson, La-toya, NY
Jacobs, Anthony C.**
Jacobs-Osborne, Guliana D.,
　NY
Jailall, Rajendra J.*
James, Michelle B., NY
Jean-felix, Stanley, NY
Jean-louis, Wigeby, NY
Jenkins, Charisse N., NY
Jenkins, Rshaun K., NY
Jimenez, Cristobal F., NY
Jimenez, Pedro A., NY
Job, Andre F.*
Joe, Lloyd D., NY
John, Lisa N., NY
Johnson, Danielle C., NY
Johnson, Everard K., NY
Johnson, Gwyn, NY
Johnson, Kim T.*
Johnson, Larry, NY
Johnson, Marcia D., NY
Johnson, Martin G., NY
Johnson, Stephanie, NY
Jones, Corey A., NY
Jones, Kevin, NY
Jones, Lateshia P., NY
Jones, Rosedale*
Jones, Yvonne, NY
Joseph, Eugenie, NY
Joseph, George J., NY
Joseph, Ms. Rhonda F., NY
Joye, Natarsia L., NY
Joyner, Anissa R.*
Joyner, Tisa S., NY
Julien, Simon, NY
Junko, Lisa M., NY
Juritsch, Martin J., NY
Kanne, Emmanuel, NY
Kanowsky, Tina M., NJ
Kaplan, Holly S., NY
Kaspiev, Mark*
Kassnoff, Erika F.*
Kateridge, Janine M., NY
Keane, Patrick J., NY
Kearins, Michael P.*
Kellier, Hayley A.*
Kelly, Michael J.*
Kennedy-Gomes, Mrs.
　Candice, NY
Khahaifa, Weslii V.*
Kim, Sonni*
Kim, Sunghoon, NY
Kinahan, Donna M., NJ
King, Rechelle L., NY
King, Rhonny S.*
Klas, Brian E., NY
Kline, Byron, NY
Knapp, Irene*
Knicos, Bessie, NJ
Knight, Angela N., NY
Knight, Lamona O., NY
Koller, Joseph J., NY
Kong, Corwin, NY
Kong, Yuen F., NY
Koopalethes, Alexander J., NJ
Korb, Adriana, NY
Kortright, Augusto, NY
Koumpouras, John, NY

Kouzel, Margarita, CA
Kozakiewicz, Jennifer L., NJ
Kramer, Sean C., NY
Krating, Mary A.*
Krishnanan, Annita, GA
Kuan, Andres, NY
Kulah, Kofua Z., NY
Kurtek, Richard, NY
Kypriotis, Theodosios, NY
Labiento, Daniel, NY
Laboy, Michelle, NY
La De, La, NY
Laguerre, John, NY
Lambert-martinez, Efrain, NY
Lambie, M'balia B., FL
Lambkin, John M., NY
Lancaster, Michael O., NY
Langan, Mary K., NY
Lanigan, Maria, NY
Lantigua, Alfa*
La Padula, Vincent A., NY
Laperuta, Domenick A., NY
Larosa, Michael A., NY
Lasanta, Vanessa L.*
Lawrence, Claude, NY
Lawson, Blair, NY
Lazzaro, Paul J., NJ
Le Barber-scully, Carole L.*
Ledford, Marsha N., NY
Lee, Yoon S., NY
Leiterman, Jason E., NY
Lenard, Jill R., NY
Leon, Angel M.*
Leventis, Angela B., NY
Levy, Amy B., NY
Levy, William, NY
Lew, Larry, NY
Lewin, Georgia M., NY
Licata, Francine M.*
Liggians, Rhonda L., NY
Lin, Nisha, NJ
Linares, Israel, NY
Lindenmayer, Rose M., NY
Lindsay, Garth, NY
Linstrom, Gregory M., CT
Liranzo, Rosemary*
Lisa, Thomas M., NY
Liscinsky, James K., NJ
Lissner, Michael A., NY
Little-Torres, Elyse, NY
Lo, Chun-on, NY
Loila, Dan, NY
Lombard, Gary J., NY
Loo, George, NY
Lopez, Aida A.*
Lopez, Diana, NY
Lopez, Frank, MD
Lopez, Jackeline Y., NY
Lopez, Linda I., NY
Lopez, Sabrina I., NY
Lopez, Sharon, NY
Lopez, Yeni A.*
Loranger, Michelle, NY
Lorello, Charles M.*
Los, Sandra A., OH
Louison, Kirk, NY
Louissaint, Halaby, NY
Louissaint, Ravhelle, NY
Lovell, David E., NY
Lowery, John P., NY
Lowery, John W., NY
Lowney, Michael P., NY
Lowy, Kenneth M., NY
Luengas, Jose A., NY
Lunn, Kitty, NY
Lutzker, Erik L., NY
Luyando, Rafael A., NY
Luyando, Ray F., NY
Lynch, Christopher B., NY
Lynch, Terry D.*
Lynn, Kandia O., NY
Lyons, Janine Q., NY
Lyons, Leonie A., NY
Macdonnell, Mark C., NY
Mack, Ms. Stephanie M., NY
Macon, Olivia Y., GA

Macwithey, Thomas J., NY
Maekawa, Yoshimitsu, NY
Maher, Anne M., NJ
Mahipat, Pamela*
Maitland, Michelle, NY
Major, Gilbert H., NY
Maldonado, David, NY
Maloney, Bryan M., NY
Maloney, Steven E., NY
Maltese, Nicole M., NY
Maltin, Nancy I., NY
Mammarelli, Christopher J., NY
Manchand, Nicole E., NY
Mangome, Victor, NY
Maniscalco, Vito, NY
Man-kong, Margaret*
Mannie, John*
Margolis, Jason S., NY
Mariolis, Aliki G.*
Markowitz, Matthew, NY
Marotta, Michelle, NY
Marquez, Jimmy, NY
Marshall, Noel, NY
Marte, Elsa, NY
Martin, Michael, NY
Martinez, Alfonso V., NY
Martinez, Janet A.*
Martinez, Jocelyne, NY
Martinez, Miguel E., NY
Martinez, Sandra, NY
Martinez, Victor M., NY
Maslova, Olga, NY
Mason, Marcia C., NY
Masri, Rana*
Massop, Carmen E.*
Masterson, Charles, NY
Mateo, Edelmira A., NY
Mateo, Edwin J.*
Mateo, Yudelca A., NY
Mathai, Satish, NY
Matheus, Janice M., NY
Matias, Edgar, NY
Matta, Maria J.*
Mattson, Andrew, NY
Maurer, Daniel E., NY
Maxwell, Peadar G., NY
Maycock, Deborah D., MN
Mayol, Gerardo, NY
Mayr, Louis A., NY
Mazza, Yoko*
Mc, Cabe, NY
Mc, Dermott*
Mc Allister, Cathleen S., NY
McAloon, Daniel K., NY
Mcbride, Trone L., NY
Mccarther, Monifa, VA
McCarthy, Jacqueline, NY
Mccavera, James, NY
Mc Caw, Tonya A.*
Mccormack, Stephen F., NY
McCray, Tara Y., NY
Mc Cullough, Valerie A.*
Mccurdy, Leslie D., NY
Mccutchan, Lisa K., NY
Mcenany, Kristen M.*
Mcfadden, Phyllis*
Mc Farlane, Charlene A., NY
Mcgregor, Karyn A., NY
Mc Innis, Michael R., NY
Mckay, Roxanne M., NY
Mckenzie, Constance, NY
McLaughlin, Kari L.*
Mcmillan, Margaret*
Mcmillion, Tony, NY
Mc Nulty, Christopher R., NY
Mc Pherson, Debbra S., NY
Mcpherson, Michele M., NY
Mcqueen, David A., NY
Meaders, Nyhisha T., NY
Medina, Francisco, NY
Mena, Bayovanex, NY
Mendez, Arturo, NY
Mendez, Francis, NY
Mendez, Yolanda*
Mendoza, Joel, CT
Mensah, Sylvester F., NY

Mercado, Robert, NY
Mercado, Wigberto, NY
Merrick, Timothy, NY
Messina, Camillo, NY
Meszaros-Brillon, A., NY
Metivier, Beverley A., NY
Meyer, Kurt P., NY
Meyers, Glenn R., NY
Miah, Mohammed*
Mila, Jennifer, NY
Miller, Angela P.*
Miller, Christopher A., NY
Miller, Deltra A.*
Miller, Edward D., NY
Miller, Oniel A.*
Millien, Tamara, NY
Miranda, Doreen, NY
Miranda, Rosina*
Mitchell, Gloria A., VA
Mitchell, Maureen, NY
Mitrctasics, Mrs. Catherine, NY
Mobley, Ayanna T., NY
Mock, Judy, NY
Moeslinger, Emma N., NY
Moffett, Anita, NY
Moffett, Melissa N., NY
Monaghan, Allene*
Moncayo, Frank J., NY
Montague, Denise*
Montalvo, Juan, NY
Montecier, Allison A., NY
Montenegro, Richard (Rich), Jr., NY
Moore, Cynthia*
Moore, Doreen, NY
Moore, Nichole K., NY
Mora, Felix, NY
Morabito, Douglas P., CT
Morales, Danisha*
Morales, Marilyn, NY
Morales, Michelle*
Morales, Sara, NY
Morales, Yvette, NY
Morales-Torres, Sandra E., NY
Morell, Edward, NY
Morris, Keisha B., VA
Morris, Walter A., NY
Morris-alston, Sophi, NY
Morrison, Donald J., Jr., NY
Moses, Deatra R., NY
Moses, Puliti, NY
Moye, Millicent L., NY
Mui, Michael S., NY
Muir, Harriette A., NY
Mulheron, Gregory S.*
Muller, Deborah, NY
Muller, John K., NY
Muniz, Mrs. Belinda, NJ
Muriel, Marianela, NY
Murray, Daniel F., NY
Murrell, Zenja J., NY
Myers, Joseph J., NY
Nachmany, Etty, NY
Nakao, Eric D., NY
Nass, Eric P., NY
Nathan, Paul A., NY
Natta, Stephenie, NY
Navarro, Jose A., NY
Nedlin, Marny B., FL
Nelligar, James E., NY
Nelson, Mennie F., NY
Nelson, Yvonne, NY
Nesmith, Phoebe R., NY
Nestor, John T., NY
Neufville, Norris, NY
Newkirk, Tabitha, NY
Newton, Samuel A., NY
Ng, Sukfong C., NY
Ngai, Kenneth, NY
Ngai-crim, Karin, NY
Nicholas, Ainsley, NY
Nieves, Ralph G., NY
Nolasco, Hector, NY
Nonis, Basil, NY
Norberg, Mark*
Norberg, Scott, NY

Normil, Marie, NY
Norton, Keith J., NJ
Norvio, Scott J., NY
Nugent, Michele D., VA
O'callaghan, Cormac D., FL
Oconnell, Edward T., NJ
O'Conner, Catherine, NY
O'Connor, Ms. Brigid, NY
O'daniels, Tiffany L., NY
Odums, Tanya S., NY
O'hara, Kerry A.*
Okeke, Ikenna*
Olijnyk, Steven A., NY
Oliver, Paul S., NY
Oliveras, Mrs. Daisy I., NY
Olivo-Perez, Sharon L., NY
Oluwa, Abiodun M.*
Onyeobia, Kelechi, NY
Organ, Mrs. Miriam, NY
Orlando, Robert A., NY
Ortega, Corinne N., NE
Ortiz, Carolina M., NY
Ortiz, Silvia T., NY
Osnato, William A.*
Osso, Donna J.*
Oyediran, Jacob O., NY
Pajooh, Rudolph R., NY
Palladino, Marie A., NY
Panagopoulos, Stilianos E., NY
Pandya-ramrikhi, A.*
Panell, Julius*
Panther, Shakira M., NY
Papson-Adams, David, NY
Pardesi, Guardial S., NY
Paredes, Ruth V., NY
Parker, Sydney H., NY
Parrom, Gigi*
Pascocello, Anthony J., Jr., NY
Patania, John, NJ
Patrizi, Dominick, NY
Patterson, Erika P., NJ
Paulino, Reynaldo M., NY
Paz, M. V.*
Pearson, Evelyn E., NY
Peart, Annmarie B., NY
Pedersen, Frank, NY
Pedro, Hakeem A., NY
Peele, Ondra T., GA
Pelepelin, Alex*
Pena, Ambioris D.*
Pena, Carmen L., NY
Pena, Eligia, NY
Pena, Jenaro R., NY
Pena, Julio, NY
Penn, Joseph C., PA
Peoples, Ms. Melissa, NY
Perez, Bianca, NY
Perez, Florence*
Perez, Lisbeth D., NY
Perez, Rosa T.*
Perez, Victor M., NJ
Perfetto, Robert M., NY
Perlleshi, Luigi, NY
Perlov, Joshua M., NY
Perry, Kevin, NY
Persaud, Annette N., NY
Persinger, Ms. Sherry L., MO
Persuad, Annette, NY
Peterson, Marlana E.*
Peterson, Sandra, NY
Peterson, Tania I., NY
Petrov, Aleksey, NY
Phelan, Thomas F.*
Philips, Janet, NY
Phillips, Leon A., PA
Philogene, Gemelyn*
Philp, Leslie-Ann C.*
Phipps, Rocio, NY
Pichardo, Ana I., NY
Pichardo, Maria F., NY
Pierre, Michael W., NY
Piliero, Giuliano, NY
Pitter, Violet M., NY
Plaia, Vito, NY
Plant, Edward J., NY
Poggi, John J., III, NY

Polanco, Lauvienska E., FL
Polin, Ms. Martha A., NY
Polite, Charntel*
Pollack, Andrew B., NJ
Poonai, Roopnarine, NY
Poppe, Matthew S., NY
Porter, Damon*
Posniack, Glenn, FL
Pouliot Grant, Anne C., NY
Powell, Shawnee, NY
Powell, Walter, NY
Pradieu, Caroline, NY
Price, Laray, NY
Prince, Ernst, NY
Proscia, Thomas G., NY
Prosper, Marlon R., NY
Pruitt, Denise L., NY
Psahos, Theodoros (Ted), NY
Puello, Miguelina, NY
Pugh, Jason M., NY
Pulgar, Paula A., NJ
Pupiales, Monica P., NY
Quartara, Vita, NY
Quinones, Giselle, NY
Rahat, Mohamed, NY
Rahat, Sheikh M.*
Ramos, Jack, NY
Ramos, Yolanda, NY
Ramos, Zenaida, NY
Ramsay, Margaret, NY
Ramsey, Darryl M., NY
Rancic, Valentino, NJ
Randle, Kevin M., NY
Rankine, Denise, NY
Rasso, Louis J., NY
Ray, Thomas B., NY
Rayford, James C., NY
Raynor, David N., NY
Rector, James A.*
Regis, Ms. K. F., NY
Rego, Simon A., Canada
Reid, Diana M., NY
Reid, Hattie, NY
Reid, Lorna P., NY
Reid, Shaun C., Esq., NY
Reilly, James P.*
Remon, Malena C., NY
Rensch, Laura, NY
Reuben, Ernest M., NY
Reyes, Olga, NY
Reynolds, George F., NY
Reynoso, Florinda, NY
Rhem, Minnie B.*
Ricci, Carmen M., NY
Richards, Lorraine, NY
Richardson, V.*
Richardson-Morris*
Ridges, Thomas C., NY
Ridley, Sandra O., NY
Rios, Jennery, NY
Rivera, Brenda, NY
Rivera, Carmen, NY
Rivera, Cesar J., NY
Rivera, Eduardo, NY
Rivera, Elizabeth, NY
Rivera, Felix*
Rivera, Maria R., NY
Rivera, Michelle, NY
Rivera, Onix, NY
Rivera, Teresita F., NY
Rivera, Yvonne, NJ
Rivero, Lisandra, NY
Rizzo, Kevin, NJ
Roach, Erle S., NY
Roan, Hope A.*
Robertson, Bruce A., NY
Robinson, Angela M., NY
Robinson, Cynthia (Cyndy), NY
Robinson, Koy E., NY
Robles, Jose E., NY
Rodriguez, Andrea B.*
Rodriguez, Araceli, NY
Rodriguez, C., NY
Rodriguez, Claudia, NY
Rodriguez, Iris J., NY
Rodriguez, Isabella, MD

Rodriguez, Jilma*
Rodriguez, Juan C., NY
Rodriguez, Julio, NY
Rodriguez, Lina B., NY
Rodriguez, Louis I., NY
Rodriguez, Michelle, NY
Rodriguez, Myrza M., NY
Rodriguez, Nelson, NY
Rodriguez, Rebecca, NY
Rodriguez, Rosa Y.*
Rodriguez, S., NY
Rodriguez, Sandra M., NY
Rodriguez, Wanda, NY
Rodriguez, Yolanda, NY
Rogaski, John, NY
Rognon, Rudolph G., NY
Rolland, Kenya*
Roman, Edwin, NY
Roman, Jose F.*
Roman, Marian C., NY
Romano, Christopher, NY
Romero, Benita A., NY
Roske, Daniel, NJ
Ross, Renee*
Roth, Paul P., NY
Rothenberg, Jackie, NY
Royce, Kevin J., NJ
Rubirosa, Natasha, NY
Ruggiero, Anthony, NY
Ruiz, Bernadette, NY
Ruiz, Nydia, NY
Ruiz, Pedro J., NY
Russell, Marsha Natasha, NY
Russell, Michael L., NY
Russo, Philip A., NY
Ryan, Christopher, NY
Ryan, Kim, NY
Sadig, Yasmin H.*
Saigo, Shondell A., NY
Salamone, Vincent, NY
Salguero, Elcida, NY
Salim, Said, NY
Samuels, Eli P.*
Samuels, Sandra E., NY
Sanchez, Carlos M., NY
Sanchez, Diana, NY
Sanchez, Felipe A., NY
Sanchez, Joseph (Joie) R., NY
Sanders, Antoinette, NY
Sandusky, Ativia S.*
Sang, Suiling, NY
Sansarran, Nirmala, NY
Santana, Felicia A., NY
Santana, Maribel, NY
Santos, Jose J., NY
Sarfo, Solomon, NY
Sargeant, Mark A., NY
Savarese, Gabriel M., NY
Saxe, Susan N., NY
Scally, Tina M., NY
Scalzo, Ronald G., NY
Scavelli, Guy V., NY
Schachter, Lisa, NY
Schifini, Thomas A., TX
Schmidt, John, NJ
Schmidt, Michael, NY
Schubert, Kristin, NY
Schultz, Matthew A.*
Scott, Coleen A.*
Scott, Edythe, NY
Scott, Lezlie A., CT
Scott, Monica, NY
Scotto-Lavino, T., NY
Scott-wilson, Nichole, NY
Sculley, Maryanne, NY
Seay, Rholanda R., NY
Sebro, Sherwin K., NY
Selvaggi, Anthony, NY
Selzner, Jennifer L., NY
Semexant, Biel, FL
Seney, Jeannette V., NY
Seraspe, Danilo, NJ
Serrano, Estella, NY
Serrano, Samantha, NY
Sharon, Elihu, NY
Sharon, Isaac, NY

Shaw, Michelle M., NY
Shea, James, NY
Shearin, John D., NJ
Shepard, Marla D.*
Shewnarain, Maya, IL
Shturmina, Marina, NY
Shulterbron, Johanna, NY
Sicurelli, Karen A., NY
Silla, Bruno A.*
Silva, Maria J., NY
Silva, Martin, NY
Silva, Roberto, Jr., NY
Silver, Alison L.*
Simeon, Esther, NY
Simmons, Yvonne, NY
Simon, Renee I.*
Simpson, Brian A.*
Simpson, Shelaine, NY
Slade, Howard M., NY
Slezak, Alice, NY
Small, Christine J., CO
Small, Erona R., NY
Small, Karen S., NY
Small, Kwame O., NY
Smit, Christie M., NY
Smith, Courtney, NY
Smith, Denise B., NY
Smith, Jonathan B.*
Smith, Melba L., NY
Smith, Michael S., NY
Smith, Michelle D., NY
Smith, Michelle S., NY
Smith, Pamela D., NY
Smith, Rodney, NY
Smith, Ronald G., MD
Solano, Silvia M., NY
Soler, Diana L., NY
Soler-lugo, Maria, NY
Somerstein, Ilyse R., NJ
Sonnetta Joyner, Tisa, NY
Soria, Katterine I., NY
Soriano, Christina, NY
Soto, Evangelina, NY
Sotolongo, Pedro, FL
Sowah, Mawuli, NJ
Spaier, Matthew H., NY
Spitzbarth, Robert, NY
Spriggs, Lashunn, NY
Stakias, Ellen S., NY
Staniek, Magdalena, NY
Stapleton, Mary A., NY
Stark, Robert M., NY
Starkes, Tommie C., NY
Staton, Keith, NY
St. Clor, Wagner P., NY
Steets, William R., VA
Stein, Heather J., NY
Stephens, Eric, NY
Stephenson, Oscar L., NY
Stern, Helen A., FL
Stevens, Nadia U.*
Stewart, Janet S., NY
Stewart, Shannon T., NY
Stiller, Marla K., NY
Stivala, Rachel D., NY
Stone, Pandora, NY
Stopler, Michael J., NY
Strickland, Annette, NY
Strong, Kevin L., NY
Stuart, Calvin, NY
Stukes, Ms. Ernestine T., NY
Suarez, Martha E.*
Subrahimovic, S.*
Sullivan, Terrence C., NY
Sultan, Patricia, NY
Swain, Connie, NY
Sweeting, Soyini T., NY
Swinton, Darlene, NY
Syed, Ghazali A., NY
Tabrizi, Ms. Monica N., CA
Talton, Simone M., NY
Tamai, Julianne Sumiyo, NY
Tancula, Aldona, NY
Taormina, Jonathan*
Tart, Angela L., MD
Taveras, Luisa J., NY

Taveras, Seny, NY
Tavitian, Lucy G., NY
Taylor, Hilton T., NY
Taylor, Rosemarie, NY
Telleria, Alberto F., NY
Temple, Canchetta*
Testa, Matthew J.*
Theodore, Leticia S., NY
Thomas, Darrell E., NY
Thomas, Joy E., NY
Thomas, Judy C., NY
Thomas, Keith B., NY
Thompson, Michele C., NY
Thornton, Alexis G.*
Thorpe, Jennifer J., NY
Tinsley, Clayton M., NY
Titus, Serina E., NY
Tomashosky, Eugene, FL
Tomlinson, Kenneth, NY
Toppin, Douglas D., NY
Tornetti, Frank J., NY
Toro, Zacarias, NY
Torrens, Mark A., NJ
Torres, Edwin*
Torres, Hector L., NY
Torres, Jesus, NY
Torres, Johnnie*
Torres, Lissette, NY
Trainor, Patrick J., PA
Trautmann, S., NY
Trentacosta, Dena M., NY
Trigo, Alejandra, NY
Triolo, Bobbi A., NJ
Tsai, Jeffrey, NY
Tseng, Chih H., NY
Tsevdos, Stefanos, NY
Tsitko, Viktoriya*
Turner, Michelle A., NY
Tutani, Sidney, NY
Tyler, Brian D., NY
Tytell, Peter V., NY
Ude, Jude M., NY
Ugo, Roy P.*
Uke, Evaristus U., NY
Uma-Omede, Tonnie*
Ungarino, Peter J., NY
Urena, Elizabeth*
Usher, Joseph J.*
Utsey, Robert E., PA
Uzcategui, Robert E., NY
Valera, Magalys, NY
Vallderuten, Fabiola, VA
Valle, Nelson, NY
Vallejo, Fanny, NY
Vanderlee, Cynthia S., NY
Vargas, Brenda*
Vargas, Dayana, NY
Vargas, Jeffrey (Jeff), NY
Varnes, Robert*
Vartabedian, Darryl, NJ
Vasquez, Migdalia*
Vaughn, Sean, NY
Vazquez-Rodriguez, Freddie, NY
Vega, Carmen M., NY
Vega, Jose R., NY
Velazquez, A.*
Velazquez, Felix J., NY
Velez, Rosendo P., NY
Velez, Theresa L., NJ
Venetis-colon, Angela*
Verapen, Latchmanen*
Vered, Merav*
Vetere, Lisa M., NY
Vilfort, Nedgine, NY
Villanueva, David, NY
Vines, Bernard A., NY
Vishnudat, Mrs. Indira D., NY
Vo, Chau, NY
Volmar, Gary P., NY
Von, Dietsch, NY
Vosmus, James F., NY
Vredenburgh, E., NY
Waite, Dahlia L., FL
Walker, Linda L.*
Wallace, Amanda L., NY

Wallen, Richard J., IN
Walsh, Matthew T., NY
Walsky, Philip J.*
Walther, Derek G., NY
Ward, Ms. Linda M., NJ
Warren, Sondra J., NY
Warren, Sophia D., NY
Washington-goeloe,
　Stephanie, NY
Wasserman, Adam*
Waters, Therese M., NJ
Webster-Springer, Michelle S.*
Weems, Scott C., NY
Weisenfeld, Marc D., NY
Welsh, Lawrence J., NY
West, Valerie, NY
Wetzel, Tracey P., NY
Wexler, Robert A.*
White, Joseph M., NY
White, Karen, NY
White, Robert L., NY
White-Joshua, Sydney M.*
Whitfield, Camille, NY
Wicker, Jason A., NJ
Wierl, Christopher, CO
Wilkerson, Walter P., NY
Williams, Alwin R., NY
Williams, Anthony R., NY
Williams, Cheryl V.*
Williams, Deborah R., NY
Williams, Denise*
Williams, Gordon, NY
Williams, Karen*
Williams, La K., NY
Williams, Michael J.*
Williams, Olin T., NY
Williams, Rhonda Y., JD, NY
Williams, Robert L., NY
Willis, Rakaiyah S.*
Wilson, Aaron, MD
Wilson, Ramika, NY
Wilson, Robert A., NJ
Wiltshire, Ms. Cheryl M., OH
Wimberly, Shamelle T.*
Windley, Tesha*
Winski, Debra L., NY
Wint, Winsome M.*
Wissert, Theresa A., NY
Won, Steven I.*
Wong, Rose, NY
Wong, Sai-Mei*
Wood, Steven R.*
Woodard, Chrystal, NY
Woodberry, Corey, NY
Woodlock, John K.*
Woods, Ms. Sheila, NY
Wooten, Jessie*
Wright, April A., NY
Wright, Kundora, NY
Wright, Roy J., NY
Wright, Tiffany E., NY
Yam, Serena J., NY
Yearwood, Lisa E., NY
Yee, Arthur, NY
Yeun, Ray B., NY
Youmans, Robin*
Young, Gail, NY
Youngblood, Schwanna, NY
Yusuf, Mohamed S., NY
Zabala, Denia*
Zartman, Brian B., CA
Zayerz, Agueybana, NY
Zevon, Robert J., FL
Zimmerman, Wheeler L., Jr.,
　NY
Zuniga, Martin, NY
Zurita, Charles N., NY

1996

Abdool, Rick E., NY
Abdur-rahim, Sharif*
Abraham, Harlan B., NY
Abreu, Francisco A.*
Adams, Christopher, NY
Agada-okeke, C.*
Agho, Jeromia, NY

Akugbe, Osagie P.*
Albright, Andrew F.*
Alcoba, Marcello, NJ
Alexander, Daniel J., NY
Alexander, Tyrone, NY
Alexandre, Nadhege M., CA
Alexandre, Natacha, NY
Alicea, Sigret, FL
Aliyev, Radmila, NY
Allen, Joseph A., NY
Almodovar, Melisa, NY
Almonte, Andy, NY
Almonte, Luis A., NY
Almusharakh, Jama A.*
Alvarez, Jeannette M., NJ
Alvarez, Ray, FL
Amaro, Ed, NJ
Ambrose, Wilma I., NY
Anastas, Anthony, NY
Anderson, Andre, NY
Anderson, Bonita M., NY
Anderson, Krik C., NY
Andino, Anita M., NY
Andress, La'donna V., TX
Andrew, Gregory, NY
Andrini, Deanna, NY
Anes, Edwin, NY
Angelosi, Anthony R.*
Anthony, Kisha S.*
Aponte, Marlene, NY
Aponte, Negron R., PR
Appiah, Amma*
Arce, Daisy, NY
Arecius, Claudine, NY
Aristy, Tommy G., NY
Armstead, Kemba A., NY
Arnold, Richard, NY
Arocho, Robert*
Arroyo, Catherine, NY
Asante, Tyberius D., NY
Asher, Jean M., NY
Augustin, Nancy, NY
Augustine, Sharmain, NY
Austin, Keisha M.*
Austrie, Gilda, NY
Aviles, Lisa, NY
Ayala, Jeanette*
Azzaro, Diana, NY
Babski, Tatjana A., NY
Bacchi, Diana E., NY
Bach, Roger J., NY
Badalamenti, Frank, NY
Baez, Mayra M., NY
Baez, Yvonne K., NY
Ballard, Celeste I., NY
Banievicz, Alexander, NY
Banks, Deborah M., NY
Bardales, Michael G., NY
Barnes, Cassandra C.*
Barnes, Shurrel Y., NY
Barometre, Reginald, NY
Barrois, Sebastien E., NY
Barrow, Jova G.*
Barrow, Mary, NY
Barry, Ann-marie T.*
Barry, James J.*
Bass, Jeffrey I., CA
Bawer, Patricia, NY
Beaman, Paige A., NY
Beaulieu, Sakeena T.*
Bejgrowicz, Lisa M., NJ
Belgrave, Jessica A., NY
Belinsky, Alexei*
Belotte, Myriam, NY
Benitez, Mariluz*
Benjamin, Helman O., NY
Bentley, Cheryl A., NY
Bernard, Derwin M., NY
Bernard, Suzie J.*
Berrios, Lynelle, NY
Bert, Gerard, NY
Berta, Anita C.*
Berube, Michael, Canada
Best, Racine A., NY
Betances, Neftali, Jr., NY
Betancourt, Brian, NY

Betts, Mary-ann C., NY
Bhola, Ms. Patti-lou S., NY
Biada, Charles, NY
Bianco, Anthony V., AZ
Biot, Deborah M., NY
Bitner, Iwona E., NV
Blackman, Colin J., NY
Blacksburg, Michael, NY
Blackshear, Norman, NY
Blanco, Fior D., NY
Bliss, Donald, CT
Blomquist, Karen A.*
Bloom, Jason S., TX
Bloom, Michael H., NY
Blum, Dominic K., NY
Boateng, Akua A., NY
Bobeczko, Aleksandra, NY
Bonano, Aracelis, NY
Bonuso, Stephen F.*
Boone, Christina L.*
Borja, Ivan, NY
Borrero, Hiram T., NY
Botello, Jacqueline*
Bothos, Demetrios, NY
Boute, Yvrande, NY
Bowen, Anthony, NY
Boyd, Tresilla G.*
Boykins, Brandi*
Boylan, Kathleen, NJ
Boylan, Lauren E., NY
Brackett, Marc A.*
Bradley, Kelly N.*
Brady, Bryan, NY
Brady, Sandra A., NJ
Brandt, Kenneth*
Brathwaite, Earl R., NY
Brathwaite, Tasha Y., NY
Brech, Todd R., NY
Breslin, Michael, NY
Broker, Steven J., NY
Brouard, Michelle, NY
Brown, Charlton A., NY
Brown, Cheryl M., NY
Brown, Derrick, NY
Brown, Janet, NY
Brown, Tara N., SC
Brown, Victor J.*
Brunetti, Joseph, NY
Bruno, Michael A., NY
Buckman, Janine N.*
Buitrago, Michael, NY
Bujold, Daniel J., NY
Buksha, Raymond M., NY
Burch, Shande D., NY
Burdiez, Ruby M., NY
Burgh, Todd D., NY
Bush, Robert C., NJ
Busi, Awilda*
Bykes, Jennifer V., NY
Byrne, George, NY
Cadet, Stanley*
Caggiano, Andrew C., NJ
Cajou, Amelica*
Cajou, Jean Claude, NY
Calandriello, Maria, NY
Callahan, Jill S.*
Callwood, Delcia I.*
Camargo, Catherine, NY
Camilleri, Michelle, NY
Camilo, Wilton, NY
Caminero, Marisol*
Campbell, Tricia T., NY
Campolo, Jennifer, NJ
Cancel, Juan A., NY
Canizales, Christina, NY
Cannady, Sheletha S., NY
Canny, Joseph, NY
Cantalupo, Lotteann, NY
Capparelli, Robert (Rob), NY
Capria, Britt A., CT
Caravello, Kelly A., NY
Carbonaro, Lawrence, NY
Carey, Arlene, NY
Carpinelli, Paul, NY
Carranza, Oscar, NY
Carrera, Miguel A., NY

Carrington, Ron E., NY
Carrion, Axel, NJ
Carter, Debbie N., NY
Casale, Donald E., II, MA
Casaletto, Craig J., NJ
Casares, Alcides, NY
Caselli, Lisa A., NY
Castro, Arlene, NY
Castro, Pacheco G.*
Cea, Ellen, NJ
Ceballos, Gloria A., NY
Cerezo, Juan E., NY
Ceron, Gladys E., NY
Chambers, Jeffrey A., NJ
Chand, Seema, NY
Chang, John K., NY
Charles, Nirlaine, NY
Chase, Lisa, NY
Chavez, Alina, NY
Chen, Johnny Y., NY
Chen, Katty, NY
Cheng, Mei, NY
Chetal, Rakesh, NY
Chevere, Beverly D., NY
Childs, Harry E., NY
Chin-sang, Helena M.*
Cho, Polly, NY
Choe, Munyong, NY
Chon, Haksoo, NY
Christ, Karen J., NY
Christine, Marc T., NJ
Cicchesi, Cynthia M., NY
Cintron, Dolores, NY
Cintron, Donna M., NY
Clark, Christopher, NY
Clarke, Al-yeru, NY
Clarke, Cleveland, NY
Coard, Toioto*
Coaxum, Stacey S., NY
Coghlan, Grace, NY
Colasurdo, James F., NY
Coleman, Antoinetta, NY
Coleman, Candance D., NY
Collado, Ms. Giselle M., NY
Collazo, Fredeswinda, NY
Collins, Barbara W., NY
Collins, Bashiek M., NY
Collins, Tara, NY
Collins, Yolanda*
Colon, Carlos, NY
Colon, Fernando L.*
Colon, Gladys I.*
Colon, Gregory, NY
Colon, Jose M., NY
Colon, Kazandra, NY
Colon, Oswald, NY
Conroy, John T., NY
Contreras, Juan A., NY
Conway, Martin J., NY
Cook, Lovely, NY
Corcoran, Michael C., NJ
Cordero, Steven M., Esq., NY
Coriano, Milagros, NY
Corprew, Nitaka, NC
Correa, Edward, NY
Coutts, Anne R., Canada
Crabb, Eric C., NJ
Crader, Clarissa T., NY
Crespo, Marivet, NY
Crespo, Richard (Richie), NY
Crichlow, Alison F., NY
Cromwell, Christine, NY
Crose, Bambi M., NY
Crump, Michael, NY
Cruz, Angel, NY
Cruz, Richard, NY
Cubero, Candido, NY
Cuevas, Johnny O., NY
Cummings, Ana, NY
Cummings, Kathy C., NY
Cummings, Orlene F., NY
Curich, Joseph, NY
Cvijic, Zora, NJ
Dabkowski, Dariusz, NY
Damms, William H.*
D'andrea, Lorenzo J., NY

Daniel-Babb, Valerie, NY
Darmstadt, Julie A.*
D'arrigo, Joseph G., NY
Dashiell, Karen, NY
Daugherty, William, NY
Dauley, Stephanie L.*
David, Lauri R.*
Davis, Chantel L., NY
Davis, Geneve E., NY
Davis, Lawrence E., NY
Davis, Mandy D., NY
Davis, Tonya, NY
Dawkins, Georgia*
De, La, NY
Dean, Everett D.*
Dechinea, Aggrey D., NY
Decker, Michael J., NY
Decresce, Christopher, NJ
Dejesus, Diana, NY
Deleo, Deirdre, NY
Delgado, Tracy L., NY
Dell'aera, Peter A., NY
Dellavalle, Anthony, NY
Delvalle, Yesenia, NY
Dennedy, James F., NY
Dennis, Ms. Tyler L., NY
Denny, Michelle T.*
Depalma, Ms. Danielle A., NJ
Depuy, Richard A., NY
Devine, Patrick, NY
Dezil, Patrick, NY
Dial, Savitri D., NY
Diamond, Darlene M., IL
Diaz, Anthony, NY
Diaz, Carmen L., NY
Diaz, Jhosandys A., NY
Diaz, Katya*
Diaz, Marcello S.*
Diaz, Maria I., NY
Diaz, Nora, NY
Dieudonne, Philome A.*
Digiam, Battista J., NY
Diorio, Vincent C.*
Dixon, Anthony A., NY
Doldron, Sherena, NY
Dominguez, Denise, NJ
Dooley, Daniel, NY
Dopfel, Robert, NY
Douglas-Richards, La, NY
Dowd, Peter J., NY
Doyle, Michael P., NY
Drake, Jeanne M., NY
Ducos, Eric, NY
Duhaney, Shirene A., NY
Dunbar, Arlene, NY
Duncan, Shakima, NY
Dunne, Charles G., NY
Durkel, Valerie E.*
Durso, Vivian V., NY
Durudogan, Agah, NY
Duville, Richard L., NY
Eccles, Kern, NY
Edmonds, Garfield N., NY
Edwards, Colleen V., NY
Ehrlich, Neil, NY
Eisenberg, Shauna L., NY
El-Amin, Ms. Zamirah K., NY
Elezi, Hana*
Elie, Yves, NY
Ellis, Anthony, NY
Ellis, Harry*
Ellison, Phillip, NY
Elmore, Eve M.*
Embry, Alicia J., NY
Ender, Glenn A.*
Espinoza, Jenny P., CT
Esposito, Angelina E., NY
Estevez, Javier G., NY
Estevez, Omar G.*
Estwick, Gerald, NY
Eva, Serge*
Evans, Aaron J., NY
Eventeris, Steve, NY
Everett, Lisa*
Facchini, Paschal, NJ
Faconti, Christiane, NY

Fahy, Blythe B.*
Fair, Craig D., NY
Farkas, Diana A., NY
Farrugia, Matthew P., NY
Febles, Aida C., NY
Fedotov, Alex V., NY
Fenty, Jill M., NJ
Ferrell, Shaniqua N., NY
Fields, William F., NY
Figueroa, Iris, NY
Figueroa, Lois M., NY
Figueroa, Maria E., NY
Finamore, James J., NY
Fine, Joselyn, NY
Finucane, Damien W.*
Fitzgerald, Kelly J., NY
Fleming-white, Merie, NY
Fleury, Renime, NY
Flyaks, Renata, NY
Fonrose, Selwyn M.*
Forde, Aine P., NY
Fortunat, Daphnee, NY
Fowler, Venae D.*
Francis, Nicke R., NY
Francois, Yurla*
Friedman, Jason A., VA
Fuentes, Christopher, NJ
Fulco, Anthony G., NJ
Fulgencio, Nederland, NY
Funk, James, NY
Fussalva, Arleene J., NY
Gallagher, Michael S., IL
Gallman, Kimberly L., NY
Gambino, Thomas, NJ
Garay, Tracy L., NY
Garcia, Doris*
Garcia, Jo-Alejandra, NY
Garcia, Louis J., NY
Garcia, Martha M., NJ
Garcia, Yesenia, NY
Gardner, Llewelyn, NY
Garrido, Francisco, NY
Gedeon, Elda, NY
Genia, James H., NY
George, Lennox, NY
Gestring, Craig R., NJ
Gialobello, Michael, NY
Gibbons, Nicole S., NY
Gibbons, Thomas E., NY
Giddings, Curtis G., Jr., NY
Gidlow, Brooke E., CO
Giffard, Sharon L.*
Gilbert, Derrick T.*
Gill, Cody, NY
Gillis, Michael H., NY
Glantz, Clarke I.*
Glover-pierce, Doree*
Go, Jamelyn, NJ
Gold, Stanley A., VA
Goldson, Marcia M.*
Goodloe, Elizabeth M.*
Goss, Agnieszka, NY
Goss, Ronald M., NY
Grady, Michael F., NY
Graham, Ardene M., NY
Granata, Bryan E., NY
Green, Calbert B., NY
Green, Douglas, NJ
Greene, Javonna*
Gregory, Rita, NY
Griffin, Brian A., NY
Griffin, Latoya S.*
Gross, Jacob A., NY
Grullon, Isaias R.*
Gu, Christopher K., NY
Guajardo, Jacqueline, NY
Guerra, Timothy A., NY
Guerrero, Katherine, NY
Guevara, Benigno*
Guevara-williams, D., NY
Guggenheim, Cordelia, AZ
Gulliver, Kimberly C., NY
Guskin, Barbara S., NY
Guy, Victor, NY
Guzman, Damary, NY
Hakim, Laurie J., NY

Hall, James, MD
Hamilton, Earl N.*
Hanley, John J., NY
Hanna, Richard, NJ
Hansberry, Wellingto, NY
Harmon, Timothy J., NY
Harrell, Dorothea M., NY
Harrington, Irwin C., NY
Harry, Lavern E., NY
Hart, Keith, MD
Hartmann, Michele*
Haseeb, Mohammad*
Hassett, Ann, NY
Hatfield, Steven J., NJ
Hayes, John R., NY
Hazarian, David J., NY
Hein, Jennifer, NY
Hellman, Karen A., AZ
Henderson, Vane B., NY
Hendricks, Andre, NY
Hendricks, Jennifer, NY
Henriquez, Siria L.*
Henry, Kirk L.*
Hernandez, Frankie*
Hernandez, Montoyo L.*
Herrera, Luis, NY
Hidalgo, Christine*
Hightower, Sadiquah, NY
Hilaire-Fisher, Marie C., NJ
Hillsman, Yequarah, NY
Hines, Sharon, NY
Hines, Sharon, NY
Hlavaty, John, NY
Hodgson, Tania, NY
Hoens, Eric P., NY
Hofacker, Patricia, NY
Hogan, Steven M., NY
Hohl, Christine, NY
Hone, Jacqueline, NJ
Hooper, Corey L.*
Horn, Helen L., NY
Hou, Julie, NY
Howard, Bernard E., NY
Huacuz, Rogers, NY
Huerta, Maricela, CA
Huett, Lori A.*
Hunter, Philip, NY
Idlett, Paul J., NY
Ifidon, Lawrence L., NY
Imariagbe, Eric*
Iovina, Kris*
Isom, Michael, NY
Ivory, Marcheta R., NY
Jackson, Carol J., NY
Jackson, Shawneequa, NY
Jain, Rajiv, NY
Jajoute, Gerald*
Jamadar, Bettyann, NY
James, Jemal, NY
James, Lisa, NJ
Jaroslow, Lori*
Javier, Jonathan, NY
Jean, Roberson D., NY
Jean-louis, Valerie, NY
Jean-philippe, Paulena, NY
Jenkins, Alice M., NY
Jenkins, Pamela S., NY
Jernigan, Maranda D., NY
Jesia, Bryan N., NY
Jeune, Sergo, NY
Johnson, Darlene R.*
Johnson, John B., NY
Johnson, Theresa M.*
Jones, Derrick A., NY
Jones, Paula, VA
Joseph, Kirt A., NY
Joseph, Ms. Tania R., NY
Joseph, Wilfredo, NY
Joyce, Jennifer, NY
Jugmohan, Gopie, NY
Julien, Erwin C.*
Kapel, Mark, NY
Kaplan, Mark, NY
Kelley, Donna L.*
Kelley, John P.*
Kennedy, Tasha K., NY

Kettrles, Tamiko N., NY
Khan, Bibi N., NY
Khwaja, Tariq M., NY
King, Edison L., NY
Kirkby, Stuart T., NY
Knight, Alisa G., NY
Ko, Michelle, NY
Kohn, Deena R., NY
Koontz, Kyristel P., NY
Koutouratsas, Nick, NY
Kreuscher, Robert L., NY
Kuhner, Vance T., NY
Kurt, Cihan, NY
Kurys, Mark C., NY
Lacobs, Scott L., NY
Laferla, Linda J., NY
Lai, Raymond, NY
Lall, Christopher, NY
Lam, Sindi H., NY
Laporte, Adam*
Laroche, Philippe*
Laurenson, Barbara J., NY
Leavitt, Catherine B., AZ
Leckler, Francis P., NY
Lee, Jin, NY
Lee, Kenneth, NY
Lee, Wai L., NY
Lefkof, Alan, NY
Leger, Reguerre, NY
Lehman, Joanne, NY
Leibowitz, Jill D., NY
Lessen, Cristina*
Lessen, Nicholas J., NY
Levy, Antoinette T., NY
Levy, Erez, NY
Levy, Shari, NY
Lewis, Alison, NY
Lewis, Arlene D.*
Lewis, Geoffrey B., NY
Lewis, Mazel S., NY
Lezcano, Eduardo D., NY
Li, James, NY
Lienhart, Richard, NY
Lifrieri, Michael D., NY
Lilley, William P., NY
Lin, Showsan, NY
Litchmore, Monique E., NY
Lloyd, Claudette, NJ
Lloyd, Donald*
Lofaro, Christian D.*
Logan, Tracy, NY
Long, Jacqueline, NY
Longo, Paul J., NY
Lopen, Nicole, NY
Lopez, Jamal D., NY
Lopez, Sandra, NY
Lopez, Terron, PR
Lore, Frank A., NY
Louallen, Fatima G., NY
Louis-jeune, Paul*
Louisor, Mike P., NY
Loureiro, Victor M.*
Lubin, Theodule B., NY
Luna, Erika, NY
Luna-gordinier, J.*
Lynch, Sean J., NY
Madrid, Fabian A.*
Madrid, Nelson, NY
Madrigal, Elvira, NY
Magistro, Anthony J., OR
Magliacano, Anthony, NJ
Maher, Lisa-marie, NY
Makanjuola, Rafiu T., MD
Maldonado, Joseph B., NY
Maldonado, Mary, NY
Maldonado, Xinmia M., NY
Maloney, Christopher, NY
Maloney, David*
Maloney, Linda*
Maloney, Vaughn, NY
Mantzaris, Demetrios (Jimmy), NY
Mapps, Valeria D., NY
Marcantuono, Melissa, NJ
Marcial, Tanya, NY
Marcus, Shurnette M., NY

Maria, Edward, NY
Marin, Vivian, NY
Marrero, Miguel, NY
Marriott, Nirvana, NY
Marshall, Cliff, NY
Marshall, Ms. Monique R., NY
Marsicano, Jon*
Martello, Michael, NY
Martinez, Oscar A., NY
Martterer, Amy K., NY
Mathwich, Mary C., NY
Matos, Wanda*
Matthews, Jermaine, NY
Matute, Gaynell, NY
Matz, Markus A., NY
Maurilus, Pierre S., NY
Mazzella, Susan I., NY
Mc, Quillan, NY
McAleer, Gerard P., VA
Mcauliffe, John, NY
Mc Cabe, Jenni, NY
McCarthy, Jennifer, NY
Mccondichie, Charise, NY
Mccullough, Ayanna, NY
Mcdesmott, James E., NY
Mcgough, John J., NY
McGowan, Sean M., NJ
Mckenna, Timothy P., NY
Mckoy, Gay L., NY
McMahon, Michael J., NJ
Mcmanus, Siobhan A., NY
McNeely, Karen T., NY
Mcnelis, Michael J., NY
McNickle, R. G. (Nick), NY
Mcwilliams, Scott R., NY
Medic, Joseph, NY
Meehan, Stephen G., OH
Mejia, Luis M.*
Mejia, Ravel E., NY
Mencia, Jose L., NY
Mendoza, John, NY
Mensler, Jeffrey, NY
Mera, Olivia E.*
Mercado, Diana, NY
Middleton, La-tonia B., NJ
Miller, Lee A., NY
Miller, Louis J., NY
Miller, Melva, NY
Millevoi, Frank, NY
Minoque, Linda A.*
Miralla, Ms. Janet, NY
Miranda, Fernando J.*
Mitchell, Jamell, DE
Modeste, Hermione A.*
Molignano, Nicole M., CO
Mollaghan, John T., NY
Moller, Kenneth C., NY
Momodu, Dove E., NY
Moncayo, Marco A.*
Mondesir, Tara M.*
Monroe, Angeline E., NY
Montero, Umberto*
Montilla, Nestor H.*
Moore, Hukm, NY
Moore, William J., NY
Mootoo, Kahli C.*
Moquete, Cesar U., NY
Morales, Auries M., NY
Morley, Michael, NY
Morris, Donna A., NJ
Moss, Geoffrey, NY
Mousadakos, Chrisoula, NY
Moya, Chico, NY
Moye, Michelle, NY
Mozie, Edie D., NY
Mundo, Reymundo, NY
Murath, Jonathan C.*
Murphy, Brian C., NY
Mustaphalli, Dean*
Mwanga, Frederick, NY
Myers, Yvette, NY
Nau, Michael, NY
Nazario, Jose, NY
Neblett, Annette, NY
Negron, Larry, NY
Nelly, Stabile, NY

Nelson, Guerline, NY
Nemorin, James V., NY
Newman, Paul R., CT
Ng, Harry J., NY
Ngai, Lauren M., NY
Nicholson, Tammy T., NY
Nicola, Maria E., NY
Niemes, Monica E., NY
Nieves, Michael A.*
Nikoloudakis, Georgi, NY
Nisely, Michelle S., FL
Noailles, Marie, NY
Noel, Gesner, NY
Nolasco, Jorge*
Norden, Paul A., NY
Norgriff, Keith A., NY
Nunez, Miguel A., NY
Nunez-torres, Julie F., NY
Nunn, Jason A., NJ
Nurse, Henry E., NY
Nyland, Charles A., NY
O'boyle, James M., NY
Ocasio, Carlos, NY
Ocasio, Jacqueline A., NY
Ogbeni, Felicia U., NY
Ogunadz, Tamara, NY
Oh, Jong, NY
Ohale, Emmanuel U., NY
Olivera, Tonia C., NY
O' Okpara, Innocent, NY
O'Reilly, John P., NY
O'Rourke, Tara A., NY
Orozco, Odalis, NY
Ortiz, Amador P., NY
Ortiz, De*
Ortiz, Edwin, NY
Ortiz, Janet, NY
Ortiz, Linnette*
Ortiz, Nora S.*
Ortiz-benjamin, Maira, NY
Ortman, Kathleen E., NY
Osamwonyi, Joseph I., VA
Otten, Kimberly A., NY
Owens, Veronica M., NY
Owie, Edwin, NY
Ozzandar, Engin, NY
Padilla, Margarita M., NY
Paik, Min K., NJ
Palumbo, Bill, NY
Papadopoulos, Theo*
Parker, Matthew W., NY
Parrales, John T., NY
Patruno, Cataldo, NY
Patterson, Rosezena, NY
Patton, Ronda Y., NY
Paylor, Lorraine F.*
Pena, Ms. Marisel C., NY
Peoples, Yasmeen (Yaszie) A.,
  NY
Perez, Alicia, NY
Perez, Emilio*
Perez, Lauro, NY
Perez, Lizabeth (Lisa), NY
Perez, Saul M.*
Perez, Vanessa, NY
Perkins, Nicole S., NY
Perkins, Tonya L.*
Petreski, Toni, NJ
Petrinc, Camille F., NY
Pfiemer, Kelley A.*
Phurchpean, Kongkrit, NY
Piazza, Karen L., NY
Pieklo, Eric J., NJ
Pimentel, Rosa A., NY
Pinto, Christine M., NY
Pinto, Giovanni V., NY
Platis, Anna C., NY
Plaza, Sandy N., NY
Polyakova, Svetlana, NY
Pomales, Mildred, NY
Porcelli, Rita, NY
Potter, Hillary A., CO
Poust, Brian J., NY
Prado, Martha E.*
Preiss, George M., NJ
Prescott, Robert E., NY

Prophete, Rachelle R.*
Pryce, Genniveive O., NY
Pucci, Mark*
Quiroz, Kathleen M., NY
Rabinovich, Billy B.*
Ragin, Kenya S., NY
Ragland, Eric, NY
Ram, Chandrowtie, NY
Ramirez, Karen Y., NY
Ramkissoon, Ricardo, NY
Ramos, Manuel, PA
Ramos, Marlene (Mandy) M.,
  NY
Ramos, Ramonita, NY
Ramsaran, Ramcharita, NY
Ravenell, Jason, NY
Rawls, Shanell, NY
Reddick, Euphemia S., NY
Redman, Stacy L., NY
Reid, Jermaine, NY
Reilly, Edward, NY
Reilly, Michael, NY
Reingold, Michael, NY
Reinhardt, Richard, NJ
Reyes, Gloria, NY
Reyes, Jose, NY
Reyna, Isabel*
Rice, Sharnik, NY
Rich, Cecelia, NY
Richards, Kimberly A., NY
Ring, Brian, NY
Rini, Kristy*
Riquelme, Peter L., NY
Rivas, Alejandro J., NY
Rivas, Fradis, NY
Rivera, Iris M., NY
Rivera, Jalika, NY
Rivera, John G., NY
Rivera, Jose, NY
Rivera, Luz A., NY
Rivera, Monica L.*
Rivera, Steven, NY
Rivera, Victor L., NY
Robinson, Quintin*
Rodriguez, Dennis*
Rodriguez, Diane*
Rodriguez, Errol O., NY
Rodriguez, Jeff D.*
Rodriguez, Jimmy, NY
Rodriguez, Lisa, NY
Rodriguez, Maria, NY
Rodriguez, Maribel, NY
Rodriguez, Morahina, NY
Rogers, Lakesha, NY
Rojas, Inez M., NY
Romero, Angela, NY
Romero, Xaviera E., NY
Rondon, Natasha J., NY
Rosado, Christine, NY
Rosario, Fernando, NY
Rose, Rodney J., NY
Rosenberger, Michael, NY
Rossi-rosen, Renee M., NJ
Ruiz, Judy, NY
Ruiz, Vicki L., NY
Ruocco, Dante, NJ
Ruotolo, Joseph C., NY
Rus, Adrian*
Rush, Vilethia, NY
Russell, Jessica K., NY
Saget, Marie P., FL
Sainnoval, Sanders*
Saintil, Naomi M., NY
Sajous, Claudine*
Salahuddin, Shaifah, NY
Sallemi, Ralph, NY
Samuels, Bradshaw, NY
Samuels, Susan R., NY
Sanborn, Laurel, NY
Sanchez, Constanza, NY
Sanchez, Luis A.*
Sanon, Farrah, NY
Santana, Ricardo, NY
Santiago, li*
Santiago, Melissa S., NY

Santiago, Raymond (Ray) S.,
  Esq., NY
Santiago, Tina M., NY
Santos, Janissett*
Satriana, Peter, NY
Saunders, Louvinia, NY
Savopoulos, Emmanuel, NY
Scalici, Joseph, NY
Scordato, Matthew, NY
Scott, Andrea, NY
Scott, Emily E., NY
Scott, Lisa A.*
Seabrook, Reginald K., DE
Segar, Yvonne, SC
Serge, Victor J., NY
Serrano, Jose, NY
Serrano, Michelle O., NY
Severino, Solangel A., NY
Sharpe, Ryan R., NY
Shaw, Colleen G.*
Shaw, La-shonda V., NY
Shaw, Yolanda L., NY
Shea, Kathleen C., NY
Sheehan, John, NY
Sherriffe, Lyndon*
Sherwood, Roxanne M., NY
Shiff-shcheransky, T.*
Shkolnik, Albina, NY
Shoaib, Mohammad*
Shohat-mandel, Orit*
Sidberry, Christina, NY
Sidman, Jerry R., NY
Sien, Tjia (Chito) T., Jr., NY
Silva, Dinorah A.*
Silva, Yahaira, NY
Silver, Sherrelle M., NY
Simenauer, David, NY
Simmons, Shelice*
Simpson, Calvin T.*
Simpson, Gerald C., NY
Sinclair, Pablo F., NY
Singh, Andrei Y., NY
Singh, Esther A., NY
Singh, Rubi K., NY
Singleton, Ms. Latanya M., NY
Singleton, Michelle, NY
Sinnott, Thomas G., NJ
Skeeter, Raymond S., NY
Slackman, Noah K.*
Slawinski, Izabela B.*
Small, Cynthia A., NY
Small, Dona S., NY
Smalls, Larue C., NY
Smith, Christopher, NY
Smith, Francis X., NY
Smith, Robin, NY
Smith, Saundra, NY
Smolensky, Glen D., NY
Snyder, Heather T., NY
So, Hong Min, NY
Somersall, Tara S., NY
Son, Keith, NY
Sordi, Joseph C., NY
Sosa, Maria R.*
Sosnowik, Daniel E., NY
Southwell, Anthony I., NY
Spagnola, Carmen T., CT
Spencer, Dahlia L., NY
Spinelli, Michael, NY
Spivey, Lettie C.*
Spriggs, Jeffrey, NY
Staab, Ryan R., VA
Staines, Alex, NY
Stanton, Robert J.*
Staples, Sharon A., NY
Steele-Baird, Svetlana, NY
Steets, Vanessa C., NY
Stella, Jason M., NY
Sten, Brian C., FL
Steo, Frank, NY
Stephen, Tyndale*
Stewart, Dianne L.*
Stillie, Elizabeth, NY
St. Jean, Fritz, NY
Stores, Latrebia R.*
Streger, Matthew R., SC

St. Surin, Mietta, NY
Stuger, Lavern N., NY
Suarez, Angel L.*
Suarez, Felix, NY
Suarez, Judith, NJ
Sullivan, Brien P., NY
Sutherland, Carla H., NY
Svagrik, Nancy J.*
Svetlov, Victoria, NY
Swain, Michael, NY
Tamaro, Loring, NY
Tapia, Arturo A., NY
Tapper, Winsome*
Taras, Lorelle S., NY
Tavares, Ana M., NY
Taylor, Erin S.*
Taylor, Junior P., NY
Taylor, Kevin L., NY
Teel, Taneka S., NY
Thomas, Danny T., NY
Thomas, Denise S., NY
Thompson, Shelby L.*
Tisdale, Kristine A., NY
Tituana, Luis, NY
Tobon, John F.*
Tocco, Stephen M., NY
Todd, Belinda A.*
Todorovic, Jelica, NY
Toliver, Vonda, NY
Tomala, Jeannette, NY
Tomlinson, Camille E., NY
Toro, Miriam, NY
Torrence, Sandra E., NY
Torres, Katherine, NY
Torres, Milly, NY
Torres, Rios*
Torres, Terence S.*
Towns, Suzanne, NY
Tramontana, G., NY
Tremblay, Helene N.*
Trenca, Michael P., NY
Trevellian, Christine, NY
Tricardo, Dominick, NY
Troyansky, Eugene, NJ
Truitt, James F., NY
Truong, Dan, NY
Trusty, Beshon, NY
Tsui-chang, Cindy*
Tuck, Christopher C., FL
Tuly, Beth M., NY
Tunca, Ms. Yasemin N., NY
Turkiya, Vladimir A., NY
Turner, Gerard, NY
Turner, Tinaddine N., NY
Tyson, Sonya L.*
Urbaez, Eliet, NY
Uria, Maria, NY
Valdez, Rosanna Y., NY
Valentin, Julio A., NY
Varela, Lillian, NY
Vargas, Madeline*
Varghese, Vinod, NY
Vasile-davila, Fern, NY
Vasquez, Ms. Daisy, NY
Vaughn, Robbie, NY
Vaz, Nitia G.*
Vazquez, Jose R., NY
Velasquez, Yanina, NY
Velez, Cindhia, NY
Velez, German J., NY
Velez, Glorialee, FL
Vigilance, Fitzroy, NY
Villanueva, Nidia*
Vines, Shari N.*
Vitolo, John J., NY
Vogel, Bruce J., NY
Vogt, Julie A., NY
Volfson, Diana*
Vouthas, Spiros, NY
Wacker, Donna A.*
Wade, Lori H., NY
Wager, Tracy A., NY
Walker, Michael J., NY
Walsh, Declan J., NY
Walters, Christy L.*
Walther, Jennifer, NY

Warren, Glenn E., NY
Waterman, Georgina L., NY
Watts, Dionne*
Wawa, Eleanor, NY
Weber, Herschel, NY
Weber, Robert D., Jr., FL
Weiss, Jason H., NJ
Wheeler, Tiffany D.*
White, Monique L., NY
White, Robin L., MD
White, Valerie, NY
Whiteside, Scott L., NY
Whitt, Kimberly D., VA
Wickham, Melanie C.*
Wiggin, Matthew J., NY
Wiley, Denise T., NY
Wilkinson, Denise, NY
Williams, Avis, NY
Williams, Cornelia M., NY
Williams, Demetrius, NY
Williams, Lisa A., MA
Williams, Myron S., NY
Williamson, Stacie, NY
Wilson, Sharon, NY
Winslow, Cynthia (Cindy) L., WI
Wislar, Margaret E., NY
Woessner, Eileen M., AZ
Wong, Rachel, NY
Wood, Joseph D., NY
Woolward, Sharon, NY
Wright, Vivene G., NY
Yamada, Stella, NY
Yancey, Davina R., NY
Yhun, Suk-han, NY
Zamorn, Esperanza, NY
Zandy, Matthew P., NY
Zeideia, Bajes M., NY
Zepf, Darin R., NY
Zorrilla, Yngrid E., NY

1997

Abousamra, Paul N., NY
Acosta, Danae, NY
Acosta, Indrani, NY
Adames, Flavio L., NY
Adams, Errol A., NY
Adams, Gina M., NY
Addelston, Adam D., NY
Adeleye, Helen, NY
Adorno, Milinda, NY
Aguilar, Joanne C., NY
Akhtab, Nazlah, NY
Alam, Ilia A., NY
Alameda, Wanda*
Albarran, Migdalia, NY
Alcee, Natalie (Giggles) S., NJ
Alerte, Richard C., NY
Alexander, Christoph, NY
Alexander, Delvia M., NY
Alexander, Neva H., NY
Alexander, Tricia, NY
Alexandre, Jean W., NY
Allert, Theresa, NY
Allette-davis, Wendy, NY
Almodovar, Lourdes, NY
Almonor, Merault K., NY
Almonte, Alex, NY
Almonte, Ervin J., NY
Alvia, Susana, NY
Amanna, Francine M., NY
Ambroise, Sabine T., NY
Amin, Mohsena F.*
Amour, Johnson N., NY
Anderson, Christeen, NY
Anderson-Edwards, Emily*
Andino, Alcides, NY
Andrade, Karol J., NY
Angueria, Elaine M.*
Annamunthodo, John C., NY
Anthony, Chailendra, NY
Anthony, Mark W., NY
Araujo, Jose M., NY
Arce, Michele, NY
Archambeau, Lincoln, NY
Arlain, Nena D., NY

Arniotes, LT James V., NY
Arocho, Sonia A., NY
Arteaga, Ms. Luz A., NY
Asencio, Stacy, NY
Ashley, Teresa L., NY
Assiff, Laurie A., NY
Augello, Brian M.*
Augustus, Antoinette J., NY
Ayala, Apollo A.*
Ayala, Jacqueline*
Ayala, Melody*
Azurdia, Gilda L., NY
Azurdia, Raul J., NY
Bacovic, Hasan, NY
BAdagliacca, Michael, NY
Badillo, Elizabeth, NY
Baek, Hyon K., NY
Bagi, Gabor R., NY
Baidy, Quillar, NY
Bailey, Anthony M., NY
Bailey, Betzaida, NY
Bailey, Edmarine A., NY
Bailey, Kimesha, NY
Bailey, Steven D., NJ
Bailey, Sweden M., NY
Baird, Scott, NY
Baker, Noel M., NY
Baker, Robert D., NY
Baliko, Jaclyn M., NJ
Bamdas, Erica*
Baraket, Tamara M., NY
Barbot, Charles G.*
Barfield, Shawn, NY
Barlow, Christopher, NY
Barr, Keith, NY
Barreiro, Ramon G., NY
Barrow, Glenda M.*
Barry, Lauren S.*
Bartley, Laverne D., NY
Basora, Karina*
Bast, Molly A., NY
Batista, Maria, NY
Battista, Michael N., NY
Baumann, Daniel, NY
Baxter, Gregory, NY
Becchina, Victoria A., NJ
Beckford, Maxine A., NY
Bedrossian, Anne-Marie M., Canada
Beekram, Anita L., NY
Belen, Irene M., NY
Belfi, Brian J., FL
Bell, Anna K., NY
Bell, James K., NY
Benaim, Charlie, NY
Benasutti, Kathleen, NY
Benbow, Engrid*
Benejan, Hobert, NY
Benitez-rivera, Mild, NY
Benjamin, Regeena*
Bent, Pamela A., NY
Berrouet, Gerard E., NY
Best, Aromah, NY
Best, Sandra, NY
Bethune, Ray*
Bevinetto, Santo, NY
Bey, Robert F., NY
Bhan, Alvin J., NY
Bido, Antonia F., NY
Biegel, Stephen W., NY
Biller, CDR Ronald D., NY
Bittmann, Brenda L., NY
Blachman, Eric J., NY
Blackwell, Dru Janin, NY
Blackwood, Nicola G., NY
Blaha, Jana L., NY
Blake, Ernestine, NY
Blue, Sheila E., NY
Blumenstein, R., NY
Boccia, Gary**
Bodden, Cheryl L., NY
Boisseau, Dominique, NY
Bolstad, Robert, NY
Bolton, Cheryl C., NY
Bonaney, Polanges R., NY

Boodhoo, Joanne, NY
Boone, Nikita M., NY
Borbon, Manuel J., NY
Borea, William P., NJ
Borker, Vito, NY
Borrero, Ormello A.*
Bourne, Krishna L.*
Bowden, Bradd D., NY
Bowman, Lawson D., NY
Boyce, Rodney C., NY
Boyd, Crystal, NY
Boyde, Diana*
Bradley, Richard A., NY
Bradshaw, Robert N., NY
Braga, Flavia R.*
Bramble, Anthony S., NY
Brannan, Amy A., NY
Brash, Ronald A., NY
Breton, Lydia E., NY
Briskie, Michael S., NY
Briu, Yolanda, NY
Broadman, Neil D.*
Brodman, Mathew H., NY
Brooks, Kathleen M.*
Brown, Herbert A., Jr., NY
Brown, Juliet D., NY
Brown, Latisha Y., NY
Brown, Moreale P., NY
Brown, Tyrone S., NY
Browning, Melissa E.*
Browning, Monique, NY
Brucculeri, Maryann, NY
Brunson, Jacqueline, NY
Bubbico, Francesco D., NJ
Buica, Lucy, NY
Bundhoo, Rakeish, NY
Bunkeddeko, Sully, NY
Buono, Alisa, NY
Burakiewicz, Lisa M., NY
Burgess, Audrey L., NY
Burke, John F., NY
Burke, Patrick, NY
Butler, Katrina A., NY
Buttaro, Victor A., NY
Bzik, Susan M., NJ
Cabrera, Milagros, NY
Cabrera, Sara, NY
Cadet, Flobert, NY
Caicedo, Jose, NY
Calderon, Marilyn, NY
Calderon, Nubia C., NY
Caldwell, Lynnette, NJ
Camacho, Angel J., NY
Cameron, Norman E., NY
Campbell, Annecia A., NY
Campbell, Sally*
Campoccio, Deborah A., NY
Cantave, Barbara E., NY
Cantwell, Dennis M.*
Capobianco, Joseph J., NY
Cappiello, Dominick A., NY
Caprices, Nadalyn, NY
Carberry, James E., NY
Cardona, Jimmy E., NY
Cardoza, Zachary A., NY
Caria, Pierluca*
Carlos, Vicente B.*
Carlton, Erik, NY
Carlucci, Jean M., RI
Carmona, Marco A., NY
Carpenter, Annissa L., FL
Carpluk, Andrew*
Carrara, Benjamin J., NJ
Carter, Ronald, NY
Carter-el, Davida A.*
Casella, Nancy E., NY
Casilla, Jose, NY
Cassidy, Thomas A., NJ
Castaneda, Urania, NY
Castillo, Gelin M., NY
Castillo, Joanna*
Castillo, Maria I., NY
Castro, Aida L., NY
Castro, Alan J., NY
Castro, Maria T., NY
Cea, Brian J.*

Cerda, Rafael A., NY
Cespedes, Luisa Y., NY
Chambers, Robert, NJ
Chan, Anthony*
Chan, Kathy, NY
Chan, Susan, NY
Charles, Victor, NY
Chattergoon, Suchetr C., NY
Chavez, Rocio E., NY
Chen, Jie Chan, NY
Cheng, Howard*
Chiu, Lim-chi, NY
Choi, Jinjong*
Choy, Yolanda, NY
Christian, Anita, NY
Cid, Maria, NY
Cintron, Anita, NY
Clahar, Winwell, NY
Clarke, Kert L., NY
Clarke, Lateacha S., NY
Clarke, Ms. Nicole A., NY
Clarke, Sonia J.*
Cohen, Jacqueline, NY
Cole, Margie, NY
Coley, Takiya Y., NY
Collazo, Marisol, NY
Collica, Kimberly A., NY
Collins, Clive M., NY
Collins, Falisha R., NY
Colon, Anthony B., NY
Colon, Carlos A., NY
Colon, Elizabeth, NY
Colon, Jose M., NY
Colon, Sandy T., NY
Columna, Walter E., NY
Concepcion, Magaly S., FL
Connolly, Mary F., NY
Connor, Ghyslaine, NY
Conte, Daniel P., NY
Conti, Richard P., NJ
Contreras, Gloria, NY
Contreras, Lillian, NY
Conway, Maryelyn, NJ
Copeland, Nyree D., NY
Corbett, La'tonia C.*
Cordes, Joseph, NY
Correa, Ruben, NY
Cosme, Maura, NY
Coyne, Susan M., NY
Craig, Jeffrey S., NY
Crawford, Randy B., NJ
Crosby, Marion T., NY
Cruz, Jamie, NJ
Cruz, Madeline*
Cruz, Naomi, NY
Cruz, Ramses*
Cuccioli, Barbara V., NY
Cudjoe, Michelle A., NY
Cuevas, Ms. Claris I., NY
Cumberbatch, Simeon, NY
Cumberland, James E.*
Cummo, Joseph A., NY
Cunningham, Lawrence (Larry) H., DC
Curtis, Doniyell L., NY
Curtis, Gayle*
D'alessandro, Joseph, NY
Dalton, Angela C., NY
D'Andrea, Leonardo, NY
Daniel, Cemon F., NY
Daouaou, Abdelilah, NY
Davidson, Paulette P., NY
Davidzon, Alexander, NY
Davila, Alfredo, NY
Davila, Luis E., NY
Davila, Nancy, NY
Davis, Felicia J., NY
Davis, Regina A., NY
Davis, Wilbert, NY
Deacon, Carol J., NY
Deans, Karen, NY
Deceglie, Louis M., NJ
Dechabert, Ms. Christina, NY
Decoteau, Francis A., NY
Deese, Gregory, NY

DeFranco, Elizabeth (Liz) C., NY
De Gaetano, Gina, NY
Degil, Rana M., NY
Degiulio, Joseph A., NY
DeGrenier, Terrence, MA
Delacruz, Cruz, NY
Delarosa, Jasmin*
Denslow, Lisa D., NY
De Paula, Alber*
Derolus, Jean P., NY
De Souza, Chris, NY
Diakos, Georgia, NJ
Diaz, Maria D., NY
Diaz, Rahsaan E., NY
Diaz, Virgil J., NY
Diggs, Sandra, NY
Dillard, Gail E., NY
Dillon, Laura A., NY
Dinkins, Benjamin S., NY
Disarno, James J., NJ
Dislaking, Antonio, NY
Doherty, Kevin M.*
Dorokhov, Marina*
Dorta, Edward, NY
Dorval, Marcoris, NY
Dos Santos, Kerry, NJ
Douglas, Darien, NY
Douglas, Suzane C.*
Dove, Sheila T., NY
Dowe, Ferron C., NY
Downs, Henry, NY
Duarte, Ms. Ruth, NY
Du La, Fonta*
Duncan, Wilburn C.*
Duque, Lupe M.*
Duque, Ruben D., NY
Duran, Heidi L., CT
Duval, Christopher D., NY
Dzairi, Ali, NY
Eckstein, Robert, NY
Edwards, Katrina, NJ
Edwards, Roxanne D., NY
Edwards, Stephen C.*
Elder, Margaret A., NY
Elliot, Kisha A.*
Emilian, Ivan, NY
Encarnacion, Gregory, NY
English, Claudia M., NY
Escobar, Nelson L., NY
Essilfie, Coretta, NY
Evans, Kenya L., NY
Evans, Michael, NY
Ezechiels, Richard E., NY
Farquhar, Chandra T.*
Farrell, Denise M., NY
Feliciano, Elsa M., NY
Feliu, Maria D., NY
Fell, Ronald, NY
Fenner, Rosalynde M., NY
Fergus, Kathyann J., NY
Fernandez, Carlos A., NY
Fernandez, Luis, NY
Ferreira, Jeannette, VA
Figueroa, Jacquelin*
Figueroa, Juana A., NY
Figueroa, Melissa, NY
Figueroa, Paola A., NY
Flannery, Timothy J., NJ
Fleming, John F., NY
Fleming, Rita M.*
Fletcherel, Ralph A., NY
Fleuriot, Delarquy*
Fogarty, Michael B., NY
Fonteboa, Elizabeth, NY
Forde, Sharon, NY
Forrester, Tamika, NY
Foster, Valerie, NY
Fowler, Stephanie, NY
Fox, Jason, NY
Frances, Quinia*
Francis, Rosemarie, NY
Francis-Lewis, Flona V., NY
Franco, Maria, NY
Frasco, Elizabeth G., NJ
Frazier, Dawn M., NY

Frias, Jose M., NY
Fuentes, James F., NY
Fuko, Curtis, NJ
Fung, Janet K., NY
Furlong, Joseph, NY
Gadlin, Igor E., NY
Galaher, Lilia, NY
Galarza, Michael M., NY
Galdamez, Laura C.*
Galeano, Sonia L., NY
Galloway, Rulisa, NY
Garcia, James D.*
Garcia, Nidya A.*
Garrett, Sabrina*
Geagan, Patrick C., NY
Geddes, Melanie D., NY
Gendell, Alexis L., NY
Genova, Chris A., NY
Georgopoulos, Antoni, NY
Geraldo, Novy E.*
Gettis, Deanne R., NJ
Gh'rael, Kelly M., NY
Giaconelli, Louis C., NY
Giangeruso, Carmine, CFPS, NJ
Gibbs, Michael J., NY
Giler, Lorena K., NY
Gill, Brian P., NY
Gilligan, Joseph P., NY
Ginel, Julio A., NY
Girshick, Jenny Y., NY
Gistenson, Svetlana*
Glenn, William, NY
Godby, Natasha L., NY
Goldberg, Daniel J., NY
Goldstein, Howard, NY
Gomez, Paula A., NJ
Gonzalez, Anilexa J., NY
Gonzalez, Elizabeth, NY
Gonzalez, Michelle, NY
Gonzalez-Usera, Jessica, NY
Gooding, Sharon, NY
Gorbett, Robert, NY
Gordon, Andrea D., NY
Gore, Michelle A., NY
Gosling, Carolin, NY
Graham, Nichole N., NY
Graham-hayward, Deb*
Granados, Alfredo E.*
Grant, Geroy C., NY
Grant, Shernette*
Gravelli, Vincent M., NY
Green, Stephen, NY
Greene, Cheree, NY
Greene, Valarie L., NY
Greenwald, Steven, NY
Gresh, Ms. Marilyn B., NJ
Grey, Natasha N., NY
Guaba, Roberto*
Guastella, Joan, NY
Guclen, Ender, NY
Guerra, Cecilia M., NY
Guglielmo, Christoph, NY
Gumbs, Nailah, NY
Gumbs, Tessa J.*
Gutierrez, Johanna, NY
Gutman, Laura, NY
Guzman, Rosa, NY
Guzzardi, Joseph, NY
Guzzo, Louis G., NY
Hadzi, Brahimovic S., NY
Haire, Christine, NY
Ham, Sung, NY
Hamilton, Donna A.*
Hamilton, Rudolph H., NY
Haniff, Zahirudeen, NY
Hansen, Ronald, NY
Haralambous, Lambros, NY
Haro, David I., NY
Harper, Fabian F., NY
Harper, Lawrence, NY
Harper, Yaphet, NY
Harris, Crystal, NY
Harrow, Tracy A., NY
Hart, Carrie A., NY
Hartl, Carolyn G.*

Hasan, Zaheeruddin S., NY
Hayes, Donald, NY
Hayes, Michael, NY
Hayes, Tevonda, NY
Headley, Paul A., NY
Hearn, Gimenez S.*
Hellner, Brian, NY
Henriquez, Deborah C., NY
Henriquez, Marlene, NY
Henry, Patrick J.*
Henry, Valerie E., NY
Heredia, Rafael J., NY
Herman, Tracy A., FL
Hernandez, Daisy, NY
Hernandez, Gretchen*
Hernandez, Jose A., NY
Hernandez, Michael E., NY
Hernandez, Michelle, NY
Herrera, Ventura M.*
Hess, Brian, NY
Hibbert, Melonie J., NY
Hidalgo, Frank, NY
Hilaire, Reginald, NY
Hill, Aiyeesha L., NY
Hill, Michael A., NY
Hill, Nadine A., NY
Hilsman, Carla D., NY
Hilton, Allison, NY
Hogan, Tamika C., NY
Holland, Jan, NY
Horford, James C.*
Hot, Zajo E., NY
Hrebenko, Aneta, NJ
Huang, Chen Tao, NY
Hughes, Christina E., NY
Huie, Brenda, NY
Huiett, Ghaironesa, NY
Hungreder, Scott G., NY
Hutchinson, Dionne, NY
Hutchinson, Nadia, NY
Hyland, Velvet A., NY
Iglesias, Nora M., NY
Ionescu-Binder, Beatrice, NY
Irizarry, Gisela, NY
Ivanova, Nathalia L., NY
Jackson, Christina, NY
James, Dale*
Janvier, Alexandra, NY
Jebavy, Judith A., AZ
Jefferson, Marsha E., NY
Jenkins, Douglas A., NY
Jenkins, Ms. Sabrina M., NY
Jerez, Victor, NY
Jerome, Lourdes M., NY
Jeselson, Paul J., NY
Jimenez, Carmen*
Jiminez, Karen, NY
John, Brentnol, NY
John, Ceres, NY
Johnson, Isaiah, NY
Johnson, Kelly S.*
Johnson, Sharon A., NY
Johnson, Theresa A., NY
Johnson, Zanetta C., NY
Jones, Felicia*
Jones, Iesha*
Jones, Margaret D., NJ
Jones, Marla V., NY
Jones, Shaamgod, NY
Jones, Stephanie E., NY
Jordan, Stephen, NY
Joseph, Jean, NY
Joseph, Philip, NY
Jourdan, Marine, NJ
Jourdan, Paul J., NY
Juman, Tarek, NY
Jun, Mary, NY
Jurado, John F.*
Kahn-Viteri, Michael A.
Kamona, Ruth N., NY
Kanokogi, Jean S., NY
Kaslofsky, Thor, NY
Kearns, Kelly E., NY
Keefe, Frances J.*
Keller, Christopher, OH
Kelly, David J., NJ

Kelly, Kevin A.*
Kelty, Patrick, NY
Kemel, Ann, NY
Kemp, Michelle B., NY
Kemp, Naomi, NY
Kennedy, Kendra L.*
Kennedy, Michael J., NJ
Kennely, Fritz S., NJ
Keown, Stephen V.*
Khan, Neil M., NY
Khobot, Aleksandr, NY
Kiely, Brian*
Kimmel, Erica B.*
Kinard, Renee R.*
King, Mrs. Crystal-Dawn, NY
King, Joan A., NY
Klucharits, John C., NJ
Knox, Trina M., NY
Koo, Andrew C.*
Kosinski, Monica D., VA
Kozicki, Susan, FL
Kozyra, Arthur*
Krol, ILya, NY
Kukurinis, Theologia, NY
Lajszky, Werner P., NY
La Madrid, Ms. Yvette, NY
Lamarca, Daniel P., NY
Lambert, Vanessa, NY
Lamour, Barbara M., NY
Lara, Guisela J., NY
Larkey, David H., NJ
La Spisa, Salva, NY
Lassi, Luisa E., NY
Lawrence, Veronie, NY
Leach, Anthony, NY
Lee, Andreas Y., NY
Lee, Sherman, NY
Lefeure, Charles*
Legiec, Mark, NJ
Lentz, Jennifer P., NY
Leone, Michell, NY
Lerner, Larisa, NY
Lewin, Ms. Ouida O., NY
Lewis, Everad H., NY
Lewis, Jasmine T.*
Lewis, Sonya A., NY
Li, Kathy, NY
Lian, Leon E., NY
Lieb, Kristen M., NY
Lights, Philip A.*
Lill, Nicholas D.*
Lippi, Ms. Francine J., NY
Little, Sheremah, NY
Livingstone, John E., NY
Lloyd, Mauline M., NY
Lochner, Colin D., NY
Lockett, Athina L., NY
Lodvil, Murielle, NY
Loerbs, Heather A., NY
Loizon, Louis*
Longo, Rudolph A., NY
Lopez, Jennifer L.*
Lopez, Kevin, NY
Lopez, Lucy*
Lopez, Malgorzata K., NY
Lopez, Melind A., NY
Lopez, Monserrate, NY
Lopez, Victoria, NY
Lorde, Shannon G., NY
Louis, Barbara, NY
Louissaint, Medeline, NY
Lovina, Richard*
Lowe, Jacqueline P., NY
Lowe, Victoria L., NC
Lubben, Kelly A.*
Lucia, Kimberly A., NY
Luck, Teresa, NY
Lugo, Elizabeth, NY
Lui, Elena, NY
Luma, Yoleine, NY
Luther, John J., NY
Luyando, Luz I., NY
Lynch, Darren R.*
Mahady, Myles, NY
Majid, Syed M., NY
Malave, Carlos J.*

Mani, Riva, India
Manna, Salvatore, NY
Manzello, Joseph, NY
Marini, Ivette, NY
Markiewicz, Tom A., NY
Marlow, Kidada, NY
Marrero, Jose L., NY
Marsh, Judy C., NY
Marshall, Paula, NY
Marshall-Myles, Coleen, NY
Martin, Alexandra, PA
Martin, Beverly S., NY
Martin, Sara*
Martinez, Edgar, NY
Martinez, Felix, Jr., NY
Martinez, Marisol, NY
Martinez, Yesenia, NY
Marty, Maritza, NY
Mason, Barbara D.*
Massey, David, NY
Mata, Angelina E., NY
Mateo, Gladys E., NY
Matos, Daniel*
Maurice, Ms. Geraldine, NY
Mayes, Denise M.*
Maynard, Joycelyn Y.*
Mazariego, Andres, NY
Mcbride, Rosemary*
Mcbride, William A., NY
Mc Callum, Dionn, NY
Mccarthy, Donna M., NY
Mccarthy, James N., NY
Mccarton, James I., NY
Mccarty, Gerard, NY
McClain, Shawn D., NY
McCollough, Charmaine, NY
Mccormack, Paul G., NY
Mccoy, Deon*
Mccutchen, Aishah K., NY
Mcdonald, Lucille A., NY
Mcgee, Patrick J., NY
Mcgovern, Rita, NY
McKenzie, Albert W., NY
Mckenzie, Mark A., NY
Mckenzie, Rohan M., NY
Mcmahon, Michael S., NY
Mc Nulty, Thomas P., NY
Meinken, Todd E., NY
Melis, Paul, NY
Melvin, Octavia F., NY
Mendal, Amy, NY
Mendez, Angela, NY
Menes, Yvette, NY
Mercado, Julio, NY
Merced, Dennis*
Mero, Mildred, NY
Merritt, Douglas, NY
Mersheimer, Chris, NY
Meszaros, Stephanie*
Meza, Edgar E., CA
Michel, Pierre M., NY
Mickens, Renee J., NY
Miles, Leon D.*
Miller, Dwight D., NY
Miller, Georgetea A., NY
Miller, Gloria L., NY
Miller, Kisha, NY
Minara, Robert J., NY
Mirand, Esther L., NY
Miranda, Celines*
Miron, Lowell S., NY
Mirza, Ashfa N., NY
Mitchell, Charles A., NY
Mitchell, Deborah, NY
Mitchell, Gary M.*
Mitchell, Sharleen J., NY
Mitton, Herns, NY
Moffatt, Maikov A., NY
Mohammed, Rijal, NY
Montalvo, Marcos*
Montgomery, Stephani, NY
Montrose, Sharon R., NY
Moon, Charles C., NY
Mora, Jessica M., NY
Mora, Madeline C., NY
Morales, Bethzaida, NY

Morales, Cesar A., NY
Morales, Hector, NY
Morales, Oscar*
Morales, Paola A., NY
Moran, Brian K., NY
Morelli, Joseph A., NY
Moreno, Miguel, FL
Morgan, Beverley D.*
Moriarty, Justine B., NY
Mornel, Theodore B., NJ
Morris, Gregory A.*
Moscoso, Emilio C., NY
Moskowitz, Ari A., NY
Moultrie, Latoya Z., NY
Mowatt, Wendy A., FL
Mullin, John H., GA
Munroe, Doris L., NY
Murillo, Cynthia T., NY
Murphy, Lisa, NY
Nadella, K., NY
Napier, Gregory M., NY
Nazaire, Magdala, NY
Nazaire, Yvana, NY
Nedderman, Dionne A., NY
Neggia, Thomas E., NJ
Nehama, Alan, NY
Nekrutman, David R., NY
Nelson, Daisy*
Nelson, Debra A., NY
Nelson, Fitzroy R., NY
Nelson, Mark E.*
Nevarez, Ms. Melissa, NY
Newell, Pauline M.*
Newton, Herold H., NY
Ng, Phillip, NY
Nguyen, Huyen M., NY
Niang, Baila*
Nicholson, Conrad R., NY
Nicks, Alfonso M., NY
Nicolaou, Carmen A., NY
Nieves, Julie A., NY
Ninburg, Svetlana, NY
Nisi, Anthony J., NJ
Niss, Oleg, NY
Nobles, Sharon V., NY
Noel, Desmond E., NY
Nunez, Janet F., NY
Nunez, Janet F., NY
Nuzzi, Laurie A., NY
Oakley, Charlene S., NY
O'callaghan, Joseph, NY
O'Connell, Sean M., NY
O'Dell, Jill C., IL
Okafor, Emeka D., NY
Okeagu, Ugochi T.*
Olivo, Jose, NY
O'Neill, Angelo L., NY
Ordonez, Julio C., NY
Ortiz, Carlos E., NY
Ortiz, Christopher W., NY
Ortiz, Dawn, NY
Ortiz, Luis E.*
Ortiz, Michael A., NY
Ortiz, Ricardo L., NY
Osbourne, Cherryann, NY
Ostrowski, Greg T., NY
Outar, Beverley, NY
Owens, Trina R.*
Pacheco, Marilyn I., NY
Pacheco, Wilfredo*
Packer, Catherine, NY
Packman, Miriam A., NY
Page, Lauren S., NY
Page-Okhiria, Carolyn D., NY
Paglino, Joseph R., NJ
Palatnik, Victoria D., NY
Palega, Paul K., NY
Palmer, Doreen O., NY
Palmer, Seth*
Panama, Maritza B., NY
Papp, Robert J., NY
Pappagallo, Joseph*
Park, Christine M., NY
Parker, Calvin N., NY
Parker, Dieshia L., NY
Parkins, Marcia D., NY

Partridge, Joseph, NY
Pascal, Sandra*
Pastrana, Angel L., NY
Patterson, Jeneva M., NY
Payne, Andrea T., NY
Peart, Donaree Y., NY
Peralta, Omar J., NY
Peralta, Vivian, NY
Perez, Alida, NY
Perez, Irving*
Perez, John T., NY
Perez, Leticia N., NY
Perez, Lourdes M., NY
Perez, Mario, NY
Perez, Mayra E., NY
Perez, Michelle, NY
Perez, Mike, NY
Perez, Sandra M., NY
Petersen, Jacqueline, NY
Peterson, Eugene, Jr., NY
Petry, Beth-anne*
Phillips, Lorraine*
Phillips, Patrick A., NY
Pichardo, Marcos, NY
Pierre, Bikens, NY
Pierre, Josephine, NY
Pierrelouis, Max, NY
Pinkney, Tamela E., NY
Pisarczyk, Edyta, NY
Pittman, Yolanda R., NY
Poglodek, Tina M., NY
Polanco, Teodoro R.*
Poland, Jeremy M., NY
Polis, Stacy A., NY
Pollard, Lisa M.*
Poma, Ms. Patricia E., NY
Pompey, Quwanna S., NY
Pondillo, Anthony, NY
Portelli, Frank, NY
Porter, Samuel A., FL
Potts, Janice P., NY
Powmesamy, Learie, NY
Prendergast, Yollette, NY
Prentis, Cheryle R., NY
Presume, Thierry, NY
Proto, Rosa M., NY
Pugliese, Naomi B., NY
Pulice, Ronnie, NY
Pysarenko, Katherine, NY
Quaranto, Annette L., NY
Quarless, Tahaiwa V., NY
Quezada, Alejandro, NY
Quinones, Milagros, NY
Quinones, Zoraida, NY
Quintana, Grisel, NY
Quintanilla, Carlos*
Quraishi, Zahid N., NJ
Railey, James A., NY
Hamirez, Lesbia, NY
Ramnarain, Kavita, NY
Ramos, Laura, NY
Ramos, Mead S., NY
Ramos, Rossan M.*
Ramsay, Nicole A.*
Randall-evans, Grace M.*
Raphael, Giselle L., FL
Ratney, Alyson D., NY
Regalado, Ana R., NY
Regus, Judith G., NY
Reid, Antoinette M., NY
Reid, Dyke O., NY
Reuben, Frank J.*
Reyes, Henry, NY
Reyes, Moses, NY
Reynoso, Marycruz*
Richards, Andrea N., NY
Riley, Dawn M., NY
Riso, Edward T., NY
Rivera, David, NY
Rivera, Eduardo, NY
Rivera, Elba, NY
Rivera, Eric, NY
Rivera, Jonathan M., NY
Rivera, Julie A., PA
Rivera, Robert O., NY
Rivera, Roberto, NY

Rivera, Selenia, NY
Rizzo, Leonard I., NY
Roach, Kairis J., NY
Roberts, Linda, NY
Roberts, Matthew A., NY
Robertson, Ms. Sallie A., NY
Robertson, Stanford B., NY
Robillard, Michelle, AZ
Robles, Lizette E.*
Rodriguez, Alba L., NY
Rodriguez, Belinda, NY
Rodriguez, Eddie, NY
Rodriguez, Herbert R.*
Rodriguez, Ivan J., NY
Rodriguez, Jeffrey, NY
Rodriguez, Joey, NY
Rodriguez, John A.*
Rodriguez, Juan C., NY
Rodriguez, Lourdes N., NY
Rodriguez, Nicholas, NY
Rodriguez, Servando, NY
Rodriguez, Sylvia, NJ
Rodriguez, Ms. Veronica, NY
Rojewski, Robert, NJ
Roman, Lisa, NJ
Ronelli, Danielle A., NY
Rorie, Scott F., NY
Rosa, Justo, NY
Rosado, Jacqueline, NY
Rosario, Jasmine E.*
Rosario, Juan, NY
Rosario, Maribel*
Rosario, Moises, NY
Ross, Stanley, NY
Rossello, Manuel, NY
Roulhac, Teresa, NY
Rowe, John M., NY
Rozier, Christopher, NY
Rudolph, Gary J., NY
Russo, Stacey A., NY
Ryan, Herman D.*
Ryan, Robert T., NY
Rye, James*
Sacipi, Bujar B., NY
Sadovskiy, Yevgeniy, NY
Sahdala, Ambiorix A., NY
Saint Victor, Lewis, NY
Salgado, Nelida, NJ
Salmon, Horace S., NY
Sambula, Anthony L., NY
Samuels, Sheila Y., NY
Sanchez, Castalia, NY
Sanchez, Catherine L., CA
Sanchez, Natasha P., NY
Sanchez, Sandra P., NY
Sandberg, Scott F.*
Sandelli, Wendy L., NY
Santiago, Lisette, NY
Santos, Tyrone S., NY
Sanzo, Esther*
Saunders, Kathyann C., NY
Scala, Richard A., NY
Scalzo, Charles, NY
Schmidt, Margaret J., NJ
Schultz, John A., Jr., PA
Schweitzer, William, NY
Scott, Alicia*
Scott, Ashaun*
Scott-hoyt, Susan M.*
Sebro, Kathy, NY
Secor, Bruce M., NY
Seelig, William (Billy), NY
Seibert, Eleanore, NY
Seide, Nadege, NY
Sell, Angela M., PA
Sena, Nino D., NY
Sequinot, Abimael*
Serling, Latonja F., NY
Sernaque, Janet, TX
Serrano, Ana S., NY
Sesay-harrell, Kadij*
Sevastyanov, Vladimir, NY
Shannon, Shiann, NY
Shavers, Donna L., NY
Shearer, Kimberley, NY
Shields, Diana L., NY

Shiva, Andrew, NY
Shu, Howard, NY
Shuford, Keisha R., NY
Sierra, Benny*
Siggeris, Tina*
Simanduyeva, Juliya, NY
Simmons-sixto, Camil*
Simon, Barry, NY
Simon, Tyrone K., NY
Simone, Christine*
Simpson, Alicia, NY
Simpson, Nicole D., NY
Simsovits, Rachel, NY
Singh, Krishna S., NY
Singh, Priya, NY
Singleton, Valerie*
Slevin, John J., NY
Small, Christopher*
Smith, Joyce E., NY
Smith, Karen R., NY
Smith, Melinda G., NY
Smith, Robert L.*
Smith, Roberta L., FL
Smith, Sabrina, GA
Smullen, Margaret, NY
Solgan, Christopher J., NY
Sosa, Ms. Kilsie, NY
Sosa, Stephanie A., NY
Sosin, Alexander, NY
Soto, David, NY
Sowah, Ayeley, NY
Spektor, Irma*
Spence, Maurice A., NY
Spiegel, Matthew, NY
Stanton, Sam M., NY
Stark, Ms. Carmen C., NY
St. Bernard, Shari, NY
Steimke, Tara, NY
Stephen, Kendrea S.*
Stephens, Gary, NJ
Steuerer, John, NY
Stewart, John D.*
Stewart, Lenore O., NY
Stewart-dixon, Cynth*
Stockhausen, Scott, NY
Stone, Carl J., NY
Strafella, Kim M., NY
Strazzullo, Salvator, NY
Stringer, Judith L., NJ
Strubbe, Maureen, NY
St. Victor, Lewis, NY
Sullivan, Joseph, NY
Sumpter, Michelle T., FL
Sumter, Antoinette, NY
Suponitskiy, Serge, NJ
Suriel, Julissa A., NY
Swinton, Victor, NY
Tabachnick, Carrie R., NY
Takeuchi, Michael, NY
Tavarez, Merrybet, NY
Taveras, Wendy, NY
Taylor, Ms. Ann L., NY
Taylor, Christopher*
Taylor, Deserie, NY
Taylor, Donnell, NY
Taylor, Jamal, NY
Taylor, Pasey N., NY
Taylor, Ms. Shernill, NY
Tejada, Jorge L., NY
Tejada, Ripcary, NY
Telford, Ken, NY
Tenenbaum, Lauren C.*
Theodore, Mornel*
Thomas, Natacha, NY
Thornton, Frank C.*
Thornton, Jenell, NY
Timm, Julianna M.*
Tobias, Joshua M.*
Tomlinson, Jodi L., NY
Torlish, Helena, NJ
Torres, Allison, NY
Torres, Damaris E., NY
Torres, Elizabeth, NY
Trause, Victoria, NJ
Travis, Jody A., NY
Triffon, George E., NY

Trofi, Angela*
Tsang, Wing C.
Ttley, Sheila A., NY
Tucker, Darlene, NY
Tulley, Dionne, NY
Tully, Rachel, NY
Tumasar, Diane M., NY
Tunis, Roberson*
Tuohy, Patrick, NY
Turner, Candia, NY
Turner, Joseph A., NY
Turner, Michele, NY
Umar, El-farouk, NY
Upsher, Denise, NY
Uwague, Nelson, NY
Valdez, Mary*
Valerio, Peter, NY
Vargas, Jose, NY
Vargas, Shirley W., NY
Vazquez, Jose*
Vega, Nanette, NY
Velasquez, Edwin, NY
Velez, David A., NY
Vickerie, Natasha P., NY
Victor, Philson J., PA
Vidal-Romero, Elida, NY
Villacorta, Adriel W., NY
Villegas, Lliana, NY
Vinales, Jose A.*
Vitale, Tammy, NY
Wachter, Mark T., NY
Waiters, Lawana*
Waite-Shuler, Yvette M., NY
Walcott, Kama E., NY
Walker, Ms. Chenyear A., NY
Walker, Lisa L., NY
Walker, Sabrina*
Walker, Sharlisa M., NY
Wall, Alysa G.*
Walsh, Kevin J.*
Ward, Clifford, NY
Ward, Roger, NY
Ward, Yvette A., NY
Warnke, Sharon E.*
Warren, Gerald, NY
Washington, Archie, NY
Waters, Sean H. T., NY
Webber, Leroy M., NY
Webley, Karen R., NY
Weidenfeld, Alan I., NY
Weiswasser, David, NY
Welsh-Shirley, Joyce L., NY
Weston, Denise M., NY
White, Letecia J., NY
White, Patrick C., NY
Whiteside, Lisa, NY
Whittaker, Ikiesha T., NY
Wilks, Daniel C.*
Williams, Angela, NY
Williams, Barbara A., NY
Williams, Deborah E., GA
Williams, Ernest M.*
Williams, Euclyn A., NY
Williams, Magdelina*
Williams, Nakesha L., NY
Williams, Patricia H., NY
Williams, Rosalyn D.*
Williams, Sonya Y., NY
Wilson, Annette G., NY
Wilson, Fertima, NJ
Wilson, Regina D., NY
Wimberly, Sheila A., NY
Wintonick, Steven G.*
Wojcik, Jerry H., NY
Wojtach, Christophe J., NJ
Wong, Fidel A., NY
Wright, Andrea A., NY
Wright, Charmone, NY
Wright, Shaulene, NY
Wright, Theresa V., NY
Wright, Wayne R., NY
Wustefeld, Janet L., NJ
Wyatt, Antoinette C., NY
Xavier, Canisius R., NY
Yan, Hon-man, NY
Yoon, Sung-pil*

Young, Dennis M., NY
Young, Felicity A., NY
Yuen, Hon, NY
Zaidenberg, Nidia, NY
Zambrano, Bethsave, NY
Zef, Aleksandr, NY
Zephirin, Nadege L., NY
Zicuis, Paul, NY
Zimmerman, Peter S., NY
Zurita, Barbara, NY

1998

Achini, Antonio, NY
Acosta, Gasmary, NY
Acosta, Gloria W., NY
Adams, Eric L., NY
Agron, Mikhail M., NY
Ahrens, Bree C., OR
Akins, Rachquel, NY
Alava, Eddie J., NY
Albornoz, Anneris T., NY
Albuja, Hugo D., NY
Aldoy, Anna M., NJ
Alejandro, Gina M., NY
Alejandro, Joseph A.*
Ali, Allison, NY
Aliha, Kourosh M., NY
Allen, Kelly J., NY
Allwood, Maria B., NY
Almonte, Ernesto R., NY
Alvarado, Ivonne C., NY
Alvarez, Michelle L., NY
Alvarez, Richard, NY
Alzate, Jorge E., NY
Amadi, Ogechi A., NY
Amaral, Patrick N., NJ
Angelucci, Joann, NY
Angermaier, Heather A., NY
Aponte, Lydia, NY
Armani, Chris G., NY
Arthur, Jude, NY
Aversa, Eileen T., NY
Ayala, Mona C., NY
Bacchus, Kimberly C., NY
Baez, Ricardo, NY
Balgobin, Ms. Julianna, NY
Bany, Peter D.*
Baptiste, Camille A., GA
Barminko, Svetlana, NY
Barrios, Luz, NY
Bartels, Ms. Elizabeth C., NJ
Batista, Shenoeck, NY
Bavolar, SGT Keith A., NY
Baxter, Katherine L.*
Bayliss, Bridget G., NY
Beatty, John P., NY
Belton, Deborah E., NY
Bencosme, Odette M., NY
Benintendo, John, NY
Bennett, Winsome Y., NY
Berkowitz, Charles R., NY
Berrios, Aaron, NY
Berrios, Johnny, NY
Birner, Jolene N., NY
Black, Samuel (Sam), CA
Blackman, Te'shanee M., NY
Blackwood-ahmed, Melrose, NY
Blaich, Charles R., NY
Blakeley, Dawn, NY
Blount, Ms. Heather, NY
Blume, Rene M., NY
Blumstein, Evan P., NY
Bobb, Gavin E., NY
Boettcher, Donna M., NJ
Bonas Benjamin, Laura Z., NY
Bonilla, Jose E., NY
Bonilla, Rosa Y., NY
Booker, Kwesi L., NY
Borbon, Daysi A., NY
Borrelli, Kristin K., NY
Borrero, Kenneth, NJ
Boyce, Robert, NY
Bracero, Denise, NY
Brathwaite, Henderson O., NY
Bravo, William A., NY

Braxton, Valerie D., NY
Brimberg, Karen J.*
Brimfield, Audrey*
Broderick, Stephen J., NY
Brown, Joseph G., Jr., NY
Brown, Milton E., NY
Brown, Paul R., NY
Brown, Paul S., NY
Brown, Ronda R., NY
Brown, Timothy, NY
Brucculeri, Giovanna R., NY
Brudent, Sandra, NY
Bruechert, Nicolle, NY
Brunson, Lakisha D., NY
Bryan, Stephanie A., NY
Bubnis, Christalie J., PA
Bull, Rhudean, CT
Burgos, Angela I., NY
Burrell, Monica, NY
Burroughs, Ninette, NY
Burshteyn, Pavel, NY
Butler, Ruth M., NY
Butler, Tawanna C., NY
Caballero, Joyce E., NY
Caban, Deboral, NY
Cala, Jerome J.*
Calise, Diane, NY
Calvert, Vashti N., NY
Camacho, Michael, NY
Camargo, Ruth E., NY
Campbell, Robert, NY
Canal, Wilvina, NY
Cannizzaro, Mariann, NY
Capellan, Awilda J., NY
Cardoza, Jamie M., NY
Carrera, Margarita, NY
Carrillo, Anaida W., NY
Carson, Jonathan, NY
Casares, 1LT John W., USA, TX
Cassidy, Jared K., NY
Castellani, Albertina, NY
Castellano, Joseph M.*
Castro, Gisele, NY
Castro, Sandra J., NY
Catana, Alexandra D., NY
Catania, Denise A., NY
Chacon, Karlene L., NY
Chapman, Marilyn, NY
Cheng, Christoph C., NY
Cherry, Alvina T., NY
Choi, Manyi*
Christie, Andrew C., NY
Chupcavich, Anna J., NY
Cicero, Alethea U., NY
Cintron, Edwin, NY
Clowes, Eric J., NJ
Clyde, Nicole, NY
Cocozza, Joseph T., NY
Cohen, David J., NY
Coker, Renee R., NY
Colclough, Andre W., NY
Coleman, Shermelle, NY
Collins, Stephen P., NY
Colon, Rafael E., NY
Conde, Matthew P., NY
Conklin, Jennifer M., NY
Connolly, Caitlin A., NY
Connor, Mrs. Katrina A., NY
Cooke, Sharon F.*
Cooper, Vikki*
Correa, Angel R., NY
Cosentino, Donna M., NY
Cossu, Jennifer K., NY
Costanzo, Keith J., NY
Coutain, Kade, NY
Crawford, Andrea (Angie) K., NY
Crawford, Mark R., NY
Cronin, Joseph M., NY
Cronin, Michael, NY
Crouthamel, David E., NJ
Cruz, Heidy A.*
Cueva, Patrica E., NY
Culella, Marycatherine E., NY
Cummings, Dalila C., NY

Curylo, Phyllis J., NY
Czarnecka, Beata, NY
Dadacay, Dominic M., NY
Daly, Elizabeth V., NY
Damon, Latricia R., NY
Dargan, Sabrina, NY
Davis, Brian P., NY
Davis, Bridgette K.*
Davis, Nakisha, NY
Davis, William T., NY
Dearson, Daniel P.*
de Beer, Rebecca, NY
Debono, Pierre C., NY
Deceilio, Andrea E., NY
De George, Joseph W., NY
Dejesus, Iris K., NY
Delacruz, Jasinta*
Delacruz, Ralph, NY
Dellorto, Nakisha A., NJ
Denis, Chester T., NY
Dennard, Debra M., NY
Desir, Wilfrid, NY
Dessources, Ralph, NY
Devonish, Winston R., NY
Deyo, LT David, NY
Diaz, Norian F., NY
Difilippo, Christopher B., NY
Diih, Sorle S., NY
Di Pane, Jodi E., NJ
Dirago, Anthony*
Dobson, Anthony, NY
Dodson, Kenneth L., NY
Dominguez, Gerardo*
Donnelly, Stephen M., NY
Donohue, Dennis W., NY
Douglas, Marsha D., NY
Douglass, Robert L., NY
Doute, Jemal L., NY
Drew, Isola S., NY
Drouillard, Julie A.*
Ductan, Cohetta, NY
Duke, Lara M., TX
Duncan, Bernadette, NY
Dupree, Angela, NY
Duran, Jimmy, NY
Durand, Maria A., NY
Duverne, Madeleine M., NY
Elcock, Mark G., NY
Elsayed, Judith, NY
Erickson, Scott W., NY
Ernst, James C., NY
Escalante, Norma E., NY
Escobar, Luis M., NY
Escobar, Veronica, NY
Espanet, Jennifer A., NY
Estevez, Mildred, NY
Esturine, Francella T., NY
Fabien, Margareth, NY
Farrell, Clare T., NY
Farrell, Mel G., NY
Fauntleroy, Irma C., NY
Felder, William J., NY
Feliciano, Elizabeth, NY
Feliz, Luisa A., NY
Ferguson, Andre, NY
Fernadez, Patricia, NY
Fernandez, Adamilka, NY
Fernandez, John A., NY
Fields, Dana, NY
Fields, Mark A., NY
Figueroa, Genoveba N., NY
Fiore, Sharon A., FL
Flores, Anibal, NY
Flores, Yvonne Y., NY
Folgar, Karen J., NY
Ford, Stacey A.*
Fox, Kevin M., NY
Fox, Thomas M., NY
Foye, Katrina, NY
Francis, Howard C., NY
Francis, Joel M., NY
Francois, Marc D., NY
Freier, Deborah A.*
French, Rollo C., NY
Frick, Henry F., NY
Frittitta, Joseph G., NY

Fuller, Joan D., NY
Gaillard, Andrea J., NY
Gallardo, Diana, NY
Galloza, Gilbert, NY
Gancitano, Victor R., NY
Garces, Felipe A., NY
Garcia, Aldo J., NY
Garcia, Camilo F.*
Garnett, Joan M., TX
Garofalo, Michael R., NY
Garrido, Richard R., NY
Garvey, Wendy, NY
Gaskin, Melissa E., NY
Gaskin, Michelle D., NY
Gaston, Kanal V., NY
Gaudiosi, Nicholas C., NY
Gayle, Cathy A., MD
Gibbons, Adam C., NJ
Gibilaro, John R.*
Gifford, Kompel, NY
Gilchrist, Beverly R., NY
Giller, Randi L., NY
Gillians, Detra S., NY
Giordano, Bryan P., NY
Giordano, Melissa A., NY
Givens, Tameika, NY
Glanstein, Janelle M., NY
Glawson, Lillian F., NY
Glemaud, Stanley, NY
Goldfarb, Matthew S., NY
Gomes, Felicia C., NY
Gonzalez, Adonis, NY
Gonzalez, Maria, NY
Gonzalez, Monica L., NY
Goodman, Sabrina B., NY
Gopee, Brenda G., NY
Gorelik, Joanna K., CA
Goris, Patricio, NY
Gossman, Craig W., NY
Graciano, Maria C., NY
Graham, Nicole S., NY
Graves, Christine H., NY
Green, Kelly A., NY
Greene, Delicia T., NY
Greene, Kenny B., NY
Greenidge, Charmaine D.*
Gridley, Shannon C., FL
Grosso, Heather L.*
Grullon, Johanny, NY
Grzanka, Emily J., IL
Guarna, Vanessa K., NY
Guillaume, Christa M., NY
Gumley, Laura M., NY
Guski, Christopher J., NY
Guzman, Elizabeth K., NY
Guzzo, Scott R., NJ
Hackenmiller, Julie, TN
Hall, Debra E., NY
Hall, Ruben T., NY
Hamm, Tushan S., NY
Hammer, Charles M., NY
Haque, Ferdous, NY
Harkins, Michella R., NY
Harris, Latonia*
Harrison, Karen M., NY
Harvey, Ms. Wendy B., NY
Hayowyk, John A., NJ
Heaney, Patrick, NY
Hemingway, Michael J.*
Henriques, Luciann, NY
Herbosch, Alessandra D., NY
Hermans, Peter L., NJ
Hernandez, Elizabeth, NY
Hernandez, Michael, NY
Herrera, Carlos R., NY
Herve, Francois, NY
Hibbert, Jacqueline M., NY
Higgins, Adrienne C., NY
Higgins, Michael S., NY
Hill, Damon A., NY
Hill, Meloney E., NY
Hills, Carlos J.*
Hilton, Quiana L., NY
Hinds, Kelvin C., NY
Hobson, Anthony E., NY
Hogan, Paul T., NY

Holder, Mark A.*
Holmes, Sharon R., NY
Horan, Denise A., NY
Howell, Paula M., NY
Hughes, John E., NY
Hull, Melanie S., NY
Hwee, Edmund, NY
Hyacinth, Mario K., NY
Hyppolite, Ms. Anne W., NY
Igiebor, Justice O., NY
Ihne, Christine M., NY
Ingram, Dawn M.*
Interlandi, Giuseppe S., NY
Irizarry, Christopher F., NJ
Isaacson, Eric M., NY
Israelov, Michelle, NY
Ives, Nicole J., NJ
Jabouin, Melone H., NY
Jackson, Adriane R., NY
Jackson, Judy, NY
Jackson, Latoya M., NY
Jacobs, Cyril C., NY
Jaigobind, Carl, NY
James, Fallarasha K., NY
Jamison, Annette, NY
Jason, Tracey, NJ
Javier, Sharon, NY
Jean-gilles, Myriam, NY
Jean-louis, Hildere, NY
Jegede, Babatunde S., NY
Jenkins, Shirley L., NY
Jimenez, Agueda M., NY
Jimenez, Ramona J., NY
Johnson, Carlton A.*
Johnson, Charles A., NY
Johnson, Gloria, NY
Johnson, Jocelyne I.*
Johnson, Kimberly A., NY
Johnson, Ms. Monique F., FL
Johnson, Niesha P., NY
Johnson, Robert J., NJ
Johnson, Shannon M.*
Johnson, Wendy R., NY
Jones, Billy M.*
Jones, Brenda L., NY
Jones, Debra D., NY
Jones, Kevin D., NY
Jones, Rehenia, NY
Jones, Venessia S., NY
Jordan, Nazly, NY
Joris, Compton, NY
Joseph, Crystal, NY
Jubak, Ms. Jennifer L., NY
Kagan, Donald R., NY
Kakar, Humyra, NY
Kalinian, Haygoush*
Kalletta, Edward D., Jr., NY
Kane, James C., NY
Kasper, Daniel T., NJ
Katzeff, Martha, NY
Kavanagh, Michael J., NY
Kayser, Steven B., NY
Keith, Ms. Stacy A., MD
Kemp, Donita M., NY
Kennedy, Deniese L., NY
Kenny, John D., NY
Kessopa-Cabrera, Pojana, NY
Khan, Angelina, NY
Khan, Arlene, NY
Khan, Sharon*
Khan, Shazad, NY
Khurana, Rajiv R., NY
King, Jerome A., NJ
King, Usheevii, NY
Kittrell, Frances E., NY
Kleinman, Mandy K., NY
Klencner, Waldemar M.*
Knezevic, Antoaneta, NY
Knorr, Jill L., NJ
Koch, Christopher J., NY
Koester, Arlene L., NY
Korneev, Tanya V., NY
Korol, Natalya, NY
Kosteas, Panagiotes, NY
Kraus, David T., NJ
Kravchenko, Leonid, NY

Kroll, Rainer D., NY
Kumagai, Koshin, NY
Kunitzky, Michael, CA
Kusmierska, Grazyna, NY
Lacicero, Diane R., NJ
Lam, Kwai, China
Lamb, James P., NY
La Morte, David, NJ
Lang, Wayne L., NY
Langarica, Ernesto, NY
La Rac, Natasha, NY
Laroc, Natasha E., NY
Lasanta, Danielle M.*
Laschet, Alice, NY
Lassen, Christopher M., NY
Laster, Keena M., NY
Lastique, Sharon D., NY
Lattner, Maryann H.*
Lawrence, Julia J., NY
Lazo, Herlis A., NY
Leandry, Victor, NY
Lee, Chon J., NY
Lee, Donald F., NY
Lee, Ms. Michele, NY
Lee, Vernon, NY
Leftt, Andrew D., NY
Leggett, Kenyon E., NY
Lempert, Vladimir, NY
Leone, Christopher M., NY
Lesser, Marc H., NY
Leung, Emily, NY
Lewis, Frederick H., NY
Lewis, Holly Y., NY
Lieberstein, Steven I., NY
Liffey, Joseph A., Jr., NY
Livingstone, Iain T.*
Lloyd, Tasha N., NY
Lobrutto, Salvatore, NY
Lockery, Jennifer A.*
Lopez, Karen*
Lopez, Michael A., NY
Lora, Krupskaia (Sky), NY
Lore, Charles J., NY
Lorenc, Iwona, NY
Louallen, Keith, NY
Louissaint, Harmelle M., NY
Loureiro, John M., NJ
Louvado, Ivo M., MD
Lovell, Frederick J., NY
Lowe, Eulisha T., NY
Lozano, Elsa M., NY
Lubin, Suze, NY
Macaluso, Leonard, NY
Macdalie, Jeeny, NY
Macpherson, Ian C., NY
Mahon, Jennifer, NY
Mailman, Kevin D.*
Major, Curstlinia S., NY
Mancuso, Donna Marie B., NY
Manjarrez, Jose L., NY
Marcellus, Algeste, NY
Marchese, Maria N., NJ
Marine, Ricardo, NY
Mark, Harry, NY
Markulin, Sheryl I.*
Marseille, Bogard, NY
Martin, James (Jim) P., NY
Martinez, Elizabeth, NY
Martinez, Maria O., NY
Marulanda, William, NY
Matos, Edwin A., NY
Matthew, Kevin S., FL
Matthews, Karen A., NY
Maturine, Latoya D., NY
Maxwell, Ellen E.*
Maxwell, Gwendolyn, NY
Mazerolle, Christian, NJ
Mccain, Shanique S., NY
Mccann, Peggy A.*
Mccants, Stephanie N., NY
McCollin, Kathy-Ann E., NY
Mccullough, Sylvia A., NY
Mcdermott, John R., NY
Mcdonald, Yajayra, NY
McEntire, Catherine Duffy, NY
McGhee, Lisa, NY

Mcgrath, Patrick M., NY
Mcguire, Patrick J., NY
Mcgurl, Thomas M., NJ
Mckenzie, Malcome, NY
Mc Queen, Norman E., Jr., NY
Mejia, Sandra M., NY
Melendez, Monserrate, NY
Melino, Albert J., NY
Melo, Yesenia E., NY
Mendez, Jeanette*
Mendez, Lisa, NY
Mendez, Marisol, NY
Mendolia, Jeffrey, NY
Mercedes, Wendy V., NY
Mereuta, Rodica D., NY
Merriweather, Michelle L., NY
Meyers, Trishonna M., NY
Michel, Nancy C., NY
Michel, Pierre R., NY
Mieles, Christina M., NY
Miladinov, Marija, NY
Miller, Ivy C., NY
Milner, Michael C., NY
Minaya, Joselinne A., NY
Mitchell, Kimberly A., NY
Mitchell, Salahadine (Sal), NY
Mitchell, Tracie-Ann N., NY
Molina, Bobby, NY
Monnay, Yves, NJ
Monplaisir, Ms. Patricia D., NY
Montague, Steven L., NY
Montijo, Maribel, NY
Moodie, Joyell T., NY
Morales, Ingrid M., NY
Moran, John A., III, NY
Moreia, Fredrick M., NY
Moreno, Karla C., NY
Moreno, Thaimi, NY
Moriarty, Edward P., NY
Motisi, Meegan T., NY
Moy, Wai*
Mulligan, Thomas M., NY
Munoz-Shivers, Rachel I., NY
Murphy, Daniel P., NY
Mylott, Robert H., NY
Myung, Ji-Man, NJ
Nachtman, Iva, VA
Nacinovich, Ms. Diane M., NY
Napoleon, Johnny L., NY
Natale, Marc J., NY
Nazamy, Najib, NY
Ndreu, Ritvan J.*
Neal, Sean M., NY
Neckin, Ian H., NY
Nedos, William T., NY
Negron, Maria E., NY
Negron, Peter, NY
Neonakis, Alecsandro, NY
Nesmith, Daron L., NY
Neuwirth-Vreeland, Denise, NY
Newkirk, Rosalind J., NY
Nicaj, Vera, NY
Nichols, James J., NY
Nieto, Mauricio*
Nieves, Linda R., NY
Nimrod, Lloyd G., NY
No, Steve, NJ
Noble, Simone A., NY
Noel, Kevin E., NY
Noel, Sean S., NY
Nozine, Josette M., NY
Nunez, Yohanna, NY
Oconnell, Daniel V., NY
Oconnor, Thomas J., NY
Ohadoma, Emmanuel O., NY
Olivares, Flor E., NY
Onwuka, Nelson O., NY
Orender, Patrick E., NY
O'Rourke, Stacey M., NY
Ortiz, Alex, NY
Ortiz, Maria, NY
Ossohou, Andre A., NY
Owens, Olga M.*
Ozuna, Maria J., NY
Pacheco, Kahilil*
Paige, Jodi W., NY

Palmer, Lorrine R., NY
Palmisano, Nicholas A., NJ
Palza, Lyz, TX
Paradiso, Michael, NY
Park, Junkyu, NY
Parris, David Mosa E., NY
Parry, Lesroy T., NY
Patti, Pasquale J., NJ
Paul, Yulonda J., NY
Payne, Jamil V., NY
Pearson, Timothy, NY
Pena, Anthony, NY
Penson, Michelle L.*
Perdomo, Kevin A., NY
Pereira, Laura, NY
Perez, Carlos M., NY
Perez, George E.*
Perez, Irma, NY
Perez, Jason*
Perez, Juan, NY
Perez, Vilma, NY
Perrotta, Michael J., NY
Perry, Ofer A., TX
Perry, Offer J.*
Persaud, Nalini, NY
Peters, Claire E., NY
Peters, Kelly A., NY
Peterson, Sandra S., NY
Peza, Miroslaw*
Phillips, Emily S., NY
Phillips, Nickie D., NY
Phillips, Timothy F., NY
Pickett, John J., NY
Pierre, Abel L., NY
Pierre-francois, Wladimir, NY
Pietrzak, Margaret M., NY
Pimenta, Paul M., NY
Pinti, Rosanne A., NY
Pinto, Diane L.*
Plawner, Thomas A., NY
Polanco, Veronica, NY
Pomerantz, Scot, NY
Pontecorvo, Thomas J., NY
Pope, Winston L., NY
Poplavskiy, Aleksandr A., NY
Porter, A. Dashiell, NY
Portorreal, Ms. Yecenia, NY
Powell, Wizdom A.*
Prashad, Dianna P., NY
Preval, Walter, NY
Pride, Kasha L., NY
Prieto, Juliza J., CA
Prioleau, Catrina C., NY
Purdie, Yvonne W., NY
Raeburn, Phyllis S., NY
Ragonese, Lisa A., NY
Ramdeholl, Neville, NY
Ramirez, Alexis, NY
Ramirez, Barry, NY
Ramirez, Giomar P., NY
Ramirez, Jessica D., NY
Ramirez, Lamberto, NY
Ramirez, Robert, NY
Ramirez, Vernon, NY
Ramjohn, Maria J., NY
Ramos, Rafanzelin, NY
Ramsay, Elcah, NY
Rankin, Ms. Louise M., NY
Raver, Deidre M., NY
Raymond, Woody, NY
Reen, Shaun M., NY
Reinert, Mendoza L., CA
Rello, John J., NJ
Reyes, Lina E., NY
Rhodes, Onesia S., NY
Rhonda, Harris L., NJ
Rios, Juan R., NY
Ritchie, Kerri, NY
Rivera, Denise, NY
Rivera, Elisha S., NY
Rivera, Jose A., NY
Rivera, Karen E., NY
Rivera, Nickcole S., NY
Roberson, Shawanda, NY
Roberts, Pamela T., NY
Roberts, Sherman S., NY

Robinson, Dwight C., NY
Robinson, Michelle D., NY
Robinson, Roberto I., NY
Robles, Nelson A., NY
Rocco, Kenneth B., NJ
Rodgers, Lamont K., NY
Rodriguez, Abigail, NY
Rodriguez, Angela E., NY
Rodriguez, Damian A., NY
Rodriguez, Lizette, NY
Rodriguez, Mashea M., NY
Rodriguez, Miriam M., NY
Rodriguez, Yara, NY
Rodriguez, Yvette*
Rodriguez, Yvonne, NY
Rojas, Luis E., NY
Rolon, Miriam, NY
Roman, Vivian, NY
Romero, Yenia J., NY
Rontanz, Richard A.*
Rosario, Rafael, NY
Rosario, Victor M., NY
Rosati, Daniel J., NY
Rosenberg, Michelle L., NY
Rosenberger, Joseph N., NY
Royer, Helena C., NY
Rue, Sheena R., NY
Ryan, John P., NY
Sabb, Jamal M., NY
Saint-fleur, Johanne A., NY
Salas, Julius O., PA
Salinas, Liz K., NY
Salvador, Selene, NY
Sam, Yolanda E.*
Samsonov, Aleksandr, NY
Samuels, Jason S., NY
Sanabria, Deborah, NY
Sanchez, Anna S., NY
Sanchez, Baldemiro, NY
Sanchez, Felix R., NY
Sanchez, Irene, NY
Sanchez, Lizabeth*
Sandiford, Jerry A., NY
Sanfilippo, Monica L., NY
Santa, Robert C., NY
Santiago, Anna P., NY
Santiago, Jessica, NY
Santiago, Mrs. Sueleyba, NY
Santiago, Zoraida, NY
Saraceni, Frank M., NJ
Satchell, Sonia E., NY
Savage, Patrick J., NY
Savva, Mary*
Saxby, Michele W., NY
Schild, Alexandra H., NY
Schild, Stephanie V., NY
Schmitz, William J., NY
Schrempp, Karen E.*
Schroeder, Thomas, NJ
Scott, Mrs. Gladys A., NY
Scotto, Joseph M., NY
Sealy, Wendell L., NY
Seeram, Jillene*
Seldner, Jenny R.*
Serra, Raphael, NY
Serrano, Millie, NY
Shabazz, Khari S.*
Shea, Patrick J., NY
Sheard, Paige C., NY
Sherlock, Gerald, NY
Sherwood, William C., NY
Shuemate, Melissa A., NY
Shulterbron, Luz M., NY
Shvartsman, Maria T., CT
Silvera, Sashika T., NY
Simion, Nicolae, NY
Simmons, Melodi K., NY
Simon, Michael, NY
Simon, Michelle R., NY
Sklyut, Olga, NY
Skrypkun, Meg E., IL
Smalls, Shameka, NY
Smigielska, Katarzyna P., NY
Smith, Arlyne D.*
Smith, Daniel J., NY
Smith, Derrick A., NY

Smith, Farah A., NY
Smith, Jacqueline D., NY
Smith, Tina P., NY
Sorensen, Bo N., Denmark
Soto, Michelle C., FL
Spady, Sonya A., NY
Sparrow, James T., NY
Spinella, Raymond, NY
Stallings, Theresa J.*
Stanley, Lynnette, NY
Stare, Renata*
Steigman, Heidi J., NY
Stevens, Tamika S., NY
Stewart, Delisia R., NY
Stewart, Karen D., NY
St. Fort, Lina, NY
Stimphil, Kathy K., NY
Stokley, Hope B., NY
Strayhorn, Ms. Michelle, NY
Sugarman, Stacy, NY
Sullivan, Jennifer C., NY
Suppa, Christina, NY
Surena, Jean Bernard C.*
Susino, Joseph, NY
Tabb, Ms. Yolanda, NY
Taboada, Yelitza C., NY
Tanella, Gerard M., NY
Tarver, Dionne E., NY
Taylor, Heidi M., CA
Tazifua, Thaddeus A.*
Teelimian, Henrik, NY
Tejada, Marianela, NY
Testa, Lawrence W., NY
Texler, Misty, NY
Thomany, Carline*
Thomas, Alisa J., NY
Thomas, Roxanne D., NY
Thompson, Sacheen L.*
Tindal, Russell*
Tocci, Daniel L., NY
Todorova, Yeleina V., NY
Toolsee, Drupatie R., NY
Torres, Daisy, NY
Torres, Ricardo, NY
Torres-hernandez, Maritza, NY
Trail, Robert L., NY
Triebel, Erika M., NY
Trinidad, Evelyn, NY
Trinidad, Linda M., NY
Tsekouras, Fay F., NY
Tuason, Aleli P., NJ
Tulloch, Natalie T., NY
Turschmann, Michelle, NY
Tyre, Iasia A., NY
Ulrich, Thomas L., NJ
Urteaga, Ana M., NY
Varela, Anthony F., NJ
Vargas, Dayanara J., NY
Varnell, Mary Allen B., MS
Varsamas, Tommy A., NY
Vasquez, Julio E., NY
Vasquez, Michael J., NY
Vaz, Fernando P., NY
Vela, Bianca M., NY
Velasquez, Katty, NY
Velez, Donato, NY
Veljanovska, Marija, NY
Veloz, Ramon, NY
Vernazza, Laurel A., NJ
Vielot, Marshka M., NY
Villanueva, Hector M., CA
Villanueva, Michelle*
Vlad, Cristian A., NY
Volmar, Marc A., Jr., NY
Volpi, Ms. Jennifer M., NY
Volynets, Anatoliy, NY
Waldron, John F., NJ
Walker, Shidina L., NY
Wallace, Roxanne S., NY
Walsh, Thomas B., NY
Ward, Orson R., NY
Wargo, Jennifer, NY
Warthen, Rodney, NY
Washington, Bernetha, NY
Waszczuk, Wieslaw, NY

Weeeks, Donnetta, NY
Weltin, Jennifer M.*
Weston, Theodore S.*
Wheatle, Kerensa C., NY
White, Norman K., NY
Whittaker, Franklin J., NY
Wiener, Lorin, NY
Wille, Diana, NY
Williams, Grace M., NY
Williams, Katrina J., NY
Williams, Kevin A., NY
Williams, Keyla N., NY
Williams, Shaundelle M.*
Williams, Suzette S., NY
Williamson, Flavia M., NY
Wilson, Richard P., NY
Witty, Marina I., NY
Wohlfiel, Allison E., CA
Wong, Selwyn M., NY
Yates, Genithia, PA
Yee, Yu S., NY
Young, Antonia R., NY
Young, Shnequa A., NY
Youngs, Chance R., NY
Zagorodnyuk, Lada, NY
Zajicek, Renee M., OH
Zavala, James E., NY
Zaveloff, Sarah H., NY
Zielinski, Peter, NY
Zouhbi, Faisal, NY
Zwerling, Gayle B., NY

1999

Abdurakhmanov, Igor F., NY
Acevedo, Maxima K., NY
Acevedo, Samantha*
Achon, Alexa M., NY
Acosta, Michelle, NY
Acosta, Pilar M., NJ
Adams, De'Ron W., NY
Ademaj, Vera, NY
Ahyoung, Gary C., NY
Aitken, Alexandra S., GA
Ajunwa, Ifeyinwa P., NY
Albert, Tracy K., NY
Alduende, Ivonne, NY
Alexander, Alison J., NY
Alexandre, Mirlene*
Ali, Anisa S., NY
Allaby, Dennis T.*
Aloia, Veanna M., NJ
Amador, Bernard, NY
Amay, Jasmin E., NY
Ambris, Ayanna E., NY
Ampie, Omar A., FL
Amundsen, James E., NY
Anatsui, Edwige M., NY
Anderson, Ms. Carmen N., NY
Anderson, Jacqueline V., NY
Antonin, Jo-Ann, NY
Antoniou, Antonios, NY
Antonucci, Robert J., NY
Arias, David S., NY
Arlen, Jennifer, NY
Armenia, Rita, NY
Armesto, Catherine P., NY
Arroyo, Kelly, NY
Askins, Jisselle F., NY
Assayag, Lyate A., NY
Atkinson, Glenroy*
Atristain, Luis, NY
Attridge, Walter J., NY
Auguste-Smith, Portia, NY
Augustin, Kisha V., NY
Auli, Karoll, NY
Ault, Colette E., NY
Avdoulos, Robert L., NY
Ayala, Irma I., NY
Babb, Jackie R., NY
Badillo, Cristina, NY
Baichoo, Linda T., NY
Baisden, Ms. Jilyon, NY
Balangon, Janelle P., NY
Balgobin, Hemant K., NY
Banks, Latisha V., NY
Banks, Sadiqa, NY

Barbosa, Jose A., NY
Barton, Claudia J., NY
Basler, Craig C., NY
Bass, Mildred C., NY
Bastidas, Patricia E., NY
Battaglia, William, NJ
Battle, Tamika S., NY
Bauer, George M., NY
Bazile, Steven G., NY
Beary, Richard A., NY
Beato, Rafael A., NY
Beattie, Henry J., NY
Belcher, Penney L., NY
Belford, Curtis S., NY
Bello, Valerie, NY
Benjamin, Paul, NY
Bennett, Ms. Kerry-Ann, NY
Berry, Siobhan L., NY
Bility, Mohammed S., NY
Biswanger, Terri P., NY
Black, David W., NY
Blaikie, Melanie A., NY
Bohringer, Ernest W., NY
Bonilla, Anthony, NY
Booncome, Sanrit, NY
Bordas, David M., NY
Bowles, Mark E., NY
Bracy, Marshandra D., NY
Breault, Suzanne M., NJ
Bredefeld, Nicole J., NJ
Brennan, Denise, NY
Brenneman, Suzanne N., NY
Brighton, China T., CA
Brock, Mrs. Daisy H., NY
Bronaugh, Ronald A., NY
Brown, Courtney L., NY
Brown, Kenya D., NY
Brown, Ketina*
Brown, Leah D., NY
Brown, Linata, NY
Brown, Tarsha S., NY
Brown, Timothy J., NY
Brown, Tracy-Ann M., NY
Browne, Phillip A., NY
Bruce, Prince A., NY
Budram, Anil, NY
Bullwinkel, John A., CO
Bundy, Elizabeth B., WI
Burgess, Victoria, NY
Burke, Kevin E., NY
Burroughs, Jamel, NY
Bush, Randall S., NY
Byer, Renee A., NY
Byrd, Shasun (Germaine), NY
Byrnes, Jennifer L., NY
Byrnes, Ms. Kirsten M., NJ
Cabral, Aileen I., NY
Caccavo, Christine, NY
Cadet, Rachelle, NY
Calin, Ovidiu M., NY
Caltabiano, Lisa J., NY
Camilo, Gilberto J., NY
Caminero, Elbi M., NY
Canning, Candia C., NY
Caraballo, Gesselle, NY
Carlson, Glenn A., NY
Carrasco, Edward (Ed) G., NY
Carrion, Ana R., NY
Carroll, Michael J., NY
Carvajal, Tania M., NY
Cassidy, Joseph T., NY
Castellano, Cayetano R., NJ
Castellar, Kane H., NY
Castro, Zinna, NY
Caver, Cynthia L., NY
Cedeno, Stacey N., NY
Challita, John-Pierre, NY
Chambers, Maxine V., NY
Chan, Suk Han H., NY
Chance-Pollard, Sarita T., NY
Chantayan, Angelika, NY
Charles, Ralph M., NY
Chen, Jennifer W., NY
Cherubin, Ms. Yadlynd R., NY
Cheung, Zulma G., NJ
Chew, Philip M., NY

Childs, Iris M., NY
Chin, Victor, NY
Chowdhury, Tarakur R., NY
Chung, James K., NY
Chyrack, Judy, NY
Cipriano, Vincent, NY
Cirillo, Maria D., NY
Clark, Shalima, NY
Clarke, Laura, NJ
Clarke, Nicole L., NY
Clarke, Rosanna, NY
Clay, Kareem, NY
Clotter, Nelly, NY
Coello, Marjorie I., NY
Cohn, Jennifer I., NY
Collins, Louis H., NY
Colon, Wendy C., NY
Cominnel, Irene D., NY
Connor, Brian W., NY
Coppock, SGT Durwin L., NJ
Corbett, Robert, NY
Cordero, Raul (Pappa Bear), NY
Cordon, Lee C., NY
Corso, David J., NY
Cotto, Veronica, NY
Coviello, Ms. Karlee M., NJ
Cox, Ethel, NY
Cozzolino, Caryn, NY
Crayton, Wanda A., NY
Creighton, Brian K., NY
Croke, Brian M., NY
Cruz, Talia C., NY
Cruz, Victor A., NY
Cummings, Ivan, NY
Cupid, Irma, NY
Curcio, Leanne T., NJ
Cusimano, Stephanie A., NJ
Dacosta, Emmy H., NY
Dalloo, Eric S., NY
D'Amore, Jessica M., NJ
Dangelo, Steven J., NY
Daniels, Mrs. Romina J., NY
Darden, Lakisha M., DC
Davidson, Terrill L., NY
Davis, Charles W., NY
Davis, Joanne, NY
Defrancesco, Rosalie A., NY
Delacruz, Claret, NY
Delerme, Carolyn, NY
Delisser, Christine A., NY
Deliu, Francisco C., NY
Denis, Iznaldy, NY
Derfinyak, Eugene S., NY
Dervin, Katharine M., NY
D'Gracia, Anthony J., NY
Diana, Charlene K., NY
Diaz, Migdalia M., NY
DiToro, Christopher J., NY
Ditto, Philip J., NY
Dolan, Daniel S., NY
Dolphy, Keri-Ann, NY
Dombrosky, Mark D., NY
Domond, Alix, NY
Donahue, Paul G., NY
Donlon, Megan, NY
Doolan, Shane R., NY
Dormena, Marie-Suze, NY
Doss, C. Brian, TN
Douglas, John F., NY
Drummond, Junior A., NY
Duncan, Jesse J., NY
Durkin, Robert T., NY
Dwyer, Lauren A., NY
Dybski, Thomas, NY
Dyminski, Edward A., NJ
Egan, Abbe I., PA
Eleftheriou, Eleftherios A., NY
Ellis, Joseph S., NY
Emanuel, Michael A., NY
Emidih, Jones F., NY
Eng, Shawn, NY
Enriquez, Lister V., NY
Eodumegwuhu, Khalika U., NY
Escobar, Marcus, NY
Esguerra, Andres, NY

Espada, Evelyn, NY
Espinal, Jacqueline, NY
Espinal, Sandra M., NY
Espinoza, Fanny G., NY
Espinoza, Susan I., NY
Esposito, Michael V., NY
Fajardo, Juan Carlos, NY
Fallon, Jeffrey C., NY
Fasano, Richard A., NY
Fayad, Abdul, NY
Fegley, Venessa M., FL
Fernandez, Maria C., NY
Fernandez, Yvette, NJ
Figueroa, Dominga, NY
Figueroa, Jodie L., NY
Filion, Elizabeth, NY
Filipowicz, Renata, NY
Finegan, Kevin J., NY
Flaherty, Jennifer J., CT
Flamarique-Vela, Susana, NY
Flanagan, Colleen M., NJ
Fleskes, Jenna M., CA
Flores, Franklin, NY
Flores, Jason D., NY
Foreman, Paulette, NY
Forlong, Pedro A., NY
Fountoulakis, Georgios, NY
Fourcell, Samantha, NY
Fox, Kemeel N., NY
Francois, Reginald*
Franklin, Raymond J., NY
Fraser, Marvin R.*
Frater, Donroy S., NY
Frates, Michaelynn J., NY
Frazier, Veronica, NY
Fredericks, Jonathan E., NY
Freilich, Mark J., NY
Frias, Maria C., NY
Fuentes, Jacqueline A., NY
Gabin, Angeli, NY
Gabriel, Anne M., NJ
Gabriel, Sandra M., NY
Gaither, Ernest, NY
Galicia, Margo V., NY
Galvin, Christopher J., NY
Gangoo, Andrea R., NY
Garcia, Dolly M.*
Garcia, Fausto, Jr., NY
Garcia, Marilyn, NY
Garcia, Rosa M., NY
Garofano, Graziella D., NY
Ge, Sylvester Y., NY
Gee, Anthony D., NY
Gelb, Nelya, NY
Gelman, Jennifer M., NY
Gely, Timothy N., NY
Gentile, Dominic A.
George, Ms. Camille A., NY
George, Sharon J., NY
Geraci, Anthony W., NY
Gerdes, Jeffrey J., NY
Gerovich, Yevgeny, NY
Gerrick, Theckla R., NY
Gibbs, Satisha E., NY
Giuliano, Diane L., NY
Gjelaj, Mark, NY
Glenn, Tyra T., NY
Gnitecki, Marcin, NY
Godfrey, David L., NY
Goldberg, Delia W., NY
Goldberg, Sheri, FL
Golden, John P., NY
Gollins, Lara S.*
Gomez, Tracie, NY
Gonzales, Helen K., NY
Gonzalez, Alicia, NY
Gonzalez, Allan W., NY
Gonzalez, Carmen L., NY
Gonzalez, Hector L., NY
Gonzalez, Jeffrey, NY
Gonzalez, Sandy J., NY
Gonzalez, Tanya N., NY
Gonzalez, Ms. Yadhira, NY
Goodwin, Ella D., NY
Gorelik, Max, CA
Gorovoy, Oleg B., NY

Grant, Harriett D., NY
Grant, Kevin C., NY
Grant, Tamika S., NY
Greenberg, Adam N., NY
Greene, Jiton T., NJ
Greene, Tamecca L., NY
Grisales, Claudia, NY
Guerrero, Noemi, NY
Guerrero, Wendy D., NY
Gutierrez, Edith, NY
Guzman, Danny R., NY
Guzman, Edward E., NY
Guzman, Nelson, NY
Guzman, Saul, NY
Habashzada, Halai, NY
Hall, John J., NY
Hamideh, Hamza, NY
Hamilton, Carlene D.*
Hamilton, Jennifer M., NY
Hamilton, Kevin P., NY
Hansen, Brett P., NY
Haran, Stephen J., NY
Harding, Jacinth A., NY
Hardy, Kimberly, NY
Harmon, Ms. Amy, NY
Harrigan, Eric J., NY
Harriott, Kerry-Ann E., NY
Harris, Onya T., NJ
Hart, Harvin, NY
Hartzog, Adam C., CT
Hatzakos, Peter, NY
Hayashi, Magen K., MI
Hayes, Miranda R., NY
Hayes, Shanise M.*
Haygood, Alia A., NY
Haynes, Lisa D., NY
Haywood, Kimberly L., NY
Heimink, Thomas H., NY
Henry, Josseth A., NY
Henry, Lowana M., NY
Henry, Mrs. Marie R., NY
Herbert, Tara V., NY
Herbst, Andrew J., NY
Hernandez, Gertrudis, NY
Hernandez, Ronald, NY
Herrell, Todd M., NY
Herrera, Eduardo J., NY
Herrera, Leslie S., NY
Herrera, Sergio R., NY
Hickey, Keri, NY
Hickey, Stephanie M., NY
Hickey, Thomas F., NY
Hill, Craig R., NY
Hinestroza, Xiomara, NY
Hirbour, Cynthia A., CT
Hodge, Ivy S., NY
Holden, Terence, NY
Holly, Erin K., NY
Holsey, Sabine N., NY
Holsten, Gary W., Jr., NJ
Hopkins, Adria D., NY
Houdek, Caroline M., NY
Houle, Ms. Genevieve L.,
　Canada
Howe, Jason B., NY
Howze, Rosa M., NY
Hsu, Peter B., CA
Huey, Ivy S., NY
Hughes, James R., NJ
Hunt, Curtis J., NY
Hunter, Tara D.*
Hunter, Yovonda (Yoyo) B., NY
Hurwitz, Brian M., NY
Ibrahim, Shorab, NY
Ifebi, Emeka C., NY
Impavido, Catherine L., NY
Isaac, Dana R., NY
Iyesi, Okpa, NY
Jackson, Alicia J., NY
Jaen, Dimas A., NY
Jagdharry, Mayleen G., NY
James, Israel, NY
Jamyang, Dekyi T., NJ
Jarjokian, Kegham A., NY
Jefferson, Kayra R., NY
Jenkins, Gary P., NY

Jennings, Sean J., MA
Jimenez, Daniel, NY
Jimenez, Ms. Julie A., NJ
Jimenez, Leyla X., NY
Jimenez, Robert, NJ
John, Carol A.*
Johns, Lashana M., NY
Johnson, Charlene A., NY
Johnson, Edna S., NY
Johnson, Mrs. Paticia A., NY
Johnson, Sheree V.*
Johnson, Tiffany R., NY
Jonas, Hazel D.*
Jonas, Heather E., NY
Jones, Eneka U., NY
Jones, Michelle A., NY
Jordan, Shamieka S., NY
Joseph, Eddison M., NY
Joseph, Patrick F., NY
Kabakoff, Robert I., NY
Kaffashan, Nazanin, OR
Kao, Pu-Mao F., NY
Kaufman, Brian R., NY
Kavanaugh, Shannon B., NJ
Kazymirczuk, Tina G., NJ
Keane, Joseph P., NJ
Keehlisen, Lynda M., NY
Keeler, Garrett L., NJ
Kellman, Rudolph*
Kelly, James F., NY
Kelly, Yvonne, NY
Kemp, Royevette, NY
Kennon, Shawn, NY
Kerr, Milagro X., NY
Khaimov, Igor I., NY
Khan, Rakeela B., NY
Khilkevich, Denis A., NY
Khiterer, Inna, NY
Killian, Becky, NY
Kinard, Tabitha, NY
King, John P., NY
Kinscherf, Cindy L., NY
Kitching, Tselanee, NY
Klein, Gilah F., CT
Knight, Petrice A., NY
Kogan, Darina, NY
Kokubun, Shoko, NY
Kolenovic, Medzit, NY
Kornegay, Kenyetta A., NY
Korolyev, Dina, NY
Kosmetatos, Marina, NY
Koumba, Patricia S., NY
Kourakos, Joseph C., NY
Kreymer, Rita, NY
Kurschner, Alexis L.*
Kurzweil, Andrew, NY
Kuzyszyn, Katrina N., NC
Kyriakides, Michael N., NY
Labus, Heather A., NY
Lacombe, Stanley B., NY
Lalak, Patsy A., NY
Lalaram, Anjani, NY
Lambrianidou, Kyriaki, NY
Lampf, Jesse D., NJ
Larroche, Odette Y., NY
Larsen, Jeremy, NY
Lavington, Chelsea R., NY
Lawrence, Talaia, NY
Lazarre, Marie, NY
Leaderman, Ian C., GA
Leckey, Sabrina M., NY
Ledroit, Delphine Y., NY
Lee, Barbara S., FL
Lee, Judy, NY
Lee, Tiffany M., VA
Leggett, Ms. Renee, NY
Lema, Kathy, NY
Lembersky, Victoria D., NY
Lemo, Edina, NY
Lenze, William R., NY
Levi, Dmitry, NY
Levien, Michael C., NY
Levine, Cari, NY
Levine, Stuart J., NY
Lewis, Michael G., NY
Lewis, Raphine J., NY

Lewis Sardia, Sardia F., NY
Li, Bonnie Y., NY
Liatto, Joann, NY
Liguori, Michael T., NY
Lim, Elizabeth O., NY
Lin, David, NY
Lindo, Renee, NY
Linetskaya, Yuliya, NY
Lipp, James O., NY
Llyod, Massa N., NY
Lobl, Alin, NY
Loecher, Daryl C., NY
Long, Jeffrey E., NY
Longaro, Brian J., NY
Looby, Lisa, NY
Lopez, Edgar, NY
Lopez, Marisel, NY
Lopez, Marla, NY
Lucas, Ms. Patricia A., NY
Lucien, Steeves, NY
Luckey, Joyce C., NY
Luna, Nallibe, NY
Lundquist, Tracey A., NJ
Lundy, Romero, NY
Luongo, Gregg A., MA
Lupi, Melissa A., NJ
Lutchmansingh, David A., NY
Lynch, Phiona D.*
Lynch, Thandi N., NY
Macari, Valerio F., NY
Mahoney, Catherine V., NY
Malagoli, Tara D., NY
Malahy, James E., NY
Malaxos, Troy-Nicholas, NY
Maldonado, Carmelo, NY
Maldonado, Evelyn J., NY
Maldonado, Ismael, NY
Manette, Sean S., NY
Mangal, Yovendra, NY
Mangarella, Anthony, NY
Manger, Nichole, NY
Manir, Zabed, NY
Manis, Ms. Jeanne D., NY
Mann, Krista J., NY
Mannino, Eulalia, NY
Marasco, Michael J., FL
Marchetti, Rossin A., NC
Marech, Craig A., NJ
Mariano, Theresa, NY
Maris, Gus*
Marita, Rose B., NY
Marley, Brian S.*
Marquez, Melinda E., NY
Marrero, Ms. Rosa M., NY
Martinez, Joselin, NY
Martinez, Margherita, NY
Martinez, Vincent O.*
Massey, Ritesh, NY
Mathews, Onica O., CT
Matos, Lisette, NY
Matos, Venessa M., NY
Matthew, Monique C., NY
Mayer, Robin L., NY
Mayers, John D., Jr., NY
Mayor, Lizette, NY
Mays, Valerie N., NY
Maysonet, Christine L., NY
McAlpine, Bill, NY
McCartha, Dawn E., NY
McGowan, Ruth M.*
McGrath, Juzann M., NY
McKinley, Tenee S., NY
MClees, John C., NY
Mc Master, John A., NY
McNeill, Ms. Jasmine K., NY
Mcwhirter, Arran R.*
Medina, Bolivar, NY
Medley, Leslie C.*
Melendez, Abel, NY
Melendez, Esi E.*
Melendez-Josey, Maritza, FL
Melgar, Silvia L., NY
Melhado, Godfrey R., NY
Melsky, SGT Ryan E., NJ
Mendez, Dennis M., NY
Mendez, Maritza, NY

Mendoza, Esther C., NY
Menos, Sedrys, NY
Mercado, Frances, NY
Mercedes, Wascar A., NY
Mesa, Nelson, NY
Messina, John J., NY
Metaxas, Alexander, NY
Michaelson, Estee M., NY
Middleton, Karen A., NY
Middleton, Ruth P., NY
Middleton, Sharon D., NY
Mihailos, Michele A., NY
Miller, Ann M., OH
Miller, Carlos M., NY
Miller, Chanell N., NY
Minier, Mildred, NY
Mirabal, Carolina, NY
Mitchell, Janet E.*
Mitchell, Natasha, NY
Mitsinikos, Nikos J.
Molina, Angelita, NY
Molina, Ariadne M., NJ
Molina, Evelyn, NY
Molina, Sandra M., NY
Monk, Marie, NY
Montague, Kathleen B., NY
Montana, Paul J., NY
Montoya, Carlos A., NY
Moonan, Ravi N., NY
Moore, Patrick, NY
Moore, Talitha, NY
Morales, Carlos E., NY
Morales, Indiana, NY
Moran, Kendre M., NY
Morasco, Benjamin J., MO
Moreira, Ms. Julie A., NY
Moriarty, Robert C., NY
Morris, Chasity L., NY
Morrissey, Timothy K., NY
Moutopoulos, Jimmy, NY
Mraz, Mrs. Leanne A., NJ
Mshvelidze, Vadim, NY
Mujica, Linda R., NY
Mulcahy, Michele A., NY
Mule, Concetta M., NJ
Mulholland, Patrick G., NY
Munroe, Simone A., NY
Murphy, Brian J., NY
Murphy, Ms. Josephine A., NY
Murphy, Kathleen E., NY
Myers, Sayeeda, NY
Nalty, Carlton J.*
Nanna, Louis J., NJ
Nasser, Sharifa M., NY
Nazarzadeh, David R., NJ
Nguyen, Deidre, NY
Niblock, Susan B., MD
Nieves, Gloria E., NY
Nieves, Jose V., NY
Nikitin, Maxim, NY
Nixon, Henry E., NY
Nocella, Adrienne L.*
Nunez, Claribel, NY
O'Brien, Keri J., NY
Obuchowski, Bart M., NJ
Ochs, Jeffrey J., NJ
Octave, Colin, NY
O'Donnell, CAPT Steven, NY
O'Dowd, Michael P., NY
Odowd, Michael P., NY
Ogula, David C.*
Okosun, Alexander E., NY
Oquendo, Olivet, NY
Orourke, Rosemarie K., NY
Ortega, Jessica, NY
Ortega, Maritza, NY
Ortega, Shirley L., NY
Ortega-Veliz, Olga, NY
Ortiz, Madeline*
Ortiz, Yolanda, NY
Orzillo, Kelly S., NJ
Osborne, Kimberly M., NY
Oseni, Yetunde A., NY
Ostrander, Anthony (Tony) S., NY
O'Sullivan, Kevin M., NY

Owens, Kelly E., NY
Oyewayo, Olusade, NY
Pabon, Karen K., NY
Pace, David R., NY
Padilla, Alfonso, NY
Padron, Ms. Linette, NY
Pahman, Marina, NY
Palmer, Nicole M., NJ
Pan, Karen V., NY
Parikh, Pragati J., NY
Parisi, Domenico J., NY
Park, Richard A., VA
Parrish, David, NY
Parrotta, Diane M.*
Parsons, Jerome C.*
Pasuizaca, Carmen L., NY
Patterson, Germaine, NY
Patterson, Ilani B., NY
Paul, Mario, NY
Paul, Nigel
Paulino, Jose P., NY
Peay, Ms. Lisa D., NY
Pelissier, Junie, NY
Pena, Erica, NY
Pena, Esther, NY
Pena, Eva M., NY
Pena, Leonel A., NY
Pena, Marisol, NY
Perales, Christopher C.*
Perez, Jaime A., NY
Perez, Omar, PR
Perez, Rosa S., NY
Perritt, William J., NY
Persaud, Amanda J., NY
Peters, Petra P., NY
Peterson, Daniel J., NY
Petrocelli, David A.*
Pettit, George J., NY
Petty, Bernard M., NY
Philbert, Donna-Marie, NY
Philippeaux, Gerard*
Phillip, Gayle D., NY
Phillips, Ernest G., NY
Phillips, Steven S., NY
Pichardo, Fausto B., NY
Pierre, Louicasse, NY
Pierre, Taciana, NY
Pierre-Louis, Ms. Audrey H., NY
Pierri, Rocco J., NY
Piil, Laura, NY
Pinkhasov, Mikhail, NY
Pitt, James R., NY
Placido, Elizabeth J., NY
Pliva, Alex, NY
Plummer, Nicolyn M.*
Polanco, Alfa C., NY
Pollard, Willette, NY
Pomales, Jessica, NY
Popovic, Jozef, NY
Portes, Francisco T., NY
Poseluzny, Janis
Powell, Veronica D., NY
Preddice, Victoria A., RI
Price, Henrimae, NY
Price, Kimberlea D.*
Prince, Natasha R.*
Prip, Ronny*
Proenza-Klein, Jennifer E., NY
Proper, Diana E., NY
Proscio, Charles J., Jr., NY
Protas, Roman, NY
Pujadas, Gemma E., NY
Purpura, Heather D., NY
Quick, Keri A., NY
Quijije, Kathy M., NJ
Quinones, Andrea, NY
Quinones, Frances, NY
Quinones, Monique, NY
Ragoonanan, Ramcharan, NY
Ramirez, Debra L., NY
Ramirez, Reynaldo, NY
Ramos, Damaso, NY
Ramos, James J., NY
Ramos, Nestor, NY
Ramoutar, Donny B., NY

Rampioray, Kamini, NY
Ranieri, Joseph N., NY
Rawlings, Karen V., NY
Ray, Donald L., NY
Raymond, Sherly, NY
Razzi, Dana L., PA
Reboyras, Jessica M., NY
Redding, Assunta S., NY
Reed, Jasmine M., NY
Reed, Rachel A., NJ
Reekie, Robert, NY
Reibel, Denise L., NJ
Reibscheid, Mark A., NY
Reid, Anne E., NY
Reis, Thomas C., NY
Renner, Nils, NY
Resko, Ronald J., NY
Reszetylo, Karen, NY
Reyes, Ana A., NY
Reyes, Jacayra C., NY
Reyes, Joselyne A., NY
Reyes, Sudhey, NY
Reyes, Yahayra, NY
Reynoso, Alexa J., NY
Rice, Damon E., MD
Richards, Jeannette R., NY
Richards, Nadege, NY
Richardson, Bruce A., NY
Richardson, Thomas, NY
Richardson, Yanicke, NY
Richiez, Irving G., NY
Rinaldi, Noel A., NY
Rivera, Cynthia M., NY
Rivera, Dana E., NY
Rivera, Joey S., NY
Rivera, Manuel S., NY
Rivera, Michael E., NJ
Rivera, Pedro, Sr., NY
Rivera, Peter, NY
Rizzuto, Zoe C., NY
Roberson, Lakeisha A., NY
Roberson, William C., NY
Robertson, Erin N., MD
Robertson, Sean J., NY
Robin, Latasha B., NY
Robinson, Daniel T., NY
Robinson, Dawn M., NJ
Robinson, Neil H., NY
Robinson, Zandra, NY
Rodgers, Sherrice T., NY
Rodriguez, Adrienne J., NY
Rodriguez, Andrew W., NY
Rodriguez, Braulio, NY
Rodriguez, Diana V.*
Rodriguez, Jhoel, NY
Rodriguez, Luis D., NY
Rodriguez, Marcos A., NY
Rodriguez, Sandra, NY
Rodriquez, William, Jr., NY
Roedell, Kristen, NJ
Rojas, Paola R., NY
Rolla, Peter J., NY
Roman, Jenny, NY
Rosa, Confesor, NY
Rosa, Vapaira M., NY
Rosado, Carmen, NY
Rosario, Cynthia A., NY
Rosner, Jennifer E.*
Rothenberg, Daniel S., NY
Rouse, Evelyn, NY
Rubero, Kenneth, NY
Rudshteyn, Yuriy, NY
Ruff, Michelle N., NY
Rufino, Annette L., NY
Ruiz, Ada, NY
Rumell, William N., NJ
Russel, Patrick O., NY
Russell, Brenda M., NY
Russell, Julie A.*
Russell, Sara, NY
Rutherford, Chauncey A., NY
Ryan, Theresa A., OH
Sack, Nichole L., NY
Salazar-Atias, Ms. Camila D., NY
Salcedo, Felix M., NY

Salcedo, Yadira I., NY
Sama, Jessica, NY
Samedi, John F., NY
Samide, Erik C., NY
Samuel, Gracita R., NY
Sanchez, Enrique, NY
Sanchez, Julie, NY
Sanders, Mrs. Jeanne F., NY
Sandy, Denise M., NJ
Santana Martuez, Odalis, NY
Santiago, Frances, NY
Santiago, Jackeline, NY
Santiago, Jeanette, NY
Santiago, Jose L., NY
Santiago, Lizabeth*
Santiago, Luz D., NY
Santiago, William, NY
Sardisco, Salvatore, NY
Sarno, Lisa D., NY
Sarro, Peter J., NY
Sasso, Jill E., CT
Savatteri, Stephine, NJ
Sawyer, Genqunic R., NY
Schmollinger, Justine M., NY
Schnell, Barry A., NY
Schulhoff, Pamela, NY
Schwartz, Thomas P., NJ
Schwenzer, Roseann, PA
Sclafani, Cara J., NY
Sconzo, Rachel L., NJ
Scott, Monica, NY
Scott, Nichole R., NY
Scott, Thorance A., NY
Seda, Sandy, NY
Selip, Raena A., NY
Sequeira, Patricia*
Serrano, Francine, MD
Sewell, Keechant L., NY
Shah, Jignesh, NY
Shamsundar, Jaso, NY
Shivers, Lashonne L., NY
Shuster, Galina V., NY
Shuster, Irina V., NY
Shvartsman, Alexander, NY
Sierra, Jennifer G., NY
Silverstein, Andrew, NY
Simmons, Clifford L., NY
Simmons, Mia, NY
Singh, Christina, NY
Singleton, Simone Y.*
Singleton, Thelia L., NY
Sjoblom, Andreas E., NY
Slater, Roxanne Y., NY
Small, Kimberly O., NY
Smallwood, Lee N., NY
Smith, Bettina J., NY
Smulczeski, Richard, NY
Soghomonian, Christine A., NY
Solomon, Osbert K., NY
Soto, Denice C., NJ
Soto, Grace M., NY
Soto, Suesette, NY
Soto, Tareva L., NY
Sotomayor, Ana R., NY
Souvenir, Latoya V., NY
Sowah, Ayiteh, NY
Spencer-Dejesus, Jesusa T., NY
Springer, Laurana M., NY
Squires, Ronald W., NJ
Starace, Theresa K., NY
Stelmach, Joanne, NJ
Stephens, Sukeena M., NY
Stewart, Juanita M., NY
Stewart, Lisa M., CA
Stewart, Marie A., NY
Stfirmin, Gyna M., NY
Stillwell, Nisha R., NY
Stone, La-Toya T., NY
Stracker, Cassandra L., NJ
Streete, Tenneshia S., NY
Strobl, Staci E., NY
Stroh, Christopher M., NY
Sullivan, Nancy G., NY
Summers, Melody Y., NY
Sundheim, Irina H., NY

Swain, Warren, NY
Sylvester, Rukiya A., NY
Symolon, Kelly M., CT
Tabor, Violet, NJ
Tai, Shuk-Yu, NY
Talamas, Jacqueline C., NY
Tanaka, Daniel S., NY
Tang, Linda Y., NY
Taylor, Aisha J., NY
Telesco, Christina B., SC
Telfer, Michael A., NY
Templier, Pierrette, GA
Tennant, Denise M., NY
Thomas, Caran C., NY
Thomas, Carl, NY
Thomas, Jennifer N., NY
Thomas, Kristal L., NY
Thomas, Melinda D., NY
Thomason, Tamika, NY
Thompson, Ms. Joan F., NY
Thompson, Nedra A., NY
Tomback, Daniel M., NY
Torres, Fernando, NY
Torres, Gerardo, NY
Torres, Tanya I., NY
Toussaint, Barbara, NY
Toussaint, Emmanuel, NY
Traino, Melissa A.*
Traore, Mory*
Trelles, Henry X., NY
Trent, Rachel S., NJ
Treyvus, Kira, NY
Trippedo, Donna M., NY
Trois, Robert F., NY
Trovillot, Claude, NY
Troy, Jacqueline D., NY
Tsang, Hitomi T., NY
Tudoriu, Opritsa E., NY
Tulloch, Macola A., NY
Tulloch, Taneese T., NY
Turnage, Tywanna E., NY
Turner, Andrew C., NY
Uffer, Roselyn, NY
Urena, Gustavo, NY
Uribe, Brian S., NY
Uveges, Michael J., NY
Vaher, Kristi L., NY
Valcarcel, Carmen E., NY
Vamvoukakis, Patricia A., NY
Van, Hien D., NY
Van Arsdel-Chimka, Alison M.,
   FL
Vara, Lisa, NJ
Vargas, Adriana, NY
Vargas, Ariel, NY
Vargas, Bernabe, NY
Varshavskiy, Yevgeniy, NY
Vasquez, Maria I., NY
Vatel, Wileen, NY
Vazquez, Daniel M., NY
Vega, Javiel, NY
Vega, Michael A., NY
Velazquez, Liz, NY
Velez, Martha S., NY
Velilla, Angel E., NY
Venezia, James A.*
Ventura, Rosanny J., NY
Venuti, Christine M., NY
Vera, Sharon L., NY
Vicente, Milagros, NY
Vickers, Maxine T., NY
Vu, Mimi, NY
Walker, Adrienne J., NY
Walker, Dana R., NY
Walker, David, NY
Wallawach, Liane C., NY
Ward, Jacqueline A., NY
Warden, Rolland L.*
Wargo, Catherine M., NJ
Washington, Theresa M., NY
Webb, Hillary D., NY
Webb, Ruth H., IA
Webb, Shaun D., NY
Wells, Marianne E., MA
Wenstrom, Erika M., CA
West, Felicia A., NY

Wharton, Arnetha N., NY
White, Caleb J., NY
White, Joseph B., NY
Whitfield, Mrs. Allison J., NY
Wicklund, Jill P., NY
Wiggins, Dionne R., NY
Wilber, BethanyAnne, NY
Wilkins, Michael R., NY
Williams, Alecia S., NY
Williams, Lillian, NY
Williams, Roderick M., NY
Williams, Vanessa E., NY
Williams, Winsome O., NY
Wilson, Keryon T., NY
Wilson-Howard, Terri, NY
Windsor, Pedro J., NY
Winfield, Karen M., NY
Wise, Lashanda M., NY
Wnuk, Kazimierz S., NY
Wojtach, Susan E., NJ
Wolfe, Timothy E., NY
Woodbyne, Maurice C., NY
Wright, Rochelle T., NY
Wright, Sharnickqua O., NY
Wysocka, Anita, NY
Xenakis, Helen, NY
Yacoob, Azimoon N., NY
Yanis, Ricardo A., NJ
Yen, Chih-Chung, CA
Yoch, Marchelle R., VA
Yoo, John, NY
Yoshizaki, Takuji, NY
Zaro, Ines A., NY
Zayas, Victor L., Jr., NY
Zenteno, Antonio, NY
Zhang, Hui, NY
Zhukovsky, Alexander, NY
Zorrilla, Agatha N., NY
Zucker, Marc T., FL
Zwickel, Randi D., NY

GEOGRAPHICAL SECTION
by Residence Address

ALABAMA

ATHENS
Watts, Timothy D., '91

BIRMINGHAM
Ackerson, Kimberley, PhD, '88
Jones, Shelanda R., '90
Ramsey, Charles E., '72 *PL*

MOBILE
Gregory, Helen A., '80

TUSCALOOSA
Scott, Mable, '79 *SW*

ALASKA

ANCHORAGE
McCole, Peter, '87 *GN*

ARIZONA

AVONDALE
Soto, Diana, '84 *PL*

CAVE CREEK
Anshanslin, James B., '80
Rall, Charles E., '76 *PL*
Sokol, Louise J., '80 *CO*

CHANDLER
Robson, Robert (Bob) J., '78 *GE*

FOUNTAIN HILLS
Jacobs, Lawrence W., '72 *PL*

GILBERT
Griffith, Anthony, '86

LAKE HAVASU CITY
Derenowski, John C., '67 *ET*

MESA
Cali, Richard J., '80

NOGALES
Jebavy, Judith A., '97 *LW*

PAYSON
Thompson, Julia E., '83

PEORIA
Hellman, Karen A., '96 *CO*
King, Eric D., '89 *CP*

PHOENIX
Bianco, Anthony V., '96
Longo, Dolores A., '94
O'hanlon, Eugene C., '72
Pelton, Gwendolyn E., '80

PRESCOTT
Salerno, Joseph J., '76 *PL*

SCOTTSDALE
Aldrich, Darcy M., '93
Cooper, Kenneth, '77
Leavitt, Catherine B., '96
Tobin, John W., '72

SEDONA
Bilello, Anthony, '79

SUN CITY
Blumenthal, George, '69

SUN LAKES
Campion, Edmund J., '74
Wegman, James L., CPP, '80 *WR*

TEMPE
Woessner, Eileen M., '96

TUCSON
Guggenheim, Cordelia, '96 *ST*
Hallett, Sarah J., '91
Thompson, Kenneth V.

YUMA
Crosby, Karen P., '81
Robillard, Michelle, '97

ARKANSAS

BOONEVILLE
Beauchaine, David J., '75

HOT SPRINGS
Connor, Steven, '89

CALIFORNIA

ALISO VIEJO
Huerta, Maricela, '96

ALTA LOMA
Catanzaro, Joseph, '81

ANTELOPE
Bruno, Joan, '77

ARROYO GRANDE
Ryan, William J., '78

BAYPOINT
Rosario, Manuel D., '75

BONITA
Demers, Martha, '91 *GN*
Gorelik, Joanna K., '98
Gorelik, Max, '99 *LW*
Reinert, Mendoza L., '98

CARMEL VALLEY
Beatty, Gerard V., '72 *ET*

CASTRO VALLEY
Young, Don, '83

CERRITOS
Yen, Chih-Chung, '99

CHULA VISTA
Salamy, Joseph M., '89 *TR*

CLAREMONT
Taylor, Heidi M., '98

CORONA
Walker, Susan M., '82 *BI*

CRESTLINE
Bramble, Rachel, '93

DANA POINT
Varney, Lillian, '78

DANVILLE
Christensen, James, '81 *GN*

ESCONDIDO
Barrett, Kevin, '91 *ET*
Falvey, Lynn R., '75 *GN*
Falvey, Stephen J., '75 *BK*

FONTANA
Brighton, China T., '99

FOUNTAIN VALLEY
Mc Coy, Felix J., '76

FREMONT
Henriques, Marie, '77

GRANITE BAY
Skinner, Elizabeth, '93

HAYWARD
La Mont, Olivia E., '77
Watkins, Ms. Tracey L., '85 *CT*

HERMOSA BEACH
Fishman, Howard (Howie) L., '78 *GN*

HUNTINGTON BEACH
Noll, Harold W., '73 *GN*
Sandin, Eric J., '91 *LW*

INGLEWOOD
Jaundoo, Madeleine, '90
Oliver, Thompson

IRVINE
Chiarini, George J., '77

LAGUNA HILLS
Sand, Valerie S., '71 *ET*

LA HABRA
Murphy, Donald R., '79

LAKE FOREST
Hughes, Timothy P., '76

LA MESA
Zartman, Brian B., '95

LAMONT
Mancera, Teresa

LOMA LINDA
Jinenez-Francis, Els, '93

LONG BEACH
Allan, Colin P., '80
Tabrizi, Ms. Monica N., '95 *SA*
Velez-cruz, Margaret R., '83

LOOMIS
Dean, Mrs. Angela R., '89 *LW*

LOS ANGELES
Alexandre, Nadhege M., '96
Derac, Yves P., '84
Hickey, L. F., '83
Loox, Michael J., '86
Molinaro, Ms. Yvette, '87 *LW*
Sorokin, Jill, '93
Weissman, David L., '75

MARTINEZ
Ojena, Stephen, '72 *LW*

MILL VALLEY
Cisneros, Albert E., '77

MODESTO
McDevitt, James P., '72

MORENO VALLEY
Jones, Gregory, '81 *LW*

OAKLAND
Alaji, Omar U., '95

OCEANSIDE
Benjamin, Edward, '75

ORANGE
Meza, Edgar E., '97

OXNARD
Mack, Robert J., '77 *GN*

PALM SPRINGS
Richards, Jodi J., '87

PETALUMA
Mc Carthy, Gerard F., '78

PLACENTIA
Burrell, Tracey, PhD, '91

PLEASANTON
Hee, Jackson, '85

POMONA
Urgo, John F., '76

RAMONA
Wohlfiel, Allison E., '98

RESEDA
Mandelbaum, Marvin H., '76 *BE*

ROCKLIN
Sanchez, Catherine L., '97

SACRAMENTO
Carthon, Arlene, '90 *NU*
Hoover, Herbert B., '69 *PL*
Saltenberger, Otto H., '68

SAN DIEGO
Acosta, Galo F., '78
Arons-Schultze, Janet A., '78 *ME*
Barbieri, Ellen B., '75 *NU*
Bass, Jeffrey I., '96 *ST*
Cronin, Kathleen V., '69 *ET*
Danjer, Marco V., '95
Dennis, Jose J., '78
Kouzel, Margarita, '95 *LW*
Mahoney, Matthew, '92
Simon, Gregory D., '83
Stewart, Lisa M., '99 *ST*
Williams, Andel G., '88 *FV*

SAN FRANCISCO
Bailey, Alban O., '77
Berrios, Carmen M., '83 *CO*
Black, Samuel (Sam), '98 *CP*
Edwards, Theresa A., '75
Fleskes, Jenna M., '99 *SW*
Grunski, Alexander F., '77
Hassett, Jean M., '72 *SW*
Kunitzky, Michael, '98 *AD*
Lam, Alfred, '87
Reid, Nora A., '85
Roe, Julie, '92

SAN JOSE
Ferguson, Craig D., '82 *TR*
Marchetta, Raymond A., '79
Maselli, John M., '83
Mc Namara, Joseph D., '68
Plamenco, Roberto C., '89 *PL*

SAN MARCOS
Hamblin, Desmond M., '75

SAN MARINO
Hsu, Peter B., '99

SAN MATEO
Rudd, Alexis H., '93 *ST*
Shea, Nicola D., '94 *SN*

SAN RAFAEL
Kenny, Robert E., CCA, '82 *GN*

SAN RAMON
McGraw, Deborah S., '91
Renois, Paul J., '79

SANTA ANA
Jones, Cassandra D., '89 *LW*

SANTA MONICA
Angeletti, Debra, '93 *LW*

SEAL BEACH
Villanueva, Hector M., '98 *PL*

SIMI VALLEY
Shortell, Robert E., '75
Wiseman, Kenneth F., '72

SUNNYVALE
Wenstrom, Erika M., '99

287

CALIFORNIA

TARZANA
Prieto, Juliza J., '98 *AD*

VAN NUYS
Forni, Mario T., '73 *ET*

VENTURA
Goff, Richard, '74

VISTA
Alamo, Ildefonso L., '81
Hoffman, Charles, '77

WEST COVINA
Hogarth, Emmanuel J., '85

COLORADO

AURORA
Delgado, Ms. Fatima A., '95 *IN*
Small, Christine J., '95
Taylor, Sandra L., '72 *EA*

COLORADO SPRINGS
Bullwinkel, John A., '99
Zlochower, Sol, '72

DENVER
Hood, Melody E., '86
Madgett, Brian, '89
Marshall, Edward S., '92
Molignano, Nicole M., '96 *CP*
Potter, Hillary A., '96 *ET*
Spano, Albert, '92

DIVIDE
Kleiner, Richard L., '81

ENGLEWOOD
Gidlow, Brooke E., '96

EVERGREEN
Goldbach, George A., '78

GRAND JUNCTION
Kroncher, Alex T., '94

LAFAYETTE
Wierl, Christopher, '95 *MG*

LAKEWOOD
Berry, BG Robert W., USA(Ret.),
  '81 *LW*
Caffrey, James D., '80

LITTLETON
Gudowitz, Peter M., '89

LONGMONT
Chaffee, David J., '75

PARKER
Joel, Kenneth W., '83

CONNECTICUT

BETHEL
Posavetz, Marilyn A., '74 *FV*
Shvartsman, Maria T., '98 *PL*

BRANFORD
Lee, Dr. Henry C., '72 *GE*

BRIDGEPORT
Carter, Michael R., '92
Donohue, Brian A., '82
Kadir, Maqsood U., PhD, '88 *ET*
Klein, Gilah F., '99
Mathews, Onica O., '99 *PL*
Mendez, Jorge A., '87 *ME*
Mendoza, Joel, '95
Schwartz, Edward H., '80
Scott, Lezlie A., '95

CROMWELL
Flaherty, Jennifer J., '99

DANBURY
Welsh, Katherine W., '80 *EA*

DERBY
Kurtyka, George F., '90

EAST HADDAM
Wasserman, David, '87 *SN*

ENFIELD
Lopez, Jose L., Sr., '82 *PL*

FAIRFIELD
Hansen, Glenn J., '80 *MG*
Mario, John R., '79

GLASTONBURY
Rivera, Wilfredo, '89

GREENWICH
Lagano, Christopher, '89 *LW*
Linstrom, Gregory M., '95

HAMDEN
Kinnebrew, Deborah, '77 *CO*

HARTFORD
Perry, Darlene L., '92

LEDYARD
Dames, Fatima C., '95

MANCHESTER
Hartzog, Adam C., '99

MILFORD
Bull, Rhudean, '98
Farrell, John R., '73

MONROE
Rich Appelberg, Lori, '85

MOUNT CARMEL
Dyer, Mark, '93 *ST*

NEW FAIRFIELD
Pastore, Michael J., '92

NEW HAVEN
Asamoah, Benoni A., '80
Bartlett-Josie, Mrs. Christine, '90
  FS

NEW MILFORD
Wodarski, Joseph P., Jr., '86 *PL*

NORTH BRANFORD
Brinkman, Mrs. Diane M., '94 *CO*
Dowtin, Ronda, '94 *ME*

NORWALK
Capria, Britt A., '96 *HM*
Mccauley, Chris, '93
Springett, Linda, '80

RIDGEFIELD
Maguire, John T., '79
Markert, Anthony, '91
Santangelo, Frank, '79
Tyrrell, Edward, '82 *MG*

RIVERSIDE
Gaffney, Kevin J., '81

ROCKY HILL
Colgan, George J., '79

SHELTON
Bliss, Donald, '96 *VL*

SHERMAN
Rowland, Eileen, *LS*

SIMSBURY
Gross, Solomon, '74

SOUTHBURY
Mc Geough, Sherry A.

SOUTHINGTON
Symolon, Kelly M., '99 *SW*
Zendzian, Craig A., '73

STAMFORD
Cornish, Michael J., '86
Dinwiddie, Harman B., '79
Doolittle, Timothy, '82
Duggan, Frank, '76
Espinoza, Jenny P., '96
Farrell, John J., '78
Howard, Timothy, '89
Newman, Paul R., '96 *PL*
Rafferty, Richard M., '89

STERLING
Parsons, Theodore, '73 *MG*

STRATFORD
Ekstrom, Charles A., '89 *LW*
Hazel, William B., III, '95 *SO*
Morabito, Douglas P., '95 *LW*
Sasso, Jill E., '99

TRUMBULL
Karayiannes, John G., '82
Spagnola, Carmen T., '96 *GN*

WALLINGFORD
Buntin, Mark M., '80 *BE*
Duran, Heidi L., '97

WATERBURY
Hirbour, Cynthia A., '99
Kennedy, Lori, '91

WATERFORD
Lovell, Brian I., '89

WEST HAVEN
Augustynowicz, Richard, '77

DELAWARE

BEAR
Seabrook, Reginald K., '96 *CO*

GREENVILLE
Gimlett, Brian F., '75
Gimlett, Linda, '77

HOCKESSIN
O'Rourke, William J., '67 *GN*

NEWARK
Jones-knight, Helen, '94
Mitchell, Jamell, '96 *LW*

REHOBOTH BEACH
Brandt, William J., '68 *PL*

WILMINGTON
Bailey, Patricia A., '81
Vaughan, Terry, '82

DISTRICT OF COLUMBIA

WASHINGTON
Cross, Michelle I., '91
Cunningham, Lawrence (Larry) H.,
  '97 *LW*
Darden, Lakisha M., '99 *GN*
Embden, David R., '95
Foley, Thomas B., ACP, '72 *GN*
Junco, Jorge N., '79
Kornblum, Allan, '69 *LW*
Melendez, Aida L., '78
Messam, Patrick, '80
Moody, Lee R., '75
Sawangnetr, Somchart, '83
Scott, Edward S., '89
Seremetis, Michael, '93 *GN*
Shattuck, John
Simon, Lennox J., '76
Williams, Hubert, '68

FLORIDA

ALTAMONTE SPRINGS
Adams, Julia V., '93

APOPKA
Espanol, Joseph L., '80

AVON PARK
Hunt, Marvin S., '75 *ET*

BAREFOOT BAY
Clinton, Brian J., '74 *PL*

BAYONET POINT
Provenza, Charles S.

BIG PINE KEY
Grimes, William P., '82
Passika, John I., '77

BOCA RATON
Anduze, Lisa M., '90
Benson, Irving, '69 *PL*
Gonzalez, Enrique, '91 *CP*
Lauda, Edward C., '80 *ME*
Mc Cutcheon, William
Murphy, Daniel J., '78
Oleksa, James S., '68 *MG*
Ravens, Carl, '68 *PL*
Strauss, Walter, '78
Trillo, Ismael, '78 *PL*
Ward, Joseph R., '75

BONITA SPRINGS
Mc Carthy, Donald F., '76

BOYNTON BEACH
Dure, Jacques P., '82
Feldman, David A., '79 *ET*
Katz, Richard, '88
Litvin, Lawrence H., '87
Rothenberg, Bruce A., '83 *GN*
Rowland, John, '76
Seedman, Albert A., '62
Taormina, Peter F., '78

BRADENTON
Logan, Mark R., '84

BRANDON
Gibbons, John W., '76
Minton, Kenneth W., '84 *PL*

CAPE CORAL
Brennan, Thomas F., '75
Kennedy, Angela, '87
Pinette, Holly, '79
Rodriguez, James, '76

CELEBRATION
Sobotor, Bonnie G., '78

CLEARWATER
Barros, Anna M., '78
Iglesias, Rosa E., '83
Passanesi, Dominick, '75

COCOA
Haughwout, Hugh O.
Taylor, Albert, '88

COCOA BEACH
O'Connell, James H., '77 *PL*
Sullivan, William T., '75

COCONUT CREEK
Lebowitz, Raymond, '79 *PL*
Myles, Miriam T., '78
Urvant, Marvin D.

CORAL GABLES
Truitt, John, '85

CORAL SPRINGS
Agosto, Barbara, '93
Brownstein, Brian J., '86
Centamore, Ronald J., '81
Dunne, Joseph A., '71
Kilmer, Joseph F., '80 *PL*
Knight, Thaddeus A., '85
Lewis, April A., '83
Mitchell, Corey, '94 *LW*
Raphael, Giselle L., '97 *EA*

CRYSTAL RIVER
Fegley, Venessa M., '99 *SO*

DAVIE
Chabrier, Lydia I., '79
Rothlein, Steve, '74 *PL*
Schwartz, Lawrence, '73
Zucker, Marc T., '99

DAYTONA BEACH
Almodovar, Steven A., '84
Greene, Marlene M., '74 *FA*
Greene, Matthew L., '75 *PL*
Wladich, Richard, '77

DELRAY BEACH
Frumin, Leonard C.
Sawyer, James W., '76
Schwartz, Louis, '81
Spiegel, Jack, '76 *PL*

SURFSIDE
Mulero, George, '76 *PL*

TALLAHASSEE
Liebert, Bennis

TAMPA
Hazel, Ms. Kim R., '91 *PL*
Molloy, Patrick J., '78

TARPON SPRINGS
Filipponi, Dominick, '77 *PL*
Foran, Philip J., '67

THE VILLAGES
Bamrick, Kenneth G., '69

TITUSVILLE
Van Arsdel-Chimka, Alison M., '99

VALRICO
Melendez-Josey, Maritza, '99

VENICE
Sexton, William A., '80
Tomashosky, Eugene, '95

WELLINGTON
Gordon, Vivian A., '85

WEST HOLLYWOOD
Cuomo, Anthony, '75

WESTON
Anaipakos, George P., '82
Bobb, Hamilton E., '82

WEST PALM BEACH
Burke, Thomas, '82
Concepcion, Magaly S., '97 *HM*
Cuomo, Vincent F., '77
Hunt, Nicole D., '91
Rodriguez, Charles, '76
Salamone, John A., '75

WINTER PARK
Gridley, Shannon C., '98 *LW*
Henderson, Joseph M., '73

WINTER SPRINGS
Cruz, Elbert, '86

GEORGIA

ACWORTH
Smith, William G., '80 *LW*
Stern, Martin, '76

ALPHARETTA
Mullin, John H., '97 *PL*

ATHENS
Smith, Sabrina, '97

ATLANTA
Abdul, Christine A., '95
Anisowicz, George, '71
Bacon, Cynthia, '89
Brown, Ronald E., '76
Crawford, Bobby G., '78
Leaderman, Ian C., '99
Macon, Olivia Y., '95 *ME*
Peele, Ondra T., '95 *BI*
Tucker, Bonita C., '76 *MG*
Williams, Deborah E., '97 *GN*

AUSTELL
Eason, Rufus J., '83

BRUNSWICK
Jones, Beverly V., '92
Jones, Seymour A., '76 *PL*

CLARKSTON
Shack, Robert C., '81 *PL*

COLUMBUS
Baptiste, Camille A., '98 *CT*

DECATUR
Hutchinson, J., '89
Hutchinson, Thomas, '91
Krishnanan, Annita, '95
Willson, Robert H., '83

DULUTH
Aitken, Alexandra S., '99 *IM*

Gheta, Barbara A., '91

FAYETTEVILLE
Maner, Benjamin, '89
Sorci, Frank X., '77 *SA*

GLYNCO
Turner, Al, '70

GRAYSON
Cortellino, Gary J., '78 *PL*

KENNESAW
Vicens, Carol, '83

LAWRENCEVILLE
Grogan, Lorna A., '84 *GE*

LILBURN
Davila, Jacinto, '87 *MG*

LITHONIA
Martin, Angela, '72

MARIETTA
Dicks, Garry S., '78 *MG*
Elliott, Sandra E., '81 *IN*
Jones, Roger, '77
Panchame, Allan G., '94 *PL*
Vistoso, Julio M., '91

NORCROSS
Maxim, Ana, '93 *CP*
Maxim, Ilie, '93 *CP*

RICHMOND HILL
Blige, Slater S., '74 *GE*

RIVERDALE
Lock, Clifford A., '77 *LW*
Normil, Chantal, '90

ROSWELL
Templier, Pierrette, '99 *LW*
Thomas, Richard G., '77

SAVANNAH
David, Harley, '78 *PL*

SMYRNA
Cox, Julie A., '95
Halley, Ms. Stacey A., '93 *LW*

STONE MOUNTAIN
Stewart, Paul L., '84

SUWANEE
Brumer, Steven N., '83 *CP*

TUNNEL HILL
Baker, Jimmie R., '77 *LW*

HAWAII

AIEA
Kendrick, John V., '80

HONOLULU
Bretton, Ronald, '76
Neary, Kathleen T., '70 *CP*
Tsuji, Marian E., '83 *GN*
Vericker, Robert W., '78

KAPAA
Angley, Richard J., '76

PEARL HARBOR
Plover, John

ILLINOIS

ARLINGTON HEIGHTS
Reilly, James P., '75 *PL*

BUFFALO GROVE
Catalano, Thomas, '73

CHAMPAIGN
Kelly, Joseph A., '72 *LW*

CHICAGO
Brown, Sherise N., '95
Gallagher, Michael S., '96
Grzanka, Emily J., '98 *ST*
Maghan, Jess, '86

Nowacoski, Michael, '93
O'Dell, Jill C., '97 *CP*
Ross Shapiro, Jennifer S., '89 *FV*
Shewnarain, Maya, '95 *ET*
Skrypkun, Meg E., '98

DARIEN
Nowicki, John F., '80

EDWARDSVILLE
Diamond, Darlene M., '96

GLEN ELLYN
Gilmartin, James J., '77

LA GRANGE
Fallon, Thomas W., '76

MUNDELEIN
Sherk, Edgar F., '78

NAPERVILLE
Nigro, Gregory, '86
Oleskowicz, John F., '83 *GN*

NILES
Zorn, Andrew G., '88

NORMAL
Ellsworth, Thomas, '76 *ET*

ROCK ISLAND
Garvin Huntley, Lynn M., PhD, '86 *ME*

URBANA
Chow, Lynette S., '95

WHEATON
Thompson, Madelyn, '81 *IN*

INDIANA

GREENCASTLE
Guyot, Dorothy, *EA*

INDIANAPOLIS
Kelly, Margo F., '75 *MG*
Kelly, Stephen P., '72
Peterson-Kimborough, Mrs. Claudette J., '79 *MG*

NOTRE DAME
Wallen, Richard J., '95

SCHERERVILLE
Sala, Eva M., '93

IOWA

CLIVE
Webb, Ruth H., '99 *ST*

INDIANOLA
Fusco, Filomena J., '84

KANSAS

MANHATTAN
Luftman, Lance J., '86 *PL*

KENTUCKY

HENDERSON
Rosario-Dixon, Maria D., '83 *HM*

LEXINGTON
Hinnrichs, Jeffery K., '75 *PL*

LOUISVILLE
Draffin, Beverly H., '78
Folsom, Norman, '84
Gordon, Abby R., '91
Mc Sharry, Talbot, '82
Wisotsky-Burt, Ms. Amy T., '77 *PN*

LOUISIANA

BATON ROUGE
Francesch, Fred R.

HARVEY
Weiler, Edward, '89 *MG*

MANDEVILLE
Ando, Scott M., '88

MARRERO
Martin, Betty J., '78

SHREVEPORT
Barton, Shari L., '93

MAINE

BIDDEFORD
Langevin, Guy, '91

TOPSFIELD
Bala, James W., '76 *PL*

WASHBURN
Maynard, Reuben W., '92

MARYLAND

ADELPHI
Gayle, Cathy A., '98 *CH*

ARNOLD
Taublib, Allan M., '75

BALTIMORE
Chittick, Diane A., '95
Douthit, Teresa M., '88 *LW*
Hall, James, '96
Hart, Keith, '96
Hibbler, Louise, '77
Keith, Ms. Stacy A., '98 *LW*
Makanjuola, Rafiu T., '96 *PL*
Parker, Kim, '88
Robertson, Erin N., '99 *PL*
Rubenstein, Hy D., '77 *LW*
Serrano, Francine, '99 *CO*

BETHESDA
Murphy, Patrick V., '60
Niblock, Susan B., '99 *GN*

BOWIE
Woodard, Richard, '75

BROOKEVILLE
Katz, Lawrence, '80 *LW*

CLINTON
Blackman, Michael J., '80 *PL*
Butcher, Margaret P., '83 *MK*

COCKEYSVILLE
Louvado, Ivo M., '98 *PL*

COLUMBIA
Cherry, Jack W.
Gross, Kenneth D., '78
Lopez, Frank, '95
Morris-english, Patricia J., '78

CROFTON
Peterson, Dennis J., '79

DISTRICT HEIGHTS
Wilson, Yolanda, '84

ELKTON
Ferrara-Machado, Vivian M., '88 *JU*

ELLICOTT CITY
Kennedy, Karen M., '90 *MG*
Smith, Teresa, '78

FINKSBURG
Bieling, Christopher, '79

GAITHERSBURG
Cousins, Thomas D., '80
Karira, Raj J., '93
Marquez, Miguel A., '80

GERMANTOWN
Garris, Tanya J., '89

GLENN DALE
Gallagher, Harold D., '76

GREENBELT
White, Robin L., '96

HURLOCK
Camper, Deborah F., Esq., '84 *LW*

HYATTSVILLE
Adade, Dr. Aaron Y., '79 *HT*
Earle, Lynda E., '86

LANDOVER
Griffins, Tml A., *HT*
Pringle, Hester V., '78 *PL*

LANDOVER HILLS
Sena, James P., '78

LARGO
Rice, Damon E., '99

LAUREL
LaMothe, Michael F., '82 *GN*
Marshall, Vanessa M., '89 *SW*

MITCHELLVILLE
Elmore, Allan F., '71

MONTGOMERY VILLAGE
Bonds, Charles W., '89

MOUNT AIRY
Smith, Ronald G., '95

NOTTINGHAM
Palmeri, LT Nicholas R., '79 *PL*

ODENTON
Ward, Florence V., '86 *TV*

OWINGS MILLS
Atkinson, Donald, '75 *MY*
Rodriguez, Isabella, '95

OXON HILL
Mimms, Yvette C., '82 *CN*

PARKVILLE
Vega, Ronald, '80 *PL*

ROCKVILLE
Agiri, Iyabo, '92
Roos, Denise, '71
Yim, Steven S., '94

SAVAGE
Tart, Angela L., '95

SEVERN
Razukas, Matthew D., '93

SILVER SPRING
Battaglia, Eugene F., '78
Jones, Gertrude E., '87
Mc Gary, Rogor A., '76
Neil, Larold C., '81 *GN*

TEMPLE HILLS
Gaston, Arnett W., '71 *ET*
Wallace, Stanley, '90

TOWSON
Behan, Cornelius (Neil) J., '68 *CN*

UPPER MARLBORO
Vicks, Leah D., '88
Wilson, Aaron, '95

WALDORF
Genovese, Alexander V., '95 *LW*

MASSACHUSETTS

ALFORD
Canning, Thomas P., '80

ANDOVER
Whitlock, Michael J., '83

ARLINGTON
Davis, Jeannette M., '81

BOSTON
Casale, Donald E., II, '96 *LW*

Swindell, Darryl A., '88

BRADFORD
DeGrenier, Terrence, '97
Keefe, Dennis C., '77

BROOKLINE
Green, Eliot, '86
Oren, Itzhak, '84

CARVER
Desurmeaux, Paul E., '77

CHARLESTOWN
Smith, Mrs. Lesley B., '95 *GN*

CHELMSFORD
Donelan, Michael J., '76

DANVERS
Ryan, Francis M., '70 *ET*

DOVER
Jensen, Glenn A., '77

DUDLEY
Brezny, Charles G., '85 *CP*

EAST HARWICH
Tyler, Edward J., '70

EAST LONGMEADOW
Britan, Judith S., '79

GRAFTON
Pijaca, John A., '89 *PL*

GREAT BARRINGTON
Cohen, Rachel L., '94 *WR*

MEDFORD
Eggleston, Lester R., *LW*

NEW BEDFORD
Boyle, William M., '84

NORWELL
Feldstein, Kenneth I., '79 *MF*

PITTSFIELD
Treible, Roy D., '89

PLAINVILLE
Williams, Lisa A., '96 *RD*

PLYMOUTH
Wilfrid, Joanne, '76

QUINCY
Wells, Marianne E., '99

READING
Luongo, Gregg A., '99

SOMERVILLE
Murphy, Joseph R.

SOUTH YARMOUTH
Flynn, Eugene W., '75

STOCKBRIDGE
Jennings, Sean J., '99

WAREHAM
Bergeron, John D., '72 *CN*

WATERTOWN
Geller, Patricia A., EdD, '80 *ME*

WESTFIELD
Hanrahan, Joseph J., '72

WESTWOOD
Loughlin, Michael, '72 *RE*
Smoke, Clinton H., '85

MICHIGAN

ANN ARBOR
Hayashi, Magen K., '99
Kamisar, Yale

BENTON HARBOR
Martin, Carol A.

BLOOMFIELD
Charla, Stephen P., '77

COTTRELLVILLE
Spreen, Johannes F., '66 *PL*

FERNDALE
Mcqueeney, Patrick, '85

FLUSHING
Ali, Mrs. Aneerah R., '93 *LW*

LANSING
Anderson, Rufus S.
Horace, Sara A., '89
Hurst, Veta P., '91

MARSHALL
O'dowd, Edward F., '77

MINNESOTA

BEMIDJI
Zamerinsky-lussier, Randy, '80

MINNEAPOLIS
Bernstein, Faye K., '94 *CO*
Maycock, Deborah D., '95

WOODBURY
Mccaffrey, Sean P., '94 *LW*

MISSISSIPPI

MC COMB
Varnell, Mary Allen B., '98

PASCAGOULA
Gadry, Albert J., '75

MISSOURI

FESTUS
Papaccio, Charles J., '80

JACKSON
Persinger, Ms. Sherry L., '95 *GN*

KNOB NOSTER
Zarilla, Anthony J., '79

SAINT LOUIS
Morasco, Benjamin J., '99 *ST*
Vazquez, Edward A., '84

MONTANA

RED LODGE
Pearson, Richard

NEBRASKA

LINCOLN
Ortega, Corinne N., '95

NEVADA

CARSON CITY
Mahoney, Patrick D., '76 *NU*

HENDERSON
Holland, Michael, '76

LAS VEGAS
Barton, Jeffrey A., '89
Bitner, Iwona E., '96
Brown, Robin, '88
Collins, Kevin P., '90
Flynn, Raymond J., '80 *PL*
Meadow, Howard S., '76
Olender, Ronald W., '75
Pearson, Joan E., '75 *PL*
Raiford, Louis G., '77 *PL*
Sakelhide, Keith A., '80 *LW*
Storch, Jerome E., '75 *ET*

NORTH LAS VEGAS
Smith, L. P., '80 *HT*

RENO
Powell, Alan C., '81 *PL*

NEW HAMPSHIRE

CONCORD
Sughrue, Daniel F., '75

EPSOM
Sheehy, John K., '72

HOOKSETT
Oliver, James H., '76

MONT VERNON
Vinton, Jeanette, '85 *LW*

PETERBOROUGH
Pucciarello, Thomas R., '78

NEW JERSEY

ABERDEEN
Cheung, Zulma G., '99
Nanna, Louis J., '99 *FV*

ABSECON
Knorr, Jill L., '98 *LW*

ADELPHIA
Paglino, Joseph R., '97 *GN*

ALLENDALE
Robotti, Carlo, '93

ANDOVER
Danielson, Eskil S., '75 *PL*
Hall, David E., '72

ANNANDALE
Rivers, John J., '82 *CP*

ASBURY PARK
Nuccio, Anthony J., '89

ATLANTIC CITY
Wenthe, Leah M., '93

AVENEL
Juliano, Maria A., '85

AVON BY THE SEA
Leather, Joseph J., '77

BARNEGAT
Magliaro, Joseph L., '78

BASKING RIDGE
Cea, Ellen, '96
Sullivan, James F., '80

BAYONNE
Cline, James, '73
Dillon, Michael P., '95
Gulinello, Joseph J., '76
Hopkins, Kevin M., '87
Rusznak, Richard C., '90
Smith, John W.
Yurchak, Karyn, '94

BAYVILLE
Velez, Alex, '84

BEACH HAVEN
Girfin, Scott

BEACHWOOD
Kowalewski, Steven A., '91
Pascalicchio, James, '71

BELFORD
Brady, Matthew, '93

BELLE MEAD
Ryan, Edward J., '73

BELLEVILLE
Bruzzichesi, William, '91 *PL*
De Vivo, Francis (Frank) W., '80 *LW*
Figueroa, Lisset, '93
Hanna, Richard, '96 *LW*
Lee, Franklin, '86 *JU*
Wells, Rory J., '92

BELMAR
Brennan, Joseph R., '83

BERGENFIELD
Allen, Jacinta, '95
Arzola, Elizabeth, '89
Collazo-soto, Ms. Desiree, '93
Commike, Eileen A., '76 *SW*
Flanagan, Colleen M., '99 *LW*
Hudyma, Amie, '85
Mc Kay, John J., '75
Sahlberg, Fred J., '78
Sylver, Peter T., '94
Ziegler, Jay E., '86

BLAIRSTOWN
Neggia, Thomas E., '97 *GN*

BLOOMFIELD
Aiello, Michael, '86
Apolinario, Marcia, '95
Brown, James M., '64
Henderson, Audrey, '83
Schwartz, Thomas P., '99 *PH*

BLOOMINGDALE
Ryniak, William A., '89 *LW*

BOGOTA
Forsthoff, SGT Roger A., '87 *PL*
Mc Elroy, Patrick J., '81
O'neill, Mark L., '78

BOONTON
Degroot, Daniel R., '85 *PL*

BORDENTOWN
Palmer, Nicole M., '99
Stelmach, Joanne, '99

BRANCHBURG
Savage, Mark J., '79

BRICK
Aldoy, Anna M., '98 *ME*
Aloia, Veanna M., '99
Clancy, William C., '66 *ET*
Dellorto, Melissa A., '98
Kenny, Michael J., '71
Mccarthy, Justin M., '92
Stefanick, Richard A., '84
Vineis, Steven S.
Wicker, Jason A., '95 *CP*

BRIDGEWATER
Chambers, Hewitt L., Jr., '81 *GN*
Dahl, Dena A., '92 *LW*

BRIELLE
Callas, George S., '69

BRIGANTINE
Griffin, Scott
Kenney, Wilson C., '70 *PL*

BUDD LAKE
DeMagistris, Scott J., '92 *LW*
Healy, Dorothy
Nesensohn, Donald O., '76
Varela, Anthony F., '98
Wargo, Catherine M., '99

BURLINGTON TOWNSHIP
Banach, Paul F., '86

BUTLER
Costabile, Michael J., '73

CALDWELL
Corcoran, Michael C., '96 *PL*
Reed, Rachel A., '99

CAPE MAY
Low, Timothy J., '81

CARLSTADT
Lavagna, Peter J., '82

CARTERET
Caldararo, John V., '76
Demby, Janice, '89
Medwick, Toni A., '74

CEDAR GROVE
Clark, Joseph F., '75
Fearon, William G., '92 *LW*

Nolan, John E., '82
Sconzo, Rachel L., '99 *MG*

CEDAR KNOLLS
Lupi, Melissa A., '99
Rocco, Kenneth B., '98 *GN*

CHATHAM
Trent, Rachel S., '99

CHERRY HILL
Beichner, Karen R., '95
Mitchelson, Thomas P., '78
O'dowd, John W., '79
Rumell, William N., '99 *CO*
Stewart, John E., Esq., '80 *LW*

CHESTER
Stracker, Cassandra L., '99 *GN*

CLARK
Fuentes, Christopher, '96
Halloran, Frank H., '80
Leglec, Mark, '97
Mannix, William R., '87
Sluka, Keith, '90

CLAYTON
Haynes, Kenneth, '83

CLIFFSIDE PARK
Alcee, Natalie (Giggles) S., '97 *LW*
Borrero, Kenneth, '98 *FV*
Prisco, John J., '87
Quijije, Kathy M., '99
Royer, Gary, '86
Santiago, George L., '94
Segal, Susanne, '83

CLIFTON
Adamiak, Alan B., '83 *BI*
Amengual, Margie, '83 *SW*
Araneo, Suzanne, '83
Boylan, Kathleen, '96 *HM*
Fernandez, Yvette, '99
Kredatus, Edward J.
Lorimer, Philip, CPM, '88 *SN*
Schulze, Raymond, '76
Solesky, Edward J., '82
Suarez-Serafin, J., '94
Tencza, Adam S., '78

CLINTON
Poynter, Charles D., '84
Snyder, Kimberly S., '93 *MG*

CLOSTER
Danese, Elizabeth Anne, '74 *PL*
Haberfeld, Maria M., '90

COLONIA
Bailey, Steven D., '97
Peterson, James J., '81
Rossi-rosen, Renee M., '96
Schneider, James T., '79 *LW*
Williams, Elizabeth, '93

CONVENT STATION
Conti, Richard P., '97 *ET*
Dangler, Donald J., '85
Lawlor, Jason A., '93
Rochford, Edward V., '72 *PL*

CRANBURY
Kantrowitz, Steven H., '80

CRANFORD
Mathews, Frank J., '77 *ME*
Ochs, Jeffrey J., '99 *GN*
Paparozzi, Sandra M., '82
Savatteri, Stephine, '99 *CO*
Sorge, Glenn W., '87

CRESSKILL
Bresnan, Eilish B., '93 *JU*
Hrebenko, Aneta, '97 *GN*
Russo, Dello A., '91

DAYTON
Ulianko, John A., '77

DEMAREST
Weiss, Jason H., '96

DENVILLE
D'angelo, Edward, '87

Rabson, Mark J., '77 *MG*

DOVER
Amaral, Patrick N., '98

DUMONT
Greene, Jiton T., '99 *LW*
Roche, Grace V., '84
Schiralli, Anthony M., '88
Wilson, Robert A., '95

DUNELLEN
Jones, Margaret D., '97 *MK*
Wojtach, Susan E., '99 *AM*

EAST BRUNSWICK
Monahan, Thomas M., '85 *LW*
Moore, Penelope A., '87 *SN*
Pasichow, Jerome N., '77
Ur, Joseph, '86 *PL*

EAST HANOVER
Fischer, Lauren A., '92
Gaughan, Edward T., '78

EAST NEWARK
Scaglione, Dominic J., '76

EAST ORANGE
Robinson, John A., '77 *LW*
Williams, Fernard M., '76
Wyatt, Paul A., '85

EAST RUTHERFORD
Brown-Cathey, Ms. Gertrude, '84 *NU*
Parrish, John F., '76
Pickett, John J., '98 *ME*

EAST WINDSOR
Horne, Peter, '87 *ET*

EATONTOWN
Fuko, Curtis, '97

EDGEWATER
Edwards, Katrina, '97 *MG*

EDISON
Akinsiku, Frederick, '85
Collins, Elliot, '91 *CN*
Curry, Heather M., '95
Dineen, William F., '94
Fenkel, Robert I., '82 *LW*
Forker, Edward C., '80
Frasco, Elizabeth G., '97
Harris, Rhonda L.
Kanowsky, Tina M., '95
Kapitan, Gary A., '84
Karras, Andrea I., '94
Kennely, Fritz S., '97 *PL*
Mcgotty, Thomas J., '85
Mc Parland, Thomas A., '75
Mraz, Mrs. Leanne A., '99 *LW*
Patania, John, '95
Rhonda, Harris L., '98
Zavistoski, Robert, '93 *LW*

EGG HARBOR TOWNSHIP
Lurry, Mary L., '85
Shapiro, Eric M., '84 *CC*

ELIZABETH
Iyoha, Friday E., '80
Juzefyk, Susan M., '83
La Morte, David, '98
Maldonado, Annette, '93
Meagher, Dr. Patrick B., '87 *TC*
Mule, Concetta M., '99

ELMWOOD PARK
Cheski, Philip M., '93 *GE*
Fulco, Anthony G., '96
Galasso, Daniel T., 2000 *LW*
Jimenez, Robert, '99 *CT*
Mazerolle, Christian, '98 *GN*
McGowan, Sean M., '96 *MG*
Rowe, Thomas P., '91
Somerstein, Ilyse R., '95
Van Loon, Gary, '83

EMERSON
Canavan, Andrew J., '80
Depalma, Ms. Danielle A., '96

Klucharits, John C., '97

ENGLEWOOD
Amaro, Ed, '96 *MG*
Clarke, Sheena D., '81
Harper, Christa J., '95
Johnson, Granville, '85 *PL*
Salim, John R., '84
Scudder, Ivy, '93
Stephens, Gary, '97
Welsh, Mrs. Venesia A., '94 *IN*

ENGLISHTOWN
Coulianidis, Michael
Jacobson, Benjamin, '76
Ricciuto, Michael, '77
Szarawarski, Michael, '79 *CC*

FAIR HAVEN
Koren, John, '70

FAIR LAWN
Bzik, Susan M., '97
Cameron, Peter F., '76
Cooper, Iris A., '80
Crugnola, Charles K., '91
Davies, Christopher J., '95
Kassai, Michael D., '93 *PL*
Kronenfeld, Jeffrey, '86
Landis, James L., '75
Suponitskiy, Serge, '97 *EN*
Talty, Richard B., '75
Vartabedian, Darryl, '95 *MG*

FAIRVIEW
Rancic, Valentino, '95

FANWOOD
Foley, Stephen P., '83
Foley, Ms. Susan, '83
Quraishi, Zahid N., '97 *LW*

FLANDERS
Dever, John A., '84 *PL*

FLEMINGTON
Melsky, SGT Ryan E., '99 *PL*
O'Grady, Dermot, '81 *GN*

FLORHAM PARK
O'connor, Andrew J., '86

FORDS
Byrnes, Ms. Kirsten M., '99 *SW*
Daly, William, '85 *MG*

FORKED RIVER
Discenza, Regina, '85 *CH*

FORT LEE
Gibbons, Adam C., '98 *CT*
Gross, Arthur, '87
Hone, Jacqueline, '96
Johnson, Ms. Nykelle S., '94 *BE*
Jourdan, Marine, '97 *BE*
No, Steve, '98 *PL*
Paik, Min K., '96
Weinberg, Jeffrey, '87

FRANKLIN PARK
Kinahan, Donna M., '95

FREEHOLD
Cappiello, James T., '90
Cook, Mrs. Leanne T., '99 *CO*
Desantis, Francesco, '76 *AC*
Henry, James W., '78
Jackson, Hazel L., '86 *LW*
Kazymirczuk, Tina G., '99 *LW*
Ng, Anthony C., '84 *GN*
Paylago, Stanley U., '91
Reibel, Denise L., '99
Vitolo, William (Billy) R., '87 *PL*

GARFIELD
Nappi, Lori A., '81 *SA*
Vanderburgh, Thomas, '87

GILLETTE
Ramirez, Richard, '76

GLEN GARDNER
Raichle, Carl J., '76 *SN*

GLEN ROCK
Cruz, Jamie, '97

Devlin, John F., '75
Dour, Daniel F., '79
Goodwin, Patrick J., '78 *CC*
McInerney, Robert (Bob) X., CPP, '77 *CN*

GREENDELL
Guzzo, Scott R., '98 *SA*

HACKENSACK
Bunch, Robert L., '74
Burgess, Mrs. Marjorie L., '71 *PL*
Fontana, John P., '81
Hayes, Dorsey L., '79
Love, Jason C., '93 *GN*
Savoia, Michael F., '82

HACKETTSTOWN
Brennan, James J., '68
Christensen, Jarl H., '75 *PL*
Wojtach, Christophe J., '97 *PL*

HALEDON
Brady, Sandra A., '96
Triolo, Bobbi A., '95

HAMILTON
Buchalter, Steven, '75 *GN*

HAMILTON SQUARE
Bartlett, Thomas W., '76 *JU*

HARRINGTON PARK
Martin, Robert A., '75 *LW*

HASBROUCK HEIGHTS
Borzotta, David R., '93
Gyenes, Albert R., Jr., '94 *PL*
Paige, John J., '77

HAWORTH
Nikac, Maria, '94
Ulrich, Michael, '92

HAWTHORNE
Majeski, William J., '76 *BE*
Vodde, Robert F., '81

HAZLET
Pladl, John R., '80

HEWITT
Ryan, Thomas P., '77 *PL*

HIGHLAND PARK
Callahan, William J., '95
Latham, John F., '85
Pollack, Andrew B., '95 *ET*

HIGHTSTOWN
Gutkin, Jonathan M., '95

HILLSDALE
Grandstaff, Glenn, '84
Kramer, David A., '81

HILLSIDE
Patterson, Erika P., '95 *LW*

HOBOKEN
Dirkin, Walter J., Esq., '95 *LW*
Kavanaugh, Shannon B., '99
Roche, Edward J., '79 *ME*

HO-HO-KUS
Baxter, George T., '79

HOLMDEL
Waldron, John F., '98 *PL*

HOPATCONG
Clowes, Eric J., '98
Kraus, David T., '98 *PL*
Scott, Cleve M., '85

HOWELL
Canady, Donna A., '96 *BI*
Keelan, James G., '73
Rizzo, Kevin, '95

IRVINGTON
Butler, Joanne L., '84

ISELIN
Barajas, Robert J., '81 *CN*

JACKSON
Bridgewater, Joel A., '74
Hercules, Keith F., '79 *EA*

Janzekovich, Robert, '88
Kennedy, Michael J., '97
Nelson, Claudette A., '96 *MG*
Williams, Albert D., '77 *SA*
Yanis, Ricardo A., '99 *PL*

JERSEY CITY
Anton, Robert W., '90
Baliko, Jaclyn M., '97
Barry, Karl S., '81
Bobb, Ms. Irma Diane, Esq., '94 *LW*
Campbell, Steven T., '78
Carrion, Axel, '96
Christine, Marc T., '96 *GD*
Decresce, Christopher, '96
Edwards, Carla, '91
Emilian, Ivan, '97
Erazo, Elliot, '89
Estrada, Mario B., '94 *GN*
Ferraioli, Steven J., '87 *PL*
Fitzgerald, Patrick J., '79
Geraghty, John F.
Hayes, Clarence E., '88
Heer, Edward
Jones, Cheryl M., '93
Lamperti, Edward P., '92
Lee, David, '83
Martino, Vincent P.
McGill, Steven J., '93
Messick, Edna, '84
Mornel, Theodore B., '97 *EM*
Neblett-ford, Jillian A., '85
Nichols, Ferdinanda W., '88
Reddington, Francis, '82
Shearin, John D., '95
Spann, Cassaundra, '92 *GN*
Stancil, Barbara A., '86
Stewart, Vivienne, '85
Tuason, Aleli P., '98
Wafula, Bramwell, '86
Wilson, Fertima, '97

KEANSBURG
Santiago, Marc A., '94 *MG*

KEARNY
Kirst, Kevin, '88
McDonald, Jeannette, '92
Warnquist, David G., '76

KENDALL PARK
Coyle, James G., '79
Dascoli, Francis, '76 *PL*

KENILWORTH
Pugliese, Ferdinando, '91

KEYPORT
Conroy, Sharon A., '94
Fleming, William, '75 *PL*
Haggorty, James J., '80

KINNELON
Mc Ginnis, Robert D., '76

LAKE HIAWATHA
Breault, Suzanne A., '99
Caggiano, Andrew C., '96
Cutler, Robin A., '82
Delrusso, Christopher, '79

LAKE HOPATCONG
Hassa, Vincent J., '75
Kupfer, James R., '82
Stanton, Mary, '85

LAKEHURST
Acosta, Pilar M., '99 *JU*
Fauci, Richard A., '71 *PL*

LAKEWOOD
Granville, Alfonso M., '80
Marchesano, Neil, '81
Murray, Robert P., '77 *PL*
O'Shea, Timothy J., '76
Rivera, Yvonne, '95 *GN*
Wendruff, Lorrie

LAMBERTVILLE
Brown, Valerie L., '77 *LW*

LANOKA HARBOR
Gresh, Ms. Marilyn B., '97
Mc Gowan, Kenneth T., '78

LAURENCE HARBOR
Brett, Veronica E., '84 *CO*

LAWRENCE
Chin, George W., '79

LAWRENCEVILLE
Burrell, William D., '76 *PL*

LEBANON
Doherty, James P., '75
Sierp, Robert W., '81

LEONIA
Alvarez, Jeannette M., '96
Cafarelli, Michael L., '88
Fontane, Rudolph

LINCROFT
Katz, Marvin A., '74 *CN*
Louden, Dr. Robert J., '77 *EA*

LINDEN
Buckley, Anna M., '85
Clark, Jeffrey W., '89
Colucci-Turbett, Joann, '75 *GN*
Daniel, William A., '78
Davis, Richard A., '82
Eichhorn, Barbara L., '79
Flynn, John, '90
Marech, Craig A., '99 *GN*
Marti, Lauren B., '82
Munoz, Antonio, '89
Obuchowski, Bart M., '99 *PL*
Patti, Pasquale J., '98 *GN*
Turbett, William F., '77

LITTLE EGG HARBOR TOWNSHIP
Sinnott, Thomas G., '96 *PL*

LITTLE FERRY
Henshaw, George V., '83
Newman, Lisa N., '85 *JU*

LITTLE SILVER
Davis, Andrew R., '68
Hogan, Robert A., '71 *CN*
Masella, Richard P., '82

LIVINGSTON
Aimone, Paul J., '83 *LW*
Danckwerth, Edward T., '75
Kunkis, Robert, '77 *GN*
Mc Intyre, John F., '75
McSpirit, Ms. Theadora P., '93 *GN*
Mooney, Richard P., '80
Myung, Ji-Man, '98

LODI
Assenheimer, Carl F., '73
Gomez, Victor R., '93 *CO*
King, Jerome A., '98
Maher, Anne M., '95 *SW*
Moschetto, Andrew J., '78

LONG BRANCH
Anglin, Brian, '86
Gorman, Albert J., '84

LONG VALLEY
Murray, John J.
Salvatore, Lawrence F., '79 *CP*

LYNDHURST
Aramino, Sandra L., '83
Feinholtz, Leslie, '95
Giangeruso, Carmine, CFPS, '97 *PL*
Hatfield, Steven J., '96 *PB*
Killeen, Michael K., '92
Kupper, Donald F., '76 *PL*
Notte, Daniel A., '83

MADISON
Cusimano, Stephanie A., '99
Kay, Paul, '94
Meeks, John A., '72

MAHWAH
Becchina, Victoria A., '97

Coviello, Ms. Karlee M., '99
Frazer, John H., '94
Jimenez, Ms. Julie A., '99 *SW*
Kozakiewicz, Jennifer L., '95
Natale, Aileen F., '93 *RL*
Robinson, Dawn M., '99
Rosen, Penny, '93

MANAHAWKIN
Courtney, William D., '80
Mayushan, Avram M., '92
Wonnum-gaines, Lora, '82

MANALAPAN
Barry, Edward P., '80
Bartkovich, Michelle
Brogan, Michael P., '80 *PL*
Burruano, Vivian S., '81
Delano, Donald F., '76 *PL*
Gordon, Benjamin A., '95
Hoffman, Neil, '79 *AC*

MANASQUAN
Nicholson, Walter A., '75 *PL*
Prusak, Patricia R., '78 *PL*

MANVILLE
Di Pane, Jodi E., '98 *CN*

MAPLE SHADE
Caldwell, Lynnette, '97 *LW*
James, Lisa, '96

MAPLEWOOD
Del, Preore S., '79
Del Preore, Salvatore, '79 *LW*
Fitzmaurice, M., '92
Gestring, Brian J., '94
Gestring, Craig R., '96
Holland, Linda J., '88
Mc Kissic, Aaron, '72
Miller, Amy B., '89
Tabor, Violet, '99
Williams, David, '86 *LW*
Wulach, James

MARLBORO
Cohen, David L., '84 *IN*
Facchini, Paschal, '96 *MG*
Lustig, Marsha L., '79
Pedone, Riccardo, '77

MARLTON
Torres, Anibal, '81
Velarides, Anastasios, '89

MATAWAN
Duesterdick, Kurt A., '82 *PL*
Dyminski, Edward A., '99
Gambino, Thomas, '96
Lee, Chak Y., '84
Manibo, Joel R., '94
Vento, Frank J., '81

MAYWOOD
Culvert, Romano, '76
Mancuso, John J., '92
Reynolds, Patrick, '85 *LW*
Romani, C., '75

METUCHEN
Houghton, Richard M., '84

MIDDLESEX
First, Jeffrey D., '90 *ME*

MIDDLETOWN
Baker, Harold C., '73 *EN*
Dressler, Marcella, '91
Ferrigno, Mario, '86
Mc Nicholas, Eveann V., '70
O'connor, Thomas P., '76

MIDLAND PARK
Macchiaroli, Joseph, '84
Marrone, Gerald H., '82 *GE*

MILFORD
Crabb, Eric C., '96

MILLBURN
Conway, Michael A., '81

MILLINGTON
Laffey, Christopher, '93

293

Schmidt, Margaret J., '97

SEWAREN
Sciandra, Joseph R., '80 *ME*

SEWELL
Anderson, Robert J., '84 *GN*

SHORT HILLS
Bartels, Ms. Elizabeth C., '98 *SO*
Bocian, Stephen J., '77

SICKLERVILLE
Ives, Nicole J., '98

SKILLMAN
Holtzman-Waranis, Cynthia R., '93 *CO*

SMITHVILLE
Zarek, Edward T., '84 *GN*

SOMERSET
Baicher, Robin M., '83 *SA*
Carroll, James W., '85
Riddick, Robert R., '85
Williams, Frank C., '70

SOMERVILLE
Dundon, Reilly J., '89
Grasso, Joseph

SOUTH AMBOY
English, Christopher, '90
Hastings, Kevin M., '83
Pieklo, Eric J., '96
Stern, Barry P., '89 *PL*

SOUTH HACKENSACK
Suarez-Figueroa, Judith, '96

SOUTH ORANGE
Coppock, SGT Durwin L., '99 *PL*
Jules, Wisner, '92 *ET*
Sacks, Barbara K., '70
Silver, Sibyl J.

SOUTH PLAINFIELD
Mehaffey, Paul R., '78

SPARTA
Carlson, Richard D., Jr., '75 *PL*
Dehlinger, Alfred, '83

SPOTSWOOD
Melendez, Eugenio, '79 *LW*
Ray, Vern, '93 *PL*
Ward, Rodney C., '80 *LW*

SPRINGFIELD
Colon, Hector E., '95 *CP*
Klar, Marc E., '75

SPRING LAKE
Kelly, William M., '75 *GN*

STANTON
Convery, James H., '76

STOCKHOLM
Fallon, Ms. Bessie A., '95 *GN*

STONE HARBOR
Kemly, Ronald H., '76

SUCCASUNNA
Campolo, Jennifer, '96 *GE*
Hayowyk, John A., '98
Rose, Richard A., '85 *PL*
Sclafani, Joseph C., '84
Smyth, Kerry M., '85

SUSSEX
Feeney, Mary D., '76

SWEDESBORO
Booker, Eric G., '84

TEANECK
Acevedo, Louis, '81
Alvarado, Darlene, '93
Banks, Demorris J., '79
Bermann, Julia, '87
Brancato, Gregory R., '87
Hodges, Warren A., '79
Jackson, Vicki D., '79
Joyner, Harry, '81
Kanrich, Susan, '88
Kraemer, Richard E., '80

Mansky, Orin, '79
Mc Mnmon, Dennis, '76
Molina, Ariadne M., '99 *MK*
Muniz, Mrs. Belinda, '95
O'brien, Patricia A., '75
Robinson, Ms. Lillian W., '77 *LW*
Spain, Pauline, '78 *ET*
Whited, Daniel F., '78

TINTON FALLS
Crawford, Randy B., '97 *PL*

TITUSVILLE
Mc, Corkle D., '84

TOMS RIVER
Barnes, Bray, '80
Budenas, John M., '91 *GN*
Durham, Elaine C., '78
Forte, Louis (Lou), '82
Frank, Rudolph A., '82 *GN*
Furey, John, '86 *ME*
Gettis, Deanne R., '97 *CO*
Goncalves, Alvaro, '90
Grillo, Richard S., '85
Gyss, Henry F., '67
Jacob, George N., '80
Kicki, Michael E., '82
Lembo, Stephen J., '76
Mastronardy, Michael, '79
Muniz, Eric R., '82
Roske, Daniel, '95

TOTOWA
Kearns, Margherita, '90
Ruocco, Dante, '96

TRENTON
Beveridge, Alvin J., '78 *GN*
Beyer, Howard L., '79
Cuyler, Julius T., '81
Dempsey, Dennis J., '79
Holloway, Harold T., '76
Iloka, Samuel C., '89
Keane, Joseph P., '99
Mollica, Joseph C., '80
Presser, Allen, '75
Pulgar, Paula A., '95 *SW*
Troyansky, Eugene, '96
Tucker, Thomas A., '82

UNION
Conway, Maryelyn, '97
Magliacano, Anthony, '96
Reale, Ronald G., '85 *LW*
Spellman, Kenneth M., '87
Stanek, Thomas, '90

UNION CITY
Audiffred, Jesus, '93 *PL*
Irizarry, Christopher F., '98 *LW*
Marchese, Maria N., '98 *ST*
Roman, Lisa, '97
Stockman, Lavelle, '94

UPPER SADDLE RIVER
Henderson, Robert A., '78

VAUXHALL
Cole, Leslie, CPP, '81 *CN*
Robinson, Walter A., '83 *PL*

VERONA
Palladino, James M., '75

VOORHEES
Baruch, Marcia L., '80
Jordan, Ms. Janet E., '74 *PL*

WALDWICK
Brady, Richard J., Esq., '82 *LW*
Corbett, Glenn P., '82
Leonard, Sean R., '89
Ratcliffe, Robert G., '78
Wekarski, Stanley P., '78

WALLINGTON
Fenty, Jill M., '98 *AA*
Garcia, Martha M., '96 *CN*
Kisala, Stanley M., '91 *PL*
Lipari, Donna M., '87
Oconnell, Edward T., '95

WARREN
Mignano, Michael J., '94 *BI*

WASHINGTON PARK
Middleton, La-tonia B., '96 *CT*

WASHINGTON TOWNSHIP
Caffrey, Ronald, '85
Ford, Matthew C., '78

WAYNE
Franco, Robert J., '95
Lazzaro, Paul J., '95 *GN*
Mendel, Alan, '76
Perez, Madeline, '86
Pignatello, Robert
Royce, Kevin J., '95
Vecchi, Louis, '76

WEEHAWKEN
Irizarry, Gisela, '97 *BI*
Lindgren, George A., '89

WEST CALDWELL
Rello, John J., '98 *LW*

WESTFIELD
Borchers, James E., '85
Castellano, John, '80 *PL*
Disarno, James J., '97
Kelly, David J., '97 *PL*
Koski, Richard A., '82
Mc Gorty, Donald J., '85
Orzillo, Kelly S., '99 *LW*
Pisane, Randolph (Randy), '72
Richardson, Randall, '76
Thorpe, Leslie P., '80

WEST MILFORD
Crouthamel, David E., '98 *PL*
Etnbinder, Leonard
Klein, Robert E., '89 *PL*
Nisi, Anthony J., '97 *PL*
Rampola, Joseph J., '94 *PL*
Rampola, Mrs. Pamela A., '94 *SW*

WEST NEW YORK
Bradley, Kevin, '95
Colon, Reinaldo, '77
Gisors, Roselyne, '87
Jamyang, Dekyi T., '99
Kluft, Elizabeth R., '91
Salgado, Nelida, '97

WEST ORANGE
Baumgart, Edward W., '80
Belgrave, Carl C., '83 *LW*
Green, Douglas, '96
Hadley-Bailey, Cynthia, '75
Hymowitz, Alan J., '84
Lampf, Jesse D., '99 *PL*
O'connor, Julie A., '78
Ronzo, Louis, '77
Ward, Ms. Linda M., '95 *CP*

WEST PATERSON
Bubbico, Francesco D., '97

WEST WINDSOR
McMahon, Michael J., '96 *PL*

WESTWOOD
Ciringione, Frank J., '88 *PL*
Ng, Grace, '77
Stella, John F., '76
Trause, Victoria, '97 *CO*

WHARTON
Colavita, Maria A., '79
Liscinsky, James K., '95

WHIPPANY
Alswang, Scott B., '80 *GN*
Hammond, Gregory C., '84
Hermans, Peter L., '98 *PL*
Petreski, Toni, '96 *PL*

WHITEHOUSE STATION
Boettcher, Donna M., '98

WHITING
Mahoney, Robert E., '82 *PL*

WILDWOOD
Beers, Albert S., '89 *MG*

WILLINGBORO
Beard, Darryl, '92
Campbell, Isaac J., '82
Carruthers, Bevan, '84
Jackson, Edward, '85 *PL*

WINFIELD
Braithwaite, Deborah, '85

WOODBRIDGE
Grogan, Dennis, '92 *AC*
Kamara, Samuel M., '91 *LW*
O'neill, Eugene F., '77

WOODCLIFF LAKE
Griffith, Todd A., '85

WOOD-RIDGE
Stuis, Charles F., '80

WYCKOFF
Cohen, Samuel, '75 *SW*
Higgins, Patrick (Pat) J., '92 *PL*

NEW MEXICO

ABIQUIU
Sellers, Terence C., '86

ALBUQUERQUE
Burgos, Brenda, '90
King, Emma C., '81
Strickland, Justin C., '78

RIO RANCHO
Sci, Paul R., '75

SANTA FE
Quinones, Hector M., '91 *MY*

NEW YORK

ACRA
Faith, Francis L., '80 *PL*

ALBANY
Brown, Deborah L., '95 *SW*
Cole, Karen E., '80 *AM*
Dunn, Thomas J., '88
Evans, April R., '79 *GN*
Gordon, Blanche M., '95
Greene, Jeanique, '93 *LW*
Nasser, Sharifa M., '99
Stillwell, Nisha R., '99
Stone, Marianne E., '77

ALBERTSON
Braun, Eileen E., '89 *LW*
Daley, Thomas J., '85 *PL*
Parrino, Irene R., '89
Parrino, Joseph J., '88
Steinmann, Robert W., '91

ALTAMONT
Tosado, Mariveila, '88 *ST*

AMAWALK
Mc Cabe, Robert K., '78

AMITY HARBOR
Mcgrath, Patrick M., '99
Zachary, William E., '76

AMITYVILLE
Bagley, Reginald N., '76
Bonacum, William T., '75
Camilleri, Michele, '94 *FV*
Chavies, Phyllis A., '93
Corbett, Ms. Heather A., '95 *ET*
Fairley, Norman S., '95
Johnson, Edward J., '85 *LW*
Jones, Bobby R., '89
Kissane, Thomas P., '75
Lawson, Mrs. Kim, '92 *LW*
Lipp, James O., '99
Nash, Joseph F., '73 *BE*
Powell, Walter, '95 *GN*

295

AMSTERDAM
Swierzowski, Christi, '92

ANNANDALE-ON-HUDSON
Stroup, Timothy

ANSONIA
Organ, Mrs. Miriam, '95 ET

ARDSLEY
Connick, Kathleen, '91
Galbreath, Lauren M., '95
Longobardi, Alfred C., '77 EA

ARMONK
Cardillo, Joseph L., '74 BE
Tallent, Thomas P., '89

ARVERNE
Anderson, Esther G., '85
Burnette, Lebro C., '86
Cheeks, Robert, '95 AM
Mitchell, Salahadine (Sal), '98 PL
Osbourne, Cherryann, '97
Thomas, Edmund, '86

ASTORIA
Adams, Christopher, '96 LW
Aguilera, Emily, '91
Akrivos, Jimmy, '95
Andrade, Karol J., '97
Antoniou, Antonios, '99
Avramidis, Georgios, '84
Azzolini, John, '90
Berdan, Warren C., '97
Bogovic, Anthony P., '79 FV
Borrelli, Kristin K., '98
Boyce, Robert, '98
Brucculeri, Giovanna R., '98
Bullaro, Marc J., '80
Byrnes, James E., '78
Calin, Ovidiu M., '99
Carter, Dawn E., '85
Celella, Carolyn C., '80
Cerasoli, Justine M., '92
Chon, Haksoo, '96
Clark, Christopher, '96
Colon, Carlos A., '97
Cruz, Margarita, '79
D'Ambrosio, Jaime, '83
Daouaou, Abdelilah, '97
Digirolomo, Nicholas, '95
Downes, Thomas A., '70
Durando, Doanld M., '76
Dzairi, Ali, '97
Eleftheriou, Eleftherios A., '99 ST
Eventeris, Steve, '96
Fernandez, Mercedes, '89
Finkelstein, Eric L., '87 PL
Fitzpatrick, Paul J., '94 PL
Fleming-white, Merie, '96
Fountoulakis, Georgios, '99 PL
Frisik, David J., '82
Galaher, Lilia, '97 AM
Garcia, Marilyn, '99
George, Ms. Camille A., '99 LW
Grippi, Ada, '91
Guerrero, Daniel G., '89
Hadjidemetriou, George, '93 GN
Hadzi, Brahimovic S., '97
Haralambous, Lambros, '97
Herrera, Jose, '93
Javier, Sharon, '98
Kalogeras, Eleni, '82
Kolarik, Sean, '81
Kolarik, Timothy D., '79
Kosteas, Panagiotes, '98
Koulombinis, Nicholas, '78
Kyriakides, Michael N., '99
Lee, Chon J., '98 PL
Lorenc, Iwona, '98
Manir, Zabed, '99 MG
Marrero, Ms. Rosa M., '99 LW
McCarthy, Jennifer, '96
Mendez, Maritza, '99 SW
Meyer, Kurt P., '95
Meyers, Trishonna M., '98
Mitrctasics, Mrs. Catherine, '95
Molina, Sandra M., '99 LW

Monokrousos, Dennis, '83
Morales, Auries M., '96 LW
Mullins, Steven J., '93
Nelly, Stabile, '96
Nieves, Linda R., '98
O'Sullivan, Kevin M., '99 LW
Panagopoulos, Stilianos E., '95
Pawelczak, Peter, '75
Pena, Eva M., '99
Pisarczyk, Edyta, '97
Price, Sherry V., '79
Rauch, Richard S., '88
Ray, Donald L., '99
Robles, Nelson A., '98
Rogaski, John, '95
Sanchez, Enrique, '99 PL
Schillinger, Robert, '81
Seda, Sandy, '99
Senise, John B.
Severino, Solangel A., '96
Snyder, Heather T., '96 SO
Soto, Tareva L., '99
Speidel, Philip G., '84
Spinelli, Michael, '96
Stasio, Marie R., '83
Steigman, Heidi J., '98
Strobl, Staci E., '99 LW
Towns, Suzanne, '96 ST
Ubelli, Michael A., '78
Varsamas, Tommy A., '98
Vincent, Nadienne K., '80
Wargo, Jennifer, '98
White, Patrick C., '97
Wong, Kenneth, '83
Xepolitos, Constance, '82
Zuccarello, Mina S., '78
Zurita, Barbara, '97

ATLANTIC BEACH
Fisch, Daniel G., '95
Hagan, William P., '79
Sanders, Liliana M., '91 ST

AUBURN
Banko -Ross, Dr. Ellen, '84 CO
Lukula, Audrey, '91

AVERILL PARK
Plante, George J., '75 PL

BABYLON
Bravo, William A., '98
Halpern, Samuel B., '89
Hernandez, Victor, '92
Jiminez, Karen, '97
Kessinger, Ann L., '77 LW
Lee, Vernon, '98
Mc Loughlin, Robert, '76
McLoughlin, Robert G.
Nicolosi, Joseph R., '78
Nugent, Andrew G., '78
Reilly, Thomas W., '74 LW
Ruotolo, Joseph C., '96
Tripp, Peter G., '89 PL
Wolfe, Timothy E., '99

BALDWIN
Bailey, William S., '82 MG
Baribault, Richard, '72
Betts, Steven D., '95
Crawford, Harold A.
Del Castillo, Vincent, '84 PL
Goldman, Stanley, '82
Gomez, Henry J., '91
Hart, Barry E.
Healy, James, '85 PL
Hernandez, Yvette, '92
Herrmann, Christophe, 2000
Hinds, Randolph A., '85
Houdek, Caroline M., '99 BE
Johnson, Bernard A., '71 GN
L'amour, Mousslin, '90
Love, William A., '84
McCarthy, Daniel, '90
Mitkish, John A., '73
Moses, Herbert J., '81
Nathaniel, Nigel M., '90 AM
O'neill, James, '75
Patton, Ronda Y., '96 LW

Rottkamp, William J., '75
Schneider, Joseph E., Jr., '78 PL
Screen, Crystal L., '86 PL
Turcic, Stefanie, '90
White, Michael W., '87

BALDWINSVILLE
Battiste, Denise, '84 FV
Ortlieb, Robert J., '89

BALLSTON LAKE
Regan, Patrick J.

BALLSTON SPA
Richardson, Maureen G., '86

BARDONIA
Borman, Gary M., '77 LW
Latarski, Sigmund J., '71

BATAVIA
Weems, Scott C., '95
Wiater, Frank F.

BAYPORT
Brady, John J., '93 GN
Gross, Jacob A., '96
Herting, Edward C., '76 GN

BAY SHORE
Adams, Bernard S., '92
Bayard, Marie-denise, '76
Blake, Christopher
Bonelli, Basil A., '79
Broderick, Stephen J., '98
Bronkhurst, Frank X., '78
Carreras, Ralph, '75
Elliott, Sean M., '88
Estrella, Yojaida, '95
Grimm, Matthew B., '95 PB
Hajaree-Ramsaran, Mrs. Sabita, '95 ST
Jacobs, Jerry L., '91 ET
Jenkins, Gary H.
Johannesen, Richard, '85
Mills, Aaron E., '80
Petrone, Elizabeth, '83
Preval, Walter, '90
Ramsey, Claude C., '93
Rentz, Tracy D., '91 ET
Robin, Latasha B., '99 CO
Saldana, N. Antonio, '92 LW
Selkowitz, Richard
Sparrow, James T., '98
Tracy, Peter, '85
Trentacosta-Rosado, Dena M., '95 PL

BAYSIDE
Aleman, Jose L., '94
Bincarowsky, George, '58 ET
Brigandi, Douglas, '76
Byrne, Lawrence P., '85 PL
Chan, Kalung, '92
Ciavarella, Joanne, '89
Fauntleroy, Irma C., '98
Foglia, Mrs. Sophia, '75 AM
Gaioni, Robert J., '76
Giller, Randi L., '98
Gribben, Richard J.
Guzzardi, Joseph, '97
Jain, Rajiv, '96
Koch, Christopher J., '98
Kouloumbinis, N., '91
Kuceluk, Joseph R., '78
Levin, David J., '78 PL
Linden, Scott L., '78
Lubomski, CAPT Joseph E., '73 PL
Maltz, Barbara K., '78 SO
Masterson, Kevin M., '89
Mckenna, Thomas, '92 LW
Melis, Paul, '97 BE
Morton, Gerald T., '81
Rumberg, Alan R.
Rush, Vilethia, '96
Sabatini, Karen, '90
Sanchez, Sandra P., '97
Schnell, Barry A., '99
Schuster, Kenneth G., '76
Seignious, Lisa A., '84
Seignious, Patricia

Seignious, Robert, '75
Spaun, Gregory (Greg) J., '86 LW
Stein, Eugene P., '88
Urprasad, Deodat, '92 PL
Yasso, Michael, '90

BAYVILLE
Carolan, John J., '79 PL
Hoy, Patrick J., '75
Sheeler, Daniel H., '71
Tice, Harry A., III, '74 LW

BEACON
Brown, James D., '83
Fountain, Belinda M., '77 LW
Good, Carlton, '86
Hockler, Terry M., '93
Macdonald, Mrs. Nirvana L., '96 FV
Murphy, Charles M., '94
Tompkins, Gail H., '77 CO
Tortora, Joseph, '88
Zias, Joanne, '78

BEDFORD
Kelly, William P., '68 PL
Sadrakula, Michael P., '76 PL
Silverman, Susan W., PhD, '93
Takeuchi, Michael, '97

BEDFORD HILLS
Dixon, Alexandreena, '84
Mascari, John C., '88 LW

BEECHHURST
Clavell, Louis F., '72
Crawford, Arthur J., '76
Garvey, James T., Jr., '74 CN
Power, Thomas J., '76 PL
Vaughan, Sheila M., '94 LW

BELLE HARBOR
Egan, Patrick J., '76 AC
Flynn, Eugene M., PL
Gray, John H., '92
Kalletta, Edward D., Jr., '98 PL
Kelly, John J., '76
Knox, Blanche M., '78
O'Connor, Ms. Brigid, '95 PL
Reen, Shaun M., '98
Savage, Patrick J., '98 PL
Taylor, Steven M., '83

BELLEROSE
Albano, Daniel J., '76
Carey, Gary T., '76
Clabby, William F., '82 PL
Cornwall, Robert J., '75
Espada-Waite, M., '90
Kinscherf, Cindy L., '99 PL
Langone, Darin, '90
Linares, Israel, '95 PL
Martinez, Santiago, '93
Mc Creary, Joanne L., '77
Montgomery, Stephani, '97
Moore, James F., '71 ET
Murawski, Walter H., '84
Palau, Luis A., '75
Patel, Mayank R., '89
Pedersen, Frank, '95
Poje, Leopold J., '63 PL
Rodriguez, Michael, '91
Schreiner, John A., '76
Serra, Raphael, '98
Shea, Patrick J., '98
Yevoli, Peter A., '78 GN
Zeman, John

BELLEROSE TERRACE
Thomas, Peter L., '87 MG
Yacoob, Azimoon N., '99 CO

BELLMORE
Biscuti, Anthony J., '93
Campbell, John J., '72 PL
Cornell, Richard R., '91 PL
Dotzler, Paul P., '80
Ham, Gustavo, '94 PL
Hayes, James J., '79
Kaufmann, Kevin J., '85 PL
Kopp, Barbara A.
Longaro, Brian J., '99

Olsson, Christopher, '82
Selover, Joan, '92
Sireci, Gerard, '76
Slavin, Dennis F., '78

BELLPORT
Cosentino, Donna M., '98 *ME*
Harrow, Tracy A., '97

BETHPAGE
Aponte, Gina, '89
Cerreta, Kenneth, '85 *PL*
Chetal, Rakesh, '96
Darcy, Thomas J., '72
Davids, Joseph Z., '80
Diem, Martin E.
Feeley, William F., '79 *CN*
James, Spencer L., '81 *CP*
Kozel, Joseph D., '76
La Veglia, Anthony J., '75 *EM*
Mayr, Louis A., '95 *PL*
Morra, Michael C., '75
Palega, Paul K., '97
Perini, Bernard J., '70 *CP*
Rolla, Peter J., '99 *MG*
Romano, George A., '85
Sicurelli, Karen A., '95

BINGHAMTON
Belcher, Penney L., '99
Bunis, Joy, '84
Fair, Craig D., '96
Nocerino, Thomas, '77 *IN*
Rounds, Thomas E., '70 *PL*
Wise, Lauren A., '75 *LW*

BLAUVELT
Carr, Robert J., '75
Dowling, Edward J., '71
Foody, Liam J., '80
Galdi, Joseph M., '83
Goldfarb, Matthew S., '98 *PL*
Goldrick, Thomas J., '78
Hackett, George A., '76 *ET*

BLOOMINGBURG
Carey, James P., '89

BLOOMING GROVE
Bailey, Alex T., '94 *PL*
Brown, Courtney L., '99 *SA*

BLUE POINT
Gazzola, Anthony J., '74

BOHEMIA
Cullum, Christopher, '86
Farino, Thomas, '93
Gottlieb, Cara, '95
Guglielmo, Christoph, '97
Kostanoski, John I., '69

BOVINA CENTER
Sangiorgio, Maryann, '90

BREEZY POINT
Donlon, John L., '89 *PL*
Higgins, William J., '80
Redmond, Robin L., '94 *SW*
Silva, Catherine C., '84

BRENTWOOD
Castro, Deron R., '89
Dellapenna, Alfrdd J.
Devlin, Patrick J., '77
Devonish, Claudette, '92
Esposito, Angelina E., '96 *TR*
Ford, Brian F.
Francis, Howard C., '98
Garvey, Michael J., Sr., '95 *MG*
Grobluski, George F., '79
Marin, Vivian, '96
Martinez, Esperanza, '78
Mills, Charles M., '76 *PL*
Moore, Hukm, '96
Prince, Gilbert D., '72
Rivera, Angel M., '83
Sganga, Richard F., '74
Torres, David, '86
Wong, Fidel A., '97
Zaragoza, Deserie M., '89

BREWSTER
Belfiore, Thomas E., '79
Bonanno, Patsy, '91
Charest, Mark F., '90
Gagatch, Robert P., '75
Lara, Manuel E., '94 *LW*
Liguori, Michael T., '99 *ST*
MacDougall, John, '76 *PL*
Zazzero, Paul W., '84 *PL*

BRIARCLIFF MANOR
Ospina, Leonard, '94
Selvaggi, Anthony, '95
Turco, Angelo J., '72

BRIARWOOD
Atristain, Luis, '99
Brown, Tracy-Ann M., '99 *PB*
Crose, Bambi M., '96
Figueroa, Lois M., '96
Hetrick, John G., '78
Jenkins, Shirley L., '98

BRIGHTWATERS
Mc Nicholas, James F., '76 *PL*

BROAD CHANNEL
Badamo, Robert T., '77 *PL*
Cordes, Joseph, '97
Medina, Bolivar, '99
Tubridy, Daniel J.

BRONX
Abamwa, Osaka M., '95 *LW*
Abdallah, Adib, '85
Abdur-Rashid, Sabura, '93
Abousamra, Paul N., '97
Abreu, Arnold, '80
Acevedo, Maxima K., '99
Acevedo, Socrates, '93
Achini, Antonio, '98 *LW*
Achon, Alexa M., '99
Acosta, Danae, '97
Acosta, Gasmary, '98 *SW*
Acosta-hancock, Dora, '85
Adeleye, Helen, '97 *SW*
Ademaj, Vera, '99
Aguiar, Yvette, '86
Ahern, Kevin, '86
Ahyoung, Gary C., '99 *ET*
Aiken, Avril A., '87 *ET*
Ajunwa, Ifeyinwa P., '99 *PN*
Akapolawal, Wasiu A., '93
Akerele, Gabriel A., '92 *NU*
Albright, Eugene T., '73 *PL*
Albury, Nicholas A., '76
Alduende, Ivonne, '99 *PB*
Alejandro, Byanca, '92
Alexander, Beverly J., '89 *LW*
Alexander, Delvia M., '97
Alexander, Lorna V., '86
Alexandre, Jphilippe, '95
Alexis, Monica, '94
Ali, Shakawat, '95 *CP*
Allen, Neil G., '94
Almedina, Joseph A., '76
Almeida, Esther M., '94 *MG*
Almonte, Andy, '96
Alston, Samuel, '82 *IN*
Alvarado, Gloria M., '91
Alvarez, Betsaira, '93
Alverio, Daisy M., '81 *LW*
Amador, Bernard, '99 *ST*
Amador, Doris, '81
Amadu, Onoriode P., '91
Amaro, Maria, '91 *PL*
Amedee, J., '93
Amelio, Anthony, '85 *LW*
Ancrum, Alberta, '89
Andaluz-scher, Maria, '87
Anders, Scott, '94 *LW*
Anderson, Kevin G., '94 *GN*
Andrini, Deanna, '96
Anello, Cathy
Angelucci, Joann, '98
Anthony, Ceredo F., '94
Anyansi, James O., '90
Aponte, Cesar, '77 *PL*
Aponte, Lydia, '98

Archambeau, Lincoln, '97
Argaluza, Roberto, '95
Argenti, Karen M., '78 *CN*
Arias, Flora, '85
Armas, Margie, '94 *PL*
Armorer, Sharifa J., '93 *SW*
Armstead, Kemba A., '96
Armstrong, Lenore, '93
Armstrong-barrows, Valerie F., '89
Arnold, Sharol A., '92
Arocho, Belinda A., '82
Arrington, Oscar P., '85
Arrington, Otis W., '78
Arroyo, Anthony, '95
Arroyo, David, '89
Arroyo, Henry, '90 *PL*
Arroyo, Jose A., '95
Asbery, Joseph, '93
Auli, Karoll, '99 *SW*
Avila, Gil, '93
Ayala, Robert, '87
Ayers, Rashida, '95
Bachmann, Peter J., '80
Bachorik, Edward S., '73
Baez, Benjamin, '84
Baez, Mayra M., '96
Bailey, Belinda A., '79
Bailey, Christine, '89
Bailey, Nigel R., '95
Baker, Teresa, '86
Ballantine, Jean M., '82
Ballard, Celeste I., '96
Ballard, Michael A., '79
Banievicz, Alexander, '96 *GN*
Banks, Hermon J., '76 *CN*
Banks, Linda, '91
Banks, Sadiqa, '99
Barfield, Shawn, '97
Barlow, Christopher, '97
Barr, Leroy, '71
Barreiro, Ramon G., '97
Barrett, Katherine E., '82
Barrios, Leonthe, '92
Barrows, Alleen A., '93
Barry, Gail L., '84
Bartolotta, John, '92
Bashir, Benjamin M., '75
Bassett, Patricia A., '84
Bast, Molly A., '97
Batista, Carmelo, '80
Batista, Maria, '97
Batista, Shenoeck, '98
Baumann, Daniel, '97 *LW*
Baxter, Gregory, '97
Beato, Marino, '93
Beatty, Cephus J., '85
Beirne, Margaret, '76
Belfon, Joyce P., '78
Belin, Thelma, '86 *AM*
Bell, Tasmiya J., '93
Bellaflores, Jamari, '95
Bellamy, Beverly J., '80
Bellamy, Myra D., '85
Bellejambe, Melanie, '80
Bello, Valerie, '99 *RD*
Benejan, Robert, '97
Benfatti, Kristeine, '90 *CO*
Benitez, Gustavo, '92 *PL*
Benitez-rivera, Mild, '97 *LW*
Benjamin, Gilda E., '94
Bennett, Curtis L., '91
Bennett, Keren M., '94
Bennett, Winsome Y., '98
Berisha, Xhavid, '84
Berkley, Desiree M., '95
Bernardez, Mirtha C., '92
Berrios, Frank J., '93
Berrios, Laura M., '83
Berrios, Lynelle, '96
Betances, Neftali, Jr., '96 *PL*
Bieniewicz, Linda M., '93
Birch, Judith E., '77
Bishop, William B., '86
Blackman, Te'shanee M., '98
Blair, Dwight A., '78
Blake, Ernestine, '97 *RE*

Bobb, Gavin E., '98
Bodden, Juana, '94
Bolt, Ronald G., '82
Bonano, Aracelis, '96
Bonilla, Nilda, '85
Borquaye, Marylin, '81 *CP*
Bossa, Anna L., '89
Bourdon, Ana M., '92 *GN*
Bowden, Bradd D., '97
Bowens, Renita D., '94 *SW*
Bowry, Letitia R., '84
Bracy, Marshandra D., '99
Bradley, Donna M., '87
Bramson, Joy A., '78 *EV*
Branch, Robert L., '77
Brash, Ronald A., '97
Brea, Lizette, '95
Breslin, Michael, '96
Breton, Lydia E., '97
Brinson, Allyson C., '83
Britton, Lyria K., '89
Briu, Yolanda, '97
Brock, Mrs. Daisy H., '99 *CO*
Brogan, Thomas M., '85
Brogli, Maria C., '91
Broker, Steven J., '96 *LW*
Brown, Arline D., '82 *ET*
Brown, Arthur M., '70 *ET*
Brown, Brian K., '89
Brown, Charles R., '89
Brown, Colin R., '95
Brown, Doslyn V., '90 *SW*
Brown, Herman, '87
Brown, Ian L., '87
Brown, Joanna U., '83
Brown, Julia C., '83
Brown, Juliet D., '97
Brown, Louis, '76
Brown, Melvin R., '81
Brown, Milton E., '98
Brown, Patricia R., '79 *SW*
Brown, Ralph J., '76
Brown, Rodney W., '93
Brown, Ronda R., '98 *GN*
Browne, Cleo-renee, '90
Bruce, Prince A., '99 *PL*
Bruce, Tommy, '93 *PL*
Brun, Gina, '88 *ET*
Brunson, Jacqueline, '97
Bryan-piper, Hannah, '92
Bucci, Joseph R., '82
Budram, Anil, '99 *ET*
Buksha, Raymond M., '96
Bunyan, Michael C., '78
Burakiewicz, Lisa M., '97 *SW*
Burbridge, Adero, '93
Burdi, Michael J., '84 *LW*
Burge, John S., '81
Burke, Redmond P., '81 *ET*
Burns-Lemp, Patricia, '78
Burshteyn, Pavel, '98
Butcher, Mrs. Judith A., '83 *GN*
Butler, Tawanna C., '98
Butterfield, Anna, '86
Byer, Charles, '92
Byrne, John T., '76
Cabrera, Marjorie, '93
Calathes, Dr. William, '83 *ET*
Calderon, Jose, '87
Calderone, William D., '80
Calhoun, James J., '73
Calise, Diane, '98
Callender, Colette D., '92
Callistro, Cynthia Y., '90 *CH*
Calzerano, Joeph P., '62
Camacho, Angel J., '97
Camacho, Edgar M., '84 *PL*
Camacho, Michael, '98
Camacho, Sarita, '93
Camilo, Gilberto J., '99 *PL*
Campbell, Duncan, '82
Campbell, Hopeton A., '90 *MD*
Campbell, Morven A., '95 *SW*
Campbell, Sheilah N., '85
Canacoo, Seth, '88
Candia, Fernando A., '89 *IN*

Matz, Markus A., '96
Maxwell, Gwendolyn, '98
May, Paul D., '84 *PL*
Maynard, Heather E., '94 *AM*
Mazzella, James, '88
Mc, Call T., '90
McAloon, Daniel K., '95 *ET*
McCabe, Patrick M., '91
McClean, Monique D., '88
McCollough, Charmaine, '97 *LW*
Mccormack, Paul G., '97 *LW*
Mccullough, Ayanna, '96
Mccullough, Sylvia A., '98
Mccutchen, Aishah K., '97
Mc Donald, Thomas T., '79
McEntire, Catherine Duffy, '98 *PL*
Mcfarlane, Barbara, '89
Mcfarlane, Elaine C., '86
Mc Geady, Robert J., '81
Mckenzie, Rohan M., '97
Mc Keon, Joseph D., '74
McKinley, Tenee S., '99
Mc Kinzie, Linda M., '82
Mc Knight, Thomas J., '72
Mc Leod, James, '77
Mc Manus, Deborah A., '81
Mc Master, John A., '99 *MG*
Mcmillion, Tony, '95
Mc Nulty, Christopher R., '95
Mc Pherson, Dianne, '79
Mcqueen, David A., '95
McShall, Florence I., '86
Mc Sherry, Martin M., '76
Medina, Deborah A., '92 *PL*
Medina, Luis A., '89
Medina, Moraima, '84
Meenan, Patrick J., '78
Melbourne, Phyllis M., '84 *EA*
Melekwe, Augustina A., '84
Melendez, Abel, '99 *PL*
Melendez, David, '89
Melendez, Michael J., '87
Melendez, Monserrate, '98 *SW*
Melino, Albert J., '98
Melrose, Valerie L., '78 *GN*
Menard, Earl J., Jr., '77 *AC*
Mencia, Jose L., '96 *ME*
Mendez, Felix R., '80
Mendez, Lucitania B., '94 *CO*
Mendez, Mrs. Milly, '96 *SO*
Mendoza, John, '96
Mercado, Diana, '96
Mercado, Frances, '99 *AM*
Mercado, Julio, '97
Mercado, Lizbeth, '84
Mercado, Raymond, '94
Mercado-Ortiz, Luciano, '76
Merced, Deborah, '90
Meszaros-Brillon, A., '95
Meyers, Mrs. WillieEarl, '79
Mickens, Renee J., '97 *FV*
Middleton, C. B., '75
Middleton, Sharon D., '99 *ET*
Mila, Jennifer, '95
Miller, Bobby, '91
Miller, Chanell N., '99
Miller, Georgetea A., '97
Miller, Lorraine E., '82
Milone, Debra D., '78
Mims, Venetia L., '89 *MG*
Minauskas, John A., '75
Miner, Juanita H., '72
Mingo, Alfred E., '76 *BE*
Mirabal, Carolina, '99 *LW*
Mirand, Esther L., '97
Moeslinger, Emma N., '95
Mohammed, Hassim, '92
Molina, Angelita, '99
Molinaro, Mario A., '83 *CO*
Momodu, Dove E., '96
Monge, Luis A., '93 *PL*
Monplaisir, Ms. Patricia D., '98 *LW*
Monroe, Alisha J., '93
Montague, Kathleen B., '99 *PL*
Montanez, Nellie, '93
Moore, Patricia M., '81

Moorehead, Claude L., '90
Moorehead, Norris E., '76
Moorehead, Henry A., '89 *LW*
Mora, Jessica M., '97 *CN*
Morales, Carlos R., '93 *TR*
Morales, Hector, '97 *ET*
Morales, Lucette, '82
Morales, Sara, '95
Morales, Yvette, '80
Morales-Torres, Sandra E., '95
Morell, Edward, '95
Morelli, Joseph A., '97
Moreno, Karla C., '98
Morgan, John P., '90 *ET*
Moriarty, Robert C., '99
Morretta, Matthew G., '92
Morris-alston, Sophi, '95
Mota, Andrea, '94
Mozie, Edie D., '96
Muir, Harriette A., '95
Mujica, Linda R., '99 *PL*
Mulligan, Thomas M., '98 *PL*
Mundo, Reymundo, '96
Munoz, John, '89
Munoz, Julio E., '89
Munroe, Simone A., '99
Murchison, James, '94
Murillo, Cynthia T., '97
Murphy, James, '85
Murray, Sheila E., '93
Myers, Ayanna C., '93
Myers, Carol A., '88 *SN*
Myers, Debra A., '80 *ET*
Myers, Noah L., '86
Myers, Sayeeda, '99
Nanton, Willena, '88 *GN*
Napolitano, Sal R., '76
Navarro, William J., '77
Nazario, Francisco, '78 *GN*
Nazario, John, '90 *LW*
Nazario, Jose, '96
Ndreu, Firdez, '89
Negron, Victor, '79
Nelligar, James E., '95
Nelms, Luonel D., '78
Nelson, Fitzroy R., '97
Nelson, Lynda D., '89
Nesmith, Daron L., '98 *PL*
Newton, Herold H., '97
Nguyen, Huyen M., '97
Nicaj, Vera, '98
Nicola, Maria E., '96 *CP*
Nieves, Jose V., '99 *PL*
Nieves, Samuel, '93
Nixon, Henry E., '99 *ST*
Nkrumah, Kafahni T., '92
Nobilione, Joseph G., '86
Nocera, Salvatore F.
Nolan, Wanda J., '80
Nonis, Basil, '95
Norflett, Ronald, '77
Nunez, Juan, '93
Nwahiri, Matthias, '91
O'brien, Hayden, '92
Obryan, Diren D., '85
O'bryan, Rupert W., '82
O'byrne, Francis M., '74
Ocampo, Mayra D., '93
Ocasio, Carlos, '96
O'conner, Hilda N., '89
O'Connoll, Thomas J.
Oconnor, John P., '91
Odita, Pauline U., '82
O'Donnell, CAPT Steven, '99 *PL*
Ohadoma, Emmanuel O., '98
Ohakamnu, George N., '92
O'hare, Aileen, '87
Okafor, Emeka D., '99
Okosun, Alexander E., '99 *PL*
Okrah, Edward K., '93 *GN*
Olinto, Luigi T., '93
Olivares, Esther, '93
Olivares, Flor E., '98 *PL*
Olivo, Jose, '97
Omotayo, Nixon O., '84 *GN*
Onyeobia, Kelechi, '95 *RE*

Orangeo, Andrew D., '75
Orozco, Odalis, '96
Ortega, Jessica, '99 *PL*
Ortega, Shirley L., '99
Ortiz, Janet, '96 *LW*
Ortiz, Joseph A., '89
Ortiz, Marilyn, '90 *SW*
Ortiz, Michael A., '97
Ortiz, Oscar J., '93
Ortiz, Yolanda R., '87
Ortiz-benjamin, Maira, '96 *AM*
Ortiz Ortiz, Ana M., '79 *LW*
Ortolano, Lisa, '87 *LW*
Oschmann, Edward J., '81
Osorio, Theodore P., '82
O'Sullivan, Christopher G., '77 *PL*
O'sullivan, Marie, '94
Otero, Mildred, '94
Ovando, Percida R., '88 *SW*
Owie, Edwin, '96 *SW*
Oyibo-Ebije, A., '93
Pacheco, Brunilda, '80
Pacheco, Jose A., Jr., '76 *PL*
Padilla, Alfonso, '99
Padilla, Anthony, '92
Padilla, Joseph A., '86
Padilla, Margarita M., '96 *ME*
Pagan, Edwin R., '90
Page-Okhiria, Carolyn D., '97
Paige, Jodi W., '98 *LW*
Palermo, Mario E., '78
Palzer, Lewis N.
Parker, George, '93
Parker, Sydney H., '95
Parkins, Marcia S., '97
Parks, Lanetta J., '80
Parrales, John T., '96
Parris, Cecilia G., '89
Parry, Lesroy T., '98 *LW*
Pastrana, Angel L., '97 *CO*
Patten, Jennifer M., '93
Patterson, Ilani B., '99
Patterson, Ison J., '93
Patterson, Rosezena, '96 *PL*
Paul, Yulonda J., '98
Paulino, Jose P., '99
Paulino, Reynaldo M., '95 *PL*
Paulk, Kim M., '93
Payne, Jesse J., '72
Pearson, Evelyn E., '95 *MG*
Pedro, Hakeem A., '95 *SW*
Pegram, John A., '76
Pena, Carmen L., '95 *SW*
Pena, Eligia, '95
Pena, Erica, '99
Perez, Irma, '98
Perez, Ismael J., '79
Perez, Jaime A., '99 *TC*
Perez, Liduvina, '79
Perez, Lizabeth (Lisa), '96 *PL*
Perez, Michelle, '89 *AM*
Perez, Sandra M., '97
Perez-ruiz, Ines, '91
Perkins, Nicole S., '96 *LW*
Peronneau, Ernest, '90
Pesante, Margarita, '78 *LW*
Peterkin, Robert N., '93
Peters, Claire E., '98 *GN*
Peters, Kelly A., '98
Petersen, Jacqueline, '97
Petty, Camille B., '89 *NU*
Phillip, Gayle D., '99
Phillips, Anthony R., '88
Pichardo, Francisca, '87
Pierce, Allison, '86
Pilny, Richard E., '78
Pinckney, Michael J., '79
Pitter, Violet M., '95
Pitts, Arthur A., '82
Pizarro, Ramona, '88
Pizzo, Dominick, '93
Poejo, Victor A., '91
Poglodek, Tina M., '97
Poisella, Michael J.
Polanco, Miosotis, '94
Polesel, Steven L., '75

Pollack, Dan L., '75
Pomales, Jessica, '99
Poonai, Roopnarine, '95 *LW*
Popper, Alan H., '86
Pouncie, Ms. Amanda M., '78 *NU*
Powell, Dalvanie K., '87
Powell, Denise K., '79
Pray, Randiolph P., '78
Price, Laray, '95
Price, Vincent C., '89
Price, Warren J., '83 *SW*
Proscia, Thomas G., '95
Prosper, Marlon R., '95
Pryce, Genniveive O., '96
Puello, Miguelina, '95 *PL*
Pulice, Ronnie, '97
Purtill, Michael, '79
Pysarenko, Katherine, '97 *SW*
Quarles, Cheryl T., '90
Quartimon, Ronald L., '93
Quattlander, Raymond, '91
Quattrucci, Elisa A., '85
Quigley, Donald M., '88
Quinones, Alma D., '76
Quinones, Frances, '99
Quinones, Giselle, '95
Quinones, Joann, '93
Quinones, Julio C., '94
Quinones, Luis A., '78
Quinones, Milagros, '97
Quinones, Richard, '92
Quintana, Lydia C., '91 *GN*
Quintero, Anthony, '85
Radcliffe, Anna J., '80 *SW*
Rakowsky, Andrew R., '82
Ramirez, Anthony J., '78
Ramirez, Barry, '98 *MG*
Ramirez, Carlos, '88
Ramirez, Debra L., '99
Ramirez, Jessica D., '98 *PL*
Ramjit, Sheriffa, '93
Ramkaran, Denyse, '91 *AP*
Ramos, Damaso, '99
Ramos, Laura, '97 *AC*
Ramos, Magda, '93
Ramos, Maria, '92
Ramos, Marisol, '91
Ramos, Mead S., '97
Ramos, Nestor, '99 *LW*
Ramsay, Margaret, '95 *GN*
Ramsey, Danette, '96
Randolph, Wanda, '91
Ravenell, Jason, '96 *SW*
Reboyras, Jessica M., '99
Rechenberg, Jan M., '76 *BE*
Reed, Jasmine M., '99 *LW*
Reid, Diana M., '95
Reid, Howard, '90
Reid, LaLisa, '89 *LW*
Reilly, Nancy A., '80
Reilly, Peter J., '88
Resto, Hipolito, '76
Resto, Lourdes, '85
Reyes, Ana A., '99 *LW*
Reyes, Joselyne A., '99 *SW*
Reynoso, Alexa J., '99 *PN*
Reynoso, Edgar, '92 *CP*
Reynoso, Florinda, '95
Rice, Sharnik, '96
Ricevuto, Anthony R., '91
Richardson, Cheryl J., '87
Richardson, Ernest V., '90
Ridley, Sandra O., '95 *ET*
Riggins, Diane
Riggio, Michael, '94
Riollano, Miriam, '79
Rios, George J., '75 *PL*
Rios, Juan R., '98 *LW*
Rios, Ruben, '93
Ristenbatt, R., '90
Rivera, Andrew A., '84
Rivera, Cynthia M., '99
Rivera, Dana E., '99 *ST*
Rivera, Denise, '98
Rivera, Eric, '97
Rivera, Evelyn, '90

West, Donna M., '89
Westcott-Marshall, Darryl A., '78 CO
Wharton, Arnetha N., '99
White, Brenda L., '89
White, Jennifer J., '93
White, Karen, '95
White, Monique L., '96
Whitfield, Kimberly, '91
Whiting, John W., '93 CP
Whitted, Frank N., '93
Wiley, Denise T., '96
Wilkins, Clarinda, '81
Williams, Alfred, '79 PL
Williams, Bridget L., '87 MG
Williams, Deborah R., '95
Williams, Demetrius, '96
Williams, Donna M., '94
Williams, Grace M., '98
Williams, Ibikunle A., '85
Williams, Jeffery L., '90
Williams, Katrina J., '98 LW
Williams, Keyla N., '98 SW
Williams, L., '80
Williams, Le'roy C., '86
Williams, Lillian, '99
Williams, Migdalia, '78
Williams, Patricia H., '97
Williams, Sonya Y., '97
Williams, Suzette S., '96
Williamson, Stacie, '96
Wilson, Desiree T., '81
Wilson, Dolores M., '76
Wimbish, Patsy, '79
Windus, James E., '81
Winston, Oscar S., '81
Wise, Edwina R., '78
Wise, Lashanda M., '99
Witty, Marina I., '98
Witty, Sandra D., '90
Woodbyne, Maurice C., '99 GN
Woods, Gail D., '85
Worley, Donna J., '86
Wray, Tasha V., '91
Wright, Mrs. Kyristel P., '96 MG
Wright, Sharnickqua O., '99 ET
Wright, Teresa A., '86
Wright, Tiffany E., '95
Wyatt, Antoinette C., '97 SW
Yee, William, '77
Young, Adrienne M., '81 ET
Young, LeRohn A., '77 FL
Yusuf, Mohamed S., '95
Zaccaro, Anthony R., '76
Zaino, James R., '79
Zamorn, Esperanza, '96
Zaro, Ines A., '99 GN
Zayas, John, '79
Zimmerman, Wheeler L., Jr., '95 IN
Zummo, Annette M., '79

BRONXVILLE
Camarda, Susan A., '86
Carpender, Scott, '90
Fetonti, Paul J., '76 MG
Horowitz, Robert B., '78
Hunce, Joseph D., '81 LW
Laperuta, Domenick A., '74 MG
Olla, Philip A., '79
Pecoraro, Diana, '86 LW
Steinfeld, Mark D., '78 LW
Varela, Lillian, '96
Vo, Chau, '95 PL

BROOKLYN
Abbott, Fern A., '85
Abbott, Milton N., '80
Abdool, Rick E., '96 LW
Abdullah, Ms. Doris T., '80 FV
Abimbola, Ayetigbo C., '88
Abolade, Wasiu A., '78
Abraham, George C., '75 CN
Abramchik, Trudy, '82
Abrams, Deon S., '94 LW
Abrams, Fay A., '80
Abreu-lotz, Yosmari M., '84
Acevedo, Carmelo, '88

Acevedo, Luz A., '77
Acevedo, Nancy, '89
Acevedo, Ramon, '80
Acosta, Indrani, '97
Actie, Winnifred, '78
Adams, Dennis A., '78
Adams, Elke, '90
Adams, Eric L., '98
Adams, Robert W., '69 CN
Adegbamigbe, Adedeji, '95 CP
Adeniran, Adeyinka, '90
Adesina, Mufutau A., '91
Adinolfi, Thomas R., '80
Adjaero, Alphonsus A., '95 LW
Adolphe, Marsiste, '94
Adum-Bawdah, Hana, PhD, '78
Agrapides, Peter, '83
Agron, Mikhail M., '98
Aguilar, Joanne C., '97
Ahmed, Abdul M., '89 EA
Aiello, Frank P., '75
Akhtab, Nazlah, '97
Akselrod, Steve, '95
Alaimo, Frank A., '77
Alaimo, William N., '80
Alava, Tricia, '93
Albert, Tracy K., '99 ME
Aibornoz, Anneris T., '98
Albuja, Hugo D., '98 LW
Alerte, Richard C., '97
Alexander, Algernon, '93 LW
Alexander, Alison J., '99 AM
Alexander, Daniel J., '96
Alexander, Dawn L., '90
Alexander, Lavern K., '92 LW
Alexander, Neva A., '97
Alexander, Samuel, '79
Alexander, Tricia, '97
Alexandre, Jean W., '97
Aleyne, Aida M., '93
Alfred, Rosa A., '86
Ali, Fyza D., '95
Alicea, Elliott J., '95
Aliyev, Radmila, '96
Allamby, Kevin, '95
AllBright, Nicole, '95
Allen, Brenda R., '81
Allen, Jerome, '93
Allen, John J., '80
Allen, Joseph A., '96 LW
Allen, Pauline L., '79
Allen, Theresa L., '77
Allen, Tonya, '92
Allen, Wayne A., '92 PL
Allert, Theresa, '97 LS
Alleva, Michael, '95
Alleyne, Pauline A., '93
Alleyne, Peter, '90
Aloi, Carole A., '80
Alongi, Michael R., '95
Alpa, Yalcin, '95
Alphonso, Errol A., '93
Alston, Harry T., '82 CO
Alston, Yvonne, '91
Alvear, Mrs. Bonnie S., '88
Amato, Peter J., '95
Amato, Ronald J., '81 MG
Amatore, Alfred, '92
Amay, Jasmin E., '99
Ambert, Ms. Arlene, '85 LW
Ambris, Ayanna E., '99 PL
Ambris, Marcia C., '95
Ambrose, Wilma I., '96
Amour, Johnson N., '97
Anderson, Ms. Carmen N., '99 GN
Anderson, Erik J., '92
Anderson, Eunice T., '82
Anderson, Jacqueline V., '99
Anderson, Luke E., '95
Anderson, Vanita M., '95
Andrew, Gregory, '96
Andrews, Benjamin (Ben), '90 FV
Andrews, Joy A., '89
Anduze, Kenneth R., '89
Anes, Edwin, '96 LW
Angilletta, Joseph A., '86

Annamunthodo, John C., '97 ET
Annarumma, Thomas P., '80
Annucci, Anthony J., '76
Anobile, John J., '80
Antab, Vaughn, '73
Anthony, Chailendra, '97
Anthony, Tyrone, '79
Antoine, Jennifer
Antoine, McFredy, '89 BE
Antoine, Phyllis A., '78
Antoine, Wayne A., '80
Antomez, SGT Herbert, '78 LW
Antrobus, Jennifer B., '79
Appel, Kenneth P., '84 MG
Appelbaum, Jed, '76 PL
Applewhite, Elsie, '84 CP
Aquino, Donald D., '73
Arce, Jose M., '89
Arce, Nancy, '90
Archer-Joefield, Shellyann M., '92
Archie, Michelle J., '93
Arecius, Claudine, '96
Arellano, Jose, '95 LW
Arlen, Jennifer, '99 ME
Armani, Chris G., '98 LW
Arniotes, LT James V., '97 PL
Arocho, Sonia A., '97
Arroyo, Catherine, '96
Arroyo, Jennifer R., '94 CP
Arroyo, Kelly, '99
Arsenakos, Stella, JD, '80 LW
Artes, Joseph
Arthur, Easlyn C., '80
Arthur, Kent, '92
Asad, Abdalla M., '95
Asad, Jamal M., '89
Asencio, Stacy, '97
Ash, Sylvia G., Esq., '76 LW
Asher, Jean M., '96
Ashley, Teresa L., '97 CP
Ashton, Cornelius M., '86
Assayag, Lyate A., '99
Assiff, Laurie A., '97
Atlas, Gary, '75
Augello, Angelo J., '76
Auguste-Smith, Portia, '99
Augustin, Kisha V., '99 LW
Augustine, Clyde L., '80 LW
Augustus Miller, Mrs. Antoinette J., '97 PL
Austin, Karen F., '76
Avila, Patricio, '95
Aviles, Lisa, '94
Avinger, Denise, '95
Babalola, Sikiru, '94 SW
Babb, Jackie R., '99 FV
Babb, Randolph, '77
Bacchi, Diana E., '96
Bacchus, Garvin W., '80
Bacchus-Larode, Mrs. Kimberly C., '98 IN
Bacovic, Hasan, '97
BAdagliacca, Michael, '97
Badillo, Cristina, '99 AM
Baez, Yvonne K., '96 MG
Bahan, Mildred, '92
Bahna, Alfred M., '88 MK
Bailey, Anthony M., '97
Bailey, Betzaida, '97
Bailey, Edmarine A., '97
Baird-alleyne, Arlene, '91
Baisden, Ms. Jilyon, '99 BI
Baker, Noel M., '97
Balcombe, Marcelle, '93
Balgobin, Ms. Julianna A., '98 ET
Balliraj, Ramjit, '79
Balogun, Raheem, '85
Banatte, Carline, '94
Band, Nora H., '77
Bank, Maurice H., '76
Banks, Celia B., '81
Banks, Shaundra L., '82
Baratta, Anthony, '80
Barbour, Ms. Susan M., '85 LW
Barfield, Miriam, '82
Barker, Cathy-anne D., '95

Barnes, Charles E., '80
Barnes, Shurrel Y., '96
Barometre, Reginald, '96 SW
Barrett, Calvin A., '77
Barrett, Doreen A., '83
Barrington, Nichelle, '94
Barriteau, Marsha A., '92
Barrow, Audra J., '92 LW
Barry, Rupert V., '78
Bartolone, Maria, '83
Barton, Wade J., '80
Batt, Jerome P., '75
Battle, Lisa M., '93 AM
Baumert, Robert (Boomer) J., '66 PL
Baxter, Katherine, '78
Baylor, Charlene, '89
Bayne, Melvin, '92 LW
Bazile, Steven G., '99
Beamon, Tanya J., '90
Beatty, Pamela Y., '94
Beauvais, Reginald, '90
Beckles, Arlene D., '87 PL
Been, Monette L., '89
Behlin, Charlotte E., '89
Beldo, Gina, '94
Belenky, Dmitry, '94 SW
Belford, Curtis S., '99 PL
Belford, Mary J., '87
Belgrave, Jessica A., '96
Bello, Joseph J., '89
Bello, Muhammad A., '82 GN
Benedetto, Anthony S., '75
Benjamin, Lesley V., '91
Benjamin, Yvonne E., '94 PL
Bennett, Sylvia L., '79 LW
Bent, Pamela A., '97 LW
Bentley, Cheryl A., '96
Benzan, Lourdes M., '82
Beritan, Jorge L., '95
Berke, Marshall L., '95 AC
Berman, Stacey, '83
Bermudez, Iris E., '86
Bermudez, Rosa A., '92
Bermudez, Yvette, '88
Bernard, Derwin M., '96
Bernstein, Stuart L., '83
Berrouet, Gerard E., '97
Best, George M., '75 ES
Best, Jennifer A., '94
Best, Racine A., '96 CT
Best, William S., '89
Bethel, Cassandra V., '83
Betso, Philip R., '79
Betts, Mary-ann C., '96
Bility, Mohammed S., '99 ET
Bittar, Dennis, '93
Bittar, Robert N., '87 BE
Black, Sylvia C., '94 PL
Blackman, Michelle, '95
Blackshear, Norman, '96
Blackwood-ahmed, Melrose, '98
Blaha, Jana L., '97
Blake, Micheryl R., '85
Blake, Ms. Vera A., '92 MG
Blank, Dorothea, '82
Bleeker, Stanley W., '78
Bleiberg, Michael S., '76
Blount, Ms. Heather, '98 GN
Blugh, Eneida A., '91
Blugh, Michael, '93
Blum, Dominic K., '96 GN
Blume, Rene M., '98
Blumstein, Evan P., '98
Boakye-yiadom, Kwame, '87 ME
Boatright, Gina E., '83
Bolden, Denise, '87
Boldin, Teresa S., '93
Bolstad, Robert, '97
Bolton, Garfield L., '93 PL
Bonaney, Polanges R., '97
Bonas Benjamin, Laura Z., '98
Bonds, Cheryl D., '89
Bonet, Deborah H., '92
Bonilla, Sandra G., '92
Booker, Kwesi L., '98 SW

Booker, Wayne R., '79
Boone, Bruce A., '94 *TR*
Borders, Delisa Y., '83
Borker, Vito, '97 *PL*
Borman, Charles J., '75
Borrero, Hiram T., '96
Boshell, Kevin M., '95
Boston, Karen, '88
Botte, Dominick, Jr., '80 *BE*
Boute, Yvrande, '96
Bovell, Donna A., '93 *PL*
Bowen, Fielding W., '91
Bowen, Gerard, '92
Bowles, Aries, '95
Bowles, Leslie M., '94
Boyce, Audrei T., '75
Boyce, Karentessa D., '92
Boyce, Rodney C., '97 *PL*
Boyd, Crystal, '97
Boyd, William S., '78
Boyle, Sheila A., '80
Bracero, Denise, '98 *CP*
Brady, Oral W., '92
Braff, Neil S., '88
Braithwaite, George F., '77
Bramble, Anthony S., '97 *AM*
Branic, Doretha, '88 *SW*
Brassington, Michael, '90
Brathwaite, Henderson O., '98
Brathwaite, Tasha Y., '96
Braxton, Aubrey S., '91 *PL*
Breder, Donald J., '95
Bren, Fern M., '85
Brennan, John P., '68
Brenord, Celius, '95
Breslin, Michael D., '94
Briggs, Errol, '95 *SW*
Briggs, Renee, '91 *CO*
Brill, John J., '76
Brinadze, Anna, '95 *LW*
Brisbane, Joyce L., '88
Briscoe, Harold P., '69
Briskie, Michael S., '97 *GN*
Brissett, Jacqueline, '93
Britt, Deborah L., '79 *MG*
Brodman, Mathew H., '97 *GN*
Brogan, Francis J., '79
Brooks, Michele, '89
Brown, Annie D., '94
Brown, Beverley M., '82
Brown, Candra L., '92
Brown, Carol N., '83
Brown, Charles L., '79
Brown, Clifford E., '90
Brown, Derrick, '96
Brown, Francisco A., '82 *PL*
Brown, Iris D., '77
Brown, Isaac L., '95
Brown, Janet, '96
Brown, Latisha Y., '97 *PL*
Brown, Leonetta M., '80
Brown, Linata, '99 *ES*
Brown, Moreale P., '97 *CH*
Brown, Myrtle M., '85
Brown, Paul R., '98
Brown, Paul S., '98
Brown, Renelle, '90
Brown, Stevelle M., '93
Brown, Tarsha S., '99
Brown, Timothy, '98 *LW*
Brown, Timothy J., '99 *PL*
Brown, Yvette E., '95 *SW*
Browne, Phillip A., '99 *GN*
Brudent, Sandra, '98 *MG*
Bruneau, Johanne, '91
Brunetti, Joseph, '96
Bruno, Daniel J., '95 *LW*
Bruno, Michael A., '96
Bryan, Annmarie L., '83
Bryan, Stephanie A., '98
Bryant, Julia
Bryant, Nicole, '95
Bucca, Maria, '94
Buffaloe, Kenneth S., '86
Buica, Lucy, '97
Buie, Deborah L., '90

Buie, Teresa, '92
Bukatman, Tessie
Bullen, Alicia
Buono, Joseph F., '77 *PL*
Burch, Felicia, '88
Burger, William C., '76
Burgh, Todd D., '96 *LW*
Burgos, Angela I., '98
Burke, Derek, '92
Burns, John W., '82 *LW*
Burton, Ines V., '95
Busby, Dyedra P., '95
Buscaglia, Joann, '88
Bute, Jessica A., '91
Butler, Jason L., '94
Butler, Katrina A., '97
Butler, Sandra, '92
Butler, Tyrone T., '77
Buttaro, Victor A., '97
Buttaro-sanchez, Joann, '90
Byer, Renee A., '99 *RE*
Byrd, Shasun (Germaine), '99
Byrd, Vanessa A., '82
Byrnes, John P., '75
Caballero, Joyce E., '98
Cabrera, Maritza, '93 *GN*
Cabrera, Milagros, '97
Caccavale, Andrew C., '90
Caddle, Carolyn A., '95
Cade, David W., '78
Cadet, Flobert, '97
Cadet, Rachelle, '99
Cadet, Robinson, '93
Cadet, Yves, '83
Caesar, Tessa V., '95 *LW*
Cagliuso, Nicholas, '95
Caicedo, Jose, '97
Cajigas, Veronica, '95
Cajou, Jean Claude, '96 *ET*
Calabro, Andrew J., '77
Caldarola, Anthony E., '80
Calderon, Angel, '77
Callender, Cynthia, '94 *GN*
Calvert, Vashti N., '98
Cameron, Norman E., '97 *GN*
Cammallere, Catherine, '82 *CN*
Cammallere, M. J., '76
Campbell, Bradley S., '90
Campbell, Carol G., '86
Campbell, Patricia A., '95
Campbell, Yolan, '94
Canaii, Angel B., '75
Canal, Wilvina, '98 *PB*
Candelaria, Gladys, '85
Cangelosi, Robert S., '93 *PL*
Canning, Candia C., '99
Cantalino, Carmen C., '79
Cantave, Alexandra M., '86
Canty, Maria A., '95
Capella, Peter C.
Capobianco, Joseph J., '97 *SA*
Capparelli, Madeline C., '95
Cappello, Edward, '77 *PL*
Caputo, Rosemarie, '84
Caravello, Kelly A., '96
Carbonaro, Lawrence, '96
Cardet, Carolyn, '93
Carlson, Karen F., '81
Carlton, Erik, '97
Carmichel, Debora L., '85
Carmona, Amada, '86
Carolina, Tanya L., '93
Carr, Autuam D., '89
Carrillo, Anaida W., '98
Carrington, Charlotte, '77
Carrington, Eric, '95
Cartagena, Hector, '94
Carter, Arnold, '91 *PL*
Carter, Corynne D., '92
Carter, Kim, '85
Carter, Melvin R., '91
Carter, Ronald, '97
Caruth, Godson R., '95 *SO*
Carvajal-Nunez, Mrs. Xiomara G.,
   '95 *ET*

Casanova-Scott, Mrs. Veronica, '89
   GN
Cashin, Margarette, '89 *LW*
Caso, Luis, '90 *JU*
Cassagnol, Nikole, '95 *EV*
Cassano, Vito M., '77
Cassidy, John J., '76 *PL*
Castro, Debra, '89
Castro, Giselle, '80
Castro, Jacqueline, '93
Castro-Gonzalez, Wilf, '78
Catalfumo, Michael, '75
Catlyn, Dasha V., '95
Cavaliere, Christopher, '95 *FV*
Cazeau, Beatrice, '94 *LW*
Cedeno, Stacey N., '99 *GN*
Cethoute, Guy J., '92
Chacon, Karlene L., '98
Chametzky, Steven A., '91 *PL*
Champagne, Nancy F., '80
Chan, Suk Han H., '99 *LW*
Chan, Wai H., '87
Chandler, Jana, '86
Chandler, Kinya, '95
Chang, John K., '96 *PL*
Chapman, Doris, '87
Charles, Joseph, '95
Charles, Marie M., '79
Charles, Nirlaine, '96 *SW*
Chase, Lisa, '96
Chavez, Rocio E., '97
Chavis, Rosezina, '95
Cheatham, Leroy R., '76
Cheng, Christoph C., '98 *PL*
Cheregotis, Peter J., '95
Cherry, Alvina T., '98
Cherubin, Ms. Yadlynd R., '99 *SW*
Chiappetta, Gennaro (Jerry), '71
   GN
Chiarantano, Daniel, '87 *PL*
Chico, Ivelisse, '95
Chillo, Generoso A., '88
Chorzewski, Robert, '89
Choy, Yolanda, '97 *PL*
Christian, Elmo E., '95 *BE*
Christiano, Michael J., '77
Christie, Andrew C., '98
Christophe, Joseph, '94 *PL*
Chung, Jane, '93
Chung, Michael, '95
Chypre, Richard L., '86
Chyrack, Judy, '99
Cicero, Alethea U., '98 *CT*
Cilione, Jeffery, '93
Cisek, Mary T., '93
Clark, Mark, '92 *PL*
Clark, William D., '89
Clarke, Al-yeru, '96
Clarke, Barry R., '93 *LW*
Clarke, Justin H., '95 *CP*
Clarke, Kathleen C., '77
Clarke, Lois G., '77
Clarke, Lynn A., '80
Clarke, Michelle Y., '81
Clarke, Nicole L., '99 *JO*
Clarke, Nuria E., '93 *ME*
Clarke, Rosanna, '99 *ET*
Clarke, Thomas J., '76
Clemente, Michael A., '89
Clouden, George, '87 *PL*
Coaxum, Teresa (Teri), '93 *PB*
Codling, Omar, '95
Codrington, Paula A., '94 *LW*
Cohen, Amy B., '91
Cohen, Faith M., '90 *PL*
Cohen, Jacqueline, '97
Cohen, Steven M., '80
Colasuonno, Dominick, '89 *PL*
Coleman, Charles E., '80 *LW*
Coleman, James J., '77 *LW*
Coley, Helen, '95
Coley, Takiya Y., '95
Coll, Thomas F., '77
Collier, Dyral, '82
Colligan, Mary E., '75
Collins, Gail M., '75

Collins, Kellis, '92
Collins, Michael, '90 *PL*
Collins, Ruby A., '93
Collins, Timothy K., '84
Colon, Ana R., '99 *LW*
Colon, Bernardo, '92
Colon, Elizabeth, '97
Colon, Jacqueline, '87
Colon, Monica, '95 *LW*
Colon, Oswald, '96
Colon, Rafael E., '98
Colon, Robert G., '73
Conboy, Raymond C., '92 *PN*
Concannon, John P., '78
Condiotti, Irving, '76
Connolly, Mary F., '97 *SW*
Connor, Charles, '92
Connor, Gregory L., '77 *ME*
Connor, Mrs. Katrina A., '98 *ET*
Conry, Terry L., '77
Contreras, Gloria, '97
Conway, Judith A., '86 *ET*
Cook, Lovely, '96
Cook, Steven W., '81
Cooper, Alfonso A., '78
Cooper, Ava A., '82
Cooper, Gavin A., '78 *GN*
Cooper, Tonya, '86
Cora -Lundquist, Marissa, '93 *PL*
Corbin, Stephen, '95
Corchado, Maribel, '93
Corcoran, James P., '74 *PL*
Coriano, Milagros, '96 *CO*
Corneh, Varney M., '80 *PL*
Corney, Raymond J., '79 *BK*
Corpening, La'tanya, '86
Correa, Jose M., '93
Corrica, Jerome S., '85
Corso, David J., '99 *FV*
Cort, Martha R., '92
Cortes, Nelson, '81
Cortese, Frank, '79
Cosentino, Louis A., '80
Cosenza, Bernard S., '77
Costas, Yvette-Marie, '80
Cotter, Daniel J., '77
Cotto, Jose L., '90 *LW*
Cotto, Veronica, '99 *GN*
Cotton, Eddie, '93 *LW*
Cowick, Gary L., '95
Cox-Alston, Ms. Stephanie A., '78
   CT
Crader, Clarissa T., '96
Crane, Ernest, '83 *ET*
Cranford, Charles, Jr., '88 *LW*
Crawford, Andrea (Angie) K., '98
   PN
Crawford, Audrey D., '78 *PL*
Crawford, Mark R., '98 *PL*
Crenshaw, Frank D., '80 *LW*
Crespo, Gladys L., '93
Crespo, Luisa E., '91 *VL*
Crespo, Marivet, '96
Crespo, Sylvia, '86
Crichlow, Alison F., '96
Crosby, Trevor, '92
Crowley, Colin, '84
Crowley, Denis F., '84
Crudup, Roslyn S., '87 *SW*
Cruz, Angel, '95
Cruz, Carlos M., '92
Cruz, Jeanette, '91
Cruz, Monica C., '92
Cruz, Roberto D., '81
Cubero, Candido, '96 *PL*
Cucaj, Xhevat, '95
Cuccia, Anthony J., '90
Cuccia, Frances E., '82
Cuccioli, Barbara V., '97
Cuciti, Nicholas S., '81
Cudjoe, Michelle A., '97 *AM*
Cuebas, Edwin, '77
Cumberbatch, Simeon, '97 *LW*
Cummings, Dalila C., '98 *PN*
Cummings, Ivan, '99 *AM*
Cummings, Orlene F., '96

Cummings, Vernessa, '84
Cupid, Irma, '99
Curran, Eleanor A., '74 AM
Curran, Maureen
Cutler, Lynn, '74
Dagnello, Rudy J., '74 GN
Daidone, Anthony, '84
D'alessandro, Joseph, '97
D'alessandro, Paul V., '83
Dallatorre, Elaine B., '79
Dalton, Angela C., '97
Daly, CAPT Francis J., '70
D'Amato, George R., '74 LW
Damon, Latricia R., '98
Dana, Robert J., '77
Dancy, Ernest A., '78
D'andrea, Lorenzo J., '96 PL
Daniel-Babb, Valerie, '96 MG
D'antonio, Steven A., '76 LW
Dargan, Sabrina, '98 GN
Daugherty, William, '96
Daughtry, Veda D., '82
David, Lafleur, '90
David, McLawrence (Max) A., 2000
    SW
David, Yves A., '77
Davidson, Leslie-Ann, '90 PL
Davidson, Paulette P., '97
Davidson, Terrill L., '99 TR
Davidzon, Alexander, '97
Davies, Charmaine A., '81
Davis, Brian P., '98 LW
Davis, Charles W., '99 GN
Davis, Regina A., '97
Davis, Roshawn B., '95
Davis, Wilbert, '97 LW
Dawson, Darlene D., '78
De, Stefano, '95
Decicco, Dominick, '93
De Cicco, Donna M., '95 FV
Decker, Michael J., '96
Decoteau, Francis A., '97 LW
Defelice, John J.
De Filippo, Michael, '80
Defina, Joseph F., '75
Defina, Louise M., '75
Defreitas, Ewald, '85
Degnan, Brian A., '85 GN
De Jesus, Evelyn A., '95
De Jesus, Nestor R., '81
De John, Gregory G., '76
Delaney, James T., '93 PL
De La Pena, Mario, '81
Deleo, Deirdre, '96 SW
Delerme, Stevenson, '95
De Luca, Lawrence J., '80
Delvalle, Carlos, '89
DeMarco, Michael
De Martini, Joseph, '77
Denardo, Jeffrey J., '80
Denis, Chester T., '98
Dennedy, James F., '96
Dennigan, Paul R., '92 PS
Denslow, Lisa D., '97 CO
De Paulo, Peter A., '76
Derolus, Jean P., '97 GN
Derring, Tremell, '90
Desaussure, Ms. Martha, '94 AM
De Serio, Joseph M., '81
DeSimone, Andrew J., '93
Desnoyers, Hans N., '87
Desola, Anthony J.
De Souza, Chris, '99
Desrouilleres, Jean, '92
Dessources, Ralph, '98
Deteskey, Henry R., '91
Detres, Cynthia, '95
Devine, Edward W., '80
Devito, Diane, '86
Devito, James M., '93
De Vito, Michael J., '80
Devlin, Kevin G., '79
Diana, Charlene K., '99
Diaz, Geneva, '87
Diaz, Juan M., '78
Diaz, Maria D., '97

Diaz, Migdalia M., '99
Diaz, Miguel A., '81
Diaz, Zulma, '92 LW
Dickerson, Joeann M., '76
Di Donato, Steven, '81
Dier, Daniel, '93
Difusco, Andrew F., '93
Diggs, Sandra, '97
Dillon, Edward J., '74
Di Matteo, Philip J., '77
Dinkins, Benjamin S., '97
Diomede, Vito S., '85
Dipaolo, Paul J., '82
Dirocco, Dana L., '83
D'Isselt, Lauren, '91
Ditto, Philip J., '99 LW
Dixon, John H., '95 PL
Dixon, Nora, '95 IN
Dixon, Paulette, '93
Dobson, Anthony, '98
Dodson, Toshia E., '90
Donadio, Randall J., '80
Donahue, Daniel J., '78
Donaldson, Irving F., '86
Donato, Roberto, '90 PL
Donohue, Brian E., '95
Donohue, Patricia M., '78
Donovan, Gerald J., '72 CN
Doolan, Shane R., '99
Dorch, Joyce M., '93
Dormena, Marie-Suze, '99 SW
Dorogoff, Paul A., '89
Dorta, Edward, '97
Dorval, Marcoris, '97
Douge, Max, '79
Dougherty, Vincent J., '75
Doughney, Joseph C., '74
Douglas, Glenda E., '79
Douglas, Marsha D., '98 ET
Douglas-Richards, La, '96
Douse, Patricia A., '79
Dove, Sheila T., '97
Dowie, Heather M., '95
Dozier, Shaunda, '90
Draghi, Paul, '71 PL
Drakes, Imogene, '94
Drew, Isola S., '98
Drucker, Mitchel E., '75
Drummond, Junior A., '99 ST
Druss, Philip M., '76
Drzewiecki, Helena D., '83
Ductan, Cohetta, '98
Dudash, Stephen, '80
Duke, Daniel L., '79 GN
Dula, Eva M., '93
Dunbar, Arlene, '96
Duncan, Garfield S., '89
Duncan, Jesse J., '99 PL
Duncan, Shakima, '96 BK
Dunlap, Daniel, '90 PL
Dunphy, Timothy G., '79
Duque, Ruben D., '97
Duran, Jimmy, '98
Durant, Portia R., '79
Durante, Eugene G., '95 PL
Durham, Bette L., '88 SW
Durr, Johershey, '76
Durso, Vivian V., '96
Dussek, Philippe R., '83
Dwyer, Donna M., '92
Dzielski, Michael, '87
Eagle-Agard, Tanya M., '95 LW
Eason, Erica M., '95 PL
Eason, Marcus, '85
Eason, Pansy, '93
Eastman, Elkan H., '95
Edison, Mel, '79 EA
Edmonds, Garfield N., '96
Edwards, Martin W., '83
Edwards, Patrick L., '89
Edwards, Randy M., '89
Egger, Stephen L., '81 CP
Eghaghe, James O., '81
Ehrlich, Neil, '96
Elcock, Mark G., '98 SN
Elisson, Chris, '90 PL

Elliott, Johnathan R., '82
Ellis, Joseph S., '99
Embry, Alicia J., '96 AM
Emidih, Jones F., '99 MG
Eng, Lorna, '79
Eng, Shawn, '99 PL
Engel, Peter W., '84
Engel, William, '95
English, Claudia M., '97
English, David J., '95 PS
Eodumegwuhu, Khalika U., '99
Epstein, Bonnie, '95
Erhunmwunsee, Isaac, '82
Erickson, Kathleen, '92
Escalante, Norma E., '98 FV
Esposito, Gerald A., '83
Esposito, Vincent P., '78
Esteban, Ricardo, '95
Estevez, Javier G., '96
Evans, Aaron J., '96
Evans, Cherisse T., '95
Evans, Kenya L., '97
Evans, Madeline C., '80
Evans, Robert C., '92 PL
Eyman, Buster D., '77
Fabien, Margareth, '98
Fabrizio, Ralph A., '81
Faconti, Christiane, '96
Faison, Venessa, '93
Falcone, Loretta T., '80
Fannon, Richard P., '89
Fares, Ali, '94
Farias, Jeanine V., '95
Farnes, Milagros, '84
Farrell, Clare T., '98
Farrell, Denise M., '97
Farrell, Kevin P., '74
Farrell, Marianne J., '77 ET
Farrice, Edward P., '89
Fassberg, Stuart L.
Febles, Aida C., '96 GN
Fedotov, Alex V., '96
Feigenbaum, Roy A.
Feinberg, Mark S., '91
Felder, Calvin L., '84
Felder, William J., '98
Feldman, Felix J., '95 LW
Feldstein, Robert A., '83
Feliciano, Elizabeth, '98 MK
Feliciano, Elsa M., '97
Feliciano, Gloria, '94 CO
Felix, Lesly, '86
Felton, Crystal Y., '86
Fergus, Kathyann J., '97
Ferguson, Andre, '98 LW
Ferguson, Deborah A., '93
Fernadez, Patricia, '98
Fernandez, Australia, '89
Ferrara, Albert A., '76
Ferrer, Awilda, '84
Fetus, Patrick, '93
Field, Heather L., '84
Fields, Bernadette (Michelle), '93
    LW
Figueroa, Ivan F., '81
Figueroa, Jodie L., '99
Figueroa, Paola A., '97 GN
Finamore, James J., '96 PL
Finamore, Sandro, '80
Findlay-Paul, S., '93
Finn, Sean P., '91 PL
Fiore, Albert J., '95 PL
Fiore, Anthony M., '75
Fischer, Maureen J., '80 SW
Fischer, William R., '78 PL
Fisher, Michael A., '86
Fitzgerald, John K., '88
Flaherty, Michael R.
Flamarique-Vela, Susana, '99
Flanigan, Sean R., '92
Flateau, Andrea, '85
Fleisher, David S., '81
Fleming, April J., '85 PN
Fleming, Arthur J., '76
Fleming, Sibyl L., '80
Fletcher, Ali A., '95

Fletcher, Daniel A., '93
Fleury, Andre, '92
Fleury, Renime, '96 CO
Flores, Anibal, '98 LW
Flores, Franklin, '99 PL
Flores, Yvonne E., '86 SW
Flores, Yvonne Y., '98
Flowers, Leon A., '76 LW
Flyaks, Renata, '96
Fodera, Robert F., '92 LW
Fofana, Unisa A., '85
Folan, John B., '93
Folgar, Karen J., '98
Follett, Mary R., '85
Fonfrias, Edna, '78
Forbes, Candace T., '95
Forbes, Carla M., '87
Ford, Leticia
Ford, Melvin, '81
Ford, Vanessa D., '84
Forde, Sharon, '97
Forteau, Clement, '93
Fortune, Patricia, '84 GN
Foster, Valerie, '97
Foti, Anthony G., '78
Fountain, Roscoe E., '78
Fournillier, Brian F., '85
Fowler, Stephanie, '97
Fox, Kemeel N., '99 LW
Foy, Lawrence B., '85
Fragapane, V., '81
Francillon, Joanne, '95 CT
Francis, Alvin D., '86
Francis, Nicke R., '96
Franks, Robert J., '75
Franzese, Paul N., '84
Frazier, Dawn M., '97
Frazier, William E., '80
Freed, Lesly W., '89
Freeman, Aldric, '88 LW
Freeman, Denise, '76 NU
Freeman, James H., '95 LW
Freeman, Thomas G., '80
Freeman, Willie
French, Rollo T., '98
Fry, James W., '77 GN
Fuentes, Jacqueline A., '99 SW
Fulgencio, Nederland, '96
Fuller, Joan D., '98
Fumai, John H., '76 LW
Furr, Angela R., '80
Fusaro, Michael J., '78
Gaaskin, Ms. Michelle D., '98 SW
Gabbin, Catherine P., '95
Gaddy, James, '91
Gadlin, Igor E., '97
Gaeta, Dominic J., '70
Gaither, Ernest, '99
Gala, Michael K., '94 GN
Gale, John D., '81 GN
Galea, John A., '76 RD
Galeano, Sonia L., '97 GN
Galletta, Cyrus B., '76
Gallman, Kimberly L., '96
Gallo, Henry A.
Gallup, Tamara, '95
Gambardella, Vincent, '78
Gamble, Derick, '92 ET
Gancitano, Victor R., '98 PL
Gannon, John J., '80 MI
Ganu, Komla S., '89
Garber, Joseph G., '70 PL
Garbow, Bruce, '79
Garcia, Daniel, '92
Garcia, Deborah S., '95
Gardner, Llewelyn, '96
Gardner, Marva, '85
Gargin, John J., '78
Garland, Daniella, '88 PL
Garnier, Joubert, '90 LW
Garofano, Graziella D., '99
Garrity, Thomas J., '78
Gartner, William C.
Gaud, Juan R., '84
Gaudet, Eugene C., '95
Gay, Joseph B., Jr., '95 ET

Jemmott, Norman A., '93 SW
Jenkins, Ernestine, '93
Jenkins, Gary P., '99 AM
Jenkins, Michele, '76
Jenkins, Rshaun K., '95 LW
Jenkins, Ms. Sabrina M., '97 BI
Jermin, Cyril E., '80
Jimenez, Cristobal F., '95
Jimenez, Leyla X., '99
Jinks, Veronica, '86
Joe, Lloyd D., '95 GN
John, Brentnol, '97 TC
John, Clayton P., '92
John, Jacqueline D., '89
Johnson, Alfred K., '85
Johnson, Charles A., '98
Johnson, Charlie L., '76
Johnson, Dean L., '80
Johnson, Evelyn, '88
Johnson, Geronia G., '81
Johnson, Herbert R., '76
Johnson, Joseph, '75
Johnson, Larry, '90
Johnson, Lucinda, '78
Johnson, Marcia D., '95
Johnson, Michael K., '87
Johnson, Niesha P., '98 ET
Johnson, Patricia R., '87
Johnson, Phyllis R., '84
Johnson, Robert, '82
Johnson, Shandel, '94
Johnson, Sharon A., '97
Johnson, Stepahnie, '79
Joiner, Joyce R., '79
Jolly, Terry E., '81
Jones, Corey A., '95
Jones, Derrick A., '96
Jones, Lateshia P., '95
Jones, Mrs. Rita G., '85 SW
Jones, Robin M., '92 LW
Jones, Ronnie A., '91
Jones, Shaamgod, '97
Jones, Shirley D., '84 AC
Jones-scott, Vena, '92
Jones-Thorpe, Jennifer J., '95 PL
Jordan, Gwendolyn, '91
Jordan, Percival A., '85
Jordan, Robbin M., '91 PN
Jordan, Sherryl D., '83
Jordan, Stephen, '97
Jordan, Thomas J., '85
Joris, Compton, '98 GN
Joseph, Andrea M., '92
Joseph, Carlas, '93
Joseph, Crystal, '98
Joseph, Eddison M., '99 PL
Joseph, Ingrid, '78 LW
Joseph, Jean, '97
Joseph, Jennifer M., '82
Joseph, Kirt A., '96
Joseph, Kisha C., '93
Joseph, Philip, '97
Joseph, Ms. Rhonda F., '95
Joseph, Sheila, '93
Joseph, Wilfredo, '96
Jourdan, Paul J., '97
Joyner, Joann, '83
Joyner, Tisa S., '95
Joyner, Valerie K., '84
Jung, Eleanor J., '78
Jurek, Theodore J.
Juris, David, '86
Jusino, Ismael, '85
Kaecker, Richard J., '73
Kagan, Donald R., '98
Kalisky, Alan M., '89
Kalmar, Roberta, '76
Kamara, Alex T., '93
Kanacki, Gaye D., '79
Kane, James A., '77
Kanne, Emmanuel, '95
Kanne, James A., '93
Kanokogi, Jean S., '97
Kaplan, Leonard A., '71 LW
Kaplan, Neil J., '79
Kaslofsky, Thor, '97 EM

Kaye, Allan H., '76
Kayser, Steven B., '98
Kayton, John J., '75
Keane, Patrick J., '95 PL
Keegan, Timothy F., '74
Keenan, Jane, '72
Keenan, Joseph P., '71
Kelly, Angela D., '91
Kelly, Cheryl R., '89
Kelly, Dennis E., '75
Kelly, James F., '76
Kemel, Ann, '97
Kemp, Royevette, '99 CO
Keniry, Jeanne F., '78
Kennedy, Henry W., '89
Kennedy-Gomes, Mrs. Candice, '95 SW
Kenny, William J., '78
Keogh, Dennis F., '80 PL
Kerr, Milagro X., '99 SW
Kettrles, Tamiko N., '96
Key, Cheryl V., '87
Key, Joseph
Khilkevich, Denis A., '99 JU
Khobot, Aleksandr, '97
Killerlane, James J., '70
Killian, Becky, '99
King, Anthony B., '85
King, Edith I., '83
King, Edwina J., '92 PL
King, Jemma F., '93 CT
King, Joseph F., PhD, '75 GN
King, Michael A., '91
Kinsey, Barbara, '88
Kippins, Susan A., '83
Kirk, John J., '80 PL
Kirschner, Edward, '78
Kirschner, Milton I., '66
Kirton, Donna C., '86
Kitching, Tselanee, '99 PL
Klaus, William A., '90
Klug, Kenneth C., '88
Knight, Alisa G., '96 HT
Knight, Petrice A., '99
Knight, Roger V., '82 SW
Knippler, Wesley R.
Kokis, Peter W., '91
Kolbeck, David A., '92
Konesky, Karilyn, '81
Kong, Yuen F., '95
Konig, Norman, '79
Korb, Alan H.
Korol, Natalya, '98 CP
Korolyev, Dina, '99
Koumba, Patricia S., '99 ST
Kraus, Andrew E., '70
Kreymer, Rita, '99
Kriegsman, Jeffrey, '79
Krivosta, George G.
Krutovsky, Mrs. Darina, '99
Kurnatowski, C., '91
Kurt, Cihan, '96
Kurzweil, Andrew, '99
Kusmierska, Grazyna, '98 SW
Kyei, Patricia C., '93
La, Rose M., '87
Laboy, Luis, '84
Lacobs, Scott L., '96
Lacombe, Stanley B., '99
Ladson, Anthony M., '90
Laferrera, Anthony F., '77
Lagoda, Anthony A., '79
Lagoff, John S.
Laguerre, John, '95
Lalaram, Anjani, '99
Lalonde, Marie, '84
Lam, Alan, '94
La Madrid, Ms. Yvette, '97 ET
Lamarca, Daniel P., '97
Lambert, Joseph M., '93
Lamberti, Anthony J., '78
Lambkin, John J., '76
Land, Johannie, '77
Landais, Martine, '92
Lang, Pamela D., '89
Langan, Mary K., '95

Laniado, Elliot J., '80
Lanier, Louis I., '90
La Rac, Natasha, '98
Larkin-Bowman, Cheryl A., '82 SW
Laroc, Natasha E., '98
LaRosa, Anthony, '93
Lashley, Michelle L., '87 RD
Lassen, Christopher M., '98
Latawiec, Robert F., '80
Latimer, George A., '73
Latora, Vincent, '81
Laurence, Oscar, '82
Laurendi, Domenick A., '82
Laurenson, Barbara J., '96 ET
Lautenberger, R., '93
Lawrence, Andrea L., '91
Lawrence, Julia J., '98
Lawson, Cecelia B., '88
Lazarre, Marie, '99
Lazo, Herlis A., '98 LW
Le, Brew V., '84
Leach, Anthony, '97
Leacock, Colleen E., '93
Leah, Magnuson, '93 LW
Leary, Jeremiah J., '85
Leckey, Sabrina M., '99
Ledesma, Andres, GE
Ledgister-dennis, Carla, '94
Lee, Brenda, '94
Lee, Donald F., '98 EA
Lee, Kenneth, '96
Lee, Ms. Michele, '98 PL
Lee, Richard, '75
Lee, Shawn A.
Lee, Sherman, '97
Lee, Theresa, '79
Lefkowitz, Abraham Z., '75
Leger, Reguerre, '96
Leibowitz, Gail D., '79
Leitch, Noel E., '93
Lema, Kathy, '99
Lembersky, Victoria D., '99 ST
Lempert, Vladimir, '98 CP
Lenze, William R., '99
Leonard, Michael M., '81 JU
Leonardi, Angela, '91
Leone, Michael J., '94 PL
Leone, Steven C., '88
Lerner, Steven A., '88 PN
Lesser, Marc H., '98 GN
Leto, Teresa A., '79 PL
Leung, Chiu H., '94
Levant, Cassandra D., '91 LW
Leventon, Douglas C., '94 MG
Levers, Leona, '85
Levi, Dmitry, '99
Levin, Michael, '94 SN
Levine, Fran N., '77 CT
Levine, Kenneth H., '80
Levitz, Jennifer, '96 SW
Levy, Erez, '96
Levy, Shari, '96
Lew, Steven, '90
Lewis, Alison, '96
Lewis, Dora M., '82 LW
Lewis, Everad H., '97
Lewis, Frederick H., '98 LW
Lewis, Geoffrey B., '96 AA
Lewis, Holly Y., '98
Lewis, Ingrid, '84
Lewis, Michael, '78
Lewis, Michael G., '99
Lewis, Roslyn R., '80 GN
Lewis, Sandra Y., '92
Lewis, Yolanda Y., '89
Lian, Leon E., '97
Liberatore, Benedett, '91
Licitra, Joseph, '81
Liede, James M., '72
Lifshutz, George, '76
Lim, Elizabeth O., '99
Linares, Antonio, '80
Lindsay, Clive B., '80
Lindsay, Garth, '95
Linetskaya, Yuliya, '99
Linn, Edith, '82 PL

Lipschitz, Stephen, '76
Liranzo, Mrs. Yahaira M., '99 PL
Lisogorsky, Michael N., '75
Litchmore, Monique E., '96 LW
Littles, Willette C., '85
Little-Torres, Elyse, '95
Livingstone, Lennox, '77
Lloyd-Bey, Ridwana, '91 SA
Locadia, Janet B., '75
Lockett, Athina L., '97
Lockwood, May R., '77
Lodvil, Murielle, '97
Logan- Watson, Mrs. Tracy R., '96
Logozzo, Allison, '92
Lombard, Gary J., '95 LW
Lombardo, Blase D., '75
Lombardo, Michael D., '75
Long, Demosthenes, '83
Long, Jacqueline, '96
Lopez, Cuahutemoe, '93
Lopez, Eric, '79
Lopez, Judith, '94
Lopez, Lisa L., '92
Lopez, Manuel W., '77
Lopez, Mayra, '89
Lopez, Melind A., '97
Lopez, Raymond J., '75
Lopez, Sabrina I., '95 SW
Lopez, Stanley, '91
Lopez, Wanda L., '90 ET
Lorde, Shannon G., '97 SW
Lotierzo, James D., '81
Louallen, Fatima G., '96
Louis, Barbara, '97
Louis, Jean R., '91
Louison, Kirk, '95
Louisor, Mike P., '96 PN
Louissaint, Halaby, '95
Louissaint, Medeline, '97
Louissaint, Ravhelle, '95
Love-fox, Chris, '84 SW
Lovell, Frederick J., '98 FV
Low, Elvis T., '89
Lowe, Jacqueline P., '97 SW
Lucas, Ms. Patricia A., '99 PL
Luces, Antoinette, '92 SW
Lucien, Steeves, '99 SW
Luck, Teresa, '97
Lugo, Jose A., '88
Lui, Alan S., '84 PL
Luis, Marvin, '93
Luma, Yoleine, '97 IN
Luquis, Annette, '91
Lynch, Christopher B., '95 PL
Lynch, Rodolfo R., '83
Lynch, Thandi N., '99 LS
Lynn, Kandia O., '95 SW
Lynn, William J., '80
Lyons, Hester, '75
Lyons, Janine Q., '95
Lyons, Robert T., '93 PL
Lyons, Ronald C., '79
Lyudmir, Alex, '92
Macdougall, Michael, '90
Mackey, Daniel, '85 PL
Mackie, Dawn R., '83
Maddux, Davina P., '94 SW
Magnuson, Ms. Leah, '92 LW
Magnussen, Erik M.
Mahfood, Jad P., '83
Mahon, John F., '76
Mahoney, Edward D., '77
Maillard, Patricia L., '88 EA
Mais, Byran R., '94
Maisano, Michael P., '93
Malapero, Raymond, '68
Malcolm, Sedrick, '82
Malcolm, Valerie V., '75
Maldonado, Mary, '96
Maldonado, Patricia A., '89
Maldonado, Rose, '76
Mallory-Canty, Debra A., '83 SW
Malone, Daniel E., '75 CT
Malpica, Betzaida, '82
Maltese, Nicole M., '95
Malvasio, Sylvia S., '94

Mancuso, Donna Marie B., '98 *PN*
Manger, Nichole, '99
Mangual, William P., '80
Manios, Louis N., '91 *CP*
Maniscalco, Raymond, '87
Maniscalco, Vito, '95
Manjarrez, Jose L., '98
Mann, Jeffrey H.
Mann, Kevin C., '94
Manning, Carl E., '94
Manning, Delores H., '84
Manning, Joni R., '84
Marcel, Jean, '85
Marcus, Edward, '86 *LW*
Marcus, Steve A., '90
Marinakos, Demos E., '92 *PL*
Markey, John F., '76
Markowitz, Paul B., '89
Markowitz, Thomas, '79
Marlin, Susan E., '75
Marooney, Margaret A., '81
Marotta, Michelle, '95 *LW*
Marquez, Elizabeth, '86
Marrero, Leticia L., '83
Mars, Emmanuel, '92
Mars, Nadeige, '94 *CO*
Marsh, Judy C., '97
Marshall, Ms. Monique R., '96 *LW*
Marshall, Vernon D., '92
Marshall-Murrell, Paula, '97 *ES*
Marsicovetere, Louis, '92
Martin, Annette M., '88
Martin, Duane, '88 *PL*
Martin-Baez, Beverly S., '97 *LW*
Martinez, Alma E., '83
Martinez, Annette, '87
Martinez, Desiree C., '86 *LW*
Martinez, Edgar, '97 *PL*
Martinez, Felix, Jr., '97
Martinez, Irving, '93
Martinez, Margaret, '91 *PL*
Martinez, Oscar A., '96 *ME*
Martino, Steven J., '76
Marucci, Barbara A., '79
Mascoll, Carolyn P., '84
Maslova, Olga, '95
Masotti, Alexander, '87
Mateo, Richard E., '76
Matera, Michael A., '73
Matheson, Alethia A., '93
Mathis, Caliph T., '87
Matias, Awilda, '85
Matias, Edgar, '95
Matos, Venessa M., '99
Matroni, Mark
Matterson, Eric, '92 *ET*
Maurer, Robert T., '75
Maurilus, Pierre S., '96 *GN*
Mauro, Patrick, '80
Maxson, Cree L., '91
Mays, Valerie N., '99 *SW*
Mazariego, Andres, '97
Mazza, Dolores R., '80
Mc, Alister K., '87
Mc, Anoff K., '87
Mc, Cabe, '95
Mc Allister, Justice, '79
Mc Cabe, Joseph T., '79
Mc Caffrey, Daniel X., '78
Mc Callum, Dionn, '97
McCarthy, Margaret G., '77
McClain, Shawn D., '97 *CO*
Mc Clellan, John J., '77
McCollin, Kathy-Ann E., '98 *SW*
Mccondichie, Charise, '96
Mc Conney, Christine, '75
Mccormack, Stephen F., '95
Mc Covery, Diane Y., '75
Mc Coy, Carl L., '81
McCray, Michelle E., '85
Mcdermott, John R., '98
Mcdonald, Lucille A., '97
Mcdonald, Yajayra, '98
McDougal, Sonya B., '83
McDuffie, Robert, '84
Mcfarlane, C., '93 *AM*

Mc Gee, Kathy, '90
Mcghee, Liza, '89 *CP*
McGill, Mrs. Katrina A., '98 *MY*
McGlinchey, Ms. Anne T., '92 *LW*
Mcgough, John J., '96
Mc Govern, Kevin M., '77
Mc Greal, James J., '76
Mcgregor, Karyn A., '95
Mc Guire, Peter A., '65 *LW*
Mc Intosh, Cheryl E., '79
McKain, Velma A., '95 *LW*
Mckay, Roxanne M., '95
McKenzie, Albert W., '97 *ET*
Mc Kenzie, Andrew O., '81
Mckenzie, Malcome, '98
McKenzie, Maribel E., '91
Mckenzie, Mark A., '97 *PL*
Mc Kie, Herman, '76
Mckinney, Tracy, '94
Mckoy, Marcia, '94
Mc Lean, Carol A., '78
Mc Leod, Kendall, '78
Mc Leod, Kirk, '87
Mcmahon, Michael, '83
Mcmanamon, Michael, '81
Mcnamara, Thomas G., '91
McNeely, Karen T., '96 *SW*
Mcneill, Denise L., '92
McNeill, Ms. Jasmine K., '99 *SW*
Mc Nichols, Keith B., '93
Mc Queen, Norman E., Jr., '98 *PL*
Mctursh, Rachel, '93
Meade, Lyndia F., '86 *SW*
Mecea, Robert, '92
Medina, Francisco, '95
Medina, Jose M., '93
Meehan, James B., '63
Mejias, Richard J., '94
Melita, Gregory V., '85
Melvin, Octavia F., '97
Menardy, Jasmine, '94
Mendez, Lourdes A., '83
Mendez, Maria, '92
Mendez, Marisol, '98
Mendez-Caban, Juan B., '78
Mendola, Philip L., '83
Mendoza, Florance W., '78 *LW*
Menes, Yvette, '97
Menkes, Andrew, '78
Mercer, C. W., '91
Mero, John R., '86
Merritt, Trica, '93
Messina, Camillo, '95
Metaxas, Mary, '92
Metivier, Beverley A., '95 *ET*
Metivier, Margaret, '79
Mevorah, Steven H., '75
Michaels, Anne M., '83 *HM*
Miohaolo, Norman M., '80
Michaelson, Estee M., '99
Michel, Nancy C., '98
Michel, Pierre M., '97 *ME*
Middleton, Karen A., '99
Mieles, Christina M., '98 *BI*
Miguel, Regina L., '82
Milien, Patricia, '95 *SW*
Millan, Gregory, '82
Miller, Carlos M., '99
Miller, Christopher A., '95 *PL*
Miller, Louis J., '96
Miller, Roy P., '80
Millien, Tamara, '95
Mills, Beverly A., '93
Mills, Lurline, '92
Minardi, Rocco N., '76 *PL*
Mintz, Irwin, '75
Miralla, Ms. Janet, '96 *LW*
Miranda, Anthony R., '92 *PL*
Miranda, Doreen, '95
Miranda, Georgina M., '92
Miro, Sandra M., '90
Miron, Lowell S., '97 *ME*
Mirza, Ashfa N., '97 *LW*
Misiano, Eugene, '77
Mitchell, Charles A., '97
Mitchell, Deborah, '97

Mitchell, James, '75
Mitchell, John M., '77
Mitchell, Kathleen G., '80
Mitchell, Natasha, '99
Mocombe, John E., '92
Moffatt, Maikov A., '97 *PL*
Moffett, Anita, '95
Moffett, Melissa N., '95 *SW*
Mohammad, Taj, '87
Mohrmann, Tina, '75 *LW*
Molina, Adnery, '84
Molina, Bobby, '98
Molina, Evelyn, '99
Molina, Maria T., '88
Molina, Sonia I., '90
Molloy, Patricia A., '93
Molloy, Sean E., '75
Moment, Keran M., '79 *PL*
Monderson, Frederick, '87
Monges, Abraham, '90
Monk, Marie, '99
Monroe, Alexis A., '90
Monsegue, Gail A., '83 *ET*
Monserrate, Juan, '85
Montague, Steven L., '98
Montalbano, Gary F., '84
Montalbano, Richard P., '79
Montana, Paul J., '99 *PL*
Montanez, Anna I., '92 *SW*
Monte, John J., '77
Montecier, Allison A., '95
Montijo, Maribel, '98
Moody, Ms. Sabrina R., '92 *SW*
Moore, Faryce B., '80 *GN*
Moore, Herman A., '81
Moore, Janet M., '83
Moore, Nilda J., '86
Moore, Sean, '92
Moore, Sherry R., '88
Moore, Tanya M., '93
Moorer, Denise W., '84
Moors, Gerald J.
Morales, Bethzaida, '97 *MG*
Morales, Marilyn, '95
Morales, Rose, '83
Morey, Jose, '82
Morey, Nadege, '88
Morgan, Diana, '92
Morgan, James, '80
Morhmann, Tina
Moriarty, Justine B., '97 *GN*
Morman, Cathy E., '80
Mormando, Joseph A., '81
Moron, Robert D., '79
Morris, Logan, '94
Morrison, Joan E., '91
Morrissey, Mary P., '91 *LW*
Morrissey, William J., '67 *PL*
Mortol, John R., '85
Mortellaro, P., '92
Mortley, James L., '85
Moscoso, Emilio C., '97
Moses, Puliti, '95
Moten, Reva G., '84 *PL*
Moye, Michelle, '96 *IN*
Mshvelidze, Vadim, '99
Muhammed, Cornetta, '92
Mui, Michael S., '95
Mullen-Morris, Veronica B., '92 *ET*
Mullings, Sandra V., '78
Mulzac, Henry, '91
Muniz, Eliu, '92 *PL*
Muniz, Inez, '83
Munoz-Shivers, Rachel I., '98
Murdaugh, Gale R., '81
Murphy, Ms. Josephine A., '99 *PL*
Murphy, Michael J., '86
Murphy, Mrs. Rochelle M., '77 *CT*
Murphy, Stephen F., '81
Murray, James E., '87 *PL*
Murray, John E., '65
Murray, Louis, '78
Murray, Lynne, '92
Murray, William T., '80
Myers, Cremston M., '92
Myers, Lonnie, '89

Myerson, Wayne B., '84
Myrie, Antonio A.
Nable, Beth R., '78
Nachmany, Etty, '95
Nacinovich, Ms. Diane M., '98 *AM*
Nahar, Yesenia, '94
Napoleon, Johnny L., '98
Napoli, George V., '79
Nash, Lois A., '82
Nass, Eric P., '95
Natale, Marc J., '98
Nath, Nirmala, '87
Navarro, Mario, '78
Nazaire, Magdala, '97
Nazaire, Yvana, '97 *MD*
Neblett, Annette, '96
Negron, Manuel A., '91
Negroni, Deborah, '87
Nehama, Alan, '97
Nekrutman, David R., '97 *GN*
Nelson, Anthony J., '75
Nelson, Guerline, '96
Nelson, Yvens, '93
Nesfield, Dale D., '89
Neuwirth-Vreeland, Denise, '98 *CN*
Nevarez, Ms. Melissa, '97 *LW*
Newkirk, Rosalind J., '98 *PL*
Newkirk, Tabitha, '95 *SW*
Newton, Cecil E.
Newton, Judy D., '92 *PL*
Ng, Frank K., '89
Ng, Phillip, '97 *PL*
Ngadi, Francis B., '91
Ngai-crim, Karin, '95
Niamonitakis, Steven, '87
Nicholas, Cyril W., '93
Nicholas, Leslie-Ann, '92
Nicholas, Lester S., '88
Nicholson, Conrad R., '97
Nicholson, Tammy T., '96
Nicholson, Ms. Terry, '94
Nicks, Alfonso M., '97 *LW*
Nicolaou, Carmen A., '97 *LW*
Nieves, Cynthia, '94
Nieves, Gilbert, '77
Nieves, Jaime, '89
Nieves, Julie A., '97 *CT*
Nieves-Cardenas, Mrs. Carmen,
  '92 *ET*
Nikitin, Maxim, '99
Nikoloudakis, Georgi, '96
Nimrod, Elvin G., '78
Nimrod, Lloyd G., '98
Ninburg, Svetlana, '99 *AC*
Niss, Oleg, '97 *CP*
Nixon, Staci E., '85
Njoku, Aloysius A., '87
Noble, Janet C., '86
Noocra, Vito, '84
Noel, Desmond E., '97
Noel, Gesner, '96 *CP*
Noel, Kevin E., '98
Noel, Samuel D., '88 *LW*
Norgriff, Keith A., '96
Norman, Kym R., '86
Norris, Edward T., '76 *EA*
Norton, Joseph M., '91
Norton, William J., '76
Nozine, Josette M., '98
Nunez, Hilda, '79
Nunez, Miguel A., '96
Nunez, Yohanna, '98
Nurse, John P., '91 *BE*
Oakley, Charlene S., '97
Obarowski, Edward A., '76
O'berg, Dennis J., '76
O'brien, Patrick J., '80
Ocasio, Jacqueline A., '96 *HM*
Oconnell, Daniel V., '98
O'connor, Roderick J., '74
Octave, Colin, '99
Odom, Oscar, III, '83
O'Donnell, Eugene, '82
O'Dowd, Michael P., '99 *EA*
Odowd, Michael P., '99 *EA*
Odums, Tanya S., '95

Odusanya, Abimbola, '85
Ogbara, Jane, '82
Ogbeni, Felicia U., '96
Oh, Jong, '96
Ohale, Emmanuel U., '96
O'halloran, Daniel, '86
O'hara, Brendan, '93
Oliphant-Cummings, H., '82
Oliver, Brenda L., '84
Oliver, Cynthia A.
Oliver, Jennifer M., '81
Olivera, Tonia C., '96
Olivo, Xavier F., '68
Olsen, Steven, '89
Olsen, Thomas J., '76
Omahony, Brian E., '91
O'Neill, Angelo U., '97 SW
Onufrak, Stephen P., '81
Onwuka, Nelson O., '98 CO
Orefice, Michael L., '75
Orellana, Alfonso J., '90
Orgias, Peter D., '94
Orlando, Dominic, '91
Orta, Aileen D., '92
Orta, Harry H., '79
Ortega, Mauricio, '92
Ortega-Veliz, Olga, '99
Ortiz, Dawn, '97
Ortiz, Elizabeth, '85
Ortiz, Johnny, '92
Ortiz, Mario, '93
Ortiz, Raymond, '90
Ortiz, Ricardo L., '97
Ortiz, Yolanda, '99 SW
Osborne, Kimberly M., '99 LW
Oseni, Yetunde A., '99
Osidele, Solomon O., '93
Ossen, Helen S., '83
Osuagwu, Emeka, '90
Ottey, Ms. Donna M., '86 LW
Outar, Gail A., '91
Ovalles, Mildred L., '85 LW
Owens, Kelly E., '99 LW
Pabon, Lisa, '92
Pace, David R., '99 ME
Pacella, Thomas A., '82
Packer, Catherine, '97
Padula, Louis J., '94
Pagano, Ms. Marci, '85 PL
Pahman, Marina, '99 LW
Paige, Dorothy M., '84 GN
Palatnik, Victoria D., '97 SW
Palmer, Donald E., '73 ET
Palmer, Robert A., '84
Palmer, Virginia L., '90 LW
Panazzolo, Glenn P., '84
Papamichael, Norma, '86
Papure, Gail, '85
Paredes, Ruth V., '95 PL
Parikh, Pragati J., '99
Paris, Jerome, '86
Parisi, Domenico J., '99 LW
Parlanti, Damiano, '94
Parris, Cyril J., '84
Parris, Jerome R., '86 EN
Parsons, Ronald D., '87
Partheymueller, Conrad, '77
Pascal, Licet, '84
Patao, Sonia, '81
Patino, Michael F., '85
Patterson, Germaine, '99
Paul, Mario, '99 PL
Paulson, Paul S., '77
Pearson, Ida, '88 LW
Peart, Donaree Y., '97 SW
Peay, Ms. Lisa D., '99 SW
Pecou, Enrique A., '83
Pedraza, Evelyn, '89
Pelle, James, '87
Pena, Ms. Marisel C., '96 MG
Pena, Marisol, '99 LW
Pender, Sylvia A., '84
Pendergast, Teresa A., '77
Peoples, Yasmeen (Yaszie) A., '96
   LW
Peralta, Angelina R., '83

Perez, Alicia, '96
Perez, Gregory R., '83
Perez, Hiede, '93
Perez, Juan, '98
Perez, Leticia N., '97
Perez, Lisbeth D., '95
Perez, Rosa S., '99
Perez Y Gonzalez, Dr. Maria E.,
   '87 ET
Pergamo, Joseph J., '76
Perillo, Lou B.
Pernice, Louis R., '87
Perricone, Gerard D., '79
Perrin, Heather K., '93
Perrina, Enrico, '93 ET
Perry, Celeste M., '84
Perry, Elaine, '78
Perry, Sandra, '82
Persaud, Amanda J., '99 ME
Persaud, Joseph M., '90
Person, Brenda, '89
Peters, Bernadette V., '98 ME
Peters, Calvin, '93
Peters, Clinton J., '91 PL
Peters, Petra P., '99 ET
Peters, Yule E., '93
Peterson, Denise, '85
Peterson, Eugene, Jr., '97
Peterson, Thomas V., '80
Petrocelli, Dennis, '76
Petrov, Aleksey, '95
Petty, Bernard M., '99
Phanor, Yves, '84
Philbert, Donna-Marie, '99 CO
Phillip, Arthur K., '81
Phillips, Ernest G., '99 LW
Phillips, Ethel J., '78
Phillips, Kevin D., '91
Phillips, Leon I., '76
Phillips, Nickie D., '98 ST
Phillips, Stephen E., '78
Phillips, Theresa A., '88
Phipps, Rocio, '95
Piccerill, Kenneth M., '75
Pierce, Latanya, '92
Piercey, Melissa A., '90
Pierre, Bikens, '97 LW
Pierre, Louicasse, '99 PL
Pierre, Michael W., '95
Pierre-jackson, Paula, '89
Pierrelouis, Max, '97
Pimentel, Rosa A., '96
Pinnisi, Daniel R., '72
Pinnock, Tania N., '88
Pintor, Felix S., '92 HT
Piotrowski, Michael, '78
Pisano, Edward J., '93 PL
Pitt, Christopher L., '87
Pitt, James R., '99
Pittman, Yolanda R., '97 SO
Pitts, Jeffrey, '80
Pizzi, Michael, '85
Pizzullo, Victor, '93
Pizzy, Michael A., '85
Plasencia, Dedie, '89
Plaza, Sandy N., '96
Poetta, Charles, '80
Poindexter, Lisa N., '85
Poland, Jeremy M., '97
Polenberg, Carole, '92
Politano, John, '92
Pollard, Melinda Y., '79
Pollard, Willette, '99 LW
Polly, Michael C., '87
Polovoy, John P., '77
Polyakova, Svetlana, '96 LW
Pomerantz, Scot, '96 PL
Pope, Winston L., '98 PL
Poplavskiy, Aleksandr A., '98 SW
Porras, Patricio G., '78
Portelli, Frank, '97
Porter, A. Dashiell, '98 AM
Porter, Robert L., '91
Portorreal, Ms. Yecenia, '98
Portuondo, Elaine L., '78
Potts, Janice P., '97

Pouliot Grant, Anne C., '95
Poulos, Harry, '84 EA
Poyerd, James D., '94
Prather, Raymond B., '77
Presume, Thierry, '97 PL
Price, Henrimae, '99
Price-Moore, Ms. Jennifer M., '86
   BE
Pride, Kasha L., '98 AM
Prime, Maria, '78
Prince, Daniel E., '79 PL
Prince, Mainert J., '80
Prioleau, Catrina C., '98
Proscio, Charles J., Jr., '99 PL
Protas, Roman, '99
Proto, Rosa M., '97 GN
Providence, Sharon, '87
Pucci, Raymond, '72 PL
Purcell, Ralph J., '83
Purdie, Yvonne W., '98
Pyronneau, Rose, '94
Qiu, Hong, '92
Quarless, Tahaiwa V., '97
Quashie, Joy V., '84
Quashie, Thelma
Quatrone, Rudolph S., '76
Quigley, M. F., '78
Quinn, Michael R., '84
Quinones, Andrea, '99
Quinones, Monique, '99 GN
Quinones, Zoraida, '97
Quiroz, Kathleen M., '96
Rabinowitz, M., '75
Rabinowitz, Stacey M., '89 ET
Raeburn, Phyllis S., '98
Rafaniello, Helen M., '91 GN
Ragguette, Wayne, '91
Ragin, Kenya S., '96 SW
Ragland, Eric, '96
Rago, Jodi J., '87
Ramdeholl, Neville, '98
Ramirez, Carlos, '93
Ramirez, Karen Y., '96
Ramirez, Lisandra, '86
Ramirez, Vernon, '98 BE
Ramos, James J., '99 LW
Ramos, Julius, '77
Ramos, Rafanzelin, '98
Ramos, Rosemary, '80
Ramos, Yolanda, '95
Ramoutar, Donny B., '99 PL
Ramsaran, Ramcharita, '96
Ramsay, Cherylann G., '83
Ramsay, Elcah, '98 AM
Ramsay, Rhona H., '85
Randazzo, Leonard, '77
Randle, Kevin M., '95 LW
Rapale, Sandra, '92
Rapp, Edward J., '79
Rasenberger, Joseph, '92
Ratney, Alyson D., '97
Rattigan, Wilfred S., '81
Ravalgi, Patrica M., '76
Rawlings, Karen V., '99
Ray, Robert J., '74
Rayford, James C., '95
Raymond, Sherly, '99
Raymond, Woody, '98 CP
Reaves-Bey, Leroy
Redding, Assunta S., '99 GN
Redman, Stacy L., '96
Redman-Modeste, Stephanie C.,
   '84 SW
Reed, Anthony, '86
Regalado, Ana R., '97
Regan, John M., '77 PL
Regester, Mrs. Kimberly, '99
Regis, Ms. K. F., '95 PL
Reibscheid, Mark A., '99 SW
Reid, Antoinette M., '97
Reid, Armando E., '77
Reid, Deborah E., '87
Reid, Dyke O., '97
Reid, Jermaine, '96
Reid, Julanne L., '78
Reid, Lorna S., '95

Reid, Shaun C., Esq., '95 LW
Reid-walston, Barbara, '93
Reilly, Rupert A., '82
Reiman, Kenneth R., '81
Reinhardt, Ronald R., '77
Reinhardt-O'brien, Mary E., '86
Reisman, Barbara, '86 ME
Renda, Eugene, '88
Repaci, Richard, '92
Reuben, Ernest M., '95
Reyes, Kimberly, '91
Reyes, Olga, '95
Reyes, Sudhey, '99 MG
Reyes, Victor L., '78
Reynolds, George F., '95 LW
Reynolds, Gertrude, '82
Reynolds, Sandra M., '93
Rhem, Karen B., '83 TR
Rhoden, Audrey E., '89
Rhoden, Horace, '87
Ricci, Carmen M., '95
Riccobono, Salvatore, '77
Richards, Felicia A., '92
Richards, Jeannette R., '99
Richards, Luis A., '84
Richards, Nadege, '99
Richards, Stephne, '93
Richardson, Barbara, '90
Richardson, Bruce A., '99
Richardson, Homer W., '76
Richardson, Kevin S., '88
Richardson, Steven J., '79
Richardson, Yanicke, '99
Ridges, Thomas C., '95
Ridley, Cathy L., '90
Riley, Dawn M., '97
Riojas, G. H.
Rios, Donald, '92 PL
Ripps, Carol A., '80 AM
Riquelme, Peter L., '96
Rister, Esther S., '79
Ritondo, Marcello, '93 CP
Rittenhouse, John P., '82
Rivas, Linda Y., '94
Rivela, Steven M., '79
Rivera, Brenda, '95
Rivera, Carmen, '95
Rivera, Cesar J., '95 PL
Rivera, David, '97 PL
Rivera, Eduardo, '97 LW
Rivera, Elba, '97
Rivera, Elizabeth, '95
Rivera, Jacqueline, '89 LW
Rivera, John G., '96
Rivera, Jonathan A., '97
Rivera, Karen E., '98
Rivera, Loyda E., '91
Rivera, Luz A., '96
Rivera, Marilyn, '92
Rivera, Marta, '84
Rivera, Michelle, '95
Rivera, Onix, '95
Rivera, Roberto, '97 LW
Rivera, Russell T., '93
Rivera, Selenia, '97
Rivera, Sergio T., '83
Rivera, Walter, '92
Rizzo, Joseph M., '85
Roach, Kairis J., '97
Roberson, Lakeisha A., '99 SA
Roberts, Diana C., '85 PL
Roberts, Matthew A., '97
Robertson, Roy, '88
Robertson, Stanford B., '97
Robinson, Alvin M., '80
Robinson, Benjamin E., '79
Robinson, Daniel T., '99
Robinson, Roberto I., '98
Robles, Jose E., '95
Robley, Vanessa, '90
Rocco, Janet N., '94 AM
Rock, Allen C., '88
Rodgers, Karen P., '87
Rodgers, Lamont K., '98 ST
Rodgers, Sherrice T., '99
Rodrigues, Maurice, '94

Wren, William, '78
Wright, Andrea A., '97
Wright, Floyd A., '83
Wright, Fred, '79
Wright, Pamela G., '91 LW
Wright, Pamela K., '90
Wright, Rochelle T., '99
Wright, Wayne R., '97
Wyatt-diaz, Lisa, '88
Yablokoff, Robin J., '83
Yancey, Davina R., '96
Yarde, Margarette R., '81
Yearwood, Lisa E., '95
Yeates, Smith L., '92
Yeboah, Stephen F., '89
Yeun, Ray B., '95
Young, Felicity A., '97
Young, Rodney, '92
Young, Trent J., '93
Youngs, Michael G., '87
Youssef, Magdi H., '77
Yu, Andy, '88
Yuhasz, Paula J., '80
Zaidenberg, Nidia, '97
Zamor, Marie, '94
Zani, Daniel J., '79
Zarrillo, Thomas, '87 SW
Zayas, Victor L., Jr., '99 LW
Zebelein, John R., '76
Zef, Aleksandr, '97 LW
Zenteno, Antonio, '99
Zephirin, Nadege L., '97
Zhukovsky, Alexander, '99 ST
Ziede, Gwen, '89
Zielinski, Peter, '98
Zimmerman, Peter S., '97 AP
Zlotnick, Jack
Zorrilla, Yngrid E., '96
Zuniga, Martin, '95
Zwickel, Randi D., '99 PL

BROOKVILLE
Grennan, Sean A., PhD, '76 ET

BUFFALO
Delprino, Robert, '86 ET
Kline, Byron, '95
Mcdonnell, Patrick, '92
Stein, Heather J., '95

CALVERTON
Griffin, Robin L., '91

CAMBRIA HEIGHTS
Avery, Earl, '80 IN
Brown, Carla S., '84 FB
Chapman, Marilyn, '98 CO
Dennard, Debra M., '98
Donaldson, Michelle, '89
Foxx, John H., '79
Francis, Mario J., '93 ME
Grant, Jule A., '88
Guillaume, Christa M., '98
Haynes, Lisa D., '99
Head, Sidney W., Sr., '89 PL
Holder, Winthrop A., '74
Jackson, Karen M., '92
Kennedy, Tasha K., '96
Langston, Sandra D., '93 PL
Lyons, Leonie A., '95
Marone, Anne L., '79
Marshall, Joseph, '73 AA
Maurice-Matthews, D., '92
Moore, Joseph, '79
Mosley, Alicia M., '85
Patterson, Jeneva M., '97
Phipps, Alfred L., '80
Pinckney, Irene C., '89
Rodriguez, Marilyn D.
Rollock, Roderick, '89 ME
Satterfield, Kevin, '87
Seales, Paul J., '75
Simmons, Melodi K., '98 VL
Stevens, Tamika S., '98
Waldon, Hon. Alton R., Jr., '68 LW
Williams, Cynthia, '88 CP
Wilson, Annette G., '97 LW

CAMBRIDGE
Armet, Thomas F., '79

CAMILLUS
Stewart, Shannon E., '95

CAMPBELL HALL
Adler, Scott J., '95
Black, Sally E., '90 PL
Brosnan, David J., '85

CARLE PLACE
Ahern, Liam G., '79
Bona, Alan J., '83
Chong, LT David E., '80 PL
Dwyer, Douglas R., '88 PL
Mcwilliams, Scott R., '96
O'rourke, Brian, '88
Veigl, Eugene E., '91

CARMEL
Bruning, Howard A., '79
Byron, Brendan
Cahill, Donna M., '77
Cavoto, Anthony, '76
Cohen, Michael J., '76
Cote, Raymond A., '92
De Leon, Rafael A., '84
Gleason, Richard J., '79
King, Michael P.
Melhado, Godfrey R., '99
Minara, Robert J., '97
Santiago, Frances, '99 PL
Scally, Tina M., '95 LW
Schanil, Robert, '90 GN
Vairo, SGT Daniel, '74 GN
Weaver, Ronald, '77
Young, Robert J., '79

CATSKILL
Neznanyj, Taras P., '83 PL

CAZENOVIA
Alvarez, Margarita, '78

CEDARHURST
Cossu, Jennifer K., '98 MG
Moon, Charles C., '97 FV
Shoenfeld, Samuel, '91
Swirsky, Sheldon, '76 LW
Uberti, Arthur A., '82

CENTEREACH
Bugge, Brian K., '78 CN
Forrester, Vincent P., '77
Haynes, Robert M., '94
Labiento, Daniel, '95
Ortiz, Alex, '98 PS
Quick, John W., '76
Raggi, Michael L., '79 GN
Taverna, Ignazio, '75 LW
Troy, Jacqueline D., '99
Whelan, William E., '79

CENTER MORICHES
Spera, David N., '87
Varanelli, Andrew, '82

CENTERPORT
Bitsimis, Jeffrey, '80 SA
Cirillo, Maria D., '99
Gallagher, Walter, '66
Hoffman, Robert J., '82
Kutcher, Raymond, '76
Lieb, Kristen M., '97
Mc Callan, Eugene F.
Mc Grath, Henry J., '79

CENTRAL ISLIP
Belle, Franklin D., '89
Calhoun, Roy L., '82
Christ, Karen J., '96
Fell, Ronald, '97
Fillyaw, Leonard D., '73 ET
Jackson, Derek A., '81 PL
Lassiter, Yvonne, '95 PL
Rolle, Robert J., '84 PL
Standard, Deborah, '92
Vinas, Paul, '94

CENTRAL VALLEY
Forshay, Karen, '95
Prestia, Michael A., '89

CHAPPAQUA
Fleming, Laqueth, '76 CC
Perlleshi, Luigi, '95 RE

CHESTER
Barry, Patrick T., '78 CN
Bernstein, Richard W., '76
Gardner, Michael L., '90
Lambkin, John M., '95
Longobardi, Ms. Josephine A., '87 JU
Moses, William (Bill) R., '75 LW
Nestor, John T., '95
Pegram, John A., '91
Shea, John W., '77 MG
Washington, Reginald, '90

CHESTNUT RIDGE
Collazo, Fredeswinda, '96
Early, Kimberly M., '85
Popovic, Jozef, '99

CLIFTON PARK
Rowan, Edward T., Sr., '77 GN
West, Janice Y., '81 LW

CLINTON CORNERS
O'Connor, Karen, '88

CLINTONDALE
Hamilton, Carl, '73 BE

COLD SPRING
Eschenberg, Conrad J., IV, '76 PL
Gallagher, Michael G., '75
Moeller, Thomas R., '80
Payumo, Kenneth C., '92
Soto, Francisco, '90 PL

COLLEGE POINT
Alvarez, Michelle L., '98 AM
Corrigan, Michael J., '82 LW
Corsentino, Anthony P., '80
Derfinyak, Eugene S., '99 ST
Diaz, LT Arthur, JD, '91 LW
Germosen, Otto, '95
Jubak, Ms. Jennifer L., '98
Lambe, Joan S., '79
Lo, Chun-on, '95 CP
Matuszak, Diane L., '99 LW
Maysonet, Christine L., '99 ST
Moran, Julia A., '83
Petersen, Eddy, '80 BK
Prestia, Michael, '89
Rodriguez, Edward N., '83
Sottolano, Steven M., '77
Urban, Daniel E., '84
Xenakis, Helen, '99 LW

COLONIAL HEIGHTS
Clark, Dennis P., '75

COMMACK
Campbell, Wilfrid R., '70
Feigenbaum, Daniel, '92 PL
Frohberg, John H., '75
Goldman, Howard F., '95
Haas, John J., '67
Kinahan, Patrick F.
Kurtzberg, Jared, '93
Malenka, Elliot, '91 ME
Mc Innis, Ronald P., '75
Minerva, Dominick J., '70
O'boyle, James M., '96
Pignataro, SGT Anthony J., '91 LW
Rayfield, Peter T., '77 MF
Sackman, David W.
Sandberg, Vilma B., '82
Sansone, Salvatore J., '73
Seelig, George W., '80 AA
Smulczeski, Richard, '99 PL
Volpe, Anthony, '76 PL

COMSTOCK
Toler, Theodore M., '76

CONGERS
Andino, Eddie, '92
Brady, Michael J., '69
Brophy, Edward J., '75 AR
Cabral, Raymond, '89
Capelli, Robert, '95

CORONA
Carroll, Michael J., '99 LW
Chomiak, Robert H., '78 EA
Flynn, Dennis J., '77
Guagenti, Alfonso P., '85
Joseph, Richard T., '79
McManus, John J., '89 PL
Mir-Elcik, Mrs. Nancy J., '90 LW
Moro, Peter L., '85 PL
Motto, Robert A., '91
Novick, David, '93
Ryan, Richard J., '75
Slattery, Joseph F., '72 PL
Smith, Arthur C., '78
Trois, Robert F., '99

COPIAGUE
Appel, Michael A., '80 MG
Aptacker, Steven I., '87 PL
Bryant, Brenda A., '86
Camilleri, Michelle, '96
Grimaldi, John
Harrison, Willie, '80 LW
Korneev, Tanya V., '98
Moeser, Laura B.
Moore, Nichole K., '95
Vega, Jose R., '95 PL
Vollmer, Paul, '77

CORAM
Cohen, Bonny A., '78
Cuebas, Tonia Y., '84
Foti, Frank G., '94 LW
Jones, Solomon, '80 PL
Latty, Gregory C., '84
Leibowitz, Harold, '76
Leiterman, Jason E., '95 PL
Lowy, Kenneth M., '95 PL
Merriam, Willard E., '76
O'callaghan, Joseph, '97
Rehal, Joseph G., '89 PL
Richards, Holly, '92
Secor, Bruce M., '97

CORNING
Fee, Christopher J., '95 PJ

CORNWALL
Figueroa, Maria E., '96
Marini de Aguilar, Mrs. Ivette, '97
O'Reilly, John P., '96 LW
Quinlan, Ms. Casey E., '94 GN
Thorpe, Richard W., '84

CORNWALL ON HUDSON
Bittles, Richard J., '83 PL
Hennen, Christopher G., '79 EA
Navarra, Angelo, '78
Shey, Jeff, '80

CORONA
Alban, Donna A., '95 LW
Anastas, Anthony, '96 FV
Anatsui, Edwige M., '99 PL
Austrie, Gilda, '96 ST
Brown, Belviana J., '77 LW
Brownbill-vega, Susan, '86 LW
Cadet, Darley, '86
Carbuccia, Julio C., '78
Carson, Jonathan, '95
Castro, Mrs. Ayanna T., '95 MG
De, La, '96
Diaz, Conception M., '89
Dongo-Williams, Mrs. Marsha M., '91 TR
Edokpolo, James O., '93
Ferdenzi, Joseph N., '75
Fernandez, Luis, '97
Fonteboa, Elizabeth, '97
Fortunato, Richard V., '77 PL
Garcia, Aldo J., '98 SW
Gordon, Henry, '85 RE
Hardy, Ernest T., '76
Houston, Bernard P., '78
Howe, Lawrence, '95
Jones, Tracey L., '91 PL
Jorge, Marcelo, '82
Lam, Sindi H., '96
Lawrence, Janet M., '83
Lui, Elena, '97
Malhotra, Ravi, '93

Marcos, Maria E., '79
Maynard, Carol R., '89
Miller, Gail E., '89 *EA*
Morgan, Kenneth, '91
O'Keefe, Mary A., '83
Onodu, Benjamin, '94 *PL*
Oyediran, Jacob O., '95
Platarote, Karla B., '91
Ramirez, Ms. Elizabeth, '89 *LW*
Roberts, Mrs. Sonya, '89 *PL*
Sanchez, Felix R., '98
Spaier, Matthew H., '95
Tejada, Marianela, '98
Tutani, Sidney, '95
Valdez, Rosanna Y., '96
Vasquez, Julio E., '98
Whittaker, Ikiesha T., '97
Williams, Kevin A., '98 *PL*

CORTLAND
Radke, Henry, '75

CORTLANDT MANOR
Anfiteatro, Andrea, '91
Bauza, Luis N., '93
Borchers, Henry J., '79
Czarnecki, Anthony, '75
Mcgreal, Edward J., '92
McLoughlin, Katharine, '86 *ET*
Miller, Kenneth L., '79 *RE*
Powell-Phillips, Shawnee E., '95 *PL*
Raymond, Zulma B., '79
Sexter, Jay
Singer, Donald L., '76
Straub, R. F., '89
Thompson, Sally A., '91
Wieting, Ernest F., *PL*

CROSS RIVER
Mc, Quillan, '96
Nosek, Frank R., '87 *PL*

CROTON-ON-HUDSON
Birnbaum, Lewis R., '90 *LD*
Calvert, John T.
Mc, Gowan W., '93
Riedy, William F., '69 *ET*
Sarcone, Richard, '85
Welch, Edward J., '93

CYPRESS HILLS
Brown, Charlton A., '96 *CO*

DEER PARK
Avdoulos, Robert L., '99
Buccino, Peter J., '89
Burns, Junious L., '81
Comenzo, Craig, '95
Flynn, Michael P., '77
Giordano, Bryan P., '98 *LW*
Glynn, Michael P., '77
Granelle, Anja E., '91
King, Stephen J., III, '79 *PL*
Kirkman, Edward J., '76
Kuhn, Donald A., '74 *PL*
Matheis, Jean, '85
Mc Cormick, Daniel, '74
Murphy, Robert E., '72 *PL*
Piagentini, Deborah, '93
Plackenmeyer, William, '75 *EA*
Raynor, David N., '95
Rodriguez, Gilbert, '89 *PL*
Ryall, Jeremiah J., '93
Tisdale, Kristine A., '96
Towner, Andrew T., '75
Viggiano, Doreen M., '87
Vigiano, John T., '83
Welch, James A.
Wolf, John H.

DELHI
Lande, John, '71 *FV*

DELMAR
Defranco, Edward J., '62

DIX HILLS
Bolz, Francis A., Jr., '68 *CN*
Desimone, Andrew, '92
Ghermezian, Lily, '84
King, R., '76

Littleberry, Dorothy, '90
Mazzone, Gregory, '85
Mcdonald, John, '92
Mc Donald, John E., '76
Murray, Gregory L., '90
Pandolfo, Edward P., '79
Raymond, Edward P., '79
Sarno, Lisa D., '99 *CO*

DOBBS FERRY
Clive, Laurence E., '80
Huey, Ivy S., '99 *LW*
Kravath, Pauline, '75 *CN*
Sullivan, John J., '86
Venditto, Anthony M., Esq., '87 *LW*

DOUGLASTON
Beneri, Fred P., '78 *PL*
Cruz, Louis A., Esq., '76 *LW*
Devins, Brian M., '95 *ET*
Di Martino, Steven J., '79
Nadel, David W., '76 *PL*
Palillo-Hoey, Ann, '90 *GN*
Tuffey, Thomas V., '89 *PL*
Wrynn, Mrs. Maura A., '82 *ET*

DREISER LOOP
Creamer, Jeanet E., '94 *LW*

EAST ATLANTIC BEACH
Griffin, Brian A., '96

EASTCHESTER
Cunningham, Thomas P., '82
Gunning, Jeanne B., '82
Macdonnell, Mark C., '95
Manna, Salvatore, '97
Ryan, Michael P., '94

EAST ELMHURST
Arteaga, Ms. Luz A., '97
Augustine, Sharmain, '96
Bastidas, Patricia E., '99
Brown, Joyce C., '80 *PL*
Camargo, Catherine, '96
Castro, Arlene, '95
Chan, Susan, '97 *LW*
Coello, Marjorie I., '99
Coveleski, Joyce E., '89
Dashiell, Karen, '96
Few, Terry R., '87
Francis, Willie W., '94
Francois, Mrs. Marie M., '95 *IN*
Gomez, Angelina, '79
Gutierrez, Edith, '99
Joseph, William, '82
Karmazin, Nancy, '85
Lebron, Nancy, '80
Morales, Paola A., '97
Neonakis, Alecsandro, '98 *LW*
Nicholas, Joanne C., '81 *MG*
Ordonez, Julio C., '97
Pelissier, Junie, '99
Pinkney, Eddie P., '82
Richards, Andrea N., '97
Stanis, Mary E., '75 *CT*
Terio, Stephen, '91
Walker, Reginald A., '92 *PL*

EAST GREENBUSH
Deluca, Henry, '89 *ET*

EAST HAMPTON
Germano, Erasmo A., '72
Smith, Marjorie (Mardie) W., '79

EAST ISLIP
Avella, Tracey A., '95
Cannon, Edward T., '95
Castro, Cristine D., '83
Cunningham, Joseph J., '65
Iannone, Barbara A., '94
Pereira, Laura, '98

EAST MARION
Angelakis, Kaliope, '86

EAST MEADOW
Adams, Partick H., '78
Bianchi, Joseph A., '75
Bradshaw, Robert N., '97
Clancy, James T., '76

Dolan, Edward G., '75 *PL*
Ferreyra, Orlando F., Jr., '81 *FV*
Fumai, Joseph F., '76 *PL*
Gilchrist, John T., '80
Grossman, David L., '80
Khan, Nezam, '85
Lampert, Donna L., '81
Massey, David, '97
McEniry, John A., '74 *PL*
Parker, Matthew W., '96
Pepe, Michael T., '87
Perry, Kevin, '95
Ricalde, Russell J., '89
Rohan, James, '87
Staniszewski, Thaddeus W.
Stivala, Rachel D., '95
Surless, James M., '89
Walsh, Jeanne M., '88
Walter, Bruce W., '75 *BE*

EAST NORTHPORT
Anastasopoulos, Mrs. Cara E., '92
Bluethgen, Jane M., '94
Bongiovanni, R., '88
Calvanese, Jerry F., '74 *BK*
Cesarano, Anthony, '95 *PL*
Eastman, Kenneth N., '87
Flores, Victor H., '95
Francis, Richard W., '71
Jonas, Heather E., '99
Klaman, Richard, '76
Laskin, Edward S., '83
Maloney, John F., '76 *TR*
Mulligan, Thomas F., '89 *PL*
Noblin, Robert K., '78
Norwood, Robert, '86
O'Rourke, Tara A., '96 *LW*
Silverman, Alex, '72 *PL*
Wallin, Dennis
Wood, David J., '85

EAST NORWICH
Lesser, Debra E., '84
Orlich, Joseph A., '73

EAST PATCHOGUE
Brooks, Gloria, '87 *GN*
Cadot, Marie M., '91 *ET*
Carradero, Wilfredo, '88
Conley, Nora, '94
Schuchman, Robert W., '74 *PL*
Schumann, Robert A., '78
Seabury, Major C., '85

EAST QUOGUE
Corrigan, Thomas F., '91

EAST ROCKAWAY
Bishun, Peter R., '81
Caffrey, James, '90
David, Denis P., '78 *PL*
Feffer, Lawrence, '75 *PL*
Fogarty, Michael B., '97
Harmon, Timothy J., '96
Hayes, Michael, '97
Hettler, Mrs. Frances, '74 *ET*
Hettler, Kenneth R., '74 *LW*
Kelleher, William J., '70
Kenny, John B., '90
Kolman, David O., '76
Lyttle, John P., '80
Parrinello, Arthur J., '76 *PL*
Stella, Jason M., '96

EAST SETAUKET
Colon, Helen, '91 *LW*
Corcoran, Michael T., '73 *MG*
Lopez, Gabriel R., '72 *PL*
Ramirez, Vincent P., '69 *PL*

EAST WILLISTON
Garvey, Martin V., '91
Hoffman, Joseph C., '76 *ET*
Pfadenhauer, Peter T.
Redmond, Thomas J., '79 *PL*

ELMHURST
Alzate, Jorge E., '98
Askins, Jisselle F., '99
Beato, Rafael A., '99
Berry, Joseph S., '84

Billie-Cosby, Bridget, '86
Bobeczko, Aleksandra, '96
Brockway, Alvin J., '87
Bunkeddeko, Sully, '97
Cabral, Aileen I., '99 *LW*
Capparelli, Robert (Rob), '96 *LW*
Checo, Christina, '95
Choe, Munyong, '96
Clermont, Maxim, '92
Colitti, Madeline, '78
Dacosta, Emmy H., '99
D'Andrea, Leonardo, '97
Davila, Jose, '95
Ekiziah, Stephen K., '95
Enriquez, Evelyn, '86
Esguerra, Andres, '99 *EA*
Esposito, Michael V., '99 *PL*
Fassnacht, Irene E., '76
Forlong, Pedro A., '99 *SW*
Garcia, Adriana
Geraghty, Christopher, '83
Guarino, Nicholas E., '76
Guzman, Edward E., '99 *SO*
Haque, Ferdous, '98 *EA*
Hoyt, Robert M., '81
Huang, Yi, '89
Hults, Carol D., '95 *ME*
Hwee, Edmund, '98
Iacopelli, Thomas A., '81
Ionescu-Binder, Beatrice, '97
Jean-felix, Stanley, '95 *PL*
Jelcic, Thomas A., '87
Korb, Adriana, '95 *GN*
Kormendi, Robert, '75
Lessen, Nicholas J., '96
Liou, Choa-po, '85
Lynch, Richard T., '70 *PL*
Madrid, Nelson, '96
Mai, Herbert L., '93
Malagoli, Tara D., '99 *ET*
Marshall, Cliff, '96 *LW*
Marshall, Mrs. Irene, '98 *AM*
Martinez, Marisol, '97 *LW*
Medows, Deborah, '89
Miele, John E., '78
Milovanovic, Dragan, '76
Morgan, Bruce, '94
Murillo, Leo, '79
Nadella, K., '97
Namour, Michael, '77
Newman, Roger K., '80 *GN*
Newsome, Theodore, '78
Ng, Harry G., '96 *SA*
Pagano, Richard J., '76
Pasuizaca, Carmen L., '99 *LW*
Perez, Michelle, '97
Remon, Malena C., '95 *LW*
Rivera, Elisha S., '98
Saccheri, Paula A., '82
Sacco, Ilene, '91
So, Hong Min, '96
Svendsen, Bruce J., '76
Szczerba, Eugenia, '77
Theard, Jacques E., '82
Thomas, Yvonne, '92
Tomassi, Garrett P., '76
Toner, Vincent E., '75
Tong, Patrick Y., '90
Vu, Mimi, '99

ELMIRA
Chapman, James L., '90
Petrick, C., '90
Rhodes, Frank J., '89
Stayments, Bruce, '89

ELMONT
Armenia, Rita, '99
Balunas, William E., '89
Belotte, Myriam, '96 *ET*
Brosokas, Victor J., '77
Burwell, Shawna M., '91 *ET*
Campion, John D., '74
Caselli, Lisa A., '96
Chudhabuddhi, Pichai, '85
Coribello, Linda, '81
Correa, Tula J., '95

Dawkins, Leslie V., '92
D'Erasmo, Maria L., '89
Dolan, Michael F., '70
Goldfinger, Mary Ann, '80 MG
Gonzalez, Grisselle, '85
Greco, Joseph P., '78
Hashimi, Muhammad, '85
Heavey, Michael F., '76
Hogan, Paul T., '98 RE
Iglesias, Nora M., '97 SW
Jones, David A., '92 SW
Kaminski, Dennis J., '80
Levy, Amir, '85
Lunn, Joyanne E., '89
Miller, Eric C., '90
Miller, Michael T., '86
Mitton, Herns, '97
Parker, Meryl L., '86
Pierre-francois, Wladimir, '98
Pierre-Louis, Ms. Audrey H., '99
    CO
Rankine, Denise, '95
Richards, Lorraine, '95
Sanchez, Carlos M., '95 GN
Sierra, Jennifer G., '99
Sinclair, Pablo F., '96
Sparling, Daniel E., '75
Thomas, Regina P., '84
Triola, Michael, '89
Wade, Ryeburn A., '74
Walters, Ms. Jacqueline M., '83 GN
Whiteside, Scott L., '96
Williams, Debra A., '91

ELMSFORD
Badillo, Elizabeth, '97
Montague, William R., '80
Thomas, Joy E., '95 EA
Tynes, Harcourt A., III, '88 PL

ENDWELL
Zandy, Matthew P., '96 PL

FAIRPORT
Vanderlee, Cynthia S., '95 CO

FALLSBURG
Lawrence, Brent L., '73 LW

FARMINGDALE
Addo-lobo, Kate, '87
Boyle, John J., '71 PL
Espina, Elizabeth, Esq., '93 LW
Fitzpatrick, Brian R., '83 PL
Fullam, Robert F., '73
Galvez, Alexander J., '94
Johnston, Deanna M., '89 SW
King, John J., '79
Lambert, Vanessa, '97
Mc, Nulty I., '86
Moschella, Salvatore, '72
Mulligan, William, '77
Novarro, Santo F., '76
Palmer, Eric T., '85 CC
Profeta, Susan L., '84
Romero, Palmira, '81
Serniak, Walter R., '81
Slane, William G., '92
Soler, Rafael, '85 PL
Yorio, James V.

FARMINGVILLE
Alvarez, Judith A., '85
Baricelli, Patrick C., '92 LW
Caban, Wilfred, '95
Cronin, Michael, '98
Connelly, John J., '80
Duarte, Delilah S., '90
Hughes, Maria, '79 LW
Sanso, Andre, '75
Schmidt, William, '90
Solgan, Christopher J., '97 LW

FAR ROCKAWAY
Abdul-Muntaqim, Sayeed, '83
Allman, Crystal C., '90
Barr, Keith, '97
Biesty, William F., '76 PL
Brosnan, Donald P., '76
Brownstein, Daniel, '77

Butler, Robert E., '88
Cancel, Juan A., '96
Carillo, C., '82
Carley, Joseph, '90
Chinchilla, Maria M., '95
Clarke, Kert L., '97
Clarke, Lateacha S., '97
Cohen, Jeffrey L., '74
Collazo, Diana, '88
Cooper, Janet, '94
Creary, Michael C., '89
Creelman, Thomas C., '76 LW
Cunneen, Joseph F., '95 PL
Curtis, Terri L., '79
Daniel-Hurry, Nadine N., '95
Doldron-Cancel, Sherena N., '96
    PL
Doyle, Michael P., '96 PL
Fackner, Robert E., '76
Farrell, John F., '80
Faustin, Brigette, '83
Fleming, Michael J.
Fleming, Patrice A., '93 GN
Forte, Jennifer M., '91
Gabriel, Sandra M., '99 SW
Gillen, Michael J., '81
Guarino, John M., '79
Hendricks, Andre, '96
Herrera, Sergio R., '99
Holland, Nelson K., '85
Howley, Maureen A., '78
Hunter, Gloria E., '92
Hynes, Walter G., '83
Jackson, Latoya M., '98
Jaffe, Lawrence B., '84
James, Claudia L., '88
Knott, Clare A., '79
Kosoff, Edward, '75
Kowsky, Claire
Larosa, Michael A., '95
Looby, Lisa, '99
Lynch, Elda M., '88
Manson, James E., '92
Martinez, Sandra, '95
Martino, Victor J., '87
Marzoli, Joseph L., '74
Mastorides, George F., '81
Matthews, Jermaine, '96
Mc Carthy, Kevin M., '81
McCoy, Robert N., '94 ET
Mc Dermott, Raymond T., '82
Mcgrath, Michael P., '83
Mcmanus, Siobhan A., '96
Mele, Elizabeth A., '93
Mele, Mary G., '91
Mitchell, Maureen, '95
Morle, Abena, '85
Mulvanerty, Daniel, '93
Murphy, Thomas D., '80
Olds, Kevin D., '83
O'shea, Thomas F., '75
Pellinger, Thomas G., '80
Pinero, Ismael J., '80
Powers, Derek L., '89 LW
Pronman, Yonaton, '85
Quinones, Emanuel J.
Reid, Hattie, '95
Rhodes, Rebecca, '75
Roberts, Pamela T., '98
Romero, Xaviera E., '96
Rorke, Charles V., '71
Salmon, Philip E., '85
Schneier, Steven, '75
Schweitzer, William, '97
Small, Karen S., '95 ET
Stack, Maurice J., '88
Stewart, Louisia, '79
Sullivan, Raymond J.
Sullivan, Terrence C., '95
Sullivan, Thomas F.
Timothy, John E., '70
Torres, Hector L., '95
Trusty, Beshon, '96
Vickerie, Dana A., '90
Villarreal, Paul H.
Ward, John J., '74

Warren, Sondra J., '95
Welsh, John J., '79
Wilkerson, Walter P., '95 LW
Williams, Myron S., '96 PL

FISHKILL
Giangrasso, F., '91
Harrington, Kevin M., '76
Moore, Patrick, '99 ET
Vincenzi, Victor A., '81

FLORAL PARK
Amorese, Sam A., '78 GN
Baranello, James P., '86
Barreyre, Raymond, '76 PL
Bird, Edwin T., '93
Caputo, James M., '89
Carey, John J., '79
Christman, Thomas V., '85 IN
Curran, John T., '76
Daly, William J., '76
Dickson, Paul, '91
Drogalis, John J., '73
Faro, James J., '74 LW
Foy, Raymond G., '90
Garside, James H., '77 LW
Grabin, Scott D., '79
Grant, John C., '81
Hagan, Andrew A., '78 PL
Hecker, Peggyanne M., '81
Hecker, William A., '81 LW
Hillery, Joseph F., '77
Holt, Kevin T., '85
Hulsmann, Robert N., '73 PL
Kelaher, Peter E., '76
Kennedy, Deniese L., '98
Klein, Leon E., '76 CO
Lettis, Paul M., '83 LW
Lombardo, Frank A., '75 CN
Martin, LCDR Vertel T., '82 PL
Mathews, Achoy O., '81
Mcallister, Stephen, '94
Mooney, Richard (Moon Man) B.,
    '71 LW
Moser, Marian C., '76
Moynihan, Thomas P., '79
Mullane, Edward F., '92
Murphy, Edwin E., '79
Natale, Ralph A., '83 LW
O'Connor, Joanne M., '76 PL
Phillips, Robert H., '74 ET
Picciochi, Richard T., '80
Piliere, Roy E., '77
Quinn, Paul G., '72
Raymond-Bitz, Catherine, RN, '85
    GN
Reategui, David, '92
Ring, William, '79
Rohan, Kevin, '87 VL
Schaaff, Henry G., '75 PI
Schilling, Francis L., '76
Schmitz, William J., '98 PL
Severin, David A.
Smith, Francis X., '96
Spagnoli, Dominick A.
Springer, Richard A., '76 LW
Sullivan, Jennifer C., '98
Sultana, John G., '76
Valentine, William C., '75
Vetere, Lisa M., '95
Vogel, Bruce J., '99

FLORIDA
Baumann, Ms. Deborah C., '84 MG
Brady, Bryan, '96
Cookingham, Vincent P., '81
Reyes, Rachel, '89 PL

FLUSHING
Acevedo, Rene, '90
Aiken, Daniel, '82
Aiosa, Claire J., '80
Aleman, Kleber E., '88
Aleman, Tania E., '95
Aleo, Vito V., '75
Alleva, Nicholas, '88
Almodovar, Michele Y., '95
Amato, Rosemarie A., '79

Ambroise, Sabine T., '97
Amplo, Anthony J., '78
Anderle, Joseph W., '89
Anderson, Christeen, '97
Anderson, Linda M., '79
Aponte, Marlene, '96
Argentine, Michele, '89
Armesto, Catherine P., '99 RE
Arneja, Mindy C., '86
Artesani, Joanne A., '79
Ashley, Jo-an G., '84
Atlas, Thomas A., '75
Attridge, Walter J., '99
Ayala, Manuel D., '92
Ayala, Maria, '89
Baek, Hyon K., '97
Bailey, Kimesha, '97
Balash, Andre
Baldwin, Robert M., '76
Barbato, Michael, '93 PL
Bardales, Michael G., '96 PL
Barlowe, Brian K., '87
Barriere, Wilfred M., '91
Barrios, Luz, '98
Barry, Charles P., '77
Batnick, Christie J., '83
Bawer, Patricia, '96
Bayliss, Bridget G., '98
Beacco, Joseph M., '88
Belluardo, Joseph B., '79
Bencosme, Odette M., '98
Benedetto, Michael, '93
Benintendo, John, '98
Benjamin, Paul, '99
Benson, Rodney B., '76 ET
Berman, Merrily A., '80
Bermudez, Leyla V., '95
Betz, William, '85
Bhojwani, Manny, '93
Bianculli, Frank C., '76
Bills, Sylvester, '80
Bliss, Stuart, '85
Bolen, Thomas J., '85
Bonanno, Douglas A., '82
Boodram, Natalie, '87
Bottarini, Carlos, '91
Boudiette, Charles T., '80
Bourquin, Peter E., '77
Boutsikakis, Margrte, '81
Bowman, Lawson D., '97 AM
Bozzi, Elissa, '77
Brodack, Jeffrey, '95
Brown, Richard W., '82
Bruckenstein, K., '92
Bujold, Daniel J., '96
Burke, Glenn E., '78
Burke, Robert M., '77
Burns, Christopher A., '77
Burroughs, Ninette, '98
Caballero, Ricardo M., '82
Cain, Thomas
Caldwell, Antilla
Callahan, Patricia, '93
Callan, Kathleen A., '93
Calle, Ana Maria, '86
Calle, Maria I., '95
Calle, Washington R., '78
Cama, Pasquale A., '75
Caminero, Elbi M., '99 MG
Campisi, Charles V., '78
Canavan, Francis P., '78
Cankat, Johnny A., '84
Cannizzaro, Mariann, '98
Canto, Salvatore, '93
Capella, Ms. Jeanette, '76 ET
Carberry, James E., '97
Carey, Vincent M., '83
Carey, William A., '79
Carrenard, Jack A.
Carrera, George, '93
Carter, Debbie N., '96
Caruso, Michael L., '94
Cassidy, Kevin A., '83 CN
Castaneda, Urania, '97
Catania, Denise A., '98 LW
Cebic, Svetlana, '92 MG

Poltorak, James T., '77
Porter, Pamela S., '90
Pride, Mashere V., '76
Proctor, Lillian N., '82
Pulisic, Zivko, '92
Punzi, Alfred M., '76
Pyne, Frederick F., '90
Quinn, Dolores T., '81
Quinn, Terrence J., '77
Quintero, Marisol K., '94 SW
Rada, Frederick L., '76
Raffa, John J., '77
Raffa, Matthew W., '74
Ramirez, Edgar, '79
Ramos, Jack, '95
Ray, Thomas B., '95
Reale, Alan P., '76
Reichenbach, Robert W., '77
Reilly, Theresa M., '94
Reyes, Alida, '78
Reyes, Josephine, '83
Reyes, William M., '87
Rich, Cecelia, '96
Riehl, Alfred P., '76
Ritchie, John D., '75
Roccomboli, Teresa, '94
Rodriguez, Lina B., '95
Rodriguez, Louis I., '95
Rodriguez, Ricardo, '81
Rodriguez, Ruth M., '88
Rolon, Miriam, '98
Romano, Christopher, '95 LW
Romano, Raymond, '83
Rooney, Joseph E., '76
Rosario, Luisa J., '95
Roslan, Gary J., '81
Rossi, Dennis J., '81
Roth, Paul P., '95
Rothman, Flora, '78
Rudawitz, Edward M., '76
Rudzianis, Patricia
Ruffinott, Robert R., '84
Rullo, Antonia, '80
Rybacki, Laureen A., '91
Rynne, John, '81
Safran, Leo, '70
Salane, Douglas
Salas, Ivan, '88
Salguero, Elcida, '95
Samide, Erik C., '99 MG
Sanabria, Mark A., '94 GN
Sanchez, Ivonne D., '93
Sanchez, John, '80
Sangiovanni, Louis
Santana, Gilbert, '79
Sarnataro, Geoffrey L., '80 AC
Sawtell, Edward, '93
Scanlon, Frances E., '78 LW
Scanlon, Kevin J., '94
Schade, Joseph, '85
Scheer, Paul J., '79
Schick, Raymond W., '79 BK
Schieck, William J., '76
Schieler, Jean M., '86
Schletter, Donna L., '89 LW
Schwartz, Stuart E., '79
Sclafani, Leonard A., '74
Scolaro, John F., '87
Scott, Andrea, '96
Scuderi, Mary L., '78 PL
Seelig, William (Billy), '97 PL
Segalini, George L., '79
Sergio, Alice E., '73 ET
Seubert, Robert J., '78
Sevastyanov, Vladimir, '97 CP
Shah, Jignesh, '99
Shayne, Alan F., '72
Shearer, Kimberley, '97
Shebo, David J., '81
Sheehan, Eileen J., '90
Sheff, Bonnie M., '93
Shu, Howard, '97
Shulman, Ronnie J., '84
Siebenkas, Joseph C., '91
Sihaga, George E., '93
Simons, Emily, '79

Simpson, Gerald C., '96
Simunovic, Nikola, '85
Sinatra, Francis A., '89
Singh, Lata, '92
Siotkas, John, '78
Siroka, Andrew L., '75
Siso, Frank, '90
Skolnick, Paul
Slagg, John J., '80
Slattery, Joseph W., '89 CN
Small, Dona S., '96
Smith, Henry G., '80 CT
Smith, James F., '76
Smith, Robert C., '80
Smith, Robin, '96
Snell, Gerald J., '76
Son, Keith, '96
Soranno, Carlo C., '76 PL
Soriano, Anthony, '91
Sorrentino, Frank, '83
Spaulding, James P., '80
Stagnari, John M., '75
Stahl, John P., '75
Stanulis, Mary W., '70
Strafella, Kim M., '97
Streffacio, Patrick, '92
Subach, Robert J., '76
Sullivan, Brien P., '96 CO
Sullivan, Claudia, '89
Summerlin, Gale P., '78
Summerlin, Gregory P., '75 CO
Sundheim, Irina H., '99
Svendsen, Christian, '77
Sweeney, Joseph M., '76
Syed, Ghazali A., '95
Sympi, Bernard, '81
Taras, Joseph G., '88
Tarver, Dionne E., '98 AM
Taveras, Jacqueline, '89 MG
Taveras, Juan A., '90
Taverni, Robert E., '75
Tavitian, Lucy G., '95
Terry, Walter P., '75
Thompson, George C., '82
Thompson, Rory S., '86
Thompson, Thomas J., '85
Timoney, Gavin J., '78 PL
Torres, Alejandra, '95 ET
Torres, Fernando, '99
Torres, Michelle, '89
Torres, Vilma T., '81 SW
Torun, Aydin N., '84 AM
Townsend, Michael C., '93 MG
Tozzo, James J.
Triebe, Michael, '90
Tsai, Jeffrey, '95
Tsekouras, Fay F., '98
Tsiames, Nicholas B., '93
Tully, Joanne M., '78
Ubwa, Hilary A., '81
Unger, Robert E., '93
Urteaga, Maria A., '98 SW
Vale, Carmen R., '92
Valentin, Elliot, '93
Vanegas, John J., '91
Vannata, Janice M., '93 PL
Vannata, Stephen L., '76
Vanofsky, Michael, '79
Vargas, Dayana, '95
Vargas, Howard R., '93
Vasquez, Maria I., '99 SW
Vazquez, George P., '76
Vedral, Chris J., '84
Velez, Cindhia, '96 ET
Veliz, Giovanni, '92
Victor, David
Viggiani, Catherine, '82
Vigilance, Fitzroy, '96 LW
Vinces, Rev. Edgar J., '82 GN
Vouthas, Spiros, '96
Vu, Peter, '94
Vyas, Ashwin G., '76
Wallace, April L., '82
Walls, Bradley J., '83
Walsh, Lawrence G., '87
Washington, Dennise Y., '90 LW

Wayne, Reva R., '83
Weber, Thomas K.
Weiner, Barry J., '78
Weiss, Rudolf, '85
Whitaker, Thelma J., '81 PL
White, Woodrow, '90
Wilkanowski, Barbara, '84
Williams, Alvin L., '77
Williams, James O., '75 BI
Williams, Theresa M., '85
Williams-Borden, Joanne L., '94
  SW
Willingham, Brenda, '94
Willis, Melvin H., '69
Willis, Yvonne A., '89 MG
Wong, Rachel, '96
Wong, Vincent M., '78
Woods, Arthur C., '70
Wunsch, John A., '75
Xavier, Canisius R., '97
Yagual, Rick W., '90
Yam, Serena J., '95
Yanofsky, Barbara I., '79 GN
Yanofsky, Michael A., '79 PL
Yee, Arthur, '95
Yoo, John, '99 PL
Young, Dawn, '87
Young, Marcia, '91
Yuneman, Thomas E., '79
Zabielski, Henry S., '81
Zaboras, John S., '79
Zalepa, Robert P., '75
Zeideia, Bajes M., '96
Zhang, Hui, '99
Ziccardi, John R.
Zietek, Stanley J., '78
Zuniga, John, '90

FOREST HILLS
Ali, Anisa S., '99
Ayala-devito, Linda, '89
Balangon, Janelle P., '99
Casella, Nancy E., '97
Castro, Alan J., '97
Chabla, Patricia A., '85 LW
Chan, Patrick, '91
Chevere, Beverly D., '96 CH
Correa-Gould, Mrs. Sonia, '90
Cuesta, George M., '78
Curti, Ms. Jennifer, '95 LW
Daniels, Eurita, '80 RE
Dolan, Bernard A., '77
Drewal, Roger F., '81
Fisher, Steven A., '88 LW
Gaviria, Janeth M., '95
Gianusso, BethanyAnne, '99 CO
Giler, Lorena K., '97 CT
Glazer, Stanley L.
Gurielov, Shalva, '84 PL
Gutman, Laura, '97
Haar, Barry M., '95
Hilario, Dilcia Y., '95
Hou, Julie, '96 LW
Iadanza, Charles, '70
Kleinman, Mandy K., '98
Kolenovic, Medzit, '99 PL
Lai, Laura, '81
Lai, Raymond, '96
Liebowitz, David A., '94 GN
Maldonado, David, '95
Manette, Sean S., '99 LW
Marchia, Ms. Theresa, '80 PL
Martinez, George A., '79
Miller, Dorothy J., '83
Montrose, Sharon R., '97 AM
Nguyen, Deidre, '99
Panagos, James W., '91 EM
Polin, Ms. Martha A., '95 EA
Pollini, Joseph A., '92
Polonetsky, Lawrence, '94
Reyes, Alma T., '85
Rivero, Lisandra, '96
Rodriguez, Awilda, '86
Salamon, Carmelita J., '79
Sanchez, Constanza, '96 PL
Santos, John J., '78
Schachinger, Mildred C., '76 WR

Schmidt, Michael, '95
Swain, Connie, '95
Theile, Jane
Toro, Salvador, '89
Villacorta, Adriel W., '97
Wong, Peter, '91
Woo, Stanley W., '78
Zappulla, Barbara J., '79
Zaveloff, Sarah H., '98
Zupka, Paul W., '85

FRANKLIN SQUARE
Battel, Patrick J., '71
Bolger, John P., '81
Bruno, Frank W., '82
Caputo, John, '88
Creighton, Brian K., '99
De Cicco, Timothy J., '95
Dooley, Joan T., '89 LW
Flynn, Hugh P., '75
Friaglia, Richard A., '82
Gentile, Janene M., '93
Kreuscher, Robert L., '96
Lee, Kin, '84 PL
Mccarthy, Donna M., '97
Pinti, Rosanne A., '98 ST
Sciarini, Charles K.
Simorella, Paul, '88
Wissert, Theresa A., '95

FREDONIA
Tramuto, Mrs. Andrea E., '98

FREEPORT
Augustin, Nancy, '96
Barry, Kevin B., '75
Benedetto, George, '89
Burke, Kevin E., '99
Cato, Kenrick F., '87
Colclough, Andre W., '98 PL
Dos Santos, Richard D., '73
Douglas-Robinson, Laura V., '88
  LW
Evans, Jonathan, '75
Ferber, Eric M., '93 PL
Graham, Nichole N., '97
Healy, John E., '80 PL
Hill, Michael A., '97
Jones, Kevin, '93
Joseph, Patrick F., '99
Lawrence, Claude, '95
Mazyck, Marshall, '93
Mcbride, William A., '97 PL
Mejia, Ravel E., '96
Peterson, Sandra, '95
Powell, Sandra C., '85
Quamina, Michelle R., '89 SW
Rinaldi, Noel A., '99
Santiago, Anna P., '98 PL
Sirlin, Jill, '78
Soto, Grace M., '99 CO
Stortz, Herbert A., '87
Taylor, Arthur, '80
Thomas, Umberto P., '80
Torres, Elizabeth, '97
Washington, Theresa M., '99
Wilson, James H., '76 LW
Wittich, Mark H., '78 PL

FRESH MEADOWS
Appadoo, Ruth S., '94
Barbetta, Mary T., '95
Barreto, Samuel, '92 TR
Basler, Craig C., '99
Bosio, Franklin J., '81 LW
Calderon, Peter, '93 LW
Caro, Shirley, '95
Cho, Polly, '96
Colon-Prezeau, Mrs. Kazandra V.,
  '96
Fleming, Donald L., '78
Hamilton, Jennifer M., '99
Hickey, Stephanie M., '99 ET
Jackson, Adriane R., '98 LW
Leung, Emily, '98
Margolis, Jason S., '95
Moss, Geoffrey, '96
Neary, Donna, '89 ME

Piedra, Dennis, '92 *PL*
Richardson, Brenda, '85
Schreiber, Robert, '93 *PL*

GANSEVOORT
Cronin, Joseph M., '98 *CO*

GARDEN CITY
Alers, Benjamin, '72
Buser, Robert J., CFE, '95 *LW*
Cavagnetto, Lawrence, '86
Collins, Michael J., '72
Dean, James C., '95 *PL*
Delaney, Melvin, '85
Dunne, Charles G., '96
Dunne, Jay C., '75 *BI*
Fallon, John G., '76
Farrell, Walter D., '75 *GN*
Hart, Robert, '95
Hussey, Robert F., '68 *EA*
Ivory, Patrick V., '78
Johnson, Frank J., '77 *PL*
Lowe, John P., '76
Murphy, Patrick J., '83 *LW*
Phillips, Edward C., '74
Schroeder, Fredric, '73
Summers, William F., '73
Sumner, Joan M., '79
Terrill, Cletus D., '78
Walsh, John J., '76 *PL*

GARDINER
Wager, Tracy A., '96

GARNERVILLE
Barna, John A., '75
Colon, Jose M., '96
Dodrill, Christopher A., '87 *PL*
Ippolito, Steve, '79
Loila, Dan, '95
O'Connell, Kevin J., '76
O'Connor, John J., '75
Pezzullo, Vito J., '70
Quinn, John F., '76 *LW*
Robinson, Christopher, '81 *PL*
Rynne, John P., '85
Rynne, Thomas M.
Stephens, Leslie A., '76
Zepf, Darin R., '96

GARRISON
Fidanque, Claudia S., '81
Martir, Kirby, '78 *SN*
Mc Coy, Michael G., '76 *CP*
Torres, Nelson, '88

GLEN COVE
Gudino, Sheila D., '95
Kost, Martin L., '71
Manasse, Gigi R., '84
Mandarino, Michael A., '80
Ortiz, Christopher W., '97
Scordato, Matthew, '96

GLENDALE
Alvarado, Ivonne C., '98 *PL*
Bevinetto, Santo, '97
Dooley, Daniel, '96
Downey, William A., 2000 *PL*
Eichner, Andrew J., '89
Espanet, Jennifer A., '98 *LW*
Fex, George T., '95
Gannon, James F., '73
Greer, Michele A., '88
Hagerty, Brian D., '89
Harfmann, Lawrence, '89
Hernandez, Jose A., '97 *CP*
Kelly, Thomas F., '79
Lewandowski, S. J., '76
Lieske, Donald G., '84
Mark, Harry, '98 *ME*
Mc Cloud, J. V.
Mcguire, George J., '91
Morse, Henry R., '75 *ET*
Pocchia, Barbara A., '78
Pugh, Jason M., '95
Rios, Diana, '88
Rizzo, Leonard I., '97
Russwurm, John C.

Schatz, John E., '79
Schnupp, Jerome E., '75 *PS*
Simion, Nicolae, '98
Stock, Edward J., '93
Tuck, Stephen J., '80 *ET*
Tucker, Julia E., '75
Valentin, Luis A.
Wachter, Mark T., '97 *PL*

GLENHAM
Williams, Lloyd C., '91 *PL*

GLEN HEAD
Gerbush, Monty H.
Ogorman, Marianne, '92
O'Shea, Kevin J., '79
Rooney, Thomas F., '75
Sang, John L., '80 *LW*

GLENMONT
Renz, Peter H., '77
Umar, Warith-Deen, '85

GLEN OAKS
Arneman, Barbara A., '82
Bavaro, Nicholas, '91
Carvajal, Patricia, '95 *MG*
Cawley, Donald F., '71
Fey, Alfred, '69
Giambalvo, Deborah, '92
Glynn, Thomas J.
Goldson, Kenneth A., '87
Houlihan, Maureen A., '83
Klingener, Lawrence J., '79
Leicht, Paul F., '90
O'brien, John F., '71

GLENWOOD LANDING
Winski, Debra L., '95

GLOVERSVILLE
Thomas, Caran C., '99

GODEFFROY
Henriquez, Deborah C., '97 *LW*

GOSHEN
Castillo, Luis R., '79
Ciampo, Michael N., '83 *PL*
Duda, Joseph (Joe) T., '76 *LW*
Hoens, Eric P., '96
Hughes, John E., '98 *PL*
Kuttler, George P., '78 *PL*
Petrizzo, Joseph P., '80
Romano, Frank J., '75 *GE*
Weir, SGT Seamus P., '91 *GN*
Wright, Garnet C., '90

GRAHAMSVILLE
Henry, Mrs. Marie R., '99 *ET*

GRANVILLE
Reid, Mrs. Dorothy L., '79
Reid, Luther, '79 *GN*

GREAT NECK
Chagrin, Jay W., '79 *BK*
Curry, Thomas P., '76
Dennelly, Lawrence E., '77
Edreira, Anna-marie, '89 *SW*
Higgins, Daniel P., '76
Lin, Showsan, '96
Malaxos, Troy-Nicholas, '99 *PL*
Mc Cann, Terence, '69
Nedd, Janine A., '94 *CP*
O'connor, John F., '71
Perez, Anthony, '93
Schwartz, Ellen R., '84
Schwimmer, Claudia, '93
Slade, Howard M., '95
Yang, Yinhui, '90

GREAT RIVER
Prost, Frank G., '72

GREENLAWN
Berkowitz, Charles R., '98
Diprenda, Daniel, '83
Stiller, Marla K., '95
Youngs, Chance R., '98

GREENPORT
Durkin, Mary A., '89

GREENVALE
De, Vertevil S., '88

GREENWOOD LAKE
Dowling, Richard J., '75
Kaplan, Mercedes M., '81
Murphy, John J., '87 *PL*

GUILDERLAND
Lovell, David E., '95 *EA*
Waite-carson, Gloria, '87 *FV*

GUILFORD
Jochim, Myron W., '88

HADLEY
Foley, William J., '95

HAMPTON BAYS
Brieba, Lorenzo A., '86
Guest, Gerard A., '76
O'flaherty, Donald M., '76
Romagnoli, Michael, '89 *PL*
Sacco, Dominick A., '74
Sommer, William J., '76
Sutley, Steven L., '85

HARRIMAN
Denzler, Thomas A., '92

HARRISON
Brown, Janean A., '95 *LW*
Flynn, Michael, '94
Hayden, Patricia M., '78
Langellotti, Phillip, '71 *ET*
Rooney, William, '74

HARTSDALE
Cox, Ayoka, '94 *CO*
Devine-Molin, Carol, '78 *PL*
Fantauzzi, Douglas, '92
Goldstein, Alan M., PhD, *ET*
Kalian, Mrs. Michelle A., '95 *GN*
La Pietra, Louis C., '91 *LW*
Mattiace, Christopher, '74
Pauls, Taisha, '92
Peifer, Ronald G., '84
Salumn, Joseph C., '80 *JU*
Sheehan, Francis X., '80
Torres, Katherine, '96

HASTINGS-ON-HUDSON
Levine, Irwin S.
Wallawach, Liane C., '99

HAUPPAUGE
Foley, MAJ Thomas P., '74 *GN*
Grattan, Walter W., '76
Harrison, Henry A., '71 *LW*
Henry, Sonya M., '93
Ledford, Kathleen T., '80
Madden, Dennis J., '77
Mendelsohn, David, '92 *ET*
Renner, Nils, '99 *ME*
Saladino, Frank N., '82
Samples, Mrs. Carole R., '86 *CO*
Sheenan, Timothy M.
Sullivan, Michael K., '87

HAVERSTRAW
Cantave, Barbara E., '97

HAWTHORNE
Cornelius, Eric J., '92 *SW*
Kretschmann, George, '70
Mcguinness, Charles, '91
Moran, Brian K., '97 *GN*
Pugliese, Naomi B., '97 *LW*
Tiedemann, LT James R., '83 *GN*

HEMPSTEAD
Arzuaga, Juan J., '92
Carr-sheppard, Kim D., '85 *PL*
Carter, James E., '76 *PL*
Delisser, Christine A., '99
Dezil, Patrick, '96 *LW*
Dopfel, Robert, '96
Frazier, Gloria D., '88
Green, Valerie M., '89
Harper, Bennie, '81 *BE*
Holmes, George R., '80 *JU*
Jennings, Rubin L., '90
Lloyd-Sealey, Michele, '90 *PL*

JOHN JAY COLLEGE
Marks, John G., '74
McBean, Mrs. Ghyslaine, '97 *PL*
Mc Farlane, Charlene A., '95
Montgomery, Angela D., '86 *LW*
Murray, Thomas K., '83 *AP*
Napier, Raymond C., '92
Nolan, Joseph J., '77
Patterson-Dandy, Creola, '90
Pearson, Timothy, '98
Ravelo, Ms. Mercedes, '91 *LW*
Sheppard, Kinsey O., '84 *PL*
Trail, Robert L., '98 *GN*
Walker, Edward, '94
Young, Gail, '95 *ET*

HEWLETT
Cichon, Michael, '85
Mulcahy, Michele A., '99

HICKSVILLE
Ahern, Dennis J., '78
Anziani, Victor, '76
Becker, Lester, '72
Beja, Zachary, '79
Bowler, William T., '77 *CP*
Cassidy, Susan E., '89 *PL*
Cavalier, Dorothy P., '91
Dielensnyder, George, '75
Durnack, Robert (Bob) P., '76 *IN*
Esperto, Patti-jo, '92
Fleming, William J., '90 *PL*
Gialobello, Michael, '96
Hawxhurst, Patricia, '85
Horvath, Robert J., '70 *IN*
Hughes, James D., '89
Kapinos, Thomas S., '71 *PJ*
Logan, Mary A., '81
Millard, Thomas G., '81
Radoslovich, Dario, '88
Russel, Patrick O., '99
Ryan, Alan G., '73
Ryan, Thomas, '75
Sinclair, Brian, '93
Sprague, Robert F., '72 *WR*
Urso, Robert M., '82
Valluzzi, Frank S., '93
Wierzbicki, Stanley, '87
Wolmer, Steven M., '81

HIGHLAND
Dillaunt, Gordon

HIGHLAND FALLS
Donnery, Mary C., '93 *LS*
Fatsis, Kyriakoula, '95

HIGHLAND LAKE
Giddings, Robert J., '73 *PL*

HIGHLAND MILLS
Cotter, Robert T., '78 *GN*
Gerstheimer, Pamela, '95
Hatzis, Gregory S., '92 *GN*
Manco, Robert E., '91
Monahan, Charles M., '74
Santos, Jose J., '95
Shea, James, '95
Sosa, Stephanie A., '97
Vredenburgh, Robert P., '74 *ET*

HILLCREST
Dodson, Kenneth L., '98 *PL*

HILTON
Maley, James E., Jr., '89 *ET*

HOLBROOK
Demirkaya, Yalkin, '85
Grosso, Joseph D., '73
Kaplan, Holly S., '95
Mendolia, Jeffrey, '98 *IN*
Oricoli, Anthony C.
Ovcoli, Anthony C.
Panico, Gene F., '76
Passano, Alexander, '76
Pearce, Edward, '75
Prescott, Kay F., '75 *ET*
Sherwood, Raymond G., '74
Stelmashuk, Joseph, '76

HOLLIS
Alberti, Leonardo L., '91

Austria, Crisanta H., '85
Bailey, April, '85
Bolton, Cheryl C., '97
Brown, Herbert, '80 PL
Brown, Valerie A., '95
Burton, Lisa L., '79
Devonish, Winston R., '98
Greenidge, Doreen T., '82
Gustave, Grevirlene, '91
Hawkins, Wallie E., '76 LW
Haynes, Veronica (Roni) T., '99 PL
Hazlewood, Gloria, '92
Jackson, Stephen C., '81
Jenkins, Douglas A., '97 ET
Johnson, Doris W., '78
Lamont, Naeemah, '92 LW
Lara, Antonio L., '91
Lawton, Kim R., '87
Lindworm, Joseph I.
Marshall, Mauline A., '88
McRae, Elizabeth A., '85
Mitchell, Tracie-Ann N., '98 SW
Outar, Beverley, '97
Santiago, Jessica, '98
Singh, Priya, '97
Tims, Claude D., '75
Toussaint, Emmanuel, '99 PL
Ward, Roger, '97 EA
White, Geneva A., '80
Worthy, Patricia A., '93 PL

HOLLIS HILLS
Okin, Avery Eli, '79 LW

HOLLISWOOD
Clifford, Timothy J., '79
Santucci, Jennifer S.
Thomas, Carl, '99

HOLTSVILLE
Biot, Deborah M., '96
Breslin, Daniel E., '77
Ernst, James C., '98
Koval, Robert, '86
Pribetich, John P., '73

HOPEWELL JUNCTION
Annetts, Paul D., '93 LW
Bolivar, Matilde, '90 CP
Byrnes, Jennifer L., '99 ME
Ford, Olga
Ng, Sukfong E., '95
Pellicano, Donna M., '93
Riedinger, Guy E., '88 PL
Spanower, Michael J., '89
Stranahan, Fred, '92
Tanaka, Daniel S., '99

HORSEHEADS
Mentuck, Bazyk S., '90
West, Clifford W., '89

HOWARD BEACH
Brindisi, Frank A., '81
Cassano, Dominick J.
Cohen, Seymour I., '77
Feely, Thomas J., '77
Fiscina, Michael J., '77
Frances, Miguel A., '95
Ghaly, Ayman N., '93 PL
Giordano, Susan E., '80
Godino, Joseph, '79 PL
Gruspier, Charles G., '87
Halbohn, Donald F., '80
Iannaco, Vincent T., '75
Johnson, Martin C., '77
Leibowitz, Jill D., '96 PL
Marchello, John A., '93
Martin, Richard A., '80
Mc Darby, Frank, '77
Mc Nevin, Arthur J., '67
Muller, John K., '95
O'Connell, Sean M., '97 ME
Pizzano, John, '76
Riccio, Arthur P., '80
Samrock, Walter P.
Scheper, Frederick W., '76 TC
Silver, Alan L., '78
Stickevers, John J., '78 LW
Ungarino, Peter J., '95

Vanrossem, Charles V., '82
Viglione, Albert J., '76 AM
Zimmerman, Richard E., '86

HUNTINGTON
Akgun-Auerbach, Ms. Alice, '92 SW
Alexander, Walter, '80
Brown, Alan R., '75
Cappiello, Dominick A., '97 PL
Castillo-mullings, Glynnis, '95
Dolan, Christine, '89 LW
Donovan, John J., '77
Dougherty, Shawn M., '94
Eilbeck, Jean C., '89
Georgopoulos, Antoni, '97
Gervasio, Louis A., '76 CN
Marcus, James A., '76
McCaffrey, James P., '84
Purpura, Heather D., '99
Sassone, Joseph
Seedman, Elizabeth, '89
Steets, Vanessa C., '96 GE

HUNTINGTON STATION
Bartlett, Glen E., '82
Brennan, Eileen M., '79
Cairl, Brian D., '83 MG
Galvin, Christopher J., '99
Holvik, Thor, '75
Indimine, Lawrence F., '78
Krueger, Robert W., '93 ET
Lamorte, Lisa, '80
Marano, Joseph C., '67
Monck, Robert F., '85
Osso, Gary, '82
Sermet, Carmen M., '89
Stewart, Carol M., '89

HURLEY
Chugerman, Jacob E., '76

HYDE PARK
Truitt, James F., '96 PL

ILION
Travis, Jody A., '97

INWOOD
Clue, Denese A., '95
Holladay, Dorothy E., '82
Resua, Ronald, '80

IRVINGTON
Gallagher, Kevin R., '78 PL
Sanchez, Anna S., '98 SW
Semetis, Arthur J., '78
Tierney, Michael N., '82 PL

ISLAND PARK
Buono, Alisa, '97
Confino, Sherry L., '81
Farrell, Patrick R., '80
Picone, Matilda, '78
Quinto, Donna M., '85
Sweeney, Gerard F., '76
Thomas, Carolyn, '90

ISLIP
Correa, Felix L., '77 PL
Hall, John J., '99 PL
Kurka, Jeffrey S., '93
Mylott, Robert H., '98 SN
Paredes, Josue, '96
Pinto, Giovanni V., '96
Scott, Nichole R., '99
Scott-wilson, Nichole, '95

ISLIP TERRACE
Birbiglia, Joseph M., '75 GN
Brady, Gerard D., '87

JACKSON HEIGHTS
Adames, Flavio L., '97
Barrois, Sebastien E., '96
Borgstrand, Margaret A., '74 CN
Brooks, Lorraine K., '81
Bueno, Josner, '95
Burdiez, Ruby M., '96
Cabrera, Sara, '97
Caicedo, Astrid, '94
Calderon, Nubia C., '97
Cardona, Jimmy E., '97 PL

Carrera, Margarita, '98
Castillo, Maria I., '97
Chen, Katty, '96
Degil, Rana M., '97
Diaz, Norian F., '98
Esnard, Richard, '76 RE
Fitzgibbon, John, '88
Galarza, Michael M., '97
Gellard, Douglas, '95
Giron, Juan C., '95
Gonzalez, Elizabeth, '97
Griffin, Richard M., '84
Grisales, Claudia, '99 AM
Haro, David I., '97 SW
Haynes, Marjorie P., '77
Helfman, Michelle, '80
Herrera, Eduardo J., '99
Karloszczuk, Monique, '86
Kornfeld, Mitchell, '94
Lezcano, Eduardo D., '96
Losak, Raymond J., '79
Luna, Nallibe, '99
Marte, Sandra, '94
Martin, Michael, '95
McCann, Patricia J., '93 CO
McCann, Robert H., '80
Mc Nickle, Litna M., '85 ET
McNickle, R. G. (Nick), '96 EA
Mercado, Robert, '95 PL
Miranda, Edwin R., '93
Morris, Chasity L., '99
Pasini, Roseann L., '77
Phurchpean, Kongkrit, '96
Proenza-Klein, Jennifer E., '99
Ramos, Adrian, '75
Schmucker, Walter M., '70
Shalom, Marietta, '79
Sherman, Antoine, '93
Solis, Susana M., '93
Torres, Jesus, '95
Velasquez, Carmen R., '84 LW
Weston, Denise M., '97 PL
Zavala, James E., '98 PL

JAMAICA
Abrams, Robert, '85 PL
Acosta, Luis, '77 GN
Acuna, George A., '95
Adams, Charles J., '67
Adams, Rafael D., '82 FN
Adams, Sabrina T., '85
Adamson, Evette C., '95
Addison, Jeanette D., '79
Alcantara, Mrs. Olga, '90 PN
Alexander, Tyrone, '96
Alexandre, Carl, '81
Alexandre, Natacha, '96
Ali, Na'imah A., '79
Allard, William J.
Allen, Kelly J., '98
Altman, Sedric D., '93
Alvarez, Ana A., '88
Amereno, Bernice O., '76
Anderson, Greta, '76
Anderson, Harold T., '78
Anderson, Otis C., '78
Anderson, Paul M., '76
Annitto, Paul E., '91
Archer, Mable L., '78
Arrieta, Marcela R., '82
Arthur, Jude, '98
Ashwood, Carlos A., '78
Austin, Barbara J., '79 CO
Austin, Reginald A., '75 BK
Baddoo-Asare, Juliana, '88 MG
Bailey, Lisa, '87
Baird, Omadeli S., '95
Baker, Candiace V., '91
Baker, Janice L., '95 LW
Baker, Robert D., '97 LW
Balfour, Joshua H., '92 LW
Ballero, Hilda E., '77
Barton, Kenneth L., '84
Bassett, Gregg R.
Battle, Tamika S., '99 LW
Bayley, George A., '77
Beaman, Paige A., '96

Beauzile, Tamara M., '92
Beckett, Michael L., '79
Beekman, Mary E., '78
Belgrave, Reginald, '74
Bell, James K., '97
Bell, Rolando J.
Beneby-plaza, Cathy, '84
Benjamin, Candace E., '93
Bennett, Margaret G., '78
Bennett, Margaret M., '79
Bentham, Colin H., '83
Benton, Delores, '85
Bernard, Diane M., '87
Berridge, Heather, '95
Berthley, Maria D., '95
Betty, Melvin L., '76
Bila, Anthony, '91 LW
Bines, Joseph G., '76
Blachman, Eric J., '97 PL
Blackshear, Cornelius, '71
Blanks, Juanita D., '81
Blueford, Helen J., '83
Blumlein, Michael, '85
Bolton, Judy L., '78
Boone, Nikita M., '97
Boone, Vernette L., '89
Bouillon, Stephen, '89
Bowen, Anthony, '96 SA
Bowens, Hermine E., '78
Bracey, Louise A.
Brancella, Silvano, '69
Brandon, John, '80
Brangman, Philip H., '77
Brathwaite, LeRoy L., '74 PL
Brathwaite, CAPT Rafael, '90 GN
Bratton, James G., '74
Braxton, Valerie D., '98
Brewer, Denize, '77
Brock, Beverly W., '90 NU
Brock, Ralph E., '91
Brown, Annette M., '81
Brown, Charlane O., '87
Brown, Cheryl M., '96
Brown, Delroy, '89
Brown, Desiree, '85
Brown, Kenya D., '99
Brown-Acosta, Marcia S., '92 SW
Bryan, Anita, '83
Bryan, Egan E., '80
Bulter, Bernard P., '95
Burger, Frederick (Fred) R., '76 PL
Burke, Jeremiah M., '76
Burkhalter, Gerald, '77
Burrows, Winston A., '80
Buylding, Douglas W., '91
Bynde, Darice B., '93 ET
Byrd, Paul H., '73
Caban, Wilfred, Sr., '75 MG
Cadet, Bella C., '93
Cadet, Myrtelle, '93
Calabria, Michael, '93
Calvo, Ramon, '82
Campbell, Annecia A., '97
Carattini, Esteban, '94
Carpenter, Taurina, '94
Carr, Dietrich M., '95
Carter, Owen, '76 RE
Casper, Rene E., '76
Cassidy, Patrick E., '76 PL
Cavuto, Michael T., '78
Chase, Garel S., '85
Chatman-Whitfield, Mayai N., '95 BE
Cheatham, Anthony, '89
Cheesman, Marguerite, '81
Chiara, Frank J., '77
Chimienti, Alexander, '76 PL
Chong, Gayle E., '88
Christopher, Lola C., '78
Chung, George, '76
Church, Robin A., '89
Clough, Francis, '95
Clyde, Nicole, '98
Cody, Gayle L., '82
Coffey, Thomas K., '89 PL
Cohen, Richard A., '93

Colon, Rubina, '91 *PL*
Comadore, Alberta, '80
Concannon, Joseph R., '93
Connaughton, Kenneth, '86
Connolly, Maryann, '86
Cook, Caudieu, '84
Cooper, Dermot A., '95 *LS*
Costello, Mary C., '92
Cotter, William J., '75
Cotton, Gloria B., '83
Court, Eric, '90
Crandell, Xavier O., '95
Crooks, Sonia E., '85
Crosby, Delois, '76
Crump, Michael, '96
Cruz, Naomi, '97
Curtis, Doniyell L., '97
Cusack, Nancy M., '83
D'agostino, John, '80
Daise, Cerita E., '95
Daniels, Renee L., '83
Dash, Randolph C., '84
David, Joycelyn P., '89
Davis, Diane L., '95
Davis, Felicia J., '97
Davis, Kelceda A., '87
Davis, Matthew, '94 *SW*
Davis, Vameershala, '93
Decanditis, Neil, '86
Dechinea, Aggrey D., '96
Demaggio, John M., '75
De Maio, Joseph, '77
Denis, Iznaldy, '99
De Nunzio, Steven M., '77
Desousa, Neil, '89
Devonish, Sharon, '95
Diegnan, John J., '75
Difiglia, Samuel J., '89
Dilan, Ivan, '92
Dillard, Gail E., '97
Dixon, Roxann T., '92
Dockery, Maria, '90
Dogan, Walter R., '80 *NT*
Dorsett, Floyd W., '74
Douglas, Gibbon E., '89
Dudley, Shawn L., '95
Dummett, Dexter C., '95
Duru, Athanasius O., '91
Duverne, Madeleine M., '98
Dwyer, Lawrence T., '79
Ears, Joannee, '76
Edwards, Evelyn M., '87
Ellison, Henry J., '75
Emlock, John S.
Ervin, Minnie G., '79
Escobar, Veronica, '98 *PL*
Espinal, Elida, '93
Essig, Frank, '85
Esturine, Francella T., '98
Evans, Doris P., '94
Evans, Elsa, '87
Ezechiels, Richard E., '97
Fairconeture, Stace, '85
Faustino, Allison, '95
Featherstone, Aubrey, '80 *SW*
Felder, Venitia, '92 *SW*
Feldman, Irene, '77
Fields, Dana, '98 *ET*
Figueroa, Blanche, '89
Figueroa, Luz I., '87
Fisher, Bobby, '90
Flemings, Elmer W., '76
Flynn, Alexander A., '85
Fox, Lawrence J., '77 *MG*
Francis, Rosemarie, '97
Franzese, Peter J., '92
Frazier, Marguerite, '92 *LW*
Freire, Richard J., '93 *LW*
Fuentes, James F., '97
Gantt, Jeffrey, '94
Garnell, David R.
Gasparino, John J., '89
Gaton, Errol C., '76
Gaynor, Rabiah M., '93 *PL*
Ginel, Julio A., '97 *CO*
Glenn, Dwight, '86

Glenn, William, '97
Goldberg, Laurence S.
Goldman, Robert M., '95 *PL*
Goode, Norma M.
Gordon, Winston A., '83
Graham, Wendy, '92
Grant, Tamika S., '99 *ES*
Grays, Marguerite, '79
Green, Andrew, '95 *PL*
Green, Cynthia A., '90
Green, Michelle, '93
Greenwood, Deidra, '88
Grieve, Daniel P., '73 *PL*
Guerrero, Katherine, '96
Guido, John, '75
Guilleabeaux, Kiesha, '92
Hamilton, Rudolph H., '97
Hamilton, Smallwood, '90
Hanna, Patrick J., '76
Hansberry, Wellingto, '96
Harden, Sheryl D., '84
Hargrave, Rhonda T., '80
Harper, Deborah A., '84
Harper, Lisa S., '83
Harvey, Charmaine P., '95 *AM*
Hasell, Henry V.
Hawkins, Crystal, '92
Hawkins, Shelly-ann L., '95
Hector, David A., '81 *PL*
Hercules, Martineau, '84
Hicks, Keith E., '92
Higgs, William T.
Hill, Arthur B., '66 *TR*
Hill, Barbara G., '83 *SW*
Hill, Calvin B., '92 *GN*
Hinds, Marcia R., '84
Hines, Vera D., '81
Hodges, Phyllis, '88
Holden, McThaddeus, '76 *EA*
Holder, Tonya, '93
Holsey, Sabine N., '99
Horn, Helen L., '96
Hosein, Richard A., '93
Howard, Bernard E., '96 *EV*
Hudson, Frances L., '42 *ME*
Hudson, Richard, '92
Hull, Melanie S., '98
Hunter, Yovonda (Yoyo) B., '99 *HT*
Igiebor, Justice O., '98
Iovino, James, '85 *GN*
Izzo, Anthony J., '78
Jackson, Archie V., '81
Jackson, Falinyi D., '84
Jackson, Mertol, '83
Jacobs, Cynthia D., '81
James, Michelle R., '91
Jaudon, David, '89
Jean-Philippe, Herro, '90
Jefferson, Alicia, '85
Jefferson, Clarett, '79
Jefferson, Kayra R., '99
Jenkins, Alexander D., '77
Jenkins, Alice M., '96
Jenkins, Charisse N., '95 *LW*
Jenkins, Elaine
Jenkins, Michael A., '83
Jenkins, Nicole, '93
Jenkins, Samuel N., '75 *LW*
Jennings, Hon. Allan W., Jr., '90 *GE*
Jeremie, Yves A., '92
Jerez, Mercedes C., '86
Jernigan, Maranda D., '96
John, Lisa N., '95
Johnson, Anthony L., '81
Johnson, Halsey J., '93
Johnson, Ramona C., '89
Johnson, Robert C., '77 *PL*
Jolly, Andrea P., '88
Jones, Clarissa A., '80
Jones, Eneka U., '99 *CP*
Jones, George E., '73
Jones, Lamont J., '83
Jones, Melissa S., '90 *PL*
Jones, Otis M., '76
Jones, Rodney S., Sr., '82 *PL*

Jones, William, '80
Joseph, George J., '95
Joseph, Ms. Tania R., '96 *LW*
Kelly, Kiely, '91
Kemp, Michelle B., '97
Kennedy, Lillian, '92 *AC*
Kenner, Marvin L., '93
Kerins, Gerard J., '75
King, Edison L., '96
King, Gillian L., '92
King, Joan A., '97
Kinley, Kevin, '89
Kinyatti, Mrs. Njoki W., '77 *LS*
Kirk, Thomas A., '80
Klein, Thomas N., '91
Klimek, Katherine A., '82
Konopka, Edward A., '71
Kosmetatos, Marina, '99 *LW*
Lacondre, Earl, '81
Lance, Deborha A., '83
Larrymore, Cynthia, '90
La Sala, Stephen F., '79
Lawrence, Darcel Y., '88
Layne, Christopher, '94
Leader, Martin L., '77
Leask, William M., '71 *PN*
Ledford, Marsha N., '95 *LW*
Lee, Shashana R., '90
Lekos, Ronald N., '78
Lemons, Henry, '78
Levy, Baron O., '86 *TR*
Levy, William, '95
Lew, Lisa A., '87
Lewis, Arnold C., '83
Lewis, Satia M., '79
Liddie, Michael A., '91
Lieberstein, Steven I., '98 *FR*
Lighty, Michael, '87
Linares, Boris, '94
Little, Sheremah, '97
Livingstone, John E., '97
Locantro, James C., '84
Loerbs, Heather A., '97
Loesch, Lawrence F., '77
Lopez, Carmen I., '88
Lopez, Eugenia, '83
Mack, Alice, '79
Mack, Gerard C., '93
Mahone, Ernest, '81
Maitland, Michelle, '95
Maldonado, Ebelia, '87
Maloney, Eileen A., '79
Manns, Olivien D., '80
Marchello, Charles J., '82
Marotta, James A., '80
Marshall, Noel, '95
Martinez, Joselin, '99
Martinez, Lucy, '91
Martini, John F., '77
Matalon, Victor C., '80
Maturine, Latoya D., '98
Matute, Gaynell, '96
Maycock, Neville G., '76
McAliney, Kevin P., '82
Mc Bride, Richard H., '78
McCabe, John P., '73 *ET*
McCain, Jamaine, '94
Mccain, Shanique S., '98 *AM*
McCallum, Sonya L., '93
Mc Clain, Joseph, '77
McCorkle, Emma, '91
Mc Coy, Henry, '72
McGrath, Juzann M., '99
Mc Junkin, William M., '80 *PL*
Mc Kenize, Reginald, '81
Mc Kenna, Michael, '87
Mckenzie, Reginald R., '81
Mckenzie, Roger A., '92
McKetney, L., '83
McKoy, Barbara S., '83
McLeod, Andrea M., '89
Mc Neal, Harry E., '76
Mcpherson, Michele M., '95
Melgar, Silvia L., '99
Messam, Carol R., '85
Metzger, Robert, '77

Michel, Pierre H., '92
Middleton, Ruth P., '99
Miley, Gregory L., '79
Miller, Melva, '96 *LW*
Miller-Diaz, Harriett, '83
Millien, Sabine M., '84
Mines, Gerald E.
Minoras, Bert, '86
Mitchell, Anthony J., '84 *SW*
Mitchell, Barbara B., '74
Montas, Roland, '81
Montgomery, Paul S., '85
Moonan, Ravi N., '99 *PL*
Moore, Doreen, '95 *MG*
Moore-Baker, Simone I., '94 *LW*
Moorer, Shannon, '92
Morales, Benito, '86
Moran, Kendre M., '99
Morris, Elaine L., '79
Morris, Rhoda M., '79
Morrow, William, '92
Moses, Stephanie M., '93 *PL*
Mosley, Michelle J., '87
Moye, Millicent L., '95 *LW*
Mugno, Richard E., '81
Mulvena, James F., '81
Murdock, Timothy P., '86
Murphy, Brian C., '96
Murphy, Steven, '75
Murray, Daniel F., '95
Murray, Gwendolyn, '92
Murrell, Michelle C., '92
Myers, Gregory, '92
Nandkisure, Shawn
Nazaire, Jacques, '93 *LW*
Nedderman, Dionne A., '97
Neumeyer, Donald G., '75
Nicholas, Ainsley, '95
Nizza, Joseph R., '74
Noble, Simone A., '98
Normil, Marie, '95
Nunez, Claribel, '99 *PL*
Nurse, Scott, '85
Odom, Annie D., '85
Odom, Gwendolyn N., '79
O'Donnell, Lorraine J., '75
Oliver, Paul S., '95
Onukogu, Ignatius J., '91
O' Okpara, Innocent, '96
Oquend, Madeline M., '82
Owens, Veronica M., '96
Owens-Duff, Sharon A., '81 *ET*
Paitakis, Terry, '92
Pannell, Derwin D., '89
Panther, Shakira L., '95
Parker, James W., '71
Parker, SGT Richard, '80
Parker, Rodney K., '82
Passero, Robert J.
Patnett-miller, Freddiemae, '93
Payne, Andrea T., '97
Pearce, William, '88 *BE*
Pearson, James T., '76
Perkins, Charles T., '83
Perkins, Christopher D.
Perry, Robin, '93
Pervis, Derrick, '86
Peterson, Kevin C., '79
Petrovitch, Diana, '90
Pettigrew, Rose A., '86
Philips, Richard E., '92
Phillip, Kyna W.
Phillips, Jennie R., '86 *LW*
Phillips, Timothy F., '98
Pierre, Taciana, '99
Pierre-Jacques, Charles, '84 *ME*
Pierre-louis, M., '92
Pierre-louis, Wilson, '96
Pierre Pierre, Eddy, '89 *LW*
Pinto, Christine M., '96
Pittelli, Valerie E., '96
Poma, Ms. Patricia E., '97 *GN*
Porter, Elnora, '82
Porter, Sandra, '81
Powell, Hettie V., '89
Powell, Howard G., '76 *PL*

Mc Hugh, Edward, '76 *LW*
Mendell, Jonathan, '94
Meyers, Harold, '74 *GN*
Monaghan, William A., '84
Morales, Nicholas F., '90
Neifeld, Robert, '72 *PL*
O'Loane, Daniel R., '71 *PL*
Poveromo, Joseph, '85 *PL*
Regan, Kevin J., '78 *GN*
Riley, James B., '75 *RE*
Ring, Brian, '96
Scumaci, Anthony J.
Spadafora, Ronald R., '86
Spinella, Raymond, '98
Stanton, Katherine A., '84
Travers, Richard A., '73
Welt, Carey A., '89 *PL*
Zena, Carlos W., '84
Zinnel, Michael G., '92
Zwerling, Gayle B., '98 *LW*

LIBERTY
Holland, Daniel J., '77

LINDENHURST
Albert, Philip J., '80
Alejandro, Gina M., '98 *IN*
Ayrovainen, Thomas, '83
Caminske, Russell L., '84
Cohane, Miriam B., '79
Desenso, Eldon
Grice, Richard G., '76
Jablonska, Beata, '95 *LW*
Kallash, Anas M., '87
Lo Braico, Mrs. Dawn M., '84
Loranger, Michelle, '95
Loughlin, Bernard E., '78
Lubin, Suze, '98
Luke, Mrs. Cherylann, '92 *LW*
Maltby, Paul H.
Mari, Daniel J., '74 *PL*
Muellers, Deborah L., '92
Negron, Diana, '90
Rodriguez, Ms. Migdalia A., '78 *PL*
Russo, Philip A., '95
Sarno, Henry C., '82
Simmons, Cathy, '92
Sottile, Marion, '86
Vega, Thomas R., '94
Whitfield, David

LITTLE FALLS
Stewart, Jeffrey, '93

LITTLE NECK
D'Arpe, Gene, '93
De George, Joseph W., '98 *CN*
Duffy, Charles P., '95 *PL*
Goncalves, Paula, '92
Hegarty, James, '84 *PL*
Ko, Ivan, '86 *LW*
Kurtz, Michael J., '76 *BI*
Manzello, Joseph, '97 *PL*
Shack, SGT Stanley

LIVINGSTON MANOR
Bauer, Michael, '80

LLOYD NECK
Wicks, Gwynne, '91 *CN*

LOCUST VALLEY
Jun, Mary, '97

LONG BEACH
Abramowitz, Michael, '87
Astrizky, Beatrice N., '80
Bacchus, Roseema S., '93
Brady, James S., '77
Brown, Raymond M., '76 *MG*
Carbin, Bernard J., '75
Cassidy, Michael A., '95
Cassidy, Sharon E., '92
Connolly, Daniel, '95
Cunningham, Edmund P., '79
Dargan, Thomas J., '76
Dolan, Maureen A., '79
Dorfman, Abraham, '73
Elfeld, Elizabeth, '83 *LW*
Hammel, Manuela M., '80
Jablons, David N., '90 *SW*

Laffey, John J., '83 *PL*
Lum, Geraldine W.
Martin, Teresa R., '93
Montagna, Frank C., '86
Pacheco, M. Yvette, Esq., '91 *MG*
Reinking, Robert F., '90
Rondina, Frederick E., '77 *GN*
Rose, Ronald M., '81
Rudolph, Gary J., '97
Shapiro, Stanley, '70
Stark, Robert M., '95 *RE*
Streber, Kathleen I., '82
Yanolatos, Michael D., '76
Zaharko, Stephen P., '78
Zedeck, Deborah S., '91 *CH*
Zinno, Lorrie A., '89 *LW*
Zummo, Michael A., '77 *LW*

LONG ISLAND CITY
Acosta, Michelle, '99
Agho, Jeromia, '96
Ahel, Sabine, '93
Ahmad, Shiraz, '95
Alanis, Kevin, '92
Alibrande, Donald, '76
Al-qadiri, Talla, '93
Alvarez, Lucrecia, '91
Amandola, Joseph J., '79
Arce, Nelson, '95
Aruz, Steve A., '95
Avila, Douglas E., '89
Azeglio, Anna M., '92
Balducci, Frank, '94 *LW*
Best, Aromah, '97 *SW*
Boggiano, Daniel, '94 *PL*
Bothos, Demetrios, '96 *LW*
Bourdon, Martha L., '99
Bratcher, Illene, '92
Brewer, Howard, '79
Bromley, Stephen T., '80
Buscemi, Salvatore, '74
Calvo, Jenny M., '89
Camargo, Ruth E., '98
Carberry, George M., '76
Carillo, Joseph A., '78
Carpanini, Nancy M., '79
Carvajal, Rita M., '86
Cepeda, Ivan A., '82
Ciccone, Frank, '93
Cini, Robert A., '83
Cocoros, Denise, '93
Colon, Nancy, '83
Colon, Walter, '81
Contino, Jeffrey J., '82
Cook, Robert A., '80
Cox, Andrea, '85
Crayton, Wanda A., '99 *ET*
Cueva, Patrica E., '98
Dallara, Mark A., '78 *GN*
DeConinck, David A., '95 *LW*
Delapaz, Frank C., '95
Dellicarpini, Joseph, '77
Demaio, Vincent, '93
Deow, Nadira, '86
Diaczuk, Peter J., '78
Di Mango, Domenick, '78
Ditto, Robbin A., '80
Donnelly, Matthew T., '79
Dourmas, Georgia, '84
Evans, Robert, '91
Fajardo, Edward, '91
Figueroa, Monica P., '89
Francis, Mildred L., '80
Franklin, Raymond J., '99
Giannoutsos, K., '93
Gladston, Lewis F., '83
Golfinopoulos, Kostas, '83 *LW*
Grant, Barbara V., '80
Green, Herman L., '76
Guarino, Jerry C., '94
Guerriero, Douglas G., '80
Guillouette, Darlay, '92
Gural, Gary P., '78
Haberstock, John G., '93
Hanrahan, Claire T., '94
Harb, Rifat A., '91
Henao, Rosa E., '77

Iacovou, Jack, '87
Jackson, Raymond, '87
Jalaf, Gabi G., '88
Jaworsky, Alice, '95 *LW*
Jordan, Nazly, '98 *CO*
Jules-Louis, C., '90
Junko, Lisa M., '95
Karageorge, Basil A., '85
Khan, Imran E., '88
Knezevic-Xanthos, Mrs. Antoaneta, '98 *ST*
Koumpouras, John, '95
Kozlow, Mary, '86 *PL*
Kumagai, Koshin, '98 *ST*
La Bozzetta, Victor, '81
La Covara, Margaret M., '77 *GN*
Lajszky, Werner P., '97
Lambrianidou, Kyriaki, '99 *ST*
Lasack, Ian N., '84 *CP*
Lavin, John F., '90
Leblanc, Louis M.
Lee, Fei, '92
Lieff, John C., '81
Liu, George, '79
Lutzker, Marilyn
MacDowell, Rick W., '88 *PL*
Mammarelli, Christopher J., '95 *TC*
Martin, Michael A., '84
Martinez, Maria O., '98
Matos, Edwin A., '98 *PL*
Matos, Nelson-Ness, '85 *PS*
Medic, Joseph, '96 *LW*
Mellado, Cristina B., '89
Mendoza, Arcadio, '81
Merrick, Timothy, '95
Metaxas, Alexander, '99
Michaelides, Vasilis, '90
Michelakou, Sophie, '88
Mihalakelis, Michael, '77 *GN*
Miller, Edward D., '95
Millevoi, Frank, '96
Mitrotasios, Chris, '91
Montalvo, Juan, '95
Moore, Talitha, '99 *MG*
Morales, Alejandra, '89
Moreia, Fredrick M., '98 *PL*
Nacinovich, Mario, '77
Napolitano, Ralph T., '76
Naughton, Thomas G., '87
Nicola, Christos, '89 *PL*
Nobles, Sharon V., '97 *LW*
Nock-Dudley, Joyce A., '82
Odabashian, Ralph, '92
O'Keefe, Patricia J., '92 *CP*
Oquendo, Vivian L., '93
Ozzandar, Engin, '96
Palazzolo, Florence F., '78
Parsons, Adrienne D., '83
Perez, Mike, '97
Perrin, Margaret B.
Peterman, Jesse E., '68
Piccirella, Pasquale, '80
Piliero, Giuliano, '95
Pomales, Mildred, '96 *HM*
Pradieu, Caroline, '95
Psahos, Theodoros (Ted), '95 *GN*
Reskow, Kristin E., '94
Rivera, Samari, '76
Rivera, Wanda L., '90
Roberts, Linda, '97
Romero, Angela, '96
Saenger, Patricia A., '79
Santora, Alexander, '74 *PL*
Schwarz, Eric E., '80
Seegopaul, B., '88
Serrano, Estella, '95
Shaw-Brewer, Cil M., '82 *LW*
Simpson, Rhoda, '91
Skuludis, Theodora, '87
Smrcka, Peter G., '85
Sribnik, Steven, '91
Stanley, Lynnette, '98
Stathopoulos, E., '80
Stefanidis, Stavros, '90
Stewart, Michelle D., '91
Strocco, Allison M., '85

JOHN JAY COLLEGE
Tomczak, Jill, '89
Torretta, Michael V., '80
Tutino, Barbara J., '90
Twu, Yu-jeng, '94
Valle, Frank V., '75
Waite-Shuler, Yvette M., '97 *SW*
Wilson, Ramika, '95
Zicuis, Paul, '97

LYNBROOK
Aloisio, Sal, '80
Birner, Jolene N., '98
Blomquist, Bryan D., '95 *PL*
Bowes, Vincent, '75 *FV*
Canny, Joseph, '96
Capàsso, Geraldine C., '79
Cervino, Anthony R., '79 *MF*
Comastri, Harold N., '80 *PL*
Conti, Jack, '78
Devine, Patrick, '96 *CO*
Fabian, Raymond, '95 *LW*
Forman, Morrey A., '68
Garry, Thomas N., '95 *PL*
Gill, Alyson J., '86
Golaszewski, Henry, '90
Kelly, Robert J., '80 *PL*
Kroll, Irwin S., '82
Largo, Alfred E., '80
Markey, Peter, '85
McAlpin, William T., '99 *PL*
Mc Knight, Walter D., '76
Medintz, Igor, '90
Randazzo, Todd, '78 *PL*
Stanton, John P., '77
Tauckus, Peter J., '83
Tomasso, Nicholas F., '75
Volin, Howard J., '82 *LW*
Watenberg, Mark, '82 *PL*
Zarate, Sandra L., '85 *PL*

MAHOPAC
Amplo, Anthony S., '90
Barquin, Armando X., '92 *PL*
Bruen, Noel F., '91
Coakley, Daniel P., '73 *BK*
Collins, Barbara W., '96 *CP*
Dardzinski, Lisa A., '95 *NU*
Guski, Christopher J., '98
Hartnett, Michael J., '77
Hughes, Mrs. Camille R., '96
Kelly, John E., '74 *CN*
Kirkman, Scott J., '92
Lamot, Michael D., '84
Lepore, Silvano, '86
Mammano, Richard A., '78 *PL*
Marrero, Jose N., '83 *PL*
Mc Carthy, Eugene F., '76
Mc Hugh, Edward C., '74
Perry, Patrick W., '77
Ryan, Michael, '78
Sheehan, Brian, '84 *PL*
Soares, Scott A., '93
Stahl, Doris A., '74 *GE*
Swarm, Edward, '83

MALVERNE
Barbera, Joseph, '92
Colon-Ramos, CAPT Miguel A., '80 *LW*
Fernandez, Michael, '92
Hunter, Philip, '96
Koonmen, Mary B.
Melchiona, Diane B., '66
Molina, Oscar M., '84
O'Grady, Martin F., '80 *PL*
Plesnitzer, Edward J., '76
Randazzo, Gary G., '88
Sotero, Robert F., '93
Vecchione, Deborah A., '76
Wadis, William A., '78
Wittrock, William G., '76 *MG*

MAMARONECK
Cavanagh, Charles W., '75
Flynn, Edward E.
Fraioli, Joyce A., '82
Mercogliano, Frank, '92
Romani, Mark A., '70 *ET*

Sudol, Richard W., '92

MANHASSET
Dowd, Timothy M., '78 *PL*
Kaplan, Dr. Lawrence J., '81 *ET*
Pezzo, Domenic, '75 *PL*
Rankin, Ms. Louise M., '98
Sala, Joseph J., '76
Sheehan, John P., '73 *RE*
Veyvoda, Joseph F., '76
Wolinski, Thomas P., '78

MANORVILLE
Blaszcyk, Theodore W., '81
Cuff, Patrick K., '78
Jablonsky, William, '92
Martino, Angelo, '76
Martorano, Thomas A., '78 *PL*
Misson, George R., '76 *GN*

MARCELLUS
Potucek, Daniel R., '88

MASPETH
Abruzzi, Raymond J., '81 *PL*
Almonte, Ernesto R., '98
Andino, Anita M., '96
Bach, Robert R., '76
Bohack, Susan, '91
Bonilla, Anthony, '99
Ciorciari, David J., '80 *PL*
Dziekonski, Barbara, '92 *BI*
Gaidis, John T.
Gibbs, Michael J., '97
Golino, Michael J., '95
Guerra, Cecilia M., '97 *GN*
Koumides, Steve, '87
Kramer, Sean C., '95
Kukurinis, Theologia, '97
Macolino, Eric J., '90
Mahady, Myles, '97 *PL*
Markiewicz, Tom A., '97
Mascia, Joseph, '81
McInerney, Joseph, '83
Mc Nulty, Daniel J., '79
Moutopoulos, Jimmy, '99
Munjack, Joel A., '82
Nostramo, Thomas, '77
Pioli, Victor J., '85
Puleo, Thomas A., '93
Rivera, Jose A., '98
Rogers, William J., '76
Rosario, Fernando, '96
Rossello, Manuel, '97 *PL*
Ruvolo, Anthony P., '79
Smallwood, William K., '83
Wysocka, Anita, '99

MASSAPEQUA
Ahlers, Kenneth W., '76
Auletta, Richard N., '77 *PL*
Bailey, Stephen H., '76 *GN*
Bert, Gerard, '91
Block, James B., '91
Bondor, Stephen A., '82
Campagnola, Alfonso, '75 *GN*
Campbell, Tricia T., '96
Carson, Andrew F., '76
Chason, Neil S., '81
Corcoran, Frank E., '80
Culella, Marycatherine E., '98
Dale, Thomas V., '90
D'ambrosio, Louis J., '76
Depierro, Joseph M., '69 *PL*
De Rosa, Vincent P., '79
Dundon, John W., '92
Durnin, Thomas A., '77
Encarnacion, Gregory, '97
Fogarty, James P., '68 *PL*
Frisco, Nick M., '84
Glavey, Edward, '91
Greco, CAPT Carl J., '74 *PL*
Gregg, Tommy L., '79
Gross, Daniel, '78
Harinski, James, '91 *LW*
Hayde, William P., '79
Healy, Regina A., '90
Jones, Joseph L., '73
Jones, Robert H., Sr., '78 *LW*

Kateridge, Janine M., '95 *CO*
Longo, Steven, '93
Lynam, David S., '86
Magnus, Connie L., '84 *PL*
Majid, Syed M., '97
Marotta, Michael G., '79
Mcdesmott, James E., '96
Mentuck, Edward M., '76
Merrifield, Lauri A., '81
Michell, Arthur N., '75
O'Brien, Stephen P., '91 *PL*
Ortiz, Carolina M., '95
Reilly, Edward, '96
Sanchez, Michael J., '93
Sawina, Gregory, '90
Schiraldi, Vito, '85
Selzner, Jennifer L., '95
Serafino, John M., '85 *AP*
Smith, Harry, CPP, '73 *BE*
Souvenir-brice, Mrs. Cassandra Y., '95 *ET*
Ward, John W., '74
Ward, Thomas J., DPA, *ET*

MASSAPEQUA PARK
Barrett, Daniel J., '81 *IN*
Bruechert, Nicolle, '98
Carroll, John J., '73
Clark, John W., '78
Danaher, James L., '76
Didonato, Anthony R., '70
Fermature, Thomas L.
Flood, James E., '75
Geist, Mitchell, '91 *LW*
Gorman, James P., '76 *MG*
Gorrasi, Joseph R., '80
Grant, Michael G., '75
Hudson, John J., '75
Hussey, Brian P., '84 *PL*
Johnson, Donald F., '75 *LW*
Katz, Robert G., '76
Kmetz, Thomas R., '90
Krutys, Edward J., '71
Leonard, Daniel F.
Louttit, Robert J., '79 *LW*
Mc Guinness, Francis, '75
Mc Williams, John J., '75
Naylor, Howard C., '79
Parrish, David, '99 *IN*
Petraco, Nicholas, '79
Raman, Fredrick C., '94
Rubinson, Scott H., '91
Scott, Mrs. Gladys A., '98 *PL*
Stanulis, Robert J.
Tamborino, Michael, '93
Tucciarone, Theodore

MASTIC
Jones, Darrell R., '85
Lane, Thomas R.
Ponzio, William P., '76 *PL*

MASTIC BEACH
Diver, Hugh J., '74 *PL*
Fahey, John W., '78
Lauria, James, '86
Nasa, Joseph
Ramos, Christopher L., '85
Solano, Elsa E., '94
White, Pamela S., '81

MATINECOCK
Masse, Jennifer

MAYBROOK
Uttendorfsky, M., '90

MECKLENBURG
Sumner, Sally L., '89

MEDFORD
Badillo, Anderson, '92 *PL*
Fredericks, Walter F., '76
Gee, Anthony D., '99
Gunn, Robert (Bob), '76
Hein, Jennifer, '96
Holub, Peter W., '78
Lewis Sardia, Sardia F., '99
Rensch, Laura, '95
Stone, Carl J., '97

Tabb, James L., '75
Tomlinson, Camille E., '96 *SW*

MELVILLE
Bach, Roger J., '96 *GN*
Blackman, Salena M., '92
Chang, Mrs. Josephine, Esq., '91 *LW*
Eisenberg, Scott, '95
Luis, Hector, '76
Roman, Hector L., '76
Salzano, Dr. Julienne, *GN*
Tow, Jonathan L., '94 *MG*
Vaher, Kristi L., '99

MERRICK
Bleiberg, Bruce A., '80
Borman, William G., '75
Cotty, Edward, '73 *PM*
Eckstein, Robert, '97
Filipiak, Paul J., '83 *PL*
Kennedy, Richard J., '75
Mccarthy, Timothy, '93 *PL*
Mckenna, Timothy P., '96
Mc Sweeney, Dennis F., '74
Nau, Michael, '96 *PL*
Petrilli, John A., '78
Pierri, Rocco J., '99
Thomann, Joseph S., '76
Vazquez, George N., '89 *LW*

MIDDLE ISLAND
Dettmann, Edmund P., '81 *LW*
Jones, Heather D., '93
Meinken, Todd E., '97
Pego, Michelle M., '89
Shivers, Lashonne L., '99 *AM*

MIDDLETOWN
Carpenter, Jeffrey S., '92
Doute, Jemal L., '98 *PL*
Emerson, James C., '90 *MG*
Flores, Jason D., '99
Giordano-Valentin, Melissa A., '98 *LW*
Goldsmith, Andrea M., '93
Gossman, Craig W., '98
Graham, Kenneth, '91 *ET*
Houston, Leonard W., PhD, '82 *LW*
Jefferson, Oubey L., '77
Jones, Kimberly A., '92
Lafemina, Ms. Eileen T., '98 *PL*
Lao, Jorge L., '94
Lopez, Miguel, '91 *PL*
Miller, Lee A., '96 *MG*
Minogue, Edward T., '75
Moskowitz, Ari A., '97 *PL*
Muratore, Anthony, '67 *ET*
Norat, Wigberto, '79 *PL*
Petersen, Alan, '86 *SN*
Rodriguez, Nicholas, '97 *PL*
Sheard, Paige C., '98
Winters, Alan J., '79
Zerbarini, John P., '83 *GN*

MIDDLE VILLAGE
Amanna, Francine M., '97
Dowd, Peter J., '96 *GN*
Fajardo, Juan Carlos, '99 *ST*
Fenrich, Ronald J., '75
Franke, Patricia D., '78
Gill, Brian P., '97
Gonzalez, Carmen L., '99
Haaland, Mrs. Jacqueline R., '93 *PL*
Huller, Thomas P., '77 *PL*
Keane, Timothy J., '67
Keeney, Brendan W., '85 *PL*
Lerner, Larisa, '97
Makahon, James R., '88
Malysz, Josephine, '92 *ME*
Mazzella, Susan I., '96
McCann, Michael
Mc Cann, Michael F., '75 *MG*
Mcmahon, Michael S., '97
Myers, Joseph A., '95
Nowak, Dennis A., '78
Rahill, Francis T., '71
Ripandelli, Alphonse, '76

Ryan, Martin J., '76
Swiatocha, Donald J., '85
Ta'Penzieri, Charles, '77
Villegas, Lliana, '97 *MG*
Vivieca, Adriana

MILAN
Haskins, Kimberley A., '89 *LW*

MILLER PLACE
Anderson, Krik C., '96
Breslin, Ethel T., '74
Conlon, Joseph, '75
Diehl, William T., '86
Hartt, Kevin J., '78
Lennek, Christopher, '92 *ET*
Maieli, Mark S., '81
Molinelli, James A., '92
Perfetto, Robert M., '95
Reilly, William F., '75

MILLERTON
Mulhall, Brian, '84

MILLWOOD
Cockburn, George A., '72 *EA*

MINEOLA
Besthoff, Eric A., '90
Crosby, Walter V., '74
D'agostino, Michael, '71
Egner, Elizabeth, '81
Eisenberg, Mark C., '75 *CN*
Fitzgerald, John W., '70
Flynn, Thomas J., '76
Gentil, Mark, '87
Hering, Robert K., '76
Herron, Francis R., '72 *PL*
Maher, John P., '78
McGahan, George E., '75
O'Brien, Dennis M., '88
Osroff, Peter H., '81
Paulsen, Maria E., '81
Rohlfing, Herbert V.
Sekesan, Maria, '93
Tolentino, Thomas N., '71
Touwsma, Geo J., '62
Trakas, Arthur G., '77 *LW*
Wall, Richard, '92

MOHEGAN LAKE
Anderson, Henry, '84 *TV*
Arrieta, Frank J., '82 *LW*
Burke, Michael N., '87
Ciccarello, Linda F., '78
Conforti, Paul J., '91 *LW*
Hayes, John R., '96 *PL*
Juliano, Richard P., '84 *PL*
Mcmahon, Patrick J., '92
Nurse, Henry E., '96
Reitano, Anthony, '77
Rogers, Timothy L., '87

MONROE
Adler, Morton N., '85 *ET*
Archibald, Emanuel, '82
Coniglio, Mary J.
Conry, Steven, '87
Fennessy, Adriana, '93 *SN*
Grasso, John P., '93 *PL*
Hopkins, John K., '79
Koshak, William, '83
McCarthy, William F., '71 *ET*
Mcknight, Margaret, '91
O'loughlin, Dennis, '87
O'neill, James P., '88 *PL*
Poka, John A., '82
Purdy, Thomas J., '86 *PL*
Rahn, Robert H., '81 *BE*
Rogers, James, '93 *LW*
Schwartz, Kenneth M., '82 *LW*
Stelling, Barbarann, '88
Volpe-Wasserman, Catherine M., '80
White, James J., '87

MONSEY
Di Stefano, Vincent M., '95 *PL*
Kane, Veronica A., '90
Marseille, Bogard, '98 *PN*
Morris, Walter A., '95

Pascale, George
Pleeter, Glenn R., '87 *PL*
Wallace, Patrick J., '79 *MG*

MONTAUK
Caserta, Joseph M., '77
Mazza, Frank, '76
Pontecorvo, Thomas J., '98 *CP*

MONTGOMERY
Algarin, Dwayne D., '90
Ihne, Christine M., '98
Long, William F., III, '93 *EA*

MONTICELLO
Carpenter, Ms. Edna E., '80 *LW*
David, Fredrick D., '89
Flood, Linda P., '87
Ramsay, Walter J., '94

MONTROSE
O'Halloran, Hugh M., '84

MORNINGSIDE
Brown, Ms. Estelle A., '93 *LW*

MORRISONVILLE
Preston, Thomas G., '73 *PL*

MOUNT KISCO
Hogan, Steven M., '96 *PL*

MOUNT SINAI
Curylo, Phyllis J., '98
Hoehl, Allan H., '76
Shields, James S., '80

MOUNT VERNON
Anderson, Timothy T., '93
Argent, Holly B., '75
Baidy, Quillar, '97
Baker, April M.
Barkley, Darlene, '89
Borwornthammarat, A., '95
Chen, Johnny Y., '96 *ME*
Clark, Kevin P., '92
Clotter, Nelly, '99
Conti, Nicholas A., '75
Cortes, Denise, '95
Davis, Johnny E., '87
Delma, Nadege, '91
Edwards, Joseph B., '77 *IN*
Evans, Michael, '97 *BE*
Geil, Terrence G., '74
Giantelli, Patricia, '94
Greaux, Roslyn A., '94
Guevara-williams, D., '96 *TV*
Hardy, Kevin A., '85
Johnson, Mrs. Paticia A., '99 *NU*
Jones, Brian T., '90
Lawrence, Veronie, '97
Lewis, Derrick L., '92
Mann, Krista U., '99 *SW*
McCauley, Marianne D., *EV*
Miller, Dwight D., '97
Mitchell, Sharleen J., '97
Montgomery, Victor, '89
Morgan, Clarence, '86
Mosca, Anthony M., '79
Parker, Calvin N., '97 *LW*
Penn, Marlon G., '83
Romain, Mario, '88
Santos, Sharon E., '92
Schoeller, Dennis M., '94
Smith, Alma D., '84
Smith, Tina P., '98
Soules, Christopher, '91 *PL*
Taylor, Pasey N., '97
Torres, Ernest, '77
Van Ronda, Joann, '90
Vernon, Patrice A., '94
Walker, Adrienne J., '99
Wilson, Keryon T., '99 *AM*

NANUET
Cox, Thomas P., '81
Gallagher, Thomas, '74
Garcia, Nonato, '79
Griffiths, William, '92
Hanney, Thomas V., '89
Healy, Patrick J., '74
Hunter, William

Kelly, Austin P., '75
Leone, Christopher M., '98
Lessner, Lee, '87
Mc Cabe, James J., '75
Mc Mahon, Daniel F., '76
Mossa, Vincent A., '89
Perlov, Jane, '92
Poleway, William P., '75
Pupino, Joseph M., '79 *PL*
Reekie, Robert, '76 *PL*
Ryan, William G., '75
Skelly, John F., '69 *PL*
Soler, Diana L., '95
Steinberg, Martin S., '80
Torres-Parks, Mrs. Evelyn, '93 *PL*
Verwoert, Brian G., '82
Wagner, Harold A., '86 *CN*

NEPONSIT
Hopkins, Warner V., '72 *GN*

NESCONSET
Betancourt, Brian, '96
Didonato, Vincent, '79
Eberhardt, Ruth A., '71
Fox, Kevin M., '93
Gagliardo, Diane M., '84
Henriques, Luciann, '98
Hinchey, Arthur F., '76 *PL*
Mauro, Mario F., '93
O'Connor Wright, Catherine, '95 *GN*
Pender, Patrick J., '76 *PL*
Santoro, Charles S., '87
Skovera, Anne F.
Villani, Michelle T., '98 *CP*
Wright, Roy J., '95 *GN*

NEWBURGH
Berrios, Rafael, '95
Bloom, Michael H., '96 *MG*
Cardoza, Zachary A., '97
Dunlop, Winston I., '92
Reis, Thomas C., '99
Santiago, Melissa S., '96 *GN*
Sinatra, Patricia M., '75
Walsh, Thomas B., '98

NEW CITY
Akalonu, Rosalyn B., '80
Alonso, Michael, '72
Bowman, William D., '83
Cavanagh, Joseph G., '77 *PL*
Chernick, Steven M., '89 *PL*
Condon, Robert A., '76
Conlon, James T., '77
Creegan, John I., '76
Currao, Thomas J., '90
Darcy, Christopher F., '83
Davan, Robert J., '78 *PL*
De Santis, Nicholas, '76 *AC*
Drucker, Eric G., '90
Ferguson, Brian, '91
Gilroy, Terence J., '78
Heyward, Richard, '78
Israel, Gary G., '76
Krivitzky, Marvin H., '68 *RE*
Laschet, Alice, '98 *LW*
Locke, Stephen R.
Lowenstein, Bruce H., '83
Marchina, John E., '77
Mc Carthy, Vincent, '75
Mc Manus, George M.
Mc Manus, Pierce B., '70 *MG*
Mcnamara, Joan B., '88
Meagher, Brian C., '78 *IN*
Murphy, Timothy J., '74 *PL*
O'connell, Terrance, '81
Olsson, Eugene C., '72
Powell, Tanya G., '77
Reekie, Robert, '99
Sabater, Barbara M., '93 *SW*
Sherwood, William C., '98
Steimke, Tara, '97
Stein, Richard E.
Stopler, Michael J., '95
Toohey, John J., '82 *PL*
Verwoert, John A., '77 *PL*

Verwoert, John S., '81
Weisberg, Daniel M., '89 *PL*
White, Douglas, '75

NEW HAMPTON
Cesarz, Christopher, '92
Fogg, Harry, '92 *PN*

NEW HYDE PARK
Andruszkewicz, Phillip M., '80
Billings, Robert P., '76
Canzoneri, Leah A., '83
Christman, SGT Dennis L., '73 *PL*
Civello, Joseph S., '83
Cummo, Joseph A., '97
Debono, Pierre C., '98
Donnelly, Stephen J., '69 *PL*
Donnelly, Stephen M., '98
Ferguson, Wanda, '84 *BE*
Gee, Leslie, '82 *GN*
Hetzel, Maureen A., '87
Hughes, Ellsworth K., '76
Hyams, Laurie, '79
Jacobs, Arthur W., '79
Kane, James C., '98
Kinsella, William F., '75
Klimas, Jeffrey W., '79
Lichtenstein, Barry J., '75
Loughlin, Terence A., '89
Lugo, Nelson J., '79
Mccarton, James I., '97 *PL*
Mcmahon-Carroll, Suzanne, '75
Pillion, George R., '90 *LW*
Ploumes, Joanne, '92 *LW*
Polak, Simone C., '82
Quinn, John W., Esq., '87
Sarkus, LT Peter J., '72 *PL*
Schaefer, Richard W., '83 *MG*
Thomas, Robert J., '81
Titterton, James, '81
Varghese, Vinod, '96 *GN*
Virzera, Victor L., '75
Wenz, Maura, '83

NEW KINGSTON
St. George, Joyce, '74

NEW PALTZ
Doyle, Catherine, '86

NEW ROCHELLE
Armiento, Michael J., '71
Brill, Adam H., '88
Brown, Tyrone S., '97
Carroll, Patrick J., '72 *LW*
Connolly, Caitlin A., '98
Dilone, Rachael, '87 *PL*
Donahue, Paul G., '99
Finney, John H., '87
Garvey Williams, Wendy, '98 *LW*
Gary, Ms. Blanca I., '84 *AM*
Gifford, Kompel, '98 *LW*
Griffith, Dorothy R., '82
Griffith, Liddon, '81
Hempfield, Linda D., '80
Johnson, Clinton, '87
Juris, John R., '73 *MG*
Kaplan, Mark, '90
Krus, Carol A., '81
Long, David S., '88 *LW*
Louis, Edward
Marine, Ricardo, '98 *BK*
Mason, Marcia C., '95 *SW*
Matheus, Janice M., '95
Motisi, Meegan T., '98 *LW*
Parris, Cherylann P., '94 *GN*
Raptis, Stacy
Rikoon, Elizabeth J., '87 *ME*
Rivera, Iris M., '96
Rizzo, Raymond
Rosario, Victor M., '98 *LW*
Rumph, Richard, '78
Satiro, Raymond, '88
Schwartz, Robert T., '94 *CO*
Spady, Sonya A., '98 *LW*
Stump, William P., '73 *MG*
Torres, Gerardo, '99
Trippedo, Donna M., '99
Wilson, John E., '76

NEW WINDSOR
Akins, Rachquel, '98 *SW*
Duarte, Anthony C., '82
Gaetano, Gregory, '91
Henderson, David R., '78
Lopez, Albertina F., '93
Marshall, Glenn T., '92 *PL*
Meyers, George, '91
Mulligan, Thomas P., '78 *PL*
Murphy, Daniel P., '98 *LW*
Roberson, William C., '99 *PL*
Ronning, Steve O., '76
Sherwood, Christopher, '91 *PL*
Skopin, Raymond P., '75 *PL*
Uhlmann, Dennis P., '83 *AM*
Van Denberg, Gregory C., '94
Voglesong, Daniel P., '92

NEW YORK
Abbatepaolo, Lisa M., '92
Abdelhady, Zamyra, '92 *SW*
Abramson, Rebecca D., '75 *SW*
Abreu, Maria A., '93
Acevedo, Javier J., '87
Acha, Beraldine L., '79
Acosta, Gloria W., '98
Adams, C. J., '81
Adams, De'Ron W., '99 *LW*
Adams, Errol A., '97 *FV*
Adams, James A., '90
Adams, Martha M., '85 *GN*
Addelston, Adam D., '97
Adebiyi, Christina, '91
Agatstein, Phyllys, '88
Aiken, Norman F., '90
Alava, Eddie J., '98
Alexander, Cheryl P., '94 *AP*
Alexander, Christoph, '97
Alexander, Saundra, '83
Allen, Allen B., '75
Allen, Beryl R., '71 *ME*
Allen, Christine V., '76
Allen, James T., '76
Alma, Gilbert J., '91
Almodovar, Lourdes, '97
Almonor, Merault K., '97 *LW*
Almonte, Alex, '97
Almonte, Luis A., '96
Aloia, Augustine C., '90
Alonzo, Barber, '95
Alston, Barbara A., '78
Alvarez, Cathy, '89
Alvarez, Elvin, '84
Alvarez, Richard, '98 *PL*
Alvia, Susana, '97
Amann, Gloria D., '87 *LS*
Amaro, Margarita, '95 *CO*
Anderson, Bonita M., '96 *GN*
Anderson, Dr. Lola H., '78 *ET*
Anderson, Margaret R., '92
Anderson, Dr. Melody M., '75 *ME*
Andiarena, Wilfredo, '93
Andino, Alcides, '97
Andrades, John, Jr., '78 *PN*
Andrews, Peter, '76 *GN*
Andujar, Diana, '93
Andujar, Michael, '75
Anthoine, Robert, '85
Arias, David S., '99
Arias, Milagros A., '95
Aristy, Tommy G., '96 *LW*
Armao, Robert
Arroyo, Miriam E., '81
Asante, Tyberius D., '96
Austin, Evelyn G., '78
Aviles, Norma, '92
Aviles, Victor R., '92
Ayala, Francisco, Jr., '78 *MG*
Ayala, Irma I., '97
Ayala, Mona C., '98 *LW*
Ayari, Dalinda C., '95
Aziz, Amina, '95
Baez, Eileen, '95
Baez, Tina M., '95 *LW*
Baird, Ernest, '75
Baird, Scott, '97
Balecha, Joanne

Ball, Raymond H., '90
Ball, Robert, '82 *LW*
Bankovic, Milan, '94 *PL*
Banks-Catoe, Latisha V., '99 *GN*
Baptiste, Wilfred E., '83 *LW*
Barbato, Ralph A., '84
Barbosa, Jose A., '99
Bargebuhr, Nancy E., '79 *SW*
Barminko, Svetlana, '98
Barmore, Ellen J., '82
Barnes, Enobia E., '80
Barnett, Rodney A., '93
Barrett, Thyrone V., '80
Barriteau, Gemma M., '86
Barrow-Baez, Mary, '96 *SW*
Barth, Christine, '85
Basil, John, '95
Batista, Julio, '86
Batista, Nelsa, '95
Batista, Ruth, '80
Beal, Susan, '95 *LW*
Beberaggi, Ralph, '78
Becker, Cynthia, '77
Becker, Robert L., '72 *PL*
Beekram, Anita L., '97
Belen, Irene M., '97
Bell, Christopher, '92
Beltre, Gustavo A., '95
Beltrez, Manuel, '91
Benaim, Charlie, '97
Bendetson, Robert, '79 *PL*
Benitez, John J., '95
Benjamin, Helman O., '96 *PL*
Benton, Stephanie G., '83
Berkley, Denise, '89
Bernard, Joseph, '93 *LW*
Berrios, Aaron, '98
Berrios, Johnny, '98 *PL*
Berroa, Ms. Janice, RN, '91 *NU*
Berry, Siobhan L., '99 *LW*
Biberaj, Hasan, '76
Bido, Antonia F., '97 *PL*
Biegel, Stephen W., '97
Billings, Saiheme, '93
Billups, Leeanna, '84
Bishop, Robert J., '92
Biswanger, Terri P., '99
Blackwell, Darius S., '93
Blanco, Fior D., '96
Blassingame, Paul, '93 *CP*
Blatt, Barry A., '84
Blotner, Roberta
Blue, Sheila E., '97
Boateng, Akua A., '96
Bochette, Louis R., '73
Bodden, Cheryl L., '97 *SN*
Boggio, Linda M., '82
Boggio, Marco A., '95
Boisrond, Marie-Fran, '92
Bolger, Barbara, '91
Bonano, Gregory, '83
Bonilla, Jose E., '98 *LW*
Bonilla, Jose L., '85
Bonita, Thomas J., '81 *LW*
Borakov, Fred S., '80
Borbon, Daysi A., '98 *LS*
Borbon, Manuel J., '97
Borges, Cibella R., '85
Bota, Heidi, '89
Bottino, Roland, '92
Bourdon, Edwin L., '91
Bowles, Mark E., '99
Bradley, Richard A., '97
Bragg, Joseph L., '76
Bramble, Michael P., '93 *PL*
Brandofino, Elaine M., '79 *LW*
Brathwaite, Earl R., '96 *ET*
Brathwaite, Sheron, '95
Brennan, Daniel K., '75
Brennan, John J., '78 *PL*
Brenneman, Suzanne N., '99
Brignoni, Amy B., '90
Bronaugh, Ronald A., '99 *PL*
Bronfman, Judith
Brooks, Ms. Marvie B., '90 *LS*
Brown, Debra E., '81

Brown, Gene A., '78
Brown, Joseph G., Jr., '98 *PL*
Brown, Marie B., '86 *RD*
Brown, Patrick J., '80 *PL*
Brown, Shanteil, '88 *AC*
Brown, Tara C., '90 *CN*
Browne, Amy (Amelia), '92 *PL*
Browne, Robert J., '71 *LW*
Browne, Vivian C., '81
Brownlee, Michelle, '86
Brunson, Sharon B., '89
Bruntel, Doris H., '95 *CP*
Bruschi, Mario J., '76
Brusco, Lisa, '93
Bryant, Kevin J., '79
Buckner, Martha, '95 *JO*
Buda, Richard, '78 *ET*
Bullock, Doris K., '83
Buonpane, Angelina, '78
Burch, Jennings
Burch, Shande D., '96
Burd, Dr. Marc A., '88 *SO*
Burgess, Victoria, '99 *SA*
Burke, Francis D., '70
Burke, Patrick, '97
Burnett, Byron K., '71 *LW*
Burnside, Robert W., '92
Bursuk, Paulette R., '78
Burwell, Louise M., '89 *ET*
Bush, Randall S., '99 *PL*
Bykes-Guzman, Jennifer V., '96 *LW*
Bynum, Nora B.
Byrne, Daniel C., '91
Cabrera, Yokasta, '95 *AM*
Cacciatore, Robert J., '92 *ET*
Caceres, Elisabeth, '95 *HT*
Calderon, Marilyn, '97
Calvosa, Ronald P., '81 *GN*
Camacho, Gabriel, '95
Camilo, Wilton, '96
Cammett, John M., PhD, *ET*
Campbell, Rita, '80
Canals-rosa, Mildred C., '80
Cancel, Blanca I., '77
Cannady, Terri, '92
Cantalupo, Lotteann, '96
Capaobianco, Sr. Carmela, '93
Carbonell, Elisa M., '95
Cardillo, Bob J., '78 *PL*
Carela, Wanda, '93
Carey, William J., '80
Carpinelli, Paul, '96
Carrasqillo, Myriam, '85
Carvajal, Tania M., '99 *CP*
Casares, Alcides, '96
Casilla, Jose, '97 *PL*
Castanza, James, '95
Castellani, Albertina, '98
Castillo, Alfredo, '01
Castillo, Ernesto (Pete) A., Jr.,
  CFE, '90 *IN*
Castillo, Gelin M., '97 *TV*
Castro, Fermin, '95
Castro, Maria T., '97 *MG*
Ceballos, Amelia A., '88
Ceballos, Gloria A., '96
Cedeno, Jaime, '82
Cedeno, Mariela, '92
Celedonio, Leonin, '92
Cendagorta, Louis M., '86
Cerda, Maria C., '95
Ceron, Gladys E., '96
Chacon, Mario E., '94
Chamorro, Sol M., '77
Chan, Danny, '92
Chan, Kathy, '97
Chan, Lai F., '94
Chan, Steven, '93
Chan, William, '89
Chance-Pollard, Sarita T., '99
Charles, Deryck, '86
Charles, Rulolph N., '78 *PL*
Chatterjee, Sheila, '94
Chau, Tony K., '94
Chavez, Alina, '96
Chavis, Malcolm L., '91

Chazan, Barbara A., '84
Checo, Manuela E., '95
Chen, Jie Chan, '97
Cherry, Julie, '94
Cherwak, Walter, '77
Chester, Rochelle, '82 *GN*
Childs, Iris M., '99 *PL*
Chiu, Lim-chi, '97 *LW*
Chorney, Tonya L., '95 *ST*
Chow, Julianne T., '81
Chow, Patty Y., '92 *LW*
Chow, Richard, '93
Christ, Lily E.
Chung, James K., '99
Chung, Victor L., '77 *MG*
Cintron, Aracelis, '95
Cintron, Dolores, '96
Cintron, Donna M., '96
Cipriano, Vincent, '99
Citron, Mary, '76
Clark, Ramsey, *LW*
Clarke, Charmaine, '94
Clarke, Selwart R., '89
Clay, Eugene S., '85
Clements, Lavonda D., '88 *JU*
Cobia, Reuben T., '95
Codispoti, Michael, '81 *BE*
Cohen, David J., '98
Cohn, Jennifer I., '99
Colasurdo, James F., '96
Cole, Margie, '97
Coleman, Candance D., '96
Coleman, Joseph W., '90
Coleman, Linda C., '91
Coleman, Shermelle, '98
Colletti, C., '94
Colon, Camille, '80
Colon, Carlos, '96
Colon, Diana A., '89 *LW*
Colon, Licelyn, '93
Colon, Nelson, '80
Colon, Norma I., '77
Colon, Wendy C., '99 *PL*
Columna, Walter E., '97
Colville, Lorraine R.
Connor, Brian W., '99 *BI*
Contreras, Lillian, '97
Conway, Loretta A.
Conway, Martin J., '96 *PL*
Cooper, Karl M., '84 *CP*
Corbett, Robert, '99 *GN*
Corcoran, William C., '79
Cordero, Javier M.
Cordero, Raul (Pappa Bear), '99 *PL*
Corey, Jessica E., CPP, '87 *PL*
Correa, Rosa M., '90
Corry, Lorraine, '95 *GN*
Corseri, Alessandra, '85
Cortoc, Nolida, '89
Cotto, Wilfredo, '81
Cox, Patricia A., '87
Cozzolino, Caryn, '99 *HT*
Craig, Jeffrey S., '97
Craven, Cheryl V., '93
Crawford, Douglas T., '78
Creary, Jemal D., '93
Crespi, Ralph M., '83
Crespo, Evelyn, '83
Crespo, Porfiro, '85
Crichlow, Tracy, '81
Crusoe, Irvin, '93
Cruz, Nancy, '88
Cruz, Richard, '96 *SW*
Cuello, Francisca, '93
Cuevas, Doris M., '89
Cummings, Ana, '96
Cummings, James P., '76
Cunningham, Dennis J., '76 *LW*
Cunningham, Eric D., '95
Cunningham, Maureen, '95
Cunningham, Sheila, '93
Curran, Catherine C., '95 *MK*
Curry, Warren P., '95 *PL*
Czarnecka, Beata, '98 *LW*
Dadacay, Dominic M., '98
Dalloo, Eric S., '99 *LW*

Dalton, Alvaro A.
Daly, Daren S., '90
Daly, David, '74
Daniels, Hilda B., '84
Daniels, Mrs. Romina J., '99
Daouphars, Jean Y., '94
Darby, Mildred E., '79
Davila, Alfredo, '97
Davis, Adrian C., '84
Davis, Dominique, '76
Davis, Mrs. Eleanor, PhD, '78 *CO*
Davis, James R., '90 *ET*
Davis, Joanne, '99 *AM*
Davis, Nakisha, '98
Davis, Ronald J., '76
Davis, Stephen P., '78
Deacon, Carol J., '97
De Caprio, Angelo, '77 *PL*
De Garcia, Carmen M., '78
Degraffenreid, Adella, '85
Deitel, Abraham, '75
De Jesus, Lisa, '95 *FV*
Dejesus, Nelly J., '94
Del, Vecchio F., '81
Delacruz, Claret, '99
De La Cruz, Ramon, '94
Delaney, Ernest S., '93
Deleon, Anna M., '95
Delgado, Benny, '82
Delgado, Tracy L., '96
Delpin, Pedro, '90
DeLuca, Lorayn, '94 *PN*
Delvalle, Yesenia, '96
Denis, Mrs. Karla J., '87
Dennis, Ms. Tyler L., '96 *SW*
De Paolo, Steven M., '80
Derenthal, Frederick E., '72 *LW*
Derr, Maria
DeVito, Louis J., '71 *RE*
Devlin, Maria M., '91
D'fora, Fred, '92
Dial, Savitri D., '96
Diaz, Andres F., '95 *LW*
Diaz, Angelica, '79
Diaz, Anthony, '96
Diaz, Gloria, '87
Diaz, Nora, '96 *CO*
Diaz, Valdez, '95
Diaz, Virgil J., '97 *MG*
Dimmock, James A., '93 *SO*
D'meza, Ruth, '89
Dolan, Daniel S., '99
Dolphy, Keri-Ann, '99 *SW*
Donato, Donna A., '81 *FV*
Donohue, Luisa M., '89
Donovan, Arundell (Tony) A., '75
  PL
Dorff, Michael G.
Dotson, Allen, '84
Dowd, Lorraine E., '89
Downs, Henry, '97
Downs, Maureen F., '78
Doyle, Arthur, '74 *WR*
Drake, Jeanne M., '96
Drayton, Sabrina R., '92
Drucker, Leslie, '86 *CN*
Duchaine, Nina S., '77
Dugan, Martha
Duhaney, Shirene A., '96
Dumois, Jesus, '91
Duncan, Kathy, '92
Dunn, Hayley, '95 *CP*
Dupoux, Mrs. Marie-Maud, '94 *BE*
Durand, Maria A., '98
Durney, William C., '83
Durudogan, Agah, '96
Eanes, Ms. Barbara A., '75 *ES*
Eccles, Kern, '96
Echols, Phyllis A., '83
Eckhoff-Pieratt, Ms. Karen, '82 *AM*
Eddy, Eric, '87
Edwards, James W., '74
Edwards, Joyce A., '81
Edwards, Rev. Michael, '80 *EA*
Effrece, Frank P., '81

Ehrlich, Sidney, '72
Eich, Thomas J., '77
Eisenhauer, Letty, '93
El-Amin, Ms. Zamirah K., '96 LW
Elcock, Erskine L., '90 LW
Elder, Margaret A., '97
Ellis, Iretha
Ellson, James P., '75 GN
Eng, Thomas, '87
English, Eleanor A., '84 LW
Enriquez, Jorge, '90
Erickson, Tom E.
Escobar, Louis, '75
Escobar, Luis M., '99
Escobar, Marcus, '99
Espada, Evelyn, '99
Esparza, Christopher, '90
Espinal, Sandra M., '99 LW
Espinosa, Patricia, '82
Estevez, Mildred, '98
Evans, Telora, '93
Faraone, Ms. Teri, '95 PB
Farkas, Diana A., '96 RE
Farkas, Howard G., '76 GN
Farmer, Clezel D., '83
Farrell, Mel G., '98 RE
Federici-LaFargue, Ms. Marietta,
  '95 CO
Fegan, Ewart, '86 MG
Feliciano, Evelyn, '87
Feliz, Luisa A., '98
Felton, Karen G., '84
Feneque, Samuel, '95
Fenner, Rosalynde M., '97
Ferdinand, Carol, '90
Ferguson, Adriane, '92 MG
Ferguson, Lisa A., '80
Fernandez, Adamilka, '98
Fernandez, Carlos A., '97 PL
Fernandez, Evelyn, '93
Fernandez, John A., '98 ST
Fernandez, Odalys, '87 AM
Fernandez, Theodore (Ted), '93 ET
Ferrell, Shaniqua N., '96
Fields, Jennifer A., '95
Fields, William F., '96
Figueroa, Carmelo J., '95
Figueroa, Cynthia L., '85
Figueroa, Dominga, '99
Figueroa, Juana A., '97
Figueroa, Saul, '83
Filingeri, Joseph J.
Fine, Barbara J., '95
Fisch, Roberta, '80
Fisher, Emily P., '98 RD
Flaherty, John P., '95 PL
Flanagan, Leonard, '72 PL
Fleetwood, Yancy, '94 LW
Fletcherel, Ralph A., '97
Flores, Primo
Flynn, Joseph E., '78
Fong, Wayne M., '85
Forestieri, Paul J., '88
Forner, Michael S., '76 PL
Forsythe, Farris B., '79 EA
Fortino, Denise M., '94 ME
Fox, Bonnie R., '93 ME
Francis, Joel M., '98
Francis, Robert H., '83
Fraser, Walter W., '75
Fraza, Louise J., '81
Fredua-Mensah
Freeman, Cynthia, '79
Freeman, Theodore R., '74 CN
Frias, Jose M., '97
Frias, Maria C., '99 LW
Fried, Howard, '82
Friedman, David
Frierson, Tom E., '73
Fries, Timothy, '95 ET
Fruscella, Paul D., '77
Fullard, David A., '93 LW
Fuller, Jane, '94
Fung, Kit T., '92
Fuster, Adam, '93
Gaillard, Andrea J., '98 CO

Galicia, Margo V., '99 RD
Gallagher, Joseph E., '91
Gallo-silver, Joan M., '75 LW
Gallo-Silver, Les I., '75 ME
Galloway, Robin L., '91
Galloway, Rulisa, '97 FV
Gantt, Larry, '78
Garbarino, Robert L.
Garces, Felipe A., '98
Garcia, Claire M., '89
Garcia, Fausto, Jr., '99 PL
Garrido, Richard R., '98 PL
Garvey, Eileen P., '88
Genova, Chris A., '97
George, Hector A., '86 ET
George, Patrick F., '85
Gera, Mary E., '86
Gholson, Leigh L., '92 PL
Gh'rael, Kelly M., '97
Giaconelli, Louis C., '97
Gibson, Sherry A., '92 EA
Gilchrist, Beverly R., '98
Gilchrist, J., '93
Girault, Marie, '89
Gitter, Elisabeth
Gives, Tillman W., '78
Goddard, Alson D., '95 GN
Godfrey, David L., '99
Goico, Noemi, '92
Goicochea-Bonilla, S., '88
Goldberg, Abigail S., '93
Golden, John P., '99 FL
Goldstein, Arthur, '74
Goldstein, Howard, '97
Goldstein, Patricia, '73
Gomez, Anibal, '95
Gomez, Elizabeth, '83
Gomez, Marina A., '81
Gomez, Orlando N., '95
Gomez, Rosa Y., '98 ET
Gonzalez, Hector, '95
Gonzalez, Janet, '80 PL
Gonzalez, Jo A., '84
Gonzalez, Jose A., '94
Gonzalez, Lourdes, '90
Gonzalez, Luis M., '79
Gonzalez, Maria, '98
Gonzalez, Nancy L., '86
Gonzalez, Reinaldo, '75
Gonzalez, Sandy J., '99 TR
Gonzalez, Tanya N., '99
Gonzalez Jimenez, Ramona G., '79
  PN
Goodman, Mary B., '89
Goodman, Milton, '91 CP
Goodwin, Ella D., '99 AM
Goon, William, '93
Gorbett, Robert, '97
Gordon, Linda, '95
Gore, Elissa, '86
Goris, Damaris T., '85
Goris, Patricio, '98
Gormley, Paula E., '89
Gorovoy, Oleg B., '99 CP
Goss, Ronald M., '96
Graham, Deborah A., '94
Graham, Patricia, '90
Grajales, Ednah, '91 PL
Grant, Calvin, '81 ME
Grant, Cheryl M., '94
Grant, Vanessa, '86
Graves, Christine H., '98
Graziani, Noel E., '88
Green, Eunice H., '85
Green, James M., '94
Green, Mark A., '93
Grice, Yvonne S., '82 WR
Grier, John E., '94
Griffin, Romania A., '95 LW
Grimes, Joann E., '76
Grossman, Lisa, '94
Grullon, Mario E., '89
Guzman, Elizabeth K., '98 PS
Guzman, Nelson, '99 GN
Hahn, Robert, '91
Hair, Robert A., '71

Hajisava, John, '83 MG
Hall, Tyson W., '93 EM
Hamm, Tushan S., '98
Hammie, Keith D., '87
Hance, Ms. Rachel, '92 PL
Harcourt, Kimberly, '95 BI
Hardy-major, Gloria, '83
Harmon, Ms. Amy, '99 PL
Harris, Gabriella, '94
Harris, Terrence H., '91
Hart, Harvin, '99 PL
Hart, Joanne
Hartnett, Sharon M., '82 ET
Hatgood, Alia A.
Hatton, Kenneth R., '75
Haugk, Charles J., '95
Hawkins, William F.
Haygood, Alia A., '99
Hazelhurst, Bernice, '76 MG
Hegemann, Elizabeth
Henri, Claudine L., '92
Henriques, Zelma W., ET
Henry, Conrad V., '75 PL
Henry, Mark A., '78
Herbosch, Alessandra D., '98 LW
Hermida, Mercedes, '93
Hernandez, Jenny, '92
Hernandez, Jose A., '82
Hernandez, Michael, '98 PL
Hernandez, Michelle, '97 AM
Hernandez, Ronald, '99
Herrera, George P., '92
Herrera, Juan, '95
Herzberg, Edward M., '82 SW
Hess, Donna A., '89
Hickey, Thomas F., '99 GN
Hickson, Wilibelle, '80
Higgins, Albert T., '70 CN
Higgins, Harry F., '76
Higgins, Kathryn, '75
Higgins, Michael S., '98 LW
Hightower, Sadiquah, '96 LW
Hill, Madlyn S., '81
Hilsman, Carla D., '97
Hines, Sharon, '96
Hines, Sharon, '96
Hlavaty, John, '96
Ho, Jon, '85
Hobson, Kendall G., '88 GN
Hobson, Richard, '89
Hochberg, Ian P., '79
Hodge, Ivy S., '99
Hodge, Loretta E., '90
Hodgson, Tania, '96 TR
Holder, Wayne A., '81
Holland, Jan, '97
Holley, James D., '95
Holloman, G. B., '88
Holly, Erin K., '99
Holman, Gregory R., '91
Hom, Tak J., '83
Hope, Jennifer, '92
Hopkins, Adria D., '99 LW
Horn, Lukas, '90
Howard, Bradley D., '87
Howard, George E., '77
Howard, Linder J., '83 ET
Hoyt, Ms. Yvette C., '93 GN
Hudson, Charles T., '76
Huggins, Eddie C., '76
Huiett, Ghaironesa, '97
Humber, Charles M., '75
Humphreys, Beverly, '93
Hurley, William T., '86
Hutchinson, Minerva, '91
Ibezim, David, '82
Isaac, Dana R., '99 AM
Isaacs, Paul K., '90 CP
Ithier, Carmen, '91 SW
Ivanova, Nathalia L., '97
Iyalla, T., '92
Iyalla, Tina A., '89
Iyesi, Okpa, '99
Jacob, Thomas P., '81 PL
Jacobs, Nancy
Jacoutot, Alfred, '78

Jaen, Dimas A., '99
Jaliyl, Mrs. Laila A., '80 SW
Jamadar, Bettyann, '96
James, Arthur, '80
James, Fallarasha K., '98
James, Peter G., '81
James, Tyrone L., '79
Jarratt, Kent D., '85
Javier, Jonathan, '96 PL
Jean-Baptiste, C., '89
Jenik, Alice J., '80
Jenik, Peter K., '87
Jenkins, Frederick V., '82
Jenny, Hernandez
Jerez, Victor, '97 LW
Jeselson, Paul J., '97
Jimenez, Agueda M., '98 PL
Jimenez, Ramona J., '98 ET
Jimperson, Mary, '94
Jirak, Donald J., '93
Johnson, Everard K., '95
Johnson, Gloria, '98 SW
Johnson, James, Jr., '80 PL
Johnson, John B., '96
Johnson, Keith M., '81
Johnson, Larry, '95
Johnson, Theresa A., '97
Johnson, Tiffany R., '99
Johnson, Walter E., '79
Johnson, Zanetta C., '97 AM
Johnston, David C., '81
Jones, Brenda L., '98 LW
Jones, Carolyn M., '88
Jones, Frances M., '86
Jones, Lois M., '81
Jones, Rehenia, '98
Jones, Venessia S., '98 SW
Jones, Yvonne, '95 CO
Jones-Allen, Mrs. Vernesa D., '87
  LW
Joseph, Clayton, '94
Julia, Veronica A., '84
Julian, Michael A., '75
Julien, Carole A.
Kabakoff, Robert I., '99 AP
Kaestle, Kathryn, '92
Kahn, Arlene
Kakar, Humyra, '98
Kamona, Ruth N., '97 EA
Kaplan, Renee E., '87
Kaplan, Robert, '80 PL
Kaplowitz, Karen
Kearns, Kelly E., '97
Kearse, Russell L., '92
Keating, Rian T., '94
Keitt, Veronica, '93
Kellebrew, Ida L., '81
Kelly, Yvonne, '99 SW
Kemp, Naomi, '97
Kenneally, James J., '66
Kennedy, Patrick C., '76
Keymer, Mary M., '93 SW
Khan, Angelina, '98 LW
Khan, Arlene, '98
Khan, Neil M., '97 ST
Khashiun, Karamah M., '78 JU
Khiterer, Inna, '99
Khurana, Rajiv R., '98 PL
Kiely, Deirdre, '85
Kiely, Mary A., '83
Kilcullen, Kevin J., '79
King, John, '87
King, Martin J., '76
King, Raymond F., '79 PL
King, Usheevii, '98
Kirby, Thomas H., '92
Kirschner, Robert D., '77
Kittrell-Coley, Frances E., '98 SW
Klein, Martha E., '79
Kleman, Marylnie E., '88
Klimoski, Frank, '92 PL
Knight, Angela N., '95
Ko, Mrs. Eliza, '89 GN
Kohn, Deena R., '96
Kokubon, Shoko
Kokubun, Shoko, '99 CN

Kolodny, Nathan, '69 *MG*
Kong, Corwin, '95 *BK*
Kornegay, Kenyetta A., '99
Krasnov, Felix, '94
Krinick, Norman, '80
Krol, ILya, '97
Krukin, Ms. Avalon S., '90 *ET*
Kuan, Andres, '95
Kuhn, Ann, '92 *AF*
Kukaj, Mustafa M., '83
Laboy, Michelle, '95
Lacassagne, Monica, '89
LaChanas, Christiano, '88
La De, La, '95
Lake, Ms. Deborah (Debbie) R., '91 *NT*
Lally, Patrick
Lamb, Owen H., '82
Lampasso, Albert J., '86
Lancaster, Michael O., '95 *AM*
Landivar, Mrs. Sandra J., '98 *HM*
Lanzilotti, Carlo J., '80
La Padula, Vincent A., '95 *LW*
Laporte, Angel L., '79
Larkin, Susan
La Rosa, Mickey, '80
Larroche, Odette Y., '99
Larsen, Jeremy, '99 *AR*
Lassi, Luisa E., '97 *SW*
Laster, Keena M., '98 *FV*
Lawrence, Barbara J., '94
Lawrence, Yvonne J., '85
Lazansky, George, '73
Leandry, Victor, '98 *PL*
Ledroit, Delphine Y., '99
Lee, Judy, '99 *MK*
Lee, Lisa, '90 *LW*
Lee, Monique L., '88
Lee, Pamela, '83
Lee, Wai L., '96
Lee, Yoon S., '95
Lee-Wyss, Mrs. Helen, '92 *SN*
Lefkof, Alan, '96 *PL*
Leftoff, Sondra
Leftt, Andrew D., '98
Leggett, Kenyon E., '98 *PL*
Lehman, Joanne, '96
Leifer, George
Lejbzon, Mimi, '79
Leonard, John J., '93
Lettieri, Peggy C., '77
Leung, Rose, '81
Leventis, Angela B., '95
Levien, Michael C., '99
Levine, Cari, '99
Levine, Harriett J., '82
Levine, Lenore H., '90
Levy, Amy B., '95
Levy, Antoinette T., '90
Lewis, Ellen R., '84
Lewis, Georgene L., '92
Lewis-Short, Verna, '94
Li, Bonnie Y., '99
Li, James, '96
Li, Kathy, '97 *LW*
Licklider, Patricia
Liendo, Luis E., '82 *ET*
Liffey, Joseph A., Jr., '98 *PL*
Lindenmayer, Rose M., '95
Linder, Myril I., '75
Lindo, Renee, '99
Liquori, Maureen A., '93
Lisa, Thomas M., '95
Litwack, Tom, *ET*
Livingston, Gregory, '85
Lochner, Colin D., '97 *ES*
Loecher, Daryl C., '99
Lombard, Alexander, '91
Longo, Rudolph A., '97
Longsworth, Patrick, '93
Loo, George, '95
Lopen, Nicole, '96
Lopez, Anthony, '91 *LW*
Lopez, Antonio E., '89
Lopez, Charles, '90
Lopez, David R., '83 *LW*

Lopez, Della L., '92 *AP*
Lopez, Diana, '95 *SO*
Lopez, Erik C., '94
Lopez, Kevin, '97
Lopez, Lucy C., '80
Lopez, Malgorzata K., '97
Lopez-Coriano, C. L., '84
Lora, Krupskaia (Sky), '98 *AM*
Lucia, Kimberly A., '97
Lugo, Elizabeth, '97 *PL*
Lugo, Olga I., '92
Luna, Erika, '96
Luncheon, Pedro O., '90
Lundy, Romero, '99 *MG*
Lunn, Kitty, '95 *AP*
Luyando, Luz I., '97 *ME*
Lynch-Ivins, Ellen P., '82
Mack, Ms. Stephanie M., '95 *BK*
Macpherson, Ian C., '98 *CN*
Maffettone, Dennis, '92 *LS*
Maggiacomo, Eddie M., '91
Mahamah, Chidinma, '86 *GN*
Maher, Lisa-marie, '96
Mahon, Jennifer, '98
Mahoney, Edward J., '80
Major, Sharon, '92
Maldonado, Aristides, '93
Maldonado, Xinmia M., '96
Malone, Patrick J., '85
Maloney, Steven E., '95
Maloney, Vaughn, '96
Maltin, Nancy I., '95 *LW*
Mancuso, Jo-Anne, '83
Mandel, Philip, '83
Manning, Trevor E., '89 *SW*
Mar, Marie A., '76 *LW*
Marcano, Maribel V., '88
Maria, Edward, '96
Marines, Henry, '93 *LW*
Marinoff, Gary A., '82 *AP*
Marita, Rose B., '99 *LW*
Markman, Michael, '80
Markowitz, Gerald
Marks, Bettina R., '93
Marks, Debbie A., '84
Marlovitch, Elaine A., '74
Marmolejos, Winston, '92
Marte, Elsa, '95
Martin, Cecelia, '94
Martin, Jeanne E., '93 *EA*
Martinetti, Tatiana, '91
Martinez, Bryant, '93
Martinez, Delfin, '91
Martinez, Kendall, '89
Martinez, Miguel E., '95
Martucci, June R., '91
Masterson, Charles, '95 *PL*
Mata, Angelina E., '97 *PL*
Mateo, Edelmira A., '05
Mateo, Josue, '81
Mateo, Yudelca A., '95
Mathwich, Mary C., '96
Matos, Willie, '94
Matthews, Eljay
Maull, Patricia
Maximum, Andre A., '96 *IN*
Mayer, Robin L., '99 *SW*
Mc, Donald R., '85
Mc Aleer, Joy
Mc Aree, Anne M., '76
Mcbain, Michael, '92
Mcbride, Trone L., '95
McCartha, Dawn E., '99
Mccavera, James, '95
Mcclelland, Laura D., '86
Mcclure, Steven M., '91
McCray, Tara Y., '95
Mc Cray, Tracey C., '82
Mc Crie, Robert D.
McEachin, Betty J., '84
Mceneaney, Catherine, '85
Mc Ganney, Mary L., '78
McGhee, Lisa, '98 *GN*
Mc Glinchey, Ms. Catherine, '71
Mc Guade, John
McInerney, SGT Brian G., '93 *LW*

Mc Kinney, Joyce F., '77
MClees, John C., '99
Mc Millan, Bonnie L., '85
McMillan, Bridgett, '93 *LW*
McMillan, Ralph E., '93
Mc Namara, Patrick, '79
Mc Nulty, Kathryn B., '81
Mc Quillan, Matthew A., '77
Mc Veety, James A., '72
Medina, Jaime, '93
Meeres, Victoria, '93
Meilleur, Leslie M., '85
Mejia, Sandra M., '98 *GN*
Melendez, Luis E., '82
Melian, Octavia A., '88
Melo, Yesenia E., '98
Mena, Bayovanex, '95
Mendez, Angel, '80 *LW*
Mendez, Angela, '97 *MG*
Mendez, Arturo, '95
Mendez, Rafael, '94
Mendez, Zenaida, '89 *GN*
Mendoza, Esther C., '99 *LW*
Menos, Sedrys, '99
Mensah, Benjamin, '94
Mensah, Sylvester F., '95
Mercado, Robertson B., '94
Mercedes, Wascar A., '99
Mercedes, Wendy V., '98 *ET*
Mercer, Jacquelyn D., '79
Mesibov, David E., '83
Meth, Jack
Meyer, Leonard A., '76
Meyers, Cheryl-ann, '84
Michel-Martinez, Mrs. Olga, '87 *SW*
Mickey, Gregory, '83 *GN*
Migdal, Sandra, '88
Might, Francis E., '80
Miladinov, Marija, '98
Miller, Gloria L., '97
Miller, Ivy C., '98
Miller, Lawrence, '85
Miller, Lionel R., '79
Miller, Marion
Miller, Mousey S., '93
Miller, Robert E., '81 *ET*
Millett, John F., '76
Milner, Michael C., '98
Minaya, Joselinne A., '98 *CO*
Mingione, Ernest R., '83
Minier, Mildred, '99
Miranda, Sandra, '85
Mitchell, Kimberly A., '98 *LW*
Mock, Judy, '95
Modeste, Elaine B., '84
Monroe, Angeline S., '96 *ME*
Montanez, Esteban, '87
Montanez, Shirley A., '88
Montgomory, Dwayno K., '84 *LW*
Montgomery, Joann, '86 *ME*
Montijo, Jose, '91
Moore, Jason, '99
Moore, Margaret M., '82
Moquete, Cesar U., '96
Mora, Felix, '95 *PL*
Mora, Madeline C., '97
Morado, Calvin P., '92 *SW*
Morales, Charles W., '88
Morales, Indiana, '99 *GD*
Morales-De Leon, Sandra, '75 *ET*
Moreno, Ms. Evelyn, '88 *LW*
Moreno, Thaimi, '98
Morillo, Luis R., '89
Moronta, Ana D., '81
Morrison, Benni S., '78
Morrison, Steven J., '89
Morrissey, Timothy K., '99
Morse, Henry P.
Mosby, Edward A., '91
Moselle, Linda H., '79
Moss, Cathy N., '89 *PL*
Moss, Kathryn A., '79 *SW*
Moultrie, Latoya Z., '97 *LW*
Mousadakos, Chrisoula, '96 *GN*
Moy, Wing, '76
Moya, Chico, '96

Mozaffar, Ahson, '91
Mui, Yet C., '80
Mulligan, Eleanor, '83
Munoz-Wiltshire, Nelly, '91
Murphy, Colin W., '79
Murphy, Eileen, '90
Murphy, Kathleen E., '99
Murphy, Lisa, '97
Murray, Lucy, '76
Murrell, Zenja J., '95
Myers, Victoria M., '75 *PL*
Nadal, Lucy, '86
Naigus, Dede N., '81
Nakao, Eric D., '95
Nardoza, Michael J., '75 *MG*
Nardoza, Robert, '76
Nassofer, Charles, '87
Natta, Stephenie, '95
Navarro, Jose A., '95
Negron, Larry, '96
Negron, Magaly, '93
Negron, Maria E., '98 *LW*
Negron, Peter, '97
Nelson, Debra A., '97 *LW*
Nelson, Haneef
Nelson, Mennie F., '95
Nelson, Nora A., '87
Nelson, Troy, '91
Nesmith, Phoebe R., '95 *SW*
Neubort, Betty, '79 *SW*
Neville, John J.
Newman, Kim, '89 *LW*
Newson, Norman, '82
Ney, Beverly E., '90
Ng, Molly C., '90
Ng, Tim, '89
Nickens- Thomas, Sheila, '85 *LW*
Nieves, Angel, '85
Nieves, Gloria E., '99
Nixon, Sandra R., '91 *PL*
Nocero, Jeanne V., '77 *NU*
Nourakis, Ana C., '75 *SW*
Noutsky, Martin, '88
Novoa, Carmen M., '77
Nugent, Martha D., '75
Nunez, Elvin, '94
Nunez, Janet F., '97 *AM*
Nunez, Janet F., '97
Nunez, Noralee, '93
Nunez-torres, Julie F., '96
O'Brien, Jeffrey S., '90 *WR*
O'Brien, Keri V., '99
O'Day, Joanne E., '85
Ogunadz, Tamara, '96
Ojeda, Gonzalo, '94
Ojeda, Rosa E., '80
Okhiku, Ayo A., '87
O'Livares, Elizabeth, '85
Oliveras, Mary G., '90
Olsen, Gary J., '76
O'Neil, Robert F., '70 *CN*
O'Neil, John P., '92 *JU*
Oneill, John P., '91 *LW*
O'Neill, John T., '76
Ong, Johnny H., '88
Orourke, Rosemarie K., '99
Orriola, Victor M., '76 *ME*
Ortega, Maritza, '99 *AM*
Ortiz, Carlos E., '97
Ortiz-cruz, Milagros, '89
Ortman, Kathleen E., '96
Orukpe, Frank, '85
Osorio, Uti, '94
Ossohou, Andre A., '98 *LW*
O'sullivan, Thomas F., '75
Otero, Victor E., '92 *PL*
Oyewayo, Olusade, '99 *AP*
Ozuna, Maria J., '98
Pabon, Karen K., '99
Pacheco, Richard, '80
Pacheco, Shirley A., '81
Padilla, Eric, '93
Padron, Ms. Linette, '99 *LW*
Pagan, Antonio, '86 *GE*
Pajooh, Rudolph R., '95 *AC*
Palazzoto, Diane, '80

Palladino, Marie A., '95 PS
Palmer, Lorrine R., '98 GN
Palozzola, Joseph R., '90
Panting, Hilda C., '94
Pardesi, Guardial S., '95
Paredes, Graisy M., '94
Park, Christine M., '97
Parker, Dieshia L., '97 LW
Parker, Lori V., '90 MG
Parker, Vanessa M., '93
Parra, Juan E., '91 PL
Paschall, Yvette M., '90
Pasichow, Steven A., '78 PL
Pastrana, Joycelynne, '92
Patrick, Michael A., '84 GN
Payne, Jamil V., '98 PL
Payne, Robert E., '82
Peasah, Joyce C., '77
Pelletier, Robert T., '93
Pena, Anthony, '98 CO
Pena, Esther, '99
Pena, Joel, '94
Pena, Julio, '95
Pena, Leonel A., '99
Pena, Miguel (Michael) A., '84 GN
Penon, David, '77
Peoples, Ms. Melissa, '95 LW
Peralta, Omar J., '97
Peralta, Vivian, '97
Perdomo, Kevin A., '98
Perez, Alida, '97
Perez, Beatriz A., '87
Perez, Bianca, '95
Perez, Carlos M., '98 ET
Perez, Francisca A., '90
Perez, Lourdes M., '97
Perez, Mayra E., '97
Perez, Melinda, '85
Perez, Milagros, '84
Perez, Sara L., '90
Perez, Vilma, '98
Perritt, William J., '99 GN
Persico, Gerald C., '93
Peters, Judy-lynne, '80
Peters, Prestina D., '93 MG
Peterson, Cynthia, '85
Peterson, Sandra S., '98
Pettignano, Charles, '82
Philips, Wilma, '82 SW
Phillips, Charles W., '74 GN
Phillips, George
Phillips, Steven S., '99 IN
Picardi, Richard, '92
Pichardo, Ana I., '95
Pichardo, Fausto B., '99
Pichardo, Maria F., '95
Pierre, Josephine, '97 SW
Pimentel, Nelson E.
Pinckney, Ramona J., '84
Pinkney, Tamela E., '97
Piri, Ms. Maria A., '92 PL
Pittinsky, Leonard, '75 PL
Placido, Elizabeth J., '99
Plawner, Thomas A., '98 LW
Pliva, Alex, '99
Polye, Arlene M., '83 VL
Pompey, Quwanna S., '97
Poole, Florence K., '80
Poole, Leslie
Portes, Francisco T., '99
Powell, Clinton R., '83
Powell, Joseph S., '74 LW
Powmesamy, Learie, '97 CP
Prahl, John F., '76
Prendergast, Yollette, '97 ST
Prentis, Cheryle R., '97
Prescott, Robert E., '96
Pressley-Collier, Sharon F., '83 SW
Prignano, Roseann B., '85
Prince, Mike K., '93
Proper, Diana E., '99
Pryjmak, Myron W., '84
Quaranto, Annette L., '97 GN
Quinn, Michael B., '76
Rader, Matthew, '79 SW
Railey, James A., '97

Rainey, Eugene, '89 GN
Ramadan, Mahmoud, '86
Ramcharan, Praimadip, '84
Ramirez, Alexis, '98 SA
Ramirez, Holli, '93 MG
Ramirez, Lamberto, '98
Ramirez, Manuel, '92 LW
Ramirez, Robert, '98
Ramirez, Mrs. Virginie, '93 ST
Ramkissoon, Ricardo, '96 PL
Ramos, Evelyn, '86
Ramos, Marlene (Mandy) M., '96 SW
Ramos, Ramonita, '96 LW
Ramos, Zenaida, '95
Ramsey, Darryl M., '95
Randolph, Kirk A., '93
Ranieri, Joseph N., '99
Rashbaum, Maurice
Rawles, Melba, '76
Rawls, Shanell, '96
Reddick, Euphemia S., '96
Reese, Lavinia, '79
Regan, James K., '78 PL
Reilly, Andrew J., '78
Reilly, Thomas J., '78
Reimann, Elsbeth, '76 GN
Reingold, Michael, '96
Reinoso, Rafael A., '88
Reiss, Gary, '89 PL
Reitkopf, Patricia B., '86
Repetto, Tom
Resko, Ronald J., '99 PL
Reszetylo, Karen, '99
Reyes, Frank M., '94
Reyes, Henry, '97
Reyes, Javier, '85
Reyes, Jose, '96
Reyes, Leila T., '92
Reyes, Lina E., '98
Reyes, Moses, '97
Reyes, William, '79
Reyna, Yocasta, '86
Reynolds, Linda-Keisha M., '80 LW
Ricardo, Pilar E., '81
Richiez, Irving G., '99 CN
Rigono, Gabriel, '93 PL
Riordan, Patricia A., '92
Rios, Edwin, '77
Rios, Nilsa M., '94
Ritchie, Kerri, '98
Rivas, Alejandro J., '96
Rivas, Fradis, '96 LW
Rivera, Daniel, '79
Rivera, David, '80
Rivera, Eduardo, '95
Rivera, Ivette M., '90
Rivera, Jalika, '96 LW
Rivera, Javier A., '90
Rivera, Jorge W., '75
Rivera, Jose, '96
Rivera, Maria F., '86
Rivera, Maria R., '95
Rivera, Nicholas, '76
Rivera, Robert O., '97
Rivera, Sandra, '85
Rivera, Steven, '96 PL
Rivera, Teresita F., '95
Rizzuto, Zoe C., '99
Roberts, Sherman S., '98 PL
Robertson, Ms. Sallie A., '97 ES
Robertson, Sean J., '99 PL
Robinson, Angela M., '95
Robinson, Cynthia (Cyndy), '95 PN
Robinson, Yolanda D., '85
Robles, Laurel, '73
Rodriguez, Albania, '85
Rodriguez, Antonio R., '90
Rodriguez, Braulio, '99
Rodriguez, Errol O., '96 CO
Rodriguez, Estela, '92
Rodriguez, Franklin Delano, '83 MG
Rodriguez, Iris J., '95
Rodriguez, Jeffrey, '97
Rodriguez, Jose M., '83

Rodriguez, Louis, '91
Rodriguez, Luis R., '92
Rodriguez, Maria, '96
Rodriguez, Marilyn, '82
Rodriguez, Miriam M., '98
Rodriguez, Morahina, '96
Rodriguez, Myrza M., '95
Rodriguez, Nelson, '95
Rodriguez-kaneyasu, Peter, '93
Rodriguez, Fernando, LW
Rodriquez, Odanis
Rogers, Lakesha, '96
Rojas, Inez M., '96
Rojas, Lee Y., '87
Rojas, Luis E., '98
Rojas, Paola R., '99
Roman, Ana J., '87 ME
Roman, Aracelio, '82
Roman, Edwin, '95 ET
Roman, Ms. Janet, '92
Roman, Marian C., '95 LW
Roman, Robert, '86
Roman, Vivian, '98
Romero, Yenia J., '98 ST
Rondon, Julia M., '89
Rosa, Evelyn, '90
Rosa, Rolando A., '85
Rosado, Carmen, '99
Rosado, Mercedes, '87
Rosa-jimenez, Anna, '90
Rosario, Miguel, '92
Rosario, Rafael, '98 PL
Rosen, David B., '83
Rosen, Marie, '82
Rosenbaum, Frances, '72
Rossi, David, '91
Roth, Joan I., '86
Rothenberg, Jackie, '95 JO
Rothlein Goldstein, Mary, EA
Rothmann, Scott F., '91
Roulhac, Teresa, '97
Rouse, Evelyn, '99 LS
Rowe, John M., '97 PL
Royer, Helena C., '98
Rozon, Xiomara A., '94
Ruben, Scott P., '84 GN
Rubirosa, Natasha, '95
Rueda, Zoila N., '88
Rufino, Annette L., '99 ET
Ruiz, Ada, '99
Ruiz, Peggy E., '83
Ruiz-Basquez, Luisa E., '87 IN
Russell, Brenda M., '99
Russell, Sara, '99
Sabala, Maritza, '78
Sabatino, Ludwig V., '73 PL
Saint-fleur, Johanne A., '98 LW
Salazar-Atias, Ms. Camila D., '99 RD
Salcedo, Felix M., '99
Salim, Said, '95
Sama, Jessica, '99 ME
Sampson, Darryl C., '80
Samuels, Bradshaw, '96 CC
Samuels, Susan R., '96 WR
Sanborn, Laurel, '96
Sanchez, Baldemiro, '98 SW
Sanchez, Johnny, '85
Sanchez, Joseph (Joie) R., '95
Sanders, Elaine M., '93
Sanders, Joann, '78
Sanford, Wexler
Sang, Suiling, '95
Sanon, Farrah, '96
Santa Ana, Richard, '84 PL
Santiago, Jeffrey, '85
Santiago, Luz D., '99
Santiago, Ruth M., '93
Santos, Edwin, '84
Sapio, Donald J., '78
Sarach, Omar J., '87 PL
Saritson, Anthony R., '93
Sarti, Annmarie, '90
Saulnier, Richard
Saunders, Leroy N., '82
Saunders, Michael R., '78

Saxe, Susan N., '95
Sayers, Donna C., '76
Scarborough, Stacey, '88
Schaeffer, Joseph J., '81
Schenck, Ginette N., '79
Schissel, Alan R., '82
Schmidt, Wayne F., '76
Schmollinger, Justine M., '99
Schneider, Gertrude
Schnell, Jeanine
Schnell, Nina A., '82
Schnitzer, Shirley R., PhD, ET
Schulz, Dr. Dórothy M., '73 ET
Schupp, Elizabeth, '93
Schuppert, Ronald, '77 BE
Schwartz, Milton, '75
Schwartz, Dr. Tony
Schwartzman, Leon, '77 LW
Sculley, Maryanne, '95
Segur, Webb, '87 CP
Seibert, Eleanore, '97 SN
Selip, Raena A., '99
Sentouktsi, C., '91
Serge, Victor J., '96
Serling, Latonja F., '97
Serrano, Michelle O., '96
Serrano, Millie, '98 GE
Serrano, Samantha, '95
Shapiro, Ruth B., PhD, ET
Shavers, Donna L., '97 CT
Shaw, Yolanda L., '96
Sheeheed, Wadeedah, '93
Sheinkopf, Henry A., '79
Sheinman, Ilana, '78 WR
Sherlock, Ralph M., '90
Sherwood, Roxanne M., '96 LW
Shields, Diana L., '97
Shinaul, Sherrisse, '86
Shiva, Andrew, '97
Shlapak, Beverly, '94
Shlapak, Myron
Shpritzer, Felicia, '61 ET
Shuford, Keisha R., '97
Shuster, Galina V., '99 CP
Shuster, Irina V., '99 CP
Siegel, Heather, '94
Sierra, Martin, Jr., '93 GN
Silva, Maria J., '95 SW
Silverman, Barry P., '80
Silverman, Neal
Simanduyeva, Juliya, '97 GN
Simenauer, David, '96
Simon, Barry, '97
Simon, Catherine G., '84
Singh, Rubi K., '96
Sirico, Michael G., '77
Sjoblom, Andreas E., '99
Skeete, Samuel, '80
Skeeter, Raymond S., '96
Skolnik, Mrs. Anita D., '77 CT
Sligh, Ms. Geneva L., '92 GN
Smalls, Larue C., '96
Smalls, Shameka, '98
Smatlick, Richard P., '85
Smit, Christie M., '95
Smit, W. R.
Smith, Clarence, Jr., Esq., '84 LW
Smith, Daniel J., '98 TR
Smith, James A., '81
Smith, Joyce C., '97 PB
Smith, Ms. Lillian B., '77 PL
Smith, Melinda G., '97 LW
Smith, Susanne M., '79
Smith, Sylvia M., '79
Smolensky, Glen D., '96
Sneed, Karen, '88
Solana, Iris E., '78
Soler, Luis, '82 MG
Solomon, Frederick, '92
Soto, Barbara M., '80
Soto, Evangelina, '95 LW
Soto, Javier, '88
Sotomayor, Celia, '78
Souffrant, Reginal, '92
Sowah, Ayeley, '97
Spann, Kim A., '94

Spearman, Larry D., '79
Stanley, Alonzo, '76
Stanton, Sam M., '97
Stapleton, Mary A., '95
Stark, Linda A., '78 *LW*
Stein, Brian, '92
Steinhauser, Ina, '87
Steo, Frank, '96
Stephenson, Michelle, '91
Stetson, Ms. Eleanor L., '89 *GN*
Steuerer, John, '97
Steuerman, Michael
St. Firmin, Bertrand, '84
Stfirmin, Gyna M., '99 *IN*
St-firmin, Wenda I., '90
Stickney, Charles
St. Leger, Lucie, '81 *NU*
Stone, Pandora, '95
Stone, Richard E., '81
Storch, Arthur S., '77
Sullivan, Angela D., '85
Sullivan, Elizabeth, '90
Sullivan, Nancy G., '99 *CO*
Summers, Cheryl A., '85
Taboada, Yelitza C., '98
Tagliaferro, Jennifer, '93
Tamai, Julianne Sumiyo, '95 *LW*
Tan, Lolito T., '79
Tanco, Jenny, '94
Tanner, Melinda, '93
Tapia, Arturo A., '96 *TR*
Taras, Lorelle S., '96
Taveras, Elvis, '90 *LW*
Taveras, Seny, '95
Taylor, Aisha J., '99 *SA*
Taylor, Ms. Ann L., '97 *ET*
Taylor, Du R., '76
Tejada, Jorge L., '97
Tejada, Ripcary, '97
Tejeda, Miguel A., '84
Telesco, Grace A., '87 *ET*
Tennent, Wayne A., '83
Terry, Lera T., '85
Thomas, Francis C., '78
Thomas, Rebecca A., '78
Thomason, Tamika, '99 *PB*
Thompson, Adam, '85 *LW*
Threat, Reginald W., '76
Tierney, James M., '78
Tinsley, Clayton M., '95
Tirado, Carol L., '83
Tobin, Erla, '94
Tocker, Leonard H., '83 *GN*
Tomala, Jeannette, '96
Topp, Viviane M., '94
Toro, Zacarias, '95
Torrence, Lorna Y., '77
Torrence, Sandra E., '96
Torres, Candy, '93
Torres, Damaris E., '97
Torres, Frank P., '81
Torres, Peter E., '82 *LW*
Torres, Ricardo, '98 *SW*
Tow, Dean O., '89
Tricomi, Carolyn, '71
Triffon, George E., '97
Trovillot, Claude, '99
Truong, Dan, '96
Tsang, Hitomi T., '99
Turner, Andrew C., '99
Turner, Gerard, '96
Tyson, Genine G., '92
Tytell, Peter V., '95 *LW*
Ude, Jude M., '95
Uribe, Brian S., '99
Valdes, Elena M., '83
Valdez, Rafaela A.
Valentin, Patricia A., '78
Valenzano, Michael D., '79
Vallejo, Fanny, '95
Vamvoukakis, Patricia A., '99 *ET*
Van, Hien D., '99
Vargas, Adriana, '99
Vargas, Ariel, '99 *MG*
Vargas, Bernabe, '99 *LW*
Vargas, Jeffrey (Jeff), '95 *AM*

Vargas, Leslie M., '91 *LW*
Vargas, Susana, '81
Vargas-Gonzalez, Ana, '90
Vaughan, Susan, '75
Vazquez, Jose R., '96
Velasquez, Katty, '98
Velazquez, Liz, '99 *AM*
Veljanovska, Marija, '98 *LW*
Veneziano, Salvatore, '80 *GN*
Ventura, Rosanny J., '99
Ventura-rosa, Rafael, '79
Vera, Ana A., '94
Vidal, Nellie R., '79
Vidal-Romero, Elida, '97 *SW*
Viggiano, Paul M., '84
Villar, Leslie A., '97 *LW*
Vitale, George E., '79 *PL*
Vosmus, James F., '95
Vrana, Dennis, '79
Wagenstein-Vega, Carla, '87
Waichman, Herbert L., '79 *LW*
Walden, Kevin J., '86 *MG*
Walker, Ms. Chenyear A., '97 *SW*
Walker, Donna M., '79
Walls, Jeanne M., '83
Walton, Joyce W., '90
Wanigasinghe, Sarath, '90
Ward, Kevin M., '79
Washington, Bernetha, '98
Waters, Sean H. T., '97 *GN*
Waxenberg, Sheldon
Webb, Amir
Webb, Hillary D., '99 *ST*
Weinbaum, Nathan, '74 *ET*
Weinberg, Blair, '93
Weinstock, Margot, '93 *LW*
Weisenfeld, Marc D., '95 *PL*
Weiswasser, David, '97
Wells, Angie Y., '81 *GN*
Welsh, Christopher, '88
Wermuth, Ezra C., '77
Wesley, Lois A., '76 *LS*
West, Valerie, '95
Westfall, Julius M.
Wheeler, James J., '80
Wheeler, Thomas J., '80
White, James, '83 *PL*
White, Joseph B., '99
White, Lisa M., '93 *PL*
White, Robert L., '95
Whitfield, Fred L., '85 *BE*
Wiggin, Matthew J., '96
Wilder, Cornell L., '93
Williams, Anthony M., '79
Williams, Brenda G., '92
Williams, Lauren E., '77
Williams, Ms. Linda, '76
Williams, Mary A., '78
Williams, Richard R., '07 *ET*
Williams, Robert L., '95 *SW*
Williams, Roderick M., '99 *GN*
Williams, Roxanne, '93
Williams, Yvonne
Wilson, Andrew J., '86 *LW*
Windsor, Pedro J., '99
Wislar, Margaret E., '96
Womble, Geraldine, '78
Wong, Rose, '95
Wood, Raymond, '82
Wortham, Robert
Wright, April A., '95
Wright, Charmone, '97
Wright, Shawanda, '98
Yamada, Stella, '96
Yanes, Francisco J., '89
Yee, Peter J., '93 *AM*
Yee, Yu S., '98 *PL*
Young, Dennis M., '97
Young, Natalia S., '90
Young, Virgil L., *NU*
Youngblood, Schwanna, '95
Yuen, Hon, '97
Zambrano, Bethsave, '97
Zambrano, Victor H., '94
Zayerz, Agueybana, '95 *GN*
Zernitsky, Jeremy D.

Zoskovitz, Mark
Zouhbi, Faisal, '98 *GN*
Zupka, Barbara J., '92
Zurita, Charles N., '95
Zwaryczuk, William, '80
Zyta, Richard E., '94 *LW*

NISKAYUNA
Greenberg, Martin A., '70 *ET*

NORTH BABYLON
Battista, Michael N., '97
Campisi, Ronald P., '80 *PL*
Doyle, Thomas M., '82
Gaby, Thomas R., '80 *PL*
James, Walter A., '89
Johnson, Francis R., '76
La Spisa, Salva, '97
Mahoney, Dawn, '90
Martinez, Margherita, '99 *IN*
Mcgovern, Rita, '97
Muldowney, Linda M., '90
Obremski, Frank L., '73 *PL*
Weis, Richard, '85 *LW*

NORTH BALDWIN
Gamber, Mark E., '76
Geschwinder, Janine, '94 *SP*
Giambrone, John J., '81
Griffith, Stanford A., '75
Jenkins, Andre H., '86 *PL*
Marvelli, Albert J., '92
Moore, Beverly A., '77
O'heir, Thomas L., '75
Ryley, Thomas, '90
Sylvester, Glen A., '81

NORTH BELLMORE
Calichio, Frank J., '78
Cannon, Austin E., '90 *TR*
Crepeau, Louis J., '75
Keegan, Scott J., '90 *PL*
La Barbera, Dennis, '77
Murawski, Marianne, '93 *PL*
Rodrigues, John, '92
Sherlock, Bernard F.
Tallon, LT Kenneth A., '76 *PL*

NORTH MASSAPEQUA
Durfee, Douglas M.
Farrugia, Matthew P., '96 *PL*
Vaccarello, Maria J.

NORTH MERRICK
Kahlon, Tejindar S., '76 *LW*
Macaluso, Leonard, '98
Santa, James M., '83 *PL*
Zagariello, Mrs. Diana S., '98 *SA*

NORTHPORT
Caldarelli, John L., '76
Hillowe-Donahue, C., '86
Mc. Nally L., '87
Mcnally, Terence E., '89
Merenda, Jean A., '76
Merenda, Stephen P., '76
Mulryan, Joseph V., '85
Page, Lauren S., '97
Pandolfo, Peter J., '78
Venuti, Christine M., '99 *CO*

NORTH SALEM
Kisling, Arnol F., '78
Newman, James V., '93
Trummer, Brian J., '85

NORTH VALLEY STREAM
Cruz, Heriberto, '80

NORWICH
Castiglione, Steven, '95 *SN*

NYACK
Ingman, Matthew A., '95 *AP*
Macchia, Anthony P., '94
Mccarty, Gerard, '97
O'daniels, Tiffany L., '95

OAKDALE
Delong, Joseph, '73
Machin, Annette M., '81
Miranda, Yvette M., '89
Stettner, Charles P., '68 *PL*

OAKLAND GARDENS
Daly, Elizabeth V., '98 *GN*
Jones, Robert L., '86
Kuhner, Vance T., '96
Patrizi, Dominick, '95

OCEANSIDE
Baney, James M., '75
Belasco, Mrs. Barbara A., '85 *ET*
Bonacorsa, Michael F., '91
Boutineau, Robert G., '76
Calkin, Ronald F., '76
Callanan, Maureen F., '78
Cerami, Victor S., '76
Greenberg, Adam N., '99
Hakim, Laurie J., '96
Hynes, Stephen D., '88
Joyce, Jennifer, '96 *PL*
Kobilinsky, Lawrence
Lee, Ruthsana M., '91
Lippi, Ms. Francine J., '97
Mc Geary, Joseph T., '82 *FV*
Mc Keegan, John J., '73
Mcnelis, Michael J., '96
Mennella, Concetta I., '79
Mills, James J., '76
Moehring, Thomas P., '75
Montaruli, Anthony M., '80
Pappas, Chris L., '81
Petito, Thomas J., '92
Race, Robert R., '70
Ramos, Michael, '77
Schechter, Marvin, '68 *PL*
Trager, Leonard, '75

OLD BETHPAGE
Poitevien, Eric, '92
Rudden, John
Scheiner, Adam, '90
Schenker, Stephen, '79 *BE*

OLD WESTBURY
Grgas, Susan M., '82 *HM*

ONEONTA
Farago, Stephen T., '79
Rose, Jack N., '73

ORANGEBURG
Cinquemani, Joseph, '78
Leavey, Marion A., '82 *PL*
Mcgann, Charles
Stanford, William G.
Velez, Donato, '98

ORCHARD PARK
Klas, Brian E., '95
Sanfilippo, Debra A., '90 *ME*

OSSINING
Aviles, Victor, '84 *PL*
Bell, Anna K., '97
Benfanti, Louis A., '93
Bishop, John H., '82 *GN*
Brickwood, Dale, '95
Carranza, Oscar, '96 *PL*
Hauptman, Eric J., '95
Johnson, Joni T., '79 *GN*
Muranelli, Joel, '82
Solorzano, Sandra, '89
Sutherland, Sharon, '90
Zadorozny, Maureen M., '75

OTISVILLE
Girolamo, Anthony, '75
Miller, Thomas J., '82

OYSTER BAY
De Luca, Fortunato J., '75
Gallardo, Diana, '98 *LW*
Morales, Ingrid M., '98

OZONE PARK
Almonte, Ervin J., '97 *PL*
Aniello, Nicholas A., '87
Baraket, Tamara M., '97 *LW*
Burns, Robert T., '82
Castillo, Elizabeth, '93
Collazo, Marisol, '97
Corke, Kathleen M., '80
Curich, Joseph, '96
D'Aquila, Maureen, '79

Echevarria, Daliza E., '85 SW
Erosa, Manuel L., '88
Fitzgibbons, Marie E., '76
Garcia, Jo-Alejandra, '96 ES
Ge, Sylvester Y., '99 PL
Geddes, Melanie D., '97
Halfpenny, Peter, '77
Halpern, Mitchell, '92
Hanson, Diane R., '81
Hartman, Donna M., '79
Heine, Susan K., '90
Henriquez, Marlene, '97 LW
Igneri, Patrick N., '78
Kavanagh, Michael J., '98
Kuehnle, William A., '78
Lane, Edward B., '76
Lee, M. J., '89
Lopez, Sharon, '95
McCabe, Mrs. Nunzia, '93 LW
Minacapelli, M., '92
Montoya, Carlos A., '99
Olga, Testa
Ostrowski, Greg T., '97
Quintana, Grisel, '97
Rampioray, Kamini, '99 ST
Rao, Anthony J., '77
Rodriguez, Barbara M.
Siccardi, Vincent F., '75 LW
Suarez, Jose, '85
Testa, Olga
Tulloch, Macola A., '99 LW
Tziazas, Pilar, '86
Wernly, Robert P., '78
Wildstein, Harold M.
Wurzbach, Stephen J., '82

PALISADES
Garrison, Wayne W., '84
Modafferi, Peter A., '76
O'Connor, Kevin M., '89

PARKCHESTER
Sosa, Ms. Kilsie, '97 FR

PARKSVILLE
Stinson, William M., '77 LW

PATCHOGUE
D'Gracia, Anthony J., '99 IN
Diaz, Diana, '95
Major, Livingstone R., '88 LW
Miller, Scott K., '94 PL
Narducci, Louis, '72
Quick, Keri A., '99
Tocci, Daniel L., '98
Tomlinson, Jodi L., '97

PATTERSON
Conklin Tetor, Mrs. Jennifer M., '98 MG
Farrell, Franklin H., '78
Herrell, Todd M., '99
Mc Leod, Donald K., '69
Mier, Jodi L., '80
Olivo-Perez, Sharon L., '95 PL

PATTERSONVILLE
Braff, Jeraldine, '75

PEARL RIVER
Anninos, John W.
Anschick, Robert H., '74 PL
Buhrmeister, Robert K., '95
Burke, John F., '97
Connolly, Charles P., '76 FV
Costanzo, Keith J., '98
Daly, Peter J., '93
Deegan, Kevin T., '95
Eanniello, Andrew, '87
Farrelly, Francis J., '74
Gallagher, Thomas E., '72
Idiart, George J., '85 PL
Kramer, William, '76
Mandel, Michael J., '94
McGourty, Michael J., '69 LW
Murtagh, James J., '72
Pascullo, Anthony, '86 PL
Sens-castet, Robert, '78
Shortell, Michael E., '90 PL
Weber, William J., '75

PECONIC
Allen, Richard E., '75

PEEKSKILL
Bass, Mildred C., '99
Farron, Mrs. Heidi M., '95 GN
Hanley, Gary T., '83
Jennings, Charles R., '89 ET
Macari, Valerio F., '99
Martinez, Carlos E., '81
Mesorana, Carmen, '93
Mignini, Leonard, '87
Moher, Jacqueline M., '83
O'shaughnessy, Jeremiah, '87
Staton, Keith, '95
Zecca, Joseph M., '77

PELHAM
Ambrosio, Ralph V., '80
Bartoszek, Peter C., '72 LW
Bonaparte, Henry, '75
Bucaj, Alfons, '93
Fleming, John M., '86 PL
Gallagher, Brian, '90
Hughes, Francis J., '69
Luyando, Rafael A., '95 PL
Nelson, Noel N., '89
Reid, Ethan E., '84
Smith, Catherine H., '75
Suppa, Christina, '98

PELHAM MANOR
Connolly, John J., '71

PHILMONT
Fafoutis, Nicholas A., '84

PHOENICIA
Pennisi, John A., '68

PINE BUSH
Levine, David A., '82
Mandile, Frank A., '89

PLAINVIEW
Auerbach, Alan R., '87
Bologna, Joe, '85
Califano, John J., '77 PL
Capponi, Louis J., '72
Coyne, Edward J., '79
D'Ambroff, Randa
Dangelo, Steven J., '99
Eisenberg, Shauna L., '96
Feliciano, George, '87
Golombek, Leonard, '87
Lustgarten, Adam, '87
Mc Nulty, Thomas P., '97 PL
Morgan, Robert F., '74
Pena, Jenaro R., '95 PL
Pendola, Charles J.
Sarter, Leonard, '75 PL
Sheerin, Brendan, '85 PL
Siotkas, John, '79

PLEASANT VALLEY
Richards, Kimberly A., '96
Van, Benschoten W., '75

PLEASANTVILLE
Barry, John J., '66
Bennetti, Joseph J., '90 PL
Bhola, Ms. Patti-lou S., '96 CO
Fortino, Richard J., '72 IN
Grimes, John J., Esq., '67 LW
Hess, Brian, '97
Kaufman, Mitchell J., '75 PL
Marengo, Christopher, '83 LW
Mclaughlin, Deborah, '92
Poulos, James A., '79
Von, Dietsch, '95

POINT LOOKOUT
Bargelini, Gionata M., '95
Bargellini, Gionata
Baumann, Kevin P., '76

POMONA
Belton, Deborah E., '98
Bittmann, Brenda L., '97
Bluszcz, Frank J., '79
Coyne, William P., '90
Loughman, Robert P., '72 ET

Prendergast, Terri B., '79 PL
Starace, Theresa K., '99

PORT CHESTER
Ciccone, Joseph F., '76
Fischer, Stephen F., '69 PL
Girardi, James J., '81
Gruenstrass, Steven, '91 SA
Juliano, Albert T., '93
Martin, James (Jim) P., '98 PL
O'Neill, Edward F., '75

PORT EWEN
Stock, Louis, '76

PORT JEFFERSON
Alvarez, Ronald J., '94 PL
Constant, Tara, '96 ET
Kenny, John D., '98 SA
Smigielska, Katarzyna P., '98

PORT JEFFERSON STATION
Adams, Gina M., '97
Aulbach, Philip E., '71
Corey, Peter
Dacken, Diane A., '83
Lento, Anthony
Mc Dermott, Thomas, '76
Murphy, Michael J., '61
Pattinson, Mrs. Helen M., '74 GN
Sullivan, Vincent T., '73
Zazeckie, William J., '86

PORT JERVIS
Farrell, John, '77
Hendrick, Carl, '88
Hoffmann, LT Russlan D., '91 GN

PORT WASHINGTON
Aylward, John, '95
Benes, Kenneth J., '76
Casey, Michael J., '95 PL
Davis, William T., '98
Dervin, Katharine M., '99
Formisano, Daniel
Hatton, Laurence F., '75 PL
Janousek, Stanislav, '76 LW

POTSDAM
Cooper, Christopher, '87

POUGHKEEPSIE
D'amicantonio, Thomas, '91
Gibbs, Nyhisha T., '95 HM
Herlihy, Patrick F., '77
Maloney, Bryan M., '95
Marshall, Luis R., '78 LW
Mc, Quade M., '90
Mensler, Jeffrey, '96
Morris, John A., '89 BE
Morris, Vincent K., '91 PL
Morrison, Donald J., Jr., '95
Ostrander, Anthony (Tony) S., '99
Parris, Stacey A., '94 LW
Rosenfeld, Marcia C., '86
Wilson, James D., '77
Young, Rodney D., '93

POUGHQUAG
Balcom, MAJ Jerome (Jerry) K., '73 JU
Balcom, Mrs. Laura, '73
Rough, Thomas C., '85

POUND RIDGE
Jeselnik, Joseph J., '75 MK

PURCHASE
Mc Elroy, Andrew C., '75

PUTNAM VALLEY
Babnik, Andrew, '77
Chany, Christopher P., '77 SN
Chernjawski, Nicholas, '92
Courtney, Diane T., '95
Kroll, Rainer D., '98
Lane, Michael
Molinaro, Louis J., '85 BI
Pagani, Donald P., '84

QUEENS
Bauso, Louis J., '81 PL

Furelli, Gianfranco, '95 PL
Harper, Lawrence, '97 PL

QUEENSBURY
O'Kane, John J., '76 ET

QUEENS VILLAGE
Acosta, Willie R., '75
Adorno, Milinda, '97
Antonin, Jo-Ann, '99 PL
Arlain, Nena D., '97 GN
Bavolar, SGT Keith A., '98 LW
Beary, Richard A., '99 LW
Bennett, Ms. Kerry-Ann, '99 ME
Bhan, Alvin J., '97
Bolling Sharpe, Mrs. Charise M., '83
Borfitz, Irving E., '77
Brant, John J., '78
Brown, Leslie C., '78
Burroughs, Jamel, '99
Carrington, Frederic, '75
Charles, Ronald, '93
Chattergoon, Suchetr C., '97 IN
Cintron, Angela, '79
Crosby-Greene, Lee, '95 PN
Crudup, Eartha L., '81
Cunneen, Judith A., '83
Daley, Robert E., '76
Diaz, Nestor H., '86 LW
Dobson, Dexter A., '87
Duville, Richard L., '96 CP
Echenique, Patricia S., '84
Eley, Regina E., '85
Escobar, Nelson L., '97 LS
Ferguson, Anselma, '92
Figueroa, Melissa, '97
Figurski, Susan A., '91
Fortunat, Daphnee, '96
Frazer, David, '87
Gaddist-Dorsey, Valerie D., '93 SW
Gentles, Andrea V., '94
Gerchak, Ralph E., '81
Griffith, Rodney F., '91 ME
Griles, Victor A., '81
Gumbs, Nailah, '97
Guzman, Paul N., '79
Haran, Patricia, '82
Harp, Jeffrey D., '91 CP
Harrington, Irwin C., '96 PL
Harriott, Kerry-Ann E., '99
Harris, Marilyn J., '76
Hilaire, Reginald, '97
Hill, Marilyn E., '80
Hill, Willie G., '79
Holder, Laura M., '82
Holmes, Reginald, '92
Hubert, Frank J., '77
Hyde, Tucker, '93
Ibrahim, Husaini, '86
Jackson, Kim A., '90
Jefferson, Gregory, '97
Johnson, Erious, '91
Johnson, Kesha Y., '93
Jones, Ursilla E., '76
Joyner, William L., '79
Khan, Salima J., '89 FV
Kobayashi, Beatriz, '85
Lawson, Blair, '95 ME
Leggett, Ms. Renee, '99 SW
Louis, Jeeny M., '98 PL
Malone, Victor L., Jr., '86
Marcus, Shurnette M., '96
Mariette, Roberto, '87
Mariette, Yvonne M., '83
Maurice, Ms. Geraldine, '97 ET
Maynard, Alicia S.
Mcclean, Sonia P., '84
Melidor, Avmart, '94
Mimms, Pauline P., '82
Mitchell, Leon A., '78
Moore, Leon A., '86
Moses, Deatra R., '95
Mwanga, Frederick, '96
Nagasar, Petamber, '93
Napier, Gregory M., '97
Nelson, Drew M., '91

Noel, Sean S., '98
O'Brien, Thomas P., '78
O'estricher, Marlo, '89
O'gara, William C., '92
O'hara, Thomas P.
Olijnyk, Steven A., '95
Palmer, Doreen O., '97
Patton, Brian V., '80 PL
Patton, Marsha N., '77
Pearce, Donald, '93
Perez, John T., '97
Persaud, Annette N., '95
Persuad, Annette, '95
Peterkin, John W., '77
Phillip, Charles, '92
Phillips, Patrick A., '97
Piwowarski, Joseph C., '79
Powell, Carol L., '90
Princivil, Rony, '90
Prophete, Marjorie, '90
Punch, Amanda, '91
Rhodes, Onesia S., '98 PL
Rosario, Phaedra, '94
Saint Victor, Lewis, '97
Sanders, Gregory L., '90
Sealy, Curtis V., '81
Seay, Rholanda R., '95
Sebro, Sherwin K., '95 TR
Secreto, James A., '80 PL
Sewnarain, Prabha, '92
Shannon, Shiann, '91
Shillingford, Wilford P., '78 PL
Singleton, Mrs. Maureen V., '92
Smith, John R., '76
Smith, Raquel L., '93
Smith, Russell, '90
St. Surin, Mietta, '96
St. Victor, Lewis, '97
Swain, Warren, '99 PL
Swanston, James E., '86
Tennell, Henrietta, '85
Thornton, Craig C., '93
Thurneau, Robert D., '76
Torres, Jeanette F., '92
Trotter, Lee E., '83
Venn, Magadlene, '93
Volkerts, Joanne, '90
Wawrzonek, Matthew, '75
White, Valerie, '96
Whitfield, Camille, '95
Williams, Deborah M., '81
Wilson, Cleveland F., '79
Wilson, Kathleen M., '85
Wise, Francis S., '92
Wright, Shaulene, '97 PL
Zaretsky, Kathie L., '77
Zummo, Michael A., '77

RAVENA
Shea, Edward M., '74

RED HOOK
Kirkley, John
Mc Andrew, Paula L., '78
Triebwasser, Jonah, Esq., '71 LW

REGO PARK
Abdurakhmanov, Igor F., '99
Ashoory, Bracha, '85
Best, Sandra, '97
Brown, Herbert A., Jr., '97 PL
Castro, Zinna, '99 PN
Clark, Shalima, '99
Feldmann, Dalia, '77
Green, Lawrence E., '75
Hobson, Anthony E., '98 PN
Jenkins, Ida F., '77
Johnson, Pamela A., '81
Kravchenko, Leonid, '98 LW
Lemo, Edina, '99
Lore, Charles J., '98
Maldonado, Evelyn J., '99 EA
Maurer, Daniel E., '95
Miller, Kisha, '97
Nadal, Edwin M., '84
Pan, Karen V., '99
Pena, Lucas, '83
Pinkhasov, Mikhail, '99

Radziewicz, Kathleen, '77
Ramirez, Giomar P., '98
Sai, Nancy M., '93
Shaw, Rudolph A., '82
Stuart, Linnea, '92 LW
Teelimian, Henrik, '98 PL
Vlad, Cristian A., '98 CP
Wassell, Michael M., '89
West, Felicia A., '99
White, Gregory A., '83
Zerner, Jeffrey, '91

REMSENBURG
Collins, Jeremiah, '84

RENSSELAER
Johnson, Roger J., '76
Lavin, Christopher, '89 PL

RICHMOND HILL
Ali, Allison, '98 RE
Azurdia, Gilda L., '97
Azurdia, Raul J., '97
Balgobin, Hemant K., '99 LW
Bundhoo, Rakeish, '97
Caballero, Nester J., '95
Carrera, Miguel A., '96
Challita, John-Pierre, '99
Cheng, Mei, '96 GE
Cordova, Leonor, '90 SW
Crawbuck, Charles R., '78 MG
Di Raimondo, Carl A., '77
Douglas, John F., '99
Duncan, Donald G., '92
Franzese, Peter P.
Garavito, George E., '79
Garcia, Evelyn M., '87
Gargano, Mark D., '82
Hibbert, Jacqueline M., '98
Jacobs-Osborne, Guliana D., '95
Kersellius, Gavin I., '89
Khaimov, Igor I., '99 PL
Khan, Rakeela B., '99
Klapakis, Diana M., '83
Kosseim, Amin, '92
Lopez, Daisy, '98 BK
Lustberg, Robert M., '75
Maldonado, Ismael, '99 EM
Mangal, Yovendra, '99
Martin, Sherly M., '89
Mitra, Diditi, '91
Morales, Yvette, '95
Nusser, Gary R., '78
Polanco, Alfa C., '99
Pondillo, Anthony, '97
Prashad, Dianna P., '98
Ramnarain, Kavita, '97
Reyes, Gloria, '96
Ribeiro, Gemma E., '99 PL
Rigney, James R., '94
Riso, Edward T., '97
Rosado, Alfredo, '82
Rudowitz, Bruce S., '88
Santiago, Zoraida, '98
Staples, Sharon A., '96
Stillie, Elizabeth, '96
Stonis, Richard V., '78
Strubbe, Maureen, '97
Tahany, John M.
Tavares, Karen C., '93
Venkersammy, Mark, '86
Zweibel, Patrick, '87

RIDGE
Cassidy, Jared K., '98
Chimenti, Frank J., '75
Drielak, Steven C., '78
Herbst, Andrew J., '99 MG
Mihalek, Donald J., '92
Pennetti, Salvatore, '88
Suss, Charles L., '73
Wrynn, James J.

RIDGEWOOD
Albarran, Migdalia, '97
Badalamenti, Frank, '96
Cannella, Joseph D., '76
Castellar, Kane H., '99 PN
Collazo, Antonio, '91 PL

Dabkowski, Dariusz, '96 MG
D'arrigo, Joseph G., '96
Di Gaetano, Alcide V., '76
Dominguez, Michelle A., '99 AM
Duignan, Daniel, '93
Franqui, Mary A., '87
Gallo, James E., '77
Godi, Mihai, '95
Gonzalez, Jeffrey, '99
Higgins, Adrienne C., '98 SO
Koester, Arlene L., '98
Lobl, Alin, '99
Lopez, Luis M., '91
Manning, George J., '76
Miller, Jonathan D., '76
Mojica, Yolanda C., '80
Muller, Deborah, '95 FV
Papp, Robert J., '97
Pettit, George J., '99
Quezada, Alejandro, '97
Ramirez, Reynaldo, '99 CP
Rodriguez, Araceli, '95
Ryan, Kim, '95 PL
Santiago, Tina M., '96
Serano, Frank R., '78
Torres, Dennisa A., '94
Urena, Haydee
Wurzel, Glenn J., '89

RIFTON
Audinot, Leila B., '79

RIVERDALE
Aliha, Kourosh M., '98
Bolger, William J., '91
Cuevas, Johnny O., '96 PL
Hicks, Netoya S., '95
Lavin, Brian F.
Marty-Cuevas, Maritza, '97

RIVERHEAD
Wicklund, Jill P., '99

ROCHDALE VILLAGE
Ledee, Robert, '76 GN

ROCHESTER
Dejohn, Regina M., '95
Destefano, Michael, '79
Kessler, Dennis, '70 BE
Podgorski, Robert B., '78 LW
Sconfietti, James, '90 ET
Vollmer, D. J.

ROCKAWAY BEACH
Donohue, Eileen, '94
Horan, Denise A., '98
Lee, Mrs. Karen B., '90 CO
Logan, Benjamin, '79
McLain, Darrell, '90
Vanager, Kenneth, '81

ROCKAWAY PARK
Balsamo, Patricia, '93
Heym, Eugene N., '79 PL
Howley, Mary E., '77
Kelly, James F., '77
Lyons, Thomas, '77 PL
McCarthy, Jacqueline, '95 PL
Mc Donald, Elizabeth, '81
McGinniss, Debra A., '85
Mc Gowan, Martin J., '75
Mc Keon, William
Morley, Michael, '96 PL
Morley, CAPT Susan, '92 PL
Staines, Alex, '96

ROCKAWAY POINT
Conroy, John T., '96 PL
Cowan, James T., '78 LW
Curry, John A., Esq., '91 PL

ROCKLAND LAKE
Duff, James P., '75

ROCK TAVERN
Gudat, John F., '83 PL
Trautmann, S., '95

ROCKVILLE CENTRE
Blakeley, Dawn, '98 IN
Campbell, Robert J., '78

Casola, Anthony, '92
Dumas, Peter R., '75
Ergun, Halime, '95
Feeney, Kathleen, '94
Hayes, Donald, '97 PL
Helmus, Harry H., '75
Howard, Gerard A., '77
Kirk, Edward J., '75
Lloyd, Tasha N., '98
Longo, Paul J., '96 JU
Mcguire, Patrick J., '98
Moriarty, Edward P., '98
Morrissey, Daniel F., '75
Murphy, Paul E., '78 SA
Varga, Donna M., '81 PL
Varga, Stephen J., '80 PL

ROCKY POINT
Catalano, John M., '90
Confusione, Michael J., '69
Schurr, John F., '91

RONKONKOMA
Auleta, Kent R., '75
Borgia, Donald D., '80
Carrigan, Richard M., '78
Casserly, Michael, '78
Cleary, Michael J., '80
Coffran, William J., '95
Cyran, Paul, '89
Degiulio, Joseph A., '97
Dobbins, William J., '83
Drayton, Kenneth R., '76 PL
Flood, William F., '78
Griffiths, Robert P., '75
Pelliccio, Anthony, '92
Powers, Robert, '89
Ragonese, Lisa A., '98
Roach, Eugene J., '79
Sprague, Steven J., '76
Valentin, Miguel A., '77 LW
Walker, Brian H., '93 PL
Wunderlich, Donald S., '75

ROOSEVELT
Burke, Donald H., '87 GN
Crawford, Todd L., '94
Davis, Anthony W., '80
Gerald, Ira, '95 ET
Hawkins, Michael L., '89
Hill, Donna, '95 IN
Hillsman, Yequarah, '96 AM
Holland, Ronald P., '76
Knight, Lamona O., '95 LW
Lane, Henry L., '76 LW
Lawrence, Robert M., '85
Michel, Pierre R., '98
Peart, Annmarie B., '95
Richardson, June L., '81
Sewer, Enrique D., '92 PL
Smith, Rose, '79
Toorie, Paula A., '91
Toorie, Trudy A., '88
Walker, Michael J., '96 PL
Walker, Sharlisa M., '97
White, Stephanie, '86

ROSEDALE
Allwood, Maria B., '98
Azzaro, Diana, '96
Bartlett, Ms. Judith R., '95 PL
Blackman, Colin J., '96
Bridges, Rhonda, '92
Cardichon, D., '92
Chong, Renee H., '93 PL
Clarke, Cleveland, '96
Clause, Smyrna E., '78
Corsey, Priscilla, '77
Herve, Francois, '98
Ingram, Garrett, '88 SO
Jabouin, Melone H., '98
John, Ceres, '97 ME
Jones, Debra D., '98 LW
Joseph, Eugenie, '95
Joseph, Michael R., '91
Kennon, Shawn, '99 BI
King, David W., '76 PL
Lamour, Barbara M., '97 LW

Lewis, Ms. Deidre Y., '85 *LW*
Lloyd, Mauline M., '97
Major, Gilbert H., '95 *LW*
Merriweather, Michelle L., '98
O'Connor, Valerie J., '75
Olu-Talabi, Akinwole, '92
Orr, Beverley B., '93
Paris, David S., '77
Peaks, Harold A., '82 *LW*
Peter, Robert R.
Polanco, Veronica, '98
Prinz, Ellen M., '89
Rosario, Percida, '89 *PL*
Ross, Stanley, '97 *PL*
Rothman, Peter L., '76
Ryan, Daniel, '67
Scott, Monica, '99 *PL*
Sharpe, Ryan R., '96 *ST*
Singh, Krishna S., '97
Smith, Courtney, '95
Stewart, Karen D., '98
Volmar, Marc A., Jr., '98 *SW*
Webster, Noel W., '78 *EN*
Williamson, Flavia M., '98
Wong, Geoffry, '79
Zelaya, Theresa M., '95 *SW*

ROSLYN
Forde, Angela E., '89
Olpe, Richard W., '78

ROSLYN HEIGHTS
Cooper, Neil J., '70
Jordan, Robert R., '73 *CO*
Melamed, Joel S., '86
Shilensky, Michael D., '69

ROTTERDAM
King-Anobile, Barbara, '84 *LW*

RYE
Boston, Denver G., '72
Bowman, Jeffrey H., '84
Frank, Kathryn K., '80 *ET*
Kelly, Timothy P., '83
Uzcategui, Robert E., '95 *LW*

RYE BROOK
Thompson-Carvelli, Amy E., '93

SAG HARBOR
Connelie, William G., '82 *PL*
Darcey, Lawrence G., '72
Mc Grath, Kevin J., '77
Neumann, John, '91

SAINT ALBANS
Allette-davis, Wendy, '97
Anthony, Mark W., '97 *CP*
Ault, Colette E., '99 *PN*
Banks, Deborah M., '96
Blackwell, Dru Janin, '97
Bramble, Elvira T., '75
Brown, Ms. Janet L., '91 *LW*
Chambers, Darrell, '92
Chisholm, Marvin A., '79
Domond, Alix, '99 *LW*
Edwards, Nicole R., '92
Gwyn, Christine, '95 *MK*
Hairston, Lucinia, '91
Hibbert, Marcia A., '93
Hogans, Mrs. Robin K., '91 *ET*
Jackson, Harvey, '70
Jones, Kevin, '95
Llyod, Massa N., '99
Maillard, James H., '75
Marcellus, Algeste, '98 *GN*
Marshall-Myles, Coleen, '97 *LW*
Mayers, John D., Jr., '99
Okeke, James, '91
Parris, David Mosa E., '98
Peterson, Carrie L., '80 *LW*
Ramsey, Richard M., '85
Stewart, Deirdre N., '94
Taylor, Robert G., '93
Tulloch, Natalie T., '98
Waller, Henry, '85
Welsh, Lawrence J., '95 *CO*
Williams, Alecia S., '95
Williams, Winsome O., '99 *SO*

Winfield, Lillian B., '75
Woodroffe, Dawn C., '89
Woolaston, Denise P., '77

SAINT JAMES
Olsen, Dr. Francis B., '74 *IN*

SARATOGA SPRINGS
Stanley, Dora L., '76 *GN*

SAYVILLE
Benasutti, Kathleen, '97
Casaburi, Joseph A., '71 *PL*
Castagna, John J., '95 *PL*
Dasilva, Gioia, '77
Erb, Kenneth G., '83
Johnson, Laurie J., '91
Messina, John J., '99 *PL*
Partridge, Joseph, '97
Robinson, Philip E.

SCARBOROUGH
Hanold, George M., '75

SCARSDALE
Benson, Michael J., '77
Bouza, Anthony V., '68
Collins, Stephen P., '98 *PL*
Daniels, Joseph R., '92
Di Giacomo, Anthony M., '87
Dupree, Angela, '98
Dwyer, Karen, '95
Fitzpatrick, Oona M., '91
Hahn, John J., '79
Hurley, Michael J., '93 *LW*
Knaplund, Virginia, '73
Littlejohn, Robert F., '73
Mersheimer, Chris, '97
Patel, Kamlesh K., '90
Rosenbaum, Meredith, '84
Rothenberg, Daniel S., '99 *SN*
Ryan, Fred C., '92
Smith, Robert A., '82 *PL*
Zwicker, Jay L., '77 *EA*

SCHENECTADY
Bornmann, Ines C., '84
Horan, Michael, '90
Rios, Jennery, '95
Steigman, Arnold L.

SCIPIO CENTER
Gulliver, Kimberly C., '96

SEAFORD
Arce, Michele, '97
Arnold, Richard, '96 *PL*
Barr, Charles S., CPP, CFE, '75 *FV*
Bonner, Edward J., '74
Boylan, Joan, '89
Brandi, Daniel J., '76
Brennan, Denise, '99
Conlon, Patricia A., '92
Daubman, Arthur G., '75
Deluca, Anthony E., '79 *LW*
Fealey, Joseph C., '76
Florkowski, Thomas, '85
Fuchsman, Alan, '74 *RE*
Kehoe, William J., '76 *PS*
Lee, Philip W., '79
Magrino, Robert, '90
Murphy, John T., '70 *BK*
Olsen, Edward H., '74
O'Rourke, John J., '75
Ottomano, Anthony R., '78
Outsen, Gregory J., '82
Reid, Thomas P., '68
Rushton, Denise A., '85
Sapraicone, Jane T., '79
Shtino, Gani, '76
Sicilia, Frank G., '80 *LW*
Smith, Lorraine E., '91
Specht, John F., '90
Stanton, Matthew S., '87
Sullivan, John M., '81 *PL*
Tighe, Michael R., '87
Weber, William P., '81

SEARINGTOWN
Schlosser, Kevin, '81 *LW*

SELDEN
Antonucci, Robert J., '99
Bernstein, Ms. Leslie, '83
Caparco, Randy M., '79
Colonnello, Karen A., '92
Dempsey, John S., '72 *ET*
De Niet, Bonnie, '82
Dunne, Peter J.
Fleming, John F., '97 *CO*
Fuchs, Deborah, '81
Halka, Jill A., '94
Iacopelli, Lisa, '81
Lavin, Michael B., '82
Marti, John L., '89 *PL*
Reddin, James P., '81

SENECA FALLS
Flynn, Kevin C., '93

SETAUKET
Ruggeri, Ronald X., '71 *AA*

SHELTER ISLAND
Quigley, John J., '73
Uhnak, Dorothy, '68

SHENOROCK
Mollaghan, John T., '96 *PL*
Vinci, Mrs. Catherine A., '92 *SA*

SHIRLEY
Cappella, Albert M., '81
Gorton, Michael J., '77
Hassett, Ann, '96
Lyons, Daphony P., '85
Rothang, Robert A., '74 *ME*
Wood, Joseph D., '96

SHOREHAM
Canal, Eugene, '72
Nedos, William T., '98 *PL*

SHRUB OAK
Aaron, Grantley W., '80
Gione, Gary J., '79 *PL*
Guerra, Timothy A., '96
Matusiak, William, '90

SLATE HILL
Hanson, Charles J., '75 *PL*
Nyland, Charles A., '96

SLEEPY HOLLOW
Bohigian, Valerie, '91 *WR*
Wendle, Thomas A., '73 *CP*

SLOATSBURG
Biggins, Patrick N., '77
Hogan, Brian F., '75
Holden, Terence, '99 *PL*
Maddalena, Leopold, '70
Moriarty, Thomas M., '75 *PL*

SMALLWOOD
Ference, Thomas J., '87

SMITHTOWN
Darsillo, Francis, '88
Fagan, Harry J., '74
Gilmartin, Kerri A., '81
Hart, Todd J., '95
Laferla, Linda J., '96
Linkletter, David P., '90
McGrann, Joseph P., '89
Mullady, Joseph R., '72
Negrycz, Raymond, '81
Nieroda, Daniel W., '86
Quinn, Lawrence T., '80 *PL*
Skelly, Patrick J., '80 *LW*
Smith, Wayne J., '87
Twiname, John J., '81
Uttaro, Raymond J., '75
Velez, David A., '97 *PL*
Zimmermann, William J., '77

SOMERS
Fahje, Donald J., '93 *PL*
Price, Fred E., '78 *LW*

SOUND BEACH
Francois, Marc D., '98
Schneider, Guy A., '84

SOUTHAMPTON
Cosumano, Robert L., '78

SOUTH FARMINGDALE
Penna, Frederick, Jr., '85 *GN*

SOUTH FLORAL PARK
Edwards, Sam L., '72 *PL*

SOUTH HEMPSTEAD
Davy, Christopher S., '92

SOUTH HUNTINGTON
Lee, Amy R., '89

SOUTHOLD
Berryman, John H., '62
Hughes, Brian J., '79 *LW*

SOUTH OZONE PARK
Bermudez, Michael, '79 *AC*
Bifulco, Anthony P., '90
Bifulco, Frank J., '84
Blair, Bernardo R., '80
Bonilla, Cesar A., '94 *PL*
Boodhoo, Joanne, '97
Briant, Anita K., '85
Brunson, Lakisha D., '98 *PB*
Carrington, Ron E., '96
Chase, Audrey, '91
Concepcion, Melissa, '84
Cordon, Lee C., '99
Dennis, Gustina M., '75
Freeman, Ronald A., '91
Fuller-bey, Tayhlia, '95
Garcia, Rosa M., '99 *PL*
Greene, Cheree, '97 *AM*
Hope, Quinzelle, '90
Iqbal, Nelly R., '84
Justice, Jeffrey
Khan, Shazad, '98 *PL*
Lalak, Patsy A., '99 *ME*
Lauther, Beverly, '83
Louissaint, Harmelle M., '98
Mc Nicholl, Robert G.
Mohammed, Rijal, '90
Nemorin, James V., '96 *PS*
O'Connor, Patricia A., '78
Parris, Marie N., '93 *LW*
Ruff, Michelle N., '99 *MK*
Spriggs, Lashunn, '95
Steinert, Rosa M., '79
Stone, La-Toya T., '99
Sumter, Antoinette, '97 *PN*
Tumasar, Diane M., '97 *AM*
Vessup, Earl L., '79
Williams, Jewel, '88
Wyre, Marcus L., '78

SOUTH RICHMOND HILL
Allen, Carl, '76
Amaya, Allan F., '88 *JU*
Baichoo, Linda T., '99
Henry, Valerie E., '97
Hibbert, Melonie J., '97
Jabouin, Alain S., '95 *PL*
Juman, Tarek, '97
Persaud, Nalini, '98 *CP*

SOUTH SALEM
Baez, Ricardo, '98

SOUTH SETAUKET
Blaikie, Melanie A., '99
Cerullo, Vincent, '72
Granata, Bryan E., '96
Granata, George M., '95 *LW*
Standel, Marie, '92
Zampieron, Paul W., '92 *SW*

SPARKILL
Wilkinson, Thomas C., '79

SPARROW BUSH
Lissner, Michael A., '95 *PL*

SPRINGFIELD GARDENS
Bailey, Sweden M., '97
Barton, Lisa M., '90
Beecher, Evelyn, '94
Bellamy, Charlie M., '78 *LW*
Blackman, David B., '90
Blackwood, Nicola G., '97

Bowman, Debra, '84 *PL*
Brouard, Michelle, '96
Butler, Ruth M., '98
Campbell, Robert, '98
Coleman, Antoinetta, '96
Daniel, George G., '71
Desir, Wilfrid, '98
Giglio, Charles J., '78
Jackson, Alicia J., '99
Jerome, Lourdes M., '97
Mc Pherson, Debbra S., '95
Meyers, John A., '75
Moore, Brigitte C., '85
Powell, Veronica D., '99 *ET*
Sealy, John, '82 *CP*
Simpson, Nicole D., '97 *AM*
St. Bernard, Shari, '97
Young, Shnequa A., '98 *LW*

SPRING VALLEY
Anthony, Wade D., '93
Ayala, Carmelo, '81
Bermudez, Carlos R., '94 *PL*
Brogan, Robert J.
Coleman, Philip W., '82
Collica, Kimberly A., '97 *ET*
Cooper, William C., '92 *LW*
Dillon, Laura A., '97
Ferman, Yolanda D., '79 *PL*
Hoch, Joseph B., '95 *PL*
King, Mrs. Crystal-Dawn, '97 *SW*
Marlow, Kidada, '97 *LW*
Mena, Eda L., '92
Mendez, Omar A., '93
Mulholland, Patrick G., '99
Ochs, Scott A., '83
Ortiz, Maria, '98
Pitts-Williams, Stacey G., '90 *SW*
Poust, Brian J., '96
Randall, Keron K., '92
Reid, Karlene, '90
Rodriguez, Victor M., '83 *LW*
Simmons, Melvin, '92 *LW*
Taveras, Wendy, '97
Tuly, Beth M., '96
Valencia, Armando, '99
Valentin, Julio A., '96 *PL*

STANFORDVILLE
Wolfmann, Monik H., '88

STATEN ISLAND
Abraham, Harlan B., '96
Abraham, Robert, '76
Adesanya, Oluwatoyin, '91
Agugliaro, John P., '86
Akerman, John M., '85 *PL*
Albanese, Philip P., '76
Alessandro, James, '76
Alzandani, Mansoor, '95
Amoruco, William M., '02
Amundsen, James E., '99
Andros, Frances S., '77
Annis, Christopher, '92
Aponte, Bianca M., '95
Arcuri, Gary, '92 *IN*
Armatti-Epstein, Linda T., '80
Askin, John P., '72 *PL*
Avallone, Carolann, '89
Aviles, LT Edwin R., '92 *PL*
Aweeky, Peter A., '84 *BK*
Ayari, Abderrahman B., '75
Backof, Richard W., '76
Baez, Henry, '76
Barbieri, William T., '95
Barry, James P., '92
Bartiromo, Michael, '89
Bartley, Laverne D., '97
Basciano, Patricia R., '80 *ET*
Batanus, John, '95 *PL*
Batista, Manuel L., '89
Becker, John J., '79
Benedict, Clare T., '77
Benedisuk, Mary R., '76 *PL*
Benevento, Peter R.
Berger, Richard, '92 *GN*
Biada, Charles, '96 *MG*
Biller, CDR Ronald D., '97 *PL*

Bishop, Barbara A., '90
Black, Anne, '79
Black, David W., '99
Blaich, Charles R., '98 *PL*
Blois, James H., '79
Blumenstein, R., '97
Bogdanowicz, Kathleen, '81
Bohrer, Philip, '80
Bole, Nicholas, '76
Bologna, Anthony (Tony) V., '92 *PL*
Bon, Johnny, '77
Bonacchi, Eugene, '76
Boresky, George M., '80
Boresky, Peter J., '78
Borruso, Mariano, '75 *UL*
Borsilli, Mildred O., '88
Bosco, Michael, '92
Boswell, Joseph A., '80
Boylan, Lauren E., '96 *PL*
Boylan, Michael P., '78
Boyle, Donald J., '77
Braccini, Stefano A., '95
Brasero, Rever, '84
Brech, Todd R., '96 *PL*
Breen, Susan L., '90
Brennan, Michael J., '75 *BK*
Brennan, Thomas H., '80
Brideson, Dawn M., '94
Brien, William E., '95
Briscoe, James J., '91 *PL*
Broadhurst, William, '75
Broderick, Harold T., '85
Brody, Stephen D., '81
Brousseau, Joseph O., '81
Browne, Samuel A., '82 *PL*
Browning, Darlene, '92
Bruno, Richard F., '91
Burgess, Audrey L., '97
Burke, James J., '77 *LW*
Butler, Raymond M., '95 *PL*
Caban-Gonzalez, Deborah, '98 *ET*
Calabro, Dennis P., '93
Calby, Paula M., '79 *CO*
Calhoun, William F., '76
Callahan, Robert M., '76 *PL*
Calouro, Joseph, '80
Camp, Nicole, '92
Campbell, Robert E., '71
Cangro, Frank F., '83
Cannata, Augustine M., '77
Cannizzo, Enzo F., '85
Capone, Peter, '92
Caputo, Joseph, '85
Caragiulo, Dominic, '90
Cardone, Robert A., '80
Carlo, John R., '69 *MY*
Carollo, Anthony M., '83
Carroll, Thomas J., '91
Caruana, Vincent J., '84
Casale, Charles
Casey, James J., '67 *LW*
Cassano, Salvatore J., '76
Castro, Robert J., '77 *TR*
Catalano, Domenick, '81
Cates, Bernice, '89
Chan, Agnes, '82
Cherry, Patrick J., '77
Chicolo, Mary E., '81
Chicolo, Michael, '81
Childs, Harry E., '96
Chille, Edward, '89
Chiriani, Daniel T., '82
Chodakiewicz, Thomas, '89 *GN*
Christiano, Steven A., '85
Chung, Thomas H., '94 *GN*
Ciepierski, Joseph R., '80
Cintron, Yvette, '94
Clark, Georganna, '88
Clark, James, '78
Clarke, James G., '76
Clarke, John, '85
Claro, Brian K., '87
Cody, Thomas E., '90
Cohen, Fern, '80
Coleman, William E., '76
Collins, Falisha R., '97

Colon, Mary, '83
Conde, Matthew P., '98 *PL*
Condon, Richard J., '78
Connolly, John J., '69
Conway, Gary F., '92 *PL*
Cooper, Charles D., '80 *PL*
Coppolo, James A., '80
Cordero, James A., '90
Corey, James A., '81
Corrado, Vincent J., '89 *ET*
Correa, Edward, '96 *PL*
Correale, Mark, '92
Costa, Richard, '80
Coticelli, Neal, '72
Coughlin, Richard D.
Coyne, Thomas R., '90
Craig, Kenneth A., '78
Cregan, Dennis J., '76
Cregan, Michael, '75
Cregan, Robert J., '76
Cregin, Matthew T., '94
Crimmins, Martin E., '79 *PL*
Crowley, John G., '80
Cruz, Angel, '83 *GN*
Cummings, Kathy C., '96
Cusumano, Charles, '90
Czajkowski, Raymond, '76 *ME*
Davis, Gideon, '73 *GN*
Davis, Lynette, '88 *GN*
De, Nigris B., '85
DeFina, Bernice, '95 *PL*
Defrancesco, Rosalie A., '99 *PL*
Delahanty, Lt Neal C., '72 *PL*
Dement, William, '92
Demeo, Teresa A., '84
Denesopolis, John, '94
Depuy, Richard A., '96
Desio, Frances M., '89
Desire, Yves C., '80 *PL*
Deyubero, Candida L., '79
Diaz, Michelle A., '85
Difilippo, Christopher B., '98
Dignon, Francis T., '76
Diih, Sorle S., '98
Di Marco, Andre N., '72
Di Meglio, Ciro P., '80
DiToro, Christopher J., '99 *PL*
Doerrbecker, George, '78 *SW*
Dolcimascolo, Jeffrey A., '83 *PL*
Dombrosky, Mark D., '99 *ME*
Domenech, Edgar A., '84
Donadio, Francis X., '74
Donnelly, James E., '90
Donohue, Patrick J., '92 *PL*
Donohue, Patrick T., '75
Dorans, Edward T., '75 *PL*
Dorvil, Rommelle T., '95
Dougherty, Roger B., '84 *GN*
Dougherty, William, '89
Dowd, Charles F., '77
Droner, Gerard P., '79
Dunigan, Bryan P., '80
Duval, Christopher D., '97
Dzieniszewska, Ewa, '95 *CP*
Edward, Selvin F., '81
Egan, Mary, '95
Eisner, Judy, '82
Enright, Mary E., '82
Erickson, Scott W., '98 *ET*
Esposito, Ralph A., '85 *LW*
Fabozzi, Michael, '93
Facciponti, Ronald, '94
Faison, Sylvia, '89
Faison, Thomas A., '90
Falkenhainer, William, '84
Fallon, Jeffrey C., '99
Fasano, Richard A., '99
Fealy, Michael D., '95 *LW*
Fedorschak, Leonard, '62
Feehan, Jeremiah K., '77
Feeley, Warren J., '76
Feit, Harvey D., '78
Ferguson, Charles J., '76
Ferris, Andrew P., '94
Fevelo, John F., '76
Finamore, Daniel J., '75

Finnerty, Frederick C., '77
Finnerty, Thomas W., '75 *RE*
Fischer, Mrs. Margaret M., '77 *MG*
Fitzgerald, Daniel J., '79 *GN*
Fitzpatrick, Thomas G., '76 *PL*
Flaherty, John H., '76
Flaherty, Richard J., '74
Flanagan, Leon E., '81
Flores, Arsenio, '89
Foresta, Jody A., '79
Francis, Charles R., '95
Frangos, Victoria H., '79
Frasco, Leonard W., '79
Fraser, Kenneth A., '80
Fredericksen, Robert, '70 *PL*
Freund, Charles G., '77
Frittitta, Joseph G., '98
Funk, James, '96
Furman, Cynthia, '95
Gabos, Mario, '66
Gagliardi, Michael J., '81
Gallo, Richard, '85
Gambichler, Edward F., '95 *CT*
Gannon, Walter E., '76
Garcia, Luis J., '78
Gardella, Ronald G., '80
Gelfman, George, '75
Genovese, Dominic A., '88 *PL*
Gentile, John R., '80
Geraci, Anthony W., '99
Gerdes, Jeffrey J., '99
Geritano, Lenore, '94
Giambrone, Alphonse, '90
Giammarino, Michael, '68
Gibbons, John M., '74
Gill, William B., '80
Gilmartin, Peter J.
Giordano, Jack J., '79
Giovinazzo, Alise, '93
Glidden, Ariana M., '93
Glynn, Keith A., '93
Gonzalez, Antonio, '91 *PL*
Goodman, Sabrina B., '98
Gottlieb, Paul, '76 *PL*
Goudie, David W., '76
Gravitch, Daniel J., '90
Gray, Donald R., '79
Graziano, Paul W., '79
Green, Stephen, '97
Greenwald, Steven, '97 *PL*
Grossman, Steven H., '93
Guarco, Anthony, '75 *GN*
Guastella, Maria, '91
Guido, William J., '76 *PL*
Hanley, John J., '96
Haran, Stephen J., '99
Harrigan, Eric J., '99 *MG*
Hartigan, George T., '77
Hazel, Amelia E., '81 *ME*
Herbert, John D., '83 *LW*
Heyward, Tina M., '88
Hickey, Keri, '99
Hickman, John J., '78
Hoffman, Howard A., '76
Holloway, Anthony, '94
Honore, Michelle M., '80
Hooper, Julian C., '82
Horan, James J., '75 *ET*
Hunt, Kathleen T., '77
Iannace, Arthur B., '78
Ingellis, Daniel A., '80 *PL*
Ingoglia, John V., '94
Irish, Carleton P., '68 *PL*
Iuliano, Stefano, '75
Jacobellis, Nicholas
Jakubowski, Thomas R., '77 *LW*
Jarecki, Jane M., '93
Jascewsky, George E., '77 *LW*
Jirak, Milton, '72 *ET*
Johnson, Isaiah, '97
Johnson, Jeanne, '79
Johnston, Gordom M., '81
Jones, Melissa R., '93
Kaj, Karen T., '93 *FV*
Kaltenmeier, John W., '78 *PL*
Kapel, Mark, '96

Kaufman, Steven, '85
Kavanagh, John P., '76 PL
Kelly, Gerard W., '72
Kelly, James F., '99 CT
Kelly, Leonard, '74
Kemp, Donita M., '98
Kenny, Raymond J., '68
Kiernan, Henry, '77 PL
Kinard, Tabitha, '99
King, Edward J., '77
King, Kenneth L., '76
Kirkman, Lisa A., '86
Kissel, John S., '94
Klein, Fredric C., '76 PL
Korzekwinski, Jack T., '75 GN
Koscinski, Robert, '77 PL
Kosowski, Mrs. Frances E., '80 RE
Krane, Thomas W., '79
Kress, Robert J., '79
Krieg, Barry M., '92
Kruesi, Arthur W., '76
Kuberski, Richard S., '82
Kulah, Kofua Z., '95
La Malfa, James J., '77
Lambert, Edwin F., '72 LW
Lampinstei, Edward S., '77
Landin, Rudolph, '93
Landsberg, Barry, '81
Lang, Wayne L., '98
Larson, Allan G., '83 PL
Lassen, Joseph, '93 PL
Latour, William J., '78
Laub, George J., '79
Lavelle, Joseph T., '91
Laverde, Jacqueline, '93
Lee, James M., '84
Lentz, Jennifer P., '97
Leone, Michell, '97 MG
Leong, Lai L., '84
Le Page, Robert J., '82
Levine, Morris, '80
Levine, Susan, '82
Lewis, Steven R., '93
Lilley, William P., '96
Logan, John J.
Logie, Mason, '84
Lopes, James, '85
Lopez, Lucy, '84
Loresto, Emil J., '89
Loschiauo, T.
Loughery, Michael J., '73 SA
Love, Archie C., '75
Lowery, John P., '95
Lucarelli, Modestino, '76 ET
Luongo, John D., '72
Lutkenhouse, Nancy E., '75
Lyons, John J., '90
Lyons, John R., '78
Maccarone, Virginia, '80
Madsen, Theodore S., '76
Maekawa, Yoshimitsu, '95
Magid, Stephen H., '77 JU
Mahon, Edward T., '78
Major, Curstlinia S., '98 SW
Maltese, Hon. Joseph J., '70 JU
Manahan, William F., '89
Mangome, Victor, '95
Manisero, Thomas R., '79
Manzione, Robert E.
Marcotrigiano, James, '79
Marcune, Patrick, '79
Marone, Dominic J., '90
Marra, Anthony J., Esq., '74 PL
Marrero, Miguel, '96
Marro, Elizabeth A., '87
Martin, Dennis E., '80
Martinez, Eugene, '77
Martocci, Rocco A., '76
Masucci, James J., '82 LW
Maybury, Kevin C., '76
Mazza, Cajetan, '76
Mc Allister, Cathleen S., '95
Mc Andrew, Lois J., '79 PL
Mcauliffe, John, '96
Mc Bride, Hugh J., '78
Mccants, Stephanie N., '98

Mccutchan, Lisa K., '95
Mcgee, Patrick J., '97
Mcgill, Richard K., '83
McGinn, LT Timothy R., '92 PL
Mc Givney, John A., '71
Mchugh, Michael J.
Mc Kay, John, '76
Mc Kenna, Daniel J., '77
Mckenzie, Constance, '95
McKeon, James E., '76 GN
McLaughlin, John P., '80 PL
Mc Loughlin, James F., '79
Mc Menemon, Thomas P., '77
Meadowcroft, James J., '83
Mealia, Robert M., '76
Medeiros, Michael, '76 PL
Medina, Ms. Marianella, '91 ME
Mejias, Edgar, '87 MG
Melendez, Mrs. Diana A., '95 LW
Melone, John E., '76
Mendez, Irma E., '91 PL
Merritt, Douglas, '97
Messina, Anthony L., '81
Meyers, Glenn R., '95
Miceli, Peter S., '77
Mihailos, Michele A., '99
Mikos, Ms. Nancy, '78 JU
Milione, James M., '74
Miller, Christine A., '78
Miller, Daniel, '88
Minto, James S., '70
Mohlenhoff, William R., '79
Moller, Kenneth C., '96
Moncayo, Frank J., '95
Mongan, Heather A., '77
Monti, Stanley P., '79
Mooney, Thomas E., '73
Moore, James E., '77
Moore, William J., '96
Morales, Carlos E., '99 RD
Morales, Cesar A., '97 LW
Moran, John P., '77
Morcelo, Domingo A., '76
Morelli, Angelo M., '78 GN
Morisano, Anthony J., '85
Mormino, Bennett, '88
Mulligan, Robert, '94
Mulligan, Thomas J., '77
Murillo, Jose P., '93
Murphy, Brian J., '99
Murphy, Patrick J., '72
Murphy, Thomas P., '91
Musarella, Mark, '85 LW
Myers-Punnette, Mrs. Yvette, '96 AM
Nanartowicz, Carol, '82
Natoli, Joseph J., '79
Neckin, Ian H., '98
Ngai, Kenneth, '95
Niemiec, Theodore, '83
Nolan, Harold F.
Nolasco, Joseph, '81
Norberg, Scott, '95
Norden, Paul A., '96
Nuzzi, Laurie A., '97
O'brian, Joseph J., '78
O'Brian, Patrick J.
O'Brien, Joseph J., '66 MG
O'Brien, Patrick J., '73
Ocasio, Roger, '87
O'Connor, Edward G., '73
O'connor, Kevin R., '78
O'Donnell, Donald P., '85 PL
O'leary, Jeremiah J., '76
Olender, Dennis J., '83
Olivieri, Richard, '73
Oquendo, Olivet, '99 IN
Orender, Patrick
Orender, Patrick E., '98 GN
Orlandella, Sandra M., '95 PL
Orlando, Robert A., '95
Orlick, Harvey A., '78
Otten, Kimberly A., '96
Paccione, Jack, '80 PL
Palesano, George J., '91 LW
Pallonetti, John R., '78 HT

Panarello, Gary R., '76
Pappalardo, Vivian, '88
Papson-Adams, David, '95 LW
Paradiso, Michael, '98
Paraskevas, Melissa, '88
Parera, Carolyn, '91
Parrilla, Steven J., '78
Patrice, Mic-arlem, '93 AM
Pavia, Edward J., '87
Pawluk, William J., '91
Pecoraro, Robert H., '83
Perez, Juan A., '89
Perez, Lauro, '96
Perez, Mario, '97 PL
Perno, John, '86
Perrine, John
Perrotta, Michael J., '98
Perry, Gregory S., '90
Petrocelli, Albert P., '79
Philips, Janet, '95 SW
Piazza, Anthony, '93
Picarello, Jodi A., '90
Pignataro, John V., '89 PL
Pincar, Barbara, '77 ET
Piotrowski, Ronald D., '78
Piraino, Joseph A., '77 PL
Pisani, Angelo L., '81
Pitrone, Alberta J., '90 PL
Plaia, Vito, '95 PL
Plant, Edward J., '95
Pontecorvo, Daniel M., '83 UL
Poppe, John D., '77
Poppe, Matthew S., '95
Powell, Gilbert R., '77
Primiano, John, '91
Procopio, Mary A., '85
Pruitt, Denise L., '95
Quill, Daniel J., '60
Quinn, James C., '80
Quinones, Mariluz, '88
Racioppo, Ralph, '76 GN
Rackmill, Stephen J.
Ramirez, Eliud, Jr., '85
Randall, Francis E., '75 IN
Rando, Gregory J., '76
Rasso, Louis J., '95
Rauchet, Joseph L., '78
Razzore, Annmarie, '93 ME
Reavis, Piar N., '85
Reed, Robert, '82
Refuto, George J., '77
Regan, Charles E., '77
Reid, Anne E., '99
Reid, Kenneth, '89
Reilly, Michael, '96
Rendeiro, Alfred P., '78
Reynolds, Stephen, '89
Rezoagli, Frank, '79 JU
Rice, Robert D., '73
Rivera, Nickcole D., '98
Rizzo, Brian J., '93 PL
Roberson, Irene, '79
Roccaro, Rosario J., '76
Rodriguez, Ms. Veronica, '97 AM
Romano, Mrs. Lisa M., '95 IN
Rondon, Natasha J., '96
Rosado, Concepcion P., '80
Rovira, Catherine
Ruffo, Robert, '74 PL
Rumpf, William R., '81
Russo, Joseph P., '89
Russo, Robert M., '93
Ryan, Kenneth J., '80
Ryan, Robert T., '97
Sacaccio, Michael J., '81
Sackel, James H., '82 PL
Salamone, Vincent, '95
Sampel, James J., '75
Sandseth, Thomas R., '86
Santa, Robert C., '98
Santangelo, Antoinett, '84
Santiago, Rose M., '76
Santimays, Alice V., '79 PL
Sanzone, Augustine, '85
Sargent, Douglas L., '83
Saryian, Paul D., '90 LW

Saviano, Mrs. Donna M., '92 PL
Scalici, Joseph, '96
Scarabino, Virginia, '84
Scarpone, Leonardo, '94 HT
Sceusa, Peter S., '79
Schaefer, Lawrence, '80
Schaffer, Scott L., '74 SA
Schauffert, R. C., '76
Schlitt, Robert W., '83
Schoen, Richard M., '87 PL
Schubert, Kristin, '95
Schwartz, Robert I., '70
Scotto, Anthony F., '90
Scotto, Joseph M., '98
Scotto-Lavino, T., '95
Scribani, Santo A., '93
Sedutto, Joseph
Seltzberg, Mark S., '81 ET
Semple, Darryl M., '79
Sena, Nino D., '97
Senerchia, Anthony G., '79
Shedden, Jennifer L., '89 LW
Shedden, Stephen B., '89
Shields, Eugene G., '75
Simmons, Karen P., '90
Simonetti, Joseph J., '91
Simonetti, Tosano J., '76
Slevin, Edward F., '81
Smith, Leo E., '75
Smith, Matthew R., '76
Smith, Michelle D., '95 CO
Smith, Peter G., '75
Smith, Saundra, '96
Sommers, Barry M., '75
Spataro, James A., '93 ET
Spector, Abraham M., '79
Spence, Robert J., '77
Spisto, Brian N., '81
Spitzbarth, Robert, '95
Springer, Louis G., '74
Squassoni, Laura C., '79 PL
Stack, John J., '83 CO
Stahl, Lowell L., '81
Stapleton, James J., '79
Stawchansky, Donna, '84
Stern, Lee R., '80
Stewart, Delisia R., '98
Straub, Jacqueline, '82
Sugarman, Stacy, '98
Suidzak, Victor J.
Sullivan, Daniel F., '68
Sullivan, James J., '75
Swartout, Peter J., '78
Taibbi, Patricia A., '77
Tarasewich, Thomas A., '76
Tarwacki, Robert E., Sr., '93 PL
Tatar, Paul A., '83
Tellefsen, Laurie J., '94
Tenzer, Mitchell R., '79
Thompson, Robert A., '83
Tobin, James J., '76 PL
Tocco, Stephen M., '96
Tracy, John C., '92 PL
Triarsi, Emmanuel, '80
Turbiak, Robert J., '78
Ucelli, Monique S., '97 SN
Ulsamer, John J., '77
Vaill, Mrs. Cara J., '99
Valentino, Michael, '91 PL
Vargas, Miriam, '78
Vecchiarelli, Dennis, '83
Vega, Ernan, Jr., '87 PL
Velez, German J., '96
Vellucci, Frank R., '79 GN
Villano, Valerie F., '96
Vinci, Donald S., '94
Vitale, Tammy, '97 PL
Volpi, Ms. Jennifer M., '98 PN
Vredenburgh, E., '95 LW
Vreeland, Nicholas F., '86
Vroom, Charles C., '79
Walsh, Ann, '94
Walsh, George J., '75
Walsh, Thomas P., '74 PL
Ward, Edward C., '79
Watt, Robert E., '81

Wazeter, Edward J., '78
Wells, Charles J., '78
Wessolock, Robert E., '81
Westrenen, Jack, '78
Wexler, Jason D., '93
White, Joseph M., '95
Wiedemann, Paul M., '82
Wiegand, Robert W.
Wilday, Robert D., '77
Wilkman, Robert A., '76
Wincelowicz, Michael, '75
Woodruff, Nancy, '93
Worth, John T., '74
Yasso, Michael, '75
Young, John W., '77 GN
Young, Michael G., '78
Yurman, Robert J., '81
Zaharuk, Joseph P., Jr., '78 GN
Zaidman, Esther
Zichettello, Thomas, '85

STEWART MANOR
Rose, Michael J., '77
Secter, Charles W., '79

STONY BROOK
Albertus, Alfred J., '72
Bruckenthal, Eric A.
Delamer, John
Goodman, Donald, PhD, ET
Jacobs, Harold, '76
Pinsent, Clarenc M., '73

STONY POINT
Bazazian, Dennis G., '77
Cahill, Angela M., '78 HM
Cahill, Patrick, '78 PL
Connolly, William J., '72
Egan, John J., '75
Ferrer, Jorge M., '94
Fox, Thomas M., '98
Giblin, John F., '85 LW
Glynn, Martin P., '77
Gonzalez, Francisco, '77 CN
Granata, Robert, '92
Herrera, Luis, '96
Hopkins, Farrell J., '95
Kitz, Alfred F., '78
Mahoney, Francis J., '79
Morales, Antonio, '77
Ocampo, Julio, '90
Ocampo, Mrs. Melisa, '96 PL
Rosado, Jose, '91
Sullivan, Timothy J., '72

STORMVILLE
Druker, Courtenae, '90
Lenard, Jill R., '95 PL

SUFFERN
Brockway, Mary Z., '84
Byrne, George, '96
Caccavo, Christine, '99
Cruz, Victor A., '99
Dieckmann, Martin W., '77
Fredericks, Andrew A., '95 CN
Irizarry, Sylvia E., '82
Perrone, Diane, '86

SUNNYSIDE
Aridas, Mrs. Nanette, '97
Boisseau, Dominique, '97
Carrasco, Edward (Ed) G., '99 PL
Chantayan, Angelika, '99
Davila, Luis E., '97
Goss, Agnieszka, '96
Jarosch, Richard A., '87
Ko, Michelle, '96
Mc Cabe, Jenni, '96
Rafferty, Thomas B., '82
Ragoonanan, Ramcharan, '99
Riccardi, Kenneth P., '76 LS
Ronelli, Danielle A., '97
Ryan, John F., '78
Samuels, Jason S., '98 GN
Sanchez, Natasha H., '97
Tabone, Michelle, '94
Tituana, Luis, '96
Valle, Nelson, '95

SYLVAN BEACH
Donlon, Megan, '99

SYOSSET
De Phillips, Alfred P., '67
Gecewicz, Edward T., '78
Gotay, Albert, '71
Holian, Kevin M., '80 GN
Jensen, Paul V., '72
Kaye, Mrs. Marion, '76 PL
Lizzio, Peter J., '81
Mc Gee, Peter P., '72
Mc Glone, Jim, '74 PL
Mihovich, Anthony M., '80
Paveglio, David J., '76
Rogdakis, Constantine
Schaefer, Deborah, '91 EA
Solano, Joseph L., '76
Sulfaro, George V., '93

SYRACUSE
Mclees, Mark J., '83
Trenca, Michael P., '96
Urrutia, Julio E., '79

TANNERSVILLE
Frick, Henry F., '98 PL

TAPPAN
Blacksburg, Michael, '96
Farry, Richard D., '75
Gerhold, Lawrence R., '75
Guthrie, Thomas J., '69
Maher, James M., '75
Manis, Ms. Jeanne D., '99
Modafferi, Anne C., '84
Schrettner, Joseph, '81
Weber, John, '72 PL

TARRYTOWN
Delaney, Ann, '81
Edelman, Steven P., '95
Garofalo, Michael R., '78
Hyland Reda, Mrs. Velvet A., '97 BK
Mertz, Mrs. Elizabeth H., '94 HM
Robinson, Edward S., '90
Todorovic, Jelica, '96 HT
Whitely, Donald H., '82

THIELLS
Billik, Philip A., '92
Ramos, Anthony J., '76
Rubino, Arthur S., '92

THOMPSON RIDGE
Neeson, Josephine A., '81

THORNWOOD
D'Alessio, Berardino
Lore, Frank A., '96 PL
Sysak, Paul J., '75 MF

TIVOLI
Lewis, Ms. Annamarie, '78

TOMKINS COVE
Lifrieri, Michael D., '96
Moran, John A., III, '98 PL

TROY
Caola-oskin, Courtney B., '95
Powell, David F., '85 PL

TUCKAHOE
Amato, Edward J., '76 LW
Campanile, Anthony, '95
De Gaetano, Gina, '97
Kennedy, Stephen R., '81
Kirk, Michael, '76
Munroe, Doris L., '97
Nelson, Warren W., '69
Perrotta, Fred J., '76
Sanclemente, Erlinda, '93
Todras, Jay P., '81
Walsh, James G., '93

UNIONDALE
Baker, Michele C., '87
Charles, Rose M., '95
Drakes, Ingrid L., '85 PL
Enriquez, Lister V., '99
Gonsalves, B., '93

Harding, Rev. Curtis T., Jr., '76 MY
Harris, Bishop Robert W., '74 MY
Healy, Craig C., '90
Horton, Edward, '95
Ibrahim, Shorab, '99 LW
James, Richard L., '92
Jimenez, Pedro A., '95
Lawrence, Denise A., '83
Prysock, Jeanine M., '87
Reid, Gloria M., '80 MG
Reynolds, Bertrand A., '88
Ross, James D., '71 LW
Wallace, Evelyn, '93

UTICA
Campoccio, Deborah A., '97 SW

VALHALLA
Bitkower, Amy J., '93
Carlson, Glenn A., '99 PL
Mignini, Annmarie, '91

VALLEY COTTAGE
Albanese, James J., '92
Brennan, Kenneth D., '77 BE
Burke, William J., '74
Cuccio, Rocco J., '75
Farley, James F., '95
Griffin, Dennis M., '89 PL
Taddeo, Jack, '76 PL

VALLEY STREAM
Baierlein, Elizabeth, '93
Beckford, Maxine A., '97 SW
Bohringer, Ernest W., '99 PL
Brown, Leah D., '99
Brown, Van, '95
Calandriello, Maria, '96
Cestare, John, '76
Chow, Frederick R., '85
Clerico, Lucien T., '80 GN
Cunneen, William A., '67
De Candia, Domenic, '72 PL
De Marino, Vincent A., '80
Dipierro, Paul, '91 JU
Dunne, Richard A., '72
Dutes, Ronald, '93 ES
Ferrall, Christopher T., '95
Giardina, Philip
Gillespie, Bernard M., '70 GN
Girimonte, Albert (Al) W., '81 PL
Gluck, Geri H., '93
Goodwin, Bruce K., '76
Greenberg, Harry, '78
Guzzo, Louis G., '97
Harmon, Michael P., '81 PL
Heaney, Patrick, '98 PL
Holihan, John W., '78 PL
Howkins, James O., '80
Ignaciuk, Stanley, '77
Jamindar, Swati P., '90
Keleman, Robert, '88
Lewis, Anthony, '90
Maini, John, '80
Mandzik, Philip J., '78 PL
Matrisciano, Joan, '91
Mattiasich, Fabio L., '77 GN
Mayer, Michael J., '84
Mc Dermott, John P., '77
Mendez, Dennis M., '99 MG
Moss, Kyna E., '93
Mueger, Warren, '85
Musmacher, Robert J., '81 PL
Panzarino, Nicholas, '81
Pellicani, Stephen P., '83 LW
Pierre, Abel L., '98
Piil, Laura, '99
Polis, Stacy A., '97
Quaranto, John C., '88
Raniola, John, '76
Reid, Trevor M., '84
Richardson, Thomas, '99 PL
Rodriguez-Barros, Tanya I., '91 ME
Rognon, Rudolph G., '95 LW
Sciarrino, S., '93
Silver, Sherrelle M., '96 PL
Smith, Richard C.
Sollitto, James R., '76

Soria, Katterine I., '95
Steele, Edward J., '91 PL
Stewart, Mrs. Wendy A., '95 BK
Thomas, Darrell E., '95
Vasquez, Ms. Daisy, '96 FV
Velasquez, Yanina, '96 LW
Walsh, Matthew T., '95
Warne, Kenneth C., '75
Werner, Edward C., '83
Wilson, Marsha M., '94

VICTOR
Davis, Jay E., '70

WADING RIVER
Angermaier, Heather A., '98
Donnellan, Roger W., '73
Montenegro, Richard (Rich), Jr., '95 FV
Wohlleb, Joanne, '85

WALTON
Bertolini, Vinicio, '81

WANTAGH
Antonelli, Ralph, '89
Bergersen, John R., '76
Cennamo, John E., '85
Church, William J., '95
Feiler, Christopher, '95
Forte, Leonard L., '77 FV
Gabora, Herman R., '73 PL
Harkins, Michella R., '98
Haviken, John J., '77
Held, Sharon Z., '85
Hennessey, Richard E., '78 PL
Kurtz, Robert T., '70 BE
Lamb, James P., '98 CP
Liptak, Thomas J., '75
Lopez, Lisa A., '91 ME
Mac Kay, Donald R., '75
Mc Crystal, Harry J., '69
Nasoff, William J., '76 LW
Norvio, Scott J., '95
Otis, David B., '79
Palumbo, Peter J., '77 PL
Phelan, Connie M., '90
Redican, Joseph E., '79 PL
Sanfilippo, Monica L., '98
Schultz, Philip R., '93
Schwartz, Ned E., '77 GN
Spyntiuk, Stephen P., '91 PL
Valdes, Jesus M., '90 PL
Vitucci, Frank, '77
Vonbargen, Philip H., '75
Weiss, Kenneth D., '80

WAPPINGERS FALLS
Cusher, Devin, '93
Diaz, Carmen I., '89 ET
Emanuel, Michael A., '99
Gibbons, Thomas F., '96 PI
Herring, John, '85
Kelly, Edward J.
Kinney, Susan, '88
O'Reilly, John, '92 GN
Rinaldi, Joseph, '90

WARWICK
Beattie, Henry J., '99 MG
Castagna, Alfred R., '89 PL
Cerezo, Juan E., '96 PL
Coiro, Robert M., '83 PL
Gillen, Brian J., '76
MacNamara, Donal E., ET
Markowitz, Matthew, '95
Page, Shawnee, '87
Pascocello, Anthony J., Jr., '95 PL
Rohrberg, George J.
Sala, John A., '78
Shields, Joseph G., '90 PL
Turner, Michele, '97
Williams, Gordon, '95
Zoufaly, Thomas M., '77

WASHINGTONVILLE
Blaha, Richard, '95
Cassidy, Joseph T., '99 PL
Coates, John R., Jr., '86 PL
Foley, Michael O., PhD, '75 ET

Lanza, James J., '83
Lara, Guisela J., '97
Lascano, Mercy, '83
Leahey, John G., '86
Levi, Barbara, '75
Lin, David, '99 AC
Lopez, Daisy, '80
Mackey, Elayne S., '82
Martinez, Yesenia, '97
Marulanda, William, '98
Marus, James L., '85
Matsuoka, Andrew H., '94
Mc Loughlin, Kevin, '82
Ngai, Lauren M., '96 LW
Oliveras, Mrs. Daisy I., '95 MG
Patruno, Cataldo, '96
Porcelli, Rita, '96
Quito, Mrs. Maritza B., NP, '97 PN
Regus, Judith G., '97
Rice, James T.
Rivera, Manuel S., '99
Robertson, Bruce A., '95 ET
Sabel, Raymond P., '78
Salley, Jacqueline M., '85
Sandiford, Jerry A., '98
Sierra, Lesly, '83
Sovulj, Josip, '81
Spinoso, Thomas D., '83
Veilson, Martin, '92
Virgilio, Thomas M., '81
Vrana, Denise L., '82
Winfield, Karen M., '99 PL
Yan, Hon-man, '97
Zimmerman, Sidney, '76
Zorrilla, Agatha N., '99

YAPHANK
Abrams, Jonathan A., '93 LW
Dilworth, Donald
Fleming, Edward J., '78 PL
Fontana, Mrs. Laura M., '98 MG
Glynn, James J., '68

YONKERS
Abreu, Maria T., '89
Acevedo, CW4 Efrain, '76 MI
Adolfsson, Boyd, '76 PL
Aglietti, C., '93
Armstead, David, '95
Bagi, Gabor R., '97
Barnes, Wallace, '89
Barnett, Robert, '95
Barrett, John J., '74
Bodkin, John E., '75
Bordas, David M., '99 ET
Bosco, Vicent I., '63
Branigan, Robert J.
Bustillos, Norma I., '93
Byrnes, Robert G., '95
Byrnes, Robert M., '76 GN
Caban, Juan A., '83
Capellan, Awilda J., '98
Carolan, Edward, '90
Carter, Luis A., '79 PL
Carter, Melvina M., '93 FV
Cepeda, Luis, Jr., '91 PL
Chavis, Shawn, '95
Clarke, Ms. Nicole A., '97 SW
Colicci, Gerald P., '79 BE
Concepcion, Aranel, '76 PL
Cosenza, Joseph, '80
Cotter, Joseph P., '75 CN
Cox, Ethel, '99
Coyne, Susan M., '97
Crawley, William J., '81
Crosby, Marion T., '97 LW
Daly, Daniel, '80 PL
David, Wilfred, '86 JO
Diaz, Fanny A., '91
Di Benedetto, Denise, '85 PL
Dixon, Shellese, '86 SW
Duncan, Abraham D., '72
Duro, Christopher M., '95
Dwyer, Lauren A., '99 ET
Dybski, Thomas, '99 PL
Faulk, Alisa, '95
Flynn, Brian P., '85

Freundlich, Jeffrey, '81
Garrido, Francisco, '96 GE
Giacobbe, Nicholas, '86
Graf, Margaret M., '91 RD
Greenberg, Gwynneth, '82
Hamideh, Hamza, '99
Hannigan, James R., '75
Harrison-Carera, Sharlene, '94 AM
Hasso, Lisa S., '95
Held, Kenneth L., '94 LW
Hill, Mercedes S., '85 PL
Hodgins, Joseph A., '83
Ingram, Margaret, '92 PL
Intrieri, Dominick D., '87
Iocco, Luigi G., '90
Isroe, Karyn E., '95 CO
James, Michelle B., '95 LW
Johnson, Wendy M., '98 TR
Jones, Ernest K., '64
Keating, Robert P., '93 GN
Kellam, Fayon
Kelly, Martin A., '63 PL
Kenny, Marie, '98
Kittrell, John E., '76
Kulyrych, Lubomyr P., '89
Lamb, Jerry D., '91 EM
Laperuta, Domenick A., '95 LW
Lienhart, Richard, '96
Lockhart, Colleen M., '87 SN
Lopez-Rivera, Pedro, '79
Mahoney, Catherine V., '99 PL
Mahoney, Sheila, '93
Martinez, Jocelyne, '95
Mccarthy, James N., '97
Mckenna, Siobhan H., '91
Mckoy, Gay L., '96
Mc Mahon, John P., '70
Mladenovic, Goran B., '93
Montalvo, Oneida, '93 SW
Moodie, Genevieve E., '83
Moodie, Joyell T., '98
Morciglio, Libertad E., '79
Moreira, Ms. Julie A., '99 SW
Mullins, Theresa B., '85 NU
Neal, Sean M., '98
Neufville, Norris, '95 SW
Newton, Samuel A., '95
Nieves, Dominick R., '88
Nieves, Ralph G., '95
Nolasco, Hector, '95
O'Connor, James F., '71 PL
O'Leary, Joseph P., '67 PL
Olley, Donald E., '82
O'Rourke, Stacey A., '98 PL
Packman, Miriam A., '97
Perry, Diane J., '81
Pimenta, Paul M., '98
Quetell, Jennifer L., '93
Raptis, Thomas N., '89 PL
Rood, Sholloy, Jr., '77 RE
Reilly, William G., '77
Renzullo, Vittoria, '82
Reyes, Jacayra C., '99
Reyes, Yahayra, '99 LW
Rodriguez, Kenneth M., '84 PL
Rodriguez, Servando, '97
Rosenberger, Joseph N., '98
Schrepel, Raymond J., '86
Shalvey, Edward P., '76
Smallwood, Lee N., '99
Stahl, John R., '75
Steward, Dominique K., '87 PL
Stewart, Hazel L., '87
Stroh, Christopher M., '99
Uveges, Michael J., '99 SW
Washington, Archie, '97 PL
Wendolski, Peter P., '75
Yoshizaki, Takuji, '99
Young, Antonia R., '98 ST
Young, John C., '91
Yurus, William, '89

YORKTOWN
Stamatelos, Danny S., '77 LW

YORKTOWN HEIGHTS
Bauer, George M., '99 PL

Byrne, James F., '92
Callahan, Michael P., '75 LW
Foubister, Arlene J., '75 MF
Frost, David, '79 IN
Gonin, Daniel O., '93
Gorsuch, Robert P., '71
Hellthaler, F. W., '82
Hernandez, Amarilyz, '95
Hernandez, Nancy M., '80
Knoblich, James P., '88
Kopstein, Jay I., '82 PL
Manus, Raymond P., '77
Mc Kenna, Peter, '77 PL
Noonan, Peter, '78
Pierce, Bruce H.
Ramsey, Waltis, Jr., '75 MG
Smith, Leroy G.
Weisfuse, Irene W., '81
Witkowich, Michael F., '78
Wojcik, Jerry H., '97 MG

NORTH CAROLINA

ASHEVILLE
George, Loise L., '75 MY

BANNER ELK
Flynn, John J., '71

BOONE
Kuzyszyn, Katrina N., '99

BURLINGTON
Ferris, Lauraine E., '90

CANDOR
Bostick, Denise G., '82

CARY
Astor, Kevin R., '81
Galiano, Richard H., '72

CHAPEL HILL
Marchetti, Rossin A., '99

CHARLOTTE
Flemmings, Lamont S., '76 PL
Piekarski-rome, Cynthia, '89
Richards, Emanuel (Manny) H., Jr.,
  '86 GN
Short, Eugene A., '76

DURHAM
Singletary, Charles R., Jr., '90 PL
Smith, Walter D., '75

FAYETTEVILLE
Brady, COL Edward T., USA(Ret.),
  '77 PL
Burgess, Thomas S., '79 ET
Corprew, Nitaka, '96

GOLDSBORO
Christman, William C., '78 PL
Murray, Clyde E., '74

GREENSBORO
Gundersen, William, '76
Lowe, Victoria L., '97 SW
Moores, Robert N., '84
Reyes, Donna, '84

HAMPSTEAD
Layne, Frederick R., '79

MONROE
Hade, Patrick J., '77 RL

MOYOCK
McGuinness, Hugh, '89

NEW BERN
Koehler, Karl F., '72 PL

RALEIGH
Harper, Leonard, '78 LW
Heineman, Frederick K., '75 PL
Mcloughlin, Thomas, '90

SALISBURY
Qadirah, Eleanor, '85 ET

SPARTA
Leiker, David C., '75

WILMINGTON
Dunican, Thomas A., '74 JU
Giammalvo, Gregory V.

WINDSOR
Hughes, Leola M., '93

NORTH DAKOTA

BISMARCK
Giesinger, Marie A., '86 MI

MINOT
Boyko, Kevin E., '76

OHIO

AKRON
Adkins, Lewis W., '87

BRUNSWICK
Los, Sandra A., '95 GN

CLEVELAND
Waye, Jane, '85 LW
Wiltshire, Ms. Cheryl M., '95

COLUMBUS
Bassinger, Deborah N., '84
Sheehan, Vincent J., '79 ET

DAYTON
Clark, Gerald C., Jr., '85 GN
Rosado, Lt Col Samuel A.,
  USAF(Ret.), '75

FAIRBORN
Zajicek, Renee M., '98

GALLOWAY
Pagan, Tina-marie, '92

MASON
O'connor, Michael J., '81

NORTH RIDGEVILLE
Miller, Ann M., '99

SANDUSKY
Keller, Christopher, '97

TOLEDO
Meehan, Stephen G., '96

WESTERVILLE
Boykin, Thomas, '78
McGehean, Donna G., '92 PN

WESTLAKE
Coniglio, Kenneth J., '93

WILLOUGHBY
Ryan, Theresa A., '99

YOUNGSTOWN
Welsh, James L., '93

OKLAHOMA

EDMOND
Canfield, Dennis V., PhD, '76 GN

YUKON
Flammang, Margaret A., '82

OREGON

BEAVERTON
Socci, Michael F., '78

BEND
Meyer, Mitchell L., '93

PORTLAND
Ahrens, Bree C., '98
Kaffashan, Nazanin, '99

WEST LINN
Davidson, Mark E., '79
Magistro, Anthony J., '96

PENNSYLVANIA

ABINGTON
Montague, Angela R., '89 *LW*

ALLENTOWN
Ramos, Manuel, '96
Rivera, Julie A., '97

BATH
Rhett, Sheila A., '83 *GN*

BENSALEM
Corson, Randi L., '80

BETHEL
Miller, Steven G., '81 *PN*

BETHLEHEM
Bush, Christopher P., '95
Kiapokas, Theodora, '91 *SW*

BLAKESLEE
Chester, Shonette A., '95

BRADFORD
Gannon, John F., '60

BRODHEADSVILLE
Cinti, John A., '75

BUSHKILL
Mc Cabe, Gregory R., '75 *BE*
Schwenzer, Roseann, '99

BUTLER
Bauer, Richard B., '81
Bauer, Richard C., '76

CAMP HILL
Grode, George F., '73 *IN*

CARVERSVILLE
Grosso, Ralph, '84

CLARKS SUMMIT
Lekach, Jakub, '75

CLYMER
Robles-nunez, Julia E., '94

CONESTOGA
Conlon, Peter J., '72 *PL*

CONSHOHOCKEN
Dooley, Bradford O., '79 *MY*

DINGMANS FERRY
Gibbs, James H., '77
Messina, Camillo J., '90 *PL*
Mueller, Paul K., '87
Penn, Joseph C., '95

DOYLESTOWN
Laughlin, Paula, '84
Ralko, Stephen E., '77

DREXEL HILL
Flanagan, Richard Y., '75

EASTON
Johnson, Darryl A., '92

EAST STROUDSBURG
Carter, Wylene Y., '81
Knox, Charles, '74
Lukowski, Fred J., '94 *PL*
Sampson, Marcia E., '87
Staines, Edmund T., '76
Utsey, Robert E., '95 *PL*

ERIE
Bukowski, Gary

EXTON
Salas, Julius O., '98 *LW*

GLENOLDEN
Razzi, Dana L., '99

GREELEY
Neenan, Kevin M., '88

HARRISBURG
Underwood, Mark, '90

HATBORO
Lasalle, Jeffrey J., '85

HAWLEY
Mc Donnell, Robert, '76
Moe, Richard, '78 *PL*

HERMITAGE
Needleman, Ira J., '89 *LW*

HUNTINGDON VALLEY
Martin, Alexandra, '97

KIMBERTON
Otto, Ms. Patricia C., '80 *CT*

LAKE ARIEL
Byrne, Therese M., '84
Carney, William F., '72
Donleavy, William P., '71
Phillips, Leon A., '95

LAMPETER
Kurau, William R., Jr., '74 *PL*

LANCASTER
Marinaro, Michael V., '85 *LW*

LANGHORNE
Aguero, Maggie, '80 *GN*

LEBANON
Branch, Joseph, '85

LEMONT
Craig, Sara Elizabeth, '95 *GN*

LEVITTOWN
Spiritosanto, Anton, '89

MERION STATION
Leibman, Faith, '85 *LW*

MILLERSVILLE
Mitro, Edward J., '81

MORRISVILLE
Goetz, John F., '75

MOSHANNON
Davis, Teresa A., '95 *TR*

MUNCY
Broach, Myra K., '92 *BE*

NEW HOPE
Mancuso, Peter J., '76 *BE*

NEWTOWN
Millman, Howard L., '81

PAOLI
Seward, James D., '84

PHILADELPHIA
Blount, Danny H., '81
Brea, John
Dowling, Jack F., '77 *PL*
Felix, Suzanne, '88
Figueroa, Luis A., '82
Gallagher, J. P.
Gianfrancesco, Paul, '89 *LW*
Gorman, Nina, '85
Haggerty, Michael C., '85 *GN*
Hague, George T., '70
Jarrett, E. C., '94
Madera, Brenda, '90
Nicholas, Florence M., '84 *GN*
Schultz, John A., Jr., '97 *LW*
Timoney, John F., '74
Trainor, Patrick J., '95 *GN*
Yates, Genithia, '98 *ST*

PITTSBURGH
Mc Glincy, Hugh J., '91
Tesfamariam, Bernice

POCONO LAKE
Bielski, Chester W., '74

RICHBORO
Gutierrez-donnard, Raisa, '84

ROXBOROUGH
Egan, Abbe I., '99

ROYERSFORD
Sell, Angela M., '97 *MG*

SAYLORSBURG
Berry, Stephen D., '86
Sullivan, Allison M., '90

SEWICKLEY
Gregorin, Dr. David, '82 *MY*

SHICKSHINNY
Pentangelo, Aniello A., '80

SHOHOLA
Kallas, Leo, '74 *PL*

STATE COLLEGE
Donovan, Edwin J., '72 *ET*

STOCKERTOWN
Bubnis, Christalie J., '98

STROUDSBURG
Epstein, Trevor J., '70
Victor, Philson J., '97

SWIFTWATER
Gander, Edward F., '82 *PL*

TOBYHANNA
Connelly, Robert T., '80
Mackesy, Richard, '84 *EA*

WALLINGFORD
Bernard, Ronald P., '78

WESTTOWN
Dunn, Michael F., '77

WHITEHALL
Karam, Anthony A., '86

WYNCOTE
Sergi, Frank, '80 *ME*

YARDLEY
Augustus, Sondra R., '75 *CP*
Constantino, Ralph V., '70
Higgins, Michael J., '77
Hyde, Phillip E., '76 *MG*
Inducci, Craig G., '80 *JU*

RHODE ISLAND

BRADFORD
Burrows, Jonathan, '94 *CO*

CRANSTON
Carlucci, Jean M., '97 *MI*

NORTH PROVIDENCE
Urrutia, Anna-Maria, '82 *ET*

WAKEFIELD
Preddice, Victoria A., '99

WARWICK
Boone, Theresa L.

SOUTH CAROLINA

BLUFFTON
Reilly, John T., '75

CHARLESTON
Aldrich, Alicia, '91 *CO*
O'Brien, Patrick T., '76
Simpson, Thomas G.

COLUMBIA
Boyeson, Warren, '85
Moore, Charles T.

FORT MILL
Brady, Matthew E., '79 *GE*

GEORGETOWN
La Vaughn, Deanna A., '80

GREENVILLE
Streger, Matthew R., '96 *ME*

HARDEEVILLE
Segar, Yvonne, '96

HILTON HEAD ISLAND
Boyle, John F., '63 *LW*

KINGSTREE
Chisolm, Karen A., '88

LITTLE RIVER
Foss, John R., '79 *LW*
Telesco, Christina B., '99 *PN*

LONGS
Ekster, Martin B.

MONCKS CORNER
Green, Vanessa M., '86

MOUNT PLEASANT
DeGiovine, Arthur M., '75 *LW*

NORTH AUGUSTA
Carter, Mary A., '81

OKATIE
Linden, Jack, '72

ORANGEBURG
Guinyard, Freddie, '95
Smith, Sarah A., '85 *CO*

RIDGELAND
Norton, Benjamin T., '86

SUMTER
White, David W., '76

WEST COLUMBIA
Brown, Tara N., '96 *GN*

WILLIAMSTON
Vargas, Mrs. Jennifer L., '91 *HM*

TENNESSEE

CHATTANOOGA
Sanderfer, Gale R., '83

CORDOVA
Griffin, Osie L., '87

MEMPHIS
Dobro, Stuart, '93 *LW*
Lewis, Diane, '81
Ridgway, Donald L., '79

NASHVILLE
Hackenmiller, Julie, '98 *LW*

NOLENSVILLE
Doss, C. Brian, '99 *RD*

OLD HICKORY
Guyet, Allan R., '74 *LW*

TEXAS

ALLEN
Raldiris, Carlos J., '89 *MG*

ARLINGTON
Arevalo, Yesenia M., '95 *SW*

AUSTIN
Garnett, Joan M., '98 *LW*
Sernaque, Janet, '97
Sita, Joseph M., '80 *PJ*

CARROLLTON
Singh, Ramkumar, '83

CORPUS CHRISTI
Gansrow, Ruth, '87 *PL*

DALLAS
Bloom, Jason S., '96 *CN*

DENTON
Boyle, Edward R., '83

EL PASO
Castricone, John A., '81
Clausen, Vincent J., '74 *GN*
Collorafi, Mrs. Lyz S., '98 *CO*
Correa, Miguel A., '79
Cotham, Jeffrey D., '94 *PL*
Torres, Mrs. Cecilia A., '82 *MF*

GEORGETOWN
Modawar, Faris A., '77

GRAND PRAIRIE
Duke, Lara M., '98

GRAPEVINE
Shinnick, Edward (Ed) J., '77

HARKER HEIGHTS
Blake, Dr. Henry E. E., '67 *ET*

HARLINGEN
Diaz, Mercedes, '79 *GN*

HENDERSON
Tiefenwerth, Thomas J., '83 *ME*

HIGHLANDS
White, John H., '76 *FV*

HOUSTON
Andress, La'donna V., '96
Arestie, Martin J., '76
Bollander, Richard C.
Boritza, Ms. Patricia A., '80 *LW*
Brook, Jonathan A., '83
Cohen, Ronald, '79
Falley, Roy B., '79
Gibbons, Oswald
Yagual, Magali E., '87

HUNTSVILLE
Ward, Richard H., '68

KEMPNER
Hendrick, John S., '81 *ET*

KILLEEN
Casares, 1LT John W., USA, '98 *MI*

LEWISVILLE
Mc Kinley, Ronald R., '78

MC ALLEN
Widnick, Steven M., '76 *LW*

MISSOURI CITY
Dodds, Dwayne M., '86 *GN*
Fullerton, Khalfani O., '83

PLANO
Connelly, Susan, '86
Rojas-dykes, Carol, '77

RICHARDSON
Abramson, Neal G., '78 *ET*

SAN ANTONIO
Cherena-Pacheco, Yvonne, '78 *LW*
Hatzis, Alexander C., '84
Johnsen, David P., '75
Shomion, Carol A., '75 *SW*

SUGAR LAND
Ramsey, Keitha Y., '80

THE COLONY
Reid, Diane P., '86 *CN*

THE WOODLANDS
Taylor, Robert F., '83 *ET*

TROPHY CLUB
Perry, Ofer J., '98 *FV*

UVALDE
Schifini, Thomas A., '95 *GN*

WILLIS
Quinn, Robert J., '72 *LW*

UTAH

DRAPER
Gregoric, Maximilian, '84

HOLLADAY
Zimmer, Marianne E., '78

LAKE POWELL
Arce, Michael H., '78

VERMONT

BURLINGTON
Shtull, Penny R., '84 *ET*

DANBY
Gaiotti, Helaine J., '87

NORTH BENNINGTON
Fay, Catherine, '89

SOUTH BURLINGTON
Aponte, Myriam, '79 *CN*

VIRGINIA

ALEXANDRIA
Adler, Harvey L., '79 *GN*
Allen, Matthew C., '86
Anderson, Martha C., '91
Mccarther, Monifa, '95
Roulston, Tammy L., '94 *PL*
Sarrantonio, Lana, '78
Vallecillo, Gonzalo A., '93 *LW*

ARLINGTON
Assante, Philip J., '73
McAleer, Gerard P., '96 *PL*
Oslyn, Morris, '64
Ponzo, Robert E., '83
Riccio, Joseph P., '78 *LW*
Stout, Donald R., '80 *GN*
Vallderuten, Fabiola, '95

ASHBURN
Mitesser, Peter C., '80 *GN*

BEALETON
Slattery, Robert J., '77

BURKE
Finnerty, Kevin
Yoch, Marchelle R., '99

CENTREVILLE
Pagano, Bruce L., '79
Shea, Cornelius P., '75
Shields, Roger L., '77 *GN*
Staab, Ryan R., '96 *GN*

CHANTILLY
Fratter, Jeffrey, '78

CHARLOTTESVILLE
Gagliano, Allene, '92

CHESAPEAKE
Cayetano, Olga, '95
Dubose, Kenneth E., '94
Gold, Stanley A., '96 *GN*
Haskett, Kathy, *ME*

CHESTER
Jones, Paula, '96

DALEVILLE
Barber, Glenn M., '78

DINWIDDIE
Chatman, Zemender, '87

DUMFRIES
Nachtman, Iva, '98 *PL*
Welch, Sylvia P., '82 *GN*

FAIRFAX
Quirindongo, Eligio, '84

FAIRFAX STATION
Friedman, Jason A., '96
Gross, Roger A., '77 *PL*

FALLS CHURCH
Adams, Farrell M., '83 *GN*

FORT MYER
Gelfand, Jeremy, '91

FREDERICKSBURG
Ayres, Richard, '85 *CN*
Leibowitz, Morton J., '72 *PL*
Neil, Harold, '75
Shields, Richard C., '77 *PL*

GLEN ALLEN
Adams, Charice Y., '95

GLOUCESTER
Nugent, Michele D., '95

GREAT FALLS
Hershman, Michael, '72 *CN*

HAMPTON
Bergner, Kevin, '88

LYNCHBURG
Strube, Edward W., '75 *PL*

MANASSAS
Glover, Elliott P., '81

MC LEAN
Sullivan, Patrick F., '75 *GN*

MIDLOTHIAN
Malcan, Jay W., '76

NEWPORT NEWS
Ferrson, Norita, '93

NORFOLK
Coleman, Frieda, *RE*
Dobay, Dominic, *CP*
Hartman, Bryant, *JO*

OAKTON
Barba, Maria E., '75

PURCELLVILLE
Yera, John, '88

QUANTICO
Amarutsanon, Kittisak, '93

QUINTON
Aiken, Iris A., '91

RICHMOND
Belviso, Lawrence M., '81 *PL*
Hunter, George A., '92
Jackson, Robert A., '83
Kosinski, Monica D., '97 *RD*
Lee, Tiffany M., '99 *PL*
Mitchell, Gloria A., '95
Morris, Keisha B., '95
Robinson, Hamilton, '72
Williams, Geraldo A., '85

SPOTSYLVANIA
Holder, Gloria I., '74 *BE*

SPRINGFIELD
Quinn, James F., '86 *MI*

STAFFORD
Arthur, Terri E., '84
Goode-Wallace, Laleatha B., '93 *CP*
Ortiz, Col Rene P., USMC, '75 *MI*
Pinizzotto, Anthony J., '81 *PL*
Thorson, Steven J., '85 *GN*

STERLING
Arthur, Mario, '81

SUFFOLK
Hall, Minnie M., '82 *RE*
Mercilliott, Frederic P., PhD, '74 *ET*

TAPPAHANNOCK
Nawrocki, Mary-lynn, '87

VIENNA
Aivazis, Elias K., '79 *PL*
Kettering, William N., '78
Monticelli Aivazis, Mrs. Mary, '81 *HM*

VIRGINIA BEACH
Hentze, Jeanette M., '84 *PL*
Laville-Wilson, Debra, '94
Mc Gill, John J., '70 *LW*
Nemara, Vanessa A., '77 *MG*
Peter, John H., '79
Powell, Hughlett O., '85
Robinson, Marilyn C., '85
Rodriguez, Mrs. Jeannette, '97 *CH*
Shazel, Everett, *FV*
Smith, James W., '76
Steets, William R., '95 *PL*
Wheeler, Jo, *AD*
Whitt, Kimberly D., '96
Wiener, Paul T., '71
Woodley, Janeth F., '80

WILLIAMSBURG
Loboda, Henry J., '79
Osamwonyi, Joseph I., '96 *BE*

WOODBRIDGE
Boyd-vega, Tracey, '79 *GN*
Matthew, Raymond T., '91
McKenzie, Laura, '91 *GN*
Park, Richard A., '99 *PL*
Stone, LTC Wayne A., USA, '82 *MI*

VIRGIN ISLANDS

WASHINGTON

BOTHELL
Kitson, Daniela S., '79 *HM*

PORT ORCHARD
Sullivan, Kathy, '90

SPOKANE
Treppiedi, Rocco N., '75

WALLA WALLA
Baker, James, '85 *CO*

WEST VIRGINIA

KEYSER
Parks, Bruce C., '88

WHEELING
Huber, Paul, '88 *LW*

WISCONSIN

MAYVILLE
Pokorny, Mrs. Cindy L., '96 *CT*

MEQUON
Annina, Ralph, '80 *CN*

MILWAUKEE
Hastings, Mark E., '95 *SO*
Logrande, Antonino, '90 *GN*

NORTH PRAIRIE
Bundy, Elizabeth B., '99 *CO*

WYOMING

CHEYENNE
DuFresne, Raymond K., '79
DuFresne, Roserita, '92 *AM*

U.S. MILITARY

Acevedo, Cruz, '75
Bandik, Mark G., '82
Cadogan, Darwin D., '73
Ferguson, James G., '76
Hart, Davis B., '82
Liscouski, Robert P., '78
Lock, Linda C., '76
Neblett, Angela M., '76
Russell, Michel M., '87
Shields, Phillip A., '81
Simpson, William, '71
Singh, Nandkumar, '91
Terilli, Michael, '88
Valenti, Philip J., '75

U.S. POSSESSIONS & TERRITORIES

PUERTO RICO
Aponte, Negron R., '96
Fernandez, Alexis V., '92
Lopez, Terron, '96
Perez, Omar, '99 *PL*

VIRGIN ISLANDS
Brady, Sylvia T., '72 *ME*
Harrigan, Justin, '85
Newton, Selassie A., '74 *ET*
Schrader, Richard A., '71 *WR*

OUTSIDE U.S.A.

CANADA
Bedrossian, Anne-Marie M., '97 *PL*
Berube, Michael, '96 *GN*
Bettman, Michael, '86
Carlson, Mary, '92
Coutts, Anne R., '96 *IN*
Houle, Ms. Genevieve L., '99 *LW*
Rego, Simon A., '95 *ST*
Vecchio, Jack, '74 *AF*
Vrantsidis, Dorothea, '91 *MF*

CHINA
Lam, Kwai, '98 *SO*

DENMARK
Sorensen, Bo N., '98

GHANA
Oppong, Martin D., '76

INDIA
Anand, Srikala, '86
Mani, Riva, '97

ISRAEL
Drobny, Charlene, '84 *SW*

ITALY
Aponte, Victor M., '76

NETHERLANDS
Bert, Richard A., '95 *PL*

NIGERIA
Nnamocha, Nestor U., '79

TAIWAN
Hung, Fu-chin, '84 *MG*
Lin, Ching-Hua, '93

CAREER NETWORKING SECTION

ACCOUNTING

Abarca, Celia J.
Andricosky, John J.
Becker, Mrs. Susan
Berke, Marshall L.
Bermudez, Michael
Brown, Shanteil
Clapp, Michelle D.
Desantis, Francesco
De Santis, Nicholas
Egan, Patrick J.
George, Sharon J.
Grogan, Dennis
Hoffman, Neil
Jones, Shirley D.
Kennedy, Lillian
Lin, David
Menard, Earl J., Jr.
Ninburg, Svetlana
Pajooh, Rudolph R.
Ramos, Laura
Rodriquez, William, Jr.
Rose, Lynn
Sarnataro, Geoffrey L.
Sohan, C.

ADMINISTRATIVE/ CLERICAL/ SECRETARIAL

Alexander, Alison J.
Alvarez, Michelle L.
Badillo, Cristina
Battle, Lisa M.
Belin, Thelma
Bowman, Lawson D.
Bramble, Anthony S.
Cabrera, Yokasta
Cheeks, Robert
Chupcavich, Anna J.
Cole, Karen E.
Cosme, Maura
Cudjoe, Michelle A.
Cummings, Ivan
Curran, Eleanor A.
Davis, Joanne
de Beer, Rebecca
Dennett, Phyllis D.
Desaussure, Ms. Martha
Di Maggio, Barbara A.
Dominguez, Michelle A.
Dove, Darlene C.
DuFresne, Roserita
Eckhoff-Pieratt, Ms. Karen
Embry, Alicia J.
Fernandez, Odalys
Foglia, Mrs. Sophia
Galaher, Lilia
Gary, Ms. Blanca I.
Gonzales, Helen K.
Goodwin, Ella D.
Greene, Cheree
Gregory, Rita
Grisales, Claudia
Harrison-Carera, Sharlene
Harvey, Charmaine P.
Hernandez, Michelle
Hillsman, Yequarah
Isaac, Dana R.
Jefferson, Marsha E.
Jenkins, Gary P.
Johnson, Charlene A.
Johnson, Franceska
Johnson, Zanetta C.
Lancaster, Michael O.
Lett, Lorraine

Lora, Krupskaia (Sky)
Marshall, Mrs. Irene
Maynard, Heather E.
Mccain, Shanique S.
Mcfarlane, C.
Mercado, Frances
Montrose, Sharon R.
Myers-Punnette, Mrs. Yvette
Nacinovich, Ms. Diane M.
Nathaniel, Nigel M.
Nunez, Janet F.
Ocasio, Yolanda M.
Ortega, Maritza
Ortiz-benjamin, Maira
Patrice, Mic-arlem
Perez, Michelle
Porter, A. Dashiell
Pride, Kasha L.
Ramsay, Elcah
Ripps, Carol A.
Rocco, Janet N.
Rodriguez, Ms. Veronica
Shivers, Lashonne L.
Simpson, Nicole D.
Tarver, Dionne E.
Taylor, Ms. Shernill
Torun, Aydin N.
Tumasar, Diane M.
Uhlmann, Dennis P.
Vargas, Jeffrey (Jeff)
Velazquez, Liz
Velez, Martha S.
Viglione, Albert J.
Warner- Lyons, Mrs. Elyse Y.
Wertkin, Stephen L.
Wiggins, Cathy
Williams, Angela
Wilson, Keryon T.
Wojtach, Susan E.
Woodberry, Corey
Yee, Peter J.

ADVERTISING

Kunitzky, Michael
Prieto, Juliza J.
Saint Cloux, Marie P.
Wheeler, Jo

ANIMAL SCIENCE/ VETERINARY MEDICINE

Lessner, Mrs. Mary V.

ART

Brophy, Edward J.
Larsen, Jeremy

ARTS - FINE

Kuhn, Ann
Vecchio, Jack

ARTS - PERFORMING/ CREATIVE

Alexander, Cheryl P.
Ingman, Matthew A.
Kabakoff, Robert I.
Lopez, Della L.
Lunn, Kitty
Marinoff, Gary A.
Murray, Thomas K.
Oyewayo, Olusade
Ramkaran, Denyse
Serafino, John M.
Taylor, Tonya
Zimmerman, Peter S.

AVIATION/AEROSPACE

Fenty, Jill M.
Fitzgerald, James J.
Lewis, Geoffrey B.
Marshall, Joseph
Ruggeri, Ronald X.
Seelig, George W.

BANKING

Austin, Reginald A.
Aweeky, Peter A.
Brennan, Michael J.
Calvanese, Jerry F.
Chagrin, Jay W.
Coakley, Daniel P.
Corney, Raymond J.
Duncan, Shakima
Falvey, Stephen J.
Hyland Reda, Mrs. Velvet A.
Kong, Corwin
Lawrence, Talaia
Lopez, Daisy
Mack, Ms. Stephanie M.
Marine, Ricardo
Murphy, John T.
Perez, Maritza
Petersen, Eddy
Salcedo, Yadira I.
Schick, Raymond W.
Stewart, Mrs. Wendy A.
Swinton, Darlene

BROKERAGE/ SECURITIES/ INVESTMENTS

Adamiak, Alan B.
Baisden, Ms. Jilyon
Bey, Robert F.
Canady, Donna A.
Connor, Brian W.
Dunne, Jay C.
Dziekonski, Barbara
Harcourt, Kimberly
Harvey, Ms. Wendy B.
Irizarry, Gisela
Jenkins, Ms. Sabrina M.
Kennon, Shawn
Kurtz, Michael J.
Mieles, Christina M.
Mignano, Michael J.
Molinaro, Louis J.
Palazzo, Thomas J.
Peele, Ondra T.
Salazar, Marcelo
Shergalis, Joseph A.
Walker, Susan M.
Welsh-Shirley, Joyce L.
Williams, James O.

BUSINESS - ENTREPRENEUR/ OWNER

Adelson, Arthur
Antoine, McFredy
Bittar, Robert N.
Botte, Dominick, Jr.
Brennan, Kenneth D.
Broach, Myra K.
Buntin, Mark M.
Cardillo, Joseph L.
Carroll, Thomas R.
Chatman-Whitfield, Mayai N.
Christian, Elmo E.
Codispoti, Michael
Colicci, Gerald P.

Dalton, Robert B.
Dupoux, Mrs. Marie-Maud
Evans, Michael
Ferguson, Wanda
Ham, Sung
Hamilton, Carl
Harper, Bennie
Hellner, Brian
Hennig, George D.
Holder, Gloria I.
Houdek, Caroline M.
Johnson, Ms. Nykelle S.
Jourdan, Marine
Kelly, Karen M.
Kessler, Dennis
Kurtz, Robert T.
Lopez, Luis A.
Majeski, William J.
Mancuso, Peter J.
Mandelbaum, Marvin H.
Mc Cabe, Gregory R.
Melis, Paul
Mingo, Alfred E.
Morris, John A.
Nash, Joseph F.
Nurse, John P.
Osamwonyi, Joseph I.
Pearce, William
Price-Moore, Ms. Jennifer M.
Rahn, Robert H.
Rainis, Edward A.
Ramirez, Vernon
Rechenberg, Jan M.
Rosenberg, Linda S.
Schenker, Stephen
Schuppert, Ronald
Smith, Harry, CPP
Smither, Mrs. Melissa
Smorto, Ivette
Tripi, Anthony F.
Tulley, Dionne
Walter, Bruce W.
White, Reginald H.
Whitfield, Fred L.

CHILDCARE

Brown, Moreale P.
Callistro, Cynthia Y.
Chevere, Beverly D
Discenza, Regina
Douglas, Darien
Gayle, Cathy A.
Rodriguez, Mrs. Jeannette
Zedeck, Deborah S.

COMMUNICATIONS

Baptiste, Camille A.
Barreto, Amelia R.
Best, Racine A.
Cicero, Alethea U.
Cox-Alston, Ms. Stephanie A.
Francillon, Joanne
Gambichler, Edward F.
Gibbons, Adam C.
Giler, Lorena K.
Isaacson, Eric M.
Jimenez, Robert
Kelly, James F.
King, Jemma F.
Langarica, Ernesto
Levine, Fran N.
Malone, Daniel E.
McCarey, Colleen A.
Middleton, La-tonia B.
Murphy, Mrs. Rochelle M.
Nieves, Julie A.

COMMUNICATIONS

Otto, Ms. Patricia C.
Phipps, Ms. April I.
Pokorny, Mrs. Cindy L.
Screen Aguilar, Cynthia A.
Shavers, Donna L.
Skolnik, Mrs. Anita D.
Smith, Henry G.
Solomon, Osbert K.
Stanis, Mary E.
Walker, Shirley E.
Watkins, Ms. Tracey L.

COMPUTER/HIGH TECHNOLOGY

Adegbamigbe, Adedeji
Ali, Shakawat
Anthony, Mark W.
Applewhite, Elsie
Arellano, Arthur Wellesley
Arroyo, Jennifer R.
Ashley, Teresa L.
Augustus, Sondra R.
Black, Samuel (Sam)
Blassingame, Paul
Bolivar, Matilde
Borquaye, Marylin
Bowler, William T.
Bracero, Denise
Brezny, Charles G.
Brumer, Steven N.
Bruntel, Doris H.
Carvajal, Tania M.
Clarke, Justin H.
Collins, Barbara W.
Colon, Hector E.
Cooper, Karl M.
Dobay, Dominic
Dunn, Hayley
Duville, Richard L.
Dzieniszewska, Ewa
Egger, Stephen L.
Frater, Donroy S.
Gonzalez, Enrique
Goode-Wallace, Laleatha B.
Goodman, Milton
Gorovoy, Oleg B.
Green, Andrew P.
Gumbs, Douglas J.
Harp, Jeffrey D.
Hernandez, Jose A.
Hyppolite, Ms. Anne W.
Isaacs, Paul K.
James, Spencer L.
Jones, Eneka U.
King, Eric D.
Korol, Natalya
Lamb, James P.
Lasack, Ian N.
Lempert, Vladimir
Lo, Chun-on
Malahy, James E.
Manios, Louis N.
Mannino, Salvatore O.
Maxim, Ana
Maxim, Ilie
Mc Coy, Michael G.
Mcghee, Liza
Molignano, Nicole M.
Neary, Kathleen T.
Nedd, Janine A.
Nicola, Maria E.
Niss, Oleg
Noel, Gesner
O'Dell, Jill C.
O'Keefe, Patricia J.
Perini, Bernard J.
Persaud, Nalini
Pontecorvo, Thomas J.
Powmesamy, Learie
Ramirez, Reynaldo
Raymond, Woody
Reynoso, Edgar
Ritondo, Marcello
Rivers, John J.
Rodriguez, Andrew W.
Russell, Marsha Natasha

Salvatore, Lawrence F.
Sealy, John
Segur, Webb
Sevastyanov, Vladimir
Shuster, Galina V.
Shuster, Irina V.
Sotomayor, John P.
Villani, Michelle T.
Vlad, Cristian A.
Ward, Ms. Linda M.
Weisberg, Elyse J.
Wendle, Thomas A.
Whiting, John W.
Wicker, Jason A.
Wilkins, Michael R.
Williams, Cynthia
Winn, Mrs. Martha D.

CONSTRUCTION/ CONTRACTING

Fleming, Laqueth
Goodwin, Patrick J.
Palmer, Eric T.
Samuels, Bradshaw
Shapiro, Eric M.
Szarawarski, Michael

CONSULTING

Abraham, George C.
Adams, Robert W.
Annina, Ralph
Aponte, Myriam
Argenti, Karen M.
Ayres, Richard
Banks, Hermon J.
Barajas, Robert J.
Barry, Patrick T.
Behan, Cornelius (Neil) J.
Bergeron, John D.
Bloom, Jason S.
Bolz, Francis A., Jr.
Borgstrand, Margaret A.
Brown, Tara C.
Bugge, Brian K.
Cammallere, Catherine
Cassidy, Kevin A.
Chung, Judy Y.
Cole, Leslie, CPP
Collins, Elliot
Cotter, Joseph P.
De George, Joseph W.
Di Pane, Jodi E.
Donovan, Gerald J.
Drucker, Leslie
Eisenberg, Mark C.
Feeley, William F.
Fredericks, Andrew A.
Freeman, Theodore R.
Garcia, Martha M.
Garvey, James T., Jr.
Gervasio, Louis A.
Gibbs, Eugene
Gonzalez, Francisco
Hershman, Michael
Higgins, Albert T.
Hogan, Robert A.
Hults, Charles E.
Jackson, Alena R.
Katz, Marvin A.
Kelly, John E.
Kokubun, Shoko
Kravath, Pauline
Lombardo, Frank A.
Macpherson, Ian C.
McInerney, Robert (Bob) X., CPP
Mimms, Yvette C.
Mora, Jessica M.
Neuwirth-Vreeland, Denise
Nolan, William F.
O'Neil, Robert F.
Prager, Keith S.
Reid, Diane P.
Richiez, Irving G.
Slattery, Joseph W.
Wagner, Harold A.

Weems, Betty P.
Wicks, Gwynne
Williams, Rhonda Y., JD
Wolowski, Richard C.

COUNSELING

Aldrich, Alicia
Alston, Harry T.
Amaro, Margarita
Austin, Barbara J.
Baker, James
Banko -Ross, Dr. Ellen
Benfatti, Kristeine
Bernstein, Faye K.
Berrios, Carmen M.
Bhola, Ms. Patti-lou S.
Brett, Veronica E.
Briggs, Renee
Brinkman, Mrs. Diane M.
Brock, Mrs. Daisy H.
Brown, Charlton A.
Bundy, Elizabeth B.
Burrows, Jonathan
Calby, Paula M.
Chapman, Marilyn
Collorafi, Mrs. Lyz S.
Cook, Mrs. Leanne T.
Coriano, Milagros
Cox, Ayoka
Cronin, Joseph M.
Cunningham, Darrow
Davis, Mrs. Eleanor, PhD
Denslow, Lisa D.
Devine, Patrick
Diaz, Nora
Duffy, Craig T.
Federici-LaFargue, Ms. Marietta
Feliciano, Gloria
Fernandez, Mrs. Daysi
Fine, Joselyn
Fleming, John F.
Fleury, Renime
Fortis, Daisy
Furtick, Anna E.
Gaillard, Andrea J.
Gettis, Deanne R.
Gianusso, BethanyAnne
Ginel, Julio A.
Gomez, Victor R.
Graciano, Maria C.
Hellman, Karen A.
Holtzman-Waranis, Cynthia R.
Isroe, Karyn E.
Johnson, Willie B.
Jones, Yvonne
Jordan, Nazly
Jordan, Robert R.
Kateridge, Janine M.
Kemp, Royevette
Kinnebrew, Deborah
Klein, Leon E.
Lee, Mrs. Karen B.
Mahany, Annemarie
Mars, Nadeige
Martterer, Amy K.
McCann, Patricia J.
McClain, Shawn D.
Mendez, Lucitania B.
Minaya, Joselinne A.
Molinaro, Mario A.
Onwuka, Nelson O.
Pastrana, Angel L.
Pena, Anthony
Philbert, Donna-Marie
Pierre-Louis, Ms. Audrey H.
Robin, Latasha B.
Rodriguez, Claudia
Rodriguez, Errol O.
Rose, Joyce H.
Rumell, William N.
Samples, Mrs. Carole R.
Sarno, Lisa D.
Savatteri, Stephine
Schwartz, Robert T.
Seabrook, Reginald K.

JOHN JAY COLLEGE

Serrano, Francine
Simon, Jacqueline L.
Smith, Michelle D.
Smith, Sarah A.
Sokol, Louise J.
Soto, Grace M.
Stack, John J.
Sullivan, Brien P.
Sullivan, Nancy G.
Summerlin, Gregory P.
Tompkins, Gail H.
Trause, Victoria
Vanderlee, Cynthia S.
Vazquez-Rodriguez, Freddie
Venuti, Christine M.
Welsh, Lawrence J.
Westcott-Marshall, Darryl A.
Yacoob, Azimoon N.

DENTISTRY

Thomas, Linda P.

EDUCATION - ADMINISTRATION

Ahmed, Abdul M.
Chisholm, Delores
Chomiak, Robert H.
Cockburn, George A.
Edison, Mel
Edwards, Rev. Michael
Esguerra, Andres
Forsythe, Farris B.
Gibson, Sherry A.
Guyot, Dorothy
Haque, Ferdous
Harper, Renee Y.
Hennen, Christopher G.
Hercules, Keith F.
Holden, McThaddeus
Hussey, Robert F.
Kamona, Ruth N.
Lavington, Chelsea R.
Lee, Donald F.
Long, William F., III
Longobardi, Alfred C.
Louden, Dr. Robert J.
Lovell, David E.
Mackesy, Richard
Maillard, Patricia L.
Maldonado, Evelyn J.
Manners-Morales, Mrs. Julia C.
Martin, Jeanne E.
McNickle, R. G. (Nick)
Meine, Manfred F., PhD CGFM
Melbourne, Phyllis M.
Miller, Gail E.
Norris, Edward T.
O'Dowd, Michael P.
Odowd, Michael P.
Plackenmeyer, William
Polin, Ms. Martha A.
Poulos, Harry
Raphael, Giselle L.
Rothlein Goldstein, Mary
Schaefer, Deborah
Smith, Launcelott
Taylor, Sandra L.
Thomas, Joy E.
Walsh, Declan J.
Ward, Roger
Weiner, Alan R.
Welsh, Katherine W.
Wong, Ms. Mareen S.
Zwicker, Jay L.

EDUCATION - STUDENT AFFAIRS

Best, George M.
Brown, Linata
Dorsinville, Yolande
Dutes, Ronald
Eanes, Ms. Barbara A.
Garcia, Jo-Alejandra
Goode, Anna R.
Grant, Tamika S.
Gray, Golda

CAREER NETWORKING SECTION

Lochner, Colin D.
Marshall-Murrell, Paula
Robertson, Ms. Sallie A.
Usera, Jessica

EDUCATION - TEACHING

Abramson, Neal G.
Adler, Morton N.
Ahyoung, Gary C.
Aiken, Avril A.
Anderson, Dr. Lola H.
Annamunthodo, John C.
Balgobin, Ms. Julianna
Barrett, Kevin
Basciano, Patricia R.
Beatty, Gerard V.
Belasco, Mrs. Barbara A.
Belotte, Myriam
Benson, Rodney B.
Bility, Mohammed S.
Bincarowsky, George
Blake, Dr. Henry E. E.
Bliach, Tinamarie
Booker, Walter L.
Bordas, David M.
Brathwaite, Earl R.
Brown, Arline D.
Brown, Arthur M.
Brun, Gina
Buda, Richard
Budram, Anil
Burgess, Thomas S.
Burke, Redmond P.
Burwell, Louise M.
Burwell, Shawna M.
Bynde, Darice B.
Caban-Gonzalez, Deborah
Cacciatore, Robert J.
Cadot, Marie M.
Cajou, Jean Claude
Calathes, Dr. William
Cammett, John M., PhD
Capella, Ms. Jeanette
Carvajal-Nunez, Mrs. Xiomara G.
Casarino, Carmine J.
Cisse, Sanah
Civitano, Danielle L.
Clancy, William C.
Clarke, Rosanna
Clifford, Maria C.
Collica, Kimberly A.
Connor, Mrs. Katrina A.
Constant, Tara
Conti, Richard P.
Conway, Judith A.
Corbett, Ms. Heather A.
Corrado, Vincent J.
Crane, Ernest
Crayton, Wanda A.
Cronin, Kathleen V.
Davis, James R.
Delprino, Robert
Deluca, Henry
Dempsey, John S.
Derenowski, John C.
De Santo, Joseph A., PhD
Devins, Brian M.
Diaz, Carmen I.
Donovan, Edwin J.
Douglas, Marsha D.
Dwyer, Lauren A.
Ellsworth, Thomas
Erickson, Scott W.
Farrell, Marianne J.
Feldman, David A.
Fernandez, Theodore (Ted)
Fields, Renata
Filipowicz, Renata
Filippini, Mrs. Nancy F.
Fillyaw, Leonard D.
Foley, Michael O., PhD
Forni, Mario T.
Frank, Kathryn K.
Fries, Timothy

Gamble, Derick
Gangoo, Andrea R.
Gaston, Arnett W.
Gay, Joseph B., Jr.
George, Hector A.
Gerald, Ira
Goldstein, Alan M., PhD
Gomez, Rosa Y.
Goode, Gail M.
Goodman, Alan Z.
Goodman, Donald, PhD
Graham, Kenneth
Graves-Parker, Ms. Tywana E.
Greenberg, Martin A.
Greene, Stephen
Grennan, Sean A., PhD
Grullon, Johanny
Hackett, George A.
Hartnett, Sharon M.
Hendrick, John S.
Henriques, Zelma W.
Henry, Mrs. Marie R.
Hernandez, Gertrudis
Hettler, Mrs. Frances
Hickey, Stephanie M.
Hoffman, Joseph C.
Hogans, Mrs. Robin K.
Horan, James J.
Horne, Peter
Howard, Linder J.
Hunt, Marvin S.
Ingram, Carlean N.
Jacobs, Jerry L.
Jenkins, Douglas A.
Jennings, Charles R.
Jimenez, Daniel
Jimenez, Ramona J.
Jirak, Milton
Johnson, Ms. Monique F.
Johnson, Niesha P.
Jules, Wisner
Kadir, Maqsood U., PhD
Kaplan, Dr. Lawrence J.
Klein, Marta A.
Klement, Susan M.
Klinkenberg, William (Bill) H.
Kouzoujian, Gary B.
Krueger, Robert W.
Krukin, Ms. Avalon S.
La Madrid, Ms. Yvette
Langellotti, Phillip
Laurenson, Barbara J.
Lennek, Christopher
Lewin, Ms. Ouida O.
Liendo, Luis E.
Litwack, Tom
Long, Jeffrey E.
Lopez, Wanda L.
Loughman, Robert P.
Lucarelli, Modestino
MacNamara, Donal E.
Malagoli, Tara D.
Maldonado, Carmelo
Maley, James E., Jr.
Marion, Dorothy M.
Matterson, Eric
Maurice, Ms. Geraldine
McAloon, Daniel K.
McCabe, John P.
McCarthy, William F.
McCoy, Robert N.
McKenzie, Albert W.
McLoughlin, Katharine
Mc Nickle, Litna M.
Mendelsohn, David
Mercedes, Wendy V.
Mercilliott, Frederic P., PhD
Metivier, Beverley A.
Middleton, Sharon D.
Miller, Robert E.
Monsegue, Gail A.
Moore, James F.
Moore, Patrick
Morales, Hector
Morales-De Leon, Sandra
Morgan, John P.

Morse, Henry R.
Mullen-Morris, Veronica B.
Muratore, Anthony
Myers, Debra A.
Newton, Selassie A.
Nieves-Cardenas, Mrs. Carmen
O'Kane, John J.
Organ, Mrs. Miriam
Owens-Duff, Sharon A.
Palmer, Donald E.
Perez, Carlos M.
Perez Y Gonzalez, Dr. Maria E.
Perrina, Enrico
Peters, Petra P.
Phillips, Robert H.
Pincar, Barbara
Pollack, Andrew B.
Porter, Samuel A.
Potter, Hillary A.
Powell, Veronica D.
Prescott, Kay F.
Qadirah, Eleanor
Rabinowitz, Stacey M.
Raines, Alfonso D.
Rentz, Tracy D.
Ridley, Sandra O.
Riedy, William F.
Robertson, Bruce A.
Rodriguez, Jimmy
Rogers-Grinage, Debra
Roman, Edwin
Romani, Mark A.
Rufino, Annette L.
Ryan, Francis M.
Saigo, Shondell A.
Salahuddin, Shaifah
Salomon, Myrna I.
Sand, Valerie S.
Santana Martuez, Odalis
Schnitzer, Shirley R., PhD
Schulz, Dr. Dorothy M.
Sconfietti, James
Seltzberg, Mark S.
Sergio, Alice E.
Shapiro, Ruth B., PhD
Sheehan, Vincent J.
Shewnarain, Maya
Shpritzer, Felicia
Shtull, Penny R.
Simms, Jacqueline
Singleton, Ms. Latanya M.
Singleton, Michelle
Small, Karen S.
Solis, John E.
Southwell, Anthony I.
Souvenir-brice, Mrs. Cassandra Y.
Sow, Ms. Cynthia B.
Spain, Pauline
Spataro, James A.
Stephenson, Beverley
Stephenson, Oscar L.
Stewart, Janet S.
Storch, Jerome E.
Sylvester, Philip
Taylor, Ms. Ann L.
Taylor, Junior P.
Taylor, Robert F.
Telesco, Grace A.
Thomas, Keith B.
Torres, Alejandra
Tuck, Stephen J.
Tully, Rachel
Tytell, Harold
Urrutia, Anna-Maria
Uwa-Omede, Susan
Valentine, Rudolph N.
Vamvoukakis, Patricia A.
Velez, Cindhia
Vigder, Melissa V.
Vilme, Jeannette
Vredenburgh, Robert P.
Wagner, Colette A.
Ward, Thomas J., DPA
Webber, Leroy M.

Weinbaum, Nathan
Williams, Nakesha L.
Williams, Richard R.
Wong, Selwyn M.
Wright, Sharnickqua O.
Wrynn, Mrs. Maura A.
Young, Adrienne M.
Young, Gail

ENGINEERING

Baker, Harold C.
Parris, Jerome R.
Suponitskiy, Serge

ENTERTAINMENT

Hall, Tyson W.
Jordan, Shamieka S.
Kaslofsky, Thor
Lamb, Jerry D.
La Veglia, Anthony J.
Maldonado, Ismael
Mornel, Theodore B.
Panagos, James W.

ENVIRONMENTAL SCIENCE

Bramson, Joy A.
Cassagnol, Nikole
Howard, Bernard E.
McCauley, Marianne D.

FASHION/BEAUTY

Brown, Carla S.
Holst, Irma R.
Pagliughi, Kathleen
Samuels, Sandra E.

FINANCIAL SERVICES

Abdullah, Ms. Doris T.
Adams, Errol A.
Anastas, Anthony
Andrews, Benjamin (Ben)
Babb, Jackie R.
Barr, Charles S., CPP, CFE
Battiste, Denise
Bogovic, Anthony P.
Borrero, Kenneth
Bowes, Vincent
Camilleri, Michele
Carter, Melvina M.
Cavaliere, Christopher
Connolly, Charles P.
Corso, David J.
De Cicco, Donna M.
De Jesus, Lisa
Donato, Donna A.
Escalante, Norma E.
Ferreyra, Orlando F., Jr.
Fonde, LTC Philip, USA(Ret.)
Galloway, Rulisa
Garcia, Michelle C.
Gonzalez, Kenneth A.
Hayes, Emogene S.
Higgins, Mrs. Sandra E.
Kaj, Karen T.
Khan, Salima J.
Lande, John
Laster, Keena M.
Liggians, Rhonda L.
Lovell, Frederick J.
Macdonald, Mrs. Nirvana L.
Maloney, Christopher
Mc Geary, Joseph T.
Mickens, Renee J.
Montenegro, Richard (Rich), Jr.
Moon, Charles C.
Muller, Deborah
Nanna, Louis J.
Perry, Ofer J.
Posavetz, Marilyn A.
Raver, Deidre M.
Rodriguez, Hector
Ross Shapiro, Jennifer S.
Shazel, Everett
Silverstein, Andrew
Sparro, Michael R.

FINANCIAL SERVICES

Tischler, Jeffrey I.
Toro, Eric
Vasquez, Ms. Daisy
Waite-carson, Gloria
White, John H.
White, Pearl E.
Williams, Andel G.
Wilson, Luana A.

FOREIGN SERVICES

Bartlett-Josie, Mrs. Christine
Gu, Christopher K.

FUND-RAISING

Lieberstein, Steven I.
Sosa, Ms. Kilsie

FUNERAL SERVICES

Adams, Rafael D.

GOVERNMENT - ELECTED

Blige, Slater S.
Brady, Matthew E.
Buska, Richard M.
Campolo, Jennifer
Cheng, Mei
Cheski, Philip M.
Garrido, Francisco
Go, Jamelyn
Grogan, Lorna A.
Hargrove, James
Jennings, Hon. Allan W., Jr.
Ledesma, Andres
Lee, Dr. Henry C.
Marrone, Gerald H.
Pagan, Antonio
Robson, Robert (Bob) J.
Romano, Frank J.
Sansarran, Nirmala
Serrano, Millie
Smith, Lawrence C.
Stahl, Doris A.
Steets, Vanessa C.
Wiener, Lorin

GOVERNMENT - NON-ELECTED

Acosta, Luis
Adams, Farrell M.
Adams, Martha M.
Adler, Harvey L.
Aguero, Maggie
Alswang, Scott B.
Amorese, Sam A.
Anderson, Bonita M.
Anderson, Ms. Carmen N.
Anderson, Kevin G.
Anderson, Robert J.
Andrews, Peter
Aponte, Ana
Arlain, Nena D.
Arzberger, Robert M.
Ayers, Charles E.
Babakitis, Paul G.
Bach, Roger J.
Bailey, Stephen H.
Banievicz, Alexander
Banks-Catoe, Latisha V.
Bayuelo, Claudia S.
Bello, Muhammad A.
Berger, Richard
Berube, Michael
Beveridge, Alvin J.
Birbiglia, Joseph M.
Bishop, John H.
Blount, Ms. Heather
Blum, Dominic K.
Bourdon, Ana M.
Boyd-vega, Tracey
Brady, John J.
Brathwaite, CAPT Rafael
Briskie, Michael S.
Brodman, Mathew H.
Brooks, Gloria
Brown, Ronda R.

Brown, Tara N.
Browne, Phillip A.
Buchalter, Steven
Budenas, John M.
Burke, Donald H.
Butcher, Mrs. Judith A.
Byrnes, Robert M.
Cabrera, Maritza
Callender, Cynthia
Calvosa, Ronald P.
Cameron, Norman E.
Campagnola, Alfonso
Canfield, Dennis V., PhD
Carlson, Todd S.
Casanova-Scott, Mrs. Veronica
Cedeno, Stacey N.
Chambers, Hewitt L., Jr.
Channell, Albert M.
Chester, Rochelle
Chiappetta, Gennaro (Jerry)
Chodakiewicz, Thomas
Christensen, James
Chung, Thomas H.
Clark, Gerald C., Jr.
Clausen, Vincent J.
Clerico, Lucien T.
Coakley, Lorianne
Colucci-Turbett, Joann
Cooper, Gavin A.
Corbett, Robert
Corry, Lorraine
Cotter, Robert T.
Cotto, Veronica
Craig, Sara Elizabeth
Cross, Darrell
Cruz, Angel
Dagnello, Rudy J.
Dallara, Mark A.
Daly, Elizabeth V.
Daniels, Yvonne
Darden, Lakisha M.
Dargan, Sabrina
Daugherty, Cassandra
Davis, Charles W.
Davis, Gideon
Davis, Lynette
Degnan, Brian A.
Del Vicario, Robert E.
Demers, Martha
Derienzo, Thomas
Derolus, Jean P.
Diaz, Mercedes
Disney, Elizabeth D.
Dodds, Dwayne M.
Dougherty, Roger B.
Dowd, Peter J.
Duke, Daniel L.
Ellson, James P.
Emanuel, Michael L.
Estrada, Jose
Estrada, Mario B.
Evans, April R.
Fallon, Ms. Bessie A.
Falvey, Lynn R.
Farkas, Howard G.
Farrell, Walter D.
Farron, Mrs. Heidi M.
Febles, Aida C.
Figueroa, Paola A.
Fishman, Howard (Howie) L.
Fitzgerald, Daniel J.
Fleming, Patrice A.
Foley, Thomas B., ACP
Foley, MAJ Thomas P.
Fortune, Patricia
Francois, Mrs. Christine
Frank, Rudolph A.
Fry, James W.
Gabin, Angeli
Gala, Michael F.
Gale, John D.
Galeano, Sonia L.
Gee, Leslie
Gillespie, Bernard M.
Goddard, Alson D.
Gold, Stanley A.

Gomez, Tracie
Grant, Lillie
Gray, Mrs. Tamika S.
Guarco, Anthony
Guerra, Cecilia M.
Gunerard, Gabrielle R.
Guy, Yvette D.
Guzman, Nelson
Hadjidemetriou, George
Haggerty, Michael C.
Hall, MSgt Everett M., USAFR
Harrell, Dorothea M.
Hatzis, Gregory S.
Herting, Edward C.
Hess, Harold J.
Heywood, Angela B.
Hickey, Thomas F.
Hill, Calvin B.
Hobson, Kendall G.
Hoffmann, LT Russlan D.
Holian, Kevin M.
Hopkins, Warner V.
Howard, Keith S.
Hoyt, Ms. Yvette C.
Hrebenko, Aneta
Huang, Chen Tao
Hunt, Obie
Iovino, James
Jackson, Dunstan O.
Jefferson, Marvella
Joe, Lloyd D.
Johnson, Bernard A.
Johnson, Joni T.
Joris, Compton
Kalian, Mrs. Michelle A.
Keating, Robert P.
Kelly, William M.
Kenny, Robert E., CCA
Kershaw, Eugene, Jr.
Kimlicka, Daniel E.
King, Joseph F., PhD
Ko, Mrs. Eliza
Korb, Adriana
Korzekwinski, Jack T.
Kourakos, Joseph C.
Kunkis, Robert
La Covara, Margaret M.
LaMothe, Michael F.
Lazzaro, Paul J.
Ledee, Robert
Lesser, Marc H.
Lewis, Roslyn R.
Liebowitz, David A.
Logrande, Antonino
Lopez-Sirvent, Fernando
Los, Sandra A.
Love, Jason C.
Mack, Robert J.
Mahamah, Chidinma
Marcellus, Algeste
Marech, Craig A.
Martinez, Elizabeth
Martos, Mrs. Elena L.
Mattiasich, Fabio L.
Maurilus, Pierre S.
Mazerolle, Christian
McCole, Peter
McGhee, Lisa
McKenzie, Laura
McKeon, James E.
McSpirit, Ms. Theadora P.
Mejia, Sandra M.
Melrose, Valerie L.
Mendez, Zenaida
Meyers, Harold
Mickey, Gregory
Mihalakelis, Michael
Misson, George R.
Mitesser, Peter C.
Mohr, Michael
Moore, Faryce B.
Moran, Brian K.
Morelli, Angelo M.
Moriarty, Justine B.
Mousadakos, Chrisoula
Mumford, Ronald A.

JOHN JAY COLLEGE

Nanton, Willena
Nazario, Francisco
Neggia, Thomas E.
Neil, Larold C.
Nekrutman, David R.
Newman, Roger K.
Ng, Anthony C.
Niblock, Susan B.
Nicholas, Florence M.
Noll, Harold W.
Ochs, Jeffrey J.
O'Connor Wright, Catherine
O'Grady, Dermot
Okrah, Edward K.
Oleskowicz, John F.
Omotayo, Nixon O.
O'Reilly, John
Orender, Patrick E.
O'Rourke, William J.
Paglino, Joseph R.
Paige, Dorothy M.
Palicia, Deborah L.
Palillo-Hoey, Ann
Palmer, Lorrine R.
Parris, Cherylann P.
Patrick, Michael A.
Patti, Pasquale J.
Pattinson, Mrs. Helen M.
Pena, Miguel (Michael) A.
Penna, Frederick, Jr.
Perritt, William J.
Persinger, Ms. Sherry L.
Peters, Claire E.
Phillips, Charles W.
Pike, Linda A.
Poma, Ms. Patricia E.
Powell, Kerwin M.
Powell, Walter
Preiss, George M.
Proto, Rosa M.
Psahos, Theodoros (Ted)
Quaranto, Annette L.
Quinlan, Ms. Casey E.
Quinn, Gerard M.
Quinones, Monique
Quintana, Lydia C.
Racioppo, Ralph
Rafaniello, Helen M.
Raggi, Michael L.
Rainey, Eugene
Ramsay, Margaret
Randazzo, Jason
Raymond-Bitz, Catherine, RN
Redding, Assunta S.
Regan, Kevin J.
Reid, Luther
Reimann, Elsbeth
Rhett, Sheila A.
Richards, Emanuel (Manny) H., Jr.
Rivera, Yvonne
Roach, Erle S.
Rocco, Kenneth B.
Rondina, Frederick E.
Roper, Kenneth A.
Rothenberg, Bruce A.
Rowan, Edward T., Sr.
Ruban, Ms. Carlyne S.
Ruben, Scott P.
Ruderman, Harriet
Sabb, Jamal M.
Salzano, Dr. Julienne
Samedi, John F.
Samuels, Jason S.
Sanabria, Mark A.
Sanchez, Carlos M.
Sanchez, Lissette
Santiago, Melissa S.
Schanil, Robert
Schifini, Thomas A.
Schwartz, Ned E.
Seremetis, Michael
Shields, Roger L.
Shulterbron, Luz M.
Sierra, Martin, Jr.
Simanduyeva, Juliya

Simon, Tyrone K.
Sinnott, George P.
Sligh, Ms. Geneva L.
Smith, Mrs. Lesley B.
Spagnola, Carmen T.
Spann, Cassaundra
Staab, Ryan R.
Stanley, Dora L.
Stetson, Ms. Eleanor L.
Stewart, Marie A.
Stout, Donald R.
Stracker, Cassandra L.
Sturman, Mitchell
Sullivan, Patrick F.
Sutherland-Simpson, Carla H.
Symon, Gordon J.
Tamaro, Loring
Thorson, Steven J.
Tiedemann, LT James R.
Tocker, Leonard H.
Trail, Robert L.
Trainor, Patrick J.
Tsuji, Marian E.
Vairo, SGT Daniel
Vann, Keith K.
Varghese, Vinod
Vellucci, Frank R.
Veneziano, Salvatore
Vinces, Rev. Edgar J.
Walker, Ms. Hillery G.
Walters, Ms. Jacqueline M.
Waters, Sean H. T.
Watlington, James L.
Weber, Robert D., Jr.
Weinstein, Jay A.
Weir, SGT Seamus P.
Welch, Sylvia P.
Wells, Angie Y.
Williams, Deborah E.
Williams, Madonna S.
Williams, Roderick M.
Wilson, Francine
Woodbyne, Maurice C.
Wright, Roy J.
Wustefeld, Janet L.
Yanofsky, Barbara I.
Yevoli, Peter A.
Young, John W.
Zaharuk, Joseph P., Jr.
Zarek, Edward T.
Zaro, Ines A.
Zayerz, Agueybana
Zerbarini, John P.
Zerella, Denise
Zouhbi, Faisal

GRAPHIC DESIGN

Christine, Marc T.
Hadley, David C.
Morales, Indiana

HOMEMAKING

Boylan, Kathleen
Cahill, Angela M.
Capria, Britt A.
Concepcion, Magaly S.
Ganpat, Mrs. Drupatie R.
Gibbs, Nyhisha T.
Goldberg, Delia W.
Gore, Barbara H.
Grgas, Susan M.
Kitson, Daniela S.
Landivar, Mrs. Sandra J.
Mertz, Mrs. Elizabeth H.
Michaels, Anne M.
Monticelli Aivazis, Mrs. Mary
Ocasio, Jacqueline A.
Pomales, Mildred
Rosario-Dixon, Maria D.
Schachter, Lisa
Seidman, Sylvia K.
Taylor, Deserie
Vargas, Mrs. Jennifer L.
Vasapollo-d'Augusta, Barbara

HOTEL/RESTAURANT/ CATERING

Adade, Dr. Aaron Y.
Caceres, Elisabeth
Cozzolino, Caryn
Griffins, Tml A.
Hunter, Yovonda (Yoyo) B.
Knight, Alisa G.
Pallonetti, John R.
Pintor, Felix E.
Reilly, Paul J.
Scarpone, Leonardo
Smith, L. P.
Todorovic, Jelica

IMPORT/EXPORT

Aitken, Alexandra S.

INSURANCE

Alejandro, Gina M.
Alston, Samuel
Arcuri, Gary
Avery, Earl
Bacchus-Larode, Mrs. Kimberly C.
Barrett, Daniel J.
Blakeley, Dawn
Candia, Fernando A.
Castillo, Ernesto (Pete) A., Jr., CFE
Chattergoon, Suchetr C.
Chew, Philip M.
Christman, Thomas V.
Ciuzio, Richard G.
Clayton, James O.
Cohen, David L.
Coutts, Anne R.
Cromwell, Christine
Delgado, Ms. Fatima A.
D'Gracia, Anthony J.
Dixon, Nora
Durnack, Robert (Bob) P.
Edwards, Joseph B.
Elliott, Sandra E.
Fortino, Richard J.
Francois, Mrs. Marie M.
Froman, Gerald A.
Frost, Harold
Grode, George F.
Henderson, Richard T.
Hill, Damon A.
Hill, Donna
Horvath, Robert J.
Jackson, La-toya
Luma, Yoleine
Martinez, Margherita
Maximum, Andre A.
Meagher, Brian C.
Mendolia, Jeffrey
Moye, Michelle
Nocerino, Thomas
Olsen, Dr. Francis B.
Oquendo, Olivet
Parrish, David
Phillips, Steven S.
Randall, Francis E.
Reilly, Janet S.
Romano, Mrs. Lisa M.
Ruiz-Basquez, Luisa E.
Stfirmin, Gyna M.
Thompson, Madelyn
Trignano, Marcia V.
Welsh, Mrs. Venesia A.
Woolfolk, Heather
Zimmerman, Wheeler L., Jr.

JOURNALISM

Buckner, Martha
Clarke, Nicole L.
David, Wilfred
Hartman, Bryant
Rothenberg, Jackie

JUDICIARY

Acosta, Pilar M.
Amaya, Allan F.

Balcom, MAJ Jerome (Jerry) K.
Bartlett, Thomas W.
Bresnan, Eilish B.
Caso, Luis
Clements, Lavonda D.
Dipierro, Paul
Dunican, Thomas A.
Ferrara-Machado, Vivian M.
Fiore, Nicholas S.
Holmes, George R.
Inducci, Craig G.
Khashiun, Karamah M.
Khilkevich, Denis A.
Lee, Franklin
Leonard, Michael M.
Longo, Paul J.
Longobardi, Ms. Josephine A.
Magid, Stephen H.
Maltese, Hon. Joseph J.
Mikos, Ms. Nancy
Newman, Lisa N.
O'Neill, John P.
Rezoagli, Frank
Salumn, Joseph C.
Stark, Ms. Carmen C.

LANDSCAPING

Birnbaum, Lewis R.

LAW/LEGAL SERVICES

Abamwa, Osaka M.
Abdool, Rick E.
Abrams, Deon S.
Abrams, Jonathan A.
Achini, Antonio
Adams, Christopher
Adams, De'Ron W.
Adjaero, Alphonsus A.
Aimone, Paul J.
Alban, Donna A.
Albuja, Hugo D.
Alcee, Natalie (Giggles) S.
Alexander, Algernon
Alexander, Beverly J.
Alexander, Lavern K.
Ali, Mrs. Aneerah R.
Allen, Joseph A.
Almonor, Merault K.
Alverio, Daisy M.
Amato, Edward J.
Ambert, Ms. Arlene
Amelio, Anthony
Anders, Scott
Anes, Edwin
Angeletti, Debra
Annetts, Paul D.
Antomez, SGT Herbert
Arellano, Jose
Aristy, Tommy G.
Armani, Chris G.
Arrieta, Frank J.
Arsenakos, Stella, JD
Ash, Sylvia G., Esq.
Augustin, Kisha V.
Augustine, Clyde L.
Ayala, Mona C.
Baez, Tina M.
Baker, Janice L.
Baker, Jimmie R.
Baker, Robert D.
Balducci, Frank
Balfour, Joshua H.
Balgobin, Hemant K.
Ball, Robert
Baptiste, Wilfred E.
Baraket, Tamara M.
Barbour, Ms. Susan M.
Baricelli, Patrick C.
Barnett, Denise E.
Barrow, Audra J.
Barry, Elaine
Bartoszek, Peter C.
Battle, Tamika S.
Baumann, Daniel
Bavolar, SGT Keith A.
Bayne, Melvin

Beal, Susan
Beary, Richard A.
Belgrave, Carl C.
Bellamy, Charlie M.
Benitez-rivera, Mild
Bennett, Sylvia L.
Bent, Pamela A.
Bernard, Joseph
Berry, BG Robert W., USA(Ret.)
Berry, Siobhan L.
Bila, Anthony
Bobb, Ms. Irma Diane, Esq.
Bonilla, Jose E.
Bonita, Thomas J.
Boritza, Ms. Patricia A.
Borman, Gary M.
Bosio, Franklin J.
Bothos, Demetrios
Boyle, John F.
Brady, COL Edward T., USA(Ret.)
Brady, Richard J., Esq.
Braithwaite, Reginald, Esq.
Brandofino, Elaine M.
Braun, Eileen E.
Brinadze, Anna
Brito, Michael J.
Broker, Steven J.
Brown, Belviana J.
Brown, Cathy
Brown, Ms. Estelle A.
Brown, Janean A.
Brown, Ms. Janet L.
Brown, Timothy
Brown, Valerie L.
Brownbill-vega, Susan
Browne, Robert J.
Bruno, Daniel J.
Burdi, Michael J.
Burgh, Todd D.
Burke, James J.
Burnett, Byron K.
Burns, John W.
Buser, Robert J., CFE
Bykes-Guzman, Jennifer V.
Cabral, Aileen I.
Caesar, Tessa V.
Calderon, Peter
Caldwell, Lynnette
Callahan, Michael P.
Camper, Deborah F., Esq.
Capparelli, Robert (Rob)
Cardona, Michael A.
Carpenter, Ms. Edna E.
Carrion, Luis A.
Carroll, Michael J.
Carroll, Patrick J.
Casale, Donald E., II
Casalins, Liana C.
Casey, James J.
Cashin, Margarette
Catania, Denise A.
Cazeau, Beatrice
Chabla, Patricia A.
Chan, Suk Han H.
Chan, Susan
Chang, Mrs. Josephine, Esq.
Charles, Alice
Charles Smiley, Isabelle
Cherena-Pacheco, Yvonne
Chiu, Lim-chi
Chow, Patty Y.
Clark, Ramsey
Clarke, Barry R.
Clarke, Joan B.
Codrington, Paula A.
Coker, Renee R.
Coleman, Charles E.
Coleman, James J.
Colon, Ana R.
Colon, Anthony B.
Colon, Diana A.
Colon, Gregory
Colon, Helen
Colon, Monica

Colon-Ramos, CAPT Miguel A.
Colvin, Bernard W.
Conforti, Paul J.
Cooper, William C.
Cordero, Steven M., Esq.
Corrigan, Michael J.
Cotto, Jose L.
Cotton, Eddie
Coutain, Kade
Cowan, James T.
Cranford, Charles, Jr.
Creamer, Jeanet E.
Creelman, Thomas C.
Crenshaw, Frank D.
Crosby, Marion T.
Cruz, Louis A., Esq.
Cumberbatch, Simeon
Cunningham, Dennis J.
Cunningham, Lawrence (Larry) H.
Curti, Ms. Jennifer
Curylo, Christopher J.
Cus, Stefanie M.
Czarnecka, Beata
Dahl, Dena M.
Dalloo, Eric S.
D'Amato, George R.
D'antonio, Steven A.
Davis, Andres F.
Davis, Jerome
Davis, Wilbert
Dean, Mrs. Angela R.
Decambre, Brenda
DeConinck, David A.
Decoteau, Francis A.
DeGiovine, Arthur M.
De Jesus-Rodriguez, Blanqui I.
Delacruz, Ralph
Deliu, Francisco C.
Dell'aera, Peter A.
Del Preore, Salvatore
Deluca, Anthony E.
DeMagistris, Scott J.
Derenthal, Frederick E.
Dettmann, Edmund P.
De Vivo, Francis (Frank) W.
Dezil, Patrick
Diaz, Andres F.
Diaz, LT Arthur, JD
Diaz, Nestor H.
Diaz, Zulma
Dirkin, Walter J., Esq.
Ditto, Philip J.
Dobro, Stuart
Dolan, Christine
Dominguez, Denise
Domond, Alix
Donnelly-Brinkley, Virginia
Dooley, Joan T.
Douglas-Robinson, Laura V.
Douthit, Teresa M.
Duda, Joseph (Joe) T.
Duncan, LT Robert W.
Eagle-Agard, Tanya M.
Eggleston, Lester R.
Ekstrom, Charles A.
El-Amin, Ms. Zamirah K.
Elcock, Erskine L.
Elfeld, Elizabeth
Encarnacion, Felicito
English, Eleanor A.
Espanet, Jennifer A.
Espina, Elizabeth, Esq.
Espinal, Sandra M.
Esposito, Ralph A.
Fabian, Raymond
Faro, James J.
Fealy, Michael D.
Fearon, William G.
Feldman, Felix P.
Fenkel, Robert I.
Ferguson, Andre
Fields, Bernadette (Michelle)
Figueroa, Melissa
Fisher, Steven A.
Flanagan, Colleen M.

Fleetwood, Yancy
Flores, Anibal
Flowers, Leon A.
Fodera, Robert F.
Ford, Christina E.
Foss, John R.
Foti, Frank G.
Fountain, Belinda M.
Fox, Daniel J., Esq.
Fox, Kemeel N.
Francois, Marlene
Frazier, Marguerite
Freckleton, Lloyd J.
Freeman, Aldric
Freeman, James H.
Freire, Richard J.
Frias, Maria C.
Fullard, David A.
Fumai, John H.
Galasso, Daniel T.
Gallardo, Diana
Gallo-silver, Joan M.
Garcia, Aixa J.
Garnett, Joan M.
Garnier, Joubert
Garside, James H.
Garvey Williams, Wendy
Gee, Peter
Geist, Mitchell
Genovese, Alexander V.
George, Ms. Camille A.
Gianfrancesco, Paul
Gibbs, Gail M.
Gibbs, Satisha E.
Giblin, John F.
Gifford, Kompel
Gill, LeRoi L.
Gilmore, Robert
Giordano, Bryan P.
Giordano-Valentin, Melissa A.
Glanstein, Janelle M.
Glynn, James M.
Goddard-Adetimirin, Mayfield
Goldberg, Daniel J.
Golfinopoulos, Kostas
Gordon, Andrea D.
Gordon, Wayne
Gorelik, Max
Gorman, Michael J.
Graham, Janet A.
Graham, Nicole S.
Granata, George M.
Granville, Stromme J., Sr.
Gray, Thomas E.
Green, Stephanie
Greene, Jeanique
Greene, Jiton T.
Gridley, Shannon C.
Griffin, Romania A.
Grimes, John J., Esq.
Guy, Victor
Guyet, Allan R.
Haag, Edward C.
Hackenmiller, Julie
Hackett, Michelle A.
Hall, James R.
Halley, Ms. Stacey A.
Hall-Martin, Mrs. Debra L.
Halton, Darreiel A.
Hamilton, H. S.
Hamilton, Kevin P.
Hanna, Richard
Hannibal, Louise
Harinski, James
Harmon, Teon
Haro, David I.
Harper, Leonard
Harrison, Henry A.
Harrison, Willie
Haskins, Kimberley A.
Hawkins, Wallie E.
Hawthorne-Archer, Latonya
Hecker, William A.
Heimink, Thomas H.
Held, Kenneth L.
Henriquez, Deborah C.

Henriquez, Marlene
Henry, Josseth A.
Herbert, John D.
Herbosch, Alessandra D.
Hettler, Kenneth R.
Hewitt, Althea E.
Higgins, Michael S.
Hightower, Sadiquah
Hinestroza, Xiomara
Hollingsworth, Jerald
Holmes, Sabrina
Hopkins, Adria D.
Hou, Julie
Houle, Ms. Genevieve L.
Houston, Leonard W., PhD
Howe, Jason B.
Howell, Paula M.
Huber, Paul
Huey, Ivy S.
Hughes, Brian J.
Hughes, Isabel
Hughes, Maria
Hunce, Joseph D.
Hurley, Michael J.
Hyacinth, Mario K.
Iannotta, Richard A.
Ibrahim, Shorab
Irizarry, Christopher F.
Jablonska, Beata
Jackson, Adriane R.
Jackson, Hazel L.
Jaffe, Joanne
Jakubowski, Thomas R.
James, Michelle B.
James, Wanda A.
Janousek, Stanislav
Jarjokian, Kegham A.
Jascewsky, George E.
Jason, Tracey
Jaworsky, Alice
Jebavy, Judith A.
Jefferson, Stephen M.
Jenkins, Charisse N.
Jenkins, Rshaun K.
Jenkins, Samuel N.
Jerez, Victor
Jeune, Sergo
Johnson, Dolores L.
Johnson, Donald F.
Johnson, Edward J.
Johnson, Kimberly A.
Johnson, Samuel M.
Jones, Brenda L.
Jones, Cassandra D.
Jones, Debra D.
Jones, Gregory
Jones, Robert H., Sr.
Jones, Robin M.
Jones-Allen, Mrs. Vernesa D.
Joseph, Ingrid
Joseph, Ms. Tania R.
Joyce, William D.
Joye, Natarsia L.
Kahlon, Tejindar S.
Kamara, Samuel M.
Kaplan, Leonard A.
Karczmer, Aaron S.
Katz, Lawrence
Katzeff, Martha
Kaufman, Brian R.
Kazymirczuk, Tina G.
Keeshan, Edward J.
Keith, Ms. Stacy A.
Kelly, Joseph A.
Kessinger, Ann L.
Khan, Angelina
Khwaja, Tariq M.
King-Anobile, Barbara
Klein, Irving
Knight, Lamona O.
Knorr, Jill L.
Ko, Ivan
Koch, Robert P.
Koenig, Patricia A.
Kornblum, Allan
Kosmetatos, Marina

Kouzel, Margarita
Kravchenko, Leonid
Lagano, Christopher
Laird, Donald (Don) A., CFE
Lambert, Edwin F.
Lamont, Naeemah
Lamour, Barbara M.
Lane, Betty A.
Lane, Henry L.
La Padula, Vincent A.
Laperuta, Domenick A.
La Pietra, Louis C.
Lara, Manuel E.
Laschet, Alice
Lawrence, Brent L.
Lawson, Mrs. Kim
Lazo, Herlis A.
Leah, Magnuson
Ledford, Marsha N.
Lee, Barbara S.
Lee, Lisa
Leibman, Faith
Lettis, Paul M.
Levant, Cassandra D.
Lewis, Ms. Deidre Y.
Lewis, Dora M.
Lewis, Frederick H.
Li, Kathy
Liatto, Joann
Lisanti, Mrs. Maria C.
Litchmore, Monique E.
Lock, Clifford A.
Lohnes, Robert C.
Lombard, Gary J.
Long, David S.
Lopez, Anthony
Lopez, David R.
Lopez, Marla
Lopez, Michael A.
Louallen, Keith
Louttit, Robert J.
Lucas, Carl
Luckey, Joyce C.
Luke, Mrs. Cherylann
Madrigal-Fernandez, Elvira
Magnuson, Ms. Leah
Major, Gilbert H.
Major, Livingstone R.
Maltin, Nancy I.
Manette, Sean S.
Mangano, Louis
Mangarella, Anthony
Mar, Marie A.
Marcus, Edward
Marengo, Christopher
Marinaro, Michael V.
Marines, Henry
Marita, Rose B.
Marlow, Kidada
Marotta, Michelle
Marrero, Ms. Rosa M.
Marshall, Cliff
Marshall, David
Marshall, Luis R.
Marshall, Ms. Monique R.
Marshall-Myles, Coleen
Martin, Robert A.
Martin-Baez, Beverly S.
Martinez, Desiree C.
Martinez, Marisol
Mascari, John C.
Masucci, James J.
Matteis, Salvatore
Matuszak, Diane L.
McCabe, Mrs. Nunzia
Mccaffrey, Sean P.
McCollough, Charmaine
Mccormack, Paul G.
McDonald, Clarence (Chris)
Mc Gill, John J.
McGlinchey, Ms. Anne T.
McGourty, Michael J.
Mc Guire, Peter A.
Mc Hugh, Edward
McInerney, SGT Brian G.
McKain, Velma A.

Mckenna, Thomas
McMillan, Bridgett
Meara, Charles E.
Medic, Joseph
Melendez, Mrs. Diana A.
Melendez, Eugenio
Mendez, Angel
Mendoza, Esther C.
Mendoza, Florance W.
Miladinov, Mrs. Zora C.
Miller, Melva
Mirabal, Carolina
Miralla, Ms. Janet
Mir-Elcik, Mrs. Nancy J.
Mirza, Ashfa N.
Mitchell, Corey
Mitchell, Jamell
Mitchell, Kimberly A.
Mohrmann, Tina
Molina, Sandra M.
Molinaro, Ms. Yvette
Monahan, Thomas M.
Monplaisir, Ms. Patricia D.
Montague, Angela R.
Montgomery, Angela D.
Montgomery, Dwayne K.
Mooney, Martin C.
Mooney, Richard (Moon Man) B.
Moore-Baker, Simone I.
Moorhead, Henry A.
Morabito, Douglas P.
Morales, Auries M.
Morales, Cesar A.
Morales, Ms. Yvonne, Esq.
Moreno, Ms. Evelyn
Morrison Black, Charmaine
Morrissey, Mary P.
Moses, William (Bill) R.
Motisi, Meegan T.
Moultrie, Latoya Z.
Moye, Millicent L.
Mraz, Mrs. Leanne A.
Murphy, Daniel P.
Murphy, Patrick J.
Murray, Lewis C.
Musarella, Mark
Nasoff, William J.
Natale, Ralph A.
Nazaire, Jacques
Nazario, John
Needleman, Ira J.
Negron, Maria E.
Nelson, Debra A.
Neonakis, Alecsandro
Nesdill, Patrick J.
Nevarez, Ms. Melissa
Newman, Kim
Ngai, Lauren M.
Nickens- Thomas, Sheila
Nicks, Alfonso M.
Nicolaou, Carmen A.
Nobles, Sharon V.
Noel, Samuel D.
Ojena, Stephen
Okin, Avery Eli
Oneill, John P.
O'Reilly, John P.
O'Reilly, Thomas V.
O'Rourke, Tara A.
Ortiz, Janet
Ortiz Ortiz, Ana M.
Ortolano, Lisa
Orzillo, Kelly S.
Osborne, Kimberly M.
Ossohou, Andre A.
O'Sullivan, Kevin M.
Ottey, Ms. Donna M.
Ovalles, Mildred L.
Owens, Kelly E.
Pace, Paul A.
Padron, Ms. Linette
Page, CW2 Wallace (Wally) B., Ret.
Pahman, Marina
Paige, Jodi W.

Palesano, George J.
Palmer, Virginia L.
Palumbo, Bill
Papson-Adams, David
Parisi, Domenico J.
Parker, Calvin N.
Parker, Dieshia L.
Parris, Marie N.
Parris, Stacey A.
Parry, Lesroy T.
Pasuizaca, Carmen L.
Patterson, Erika P.
Patton, Ronda Y.
Peaks, Harold A.
Pearson, John
Pecoraro, Diana
Pellicani, Stephen P.
Pena, Marisol
Peoples, Ms. Melissa
Peoples, Yasmeen (Yaszie) A.
Perkins, Nicole S.
Pesante, Margarita
Peterson, Carrie L.
Phillips, Ernest G.
Phillips, Jennie R.
Picarillo, Anthony P.
Pierre, Bikens
Pierre Pierre, Eddy
Pignataro, SGT Anthony J.
Pillion, George R.
Pizzo, Vincent
Plawner, Thomas A.
Ploumes, Joanne
Pluciennik, Thomas C.
Podgorski, Robert B.
Politis, Steven, Esq.
Pollard, Willette
Polyakova, Svetlana
Poonai, Roopnarine
Powell, Joseph S.
Powers, Derek L.
Price, Fred E.
Pugliese, Naomi B.
Quinn, John F.
Quinn, Robert J.
Quraishi, Zahid N.
Raines, Jonathan E.
Ramirez, Ms. Elizabeth
Ramirez, Hector V., Esq.
Ramirez, Manuel
Ramos, James J.
Ramos, Nestor
Ramos, Ramonita
Randle, Kevin M.
Ravelo, Ms. Mercedes
Reale, Ronald G.
Reed, Jasmine M.
Reid, LaLisa
Reid, Shaun C., Esq.
Reilly, Thomas W.
Rello, John J.
Remon, Malena C.
Reyes, Ana A.
Reyes, Yahayra
Reynolds, George F.
Reynolds, Linda-Keisha M.
Reynolds, Patrick
Riccio, Joseph P.
Richardson Anthony, Joanne A., Esq.
Rigney, James C.
Rios, Juan R.
Rivas, Fradis
Rivera, Eduardo
Rivera, Jacqueline
Rivera, Jalika
Rivera, Jo Anne
Rivera, Roberto
Roberson, Margie
Roberts, Cheri A.
Robinson, John A.
Robinson, Ms. Lillian W.
Rodriguez, Betty
Rodriguez, Ms. Fiordaliza A.
Rodriguez, Juan C.
Rodriguez, Victor M.

Rodriquez, Fernando
Rogers, James
Rognon, Rudolph G.
Rohan, Robert V.
Roman, Marian C.
Romano, Christopher
Rosario, Victor M.
Rose, Jacqueline A.
Ross, James D.
Rozier, Christopher
Rubenstein, Hy D.
Ruiz-Velez, Mrs. Nydia
Ryan, Edward J.
Ryniak, William A.
Saint-fleur, Johanne A.
Sakelhide, Keith A.
Salas, Julius O.
Saldana, N. Antonio
Salim-Rasheed, Bibi Zameena
Sandin, Eric J.
Sang, John L.
Santiago, Jeanette
Santiago, Jose A.
Santiago, Raymond (Ray) S., Esq.
Santiago, Ricardo N.
Sar, Steve N.
Sardisco, Salvatore
Sarro, Peter J.
Saryian, Paul D.
Scally, Tina M.
Scanlon, Frances E.
Schletter, Donna L.
Schlosser, Kevin
Schneider, James T.
Schryver, Harold
Schultz, John A., Jr.
Schwartz, Kenneth M.
Schwartzman, Leon
Scott, Emily E.
Serrano, Jose
Servis, Anthony
Shamsundar, Jaso
Shaw, Mrs. Alexandria
Shaw-Brewer, Cil M.
Shedden, Jennifer L.
Sherwood, Roxanne M.
Siccardi, Vincent F.
Sicilia, Frank G.
Simmons, Melvin
Simmons-Broadbelt, Cheryl D.
Simons, Basilio A.
Skelly, Patrick J.
Smith, Clarence, Jr., Esq.
Smith, Florita E.
Smith, Melinda G.
Smith, Roberta L.
Smith, William G.
Smolowitz, Barry M.
Solgan, Christopher J.
Soo-hoo, William
Soto, Evangelina
Soto, Suesette
Sowah, Ayiteh
Spady, Sonya A.
Spaun, Gregory (Greg) J.
Springer, Richard L.
Springle, Stephen V.
Squillacioti, Vita
Stamatelos, Danny S.
Stark, Linda A.
Steele-Baird, Svetlana
Stein, Sherry
Steinfeld, Mark D.
Stephens, Sukeena M.
Stewart, John E., Esq.
Stickevers, John J.
Stimphil, Kathy K.
Stinson, William M.
Strobl, Staci E.
Stuart, Linnea
Surgeon, Clarence M.
Swirsky, Sheldon
Tabachnick, Carrie R.
Tam, Joemy C.
Tamai, Julianne Sumiyo

Taveras, Elvis
Taverna, Ignazio
Taylor, M. L.
Telesford, Janelle R.
Templier, Pierrette
Tennant, Denise M.
Tersigni, Christopher T.
Thomas, Alisa J.
Thompson, Adam
Thompson, Ms. Joan F.
Thompson, Kenneth
Thorbs, Carlene O.
Tice, Harry A., III
Todorova, Yeleina V.
Tomlinson, Mrs. Beatrice E.
Torres, Ana D.
Torres, Peter E.
Toussaint, Leveque
Trakas, Arthur G.
Treyvus, Kira
Trice Williams, Ms. Leona
Triebwasser, Jonah, Esq.
Trinidad, Linda M.
Tucker, Darlene
Tulloch, Macola A.
Tytell, Peter V.
Uke, Evaristus U.
Underwood, James S.
Uzcategui, Robert E.
Valentin, Miguel A.
Vallecillo, Gonzalo A.
Valles, LT Evelyn
Vargas, Bernabe
Vargas, Leslie M.
Vaughan, Sheila M.
Vaughn, Robbie
Vazquez, Carlos E.
Vazquez, George N.
Velasquez, Carmen R.
Velasquez, Yanina
Velez, Glorialee
Veljanovska, Marija
Venditto, Anthony M., Esq.
Vigilance, Fitzroy
Villar, Leslie A.
Vinton, Jeanette
Viollis, Paul M., Sr.
Viskup, Milly A.
Volin, Howard J.
Vredenburgh, E.
Waichman, Herbert L.
Waldon, Hon. Alton R., Jr.
Walker, Theodore, Jr.
Wallace, Amanda L.
Walsh, Paul
Ward, Rodney C.
Washington, Dennise Y.
Waszczuk, Wieslaw
Watson, Alwyn
Waye, Jane
Weinstock, Margot
Weis, Richard
Welch, Nicole D.
West, Janice Y.
Widnick, Steven M.
Wilkerson, Walter P.
Williams, Alwin R.
Williams, David
Williams, Katrina J.
Williams, Kimberly
Wilson, Andrew J.
Wilson, Annette G.
Wilson, James H.
Wilson, Nina M.
Wise, Lauren A.
Woolward, Sharon
Wright, Pamela G.
Xenakis, Helen
Yhun, Suk-han
Young, Shnequa A.
Zavistoski, Robert
Zayas, Victor L., Jr.
Zef, Aleksandr
Zinno, Lorrie A.
Zummo, Michael A.
Zwerling, Gayle B.

Zyta, Richard E.

LIBRARY SCIENCE

Allert, Theresa
Amann, Gloria D.
Borbon, Daysi A.
Brooks, Ms. Marvie B.
Cooper, Dermot A.
Donnery, Mary C.
Escobar, Nelson L.
Greene, Delicia T.
Kinyatti, Mrs. Njoki W.
Lynch, Thandi N.
Maffettone, Dennis
Riccardi, Kenneth P.
Rouse, Evelyn
Rowland, Eileen
Wesley, Lois A.

MANAGEMENT

Almeida, Esther M.
Amaro, Ed
Amato, Ronald J.
Appel, Kenneth P.
Appel, Michael A.
Ayala, Francisco, Jr.
Baddoo-Asare, Juliana
Baez, Yvonne K.
Bailey, William S.
Baumann, Ms. Deborah C.
Beattie, Henry J.
Beers, Albert S.
Bender, John R.
Biada, Charles
Blake, Ms. Vera A.
Bloom, Michael H.
Britt, Deborah L.
Brown, Raymond M.
Brudent, Sandra
Burgois, John M.
Caban, Wilfred, Sr.
Cairl, Brian D.
Caminero, Elbi M.
Carvajal, Patricia
Castro, Mrs. Ayanna T.
Castro, Maria T.
Cebic, Svetlana
Channell, Warren T.
Chen, Jennifer W.
Chin, Tin Y.
Chung, Victor L.
Cintron, Anita
Conklin Tetor, Mrs. Jennifer M.
Corcoran, Michael T.
Cossu, Jennifer K.
Crawbuck, Charles R.
Dabkowski, Dariusz
Daly, William
Daniel-Babb, Valerie
Davila, Jacinto
Devine, James J.
Diaz, Janice
Diaz, Virgil J.
Dicks, Garry S.
Edwards, Katrina
Emerson, James C.
Emidih, Jones F.
Facchini, Paschal
Fayad, Abdul
Fegan, Ewart
Ferguson, Adriane
Fetonti, Paul J.
Fischer, Mrs. Margaret M.
Fonseca, Ms. Lisa A.
Fontana, Mrs. Laura M.
Forbell, Michael P.
Fox, Lawrence J.
Garvey, Michael J., Sr.
Goldfinger, Mary Ann
Gorman, James P.
Grant, Kenneth G.
Hajisava, John
Hansen, Glenn J.
Harrigan, Eric J.
Harris, Arthur J.
Harrison, Karen M.

Hazelhurst, Bernice
Herbst, Andrew J.
Hughes, Christina E.
Hung, Fu-chin
Hyde, Phillip E.
Juris, John R.
Kanterman, Ronald E.
Kashimer, Irene
Kelly, Margo F.
Kennedy, Karen M.
Kolodny, Nathan
Laperuta, Domenick A.
Leone, Michell
Leventon, Douglas C.
Loureiro, John M.
Lundy, Romero
Manir, Zabed
Mc Cann, Michael F.
McGowan, Sean M.
Mc Manus, Pierce B.
Mc Master, John A.
Mejias, Edgar
Mendez, Angela
Mendez, Dennis M.
Miller, James O.
Miller, Lee A.
Mims, Venetia L.
Mitchell, Ms. Carolyn
Moore, Doreen
Moore, Talitha
Morales, Bethzaida
Morales, William
Moss, Joel W.
Nardoza, Michael J.
Nelson, Claudette A.
Nemara, Vanessa A.
Nicholas, Joanne C.
O'Brien, Joseph J.
Oleksa, James S.
Oliveras, Mrs. Daisy I.
Pacheco, M. Yvette, Esq.
Parker, Lori V.
Parsons, Theodore
Pearson, Evelyn E.
Pelaez, Armando L.
Pena, Ms. Marisel C.
Peters, Prestina D.
Peterson-Kimborough, Mrs.
   Claudette J.
Posniack, Glenn
Rabson, Mark J.
Raldiris, Carlos J.
Ramirez, Barry
Ramirez, Holli
Ramsey, Waltis, Jr.
Reid, Gloria M.
Reyes, Sudhey
Robinson, Dwight C.
Rodriguez, Franklin Delano
Rolla, Peter J.
Samide, Erik C.
Santiago, Marc A.
Schaefer, Richard W.
Schellhass, Kenneth J.
Sconzo, Rachel L.
Sell, Angela M.
Shea, John W.
Silva, Roberto, Jr.
Smith, Bettina J.
Snyder, Kimberly S.
Soler, Luis
Sousa, Robert
Stump, William P.
Taveras, Jacqueline
Taylor, Jeanette R.
Testa, Lawrence W.
Thomas, Peter L.
Tobin, Eileen M.
Tow, Jonathan L.
Townsend, Michael C.
Tucker, Bonita C.
Tyrrell, Edward
Vargas, Ariel
Vartabedian, Darryl
Vega, Carmen M.
Vega, Michael A.

Ventimiglia, Vincent
Villegas, Lliana
Walden, Kevin J.
Wallace, Patrick J.
Walz, Thomas M.
Warner, Philip R.
Weiler, Edward
Wierl, Christopher
Williams, Bridget L.
Willis, Yvonne A.
Wilson, Richard P.
Wittrock, William G.
Wojcik, Jerry H.
Wright, Mrs. Kyristel P.

MANUFACTURING

Cervino, Anthony R.
Feldstein, Kenneth I.
Foubister, Arlene J.
James, Dina M.
Rayfield, Peter T.
Sysak, Paul J.
Torres, Mrs. Cecilia A.
Vrantsidis, Dorothea

MARKETING

Bahna, Alfred M.
Butcher, Margaret P.
Curran, Catherine C.
Feliciano, Elizabeth
Fox, Jason
Gwyn, Christine
Jeselnik, Joseph J.
Johnson, Ava Y.
Jones, Margaret D.
Lee, Judy
Lundquist, Tracey A.
Molina, Ariadne M.
Ruff, Michelle N.
Strayhorn, Ms. Michelle
Velez, Theresa L.
Walker, Mala D.

MEDIA

Campbell, Hopeton A.
Nazaire, Yvana
Tinglin, Morris C.

MEDICAL/HEALTH SERVICES

Albert, Tracy K.
Aldoy, Anna M.
Allen, Beryl R.
Anderson, Dr. Melody M.
Arlen, Jennifer
Arons-Schultze, Janet A.
Bennett, Ms. Kerry-Ann
Boakye-yiadom, Kwame
Brady, Sylvia T.
Byrnes, Jennifer L.
Chen, Johnny Y.
Clarke, Denise L.
Clarke, Nuria E.
Connor, Gregory L.
Cosentino, Donna M.
Czajkowski, Raymond
Dombrosky, Mark D.
Dowtin, Ronda
Espinal, Jacqueline
Filion, Elizabeth
First, Jeffrey D.
Fortino, Denise M.
Fox, Bonnie R.
Francis, Mario J.
Furey, John
Gallo-Silver, Les I.
Garvin Huntley, Lynn M., PhD
Geller, Patricia A., EdD
Glemaud, Stanley
Grant, Calvin
Griffith, Rodney F.
Gutierrez, Geraldine
Hahn, Harold
Haskett, Kathy
Hazel, Amelia E.
Henry, Shirley M.

Hudson, Frances L.
Hults, Carol D.
John, Ceres
Lalak, Patsy A.
Lauda, Edward C.
Lawson, Blair
Lopez, Lisa J.
Luyando, Luz I.
Macon, Olivia Y.
Malenka, Elliot
Malysz, Josephine
Mark, Harry
Martinez, Oscar A.
Mathews, Frank J.
Medina, Ms. Marianella
Mencia, Jose L.
Mendez, Jorge A.
Michel, Pierre M.
Miron, Lowell S.
Monroe, Angeline E.
Montgomery, Joann
Neary, Donna
Ninomiya, Marilyn J.
O'Connell, Sean M.
Orriola, Victor M.
Pace, David R.
Padilla, Margarita M.
Persaud, Amanda J.
Peters, Bernadette V.
Pickett, John J.
Pierre-Jacques, Charles
Razzore, Annmarie
Reisman, Barbara
Renner, Nils
Rikoon, Elizabeth J.
Roche, Edward J.
Rodriguez, Sylvia
Rodriguez-Barros, Tanya I.
Rollock, Roderick
Roman, Ana J.
Rothang, Robert A.
Sama, Jessica
Sanders, Mrs. Jeanne F.
Sanfilippo, Debra A.
Sciandra, Joseph R.
Sergi, Frank
Streger, Matthew R.
Tiefenwerth, Thomas J.
Valera, Magalys
Whitaker, M. Katrina
Williams, Richelle

MILITARY

Acevedo, CW4 Efrain
Burgess, SGT Irving, Jr.
Carlucci, Jean M.
Casares, 1LT John W., USA
Durkin, Robert T.
Gaillard, Leroy
Gannon, John J.
Giesinger, Marie A.
Maughan, William F.
Ortiz, Col Rene P., USMC
Quinn, James F.
Rodriguez, Juan C.
Stone, LTC Wayne A., USA

MINISTRY

Atkinson, Donald
Carlo, John R.
Dooley, Bradford O.
George, Loise L.
Gregorin, Dr. David
Harding, Rev. Curtis T., Jr.
Hare, Ruby E.
Harris, Bishop Robert W.
Hazzard, Rev. Carrie L.
McGill, Mrs. Katrina A.
Quinones, Hector M.

NURSING

Akerele, Gabriel A.
Barbieri, Ellen B.
Berroa, Ms. Janice, RN
Brock, Beverly W.
Brown-Cathey, Ms. Gertrude

CAREER NETWORKING SECTION

Cameron, Rosalind R.
Carthon, Arlene
Dardzinski, Lisa A.
de Holczer, Lauren J.
Freeman, Denise
Johnson, Mrs. Paticia A.
Lopez, Lorraine
Mahoney, Patrick D.
Mullins, Theresa B.
Nocero, Jeanne V.
Ortiz, Anne M.
Petty, Camille B.
Pouncie, Ms. Amanda M.
St. Leger, Lucie
Young, Virgil L.

NUTRITION

Dogan, Walter R.
Lake, Ms. Deborah (Debbie) R.
Lindsay, Cordelia

PERSONAL SERVICES

Dennigan, Paul R.
English, David J.
Guzman, Elizabeth K.
Kehoe, William J.
Kelty, Patrick
Maldonado, Edwin
Matos, Nelson-Ness
Nemorin, James V.
Ortiz, Alex
Palladino, Marie A.
Schnupp, Jerome E.
Valcarcel, Carmen E.

PERSONNEL/HUMAN RESOURCES

Ajunwa, Ifeyinwa P.
Alcantara, Mrs. Olga
Andrades, John, Jr.
Ault, Colette E.
Castellar, Kane H.
Castro, Zinna
Chowdhury, Tarakur R.
Comninel, Irene D.
Conboy, Raymond C.
Crawford, Andrea (Angie) K.
Crosby-Greene, Lee
Cummings, Dalila C.
DeLuca, Lorayn
Fleming, April J.
Fogg, Harry
Gonzalez, Anilexa J.
Gonzalez Jimenez, Ramona G.
Hickman, Lynn B.
Hobson, Anthony E.
Jordan, Robbin M.
Leask, William M.
Lerner, Steven A.
Louisor, Mike P.
Mancuso, Donna Marie B.
Marseille, Bogard
Matthews, Karen A.
McGehean, Donna G.
Michaels, Carol
Miller, Steven G.
Nadelbach, Lisa M.
Quito, Mrs. Maritza B., NP
Reynoso, Alexa J.
Robinson, Cynthia (Cyndy)
Rogers, Katherine C.
Shepard, Frederick A.
Slater, Roxanne Y.
Small, Darnley E.
Smith, Maria L.
Sumter, Antoinette
Telesco, Christina B.
Volpi, Ms. Jennifer M.
Weber, Herschel
Williams, Donna A.
Wisotsky-Burt, Ms. Amy T.

PHARMACY

Cotty, Edward

PHYSICIAN

Concepcion, Dr. Lydia
Guajardo, Jacqueline
Schwartz, Thomas P.

PUBLIC RELATIONS

Alduende, Ivonne
Brown, Tracy-Ann M.
Brunson, Lakisha D.
Canal, Wilvina
Coaxum, Teresa (Teri)
Faraone, Ms. Teri
Grimm, Matthew B.
Hatfield, Steven J.
Kessopa-Cabrera, Pojana
Lee, Jin
Smith, Joyce E.
Thomason, Tamika

PUBLIC SERVICE

Abrams, Robert
Abruzzi, Raymond J.
Acevedo, Edward T.
Adolfsson, Boyd
Aivazis, Elias K.
Akerman, John M.
Albright, Eugene T.
Allen, Wayne A.
Almonte, Ervin J.
Alvarado, Ivonne C.
Alvarez, Richard
Alvarez, Ronald J.
Amaro, Marta
Ambris, Ayanna E.
Anatsui, Edwige M.
Anderson, Charles P.
Anschick, Robert H.
Antonin, Jo-Ann
Aponte, Cesar
Appelbaum, Jed
Aptacker, Steven I.
Armas, Margie
Arniotes, LT James V.
Arnold, Henry C.
Arnold, Richard
Arroyo, Henry
Askin, John P.
Audiffred, Jesus
Augustus Miller, Mrs.
    Antoinette J.
Auletta, Richard N.
Autera, Marysusan D.
Aviles, LT Edwin R.
Aviles, Victor
Babbini, Patricia A.
Badamo, Robert T.
Badillo, Anderson
Bailey, Alex T.
Bala, James W.
Bankovic, Milan
Barbato, Michael
Bardales, Michael G.
Barquin, Armando X.
Barrett, Kevin J.
Barreyre, Raymond
Bartlett, Ms. Judith R.
Batanus, John
Bauer, George M.
Baumert, Robert (Boomer) J.
Bauso, Louis J.
Bax, Wayne F.
Becker, Robert L.
Beckles, Arlene D.
Bedrossian, Anne-Marie M.
Belford, Curtis S.
Belviso, Lawrence M.
Bendetson, Robert
Benedisuk, Mary R.
Beneri, Fred P.
Benitez, Gustavo
Benjamin, Helman O.
Benjamin, Yvonne E.
Bennetti, Joseph J.
Benson, Irving
Bermudez, Carlos R.
Berrios, Johnny

Bert, Richard A.
Betances, Neftali, Jr.
Bianco, Aniello R.
Bido, Antonia F.
Biesty, William F.
Biller, CDR Ronald D.
Bittles, Richard J.
Blachman, Eric J.
Black, Sally E.
Black, Sylvia C.
Blackman, Michael J.
Blaich, Charles R.
Blake, Richard A.
Blomquist, Bryan D.
Boggiano, Daniel
Bohringer, Ernest W.
Bologna, Anthony (Tony) V.
Bolton, Garfield L.
Bonilla, Cesar A.
Borker, Vito
Bosko, George M.
Bovell, Donna A.
Bowman, Debra
Boyce, Rodney C.
Boylan, Lauren E.
Boyle, James J.
Boyle, John J.
Bramble, Michael P.
Brandt, William J.
Brathwaite, LeRoy L.
Braxton, Aubrey S.
Brech, Todd R.
Brennan, John J.
Brienza, Jeffrey T.
Briscoe, James J.
Britton, John J.
Brogan, Michael P.
Bronaugh, Ronald A.
Brown, Francisco A.
Brown, Herbert
Brown, Herbert A., Jr.
Brown, Joseph G., Jr.
Brown, Joyce C.
Brown, Latisha Y.
Brown, Patrick J.
Brown, Timothy J.
Browne, Amy (Amelia)
Browne, Samuel A.
Bruce, Prince A.
Bruce, Tommy
Bruzzichesi, William
Buono, Joseph F.
Burger, Frederick (Fred) R.
Burgess, Mrs. Marjorie L.
Burke, Robert F.
Burrell, William D.
Bush, Randall S.
Butler, Raymond M.
Byrne, Lawrence P.
Cahill, Patrick
Califano, John J.
Callahan, Robert M.
Camacho, Edgar M.
Camilo, Gilberto J.
Campbell, John J.
Campisi, Ronald P.
Cangelosi, Robert S.
Cappello, Edward
Cappiello, Dominick A.
Cardillo, Bob J.
Cardona, Jimmy E.
Carlson, Glenn A.
Carlson, Richard D., Jr.
Carolan, John J.
Carranza, Oscar
Carrasco, Edward (Ed) G.
Carr-sheppard, Kim D.
Carter, Arnold
Carter, James E.
Carter, Luis A.
Caruso, Rosemary
Casaburi, Joseph A.
Casey, Michael J.
Casilla, Jose
Cassidy, John J.
Cassidy, Joseph T.

PUBLIC SERVICE

Cassidy, Patrick E.
Cassidy, Susan E.
Castagna, Alfred R.
Castagna, John J.
Castellano, John
Cavanagh, Joseph G.
Caver, Cynthia L.
Cepeda, Luis, Jr.
Cerezo, Juan E.
Cerreta, Kenneth
Cesarano, Anthony
Chambers, Jeffrey A.
Chametzky, Steven A.
Chang, John K.
Charles, Rulolph N.
Cheng, Christoph C.
Chernick, Steven M.
Chiarantano, Daniel
Childs, Iris M.
Chimienti, Alexander
Chong, LT David E.
Chong, Renee H.
Choy, Yolanda
Christensen, Jarl H.
Christman, SGT Dennis L.
Christman, William C.
Christophe, Joseph
Ciampo, Michael N.
Ciorciari, David J.
Ciringione, Frank J.
Clabby, William F.
Clark, Kevin M.
Clark, Mark
Clark, William R.
Clinton, Brian J.
Clouden, George
Coates, John R., Jr.
Coffey, Thomas K.
Cohen, Faith M.
Coiro, Robert M.
Colasuonno, Dominick
Colclough, Andre W.
Collado, Ms. Giselle M.
Collazo, Antonio
Collins, Michael
Collins, Stephen P.
Colon, Rubina
Colon, Wendy C.
Comastri, Harold N.
Comperiati, Joseph A.
Concepcion, Angel
Conde, Matthew P.
Conlon, Peter J.
Connelie, William G.
Connelly, Karen T.
Conroy, Edward A.
Conroy, John T.
Conte, Daniel P.
Conversano, Victor M.
Conway, Gary F.
Conway, Martin J.
Cook, Mrs. Lisa M.
Cooper, Charles D.
Cooper, Edwin B.
Coppock, SGT Durwin L.
Cora -Lundquist, Marissa
Corcoran, James P.
Corcoran, Michael C.
Cordero, Raul (Pappa Bear)
Corey, Jessica E., CPP
Corneh, Varney M.
Cornell, Richard R.
Correa, Angel R.
Correa, Edward
Correa, Felix L.
Cortellino, Gary J.
Cotham, Jeffrey D.
Cozens, Mark P.
Crawford, Audrey D.
Crawford, Mark R.
Crawford, Michelle D.
Crawford, Ollie A.
Crawford, Randy B.
Crespo, Richard (Richie)
Crimmins, Martin E.
Crouthamel, David E.

PUBLIC SERVICE

JOHN JAY COLLEGE

Cubero, Candido
Cuevas, Johnny O.
Cugliandro, Pasquale
Cunneen, Joseph F.
Curran, James E.
Curry, John A., Esq.
Curry, Warren P.
Daley, Thomas J.
Daly, Daniel
D'andrea, Lorenzo J.
Danese, Elizabeth Anne
Danielson, Eskil S.
Danik, Mark D.
Dascoli, Francis
Davan, Robert J.
David, Denis P.
David, Harley
Davidson, Leslie-Ann
Dean, James C.
Deane, Eric
De Candia, Domenic
De Caprio, Angelo
DeCastro, Janet L.
DeFina, Bernice
Defrancesco, Rosalie A.
Degroot, Daniel R.
Delahanty, Lt Neal C.
Delaney, James T.
Delano, Donald F.
Del Castillo, Vincent
Depierro, Joseph M.
Deravin, MAJ Eric H., USAR(Ret.)
Desire, Yves C.
Dever, John A.
Devine-Molin, Carol
Deyo, LT David
Di Benedetto, Denise
DiBrizzi, Michael A., Esq.
Dicks, Daniel M.
Dilone, Rafael
Di Stefano, Vincent M.
DiToro, Christopher J.
Diver, Hugh J.
Dixon, John H.
Dixon, Sharon H.
Dodrill, Christopher A.
Dodson, Kenneth L.
Doherty, CAPT Michael J.
Dolan, Edward G.
Dolcimascolo, Jeffrey A.
Doldron-Cancel, Sherena N.
Donato, Roberto
Donlon, John L.
Donnelly, Stephen J.
Donohue, Patrick J.
Donovan, Arundell (Tony) A.
Dorans, Edward T.
Doute, Jemal L.
Dowd, Timothy M.
Dowling, Jack F.
Downey, John R.
Downey, William A.
Doyle, Michael P.
Draghi, Paul
Drakes, Ingrid L.
Drayton, Kenneth R.
Duesterdick, Kurt A.
Duffy, Charles P.
D'ulisse, Carl
Duncan, Jesse J.
Duncan, Mrs. Louise L.
Dunlap, Daniel
Durante, Eugene G.
Dwyer, Douglas R.
Dybski, Thomas
Eason, Erica M.
Eddington, Mark
Edwards, Sam L.
Elisson, Chris
Elmore, William (Bill) L.
Eng, Shawn
Eschenberg, Conrad J., IV
Escobar, Veronica
Esposito, Michael V.
Evans, Jasseth M.

Evans, Robert C.
Faherty, Donald J.
Fahje, Donald
Faith, Francis L.
Farrugia, Matthew P.
Fauci, Richard A.
Feffer, Lawrence
Feigenbaum, Daniel
Ferber, Eric M.
Ferman, Yolanda D.
Fernandez, Carlos A.
Ferraioli, Steven J.
Ferrante, Victor
Filipiak, Paul J.
Filipponi, Dominick
Finamore, James J.
Finkelstein, Eric L.
Finlayson, Thomas C., Jr.
Finn, Sean P.
Fiore, Albert J.
Fischer, Stephen F.
Fischer, William R.
Fitzpatrick, Brian R.
Fitzpatrick, Paul J.
Fitzpatrick, Thomas G.
Flaherty, John P.
Flanagan, Leonard
Fleming, Edward J.
Fleming, John M.
Fleming, William
Fleming, William J.
Flemmings, Lamont S.
Flores, Franklin
Flynn, Eugene M.
Flynn, Raymond J.
Flynn, William J.
Fogarty, James P.
Forner, Michael S.
Forsthoff, SGT Roger A.
Forte, Leonard L.
Fortunato, Richard V.
Fountoulakis, Georgios
Fredericks, Jonathan E.
Fredericksen, Robert
Frick, Henry F.
Friedman, Jenna
Fumai, Joseph F.
Furelli, Gianfranco
Gabora, Herman R.
Gaby, Thomas R.
Gallagher, Kevin R.
Gancitano, Victor R.
Gander, Edward F.
Gansrow, Ruth
Garber, Joseph G.
Garcia, Fausto, Jr.
Garcia, Jason K.
Garcia, Rosa M.
Garland, Daniella
Garrido, Richard R.
Garry, Thomas N.
Gaston, Kanal V.
Gaudiosi, Nicholas C.
Gaynor, Rabiah M.
Ge, Sylvester Y.
Genovese, Dominic A.
Gentile, Dominic A.
Gesualdi, Frank J.
Ghaly, Ayman N.
Gholson, Leigh L.
Giangeruso, Carmine, CFPS
Gibbons, Thomas E.
Giddings, Curtis G., Jr.
Giddings, Robert J.
Gione, Gary J.
Girimonte, Albert (Al) W.
Godino, Joseph
Golden, John P.
Goldfarb, Matthew S.
Goldman, Robert M.
Gonzales, Burt R.
Gonzalez, Anthony
Gonzalez, Antonio
Gonzalez, Hector L.
Gonzalez, Janet
Gonzalez, Manuel

Gooden, Herman
Gottlieb, Paul
Grajales, Ednah
Grasso, John P.
Gravelli, Vincent M.
Greco, CAPT Carl J.
Green, Andrew
Green, Vincent E.
Greene, Marlene M.
Greene, Matthew L.
Greenwald, Steven
Grieve, Daniel P.
Griffin, Dennis M.
Grinage, David F.
Gross, Roger A.
Gudat, John F.
Guido, William J.
Gurielov, Shalva
Guzman, Danny R.
Gyenes, Albert R., Jr.
Haaland, Mrs. Jacqueline R.
Hagan, Andrew A.
Haines, James V.
Hall, John J.
Hall, Ruben T.
Ham, Gustavo
Hammer, Charles M.
Hammer, David S.
Hance, Ms. Rachel
Hanover, Scott W.
Hanson, Charles J.
Harmon, Ms. Amy
Harmon, Michael P.
Harper, Lawrence
Harrington, Irwin C.
Harris, Onya T.
Hart, Harvin
Hartley, Wayne
Harvey, Beverly
Hatton, Laurence F.
Hayes, Donald
Hayes, John R.
Haynes, Veronica (Roni) T.
Hazel, Ms. Kim R.
Head, Sidney W., Sr.
Healy, James
Healy, John E.
Heaney, Patrick
Hector, David A.
Hegarty, James
Heineman, Frederick K.
Hennessey, Richard E.
Henry, Conrad V.
Hentze, Jeanette M.
Hermans, Peter L.
Hernandez, Michael
Herron, Francis R.
Heym, Eugene
Higgins, Patrick (Pat) J.
Hill, Mercedes S.
Hinchey, Arthur F.
Hinds, Kelvin C.
Hines, James R.
Hinnrichs, Jeffery K.
Hoch, Joseph B.
Hochstadt, Marc M.
Hodges, Rodney R.
Hogan, Steven M.
Holden, Terence
Holihan, John W.
Holmes, Ms. Angela A.
Holsten, Gary W., Jr.
Hoover, Herbert B.
Hot, Zajo E.
Howard, Theodora E.
Huacuz, Rogers
Hughes, James R.
Hughes, John E.
Huller, Thomas P.
Hulsmann, Robert N.
Hunt, Curtis J.
Hussey, Brian P.
Idiart, George J.
Ierardi, Andrew J.
Ingellis, Daniel A.
Ingram, Margaret

Irish, Carleton P.
Jabouin, Alain S.
Jack, Bryan A.
Jackson, Derek A.
Jackson, Edward
Jackson, Katherine L.
Jacob, Thomas P.
Jacobs, Lawrence W.
Jaigobind, Carl
James, Ainsworth
James, Israel
Javier, Jonathan
Jay, Henry, Jr.
Jean-felix, Stanley
Jenkins, Andre H.
Jimenez, Agueda M.
Johnson, Danielle C.
Johnson, Frank J.
Johnson, Granville
Johnson, James, Jr.
Johnson, Robert C.
Jones, Melissa S.
Jones, Rodney S., Sr.
Jones, Seymour A.
Jones, Solomon
Jones, Tracey L.
Jones-Thorpe, Jennifer J.
Jordan, Ms. Janet E.
Joseph, Eddison M.
Joseph, Essy A.
Joyce, Jennifer
Juliano, Richard P.
Kallas, Leo
Kalletta, Edward D., Jr.
Kaltenmeier, John W.
Kaplan, Robert
Karlovitch, Jay
Kassai, Michael D.
Kaufman, Mitchell J.
Kaufmann, Kevin J.
Kavanagh, John P.
Kaye, Mrs. Marion
Kealy, Thomas J.
Keane, Patrick J.
Keegan, Scott J.
Keeney, Brendan W.
Kelly, David J.
Kelly, James P.
Kelly, Martin A.
Kelly, Robert J.
Kelly, William P.
Kennely, Fritz S.
Kenney, Wilson C.
Keogh, Dennis F.
Kerton, Ervin (Ernie)
Khaimov, Igor I.
Khan, Shazad
Khurana, Rajiv R.
Kiernan, Henry
Kilmer, Joseph F.
King, David W.
King, Edwina J.
King, Raymond F.
King, Stephen J., III
Kinscherf, Cindy L.
Kirk, John J.
Kisala, Stanley M.
Kitching, Tselanee
Klein, Fredric C.
Klein, Richard J.
Klein, Robert E.
Klimoski, Frank
Knights, Robert A.
Koehler, Karl F.
Kolenovic, Medzit
Kopstein, Jay I.
Koscinski, Robert
Kozlow, Mary
Kraus, David T.
Kruger, Henry J.
Kuhn, Donald A.
Kulesa, LT Edward J.
Kupper, Donald F.
Kurau, William R., Jr.
Kurz, Edward A.
Kuttler, George P.

348

Lafemina, Ms. Eileen T.
Laffey, John J.
Lampf, Jesse D.
Langston, Sandra D.
Larson, Allan G.
Lassen, Joseph
Lassiter, Yvonne
Lavin, Christopher
Leandry, Victor
Leavey, Marion A.
Lebowitz, Raymond
Leckler, Francis P.
Lee, Chon J.
Lee, Kin
Lee, Ms. Michele
Lee, Tiffany M.
Lefkof, Alan
Leggett, Kenyon E.
Leibowitz, Jill D.
Leibowitz, Morton J.
Leiterman, Jason E.
Lenard, Jill R.
Leone, Michael J.
Leto, Teresa A.
Lett, John A.
Levin, David J.
Liffey, Joseph A., Jr.
Linares, Israel
Lindner, LT Peter M.
Linn, Edith
Lipari, Anthony J.
Liranzo, Mrs. Yahaira M.
Lissner, Michael A.
Lloyd-Sealey, Michele
LoCascio, Salvatore
Lopez, Gabriel R.
Lopez, Jose L., Sr.
Lopez, Miguel
Lore, Frank A.
Louis, Jeeny M.
Louvado, Ivo M.
Lowe, Eulisha T.
Lowy, Kenneth M.
Lubomski, CAPT Joseph E.
Lucas, Ms. Patricia A.
Luftman, Lance J.
Lugo, Elizabeth
Lugo, Mrs. Sylvia
Lui, Alan S.
Lukowski, Fred J.
Lutzker, Erik L.
Luyando, Rafael A.
Lynch, Christopher B.
Lynch, Richard T.
Lyons, Robert T.
Lyons, Thomas
MacDougall, John
MacDowell, Rick W.
Mackey, Daniel
Magnus, Connie L.
Mahady, Myles
Mahoney, Catherine V.
Mahoney, Robert E.
Maillard, William L.
Makanjuola, Rafiu T.
Malaxos, Troy-Nicholas
Malool, Paul G.
Mammano, Richard A.
Mandzik, Philip J.
Mantzaris, Demetrios (Jimmy)
Manzello, Joseph
Marchia, Ms. Theresa
Mari, Daniel J.
Marinakos, Demos E.
Marra, Anthony J., Esq.
Marrero, Jose N.
Marrero, William
Marshall, Glenn T.
Marti, John L.
Martin, Duane
Martin, James (Jim) P.
Martin, LCDR Vertel T.
Martinez, Edgar
Martinez, Joseph
Martinez, Margaret
Martorano, Thomas A.

Massey, Ritesh
Masterson, Charles
Mata, Angelina E.
Mathews, Onica O.
Matos, Edwin A.
May, Paul D.
Mayr, Louis A.
McAleer, Gerard P.
McAlpin, William T.
Mc Andrew, Lois J.
McBean, Mrs. Ghyslaine
Mcbride, William A.
McCarthy, Jacqueline
Mccarthy, Timothy
Mccarton, James I.
McEniry, John A.
McEntire, Catherine Duffy
Mc Garry, MAJ Frederick S., USA(Ret.)
McGinn, LT Timothy R.
Mc Glone, Jim
McGowan, Hugh M.
Mc Junkin, William M.
Mc Kenna, Peter
Mckenzie, Mark A.
McLaughlin, John P.
McMahon, Michael J.
McManus, John J.
Mc Nicholas, James F.
Mc Nulty, Thomas P.
Mc Queen, Norman E., Jr.
Medeiros, Michael
Medina, Deborah
Melendez, Abel
Melsky, SGT Ryan E.
Mendez, Irma E.
Mercado, Robert
Messina, Camillo J.
Messina, John J.
Metzler, Arthur J.
Miller, Christopher A.
Miller, Robert
Miller, Scott K.
Mills, Charles M.
Minardi, Rocco N.
Minton, Kenneth W.
Miranda, Anthony R.
Mitchell, Salahadine (Sal)
Moe, Richard
Moffatt, Maikov A.
Mollaghan, John T.
Moment, Keran M.
Monge, Luis A.
Monnay, Yves
Montague, Kathleen B.
Montali, Joseph R.
Montana, Paul J.
Moonan, Ravi N.
Mora, Felix
Moran, John A., III
Moreia, Fredrick M.
Moreno, Juan, Jr.
Moriarty, Thomas M.
Morley, Michael
Morley, CAPT Susan
Moro, Patrick J.
Morris, Vincent K.
Morrissey, William J.
Moses, Stephanie M.
Moskowitz, Ari A.
Moss, Cathy N.
Moten, Reva G.
Mujica, Linda R.
Mulero, George
Mulligan, Thomas F.
Mulligan, Thomas M.
Mulligan, Thomas P.
Mullin, John H.
Muniz, Eliu
Murawski, Marianne
Murphy, John J.
Murphy, Ms. Josephine A.
Murphy, Robert E.
Murphy, Timothy J.
Murray, James E.
Murray, Robert P.

Musmacher, Robert J.
Myers, Victoria M.
Nachtman, Iva
Nadel, David W.
Nau, Michael
Nedos, William T.
Neifeld, Robert
Nesmith, Daron L.
Neumayer, August F.
Newkirk, Rosalind J.
Newman, Paul R.
Newton, Judy D.
Neznanyj, Taras P.
Ng, Phillip
Nicholson, Walter A.
Nicola, Christos
Nieves, Jose V.
Nisi, Anthony J.
Nixon, Sandra R.
No, Steve
Norat, Wigberto
Nosek, Frank R.
Nunez, Claribel
Obremski, Frank L.
O'Brien, Stephen P.
Obuchowski, Bart M.
Ocampo, Mrs. Melisa
O'Connell, James H.
O'Connor, Ms. Brigid
O'Connor, James F.
O'Connor, Joanne M.
O'Donnell, Donald P.
O'Donnell, CAPT Steven
O'Grady, Martin F.
Okosun, Alexander E.
O'Leary, Joseph P.
Olivares, Flor E.
Olivo-Perez, Sharon L.
O'Loane, Daniel R.
O'neill, James P.
Onodu, Benjamin
O'Reilly, Thomas C.
Orlandella, Sandra M.
O'Rourke, Stacey M.
Ortega, Jessica
Ortiz, Amador P.
O'Sullivan, Christopher G.
Otero, Victor E.
Paccione, Jack
Pacheco, Jose A., Jr.
Pagan, Michele D.
Pagano, Ms. Marci
Palmeri, LT Nicholas R.
Palumbo, Peter J.
Panchame, Allan G.
Paredes, Ruth V.
Park, Richard A.
Parra, Juan E.
Parrinello, Arthur J.
Pascocello, Anthony J., Jr.
Pascullo, Anthony
Pasichow, Steven A.
Patterson, Rosezena
Patton, Brian V.
Paul, Mario
Paul, Nigel
Paulino, Reynaldo M.
Payne, Jamil V.
Pearson, Joan E.
Pena, Jenaro R.
Pender, Patrick J.
Pennes, Emilio
Perez, Lizabeth (Lisa)
Perez, Mario
Perez, Omar
Perez, Vanessa
Pesce, Frank J., Jr.
Peters, Clinton J.
Petreski, Toni
Pezzo, Domenic
Piazza, Karen L.
Piedra, Dennis
Pierre, Louicasse
Pignataro, John V.
Pijaca, John A.
Pinizzotto, Anthony J.

Piraino, Joseph A.
Piri, Ms. Maria A.
Pisano, Edward J.
Pitrone, Alberta J.
Pittinsky, Leonard
Plaia, Vito
Plamenco, Roberto C.
Plante, George J.
Pleeter, Glenn R.
Poggi, John J., III
Poje, Leopold J.
Pomerantz, Scot
Ponzio, William P.
Pope, Winston L.
Poveromo, Joseph
Powell, Alan C.
Powell, David F.
Powell, Howard G.
Powell, William M.
Powell-Phillips, Shawnee E.
Power, Thomas J.
Prendergast, Terri B.
Preston, Alvin E.
Preston, Thomas G.
Presume, Thierry
Prince, Daniel E.
Pringle, Hester V.
Proscio, Charles J., Jr.
Prusak, Patricia R.
Pucci, Raymond
Puello, Miguelina
Pupino, Joseph M.
Purdy, Thomas J.
Quinn, Lawrence T.
Rabel, Ilzee
Raiford, Louis G.
Rall, Charles E.
Ramirez, Jessica D.
Ramirez, Vincent P.
Ramkissoon, Ricardo
Ramos-Sololongo, Denyse N.
Ramoutar, Donny B.
Rampolla, Joseph J.
Ramsey, Charles E.
Randazzo, Todd
Raptis, Thomas N.
Ravens, Carl
Ray, Vern
Redican, Joseph E.
Redmond, Thomas J.
Reekie, Robert
Reeves, Lee
Regan, James K.
Regan, John M.
Regis, Ms. K. F.
Rehal, Joseph G.
Reid, Keith L.
Reilly, James P.
Reiss, Gary
Resko, Ronald J.
Reyes, Rachel
Rhodes, Onesia S.
Ribeiro, Gemma E.
Richardson, Thomas
Ridley, Grace E.
Riedinger, Guy E.
Rigono, Gabriel
Rios, Donald
Rios, George J.
Rivera, Cesar J.
Rivera, David
Rivera, SGT Mario L.
Rivera, Peter
Rivera, Steven
Rizzo, Brian J.
Roberson, William C.
Roberts, Diana C.
Roberts, Richard H.
Roberts, Sherman S.
Roberts, Mrs. Sonya
Robertson, Erin N.
Robertson, Sean J.
Robinson, Christopher
Robinson, Walter A.
Roca, Randall S.
Rochford, Edward V.

Chany, Christopher P.
Elcock, Mark G.
Fennessy, Adriana
Lee-Wyss, Mrs. Helen
Levin, Michael
Lockhart, Colleen M.
Lorimer, Philip, CPM
Martir, Kirby
Moore, Penelope A.
Myers, Carol A.
Mylott, Robert H.
Petersen, Alan
Raichle, Carl J.
Rothenberg, Daniel S.
Seibert, Eleanore
Shea, Nicola D.
Talbot, Richard J.
Ucelli, Monique S.
Wasserman, David

SOCIAL SCIENCE

Alvarez, Ray
Bartels, Ms. Elizabeth C.
Burd, Dr. Marc A.
Caruth, Godson R.
Dimmock, James A.
Fegley, Venessa M.
Guzman, Damary
Guzman, Edward E.
Hastings, Mark E.
Hazel, William B., III
Higgins, Adrienne C.
Hilaire-Fisher, Marie C.
Ingram, Garrett
Keehlisen, Lynda M.
Lam, Kwai
Lopez, Diana
Maltz, Barbara K.
Mendez, Mrs. Milly
Pittman, Yolanda R.
Snyder, Heather T.
Tillett, Vincent A.
Williams, Winsome O.

SOCIAL WORK

Abdelhady, Zamyra
Abramson, Rebecca D.
Acosta, Gasmary
Adeleye, Helen
Akgun-Auerbach, Ms. Alice
Akins, Rachquel
Amengual, Margie
Arevalo, Yesenia M.
Armorer, Sharifa J.
Auli, Karoll
Babalola, Sikiru
Bargebuhr, Nancy E.
Barometre, Reginald
Barrow-Baez, Mary
Beckford, Maxine A.
Belenky, Dmitry
Best, Aromah
Booker, Kwesi L.
Bowens, Renita D.
Branic, Doretha
Briggs, Errol
Brown, Deborah L.
Brown, Doslyn V.
Brown, Patricia R.
Brown, Yvette E.
Brown-Acosta, Marcia S.
Buggs, Mrs. Veronica V.
Burakiewicz, Lisa M.
Byrnes, Mrs. Kirsten M.
Caltabiano, Lisa J.
Campbell, Morven A.
Campoccio, Deborah A.
Cardoza, Jamie M.
Chamagua, Iris E.
Charles, Nirlaine
Cherubin, Ms. Yadlynd R.
Clarke, Ms. Nicole A.
Cobb, Mrs. Mamie O.
Cohen, Samuel
Colon, Sandy T.
Commike, Eileen A.

Connolly, Mary F.
Contreras, Juan A.
Cordova, Leonor
Cornelius, Eric J.
Crudup, Roslyn S.
Crummell, Donna
Cruz, Richard
Curran, Matthew F.
D'Amore, Jessica M.
David, McLawrence (Max) A.
Davis, Matthew
Deans, Karen
Deleo, Deirdre
Dennis, Ms. Tyler L.
Desir, Nadine (Nadia) O.
Dewberry, Valerie M.
Diaz, Fatima
Diaz, Maria I.
Dixon, Shellese
Doerrbecker, George
Dolphy, Keri-Ann
Dormena, Marie-Suze
Drobny, Charlene
Durham, Bette L.
Echevarria, Daliza E.
Edreira, Anna-marie
Ervin Bullock, Irene E.
Essilfie, Coretta
Featherstone, Aubrey
Felder, Venitia
Fischer, Maureen J.
Fleskes, Jenna M.
Flores, Yvonne E.
Forlong, Pedro A.
Fuentes, Jacqueline A.
Fung, Janet K.
Fussalva, Arleene J.
Gaaskin, Ms. Michelle D.
Gabriel, Sandra M.
Gaddist-Dorsey, Valerie D.
Garay, Tracy L.
Garcia, Aldo J.
Garcia, Louis J.
Giustra, Robert
Goldberg, Mrs. Denise M.
Gomez, George
Green, Calbert B.
Hackett-Viera, Tessa I.
Haire, Christine
Harris, Will C., III
Hassett, Jean M.
Haywood, Kimberly L.
Henry, Lowana M.
Hernandez, Rosalia
Hernandez, Virginia
Herzberg, Edward M.
Hill, Barbara G.
Holmes, Ms. Gloria
Hugee, Angela L.
Iglesias, Nora M.
Ithier, Carmen
Jablons, David N.
Jaliyl, Mrs. Laila A.
Jemmott, Norman A.
Jimenez, Ms. Julie A.
Johnson, Anne T.
Johnson, Gloria
Johnston, Deanna M.
Jones, David A.
Jones, Mrs. Rita G.
Jones, Venessia S.
Kelly, Yvonne
Kennedy-Gomes, Mrs.
    Candice
Kerr, Milagro X.
Keymer, Mary M.
Kiapokas, Theodora
King, Mrs. Crystal-Dawn
Kittrell-Coley, Frances E.
Knight, Roger V.
Kusmierska, Grazyna
Lacicero, Diane R.
Larkin-Bowman, Cheryl A.
Lassi, Luisa E.
Leggett, Ms. Renee
Levitz, Jennifer

Lopez, Sabrina I.
Lorde, Shannon G.
Love-fox, Chris
Lowe, Jacqueline P.
Lowe, Victoria L.
Lozano, Elsa M.
Lubin, Theodule B.
Luces, Antoinette
Lucien, Steeves
Lynn, Kandia O.
Maddux, Davina P.
Maher, Anne M.
Major, Curstlinia S.
Mallory-Canty, Debra A.
Mann, Krista J.
Manning, Trevor E.
Marshall, Vanessa M.
Mason, Vanessa M.
Mayer, Robin L.
Mayor, Lizette
Mays, Valerie N.
Mc Carthy, Timothy J.
McCollin, Kathy-Ann E.
McNeely, Karen T.
McNeill, Ms. Jasmine K.
Meade, Lyndia F.
Melendez, Monserrate
Mendez, Maritza
Michel-Martinez, Mrs. Olga
Milien, Patricia
Mitchell, Anthony J.
Mitchell, Tracie-Ann N.
Moffett, Melissa N.
Montalvo, Oneida
Montanez, Anna I.
Moody, Ms. Sabrina R.
Morado, Calvin P.
Morales, Wilfredo E.
Moreira, Ms. Julie A.
Moss, Kathryn A.
Nesmith, Phoebe R.
Neubort, Betty
Neufville, Norris
Newkirk, Tabitha
Nourakis, Ana C.
O'Neill, Angelo L.
Ortiz, Marilyn
Ortiz, Yolanda
Ovando, Percida R.
Owie, Edwin
Palatnik, Victoria D.
Peart, Donaree Y.
Peay, Ms. Lisa D.
Pedro, Hakeem A.
Pena, Carmen L.
Peterson, Tania I.
Philips, Janet
Philips, Wilma
Pierre, Josephine
Pitts-Williams, Stacey G.
Poplavskiy, Aleksandr A.
Pressley-Collier, Sharon F.
Price, Warren J.
Pulgar, Paula A.
Pysarenko, Katherine
Quamina, Michelle R.
Quintero, Marisol K.
Radcliffe, Anna J.
Rader, Matthew
Ragin, Kenya S.
Ramos, Marlene (Mandy) M.
Rampolla, Mrs. Pamela A.
Ravenell, Jason
Redman-Modeste, Stephanie
    C.
Redmond, Robin L.
Reibscheid, Mark A.
Reyes, Joselyne A.
Rivera, Herman
Robinson, Barbara E.
Rodriguez, Maribel
Roldan, Mrs. Eleanor J.
Roman, Jenny
Rorie, Scott F.
Rubino, Charles J.
Ruiz, Judy

Russo, Stacey A.
Sabater, Barbara M.
Samuel, Gracita R.
Sanchez, Anna S.
Sanchez, Baldemiro
Sanders, Antoinette
Santiago, Jackeline
Sasson, Dina J.
Scott, Mable
Shannon, Doris
Shinaba, Jumoke D.
Shomion, Carol A.
Silva, Maria J.
Smith, Kundora
Smith, Ms. Ruth D.
Spencer-Dejesus, Jesusa T.
Spriggs, Jeffrey
Staniek, Magdalena
Stone, Lada
Symolon, Kelly M.
Tain-Slater, Mrs. Valerie
Talton, Simone M.
Thomas, Kristal L.
Thornton, Jenell
Tomback, Daniel M.
Tomlinson, Camille E.
Torres, Ricardo
Torres, Talia C.
Torres, Vilma T.
Tunca, Ms. Yasemin N.
Turner, Tinaddine N.
Tyre, Iasia A.
Urteaga, Ana M.
Uveges, Michael J.
Vargas, Shirley W.
Vasquez, Maria I.
Vega, Javiel
Vicente, Milagros
Vidal-Romero, Elida
Vielot, Marshka M.
Volmar, Marc A., Jr.
Waite-Shuler, Yvette M.
Walker, Ms. Chenyear A.
West, Deborah
Whitfield, Mrs. Allison J.
Williams, Kenneth R.
Williams, Keyla N.
Williams, Robert L.
Williams-Borden, Joanne L.
Williams-Carr, Ivy C.
Wilson, Mrs. Cynthia E.
Wilson, Ms. Myrna
Witt, Olin T.
Wyatt, Antoinette C.
Zampieron, Paul W.
Zarrillo, Tina
Zelaya, Theresa M.

SPORTS

Geschwinder, Janine
Lenahan, William R.

STUDENT

Amador, Bernard
Austrie, Gilda
Bass, Jeffrey I.
Chorney, Tonya L.
Derfinyak, Eugene S.
Drummond, Junior A.
Dyer, Mark
Edwards, Roxanne D.
Eleftheriou, Eleftherios A.
Fajardo, Juan Carlos
Fernandez, John A.
Gomez, Carmen M.
Gonzalez, Ms. Yadhira
Grant, Kevin C.
Greene, Tamecca L.
Grzanka, Emily J.
Guerrero, Noemi
Guggenheim, Cordelia
Guzman, Saul
Hajaree-Ramsaran, Mrs.
    Sabita
Hansen, Brett P.
Impavido, Catherine L.

351

Khan, Neil M.
Knezevic-Xanthos, Mrs. Antoaneta
Koumba, Patricia S.
Kumagai, Koshin
Lambrianidou, Kyriaki
Lembersky, Victoria D.
Liguori, Michael T.
Marchese, Maria N.
Maysonet, Christine L.
Morasco, Benjamin J.
Nixon, Henry E.
Phillips, Nickie D.
Pinti, Rosanne A.
Prendergast, Yollette
Ramirez, Mrs. Virginie
Rampioray, Kamini
Rego, Simon A.
Rivera, Dana E.
Rivera, Michael E.
Rodgers, Lamont K.
Rodriguez, Alba L.
Romero, Yenia J.
Rudd, Alexis H.
Sanders, Liliana M.
Sharpe, Ryan R.
Sidman, Jerry R.
Stewart, Lisa M.
Tosado, Mariveila
Toussaint, Barbara
Towns, Suzanne
Trinidad, Evelyn
Webb, Hillary D.
Webb, Ruth H.
Yates, Genithia
Young, Antonia R.
Zhukovsky, Alexander

TRADE/CRAFT

Jagdharry, Mayleen G.
John, Brentnol
Mammarelli, Christopher J.
Meagher, Dr. Patrick B.
Perez, Jaime A.
Scheper, Frederick W.

TRANSPORTATION

Barreto, Samuel
Boone, Bruce A.
Cannon, Austin E.
Carney, Raymond J.
Castro, Robert J.
Daniels, Thomas L.
Davidson, Terrill L.
Davis, Teresa A.
Dongo-Williams, Mrs. Marsha M.
Esposito, Angelina E.
Ferguson, Craig D.
Gonzalez, Sandy J.
Gooden, Elsa G.
Handman, Stuart W.
Hill, Arthur B.
Hodgson, Tania
Jackson, Christina
Johnson, Martin G.
Johnson, Robert J.
Johnson, Wendy R.
Levy, Baron O.
Maloney, John F.
Morales, Carlos R.
Rhem, Karen B.
Salamy, Joseph M.
Sanchez, Julie
Sebro, Sherwin K.
Simms, Clarence J.
Smith, Daniel J.
Tapia, Arturo A.
Turbee, Patricia A.
Turner, Mrs. Regina

TRAVEL INDUSTRY

Anderson, Henry
Castillo, Gelin M.
Guevara-williams, D.
Ward, Florence V.

Zazzi, Marie L.

UTILITIES

Borruso, Mariano
Pontecorvo, Daniel M.
Russo, John

VOLUNTEERISM

Bliss, Donald
Crespo, Luisa E.
Polye, Arlene M.
Rohan, Kevin
Simmons, Melodi K.

WRITING

Bohigian, Valerie
Cohen, Rachel L.
DeFranco, Elizabeth (Liz) C.
Doyle, Arthur
Grice, Yvonne S.
James, Sharon
O'Brien, Jeffrey S.
Samuels, Susan R.
Schachinger, Mildred C.
Schatzberg, Rufus
Schrader, Richard A.
Sheinman, Ilana
Sprague, Robert F.
Stewart, Lenore O.
Tesoriero, Thomas J.
Wegman, James L., CPP

E-MAIL ADDRESS SECTION

A

Abarca, Celia J., '78,   violinmom1@aol.com
Abdool, Rick E., '96,   ABDOOL@DPW.COM
Abdullah, Ms. Doris T., '80,   doris_abdullah@pechiney.com
Abraham, George C., '75,   bossi@aol.com
Abraham, Harlan B., '96,   hbabrbiz@aol.com
Abruzzi, Raymond J., '81,   cougar90@prodigy.net
Acevedo, CW4 Efrain, '76,   papiace2@hotmail.com
Achon, Alexa M., '99,   aachon@hotmail.com
Acosta, Gasmary, '98,   destiny2tasia@aol.com
Acosta, Luis, '77,   lacosta@dhcr.state.ny.us
Adamiak, Alan B., '83,   aadamiak@aol.com
Adams, De'Ron W., '99,   deronwadams@aol.com
Adams, Errol A., '97,   easa71@yahoo.com
Adams, Julia V., '93,   juliava@prodigy.net
Adegbamigbe, Adedeji, '95,   dejisr@earthlink.net
Ademaj, Vera, '99,   beri1224@aol.com
Adjaero, Alphonsus A., '95,   ocnet@msn.com
Adler, Harvey L., '79,   harvey.l.adler@usdoj.gov
Adler, Morton N., '85,   samrelda@frontiernet.net
Ahyoung, Gary C., '99,   jerrydman@aol.com
Aiken, Iris A., '91,   iaiken@aol.com
Aimone, Paul J., '83,   pjaimone@prodigy.net
Aitken, Alexandra S., '99,   alexaitken@hotmail.com
Aivazis, Elias K., '79,   eaivazis@usss.treas.gov
Ajunwa, Ifeyinwa P., '99,   pajunwa@hotmail.com
Akerele, Gabriel A., '92,   akerele@freewwweb.com
Akgun-Auerbach, Ms. Alice, '92,   scandalice@aol.com
Albright, Eugene T., '73,   eta55@aol.com
Alcantara, Mrs. Olga, '90,   olga_alcantara@rfcuny.org
Alcee, Natalie (Giggles) S., '97,   nalcee@ckslaw.com
Aldoy, Anna M., '98,   annaaldoy@aol.com
Aldrich, Alicia, '91,   aldricha@hotmail.com
Alduende, Ivonne, '99,   ALDUENDE@AOL.COM
Alexander, Lavern K., '92,   TYECE@AOL.COM
Alexandre, Jean W., '97,   winchel2@aol.com
Ali, Mrs. Aneerah R., '93,   alifam1@usol.com
Ali, Shakawat, '95,   dostho@netzero.net
Allen, Alton D., '76,   sgtaa641@aol.com
Allen, Joseph A., '96,   joseph_allen@hotmail.com
Allen, Wayne A., '92,   wallen8736@aol.com
Almeida, Esther M., '94,   apparellak@aol.com
Alswang, Scott B., '80,   salswang@aol.com
Alvarez, Elvin, '84,   ea95@columbia.edu
Alvarez, Michelle L., '98,   evita574@aol.com
Alvarez, Ray, '96,   miamialvarez@aol.com
Alverio, Daisy M., '81,   dalverio@aol.com
Amador, Bernard, '99,   bamador813@aol.com
Amato, Edward J., '76,   eamato@flashcom.net
Amaya, Allan F., '88,   ipecacuana@hotmail.com
Amengual, Margie, '83,   margie@praxisint.net
Ampie, Omar A., '99,   bmelon95@aol.com
Anatsui, Edwige M., '99,   aiban64@gateway.net
Anderson, Bonita M., '96,   silversneakers1@ivillage.com
Anderson, Charles P., '75,   charlesjud@aol.com
Anderson, Kevin G., '94,   kanderson@doblan.cn.ci-nyc.ny.us
Anderson, Dr. Lola H., '78,   lora621@aol.com
Anderson, Dr. Melody M., '75,   mmanderson@mindspring.com
Anderson, Robert J., '84,   rjapd@gateway.net
Andrades, John, Jr., '78,   acoljon@aol.com
Andrews, Benjamin (Ben), '90,   bacomm@aol.com
Andrews, Peter, '76,   us5136@onebox.com
Andricosky, John J., '76,   jjaact@aol.com
Anes, Edwin, '96,   edanes@aol.com
Annina, Ralph, '80,   rannina@execpc.com
Antonin, Jo-Ann, '99,   dulcemajo@earthlink.net
Aponte, Ana, '90,   ana-aponte@webtv.net
Aponte, Myriam, '79,   myraima@hotmail.com
Aponte, Victor M., '76,   cvaponterome@yahoo.com
Appel, Kenneth P., '84,   kenneth@peoplepc.com
Appel, Michael A., '80,   mappel1209@aol.com
Aptacker, Steven I., '87,   saptacker@aol.com
Arce, Michele, '97,   marce00123@aol.com
Arellano, Arthur Wellesley,   narco.trafficker@slortar.com
Arellano, Jose, '95,   offwheeler@hotmail.com

Arevalo, Yesenia M., '95,   smerphett@aol.com
Argenti, Karen M., '78,   kabx101@aol.com
Aridas, Mrs. Nanette, '97,   nanettearidas@hotmail.com
Aristy, Tommy G., '96,   tommya_dbl@yahoo.com
Arlain, Nena D., '97,   just1diva@hotmail.com
Arlen, Jennifer, '99,   j_arlen@yahoo.com
Armani, Chris G., '98,   bklynsexx@aol.com
Armas, Margie, '94,   margieacop@yahoo.com
Armatti-Epstein, Linda T., '80,   bigje@aol.com
Armesto, Catherine P., '99,   pinkpwdr5@aol.com
Arniotes, LT James V., '97,   jarniotes@juno.com
Arnold, Richard, '96,   rearnold@optonline.net
Arons-Schultze, Janet A., '78,   JANSCHULTZE@HOTMAIL.COM
Arroyo, Jennifer R., '94,   jrarroyo@wlrk.com
Arteaga, Ms. Luz A., '97,   uarteaga19@aol.com
Ash, Sylvia G., Esq., '76,   sylviag85@aol.com
Ashley, Teresa L., '97,   tashley330@aol.com
Atkinson, Donald, '75,   dratkin@bellatlantic.net
Augustin, Kisha V., '99,   kishany@hotmail.com
Augustine, Clyde L., '80,   augustic@brooklynda.org
Augustus Miller, Mrs. Antoinette J., '97,   imiller379@aol.com
Augustynowicz, Richard, '77,   ramaka3@gateway.net
Auli, Karoll, '99,   kk5700@acs.dfa.state.ny.us
Austrie, Gilda, '99,   aga@pophost.com
Autera, Marysusan D., '93,   aretua@aol.com
Avery, Earl, '80,   chibinc@aol.com
Aweeky, Peter A., '84,   paweeky@bloomberg.net
Ayala, Francisco, Jr., '78,   hnleanyvp1@aol.com
Ayres, Richard, '85,   ayresclms@rcn.com

B

Babakitis, Paul G., '83,   nysabas@optonline.net
Babisco, Stephen G., '77,   babiscko@aol.com
Bahna, Alfred M., '88,   abahna@aol.com
Baicher, Robin M., '83,   justjewl@aol.com
Bailey, Stephen H., '76,   POPDOGG1@AOL.COM
Bailey, William S., '82,   beelmnf@aol.com
Baisden, Ms. Jilyon, '99,   jhbai@aol.com
Baker, Harold C., '73,   hcbaker@worldnet.att.net
Baker, Janice L., '95,   janice.baker@cliffordchance.com
Baker, Jimmie R., '77,   jbaker@ocs.com
Baker, Robert D., '97,   duvalny@juno.com
Bala, James W., '76,   jsbala@nemaine.com
Balcom, MAJ Jerome (Jerry) K., '73,   jbalcom@courts.state.ny.us
Balcom, Mrs. Laura, '73,   lbb120@aol.com
Baldwin, Robert M., '76,   bbaldwin@movadogroup.com
Ball, Robert, '82,   rballjar4@hotmail.com
Bamrick, Kenneth G., '69,   kgfb918@aol.com
Bank, Maurice H., '76,   joelmcrea@worldnet.att.net
Bankovic, Milan, '94,   sabank99@yahoo.com
Banks, Hermon J., '76,   hbanks@aol.com
Banks-Catoe, Latisha V., '99,   lcatoe4346@aol.com
Baptiste, Camille A., '98,   gt98law@compuserve.com
Baptiste, Wilfred E., '83,   bappo1@aol.com
Barajas, Robert J., '81,   derventa98@aol.com
Baraket, Tamara M., '97,   PRININCA@AOL.COM
Barbato, Michael, '93,   ladder143@aol.com
Barbieri, Ellen B., '75,   elsal@cts.com
Bargebuhr, Nancy E., '79,   ccrly0903@aol.com
Barnett, Denise E., '90,   dbarn42824@aol.com
Barquin, Armando X., '92,   j71032@aol.com
Barr, Charles S., CPP, CFE, '75,   csb617@aol.com
Barreto, Amelia R., '90,   ambarr@aol.com
Barreto, Samuel, '92,   sambarreto@mindspring.com
Barreyre, Raymond, '76,   raybarre@aol.com
Barrow-Baez, Mary, '96,   mbaez@juno.com
Barry, Elaine, '82,   ebarry@richoneil.com
Barry, Kevin B., '75,   iabtibarry@aol.com
Barry, Patrick T., '78,   paddy_barry@aigltd.net
Bartels, Ms. Elizabeth C., '98,   lizbartels@home.com
Bartlett-Josie, Mrs. Christine, '90,   chbjosie@yahoo.com
Bartoszek, Peter C., '72,   peanlet@aol.com
Baruch, Marcia L., '80,   mbaruch@bop.gov
Basciano, Patricia R., '80,   prb704@aol.com
Bass, Jeffrey I., '96,   puravida@dellnet.com
Bauer, George M., '99,   gmb6155@aol.com

Baumann, Ms. Deborah C., '84,   duffyblack@aol.com
Bavolar, SGT Keith A., '98,   bav293@aol.com
Beal, Susan, '95,   susan@bealejohnson.com
Beary, Richard A., '99,   YELLADLO@HOTMAIL.COM
Beattie, Henry J., '99,   pi@warwic.net
Beatty, Gerard V., '72,   gbeatty@jafar.hartnell.cc.ca.us
Beckford, Maxine A., '97,   mladybug70@aol.com
Beckles, Arlene D., '87,   beckles1@mindspring.com
Bedrossian, Anne-Marie M., '97,   ambedross@hotmail.com
Beers, Albert S., '89,   abeers@jerseycape.com
Behan, Cornelius (Neil) J., '68,   nbehan@sprynet.com
Belasco, Mrs. Barbara A., '85,   bmtmss@imcnyc.com
Beldo, Gina, '94,   gbeldo5576@aol.com
Belenky, Dmitry, '94,   masterdee31@netzero.net
Belgrave, Carl C., '83,   ccbelgrave@aol.com
Bello, Valerie, '99,   valstacey@rocketmail.com
Belviso, Lawrence M., '81,   bel@co.henrico.va.us
Benaim, Charlie, '97,   mntf35@aol.com
Bender, John R., '77,   jbender@triarc.com
Benfatti, Kristeine, '90,   kristeineb@aol.com
Benjamin, Helman O., '96,   hbenja1387@aol.com
Benjamin, Yvonne E., '94,   vonne8@juno.com
Bennett, Ms. Kerry-Ann, '99,   kben698724@aol.com
Bennett, Sylvia L., '79,   sylben914@aol.com
Bergeron, John D., '72,   bergersonj@aol.com
Berke, Marshall L., '95,   mberke@ccfa.org
Bermudez, Carlos R., '94,   cptbermudez@earthlink.net
Bernard, Joseph, '93,   gybernard@aol.com
Bernstein, Faye K., '94,   FAYERACE@AOL.COM
Berroa, Ms. Janice, RN, '91,   ladij168@aol.com
Berry, BG Robert W., USA(Ret.), '81,   rberry@mprlaw.com
Bert, Richard A., '95,   richardbert@hotmail.com
Betances, Neftali, Jr., '96,   nefty007@mindspring.com
Bitsimis, Jeffrey, '80,   jbitsimis@srtnyc.com
Black, Samuel (Sam), '98,   sblack@streetfusion.com
Blaha, Jana L., '97,   jbksk@erols.com
Blaich, Charles R., '98,   bcb6@aol.com
Blake, Richard A., '93,   rblake@ci.ocoee.fl.us
Blakeley, Dawn, '98,   dblakeley@rockco.com
Bliss, Donald, '96,   db5847@aol.com
Bloom, Jason S., '96,   jbloom@courtroomsciences.com
Bloom, Michael H., '96,   ym7277@usma.army.edu
Blount, Ms. Heather, '98,   heatherhys@aol.com
Bobb, Ms. Irma Diane, Esq., '94,   idbobb@aol.com
Boggiano, Daniel, '94,   BOGGIANO@EROLS.COM
Boggio, Linda M., '82,   lin600@aol.com
Bogovic, Anthony P., '79,   abogovic@painewebber.com
Bohigian, Valerie, '91,   a1valian@aol.com
Bohringer, Ernest W., '99,   ewb346@aol.com
Bolivar, Matilde, '90,   mbolivar@cunyvm.cuny.edu
Bolling Sharpe, Mrs. Charise M., '83,   charise.bollingsharpe@ssmb.com
Bologna, Anthony (Tony) V., '92,   sqdcmdr30@aol.com
Bolz, Francis A., Jr., '68,   hntone@aol.com
Bonaney, Polanges R., '97,   hotsauce01@msn.com
Bonilla, Jose E., '98,   jbonij@aol.com
Booker, Kwesi L., '98,   KWESMAC2@AOL.COM
Boone, Bruce A., '94,   boonekungfu@gateway.net
Bordas, David M., '99,   dm_publius@yahoo.com
Boritza, Ms. Patricia A., '80,   pboritza@mayerbrown.com
Borker, Vito, '97,   nfinti92@aol.com
Borquaye, Marylin, '81,   mreed1@worldnet.att.net
Borrero, Kenneth, '98,   ken_borrero@stbarnabas-ny.org
Borruso, Mariano, '75,   utiltiesmet@aol.com
Bosko, George M., '81,   geobos@gate.net
Boston, Denver G., '72,   dgboston1@aol.com
Botte, Dominick, Jr., '80,   nyf542@aol.com
Bourdon, Ana M., '92,   AMBOURDON@USPIS.GOV
Bove, John D., '78,   bovej@labs.wyeth.com
Bovell, Donna A., '93,   dbforreal@aol.com
Bowen, Anthony, '96,   anthony.bowen4@gte.net
Bowens, Renita D., '94,   rbowen370@aol.com
Bowes, Vincent, '75,   vincentobowes@ssmb.com
Bowler, William T., '77,   cbbowler@spreynet.com
Bowman, Debra, '84,   debra@sumter.net
Bowman, Lawson D., '97,   lawsonbowman@aol.com
Boylan, Kathleen, '96,   kmboylan@aol.com
Boylan, Lauren E., '96,   lau.irish@gateway.ret
Boyle, James J., '77,   jboyle@optimum.com
Boyle, John J., '71,   margejohnboyle@worldnet.att.net
Bracero, Denise, '98,   dbracero25@aol.com
Brady, COL Edward T., USA(Ret.), '77,   arsenal@fayettevillenc.com
Brady, John J., '93,   jjbrady@bop.gov
Braithwaite, Reginald, Esq., '75,   rlbnyesq@aol.com
Bramble, Anthony S., '97,   antbra07@aol.com
Brandt, William J., '68,   256@aol.com
Brathwaite, LeRoy L., '74,   anaconda@webcombo.net

Brathwaite, CAPT Rafael, '90,   rafaob@yahoo.com
Brech, Todd R., '96,   TODDRB@HOTMAIL.COM
Brennan, Kenneth D., '77,   smallfatthumbs@aol.com
Bresnan, Eilish B., '93,   ebresnan1@aol.com
Brett, Veronica E., '84,   addictdoc@aol.com
Briggs, Errol, '95,   ebinc123@aol.com
Brinadze, Anna, '95,   annflx@aol.com
Brinkman, Mrs. Diane M., '94,   timpus@aol.com
Briscoe, James J., '91,   jimbrik@aol.com
Brito, Michael J., '95,   mboogie29@hotmail.com
Britton, John J., '77,   john.britton@usdoj.gov
Brodman, Mathew H., '97,   brodmanmh@state.gov
Brogan, Michael P., '80,   mpb46@aol.com
Broker, Steven J., '96,   sb9701@aol.com
Bronaugh, Ronald A., '99,   rbronaugh@aol.com
Brooks, Ms. Marvie B., '90,   marvie.brooks@jj.cuny.edu
Brown, Cathy, '94,   cbrown@riker.com
Brown, Courtney L., '99,   courtney_brown@globalcrossing.com
Brown, Deborah L., '95,   DB3037@ESC.ALBANY.EDU
Brown, Francisco A., '82,   francisco.brown@worldnet.att.net
Brown, Herbert, '80,   JLBHAB@AOL.COM
Brown, Herbert A., Jr., '97,   tjphab@aol.com
Brown, Janean A., '95,   jbown8710@aol.com
Brown, Ms. Janet L., '91,   jbrown1728@aol.com
Brown, Latisha Y., '97,   teetee329@aol.com
Brown, Patricia R., '79,   pbrownlpyr@aol.com
Brown, Ronda R., '98,   b945@aol.com
Brown, Shanteil, '88,   shangary@msn.com
Brown, Tara C., '90,   tcbnharlem@aol.com
Brown, Tara N., '96,   sweetpeay@ivillage.com
Brown, Timothy, '98,   mysuite@netzero.net
Brown, Tracy-Ann M., '99,   tbrown@jmhcomm.com
Brown, Valerie L., '77,   vbrown@njsba.com
Brown, Yvette E., '95,   yebony@aol.com
Browne, Phillip A., '99,   phillip11207@hotmail.com
Browning, Darlene, '92,   chanel8107@aol.com
Bruce, Prince A., '99,   obigie@hotmail.com
Bruce, Tommy, '93,   brucet@un.org
Brudent, Sandra, '98,   sbrudent@yahoo.com
Brumer, Steven N., '83,   sbrumer@wireless-data.com
Bruno, Daniel J., '95,   danou1@aol.com
Bruno, Frank W., '82,   fbear3@aol.com
Brunson, Lakisha D., '98,   lbrunson@optonline.net
Buckley, Maurice, '80,   emb31473@aol.com
Buda, Richard, '78,   richard.buda@hofstra.edu
Budram, Anil, '99,   jjckid@aol.com
Bugge, Brian K., '78,   icfleso@aol.com
Bull, Rhudean, '98,   rbull@ci.stanford.ct.us
Bundy, Elizabeth B., '99,   bethbundy@juno.com
Bunkeddeko, Sally, '97,   jajjag@aol.com
Buntin, Mark M., '80,   newwinc@aol.com
Buono, Joseph F., '77,   jbodega@aol.com
Burd, Dr. Marc A., '88,   drburd@worldnet.att.net
Burger, Frederick (Fred) R., '76,   freddieb6@juno.com
Burgh, Todd D., '96,   tburgh@netscape.com
Burnett, Byron K., '71,   bkbfly@aol.com
Burns, John W., '82,   jburns@cbhl.com
Burrell, Tracey, PhD, '91,   tburrell@aol.com
Burrows, Jonathan, '94,   jburrows500@aol.com
Burwell, Shawna M., '91,   muffin8778@aol.com
Buser, Robert J., CFE, '95,   brixbunch@aol.com
Buska, Richard M., '86,   nyumpa@aol.com
Butcher, Margaret P., '83,   cherub51@juno.com
Butler, Tawanna C., '98,   tcbbrighteyes@aol.com
Byer, Renee A., '99,   rbyer@peguinputnam.com
Bynum, Nora B.,   eternal50@juno.com
Byrnes, Jennifer L., '99,   jby8099650@aol.com
Byrnes, Ms. Kirsten M., '99,   byrnes_k@worldnet.att.net

C

Cabral, Aileen I., '99,   aicarbal@yahoo.com
Cacciatore, Robert J., '92,   rjpc@aol.com
Caceres, Elisabeth, '95,   lcaceres@peninsular.com
Cadot, Marie M., '95,   MCHILAIRE@AOL.COM
Caesar, Tessa V., '95,   bribri1067@aol.com
Cafarelli, Michael L., '88,   mlccrc@erols.com
Cahill, Patrick, '78,   palkp@aol.com
Cairl, Brian D., '83,   bcairl@kroll-ogara.com
Cajou, Jean Claude, '96,   PILOT703@AOL.COM
Calathes, Dr. William, '83,   wcalathes@aol.com
Calby, Paula M., '79,   pcalby@victimsservices.org
Calise, Diane, '98,   dinee@msn.com
Callender, Cynthia, '94,   esyllar1218@worldnet.att.net
Camacho, Edgar M., '84,   camperez@aol.com
Camacho, Gabriel, '95,   investigate@mail.com
Camilleri, Michele, '94,   cmcvac@msn.com

Camilo, Gilberto J., '99, LOFTY45@AOL.COM
Cammett, John M., PhD, jmcjj@cunyvm.cuny.edu
Campbell, Annecia A., '97, imod64@aol.com
Campbell, Hopeton A., '90, hcampbell@fordham.edu
Campbell, Steven T., '78, csr_inc@compuserve.com
Camper, Deborah F., Esq., '84, slake@fastol.com
Campoccio, Deborah A., '97, qtpie7i997@aol.com
Canady, Donna A., '96, dcanady29@aol.com
Cancel, Juan A., '96, ebonycoqui@aol.com
Candia, Fernando A., '89, fernando.candia@progressiveinsurance.com
Canfield, Dennis V., PhD, '76, dennis_canfield@mmac.jccbi.gov
Canning, Candia C., '99, ccan266911@aol.com
Cannon, Austin E., '90, austin.cannon@airborne.com
Capaobianco, Sr. Carmela, '93, gs17street.com
Capella, Ms. Jeanette, '76, spirittry@aol.com
Capparelli, Robert (Rob), '96, rcappare@pryorcashman.com
Cappello, Edward, '77, edcapp203@aol.com
Cappiello, Dominick A., '97, dc1527@aol.com
Capria, Britt A., '96, britt_capria@hotmail.com
Cardillo, Bob J., '78, bob060@aol.com
Cardillo, Joseph L., '74, joecardillo@arrow.com
Cardoza, Zachary A., '97, zachary.cardoza@responseinsurance.com
Carlo, John R., '69, cpc@nac.net
Carlson, Glenn A., '99, gc5317@aol.com
Carlson, Richard D., Jr., '75, carl4@sparta.csnet.net
Carlucci, Jean M., '97, dduck275@hotmail.com
Carolan, Edward, '90, ecarolan@worldnet.att.net
Carpenter, Ms. Edna E., '80, eddy@in4web.com
Carpinelli, Paul, '96, paulcarpin@aol.com
Carranza, Oscar, '96, oscardos@hotmail.com
Carrasco, Edward (Ed) G., '99, ecarr15479@aol.com
Carrera, Margarita, '98, gozque@hotmail.com
Carrion, Luis A., '93, carrionfa@aol.com
Carroll, Patrick J., '72, pcarroll@ci.new-rochelle.ny.us
Carroll, Thomas R., '73, carroll@aol.com
Carter, James E., '76, j.e.carter@systec.com
Carter, Mary A., '81, w1m2carter@aol.com
Carter, Owen, '76, omcre@aol.com
Caruso, Rosemary, '85, ro6425@aol.com
Carvajal, Tania M., '99, tmcarvajal@netscape.net
Carvajal-Nunez, Mrs. Xiomara G., '95, eroidis@aol.com
Casale, Donald E., II, '96, decii@erols.com
Casalins, Liana C., '89, m52maya@aol.com
Casanova-Scott, Mrs. Veronica, '89, vscotties7@aol.com
Casares, 1LT John W., USA, '98, wcasa@aol.com
Casarino, Carmine J., '70, melcasa@aol.com
Cassidy, Susan E., '89, susan_cass@hotmail.com
Castagna, John J., '89, johnnyc972@aol.com
Castellano, John, '80, jcastjets@aol.com
Castellar, Kane H., '99, kcast11@aol.com
Castiglione, Steven, '95, castiglione.sl@pg.com
Castillo, Ernesto (Pete) A., Jr., CFE, '90, ernesto.castillo@aig.com
Castillo, Gelin M., '97, loiinte4@aol.com
Castro, Mrs. Ayanna T., '95, ayanna_castro@hotmail.com
Castro, Robert J., '77, mayanman@hotmail.com
Catania, Denise A., '98, dcatania@ebglaw.com
Cavagnetto, Lawrence, '86, proflarry@earthlink.net
Cavaliere, Christopher, '95, tnc917@aol.com
Cavanagh, James P., '79, cavna2@optonline.net
Caver, Cynthia L., '99, cysyca@aol.com
Cazeau, Beatrice, '94, cdzeau@sall.state.fl.us
Cebic, Svetlana, '92, scebic@aol.com
Cepeda, Luis, Jr., '91, luisfjr63@aol.com
Cerezo, Juan E., '96, jcerezo@manhattancollege.edu
Cesarano, Anthony, '95, leadviper@aol.com
Challita, John-Pierre, '99, jchallita@aol.com
Chambers, Jeffrey A., '96, jchamb7192@aol.com
Chambers, Maxine V., '99, sbegodon@aol.com
Chametzky, Steven A., '91, saco@aol.com
Chan, David, '95, dachan@bankofny.com
Chan, Suk Han H., '99, hantra72@aol.com
Chan, Susan, '97, suschan@dpw.com
Chang, Mrs. Josephine, Esq., '91, jchang@fulbright.com
Chapman, Marilyn, '98, chapcut@juno.com
Charles, Alice, '95, alicecharles@msn.com
Charles Smiley, Isabelle, '90, igrits@aol.com
Chatman-Whitfield, Mayai N., '95, wednday.com
Chavis, Rosezina, '95, rdavis@johnj.cuny.edu
Cheeks, Robert, '95, robcheeks@aka.com
Chen, Johnny Y., '96, chenyen32@yahoo.com
Chen, Katty, '96, kchbh@cunyvm.cuny.edu
Cherena-Pacheco, Yvonne, '78, cherenay@law.stmarytx.edu
Chernick, Steven M., '89, schernick@netzero.net
Cherubin, Ms. Yadlynd R., '99, yadlynd@mailcity.com
Cheski, Philip M., '93, pcheski@hotmail.com
Chiarini, George J., '77, chiarinmarble@aol.com

Childs, Iris M., '99, butbrown@aol.com
Chin, George W., '79, gc4nfic@aol.com
Chisholm, Delores, '82, deloreschisholm@hotmail.com
Chomiak, Robert H., '78, rohcho@aol.com
Chorney, Tonya L., '95, tlchorney@aol.com
Chowdhury, Tarakur R., '99, tarakur@aol.com
Christensen, James, '81, raboworld@aol.com
Christian, Elmo E., '95, mistamagic@aol.com
Christman, William C., '78, eagle524@aol.com
Chugerman, Jacob E., '76, jec622@pb.seflin.org
Chung, Thomas H., '94, hojoonc@aol.com
Chung, Victor L., '77, vchung@webtv.net
Ciampo, Michael N., '83, champ44@warwick.net
Cicero, Alethea U., '98, aletheacic@aol.com
Cisse, Sanah, '85, ccsanah@educ.umass.edu
Ciuzio, Richard G., '78, qzo55@aol.com
Clapp, Michelle D., '95, michelle.clapp@nyu.edu
Clark, Kevin M., '80, tuvokclark@netscape.net
Clark, Mark, '92, mclark5476@aol.com
Clarke, Barry R., '93, bclarke@courts.state.ny
Clarke, Ms. Nicole A., '97, nstorm7@aol.com
Clarke, Nuria E., '93, levyja@webtv.com
Clausen, Vincent J., '76, VINCENTCKA@AOL.COM
Clayton, James O., '83, jameso0504@aol.com
Clements, Lavonda D., '88, msgiab@aol.com
Clerico, Lucien T., '90, tshot63@aol.com
Clifford, Maria C., '77, iluvny6034@aol.com
Coaxum, Teresa (Teri), '93, coaxumt@brooklynda.org
Cockburn, George A., '72, georgec@jjay.cumy.edu
Codispoti, Michael, '81, soarvideos@aol.com
Codrington, Paula A., '94, rhema20@juno.com
Coello, Marjorie I., '99, mimc200@aol.com
Cohen, Bonny A., '78, frogbare@hotmail.com
Cohen, David J., '98, djcjc@aol.com
Cohen, David L., '84, sleuth29@aol.com
Cohn, Jennifer I., '99, jicohn@legal_aid.org
Coiro, Robert M., '83, libo@warwick.net
Coker, Renee R., '98, rcoker220@aol.com
Colasurdo, James F., '96, jfsolas@aol.com
Colclough, Andre W., '98, wecer@aol.com
Cole, Leslie, CPP, '81, les.cole@worldnet.att.net
Coleman, Charles E., '80, ccoleman@nyctc.cuny.edu
Colicci, Gerald P., '79, spci291@aol.com
Collado, Ms. Giselle M., '96, gis1972@aol.com
Collazo, Antonio, '91, acollaz@aol.com
Collazo-soto, Ms. Desiree, '93, micdezco@ix.netcom.com
Collica, Kimberly A., '97, kimjail@aol.com
Collins, Elliot, '91, hhd123@bellatlantic.net
Collins, Michael, '90, MCOLLINS@NYPD.ORG
Collorafi, Mrs. Lyz S., '98, peruana24@cs.com
Colon, Ana R., '99, acolon@kkwc.com
Colon, Anthony B., '97, acolon16@webtv.net
Colon, Gregory, '96, peddy75@earthlink.net
Colon, Hector E., '95, hmjcolon@yahoo.com
Colon, Helen, '91, ladyblue20@aol.com
Colon, Licelyn, '93, vigor217@aol.com
Colon, Monica, '95, faith11000@aol.com
Colon, Robert G., '73, harleyrob@webtv.net
Colon, Wendy C., '99, wcwhatever@aol.com
Colonnello, Karen A., '92, fong6689@aol.com
Colon-Prezeau, Mrs. Kazandra V., '96, skprezeau@aol.com
Colucci-Turbett, Joann, '75, watson3716@aol.com
Colvin, Bernard W., '94, threequarters@prodigy.net
Comastri, Harold N., '80, dean86@aol.com
Concepcion, Dr. Lydia, '92, lconcrpcion@pol.net
Conde, Matthew P., '98, thewter77@aol.com
Conklin Tetor, Mrs. Jennifer M., '98, jmcejt@aol.com
Connelly, Robert T., '80, poconoirish@webtv.net
Connolly, Charles P., '76, cconnolly@exchange.ml.com
Connolly, John J., '69, john1885e@aol.com
Connolly, Mary F., '97, maddyooch@aol.com
Connor, Brian W., '99, bconnor924@aol.com
Conroy, John T., '96, conjohnroy@aol.com
Conry, Steven, '87, conry@frontiernet.net
Conte, Daniel P., '97, dan@conte.com
Conti, Richard P., '97, lewybodies@aol.com
Conway, Gary F., '92, rhpllios@aol.com
Conway, Judith A., '86, www.jconway.com
Conway, Martin J., '96, mcnkc88@aol.com
Cook, Mrs. Leanne T., '99, leacook@cs.com
Cooper, Dermot A., '95, dermotcooper@hotmail.com
Cooper, Karl M., '94, y2kmc@mindspring.com
Coppock, SGT Durwin L., '99, sgt_coppock@hotmail.com
Cora -Lundquist, Marissa, '93, aroc020@aol.com
Corbett, Glenn P., '82, jcorbett@jjay.cuny.edu
Corbin, Stephen, '95, 17183193334@orchestrate.net

Corcoran, Michael C., '96, mccorcoran@worldnet.att.net
Corcoran, Michael T., '73, wllind703@aol.com
Cordero, Raul (Pappa Bear), '99, cordero55@netscape.net
Cordero, Steven M., Esq., '96, scordero@msn.com
Corey, Jessica E., CPP, '87, jecnypd@aol.com
Coriano, Milagros, '96, mayli26@hotmail.com
Cornelius, Eric J., '92, ejcjoep@aol.com
Cornell, Richard R., '91, corncars@aol.com
Corrigan, Michael J., '82, antrimmgt@aol.com
Corso, David J., '99, jurist@mail.com
Cortellino, Gary J., '78, garycortel@aol.com
Cosentino, Donna M., '98, showmethemoney@bigplanet.com
Cosme, Maura, '97, medeira@yahoo.com
Cossu, Jennifer K., '98, demijenna@aol.com
Cote, Raymond A., '92, rote97642@aol.com
Cotham, Jeffrey D., '94, armymanret@aol.com
Cotter, Robert T., '78, shadrav@frontiernet.net
Cotto, Jose L., '90, jcotto007@earthlink.net
Cotty, Edward, '73, ecotty@altanainc.com
Courtney, William D., '80, b.courtney@control-risks.com
Coutts, Anne R., '96, car33263@ibmmail.com
Coviello, Ms. Karlee M., '99, k23ar@aol.com
Cowan, James T., '78, jtcjr@hotmail.com
Cox, Ayoka, '94, nnuego@aol.com
Cox, Daniel H., '92, dhcox58@hotmail.com
Cox-Alston, Ms. Stephanie A., '78, coxalston@yahoo.com
Cozzolino, Caryn, '99, cozz1974@hotmail.com
Craig, Sara Elizabeth, '95, sec@vicon.net
Crawford, Andrea (Angie) K., '98, andrea.crawfor@nike.com
Crawford, Mark R., '98, gmc113096@aol.com
Crawford, Randy B., '97, rcrawford23@aol.com
Crayton, Wanda A., '99, wcra18936@aol.com
Creamer, Jeanet E., '94, jcre993718@aol.com
Creegan, John I., '76, hbfluke@aol.com
Creque, Romelia Y., '82, lavendarflower@msn.com
Cronin, Joseph M., '98, joecronin@aol.com
Crosby, Marion T., '97, keytho@hotmail.com
Crouthamel, David E., '98, davecrout@aol.com
Cruz, Louis A., Esq., '76, lacruz@banet.net
Cruz, Richard, '96, richardcruz@law.com
Cruz, Victor A., '99, victorcruz@banet.net
Cudjoe, Michelle A., '97, michibu@aol.com
Cuebas, Edwin, '77, ekcuebas@uspis.gov
Cuevas, Ms. Claris I., '97, sanalejo@cs.com
Cumberbatch, Simeon, '97, cumberbatchlaw@worldnet.att.net
Cunningham, Darrow, '79, blkconscious@msn.com
Cunningham, Lawrence (Larry) H., '97, cunningham@ibm.net
Curran, Catherine C., '95, cccurranny@hotmail.com
Curran, Matthew F., '74, mcurran105@aol.com
Cusumano, Patricia (Tricia), '92, MYWAY444444@AOL.COM
Czarnecka, Beata, '98, beata707@aol.com

D

Dacosta, Emmy H., '99, emmyVC@aol.com
Dagnello, Rudy J., '74, rjdejkaf@aol.com
Dahl, Dena M., '92, CDRDAHL100@NETZERO.NET
Dalloo, Eric S., '99, edalloo@hklaw.com
Dalton, Robert B., '81, rdalton138@aol.com
Daly, Elizabeth V., '98, lizd233@aol.com
D'Amato, George R., '74, george-damato@tax.state.ny.us
Dames, Fatima C., '95, fdames@mptn.org
D'Amore, Jessica M., '99, jdamore@iwon.com
D'andrea, Lorenzo J., '96, ld09@aol.com
Daniel-Babb, Valerie, '96, lesamaa@earthlink.com
Daniels, Eurita, '80, rere1218@aol.com
Danielson, Eskil S., '75, eskild@interactive.net
Danik, Mark D., '76, tigrevp@earthlink.net
Danjer, Marco V., '95, krooklyn@aol.com
D'antonio, Steven A., '76, auico@aol.com
Daouaou, Abdelilah, '97, adaouaou@aol.com
Davan, Robert J., '78, davanclan@aol.com
David, McLawrence (Max) A., 2000, mclawdav@hotmail.com
Davies, Christopher J., '95, cdavies1985@prodigy.net
Davis, Brian P., '98, JJCGRAD98@HOTMAIL.COM
Davis, Mrs. Eleanor, PhD, '78, nelledav@aol.com
Davis, Gideon, '73, gdavis276@aol.com
Davis, Joanne, '99, joanne.davis@msdw.com
Davis, Teresa A., '95, tad6@psu.edu
Davis, Vameershala, '93, meeshoo@msn.com
Davis, Wilbert, '97, williewild@earthlink.com
Davy, Christopher S., '92, cdavy@ora.fda.gov
Deacon, Carol J., '97, cdeacon727@aol.com
Dean, Mrs. Angela R., '89, stngry00@pacbell.net
Decambre, Brenda, '95, bdecambre@netzero.net
Defranco, Edward J., '62, defranco@dcjs.state.ny.us
DeFranco, Elizabeth (Liz) C., '97, hozro@usa.net

De George, Joseph W., '98, jodegeorge@juno.com
DeGrenier, Terrence, '97, TERRENCE_DEGRENIER@BIO-RAD.COM
de Holczer, Lauren J., '80, lnypd@aol.com
Dejesus, Iris K., '98, keyla@hotmail.com
De Jesus, Lisa, '95, lisa.dejesus@fmr.com
De Jesus-Rodriguez, Blanqui I., '90, blanqui@earthlink.net
Delahanty, Lt Neal C., '72, nealdel@aol.com
Deleo, Deirdre, '96, deirdre_deleo@yahoo.com
Delerme, Carolyn, '99, carolyndelerme@compuserve.com
Delgado, Ms. Fatima A., '95, fdel513@cs.com
Delprino, Robert, '86, delprirp@buffalo.edu
Deluca, Anthony E., '79, adeluca1@optonline.net
Deluca, Henry, '89, hrdeluca@aol.com
DeLuca, Lorayn, '94, hrmsyndhe@aol.com
Del Vicario, Robert E., '91, bawbsvet@aol.com
Demers, Martha, '91, mpdemers@reg9.med.navy.mil
Dempsey, John S., '72, profjacks1@aol.com
De Niet, Bonnie, '82, bonnie.msgarrell@wcb.state.ny.us
Denis, Mrs. Karla J., '87, kdbd2@aol.com
Dennett, Phyllis D., '83, internetpdennett@courts.state.ny.us
Denslow, Lisa D., '96, bmczick@hotmail.com
Derenowski, John C., '67, barbderenowski@hotmail.com
Derienzo, Thomas, '92, tderien@netrom.com
Derolus, Jean P., '97, jder454916@aol.com
Dettmann, Edmund P., '81, dettmanne@wwdb.org
Devine, Patrick, '96, ped72@yahoo.com
Devins, Brian M., '95, bshark17@aol.com
De Vivo, Francis (Frank) W., '80, FD111@AOL.COM
Dewberry, Valerie M., '89, queenzuelaaol.com
Deyo, LT David, '98, gddndd@webtv.net
Dezil, Patrick, '96, pdezil@dpw.com
Diakos, Georgia, '97, dkatzos@ix.netcom.com
Diaz, Andres F., '95, crookways@aol.com
Diaz, LT Arthur, JD, '91, best.attorney@mindspring.com
Diaz, Janice, '95, janice_10468@yahoo.com
Diaz, Nestor H., '86, oro612@gateway.net
Diaz, Virgil J., '97, vjdiaz@aol.com
DiBrizzi, Michael A., Esq., '88, michael752@aol.com
Dicks, Daniel M., '93, fendi954@aol.com
Dielensnyder, George, '75, gdielen@banet.net
Di Maggio, Barbara A., '81, basketlov6@aol.com
Dimmock, James A., '93, james_maddock@edalliance.org
Di Pane, Jodi E., '98, aajodi@hotmail.com
Dirkin, Walter J., Esq., '95, walterdirkin@yahoo.com
Diver, Hugh J., '74, hq245@aol.com
Dobro, Stuart, '93, stugotz@worldnet.att.net
Dodson, Kenneth L., '98, lionkng63@aol.com
Dogan, Walter R., '80, jarrett2796@aol.com
Dolan, Edward G., '75, edolan2406@aol.com
Doldron-Cancel, Sherena N., '96, ebonycoqui@aol.com
Dolphy, Keri-Ann, '99, hazel010@hotmail.com
Dombrosky, Mark D., '99, markdomb@hotmail.com
Domingo, Joel J., '77, joel127@aol.com
Dominguez, Denise, '96, ddenise@pegasus.rutgers.edu
Dominguez, Thomas, '95, sprongboy53@cs.com
Donato, Donna A., '81, addonato@tiaa-cref.org
Donato, Roberto, '97, rbd80@aol.com
Dongo-Williams, Mrs. Marsha M., '91, dougjr@webtv.net
Donnelly, Stephen J., '69, sjdon233@cs.com
Donnelly-Brinkley, Virginia, '94, vadonnie@cs.com
Donnery, Mary C., '93, mdonnery@wls.lib.ny.us
Donovan, Edwin J., '72, ejd3@psu.edu
Donovan, Gerald J., '72, protectors3@aol.com
Dorvil, Rommelle T., '95, rommelle04@cs.com
Doss, C. Brian, '99, bdoss@mail.state.tn.us
Douglas, Darien, '97, ddouglas@leakeandwatts.org
Douglas, Marsha B., '98, marsha27@netzero.net
Douglas-Robinson, Laura V., '88, sergantbuster@aol.com
Dour, Daniel F., '79, darecopl@juno.com
Doute, Jemal L., '98, doute@compuserve.com
Dove, Darlene C., '89, ddove@courts.state.ny.us
Dowd, Peter J., '96, pd71@accesshub.net
Dowling, Jack F., '77, dowlingj@philau.edu
Downey, William A., 2000, willd44@aol.com
Draghi, Paul, '71, pdraghi@aol.com
Drakes, Ingrid L., '85, mrscarib@aol.com
Drayton, Kenneth R., '76, draytoke@sfitva.cc.fitsuny.edu
Drucker, Eric G., '90, cdrucker@jjay.cuny.edu
Drucker, Leslie, '86, lmdrucker@aol.com
Drummond, Junior A., '99, nokijun@aol.com
Duesterdick, Kurt A., '82, rdwykurt@aol.com
Duffy, Charles P., '95, cduffy@nypd.org
Duffy, Craig T., '94, craigduffy@nac.net
DuFresne, Raymond K., '79, ray41950@aol.com
DuFresne, Roserita, '92, wyomama@aol.com
Duke, Daniel L., '79, dan.duke@gsa.gov

Duncan, Jesse J., '99, psuedos@aol.com
Dunican, Thomas A., '74, tomd46@aol.com
Dunne, Jay C., '75, sgadilla@aol.com
Dupoux, Mrs. Marie-Maud, '94, ricawemungu@aol.com
Duque, Ruben D., '97, elduque083@hotmail.com
Duran, Heidi L., '97, rosabr34@aol.com
Duran, Jimmy, '98, jimmyduran@jimmysmail.com
Durante, Eugene G., '95, oogles72@aol.com
Dutes, Ronald, '93, rdutes@aol.com
Dybski, Thomas, '99, dybi@aol.com
Dyer, Mark, '93, justcauze@yahoo.com
Dziekonski, Barbara, '92, proxxie@aol.com
Dzieniszewska, Ewa, '95, ewa.dzieniszewska@ssmb.com

E

Eanes, Ms. Barbara A., '75, eanes123@worldnet.att.net
Eastman, Kenneth N., '87, kne123@hotmail.com
Echevarria, Daliza E., '85, decheva@cmcny.com
Edison, Mel, '79, medison@jjay.cuny.edu
Edokpolo, James O., '93, jedokpolo@aol.com
Egan, Abbe I., '99, aegan@law.villanova.edu
Egan, Patrick J., '76, pegan49194@aol.com
Egger, Stephen L., '81, segger@banet.net
Eisenberg, Mark C., '75, mce2@juno.com
El-Amin, Ms. Zamirah K., '96, mahasin@ix.netcom.com
Elfeld, Elizabeth, '83, liz@beachoffice.com
Ellsworth, Thomas, '76, tellswor@ilstu.edu
Emanuel, Michael L., '84, longsnap.74@hotmail.com
Embry, Alicia J., '96, awalton364@aol.com
Emerson, James C., '90, james_emerson@global crossing.com
Eng, Shawn, '99, sengssk@hotmail.com
Erickson, Scott W., '98, jjcscott@aol.com
Eschenberg, Conrad J., IV, '76, comicart@pcrealm.net
Escobar, Nelson L., '97, iliegal2u@aol.com
Espina, Elizabeth, Esq., '93, espina231@aol.com
Espinal, Sandra M., '99, espinals@coudert.com
Esposito, Michael V., '99, mveny@aol.com
Esposito, Ralph A., '85, respo@pipeline.com
Evans, April R., '79, aevans@scoc.state.ny.us
Evans, Michael, '97, www.mikedaddy.com

F

Fabian, Raymond, '95, fab4242@aol.com
Facchini, Paschal, '96, pat1951@excite.com
Fallon, Ms. Bessie A., '95, bafallon@uspis.gov
Faraone, Ms. Teri, '95, faraone6@ibm.net
Farkas, Howard G., '76, zachfwa@aol.com
Faro, James J., '74, k2pkr@optonline.net
Farrell, Mel G., '98, mel10128@aol.com
Farrugia, Matthew P., '96, farrugian@aol.com
Fasano, Richard A., '99, raf1223@aol.com
Fauci, Richard A., '71, richmc4c@aol.com
Fayad, Abdul, '99, sinistersire@aol.com
Fearon, William G., '92, mav924@aol.com
Federici-LaFargue, Ms. Marietta, '95, mlafargue@law.columbia.edu
Fee, Christopher J., '95, cfee@stny.rr.com
Fegan, Ewart, '86, broadwayeddie@yahoo.com
Fegley, Venessa M., '99, vfegley@aol.com
Feigenbaum, Daniel, '92, thunderdan01@aol.com
Feldstein, Kenneth I., '79, kif2000@aol.com
Feliciano, Elizabeth, '98, efelicia@hmsy.com
Feliciano, Gloria, '94, babypaz27@aol.com
Fennessy, Adriana, '93, adriana.mairanda@novartis.farmer.com
Ferber, Eric M., '93, easye2703@aol.com
Ferguson, Andre, '98, prophets17@hotmail.com
Fernandez, John A., '98, ferja@worldnet.att.net
Fernandez, Odalys, '87, storm1500@aol.com
Fernandez, Theodore (Ted), '93, ted_fernandez@hotmail.com
Fernandez, Yvette, '99, djpride@aol.com
Ferrante, Victor, '95, termitevic@aol.com
Ferrara-Machado, Vivian M., '88, jvee1@eclipsetell.net
Ferreyra, Orlando F., Jr., '81, ltfrank4@aol.com
Fetonti, Paul J., '76, teemch5@compuserve.com
Fields, Bernadette (Michelle), '93, cutey_99_2000@yahoo.com
Fields, Dana, '98, danfiel@aol.com
Figueroa, Paola A., '97, figgy1122@aol.com
Filipiak, Paul J., '83, paul@visitli.com
Filipowicz, Renata, '99, rfilip9556@aol.com
Filippini, Mrs. Nancy F., '83, nanc761@aol.com
Filipponi, Dominick, '77, dfilipp1@tampabay.rr.com
Fillyaw, Leonard D., '73, lflenny@aol.com
Finamore, James J., '96, RDO98@AOL.COM
Finlayson, Thomas C., Jr., '95, tee721@aol.com
Finnerty, Thomas W., '75, redgate@msn.com
Fiore, Albert J., '95, bigal1575@aol.com
Fiore, Nicholas S., '75, nfior@aol.com

Fisher, Emily P., '98, esphil@aol.com
Fishman, Howard (Howie) L., '78, kkfish@earthlink.net
Fitzgerald, James J., '93, james.j.fitzgerald@faa.gov
Flaherty, John P., '95, jflaherty@gc.cuny.edu
Flanagan, Colleen M., '99, colleen@dsslaw.com
Fleetwood, Yancy, '94, yfleetwood@phillipsnizer.com
Fleming, John F., '97, frmcknz@msn.com
Fleming, Laqueth, '76, lqfleming@aol.com
Fleming, Patrice A., '83, patrice_fleming@ed.gov
Fleskes, Jenna M., '99, jfleskes@juno.com
Fleury, Renime, '96, renime@hotmail.com
Flores, Anibal, '98, afq2346@aol.com
Flores, Franklin, '99, fflores104@aol.com
Flyaks, Renata, '96, RFLYAKS@IMPATH.COM
Flynn, Raymond J., '80, r2201@lvmpd.com
Flynn, William J., '94, flynnw@aol.com
Fodera, Robert F., '92, rfodera@aol.com
Foglia, Mrs. Sophia, '75, sophiaqso@aol.com
Foley, Michael O., PhD, '75, foleym@wcsu.edu
Foley, Ms. Susan, '83, olbklynbal@aol.com
Foley, Thomas B., ACP, '72, erols@budy.com
Fonseca, Ms. Lisa A., '91, chical@bellatlantic.net
Fontana, Mrs. Laura M., '98, lfontana@fala.com
Forbell, Michael P., '67, mnmteeup@aol.com
Forlong, Pedro A., '99, war19k10@aol.com
Forsthoff, SGT Roger A., '87, frostyhc@aol.com
Forsythe, Farris B., '79, fforsyth@jjay.cuny.edu
Fortino, Denise M., '94, dfortinoma@aol.com
Fortune, Patricia, '84, patriciafortune@aol.com
Foss, John R., '79, ncscpi@aol.com
Fountoulakis, Georgios, '99, fizzo2000@aol.com
Fox, Jason, '97, jayfox21@aol.com
Fox, Lawrence J., '77, ljfoxfamily@worldnet.att.net
Foy, Lawrence B., '85, rok257@aol.com
Francillon, Joanne, '95, jfrancillon@mindspring.com
Francis, Joel M., '98, nyrebel@aol.com
Francois, Mrs. Christine, '92, ncfrancois@aol.com
Francois, Marlene, '90, marle999@aol.com
Frates, Michaelynn J., '99, mfrates@hotmail.com
Frazier, Marguerite, '92, mafraz30@iwon.com
Freckleton, Lloyd J., '91, mptopdog@aol.com
Fredericks, Andrew A., '95, aafredinc@aol.com
Freeman, James H., '95, jafree830@aol.com
Freilich, Mark J., '99, mezic@aol.com
Frias, Maria C., '99, frias160@aol.com
Frick, Henry F., '98, tannersville@hotmail.com
Fries, Timothy, '95, tfriessr@visto.com
Frost, David, '79, difrosted@aol.com
Fuko, Curtis, '97, sbuck74@aol.com
Fumai, John H., '76, pepaw36@aol.com
Fung, Janet K., '97, violin176@aol.com
Furey, John, '86, chiromule@aol.com
Furtick, Anna E., '92, car5683@earthlink.net
Fussalva, Arleene J., '96, ajfcsw@aol.com

G

Gaaskin, Ms. Michelle D., '98, mdgaskin@aol.com
Gabora, Herman R., '73, arobag01@aol.com
Gaby, Thomas R., '80, goodgrab@aol.com
Gadlin, Igor E., '97, uilaw@netzero.net
Gagliano, Allene, '92, ag6d@virginia.edu
Gaillard, Andrea J., '98, ajatal@looksmart.com
Gala, Michael F., '94, superbuff1@aol.com
Galea, John A., '76, johngalea@oasas.state.ny.us
Galeano, Sonia L., '97, sonia_galeano@nyed.uscourts.gov
Galiano, Richard H., '72, duck83@aol.com
Galicia, Margo V., '99, mgalicia@prodigy.net
Gallardo, Diana, '98, zephyr011675@aol.com
Gallo-silver, Joan M., '75, jogallo@cwt.com
Gallo-Silver, Les I., '75, jillino@aol.com
Galloway, Rulisa, '97, rgallowa@jjay.cuny.edu
Gambichler, Edward F., '95, efg72@aol.com
Garay, Tracy L., '96, tlgaray96@aol.com
Garcia, Jo-Alejandra, '96, jgarcia@jjay.cuny.edu
Garcia, Martha M., '96, garschup@msn.com
Garcia, Michelle C., '98, michelle.garcia@bowne.com
Garnett, Joan M., '98, jgarnett@supportkids.com
Garrido, Richard R., '98, jrgar711@aol.com
Garry, Thomas N., '95, tomikat22@aol.com
Garvey, James T., Jr., '74, curnyna@aol.com
Garvey, Michael J., Sr., '95, trekII@aol.com
Garvey Williams, Wendy, '98, wendyws500@cs.com
Gary, Ms. Blanca I., '84, ngbig@aol.com
Gaston, Arnett W., '71, awgaston@ix.netcom.com
Gaston, Kanal V., '98, kvgaston@aol.com
Gaudiosi, Nicholas C., '98, nick7@optonline.net

Hernandez, Jose A., '97, hernaj83@yahoo.com
Hernandez, Michael, '98, mikeh4@frontiernet.net
Hernandez, Michelle, '97, mpadilla@stroock.com
Herrmann, Christophe, 2000, cherrmann@att.net
Herron, Francis R., '72, fherron2@juno.com
Hershman, Michael, '72, mhershman@dsfx.com
Herve, Francois, '98, herve71@hotmail.com
Hewitt, Althea E., '92, hewitt@com.com
Hickey, Thomas F., '99, thomasfhickey@aol.com
Hicks, Keith E., '92, clefb@aol.com
Higgins, Adrienne C., '98, aragwan@aol.com
Higgins, Malachy T., '70, higgins334@aol.com
Higgins, Michael S., '98, mrhig@aol.com
Higgins, Mrs. Sandra E., '82, shiggins.nyctc@cuny.edu
Hightower, Sadiquah, '96, dak2010@hotmail.com
Hilaire-Fisher, Marie C., '96, marie_fisher@goodshepherds.org
Hill, Donna, '95, mydonnna@aol.com
Hillsman, Yequarah, '96, quarah@aol.com
Hirsch, Karl W., '80, carlh@ci.ftlaud.fl.us
Hobson, Anthony E., '98, ahobson@cbs.com
Hoch, Joseph B., '95, jorob26@aol.com
Hodgson, Tania, '96, chodg82974@aol.com
Hoffman, Joseph C., '76, jchoffmansr@aol.com
Hoffmann, LT Russlan D., '91, rhoffman@ramapo.edu
Hogan, Paul T., '98, tessmaster@aol.com
Hogan, Robert A., '71, hogansec@aol.com
Holden, McThaddeus, '76, mac.holden@bcc.cuny.edu
Holder, Gloria I., '74, doeji41@aol.com
Holian, Kevin M., '80, kevin.m.holian@irs.gov
Holmes, Sabrina, '81, holmess@sullcorm.com
Holst, Irma R., '78, irmaholst@aol.com
Holsten, Gary W., Jr., '99, garywes8@aol.com
Holub, Peter W., '78, pholub@earthlink.net
Hoover, Herbert B., '69, hhoover983@aol.com
Hopkins, Adria D., '99, adee7@juno.com
Horne, Peter, '87, hornep@mccc.edu
Hou, Julie, '96, julie_hou@hotmail.com
Houle, Ms. Genevieve L., '99, houlegenevieve@hotmail.com
Howard, Bernard E., '96, bhoward@nyh.org
Howard, Keith S., '89, keith7132@msn.com
Howard, Theodora E., '85, theodorahoward@hotmail.com
Howell, Paula M., '98, phowell@law.harvard.edu
Hrebenko, Aneta, '97, ahrebenko@doleta.gov
Huang, Chen Tao, '97, chentaohuang@aol.com
Huey, Ivy S., '99, stista1@aol.com
Hugee, Angela L., '89, canjazjon@aol.com
Hughes, Brian J., '79, brhughes@suffolk.lib.ny.us
Hughes, Christina E., '97, cadc@ix.netcom.com
Hughes, Maria, '79, mhughe@suffolk.lib.ny.us
Hung, Fu-chin, '84, henrysh@msio.hinet.net
Hunt, Marvin S., '75, hunt_marvin@hotmail.com
Hunter, Gloria E., '92, ghu5227240@aol.com
Hurley, Michael J., '93, hurl230@aol.com
Hyacinth, Mario K., '98, m_hyacinth@stblaw.com
Hyde, Phillip E., '76, philhyde99@cs.com
Hyland Reda, Mrs. Velvet A., '97, vhyland@fffc.com
Hyppolite, Ms. Anne W., '98, ahyppolite@nypl.org

I

Iannotta, Richard A., '75, riorimm@aol.com
Ibrahim, Shorab, '99, shorabi@hotmail.com
Idiart, George J., '85, gmidiart@ix.netcom.com
Ihne, Christine M., '98, ihne@frontiernet.net
Impavido, Catherine L., '97, cat9110@aol.com
Ingman, Matthew A., '95, mingman@usa.net
Ingram, Carlean N., '94, cningram@concentric.net
Irizarry, Christopher F., '98, calbo1@aol.com
Irizarry, Gisela, '97, gisela1pr@aol.com
Isaac, Dana R., '99, rndi726@aol.com
Isaacs, Paul K., '90, microappld@aol.com
Isaacson, Eric M., '98, happy715@msn.com
Isom, Michael, '96, misom90@hotmail.com
Isroe, Karyn E., '95, isroek@brooklynda.org

J

Jablonska, Beata, '95, beacinska@aol.com
Jabouin, Alain S., '95, aj34@email.msn.com
Jack, Bryan A., '95, bjack@brooklyn.cuny.edu
Jackson, Adriane R., '98, pisces523@earthlink.net
Jackson, Christina, '97, ljack83622@aol.com
Jackson, Derek A., '81, djackson@nynjhidta.org
Jackson, Dunstan O., 2000, dunstanj@yahoo.com
Jackson, Judy, '98, jujumajik@yahoo.com
Jackson, Katherine L., '87, kittkatt1899@aol.com
Jackson, La-toya, '95, jusone2001@yahoo.com
Jacobs, Jerry L., '91, boleg21@aol.com

Jaen, Dimas A., '99, djaen97963@aol.com
Jagdharry, Mayleen G., '99, mmusicmay@aol.com
Jaliyl, Mrs. Laila A., '80, lailaamatullah@aol.com
James, Ainsworth, '90, ainsjames@yahoo.com
James, Dina M., '94, djames@manheimer.com
James, Spencer L., '81, sjames@bankofny.com
James, Wanda A., '91, DONDO@EROLS.COM
Jarjokian, Kegham A., '99, lawcrj99@aol.com
Jason, Tracey, '98, fugees007@aol.com
Jaworsky, Alice, '95, powwowali@aol.com
Jefferson, Stephen M., '83, hwyblu315@aol.com
Jemmott, Norman A., '93, blakryme@aol.com
Jenkins, Douglas A., '97, lexetc426@juno.com
Jenkins, Gary P., '99, jenks1032@aol.com
Jenkins, Ms. Sabrina M., '97, jinksgogeta@aol.com
Jennings, Charles R., '89, nofires@ix.netcom.com
Jeselnik, Joseph J., '75, joeyj51@aol.com
Jimenez, Agueda M., '98, AJR612@AOL.COM
Jimenez, Daniel, '99, danny10462@yahoo.com
Johnson, Ava Y., '93, avehoney@hotmail.com
Johnson, Charlene A., '99, cheln@ny.freei.net
Johnson, Danielle C., '95, kawsul@msn.com
Johnson, Dolores L., '95, shark94@netzero.net
Johnson, Granville, '85, originalgque@hotmail.com
Johnson, John B., '96, umojaj@aol.com
Johnson, Kimberly A., '98, miss1775@aol.com
Johnson, Kristel A., '92, kalcine@hotmail.com
Johnson, Ms. Monique F., '98, KNABBI1974@AOL.COM
Johnson, Ms. Nykelle S., '94, nyk145@webtv.com
Johnson, Robert J., '98, bob3451@aol.com
Johnson, Wendy A., '98, wendoe@netscape.com
Johnson, Zanetta C., '97, zeecj@msn.com
Jones, Brenda L., '98, brenda89aka@aol.com
Jones, David A., '92, 110256.2163@compuserve.com
Jones, Debra D., '99, pallucci@aol.com
Jones, Eneka U., '99, nekesj@aol.com
Jones, Gregory, '81, ispy4jones@msn.com
Jones, Paula, '96, pj4n@virginia.edu
Jones, Mrs. Rita G., '85, jkree@aol.com
Jones, Robert H., Sr., '78, brhjones@yahoo.com
Jones, Robin M., '92, rmjones33@hotmail.com
Jones, Seymour A., '76, sjones@fletc.treas.gov
Jones, Shirley D., '84, sdjon45@aol.com
Jones, Tracey L., '91, tlj29@aol.com
Jones-Thorpe, Jennifer J., '95, judmel@aol.com
Jordan, Nazly, '98, sticky29@juno.com
Jordan, Robbin M., '91, rjordan@nfam.com
Jordan, Shamieka S., '99, ssjordan@lycosmasmail.com
Joseph, Eddison M., '99, ark255@aol.com
Joseph, Ingrid, '78, joseing@aol.com
Joseph, Patrick F., '99, patjos1@msn.com
Joseph, Ms. Rhonda F., '95, rfj@netnoir.net
Jourdan, Marine, '97, thepeoplesparalegal@hotmail.com
Joyce, Jennifer, '96, jenjyc@aol.com
Joye, Natarsia L., '95, njoye92857@aol.com
Jubak, Ms. Jennifer L., '98, gennie@yahoo.com
Jules, Wisner, '92, alies92168@aol.com
Juris, John R., '73, ny420@bestweb.net

K

Kabakoff, Robert I., '99, kabakoff@hotmail.com
Kadir, Maqsood U., PhD, '88, mkadir@optonline.net
Kaj, Karen T., '93, kkaj@rnb.com
Kalletta, Edward D., Jr., '98, battchies3@aol.com
Kamara, Samuel M., '91, skamaralaw@hotmail.com
Kamona, Ruth N., '97, rkamona@hotmail.com
Kanterman, Ronald E., '80, ronald_kanterman@merck.com
Kapinos, Thomas S., '71, cjmi@erols.com
Kaplan, Robert, '80, hrkaplan@aol.com
Karam, Anthony A., '86, TONYKARAM1@PRODIGY.NET
Kashimer, Irene, '81, cookie22@prodigy.net
Kaslofsky, Thor, '97, thorworld@aol.com
Kateridge, Janine M., '95, kt938@aol.com
Katz, Lawrence, '80, lkatz@uspis.gov
Katz, Marvin A., '74, mkatbii@yahoo.com
Katzeff, Martha, '98, mkatzeff@winston.com
Kaufman, Brian R., '99, brkauf2@aol.com
Kaufman, Mitchell J., '75, mjk0036@aol.com
Kayser, Steven B., '98, elvisthedog75@aol.com
Kazymirczuk, Tina G., '99, tkazymirczuk@willkie.com
Keane, Patrick J., '95, pkeane2980@aol.com
Keating, Robert P., '93, rob023k@aol.com
Keehlisen, Lynda M., '99, lscooby@optonline.net
Keith, Ms. Stacy A., '98, sconaway@mdot.state.md.us
Kelly, James F., '99, pappyjfk@cs.com
Kelly, John E., '74, jkellyisc@earthlink.net

Kelly, Karen M., '81, crownalt@aol.com
Kelly, Margo F., '75, margo.kelly@marchfirst.com
Kelly, Stephen P., '72, spk@iquest.net
Kelly, William M., '75, kellyw@dcj.lps.state.nj.us
Kelly, Yvonne, '99, ykellyma@yahoo.com
Kennedy, Karen M., '90, karekennedy@aol.com
Kennedy, Lillian, '92, lkenn855351@aol.com
Kennon, Shawn, '99, skennon@bloomberg.net
Kenny, John D., '98, jkenny@gis.net
Kenny, Robert E., CCA, '82, bken@pacbell.net
Kessinger, Ann L., '77, annielk52@aol.com
Kessler, Dennis, '70, kitch48@aol.com
Kessopa-Cabrera, Pojana, '98, cabrerapj@aol.com
Keymer, Mary M., '93, keymer@erols.com
Khan, Angelina, '98, ak@aol.com
Khan, Neil M., '97, nkhan.s@nyls.edu
Khan, Rakeela B., '99, jamnavned@aol.com
Khashiun, Karamah M., '78, kmkhas@aol.com
Khilkevich, Denis A., '99, dennnis@accesshub.net
Khiterer, Inna, '99, serega@aol.com
Khurana, Rajiv R., '98, RAJIV2@JUNO.COM
Khwaja, Tariq M., '96, tkhwaja@kayescholer.com
Kiapokas, Theodora, '91, dorainpa@hotmail.com
King, Eric D., '89, blkbro123@aol.com
King, Jemma F., '93, jemma@home.com
King, Joseph F., PhD, '75, jfking1@aol.com
King, Raymond F., '79, rfgk46@hotmail.com
King, Stephen J., III, '79, tikitai@aol.com
King, Vera L., '77, vlking02@bellsouth.net
King-Anobile, Barbara, '84, bking@gordonsiegel.com
Kinscherf, Cindy L., '99, kinsch@msn.com
Kinyatti, Mrs. Njoki W., '77, kinyatti@york.cuny.edu
Kittrell-Coley, Frances E., '98, coleyqueen@aol.com
Klein, Fredric C., '76, bandit7558@aol.com
Klein, Robert E., '89, rklein@njcu.edu
Klimoski, Frank, '92, MRFK73@AOL.COM
Klotko, Steven G., '92, mockachild@aol.com
Knezevic-Xanthos, Mrs. Antoaneta, '98, SANYA523@AOL.COM
Knight, Lamona O., '95, whimhill@hotmail.com
Knight, Petrice A., '99, pet32@juno.com
Knights, Robert A., '89, irondukeny@aol.com
Knoblich, James P., '88, knobby20001@excite.com
Knorr, Jill L., '98, libertyb@gateway.net
Ko, Mrs. Eliza, '89, eliza_lo@huda.gov
Koehler, Karl F., '72, rmk1@always-online.com
Koehler, Richard J., JD, '73, rkoehler@koehler_isaacs.com
Kokubun, Shoko, '99, skokubun@forensicpanel.com
Kolenovic, Medzit, '99, nysfnest@aol.com
Kolman, David O., '76, kinckole@worldnet.att.net
Kolodny, Nathan, '69, NATHANKOLODNY@ABC.COM
Kong, Corwin, '95, c_kong@juno.com
Kopstein, Jay I., '82, kopstein@computer.net
Korol, Natalya, '98, nycoder@aol.com
Koshak, William, '83, mrbill@frontiernet.net
Kosinski, Monica D., '97, mdkosinski@yahoo.com
Kosowski, Mrs. Frances E., '80, franppc@aol.com
Koumba, Patricia S., '99, patstel@collegeclub.com
Kourakos, Joseph C., '99, JCK2276@AOL.COM
Kouzel, Margarita, '95, margaritak@hotmail.com
Kouzoujian, Gary B., '85, garyk616@aol.com
Kraus, David T., '98, dtk16@hotmail.com
Krueger, Robert W., '93, licyclists@aol.com
Kuceluk, Joseph R., '78, momo60@aol.com
Kulesa, LT Edward J., '80, hoosyerdaddy@att.net
Kumagai, Koshin, '98, kkoshin@worldnet.att.net
Kunitzky, Michael, '98, mkunitzky@hotmail.com
Kupper, Donald F., '76, dfk305@aol.com
Kurau, William R., Jr., '74, 1ampeter@epix.net
Kurtz, Michael J., '76, miketjkurtz@yahoo.com
Kurzweil, Andrew, '99, ackurz@bigfoot.com
Kushner, Abraham, '73, kamvi2@webtv.net

L

Labus, Heather A., '99, odysseyhl@aol.com
Lagano, Christopher, '89, chrislagano@snet.net
Laird, Donald (Don) A., CFE, '74, lairddon@aol.com
Lake, Ms. Deborah (Debbie) R., '91, DRLAKE66@AOL.COM
Lam, Kwai, '98, lam7@hotmail.com
La Madrid, Ms. Yvette, '97, yvettelamadrid@aol.com
Lamb, James P., '98, jlamb@staff.mail.com
Lamb, Jerry D., '91, vmillennia@aol.com
Lambert, Edwin F., '72, efl1800@aol.com
Lamberti, Anthony J., '78, alambertiesq31@aol.com
Lambrianidou, Kyriaki, '99, kouwlalla@worldnet.att.net
Lamont, Naeemah, '92, naeemahl@aol.com
La Mont, Olivia E., '77, olive.lamont@fhwa.dot.gov

La Morte, David, '98, bestnut@aol.com
LaMothe, Michael F., '82, laMotheM@aol.com
Lamour, Barbara M., '97, manoussos@pilaw.org
Lampf, Jesse D., '99, jlampf@aol.com
Lande, John, '71, jlande@dmcom.net
Landivar, Mrs. Sandra J., '98, delicious@handtech.com
Lane, Henry L., '76, henrymmmlane@tahoe.com
Lang, Wayne L., '98, wllstar@aol.com
Langarica, Ernesto, '98, boogernica@aol.com
Langellotti, Phillip, '71, pappil@hotmail.com
Langston, Sandra D., '93, S.D.LANGSTON@ONEBOX.COM
Laperuta, Domenick A., '74, laperuta@alpha.lehman.cuny.edu
Laperuta, Domenick A., '95, starquest98@netscape.com
La Pietra, Louis C., '91, lapietra@law.com
Lara, Manuel E., '94, mlara!@coolemail.com
Larkin-Bowman, Cheryl A., '82, sailorbk@aol.com
Larsen, Jeremy, '99, jcwl40@hotmail.com
Lashley, Michelle L., '87, jharod1216@aol.com
Lassen, Joseph, '93, MAKAHAII@AOL.COM
Lassiter, Yvonne, '95, lord12qv@aol.com
Laster, Keena M., '98, marie072@aol.com
La Veglia, Anthony J., '75, ajl@cablevision.com
Laville-Wilson, Debra, '94, laville@gte.net
Lavin, Christopher, '89, CLAVIN3366@AOL.COM
Lavington, Chelsea R., '99, c.lavington@mailcity.com
Lawrence, Talaia, '99, tlawr25338@aol.com
Lawson, Blair, '95, bfree2me@aol.com
Leah, Magnuson, '93, leahmagnuson@aol.com
Lebowitz, Raymond, '79, rl171@aol.com
Ledesma, Andres, aledesma25@hotmail.com
Lee, Barbara S., '99, bsl@proedge-group.com
Lee, Chon J., '98, junel0826@hotmail.com
Lee, Jin, '96, jlee@bsa-gnyc.org
Lee, Judy, '99, judy0123ny@yahoo.com
Lee, Kin, '84, ster108@hotmail.com
Lee, Lisa, '90, llee@doilan.ci.nyc.ny.us
Lee-Wyss, Mrs. Helen, '92, helenandco@erols.com
Leggett, Kenyon E., '98, aharvey@bellatlantic.net
Leggett, Ms. Renee, '99, cheezepleez@aol.com
Leibowitz, Morton J., '72, mfl48@aol.com
Lekach, Jakub, '75, icam2@aol.com
Lema, Kathy, '99, kated63@aol.com
Lembersky, Victoria D., '99, caution286@aol.com
Lempert, Vladimir, '98, lempertv@doe.org
Lenahan, William R., '78, billenahan@aol.com
Lennek, Christopher, '92, IMPERIALPINTS@MSN.COM
Lenze, William R., '99, wrl124@aol.com
Leone, Michael J., '94, zig5288@aol.com
Leone, Michell, '97, looneymich@aol.com
Lesser, Marc H., '98, waynmess@aol.com
Lessner, Mrs. Mary V., '77, mouseveronica@netzero.net
Leto, Teresa A., '79, taleto@aol.com
Levant, Cassandra D., '91, clevant@xena.jay.cuny.edu
Levin, David J., '78, gumshoe@pipeline.com
Levine, Fran N., '77, fran.levine@wcom.com
Levitz, Jennifer, '96, jlevitz_coa@yahoo.com
Levy, Baron O., '86, baronlevy@aol.com
Lew, Steven, '90, steve5728@hotmail.com
Lewin, Ms. Ouida O., '97, 00LEWINS1@AOL.COM
Lewis, Ms. Annamarie, '78, anna@webjogger.net
Lewis, Ms. Deidre Y., '85, dejoi@msn.com
Lewis, Frederick H., '98, calpech@aol.com
Lewis, Geoffrey B., '96, kimik2@msn.com
Lewis, Michael G., '99, tru113@hotmail.com
Lewis, Roslyn R., '80, coco487@aol.com
Lieberstein, Steven I., '98, sliebers@worldnet.att.net
Liebowitz, David A., '94, ddallytc@aol.com
Liendo, Luis E., '82, lliendo@worldnet.att.net
Liffey, Joseph A., Jr., '98, joseph.liffey@usdoj.gov
Liggians, Rhonda L., '95, mstehilah7@aol.com
Lightfoot, Jerome, '71, lcub3@aol.com
Liguori, Michael T., '99, liguori@lawyer.com
Lindenmayer, Rose M., '95, lindaroli@aol.com
Lindner, LT Peter M., '90, us21angel@aol.com
Lindsay, Cordelia, '92, hglindsay@worldnet.att.net
Lippi, Ms. Francine J., '97, frenchi@systec.com
Litwack, Tom, tlitwach@jjay.cuny.edu
Lloyd, Mauline M., '97, alaoyd@aol.com
Lloyd-Bey, Ridwana, '91, ridwanal@yahoo.com
Lo, Chun-on, '95, lydiabern@mindspring.com
Lobl, Alin, '99, alobl@prodigy.net
Loboda, Henry J., '79, lobada75@aol.com
Lochner, Colin D., '97, colindlbehner@yahoo.com
Lock, Clifford A., '77, clock13049@cs.com
Lockhart, Colleen M., '97, ido34@aol.com
Logan- Watson, Mrs. Tracy R., '96, log2wat@aol.com

Logrande, Antonino, '90, nino165@yahoo.com
Lohnes, Robert C., '78, boblohnes@aol.com
Lombard, Gary J., '95, bardlom@aol.com
Lombardo, Frank A., '75, rems_tutuorial@yahoo.com
Long, William F., III, '93, longw@newpaltz.edu
Longobardi, Ms. Josephine A., '87, www.excelsior3.com
Looby, Lisa, '99, llooby411@aol.com
Loox, Michael J., '86, myklox@aol.com
Lopez, David R., '83, davidlopez@nysp.uscourts.gov
Lopez, Israel, '90, lopezi@tvratings.com
Lopez, Lisa J., '91, ZEPOL564@AOL.COM
Lopez, Luis A., '79, alantesecurity@prodigy.net
Lopez, Miguel, '91, tickerfied@email.msn.com
Lopez-Sirvent, Fernando, '81, fernandolsirvent@hotmail.com
Lora, Krupskaia (Sky), '98, lkrups@jjay.cuny.edu
Los, Sandra A., '95, coholic@aol.com
Louallen, Keith, '98, klouallen@aol.com
Louden, Dr. Robert J., '77, rjlouden@jjay.cuny.edu
Loughery, Michael J., '73, michael.loughery@spectaguard.com
Loureiro, John M., '98, z_e_u_s7@hotmail.com
Louttit, Robert J., '79, EL5BID@AOL.COM
Love, Jason C., '93, jlove399@aol.com
Lovell, Brian I., '89, lovellb@juno.com
Lovell, David E., '95, dlovell@mail.nysed.gov
Lovell, Frederick J., '98, gamfa@aol.com
Lowe, Jacqueline P., '97, belmontrd@aol.com
Lowe, Victoria L., '97, VICKPSY@AOL.COM
Lowy, Kenneth M., '95, sleeponjob@aol.com
Lozano, Elsa M., '98, mirella35@earthlink.net
Lubin, Theodule B., '96, theolubin@yahoo.com
Lubomski, CAPT Joseph E., '73, joel461@aol.com
Lucas, Carl, '82, esqcarl@aol.com
Luckey, Joyce C., '99, jluckeys@aol.com
Luftman, Lance J., '86, lancel47@interkan.net
Luke, Mrs. Cherylann, '92, mocha10@earthlink.net
Lukowski, Fred J., '94, lukowskif@admin.njit.edu
Luma, Yoleine, '97, lumas@netnore.net
Lundquist, Tracey A., '99, intlaromatic@aol.com
Lundy, Romero, '99, rlundyrjs@aol.com
Lunn, Kitty, '95, k1infinity@aol.com
Lynch, Christopher B., '95, cblove4u@aol.com
Lynch, Rodolfo R., '83, perci73@aol.com
Lynch, Thandi N., '99, thandil@excite.com

M

Macdonald, Mrs. Nirvana L., '96, nirvana.l.marriott@bellatlantic.net
Mack, Ms. Stephanie M., '95, stephanie.mack@chase.com
Mackesy, Richard, '84, rmackesy@sussex.cc.nj.us
Mackey, Daniel, '85, sais627@hotmail.com
Macpherson, Ian C., '98, i.macpherson@worldnet.att.net
Maddux, Davina P., '94, 4347ww@acs.dfa.state.ny.us
Maekawa, Yoshimitsu, '95, ymaekawa79@aol.com
Maffettone, Dennis, '92, dmaffett@mtahq.org
Magnus, Connie L., '84, CMAGNUS@OPTONLINE.NET
Magnuson, Ms. Leah, '92, leahmagnuson@aol.com
Mahady, Myles, '97, myler@akula.com
Mahamah, Chidinma, '86, moha0000@mindspring.com
Mahany, Annemarie, '89, mahanyannie@hotmail.com
Mahoney, Robert E., '82, rrmahoney@aol.com
Maillard, James H., '75, csmajor@aol.com
Maillard, Patricia L., '88, bang007@aol.com
Maillard, William L., '73, kylapapa@bellsouth.net
Majeski, William J., '76, majeski@worldnet.att.net
Malahy, James E., '99, malja316@yahoo.com
Malaxos, Troy-Nicholas, '99, tnmalaxos@juno.com
Maldonado, Carmelo, '99, dvdforever@aol.com
Maldonado, Edwin, '92, lv2div@aol.com
Maldonado, Evelyn J., '99, leosophia@hotmail.com
Maldonado, Ismael, '99, blaznhotpro@aol.com
Maley, James E., Jr., '89, jmaley@monroecc.edu
Malone, Daniel E., '75, dem2@nyu.edu
Malone, Victor E., Jr., '86, VEMALONEJR@AOL.COM
Maloney, Bryan M., '95, bmaloney@bnkst.edu
Malool, Paul G., '93, pgm1@home.com
Mammano, Richard A., '78, tii74@yahoo.com
Mancuso, Donna Marie B., '98, domancuso@dttus.com
Mancuso, Peter J., '76, mancuso@quiltfest.com
Mandelbaum, Marvin H., '76, pimarv@aol.com
Mandzik, Philip J., '78, nyphilm@aol.com
Manette, Sean S., '99, SSMANETTE@AOL.COM
Mangarella, Anthony, '99, axm23@yahoo.com
Manios, Louis N., '91, lmanios@mindspring.com
Manir, Zabed, '99, ztmanir@cs.com
Manis, Ms. Jeanne D., '99, RMANIS@BIGPLANET.COM
Mann, Krista J., '99, quietstorm_3_99@hotmail.com
Manners-Morales, Mrs. Julia C., '80, mannersj@aol.com

Mannino, Salvatore O., '94, smannino@welbro.com
Manzello, Joseph, '97, bigmetfn@aol.com
Marasco, Michael J., '99, micrasco@aol.com
Marcellus, Algeste, '98, amarcell@mail.nysed.com
Marchese, Maria N., '98, mnmarchese@aol.com
Marchia, Ms. Theresa, '80, rainbow15@msn.com
Mariano-Noreiga, Mrs. Theresa, '99, ladom69@aol.com
Marin, Vivian, '96, vivian_marin@yr.com
Marine, Ricardo, '98, ricardo.marine@citicorp.com
Marines, Henry, '93, MARINESH@BROOKLYNDA.ORG
Mark, Harry, '98, hmark@asia.com
Marks, John G., '74, jmarks@courts.state.ny.us
Marseille, Bogard, '98, gromosso@hotmail.com
Marshall, David, '92, marsh91469@aol.com
Marshall, Glenn T., '92, historynw@aol.com
Marshall, Mrs. Irene, '98, isanchez@dpw.com
Marshall-Myles, Coleen, '97, cmyles8858@aol.com
Martin, Robert A., '75, ramartinpi@aol.com
Martin, LCDR Vertel T., '82, vtm3@columbia.edu
Martinez, Edgar, '97, edcin912@aol.com
Martinez, Elizabeth, '98, 1580super@msn.com
Martinez, Margaret, '91, geeko1005@aol.com
Martinez, Marisol, '97, mmartinezny@aol.com
Martinez, Theresa, '92, tita11211@aol.com
Martir, Kirby, '78, YPDLAB@WESTNET.COM
Martorano, Thomas A., '78, tmartora@suffolk.lib.ny.us
Mascari, John C., '88, johnnymasc@aol.com
Massey, Ritesh, '99, seth1013@aol.com
Masterson, Charles, '95, charterny@aol.com
Mata, Angelina E., '97, pocahonta@operamill.com
Mateo, Gladys E., '97, medviewer@yahoo.com
Mathews, Frank J., '77, teacher@qigongway.com
Mathews, Onica O., '99, onicam2000@yahoo.com
Matos, Nelson-Ness, '85, matos17@freewwweb.com
Matthews, Karen A., '98, K_MATTHEWS@SMTPLINK.MSSM.EDU
Maurice, Ms. Geraldine, '87, gerry@2key.com
Maurilus, Pierre S., '96, havenajaz@aol.com
Maxim, Ilie, '93, maxima5@hotmail.com
Maximum, Andre A., '96, maxinum55@aol.com
May, Paul D., '84, pauldmay@aol.com
Mayers, John D., Jr., '99, jdmj2000@aol.com
Mayr, Louis A., '95, ltjjm@aol.com
Maysonet, Christine L., '99, clmaysonet@aol.com
Mcallister, Stephen, '94, npsflprz@aol.com
Mcbride, William A., '97, billy2339@aol.com
Mc Cabe, James J., '75, wemccabes@aol.com
Mccaffrey, Sean P., '94, sean.mccaffrey@usdaj.gov
Mccarthy, Timothy, '93, tmcny04@aol.com
McCarthy, William F., '71, wmccarthy@frontiernet.net
McCauley, Marianne D., mmccauley@gc.cuny.edu
McClain, Shawn D., '97, shawntaramcclain@aol.com
McCollin, Kathy-Ann E., '98, enchio@aol.com
Mccormack, Paul G., '97, pauleymac@aol.com
Mc Coy, Henry, '72, dlhmj@aol.com
Mc Coy, Michael G., '76, mccoy7111@aol.com
McDevitt, James P., '72, jmcdev9374@aol.com
McDonald, Clarence (Chris), '79, policeolympics@mindspring.com
Mcfarlane, C., '93, adv37539@netzero.net
McGehean, Donna G., '92, domcgehean@msn.com
Mcghee, Liza, '89, izamcghee@mciworld.com
McGlinchey, Ms. Anne T., '92, amcglinc@courts.state.ny.us
McGowan, Hugh M., '94, mcgowanmob@aol.com
McGowan, Sean M., '96, smcgowan01@sprynet.com
Mc Hugh, Edward, '76, mchugh14@aol.com
McInerney, SGT Brian G., '93, bmcin@yahoo.com
McInerney, Robert (Bob) X., CPP, '77, rxmjm@aol.com
Mc Kenna, Peter, '77, noeraider@aol.com
McKeon, James E., '76, jimmyjim643@aol.com
McLoughlin, Katharine, '86, delany@bestweb.net
Mcloughlin, Thomas, '90, tmcloughlin@magicaldesk.com
McMahon, Michael J., '96, mjm4571@aol.com
Mc Master, John A., '99, murphylaw@aol.com
McMillan, Bridgett, '93, msesquire8@aol.com
Mc Nicholas, James F., '76, jmcnicholas1@cs.com
McNickle, R. G. (Nick), '96, nmcnickle@jjay.cuny.edu
Meade, Lyndia F., '86, lyndiam@susnyc.org
Meagher, Brian C., '78, brianmeagher@travelers.com
Mealia, Robert M., '76, rmealia@iona.edu
Medic, Joseph, '96, vulturelaw@yahoo.com
Medina, Bolivar, '99, boli85@worldnet.att.net
Medina, Ms. Marianella, '91, marianellamedina@slrhc.org
Meine, Manfred E., PhD CGFM, '90, drmneine@tsufl.edu
Melendez, Eugenio, '79, emelendez@home.com
Melis, Paul, '97, krokea@aol.com
Melsky, SGT Ryan E., '99, rmelsky@temple.ocis.edu
Mena, Bayovanex, '95, bohemio111@aol.com

Menard, Earl J., Jr., '77, ejm124@aol.com
Mencia, Jose L., '96, jmencia@cccare.org
Mendez, Angel, '80, cupid13548@aol.com
Mendez, Jorge A., '87, mendezjmen@aol.com
Mendez, Maritza, '99, maritzamendez@aol.com
Mendez, Mrs. Milly, '96, rubia6969@yahoo.com
Mendez, Rafael, '94, gemini94@worldnet.att.net
Mendez, Zenaida, '89, mendez2@gateway.net
Mendoza, Esther C., '99, ec_mendoza@hotmail.com
Mendoza, Florance W., '78, florance.mendozu@cie.net
Mennella, Concetta I., '79, cimny@cunyvm.cuny.edu
Mercado, Frances, '99, ktv2000@aol.com
Mercedes, Wendy V., '98, wmercedes@aol.com
Mercilliott, Frederic P., PhD, '74, mercif@chowan.edu
Messina, Anthony L., '81, louam@aol.com
Messina, John J., '99, jmessina@oem.cn.ci.nyc.ny.us
Metivier, Beverley A., '95, beverleym@mindspring.com
Metzler, Arthur J., '81, titanicSOS@juno.com
Michaels, Anne M., '83, tomjoe@gateway.net
Michel, Pierre M., '97, neig@hotmail.com
Mickens, Renee J., '97, renee.j.mickens@marshmc.com
Middleton, Sharon D., '99, alwaysva96@aol.com
Mignano, Michael J., '94, mmignano@knight-sec.com
Miladinov, Mrs. Zora C., '96, zora@hendrickslaw.com
Milien, Patricia, '95, neilim@aol.com
Miller, Carlos M., '99, NASTYCEE@AOL.COM
Miller, Chanell N., '99, cmill2001@yahoo.com
Miller, Gail E., '89, gmiller@jjay.cuny.edu
Miller, Lee A., '96, lee_miller@pepboys.com
Miller, Melva, '96, mmiller@thefamilycenter.org
Miller, Steven G., '81, smiller@cor.state.pa.us
Mills, Charles M., '76, cmills1215@aol.com
Mimms, Yvette C., '82, ycw5et79@aol.com
Mims, Venetia L., '89, mimsy1@webtv.net
Mingo, Alfred E., '76, aemsec@aol.com
Minton, Kenneth W., '84, kminton@gte.net
Mirabal, Carolina, '99, cmirabal@bu.edu
Miralla, Ms. Janet, '96, lassoff@ibm.com
Miranda, Anthony R., '92, STMPFS@AOL.COM
Mir-Elcik, Mrs. Nancy J., '90, nanme924@cs.com
Miron, Lowell S., '97, toucans@prodigy.net
Mirza, Ashfa N., '97, aisha.a@usa.net
Mitchell, Ms. Carolyn, '85, cmitch4730@aol.com
Mitchell, Douglas J., '83, dmitch@frontiernet.net
Mitchell, Harry J., '78, hmitch@freewwweb.com
Mitchell, Tracie-Ann N., '98, tmitchell247@aol.com
Mitro, Edward J., '81, edmitro@hotmail.com
Mitsinikos, Nikos J., '99, nikomits@aol.com
Moffatt, Maikov A., '97, investigator10@hotmail.com
Mohr, Michael, '90, mdmohr@atf.treas.gov
Molignano, Nicole M., '96, molignano@juno.com
Molina, Ariadne M., '99, ariane967@aol.com
Molinaro, Louis J., '85, lmolinar@siac.com
Molinaro, Mario A., '83, mmoli66384@aol.com
Molinaro, Ms. Yvette, '87, yxm@msk.com
Montague, William R., '80, monty55@aol.com
Montali, Joseph R., '86, PDBLUE806@AOL.COM
Montalvo, Oneida, '93, onedamg@juno.com
Montenegro, Richard (Rich), Jr., '95, richmonte@netzero.net
Montgomery, Angela D., '86, jPupsly@aol.com
Montgomery, Dwayne K., '84, dkm1025@aol.com
Montrose, Sharon R., '97, srmontrose@hotmail.com
Moody, Ms. Sabrina R., '92, bebesrm@aol.com
Moon, Charles C., '91, cpmoon@erols.com
Moonan, Ravi N., '99, femperfi27@hotmail.com
Mooney, Martin C., '76, mmooney@aol.com
Moore, Patrick, '99, pjm77@juno.com
Moore, Talitha, '99, rred28@gateway.net
Moore-Baker, Simone I., '94, duvalny@juno.com
Moquete, Cesar U., '96, guiraguy@aol.com
Mora, Felix, '95, tapnrack9@aol.com
Mora, Jessica M., '97, boki@gateway.net
Morabito, Douglas P., '95, douglas/morabito@ctd.uscourts.gov
Morado, Calvin P., '92, ceepmo@gateway.net
Morales, Bethzaida, '99, bmorales@jjay.cuny.edu
Morales, Carlos E., '99, kaminal@hotmail.com
Morales, Carlos R., '93, cmorales@northbergen.kmart.com
Morales, Cesar A., '97, tonee175@aol.com
Morales, Hector, '97, hctrmis@aol.com
Morales, Indiana, '99, imorales@qgraph.com
Morales, Wilfredo E., '84, sfprparade@cs.com
Morales, Ms. Yvonne, Esq., '94, moralesy@brooklynda.org
Morales-De Leon, Sandra, '75, reslv2270@aol.com
Morasco, Benjamin J., '99, morascob@slu.edu
Moreia, Fredrick M., '98, mike716305@aol.com
Moreira, Ms. Julie A., '99, jujum8@cs.com

Moreno, Juan, Jr., '88, juacor05@aol.com
Mornel, Theodore B., '97, tmornel@aol.com
Morris, Vincent K., '91, topcat294@aol.com
Mosca, Anthony M., '79, carmendee@bestnetpc.com
Moskowitz, Ari A., '97, nighteyes@pioneeris.net
Moss, Joel W., '76, sjmoose@juno.com
Motisi, Meegan T., '98, meeganmo@aol.com
Mousadakos, Chrisoula, '96, bill18@onebox.com
Mraz, Mrs. Leanne A., '99, lmraz@corus.jnj.com
Mujica, Linda R., '99, sunyleo@aol.com
Mulligan, Thomas P., '78, moodyblu1@earthlink.net
Mullin, John H., '97, mullinfcpd@aol.com
Mumford, Ronald A., '82, ronald.mumford@djj.state.fl.us
Muniz, Mrs. Belinda, '95, oyebeli@aol.com
Muniz, Eliu, '92, nmuniz5717@aol.com
Muratore, Anthony, '67, atmsr@compuserve.com
Murphy, John J., '87, murphy1jj@aol.com
Murphy, Ms. Josephine A., '99, pomurphy@noparole.com
Murphy, Robert E., '72, murf415@aol.com
Murphy, Mrs. Rochelle M., '77, murf15@aol.com
Murray, James E., '87, jefm@msn.com
Murtagh, James J., '72, jjmurtag@redconnect.com
Myers, Carol A., '88, kobeko527@hotmail.com
Mylott, Robert H., '98, rmylott@aol.com

N

Nacinovich, Ms. Diane M., '98, dianen1@aol.com
Nadel, David W., '76, liaison@nypd.org
Nadelbach, Lisa M., '98, lmendez@liscnet.org
Nanton, Willena, '88, nyccsc@prodigy.net
Nappi, Lori A., '81, lorrian59@aol.com
Nash, Joseph F., '73, cjnash65@juno.com
Nasser, Sharifa M., '99, snasser@mail.als.edu
Neary, Donna A., '89, nearyd@aol.com
Neary, Kathleen T., '70, kneary@wwdb.org
Nedos, William T., '98, wnedos@sprynet.com
Neggia, Thomas E., '97, nege74@erols.com
Negron, Maria E., '98, negronm@wemed.com
Nekrutman, David R., '97, netrutman@aol.com
Nelson, Claudette A., '96, claudette.a.nelson@chase.com
Nelson, Debra A., '97, chocve2362@aol.com
Nemara, Vanessa A., '77, vnemara@mlca.uscg.mil
Nesmith, Daron L., '98, dnesmith1@aol.com
Nesmith, Phoebe R., '95, phoebenesmith5690ww@acs.dsa.state.ny.us
Nevarez, Ms. Melissa, '97, geminimn@aol.com
Newkirk, Tabitha, '96, trrng@aol.com
Newman, Lisa N., '85, francquie@aol.com
Newman, Paul R., '96, prnewm@home.com
Newton, Judy D., '92, daos27@msn.com
Ng, Anthony C., '84, anthony.ng@gsa.gov
Ng, Phillip, '97, VAC@AOL.COM
Ngai, Lauren M., '96, lmn8050@aol.com
Niblock, Susan B., '99, sniblock@hotmail.com
Nicholas, Florence M., '84, florence.nicholas@pha.phila.gov
Nicholas, Joanne C., '81, jcn95@aol.com
Nicholson, Walter A., '75, mcglynnnich@worldnet.att.net
Nickens-Thomas, Sheila, '85, sheila.nickens@usdoj.gov
Nicks, Alfonso M., '97, siskod59@cs.com
Nicola, Christos, '89, cnicola@juno.com
Nicola, Maria E., '96, mnicola@comlan.ci.nyc.ny.us
Nicolaou, Carmen A., '97, goods1031@aol.com
Nieves, Julie A., '97, bellnorth1@juno.com
Nieves-Cardenas, Mrs. Carmen, '92, tcncarc@tc.cc.va.us
Nikitin, Maxim, '99, maxnikitin@hotmail.com
Ninburg, Svetlana, '99, sninburg@aol.com
Ninomiya, Marilyn J., '88, maraherbal@aol.com
Nisely, Michelle S., '96, dmjpm@aol.com
Nisi, Anthony J., '97, cobra@intac.com
Nixon, Henry E., '99, biggamann@aol.com
Nkrumah, Kafahni T., '92, knnkrumah@legal-aid.org
Nobles, Sharon V., '97, SCNOBLES@HOTMAIL.COM
Nocerino, Thomas, '77, tnocer@smlny.com
Noel, Gesner, '96, gesnern@msn.com
Noel, Samuel D., '98, samuel.noel@usdoj.gov
Nolan, William F., '73, firesleuthny@msn.com
Noll, Harold W., '73, haroldn999@aol.com
Nugent, Michele D., '95, mdn073@central.dss.state.va.us
Nunez, Claribel, '99, claribelnunez@aol.com
Nunez, Janet F., '97, jfnc@aol.com
Nuzzi, Laurie A., '97, lanizzi21@aol.com

O

O'Brien, Stephen P., '91, sob711@optonline.net
Ocampo, Mrs. Melisa, '96, ocampoclan@hotmail.com
Ocasio, Jacqueline A., '96, jackieo_11237@yahoo.com
Ocasio, Yolanda M., '83, ymocasio@sjulaw.stjohns.edu

O'Connell, Sean M., '97, ragazzomal@aol.com
O'Connor Wright, Catherine, '95, catherine.o'conner@usdoj.gov
O'Dell, Jill C., '97, jcodell1@hotmail.com
O'Donnell, CAPT Steven, '99, firedude47@aol.com
O'Dowd, Michael P., '99, modowd@jjay.cuny.edu
Odowd, Michael P., '99, modowd@jjay.cuny.edu
Ojena, Stephen, '72, kinderprint@kinderprint.com
O'Kane, John J., '76, driver41@aol.com
O'Keefe, Patricia J., '92, patricia40@mindspring.com
Okin, Avery Eli, '79, aokin@bklynbar.org
Okosun, Alexander E., '99, aokosun@jj.cuny.edu
Okrah, Edward K., '93, hotpapa1@netzero.net
Oliveras, Mrs. Daisy I., '95, leowhispers@aol.com
Olsen, Dr. Francis B., '74, drfo@prodigy.net
Omotayo, Nixon O., '84, daysi57@aol.com
O'Neil, Robert F., '70, roonassociates@aol.com
Onyeobia, Kelechi, '95, konyeobia@law.pace.edu
Oquendo, Vivian L., '93, voquendo@aol.com
Orender, Patrick E., '98, patrick.jr.orender@customs.treas.gov
Orlandella, Sandra M., '95, sorlan123@aol.com
Orlick, Harvey A., '78, lorlick@ibm.net
O'Rourke, Stacey M., '98, smor958@aol.com
O'Rourke, William J., '67, wjtorourke@aol.com
Orozco, Odalis, '96, perozco@aol.com
Orriola, Victor M., '76, lahadtr@aol.com
Ortiz, Amador P., '96, PEANUT9292@WEBTV.NET
Ortiz, Anne M., '75, anneannop@aol.com
Ortiz, Janet, '96, jantiz2@aol.com
Ortiz, Maria, '98, MARUKA1@EARTHLINK.NET
Ortiz, Col Rene P., USMC, '75, MICPAUL1@AOL.COM
Ortiz, Yolanda, '99, yov419@aol.com
Orzillo, Kelly S., '99, korzillo@yahoo.com
Osamwonyi, Joseph I., '96, josamwon@waldenu.edu
Ostrander, Anthony (Tony) S., '99, tony5star@vh.net
Otto, Ms. Patricia C., '80, patriciaotto@aol.com
Owens, Veronica M., '96, veronica_owens@usa.net

P

Pace, Paul A., '84, prpace@aol.com
Packman, Miriam A., '97, macabrewmn@worldnet.att.net
Padilla, Margarita M., '96, padilla@pi.cpmc.columbia.edu
Padron, Ms. Linette, '99, lpadron@bear.com
Pagan, Michele D., '91, mpagan@palmbeachpolice.com
Pagan, Tina-marie, '92, wpaganjr@megsinet.net
Pagano, Ms. Marci, '85, mushmouse513@aol.com
Page, CW2 Wallace (Wally) B., Ret., '77, nitwite@webtv.com
Paglino, Joseph R., '97, jrpags@webspan.net
Paige, Jodi W., '98, jpaige@morganlawfirm.com
Palazzo, Thomas J., '93, tpalazzo@bear.com
Palesano, George J., '91, gp2814@aol.com
Palicia, Deborah L., '96, deborah_palicia@njpt.uscourts.gov
Palladino, Marie A., '95, mpalla1006@earthlink.net
Palmer, Lorrine R., '98, mom0024@flashnet.com
Palmeri, LT Nicholas R., '79, nickpalm@erols.com
Palumbo, Bill, '96, anthony0868@aol.com
Papson-Adams, David, '95, dpapson-adams@mcsw.com
Park, Richard A., '99, aquacop1173@yahoo.com
Parrinello, Arthur J., '76, hapool@msn.com
Parry, Lesroy T., '98, lesroynyc@cs.com
Parsons, Theodore, '73, tparsonsj@prodigy.net
Pascocello, Anthony J., Jr., '95, ltp400@aol.com
Pastrana, Angel J., '97, brolic3514@aol.com
Pasuizaca, Carmen L., '99, clps74@aol.com
Patrice, Mic-arlem, '93, rockthehill@aol.com
Patterson, Erika J., '95, akiree@aol.com
Patti, Pasquale J., '98, pasqualepj@aol.com
Pattinson, Mrs. Helen M., '74, hpattinson@yahoo.com
Patton, Ronda Y., '96, ronda22@juno.com
Paul, Nigel, '99, nplegin7@aol.com
Paulino, Reynaldo M., '95, reypaulino@cs.com
Payne, Andrea T., '97, andrea.payne@mail.house.gov
Payne, Jamil V., '98, payne3373@hotmail.com
Peaks, Harold A., '82, HPEAKS@LEGAL-AIDE.ORG
Pearson, Evelyn E., '95, evelyn_pearson@mastercard.com
Peart, Donaree Y., '97, crazysexykooldee@aol.com
Peay, Ms. Lisa D., '99, heyluvv@hotmail.com
Pecoraro, Diana, '86, diana613@mindspring.com
Pedro, Hakeem A., '95, latkesh@aol.com
Pena, Jenaro R., '95, merlin19th@aol.com
Pena, Ms. Marisel C., '96, mpena1127@aol.com
Pena, Marisol, '99, solimar27@hotmail.com
Pennes, Emilio, '86, epennes@aol.com
Peoples, Ms. Melissa, '95, mpeoples27@yahoo.com
Peoples, Yasmeen (Yaszie) A., '96, darquale@hotmail.com
Perez, Carlos M., '98, perez_gtm@fc1.nycenet.edu
Perez, Jaime A., '99, lasalle33@hotmail.com

Perez, Lizabeth (Lisa), '96, lee255@aol.com
Perez, Michelle, '89, mlperez@courts.state.ny.us
Perez Y Gonzalez, Dr. Maria E., '87, mariapg@brooklyn.cuny.edu
Perini, Bernard J., '70, winnlink@aol.com
Perkins, Nicole S., '96, nikky10139@aol.com
Perlleshi, Luigi, '95, luigji123@aol.com
Perritt, William J., '99, williamperritt@netscape.net
Perry, Ofer J., '98, jperry@unforgettable.com
Persaud, Amanda J., '99, ajpers@aol.com
Persaud, Nalini, '98, nalpersd@aol.com
Persico, Gerald C., '93, gpersico@worldnet.att.net
Pesante, Margarita, '78, mpesante98@hotmail.com
Pesce, Frank J., Jr., '71, fish6531@gte.net
Peters, Bernadette V., '98, SEXYNESS925@HOTMAIL.COM
Peters, Petra P., '99, petreppeters@aol.com
Peters, Prestina D., '93, ppeters@bn.com
Peterson, Eugene, Jr., '97, geno2000@aol.com
Peterson, Tania I., '95, mstpeterson@aol.com
Petreski, Toni, '96, petreskit@dcj.lps.state.nj.us
Petty, Camille B., '89, pettyrn@webtv.net
Pezzo, Domenic, '75, newyork27@aol.com
Philips, Wilma, '82, 300x63@acs.dfa.state.ny.us
Phillips, Ernest G., '99, gpeall@hotmail.com
Phillips, Nickie D., '98, KNICKIT@AOL.COM
Phillips, Steven S., '99, stevphil@aol.com
Phillips, Timothy F., '98, tim@phillipsenterprises.com
Phipps, Ms. April I., '81, afvdillon@aol.com
Picarillo, Anthony P., '83, pete.picarillo@bulgari.com
Pickett, John J., '98, forensic3@juno.com
Piedra, Dennis, '92, piedradennis@hotmail.com
Pierre, Bikens, '97, biky55@aol.com
Pierre, Louicasse, '99, lpierrejjstudent@aol.com
Pierre-Louis, Ms. Audrey H., '99, audreyp18@aol.com
Pignataro, John V., '89, jpignat143@aol.com
Piil, Laura, '99, lnp1237@hotmail.com
Pijaca, John A., '89, pijaca325@aol.com
Pincar, Barbara, '77, CARPIN065@AOL.COM
Pinizzotto, Anthony J., '81, ajp939@erols.com
Pinti, Rosanne A., '98, rosalipsy@aol.com
Piri, Ms. Maria A., '92, mariaabbey@aol.com
Pitrone, Alberta J., '90, sitf@aol.com
Pittman, Yolanda R., '97, yoyo@vsa.com
Plackenmeyer, William, '75, wplackenmeyer@barnard.edu
Plamenco, Roberto C., '89, RP3296@AOL.COM
Plawner, Thomas A., '98, suave@mindspring.com
Pleeter, Glenn R., '87, mrgus911@aol.com
Poggi, John J., III, '95, JOHNPOGGIII@MSN.COM
Pokorny, Mrs. Cindy L., '96, cindip@powercom.net
Poland, Jeremy M., '97, cdarrow3@aol.com
Polin, Ms. Martha V., '95, mmhobbs@msn.com
Politis, Steven, Esq., '93, spol104708@aol.com
Pollack, Andrew B., '95, apollack@havlet.org
Polyakova, Svetlana, '96, ctapyxa@aol.com
Pontecorvo, Daniel M., '83, pontecorvod@coned.com
Pontecorvo, Thomas J., '99, pontecorvothomas@hotmail.com
Poplavskiy, Aleksandr A., '98, spider332@excite.com
Porter, Samuel A., '97, jackap91@email.com
Posniack, Glenn, '95, gposniack@adt.com
Potter, Hillary A., '96, hillaryap@aol.com
Poulos, Harry, '84, hpoulos@nycboe.net
Powell, David F., '85, blkwolf226@hotmail.com
Powell, Hughlett O., '85, vencat@mindspring.com
Powell, Kerwin M., '88, swapow@yahoo.com
Powell, William M., '77, irie5517@aol.com
Powers, Derek L., '89, dbb72@aol.com
Powmesamy, Learie, '97, leariep@yahoo.com
Prager, Keith S., '72, kprager107@aol.com
Preiss, George M., '96, gmpjjc@worldnet.att.com
Prendergast, Yollette, '97, lettielove@aol.com
Pressley-Collier, Sharon F., '83, spres57577@aol.com
Prestia, Charles R., '81, charlesprestia@prodigy.net
Preston, Thomas G., '73, elkter@togetherness.net
Presume, Thierry, '97, leftee69@aol.com
Price, Fred E., '78, pricefejd@hotmail.com
Price, Laray, '95, lprice1062@aol.com
Price-Moore, Ms. Jennifer M., '86, pripro@aol.com
Pride, Kasha L., '97, kasha.pride@usdoj.gov
Prime, Maria, '78, evidence@nmail.com
Proscio, Charles J., Jr., '99, cpro2@aol.com
Psahos, Theodoros (Ted), '95, scopelos@aol.com
Pucci, Raymond, '72, rjp@voicenet.com
Puello, Miguelina, '95, domreppr@aol.com
Pugliese, Naomi B., '97, PIXIE99105@AOL.COM
Puleo, Thomas A., '93, t_puleo@aol.com
Purdy, Thomas J., '86, tjdp1814@excite.com

Q

Qadirah, Eleanor, '85,　eqadirah@tcdi.net
Quaranto, Annette L., '97,　meethos@webtv.net
Quijije, Kathy M., '99,　pollita@bellatlantic.net
Quinn, James F., '86,　quinn@hq.penfed.org
Quinn, John F., '76,　quinnnor@aol.com
Quinn, John W., Esq., '87,　jwquinn@chubb.com
Quinn, Robert J., '72,　thequinns@aol.com
Quinones, Hector M., '91,　hectorq@earthlink.net
Quintana, Lydia C., '91,　lydia.quintana@usdoj.gov
Quintero, Marisol K., '94,　colombianqueen@netzero.net
Quraishi, Zahid N., '97,　znq@pegasus.rutgers.edu

R

Rabson, Mark J., '77,　mrabson@aol.com
Racioppo, Ralph, '76,　rleonard38@aol.com
Raggi, Michael L., '79,　michaelraggi@dodig.osd.mil
Ragin, Kenya S., '96,　cookiemay90@ya.com
Ragoonanan, Ramcharan, '99,　ragoo16@aol.com
Rahn, Robert H., '81,　bobrahn@frontiernet.net
Raichle, Carl J., '76,　cjraichle@uspis.gov
Rainis, Edward A., '73,　fasteddie66@juno.com
Raldiris, Carlos J., '89,　carlos_raldiris@vpsu.com
Rall, Charles E., '76,　lawman022@aol.com
Ramirez, Alexis, '98,　alexis_ramirez@hotmail.com
Ramirez, Ms. Elizabeth, '89,　adreamsnatcher@aol.com
Ramirez, Hector V., Esq., '92,　hvram@aol.com
Ramirez, Vernon, '98,　vernon15hr@aol.com
Ramos, James J., '99,　jramosjoe@aol.com
Ramos, Laura, '97,　lramos11@hotmail.com
Ramos, Marlene (Mandy) M., '96,　mandylgl@aol.com
Ramos, Nestor, '99,　ronin7@flash.net
Ramos, Ramonita, '96,　lightupmyfire@aol.com
Ramos, Yolanda, '95,　yolanda_ramos@elnotes5.bankofny.com
Ramos-Sololongo, Denyse N., '89,　mtmt007@aol.com
Rampioray, Kamini, '99,　hercules01@email.msn.com
Rampolla, Joseph J., '94,　joepam@bellatlantic.net
Rampolla, Mrs. Pamela A., '94,　joepam@bellatlantic.net
Ramsay, Margaret, '95,　PUNANY4@JUNO.COM
Randall, Francis E., '75,　randalfr@tokiom.com
Raptis, Thomas N., '89,　tnr22@aol.com
Ratney, Alyson D., '97,　neyaabrej@juno.com
Ravelo, Ms. Mercedes, '91,　merecedes.ravelo@hofstra.edu
Ravenell, Jason, '96,　1252xx@acs.dfa.state.ny.us
Ravens, Carl, '68,　carlil@juno.com
Raver, Deidre M., '98,　dederave@aol.com
Ray, Donald L., '99,　dywray@aol.com
Ray, Vern, '93,　wwic666@aol.com
Rayfield, Peter T., '77,　prayfield2@aol.com
Raymond, Woody, '98,　wraymond@hotmail.com
Rechenberg, Jan M., '76,　goldtrains@aol.com
Reed, Jasmine M., '99,　jasminedaniel@aol.com
Reed, Shelley, Jr., '77,　sreedjr@hotmail.com
Reekie, Robert, '76,　reekiebsr@yahoo.com
Reeves, Lee, '82,　marathon@frontiernet.net
Regan, John M., '77,　johntpd84@aol.com
Regan, Patrick J.,　184578406regan@dcjs.state.ny.us
Regester, Mrs. Kimberly, '99,　kimski546@aol.com
Regis, Ms. K. F., '95,　kfreya1@aol.com
Rego, Simon A., '95,　rego@doctor.com
Reibscheid, Mark A., '99,　marcosegundo@hotmail.com
Reid, Gloria M., '80,　greid001@email.usps.gov
Reid, Julanne L., '78,　jreid@mec.cuny.edu
Reid, Shaun C., Esq., '95,　reids@gghlaw.com
Reilly, James P., '75,　reilsdat@aol.com
Reilly, Paul J., '76,　jags08@aol.com
Reilly, Thomas W., '74,　tbone1136@aol.com
Reisman, Barbara, '86,　hreis72241@aol.com
Remon, Malena C., '95,　malenaremo@aol.com
Renner, Nils, '99,　nils666@gateway.net
Rentz, Tracy D., '91,　mftd5050@aol.com
Renz, Peter H., '77,　repete700@aol.com
Reyes, Ana A., '99,　anarherrique2@yahoo.com
Reyes, Joselyne A., '99,　avocette@prodigy.net
Reyes, Olga, '95,　cookieluv00@aol.com
Reyes, Sudhey, '99,　reyes53@aol.com
Reyes, Yahayra, '99,　yreyes@windelsmarx.com
Reynolds, George F., '95,　imabroker@aol.com
Reynolds, Linda-Keisha M., '80,　maxide@aol.com
Reynolds, Patrick, '85,　preynolds@maywoodpd.org
Reynoso, Alexa J., '99,　drew0320@aol.com
Reynoso, Edgar, '92,　kretai@netzero.net
Rezoagli, Frank, '79,　tillojr@aol.com
Ribeiro, Gemma E., '99,　gembeiro@aol.com
Richards, Emanuel (Manny) H., Jr., '86,　emanrich.3@aol.com

Richardson, Thomas, '99,　lt727@aol.com
Richardson Anthony, Joanne A., Esq., '89,　janthony299@aol.com
Ridley, Sandra O., '95,　soridley@aol.com
Rios, Donald, '92,　donaldo@gateway.net
Rios, Juan R., '98,　jrios@law.harvard.edu
Ripps, Carol A., '80,　cripps@brooklyn.cuny.edu
Ritondo, Marcello, '93,　lanman111@netzero.net
Rivas, Fradis, '96,　elsheriff@freedom.usa.com
Rivera, Cesar J., '95,　ZALE69@YAHOO.COM
Rivera, Dana E., '99,　six9spdstr@aol.com
Rivera, David, '97,　dav9768@aol.com
Rivera, Eduardo, '97,　erivera@osborneny.org
Rivera, Jalika, '96,　jrivera74@aol.com
Rivera, SGT Mario L., '92,　mlrivera65@aol.com
Rivera, Pedro, Sr., '99,　mason4524@netzero.net
Rivera, Peter, '99,　pri6307860@aol.com
Rivera, Roberto, '97,　rrivy@aol.com
Rivera, Steven, '96,　srivera69@aol.com
Rivers, John J., '82,　jrivers@us.oracle.com
Rizzuto, Zoe C., '99,　zrizzuto@ccrblan.cn.ci.nyc.ny.us
Roach, Erle S., '95,　eroach2005@aol.com
Roberson, William C., '99,　interpidg@aol.com
Roberts, Sherman S., '98,　sassperilla1@aol.com
Robertson, Erin N., '99,　teezagtr@aol.com
Robin, Latasha B., '99,　lrobin@mbc-net.com
Robinson, Christopher, '81,　chrisr413@aol.com
Robinson, Cynthia (Cyndy), '95,　cyndy31@aol.com
Robinson, Dwight C., '98,　futureflex@aol.com
Robinson, Zandra, '99,　zhayabusa@aol.com
Rochford, Edward V., '72,　evrochford@prodigy.net
Rodgers, Lamont K., '98,　popdog@rocketmail.com
Rodriguez, Adrienne J., '98,　ajar26@cs.com
Rodriguez, Alba L., '97,　albalima@yahoo.com
Rodriguez, Andres E., '93,　nysinvaer@aol.com
Rodriguez, Andrew W., '99,　arodriguez@ascap.com
Rodriguez, Betty, '93,　rodrigub@brooklynda.org
Rodriguez, Claudia, '95,　scam9731@aol.com
Rodriguez, Errol O., '96,　erodpsyche@aol.com
Rodriguez, Ms. Fiordaliza A., '93,　kk5640@acs.dfa.state.ny.us
Rodriguez, Gilbert, '89,　gr14dren@aol.com
Rodriguez, Jose J., '81,　rekers289@aol.com
Rodriguez, Juan C., '95,　UC520@HOTMAIL.COM
Rodriguez, Lizette, '98,　lissy_80@hotmail.com
Rodriguez, Luis D., '99,　crash1r@aol.com
Rodriguez, Maribel, '96,　maribelrodriguez@nmic.org
Rodriguez, Ms. Migdalia A., '78,　miggier@aol.com
Rodriguez, Nicholas, '97,　nickr74@hotmail.com
Rodriguez, Sylvia, '97,　charlie05@webtv.net
Rodriguez, Ms. Veronica, '97,　veronica.rodriquez@umusic.com
Rodriguez, Yara, '98,　yara_rodriguez@timeinc.com
Rodriquez, Yolanda, '95,　cjn1011@aol.com
Rodriguez-Aviles, Wanda, '95,　wrodriguinv@aol.com
Rodriquez, William, Jr., '99,　wrodriguez@primediasi.com
Rogers, James, '93,　rogers@nypd.org
Rogers, Jennifer L., '88,　jrg818@aol.com
Rogers-Grinage, Debra, '83,　debgrinage@aol.com
Rojas, Paola R., '99,　PAOLANY1@EXCITE.COM
Roldan, Mrs. Eleanor J., '96,　mopies@aol.com
Rollock, Roderick, '89,　introdjo@hotmail.com
Roman, Ana J., '87,　AROMAN@PANYNJ.GOV
Roman, Edwin, '95,　er52@cornell.edu
Roman, Marian C., '95,　piru70@aol.com
Roman, Vivian, '98,　kk4620@dfa.state.ny.us
Romano, Mrs. Lisa M., '95,　charlesandlisa@prodigy.net
Romero, Yenia J., '98,　YENIA2@AOL.COM
Roper, Kenneth A., '87,　kar1056@cs.com
Rosado, Lt Col Samuel A., USAF(Ret.), '75,　sam_rosado@mns.com
Rosario, Luisa J., '95,　rxjohnny@aol.com
Rosario, Victor M., '98,　vic0072000@aol.com
Rosenberg, Linda S., '80,　btlinda@juno.com
Roske, Daniel, '95,　dr275@hotmail.com
Ross, James D., '71,　jross93027@aol.com
Ross, Stanley, '97,　vestout@aol.com
Ross Shapiro, Jennifer S., '89,　jshapiro@ci.chi.il.us
Rothenberg, Bruce A., '83,　bruceroth1@aol.com
Rothenberg, Daniel S., '99,　danrothen@aol.com
Rothlein, Steve, '74,　sterothle.nugs.com
Rouse, Evelyn, '99,　evelyn@cassidycat.com
Rowan, Edward T., Sr., '77,　erowan@lottery.state.ny.us
Rowe, John M., '97,　jrowe9@yahoo.com
Rozier, Christopher, '97,　cwr24@hotmail.com
Ruban, Ms. Carlyne S., '92,　carly467@hotmail.com
Ruben, Scott P., '84,　zaaphantam@cs.com
Rubenstein, Hy D., '77,　hy.rubenstein@haledoor.com
Rubero, Kenneth, '99,　ruberk@aol.com
Rudd, Alexis H., '93,　ahrjj@cunyvm.cuny.edu

Rudowitz, Bruce S., '88,   aetro@juno.com
Ruff, Michelle N., '99,   michruff77@hotmail.com
Ruggeri, Ronald X., '71,   towerafss@aol.com
Ruiz, Judy, '96,   toppdiva@aol.com
Ruiz-Basquez, Luisa E., '87,   ruiz_luisa@hotmail.com
Ruiz-Velez, Mrs. Nydia, '95,   coqui8673@aol.com
Russell, Brenda M., '99,   bmrussel@dpw.com
Russell, Marsha Natasha, '95,   mnrussell@worldnet.att.net
Russo, John, '81,   jrusso@keyspanenergy.com
Ryniak, William A., '89,   gunslin330@aol.com

S

Sabater, Barbara M., '93,   bmsabater@aol.com
Sackel, James H., '82,   jhs107@aol.com
Saigo, Shondell A., '95,   cat217173@aol.com
Saint Cloux, Marie P., '96,   steevem@prodigy.net
Saint-fleur, Johanne A., '98,   chipipi1@aol.com
Sakelhide, Keith A., '80,   sakelhide@msn.com
Salamy, Joseph M., '85,   jsalamy@home.com
Salas, Julius O., '98,   fop189@aol.com
Salazar, Marcelo, '94,   swimmer1971@aol.com
Salazar-Atias, Ms. Camila D., '99,   csalazar7@hotmail.com
Salcedo, Yadira I., '99,   yadirasalcedo@hotmail.com
Saldana, N. Antonio, '92,   sald297@aol.com
Salerno, Joseph J., '76,   jsalerno@primenet.com
Salim-Rasheed, Bibi Zameena, '92,   zameenarasheed@aol.com
Salinas, Liz K., '98,   firejan27@aol.com
Salvatore, Lawrence F., '79,   lsalvatore@lucent.com
Salzano, Dr. Julienne,   jsalzano@hoflink.com
Sama, Jessica, '95,   jsama1@hotmail.com
Sambula, Anthony L., '97,   lukeizm1@earthlink.net
Samedi, John F., '99,   jsamedi@aol.com
Samuels, Jason S., '98,   JSS75@MSN.COM
Samuels, Sheila Y., '97,   ssamuels@law.pac.edu
Samuels, Susan R., '96,   suzeysam@aol.com
Sanchez, Carlos M., '95,   procast@msn.com
Sanchez, Enrique, '99,   forensicsdoctor@aol.com
Sanchez, Joseph (Joie) R., '95,   jsanchez3@juno.com
Sanchez, Julie, '99,   jsanchez33@yahoo.com
Sand, Valerie S., '71,   valeriesand@fea.net
Sanders, Liliana M., '91,   forensicdx@aol.com
Sanderson, Paul M., '76,   paul_sanderson@msn.com
Sandin, Eric J., '91,   ericsandin@msn.com
Sandseth, Thomas R., '86,   102656.3042@compuserve.com
Sanfilippo, Debra A., '90,   diby@aol.com
Sang, John L., '80,   sangjohn@aol.com
Sansone, Salvatore J., '73,   ssansone@suffolk.lib.ny.us
Santa Ana, Richard, '84,   75707.3355@compuserve.com
Santana Martuez, Odalis, '99,   anbthentherewasodie@hotmail.com
Santiago, Frances, '99,   franjafo@aol.com
Santiago, Jackeline, '99,   feburarytwo@hotmail.com
Santiago, Jeanette, '99,   santiagocentan@aol.com
Santiago, Jose A., '94,   jsalinas63@cs.com
Santiago, Marc A., '94,   marcsantim@aol.com
Santiago, Melissa S., '96,   melissa.santiago@ssa.gov
Santiago, Raymond (Ray) S., Esq., '96,   raysantiago@juno.com
Santiago, Ricardo N., '64,   rsant73066@aol.com
Santiago, Mrs. Sueleyba, '98,   sueleyba@eskimo.com
Santiago, Zoraida, '98,   zsaint40@hotmail.com
Santora, Alexander, '74,   almau12345@aol.com
Sarach, Omar J., '87,   trek621@cs.com
Sarnataro, Geoffrey L., '80,   geoffreysarnataro@ibi.com
Sarrantonio, Lana, '78,   032287075lsarra@co.arlington.va.us
Sarro, Peter J., '99,   thirtn13@aol.com
Sarter, Leonard, '75,   jansa19@aol.com
Sasson, Dina J., '92,   dsasson@aol.com
Savage, Patrick J., '98,   tralee65@worldnet.att.net
Savatteri, Stephine, '99,   auxano8810@aol.com
Saviano, Mrs. Donna M., '92,   abettrday@aol.com
Scally, Tina M., '95,   tms1@co.westchester.ny.us
Scalzo, Ronald G., '95,   brooklynron@aol.com
Scanlon, Frances E., '78,   feslaw@aol.com
Scanlon, Kevin J., '94,   kjsij@cuny.edu
Scarpone, Leonardo, '94,   italvisionz@aol.com
Schaefer, Deborah, '91,   dschaefer@animail.com
Schaefer, Richard W., '83,   rschaefer@keyspanenergy.com
Schaffer, Scott L., '74,   ubiscott@aol.com
Schanil, Robert, '90,   stanglovr66@cs.com
Schatzberg, Rufus, '89,   rufusschatzberg@cs.com
Schellhass, Kenneth J., '83,   kenneth.j.schellhaas@aexp.com
Schenker, Stephen, '79,   lie@aol.com
Schifini, Thomas A., '95,   schifit@yahoo.com
Schletter, Donna L., '89,   hpocus217@yahoo.com
Schlosser, Kevin, '81,   kschlosser@rmefpc.com
Schmitz, William J., '98,   wschmitz@bmcc.cuny.edu
Schmollinger, Justine M., '99,   JMSTHMOLL@NETSCAPE.NET

Schnitzer, Shirley R., PhD,   schnitzer@earthlink.net
Schreiber, Robert, '93,   blueey26@aol.com
Schultz, John A., Jr., '97,   jas@astro.temple.edu
Schulz, Dr. Dorothy M., '73,   dschulz@jjay.cuny.edu
Schuppert, Ronald, '77,   rschuppert@iopener.net
Schwartz, Kenneth M., '82,   bronx59@frontiernet.net
Schwartz, Milton, '75,   tsecuve@dtl.net
Schwartz, Thomas P., '99,   tps90@hotmail.com
Schwartzman, Leon, '77,   poc12@worldnet.att.net
Sciandra, Joseph R., '80,   joseph.sciandra@roche.com
Sclafani, Joseph C., '84,   jcs74@juno.com
Sconfietti, James, '90,   jscon45@aol.com
Sconzo, Rachel L., '99,   divynemsr@aol.com
Scott, Mrs. Gladys A., '98,   catwoman060@aol.com
Scott, Ivory L., '86,   finest1011@aol.com
Scott, Monica, '99,   moni49@juno.com
Scott, Thorance A., '99,   t5219@aol.com
Scotto-Lavino, T., '95,   joenteri@erols.com
Seabrook, Reginald K., '96,   brook8@aol.com
Sebro, Sherwin K., '95,   transitclub@yahoo.com
Seedman, Albert A., '62,   bbeck592@aol.com
Seelig, George W., '80,   george.seelig@lmco.com
Segarra, Elsie, '92,   LCSSPACE@AOL.COM
Seibert, Eleanore, '97,   seibee01@doc.mssm.edu
Sell, Angela M., '97,   NOONIT@BELLATLANTIC.NET
Seltzberg, Mark S., '81,   coachms@aol.com
Serafino, John M., '85,   docsera@aol.com
Seraspe, Danilo, '95,   dseraspe@aol.com
Seremetis, Michael, '93,   MSEREMETIS@USSS.TREAS.GOV
Sergi, Frank, '80,   snarth@aol.com
Serrano, Jose, '96,   jayarees@excite.com
Servis, Anthony, '88,   ltnj@aol.com
Sevastyanov, Vladimir, '97,   valad794@aol.com
Sewer, Enrique D., '92,   rico327che@aol.com
Shack, SGT Stanley,   ssbshack8@aol.com
Shaleesh, LT William, '89,   wmsshiek@aol.com
Shamsundar, Jaso, '99,   j.shamsunder@yahoo.com
Sharpe, Ryan R., '96,   rysee@hotmail.com
Shavers, Donna L., '97,   SDREAMIED@AOL.COM
Shaw, Mrs. Alexandria, '95,   matnjuss@aol.com
Shaw, Rudolph A., '82,   shawr@un.org
Shea, John W., '77,   jshea@warwick.net
Shea, Nicola D., '94,   nshea@forensica.com
Sheard, Paige C., '98,   paigesheard@hotmail.com
Shedden, Jennifer L., '89,   jest894010@aol.com
Sheehan, Brian, '84,   briansheehan@worldnet.att.net
Sheehan, Vincent J., '79,   vince9951@aol.com
Sheerin, Brendan, '85,   msgfan1@aol.com
Shewnarain, Maya, '99,   msshew@aol.com
Shields, Joseph G., '90,   lttrainman@webtv.net
Shomion, Carol A., '75,   cshomion@aol.com
Shortell, Michael E., '90,   shortyek@gateway.net
Shuster, Galina V., '99,   galina@oven.com
Shuster, Irina V., '99,   irina@oven.com
Siccardi, Vincent F., '75,   vsiccardi@aol.com
Sidman, Jerry R., '96,   tynails@aol.com
Sien, Tjia (Chito) T., Jr., '96,   chitocn@hotmail.com
Sierra, Martin, Jr., '93,   msierrajr@aol.com
Silva, Maria J., '95,   mimj2@aol.com
Silva, Roberto, Jr., '95,   christinesilva@webtv.net
Silverman, Susan W., PhD, '93,   sueangler@aol.com
Silverstein, Andrew, '99,   asilver570@earthlink.net
Simmons, Melodi K., '98,   msimm19@hotmail.com
Simmons-Broadbelt, Cheryl D., '92,   csimmons@wlrk.com
Simms, Jacqueline, '93,   jbsimms1@netzero.net
Simon, Jacqueline L., '93,   jacquelinesimon@aol.com
Simpson, Shelaine, '95,   sfimp1075@aol.com
Singleton, Ms. Latanya M., '96,   lsingle733@aol.com
Siotkas, John, '79,   john_siotkas@baruch.cuny.edu
Sita, Joseph M., '80,   riv1966@sc.com
Skelly, John G., '77,   jgskelly@bellsouth.net
Skopin, Raymond P., '75,   rskopin@mtahq.org
Slater, Roxanne Y., '99,   rslater@nycl.com
Slattery, Joseph W., '89,   ajl@lcconsultants.com
Small, Karen S., '95,   ksmall@thehopeprogram.org
Small, Kimberly O., '99,   shooklove@aol.com
Smalls, Larue C., '96,   ruester44@hotmail.com
Smallwood, Lee N., '99,   lee93074@aol.com
Smith, Allen J., '80,   ajsmith@restorationplaza.org
Smith, Bettina J., '99,   bsmith@brooklyn.cuny.edu
Smith, Clarence, Jr., Esq., '84,   bubbycs@hotmail.com
Smith, Harry, CPP, '73,   hsmith4cpp@aol.com
Smith, Henry G., '80,   lenrygsmith@nyi.com
Smith, L. P., '80,   fastcar@webtv.net
Smith, Launcelott, '74,   lsmith@cjrc.org
Smith, Mrs. Lesley B., '95,   lesley.smith@ci-boston.ma.us

Smith, Marjorie (Mardie) W., '79, mardie@hamptons.com
Smith, Melinda G., '97, n.g.mess@fordfound.org
Smith, Robert A., '82, rsmith@ci.new-rochelle.ny.us
Smith, Roberta L., '97, honeybabe39@yahoo.com
Smith, Ms. Ruth D., '78, rdsmith01@aol.com
Smith, Sarah A., '85, ssmith9150@aol.com
Smith, Susanne M., '79, ssislar@aol.com
Smith, William G., '80, glenn5623@aol.com
Smither, Mrs. Melissa, '91, javabiz@aol.com
Smolowitz, Barry M., '79, johnjay@smolowitz.com
Smorto, Ivette, '83, isbyphesea@aol.com
Smulczeski, Richard, '99, ltrs579@aol.com
Smyth, Kerry M., '85, 733606497ksmyth@chubb.com
Snyder, Heather T., '96, snyder@murray.fordham.edu
Soghomonian, Christine A., '99, kostasone@earthlink.net
Sohan, C., '90, nalini1124@cs.com
Sokol, Louise J., '80, cavecreek@aol.com
Soler, Rafael, '85, ralo@coqui.net
Solgan, Christopher J., '97, csolgan@hotmail.com
Sorci, Frank X., '77, fxs2@gateway.net
Sosa, Ms. Kilsie, '97, ksosa@jjay.cuny.edu
Sosnowik, Daniel E., '96, dsosnowi@gw.nypd.org
Soto, David, '97, pito_54@hotmail.com
Soto, Evangelina, '95, eveair@aol.com
Soto, Francisco, '90, ln.cisco4448@cs.com
Soto, Grace M., '99, sun12beach@aol.com
Sotomayor, John P., '90, TAZ521@AOL.COM
Soules, Christopher, '91, cpsoules@yahoo.com
Sousa, Robert, '87, gonyjetsgo@aol.com
Southerland, Gilbert A., '76, gillowsouth@aol.com
Souvenir-brice, Mrs. Cassandra Y., '95, baboubrice@aol.com
Sow, Ms. Cynthia B., '81, hipas@aol.com
Spagnola, Carmen T., '96, robinspag@prodigy.net
Spain, Pauline, '78, lene1019@aol.com
Spann, Cassaundra, '92, cassaundra.spann@gsa.gov
Sparro, Michael R., '92, mrsparro@earthlink.net
Spaun, Gregory (Greg) J., '86, gspaun@tiny.brooklaw.edu
Spencer-Dejesus, Jesusa T., '99, seken2none@aol.com
Spriggs, Jeffrey, '96, wood163@aol.com
Springle, Stephen V., '93, svspringle@yahoo.com
Squassoni, Laura C., '79, lcssnj@gateway.net
Squires, Ronald W., '99, rwsjunk@hotmail.com
Staab, Ryan R., '96, rrstmtg@aol.com
Stahl, Doris A., '74, dorisle@aol.com
Stanley, Dora L., '76, dstanley@nysnet.net
Stapleton, James W., '72, grampyjim2@aol.com
Stark, Ms. Carmen C., '97, cceestark@aol.com
Stark, Robert M., '95, realbob1@aol.com
Steets, William R., '95, wrsteets@aol.com
Stephens, Sukeena M., '99, forbid3@aol.com
Stephenson, Beverley, '92, agie2@yahoo.com
Stephenson, Oscar L., '95, oscarstep@aol.com
Sternblitz, Paul S., '76, icebreaker@rocketmail.com
Stettner, Charles P., '68, patchas2@aol.com
Steuerer, John, '97, jsteurer@aol.com
Stevens, Gordon F., '72, cragrat@earthlink.net
Stewart, Deirdre N., '94, deirdrgs@hotmail.com
Stewart, Hazel L., '87, hlslan@aol.com
Stewart, Janet S., '95, JANSTEW@ACNIC.COM
Stewart, Lenore O., '97, satanfox@aol.com
Stewart, Lisa M., '99, lmsnew@aol.com
Stickevers, John J., '78, jstickevers@ibm.net
Stimphil, Kathy K., '98, kstimphil@aol.com
St. Jean, Fritz, '96, fst65@aol.com
Stone, LTC Wayne A., USA, '82, wayn75196@aol.com
Storch, Jerome E., '75, jestorch@aol.com
Stracker, Cassandra L., '99, CLSTRACKER@USPIS.GOV
Streger, Matthew R., '96, medic152@mindspring.com
Strobl, Staci E., '99, staci_strobl@nyep.uscourts.gov
Strube, Edward W., '75, eutrube@surfree.com
Stuart, Calvin, '95, stulove@aol.com
Stump, William P., '73, ssiprogram@aol.com
Sturman, Mitchell, '76, msturman@email.usps.gov
Sullivan, Brien P., '96, brien@asan.com
Sullivan, Patrick F., '75, sullivanp.osi@gao.gov
Sumter, Antoinette, '97, asumter@york.cuny.edu
Suponitskiy, Serge, '97, ssuponitskiy@scholastic.com
Surgeon, Clarence M., '77, csurgeon@aol.com
Swain, Michael, '96, swainsecuritcons@aol.com
Swain, Warren, '99, luvecho69@aol.com
Sweeting, Soyini T., '95, ifealoha@aol.com
Swinton, Darlene, '95, divalarue34@aol.com
Sylvester, Philip, '85, phsylvester726@yahoo.com
Szarawarski, Michael, '79, carollee43@aol.com

T

Tabachnick, Carrie R., '97, tabachnc@brooklynda.org
Tabb, Ms. Yolanda, '98, y_tabb@hotmail.com
Taddeo, Jack, '76, jtaddeo520@aol.com
Tagarelli, Nicholas A., '79, papdhockey@aol.com
Talamas, Jacqueline C., '99, latinladyj@aol.com
Tallon, LT Kenneth A., '76, sargekt@aol.com
Tam, Joemy C., '82, joemytam@hotmail.com
Tamai, Julianne Sumiyo, '95, jstamai@aol.com
Tamaro, Loring, '96, lortam1@aol.com
Tarver, Dionne E., '98, dta3880216@aol.com
Tarwacki, Robert E., Sr., '93, fop145@geocities.com
Taveras, Elvis, '90, taverases@msn.com
Taylor, Junior P., '96, southfork@aol.com
Taylor, Robert F., '83, irish@wt.net
Taylor, Sandra L., '72, SANDSTAR60@YAHOO.COM
Taylor, Ms. Shernill, '97, shernill_taylor@baruch.cuny.edu
Taylor, Tonya, '93, tlewis1059@aol.com
Taylor, Virginia, '87, ronnet695@aol.com
Teachey, George A., '81, teach1065@aol.com
Teelimian, Henrik, '98, hteelimian@aol.com
Telesco, Grace A., '87, kdgt@aol.com
Telesford, Janelle R., '94, jtelesford@emmetmarvin.com
Telfer, Michael A., '99, abeylabyln@aol.com
Tellefsen, Laurie J., '94, ljt0110@aol.com
Templier, Pierrette, '99, pierrettetemp@aol.com
Thomas, Keith B., '95, avrilkeith@hotmail.com
Thompson, Adam, '85, amtlaw@aol.com
Thompson, Kenneth, '89, kthom0314@aol.com
Thompson, Madelyn, '81, madelyn.thompson@zurichus.com
Thompson-Carvelli, Amy E., '93, jcarve7950@aol.com
Thornton, Jenell, '97, dimples283@juno.com
Thorson, Steven J., '85, sthorson@camber.com
Tiedemann, LT James R., '83, jrt1@westchestergov.com
Tiefenwerth, Thomas J., '83, tjtiefenwerth@aol.com
Tierney, Michael N., '82, oceanybreeze@aol.com
Tischler, Jeffrey I., '80, klrwayl1@aol.com
Toal, Joseph V., '76, toal2027@aol.com
Tocker, Leonard H., '83, ltocker@ins.state.ny.us
Todorovic, Jelica, '96, LELA72@AOL.COM
Tomback, Daniel M., '99, cobretti@aol.com
Tomlinson, Mrs. Beatrice E., '77, terry@tbol.net
Tomlinson, Camille E., '96, keishcam@aol.com
Tompkins, Gail H., '77, ghtompkins@aol.com
Toro, Eric, '84, etoro@aol.com
Torres, Alejandra, '95, alexis167@aol.com
Torres, Mrs. Cecilia A., '82, hawaiisunset99@aol.com
Torres, Dennisa A., '94, datorres@legal_apd.org
Torres, Talia C., '99, madisonsquarejrt@aol.com
Tosado, Mariveila, '88, mt926@aol.com
Toussaint, Emmanuel, '99, eman2193@yahoo.com
Toussaint, Leveque, '91, toussaint99@aol.com
Townsend, Michael C., '93, bitterman@juno.com
Trakas, Arthur G., '77, atrakas@esq.com
Tramuto, Mrs. Andrea E., '98, jeffnnancybre@netsync.net
Trause, Victoria, '97, vhtrau@bellatlantic.net
Trelles, Henry X., '99, mudodgaf@aol.com
Triebwasser, Jonah, Esq., '71, jonaht@juno.com
Trignano, Marcia V., '78, marciatrig@hotmail.com
Trillo, Ismael, '78, ismealt@aol.com
Trinidad, Linda M., '98, linda_trinidad@yahoo.com
Tripi, Anthony F., '88, healthybodyworks@juno.com
Truitt, James F., '96, lobo@vh.net
Tsang, Wing C., '97, chucktsang@yahoo.com
Tsevdos, Stefanos, '95, stefanos@aol.com
Tsuji, Marian E., '83, metsuji@aloha.net
Tuck, Stephen J., '80, nysjt@aol.com
Tucker, Bonita C., '76, bcarment@aol.com
Tucker, Darlene, '97, dct342@aol.com
Tumasar, Diane M., '97, ds932@aol.com
Turner, Mrs. Regina, '92, rcros26759@aol.com
Tyre, Iasia A., '98, iatyre@aol.com
Tyrrell, Edward, '82, edward.tyrrell@usdoj.gov
Tytell, Harold, '68, atytell@juno.com
Tytell, Peter V., '95, typeter@aol.com

U

Ucelli, Monique S., '97, mahi1129@aol.com
Uhlmann, Dennis P., '83, oldmann7@compuserve.com
Uke, Evaristus U., '95, unimke@msn.com
Umar, Warith-Deen, '85, deenworks@aol.com
Ur, Joseph, '96, ru094@aol.com
Urrutia, Anna-Maria, '82, spenurr@aol.com
Usera, Jessica, '97, jusera@jjay.cuny.edu
Utsey, Robert E., '95, senseidoc@compuserve.com
Uveges, Michael J., '99, cyko1197@aol.com

Uwa-Omede, Tonnie, '92,   osazz@aol.com

V

Valcarcel, Carmen E., '99,   cval58@aol.com
Valdes, Jesus M., '90,   radtrainer@aol.com
Vale, Carmen R., '92,   crvalei@aol.com
Valentin, Miguel A., '77,   mike16397@yahoo.com
Valentine, Hillel J.,   josiahv@aol.com
Valles, LT Evelyn, '76,   TATSINGTAM@AOL.COM
Vanderlee, Cynthia S., '95,   cvanderlee@wfmail.canandaigua.k12.ny.us
Vann, Keith K., '91,   kkvann@webtv.net
Vannata, Janice M., '93,   svannata@aol.com
Varga, Donna M., '81,   inthenet@iwon.com
Varga, Stephen J., '80,   inthenet@iwon.com
Vargas, Bernabe, '99,   bza3502894@aol.com
Vargas, Jeffrey (Jeff), '95,   jvargas_81@hotmail.com
Vargas, Mrs. Jennifer L., '91,   jlvargas@juno.com
Vargas, Leslie M., '91,   rosie7002@aol.com
Varghese, Vinod, '96,   vinodvarghese@netscape.com
Vartabedian, Darryl, '95,   dhv1@hotmail.com
Vasapollo-d'Augusta, Barbara, '92,   daugusta@cybernex.net
Vasquez, Ms. Daisy, '96,   maesid@aol.com
Vaughan, Sheila M., '94,   curnyna@aol.com
Vaughn, Robbie, '96,   my29s@aol.com
Vazquez, Edward A., '84,   eavazquez@aol.com
Vecchio, Jack, '74,   jackvecchio@hotmail.com
Vega, Javiel, '99,   jv68@gateway.net
Vega, Michael A., '99,   mav226b@aol.com
Vega, Thomas, '84,   tomstoy8@aol.com
Veilson, Martin, '92,   martinveilson@aol.com
Vela, Bianca M., '98,   bvela87789@aol.com
Velasquez, Carmen R., '94,   carmenvelasquez@lawyer.com
Velasquez, Katty, '98,   velasquez84@aol.com
Velasquez, Yanina, '96,   yanivebe@gateway.net
Velazquez, Liz, '99,   lizzy717@aol.com
Velez, Cindhia, '96,   jrodrig9195@aol.com
Velez, Glorialee, '96,   GLVELEZ@AOL.COM
Velez, Rosendo P., '95,   ltchendo@aol.com
Velez-cruz, Margaret R., '83,   VELEZCRUZ@EXCITE.COM
Velilla, Angel E., '99,   kidange@aol.com
Veneziano, Salvatore, '80,   svenezi456@aol.com
Ventimiglia, Vincent, '74,   jimmyboya@aol.com
Venuti, Christine M., '99,   dharmacv@yahoo.com
Vera, Sharon L., '99,   skorpia76@aol.com
Vessio, Nicholas P., '76,   nick124162@aol.com
Vidal-Romero, Elida, '97,   ely52@juno.com
Villanueva, Hector M., '98,   vee582@aol.com
Villegas, Liana, '97,   lliana@excite.com
Vinces, Rev. Edgar J., '82,   8198ww@acs.dfa.state.ny.us
Vinci, Mrs. Catherine A., '92,   cathy_vinci@faulknergrey.com
Viollis, Paul M., Sr., '83,   pviollis@kroll-ogara.com
Vishnudat, Mrs. Indira D., '95,   khankadir@aol.com
Vitale, George E., '79,   nystnyc@aol.com
Vlad, Cristian A., '98,   c.vlad@worldnet.att.net
Volmar, Marc A., Jr., '98,   keamar@mailcity.com
Volpe, Anthony, '76,   gloria890@aol.com
Vrantsidis, Dorothea, '91,   dv11@daimlerchrysler.com
Vredenburgh, Robert P., '74,   vredeo@frontiernet.net

W

Wachter, Mark T., '97,   marktpd@aol.com
Wagner, Colette A., '79,   COLETTE.WAGNER@MAIL.CUNY.EDU
Waite-carson, Gloria, '87,   legal@ayco.com
Walden, Kevin J., '86,   kjwaldenl@aol.com
Walden, Moises J., '94,   popco718@aol.com
Waldron, John F., '98,   jackwaldronspd@aol.com
Walker, Brian H., '93,   tex88@webtv.net
Walker, Ms. Chenyear A., '97,   blesinns@aol.com
Walker, Darrell, '76,   doewalk111@aol.com
Walker, Ms. Hillery G., '83,   hillawalk@hotmail.com
Walker, Mala D., '78,   darcelunltd@aol.com
Walker, Michael J., '96,   MJW9432@AOL.COM
Wallace, Patrick J., '79,   firemar@aol.com
Walsh, Declan J., '96,   dwalsh@jjay.cuny.edu
Walsh, George J., '75,   gwalsh122@earthlink.net
Walsh, Thomas P., '74,   tpwosh@aol.com
Walter, Bruce W., '75,   lwalter005@aol.com
Ward, Esther L., '80,   tobu006@aol.com
Ward, Florence V., '86,   fvward@juno.com
Ward, Jacqueline A., '99,   wdestinee@aol.com
Ward, Ms. Linda M., '95,   lward@skadden.com
Ward, Richard H., '68,   onwardvic@aol.com
Ward, Roger, '97,   rward776@aol.com
Ward, Thomas J., DPA,   wardt@stjohn.edu
Ward, Yvette A., '97,   moticia@aol.com
Wargo, Catherine M., '99,   cmwargo@aol.com

Warley, Raquel-Maria, '93,   gerroyroc@aol.com
Warner, Philip R., '85,   WARBRO3@CS.COM
Warner- Lyons, Mrs. Elyse Y., '94,   elyse.warner@mendes.com
Washington, Dennise Y., '90,   dwashing@courts.state.ny.us
Wasserman, David, '87,   david_wasserman@groton.pfizer.com
Waszczuk, Wieslaw, '98,   juniorlj1@aol.com
Watenberg, Mark, '82,   wat344@aol.com
Watkins, Ms. Tracey L., '85,   twatkins@northpointcom.com
Waxman, Mrs. Lorraine, '79,   babybiz20a@aol.com
Webb, Hillary D., '99,   hwebb@gccuny.edu
Webb, Shaun D., '99,   webb4049@aol.com
Weber, Robert D., Jr., '96,   bobpcfl@mindspring.com
Weems, Betty P., '93,   weemsbetty@hotmail.com
Weiler, Edward, '89,   amweiler@mindspring.com
Weinbaum, Nathan, '74,   nncb@msn.com
Weinstein, Jay A., '71,   weins2393@aol.com
Weinstock, Margot, '93,   alexkur@ix.netcom.com
Weir, SGT Seamus P., '91,   weir@fcc.net
Weisberg, Daniel M., '89,   dmwesq@rockland.net
Weisberg, Elyse J., '90,   ejweisberg@aol.com
Welch, Nicole D., '93,   NIKNAK97@AOL.COM
Wells, Marianne E., '99,   nicolove@excite.com
Welsh, Katherine W., '80,   mbkpmb@aol.com
Welsh, Mrs. Venesia A., '94,   vcr1028268@aol.com
Welt, Carey A., '89,   ncfm17@aol.com
Wempe, Raymond H., '81,   mtplaw@gateway.com
Wendle, Thomas A., '73,   thomas.wendle@equitable.com
Weston, Denise M., '97,   fairyworse@aol.com
White, John H., '76,   jhwhite923@netzero.com
White, Reginald H., '83,   rvp2be2@webtv.net
Whitfield, Fred L., '85,   FWHITFIELD@EARTHLINK.NET
Whiting, John W., '93,   whitingj@rnj-consulting.com
Wicker, Jason A., '95,   wic1111@yahoo.com
Wicks, Gwynne, '95,   gjwicks@cs.com
Widnick, Steven M., '76,   tuewid@webtv.net
Wiener, Lorin, '98,   drwiener@hotmail.com
Wierl, Christopher, '95,   cwierl@yahoo.com
Wilday, Robert D., '77,   popyseedr1@aol.com
Wilkerson, Walter P., '95,   wpwee21@aol.com
Wilkins, Michael R., '99,   mwill23@mail.com
Williams, Albert D., '77,   aldarrwill@cs.com
Williams, Alecia S., '99,   aswilliams@nypl.org
Williams, Alwin R., '95,   DEEPCVR91@AOL.COM
Williams, Andel G., '88,   ANWILLIA@ADVANTA.COM
Williams, Angela, '97,   angelamw@prodigy.net
Williams, Bridget L., '87,   mid2@mail.com
Williams, Geraldo A., '85,   geraldowms@aol.com
Williams, Kimberly, '90,   smiley8554@aol.com
Williams, Ms. Linda, '76,   zlawell@earthlink.net
Williams, Lloyd C., '91,   cagway@aol.com
Williams, Madonna S., '94,   dstorm28@yahoo.com
Williams, Nakesha L., '97,   girl6ny@aol.com
Williams, Rhonda Y., JD, '95,   esq99jd@aol.com
Williams, Richelle, '88,   mightymahonone@aol.com
Williams, Roderick M., '99,   wildbill34@hotmail.com
Willis, Yvonne A., '89,   dhri@msn.com
Wilson, James H., '76,   jameshwilson@msn.com
Wilson, Keryon T., '99,   JUSTICEJAZZ@AOL.COM
Wilson, Luana A., '89,   lwilson1@lehman.com
Wilson, Ms. Myrna, '93,   myrnaw@susnyc.org
Wilson, Richard P., '98,   infant@earthlink.net
Wilson-Howard, Terri, '99,   sutra7@earthlink.net
Wiltshire, Ms. Cheryl M., '95,   cheryl.wiltshire@law.csuohio.edu
Wimberly, Sheila A., '97,   swimbe6642@aol.com
Windsor, Pedro J., '99,   pedrojw@aol.com
Winfield, Karen M., '99,   contackmw@aol.com
Winn, Mrs. Martha D., '87,   mwinn@dycdlan.cn.ci.nyc.ny.us
Wise, Lauren A., '75,   law132@aol.com
Wisotsky-Burt, Ms. Amy T., '77,   amy_wisotsky@b-f.com
Witt, Olin T., '86,   the5witt@aol.com
Wittich, Mark H., '78,   m.wittich@police.vil.freeport.ny.us
Wodarski, Joseph P., Jr., '86,   suinjoe@aol.com
Wojtach, Susan E., '99,   jmwojtach@worldnet.att.net
Wolowski, Richard C., '74,   richwolo@ix.netcom.com
Woodbyne, Maurice C., '99,   moscun1@aol.com
Worthy, Patricia A., '93,   gapeach@aol.com
Wright, Rochelle T., '99,   rwright810@aol.com
Wright, Roy J., '95,   ROY.WRIGHT@USDOJ.GOV
Wrynn, Mrs. Maura A., '82,   love2skimaura@aol.com

X

Xenakis, Helen, '99,   agapi15@yahoo.com

Y

Yacoob, Azimoon N., '99,   aby@dellnet.com
Yanis, Ricardo A., '99,   ptlray@aol.com

Yanofsky, Barbara I., '79,   BYANDCATS@AOL.COM
Yanolatos, Michael D., '76,   ironmikeya@aol.com
Yates, Genithia, '98,   genithia@aol.com
Yee, Peter J., '93,   peterjy@juno.com
Yee, Yu S., '98,   sgtsingyee@aol.com
Yoo, John, '99,   jhny007@aol.com
Young, Adrienne M., '81,   threemasters@aol.com

Z

Zagariello, Mrs. Diana S., '98,   dswmz@aol.com
Zaharuk, Joseph P., Jr., '78,   jozie001@yahoo.com
Zandy, Matthew P., '96,   mzandy@juno.com
Zarek, Edward T., '84,   fed2022@worldnet.att.net
Zaro, Ines A., '99,   aguta28@aol.com
Zarrillo, Tina, '87,   tzsjk@worldnet.att.net
Zavala, James E., '98,   crazytony72@hotmail.com
Zaveloff, Sarah H., '98,   scz100@aol.com
Zavistoski, Robert, '93,   zav43@aol.com
Zayas, Victor L., Jr., '99,   bkbadboy4u@email.msn.com
Zayerz, Agueybana, '95,   solohutt@aol.com
Zazzi, Marie L., '72,   zazzi.marie@alitalia.it
Zelaya, Theresa M., '95,   luckeee23@aol.com
Zerella, Denise, '89,   trainerdz@aol.com
Zucker, Marc T., '99,   mz3@aol.com
Zummo, Michael A., '77,   mzummo@courts.state.ny.us
Zwicker, Jay L., '77,   zwickerj@mmc.marymt.edu